Algebra 2

Common Core

Randall I. Charles
Basia Hall
Dan Kennedy
Allan E. Bellman
Sadie Chavis Bragg
William G. Handlin
Stuart J. Murphy
Grant Wiggins

PEARSON

Boston, Massachusetts • Chandler, Arizona • Glenview, Illinois • Hoboken, New Jersey

Acknowledgments appear on page T574, which constitutes an extension of this copyright page.

PEARSON

ISBN-13: 978-0-13-328124-8
ISBN-10:   0-13-328124-8

6   16

Algebra 2 *Teacher's Edition Contents*

Teacher Handbook

VOLUME 1

CC Content Focus: Seeing Structure in Expressions

CC Content Focus: Interpreting and Building Functions

VOLUME 2

CC Content Focus: Expressing Geometric Properties with Equations

CC Content Focus: Conditional Probability and Matrices

CC Content Focus: Trigonometric Functions

Series *Authors*

Randall I. Charles, Ph.D., is Professor Emeritus in the Department of Mathematics and Computer Science at San Jose State University, San Jose, California. He began his career as a high school mathematics teacher, and he was a mathematics supervisor for five years. Dr. Charles has been a member of several NCTM committees and is the former Vice President of the National Council of Supervisors of Mathematics. Much of his writing and research has been in the area of problem solving. He has authored more than 90 mathematics textbooks for kindergarten through college.

Dan Kennedy, Ph.D., is a classroom teacher and the Lupton Distinguished Professor of Mathematics at the Baylor School in Chattanooga, Tennessee. A frequent speaker at professional meetings on the subject of mathematics education reform, Dr. Kennedy has conducted more than 50 workshops and institutes for high school teachers. He is coauthor of textbooks in calculus and precalculus, and from 1990 to 1994, he chaired the College Board's AP Calculus Development Committee. He is a 1992 Tandy Technology Scholar and a 1995 Presidential Award winner.

Basia Hall currently serves as Manager of Instructional Programs for the Houston Independent School District. With 33 years of teaching experience, Ms. Hall has served as a department chair, instructional supervisor, school improvement facilitator, and professional development trainer. She has developed curricula for Algebra 1, Geometry, and Algebra 2 and co-developed the Texas state mathematics standards. A 1992 Presidential Awardee, Ms. Hall is past president of the Texas Association of Supervisors of Mathematics and is a state representative for the National Council of Supervisors of Mathematics (NCSM).

Consulting *Authors*

Stuart J. Murphy is a visual learning author and consultant. He is a champion of helping students develop learning skills so they become more successful students. He is the author of *MathStart*, a series of children's books that presents mathematical concepts in the context of stories and *I See I Learn*, a Pre-Kindergarten and Kindergarten learning initiative that focuses on social and emotional skills. A graduate of the Rhode Island School of Design, he has worked extensively in educational publishing and has been on the authorship teams of a number of elementary and high school mathematics programs. He is a frequent presenter at meetings of the National Council of Teachers of Mathematics, the International Reading Association, and other professional organizations.

Grant Wiggins, Ed.D., is the President of Authentic Education in Hopewell, New Jersey. He earned his B.A. from St. John's College in Annapolis and his Ed.D. from Harvard University. Dr. Wiggins consults with schools, districts, and state education departments on a variety of reform matters; organizes conferences and workshops; and develops print materials and Web resources on curricular change. He is perhaps best known for being the coauthor, with Jay McTighe, of *Understanding by Design* and *The Understanding by Design Handbook*[1], the award-winning and highly successful materials on curriculum published by ASCD. His work has been supported by the Pew Charitable Trusts, the Geraldine R. Dodge Foundation, and the National Science Foundation.

[1] ASCD, publisher of "The Understanding by Design Handbook" coauthored by Grant Wiggins and registered owner of the trademark "Understanding by Design," has not authorized or sponsored this work and is in no way affiliated with Pearson or its products.

Program *Authors*

Algebra 1 and Algebra 2

Allan E. Bellman, Ph.D., is an Associate Professor of Mathematics Education at the University of Mississippi. He previously taught at the University of California, Davis for 12 years and in public school in Montgomery County, Maryland for 31. He has been an instructor for both the Woodrow Wilson National Fellowship Foundation and the Texas Instruments' T³ program. Dr. Bellman has a expertise in the use of technology in education and assessment-driven instruction, and speaks frequently on these topics. He was a 1992 Tandy Technology Scholar and has twice been listed in Who's Who Among America's Teachers.

Sadie Chavis Bragg, Ed.D., is Senior Vice President of Academic Affairs and professor of mathematics at the Borough of Manhattan Community College of the City University of New York. She is a past president of the American Mathematical Association of Two-Year Colleges (AMATYC). In recognition of her service to the field of mathematics locally, statewide, nationally, and internationally, she was awarded AMATYC's most prestigious award, the Mathematics Excellence Award for 2010. Dr. Bragg has coauthored more than 50 mathematics textbooks for kindergarten through college.

William G. Handlin, Sr., is a classroom teacher and Department Chair of Mathematics and former Department Chair of Technology Applications at Spring Woods High School in Houston, Texas. Awarded Life Membership in the Texas Congress of Parents and Teachers for his contributions to the well-being of children, Mr. Handlin is also a frequent workshop and seminar leader in professional meetings.

Geometry

Laurie E. Bass is a classroom teacher at the 9–12 division of the Ethical Culture Fieldston School in Riverdale, New York. A classroom teacher for more than 30 years, Ms. Bass has a wide base of teaching experience, ranging from Grade 6 through Advanced Placement Calculus. She was the recipient of a 2000 Honorable Mention for the Radio Shack National Teacher Awards. She has been a contributing writer for a number of publications, including software-based activities for the Algebra 1 classroom. Among her areas of special interest are cooperative learning for high school students and geometry exploration on the computer. Ms. Bass is a frequent presenter at local, regional, and national conferences.

Art Johnson, Ed.D., is a professor of mathematics education at Boston University. He is a mathematics educator with 32 years of public school teaching experience, a frequent speaker and workshop leader, and the recipient of a number of awards: the Tandy Prize for Teaching Excellence, the Presidential Award for Excellence in Mathematics Teaching, and New Hampshire Teacher of the Year. He was also profiled by the Disney Corporation in the American Teacher of the Year Program. Dr. Johnson has contributed 18 articles to NCTM journals and has authored over 50 books on various aspects of mathematics.

Reviewers *National*

Tammy Baumann
K-12 Mathematics Coordinator
School District of the City
 of Erie
Erie, Pennsylvania

Sandy Cowgill
Mathematics Department Chair
Muncie Central High School
Muncie, Indiana

Sheryl Ezze
Mathematics Chairperson
DeWitt High School
Lansing, Michigan

Dennis Griebel
Mathematics Coordinator
Cherry Creek School District
Aurora, Colorado

Bill Harrington
Secondary Mathematics
 Coordinator
State College School District
State College, Pennsylvania

Michael Herzog
Mathematics Teacher
Tucson Small School Project
Tucson, Arizona

Camilla Horton
Secondary Instruction Support
Memphis School District
Memphis, Tennessee

Gary Kubina
Mathematics Consultant
Mobile County School System
Mobile, Alabama

Sharon Liston
Mathematics Department Chair
Moore Public Schools
Oklahoma City, Oklahoma

Ann Marie Palmeri Monahan
Mathematics Supervisor
Bayonne Public Schools
Bayonne, New Jersey

Indika Morris
Mathematics Department Chair
Queen Creek School District
Queen Creek, Arizona

Jennifer Petersen
K-12 Mathematics Curriculum
 Facilitator
Springfield Public Schools
Springfield, Missouri

Tammy Popp
Mathematics Teacher
Mehlville School District
St. Louis, Missouri

Mickey Porter
Mathematics Teacher
Dayton Public Schools
Dayton, Ohio

Steven Sachs
Mathematics Department Chair
Lawrence North High School
Indianapolis, Indiana

John Staley
Secondary Mathematics
 Coordinator
Office of Mathematics, PK-12
Baltimore, Maryland

Robert Thomas, Ph.D.
Mathematics Teacher
Yuma Union High School
 District #70
Yuma, Arizona

Linda Ussery
Mathematics Consultant
Alabama Department of
 Education
Tuscumbia, Alabama

Denise Vizzini
Mathematics Teacher
Clarksburg High School
Montgomery County,
 Maryland

Marcia White
Mathematics Specialist
Academic Operations,
 Technology and Innovations
Memphis City Schools
Memphis, Tennessee

Merrie Wolf
Mathematics Department Chair
Tulsa Public Schools
Tulsa, Oklahoma

Contents *in Brief*

Welcome to *Pearson Algebra 2 Common Core Edition* student book. Throughout this textbook, you will find content that has been developed to cover many of the High School Standards for Mathematical Content and all of the Standards for Mathematical Practice. The End-of-Course Assessment provides students with practice with all of the Standards for Mathematical Content listed on pages xx to xxiii.

A New Way to *Experience Math*

Pearson Algebra 2 Common Core Edition offers a whole new way to look at mathematics. This **blended print and digital** curriculum is built on a foundation of problem solving and visual learning. Students will experience math like never before. See for yourself!

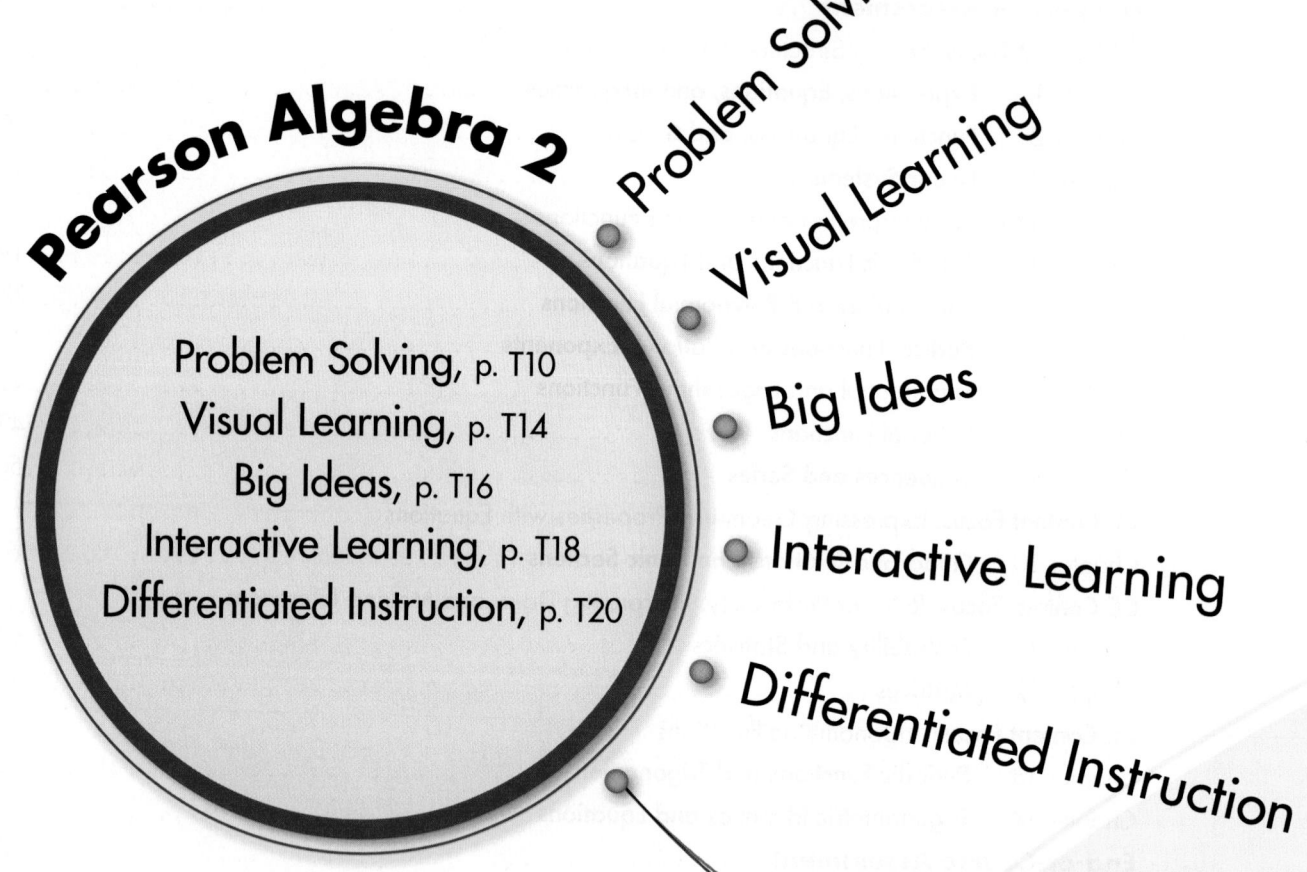

Pearson Algebra 2

Problem Solving, p. T10
Visual Learning, p. T14
Big Ideas, p. T16
Interactive Learning, p. T18
Differentiated Instruction, p. T20

Problem Solving

Visual Learning

Big Ideas

Interactive Learning

Differentiated Instruction

These five essential components of learning – problem solving, visual learning, focused and coherent curriculum development through Big Ideas, interactive learning, and differentiated instruction – are skillfully interwoven throughout *Pearson Algebra 2 Common Core Edition* to offer students a pedagogically rich, conceptually rigorous, and visually engaging program.

The **Common Core State Standards for Mathematics** call for a new approach to mathematics education. They challenge educators to rethink math curriculum at all levels. They push teachers and students to strive to achieve ever higher expectations. They set **college and career readiness** as the goal for all students.

Developing Mathematically Proficient Students

The **Standards for Mathematical Practice** describe behaviors of mathematically proficient students that all teachers should seek to develop in their students. They draw from both problem solving and reasoning skills and mathematical ways of thinking.

The **Standards for Mathematical Content** define what students should understand and be able to do. When students understand mathematical concepts, they can explain why a mathematical statement is true or where a mathematical rule comes from.

Problem *Solving*

Problem solving is one of the foundations of *Pearson High School Mathematics Common Core Edition*. The **Solve It!,** found in every lesson, provides students opportunities to refine their problem-solving skills. Guided instruction to help students further develop their problem-solving skills is found in the blue boxes (*Plan, Think, Think-Write*, and *Know-Need-Plan*) throughout the program.

The Standards for Mathematical Practice in the Common Core State Standards stress the importance of strong problem-solving and reasoning abilities to develop mathematical proficiency.

Developing Mathematically Proficient Students

© **Problem 3** Solving a Work Problem

Painting Amy can paint a loft apartment in 7 h. Jeremy can paint a loft apartment of the same size in 9 h. If they work together, how long will it take them to paint a third loft apartment of the same size?

Know	Need	Plan
• Amy's painting time is 7 h. • Jeremy's painting time is 9 h.	Amy and Jeremy's combined painting time	Find what fraction of a loft each person can paint in 1 h. Then write and solve a rational equation.

Know-Need-Plan Boxes step out the problem-solving process, helping students find entry points, analyze givens, and *decontextualize* the problem—that is, represent the problem situation symbolically.

"Research shows that understanding develops during the process of solving problems in which important math concepts and skills are embedded."—Randall Charles

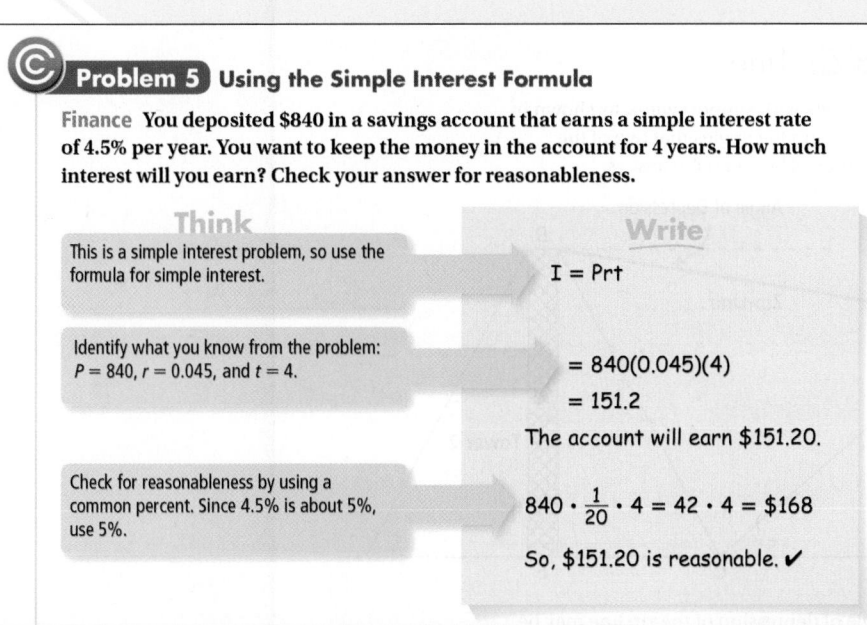

Problem 5 Using the Simple Interest Formula

Finance You deposited $840 in a savings account that earns a simple interest rate of 4.5% per year. You want to keep the money in the account for 4 years. How much interest will you earn? Check your answer for reasonableness.

Think

This is a simple interest problem, so use the formula for simple interest.

Identify what you know from the problem: $P = 840$, $r = 0.045$, and $t = 4$.

Check for reasonableness by using a common percent. Since 4.5% is about 5%, use 5%.

Write

$I = Prt$

$= 840(0.045)(4)$

$= 151.2$

The account will earn $151.20.

$840 \cdot \frac{1}{20} \cdot 4 = 42 \cdot 4 = \$168$

So, $151.20 is reasonable. ✔

Think-Write Boxes
also help students develop mathematical proficiency by modeling the thinking and reasoning of proficient problem solvers.

Do you UNDERSTAND? MATHEMATICAL PRACTICES

5. **Vocabulary** Describe the differences between a linear function and an exponential function.

6. **Reasoning** Is $y = (-2)^x$ an exponential function? Justify your answer.

7. **Error Analysis** A student evaluated the function $f(x) = 3 \cdot 4^x$ for $x = -1$ as shown at the right. Describe and correct the student's mistake.

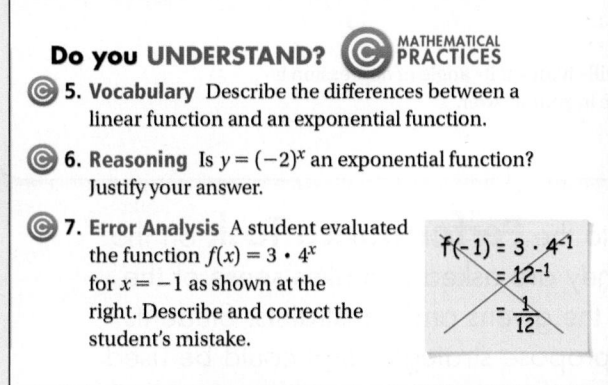

$f(-1) = 3 \cdot 4^{-1}$
$= 12^{-1}$
$= \frac{1}{12}$

Reasoning and Error Analysis exercises have students justify their thinking and critique the reasoning of others to help them become proficient thinkers and problem solvers.

Solving *Rich Problems*

Pearson Algebra 2 Common Core Edition includes regular opportunities for students to become proficient with solving rich mathematical and real-world problems. Each chapter includes a **Common Core Performance Task** that students solve throughout the chapter.

Common Core Performance Task

Determining the Length of a Zip Line

A crew is setting up a zip line between two towers with support wires, as shown in the figure. They know the heights of the towers and the angles that two of the support wires make with the ground, which is level between the towers.

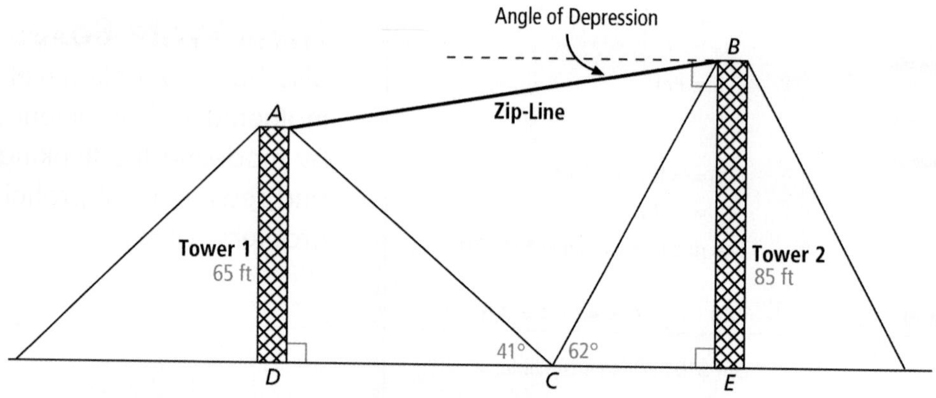

The crew's leader is concerned that the angle of depression of the zip line may be too great, resulting in a ride that is too fast. She wants to know how the length of the zip line will change if the angle of depression is halved. (In this case, the crew would set up a taller Tower 1.)

Task Description
Describe how the length of the zip line will change if its angle of depression is halved. Include the length of each zipline in your answer.

Students are introduced to the **Performance Task** on the **Chapter Opener.** They are asked to makes sense of the problem and to analyze the givens and constraints. Students are also encouraged to propose strategies that could be used to solve the problem.

Students revisit the *Common Core Performance Task* at least two times in a chapter, where they **apply what they have learned** in the lessons. Each application task also focuses on one or more of the Math Practices.

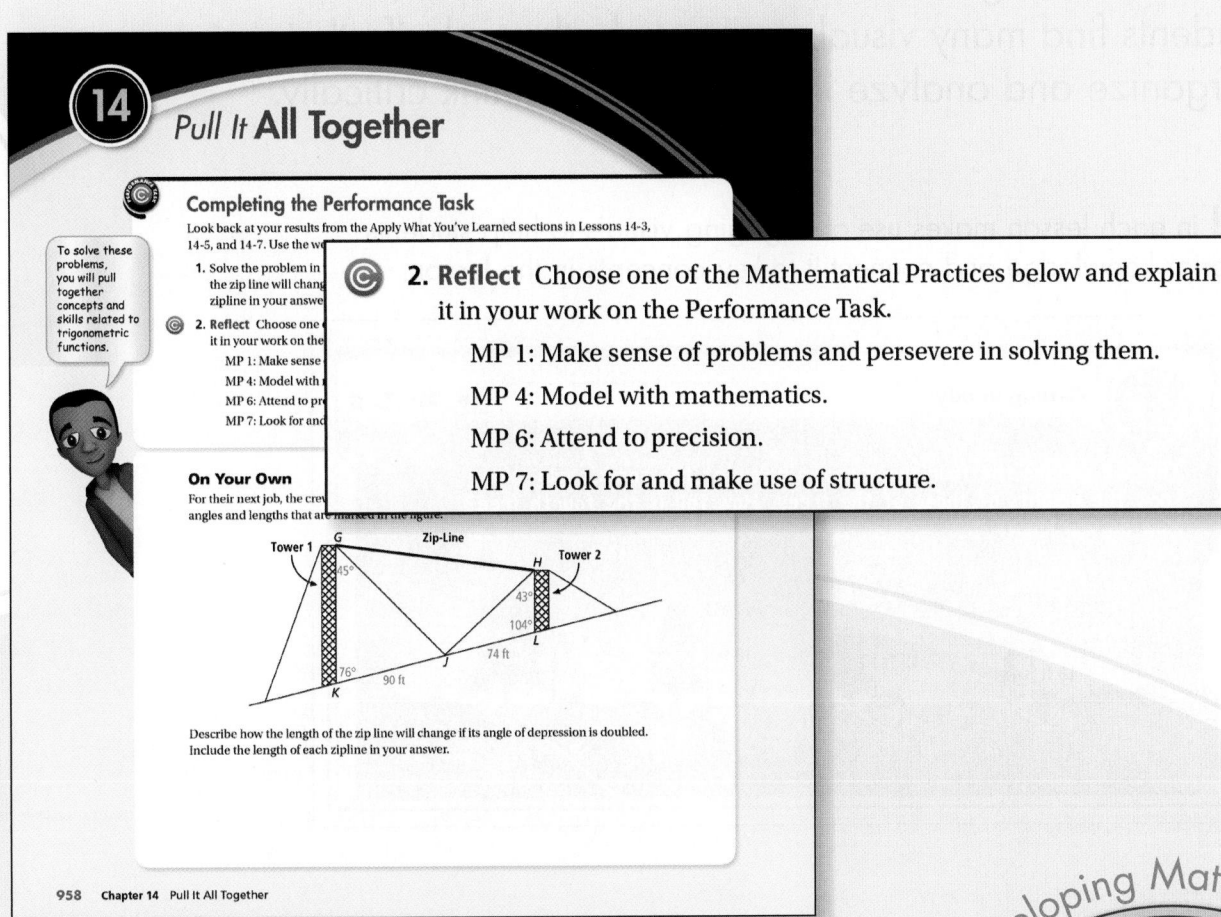

2. Reflect Choose one of the Mathematical Practices below and explain how you applied it in your work on the Performance Task.

MP 1: Make sense of problems and persevere in solving them.

MP 4: Model with mathematics.

MP 6: Attend to precision.

MP 7: Look for and make use of structure.

In the **Pull It All Together** at the end of the chapter, students complete their solution to the task. The Pull It All Together always includes a **Reflect** question that asks students to think about one or more of the Math Practices that they drew on as they worked through the solutions. Then students complete **On Your Own,** a task that requires the application of similar concepts and skills.

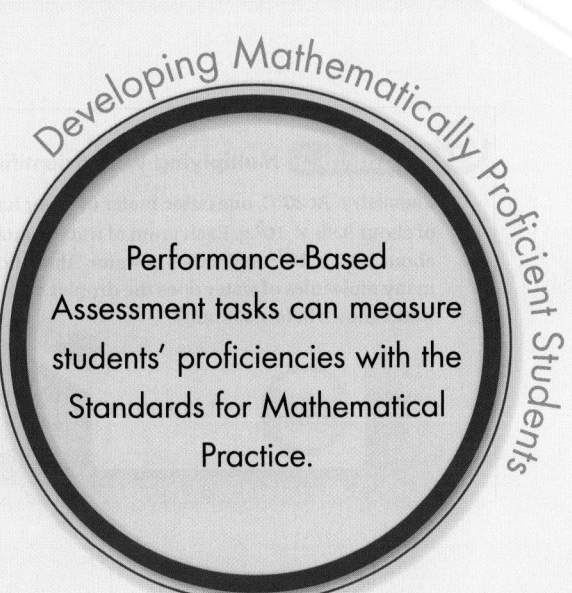

Performance-Based Assessment tasks can measure students' proficiencies with the Standards for Mathematical Practice.

Developing Mathematically Proficient Students

Visual *Learning*

Visual learning, a powerful method for making abstract ideas concrete and for connecting prior knowledge to new concepts, makes use of graphics and other visuals to present concepts. Throughout *Pearson High School Mathematics Common Core Edition*, students find many visual cues to help them clarify their thinking, organize and analyze information, and think critically.

The **Solve It!** in each lesson makes use of engaging visuals to help students tap into their prior knowledge and connect it to key concepts in the lesson.

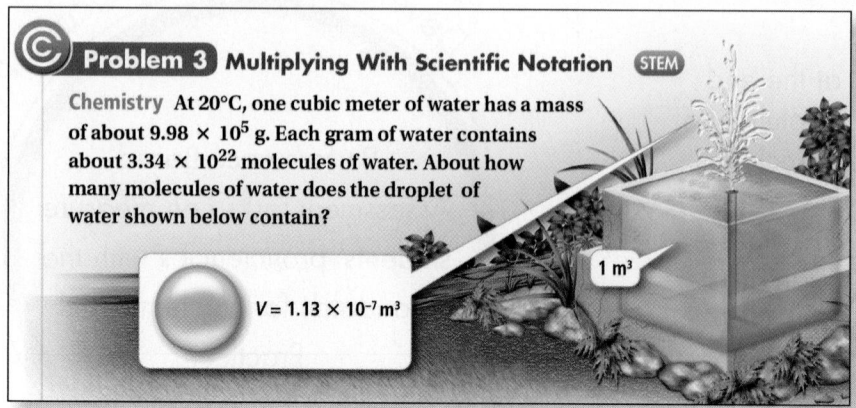

Some problems are visually rich, helping students clarify their thinking about the problem presented. The call-outs serve as **advanced organizers** as students develop solution plans.

"Through visual models, students interact with mathematical concepts, process information, reflect on their experiences, and draw conclusions. They learn."
—Stuart J. Murphy

Developing Mathematically Proficient Students

Through visual learning, students make sense of problems, develop solutions plans, and use tools appropriately, all leading to mathematical proficiency.

Some **Essential Understandings** present key concepts using visually rich images.

Essential Understanding You can find the volume of a prism or a cylinder when you know its height and the area of its base.

Both stacks of paper below contain the same number of sheets.

The first stack forms an oblique prism. The second forms a right prism. The stacks have the same height. The area of every cross section parallel to a base is the area of one sheet of paper. The stacks have the same volume. These stacks illustrate the following principle.

Big *Ideas*

Big Ideas and Essential Questions provide the organizing structure of the program and are based on the principles of Understanding by Design[1], which uses a backward design to develop curriculum. Planning the curriculum with the end results in mind leads to a more coherent program of instruction.

Big Ideas and **Essential Questions,** found on each chapter opener, help students focus on the key mathematical concepts of the chapter.

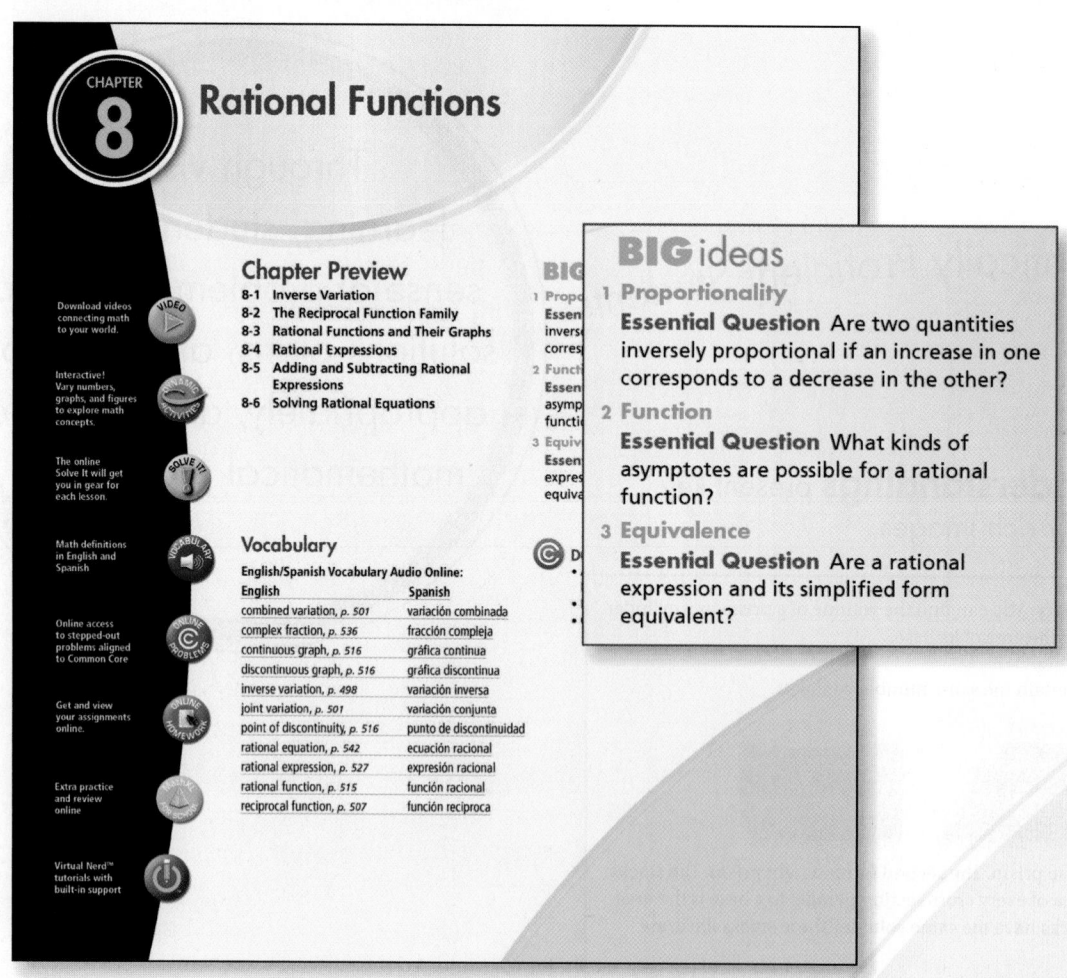

CHAPTER 8

Rational Functions

Download videos connecting math to your world.

Interactive! Vary numbers, graphs, and figures to explore math concepts.

The online Solve It will get you in gear for each lesson.

Math definitions in English and Spanish

Online access to stepped-out problems aligned to Common Core

Get and view your assignments online.

Extra practice and review online

Virtual Nerd™ tutorials with built-in support

Chapter Preview
8-1 Inverse Variation
8-2 The Reciprocal Function Family
8-3 Rational Functions and Their Graphs
8-4 Rational Expressions
8-5 Adding and Subtracting Rational Expressions
8-6 Solving Rational Equations

Vocabulary

English/Spanish Vocabulary Audio Online:

English	Spanish
combined variation, p. 501	variación combinada
complex fraction, p. 536	fracción compleja
continuous graph, p. 516	gráfica continua
discontinuous graph, p. 516	gráfica discontinua
inverse variation, p. 498	variación inversa
joint variation, p. 501	variación conjunta
point of discontinuity, p. 516	punto de discontinuidad
rational equation, p. 542	ecuación racional
rational expression, p. 527	expresión racional
rational function, p. 515	función racional
reciprocal function, p. 507	función recíproca

BIG ideas

1 Proportionality
Essential Question Are two quantities inversely proportional if an increase in one corresponds to a decrease in the other?

2 Function
Essential Question What kinds of asymptotes are possible for a rational function?

3 Equivalence
Essential Question Are a rational expression and its simplified form equivalent?

1 ASCD, publisher of "The Understanding by Design Handbook" coauthored by Grant Wiggins and registered owner of the trademark "Understanding by Design," has not authorized, approved, or sponsored this work and is in no way affiliated with Pearson or its products.

"A Big Idea is a way of seeing better and working smarter, not just another piece of knowledge."
—Grant Wiggins

The Big Ideas in *Pearson High School Mathematics Common Core Edition* align closely to the Conceptual Categories and Domains of the Standards for Mathematical Content in the Common Core State Standards.

Developing Mathematically Proficient Students

8 Chapter Review

Connecting **BIG** ideas and Answering the Essential Questions

1 Proportionality
Quantities x and y are inversely proportional only if growing x by the factor k ($k > 1$) means shrinking y by the factor $\frac{1}{k}$.

2 Function
A rational function may have no asymptotes, one horizontal or oblique asymptote, and any number of vertical asymptotes.

3 Equivalence
$f(x) = \frac{x+a}{x^2-a^2}$, $x \neq \pm a$, and $g(x) = \frac{1}{x-a}$, $x \neq \pm a$, are equivalent.

Inverse Variation (Lesson 8-1)
Are ℓ and w inversely proportional?
$A = \ell w$
$P = 2\ell + 2w$
• for a constant area—yes
• for a constant perimeter—no

Rational Functions and Their Graphs (Lesson 8-3)
Asymptotes:
For $y = \frac{2x^2}{x^2-9}$
horizontal: $y = 2$
vertical: $x = \pm 3$
For $y = \frac{2x^3+6x^2}{x^2+1}$
oblique: $y = 2x + 6$.
$y = \frac{x^4+5}{x^2+1}$ has no asymptotes.

The Reciprocal Function Family (Lesson 8-2)
$A(\ell) = \frac{5}{\ell}$
is a stretch of the graph of $A(\ell) = \frac{1}{\ell}$ by a factor of 5.

Solving Equations Involving Rational Expressions (Lessons 8-4, 8-5, and 8-6)
$\frac{2x^2}{x^2-9} = \frac{x-6}{x-3} + \frac{18}{x^2-9}$
$\frac{2x^2}{x^2-9} = \frac{(x-6)(x+3)}{(x-3)(x+3)} + \frac{18}{x^2-9}$
$2x^2 = x^2 - 3x - 18 + 18$
$x^2 + 3x = 0$
$x(x+3) = 0$
$x = 0 \checkmark$ or $x = -3 \cancel{x}$

In the **Chapter Review,** students will find answers to the Essential Questions for the Big Ideas. The Chapter Review also provides a comprehensive set of notes for student reference.

Interactive *Learning*

PowerAlgebra.com provides a robust interface through which you can access pedagogically rich content. PowerAlgebra.com can be used as a stand-alone digital course or integrated with print materials to provide a blended learning experience for your students. This online learning environment allows you to access resources and plan lessons easily, incorporate presentation tools, assign student work, and support student understanding.

Developing Mathematically Proficient Students

The robust digital features of PowerAlgebra.com help students to make strategic decisions about using tools appropriately, an important skill in the Common Core State Standards.

PowerAlgebra.com is the gateway for students and teachers to all digital components for *Pearson Algebra 2 Common Core Edition.* This includes access to the complete Student Edition and Teacher's Edition, editable worksheets, presentation tools and a sophisticated classroom management system.

PowerAlgebra.com

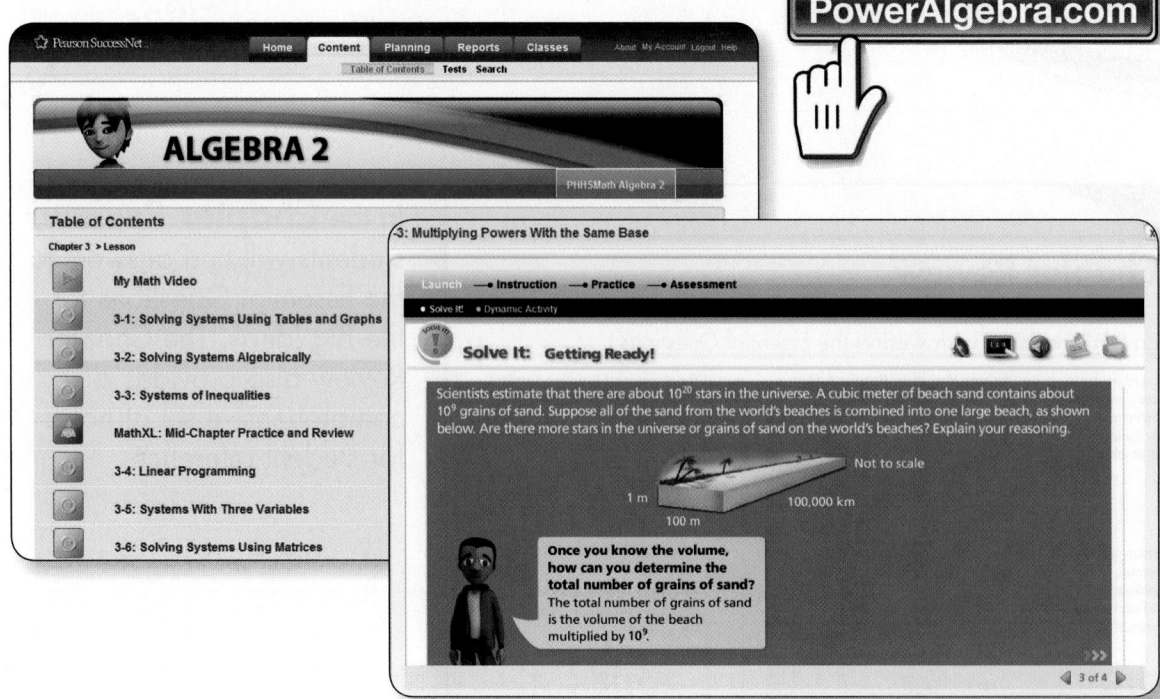

"Today's students are digital natives. They approach their lives differently as they integrate digital technologies seamlessly in their daily activities. Let's not have them power down when they get to math class." —Laurie Bass

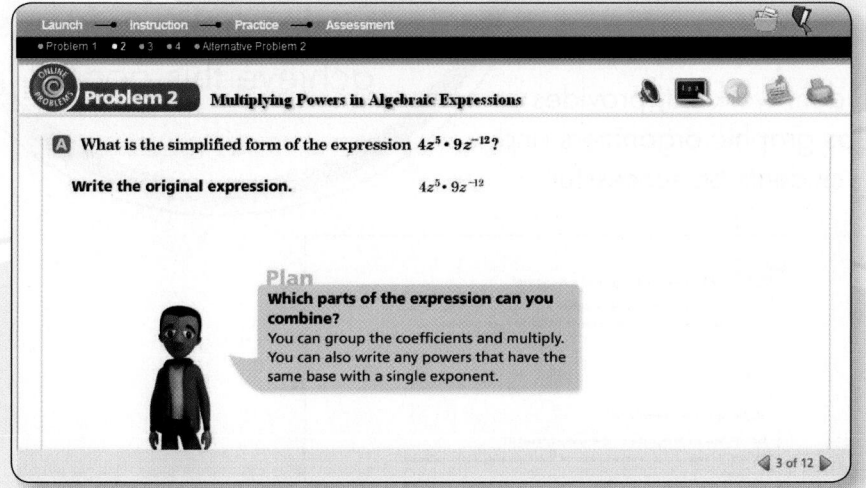

The Portable Study Center provides access to and control over the learning process. Students can download audio, video, and key lesson concepts to support their learning.

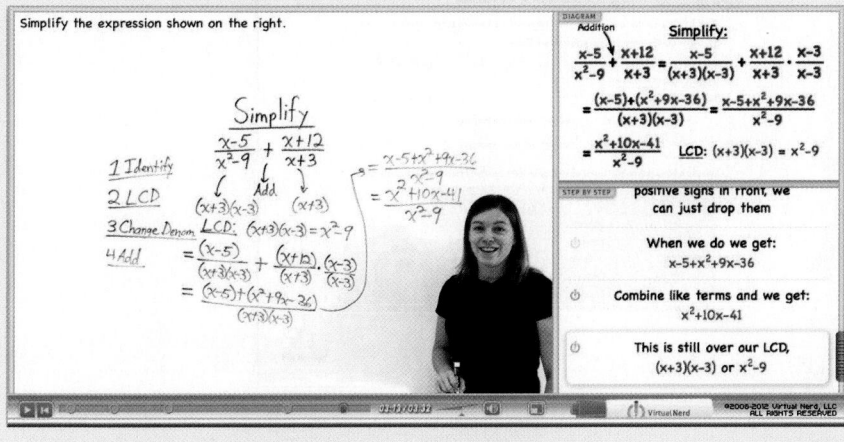

The Virtual Nerd™ videos offer additional instructional support for students as they work independently on the Practice and Problem-Solving exercises.

Differentiated *Instruction*

Differentiating instruction helps all students develop conceptual understanding, strengthen mathematical reasoning and problem-solving skills. *Pearson High School Mathematics Common Core Edition* offers many options for differentiating instruction throughout the lessons.

Developing Mathematically Proficient Students

The Common Core State Standards insist that all students must be supported in their learning so they can meet all of the standards. Differentiating instruction helps students achieve this goal.

The Student Companion, a student worktext, provides visuals and other learning aids, such as graphic organizers and vocabulary builders, that can help all students be successful.

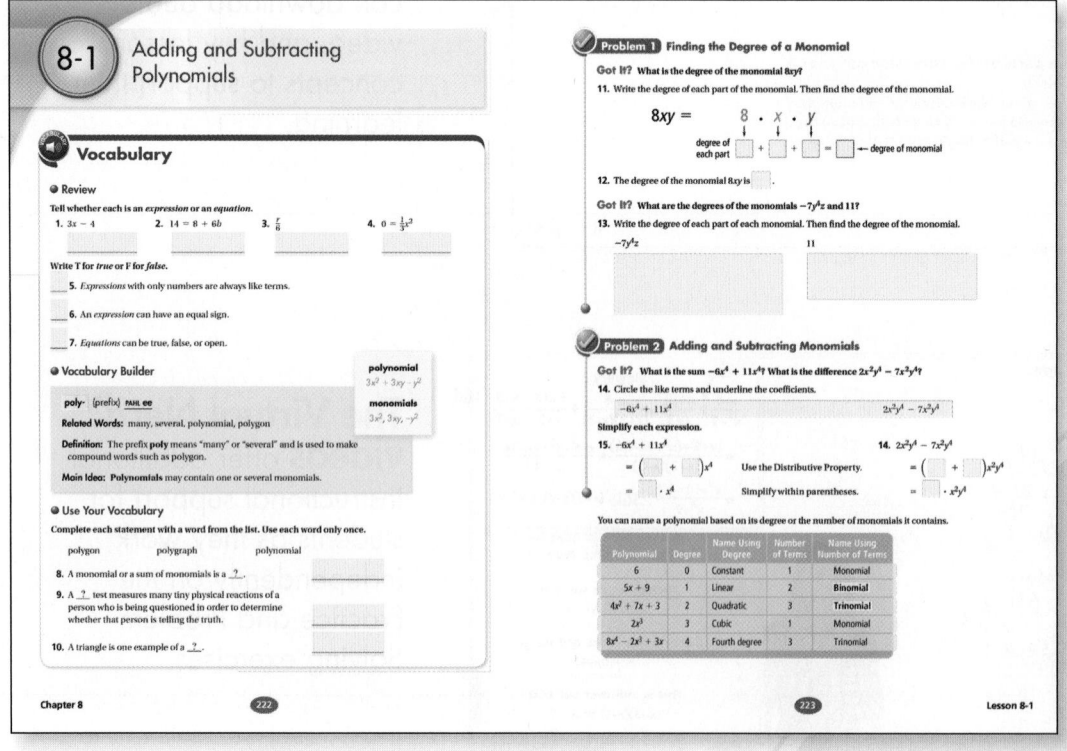

"Differentiated instruction does not change what is taught; it changes how it is taught."—Basia Hall

Lesson Resources include print and digital resources to assess, remediate, or enrich. Teachers will also find teaching tips and support for English Language Learners.

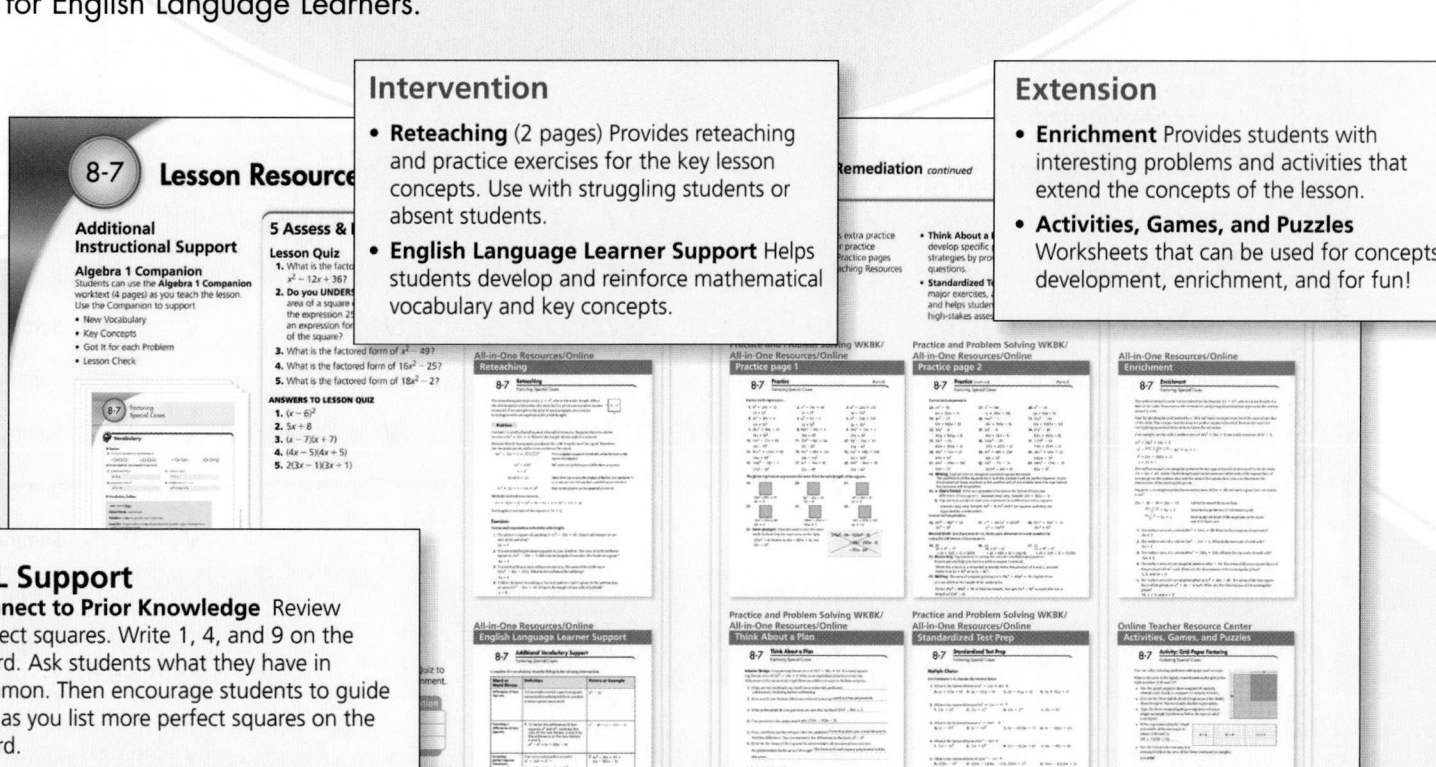

Intervention

- **Reteaching** (2 pages) Provides reteaching and practice exercises for the key lesson concepts. Use with struggling students or absent students.
- **English Language Learner Support** Helps students develop and reinforce mathematical vocabulary and key concepts.

Extension

- **Enrichment** Provides students with interesting problems and activities that extend the concepts of the lesson.
- **Activities, Games, and Puzzles** Worksheets that can be used for concepts development, enrichment, and for fun!

ELL Support

Connect to Prior Knowledge Review perfect squares. Write 1, 4, and 9 on the board. Ask students what they have in common. Then encourage students to guide you as you list more perfect squares on the board.

Use Manipulatives Model to students how to use grid paper to show a trinomial is a perfect square. One unit on the grid paper is "1", two vertical units is x, and a 2×2 square unit is x^2. $4x^2 + 4x + 1$ can be arranged into a perfect square. Challenge students to arrange other trinomials into squares and write the factors.

Assessment

Pearson High School Mathematics Common Core Edition offers a wealth of formative and summative assessments, all of which are aligned to the Standards for Mathematical Content and the Standards for Mathematical Practices.

All students will be held to the same expectations and will be assessed with a common assessment.

Developing Mathematically Proficient Students

		Textbook	PowerAlgebra.com	CD/DVD	Print Ancillary	Type
Course Level	**Diagnostic Assessments** • Screening Test • Entry Level Assessment • Diagnostic Tests	√	√	√	√	Diagnostic
	Summative Assessments • Quarter Test • Mid-course Test • Final Test • End-of-course Test	√	√	√	√	Summative
Chapter Level	Mid-Chapter Quiz	√	√			Formative
	Put It All Together	√	√			Summative
	Chapter Tests		√	√	√	Summative
	Cumulative Standards Practice	√	√			Summative
	Benchmark Tests		√	√	√	Summative
	Chapter Projects	√	√			Summative
	Performance Tasks	√	√	√	√	Summative
Lesson Level	Get Ready	√	√			Diagnostic
	Got It?	√	√			Formative
	Lesson Check	√	√			Formative
	Lesson Quizzes	√	√	√	√	Formative
	Self-Assessment		√			Formative
	Test Prep	√	√	√	√	Formative
Multi-level Assessments	Math XL for School		√			Formative
	ExamView			√		Formative, Summative
	SuccessTracker • Teacher Build-A-Test • Pre-made assessments		√			Formative, Summative

> "Fair, consistent, quality assessment is the only way to ensure that students are learning what you are teaching."
> —Bill Handlin

MathXL® for School
Go to PowerAlgebra.com

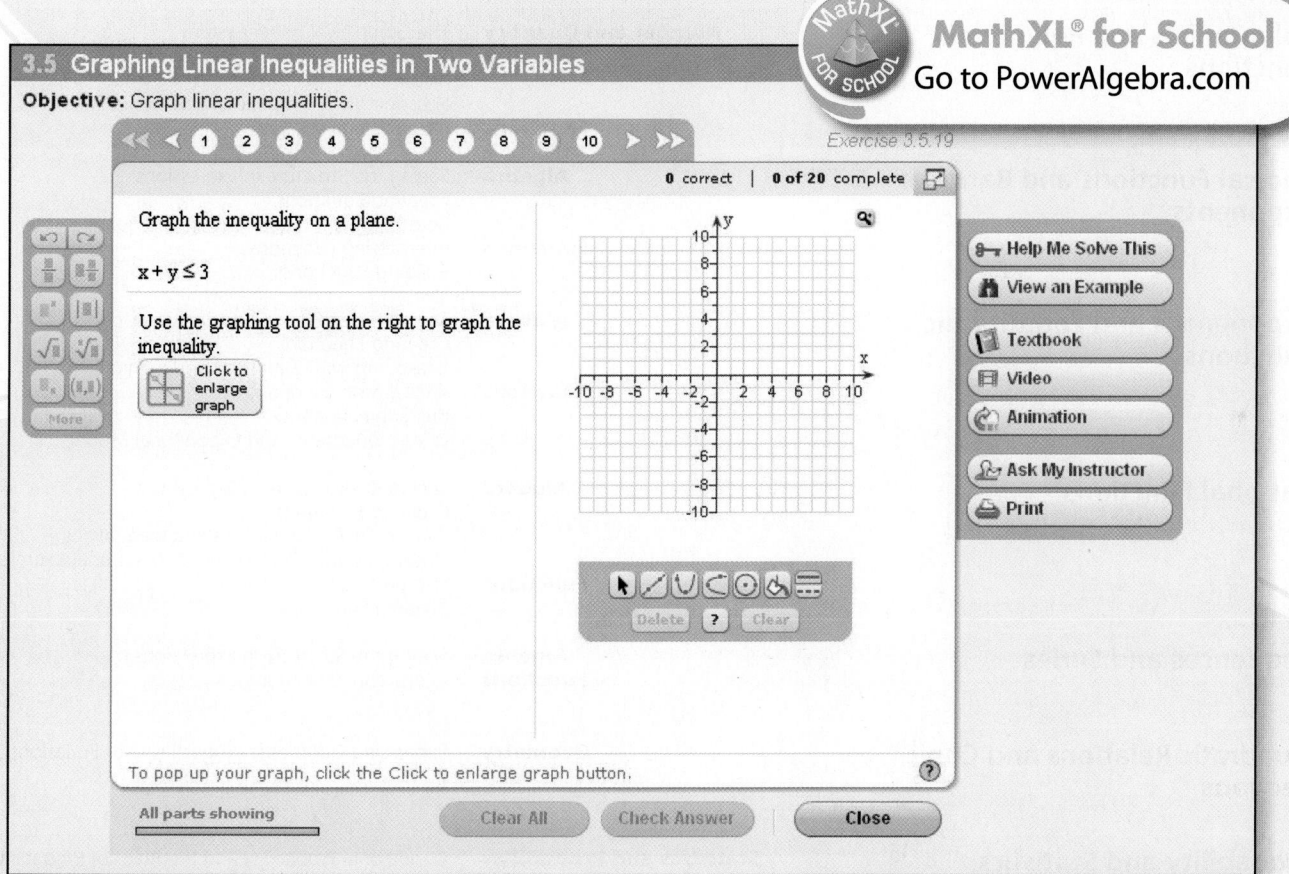

3.5 Graphing Linear Inequalities in Two Variables

Objective: Graph linear inequalities.

Exercise 3.5.19

1 2 3 4 5 6 7 8 9 10

0 correct | 0 of 20 complete

Graph the inequality on a plane.

$x + y \le 3$

Use the graphing tool on the right to graph the inequality.

Click to enlarge graph

To pop up your graph, click the Click to enlarge graph button.

Help Me Solve This
View an Example
Textbook
Video
Animation
Ask My Instructor
Print

All parts showing   Clear All   Check Answer   Close

MathXL for School is a powerful online homework, tutorial, and assessment system. It assigns students homework problems, automatically grades their work, and then provides immediate feedback and tutorial assistance to ensure mastery before high-stakes tests.

Big Ideas *and the* Common Core

Chapter Title	Common Core Conceptual Categories and Domains	
1 Expressions, Equations and Inequalities	Algebra	Seeing the Structure in Expressions Creating Equations
2 Functions, Equations, and Graphs	Algebra Functions	Creating Equations Interpreting Functions Building Functions
3 Linear Systems	Algebra	Creating Equations Reasoning with Equations and Inequalities
4 Quadratic Functions and Equations	Number and Quantity Algebra Functions	The Complex Number System Seeing the Structure in Expressions Creating Equations Arithmetic with Polynomials and Rational Expressions Interpreting Functions
5 Polynomials and Polynomial Functions	Number and Quantity Algebra Functions	The Complex Number System Seeing the Structure in Expressions Arithmetic with Polynomials and Rational Expressions Reasoning with Equations and Inequalities Interpreting Functions
6 Radical Functions and Rational Exponents	Algebra Functions	Seeing the Structure in Expressions Creating Equations Reasoning with Equations and Inequalities Interpreting Functions Building Functions
7 Exponential and Logarithmic Functions	Algebra Functions	Seeing the Structure in Expressions Creating Equations Reasoning with Equations and Inequalities Interpreting Functions Building Functions Linear, Quadratic, and Exponential Models
8 Rational Functions	Algebra Functions	Seeing the Structure in Expressions Creating Equations Reasoning with Equations and Inequalities Arithmetic with Polynomials and Rational Expressions Interpreting Functions Building Functions
9 Sequences and Series	Algebra Functions	Seeing the Structure in Expressions Interpreting Functions
10 Quadratic Relations and Conic Sections	Geometry	Expressing Geometric Properties with Equations
11 Probability and Statistics	Statistics and Probability	Conditional Probability and the Rules of Probability Using Probability to Make Decisions Making Inferences and Justifying Conclusions Interpreting Categorical and Quantitative Data
12 Matrices	Number and Quantity Geometry	Vectors and Matrix Quantities Expressing Geometric Properties with Equations Geometric Measurement and Dimension Congruence
13 Periodic Functions and Trigonometry	Functions	Interpreting Functions Trigonometric Functions
14 Trigonometric Identities and Equations	Functions Geometry	Trigonometric Functions Similarity, Right Triangles, and Trigonometry

The Big Ideas, the organizing structure of *Pearson Algebra 2 Mathematics Common Core Edition*, are closely aligned to the Conceptual Categories and Domains found in the Common Core State Standards.

Big Ideas	Essential Questions
Variable **Properties** **Solving Equations and Inequalities**	How do variables help you model real-world situations? How can you use the properties of real numbers to simplify algebraic expressions? How do you solve an equation or inequality?
Equivalence **Function** **Modeling**	Does it matter which form of a linear equation you use? How do you use transformations to help graph absolute value functions? How can you model data with a linear function?
Function **Equivalent** **Solving Equations and Inequalities**	How does representing functions graphically help you solve a system of equations? How does writing equivalent equations help you solve a system of equations? How are the properties of equality used in the matrix solution of a system of equations?
Equivalence **Function** **Solving Equations and Inequalities**	What are the advantages of a quadratic function in vertex form? In standard form? How is any quadratic function related to the parent quadratic function $y = x^2$? How are the real solutions of a quadratic equation related to the graph of the related quadratic function?
Function **Equivalence** **Solving Equations and Inequalities**	What does the degree of a polynomial tell you about its related polynomial function? For a polynomial function, how are factors, zeros, and x-intercepts related? For a polynomial equation, how are factors and roots related?
Equivalence **Solving Equations and Inequalities** **Function**	To simplify the nth root of an expression, what must be true about the expression? When you square each side of an equation, is the resulting equation equivalent to the original? How are a function and its inverse function related?
Modeling **Equivalence** **Function**	How do you model a quantity that changes regularly over time by the same percentage? How are exponents and logarithms related? How are exponential functions and logarithmic functions related?
Proportionality **Function** **Equivalence**	Are two quantities inversely proportional if an increase in one corresponds to a decrease in the other? What kinds of asymptote are possible for a rational function? Are a rational expression and its simplified form equivalent?
Variable **Equivalence** **Modeling**	How can you represent the terms of a sequence explicitly? How can you represent them recursively? What are equivalent explicit and recursive definitions for an arithmetic sequence? How can you model a geometric sequence? How can you model its sum?
Modeling **Equivalence** **Coordinate Geometry**	What is the intersection of a cone and a plane parallel to a line along the side of the cone? What is the graph of $\frac{x^2}{9} = \frac{y^2}{9} = 1$ What is the difference between the algebraic representations of ellipses and hyperbolas?
Probability **Data Collection and Analysis**	What is the difference between a permutation and a combination? What is the difference between experimental and theoretical probability? How are measures of central tendency different from standard deviation?
Data Representation **Modeling** **Transformations**	How can you use a matrix to organize data? How can you use a matrix equation to model a real-world situation? How can a matrix represent a transformation of a geometric figure in the plane?
Modeling **Function**	How can you model periodic behavior? What function has as its graph a sine curve with amplitude 4, period π, and a minimum at the origin? If you know the value of $\sin \theta$, how can you find $\cos \theta$, $\tan \theta$, $\csc \theta$, $\sec \theta$, and $\cot \theta$?
Equivalence **Function**	How do you verify that an equation involving the variable x is an identity? A trigonometric function corresponds one number to many, so how can its inverse be a function? How do the trigonometric functions relate to the trigonometric ratios for a right triangle?

BIGideas

These Big Ideas are the organizing ideas for the study of important areas of mathematics: algebra, geometry, and statistics.

Stay connected! These Big Ideas will help you understand how the math you study in high school fits together.

Algebra

Properties
- In the transition from arithmetic to algebra, attention shifts from arithmetic operations (addition, subtraction, multiplication, and division) to use of the *properties* of these operations.
- All of the facts of arithmetic and algebra follow from certain properties.

Variable
- Quantities are used to form expressions, equations, and inequalities.
- An expression refers to a quantity but does not make a statement about it. An equation (or an inequality) is a statement about the quantities it mentions.
- Using variables in place of numbers in equations (or inequalities) allows the statement of relationships among numbers that are unknown or unspecified.

Equivalence
- A single quantity may be represented by many different expressions.
- The facts about a quantity may be expressed by many different equations (or inequalities).

Solving Equations & Inequalities
- Solving an equation is the process of rewriting the equation to make what it says about its variable(s) as simple as possible.
- Properties of numbers and equality can be used to transform an equation (or inequality) into equivalent, simpler equations (or inequalities) in order to find solutions.
- Useful information about equations and inequalities (including solutions) can be found by analyzing graphs or tables.
- The numbers and types of solutions vary predictably, based on the type of equation.

Proportionality
- Two quantities are *proportional* if they have the same ratio in each instance where they are measured together.
- Two quantities are *inversely proportional* if they have the same product in each instance where they are measured together.

Function
- A function is a relationship between variables in which each value of the input variable is associated with a unique value of the output variable.
- Functions can be represented in a variety of ways, such as graphs, tables, equations, or words. Each representation is particularly useful in certain situations.
- Some important families of functions are developed through transformations of the simplest form of the function.
- New functions can be made from other functions by applying arithmetic operations or by applying one function to the output of another.

Modeling
- Many real-world mathematical problems can be represented algebraically. These representations can lead to algebraic solutions.
- A function that models a real-world situation can then be used to make estimates or predictions about future occurrences.

Statistics and Probability

Data Collection and Analysis

- Sampling techniques are used to gather data from real-world situations. If the data are representative of the larger population, inferences can be made about that population.
- Biased sampling techniques yield data unlikely to be representative of the larger population.
- Sets of numerical data are described using measures of central tendency and dispersion.

Data Representation

- The most appropriate data representations depend on the type of data—quantitative or qualitative, and univariate or bivariate.
- Line plots, box plots, and histograms are different ways to show distribution of data over a possible range of values.

Probability

- Probability expresses the likelihood that a particular event will occur.
- Data can be used to calculate an experimental probability, and mathematical properties can be used to determine a theoretical probability.
- Either experimental or theoretical probability can be used to make predictions or decisions about future events.
- Various counting methods can be used to develop theoretical probabilities.

Geometry

Visualization

- Visualization can help you connect properties of real objects with two-dimensional drawings of these objects.

Transformations

- Transformations are mathematical functions that model concrete operations with figures.
- Transformations may be described geometrically or by coordinates.
- Symmetries of figures may be defined and classified by transformations.

Measurement

- Some attributes of geometric figures, such as length, area, volume, and angle measure, are measurable. Units are used to describe these attributes.

Reasoning & Proof

- Definitions establish meanings and remove possible misunderstanding.
- Other truths are more complex and difficult to see. It is often possible to verify complex truths by reasoning from simpler ones by using deductive reasoning.

Similarity

- Two geometric figures are similar when corresponding lengths are proportional and corresponding angles are congruent.
- Areas of simlar figures are proportional to the squares of their corresponding lengths.
- Volumes of similar figures are proportional to the cubes of their corresponding lengths.

Coordinate Geometry

- A coordinate system on a line is a number line on which points are labeled, corresponding to the real numbers.
- A coordinate system in a plane is formed by two perpendicular number lines, called the x-and y-axes, and the quadrants they form. The coordinate plane can be used to graph many functions.
- It is possible to verify some complex truths using deductive reasoning in combination with Distance, Midpoint, and Slope formulas.

Efficacy *Research*

Proven Effective *Pearson High School Mathematics Common Core Edition* is built on the pedagogical approach of the successful *Prentice Hall High School Mathematics* © 2011 with proven efficacy.

Successful Results with *Prentice Hall Algebra 1!* After two years of use, students using *Prentice Hall Algebra 1* © 2011 showed significant learning gains in math achievement. Students scored higher on both multiple-choice and open-response items than their peers in the control group using a different high school math program.

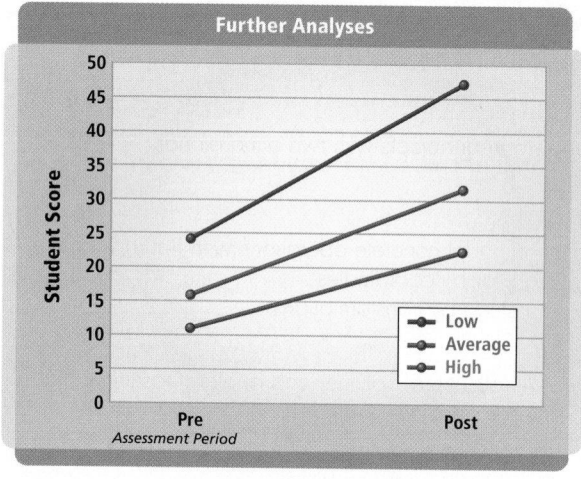

Further analyses indicate that *Prentice Hall Algebra 1* students of **all math ability** levels showed **greater gains** on the Algebra 1 open-response test than their comparison peers.

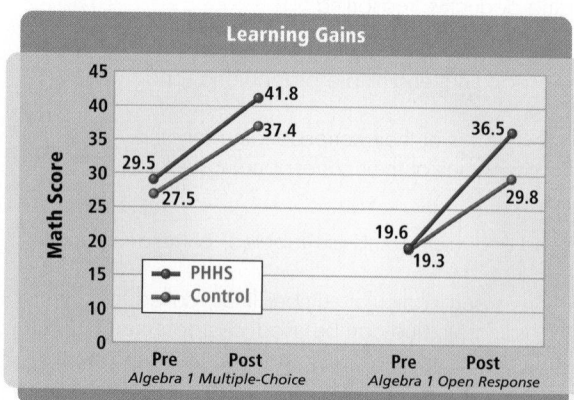

The results for students in **all subgroups**—females and males, special education students and regular education, students of various ethnic/racial backgrounds, and students receiving free/reduced lunch and those not—**showed significant learning gains,** according to study data.

PRES Associates conducted the randomized control trial study during the 2009–2010 and 2010–2011 school years, studying 1069 students in grades 8–12 and 32 math teachers. The full report of results can be accessed at www.pearsoned.com.

Behind the Research Equally as important, students using Pearson's *Prentice Hall Algebra 1* reported feeling more prepared for college math courses and perceived their math program more favorably than students using other math programs. Teachers also responded very positively to the features of the program.

> I like *Prentice Hall High School Mathematics* better than other programs because it is easier to understand. It's also more interesting.
>
> - Washington Student

> I'm glad that you have made this program for Algebra 1 because now I have a better understanding of what I'm working on. Rather than just doing work out of the textbook all the time, I can have fun with math finally!
>
> - New Jersey Student

> The technology helps to enhance what I am learning. When I look at the technology, I am able to really understand the material I am being taught.
>
> - Rhode Island Student

> I really liked the opening Solve It; I thought they were really great at getting the kids thinking and bringing out divergent answers.
>
> - Idaho Teacher

> I think *Prentice Hall High School Mathematics* has enough material to be challenging to students of all levels and meet them where they are.
>
> - Ohio Teacher

> I wasn't sure I would like *Prentice Hall High School Mathematics* at the beginning of the year, but I love it now and can't imagine teaching without it!
>
> - New Jersey Teacher

Standards *for Mathematical Practice*

The Standards for Mathematical Practice are an important part of the Common Core State Standards. They describe varieties of proficiency that teachers should focus on helping their students develop. These practices draw from the NCTM Process Standards of problem solving, reasoning and proof, communication, representation, and connections and the strands of mathematical proficiency specified in the National Research Council's report *Adding It Up*: adaptive reasoning, strategic competence, conceptual understanding, procedural fluency, and productive disposition.

These eight Standards for Mathematical Practice are often put into four groups.

Making Sense of and Solving Problems

1 Make sense of problems and persevere in solving them.

Proficient math thinkers are able to read through a problem situation and can put together a workable solution path to solve the problem posed. They are able to analyze the information provided and identify constraints and dependencies. Students can identify multiple entries to a problem solution and will choose an efficient and effective entry point.

To help students develop proficiency with this Standard, teachers should provide enough time for students to explore the problem situations. As needed, teachers can facilitate students' discussion by asking them to identify the problem they are asked to solve, to think about similar problems that they have previously solved, and to describe their solution plan.

6 Attend to precision.

Proficient math thinkers communicate clearly and precisely the approach they are using. They can identify the meaning of symbols that they use and always remember to specify units of measure and to label accurately graphical models. They use mathematical terms precisely and express their answers with the appropriate degree of accuracy.

To help students develop proficiency with this Standard, teachers should encourage clear and precise mathematical discourse in the classroom. As needed, teachers can help students attend to precision by asking them to identify the symbols that they use in their mathematical models, to specify the units of measures called for in the problem, and to explain mathematical terms and expressions. Ask students to describe an alternate strategy or method that they can use to check their solutions to problems.

Reasoning and Communicating

2 Reason abstractly and quantitatively.

Proficient math thinkers make sense of quantities in problem situations. They are able to both represent a problem situation using symbols or equations and explain what the symbols or equation represent in relationship to a problem situation. As they model a situation symbolically or mathematically, they can explain the meaning of the quantities.

To help students develop proficiency with this Standard, teachers should help students break down a problem situation and analyze options for modeling or representing the problem situation mathematically. Teachers can ask students what the quantities or variables in an equation represent and how they relate to each other.

3 Construct viable arguments and critique the reasoning of others.

Proficient math thinkers and problem solvers communicate clearly and convincingly their problem solutions. They are able to construct sound mathematical arguments and develop and defend conjectures to explain mathematical situations. They make use of examples and counterexamples to support their arguments and justify their conclusions. When asked, they are able to respond clearly and logically to the positions and conclusions of others, and are able to compare two arguments, identifying any flaws in logic or reasoning that the arguments may contain. They ask questions to clarify or improve the position of a classmate.

To help students develop proficiency with this Standard, teachers can provide frequent opportunities for students to engage in mathematical discourse in the classroom. Teachers should have students share their solution strategies, explain what their solution means, and defend their selected strategies. Teachers can also encourage students to compare and contrast different strategies used to solve a given problem. Teachers can ask students to explain how they know their solutions are correct or those of classmates may not be correct.

Representing and Connecting ....

4 Model with mathematics.

Strong math thinkers are able to use mathematics to represent a problem situation and can make connections between a real-world problem situation and mathematics. They see the applicability of mathematics to solve every-day problems and can explain how geometry can be used to solve a carpentry problem or algebra to solve a proportional relationship problem. They are able to define and map relationships among quantities in a problem, using appropriate tools to do so. They analyze the relationships and draw conclusions about the solutions.

To help students develop proficiency with this Standard, teachers can provide a variety of contexts for students to apply mathematics. For each problem situation, teachers can ask students to think of an equation or a graphical representation that describes the problem. Teachers can also ask students to identify what quantities they should use to solve the problem and what the numbers in the solution represent. Teachers should also ask students to defend their solutions, explaining how they know their solutions are correct.

5 Use appropriate tools strategically.

Strong math thinkers strategize about which tools are more helpful to solve a problem situation. They consider all tools, from paper and pencil to protractors and rulers, to calculators and software applications. They are able to articulate the appropriateness of different tools and recognize which would best serve the needs for a given problem. They are especially insightful about technological tools and use them in ways that deepen or extend their understanding of concepts. They also make use of mental tools, such as estimation, to determine the appropriateness of a solution.

To help students develop proficiency with this Standard, teachers can encourage students to think about the range of tools that might be used to solve a given problem and then to justify their selection of a tool. Teachers should have students articulate the strengths and weaknesses of different tools as part of their selection process. Teachers should also encourage students to estimate a solution before they begin to solve the problem to help them monitor whether their solution path is helping them reach an accurate solution.

Seeing Structure and Generalizing ....

7 Look for and make use of structure.

Strong math thinkers go beyond simply solving problems presented to see the structure of mathematics in these problems and to generalize mathematics principles from this structure. They are able to see complicated expressions or equations as single objects composed of many parts.

To help students develop proficiency with this Standard, teachers should spend time having students look at the structure of an equation or expression. Teachers can ask students to talk about what they notice about a given solution and what would change if different numbers or quantities were used. Teachers should also encourage students to analyze an expression, asking what each term in an expression or equation represents.

8 Look for and express regularity in repeated reasoning.

Proficient math thinkers notice when calculations are repeated and can uncover both general methods and shortcuts for solving similar problems.

To help students develop proficiency with this Standard, teachers can encourage students to engage in mathematical discourse about solutions to find and express regularity in reasoning about concepts. As students uncover regularity in mathematical behavior, teachers should ask students to propose shortcuts or generalized methods for solving similar types of problems.

Pearson High School Mathematics Common Core

This **lesson walk-through** provides an overview of the instructional structure of each lesson. It also highlights the many opportunities each lesson presents to help students become proficient with the **Standards for Mathematical Practice** (MP) in the Common Core State Standards.

1 Interactive *Learning*

Each lesson opens with a **Solve It!**, the key feature in the Interactive Learning phase of the lesson. The Solve It! presents a problem situation that relates to the math concepts of the lesson. Students interact with these concepts as they work individually or collaboratively to find a solution to the problem.

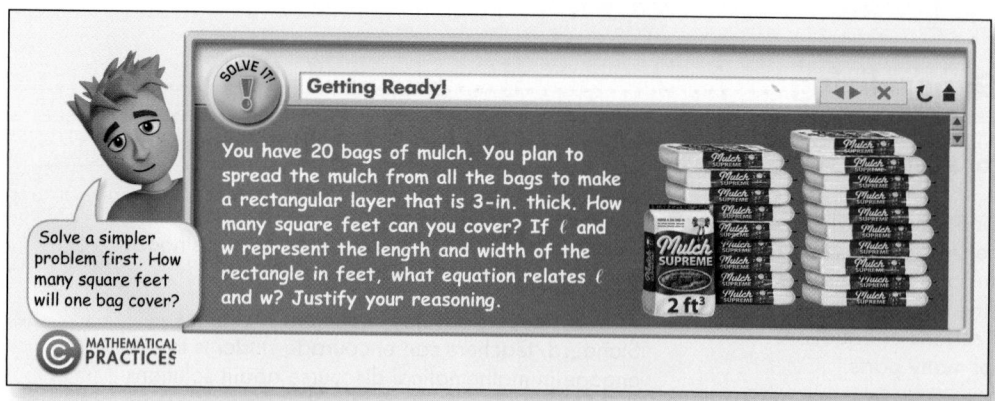

Students first look to **make sense of the problem** and to come up with a solution plan. (MP 1)

They frequently **build mathematical models** to represent a problem (MP 4) and are asked to **construct viable arguments** to justify their conclusions. (MP 3)

2 Guided *Instruction*

The Guided Instruction phase of the lesson begins with the **Essential Understanding** in which the focus of study for the lesson is formalized. The frequent **Take Note** boxes present key concepts in precise mathematical language.

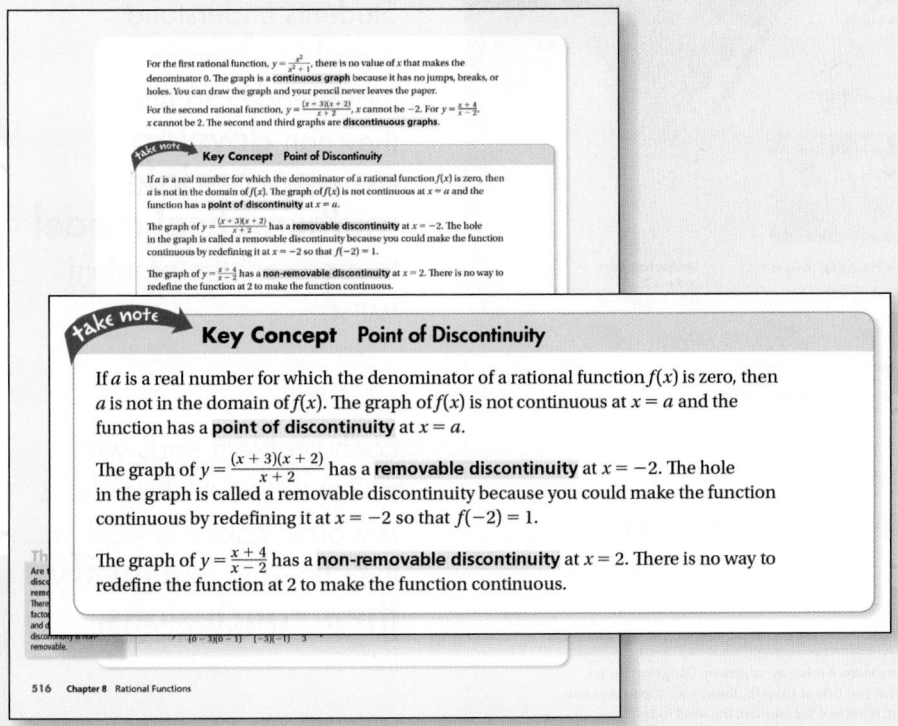

In the Take Note boxes, students are presented with clear explanations of key terms and concepts to help them **communicate precisely.** (MP 6)

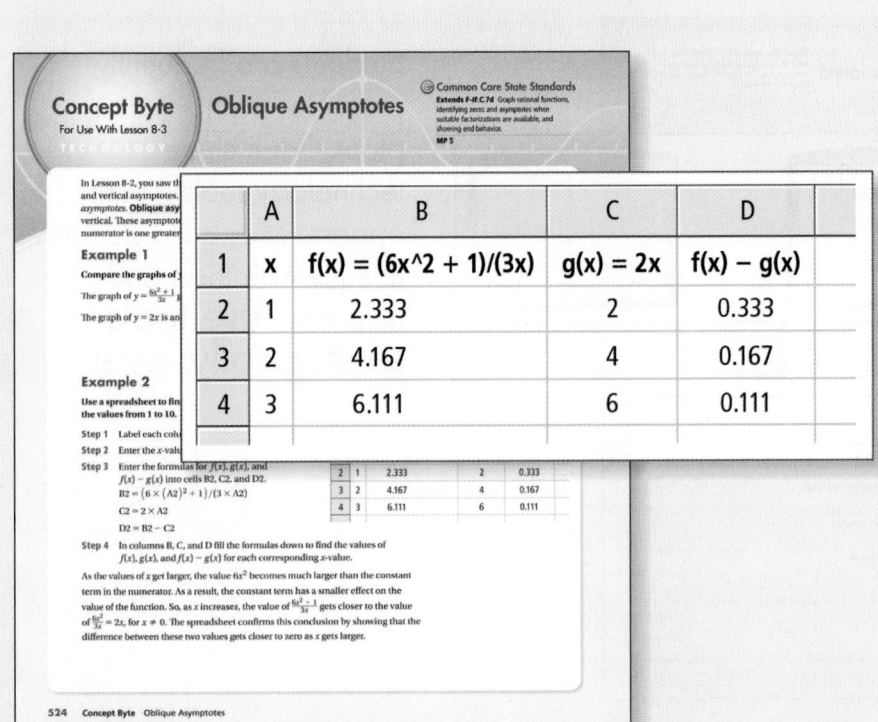

Students' experiences with a range of tools throughout the program help them become fluent with their uses so they can **choose tools strategically** when solving problems. (MP 5)

Visually rich problems, found throughout the program, present the problem situation in a medium that many young people find more relevant.

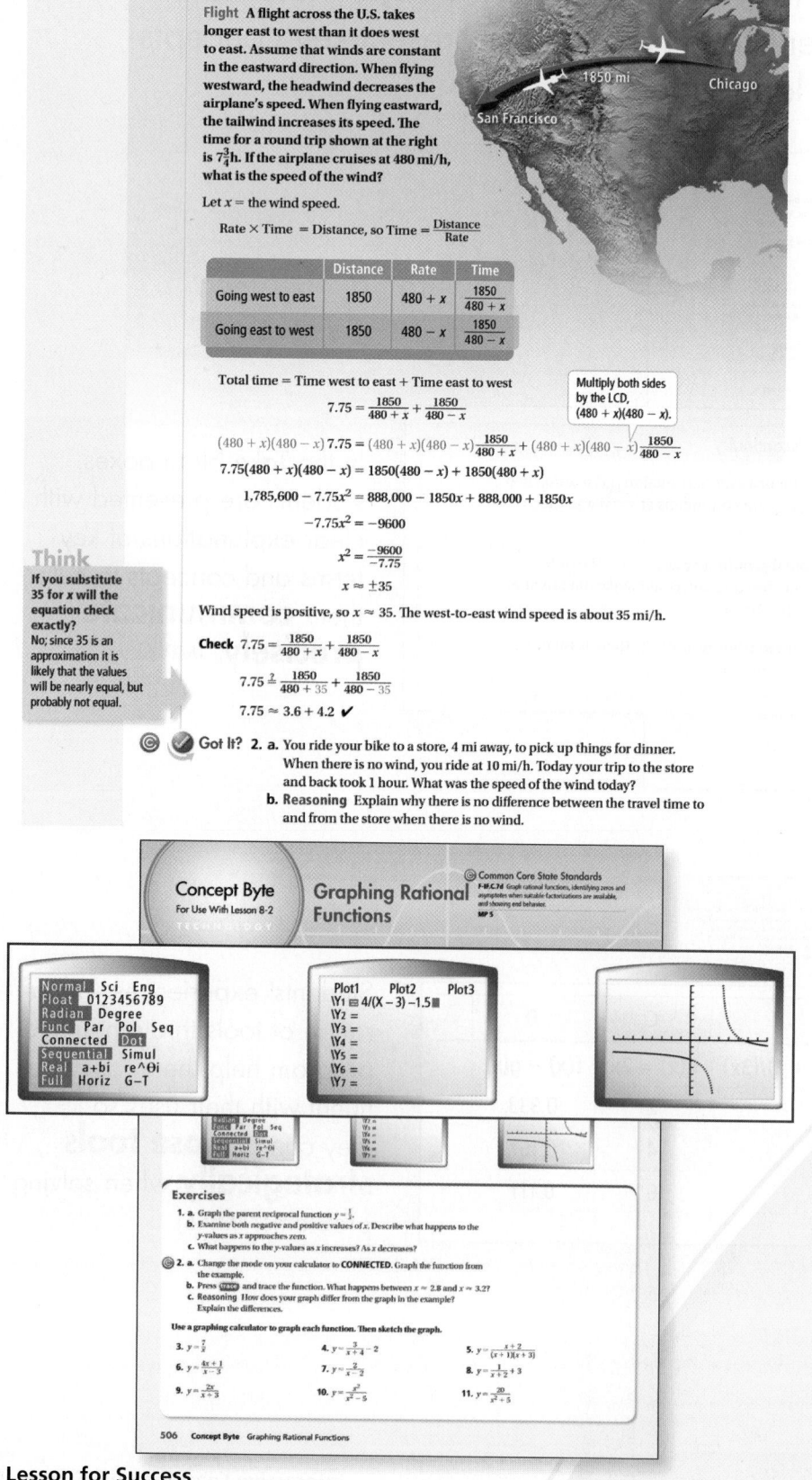

Students understand a problem situation more readily so that they can **develop an appropriate mathematical model** to represent the problem. (MP 4)

Each problem ends with a Got It? in which students are often asked to explain their thinking and **justify their conclusions.** (MP 3)

Students are frequently presented with solution plans that include technology tools. These opportunities build students' fluency with tools and help them **use tools strategically.** (MP 5)

Students encounter **Plan** and **Think**, boxes, key features of the program. These boxes model through questions and answers the thinking that *proficient problem solvers* use. Students also encounter **Know-Need-Plan** boxes, another key feature of the program. These boxes model phases of the problem-solving process to help students strengthen their problem-solving abilities.

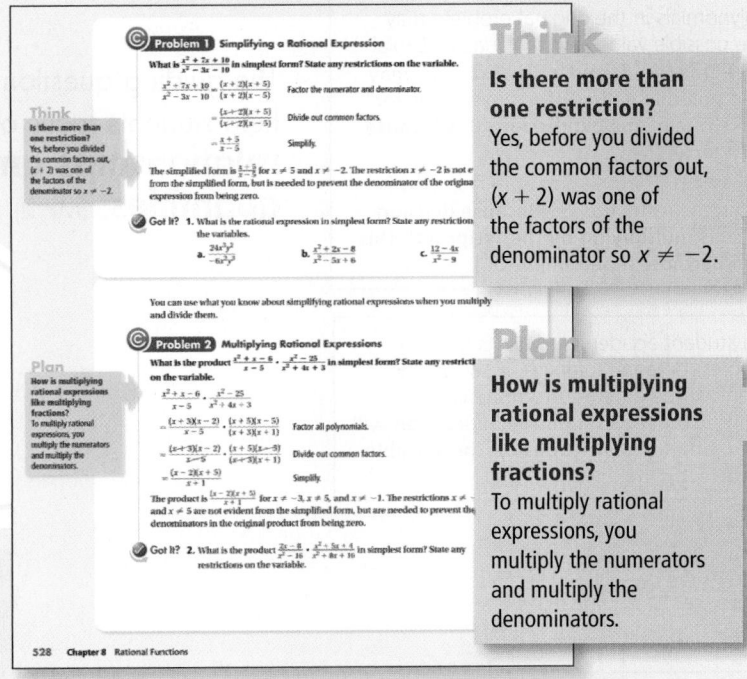

Is there more than one restriction?
Yes, before you divided the common factors out, $(x + 2)$ was one of the factors of the denominator so $x \neq -2$.

How is multiplying rational expressions like multiplying fractions?
To multiply rational expressions, you multiply the numerators and multiply the denominators.

The Think and Plan boxes can model thinking to **represent problem situations symbolically.** (MP 2)

They remind students to look for **similar problem situations** that they previously solved. (MP 1)

They also help students step back from a process to **recognize the structure** of a mathematical solution. (MP 7)

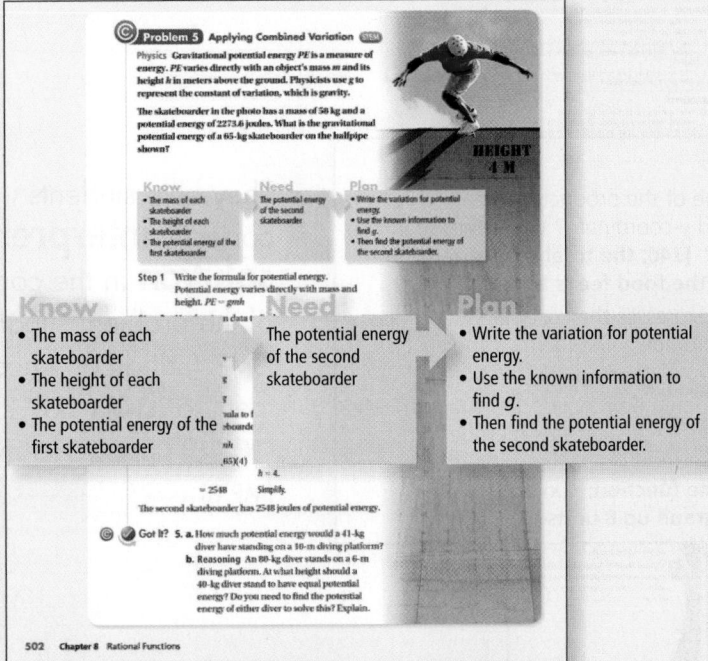

- The mass of each skateboarder
- The height of each skateboarder
- The potential energy of the first skateboarder

The potential energy of the second skateboarder

- Write the variation for potential energy.
- Use the known information to find g.
- Then find the potential energy of the second skateboarder.

The Know-Need-Plan boxes guide students to **make a solution plan.** (MP 1)

Using the Lesson for Success

Guiding questions in the Teacher's Edition offer prompts that teachers can ask to help students **persevere** in finding a workable entry point for the the problem. (MP 1) Guiding questions can also help students **reason quantitatively.** (MP 2)

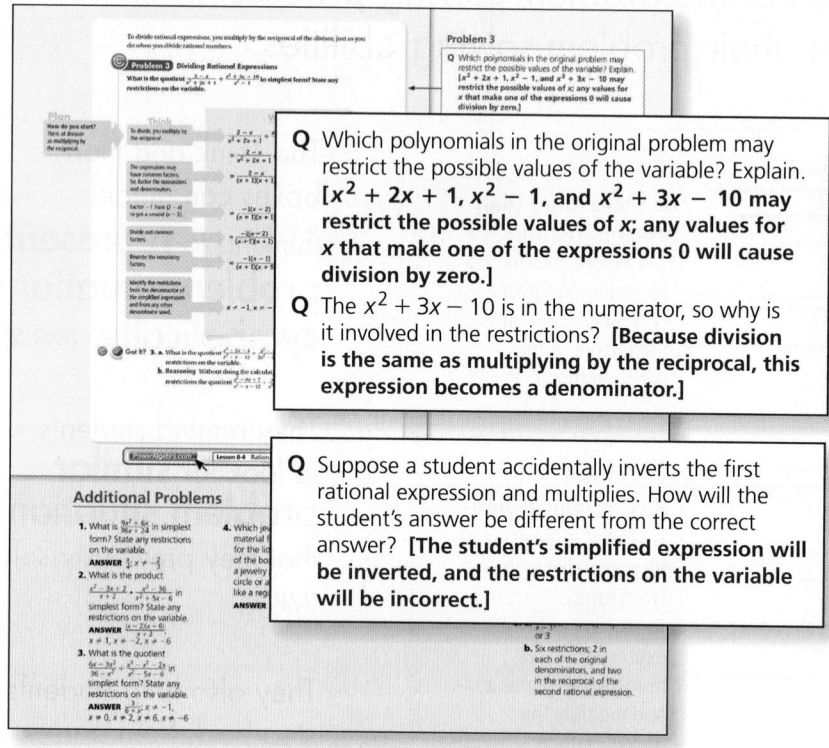

Q Which polynomials in the original problem may restrict the possible values of the variable? Explain. [$x^2 + 2x + 1$, $x^2 - 1$, and $x^2 + 3x - 10$ may restrict the possible values of x; any values for x that make one of the expressions 0 will cause division by zero.]

Q The $x^2 + 3x - 10$ is in the numerator, so why is it involved in the restrictions? [Because division is the same as multiplying by the reciprocal, this expression becomes a denominator.]

Q Suppose a student accidentally inverts the first rational expression and multiplies. How will the student's answer be different from the correct answer? [The student's simplified expression will be inverted, and the restrictions on the variable will be incorrect.]

The guiding questions help students focus on the **relationships among quantities.** (MP 2)

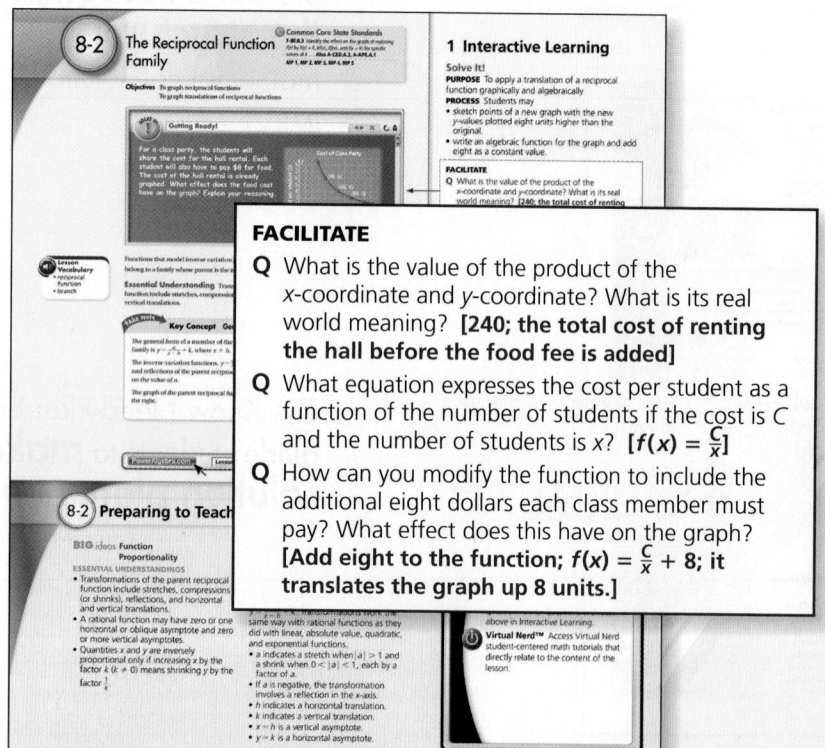

FACILITATE

Q What is the value of the product of the x-coordinate and y-coordinate? What is its real world meaning? [240; the total cost of renting the hall before the food fee is added]

Q What equation expresses the cost per student as a function of the number of students if the cost is C and the number of students is x? [$f(x) = \frac{C}{x}$]

Q How can you modify the function to include the additional eight dollars each class member must pay? What effect does this have on the graph? [Add eight to the function; $f(x) = \frac{C}{x} + 8$; it translates the graph up 8 units.]

They help students correctly **interpret a solution** in the context of the problem situation (SMP 4) and can encourage them to **look for generalizable** methods. (MP 8)

3 Lesson *Check*

The Lesson Checks present timely opportunities for assessing students' understanding of the lesson content. The questions in **Do You Know HOW?** assess students' procedural fluency while the questions in **Do You UNDERSTAND?** focus on students' conceptual understanding of the concepts. Together, they provide a comprehensive assessment of students' proficiency with the lesson content.

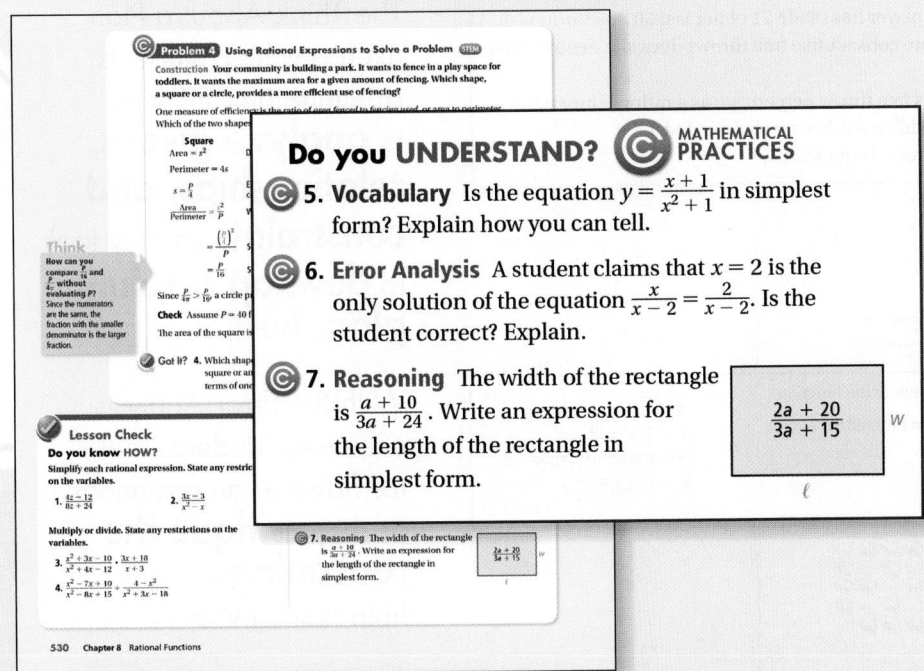

Do you UNDERSTAND? — **MATHEMATICAL PRACTICES**

5. **Vocabulary** Is the equation $y = \frac{x+1}{x^2+1}$ in simplest form? Explain how you can tell.

6. **Error Analysis** A student claims that $x = 2$ is the only solution of the equation $\frac{x}{x-2} = \frac{2}{x-2}$. Is the student correct? Explain.

7. **Reasoning** The width of the rectangle is $\frac{a+10}{3a+24}$. Write an expression for the length of the rectangle in simplest form.

$\frac{2a+20}{3a+15}$ w

ℓ

The Vocabulary exercises require that students **attend to precision** in communicating mathematical concepts. (MP 6)

Reasoning and Writing exercises ask students to **construct arguments** to justify their conclusions. (MP 3)

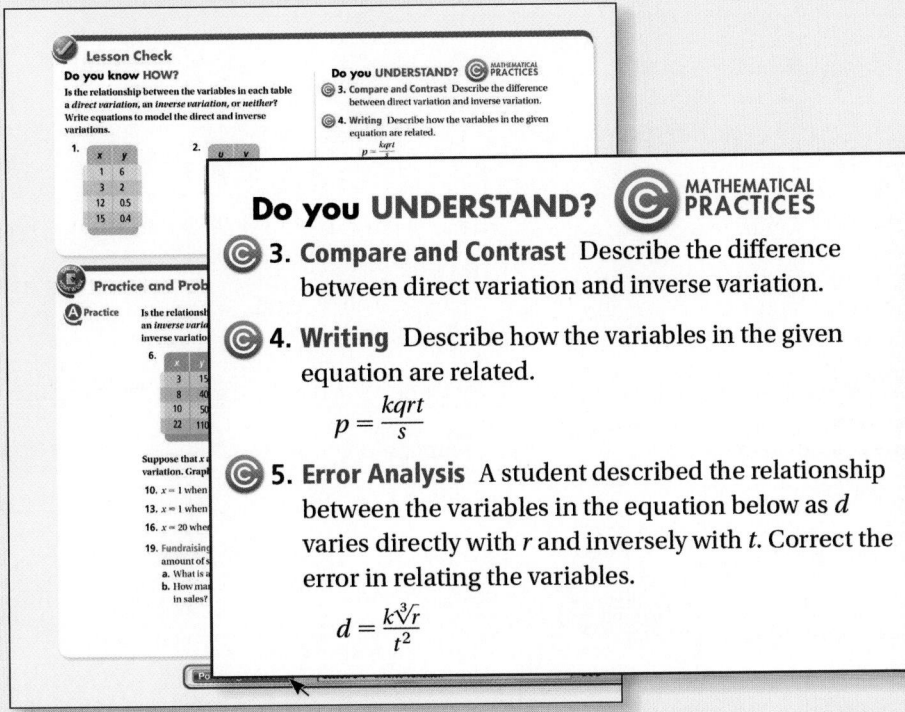

Do you UNDERSTAND? — **MATHEMATICAL PRACTICES**

3. **Compare and Contrast** Describe the difference between direct variation and inverse variation.

4. **Writing** Describe how the variables in the given equation are related.

$$p = \frac{kqrt}{s}$$

5. **Error Analysis** A student described the relationship between the variables in the equation below as d varies directly with r and inversely with t. Correct the error in relating the variables.

$$d = \frac{k\sqrt[3]{r}}{t^2}$$

Compare and Contract exercises can focus students on mathematical structures from which they can **generalize methods** or **find efficient shortcuts.** (MP 8)

4 Practice

The Practice phase offers students opportunities to solidify their procedural fluency and conceptual understanding of the lesson content. The exercises with **red headings** and the CC logo © indicate opportunities for students to build on the Standards for Mathematical Practice.

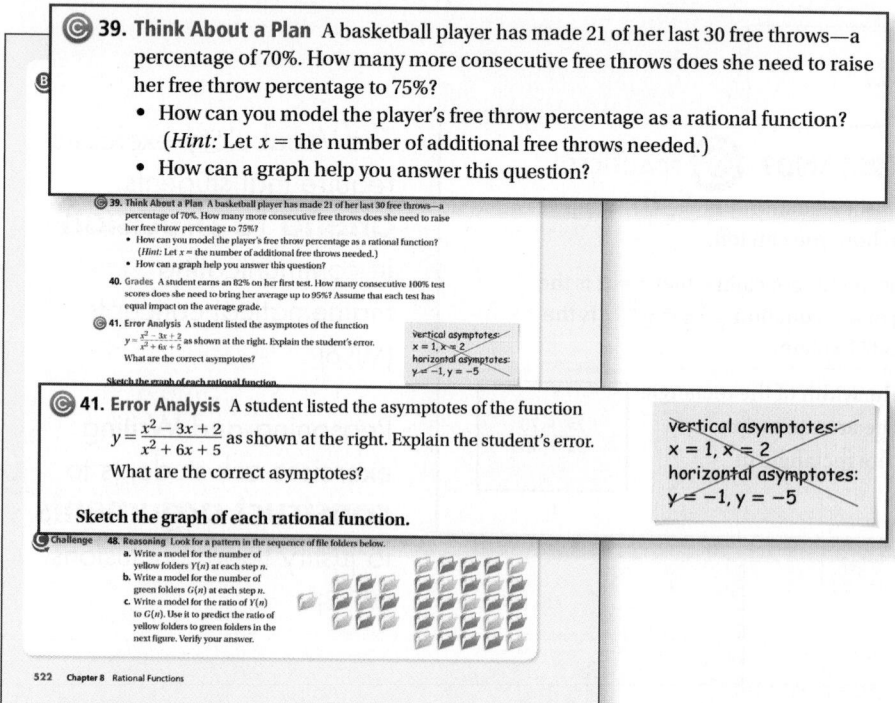

© **39. Think About a Plan** A basketball player has made 21 of her last 30 free throws—a percentage of 70%. How many more consecutive free throws does she need to raise her free throw percentage to 75%?
  • How can you model the player's free throw percentage as a rational function? (*Hint:* Let x = the number of additional free throws needed.)
  • How can a graph help you answer this question?

© **41. Error Analysis** A student listed the asymptotes of the function
$y = \dfrac{x^2 - 3x + 2}{x^2 + 6x + 5}$ as shown at the right. Explain the student's error.
What are the correct asymptotes?

vertical asymptotes:
$x = 1, x = 2$
horizontal asymptotes:
$y = -1, y = -5$

Sketch the graph of each rational function.

The Think About a Plan exercises help students structure their thinking to **analyze givens, relationships, and constraints** as they look to **develop a solution plan.** (MP 1)

With the Error Analysis exercises, students look for flaws in an argument as they **critique the reasoning** of others to help them (MP 3)

The exercises with **blue run-in heads** are multidisciplinary problem situations, including many STEM-related situations.

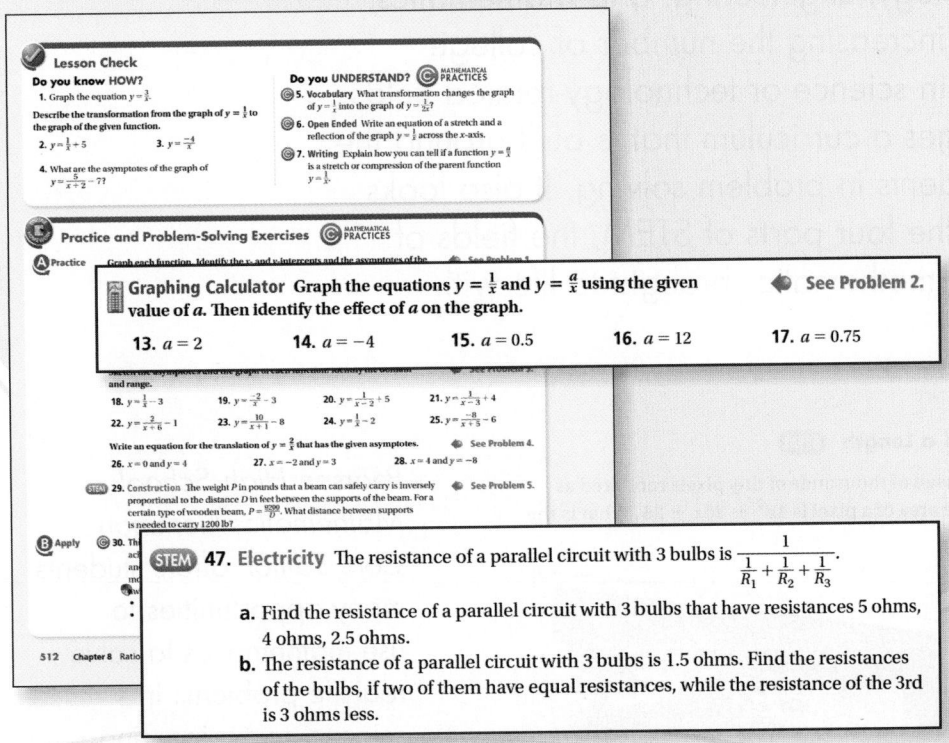

Graphing Calculator exercises help students refine their strategic understanding of **appropriate uses of tools.** (MP 5)

Some reasoning exercises help students call for **repeated reasoning** about mathematical processes or methods. (MP 8)

5 Assess and Remediate

Each lesson ends with a **Lesson Quiz** and options for differentiated instruction. On the Lesson Resources pages of the Teacher's Edition, personalized prescriptions are available based on a student's Lesson Quiz results. These prescriptions enable teachers to make data-driven decisions about assignments for intervention, on-level, and extension.

PRESCRIPTION FOR REMEDIATION
Use the student work on the Lesson Quiz to prescribe a differentiated review assignment.

Points	Differentiated Remediation
0–2	Intervention
3–4	On-level
5	Extension

What is STEM education?

STEM, or **S**cience, **T**echnology, **E**ngineering, and **M**athematics, Education has as its goal increasing the number of college students choosing majors in science or technology-related fields. STEM Education encourages a curriculum that is built around the active engagement of students in problem solving. It also looks for greater integration of the four parts of STEM, the fields of science, engineering, and mathematics brought to life with innovative technologies.

ⓒ **Problem 2** Factoring to Find a Length **STEM**

Computers Digital images are composed of thousands of tiny pixels rendered as squares, as shown below. Suppose the area of a pixel is $4x^2 + 20x + 25$. What is the length of one side of the pixel?

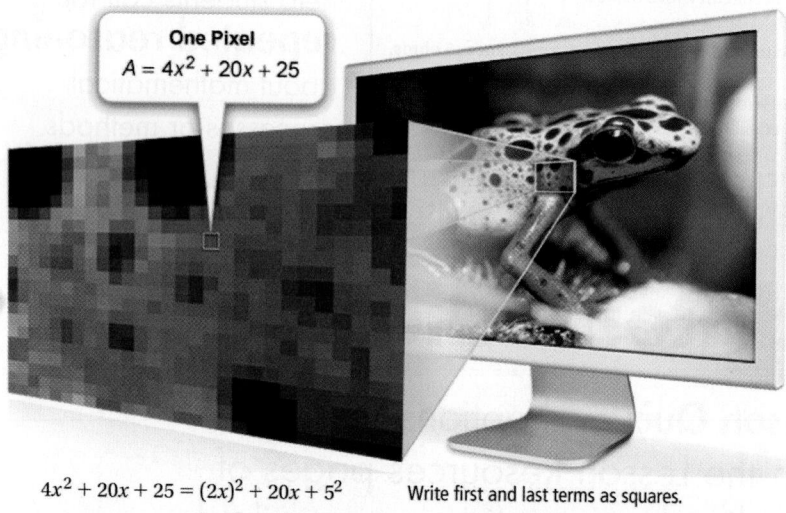

One Pixel
$A = 4x^2 + 20x + 25$

$$4x^2 + 20x + 25 = (2x)^2 + 20x + 5^2$$ Write first and last terms as squares.
$$= (2x)^2 + 2(2x)(5) + 5^2$$ Does middle term equal $2ab$? $20x = 2(2x)(5)$ ✔
$$= (2x + 5)^2$$ Write as the square of a binomial.

The length of one side of the pixel is $2x + 5$.

Pearson High School Mathematics Common Core Edition offers students many opportunities to use mathematics to solve real-life problems in science or engineering. These opportunities are highlighted with a **STEM** icon that reminds students that the problem they are to work on has a tie-in to science, engineering, or technology.

STEM **64. Manufacturing** A company is making metal rods with a target diameter of 1.5 mm. A rod is acceptable when its diameter is within 10^{-3} mm of the target diameter. Write an inequality for the acceptable range of diameters.

STEM **20. Biology** A human body contains about 2.7×10^4 microliters (μL) of blood for each pound of body weight. Each microliter of blood contains about 7×10^4 white blood cells. About how many white blood cells are in the body of a 140-lb person?

Students will also find exercises with a STEM connection in the exercise sets.

College and Career *Readiness*

Success in mathematics is essential for students preparing for **college coursework, career challenges, and global competitiveness.** But success cannot be determined solely by a student's performance on assessments. Students need to develop the thinking and reasoning habits that will empower them to reach full potential in their college work and in their career paths.

Only some students will pursue careers in math and science, still, all students will benefit from learning to analyze problem situations and developing effective and efficient solution plans. They will need those abilities to be **college- and career-ready** and to lead successful lives as citizens and leaders of the 21st century.

To promote college and career readiness, teachers use *Pearson High School Mathematics Common Core Edition* to:

Engage Students

- Blended environment of print and digital motivates students.
- Different approaches make learning accessible to more students.
- Visual approach makes math more interesting.

Teach for Understanding

- Comprehensive coverage of Common Core State Standards for High School Mathematics.
- Stepped-out instruction reduces cognitive load.
- Emphasis on Standards for Mathematical Practice helps students make sense of math and reason abstractly and quantitatively.

Promote Mastery

- Ongoing formative assessment cements skills.
- Teacher and students ask and answer questions to reinforce understanding.
- Development of math reasoning results in transferability of skills.

SUCCESS
College • Career • Life

Teaching *Resources*

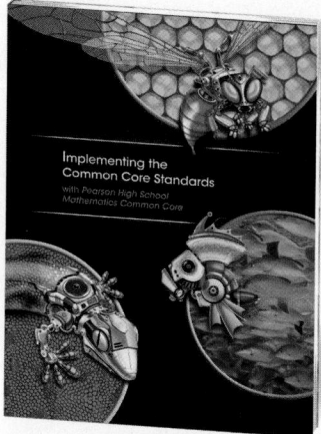

Common Core
Implementation Guide

Student Companion
Teacher's Guide

All-in-One
Teaching Resources

Common Core
Standards Practice and
Review Workbook

Practice and Problem
Solving Workbook
Teacher's Guide

Teaching with
TI-Technology CD

TI-Nspire Support CD

Answers
and Solutions CD

ExamView

PowerAlgebra.com
(Student and
Teacher Access)

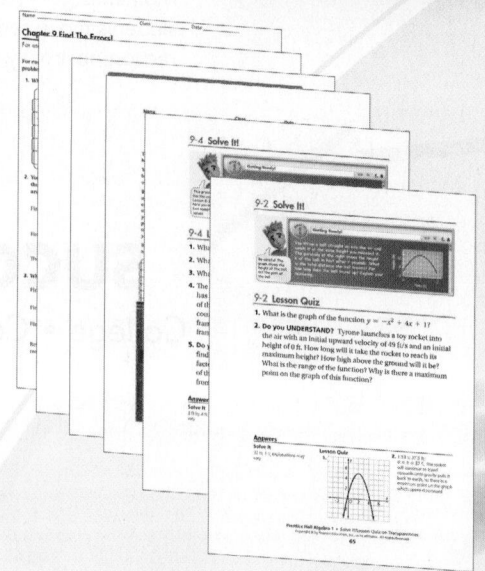

Online
Resource
Center

Teaching Resources		Intervention	On-Level	Enrichment	ELL
Student Practice and Assessment Workbooks (Print and Online)	Student Companion	√	√		√
	Practice and Problem Solving Workbook	√	√	√	√
	Common Core Test Prep Workbook	√	√	√	√
All-In-One Teaching Resources (Print, Online, and DVD)	Think about a Plan Worksheet	√	√	√	√
	Practice Form G		√	√	
	Practice Form K	√			√
	Standardized Test Prep Worksheet	√	√	√	√
	Reteaching	√			√
	Enrichment		√	√	
	ELL Support	√			√
	Performance Tasks	√	√	√	√
	Chapter Projects	√	√	√	√
All-In-One Teaching Resources (Online and DVD)	Extra Practice *(per chapter)*	√	√	√	√
	Find the Errors!		√	√	
	Activities	√	√	√	√
	Games		√	√	
	Puzzles		√	√	
	Multilingual Handbook				√
	Teaching with TI Technology		√	√	
TI-Nspire Lesson Support CD-ROM	TI-Nspire Documents *(per lesson)*	√	√	√	√
www.PowerAlgebra.com www.PowerGeometry.com (Student and Teacher Access)	Homework Video Tutors *(in English and Spanish)*	√	√		√
	My Math Videos	√	√	√	√
	Virtual Nerd™ videos	√	√	√	√
	Solve It	√	√	√	√
	Visual Glossary *(in English and Spanish)*	√	√	√	√
	Online Problems with audio	√	√	√	√
	Math Tools	√	√	√	√
	Dynamic Activities	√	√	√	√
	MathXL for School	√	√	√	√
www.InteractMath.com	Interact Math	√	√	√	√

Common Core State Standards
for Mathematical Content

The following shows the High School Standards for Mathematical Content that are taught in *Pearson Algebra 2 Common Core Edition* ©2015. Included are all of the standards that make up Achieve's Pathway for Algebra 2 and PARCC's Model Content Frameworks. Standards that are part of Achieve's Pathway are indicated with an (A) on the standard code. Those that are part of the PARCC Model Content Frameworks are indicated with (P) on the standard code. Standards that begin with (+) indicate additional mathematics that students should learn in order to take advanced courses such as calculus, advanced statistics, or discrete mathematics.

Number and Quantity		Where to Find
The Read Number System		
Extend the properties of exponents to rational exponents		
N-RN.A.1(P)	Explain how the definition of the meaning of rational exponents follows from extending the properties of integer exponents to those values, allowing for a notation for radicals in terms of rational exponents.	6-4
N-RN.A.2(P)	Rewrite expressions involving radicals and rational exponents using the properties of exponents.	6-4
Quantities		
Reason quantitatively and use units to solve problems		
N-Q.A.2(P)	Define appropriate quantities for the purpose of descriptive modeling.	1-3, 4-3
The Complex Number System		
Perform arithmetic operations with complex numbers		
N-CN.A.1(A) (P)	Know there is a complex number i such that $i^2 = -1$, and every complex number has the form $a + bi$ with a and b real.	4-8
N-CN.A.2(A) (P)	Use the relation $i^2 = -1$ and the commutative, associative, and distributive properties to add, subtract, and multiply complex numbers.	4-8
Use complex numbers in polynomial identities and equations		
N-CN.C.7(A) (P)	Solve quadratic equations with real coefficients that have complex solutions.	4-8, 5-5, 5-6
N-CN.C.8(A)	(+) Extend polynomial identities to the complex numbers.	4-8, 5-5, 5-6
N-CN.C.9(A)	(+) Know the Fundamental Theorem of Algebra; show that it is true for quadratic polynomials.	5-6

Number and Quantity		Where to Find
Vector and Matrix Quantities		
Perform operations on vectors		
N-VM.B.4	Add and subtract vectors.	12-6
N-VM.B.4a	Add vectors end-to-end, component-wise, and by the parallelogram rule. Understand that the magnitude of a sum of two vectors is typically not the sum of the magnitudes.	12-6
N-VM.B.4b	Given two vectors in magnitude and direction form, determine the magnitude and direction of their sum.	12-6
N-VM.B.4C	Understand vector subtraction $v - w$ as $v + (-w)$, where $-w$ is the additive inverse of w, with the same magnitude as w and pointing in the opposite direction. Represent vector subtraction graphically by connecting the tips in the appropriate order, and perform vector subtraction component-wise.	12-6
N-VM.B.5	(+) Multiply a vector by a scalar.	12-6
N-VM.B.5a	(+) Represent scalar multiplication graphically by scaling vectors and possibly reversing their direction; perform scalar multiplication component-wise, e.g., as $c(vx, vy) = (cvx, cvy)$.	12-6
N-VM.B.5b	(+) Compute the magnitude of a scalar multiple cv using $\|cv\| = \|c\|v$. Compute the direction of cv knowing that when $\|c\|v \neq 0$, the direction of cv is either along v (for $c > 0$) or against v (for $c < 0$). Perform operations on matrices and use matrices in applications.	12-6

Algebra		Where to Find
Seeing Structure in Expressions		
Interpret the structure of expressions		
A-SSE.A.1	Interpret expressions that represent a quantity in terms of its context.	1-6, 4-5, 5-1, 7-1, 7-2, 7-3, 8-4
A-SSE.A.1a[A]	Interpret parts of an expression, such as terms, factors, and coefficients.	4-5, 5-1, 8-4
A-SSE.A.1b[A]	Interpret complicated expressions by viewing one or more of their parts as a single entity.	1-6, 7-1, 7-2, 7-3, 8-4
A-SSE.A.2[A] [P]	Use the structure of an expression to identify ways to rewrite it.	4-4, 5-3, 6-1, 6-2, 6-3, 8-4
Write expressions in equivalent forms to solve problems		
A-SSE.B.3	Choose and produce an equivalent form of an expression to reveal and explain properties of the quantity represented by the expression.	1-1, 7-5
A-SSE.B.3c[P]	Use the properties of exponents to transform expressions for exponential functions.	7-5
A-SSE.B.4[A] [P]	Derive the formula for the sum of a finite geometric series (when the common ratio is not 1), and use the formula to solve problems.	9-5, CB 9-5

Algebra		Where to Find

Arithmetic with Polynomials and Rational Expressions

Perform arithmetic operations on polynomials

A-APR.A.1[(A)]	Understand that polynomials form a system analogous to the integers, namely, they are closed under the operations of addition, subtraction, and multiplication; add, subtract, and multiply polynomials.	5-4

Understand the relationship between zeros and factors of polynomial

A-APR.B.2[(A) (P)]	Know and apply the Remainder Theorem: For a polynomial $p(x)$ and a number a, the remainder on division by $x - a$ is $p(a)$, so $p(a) = 0$ if and only if $(x - a)$ is a factor of $p(x)$.	5-4
A-APR.B.3[(A) (P)]	Identify zeros of polynomials when suitable factorizations are available, and use the zeros to construct a rough graph of the function defined by the polynomial.	4-5, 5-2, 5-6, CB 5-6

Use polynomial identities to solve problems

A-APR.C.4[(A) (P)]	Prove polynomial identities and use them to describe numerical relationships.	CB 5-5
A-APR.C.5[(A)]	(+) Know and apply the Binomial Theorem for the expansion of $(x + y)^n$ in powers of x and y for a positive integer n, where x and y are any numbers, with coefficients determined for example by Pascal's Triangle.	5-7

Rewrite rational expressions

A-APR.D.6[(A) (P)]	Rewrite simple rational expressions in different forms; write $a(x)/b(x)$ in the form $q(x) + r(x)/b(x)$, where $a(x)$, $b(x)$, $q(x)$, and $r(x)$ are polynomials with the degree of $r(x)$ less than the degree of $b(x)$, using inspection, long division, or, for the more complicated examples, a computer algebra system.	5-4, 8-6
A-APR.D.7[(A)]	(+) Understand that rational expressions form a system analogous to the rational numbers, closed under addition, subtraction, multiplication, and division by a nonzero rational expression; add, subtract, multiply, and divide rational expressions.	8-5, 8-6

Creating Equations

Create equations that describe numbers or relationships

A-CED.A.1[(A) (P)]	Create equations and inequalities in one variable and use them to solve problems. *Include equations arising from linear and quadratic functions, and simple rational and exponential functions.*	1-4, 1-5, 1-6, 4-1, 4-5, 8-6
A-CED.A.2[(A)]	Create equations in two or more variables to represent relationships between quantities; graph equations on coordinate axes with labels and scales.	2-2, 2-3, 2-4, 2-5, 2-8, 3-1, 3-2, 4-2, CB 4-5, 7-1, 7-2, 8-1, 8-2, 8-3
A-CED.A.3[(A)]	Represent constraints by equations or inequalities, and by systems of equations and/or inequalities, and interpret solutions as viable or non-viable options in a modeling context.	3-1, 3-2, 3-3, 3-4, CB 3-4, 4-9, CB 7-6
A-CED.A.4[(A)]	Rearrange formulas to highlight a quantity of interest, using the same reasoning as in solving equations.	1-4, 6-5, 8-1

Reasoning with Equations and Inequalities

Understand solving equations as a process of reasoning and explain the reasoning

	Algebra	Where to Find
A-REI.A.1[P]	Explain each step in solving a simple equation as following from the equality of numbers asserted at the previous step, starting from the assumption that the original equation has a solution. Construct a viable argument to justify a solution method.	1-4
A-REI.A.2[A] [P]	Solve simple rational and radical equations in one variable, and give examples showing how extraneous solutions may arise.	6-5, 8-6

Solve equations and inequalities in one variable

	Algebra	Where to Find
A-REI.B.4	Solve quadratic equations in one variable.	4-5, 4-6, 4-7, 4-8
A-REI.B.4b[P]	Solve quadratic equations by inspection (e.g., for $x^2 = 49$), taking square roots, completing the square, the quadratic formula and factoring, as appropriate to the initial form of the equation. Recognize when the quadratic formula gives complex solutions and write them as $a \pm bi$ for real numbers a and b.	4-5, 4-6, 4-7, 4-8

Solve systems of equations

	Algebra	Where to Find
A-REI.C.5	Prove that, given a system of two equations in two variables, replacing one equation by the sum of that equation and a multiple of the other produces a system with the same solutions.	3-2
A-REI.C.6[P]	Solve systems of linear equations exactly and approximately (e.g., with graphs), focusing on pairs of linear equations in two variables.	3-1, 3-2, 3-3
A-REI.C.7[P]	Solve a simple system consisting of a linear equation and a quadratic equation in two variables algebraically and graphically.	4-9

Represent and solve equations and inequalities graphically

	Algebra	Where to Find
A-REI.D.11[A] [P]	Explain why the x-coordinates of the points where the graphs of the equations $y = f(x)$ and $y = g(x)$ intersect are the solutions of the equation $f(x) = g(x)$; find the solutions approximately, e.g., using technology to graph the functions, make tables of values, or find successive approximations. Include cases where $f(x)$ and/or $g(x)$ are linear, polynomial, rational, absolute value, exponential, and logarithmic functions.	3-1, 4-9, 5-3, 7-5, CB 7-6, 8-6, CB 10-6
A-REI.D.12	Graph the solutions to a linear inequality in two variables as a half-plane (excluding the boundary in the case of a strict inequality), and graph the solution set to a system of linear inequalities in two variables as the intersection of the corresponding half-planes.	3-3

Functions	Where to Find

Interpreting Functions

Understand the concept of a function and use function notation

F-IF.A.1	Understand that a function from one set (called the domain) to another set (called the range) assigns to each element of the domain exactly one element of the range. If f is a function and x is an element of its domain, then $f(x)$ denotes the output of f corresponding to the input x. The graph of f is the graph of the equation $y = f(x)$.	2-1
F-IF.A.3 (P)	Recognize that sequences are functions, sometimes defined recursively, whose domain is a subset of the integers.	9-2, CB 9-2, 9-3

Interpret functions that arise in applications in terms of the context

F-IF.B.4 (A) (P)	For a function that models a relationship between two quantities, interpret key features of graphs and tables in terms of the quantities, and sketch graphs showing key features given a verbal description of the relationship. *Key features include: intercepts; intervals where the function is increasing, decreasing, positive, or negative; relative maximums and minimums; symmetries; end behavior; and periodicity.*	2-3, 2-5, 4-1, 4-2, 4-3, 5-1, 5-8, CB 7-3, 13-1, 13-4, 13-5
F-IF.B.5 (A)	Relate the domain of a function to its graph and, where applicable, to the quantitative relationship it describes.	4-3, 5-8
F-IF.B.6 (A) (P)	Calculate and interpret the average rate of change of a function (presented symbolically or as a table) over a specified interval. Estimate the rate of change from a graph.	2-5, 4-1, 4-2, CB 4-3, 5-8

Analyze functions using different representations

F-IF.C.7	Graph functions expressed symbolically, and show key features of the graph, by hand in simple cases and using technology for more complicated cases.	CB 2-4, 2-7, 2-8, 5-1, 5-2, 5-9, 6-8, 7-1, 7-2, 7-3, CB 7-5, CB 8-2, 8-3, 13-4, 13-5, 13-6, 13-7, 13-8
F-IF.C.7b (A)	Graph square root, cube root, and piecewise-defined functions, including step functions and absolute value functions.	CB 2-4, 2-7, 2-8, 6-8
F-IF.C.7c (A) (P)	Graph polynomial functions, identifying zeros when suitable factorizations are available, and showing end behavior.	5-1, 5-2, 5-9
F-IF.C.7d	Graph rational functions, identifying zeros and asymptotes when suitable factorizations are available, and showing end behavior.	CB 8-2, 8-3
F-IF.C.7e (A) (P)	Graph exponential and logarithmic functions, showing intercepts and end behavior, and trigonometric functions, showing period, midline, and amplitude.	7-1, 7-2, 7-3, CB 7-5, 13-4, 13-5, 13-6, 13-7, 13-8
F-IF.C.8	Write a function defined by an expression in different but equivalent forms to reveal and explain different properties of the function.	4-2, 4-5, 4-6, 5-9, 6-8, 7-1, 7-2, 7-3, CB 7-5, 10-6
F-IF.C.8a (A)	Use the process of factoring and completing the square in a quadratic function to show zeros, extreme values, and symmetry of the graph, and interpret these in terms of a context.	4-5, 4-6
F-IF.C.8b (A) (P)	Write a function defined by an expression in different but equivalent forms to reveal and explain different properties of the function. Use the properties of exponents to interpret expressions for exponential functions.	7-2
F-IF.C.9 (A) (P)	Compare properties of two functions each represented in a different way (algebraically, graphically, numerically in tables, or by verbal descriptions.	2-4, 4-2, 5-9, 7-3

Functions	Where to Find

Building Functions

Build a function that models a relationship between two quantities

F-BF.A.1	Write a function that describes a relationship between two quantities.	2-2, 2-5, 5-2, 6-6, 7-2, 8-3
F-BF.A.1a[(P)]	Determine an explicit expression, a recursive process, or steps for calculation from a context.	5-2, 7-2
F-BF.A.1b[(A) (P)]	Combine standard function types using arithmetic operations.	6-6, 7-2, 8-3
F-BF.A.1c	(+) Compose functions.	6-6
F-BF.A.2[(P)]	Write arithmetic and geometric sequences both recursively and with an explicit formula, use them to model situations, and translate between the two forms.	9-2, 9-3

Build new functions from existing functions

F-BF.B.3[(A) (P)]	Identify the effect on the graph of replacing $f(x)$ by $f(x) + k$, $kf(x)$, $f(kx)$, and $f(x + k)$ for specific values of k (both positive and negative); find the value of k given the graphs. Experiment with cases and illustrate an explanation of the effects on the graph using technology. *Include recognizing even and odd functions from their graphs and algebraic expressions for them.*	2-6, 2-7, 4-1, 5-9, 8-2
F-BF.B.4	Find inverse functions.	6-7, 7-3
F-BF.B.4a[(A)]	Solve an equation of the form $f(x) = c$ for a simple function f that has an inverse and write an expression for the inverse.	6-7, 7-3
F-BF.B.4c	(+) Read values of an inverse function from a graph or a table, given that the function has an inverse.	6-7

Linear, Quadratic, and Exponential Models

Construct and compare linear, quadratic, and exponential models and solve problems

F-LE.A.2[(P)]	Construct linear and exponential functions, including arithmetic and geometric sequences, given a graph, a description of a relationship, or two input-output pairs (include reading these from a table).	2-5, 2-6, 7-1, 7-2, 9-2, 9-3
F-LE.A.4[(A) (P)]	For exponential models, express as a logarithm the solution to $ab^{ct} = d$ where a, c, and d are numbers and the base b is 2, 10, or e; evaluate the logarithm using technology.	7-5, 7-6

Interpret expressions for functions in terms of the situation they model

F-LE.B.5[(P)]	Interpret the parameters in a linear or exponential function in terms of a context.	2-3, 2-4, 7-1, 7-2

Trigonometric Functions

Extend the domain of trigonometric functions using the unit circle

F-TF.A.1[(A) (P)]	Understand radian measure of an angle as the length of the arc on the unit circle subtended by the angle.	13-3
F-TF.A.2[(A) (P)]	Explain how the unit circle in the coordinate plane enables the extension of trigonometric functions to all real numbers, interpreted as radian measures of angles traversed counterclockwise around the unit circle.	13-4, 13-5, 13-6

Model periodic phenomena with trigonometric functions

F-TF.B.5[(A) (P)]	Choose trigonometric functions to model periodic phenomena with specified amplitude, frequency, and midline.	13-4, 13-5, 13-6, 13-7
F-TF.B.6	Understand that restricting a trigonometric function to a domain on which it is always increasing or decreasing allows its inverse to be constructed.	14-2
F-TF.B.7	Use inverse functions to solve trigonometric equations that arise in modeling contexts; evaluate the solutions using technology, and interpret them in terms of the context.	14-2

Prove and apply trigonometric identities

F-TF.C.8[(A) (P)]	Prove the Pythagorean identity $\sin^2(\theta) + \cos^2(\theta) = 1$ and use it to find $\sin(\theta)$, $\cos(\theta)$, or $\tan(\theta)$ given $\sin(\theta)$, $\cos(\theta)$, or $\tan(\theta)$ and the quadrant of the angle.	14-1
F-TF.C.9	Prove the addition and subtraction formulas for sine, cosine, and tangent and use them to solve problems.	14-6, 14-7

Geometry		Where to Find
Similarity, Right Triangles, and Trigonometry		
Define trigonometric ratios and solve problems involving right triangles		
G-SRT.C.6	Represent transformations in the plane using, e.g., transparencies and geometry software; describe transformations as functions that take points in the plane as inputs and give other points as outputs. Compare transformations that preserve distance and angle to those that do not (e.g., translation versus horizontal stretch).	CB 13-1, 14-3
G-SRT.C.8	Given a geometric figure and a rotation, reflection, or translation, draw the transformed figure using, e.g., graph paper, tracing paper, or geometry software. Specify a sequence of transformations that will carry a given figure onto another.	14-3
Apply trigonometry to general triangles		
G-SRT.D.9	Represent transformations in the plane using, e.g., transparencies and geometry software; describe transformations as functions that take points in the plane as inputs and give other points as outputs. Compare transformations that preserve distance and angle to those that do not (e.g., translation versus horizontal stretch).	14-4
G-SRT.D.10	Given a geometric figure and a rotation, reflection, or translation, draw the transformed figure using, e.g., graph paper, tracing paper, or geometry software. Specify a sequence of transformations that will carry a given figure onto another.	14-4, 14-5
G-SRT.D.11	Understand and apply the Law of Sines and the Law of Cosines to find unknown measurements in right and non-right triangles (e.g., surveying problems, resultant forces).	14-4, CB 14-4, 14-5
Expressing Geometric Properties with Equations		
Translate between the geometric description and the equation for a conic section		
G-GPE.A.1	Derive the equation of a circle of given center and radius using the Pythagorean Theorem; complete the square to find the center and radius of a circle given by an equation.	10-3, 10-6
G-GPE.A.2(P)	Derive the equation of a parabola given a focus and directrix.	10-2, 10-6
G-GPE.A.3	Derive the equations of ellipses and hyperbolas given foci and directrices.	10-4, 10-5

Statistics and Probability		Where to Find
Interpreting Categorical and Quantitative Data		
Summarize, represent, and interpret data on a single count or measurement variable		
S-ID.A.2	Use statistics appropriate to the shape of the data distribution to compare center (median, mean) and spread (interquartile range, standard deviation) of two or more different data sets.	11-10
S-ID.A.4(A) (P)	Use the mean and standard deviation of a data set to fit it to a normal distribution and to estimate population percentages. Recognize that there are data sets for which such a procedure is not appropriate. Use calculators, spreadsheets, and tables to estimate areas under the normal curve.	11-7, 11-10
Summarize, represent, and interpret data on two categorical and quantitative variables		
S-ID.B.6	Represent data on two quantitative variables on a scatter plot, and describe how the variables are related.	2-5, 7-2
S-ID.B.6a(P)	Fit a function to the data; use functions fitted to data to solve problems in the context of the data. Use given functions or choose a function suggested by the context. Emphasize linear and exponential models.	2-5, 7-2

Statistics and Probability		Where to Find
Making Inferences and Justifying Conclusions		
Understand and evaluate random processes underlying statistical experiments		
S-IC.A.1[(A) (P)]	Understand statistics as a process for making inferences to be made about population parameters based on a random sample from that population.	11-8
S-IC.A.2[(A) (P)]	Decide if a specified model is consistent with results from a given data-generating process, e.g., using simulation.	CB 11-3
Make inferences and justify conclusions from sample surveys, experiments, and observational studies		
S-IC.B.3[(A) (P)]	Recognize the purposes of and differences among sample surveys, experiments, and observational studies; explain how randomization relates to each.	11-8
S-IC.B.4[(A) (P)]	Use data from a sample survey to estimate a population mean or proportion; develop a margin of error through the use of simulation models for random sampling.	11-8, CB 11-10a
S-IC.B.5[(A) (P)]	Use data from a randomized experiment to compare two treatments; use simulations to decide if differences between parameters are significant.	CB 11-10b
S-IC.B.6[(A) (P)]	Evaluate reports based on data.	11-7, 11-8
Conditional Probability and the Rules of Probability		
Understand independence and conditional probability and use them to interpret data		
S-CP.A.1[(P)]	Describe events as subsets of a sample space (the set of outcomes) using characteristics (or categories) of the outcomes, or as unions, intersections, or complements of other events ("or," "and," "not").	11-4
S-CP.A.2[(P)]	Understand that two events A and B are independent if the probability of A and B occurring together is the product of their probabilities, and use this characterization to determine if they are independent.	11-3
S-CP.A.3[(P)]	Understand the conditional probability of A given B as $P(A$ and $B)/P(B)$, and interpret independence of A and B as saying that the conditional probability of A given B is the same as the probability of A, and the conditional probability of B given A is the same as the probability of B.	11-4
S-CP.A.4[(P)]	Construct and interpret two-way frequency tables of data when two categories are associated with each object being classified. Use the two-way table as a sample space to decide if events are independent and to approximate conditional probabilities.	11-4
S-CP.A.5[(P)]	Recognize and explain the concepts of conditional probability and independence in everyday language and everyday situations.	11-3, 11-4
Use the rules of probability to compute probabilities of compound events in a uniform probability model		
S-CP.B.6[(P)]	Find the conditional probability of A given B as the fraction of B's outcomes that also belong to A, and interpret the answer in terms of the model.	11-4
S-CP.B.7[(P)]	Apply the Addition Rule, $P(A$ or $B) = P(A) + P(B) - P(A$ and $B)$, and interpret the answer in terms of the model.	11-3
S-CP.B.8	(+) Apply the general Multiplication Rule in a uniform probability model, $P(A$ and $B) = P(A)P(B|A) = P(B)P(A|B)$, and interpret the answer in terms of the model.	11-4
S-CP.B.9	(+) Use permutations and combinations to compute probabilities of compound events and solve problems.	11-1
Using Probability to Make Decisions		
Use probability to evaluate outcomes of decisions		
S-MD.B.6[(A)]	(+) Use probabilities to make fair decisions (e.g., drawing by lots, using a random number generator).	11-5, 11-6
S-MD.B.7[(A)]	(+) Analyze decisions and strategies using probability concepts (e.g., product testing, medical testing, pulling a hockey goalie at the end of a game).	11-5

Algebra 2 *Pacing Guide*

This Pacing Guide identifies lessons that have content that aligns with content expectations for Appendix A of the Common Core State Standards and with content expectations for PARCC. The suggested number of days for each chapter is based on a traditional 45-minute class period and on a 90-minute block period. The total of 160 days of instruction allows time for assessments, projects, assemblies, or other special days that vary from school to school.

KEY

✓ = Algebra 2 Content
○ = Foundational for Algebra 2
❑ = Content for Enrichment

		Common Core State Standards	PARCC	Appendix A
Chapter 1 Expressions, Equations, and Inequalities			**Traditional 6**	**Block 3**
1-1	Patterns and Expressions	A-SSE.B.3	○	○
1-2	Properties of Real Numbers	Prepares for N-RN.B.3	○	○
1-3	Algebraic Expressions	N-Q.A.2, A-SSE.A.1a	○	○
1-4	Solving Equations	A-CED.A.1, A-CED.A.4	✓	✓
1-5	Solving Inequalities	A-CED.A.1	✓	✓
1-6	Absolute Value Equations and Inequalities	A-SSE.A.1b, A-CED.A.1	✓	✓
Chapter 2 Functions, Equations, and Graphs			**Traditional 10**	**Block 5**
2-1	Relations and Functions	Reviews F-IF.A.1, Reviews F-IF.A.2	○	○
2-2	Direct Variation	A-CED.A.2, F-IF.A.1, F-BF.A.1	✓	✓
2-3	Linear Functions and Slope-Intercept Form	A-CED.A.2, F-IF.B.4, F-IF.C.7, F-LE.B.5	✓	✓
2-4	More About Linear Equations	A-CED.A.2, F-IF.A.2, F-IF.B.4, F-IF.C.7, F-IF.C.8, F-IF.C.9, F-LE.B.5	✓	✓
Concept Byte: Piecewise Functions		F-IF.C.7b	✓	✓
2-5	Using Linear Models	A-CED.A.2, F-IF.B.4, F-IF.B.6, F-BF.A.1, F-LE.A.2, S-ID.B.6a	✓	✓
2-6	Families of Functions	F-IF.C.7, F-BF.B.3, F-LE.A.2	✓	✓
2-7	Absolute Value Functions and Graphs	F-IF.C.7b, F-BF.B.3	✓	✓
2-8	Two-Variable Inequalities	A-CED.A.2, F-IF.C.7b	✓	✓
Chapter 3 Linear Systems			**Traditional 8**	**Block 4**
3-1	Solving Systems Using Tables and Graphs	A-CED.A.2, A-CED.A.3, A-REI.C.6, A-REI.D.11	✓	✓
3-2	Solving Systems Algebraically	A-CED.A.2, A-CED.A.3, A-REI.C.5, A-REI.C.6	✓	✓
3-3	Systems of Inequalities	A-CED.A.3, A-REI.C.6, A-REI.D.12	✓	✓
3-4	Linear Programming	A-CED.A.3	❑	✓
Concept Byte: Linear Programming		A-CED.A.3	❑	✓
Concept Byte: Graphs in Three Dimensions		Extends A-REI.C.6	❑	❑
3-5	Systems With Three Variables	Extends A-REI.C.6	❑	❑
3-6	Solving Systems Using Matrices	A-REI.C.8	❑	❑

	Common Core State Standards	PARCC	Appendix A
Chapter 4 Quadratic Functions and Equations		**Traditional 16 Block 8**	
4-1 Quadratic Functions and Transformations	A-CED.A.1, F-IF.B.4, F-IF.B.6, F-IF.C.7a, F-BF.B.3	✓	✓
4-2 Standard Form of a Quadratic Function	A-CED.A.2, F-IF.B.4, F-IF.B.6, F-IF.C.7a, F-IF.C.8, F-IF.C.9, F-BF.A.1	✓	✓
4-3 Modeling With Quadratic Functions	N-Q.A.2, F-IF.B.4, F-IF.B.5	✓	✓
Concept Byte: Identifying Quadratic Data	F-IF.C.6	✓	✓
4-4 Factoring Quadratic Expressions	A-SSE.A.2	✓	✓
Algebra Review: Square Roots and Radicals	Prepares for N-RN.A.2	✓	✓
4-5 Quadratic Equations	A-SSE.A.1a, A-SSE.2.3a, A-APR.B.3, A.CED.A.1, A-REI.B.4b, F-IF.C.8	✓	✓
Concept Byte: Writing Equations From Roots	A-CED.A.2	✓	✓
4-6 Completing the Square	A-REI.B.4a, A-REI.B.4b, F-IF.C.8	✓	✓
4-7 The Quadratic Formula	A-REI.B.4a, A-REI.B.4b	✓	✓
4-8 Complex Numbers	N-CN.A.1, N-CN.A.2, N-CN.C.7, N-CN.C.8, A-REI.B.4b	✓	✓
Concept Byte: Quadratic Inequalities	A-APR.B.3, A-CED.A.3	✓	✓
4-9 Quadratic Systems	A-CED.A.3, A-REI.C.7, A-REI.D.11	✓	✓
Concept Byte: Powers of Complex Numbers	Extends N-CN.A.2	❑	❑
Chapter 5 Polynomials and Polynomial Functions		**Traditional 14 Block 7**	
5-1 Polynomial Functions	A-SSE.A.1a, F-IF.B.4, F-IF.C.7c	✓	✓
5-2 Polynomials, Linear Factors, and Zeros	A-SSE.A.1a, A-APR.B.3, F-IF.C.7c, F-BF.A.1	✓	✓
5-3 Solving Polynomial Equations	A-SSE.A.2, A-REI.D.11	✓	✓
5-4 Dividing Polynomials	A-APR.A.1, A-APR.B.2a, A-APR.D.6	✓	✓
5-5 Theorems About Roots of Polynomial Equations	N-CN.C.7, N-CN.C.8	✓	✓
Concept Byte: Solving Polynomial Inequalities	A-APR.C.4	❑	✓
5-6 The Fundamental Theorem of Algebra	N-CN.C.7, N-CN.C.8, N-CN.C.9, A-APR.B.3	✓	✓
Concept Byte: Graphing Polynomials Using Zeros	A-APR.B.3	✓	✓
5-7 The Binomial Theorem	A-APR.C.5	✓	✓
5-8 Polynomial Models in the Real World	F-IF.B.4, F-IF.B.5, F-IF.B.6, F-IF.C.7	✓	✓
5-9 Transforming Polynomial Functions	F-IF.C.7c, F-IF.C.8, F-IF.C.9, F-BF.B.3	✓	✓
Chapter 6 Radical Functions and Rational Exponents		**Traditional 14 Block 7**	
Algebra Review: Properties of Exponents	Prepares for N.RN.1	○	○
6-1 Roots and Radical Expressions	A-SSE.A.2	✓	✓
6-2 Multiplying and Dividing Radical Expressions	A-SSE.A.2	✓	✓
6-3 Binomial Radical Expressions	A-SSE.A.2	✓	✓
6-4 Rational Exponents	N-RN.A.1, N-RN.A.2	○	○
6-5 Solving Square Root and Other Radical Equations	A-CED.A.4, A-REI.A.2	✓	✓
6-6 Function Operations	F-BF.A.1b, F-BF.A.1c	✓	✓
6-7 Inverse Relations and Functions	F-BF.B.4a, F-BF.B.4c	✓	✓
Concept Byte: Graphing Inverses	Extends F-BF.B.4a	❑	❑
6-8 Graphing Radical Functions	F-IF.C.7b, F-IF.C.8	✓	✓

	Common Core State Standards	PARCC	Appendix A
Chapter 7 Exponential and Logarithmic Functions		**Traditional 10 Block 5**	
7-1 Exploring Exponential Models	A-SSE.A.1b, A-CED.A.2, F-IF.C.7e, F-IF.C.8, F-LE.A.2, F-LE.B.5	✓	✓
7-2 Properties of Exponential Functions	A-SSE.A.1b, A-CED.A.2, F-IF.C.7e, F-BF.A.1b, F-IF.C.8b, F-LE.A.2, F-LE.B.5, S-ID.B.6a	✓	✓
7-3 Logarithmic Functions as Inverses	A-SSE.A.1b, F-IF.C.7e, F-IF.C.8, F-IF.C.9, F-BF.B.4a	✓	✓
Concept Byte: Fitting Curves to Data	F-IF.B.4	✓	✓
7-4 Properties of Logarithms	Prepares for F-LE.A.4	✓	✓
7-5 Exponential and Logarithmic Equations	A-SSE.B.3c, A-REI.D.11, F-LE.A.4	✓	✓
Concept Byte: Using Logarithms for Exponential Models	F-IF.C.7e, F-IF.C.8	✓	✓
7-6 Natural Logarithms	F-LE.A.4	✓	✓
Concept Byte: Exponential and Logarithmic Inequalities	A-CED.A.3, A-REI.D.11	✓	✓
Chapter 8 Rational Functions		**Traditional 14 Block 7**	
8-1 Inverse Variation	A-CED.A.2, A-CED.A.4	○	✓
Concept Byte: Graphing Rational Functions	F-IF.C.7d	□	✓
8-2 The Reciprocal Function Family	A-CED.A.2, F-BF.B.3	✓	✓
8-3 Rational Functions and Their Graphs	A-CED.A.2, F-IF.C.7d, F-BF.A.1b	✓	✓
Concept Byte: Oblique Asymptotes	Extends F-IF.C.7d	□	□
8-4 Rational Expressions	A-SSE.A.1a, A-SSE.A.1b, A-SSE.A.2	✓	✓
8-5 Adding and Subtracting Rational Expressions	A-APR.C.7	✓	✓
8-6 Solving Rational Equations	A-APR.C.6, A-APR.C.7, A-CED.A.1, A-REI.A.2, A-REI.D.11	✓	✓
Concept Byte: Systems With Rational Equations	Extends A-REI.D.11	□	□
Concept Byte: Rational Inequalities	Extends A-REI.D.11	□	□
Chapter 9 Sequences and Series		**Traditional 8 Block 4**	
9-1 Mathematical Patterns	Prepares for A-SSE.B.4	○	○
9-2 Arithmetic Sequences	F-IF.A.3, F-BF.A.2, F-LE.A.2	○	○
Concept Byte: The Fibonacci Sequence	F-IF.A.3	○	○
9-3 Geometric Sequences	Prepares for A-SSE.B.4, F-IF.A.3, F-BF.A.2, F-LE.A.2	○	○
9-4 Arithmetic Series	Extends F-IF.A.3	□	□
Concept Byte: Geometry and Infinite Series	A-SSE.B.4	✓	✓
9-5 Geometric Series	A-SSE.B.4	✓	✓
Chapter 10 Quadratic Relations and Conic Sections		**Traditional 12 Block 6**	
10-1 Exploring Conic Sections	Prepares for G-GPE.A.1, G-GPE.A.2, and G-GPE.A.3	✓	□
Concept Byte: Graphing Conic Sections	Prepares for G-GPE.A.1, G-GPE.A.2, and G-GPE.A.3	✓	□
10-2 Parabolas	G-GPE.A.2	✓	□
10-3 Circles	G-GPE.A.1	□	□
10-4 Ellipses	G-GPE.A.3	□	□
10-5 Hyperbolas	G-GPE.A.3	□	□
10-6 Translating Conic Sections	G-GPE.A.1, G-GPE.A.2, F-IF.C.8	✓	□
Concept Byte: Solving Quadratic Systems	Extends A-REI.C.7, A-REI.D.11	□	□

		Common Core State Standards	PARCC	Appendix A
Chapter 11 Probability and Statistics			**Traditional 10**	**Block 5**
11-1	Permutations and Combinations	S-CP.B.9	✓	❑
11-2	Probability	Prepares for S-IC.A.2, S-CP.A.1	✓	✓
11-3	Probability of Multiple Events	S-CP.A.2, S-CP.A.5, S-CP.B.7	✓	❑
Concept Byte: Probability Distributions		S-IC.A.2	✓	✓
11-4	Conditional Probability	S-CP.A.1, S-CP.A.3, S-CP.A.4, S-CP.A.5, S-CP.B.6, S-CP.B.8	✓	✓
11-5	Probability Models	S-MD.B.6, S-MD.B.7	✓	✓
11-6	Analyzing Data	S-IC.B.6, S-MD.B.6	✓	✓
11-7	Standard Deviation	S-ID.A.4, S-IC.B.6	✓	✓
11-8	Samples and Surveys	S-IC.A.1, S-IC.B.3, S-IC.S.B.4, S-IC.B.6	✓	✓
11-9	Binomial Distributions	Extends S-CP.B.9	❑	❑
11-10	Normal Distributions	S-ID.A.2, S-ID.A.4	✓	✓
Concept Byte: Margin of Error		S-IC.B.4	✓	✓
Concept Byte: Drawing Conclusions from Samples		S-IC.B.5	✓	✓
Chapter 12 Matrices			**Traditional 12**	**Block 6**
12-1	Adding and Subtracting Matrices	N-VM.B.8, N.VM.B.9	❑	❑
Concept Byte: Working With Matrices		N-VM.B.8	❑	❑
12-2	Matrix Multiplication	N-VM.B.6, N-VM.B.7, N-VM.B.8, N.VM.B.9	❑	❑
Concept Byte: Networks		N-VM.B.6	❑	❑
12-3	Determinants and Inverses	N-VM.B.10, N.VM.B.12	❑	❑
12-4	Inverse Matrices and Systems	N-VM.B.8	❑	❑
12-5	Geometric Transformations	N-VM.B.6, N.VM.B.7, N-VM.B.8, G-CO.A.2, G-CO.B.5	❑	❑
12-6	Vectors	N-VM.B.4a, N-VM.B.4b, N.VM.B.4c, N-VM.B.5a, N-VM.B.5b	❑	❑
Chapter 13 Periodic Functions and Trigonometry			**Traditional 14**	**Block 7**
13-1	Exploring Periodic Data	F-IF.B.4, Prepares for F-TF.B.5	✓	✓
Geometry Review: Special Right Triangles		Reviews G-SRT.C.6	○	○
13-2	Angles and the Unit Circle	Prepares for F-TF.A.2	○	○
Concept Byte: Measuring Radians		Prepares for F-TF.A.1	○	○
13-3	Radian Measure	F-TF.A.1	✓	✓
13-4	The Sine Function	F-IF.B.4, F-IF.C.7e, F-TF.A.2, F-TF.B.5	✓	✓
Concept Byte: Graphing Trigonometric Functions		Prepares for F-TF.B.5	○	○
13-5	The Cosine Function	F-IF.B.4, F-IF.C.7e, F-TF.A.2, F-TF.B.5	✓	✓
13-6	The Tangent Function	F-IF.C.7e, F-TF.A.2, F-TF.B.5	✓	✓
13-7	Translating Sine and Cosine Functions	F-IF.C.7e, F-TF.B.5	✓	✓
13-8	Reciprocal Trigonometric Functions	F-IF.C.7e	✓	✓
Chapter 14 Trigonometric Identities and Equations			**Traditional 12**	**Block 6**
14-1	Trigonometric Identities	F-TF.C.8	✓	✓
14-2	Solving Trigonometric Equations Using Inverses	F-TF.B.6, F-TF.B.7	❑	❑
14-3	Right Triangles and Trigonometric Ratios	G-SRT.C.6, G-SRT.C.8	❑	❑
14-4	Area and the Law of Sines	G-SRT.D.9, G-SRT.D.10, G-SRT.D.11	❑	❑
Concept Byte: The Ambiguous Case		G-SRT.D.11	❑	❑
14-5	The Law of Cosines	G-SRT.D.10, G-SRT.D.11	❑	❑
14-6	Angle Identities	F-TF.C.9	❑	❑
14-7	Double-Angle and Half-Angle Identities	F-TF.C.9	❑	❑

1

Expressions, Equations, and Inequalities

Chapters 1 & 2

Algebra
Seeing Structure in Expressions
   Interpret the structure of expressions
Creating Equations
   Create equations that describe numbers or relationships

Functions
Interpreting Functions
   Interpret functions that arise in applications in terms of the context
   Analyze functions using different representations
Building Functions
   Build a function that models a relationship between two quantities

2

Functions, Equations, and Graphs

Visual See It!

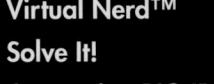

Reasoning Try It!

Practice Do It!

3

Linear Systems

Chapters 3 & 4

Number and Quantity
The Complex Number System
  Perform arithmetic operations with complex numbers
  Use complex numbers in polynomial identities and equations
Functions
Interpreting Functions
  Interpret functions that arise in applications in terms of the context
  Analyze functions using different representations
Building Functions
  Build new functions from existing functions

Algebra
Seeing Structure in Expressions
  Interpret the structure of expressions
Arithmetic with Polynomials and Rational Expressions
  Understand the relationship between zeros and factors of polynomials
Creating Equations
  Create equations that describe numbers or relationships
Reasoning with Equations and Inequalities
  Solve systems of equations
  Represent and solve equations and inequalities graphically

4 Quadratic Functions and Equations

Visual See It!

Reasoning Try It!

Practice Do It!

5

Polynomials and Polynomial Functions

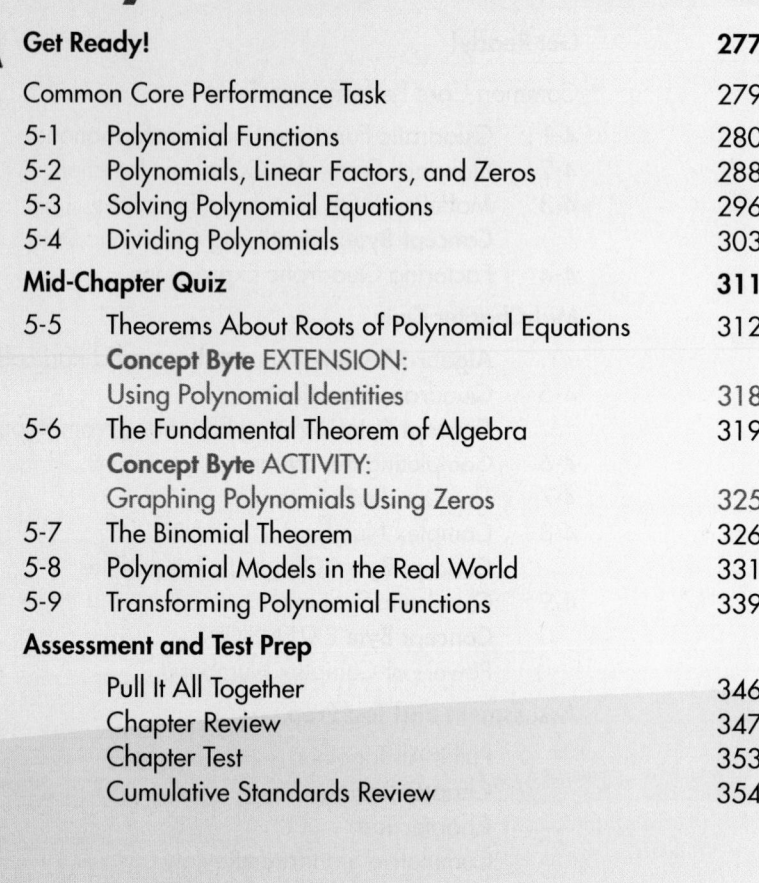

Chapters 5 & 6

Number and Quantity
The Complex Number System
  Use complex numbers in polynomial identities and equations
Functions
Interpreting Functions
  Interpret functions that arise in applications in terms of the context
  Analyze functions using different representations
Building Functions
  Build a function that models a relationship between two quantities
  Build new functions from existing functions

Algebra
Seeing Structure in Expressions
  Interpret the structure of expressions
Creating Equations
  Create equations that describe numbers or relationships
Arithmetic with Polynomials and Rational Expressions
  Understand the relationship between zeros and factors of polynomials
  Use polynomial identities to solve problems

6 Radical Functions and Rational Exponents

Visual **See It!**

Reasoning **Try It!**

Practice **Do It!**

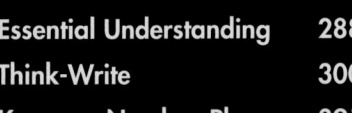

7

Exponential and Logarithmic Functions

Chapters 7 & 8

Algebra
Seeing Structure in Expressions
Interpret the structure of expressions
Creating Equations
Create equations that describe numbers or relationships
Arithmetic with Polynomials and Rational Expressions
Rewrite rational expressions
Reasoning with Equations and Inequalities
Represent and solve equations and inequalities graphically

Functions
Interpreting Functions
Analyze functions using different representations
Building Functions
Build a function that models a relationship between two quantities
Build new functions from existing functions
Linear and Exponential Models
Construct and compare linear and exponential models and solve problems

8 Rational Functions

Visual See It!

Reasoning Try It!

Practice Do It!

9

Sequences and Series

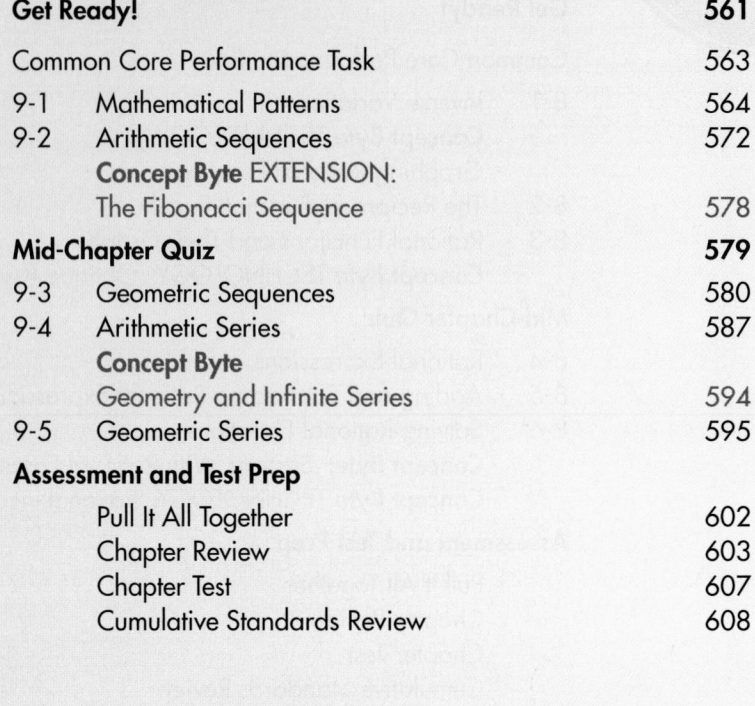

Chapters 9 & 10

Algebra
Seeing Structure in Expressions
Write expressions in equivalent forms to solve problems
Functions
Interpreting Functions
Understand the concept of a function and use function notation
Analyze functions using different representations

Geometry
Expressing Geometric Properties with Equations
Translate between the geometric description and the equation
for a conic section

10 Quadratic Relations and Conic Sections

Probability and Statistics

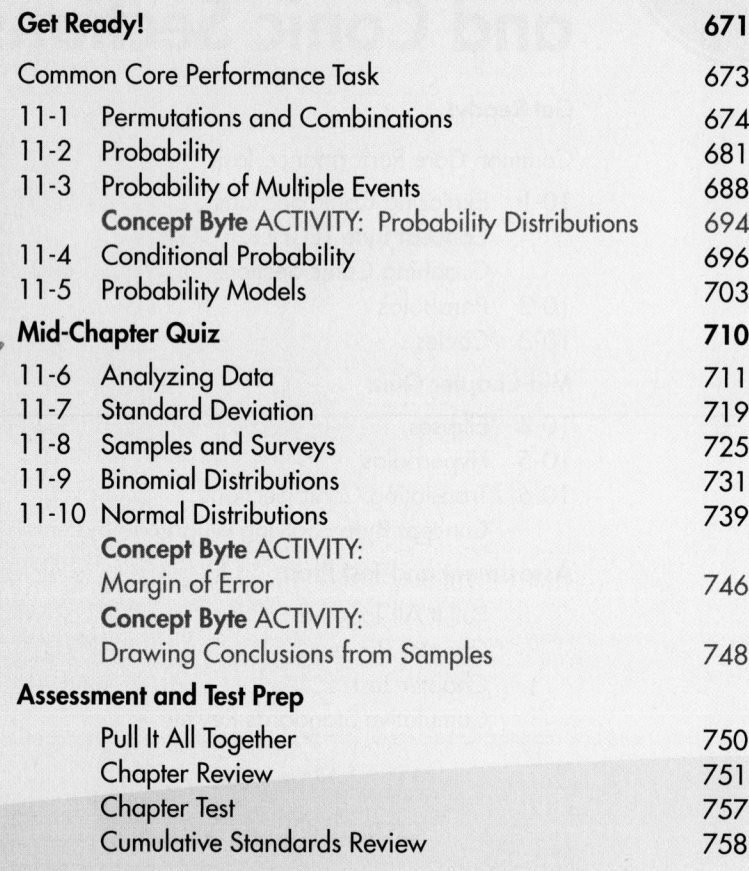

Chapters 11 & 12

Number and Quantity
Vector and Matrix Quantities
Represent and model with vector quantities
Perform operations on vectors
Perform operations on matrices and use matrices in applications

Statistics and Probability
Interpreting Categorical and Quantitative Data
Summarize, represent, and interpret data on a single count or measurement variable

Making Inferences and Justifying Conclusions
Understand and evaluate random processes underlying statistical experiments
Make inferences and justify conclusions from sample surveys, experiments, and observational studies

Conditional Probability and the Rules of Probability
Understand independence and conditional probability and use them to interpret data
Use the rules of probability to compute probabilities of compound events in a uniform probability model

Use Probability to Make Decisions
Use probability to evaluate outcomes of decisions

Matrices

Visual **See It!**

Reasoning **Try It!**

Practice **Do It!**

Periodic Functions and Trigonometry

Functions
Interpreting Functions
   Interpret functions that arise in applications in terms of the context
   Analyze functions using different representations
Trigonometric Functions
   Extend the domain of trigonometric functions using the unit circle
   Model periodic phenomena with trigonometric functions
   Prove and apply trigonometric identities

Geometry
Similarity, Right Triangles, and Trigonometry
   Define trigonometric ratios and solve problems involving right triangles
   Apply trigonometry to general triangles

Chapters 13 & 14

14 Trigonometric Identities and Equations

Visual See It!

Reasoning Try It!

Practice Do It!

Answers

1. B
2. F
3. A
4. F
5. D
6. G
7. B
8. G
9. A
10. H

Entry-Level Assessment

Multiple Choice

Read each question. Then write the letter of the correct answer on your paper.

1. Let $A = \{1, 2, 3, 4\}$ be a set in the universe $U = \{1, 2, 3, 4, 5, 6, 7, 8\}$. What is the complement of A?

  Ⓐ $\{2, 3\}$ Ⓒ $\{1, 2, 3, 4\}$

  Ⓑ $\{5, 6, 7, 8\}$ Ⓓ $\{2, 3, 7, 8\}$

2. Solve $x^2 + 2x - 3 = 0$ by factoring.

  Ⓕ $x = -3$ and $x = 1$

  Ⓖ $x = -1$ and $x = 3$

  Ⓗ $x = 0$

  Ⓘ $x = -3$ and $x = 0$

3. Simplify $\dfrac{3a^2b^3 - 12a^4b^3 + 6a^4b^2}{3a^2b}$.

  Ⓐ $b^2 - 4a^2b^2 + 2a^2b$

  Ⓑ $a^2b - 4a^2b^2 + 2a^2b$

  Ⓒ $3b^2 - 12a^2b + 6b^2$

  Ⓓ $3ab^2 - 4a^2b + 2ab^2$

4. Which relation is not a function?

  Ⓕ $\{(1, -5), (2, 4), (1, -4)\}$

  Ⓖ $\{(1, -5), (2, 4), (3, -3)\}$

  Ⓗ $\{(1, -5), (2, 4), (3, 2)\}$

  Ⓘ $\{(1, -5), (2, 4), (3, -4)\}$

5. In the diagram, m and n are parallel.

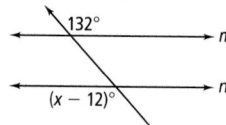

What is the value of x?

  Ⓐ 36   Ⓒ 120

  Ⓑ 60   Ⓓ 144

6. Solve $2(1 - 2w) = 4w + 18$.

  Ⓕ -4 Ⓗ 8

  Ⓖ -2 Ⓘ 16

7. Which of the following lines is perpendicular to the line $3x + y = 2$?

  Ⓐ $y = 3x + 4$

  Ⓑ $y = \frac{1}{3}x - 2$

  Ⓒ $y = -3x + 3$

  Ⓓ $y = -\frac{1}{3}x + 1$

8. If $y = 1$, then $(x + 5) \cdot y = x + 5$. Which property supports this statement?

  Ⓕ Inverse Property of Multiplication

  Ⓖ Identity Property of Multiplication

  Ⓗ Associative Property of Addition

  Ⓘ Commutative Property of Addition

9.

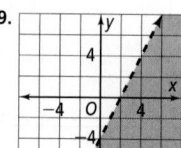

Which inequality does the graph represent?

  Ⓐ $y < 2x - 4$

  Ⓑ $y > -4x + 2$

  Ⓒ $y > 2x - 4$

  Ⓓ $y < -4x + 2$

10. The area of a trapezoid is $A = \frac{1}{2}h(b_1 + b_2)$. Solve for b_1.

  Ⓕ $b_1 = \dfrac{2A - b_2}{h}$

  Ⓖ $b_1 = \dfrac{2A - h}{b_2}$

  Ⓗ $b_1 = \dfrac{2A}{h} - b_2$

  Ⓘ $b_1 = 2A - b_2$

11. Let $\overleftrightarrow{AB}$ be parallel to $\overleftrightarrow{CD}$, with $A(-2, 3)$, $B(1, 4)$, and $C(1, 2)$. Which of the following could be the coordinates of point D?

- (A) $(4, 1)$
- (B) $(-2, -1)$
- (C) $(-2, 3)$
- (D) $(4, 3)$

12. Solve $3 \geq 4g - 5 \geq -1$.

- (F) $-\frac{3}{2} \leq g \leq 2$
- (G) $-1 \leq g \leq \frac{3}{4}$
- (H) $-4 \leq g \leq 8$
- (I) $1 \leq g \leq 2$

13. Which is *not* a solution of $5(2x + 4) \geq 2(x + 34)$?

- (A) 48
- (B) 8
- (C) 6
- (D) 3

14. Factor $6x^2 - 216$.

- (F) $6(x - 6)(x + 6)$
- (G) $(6x - 36)(6x + 36)$
- (H) $6(x - 6)$
- (I) $6(x - 36)(x + 6)$

15. Mike and Jane leave their home on bikes traveling in opposite directions on a straight road. Mike rides 5 mi/h faster than Jane. After 4 h they are 124 mi apart. At what rate does Mike ride his bike?

- (A) 5 mi/h
- (B) 13 mi/h
- (C) 18 mi/h
- (D) 31 mi/h

16. What is the point-slope form for the equation of the line in the graph?

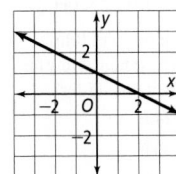

- (F) $y - 2 = \frac{3}{2}(x + 2)$
- (G) $y - 2 = \frac{1}{2}(x + 2)$
- (H) $y - 2 = -\frac{1}{2}(x + 2)$
- (I) $y - 2 = -\frac{2}{3}(x + 2)$

17. A rectangular photograph is being enlarged to poster size by making both the length and width six times as large as the original. How many times as large as the area of the original photograph is the area of the poster?

- (A) $\frac{1}{6}$
- (B) 6
- (C) 12
- (D) 36

18. A rectangle has a length of $2x + 3$ and a width of $x - 4$. Find the area of the rectangle.

- (F) $2x^2 - 12$
- (G) $2x^2 - 8x$
- (H) $2x^2 - 5x - 12$
- (I) $2x^2 - 11x - 12$

19. What is the y-intercept of the line that passes through the points $(-4, 4)$ and $(2, -5)$?

- (A) -2
- (B) $-\frac{3}{2}$
- (C) $\frac{3}{2}$
- (D) 2

20. Which of the following is equivalent to $\sqrt{2}(\sqrt{6} - 4)$?

- (F) $\sqrt{12} - 4$
- (G) $2\sqrt{3} - 2\sqrt{2}$
- (H) $\sqrt{12} - 8$
- (I) $2\sqrt{3} - 4\sqrt{2}$

21. Which of the following represents the system shown in the graph?

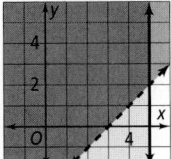

- (A) $\begin{cases} y = x - 3 \\ x \geq 5 \end{cases}$
- (B) $\begin{cases} y \leq x - 3 \\ x > 5 \end{cases}$
- (C) $\begin{cases} y < x - 3 \\ x = 5 \end{cases}$
- (D) $\begin{cases} y > x - 3 \\ x \leq 5 \end{cases}$

22. Which of the following equations represents the line that is parallel to the line $y = 5x + 2$ and that passes through the point $(1, -3)$?

- (F) $y = -5x + 2$
- (G) $y = 5x + 8$
- (H) $y = \frac{1}{5}x - 8$
- (I) $y = 5x - 8$

11. D
12. I
13. D
14. F
15. C
16. H
17. D
18. H
19. A
20. I
21. D
22. I

Answers

23. A
24. G
25. A
26. G
27. D
28. H
29. A
30. F
31. A
32. I
33. A
34. H

23. Which equation represents a line that would be perpendicular to a second line with a slope of $\frac{1}{5}$?

A $y = -5x + 2$

B $y = -\frac{1}{5}x + 3$

C $y = 5x - 2$

D $5y + x = 2$

24. $\triangle ABC$ is similar to $\triangle DEF$.

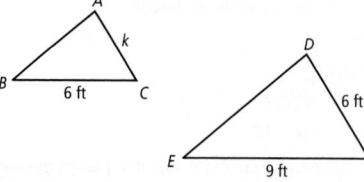

What is the value of k?

F   3 ft   H   6 ft

G   4 ft   I   9 ft

25. Solve the equation using the Quadratic Formula.
$6x^2 - 10x + 3 = 0$

A $\frac{5 \pm \sqrt{7}}{6}$

B $\frac{3 \pm \sqrt{5}}{6}$

C -2 and 5

D $\frac{3}{4}$ and $\frac{2}{3}$

26. A rectangle in the coordinate plane has vertices $(3, 2)$, $(8, 2)$, $(3, 6)$, and $(8, 6)$. Which of the following sets of vertices describes a rectangle that is congruent to this one?

F $(3, -2), (3, -8), (5, -8), (5, -2)$

G $(-2, -4), (-2, -8), (3, -8), (3, -4)$

H $(0, 0), (5, 0), (5, 5), (0, 5)$

I $(-3, 2), (1, 2), (1, 6), (-3, 6)$

27. Simplify the expression below.
$(-6y^{-4})^5$

A $7776y^{20}$ C $-7776y^{20}$

B $\frac{7776}{y^{20}}$ D $-\frac{7776}{y^{20}}$

28. What is the solution to $\frac{2n+8}{3} = \frac{n+7}{2}$?

F -9 H   5

G -1 I   13

29. Solve the system of equations below.
$$\begin{cases} 3x + y = -7 \\ 4x - y = -14 \end{cases}$$

A $(-3, 2)$ C $(-3, -2)$

B $(3, 2)$ D   no solution

30. Which of the following is equivalent to $\frac{2x - 12}{x^2 - 2x - 24}$?

F $\frac{2}{x+4}$ H $\frac{1}{x^2 - 2}$

G $\frac{1}{x+2}$ I $\frac{2x-3}{x-6}$

31. What is (are) the solution(s) of the graphed function when the value of the function is 0?

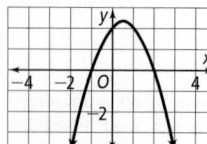

A -1 and 2 C   2

B 1 and -2 D   2.2

32. Which of the following is true?

F $\sqrt{85} < 9$ H $\sqrt{\frac{16}{25}} > \sqrt{\frac{16}{4}}$

G $8 < \sqrt{62}$ I $\sqrt{121} < \sqrt{144}$

33. A firefighter leans a 30-ft ladder against a building in order to reach a window that is 24 ft high. How far away from the building is the base of the ladder?

A   18 ft   C   24 ft

B   20 ft   D   30 ft

34. What is the number of x-intercepts of the parabola with equation $y = 6x^2 - 4x - 3$?

F   0   H   2

G   1   I   3

Get Ready!

Skills Handbook, page 973

Adding Rational Numbers

Find each sum.

1. $6 + (-6)$ **2.** $-8 + 6$ **3.** $5.31 + (-7.40)$ **4.** $-1.95 + 10$

5. $7\frac{3}{4} + \left(-8\frac{1}{2}\right)$ **6.** $-2\frac{1}{3} + 3\frac{1}{4}$ **7.** $6\frac{2}{5} + 4\frac{3}{10}$ **8.** $-1\frac{5}{6} + 5\frac{1}{3}$

Skills Handbook, page 973

Subtracting Rational Numbers

Find each difference.

9. $-28 - 14$ **10.** $61 - (-11)$ **11.** $-16 - (-25)$ **12.** $-6.2 - 3.6$

13. $-5\frac{2}{3} - \left(-2\frac{1}{3}\right)$ **14.** $-2\frac{1}{4} - 3\frac{1}{4}$ **15.** $2\frac{2}{3} - 7\frac{1}{3}$ **16.** $\frac{5}{2} - \frac{13}{4}$

Skills Handbook, page 973

Multiplying and Dividing Rational Numbers

Find each product or quotient.

17. $-3 \cdot 7$ **18.** $-2.1 \cdot (-3.5)$ **19.** $-\frac{2}{3} \div 4$ **20.** $-\frac{3}{8} \div \frac{5}{8}$

Skills Handbook, page 975

Using the Order of Operations

Simplify each expression.

21. $8 \cdot (-3) + 4$ **22.** $3 \cdot 4 - 8 \div 2$ **23.** $1 \div 2^2 - 0.54 + 1.26$

24. $9 \div (-3) - 2$ **25.** $5(3 \cdot 5 - 4)$ **26.** $1 - (1 - 5)^2 \div (-8)$

27. Reasoning Why don't the expressions $3 + 5^2 \cdot 3 \div 15$ and $(3 + 5^2) \cdot 3 \div 15$ yield the same answer?

Looking Ahead Vocabulary

28. The current of a river flows north at a *constant* rate. What is the constant in the mathematical expression $3x + 5y + 3$?

29. Before signing a contract, you must review the *terms* and conditions of the contract. How many terms are there in the surface area formula below?
$$2(\ell w + wh + h\ell)$$

30. Engineers *evaluate* the efficiency of the memory and speed of a computer. What does evaluate mean in mathematics?

31. Smiling is a facial *expression* of happiness or contentment. In math, what is the expression that represents the quotient of 3 and 3 less than a number?

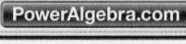

Get Ready!

Get Ready!

Assign this diagnostic assessment to determine if students have the prerequisite skills for Chapter 1.

Lesson	Skill
Skills Handbook, p. T497	Add Rational Numbers
Skills Handbook, p. T497	Subtract Rational Numbers
Skills Handbook, p. T497	Multiply and Divide Rational Numbers
Skills Handbook, p. T499	Use the Order of Operations

To remediate students, select from these resources (available for every lesson).
• Online Problems (PowerAlgebra.com)
• Reteaching (All-in-One Teaching Resources)
• Practice (All-in-One Teaching Resources)

Why Students Need These Skills

ADDING RATIONAL NUMBERS
The addition of rational numbers is essential to the application of the Addition Property of Equality.

SUBTRACTING RATIONAL NUMBERS
The subtraction of rational numbers is essential to the application of the Subtraction Property of Equality.

MULTIPLYING AND DIVIDING RATIONAL NUMBERS
The multiplication and division of rational numbers is essential to the application of the Multiplication and Division Properties of Equality.

USING THE ORDER OF OPERATIONS
The order of operations is necessary when simplifying expressions with exponents.

Looking Ahead Vocabulary

CONSTANT Tell students that a constant friend is someone who remains your friend no matter what. Ask them how a constant is different from a variable.

TERMS If students do not understand how a legal provision of a contract relates to a mathematical formula, explain that a term can also refer to a component of a mathematical expression.

EVALUATE Tell students that real estate agents evaluate properties to determine the worth or value. Ask them how they would evaluate the expression $2x + 3$ if they knew that x is 5.

EXPRESSION Tell students that an idiomatic expression is a phrase with a meaning that is different from the individual meanings of the words. Ask for an example. Ask students how the value of an expression is different from the value of each number and operation by itself.

Answers

Get Ready!

1. 0   **2.** -2

3. -2.09 **4.** 8.05

5. $-\frac{3}{4}$ **6.** $\frac{11}{12}$

7. $10\frac{7}{10}$ **8.** $3\frac{1}{2}$

9. -42 **10.** 72

11. 9   **12.** -9.8

13. $-3\frac{1}{3}$ **14.** $-5\frac{1}{2}$

15. $-4\frac{2}{3}$ **16.** $-\frac{3}{4}$

17. -21 **18.** 7.35

19. $-\frac{1}{6}$ **20.** $-\frac{3}{5}$

21. -20 **22.** 8

23. 0.97   **24.** -5

25. 55   **26.** 3

27. because the placement of the parentheses changes the order of operations

28. 3

29. 3 terms

30. Calculate the answer numerically.

31. $\frac{3}{n-3}$

Chapter 1 Overview

Chapter 1 expands on students' understandings and skills related to expressions, equations, and inequalities. In this chapter, students will develop the answers to the Essential Questions as they learn the concepts and skills bulleted below.

BIG idea Variable

ESSENTIAL QUESTION How do variables help you model real-world situations?

- Students will use an expression to model the *n*th term of a pattern.
- Students will use variables to represent unknown quantities in real-world situations.

BIG idea Properties

ESSENTIAL QUESTION How can you use the properties of real numbers to simplify algebraic expressions?

- Students will apply properties of real numbers to simplify algebraic expressions.

BIG idea Solving Equations and Inequalities

ESSENTIAL QUESTION How do you solve an equation or inequality?

- Students will apply the Properties of Equality to solve an equation.
- Students will apply the Properties of Inequality to solve an inequality.
- Students will find all of the values of a variable that make an equation or inequality true.

Content Standards

Following are the standards covered in this chapter. Modeling standards are indicated by a star symbol (★).

CONCEPTUAL CATEGORY Algebra

Domain Seeing Structure in Expressions A-SSE
Cluster Interpret the structure in expressions. (Standard A-SSE.A.1b★)
LESSON 1-6

Domain Creating Equations A-CED
Cluster Create equations that describe numbers or relationships. (Standard A-CED.A.1★)
LESSONS 1-4, 1-5, 1-6

CHAPTER 1
Expressions, Equations, and Inequalities

Download videos connecting math to your world.

Interactive! Vary numbers, graphs, and figures to explore math concepts.

The online Solve It will get you in gear for each lesson.

Math definitions in English and Spanish

Online access to stepped-out problems aligned to Common Core

Get and view your assignments online.

Extra practice and review online

Virtual Nerd™ tutorials with built-in support

Chapter Preview

1-1 Patterns and Expressions
1-2 Properties of Real Numbers
1-3 Algebraic Expressions
1-4 Solving Equations
1-5 Solving Inequalities
1-6 Absolute Value Equations and Inequalities

Vocabulary

English/Spanish Vocabulary Audio Online:

English	Spanish
absolute value, *p. 41*	valor absoluto
algebraic expression, *p. 5*	expresión algebraica
compound inequality, *p. 36*	desigualdad compuesta
like terms, *p. 21*	términos semejantes
literal equation, *p. 29*	ecuación literal
term, *p. 20*	término
variable, *p. 5*	variable

BIG ideas

1 Variable
Essential Question How do variables help you model real-world situations?

2 Properties
Essential Question How can you use the properties of real numbers to simpli' algebraic expressions?

3 Solving Equations and Inequalities
Essential Question How do you solve equation or inequality?

DOMAINS
- Seeing Structure in Expressions
- Creating Equations

Chapter 1 Overview

Use these online assets to engage your students. These include support for the Solve It and step-by-step solutions for Problems.

 Show the student-produced video demonstrating relevant and engaging applications of the new concepts in the chapter.

 Find online definitions for new terms in English and Spanish.

 Start each lesson with an attention-getting Problem. View the Problem online with helpful hints.

Common Core Performance Task

Where's My Car?

Cody leaves his friend Mia's house and drives along the road shown in the diagram below. Somewhere between Mia's house and the restaurant, Cody's car runs out of gas.

Mia's House	Gas Station	Restaurant
9 mi	11 mi	

Cody has an empty gas can in his car, but he does not want to leave the car unattended. Cody calls Mia, who drives to Cody's car to pick up his gas can. She then drives to the gas station that is located on the same road. After Mia fills the gas can, she drives back to Cody's car. She gives Cody the gas can, and then drives to the restaurant along the same road to meet another friend for lunch. When she reaches the restaurant, Mia has driven a total of 34 mi.

Task Description

Determine how far Cody is from Mia's house when his car runs out of gas. Find all possible distances.

Connecting the Task to the Math Practices

MATHEMATICAL PRACTICES

As you complete the task, you'll apply several Standards for Mathematical Practice.

- You'll draw diagrams to help you make sense of the problem. (MP 1)
- You'll assign a variable to an unknown distance and use your variable to write expressions that represent other distances. (MP 2)
- You'll model the problem situation with an equation. (MP 4)

 Increase students' depth of knowledge with interactive online activities.

 Show Problems from each lesson solved step by step. Instant replay allows students to go at their own pace when studying online.

Assign homework to individual students or to an entire class.

 Prepare students for the Mid-Chapter Quiz and Chapter Test with online practice and review.

 Virtual Nerd™ Access Virtual Nerd student-centered math tutorials that directly relate to the content of the lesson.

 Overview of the Performance Task

Students will write expressions to represent distances in a diagram. They will also write and solve an equation that represents the relationship among several distances.

Students will work on the Performance Task in the following places in the chapter.

- Lesson 1-2 (p. 17)
- Lesson 1-3 (p. 24)
- Lesson 1-4 (p. 32)
- Pull It All Together (p. 49)

Introducing the Performance Task

Tell students to read the problem on this page. Do not have them start work on the problem at this time, but ask them the following questions.

Q What is a strategy you could try in order to solve the problem? **[Sample: I could assign a variable to the distance between Cody's car and the gas station, and look for a way to write an equation relating this distance to other distances in the diagram.]**

Q How many stops does Mia make on her drive? Explain. **[Mia makes four stops: Cody's car, gas station, Cody's car again, restaurant.]**

PARCC CLAIMS

Sub-Claim A: Major Content with Connections to Practices
Sub-Claim D: Highlighted Practice MP 4 with Connections to Content

SBAC CLAIMS

Claim 2: Problem Solving
Claim 4: Modeling and Data Analysis

EXPRESSIONS, EQUATIONS, AND INEQUALITIES
Math Background © PROFESSIONAL DEVELOPMENT

The Understanding by Design® methodology was central to the development of the Big Ideas and the Essential Understandings. These will help your students build a structure on which to make connections to prior learning.

Variable

BIG idea Quantities are used to form expressions, equations, and inequalities. An expression refers to a quantity but does not make a statement about it. An equation (or an inequality) is a statement about the quantities it mentions. Using variables in place of numbers in equations (or inequalities) allows the statement of relationships among numbers that are unknown or unspecified.

ESSENTIAL UNDERSTANDINGS

1-1 You can represent some patterns using diagrams, words, numbers, or algebraic expressions.

1-3 You can represent some mathematical phrases and real-world quantities using algebraic expressions.

Properties

BIG idea All of the facts of arithmetic and algebra follow from certain properties.

ESSENTIAL UNDERSTANDINGS

1-2 The set of real numbers has several special subsets related in particular ways.

1-3 You can represent some mathematical phrases and real-world quantities using algebraic expressions.

Solving Equations and Inequalities

BIG idea Solving an equation is the process of rewriting the equation to make what it says about its variable(s) as simple as possible. Properties of numbers and equality can be used to transform an equation (or inequality) into equivalent, simpler equations (or inequalities) in order to find solutions. Useful information about equations and inequalities (including solutions) can be found by analyzing graphs or tables. The numbers and types of solutions vary predictably, based on the type of equation.

ESSENTIAL UNDERSTANDINGS

1-4 You can use the properties of equality and inverse operations to solve equations.

Sometimes, no value of the variable makes an equation true. For identities, all values of the variable make the equation true.

1-5 Just as you use properties of equality to solve equations, you can use properties of inequality to solve inequalities.

1-6 An absolute value quantity is nonnegative. Since opposites have the same absolute value, an absolute value equation can have two solutions.

You can write an absolute value inequality as a compound inequality without absolute value signs.

Variable

A variable is a symbol, usually a letter, which represents one or more numbers.

The context of a problem will determine the set of values for which a variable is defined. If p represents the number of people that use a certain airport each day, then p must take on whole number values. If t is the lifetime of a light bulb, then it can be any positive real number.

Variables allow scientists and mathematicians to summarize data as a general rule. For example, you could write the following table with columns for the side length and the perimeter of a square.

Length of a side	Perimeter of square
1	4
2	8
3	12
4	16
5	20
6	24

It is much easier, however, to summarize the relationship between side length and perimeter with the equation $p = 4s$, where p represents perimeter, and s represents side length. Because we discover general laws from observations, the use of variables to state relationships is important.

An *open sentence* is an equation that contains one or more variables. To solve the equation is to find the value of the variable that makes the equation true. For example, $x = 2$ is a solution to the open sentence $x^2 = 4$ ($x = -2$ is also a solution).

Common Errors With Variables

Many different letters and symbols can represent variables. Students may be confused when confronted with the symbols e and π. They conventionally stand for specific irrational numbers and not variables.

© Mathematical Practices

Look for and make use of structure. Reason abstractly and quantitatively. Through motivating Solve It! activities, students analyze patterns to appreciate the usefulness of variable expressions. Real-world problems motivate the usefulness of algebraic equations and inequalities.

Solving Equations and Inequalities

An equation is a statement that two expressions are equal. Solving an algebraic equation means finding all of the values of the variable that make the equation true. The Properties of Equality and inverse operations are used to solve equations.

The Properties of Equality for real numbers include the following:

Reflexive	Symmetric
$a = a$	$a = b \longrightarrow b = a$
Transitive	**Substitution**
$a = b, b = c \longrightarrow a = c$	$a = b \longrightarrow 2a + 3 = 2b + 3$

Inverse operations are operations that "undo" each other.
- Addition and subtraction are inverse operations.
- Multiplication and division are inverse operations.

Some equations are never true (no solutions):

$x + 1 = x + 2$

Some equations are always true (Identities):

$x + 2 = x + 2$

Solving an inequality means finding the range of values of the variable. The properties of inequalities are similar to the properties used for solving equations, with an important difference: when you multiply or divide each side of an inequality by a negative number, you must reverse the inequality symbol.

A compound inequality is two inequalities joined by the word *and* or *or*.

Compound inequality containing and

$a > 3$ $a < 5$

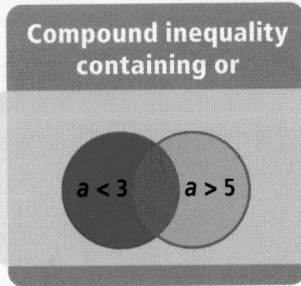

Compound inequality containing or

$a < 3$ $a > 5$

ⓒ Mathematical Practices

Model with mathematics. Look for and express regularity in repeated reasoning. Modeling is emphasized throughout the chapter as the motivation for constructing algebraic equations and inequalities. Students learn that the context changes but the algebraic structure remains the same.

Absolute Value

The absolute value of a number x, written $|x|$, represents the distance from any number x to 0 on the number line. As the diagram makes clear, for example, $|4| = |-4| = 4$.

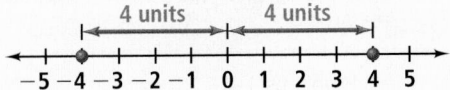

4 units   4 units

$-5\ -4\ -3\ -2\ -1\ \ 0\ \ 1\ \ 2\ \ 3\ \ 4\ \ 5$

With this in mind, the following properties are reasonable:

(1) $|x| \geq 0$

(2) $|x| = 0$ if and only if $x = 0$

(3) $|x - y| \leq |x| + |y|$

(1) just says that all distances are nonnegative. (2) says that only zero is a distance of zero from zero on the number line. (3) tells you that it is not farther to go directly from x to y than it is to go from zero to x and then from zero to y. In three-dimensions, this is the triangle inequality. In popular speech, we say that it is faster to go "as the crow flies."

In more advanced math courses, students will see that the absolute value function is generalized as the *distance function*, $d(x, y)$. Compare the following properties of $d(x, y)$ to the properties of the absolute value function:

(1') $d(x, y) \geq 0$

(2') $d(x, y) = 0$ if and only if $x = y$

(3') $d(x, y) \leq d(x, y) + d(x, z)$

(1') again says that distances are nonnegative. (2') states that two different points cannot be located in exactly the same place. (3') is the triangle inequality.

Absolute values have many applications.

ⓒ Mathematical Practices

Attend to precision. Construct viable arguments and critique the reasoning of others. Properties of real numbers are used to explain algebraic operations. Do You Understand? exercises in every lesson ensure that students can justify true statements and analyze flawed statements.

CHAPTER 1

EXPRESSIONS, EQUATIONS, AND INEQUALITIES
Pacing and Assignment Guide

		TRADITIONAL			BLOCK
Lesson	Teaching Day(s)	Basic	Average	Advanced	Block
1-1	1	Problems 1–3 Exs. 8–24, 26–32 even, 33, 34–38 even, 43–57	Problems 1–3 Exs. 9–23 odd, 25–39, 43–57	Problems 1–3 Exs. 9–23 odd, 25–57	**Day 1** Problems 1–3 Exs. 9–23 odd, 25–39, 43–57
1-2	1	Problems 1–4 Exs. 10–40, 42–48 even, 49, 58–66 even, 72–74	Problems 1–4 Exs. 11–39 odd, 41–67, 72–74	Problems 1–4 Exs. 11–39 odd, 41–74	Problems 1–4 Exs. 11–39 odd, 41–67, 72–74
1-3	1	Problems 1–5 Exs. 10–38, 40–46 even, 51	Problems 1–5 Exs. 11–37 odd, 39–60	Problems 1–5 Exs. 11–37 odd, 39–62	**Day 2** Problems 1–5 Exs. 11–37 odd, 39–60
1-4	1	Problems 1–5 Exs. 10–40, 43–45, 52, 53, 58–62 even	Problems 1–5 Exs. 11–39 odd, 41–63	Problems 1–5 Exs. 11–39 odd, 41–65	Problems 1–5 Exs. 11–39 odd, 41–63
1-5	1	Problems 1–4 Exs. 10–35, 44–50 even, 51	Problems 1–4 Exs. 11–35 odd, 44–53	Problems 1–4 Exs. 11–35 odd, 44–53	**Day 3** Problems 1–6 Exs. 11–43 odd, 44–61, 67–78
	2	Problems 5–6 Exs. 36–43, 57, 60, 67–78	Problems 5–6 Exs. 37–43 odd, 54–61, 67–78	Problems 5–6 Exs. 37–43 odd, 78	
1-6	1	Problems 1–3 Exs. 10–24 all, 48–52 even	Problems 1–3 Exs. 11–23 odd, 43–52	Problems 1–3 Exs. 11–23 odd, 43–52	**Day 4** Problems 1–5 Exs. 11–41 odd, 43–81, 90–102
	2	Problems 4–6 Exs. 25–42 all, 53, 58–66 even, 69, 81, 90–102	Problems 4–6 Exs. 25–41 odd, 53–81, 90–102	Problems 4–6 Exs. 25–41 odd, 53–89, 90–102	
Review	1	Chapter 1 Review	Chapter 1 Review	Chapter 1 Review	**Day 5** Chapter 1 Review Chapter 1 Test
Assess	1	Chapter 1 Test	Chapter 1 Test	Chapter 1 Test	
Total		**10 Days**	**10 Days**	**10 Days**	**5 Days**

Note: Pacing does not include Concept Bytes and other feature pages.

Resources

	For the Chapter	1-1	1-2	1-3	1-4	1-5	1-6
Planning							
Teacher Center Online Planner & Grade Book	I	I	I	I	I	I	I
Interactive Learning & Guided Instruction							
My Math Video	I						
Solve It!		I M	I M	I M	I M	I M	I M
Student Companion		P M	P M	P M	P M	P M	
Vocabulary Support		I P M	I P M	I P M	I P M	I P M	I P M
Got It? Support		I P	I P	I P	I P	I P	I P
Online Problems		I	I	I	I	I	I
Additional Problems		M	M	M	M	M	M
English Language Learner Support (TR)		E P M	E P M	E P M	E P M	E P M	E P M
Activities, Games, and Puzzles		E M	E M	E M	E M	E M	E M
Teaching With TI Technology With CD-ROM							
TI-Nspire™ Support CD-ROM		✓	✓	✓	✓	✓	✓
Lesson Check & Practice							
Student Companion		P M	P M	P M	P M	P M	P M
Lesson Check Support		I P	I P	I P	I P	I P	I P
Practice and Problem Solving Workbook		P	P	P	P	P	P
Think About a Plan (TR)		E P M	E P M	E P M	E P M	E P M	E P M
Practice Form G (TR)		E P M	E P M	E P M	E P M	E P M	E P M
Standardized Test Prep (TR)		P M	P M	P M	P M	P M	P M
Practice *Form K* (TR)		E P M	E P M	E P M	E P M	E P M	E P M
Extra Practice	E M						
Find the Errors!		M					
Enrichment (TR)		E P M	E P M	E P M	E P M	E P M	E P M
Answers and Solutions CD-ROM	✓	✓	✓	✓	✓	✓	✓
Assess & Remediate							
ExamView CD-ROM	✓	✓	✓	✓	✓	✓	✓
Lesson Quiz		I M	I M	I M	I M	I M	I M
Quizzes and Tests *Form G* (TR)	E P M			E P M			E P M
Quizzes and Tests *Form K* (TR)	E P M			E P M			E P M
Reteaching (TR)		E P M	E P M	E P M	E P M	E P M	E P M
Performance Tasks (TR)	P M						
Cumulative Review (TR)	P M						
Progress Monitoring Assessments	I P M						

(TR) Available in All-In-One Teaching Resources

1 Interactive Learning

Solve It!

PURPOSE To describe a geometric pattern and extend it to find the eighth term

PROCESS Students may
- trace the first pattern of squares and then rotate it clockwise 90° to see the next image.
- realize the 4th and 8th figures are the same.

FACILITATE

Q Why is the middle square always the same? **[It is at the center of the rotation.]**

Q How do the 5th and 1st figures compare? **[They are identical.]**

Q Must you draw 8 figures to solve the problem? Explain. **[No; the 4th and 8th figures match.]**

ANSWER See Solve It in Answers on next page.

CONNECT THE MATH In the Solve It, students find a pattern in a video game. In this lesson, they continue to discover patterns and express them mathematically.

2 Guided Instruction

Problem 1

Q Number the figures 1, 2, 3, and 4. How does the figure number relate to the number of sides? **[The figure number is 2 less the number of sides.]**

Got It?   **VISUAL LEARNERS**

Q What changes in each figure? **[The length of each arm increases by 1 block.]**

Q What remains the same? **[the center]**

Patterns and Expressions

Common Core State Standards
A-SSE.B.3 Choose and produce an equivalent form of an expression to reveal and explain properties of the quantity represented by the expression.
MP 1, MP 2, MP 3, MP 7

Objective To identify and describe patterns

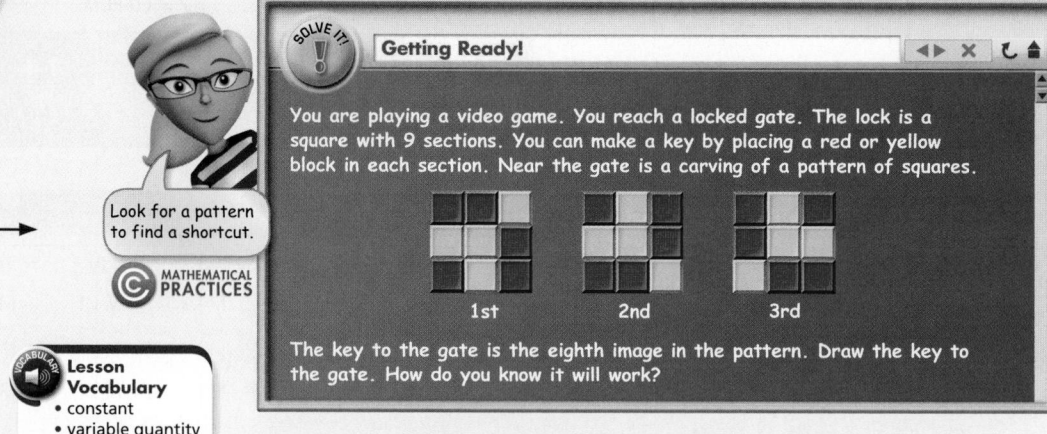

Look for a pattern to find a shortcut.

MATHEMATICAL PRACTICES

Getting Ready!

You are playing a video game. You reach a locked gate. The lock is a square with 9 sections. You can make a key by placing a red or yellow block in each section. Near the gate is a carving of a pattern of squares.

1st   2nd   3rd

The key to the gate is the eighth image in the pattern. Draw the key to the gate. How do you know it will work?

In the Solve It, you identified and used a geometric pattern. In this lesson, you will identify patterns in pictures, tables, and graphs and describe them using numbers and variables.

Essential Understanding You can represent some patterns using diagrams, words, numbers, or algebraic expressions.

Lesson Vocabulary
- constant
- variable quantity
- variable
- numerical expression
- algebraic expression

Problem 1 Identifying a Pattern

Think
How can you identify a pattern?
Look for the same type of change between consecutive figures.

Look at the figures from left to right. What is the pattern? What would the next figure in the pattern look like?

The pattern shows regular polygons with the number of sides increasing by one.

The last figure shown above has six sides, so the next figure would have seven sides. This is a heptagon: 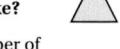.

Got It? 1. Look at the figures from left to right. What is the pattern? Draw the next figure in the pattern.

Preparing to Teach

BIG idea Variable

ESSENTIAL UNDERSTANDINGS
- Some patterns can be represented using diagrams, words, numbers, or algebraic expressions.
- Variables can represent variable quantities in real world situations and in patterns.

Math Background

This lesson illustrates that searching for patterns underlies much of mathematical knowledge. The lesson builds on students' previous experience with patterns by discussing both geometric and numeric patterns. Most of the patterns are arithmetic in nature, having the form an, $n + a$, or $an + b$. Patterns of this type are linear functions.

This lesson uses the three-column tables to organize information. The input and output values in the tables represent the independent and dependent variables.

Mathematical Practices
Look for and make use of structure.
The introduction to geometric and numeric patterns will aid students in discerning and expressing patterns from numeric and algebraic expressions.

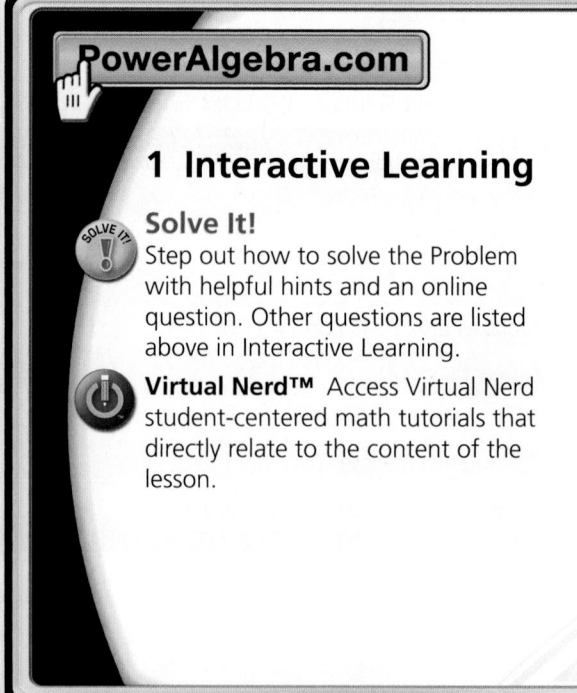

PowerAlgebra.com

1 Interactive Learning

Solve It!
Step out how to solve the Problem with helpful hints and an online question. Other questions are listed above in Interactive Learning.

Virtual Nerd™ Access Virtual Nerd student-centered math tutorials that directly relate to the content of the lesson.

A mathematical *quantity* is anything that can be measured or counted. The *value* of the quantity is its measure or the number of items that are counted. Quantities whose values do not change are called **constants**. In other situations, the value of a quantity can change. Quantities whose values change or vary are called **variable quantities**.

take note

Key Concepts   Variables and Expressions

Definition	Examples	
A **variable** is a symbol, usually a letter, that represents one or more numbers.	n	x
A **numerical expression** is a mathematical phrase that contains numbers and operation symbols.	$3 + 5$	$(8 - 2) + 5$
An **algebraic expression** is a mathematical phrase that contains one or more variables.	$3n + 5$	$(8x - 2) + 5n$

Tables are a convenient way to organize data and discover patterns. They work much like an "input/output" machine: a machine that takes one value as an input, processes it, and gives a value as an output. A process column in the table provides a way to understand what happens to the input values.

© Problem 2   Expressing a Pattern With Algebra

Use a pattern to answer each question.

A How many toothpicks are in the 20th figure?

Use a table. Look for a pattern that relates the figure number to the number of toothpicks.

Figure Number (Input)	Process Column	Number of Toothpicks (Output)
1	1(4)	4
2	2(4)	8
3	3(4)	12
⋮	⋮	⋮
n	■	■

To get the output, multiply the input by 4.

Pattern: Multiply the figure number by 4 to get the number of toothpicks. So, there are $20(4) = 80$ toothpicks in the 20th figure.

B What is an expression that describes the number of toothpicks in the *n*th figure?

Use the pattern from part (A). There are $4n$ toothpicks in the *n*th figure.

Think

What would the process look like for the *n*th row?
Multiply the figure number, *n*, by 4.

 Got It? 2. How many tiles are in the 25th figure in this pattern? Show a table of values with a process column.

Take Note

Q What is the only difference between algebraic expressions and numerical expressions? **[An algebraic expression contains one or more variables while a numerical expression contains no variables.]**

Problem 2

In analyzing the process, students may look at the pattern and think of it as adding 4 each time. Remind them that multiplication is repeated addition.

Have volunteers come to the board and draw the next two or three figures in the pattern to make sure all students see how it works.

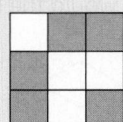

Q The numbers of toothpicks form the pattern 4, 8, 12, and so on. Describe this pattern. **[multiples of 4]**

Q How does the Process Column relate the numbers in the Input and Output columns? **[The Process Column shows that the input number is always multiplied by 4.]**

Q A student described this pattern as "add 4." Why is this not as useful as "multiply by 4"? **["Add 4" tells how the output numbers are increasing, but it does not relate the output numbers to the input numbers.]**

Got It?

Q What is the total number of squares in each figure? **[4, 6, 8]**

Q How is the 2nd figure different from the first? **[It has two more yellow squares on the right.]**

Q How is the 3rd figure different from the second? **[The 3rd figure has two more yellow squares on the right.]**

---

2 Guided Instruction

© Each Problem is worked out and supported online.

Support in Algebra 2 Companion
- Vocabulary
- Key Concepts
- Got It?

Problem 1
Identifying a Pattern
Animated

Problem 2
Expressing a Pattern with Algebra
Animated

Problem 3
Using a Graph
Animated

Answers

Solve It!

You can get each image in the pattern by turning the image before it clockwise 90°. Notice that the pattern begins to repeat with the fifth image. So, the 4th and 8th images will be the same.

Got It?

1. The pattern shows a center square and a yellow square added to each side with the number of squares per side increasing by one.

2. 52 tiles

Problem 3

Many mathematical patterns can be shown with graphs. Make sure all students know how to use ordered pairs to describe the coordinates of points on Cartesian grids.

Q Use an ordered pair to describe a point on the line. What do the coordinates of the ordered pair represent? **[Answers may vary. Sample: (6, 8); if the total of all the fish lengths is 6 inches, you need an 8 gallon tank.]**

Q The line rises from left to right, so the relationship is increasing. Why? **[As you get more fish, you need a bigger tank.]**

Q You can use the variables L and G for the quantities in this relationship. What equation relates L and G? **[$G = L + 2$]**

Q If a tank held 12 gallons, what would that mean in terms of fish length? **[The tank could hold 10 inches of fish.]**

Got It?

Q Using the graph, what is the cost of one platy? Explain. **[$2; when $x = 1$, $y = 2$.]**

Q If you continue the graph, what figure would contain all of the points? **[a line]**

Q Do you need the entire graph to determine the cost of 40 platys? Explain. **[No; if you know the cost of one you can calculate the cost for 40.]**

Problem 3 Using a Graph

Aquarium You want to set up an aquarium and need to determine what size tank to buy. The graph shows tank sizes using a rule that relates the capacity of the tank to the combined lengths of the fish it can hold.

If you want five 2-in. platys, four 1-in. guppies, and a 3-in. loach, which is the smallest capacity tank you can buy: 15-gallon, 20-gallon, or 25-gallon? Use a table to find the answer.

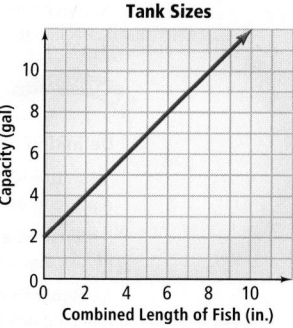
Tank Sizes

Plan

How can you use the given graph?
You can use the graph to make a table and find a pattern relating capacity and combined fish length.

Think

Choose some points on the graph.

Make a table using the input and output values shown in the ordered pairs.
Find a pattern in the process column. Each output is 2 more than the corresponding input.

You want 5 platys, 4 guppies, and 1 loach. So, you will have a total of 17 in. of fish. Find the output when the input is 17.

Write the answer in words.

Write

(0, 2), (5, 7), (10, 12)

Input	Process Column	Output
0	0 + 2	2
5	5 + 2	7
10	10 + 2	12

output = input + 2
= 17 + 2
= 19

You need to buy the 20-gal tank.

Got It? 3. The graph at the right shows the total cost of platys at the aquarium shop. Use a table to answer the questions.
a. How much do six platys cost?
b. How much do ten platys cost?
c. **Reasoning** Why is the graph in Problem 3 a line while the graph at the right is a set of points?

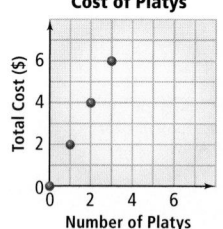
Cost of Platys

Additional Problems

1. Describe the pattern. What would the next figure in the pattern look like?

 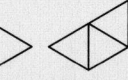 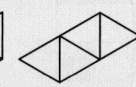

ANSWER Answers may vary. Sample: Each figure has one more equilateral triangle. The next figure will have 5 triangles, arranged like this:

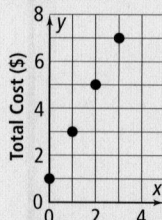

2. These figures are made with toothpicks.

a. How many toothpicks are in the 20th figure? Use a table of values with a process column to justify your answer.

b. What expression describes the number of toothpicks in the *n*th figure?

ANSWERS 100; 5*n*

3. You buy a bag of fish food and some goldfish. The graph shows the total cost depending on how many goldfish you buy.

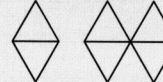
Number of Goldfish

What is your total cost if you buy the food plus 9 goldfish? Use a table to find the answer.

ANSWER $19

Answers

Got It? (continued)
3. a. $12
b. $20
c. The number of platys must be a whole number whereas the lengths of fish can be a fraction or decimal.

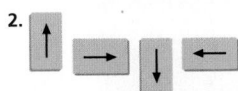

Lesson Check

Do you know HOW?

Describe a rule for each pattern.

1. 35, 70, 105, 140, . . .

2.

Make a table to represent each pattern. Use a process column.

3. 2, 4, 6, 8, . . .

4. ▌▌ ▌▌▌▌ ▌▌ ▌▌▌▌▌▌▌

Do you UNDERSTAND?  MATHEMATICAL PRACTICES

5. Explain the strategy you use to identify a pattern.

6. Compare and Contrast How are tables of values like pictorial representations? How are they different?

7. Error Analysis Your friend looks for a pattern in the table below and claims that the output equals the input divided by 2. Is your friend correct? Explain.

Input	3	6.8	8	10	25
Output	2	3.4	4	5	12.5

Practice and Problem-Solving Exercises  MATHEMATICAL PRACTICES

Ⓐ Practice   Describe each pattern using words. Draw the next likely figure in each pattern.   ◀ **See Problem 1.**

8.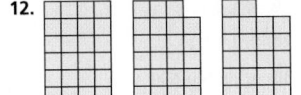

9.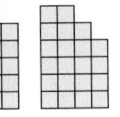

10.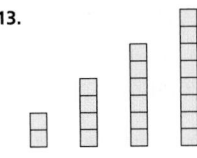

11.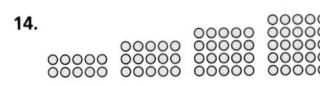

Make a table with a process column to represent each pattern. Write an expression for the number of tiles or circles in the *n*th figure.   ◀ **See Problem 2.**

12.

13.

14.

15.

---

3 Lesson Check

Do you know HOW?

- For Exercise 1, compare the rules "add 35" and "multiply the term number by 35." Only the second type can be used to find the value of the *n*th term.
- For Exercises 3–4, students may need to be told to use the term numbers 1, 2, 3, and 4 as the input numbers in the chart. Most students should recognize these patterns as the even numbers and the doubling pattern. For students who do not recognize patterns, help them make a list of patterns they have seen in this lesson. They can use this list for ideas on future problems.

Do you UNDERSTAND?

- For Exercise 5, ask how patterns can be represented. Ask students if the representation of the pattern affects the solution strategy.
- For Exercise 6, "pictorial representation" could be a graph or a series of figures. Have students discuss both interpretations of the question.

Close

> **Q** Why is it useful to be able to describe patterns?
> **[Answers may vary. Sample: If you can describe a pattern, you can use the description to make predictions.]**

Answers

Lesson Check

1. add 35

2. rotate 90° clockwise

3.

Input	Process Column	Output
1	2(1)	2
2	2(2)	4
3	2(3)	6
4	2(4)	8
⋮	⋮	⋮
n	2(*n*)	2*n*

4.

Input	Process Column	Output
1	3(1)	3
2	3(2)	6
3	3(3)	9
4	3(4)	12
⋮	⋮	⋮
n	3(*n*)	3*n*

5. Check students' work.

6. Answers may vary. Sample: Tables of values and pictorial representations are both convenient ways to organize data and discover patterns. Tables give more detail. Pictorial representations are visual.

7. No; the output is $\frac{1}{2}$ the input for all values except the first (Input: 3; Output: 2).

8–15. See next page.

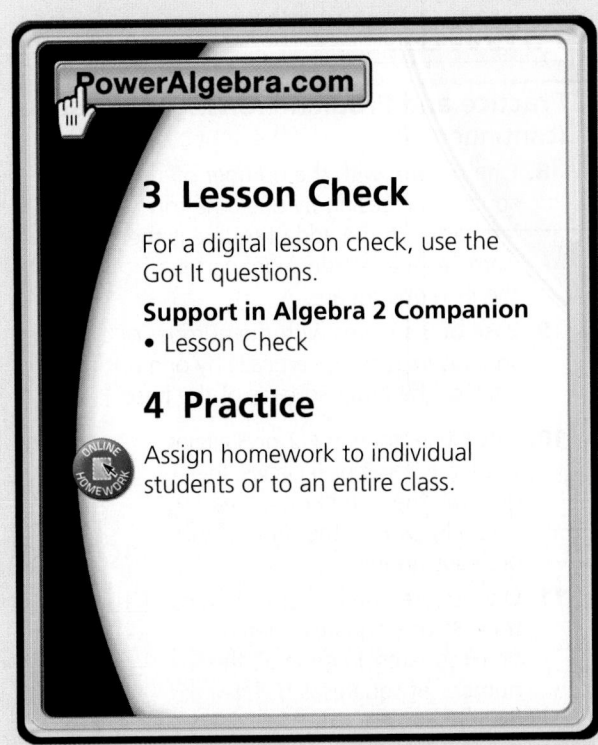

4 Practice

ASSIGNMENT GUIDE

Basic: 8–24 all, 26–32 even, 33, 34–38 even

Average: 9–23 odd, 25–39

Advanced: 9–23 odd, 25–42

Standardized Test Prep: 43–45

Mixed Review: 46–57

© **Mathematical Practices** are supported by exercises with red headings. Here are the Practices supported in this lesson:

MP 1: Make Sense of Problems Ex. 33
MP 2: Reason Abstractly Ex. 32, 40
MP 3: Critique the Reasoning of Others Ex. 7, 41
MP 3: Construct Arguments Ex. 6

Applications exercises have red headings.

EXERCISE 34: Use the Think About a Plan worksheet in the **Practice and Problem Solving Workbook** (also available in the Teaching Resources in print and online) to further support students' development in becoming independent learners.

HOMEWORK QUICK CHECK

To check students' understanding of key skills and concepts, go over Exercises 13, 21, 33, 34, and 38.

Copy and complete each table. Include a process column.

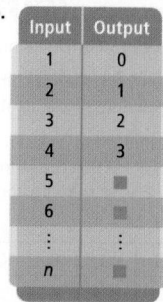

Identify a pattern by making a table. Include a process column.

◀ See Problem 3.

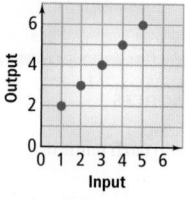

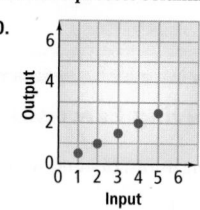

The graph shows the number of bottles of water needed for students going on a field trip.

22. How many bottles of water are needed if 5 students attend?

23. How many bottles of water are needed if 20 students attend?

24. How many bottles of water are needed if n students attend?

B Apply

Identify a pattern and find the next three numbers in the pattern.

25. 6, 12, 18, 24, . . .

26. 1, 4, 3, 6, 5, . . .

27. 3, 6, 10, 15, . . .

28. 2, 6, 10, 14, . . .

29. 1, 3, 9, 27, 81, . . .

30. 4, 20, 100, 500, . . .

31. Identify a pattern and draw the next three figures in the pattern.

© **32. Open-Ended** Write a rule so that for every input, the output is an even number.

Answers

Practice and Problem-Solving Exercises
(continued)

8. One square, with the number of squares increasing by one. The top left vertex of the added square is the same as the bottom right vertex of the previous square.

9. Base of 3 squares with the number of squares increasing vertically by one on each of the outer squares of the base.

10. One circle, then $1 + 2$ or 3 circles, then $1 + 2 + 3$ or 6 circles. In general, the number is increasing vertically by n to the right of the previous figure.

11. One square, then 2^2 or 4 squares, then 3^2 or 9 squares, then 4^2 or 16 squares. In general, the number of squares is $n \times n$ or n^2.

12. $25 - n$

Input	Process Column	Output
1	24	24
2	$24 - 1$	23
3	$24 - 2$	22
4	$24 - 3$	21
⋮	⋮	⋮
n	$24 - (n - 1)$	$25 - n$

13. $2n$

Input	Process Column	Output
1	$2(1)$	2
2	$2(2)$	4
3	$2(3)$	6
4	$2(4)$	8
⋮	⋮	⋮
n	$2(n)$	$2n$

14. $5 + 5n$

Input	Process Column	Output
1	$5 + 5(1)$	10
2	$5 + 5(2)$	15
3	$5 + 5(3)$	20
4	$5 + 5(4)$	25
⋮	⋮	⋮
n	$5 + 5(n)$	$5 + 5n$

15. $4n - 1$

Input	Process Column	Output
1	$4(1) - 1$	3
2	$4(2) - 1$	7
3	$4(3) - 1$	11
4	$4(4) - 1$	15
⋮	⋮	⋮
n	$4(n) - 1$	$4n - 1$

16–32. See next page.

33. Think About a Plan A moving company sells different sizes of boxes as shown. The extra-large box is one size larger than the third box shown. What is its volume?
- Identify a pattern of the dimension changes.
- What is the formula for the volume of a rectangular prism?

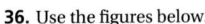

34. Use the graph shown.
  a. Identify a pattern of the graph by making a table of the inputs and outputs.
  b. What are the outputs for inputs 6, 7, and 8?

35. Collecting Jay has a rare baseball card collection. He currently owns 10 baseball cards. Each month, he purchases a new card for his collection. Write a model to represent the number of cards in Jay's collection after n months.

36. Use the figures below.

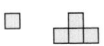

Figure (Input)	Process Column	Number of Squares (Output)
1	■	■
2	■	■
3	■	■
4	■	■
5	■	■

  a. Draw the next two figures.
  b. Copy and complete the table to find the number of squares in each figure.
  c. What is the number of squares in the nth figure? Explain your reasoning.

Copy and complete each table.

37.

Input	Output
1	5
2	9
3	13
4	17
5	■
⋮	⋮
n	■

38.

Input	Output
1	2
2	−3
3	−8
4	−13
5	■
⋮	⋮
n	■

39.

Input	Output
1	3
2	−1
3	−5
4	−9
5	■
⋮	⋮
n	■

 **Challenge**

40. Open-Ended Write the first five numbers of two different patterns in which 12 is the third number.

41. Reasoning For the past 4 years, Jesse has grown 3 inches each year. He is now 15 years old and is 5 feet 6 inches tall. He predicts that when he is 20 years old, he will be 6 feet 9 inches tall. What would you tell Jesse about his prediction?

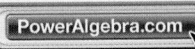
16. 4; 5; $n − 1$

17. 7; 8; $n + 2$

18. −15; −18; −3n

19. Output = Input + 1

Input	Process Column	Output
1	(1) + 1	2
2	(2) + 1	3
3	(3) + 1	4
4	(4) + 1	5
5	(5) + 1	6
⋮	⋮	⋮
n	(n) + 1	n + 1

20. Output = $\frac{1}{2}$ Input

Input	Process Column	Output
1	(1) · $\frac{1}{2}$	$\frac{1}{2}$
2	(2) · $\frac{1}{2}$	1
3	(3) · $\frac{1}{2}$	$1\frac{1}{2}$
4	(4) · $\frac{1}{2}$	2
5	(5) · $\frac{1}{2}$	$2\frac{1}{2}$
⋮	⋮	⋮
n	(n) · $\frac{1}{2}$	$\frac{1}{2}n$

21. Output = Input − 1

Input	Process Column	Output
1	(1) − 1	0
2	(2) − 1	1
3	(3) − 1	2
4	(4) − 1	3
5	(5) − 1	4
⋮	⋮	⋮
n	(n) − 1	n − 1

22. 10   **23.** 40   **24.** 2n

25. add 6 or 6n; 30, 36, 42

26. add 3; subtract 1; 8, 7, 10

27. add 3, then add 4, then add 5, and so on; 21, 28, 36

28. add 4; 18, 22, 26

29. multiply by 3; 243, 729, 2187

30. multiply by 5; 2500, 12,500, 62,500

31. The black square and dot each move clockwise one block.

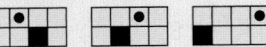

32. Answers may vary. Sample: multiply each input by 4

33. 9216 in.^{3}

34. a.

Input	Output
1	3
2	6
3	9
4	12
5	15
⋮	⋮
n	3n

  b. 18; 21; 24

35. $n + 10$, where n is the number of months

36. a.

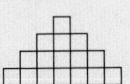 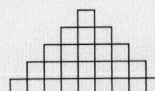

  b. Process Column: (1), 2(2), 3(3), 4(4), 5(5); Number of squares: 1, 4, 9, 16, 25

  c. n^2; Since the number of squares for each figure is the square of the figure number, the number of squares for the nth figure is $n(n)$ or n^2.

37. 21; 4n + 1

38. −18; 7 − 5n; or −5n + 7

39. −13; 7 − 4n; or −4n + 7

40. Check students' work.

41. Answers may vary. Sample: Jesse will not grow at the same rate between the ages of 15 and 20 as he has during the 4 years prior to age 15.

Answers

Practice and Problem-Solving Exercises
(continued)

42. The Sierpinski Triangle is formed by connecting the midpoints of the sides of an equilateral triangle, forming 4 smaller triangles, deleting the middle triangle. Repeat the process of connecting the midpoints of the sides of the remaining 3 triangles and deleting the middle triangle of each new set of triangles.

Standardized Test Prep

43. D

44. H

45. [2] **a.** Each number is a result of the division of the previous number by 2.

   b. $36 \div 2 = 18$, $18 \div 2 = 9$, $9 \div 2 = 4.5$, so 4.5 is the first non-integer number.

   [1] First non-integer number is not correct.

Mixed Review

46. 1.9	**47.** −3.8
48. 27	**49.** 0
50. −0.4	**51.** 7
52. 50%	**53.** 25%
54. 33.33%	**55.** 140%
56. 172%	**57.** 123%

42. This pattern shows the first five steps in constructing the Sierpinski Triangle. Use a pattern to describe the figures.

Standardized Test Prep

SAT/ACT

43. Which of the following is the best statement about the graph?

   Ⓐ After 4 weeks, the plant will be 7 inches tall.

   Ⓑ The plant was 1 inch tall at the beginning of the experiment.

   Ⓒ After 2 weeks, the plant was 3 inches tall.

   Ⓓ After 6 weeks, the plant will be 8 inches tall.

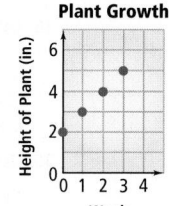

Plant Growth

44. Which is the 7th number in this pattern?

   8, 13, 18, 23, . . .

   Ⓕ 28   Ⓗ 38

   Ⓖ 33   Ⓘ 43

Short Response

45. Look at the pattern shown.

   144, 72, 36, . . .

   a. What is a rule for the pattern?

   b. What is the first non-integer number in this pattern?

Mixed Review

Simplify each expression.

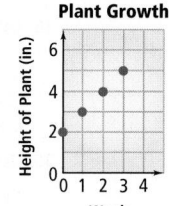 *(see reference)*

◀ See p. 975.

46. $3.6 + (-1.7)$	**47.** $1.2 - 5$
48. $(-3)(-9)$	**49.** $0(-8)$
50. $-2.8 \div 7$	**51.** $-35 \div (-5)$

Get Ready!   **To prepare for Lesson 1-2, do Exercises 52–57.**

Write each number as a percent.

◀ See p. 972.

52. 0.5	**53.** 0.25
54. $\frac{1}{3}$	**55.** $1\frac{2}{5}$
56. 1.72	**57.** 1.23

Lesson Resources

Additional Instructional Support

Algebra 2 Companion

Students can use the **Algebra 2 Companion** worktext (4 pages) as you teach the lesson. Use the Companion to support

• New Vocabulary
• Key Concepts
• Got It for each Problem
• Lesson Check

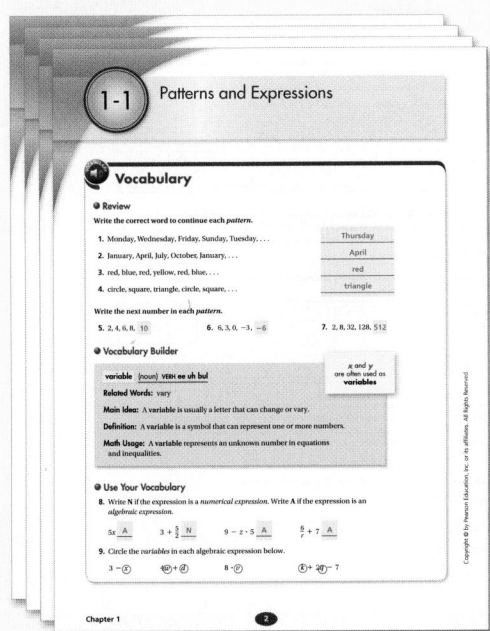

ELL Support

Use Manipulatives Have students work in pairs. One student makes a pattern with available materials, such as one pencil, one eraser, two pencils, two erasers. The other student describes the pattern in words and builds the next part of the pattern. Students reverse roles and repeat with a different set of materials, such as coins.

Use Graphic Organizers Have groups of students make a graphic organizer covering the mathematics they already know. Students might include numbers, operations, fractions, decimals, and percents. Congratulate students on the great amount of mathematics they have already learned.

5 Assess & Remediate

Lesson Quiz

1. Describe the pattern. Sketch the next figure in the pattern.

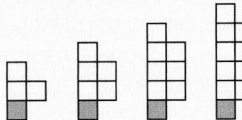

2. How many tiles are in the *n*th figure?

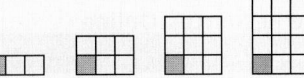

3. Do you UNDERSTAND? The graph shows the cost of bowling for one person. What is the total cost if four people each bowl four games? Explain your answer.

Bowling

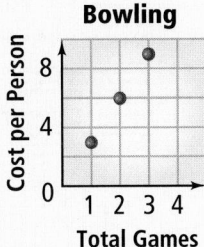

ANSWERS TO LESSON QUIZ

1. The pattern shows groups of squares with the number of squares increasing by 2. The next figure has 12 squares.

2. 3*n*

3. $48; each game cost $3 per person, so 16 total games costs $48.

PRESCRIPTION FOR REMEDIATION

Use the student work on the Lesson Quiz to prescribe a differentiated review assignment:

Points	Differentiated Remediation
0–1	Intervention
2	On-level
3	Extension

PowerAlgebra.com

5 Assess & Remediate

Assign the Lesson Quiz. Appropriate intervention, practice, or enrichment is automatically generated based on student performance.

Differentiated Remediation

Available in editable format online.

Intervention

• **Reteaching** (2 pages) Provides reteaching and practice exercises for the key lesson concepts. Use with struggling students or absent students.

• **English Language Learner Support** Helps students develop and reinforce mathematical vocabulary and key concepts.

All-in-One Resources/Online
Reteaching

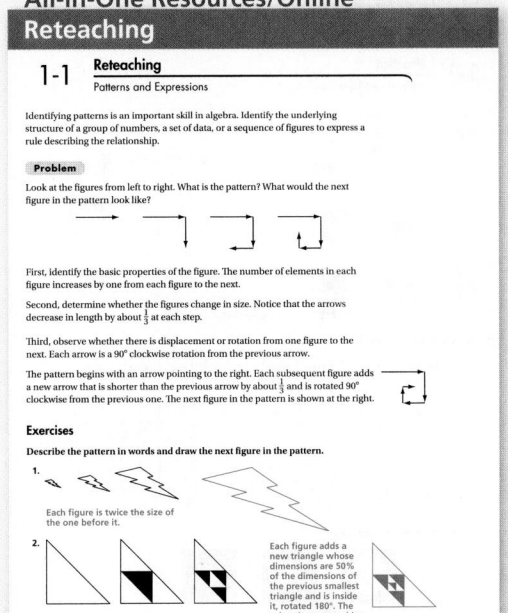

All-in-One Resources/Online
English Language Learner Support

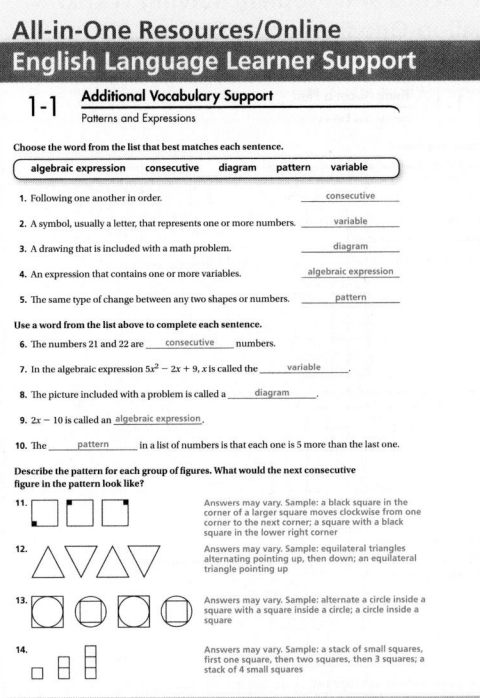

Differentiated Remediation *continued*

Available in editable format online.

On-Level

- **Practice** (2 pages) Provides extra practice for each lesson. For simpler practice exercises, use the Form K Practice pages found in the All-in-One Teaching Resources and online.

- **Think About a Plan** Helps students develop specific problem-solving skills and strategies by providing scaffolded guiding questions.

- **Standardized Test Prep** Focuses on all major exercises, all major question types, and helps students prepare for the high-stakes assessments.

Extension

- **Enrichment** Provides students with interesting problems and activities that extend the concepts of the lesson.

- **Activities, Games, and Puzzles** Worksheets that can be used for concepts development, enrichment, and for fun!

Practice and Problem Solving Wkbk/ All-in-One Resources/Online

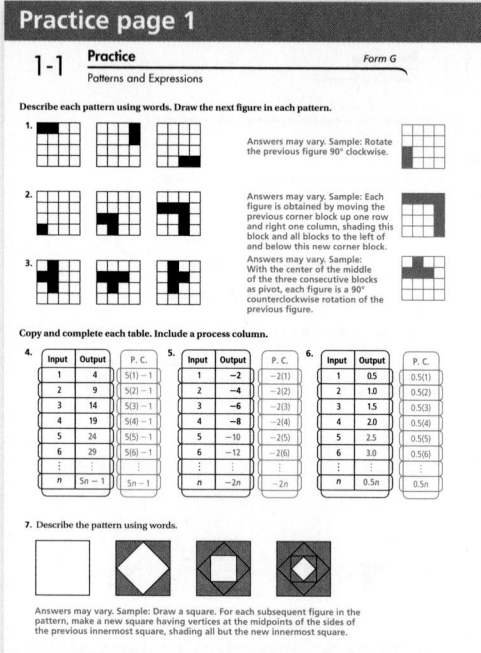

Practice and Problem Solving Wkbk/ All-in-One Resources/Online

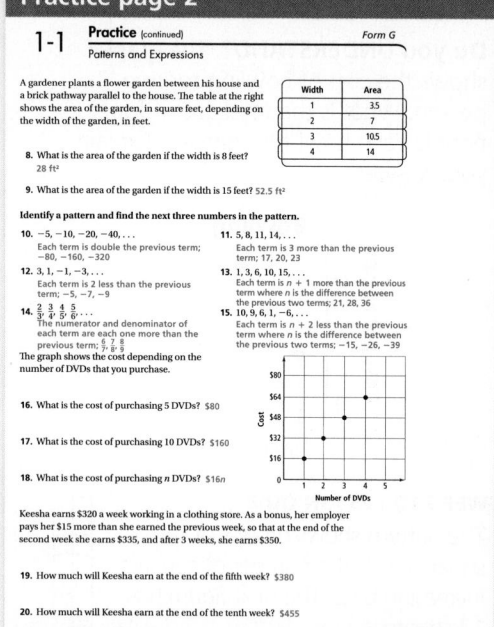

All-in-One Resources/Online

(Enrichment)

Practice and Problem Solving Wkbk/ All-in-One Resources/Online

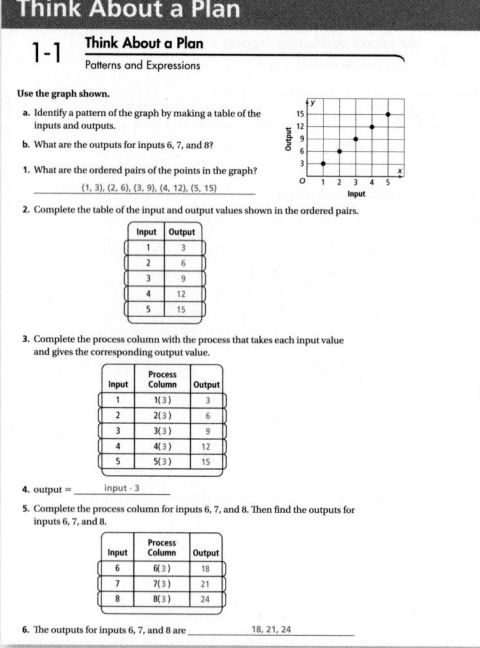

Practice and Problem Solving Wkbk/ All-in-One Resources/Online

(Standardized Test Prep)

Online Teacher Resource Center

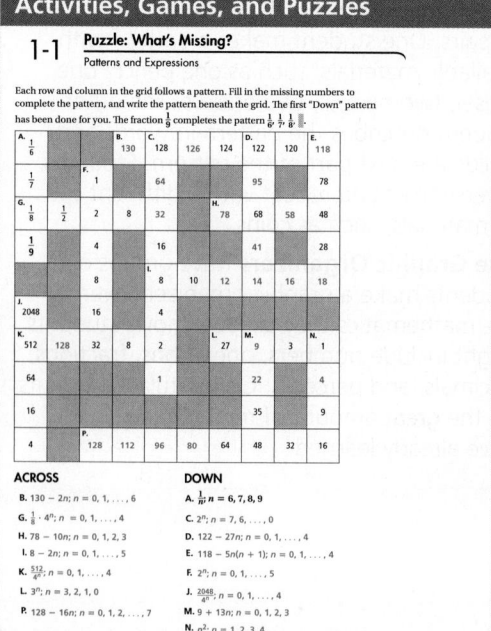

1-2 Properties of Real Numbers

Objectives To graph and order real numbers
To identify properties of real numbers

© **Common Core State Standards**
Reviews N-RN.B.3 Explain why the sum or product of two rational numbers is rational; that the sum of a rational number and an irrational number is irrational, and that the product of a nonzero rational number and an irrational number is irrational.
MP 1, MP 3, MP 6

SOLVE IT!

Getting Ready!

You use emoticons in text messages to help you communicate. Here are six emoticons. How can you describe a set that includes five of the emoticons but not the sixth?

Lesson Vocabulary
• opposite
• additive inverse
• reciprocal
• multiplicative inverse

In the Solve It, you classified sets of emoticons. In this lesson, you will classify real numbers into special subsets.

Essential Understanding The set of real numbers has several special subsets related in particular ways.

Algebra involves operations on and relations among numbers, including real numbers and imaginary numbers. (You will learn about imaginary numbers in Chapter 4.) Rational numbers and irrational numbers form the set of real numbers.

You can graph every real number as a point on the number line.

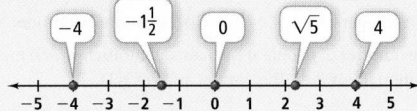

---

1 Interactive Learning

Solve It!

PURPOSE To classify objects according to common features
PROCESS Students may
• identify a feature that only five of the emoticons have in common.
• look for an emoticon with a unique feature and exclude that emoticon from the set.

FACILITATE

Q What are some features that only one emoticon has? **[glasses, wink, tongue, frown, toothy smile, round mouth]**

Q What sets could you define that include only five emoticons? **[Samples: both eyes open, no glasses, not unhappy]**

ANSWER See Solve It in Answers on next page.
CONNECT THE MATH In the Solve It, students group emoticons into subsets by common characteristics. In the lesson, students classify numbers into subsets.

1-2 Preparing to Teach

BIG idea Properties
ESSENTIAL UNDERSTANDINGS
• The set of real numbers has several subsets related in particular ways.
• Algebra involves operations on and relations among numbers, including real and imaginary numbers.
• The properties of real numbers are relationships that are true for all real numbers (except, in one case, zero).

Math Background

Students may take the properties of real numbers for granted. It seems clear, for example, that $3 + 5 = 5 + 3$, and that the sum of two real numbers is a real number. Point out that some sets of mathematical objects do not obey these rules.

For example, the set of real-valued functions is not commutative. In other words, it matters in what order functions are applied

to a number. For example, let $f(x) = |x|$ and $g(x) = -x$. If we first apply g to a positive number a, and then apply f, the result is again a. However, if we first apply f and then g, we get $-a$. You can summarize this by saying that the set of real-valued functions is not commutative.

A more familiar mathematical example is that the set of integers is not closed under division. A not mathematical example is that the putting on shoes and putting on socks are not commutative actions. Can students think of other examples from math or every day life that do not follow these rules?

On the other hand, the set of real numbers is not the only set that has these properties. For example, the set of all even integers is closed under addition and multiplication. It may be helpful for students to think of other sets that have these properties.

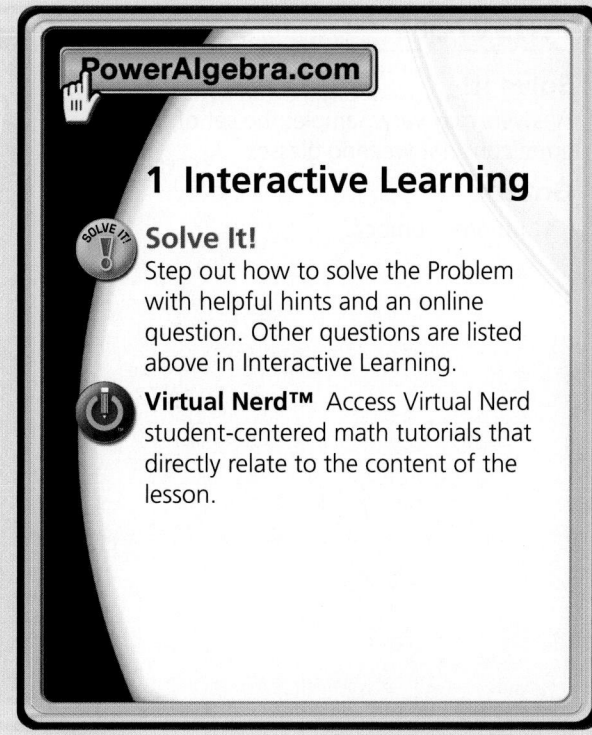

PowerAlgebra.com

1 Interactive Learning

SOLVE IT! **Solve It!**
Step out how to solve the Problem with helpful hints and an online question. Other questions are listed above in Interactive Learning.

Virtual Nerd™ Access Virtual Nerd student-centered math tutorials that directly relate to the content of the lesson.

2 Guided Instruction

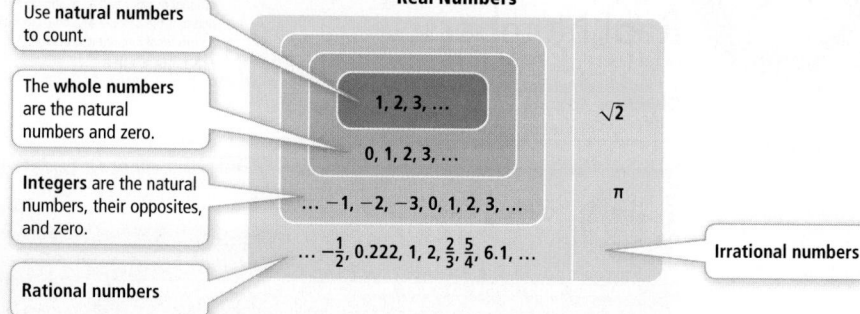

The diagram shows how subsets of the real numbers are related.

Real Numbers

Use **natural numbers** to count.

1, 2, 3, …

The **whole numbers** are the natural numbers and zero.

0, 1, 2, 3, …

Integers are the natural numbers, their opposites, and zero.

… −1, −2, −3, 0, 1, 2, 3, …

… −$\frac{1}{2}$, 0.222, 1, 2, $\frac{2}{3}$, $\frac{5}{4}$, 6.1, …

Rational numbers

$\sqrt{2}$

π

Irrational numbers

Rational numbers

- are all numbers you can write as a quotient of integers $\frac{a}{b}$, $b \neq 0$.
- include terminating decimals. For example, $\frac{1}{8} = 0.125$.
- include repeating decimals. For example, $\frac{1}{3} = 0.\overline{3}$.

Irrational numbers

- have decimal representations that neither terminate nor repeat. For example, $\sqrt{2} = 1.414213\ldots$.
- cannot be written as quotients of integers.

Problem 1

Q Would it make sense to use the set of integers to describe the number of people who participated in the race? The set of rational numbers? Explain. **[No; that would indicate a negative number of participants in the race. No; that would indicate a fractional number of participants in the race.]**

Got It?

Q Would the answer change if you were referring to the amount of money in pennies rather than in dollars? Explain. **[Yes; $15.50 in dollars is best described by the set of rational numbers but in pennies is best described by the set of natural numbers.]**

You classify a variable by naming the subset that gives you the most information about the numbers the variable represents.

Ⓒ **Problem 1** Classifying a Variable

Multiple Choice Your school is sponsoring a charity race. Which set of numbers does not contain the number of people p who participate in the race?

- Ⓐ natural numbers
- Ⓒ rational numbers
- Ⓑ integers
- Ⓓ irrational numbers

The number of people p is a natural number, which means that it is also an integer and a rational number. The correct answer is D.

Think

What are some examples of possible values of p?
The number of people p must be represented by a whole number. Determine which other sets of numbers include the whole numbers.

✓ **Got It?** **1.** In Problem 1, if each participant made a donation d of $15.50 to a local charity, which subset of real numbers best describes the amount of money raised?

Answers

Solve It!

Answers may vary. Sample: the set of the emoticons not wearing glasses

Got It?

1. rational numbers

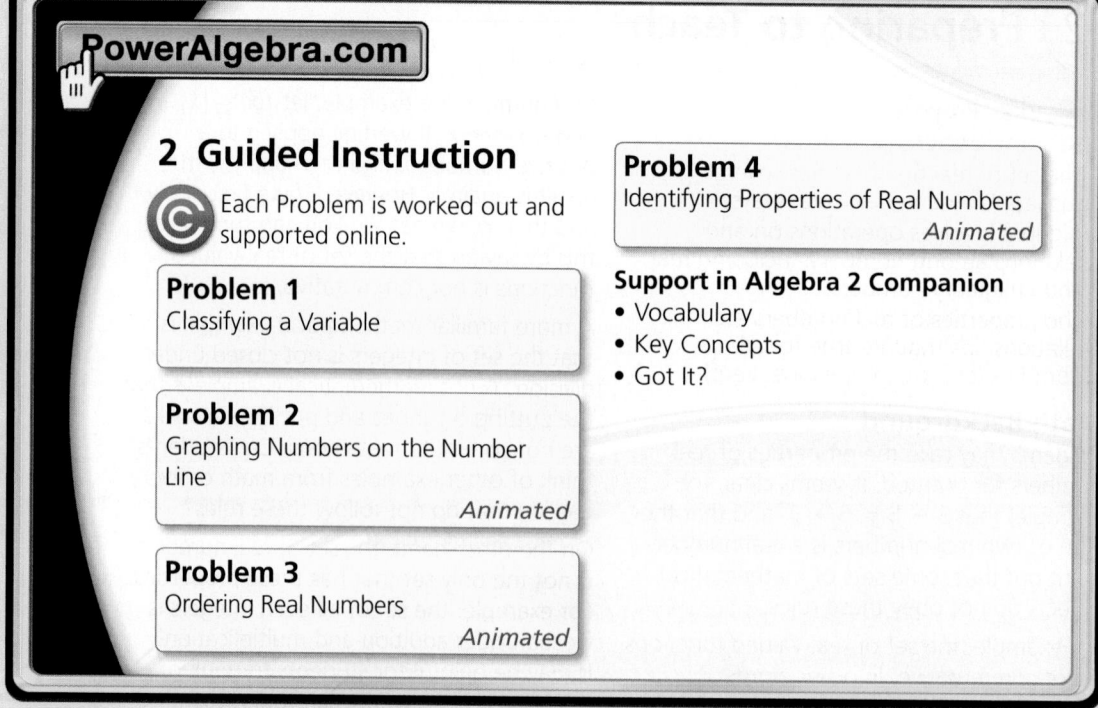

PowerAlgebra.com

2 Guided Instruction

Ⓒ Each Problem is worked out and supported online.

Problem 1
Classifying a Variable

Problem 2
Graphing Numbers on the Number Line
Animated

Problem 3
Ordering Real Numbers
Animated

Problem 4
Identifying Properties of Real Numbers
Animated

Support in Algebra 2 Companion
- Vocabulary
- Key Concepts
- Got It?

 **Problem 2** Graphing Numbers on the Number Line

What is the graph of the numbers $-\frac{5}{2}$, $\sqrt{2}$, and $2.\overline{6}$?

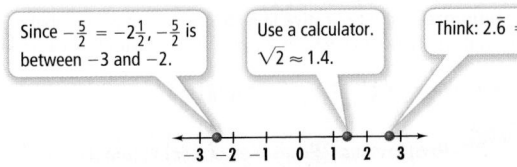

Since $-\frac{5}{2} = -2\frac{1}{2}$, $-\frac{5}{2}$ is between -3 and -2.

Use a calculator. $\sqrt{2} \approx 1.4$.

Think: $2.\overline{6} = 2\frac{2}{3}$.

Got It? 2. What is the graph of the numbers $\sqrt{3}$, $-1.\overline{4}$, and $\frac{1}{3}$?

Plan

How do you graph a number on the number line?

If the number is an integer, determine whether it is positive or negative. If it's not an integer, determine which integer it's closest to.

The number line is helpful for ordering several real numbers. For two numbers, however, it is easier to show order, or compare, using one of the inequality symbols $>$ or $<$.

 Problem 3 Ordering Real Numbers

How do $\sqrt{17}$ and 3.8 compare? Use $>$ or $<$.

Compare both numbers to $\sqrt{16}$.

$\sqrt{16} < \sqrt{17}$ 16 is less than 17.

$3.8 < \sqrt{16}$ $\sqrt{16} = 4$ and $3.8 < 4$.

Therefore, $3.8 < \sqrt{17}$, or $\sqrt{17} > 3.8$.

Check Use a calculator.

$\sqrt{17} \approx 4.123$

$3.8 < 4.123$ ✔

Got It? 3. a. How do $\sqrt{26}$ and 6.25 compare? Use $>$ or $<$.
   b. **Reasoning** Let a, b, and c be real numbers such that $a < b$ and $b < c$. How do a and c compare? Explain.

Think

Why compare $\sqrt{17}$ to the square root of a perfect square?

It makes it easier to determine which two integers $\sqrt{17}$ is between.

Essential Understanding The properties of real numbers are relationships that are true for all real numbers (except, in one case, zero).

One property of real numbers excludes a single number, zero. Zero is the *additive identity* for the real numbers, and zero is the one real number that has no *multiplicative inverse*.

Problem 2
Review how to find square roots and how to convert fractions to decimals and decimals to fractions on a calculator.

Q Which two integers is $\sqrt{2}$ between? [**1 and 2**]

Got It?

Q What decimal equals $\frac{1}{3}$? [**0.$\overline{3}$**]

Problem 3

Q What two square roots of perfect squares is $\sqrt{17}$ between? [$\sqrt{16}$ **and** $\sqrt{25}$]

Got It?

Q The square root of what perfect square is between 6.25 and $\sqrt{26}$? [**36**]
Q How does $\sqrt{36}$ compare to 6.25? [$\sqrt{36} = 6 < 6.25$]
Q How does $\sqrt{36}$ compare to $\sqrt{26}$? [$\sqrt{26} < \sqrt{36}$]

Additional Problems

1. Bankers and investors use "The rule of 72," which is modeled by $y = \frac{72}{x}$, where x is the percent interest rate and y is the years it takes an investment to double. Which set of numbers best describes the number of years y it takes for an investment to double when x is a natural number?

ANSWER Rational numbers

2. What is the graph of the numbers $-\frac{5}{3}$, $-\sqrt{8}$, and $-2.\overline{3}$?

ANSWER

3. How do $\sqrt{85}$ and 8.9 compare? Use $>$ or $<$.

ANSWER $\sqrt{85} > 8.9$

4. What property is illustrated by each of the following equations?

a. $xyz = xzy$
b. $(fg)h = f(gh)$
c. $(p + q)r = (q + p)r$
d. $(5 + y)x = x(5 + y)$
e. $8 + 0 = 0 + 8$
f. $v + 0 + w = v + w$

ANSWER 'a,' and 'd' show the Commutative Property of Multiplication; 'b' shows the Associative Property of Multiplication; 'c' and 'e' show the Commutative Property of Addition; 'f' shows the Identity Property of Addition.

Answers

Got It? (continued)

2.

3. a. $\sqrt{26} < 6.25$ or $6.25 > \sqrt{26}$

   b. $a < c$; a will be to the left of c on the number line.

The **opposite** or **additive inverse** of any number a is $-a$.
The sum of a number and its opposite is 0, the additive identity.

Examples $12 + (-12) = 0$ $-7 + 7 = 0$

The **reciprocal** or **multiplicative inverse** of any nonzero number a is $\frac{1}{a}$.
The product of a number and its reciprocal is 1, the multiplicative identity.

Examples $8\left(\frac{1}{8}\right) = 1$ $-5\left(-\frac{1}{5}\right) = 1$

Properties   Properties of Real Numbers

Let a, b, and c represent real numbers.

Property	Addition	Multiplication
Closure	$a + b$ is a real number.	ab is a real number.
Commutative	$a + b = b + a$	$ab = ba$
Associative	$(a + b) + c = a + (b + c)$	$(ab)c = a(bc)$
Identity	$a + 0 = a, 0 + a = a$ 0 is the additive identity.	$a \cdot 1 = a, 1 \cdot a = a$ 1 is the multiplicative identity.
Inverse	$a + (-a) = 0$	$a \cdot \frac{1}{a} = 1, a \neq 0$
Distributive	$a(b + c) = ab + ac$	

Problem 4   Identifying Properties of Real Numbers

Which property does the equation illustrate?

A $\left(-\frac{2}{3}\right)\left(-\frac{3}{2}\right) = 1$

The product of the numbers is 1.

Inverse Property of Multiplication

B $(3 \cdot 4) \cdot 5 = (4 \cdot 3) \cdot 5$

The equation reorders 3 and 4.

Commutative Property of Multiplication

 Got It? **4. a.** Which property does the equation $3(g + h) + 2g = (3g + 3h) + 2g$ illustrate?
  b. Reasoning Use properties of real numbers to show that $a + [3 + (-a)] = 3$. Justify each step of your solution.

Answers

Got It? (continued)
4. a. Distributive Property
  b. $a + [3 + (-a)] = a + [(-a) + 3]$ Comm.
  $= [a + (-a)] + 3$ Assoc.
  $= 0 + 3$ Inverse Identity
  $= 3$

Lesson Check

Do you know HOW?

Write an example from daily life that uses each type of real number.

1. whole numbers

2. integers

3. rational numbers

Identify the property illustrated by the equation.

4. $5 + (-5) = 0$

5. $2 \cdot (4 \cdot 5) = (2 \cdot 4) \cdot 5$

Do you UNDERSTAND?  MATHEMATICAL PRACTICES

6. Vocabulary Identify another name for a reciprocal.

7. Compare and Contrast How is the Additive Identity Property similar to the Multiplicative Identity Property? How is it different?

8. Reasoning There are grouping symbols in the equation $(5 + w) + 8 = (w + 5) + 8$, but it does not illustrate the Associative Property of Addition. Explain.

9. Give an example of a number that is not a rational number. Explain why it is not rational.

Practice and Problem-Solving Exercises  MATHEMATICAL PRACTICES

A Practice Classify each variable according to the set of numbers that best describes its values.

See Problem 1.

10. the number of times n a ball bounces; the height h from which the ball is dropped

11. the year y; the median selling price p for a house that year

12. the circumference C of a circle found by using the formula $C = 2\pi r$

Graph each number on a number line.

See Problem 2.

13. 0   **14.** $-\sqrt{24}$ **15.** -2 **16.** $2\frac{1}{2}$ **17.** $-4\frac{2}{3}$

18. 3.5   **19.** -1.4 **20.** $\sqrt{10}$ **21.** $-2\frac{1}{5}$ **22.** 4.8

Compare the two numbers. Use $>$ or $<$.

See Problem 3.

23. $16, \sqrt{16}$ **24.** $-4, -\sqrt{4}$ **25.** $\sqrt{5}, \sqrt{7}$

26. $-\sqrt{3}, -\sqrt{5}$ **27.** $5, \sqrt{22}$ **28.** $-\sqrt{38}, 6$

29. $4, \sqrt{12}$ **30.** $-8, \sqrt{70}$ **31.** $\sqrt{63}, 7.5$

32. $4.7, \sqrt{26}$ **33.** $\sqrt{75}, 9$ **34.** $12, -\sqrt{150}$

Name the property of real numbers illustrated by each equation.

See Problem 4.

35. $\pi(a + b) = \pi a + \pi b$ **36.** $-10 + 4 = 4 + (-10)$

37. $(2\sqrt{7}) \cdot \sqrt{3} = 2(\sqrt{7} \cdot \sqrt{3})$ **38.** $29 \cdot \pi = \pi \cdot 29$

39. $-\sqrt{5} + 0 = -\sqrt{5}$ **40.** $\frac{4}{7} \cdot \frac{7}{4} = 1$

---

3 Lesson Check

Do you know HOW?   ERROR INTERVENTION

- For Exercise 5, if students confuse the Associative Property with the Distributive Property, explain that the difference between them is that the Associative Property can be applied to an expression involving either multiplication or addition, while the Distributive Property can be applied to an expression involving both addition and multiplication.

Do you UNDERSTAND? ERROR INTERVENTION

- Exercise 8 may be difficult for students unless they ask: How are the expressions on each side of the equation different? Students will answer correctly if they ignore the term that is not contained in grouping symbols.

Close

Q Why is it important to know the properties of real numbers? [Answers may vary. Sample: They are needed to solve equations.]

Lesson Check

1. Answers may vary. Sample: the number of times a cricket chirps

2. Answers may vary. Sample: the change in number of people on a bus after a stop

3. Answers may vary. Sample: the outdoor temperature in tenths of a degree

4. Inverse Prop. of Add.

5. Assoc. Prop. of Mult.

6. multiplicative inverse

7. Both properties result in the original term; 0 is the additive identity, whereas 1 is the multiplicative identity.

8. The equation illustrates the Comm. Prop. of Add.

9. Answers may vary. Sample: $\sqrt{2}$ is not a rational number because it cannot be written as a quotient of integers.

Practice and Problem-Solving Exercises

10. n, whole numbers; h, rational numbers

11. y, natural numbers; p, rational numbers

12. C, irrational numbers; r, rational numbers

13. (number line: point at 0, from -3 to 2)

14. (number line: point near -5, from -6 to 1)

15. (number line: point at -2, from -4 to 2)

16. (number line: point between 2 and 3, from -1 to 4)

17. (number line: point near $-4\frac{2}{3}$, from -6 to 1)

18. (number line: point between 3 and 4, from -1 to 5)

19. (number line: point near -1.4, from -3 to 1)

20. (number line: point near 3, from -1 to 5)

21. (number line: point near -2, from -4 to 1)

22. (number line: point between 4 and 5, from -1 to 6)

23. $>$ **24.** $<$ **25.** $<$

26. $>$ **27.** $>$ **28.** $<$

29. $>$ **30.** $<$ **31.** $>$

32. $<$ **33.** $<$ **34.** $>$

35. Distr. Prop.

36. Comm. Prop. of Add.

37–40. See next page.

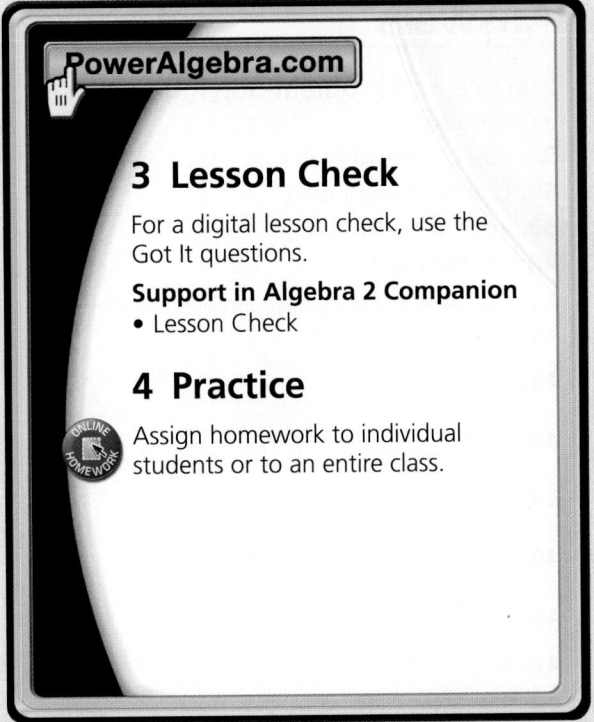

PowerAlgebra.com

3 Lesson Check

For a digital lesson check, use the Got It questions.

Support in Algebra 2 Companion
- Lesson Check

4 Practice

Assign homework to individual students or to an entire class.

4 Practice

ASSIGNMENT GUIDE

Basic: 10–40 all, 42–48 even, 49, 58–66 even

Average: 11–39 odd, 41–67

Advanced: 11–39 odd, 41–71

Standardized Test Prep: 72–74

 Mathematical Practices are supported by exercises with red headings. Here are the Practices supported in this lesson:

MP 1: Make Sense of Problems Ex. 49

MP 3: Communicate Ex. 65, 68

MP 3: Construct Arguments Ex. 7, 60–64, 67

MP 3: Critique the Reasoning of Others Ex. 50

MP 6: Attend to Precision Ex. 8

Applications exercises have blue headings.

STEM exercises focus on science or engineering applications.

EXERCISE 66: Use the Think About a Plan worksheet in the **Practice and Problem Solving Workbook** (also available in the Teaching Resources in print and online) to further support students' development in becoming independent learners.

HOMEWORK QUICK CHECK

To check students' understanding of key skills and concepts, go over Exercises 21, 39, 49, 58, and 66.

B Apply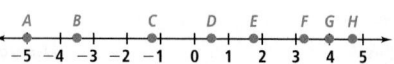

Estimate the numbers graphed at the labeled points.

41. point A **42.** point B **43.** point C **44.** point D

45. point E **46.** point F **47.** point G **48.** point H

49. Think About a Plan A cube-shaped jewelry box has a surface area of 300 square inches. What are the dimensions of the jewelry box?
- Write an algebraic expression to find the total surface area of a cube. What is the surface area of one side of a cube?
- How is the side length of a square related to its area?

50. Error Analysis A student labeled the points on the number line as shown. Explain the student's error.

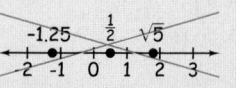

STEM **Science** The formula $I = \sqrt{\dfrac{W}{R}}$ gives the electric current I in amperes that flows through an appliance, where W is the power in watts and R is the resistance in ohms. Which set of numbers best describes the value of I for the given values of W and R?

51. $W = 100, R = 25$ **52.** $W = 100, R = 5$ **53.** $W = 500, R = 100$

54. $W = 50, R = 200$ **55.** $W = 250, R = 100$ **56.** $W = 240, R = 100$

Write the numbers in decreasing order.

57. $1, -3, -\sqrt{2}, 8, \frac{1}{3}$ **58.** $\sqrt{14}, \frac{5}{2}, -\frac{9}{16}, 1, 11$ **59.** $-17, -0.06, -3\sqrt{3}, 5.73, \frac{1}{4}$

Reasoning An example is a *counterexample* to a general statement if it makes the statement false. Show that each of the following statements is false by finding a counterexample.

60. The reciprocal of each natural number is a natural number.

61. The opposite of each whole number is a whole number.

62. There is no integer that has a reciprocal that is an integer.

63. The product of two irrational numbers is an irrational number.

64. All square roots are irrational numbers.

65. Writing Write an example of each of the 11 properties of real numbers shown on page 14.

66. Restaurant Five friends each ordered a sandwich and a drink at a restaurant. Each sandwich costs the same amount and each drink costs the same amount. What are two ways to compute the bill? What property of real numbers is illustrated by the two methods?

67. Open-Ended Write an algebraic problem that requires the use of the real-number properties to solve. Then solve the problem.

Answers

Practice and Problem-Solving Exercises
(continued)

37. Assoc. Prop. of Mult.

38. Comm. Prop. of Mult.

39. Ident. Prop. of Add.

40. Inv. Prop. of Mult.

41–48. Answers may vary. Samples are given.

41. -5

42. $-3\frac{1}{2}$

43. $-1\frac{1}{4}$

44. $\frac{1}{2}$

45. $1\frac{2}{3}$

46. $3\frac{1}{3}$

47. 4

48. 4.8

49. $\sqrt{50}$ in. $\times \sqrt{50}$ in. $\times \sqrt{50}$ in.

50. The point for $\sqrt{5}$ is not at the correct position on the number line; $\sqrt{5} \approx 2.24$.

51. natural numbers

52. irrational numbers

53. irrational numbers

54. irrational numbers

55. irrational numbers

56. irrational numbers

57. $8, 1, \frac{1}{3}, -\sqrt{2}, -3$

58. $11, \sqrt{14}, \frac{5}{2}, 1, -\frac{9}{16}$

59. $5.73, \frac{1}{4}, -0.06, -3\sqrt{3}, -17$

60. Answers may vary. Sample: 4

61. Answers may vary. Sample: 7

62. Answers may vary. Sample: -1

63. Answers may vary. Sample: $\sqrt{2}$ and $\sqrt{2}$

64. Answers may vary. Sample: $\sqrt{4}$

65. Check students' work.

66. Multiply the cost of a drink by 5 and multiply the cost of a sandwich by 5, then add, or add the cost for one drink and one sandwich, then multiply by 5; Distr. Prop., $5s + 5d = 5(s + d)$

67. Check students' work.

68. Writing Are there two integers with a product of −12 and a sum of −3? Explain.

69. Your friend used the Distributive Property and got the expression $5x + 10y - 35$. What algebraic expression could your friend have started with?

70. Geometry π is an irrational number you can use to calculate the circumference or area of a circle.
a. Find the value of π on your calculator. Can you obtain an exact representation? Explain.
b. The value of π is often represented as $\frac{22}{7}$. How does this representation compare to the decimal representation your calculator gives using the π key?

71. Does zero have a multiplicative inverse? Explain.

Standardized Test Prep

SAT/ACT

72. Which of the following shows the numbers π, $\sqrt{8}$, and 3.5 in the correct order from greatest to least?
Ⓐ $\pi, \sqrt{8}, 3.5$　　Ⓑ $3.5, \pi, \sqrt{8}$　　Ⓒ $\sqrt{8}, \pi, 3.5$　　Ⓓ $\sqrt{8}, 3.5, \pi$

73. Which of the following is the best statement about the graph?
Ⓕ A 400-minute plan costs $40.
Ⓖ A 100-minute plan costs $10.
Ⓗ A 1000-minute plan costs $110.
Ⓘ A 200-minute plan costs $35.

Cell Phone Plan

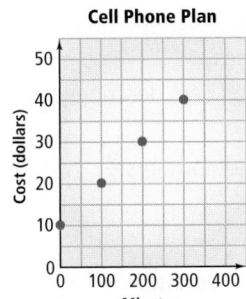

Short Response

74. Why is the opposite of the reciprocal of 5 the same as the reciprocal of the opposite of 5?

Apply What You've Learned

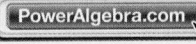 MATHEMATICAL PRACTICES
MP 1

Look back at the information on page 3 about Cody's car running out of gas.

a. Copy the diagram shown on page 3. Place a point C along the line at a point where Cody's car could be when it runs out of gas. Draw as many diagrams as needed to show the possible locations of Cody's car relative to the locations of Mia's house, the gas station, and the restaurant.

b. How many diagrams did you draw in part (a)? Explain why you needed that number of diagrams to account for all possible locations of Cody's car relative to the other three locations.

Answers

68. No; answers may vary. Sample: The only pairs of integers that have a product of −12 are −1 and 12, −2 and 6, −3 and 4, −4 and 3, −6 and 2, and −12 and 1. None of these pairs has a sum of −3.

69. $5(x + 2y - 7)$

70. a. 3.141592654 . . . ; No, π is an irrational number.
b. $\frac{22}{7} \approx 3.142857143 \ldots$; $\frac{22}{7} > \pi$

71. No; $\frac{1}{0}$ is undefined.

Standardized Test Prep

72. B

73. H

74. [2] To find the opposite of the reciprocal of 5, divide 1 by 5 and then multiply the quotient by −1. To find the reciprocal of the opposite of 5, multiply 5 by −1 and then divide 1 by the product. Both methods result in the same answer $\left(-\frac{1}{5}\right)$ because the order of operations does not matter for mult. and div.
[1] incomplete explanation

 Apply What You've Learned
Here students copy the diagram shown on page 3 and show possible locations along the road for where Cody's car runs out of gas. Later in the chapter, students will write algebraic expressions to represent distances in their diagrams.

Ⓒ **Mathematical Practices**
Students **make sense of the problem** by drawing diagrams to understand where Cody's car can be relative to the locations of Mia's house, the gas station, and the restaurant. (MP 1)

ANSWERS
a. Check students' diagrams; students should draw two diagrams: one showing point C between Mia's house and the gas station, and one showing point C between the gas station and the restaurant.

b. 2; Cody's car could have been on either side of the gas station when it ran out of gas.

Lesson Resources

Differentiated Remediation
Available in editable format online.

Additional Instructional Support

Algebra 2 Companion
Students can use the **Algebra 2 Companion** worktext (4 pages) as you teach the lesson. Use the Companion to support

- New Vocabulary
- Key Concepts
- Got It for each Problem
- Lesson Check

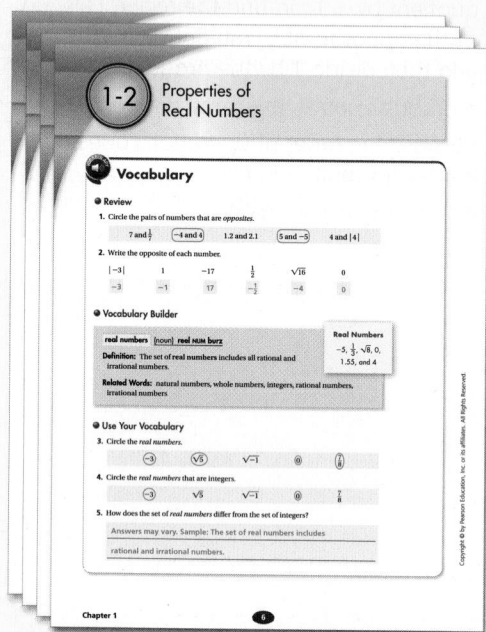

ELL Support
Use Graphic Organizers Have groups of students make a graphic organizer showing different subsets of real numbers. Students may refer to the organizer on page 12 to help them get started. Have students illustrate their graphic organizers. They might use countable objects with whole numbers, a pie with a slice cut out for rational numbers, or a number line for integers. Have students label their graphic organizers with correct terminology and with familiar words that will remind them of the meanings. When they are finished, have students compare and discuss their diagrams with another group.

5 Assess & Remediate

Lesson Quiz

1. **Do you UNDERSTAND?** The height of an equilateral triangle h equals $\frac{\sqrt{3}}{2}s$ where s is the length of a side. Suppose an equilateral triangle is made with 2-inch toothpicks.
   a. Which set of numbers best describes the value of s in inches?
   b. Which set of numbers best describes the value of h in inches?

2. What is the graph of the numbers $\frac{9}{4}$, $-\sqrt{7}$, and $1.\overline{2}$?

3. Compare $\sqrt{37}$ and 5.9.

4. Which property does the equation illustrate? $1 \cdot \frac{4}{5} = \frac{4}{5}$

ANSWERS TO LESSON QUIZ

1. **a.** natural numbers
   b. irrational numbers

2.

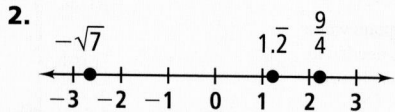

$$-\sqrt{7} \qquad 1.\overline{2} \quad \frac{9}{4}$$

```
  ─┼──┼──┼──┼──┼──┼──┼─
  -3 -2 -1  0  1  2  3
```

3. $\sqrt{37} > 5.9$

4. Identity Property of Multiplication

PRESCRIPTION FOR REMEDIATION
Use the student work on the Lesson Quiz to prescribe a differentiated review assignment:

Points	Differentiated Remediation
0–2	Intervention
3	On-level
4	Extension

PowerAlgebra.com

5 Assess & Remediate
Assign the Lesson Quiz. Appropriate intervention, practice, or enrichment is automatically generated based on student performance.

Intervention

- **Reteaching** (2 pages) Provides reteaching and practice exercises for the key lesson concepts. Use with struggling students or absent students.

- **English Language Learner Support** Helps students develop and reinforce mathematical vocabulary and key concepts.

All-in-One Resources/Online
Reteaching

1-2 Reteaching
Properties of Real Numbers

All-in-One Resources/Online
English Language Learner Support

1-2 Additional Vocabulary Support
Properties of Real Numbers

Differentiated Remediation *continued*

Available in editable format online.

On-Level

- **Practice** (2 pages) Provides extra practice for each lesson. For simpler practice exercises, use the Form K Practice pages found in the All-in-One Teaching Resources and online.

- **Think About a Plan** Helps students develop specific problem-solving skills and strategies by providing scaffolded guiding questions.

- **Standardized Test Prep** Focuses on all major exercises, all major question types, and helps students prepare for the high-stakes assessments.

Extension

- **Enrichment** Provides students with interesting problems and activities that extend the concepts of the lesson.

- **Activities, Games, and Puzzles** Worksheets that can be used for concepts development, enrichment, and for fun!

Practice and Problem Solving Wkbk/All-in-One Resources/Online
Practice page 1

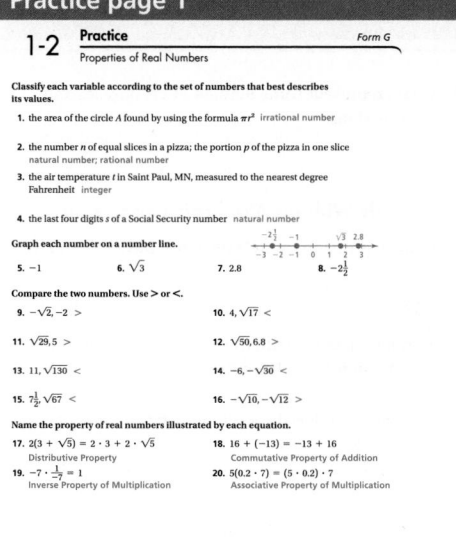

Practice and Problem Solving Wkbk/All-in-One Resources/Online
Practice page 2

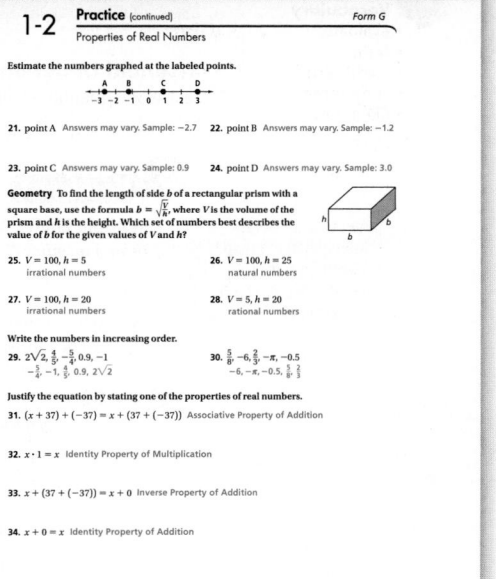

All-in-One Resources/Online
Enrichment

1-2 Enrichment
Properties of Real Numbers

There are four words beginning with the letter "I" that describe certain types of operations:

a. Identity: an operation that does not change anything. For example, adding 0 to a number is an identity operation, because adding 0 does not change the original number.

b. Inverse: an operation that can be undone by another operation. For instance, the operation of adding 2 to a number can be undone by subtracting 2 from the number. However, the operation of multiplying a number by 0 cannot be undone.

c. Idempotent: an operation that, when done twice, is the same as doing it once. For example, multiplying a number by 1 and then multiplying the result by 1 again has exactly the same effect as multiplying the number by 1 only once.

d. Involutory: an operation that, when done twice, leaves a number unchanged. For instance, multiplying a number by −1 and then multiplying the result by −1 again returns the original number.

For each of the following operations, state which of the "I" words apply. If none apply, write *none*.

1. finding the absolute value of a number idempotent
2. dividing a number by 1 identity, inverse, idempotent, involutory
3. multiplying the absolute value of a number by −1 idempotent
4. finding the reciprocal of a nonzero number inverse, involutory
5. dividing a number by −1 inverse, involutory
6. multiplying a number by 0 idempotent
7. adding 0 to the reciprocal of a nonzero number inverse, involutory
8. multiplying the reciprocal of a nonzero number by 2 inverse, involutory
9. adding the absolute value of a nonzero number to the absolute value of its reciprocal none
10. finding the reciprocal of the absolute value of the reciprocal of a nonzero number idempotent
11. finding the absolute value of −1 times a nonzero number, then taking the reciprocal none

---

Practice and Problem Solving Wkbk/All-in-One Resources/Online
Think About a Plan

1-2 Think About a Plan
Properties of Real Numbers

Five friends each ordered a sandwich and a drink at a restaurant. Each sandwich costs the same amount, and each drink costs the same amount. What are two ways to compute the bill? What property of real numbers is illustrated by the two methods?

Understanding the Problem

1. There are ☐5 sandwiches and ☐5 drinks on the bill.

2. What is the problem asking you to determine?
   two ways to represent the cost of 5 sandwiches and 5 drinks, and the property of real numbers illustrated by the two representations

Planning the Solution

3. How can you represent the cost of five sandwiches?
   Answers may vary. Sample: 5s

4. How can you represent the cost of five drinks?
   Answers may vary. Sample: 5d

5. How can you represent the cost of the items ordered by one friend?
   Answers may vary. Sample: d + s

Getting an Answer

6. Write an expression that represents the cost of five drinks and the cost of five sandwiches.
   Answers may vary. Sample: 5d + 5s

7. Write an expression that represents the cost of the items ordered by five friends.
   Answers may vary. Sample: 5(d + s)

8. What property of real numbers tells you that these two expressions are equal? Explain.
   Distributive Property; the Distributive Property states a(b + c) = ab + ac.

Practice and Problem Solving Wkbk/All-in-One Resources/Online
Standardized Test Prep

1-2 Standardized Test Prep
Properties of Real Numbers

Multiple Choice

For Exercises 1–5, choose the correct letter.

1. Which letter on the graph corresponds to $\sqrt{5}$? C

2. Which letter on the graph corresponds to -1.5? F

What property of real numbers is illustrated by the equation?

3. $-6 + (6 + 5) = (-6 + 6) + 5$ D
   (A) Identity Property of Addition
   (B) Inverse Property of Addition
   (C) Commutative Property of Addition
   (D) Associative Property of Addition

4. $2(-4 + x) = 2(-4) + 2 \cdot x$ G
   (F) Associative Property of Multiplication
   (G) Distributive Property
   (H) Associative Property of Addition
   (I) Closure Property of Multiplication

5. Which of the following shows the numbers 13, 1.3, $1\frac{2}{3}$, −4, and $-\sqrt{10}$ in order from greatest to least? B
   (A) 13, 1.3, $1\frac{2}{3}$, −4, $-\sqrt{10}$
   (B) 13, 1.3, $1\frac{2}{3}$, $-\sqrt{10}$, −4
   (C) 13, $1\frac{2}{3}$, 1.3, $-\sqrt{10}$, −4
   (D) −4, $-\sqrt{10}$, $1\frac{2}{3}$, 1.3, 13

Short Response

Geometry The length c of the hypotenuse of a right triangle with legs having lengths a and b is found by using the formula $c = \sqrt{a^2 + b^2}$. Which set of numbers best describes the value of c for the given values of a and b?

6. $a = 3, b = 4$ [2] natural numbers [1] incorrect set of numbers [0] no answer given

7. $a = \frac{1}{3}, b = \frac{1}{4}$ [2] rational numbers [1] incorrect set of numbers [0] no answer given

8. $a = \sqrt{3}, b = \sqrt{4}$ [2] irrational numbers [1] incorrect set of numbers [0] no answer given

---

Online Teacher Resource Center
Activities, Games, and Puzzles

1-2 Activity: Property Patterns
Properties of Real Numbers

Examples of the properties of real numbers with addition and multiplication follow patterns. These patterns can be identifiable even if numbers and symbols are not used. For example, consider the following phrase. It does not make any sense, but it illustrates a property of real numbers.

peanuts bake apples inside apples

This word structure follows the pattern for the Identity Property of Addition.

$$
\begin{array}{ccccc}
peanuts & bake & apples & inside & apples \\
\downarrow & \downarrow & \downarrow & \downarrow & \downarrow \\
0 & + & a & = & a
\end{array}
$$

Likewise, you can designate a word to indicate grouping.

twisted apples bake bananas bake coconuts inside apples bake twisted bananas bake coconuts
$$
\begin{array}{ccccccccccc}
\downarrow & \downarrow & \downarrow & \downarrow & \downarrow & & \downarrow & \downarrow & \downarrow & \downarrow & \downarrow \\
(& a & + & b) & + & c & = & a & + & (& b & + & c)
\end{array}
$$

The equation above illustrates the Associative Property of Addition. The word "twisted" is used for grouping. In translating the two phrases above, "bake" represents addition, "inside" represents equal to, "twisted" represents grouping, and "peanuts" represents the additive identity. A word can also be used to designate an additive inverse. For example, "sour" can be used to make "sour apples," the additive inverse of "apples."

Determine which properties are illustrated using the phrases below, and which words represent *addition, multiplication, equal to, grouping, the additive identity, the additive inverse, the multiplicative identity,* and *the multiplicative inverse*. Record these at the bottom of the page.

1. lizards slap frogs over frogs slap lizards ___Commutative Property of Addition___
2. lizards jump crickets jump lizards ___Identity Property of Multiplication___
3. frogs slap green frogs over toads ___Additive Inverse Property___
4. crickets over yellow snakes jump snakes ___Multiplicative Inverse Property___
5. snakes jump slimy frogs jump lizards over slimy snakes jump frogs jump lizards ___Associative Property of Multiplication___
6. lizards jump frogs slap snakes over lizards jump frogs slap lizards jump snakes ___Distributive Property___

additive identity ___toads___   multiplicative inverse ___crickets___
additive inverse ___green___   multiplicative inverse ___yellow___
addition ___slap___   multiplication ___jump___
grouping ___slimy___   equal to ___over___

1 Interactive Learning

Solve It!

PURPOSE To find a value by applying the correct operations to given values in an appropriate order

PROCESS Students may
- find weekly amounts earned, add them, and multiply the sum by number of weeks.
- add each ten-week amount earned.

FACILITATE

Q How much do you earn each week by walking dogs? Explain. **[$60; 3 dogs × $20 per week per dog = $60]**

Q How much do you earn each week working in the studio? Explain. **[$160; you work 5 days, 4 hours each day, at $8 per hour. 5 × 4 × $8 = $160]**

ANSWER See Solve It in Answers on next page.

CONNECT THE MATH Students perform operations in the Solve It that can be represented by an expression. One focus of the lesson will be on writing and evaluating expressions.

2 Guided Instruction

Problem 1

Q Is subtraction commutative? Explain. **[No. Answers may vary. Sample: Let $t = 9$; $9 - 7 = 2$ and $7 - 9 = -2$.]**

Got It?   EXTENSION

Q If you distribute the answer, what word phrase represents the new but equivalent expression? **[the sum of two a and two b]**

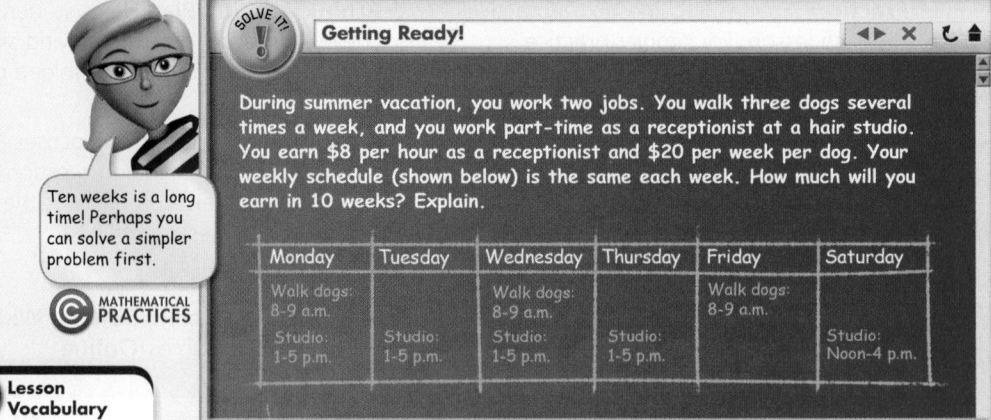

Common Core State Standards

Reviews A-SSE.A.1a Interpret parts of an expression, such as terms, factors, and coefficients. **Also reviews** A-SSE.B.3

MP 1, MP 2, MP 3

Objectives To evaluate algebraic expressions
To simplify algebraic expressions

> **Getting Ready!**
>
> During summer vacation, you work two jobs. You walk three dogs several times a week, and you work part-time as a receptionist at a hair studio. You earn $8 per hour as a receptionist and $20 per week per dog. Your weekly schedule (shown below) is the same each week. How much will you earn in 10 weeks? Explain.

Ten weeks is a long time! Perhaps you can solve a simpler problem first.

Monday	Tuesday	Wednesday	Thursday	Friday	Saturday
Walk dogs: 8-9 a.m.		Walk dogs: 8-9 a.m.		Walk dogs: 8-9 a.m.	
Studio: 1-5 p.m.	Studio: 1-5 p.m.	Studio: 1-5 p.m.	Studio: 1-5 p.m.		Studio: Noon-4 p.m.

Lesson Vocabulary
- evaluate
- term
- coefficient
- constant term
- like terms

Essential Understanding You can represent some mathematical phrases and real-world quantities using algebraic expressions.

Think

What does "seven fewer than t" mean? "Seven fewer than t" means your answer will be less than t.

Problem 1 **Modeling Words With an Algebraic Expression**

Multiple Choice Which algebraic expression models the word phrase *seven fewer than a number t*?

    Ⓐ $t + 7$ Ⓑ $-7t$ Ⓒ $t - 7$ Ⓓ $7 - t$

"Seven fewer than" suggests subtraction. Begin with the number t and subtract 7. This can be represented by the expression $t - 7$. The correct answer is C.

Got It? 1. Which algebraic expression models the word phrase *two times the sum of a and b*?

    Ⓕ $a + b$ Ⓗ $2(a + b)$

    Ⓖ $2a + b$ Ⓘ $a + 2b$

1-3 Preparing to Teach

BIG ideas Variables
Properties

ESSENTIAL UNDERSTANDINGS
- Some mathematical phrases and real-world quantities can be represented using algebraic expressions.
- Variables can represent variable quantities in real world situations and in patterns.
- The properties that apply to real numbers also apply to variables that represent them.

Math Background

The difference between a numeric expression and an algebraic expression is that an algebraic expression contains one or more variables.

These variables model a changing or unknown number, and the expression may have different values depending on this quantity. Algebraic expressions can be mathematical models for the real-world situations.

Algebraic expressions can be simplified, forming equivalent expressions, or evaluated for given values of the variables.

Review the order of operations with students as needed. You may also have students study their calculator manuals or experiment to see how their calculators handle the order of operations.

Mathematical Practices

Reason abstractly and quantitatively. In Problems 1 and 2, students will form habits of coherently representing a verbal situation with an algebraic expression.

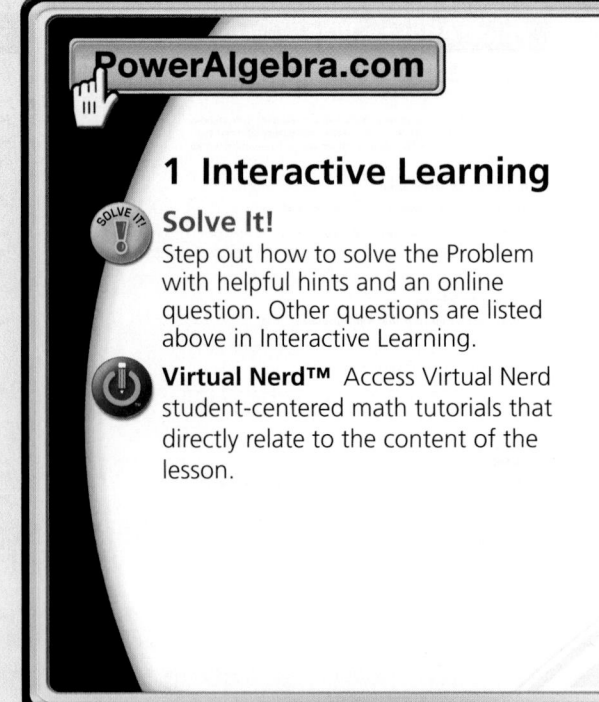

PowerAlgebra.com

1 Interactive Learning

Solve It!
Step out how to solve the Problem with helpful hints and an online question. Other questions are listed above in Interactive Learning.

Virtual Nerd™ Access Virtual Nerd student-centered math tutorials that directly relate to the content of the lesson.

To model a situation with an algebraic expression, do the following:
- Identify the actions that suggest operations.
- Define one or more variables to represent the unknown(s).
- Represent the actions using the variables and the operations.

 Problem 2 Modeling a Situation

Savings You start with $20 and save $6 each week. What algebraic expression models the total amount you save?

Plan
How can you identify the variable?
Determine which quantity is unknown.

| **Relate** | starting amount | plus | amount saved | times | number of weeks |

Define Let w = the number of weeks.

Write 20 + 6 · w

The expression $20 + 6w$ models the situation.

 Got It? 2. You had $150, but you are spending $2 each day. What algebraic expression models this situation?

To **evaluate** an algebraic expression, substitute a number for each variable in the expression. Then simplify using the order of operations.

 **Problem 3** Evaluating Algebraic Expressions

What is the value of the expression for the given values of the variables?

Plan
What operations should you start with?
Do operations that occur in grouping symbols first. Parentheses are grouping symbols.

A $7(a + 4) + 3b - 8$ for $a = -4$ and $b = 5$

$7(-4 + 4) + 3(5) - 8$ Substitute the value for each variable.

$= 7(0) + 3(5) - 8$ Perform operations within grouping symbols.

$= 0 + 15 - 8$ Multiply.

$= 15 - 8$ Add and subtract from left to right.

$= 7$

B $\frac{x}{2} + y^2$ for $x = 1$ and $y = \frac{1}{2}$

$\frac{1}{2} + \left(\frac{1}{2}\right)^2$ Substitute the value for each variable.

$= \frac{1}{2} + \frac{1}{4}$ Simplify the power.

$= \frac{3}{4}$ Add.

Got It? 3. a. What is the value of the expression $\frac{2(x^2 - y^2)}{3}$ for $x = 6$ and $y = -3$?

b. Reasoning Will the value of the expression change if the parentheses are removed? Explain.

Problem 4

VISUAL LEARNERS

This problem presents two tasks. Organize the information by completing the tables below.

Writing the expression

Type of scoring play	Number of points the play is Worth	Number of scoring plays
TD	6	t
EPK	1	k
FG	3	f

Finding the number of points scored (Evaluating the expression)

Type of scoring play	Number of points the play is Worth	Number of scoring plays
TD	6	3
EPK	1	2
FG	3	4

Got It?

Q What information do you know? **[the number of points each scoring play is worth and the number of each type of score]**

Q Determine what you need and how you will plan for this problem. How does this problem compare to Problem 4? **[You need the same things and have the same plan.]**

 Problem 4 Writing and Evaluating an Expression

Sports In football, a touchdown (TD) is worth six points, an extra-point kick (EPK) one point, and a field goal (FG) three points. What algebraic expression models the total number of points that a football team scores in a game, assuming each scoring play is one of the three given types? Suppose a football team scores 3 touchdowns, 2 extra-point kicks, and 4 field goals. How many points did the team score?

Know	Need	Plan
• Number of points each scoring play is worth • Number of each type of score	• Algebraic expression to model points scored • Total number of points scored	• Determine the variables. • Write an expression. • Evaluate the expression.

Think

How many points come from touchdowns?
The number of points from touchdowns is six times the number of touchdowns.

Relate $\dfrac{\text{points}}{\text{per TD}} \cdot \dfrac{\text{number}}{\text{of TDs}} + \dfrac{\text{points}}{\text{per EPK}} \cdot \dfrac{\text{number}}{\text{of EPKs}} + \dfrac{\text{points}}{\text{per FG}} \cdot \dfrac{\text{number}}{\text{of FGs}}$

Define Let t = the number of touchdowns.

Let k = the number of extra-point kicks.

Let f = the number of field goals.

Write $6 \cdot t + 1 \cdot k + 3 \cdot f$

The expression $6t + 1k + 3f$ models the team's total score.

The football team scores 3 touchdowns, 2 extra-point kicks, and 4 field goals, so $t = 3$, $k = 2$, and $f = 4$.

$6(3) + 1(2) + 3(4)$ Substitute the value for each variable.

$= 18 + 2 + 12$ Multiply.

$= 32$ Add.

The team scored 32 points.

✔ **Got It?** **4.** In basketball, teams can score by making two-point shots, three-point shots, and one-point free throws. What algebraic expression models the total number of points that a basketball team scores in a game? If a team makes 10 two-point shots, 5 three-point shots, and 7 free throws, how many points does it score in all?

An expression that is a number, a variable, or the product of a number and one or more variables is a **term**. A **coefficient** is the numerical factor of a term. A **constant term** is a term with no variables. You can add terms to form longer expressions. The expression below has three terms.

$$-4ax + 7w - 6$$

constant term
Think of $7w - 6$ as $7w + (-6)$. The constant term is -6.

coefficients
The numerical coefficient of $-4ax$ is -4.

Additional Problems

1. Which algebraic expression models the word phrase *one less than the product of six and w*?

A. $1 - 6 \cdot w$ **B.** $6 \cdot w - 1$

C. $w \cdot 1 - 6$ **D.** $1 \cdot 6 - w$

ANSWER B

2. You are on a bicycle trip. You traveled 52 miles the first day. Since then, your average rate has been 12 miles per hour. What algebraic expression models the distance you traveled so far?

ANSWER $52 + 12h$; h represents the number of hours since the first day.

3. What is the value of the expression for the given values of the variables?

a. $2r + 5(s + 6) - 1$ for $r = 3$ and $s = -9$

b. $c^3 - \dfrac{d}{8}$ for $c = \dfrac{1}{4}$ and $d = 1$

ANSWERS

a. -10

b. $-\dfrac{7}{64}$

4. Ticket prices for admission to a museum are $8 for adults, $5 for children, and $6 for seniors.

a. What algebraic expression models the total number of dollars collected in ticket sales?

b. If 20 adult tickets, 16 children's tickets, and 10 senior tickets are sold one morning, how much money is collected in all?

ANSWERS

a. The expression $8a + 5c + 6s$ models the total number of dollars collected; a is the number of adult tickets; c is the number of children's tickets; and s is the number of senior tickets.

b. The total amount collected is $300.

5. What is the simplified form of each expression?

a. $2a^2 + 3b^2 + 6b^2 + 5a^2$

b. $-(x + 4y) + 5(3x - y)$

ANSWERS

a. $7a^2 + 9b^2$

b. $14x - 9y$

Answers

Got It? (continued)

4. Let x = the number of two-point shots, y = the number of three-point shots, z = the number of one-point free throws, $2x + 3y + 1z$; 42 points

Like terms have the same variables raised to the same powers.

like terms   like terms

$$3x^2 + 5x^2 + 9y^3z + 2yz - 4y^3z$$

You can simplify an algebraic expression that has like terms. You combine like terms using the properties of real numbers (Lesson 1-2). An expression and its simplified form are equivalent. Their values are equal for all values of their variables.

 Concept Summary   **Properties for Simplifying Algebraic Expressions**

Let a, b, and c represent real numbers.

Definition of Subtraction	$a - b = a + (-b)$
Definition of Division	$a \div b = \frac{a}{b} = a \cdot \frac{1}{b}, b \neq 0$
Distributive Property for Subtraction	$a(b - c) = ab - ac$
Multiplication by 0	$0 \cdot a = 0$
Multiplication by -1	$-1 \cdot a = -a$
Opposite of a Sum	$-(a + b) = -a + (-b) = -a - b$
Opposite of a Difference	$-(a - b) = -a + b = b - a$
Opposite of a Product	$-(ab) = -a \cdot b = a \cdot (-b)$
Opposite of an Opposite	$-(-a) = a$

Problem 5   **Simplifying Algebraic Expressions**

Combine like terms. What is a simpler form of each expression?

 Think
Are $7x^2$ and $3y^2$ like terms?
No; they have different variables.

A $7x^2 + 3y^2 + 2y^2 - 4x^2$

$7x^2 + 3y^2 + 2y^2 - 4x^2$	Identify like terms.
$= 7x^2 - 4x^2 + 3y^2 + 2y^2$	Commutative Property of Addition
$= (7 - 4)x^2 + (3 + 2)y^2$	Distributive Property
$= 3x^2 + 5y^2$	Combine like terms.

B $-(3k + m) + 2(k - 4m)$

$-3k - m + 2k - 8m$	Opposite of a Sum and Distributive Property
$= -k - 9m$	Combine like terms.

Got It?   **5.** Combine like terms. What is a simpler form of each expression?
    a. $-4j^2 - 7k + 5j + j^2$ **b.** $-(8a + 3b) + 10(2a - 5b)$

Take Note

Q How do the Distributive Property of Addition and Subtraction compare? **[They are the same except + is replaced by − .]**

Q How can you rewrite the Opposite of a Sum Property to show that it is just a special case of the Distributive Property? **[$-(a + b) = -1(a + b) = -1a + (-1)b = -a - b$]**

Q How can you rewrite the Opposite of a Difference Property to show that it is just a special case of the Distributive Property? **[$-(a - b) = -1(a - b) = -1a - (-1)b = -a + b$]**

Problem 5

Q In 5B, how is the Distributive Property used? **[It is used to write $2(k - 4m)$ as $2k - 8m$. It is used again to combine like terms: $-3k + 2k = (-3 + 2)k = -1k = -k$ and $-m - 8m = -1m - 8m = (-1 - 8)m = -9m$.]**

Got It?   **ERROR PREVENTION**

In 5a, students may incorrectly identify $-4j^2$, $5j$, and j^2 as like terms. Like terms require the same exponents. Only $-4j^2$ and j^2 are like terms. In 5b, if students write $-8a + 3b$, they did not apply the Opposite of a Sum Property correctly: $-(8a + 3b) = -8a - 3b$.

Answers

5. a. $-3j^2 - 7k + 5j$
   b. $12a - 53b$

3 Lesson Check

Do you know HOW? — ERROR INTERVENTION

- If students have trouble substituting in Exercises 3–6, suggest they rewrite the problem, replacing the variables with parentheses and writing the variable above it. For example: $2(\underset{x}{\ }) - 3(\underset{y}{\ })$.

Do you UNDERSTAND?

- If students have trouble with Exercise 9, look at Problem 4. An algebraic expression becomes a numeric expression when values are substituted for the variables.

Close

> **Q** How do you evaluate an algebraic expression? **[Substitute values for the variables, then find the value of the resulting numeric expression.]**
>
> **Q** What does it mean to simplify an algebraic expression of the type in this lesson? **[Combine like terms.]**
>
> **Q** To model a situation with an expression, what are some tasks you might need to do? **[Answers may vary. Sample: identify the action(s), choose the correct operation(s), identify how quantities are related, define variables to represent unknown quantities]**

 Lesson Check

Do you know HOW?

Write an algebraic expression that models each word phrase.

1. the quotient of the sum of 2 and a number b, and 3

2. the sum of the product of a number k and 4, and a number m

Evaluate each algebraic expression for $x = 3$ and $y = -2$.

3. $2x - 3y$ 4. $5x + y$

5. $y - x$ 6. $x + 4y$

Do you UNDERSTAND? 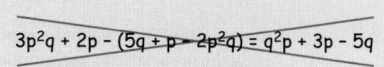 MATHEMATICAL PRACTICES

7. **Error Analysis** A student simplified the expression as shown.

$$3p^2q + 2p - (5q + p - 2p^2q) = q^2p + 3p - 5q$$

Identify the errors and correct them.

8. **Vocabulary** Explain the difference between a constant and a coefficient.

9. **Compare and Contrast** How are algebraic expressions and numerical expressions alike? How are they different? Include examples to justify your reasoning.

 Practice and Problem-Solving Exercises MATHEMATICAL PRACTICES

Ⓐ Practice

Write an algebraic expression that models each word phrase.   ◀ See Problem 1.

10. four more than a number b

11. the product of 8 and the sum of a number x and 3

12. the quotient of the difference between 5 and a number n, and 2

Write an algebraic expression that models each situation.   ◀ See Problem 2.

13. Jenny had $130, but she is spending $10 per week.

14. The piggy bank contained $25, and $1.50 is added each day.

15. You had 250 minutes left on your cell phone, and you talk an hour a week.

Evaluate each expression for the given values of the variables.   ◀ See Problem 3.

16. $4a + 7b + 3a - 2b + 2a$; $a = -5$ and $b = 3$

17. $-k^2 - (3k - 5n) + 4n$; $k = -1$ and $n = -2$

18. $-5(x + 2y) + 15(x + 2y)$; $x = 7$ and $y = -7$

19. $4(2m - n) - 3(2m - n)$; $m = -15$ and $n = -18$

STEM Physics The expression $16t^2$ models the distance in feet that an object falls during the first t seconds after being dropped. What is the distance the object falls during each time?

20. 0.25 second   21. 0.5 second   22. 2 seconds   23. 10 seconds

---

 PowerAlgebra.com

3 Lesson Check

For a digital lesson check, use the Got It questions.

Support in Algebra 2 Companion
- Lesson Check

4 Practice

Assign homework to individual students or to an entire class.

Answers

Lesson Check

1. $\dfrac{2 + b}{3}$

2. $4k + m$

3. 12

4. 13

5. -5

6. -5

7. The student did not distribute the -1.
$3p^2q + 2p - (5q + p - 2p^2q) =$
$3p^2q + 2p - 5q - p + 2p^2q =$
$5p^2q + p - 5q$

8. A constant is a term with no variables, whereas a coefficient is the numerical factor in a term.

9. Answers may vary. Sample: Both algebraic expressions and numerical expressions represent a quantity using numbers, operations and grouping symbols. An algebraic expression includes variables when representing a quantity. Examples: numerical expression: $3 + 6(5 - 2)$; algebraic expression: $2z + 3z(6 + 5z)$.

Practice and Problem-Solving Exercises

10. $b + 4$

11. $8(x + 3)$

12. $\dfrac{5 - n}{2}$

13. $130 - 10w$; with w = number of weeks

14. $25 + 1.5d$; with d = number of days

15. $250 - 60w$; with w = number of weeks

16. -30 17. -16

18. -70 19. -12

20. 1 ft

21. 4 ft

22. 64 ft

23. 1600 ft

Investing The expression $1000(1.1)^t$ represents the value of a $1000 investment that earns 10% interest per year, compounded annually for t years. What is the value of a $1000 investment at the end of each period?

24. 2 years   **25.** 3 years   **26.** 4 years   **27.** 5 years

Write an algebraic expression to model the total score in each situation. Then evaluate the expression to find the total score.   **See Problem 4.**

28. In the first set, the volleyball team made only 8 shots worth one point each.

29. In the last baseball game, there were two 3-run home runs and 4 hits that each scored 2 runs.

Simplify by combining like terms.   **See Problem 5.**

30. $5a - a$ **31.** $5 + 10s - 8s$ **32.** $-5a - 4a + b$

33. $2a + 3b + 4a$ **34.** $6r + 3s + 2s + 4r$ **35.** $0.5x - x$

36. $7b - (3a - 8b)$ **37.** $5 + (4g - 7)$ **38.** $-(3x - 4y) + x$

B Apply   Evaluate each expression for the given value of the variable.

39. $x + 2x - x - 1; x = 2$ **40.** $2z + 3 + 5 - 3z; z = -3$ **41.** $3(2a + 5) + 2(3 - a); a = 4$

42. $\frac{5(2k - 3) - 3(k + 4)}{3k + 2}; k = -2$ **43.** $y^2 + 3; y = \sqrt{7}$ **44.** $5c^3 - 6c^2 - 2c; c = -5$

45. Think About a Plan Tran's truck gets very poor gas mileage. If Tran pays $84 to fill his truck with gas and is able to drive m miles on a full tank, what expression shows his gas cost per mile?
- What operation does "per" indicate?
- Check your expression by substituting 200 miles for m. Does your answer make sense?

Simplify by combining like terms.

46. $-a^2 + 2b^2 + \frac{1}{4}a^2$ **47.** $x + \frac{x^2}{2} + 2x^2 - x$ **48.** $\frac{y^2}{4} + \frac{y}{3} + \frac{y^2}{3} - \frac{y}{5}$

49. $-(2x + y) - 2(-x - y)$ **50.** $x(3 - y) + y(x + 6)$ **51.** $\frac{1}{2}(x^2 - y^2) - \frac{5}{2}(x^2 - y^2)$

Write an algebraic expression to model each situation.

52. Class Project The freshman class will be selling carnations as a class project. What is the class's income after it pays the florist a flat fee of $200 and sells x carnations for $2 each?

53. Jobs You have a summer job at a car wash. You earn $8.50 per hour and are expected to pay a one-time fee of $15 for the uniform. If you work x hours per week, how much will you make during the first week?

54. Reasoning Suppose you need to subtract a from b but mistakenly subtract b from a instead. How is the answer you get related to the correct answer? Explain.

---

4 Practice

ASSIGNMENT GUIDE
Basic: 10–38 all, 39–46 even, 51
Average: 11–37 odd, 39–60
Advanced: 11–37 odd, 39–62

ⓒ **Mathematical Practices** are supported by exercises with red headings. Here are the Practices supported in this lesson:

MP 1: Make Sense of Problems   Ex. 45
MP 3: Communicate   Ex. 56, 62
MP 3: Construct Arguments   Ex. 54
MP 3: Critique the Reasoning of Others   Ex. 7, 9, 55

Applications exercises have blue headings.

STEM exercises focus on science or engineering applications.

EXERCISE 51: Use the Think About a Plan worksheet in the **Practice and Problem Solving Workbook** (also available in the Teaching Resources in print and online) to further support students' development in becoming independent learners.

HOMEWORK QUICK CHECK
To check students' understanding of key skills and concepts, go over Exercises 21, 31, 40, 44, and 51.

---

24. $1210

25. $1331

26. $1464.10

27. $1610.51

28. Let s = number of shots, $1s$; 8

29. Let x = 3-run home runs and y = 2-run hits; $3x + 2y$; 14

30. $4a$

31. $2s + 5$

32. $-9a + b$

33. $6a + 3b$

34. $10r + 5s$

35. $-0.5x$

36. $-3a + 15b$

37. $4g - 2$

38. $-2x + 4y$

39. 3

40. 11

41. 37

42. $\frac{41}{4}$

43. 10

44. -765

45. $\frac{\$84}{m}$

46. $-\frac{3}{4}a^2 + 2b^2$

47. $\frac{5x^2}{2}$

48. $\frac{7y^2}{12} + \frac{2y}{15}$

49. y

50. $3x + 6y$

51. $-2x^2 + 2y^2$

52. $2x - 200$

53. $8.5x - 15$

54. It is the correct answer's opposite; $a - b = -b + a = -(b - a)$

Answers

Practice and Problem-Solving
Exercises (continued)

55. No; John did not use the Distr. Prop. correctly.
$-(x + y) + 3(x - 4y)$
$-x - y + 3x - 12y$
$2x - 13y$

56. Answers may vary. Sample: x^2

57. Distr. Prop.

58. Opposite of an Opposite or Opposite of a Difference used twice

59. Opposite of a Difference

60. Mult. by -1

61. Answers may vary. Sample:
$2(b - a) + 5(b - a)$
$= (2 + 5)(b - a)$ Distr. Prop.
$= 7(b - a)$ Add.
$= 7b - 7a$ Distr. Prop.

62. a. 18
b. $2x^2$; 18
c. Properties of operations were used to simplify the original expression into an equivalent expression. Equivalent expressions have equal values for all values of their variables.

 **55. Error Analysis** John simplified the expression as shown. Is his work correct? Explain.

$-(x + y) + 3(x - 4y)$
$-x + y + 3x - 4y$
$2x - 3y$

 **56. Open-Ended** Write an example of an algebraic expression that has a nonnegative value regardless of the value of the variable.

Name the property of real numbers illustrated by the equation.

57. $2(s - t) = 2s - 2t$

58. $-[-(x - 10)] = x - 10$

59. $-(2t - 11) = 11 - 2t$

60. $-(a - b) = (-1)(a - b)$

 Challenge   **61.** Simplify $2(b - a) + 5(b - a)$ and justify each step in your simplification.

 **62. a.** Evaluate the expression $2(2x^2 - x) - 3(x^2 - x) + x^2 - x$ for $x = 3$. Do *not* simplify the expression before evaluating it.
b. Simplify the expression in part (a) and then evaluate your answer for $x = 3$.
c. Writing Explain why the values in parts (a) and (b) should be the same.

 Apply What You've Learned

MATHEMATICAL PRACTICES
MP 2

Look back at the information on page 3 about Mia helping her friend Cody after Cody's car runs out of gas.

In the Apply What You've Learned in Lesson 1-2, you drew diagrams to show possible locations of Cody's car when it runs out of gas. Choose one of these diagrams to use for parts (a)–(d) below.

a. Assign a variable to one unknown distance in your diagram.

Use your variable from part (a) to write an algebraic expression for each of the following distances.

b. the distance Mia drove from her house to Cody's car

c. the distance Mia drove between the time she picked up Cody's gas can and the time she delivered the full gas can to Cody

d. the distance Mia drove to the restaurant after leaving Cody

---

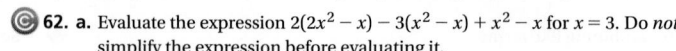 **Apply What You've Learned**

In the Apply What You've Learned for Lesson 1-2, students copied the diagram shown on page 3 and showed possible locations for where along the road Cody's car runs out of gas. Now, they write algebraic expressions to represent distances in one of their diagrams.

Mathematical Practices
Students **reason abstractly** to assign a variable to an unknown distance and express other distances in terms of that variable. (MP 2)

ANSWERS
Answers may vary. The following sample answers are for a diagram in which Cody's car is placed between Mia's house and the gas station.

a. Let x represent the distance from Cody's car to the gas station.

b. $9 - x$

c. $2x$

d. $11 + x$

1-3 Lesson Resources

Additional Instructional Support

Algebra 2 Companion

Students can use the **Algebra 2 Companion** worktext (4 pages) as you teach the lesson. Use the Companion to support

- New Vocabulary
- Key Concepts
- Got It for each Problem
- Lesson Check

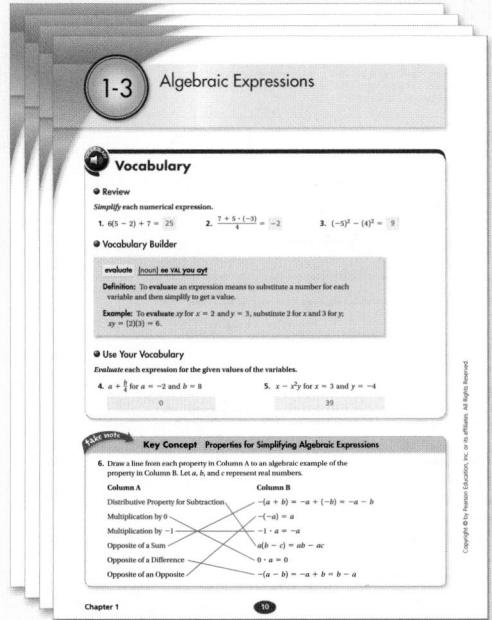

ELL Support

Focus on Language After students have studied the information about terms, coefficients, and constant terms, reinforce the vocabulary. Have students work in pairs. One student writes an expression and the other student answers the following questions: What are the terms? What is the constant term? What are the coefficients?

5 Assess & Remediate

Lesson Quiz

1. Which algebraic expression models the word phrase *three fewer than the sum of c and d*?

   (a) $3 - c + d$ (b) $(c + d) - 3$

   (c) $c + 3 - d$ (d) $d + 3 - c$

2. You have 128 ounces of milk and drink 16 ounces per day. What algebraic expression models the amount of milk you have?

3. Evaluate the expression for the given variables.

   $-a^2 - (2a - 7b) + b$ for $a = -2$ and $b = 3$

4. **Do you UNDERSTAND?** You have a summer job detailing cars. You charge $5 to wash a car, $25 to wax a car, and $2 to vacuum a car. What algebraic expression models the total amount you earn? If you wash 8 cars, wax 2 cars, and vacuum 6 cars, how much will you earn in all?

5. What is the simplified form of the expression $-(2a + 5s) + 10(a - 3s)$?

ANSWERS TO LESSON QUIZ

1. (b)
2. $128 - 16d$; d is the number of days
3. 24
4. $5w + 25x + 2v$; w is number of washes; x is number of waxes; and v is number of vacuums; $102
5. $8a - 35s$

PRESCRIPTION FOR REMEDIATION

Use the student work on the Lesson Quiz to prescribe a differentiated review assignment:

Points	Differentiated Remediation
0–2	Intervention
3–4	On-level
5	Extension

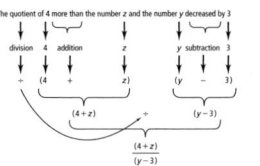

5 Assess & Remediate

Assign the Lesson Quiz. Appropriate intervention, practice, or enrichment is automatically generated based on student performance.

Differentiated Remediation
Available in editable format online.

Intervention

- **Reteaching** (2 pages) Provides reteaching and practice exercises for the key lesson concepts. Use with struggling students or absent students.
- **English Language Learner Support** Helps students develop and reinforce mathematical vocabulary and key concepts.

All-in-One Resources/Online
Reteaching

1-3 Reteaching
Algebraic Expressions

You can model words with algebraic expressions. In a word problem, look for words and word phrases that indicate mathematical operations.

Addition	Subtraction	Multiplication	Division
added to	subtracted from	multiplied by	divided by
plus	minus	product	quotient
sum	difference	times	fraction of
more than	less than	of	per
longer than	shorter than		
increased by	decreased by		
total	fewer than		
in all			

Problem

What is an algebraic expression that models the given word phrase?

The quotient of 4 more than the number z and the number y decreased by 3

$\frac{(4+z)}{(y-3)}$

Exercises

Write an algebraic expression that models each word phrase.

1. nine less than 5 multiplied by the number p $5p - 9$
2. the product of 2 divided by the number h and 8 more than the number k $\frac{2}{h}(k + 8)$
3. two decreased by the quotient of the number a and 7 and increased by a multiplied by 3 $2 - \frac{a}{7} + 3a$

All-in-One Resources/Online
English Language Learner Support

1-3 Additional Vocabulary Support
Algebraic Expressions

Use the chart below to review vocabulary. These vocabulary words will help you complete this page.

Addition (+)	Subtraction (−)	Multiplication (×)	Division (÷)
sum	difference	product	quotient
more than	less than	times	divided by
increased by	fewer than		
total	subtracted from		
added to			

Circle the word or words in each word phrase that tell you what operations to use. Write the operation symbol word (+, −, ×, ÷) next to the algebraic expression.

1. the ⟨sum⟩ of a number m and −12 +
2. the ⟨product⟩ of b and c ×
3. 14 ⟨less than⟩ p −
4. the ⟨total⟩ of −75 and t +
5. the ⟨quotient⟩ of d and 28 ÷

Match each word phrase in Column A with the matching algebraic expression in Column B.

Column A	Column B
6. the difference of a number p and 36	A. $y + 9$
7. 15 more than the number q	B. $10(r)$
8. the product of 10 and a number r	C. $q + 15$
9. the total of a number y and 9	D. $p - 36$

Match each algebraic expression in Column A with the matching word phrase in Column B.

Column A	Column B
10. $m + 45$ C	A. 45 less than a number m
11. $\frac{m}{45}$ D	B. 45 times the sum of a number m and 1
12. $m - 45$ A	C. a number m increased by 45
13. $45(m + 1)$ B	D. a number m divided by 45

Differentiated Remediation *continued*

Available in editable format online.

On-Level

- **Practice** (2 pages) Provides extra practice for each lesson. For simpler practice exercises, use the Form K Practice pages found in the All-in-One Teaching Resources and online.

- **Think About a Plan** Helps students develop specific problem-solving skills and strategies by providing scaffolded guiding questions.
- **Standardized Test Prep** Focuses on all major exercises, all major question types, and helps students prepare for the high-stakes assessments.

Extension

- **Enrichment** Provides students with interesting problems and activities that extend the concepts of the lesson.
- **Activities, Games, and Puzzles** Worksheets that can be used for concepts development, enrichment, and for fun!

Practice and Problem Solving Wkbk/All-in-One Resources/Online
Practice page 1

1-3 **Practice**   Form G
Algebraic Expressions

Write an algebraic expression that models each word phrase.

1. seven less than the number t $t - 7$

2. the sum of 11 and the product of 2 and a number r $11 + 2r$

Write an algebraic expression that models each situation.

3. Arin has $520 and is earning $75 each week babysitting. $520 + 75w$

4. You have 50 boxes of raisins and are eating 12 boxes each month. $50 - 12m$

Evaluate each expression for the given values of the variables.

5. $-4v + 3(w + 2v) - 5w$; $v = -2$ and $w = 4$ -12

6. $c(3 - a) - c^2$; $a = 4$ and $c = -1$ 0

7. $2(3e - 5f) + 3(e^2 + 4f)$; $e = 3$ and $f = -5$ 35

Surface Area The expression $6s^2$ represents the surface area of a cube with edges of length s. What is the surface area of a cube with each edge length?

8. 3 inches 54 in.^{2}

9. 1.5 meters 13.5 m^2

The expression $4.95 + 0.07x$ models a household's monthly long-distance charges, where x represents the number of minutes of long-distance calls during the month. What are the monthly charges for each number of long-distance minutes?

10. 73 minutes $10.06

11. 29 minutes $6.98

Simplify by combining like terms.

12. $5x - 3x^2 + 16x^2$ $13x^2 + 5x$

13. $\frac{3(a-b)}{9} + \frac{4}{9}b$ $\frac{1}{3}a + \frac{1}{9}b$

14. $t + \frac{t^2}{2} + t^2 + t$ $\frac{3}{2}t^2 + 2t$

15. $4a - 5(a + 1)$ $-a - 5$

16. $-2(j^2 - k) - 6(j^2 + 3k)$ $-8j^2 - 16k$

17. $x(x - y) + y(y - x)$ $x^2 - 2xy + y^2$

Practice and Problem Solving Wkbk/All-in-One Resources/Online
Practice page 2

1-3 **Practice** (continued)   Form G
Algebraic Expressions

18. In a soccer tournament, teams receive 6 points for winning a game, 3 points for tying a game, and 1 point for each goal they score. What algebraic expression models the total number of points that a soccer team receives in a tournament? Suppose one team wins two games and ties one game, scoring a total of five goals. How many points does the team receive? $6w + 3t + 1g$; 20 points

Evaluate each expression for the given value of the variable.

19. $-t^2 - (3t + 2)$; $t = 5$ -42

20. $i^2 - 5(i^3 - i^2)$; $i = 4$ -224

21. **Perimeter** Write an expression for the perimeter of the figure at the right as the sum of the lengths of its sides. What is the simplified form of this expression?
$a + (a - b) + c + b + (a - 2c) + b + c + (a - b)$; $4a$

22. Simplify $-(2x - 5y) + 3(4x + 2y)$ and justify each step in your simplification. $-2x + 5y + 12x + 6y$, Opposite of a Difference and Distributive Property; $10x + 11y$; Combine like terms using the Distributive Property

23. **Error Analysis** Alana simplified the expression as shown. Do you agree with her work? Explain.   No; Dist. Prop. and Opp. of a Diff. incorrectly applied. Correct simplification: $2x + 8 - 5x + 7 = -3x + 15$

24. **Open-Ended** Write an example of an algebraic expression that always has the same value regardless of the value of the variable.   Answers may vary. Sample: any expression that results in the variable having a coefficient of 0; sample: $x - x$

Match the property name with the appropriate equation.

25. Opposite of a Difference   E

A. $-[(-r) + 2p] = -(-r) - 2p$

26. Opposite of a Sum   A

B. $16d - (3d + 2)(0) = 16d - 0$

27. Opposite of an Opposite   F

C. $5(2 - x) = 10 - 5x$

28. Multiplication by 0   B

D. $-(4r + 3s) + t = (-1)(4r + 3s) + t$

29. Multiplication by -1 D

E. $-(8 - 3m) = 3m - 8$

30. Distributive Property   C

F. $-[-(9 - 2w)] = 9 - 2w$

Practice and Problem Solving Wkbk/All-in-One Resources/Online
Think About a Plan

1-3 **Think About a Plan**
Algebraic Expressions

Write an algebraic expression to model the situation.

The freshman class will be selling carnations as a class project. What is the class's income after it pays the florist a flat fee of $200 and sells x carnations for $2 each?

1. What does the variable represent?
the number of carnations sold

2. How will the class's income change for each carnation sold?
It will increase by $2.

3. Will paying the florist increase or decrease their income? By how much?
decrease; $200

4. Will the expression include both the income for each carnation and the florist's fee? Explain.
Yes; the class's profit is a function of the proceeds from carnation sales
and the florist's fee.

5. Write the expression in words.

The | income | is | -200 | and | 2 | times | x

6. Write the expression using symbols.

income | = | -200 | + | 2 | · | x

7. Check your expression by substituting 300 for the number of carnations. Does your answer make sense? Explain.
$-200 + 2(300) = -200 + 600 = 400$; yes; the class has an income of $400 after they
make $600 and pay the florist $200.

8. The algebraic expression $-200 + 2x$ models the freshman class income.

Practice and Problem Solving Wkbk/All-in-One Resources/Online
Standardized Test Prep

1-3 **Standardized Test Prep**
Algebraic Expressions

Multiple Choice

For Exercises 1–3, choose the correct letter.

1. The expression $2\pi(rh + r^2)$ represents the total surface area of a cylinder with height h and radius r. What is the surface area of a cylinder with height 6 centimeters and radius 2 centimeters?   C
   Ⓐ 16π cm^2
   Ⓑ 28π cm^2
   Ⓒ 32π cm^2
   Ⓓ 96π cm^2

2. Which expression best represents the simplified form of $3(m - 3) + m(5 - m) - m^2$?   F
   Ⓕ $-2m^2 + 8m - 9$
   Ⓖ $8m - 9$
   Ⓗ $-2m^2 - 2m - 9$
   Ⓘ $-2m - 9$

3. The price of a discount airline ticket starts at $150 and increases by $30 each week. Which algebraic expression models this situation?   D
   Ⓐ $30 + w$
   Ⓑ $150 - 30w$
   Ⓒ $30 - 150w$
   Ⓓ $150 + 30w$

Extended Response

4. Members of a club are selling calendars as a fundraiser. The club pays $100 for a box of wall and desk calendars. They sell wall calendars for $12 and desk calendars for $8.
   a. Write an algebraic expression to model the club's profit from selling w wall calendars and d desk calendars. Explain in words or show work for how you determined the expression.
   b. What is the club's profit from selling 9 wall calendars and 7 desk calendars? Show your work.

   a. The income from wall calendars is $12w$. The income from desk calendars is $8d$. The total income is $12w + 8d$. The club must pay $100 from the total income, so the profit is $12w + 8d - 100$. (OR equivalent explanation.)
   b. $12w + 8d - 100 = 12(9) + 8(7) - 100 = 108 + 56 - 100 = 64$; $64

[4] appropriate methods and correct expression with no computational errors

[3] appropriate methods and correct expression, but minor computational error

[2] incorrect expression or multiple computational errors

[1] correct expression and profit, without work shown

[0] no answer or no attempt made

All-in-One Resources/Online
Enrichment

1-3 **Enrichment**
Algebraic Expressions

Math Puzzle

Algebraic expressions can help reveal the secret behind number puzzles that appear to be magic. Start by trying the puzzle below. Complete the puzzle two times and record each step in the table.

Directions	First Guess	Second Guess
Think of a number.		
Add 1 to your number.		
Multiply your answer by 2.		
Subtract 2 from your answer.		
Finally, subtract your original number.		

What did you notice about your final answer each time?
Answers may vary. Sample: The final number is the same as the original number.

By writing and simplifying algebraic expressions, you can explain the puzzle.

Let n represent your number. Write an algebraic expression for each of the steps in the puzzle above.

1. Add 1 to your number. $n + 1$

2. Multiply your answer by 2. $2n + 2$

3. Subtract 2 from your answer. $2n$

4. Subtract your original number. n

5. Explain how your algebraic expressions show why the puzzle always ends with the original number.
Answers may vary. Sample: The final expression is the same as the original expression.

Write and simplify algebraic expressions for the puzzle below.

6. Think of a number. n

7. Multiply your number by 4. $4n$

8. Subtract 2. $4n - 2$

9. Divide your number by 2. $2n - 1$

10. Add 1. $2n$

11. Subtract your original number. n

Online Teacher Resource Center
Activities, Games, and Puzzles

1-3 **Game: Number-Cube Substitution**
Algebraic Expressions

Material

- 1 six-sided number cube

Game Play

Play this game in pairs. Each player takes a turn and rolls the number cube. Whoever rolls the lowest number goes first.

On your turn, roll the number cube. This number is the value of x for the first expression shown, $x + 32$. Substitute the value of x in the expression to calculate your score for the first roll. Record your roll and score on the scorecard.

Players take turns evaluating each expression. Then each player totals up his or her score, and the player with the higher total wins.

Scorecard   Check students' work.

	Player 1		Player 2	
	Number rolled, x	Score	Number rolled, x	Score
$x + 32$				
$x^2 - 3x$				
$\frac{120}{x}$				
$6x - 10$				
$-x^2$				
$-2 - x$				
$(x - 3)(x + 2)$				
$x^2 - 5x - 3$				
$(x + 3)^2 - 7$				
$-3x + 5$				
$\frac{60}{x - 7}$				
Total				

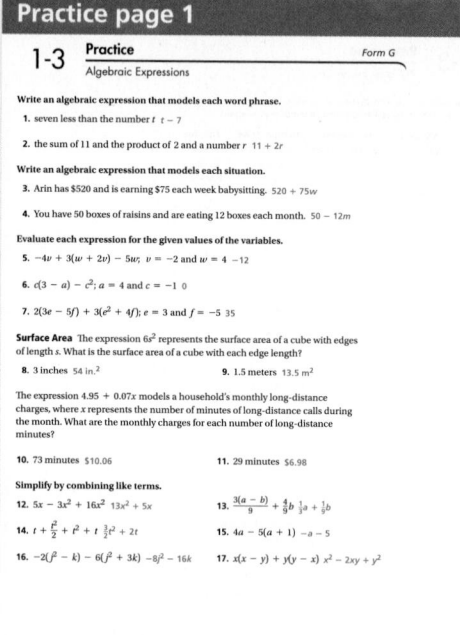

MathXL® for School
Go to PowerAlgebra.com

Do you know HOW?

1. Draw the next figure in the pattern.

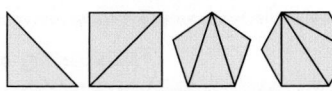

Identify a pattern and find the next number in the pattern.

2. $-405, -135, -45, -15, \ldots$

3. $\frac{2x}{3}, \frac{x}{3}, \frac{x}{6}, \frac{x}{12}, \ldots$

4. $101, 92, 83, 74, \ldots$

5. $0.4, 1.2, 3.6, 10.8, \ldots$

Name the property of real numbers illustrated by the equation.

6. $7(x - y) = 7x - 7y$

7. $\sqrt{7} \cdot 1 = \sqrt{7}$

8. $-2 \cdot \left(-\frac{1}{2}\right) = 1$

9. $2.3(3.4 \cdot 12.9) = (2.3 \cdot 3.4)(12.9)$

Write an algebraic expression to model each word phrase.

10. eight times the sum of a and b

11. four more than the product of x and y

12. six less than the quotient of d and g

13. ten less than twice the product of s and t

Simplify each expression.

14. $-x^2 + 2y - 3x^2 + 10$

15. $-2(d + 2e) + 5(3d - 8e)$

16. $-(a + 2b) + 4(a + 2b) - 2(a + 2b)$

17. $-3x + 14x + 7x^2 - 3x + 4x(x + 1)$

Identify a pattern by making a table of the inputs and outputs. Include a process column.

18.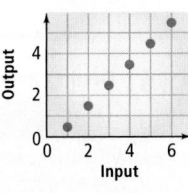

19.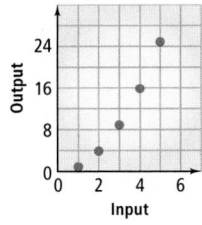

Evaluate each expression for $a = 4$, $b = -3$, and $c = 10$.

20. $7a - 5b$

21. $4a + b - |2c|$

22. $|a - b - c^2|$

Write an algebraic expression to model each situation.

23. You have 16 tomatoes, and your tomato plants produce 5 tomatoes each day.

24. Your car's gas tank holds 25 gallons, and you use 1.5 gallons of gas each day.

Do you UNDERSTAND?

25. Writing Explain why every integer is also a rational number.

26. Reasoning What expression describes the number of squares in the nth figure?

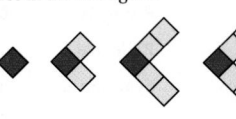

27. Reasoning Is there a Closure Property of Subtraction that applies to whole numbers? Explain.

19. Output = Input²

Input	Process Column	Output
1	$(1) \times (1)$	1
2	$(2) \times (2)$	4
3	$(3) \times (3)$	9
4	$(4) \times (4)$	16
5	$(5) \times (5)$	25
⋮	⋮	⋮
n	$(n) \times (n)$	n^2

20. 43

21. -7

22. 93

23. $16 + 5d$; Let d = number of days

24. $25 - 1.5d$; Let d = number of days

25. Every integer can be written as a quotient of integers.

26. $2n - 1$

27. No; the subtraction of a larger number from a smaller number results in a negative number, which is not a whole number.

Answers

Mid-Chapter Quiz

1.

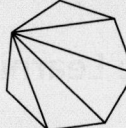

2. div. by 3; -5

3. mult. by $\frac{1}{2}$; $\frac{x}{24}$

4. subtr. 9; 65

5. mult. by 3; 32.4

6. Distr. Prop.

7. Ident. Prop. of Mult.

8. Inv. Prop. of Mult.

9. Assoc. Prop. of Mult.

10. $8(a + b)$

11. $xy + 4$

12. $\frac{d}{g} - 6$

13. $2st - 10$

14. $-4x^2 + 2y + 10$

15. $13d - 44e$

16. $a + 2b$

17. $12x + 11x^2$

18. Output = Input − 0.5

Input	Process Column	Output
1	$(1) - 0.5$	0.5
2	$(2) - 0.5$	1.5
3	$(3) - 0.5$	2.5
4	$(4) - 0.5$	3.5
5	$(5) - 0.5$	4.5
6	$(6) - 0.5$	5.5
⋮	⋮	⋮
n	$(n) - 0.5$	$n - 0.5$

PowerAlgebra.com

MathXL for School
Prepare students for the Mid-Chapter Quiz and Chapter Test with online practice and review.

1 Interactive Learning

Solve It!

PURPOSE Find unknown quantities by relating them to known quantities

PROCESS Students may
- first solve for the figure on the left.
- write and solve equations that use the idea of balance.

FACILITATE

Q What does half the mobile weigh? **[20 oz]**

Q What is the weight of the crossbar on the left side? How do you know? **[4 oz; each inch weighs 1 oz.]**

Q How much does the figure on the left weigh? **[16 oz]**

Q What is the total weight of all objects on the right side below the 4-oz crossbar? Explain. **[16 oz; their total weight must equal the weight of the figure on the left.]**

Q What does the figure on the right weigh? **[6 oz]**

Q How much does each of the middle figures weigh? Explain. **[2 oz; 8 − 2 − 1 − 1 = 4 and 4 ÷ 2 = 2]**

ANSWER See Solve It in Answers on next page.

CONNECT THE MATH In the Solve It, students implicitly use the Properties of Equality to find unknown quantities. The properties are formally introduced in this lesson and used to solve equations.

2 Guided Instruction

Take Note

The Properties of Equality hold for all real numbers, even though the examples shown are rational numbers. Challenge students to give some examples using other numbers.

Common Core State Standards

A-CED.A.1 Create equations and inequalities in one variable and use them to solve problems. **Also A-CED.A.4**

MP 1, MP 2, MP 3, MP 4, MP 6

Objectives To solve equations
To solve problems by writing equations

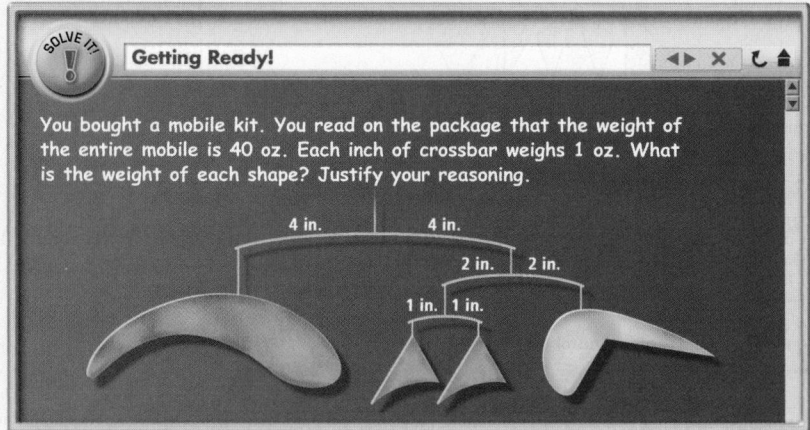

Getting Ready!

You bought a mobile kit. You read on the package that the weight of the entire mobile is 40 oz. Each inch of crossbar weighs 1 oz. What is the weight of each shape? Justify your reasoning.

4 in. 4 in. 2 in. 2 in. 1 in. 1 in.

Lesson Vocabulary
- equation
- solution of an equation
- inverse operations
- identity
- literal equation

An **equation** is a statement that two expressions are equal. In this lesson you will use equations to model and solve problems.

Essential Understanding You can use the properties of equality and inverse operations to solve equations.

take note

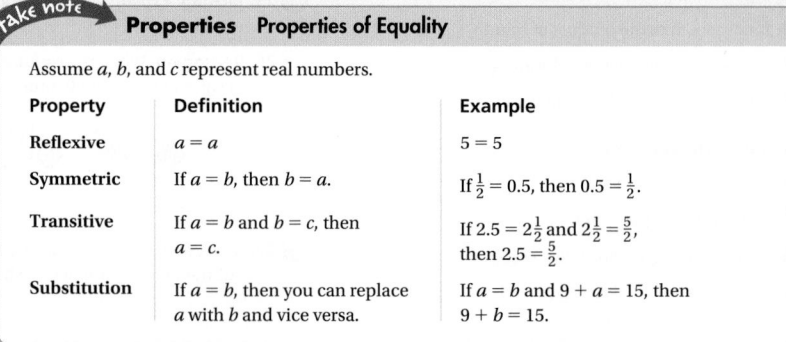

Properties Properties of Equality

Assume a, b, and c represent real numbers.

Property	Definition	Example
Reflexive	$a = a$	$5 = 5$
Symmetric	If $a = b$, then $b = a$.	If $\frac{1}{2} = 0.5$, then $0.5 = \frac{1}{2}$.
Transitive	If $a = b$ and $b = c$, then $a = c$.	If $2.5 = 2\frac{1}{2}$ and $2\frac{1}{2} = \frac{5}{2}$, then $2.5 = \frac{5}{2}$.
Substitution	If $a = b$, then you can replace a with b and vice versa.	If $a = b$ and $9 + a = 15$, then $9 + b = 15$.

BIG idea Solving Equations and Inequalities

ESSENTIAL UNDERSTANDINGS
- Properties of numbers and equality and inverse operations can be used to solve an equation by finding increasingly simpler equations that have the same solution as the original equation.
- Important properties of equality include reflexive, symmetric, transitive, substitution, addition, subtraction, multiplication and division.

Math Background

All of the one-variable equations in this lesson are linear (first degree) equations. Usually if a one-variable linear equation has a solution, then it has exactly one real solution. One-variable equations of higher degrees can have more than one real solution.

An identity is an equation that is true for all permissible values of the variable(s). Consider:

1. $x + 5 = x + 8 - 3$

2. $x + \dfrac{x}{x-3} = \dfrac{x^2 - 2x}{x-3}$

3. $(x + y)(x - y) = x^2 - y^2$

The first and third statements are identities, but the second is not. The second statement is true for all values of x except 3. Three is not in the domain since it makes the equation undefined.

Mathematical Practices

Reason abstractly and quantitatively. Students will flexibly use the four basic operations (addition, subtraction, multiplication, and division) to solve algebraic expressions.

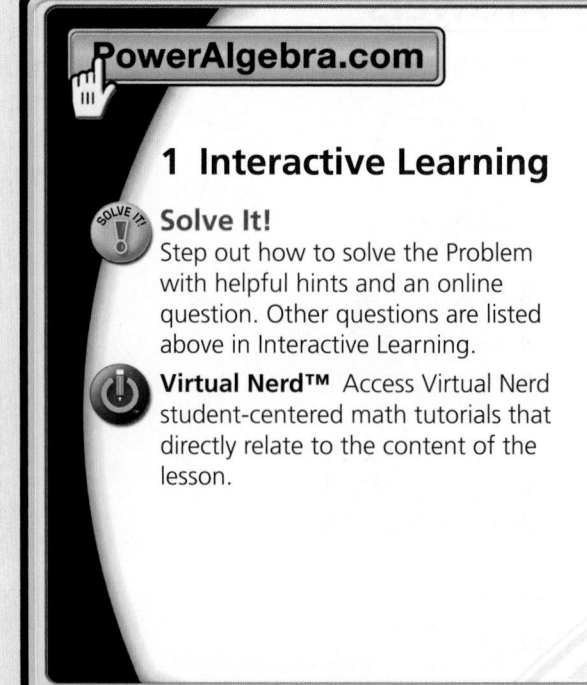

PowerAlgebra.com

1 Interactive Learning

Solve It!
Step out how to solve the Problem with helpful hints and an online question. Other questions are listed above in Interactive Learning.

Virtual Nerd™ Access Virtual Nerd student-centered math tutorials that directly relate to the content of the lesson.

Properties Properties of Equality, Continued

Assume a, b, and c represent real numbers.

Property	Definition	Example
Addition	If $a = b$, then $a + c = b + c$.	If $x = 12$, then $x + 3 = 12 + 3$.
Subtraction	If $a = b$, then $a - c = b - c$.	If $x = 12$, then $x - 3 = 12 - 3$.
Multiplication	If $a = b$, then $a \cdot c = b \cdot c$.	If $x = 12$, then $x \cdot 3 = 12 \cdot 3$.
Division	If $a = b$, then $a \div c = b \div c$ (with $c \neq 0$).	If $x = 12$, then $x \div 3 = 12 \div 3$.

Solving an equation that contains a variable means finding all values of the variable that make the equation true. Such a value is a **solution of the equation**. To find a solution, isolate the variable on one side of the equation using *inverse operations*.

Inverse operations are operations that "undo" each other. Addition and subtraction have this inverse relationship, as do multiplication and division.

Problem 1 Solving a One-Step Equation

What is the solution of $x + 4 = -12$?

> Subtraction is the inverse operation of addition, so subtract 4 from each side.

$$x + 4 = -12$$
$$x + 4 - 4 = -12 - 4 \quad \text{Subtraction Property of Equality}$$
$$x = -16 \quad \text{Simplify.}$$

Check $-16 + 4 \overset{?}{=} -12$

$$-12 = -12 ✔$$

Plan

How can you isolate the variable?
To isolate the variable, you have to remove the +4 from the left side of the equation.

Got It? 1. What is the solution of $12b = 18$?

Problem 2 Solving a Multi-Step Equation

What is the solution of $-27 + 6y = 3(y - 3)$?

$$-27 + 6y = 3(y - 3)$$
$$-27 + 6y = 3y - 9 \quad \text{Distributive Property}$$
$$6y = 3y + 18 \quad \text{Add 27 to each side.}$$
$$3y = 18 \quad \text{Subtract } 3y \text{ from each side.}$$
$$y = 6 \quad \text{Divide each side by 3.}$$

GRIDDED RESPONSE

Plan

How do you solve an equation with the variable on both sides?
Choose a side for the variable and remove it from the other side.

Got It? 2. What is the solution of $3(2x - 1) - 2(3x + 4) = 11x$?

PowerAlgebra.com | **Lesson 1-4** Solving Equations | 27

Problem 1

Q Why do you subtract 4 from the left and right sides of the equation? **[The left side indicates that 4 is added to x. The inverse operation of addition is subtraction, so subtract 4 to undo the addition, isolating x on the left side. Subtract 4 from the right side by the Subtraction Property of Equality.]**

Got It? ERROR PREVENTION

Watch for $18 - 12$. Accept the answer in simplified fraction form, simplified mixed number form, or decimal form.

Q How do you isolate the variable? **[Divide both sides by 12.]**

Problem 2

Students use the Distributive Property to remove parentheses before isolating the variable on one side.

Q What property do you apply when you add 27 to each side? **[Addition Property of Equality]**

Q What property do you apply when you subtract $3y$ from each side? **[Subtraction Property of Equality]**

Q What property do you apply when you divide each side by 3? **[Division Property of Equality]**

Got It? ERROR PREVENTION

Watch for the incorrect distribution of -2 on the left side of the equation.

---

2 Guided Instruction

 Each Problem is worked out and supported online.

Problem 1
Solving a One-Step Equation

Problem 2
Solving a Multi-Step Equation
Animated

Problem 3
Using an Equation to Solve a Problem
Animated

Problem 4
Equations with No Solutions and Identities

Problem 5
Solving a Literal Equation
Animated

Support in Algebra 2 Companion
- Vocabulary
- Key Concepts
- Got It?

Answers

Solve It!

The orange shape weighs 16 oz, yellow shape weighs 6 oz, and each green shape weighs 2 oz. When you add the weight of the shapes and the crossbars, you have 20 oz on each side of the mobile.

Got It?

1. $\frac{3}{2}$

2. -1

Problem 3

Q What does the picture tell you about the ratio of length to width of the flower carpet? **[The carpet is three times as long as it is wide; the ratio of length to width is 3:1.]**

Q Could you determine the dimensions if you did not know this ratio? Explain. **[No; answers may vary. Sample: There are many different possible lengths and widths of a rectangle whose perimeter is 200.]**

Q How can you check that the final answer is correct? **[Answers may vary. Sample: Two times the width plus two times the length equals the perimeter: 2(25) + 2(75) = 200.]**

Got It?

Q What is the only difference between this question and the one in Problem 3? **[The perimeter is 320 meters instead of 200 meters.]**

Q How does that difference affect the answer? How will it still be the same? **[The length and width of this carpet are greater than the carpet in Problem 3. The ratio of length to width is still 3:1.]**

Problem 3 Using an Equation to Solve a Problem

Flowers "Flower carpets" incorporate hundreds of thousands of brightly-colored flowers as well as grass, tree bark, and sometimes fountains to form intricate designs and motifs. The flower carpet shown here, from Grand Place in Brussels, Belgium, has a perimeter of 200 meters. What are the dimensions of the flower carpet?

Plan

How can you relate the dimensions to the perimeter?
Use the formula for the perimeter of a rectangle.

Relate 2 · width plus 2 · length equals perimeter

Define Let x = the width.

Then $3x$ = the length.

Write 2 · x + 2 · $3x$ = 200

$2x + 2 \cdot 3x = 200$

$2x + 6x = 200$ Multiply.

$8x = 200$ Combine like terms.

$\frac{8x}{8} = \frac{200}{8}$ Divide each side by 8.

$x = 25$ Simplify.

Find the length: $3x = 3 \cdot 25 = 75$.

The width is 25 meters. The length is 75 meters.

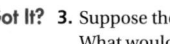 **Got It? 3.** Suppose the flower carpet from Problem 3 had a perimeter of 320 meters. What would the dimensions of the flower carpet be?

An equation does not always have one solution. An equation has no solution if no value of the variable makes the equation true. An equation that is true for every value of the variable is an **identity**.

Additional Problems

1. What is the solution of $x - 8 = -10$?

ANSWER $x = -2$

2. What does y equal in $-2(y - 1) = -16 + y$?

ANSWER $y = 6$

3. The map shows distances between towns in miles. You and your friend drive together from Newtown to Essex. You drive first, for a total of 40 miles. Then your friend drives 1.5 hours, reaching Essex. What is your friend's average rate?

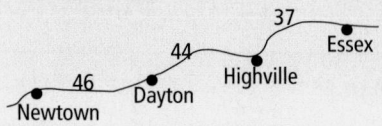

ANSWER 58 miles per hour

4. Is the equation *sometimes*, *always*, or *never* true?

a. $1 + 5x - 6 = 6x - 5 - x$

b. $-x + 2(5x - 1) = 2(3x + 4) + x$

ANSWER

a. always true

b. sometimes true

5. If $1000 is in a bank account earning 5% simple interest, the dollar value of the account A in t years is given by $A = 1000(1 + 0.05t)$. What is t in terms of A?

ANSWER $t = \frac{1}{50}A - 20$

Answers

Got It? (continued)

3. 40 m × 120 m

Essential Understanding Sometimes, no value of the variable makes an equation true. For identities, all values of the variable make the equation true.

Think

What does it mean for an equation to be sometimes true?
An equation is sometimes true if it is true for some, but not all, values of the variable.

© **Problem 4** Equations With No Solution and Identities

Is the equation *always*, *sometimes*, or *never* true?

Ⓐ $11 + 3x - 7 = 6x + 5 - 3x$

$$4 + 3x = 3x + 5$$

$$4 = 5 \quad \boxed{\text{Never true!}}$$

The last equation is not true, so no value of x makes the first two equations true. The original equation has no solution. It is never true.

Ⓑ $6x + 5 - 2x = 4 + 4x + 1$

$$4x + 5 = 4x + 5$$

$$4x = 4x$$

$$0 = 0 ✔ \quad \boxed{\text{Always true!}}$$

The last equation is true, so any value of x makes the first three equations true. The original equation is always true. It is an identity.

Got It? **4.** Is the equation *always*, *sometimes*, or *never* true?

   a. $7x + 6 - 4x = 12 + 3x - 8$ **b.** $2x + 3(x - 4) = 2(2x - 6) + x$

A **literal equation** is an equation that uses at least two different letters as variables. You can solve a literal equation for any one of its variables by using the properties of equality. You solve for a variable "in terms of" the other variables.

© **Problem 5** Solving a Literal Equation

The equation $C = \frac{5}{9}(F - 32)$ relates temperatures in degrees Fahrenheit F and degrees Celsius C. What is F in terms of C?

Plan

How do you solve a literal equation for one of its variables?
Use inverse operations to isolate the indicated variable.

$$C = \frac{5}{9}(F - 32)$$

$$\frac{9}{5}C = F - 32 \qquad \text{Multiply each side by } \frac{9}{5}.$$

$$\frac{9}{5}C + 32 = F \qquad \text{Add 32 to each side.}$$

$$F = \frac{9}{5}C + 32 \qquad \text{Symmetric Property}$$

© **Got It?** **5. a.** The equation $K = C + 273$ relates temperatures kelvins K and degrees Celsius C. What is C in terms of K?

      b. Reasoning Is the equation relating temperatures in kelvins and degrees Celsius *always*, *sometimes*, or *never* true? Explain your answer.

Problem 4

In 4A, each new equation is equivalent to the previous one. If the last equation in the solving process is false, then all equations in the process are false. Equations with the same solution set are called equivalent equations.

Got It?

> **Q** In 4b, what property is used to remove parentheses? **[Distributive Property for Subtraction]**

Problem 5

> **Q** This solution method did not use the Distributive Property to remove parentheses. Why? **[Answers may vary. Sample: You want to solve for F, not $\frac{5}{9}F$.]**

Here is an alternate solution method.

$$C = \frac{5}{9}(F - 32) \qquad C = \frac{5}{9}F - \frac{160}{9}$$

$$C + \frac{160}{9} = \frac{5}{9}F$$

$$\frac{9}{5}\left(C + \frac{160}{9}\right) = \frac{9}{5} \cdot \frac{5}{9}F$$

$$\frac{9}{5}C + 32 = F$$

> **Q** Which method do you prefer? Why? **[Answers may vary. Sample: The first method; it is shorter, so there are fewer chances to make errors.]**

Got It?

> **Q** What operation is applied to C? **[Addition; C is added to 273.]**

Answers

4. a. never

  b. always

5. a. $C = K - 273$

  b. always

PowerAlgebra.com

3 Lesson Check

For a digital lesson check, use the Got It questions.

Support in Algebra 2 Companion
• Lesson Check

4 Practice

Assign homework to individual students or to an entire class.

3 Lesson Check

Do you know HOW? ERROR INTERVENTION

- Exercises 4–6 are literal equations. Ask students to restate the direction line to match the style in Problem 5. For example, for Exercise 4, ask: What is k in terms of r?
- If students have trouble with Exercise 6, remind them that to undo multiplication by -2, divide by -2, which is the same as multiplying by $-\frac{1}{2}$. Distribute $-\frac{1}{2}$ on the right side.

Do you UNDERSTAND?

- In Exercise 8, if students do not understand what 4.3 buses means, ask them whether 4 buses is enough. It is not, so you need 5 buses; the .3 means that the fifth bus would only be partly filled.

Close

> **Q** How is solving a literal equation like solving an equation containing one variable? **[Answers may vary. Sample: In both cases, you need to isolate a variable on one side of the equation.]**

 Lesson Check

Do you know HOW?

Solve each equation.

1. $w - 15 = 8.2$

2. $\frac{x}{3} = -30$

3. $2y - 1 = y + 11$

Solve each equation for k.

4. $r - 2k = 15$

5. $6k - 2z = 12$

6. $4k + h = -2k - 14$

Do you UNDERSTAND?  MATHEMATICAL PRACTICES

 7. **Vocabulary** Explain what it means to find a solution of an equation.

8. **Reasoning** Suppose you solve an equation and find that your school needs 4.3 buses for a class trip. Explain how to interpret this solution.

9. **Error Analysis** Find the error(s) in the steps shown.

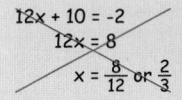

$$12x + 10 = -2$$
$$12x = 8$$
$$x = \frac{8}{12} \text{ or } \frac{2}{3}$$

Practice and Problem-Solving Exercises  MATHEMATICAL PRACTICES

A **Practice**

Solve each equation. ◆ See Problem 1.

10. $h - 12 = 6$

11. $-\frac{x}{3} = 27$

12. $4t = 48$

13. $22 + r = 36$

Solve each equation. Check your answer. ◆ See Problem 2.

14. $7w + 2 = 3w + 94$

15. $15 - g = 23 - 2g$

16. $43 - 3d = d + 9$

17. $5y + 1.8 = 4y - 3.2$

18. $6a - 5 = 4a + 2$

19. $7y + 4 = 3 - 2y$

20. $5c - 9 = 8 - 2c$

21. $4y - 8 - 2y + 5 = 0$

22. $6(n - 4) = 3n$

23. $2 - 3(x + 4) = 8$

24. $5(2 - g) = 0$

25. $2(x + 4) = 8$

Write an equation to solve each problem. ◆ See Problem 3.

26. **Bus Travel** Two buses leave Houston at the same time and travel in opposite directions. One bus averages 55 mi/h and the other bus averages 45 mi/h. When will they be 400 mi apart?

27. **Aviation** Two planes left an airport at noon. One flew east and the other flew west at twice the speed. After 3 hours the planes were 2700 mi apart. How fast was each plane flying?

28. **Geometry** The length of a rectangle is 3 cm greater than its width. The perimeter is 24 cm. What are the dimensions of the rectangle?

Determine whether the equation is *always*, *sometimes*, or *never* true. ◆ See Problem 4.

29. $5x + 3 - 2x = 7x + 3$

30. $2(5x + 4) = 10x + 6$

31. $\frac{2}{3}x + 4 = 2x$

32. $6x - 12 + 2x = 3 + 8x - 15$

Answers

Lesson Check

1. 23.2

2. -90

3. 12

4. $K = \frac{1}{2}(r - 15)$

5. $K = \frac{1}{3}(z + 6)$

6. $K = -\left(\frac{1}{6}\right)(h + 14)$

7. To find a solution of an equation means to find the value of the variable that makes the equation true.

8. Four buses are not enough. The number of buses must be a whole number, so round the number of buses to 5.

9. The second line is incorrect; subtract 10 from both sides:
$$12x = -12$$
$$x = -1$$

Practice and Problem-Solving Exercises

10. 18

11. -81

12. 12

13. 14

14. 23

15. 8

16. $\frac{17}{2}$

17. -5

18. $\frac{7}{2}$

19. $-\frac{1}{9}$

20. $\frac{17}{7}$

21. $\frac{3}{2}$

22. 8

23. -6

24. 2

25. 0

26. 4 h

27. 300 mi/h; 600 mi/h

28. width = 4.5 cm, length = 7.5 cm

29. sometimes

30. never

31. sometimes

32. always

Solve each formula for the indicated variable.

See Problem 5.

33. $A = \frac{1}{2}bh$, for h 34. $s = \frac{1}{2}gt^2$, for g 35. $V = lwh$, for w 36. $I = prt$, for r

Solve each equation for x.

37. $ax + bx = c$ 38. $\frac{x}{a} - 5 = b$ 39. $\frac{x-2}{2} = m + n$ 40. $\frac{2}{5}(x + 1) = g$

B Apply   Solve each equation.

41. $0.2(x + 3) - 4(2x - 3) = 0.9$ 42. $12 - 3(2w + 1) = 7w - 3(7 + w)$

43. $(m - 2) - 5 = 8 - 2(m - 4)$ 44. $7(a + 1) - 3a = 5 + 4(2a - 1)$

45. **Think About a Plan** The measures of an angle and its complement differ by 22°. What are the measures of the angles?
   - What is true about the sum of the measures of an angle and its complement?
   - When modeling the problem with an equation, how can you algebraically represent that the two angle measures differ by 22°?

Solve each formula for the indicated variable.

46. $R(r_1 + r_2) = r_1 r_2$, for R 47. $A = \frac{1}{2}h(b_1 + b_2)$, for b_2 48. $S = 2\pi r^2 + 2\pi rh$, for h

49. $h = vt - 5t^2$, for v 50. $v = s^2 + \frac{1}{2}sh$, for h 51. $R(r_1 + r_2) = r_1 r_2$, for r_2

52. **Writing** Suppose you write and solve an equation to determine the amount of money m you have in your bank account after several weeks. You find that $m = -36$. What does this solution mean?

53. **Geometry** The measure of the supplement of an angle is 20° more than three times the measure of the original angle. Find the measures of the angles.

54. Find 4 consecutive odd integers with a sum of 184.

Solve each equation for x.

55. $c(x + 2) - 5 = b(x - 3)$ 56. $a(3tx - 2b) = c(dx - 2)$ 57. $b(5px - 3c) = a(qx - 4)$

58. $\frac{a}{b}(2x - 12) = \frac{c}{d}$ 59. $\frac{3ax}{5} - 4c = \frac{ax}{5}$ 60. $\frac{a-c}{x-a} = m$

Write an equation to solve each problem.

61. **Swimming** A city park is opening a new swimming pool. You can pay a daily entrance fee of \$3 or purchase a membership for the 12-week summer season for \$82 and pay only \$1 per day to swim. How many days would you have to swim to make the membership worthwhile?

STEM 62. **Rocket** The first stage of a rocket burns 28 s longer than the second stage. If the total burning time for both stages is 152 s, how long does each stage burn?

63. **Error Analysis** Your friend says that the equations shown are two ways to write the same formula. Is your friend correct? Explain your answer.

$$s = \frac{n}{n+1} \quad \frac{s}{s-1} = n$$

ASSIGNMENT GUIDE
Basic: 10–40 all, 43–45, 52, 53, 58–62 even
Average: 11–39 odd, 41–63
Advanced: 11–39 odd, 41–65

Mathematical Practices are supported by exercises with red headings. Here are the Practices supported in this lesson:

MP 1: Make Sense of Problems Ex. 45
MP 3: Communicate Ex. 52, 65
MP 3: Construct Arguments Ex. 64
MP 3: Critique the Reasoning of Others Ex. 63
MP 4: Model with Mathematics Ex. 8
MP 6: Attend to Precision Ex. 9

Applications exercises have blue headings. Exercises 28 and 61 support MP 4: Model.

EXERCISE 53: Use the Think About a Plan worksheet in the **Practice and Problem Solving Workbook** (also available in the Teaching Resources in print and online) to further support students' development in becoming independent learners.

HOMEWORK QUICK CHECK
To check students' understanding of key skills and concepts, go over Exercises 27, 37, 45, 53, and 62.

---

33. $h = \frac{2A}{b}$

34. $g = \frac{2s}{t^2}$

35. $w = \frac{V}{\ell h}$

36. $r = \frac{I}{pt}$

37. $x = \frac{c}{a+b}$, $a \neq -b$

38. $x = a(b + 5)$, $a \neq 0$

39. $x = 2(m + n) + 2$

40. $x = \frac{5g}{2} - 1$

41. 1.5

42. 3

43. $\frac{23}{3}$, or $7\frac{2}{3}$

44. $\frac{3}{2}$

45. 34° and 56°

46. $R = \frac{r_1 r_2}{r_1 + r_2}$

47. $b_2 = \frac{2A}{h} - b_1$

48. $h = \frac{S - 2\pi r^2}{2\pi r}$

49. $v = \frac{h + 5t^2}{t}$

50. $h = \frac{2(v - s^2)}{s}$

51. $r_2 = \frac{Rr_1}{r_1 - R}$

52. The account has a balance less than \$0, or you overdrew on the account by \$36.

53. 40°, 140°

54. 43, 45, 47, and 49

55. $x = \frac{3b + 2c - 5}{b - c}$, $b \neq c$

56. $x = \frac{2ab - 2c}{3at - cd}$, $3at \neq cd$

57. $x = \frac{4a - 3bc}{aq - 5bp}$, $5bp \neq aq$

58. $x = \frac{cb}{2da} + 6$, $a, b, d \neq 0$

59. $x = \frac{10c}{a}$, $a \neq 0$

60. $x = \frac{a - c}{m} + a$, $m \neq 0$, $x \neq a$

61. Let c = number of swim days; $3c = 82 + c$; 41 days

62. Let s = burning time for second stage; $s + 28 + s = 152$; first stage, 90 s; second stage, 62 s

63. No; $n = \frac{s}{1 - s}$ not $\frac{s}{s - 1}$.

Answers

Practice and Problem-Solving Exercises
(continued)

64. a. Check students' work. Sample: If you solve
$ax - b = c$ for x, you get $x = \frac{b+c}{a}$. Since
b and c are integers, $b + c$ is an integer.
But a is a nonzero integer. So $\frac{b+c}{a}$ is the
quotient of two integers and hence, by the
definition of a rational number, $\frac{b+c}{a}$ is a
rational number.

b. Solutions are rational when
$\frac{c-b}{a} \geq 0$, $a \neq 0$, and $\frac{c-b}{a}$ is a square of
a rational number.

65. about 269.4 ft

 Challenge   **64.** Assume that a, b, and c are integers and $a \neq 0$.
   a. Proof Prove that the solution of the linear equation $ax - b = c$ must be
   a rational number.
    **b. Writing** Describe the values of a, b, and c for which the solutions of
   $ax^2 + b = c$ are rational.

65. A tortoise crawling at a rate of 0.1 mi/h passes a resting hare. The hare wants to rest
another 30 min before chasing the tortoise at a rate of 5 mi/h. How many feet must
the hare run to catch the tortoise?

Apply What You've Learned

MATHEMATICAL PRACTICES
MP 4

Look back at the information on page 3 about Mia helping her friend Cody after
Cody's car runs out of gas. In the Apply What You've Learned in Lesson 1-2, you
thought about the possible locations of Cody's car when it runs out of gas.

Suppose Cody runs out of gas between the gas station and the restaurant. Let
x represent the distance between Cody's car and the gas station. Choose from
the following numbers and expressions to complete the equation below. The
equation represents the relationship among the distances Mia drives.

9	11	20	34
$2x$	x	$9 + x$	$x - 9$
$9 - x$	$x + 11$	$x - 11$	$11 - x$

a. __?__ + **b.** __?__ + **c.** __?__ = **d.** __?__

from Mia's house to Cody's car

from Cody's car to gas station, then back to Cody's car

from Cody's car to the restaurant

total distance Mia drives

Apply What You've Learned
In the Apply What You've Learned
for Lessons 1-2 and 1-3, students
considered two cases for where Cody is
when his car runs out of gas, as described
on page 3. Now, they write an equation
that represents one of the two cases.

 Mathematical Practices
Students write an equation to **model**
the relationship among the distances
Mia drives if Cody's car runs out of
gas between the gas station and the
restaurant. (MP 4)

ANSWERS
a. $9 + x$
b. $2x$
c. $11 - x$
d. 34

1-4 Lesson Resources

Additional Instructional Support

Algebra 2 Companion

Students can use the **Algebra 2 Companion** worktext (4 pages) as you teach the lesson. Use the Companion to support

- New Vocabulary
- Key Concepts
- Got It for each Problem
- Lesson Check

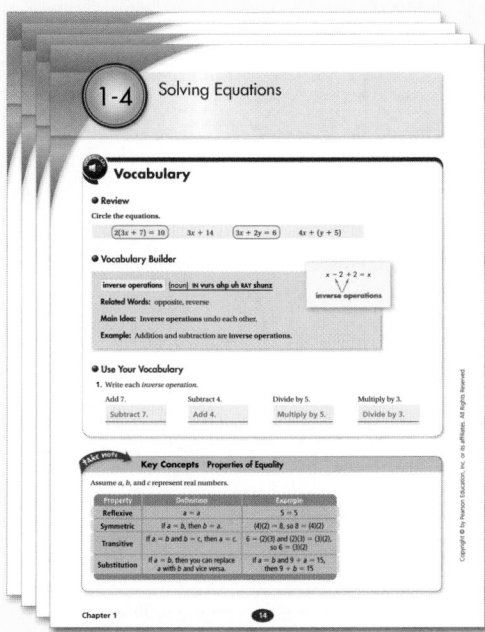

ELL Support

Use Role Playing Have groups of eight to ten students play the roles of the parts of an expression. Students can play the role of a coefficient, variable, exponent, or operator. For instance, a student might be the coefficient 8 in the expression $3x - 8y^2$. Have students first act out their expression by standing in the correct order and saying their parts and then explain how their role as a coefficient, variable, exponent, or operator changes the expression.

Next, have students keep the same roles but form new groups acting out new expressions.

5 Assess & Remediate

Lesson Quiz

1. What is the solution of $6x = 15$?
2. What does n equal in $6(2n - 3) - 2(6n + 1) = 10n$?
3. **Do you UNDERSTAND?** You manage a coffee shop. You begin the day with 25 pounds of coffee beans. You use 4 pounds of beans to brew coffee and sell 20 equal-weight bags of beans. At the end of the day you have 6 pounds of beans left. What is the weight of each bag of beans you sell?
4. Is the equation *sometimes*, *always*, or *never* true?
   a. $15 + 2x - 4 = 9x + 11 - 7x$
   b. $2x + 3(4x - 1) = 2(5x + 3) + 4x$
5. The equation $V = \frac{1}{3}\pi r^2 h$ relates the volume V, the radius r, and the height h of a cone. Write h in terms of V and r.

ANSWERS TO LESSON QUIZ

1. $x = 2.5$
2. $n = -2$
3. 0.75 pound
4. a. always true   b. never true
5. $h = \dfrac{3V}{\pi r^2}$

PRESCRIPTION FOR REMEDIATION
Use the student work on the Lesson Quiz to prescribe a differentiated review assignment:

Points	Differentiated Remediation
0–2	Intervention
3–4	On-level
5	Extension

PowerAlgebra.com

5 Assess & Remediate

Assign the Lesson Quiz. Appropriate intervention, practice, or enrichment is automatically generated based on student performance.

Differentiated Remediation
Available in editable format online.

Intervention

- **Reteaching** (2 pages) Provides reteaching and practice exercises for the key lesson concepts. Use with struggling students or absent students.
- **English Language Learner Support** Helps students develop and reinforce mathematical vocabulary and key concepts.

All-in-One Resources/Online
Reteaching

All-in-One Resources/Online
English Language Learner Support

Differentiated Remediation *continued*

Available in editable format online.

On-Level

- **Practice** (2 pages) Provides extra practice for each lesson. For simpler practice exercises, use the Form K Practice pages found in the All-in-One Teaching Resources and online.

- **Think About a Plan** Helps students develop specific problem-solving skills and strategies by providing scaffolded guiding questions.

- **Standardized Test Prep** Focuses on all major exercises, all major question types, and helps students prepare for the high-stakes assessments.

Extension

- **Enrichment** Provides students with interesting problems and activities that extend the concepts of the lesson.

- **Activities, Games, and Puzzles** Worksheets that can be used for concepts development, enrichment, and for fun!

Practice and Problem Solving Wkbk/All-in-One Resources/Online
Practice page 1

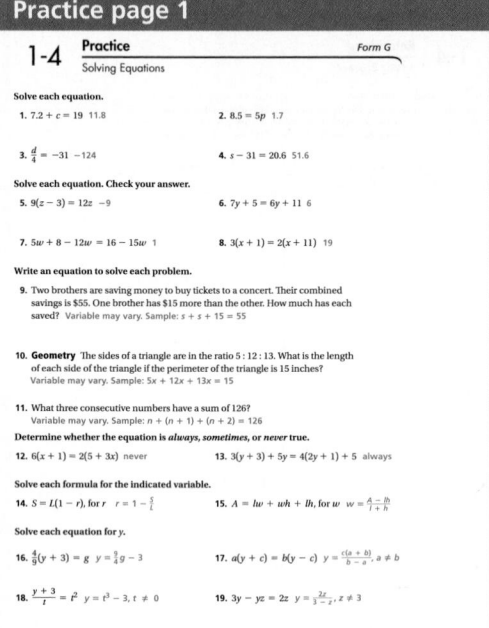

1-4 Practice — Form G
Solving Equations

Solve each equation.

1. $7.2 + c = 19$ 11.8
2. $8.5 = 5p$ 1.7
3. $\frac{d}{4} = -31$ −124
4. $s - 31 = 20.6$ 51.6

Solve each equation. Check your answer.

5. $9(z - 3) = 12z$ −9
6. $7y + 5 = 6y + 11$ 6
7. $5w + 8 - 12w = 16 - 15w$ 1
8. $3(x + 1) = 2(x + 11)$ 19

Write an equation to solve each problem.

9. Two brothers are saving money to buy tickets to a concert. Their combined savings is $55. One brother has $15 more than the other. How much has each saved? Variable may vary. Sample: $s + s + 15 = 55$
10. **Geometry** The sides of a triangle are in the ratio 5 : 12 : 13. What is the length of each side of the triangle if the perimeter of the triangle is 15 inches? Variable may vary. Sample: $5x + 12x + 13x = 15$
11. What three consecutive numbers have a sum of 126? Variable may vary. Sample: $n + (n + 1) + (n + 2) = 126$

Determine whether the equation is *always, sometimes,* or *never* true.

12. $6(x + 1) = 2(5 + 3x)$ never
13. $3(y + 3) + 5y = 4(2y + 1) + 5$ always

Solve each formula for the indicated variable.

14. $S = L(1 - r)$, for r $r = 1 - \frac{S}{L}$
15. $A = lw + wh + lh$, for w $w = \frac{A - lh}{l + h}$

Solve each equation for y.

16. $\frac{4}{9}(y + 3) = g$ $y = \frac{9}{4}g - 3$
17. $a(y + c) = b(y - c)$ $y = \frac{c(a + b)}{b - a}, a \neq b$
18. $\frac{y + 3}{t} = t^2$ $y = t^3 - 3, t \neq 0$
19. $3y - yz = 2z$ $y = \frac{2z}{3 - z}, z \neq 3$

Practice and Problem Solving Wkbk/All-in-One Resources/Online
Think About a Plan

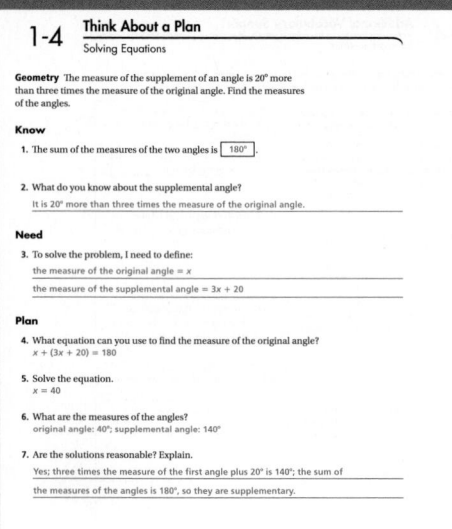

1-4 Think About a Plan
Solving Equations

Geometry The measure of the supplement of an angle is 20° more than three times the measure of the original angle. Find the measures of the angles.

Know

1. The sum of the measures of the two angles is [180°]

2. What do you know about the supplemental angle?
   It is 20° more than three times the measure of the original angle.

Need

3. To solve the problem, I need to define:
   the measure of the original angle = x
   the measure of the supplemental angle = $3x + 20$

Plan

4. What equation can you use to find the measure of the original angle?
   $x + (3x + 20) = 180$

5. Solve the equation.
   $x = 40$

6. What are the measures of the angles?
   original angle: 40°; supplemental angle: 140°

7. Are the solutions reasonable? Explain.
   Yes; three times the measure of the first angle plus 20° is 140°; the sum of the measures of the angles is 180°, so they are supplementary.

Practice and Problem Solving Wkbk/All-in-One Resources/Online
Practice page 2

1-4 Practice *(continued)* — Form G
Solving Equations

Solve each equation.

20. $0.5(x - 3) + (1.5 - x) = 5x$ 0
21. $1.2(x + 5) = 1.6(2x + 5)$ −1
22. $0.5(c + 2.8) - c = 0.6c + 0.3$ 1
23. $\frac{u}{5} + \frac{u}{10} - \frac{u}{6} = 1$ $1\frac{1}{2}$

Solve each formula for the indicated variable.

24. $V = \frac{\pi}{3}r^2h$, for h $h = \frac{3V}{\pi r^2}$
25. $D = kA\left[\frac{T_2 - T_1}{L}\right]$ for T_1 $T_1 = T_2 - \frac{DL}{kA}$

Write an equation to solve each problem.

26. Two trains left a station at the same time. One traveled north at a certain speed and the other traveled south at twice that speed. After 4 hours, the trains were 600 miles apart. How fast was each train traveling? Variable may vary. Sample: $4r + 4(2r) = 600$
27. **Geometry** The sides of one cube are twice as long as the sides of a second cube. What is the side length of each cube if the total volume of the cubes is 72 cm³? Variable may vary. Sample: $s^3 + (2s)^3 = 72$

28. **Error Analysis** Brenna solved an equation for m. Do you agree with her? Explain your answer.
   No; there is an m on both sides of the equation; the correct result should be $m = \frac{Mv_2}{v_1 - v_2}$

$Mv_1 = (m + M)v_2$
$\frac{Mv_1}{m} = Mv_2$

Solve each problem.

29. You and your friend left a bus terminal at the same time and traveled in opposite directions. Your bus was in heavy traffic and had to travel 20 miles per hour slower than your friend's bus. After 3 hours, the buses were 270 miles apart. How fast was each bus going? Your bus: 35 mi/h; Your friend's bus: 55 mi/h
30. **Geometry** The length of a rectangle is 5 centimeters greater than its width. The perimeter is 58 centimeters. What are the dimensions of the rectangle? $w = 12$ cm, $l = 17$ cm
31. What four consecutive odd integers have a sum of 336? 81, 83, 85, 87

Practice and Problem Solving Wkbk/All-in-One Resources/Online
Standardized Test Prep

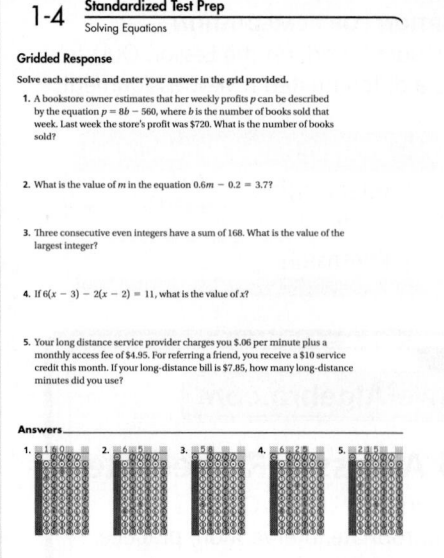

1-4 Standardized Test Prep
Solving Equations

Gridded Response

Solve each exercise and enter your answer in the grid provided.

1. A bookstore owner estimates that her weekly profits p can be described by the equation $p = 8b - 560$, where b is the number of books sold that week. Last week the store's profit was $720. What is the number of books sold?

2. What is the value of m in the equation $0.6m - 0.2 = 3.7$?

3. Three consecutive even integers have a sum of 168. What is the value of the largest integer?

4. If $6(x - 3) - 2(x - 2) = 11$, what is the value of x?

5. Your long distance service provider charges you $.06 per minute plus a monthly access fee of $4.95. For referring a friend, you receive a $10 service credit this month. If your long-distance bill is $7.85, how many long-distance minutes did you use?

Answers

1. 180   2.   3.   4.   5.

All-in-One Resources/Online
Enrichment

1-4 Enrichment
Solving Equations

Equations can be subdivided into three distinct types:

a. **conditional equations,** or equations that are true for some values of x. For example, the equation $x + 1 = 0$ is true only for $x = -1$.

b. **identities,** for which every possible value of the variable belongs to the solution set. For example, the equation $x = x$ is an identity, as it is true for all values of x.

c. **impossibilities,** for which no possible values of the variable belong to the solution set. For example, the equation $x = x + 1$ is an impossibility, as it is never true.

For each of the following equations, find the solution if it is a conditional equation, or classify the equation as an *identity* or an *impossibility*.

1. $x + (2x - 4) = 11$ 5
2. $x = x + 2$ impossibility
3. $x + (2x - 1) = 3x - 1$ identity
4. $x = (2 + 2x) - x$ impossibility
5. $(x - 2) + (2x + 4) = x$ −1
6. $x + 2 = x + 3$ impossibility
7. $2x = 3x$ 0
8. $2x + 8 = 6 - x$ $-\frac{2}{3}$
9. $2x - 4 + 3x = 8x - 5$ $\frac{1}{3}$
10. $2x + 5 = 5 + 2x$ identity
11. $2(x + 3) = 5x - (3x - 6)$ identity
12. $x + 3(x + 3) = 3(x - 3)$ −18
13. $(x + 3) + (x - 3) = 3$ $\frac{3}{2}$
14. $(x + 3) - (x - 3) = 3$ impossibility
15. $2(x + 5) - 4 = 3(x + 2) - 1$ 1
16. $1 - (x - 5) = 3 - (x - 5)$ impossibility
17. $4(x - 1) + 3 = 4x - (x + 1)$ 0

Online Teacher Resource Center
Activities, Games, and Puzzles

1-4 Game: Solve That Equation
Solving Equations

Provide the host with the following questions and answers. The host keeps score in the columns on the right.

		Player 1	Player 2
		100	100
	Properties of Equality		
1.	Name this property: $a = a$ Answer: Reflexive Property		
2.	Name this property: If $a = b$, then $a - c = b - c$. Answer: Subtraction Property of Equality		
3.	Name this property: If $a = b$ and $b = c$, then $a = c$. Answer: Transitive Property of Equality		
4.	Name this property: If $a = b$, then you can replace a with b and vice versa. Answer: Substitution Property		
	Solve a Multi-Step Equation		
5.	Solve $3x - 2 = 2(4 - x)$. Answer: $x = 2$		
6.	Solve $3x - 1 = (8 - 2x)$. Answer: $x = 3$		
7.	Solve $-9(4 - y) = 2(2y + 2)$. Answer: $y = 8$		
8.	Solve $4(5 - 2y) = 5(-y + 2) - 20$. Answer: $y = 10$		
	Sometimes, Always, or Never		
9.	Is $12(x + 5) - 4x = 2(4x - 30)$ sometimes, always, or never true? Answer: never		
10.	Is $5(-2x + 2) + 7x = (3x - 10)$ sometimes, always, or never true? Answer: always		
11.	Is $12x + 10 - 4x = 6x - 30 + 3x$ sometimes, always, or never true? Answer: sometimes		
12.	Is $5x + 8 - 2x = 2(4x - 5) - 5x$ sometimes, always, or never true? Answer: never		
	Literal Equations		
13.	Solve $ac - 2b = 3a + bc$ for b. Answer: $b = \frac{ac - 3a}{c + 2}$		
14.	Solve $ac - 3b = 2a + bc$ for c. Answer: $c = \frac{2a + 3b}{a - b}$		
15.	Solve $a + b = ab + 2ac$ for a. Answer: $a = \frac{b}{b + 2c - 1}$		
16.	Solve $3ab + b = a + bc$ for b. Answer: $b = \frac{a}{3a - c + 1}$		

1-5 Solving Inequalities

© **Common Core State Standards**
A-CED.A.1 Create equations and inequalities in one variable and use them to solve problems.
MP 1, MP 3, MP 4, MP 7

Objectives To solve and graph inequalities
To write and solve compound inequalities

Does your answer make sense? Check it using a different method.

© MATHEMATICAL **PRACTICES**

Getting Ready!

You want to download some new songs on your MP3 player. Each song will use about 4.3 MB of space. The amount of storage space on your MP3 player is shown at the right. At most how many songs can you download? Explain. (Hint: 1 GB = 1000 MB)

7.8 GB free of 19.5 GB

Words like "at most" and "at least" suggest a relationship in which two quantities may not be equal. You can represent such a relationship with a mathematical inequality.

Essential Understanding Just as you use properties of equality to solve equations, you can use properties of inequality to solve inequalities.

Lesson Vocabulary
• compound inequality

take note

Key Concept   Writing and Graphing Inequalities

Inequality	Word Sentence	Graph
$x > 4$	x is greater than 4.	open dot at 4, arrow right; -1 0 1 2 3 4 5
$x \geq 4$	x is greater than or equal to 4.	closed dot at 4, arrow right; -1 0 1 2 3 4 5
$x < 4$	x is less than 4.	open dot at 4, arrow left; -1 0 1 2 3 4 5
$x \leq 4$	x is less than or equal to 4.	closed dot at 4, arrow left; -1 0 1 2 3 4 5

In the graphs above, the point at 4 is a boundary point because it separates the graph of the inequality from the rest of the number line. An open dot at 4 means that 4 *is not* a solution. A closed dot at 4 means that 4 *is* a solution.

---

1 Interactive Learning

Solve It!

PURPOSE To distinguish between situations that involve equations and those that involve inequalities
PROCESS Students may
• multiply 7.8 by 1000 to find the number of available MB and then divide by 4.3.
• solve $4.3x = 7800$ and then use context to round to the nearest whole number.

FACILITATE

Q Why is it necessary to know 1 GB = 1000 MB? **[The songs are given in MB; the space is given in GB.]**

Q How many MB of space are available? **[7800]**

Q Does $\frac{7800}{4.3}$ give you the answer? Why or why not? **[No; it is not a whole number, and you cannot download part of a song.]**

Q What is the greatest number of songs that can still be downloaded? **[1813 songs]**

ANSWER See Solve It in Answers on next page.
CONNECT THE MATH The context of the Solve It requires students to use the concept of an inequality. The lesson formally introduces writing, solving, and graphing inequalities.

2 Guided Instruction

Take Note   VISUAL LEARNERS
When the variable is on the left of the inequality, the arrow on the graph points the same way as the pointed end of the inequality symbol.

1-5 Preparing to Teach

BIG idea Solving Equations and Inequalities

ESSENTIAL UNDERSTANDINGS

• Just as properties of equality can be used to solve equations, properties of inequality can be used to solve inequalities.
• Properties of numbers and inequality can be used to solve an inequality by finding increasingly simpler inequalities that have the same solution as the original inequality.

Math Background
Students are familiar with the Properties of Equality. In this lesson, they will learn the Properties of Inequality. These properties are closely related.

For example, the Addition Property of Equality states that if $a = b$, then $a + c = b + c$. In the Addition Property of Inequality, the difference is that the equality symbol is replaced with an inequality symbol: If $a < b$, then $a + c < b + c$.

The Multiplication and Division Properties of Equality and the corresponding Properties of Inequality are also related, provided that students multiply or divide by a positive number. When multiplying or dividing by a negative number, students must remember to change the direction of the inequality symbol.

© Mathematical Practices
Make sense of problems and persevere in solving them. Students will write and graph inequalities and explain correspondences between inequalities, verbal descriptions, and simple line graphs.

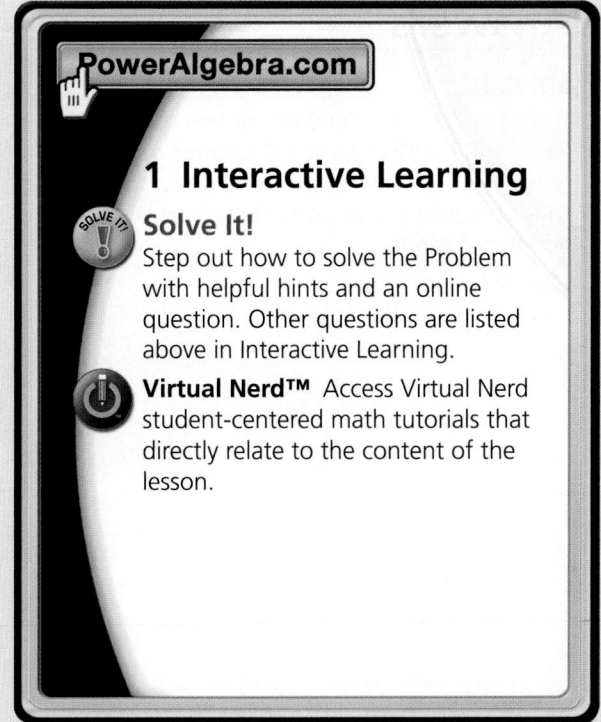

PowerAlgebra.com

1 Interactive Learning

Solve It!
Step out how to solve the Problem with helpful hints and an online question. Other questions are listed above in Interactive Learning.

Virtual Nerd™ Access Virtual Nerd student-centered math tutorials that directly relate to the content of the lesson.

Problem 1 ERROR PREVENTION

Students may use the symbol > instead of ≥. Use the sentence, "You must be at least 18 to vote" to show that 18 is included in the allowable age range.

> **Q** Explain why $5 - x \geq 12$ is incorrect. **[5 fewer than a number means 5 is being subtracted from the number; the expression $5 - x$ means a number is being subtracted from 5.]**

Got It? ERROR PREVENTION

If students write $\frac{3}{x} \leq 15$, remind them that, as with subtraction, the order of division matters: $\frac{3}{45}$ is not the same as $\frac{45}{3}$. The first value stated after the phrase "the quotient of" is the numerator; the second is the denominator.

Take Note

When reading the chart, you may need to remind students that $c < 0$ is just a symbolic way of writing that c is negative.

Here's Why It Works

Sketch a number line with $-2, -1, 0, 1,$ and 2 on it. Remind students that the number to the right of another number is always greater. Therefore, $2 > 1$. Also, $-1 > -2$. If we say the number to the left of another number is the lesser number, then $-2 < -1$. Have students compare this inequality to the first inequality.

Plan

How can you translate a sentence into an inequality?
Look for key words, such as "at least" or "greater than."

 Problem 1 Writing an Inequality From a Sentence

What inequality represents the sentence, "5 fewer than a number is at least 12."?

5 fewer than a number is at least 12.

> "Fewer" indicates subtraction.   "At least" indicates greater than or equal to.

$x - 5 \geq 12$

✓ **Got It?** **1.** What inequality represents the sentence, "The quotient of a number and 3 is no more than 15."?

The solutions of an inequality are the numbers that make it true. The properties you use for solving inequalities are similar to the properties you use for solving equations. However, when you multiply or divide each side of an inequality by a negative number, you must reverse the inequality symbol.

take note

Properties   Properties of Inequalities

Let $a, b, c,$ and d represent real numbers.

Property	Definition	Example
Transitive	If $a > b$ and $b > c$, then $a > c$.	$5 > 3$ and $3 > 1$, so $5 > 1$
Addition	If $a > b$, then $a + c > b + c$.	$4 > 2$, so $4 + 1 > 2 + 1$
Subtraction	If $a > b$, then $a - c > b - c$.	$7 > 4$, so $7 - 3 > 4 - 3$
Multiplication	If $a > b$ and $c > 0$, then $ac > bc$.	$6 > 5$ and $3 > 0$, so $6(3) > 5(3)$
	If $a > b$ and $c < 0$, then $ac < bc$.	$3 > 2$ and $-4 < 0$, so $3(-4) < 2(-4)$
Division	If $a > b$ and $c > 0$, then $\frac{a}{c} > \frac{b}{c}$.	$9 > 3$ and $3 > 0$, so $\frac{9}{3} > \frac{3}{3}$
	If $a > b$ and $c < 0$, then $\frac{a}{c} < \frac{b}{c}$.	$12 > 6$ and $-6 < 0$, so $\frac{12}{-6} < \frac{6}{-6}$

Here's Why It Works The steps below show that if $a > b$, then $-a < -b$. Therefore, you need to reverse the inequality symbol when multiplying each side of the inequality $a > b$ by -1.

$$a > b$$
$$a - b > 0 \quad \text{Subtract } b \text{ from each side.}$$
$$-b - (-a) > 0 \quad a - b = -b + a = -b - (-a).$$
$$-b > -a \quad \text{Add } -a \text{ to each side.}$$
$$-a < -b \quad \text{Rewrite the inequality with } -a \text{ on the left side.}$$

Answers

Solve It!

You have 7.8 GB = 7800 MB of free space. $7800 \div 4.3 = 1813.95$ is the greatest number of songs you can download. Round down to 1813 songs because you can only download a whole number of songs.

Got It?

1. $\frac{x}{3} \leq 15$

PowerAlgebra.com

2 Guided Instruction

Each Problem is worked out and supported online.

Problem 1
Writing an Inequality From a Sentence

Problem 2
Solving and Graphing an Inequality

Problem 3
Using an Inequality
Animated

Problem 4
No Solution or All Real Numbers as Solution
Animated

Problem 5
Solving an *And* Inequality
Animated

Problem 6
Solving an *Or* Inequality

Support in Algebra 2 Companion
• Vocabulary
• Key Concepts
• Got It?

Problem 2 Solving and Graphing an Inequality

Plan

How is solving an inequality like solving an equation?
You isolate the variable by doing the same things to each side of the inequality.

What is the solution of $-3(2x - 5) + 1 \geq 4$? Graph the solution.

$$-3(2x - 5) + 1 \geq 4$$

$-6x + 15 + 1 \geq 4$	Distributive Property
$-6x + 16 \geq 4$	Simplify.
$-6x \geq -12$	Subtraction Property of Inequality
$x \leq 2$	Divide each side by -6. Reverse the inequality symbol.

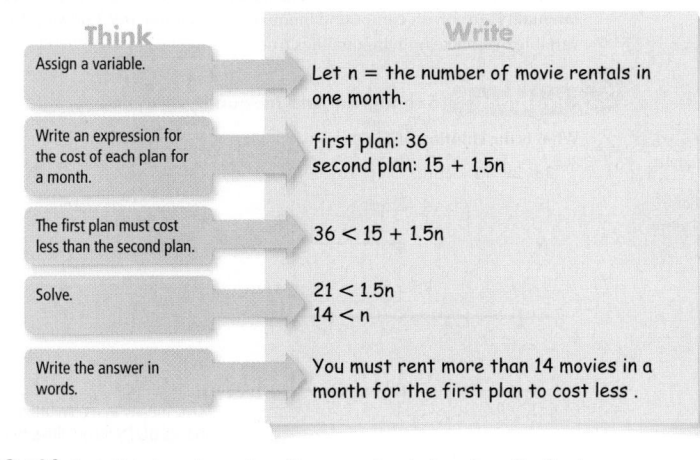

Got It? 2. What is the solution of $-2(x + 9) + 5 \geq 3$? Graph the solution.

Problem 3 Using an Inequality

Plan

How will an inequality help answer this question?
The cost of the first plan must be less than the cost of the second plan, so an inequality can be used to determine the number of movies.

Movie Rentals A movie rental company offers two subscription plans. You can pay $36 a month and rent as many movies as desired, or you can pay $15 a month and $1.50 to rent each movie. How many movies must you rent in a month for the first plan to cost less than the second plan?

Think	Write
Assign a variable.	Let n = the number of movie rentals in one month.
Write an expression for the cost of each plan for a month.	first plan: 36 second plan: $15 + 1.5n$
The first plan must cost less than the second plan.	$36 < 15 + 1.5n$
Solve.	$21 < 1.5n$ $14 < n$
Write the answer in words.	You must rent more than 14 movies in a month for the first plan to cost less.

Got It? 3. A digital music service offers two subscription plans. The first has a $9 membership fee and charges $1 per download. The second has a $25 membership fee and charges $.50 per download. How many songs must you download for the second plan to cost less than the first plan?

Problem 2

When the solution of an inequality is a range of numbers, it is impossible to list them all. There are an infinite number of solutions to $x \leq 2$.

> **Q** Up to which point is the process of finding the solution the same as it would be if the inequality were an equation instead? **[up to the point of dividing both sides by -6]**
>
> **Q** How can you check that you drew the arrow in the correct direction? **[Substitute any point that is shaded, such as 0, for x in the original inequality to see if the statement is true.]**

Got It?

> **Q** Did you have to reverse the direction of the inequality symbol? Why or why not? **[Yes; both sides are divided by a negative number.]**

Problem 3

> **Q** How do you determine whether to use $<$ or $\leq$ in the inequality? **[The problem asks for the number of rentals that make the first plan less than the second, not less than or equal to.]**

Got It?

If a student says 32 downloads, show them that the cost is the same for both plans ($41). For the second plan to cost less, you must download *more* than 32 songs or *at least* 33.

Additional Problems

1. What inequality represents the sentence, "The product of 7 and a number is no more than 50"?

ANSWER $7n \leq 50$

2. What is the solution of $4(x - 7) > -20$? Graph the solution.

ANSWER $x > 2$

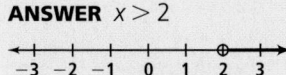

3. Plumber A charges $75 for a service charge and $40 per hour. Plumber B charges $50 per hour but no service charge. How many hours must a plumbing job last for Plumber A to cost less than Plumber B?

ANSWER greater than 7.5 hours

4. Is the inequality sometimes, always, or never true?

a. $3(x + 3) \geq 3(2 + x)$

b. $9 - x - 5 < -x + 4$

ANSWERS

a. always true

b. never true

5. What is the solution of $\frac{a}{2} < 3$ and $-3a + 5 < 8$? Graph the solution.

ANSWER $a < 6$ and $a > -1$

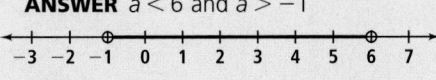

6. What is the solution of $5 - 2m \geq 21$ or $4m - 1 \geq -21$? Graph the solution.

ANSWER $m \leq -8$ or $m \geq -5$

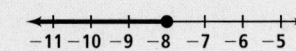

Answers

Got It? (continued)

2. $x \leq -8$

3. more than 32 songs

Problem 4

Q How would you graph the result of 4A? **[Draw a number line. Graph nothing on it.]**

Q How do the last inequalities in 4A and 4B compare? **[Answers may vary. Sample: In simplified form neither inequality contains variables. In both cases, the variable was divided out, leaving either a false (for no solutions) or a true (for all real numbers as solution) numerical statement.]**

Got It?   AUDITORY LEARNERS

After distributing, tell students that 8x represents some number, so the statement can be read as "twelve less than some number is less than eight more than the number."

Problem 5

Any solution to a compound inequality joined by *and* must make both inequalities true. Because 7 < 9 and 12 ≤ 18, 4 makes both inequalities true. However, 7 only makes the first inequality true.

Q Does the fact that there are no arrows on the graph of the solution indicate that there are a finite number of solutions? Explain. **[No; there are an infinite number of rational numbers between 3 and 6, such as 3.1, 3.11, 3.111, etc.]**

Got It?

Q What does the graph of an inequality that is sometimes true look like? **[The solution covers part but not all of a number line.]**

 Problem 4 No Solution or All Real Numbers as Solutions

Is the inequality *always*, *sometimes*, or *never* true?

A $-2(3x + 1) > -6x + 7$

$\qquad -6x - 2 > -6x + 7$ Distributive Property

$\qquad\qquad -2 > 7$ Add 6x to each side.

The last inequality $-2 > 7$ is false, so $-2(3x + 1) > -6x + 7$ is always false. It has no solution, so it is never true.

B $5(2x - 3) - 7x \le 3x + 8$

$\qquad 10x - 15 - 7x \le 3x + 8$ Distributive Property

$\qquad\qquad 3x - 15 \le 3x + 8$ Combine like terms.

$\qquad\qquad\qquad -15 \le 8$ Subtract 3x from each side.

The inequality $-15 \le 8$ is true, so $5(2x - 3) - 7x \le 3x + 8$ is always true. All real numbers are solutions.

Think
How did you determine that an *equation* has no solution?
If you solve an equation and obtain a false statement, then the equation has no solution.

✔ **Got It? 4.** Is $4(2x - 3) < 8(x + 1)$ *always*, *sometimes*, or *never* true?

You can join two inequalities with the word *and* or the word *or* to form a **compound inequality**. To solve a compound inequality containing *and*, find all values of the variable that make both inequalities true.

Think
How do you graph a compound inequality with *and*?
Find the intersection of the solutions of the two inequalities.

 Problem 5 Solving an *And* Inequality

What is the solution of $7 < 2x + 1$ and $3x \le 18$? Graph the solution.

$7 < 2x + 1$ and $3x \le 18$

$3 < x$ and $x \le 6$ Solve each inequality.

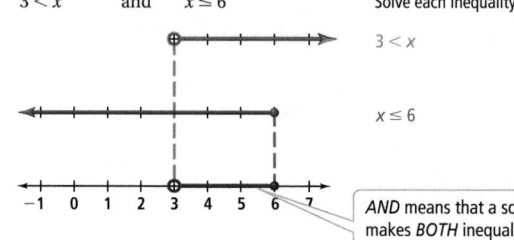

AND means that a solution makes *BOTH* inequalities true.

✔ **Got It? 5. a.** What is the solution of $5 \le 3x - 1$ and $2x < 12$? Graph the solution.
b. Reasoning Is the compound inequality in Problem 5 *always*, *sometimes*, or *never* true? Explain your reasoning.

Answers

Got It? (continued)

4. always

5. a. $x \ge 2$ and $x < 6$

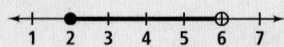

b. sometimes; The compound inequality is true when $x = 5$ and not true when $x = 7$.

You can collapse a compound *and* inequality, like $5 < x + 1$ and $x + 1 < 13$, into a simpler form, $5 < x + 1 < 13$. You read $5 < x + 1 < 13$ as "$x + 1$ is greater than 5 and less than 13."

To solve a compound inequality containing *or*, find all values of the variable that make at least one of the inequalities true.

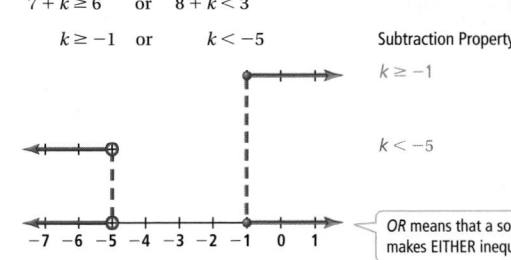

Problem 6 Solving an *Or* Inequality

What is the solution of $7 + k \geq 6$ or $8 + k < 3$? Graph the solution.

$$7 + k \geq 6 \quad \text{or} \quad 8 + k < 3$$

$$k \geq -1 \quad \text{or} \quad k < -5 \qquad \text{Subtraction Property of Inequality}$$

$k \geq -1$

$k < -5$

OR means that a solution makes EITHER inequality true.

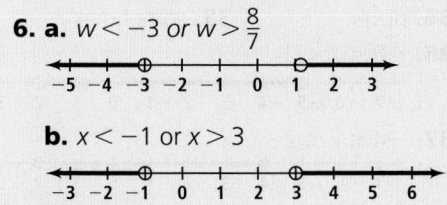 **Got It? 6.** What is the solution of each compound inequality? Graph the solution.
  a. $7w + 3 > 11$ or $4w - 1 < -13$ **b.** $16 < 5x + 1$ or $3x + 9 < 6$

Think

How does the solution to an *or* inequality differ from the solution to an *and* inequality?
The solution to an *or* inequality includes all of the solutions of each inequality, not just the solutions of both inequalities.

Lesson Check

Do you know HOW?

Write an inequality that represents each sentence.

1. Rachel's hair is at least as long as Julia's.

2. The wind speeds of tropical storms are at least 40 mi/h, but less than 74 mi/h.

Solve each inequality. Graph the solution.

3. $-4(3x + 2) \geq 16$

4. $3 < 5x - 2 < 7$

5. $7x - 3 > 18$ or $3x - 2 \leq -2$

Do you UNDERSTAND? MATHEMATICAL PRACTICES

6. Reasoning Make up an example to help explain why you must reverse the inequality symbol when you multiply or divide by a negative number.

7. Compare and Contrast Describe how the properties of inequality are similar to the properties of equality and how they differ.

8. Write an inequality for which the solution is the set of all real numbers.

9. Error Analysis Your classmate says that you cannot write a compound inequality that has no solution. Do you agree? If so, explain why. If not, give a counterexample.

Problem 6

Any solution to a compound inequality joined by *or* will make one or both of the inequalities true. If it makes *neither* inequality true, it is not a solution.

Got It?

Zero is not a solution in either question because it is in the region between the two rays and it makes both equations false.

3 Lesson Check

Do you know HOW?

• In Exercise 2, if students use the wrong inequality symbols, ask them questions such as: Can the wind speeds be 39 mi/h? 40 mi/h? Can the wind speeds be 74 mi/h? 75 mi/h?

Do you UNDERSTAND?

• For Exercise 9, refer to the solutions shown for Problem 6. The region between -5 and -1 does not make either solution true, so changing the *or* to an *and* for the two separate inequalities will result in a compound inequality with no solutions.

Close

Q How are the solutions to a compound inequality joined by *and* different from those joined by *or*? **[Answers may vary. Sample: Solutions to the former must make both individual inequalities true; solutions to the latter must only make at least one of the inequalities true.]**

---

6. a. $w < -3$ or $w > \dfrac{8}{7}$

-5 -4 -3 -2 -1 0 1 2 3

b. $x < -1$ or $x > 3$

-3 -2 -1 0 1 2 3 4 5 6

Lesson Check

1. $R \geq J$

2. $w \geq 40$ and $w < 74$

3. $x \leq -2$

-5 -4 -3 -2 -1 0 1

4. $1 < x < \dfrac{9}{5}$

-2 -1 0 1 2 3 4

5. $x \leq 0$ or $x > 3$

-2 -1 0 1 2 3 4 5

6. Answers may vary. Sample: $5 < 6$, but $-5 > -6$.

7. The transitive, addition and subtraction properties of inequality are similar to the properties of equality. The multiplication and division properties differ. Multiplying or dividing each side of an inequality by a negative number reverses the direction of the inequality symbol.

8. Answers may vary. Sample: $3x + 5 < 3(x + 5)$

9. No; Answers may vary. Sample: $2x < x + 1$ and $x + 1 > 3$

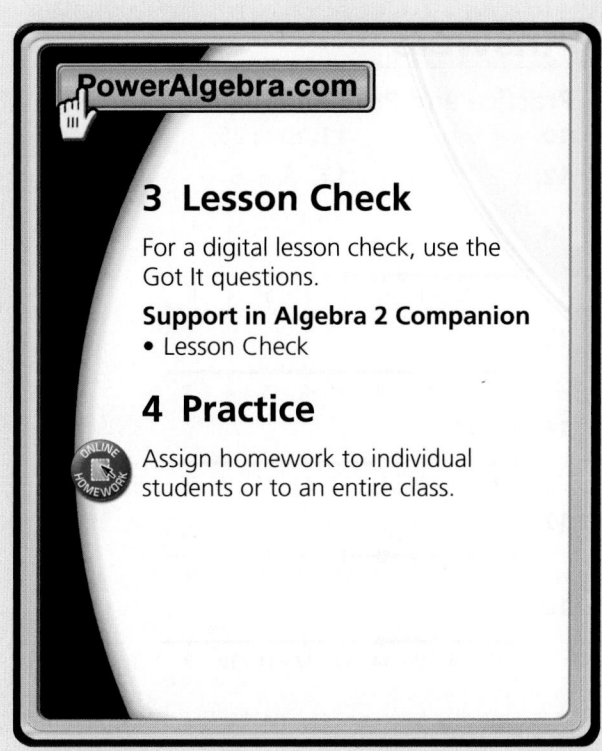

PowerAlgebra.com

3 Lesson Check

For a digital lesson check, use the Got It questions.

Support in Algebra 2 Companion
• Lesson Check

4 Practice

Assign homework to individual students or to an entire class.

4 Practice

ASSIGNMENT GUIDE

Basic: 10–43 all, 44–50 even, 51, 57, 60

Average: 11–43 odd, 44–61

Advanced: 11–43 odd, 44–66

Standardized Test Prep: 67–70

Mixed Review: 71–78

Mathematical Practices are supported by exercises with red headings. Here are the Practices supported in this lesson:

MP 1: Make Sense of Problems Ex. 44
MP 3: Communicate Ex. 7, 54
MP 3: Construct Arguments Ex. 6, 57, 66
MP 3: Critique the Reasoning of Others Ex. 9, 55
MP 7: Use Structure Ex. 62–65

Applications exercises have blue headings. Exercise 53 supports MP 4: Model.

STEM exercises focus on science or engineering applications.

EXERCISE 51: Use the Think About a Plan worksheet in the **Practice and Problem Solving Workbook** (also available in the Teaching Resources in print and online) to further support students' development in becoming independent learners.

HOMEWORK QUICK CHECK

To check students' understanding of key skills and concepts, go over Exercises 23, 39, 44, 51, and 57.

Practice and Problem-Solving Exercises  MATHEMATICAL PRACTICES

Ⓐ Practice Write the inequality that represents the sentence. ◀ See Problem 1.

10. The sum of a number and 5 is less than -7.

11. The product of a number and 8 is at least 25.

12. Six less than a number is greater than 54.

13. The quotient of a number and 12 is no more than 6.

Solve each inequality. Graph the solution. ◀ See Problem 2.

14. $-12 \geq 24x$
15. $-7k < 63$
16. $8a - 15 > 73$
17. $57 - 4t \geq 13$
18. $-18 - 5y \geq 52$
19. $14 - 4y \geq 38$
20. $4(x + 3) \leq 44$
21. $2(m - 3) + 7 < 21$
22. $4(n - 2) - 6 > 18$
23. $-2(w + 4) + 9 < -11$

Solve each problem by writing an inequality. ◀ See Problem 3.

24. The length of a picture frame is 3 in. greater than the width. The perimeter is less than 52 in. Describe the dimensions of the frame.

25. The lengths of the sides of a triangle are in the ratio 5 : 6 : 7. Describe the length of the longest side if the perimeter is less than 54 cm.

26. Find the lesser of two consecutive integers with a sum greater than 16.

27. The cost of a field trip is $220 plus $7 per student. If the school can spend at most $500, how many students can go on the field trip?

Is the inequality *always, sometimes,* or *never* true? ◀ See Problem 4.

28. $9(x + 2) > 9(x - 3)$
29. $6x - 13 < 6(x - 2)$
30. $-6(2x - 10) + 12x \leq 180$
31. $-7(3x - 7) + 21x \geq 50$
32. $3 + 5x < 5(x + 1)$
33. $2(x + 6) < 30$
34. $4x - 8 > 1 + 4(x + 3)$
35. $9x + 2(2 + x) < 5 + 9x$

Solve each compound inequality. Graph the solution. ◀ See Problems 5 and 6.

36. $2x > -10$ and $9x < 18$
37. $3x \geq -12$ and $8x \leq 16$
38. $6x \geq -24$ and $9x < 54$
39. $7x > -35$ and $5x \leq 30$
40. $4x < 16$ or $12x > 144$
41. $3x \geq 3$ or $9x < 54$
42. $8x > -32$ or $-6x \geq 48$
43. $9x \leq -27$ or $4x \geq 36$

Answers

Practice and Problem-Solving Exercises

10. $x + 5 < -7$
11. $8x \geq 25$
12. $x - 6 > 54$
13. $\frac{x}{12} \leq 6$

14. $x \leq -\frac{1}{2}$

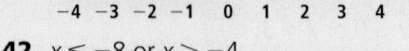

15. $k > -9$

16. $a > 11$

17. $t \leq 11$

18. $y \leq -14$

19. $y \leq -6$

20. $x \leq 8$

21. $m < 10$

22. $n > 8$

23. $w > 6$

24. The width is less than 11.5 in., and the length is 3 in. greater than the width.

25. The longest side is less than 21 cm.

26. The smaller number is an integer greater than or equal to 8.

27. at most 40 students

28. always   29. always   30. always

31. never   32. always   33. sometimes

34. never   35. sometimes

36. $-5 < x < 2$

37. $-4 \leq x \leq 2$

38. $-4 \leq x < 6$

39. $-5 < x \leq 6$

40. $x < 4$ or $x > 12$

41. all real numbers

42. $x \leq -8$ or $x > -4$

43. $x \leq -3$ or $x \geq 9$

44. Think About a Plan The diagram shows the scores in seconds of a skater's first three trials in a speed-skating event. What is the maximum time she can score on her last trial so that her average time on all four trials is under 36 seconds?

- What do you need to find an average?
- What inequality can you use to model the situation?

Solve each inequality. Graph the solution.

45. $2 - 3z \geq 7(8 - 2z) + 12$

46. $6(x - 2.5) \geq 8 - 6(3.5 + x)$

47. $\frac{2}{3}(x - 12) \leq x + 8$

48. $\frac{3}{5}(x - 12) > x - 24$

49. $3[4x - (2x - 7)] < 2(3x - 5)$

50. $6[5y - (3y - 1)] \geq 4(3y - 7)$

51. Grades Your math test scores are 68, 78, 90, and 91. What is the lowest score you can earn on the next test and still achieve an average of at least 85?

STEM 52. Chemistry The pH level of a popular shampoo is between 6.0 and 6.5 inclusive. What compound inequality shows the pH levels of this shampoo? Graph the solution.

53. Geometry The sum of the lengths of any two sides of a triangle is greater than the length of the third side. In $\triangle ABC$, $BC = 4$ and $AC = 8 - AB$. What can you conclude about AB?

54. Writing Write a word problem that can be solved using $25 + 0.5x \leq 60$.

55. Error Analysis A classmate solved the inequality $\frac{1}{2}(y - 16) \geq y + 2$ as shown. Prove that his answer is incorrect by checking a number that is less than -20. (Select a number that makes the computation easy.) What was his error?

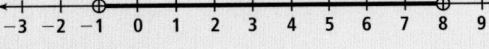

$\frac{1}{2}(y - 16) \geq y + 2$

$\frac{1}{2}y - 8 \geq y + 2$

$-10 \geq \frac{1}{2}y$

$-20 \leq y$

56. Construction A contractor estimated that her expenses for a construction project would be between \$700,000 and \$750,000. She has already spent \$496,000. How much more can she spend and remain within her estimate?

Justifying Steps Justify each step by identifying the property used.

57. $3x \leq 4(x - 1) - 8$

$3x \leq 4x - 4 - 8$

$3x \leq 4x - 12$

$-x \leq -12$

$x \geq 12$

58. $\frac{1}{2}(y + 3) > \frac{1}{3}(4 - y)$

$3(y + 3) > 2(4 - y)$

$3y + 9 > 8 - 2y$

$5y + 9 > 8$

$5y > -1$

$y > -0.2$

Solve each compound inequality. Graph the solution.

59. $-6 < 2x - 4 < 12$

60. $4x \leq 12$ and $-7x \leq 21$

61. $15x > 30$ or $18x < -36$

44. less than 36.57 seconds

45. $z \geq 6$

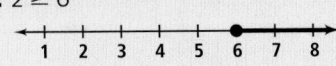

46. $x \geq \frac{1}{6}$

47. $x \geq -48$

48. $x < 42$

49. no solution

50. all real numbers

51. 98

52. $6.0 \leq x \leq 6.5$

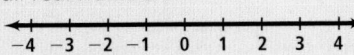

53. $2 < AB < 6$

54. Check students' work.

55. The classmate reversed the direction of the $\geq$ symbol to $\leq$ incorrectly. The correct answer is $y \leq -20$.

56. between \$204,000 and \$254,000

57. Distr. Prop.; arithmetic; Subtr. Prop. of Inequality; Mult. Prop. of Inequality

58. Mult. Prop. of Inequality; Distr. Prop.; Add. Prop. of Inequality; Subtr. Prop. of Inequality; Div. Prop. of Inequality

59. $-1 < x < 8$

60. $-3 \leq x \leq 3$

61. $x < -2$ or $x > 2$

Answers

Practice and Problem-Solving Exercises
(continued)

62. Answers may vary. Sample: $2x - 7 \geq -11$

63. Answers may vary. Sample: $-3x + 1 > 4$

64. Answers may vary. Sample: $-9 < 5x + 1 < 6$

65. Answers may vary. Sample: $2x + 4 \leq 0$ or $-3x - 3 \leq 0$

66. a. no

    b. yes; values of a that are 8 or greater

    c. (a) yes; values of a that are less than 8

        (b) no

Standardized Test Prep

67. D

68. I

69. D

70. [4] $3(x - 2) + 8 = 12$

$$3x - 6 + 8 = 12 \quad \text{Distr. Prop.}$$
$$3x + 2 = 12 \quad \text{Simplify.}$$
$$3x = 10 \quad \text{Subtr. Prop. of Eq.}$$
$$x = \frac{10}{3} \quad \text{Div. Prop. of Eq.}$$

[3] all steps and properties, but with one computational error

[2] two computational errors OR an incorrect property

[1] correct solution, without properties identified

Mixed Review

71. $7a + 5$

72. $-2x + 14y$

73. $\frac{b}{12} + 1$

74. $1.61 - 0.1k$

75. 4

76. no solution

77. $\frac{9}{10}$

78. -20

Challenge — **Open-Ended** Write an inequality with a solution that matches the graph. At least two steps should be needed to solve your inequality.

62.
$$\overset{-4\ -3\ -2\ -1\ \ 0\ \ 1\ \ 2\ \ 3\ \ 4}{\longleftrightarrow}$$

63.
$$\overset{-4\ -3\ -2\ -1\ \ 0\ \ 1\ \ 2\ \ 3\ \ 4}{\longleftrightarrow}$$

64.
$$\overset{-4\ -3\ -2\ -1\ \ 0\ \ 1\ \ 2\ \ 3\ \ 4}{\longleftrightarrow}$$

65.
$$\overset{-4\ -3\ -2\ -1\ \ 0\ \ 1\ \ 2\ \ 3\ \ 4}{\longleftrightarrow}$$

66. Reasoning Consider the compound inequality $x < 8$ and $x > a$.

    a. Are there any values of a such that all real numbers are solutions of the compound inequality? If so, what are they?

    b. Are there any values of a such that no real numbers are solutions of the compound inequality? If so, what are they?

    c. Repeat parts (a) and (b) for the compound inequality $x < 8$ or $x > a$.

Standardized Test Prep

SAT/ACT

67. What is the solution of $1 < 2x + 3 < 9$?

    Ⓐ $-1 > x < 2$ Ⓑ $2 < x < 3$ Ⓒ $-1 < x < 2$ Ⓓ $-1 < x < 3$

68. Which expression best represents the value of x in $y = mx + b$?

    Ⓕ $\frac{b - y}{m}$ Ⓖ $\frac{y + b}{m}$ Ⓗ $m(y - b)$ Ⓘ $\frac{y - b}{m}$

69. The hourly rate of a waiter is \$4 plus tips. On a particular day, the waiter worked 8 hours and received more than \$150 in pay. Which could be the amount of tips the waiter received?

    Ⓐ \$18.75   Ⓑ \$32   Ⓒ \$118   Ⓓ \$120.75

Extended Response

70. Solve $3(x - 2) + 8 = 12$. Identify each property of real numbers or equality you use.

Mixed Review

Simplify each expression.   ◀ See Lesson 1-3.

71. $(2a - 4) + (5a + 9)$ **72.** $3(x + 3y) - 5(x - y)$

73. $\frac{1}{3}(b + 12) - \frac{1}{4}(b + 12)$ **74.** $0.4(k - 0.1) + 0.5(3.3 - k)$

Get Ready! To prepare for Lesson 1-6, do Exercises 75–78.

Solve each equation. Check your answers.   ◀ See Lesson 1-4.

75. $7x - 6(11 - 2x) = 10$ **76.** $10x - 7 = 2(13 + 5x)$

77. $4y - \frac{1}{10} = 3y + \frac{4}{5}$ **78.** $0.4x + 1.18 = -3.1(2 - 0.01x)$

Lesson Resources

Additional Instructional Support

Algebra 2 Companion

Students can use the **Algebra 2 Companion** worktext (4 pages) as you teach the lesson. Use the Companion to support

- New Vocabulary
- Key Concepts
- Got It for each Problem
- Lesson Check

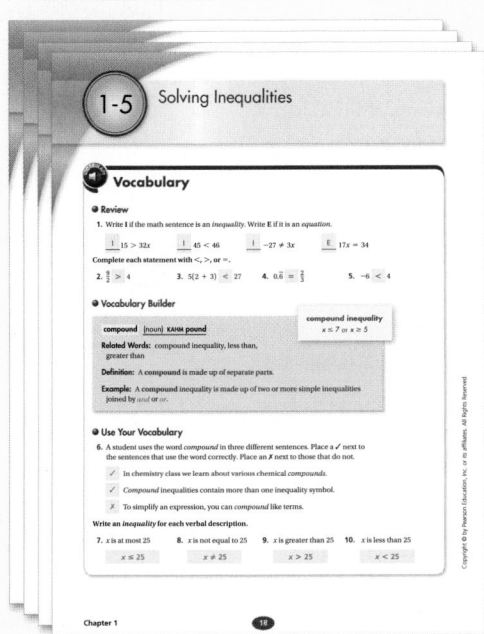

ELL Support

Use Graphic Organizers To assist students in understanding inequality word problems, help them make a graphic organizer including words for each symbol, such as the following: < less than, less, fewer; > more than, more, greater; ≤ less than or equal to, no more than, at most; ≥ greater than or equal to, no less than, at least. Then have students rewrite an inequality in English several different ways. For example, $2x - 5 \geq 4$ could be "five less than the product of 2 and x is at least 4" or "five fewer than the product of x and 2 is greater than or equal to 4."

Encourage students to illustrate their graphic organizer and to add any familiar words which will help them to understand each concept.

Next have students compare their graphic organizer with a partner's and add any new ideas to their organizer.

5 Assess & Remediate

Lesson Quiz

1. What inequality represents the sentence, "The product of 6 and a number is less than 20"?
2. What is the solution of $-5(2x - 1) + 3 \leq -2$? Graph the solution.
3. **Do you UNDERSTAND?** Eastside Gym charges a $60 initial fee and $28.50 per month. Valley Gym charges $36 per month, and no initial fee. After how many months of use would Eastside cost less than Valley?
4. Is the inequality *sometimes, always,* or *never* true?

   $3(4x + 2) + x \leq 1 + 13x$
5. What is the solution of $2 \leq 3x + 8$ and $20 > 4x$? Graph the solution.

ANSWERS TO LESSON QUIZ

1. $6x < 20$
2. $x \geq 1$

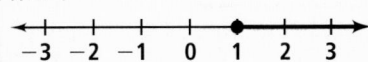

3. More than 8 months.
4. never true
5. $-2 \leq x < 5$

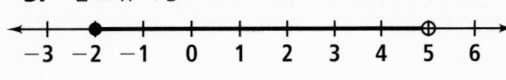

PRESCRIPTION FOR REMEDIATION

Use the student work on the Lesson Quiz to prescribe a differentiated review assignment:

Points	Differentiated Remediation
0–2	Intervention
3–4	On-level
5	Extension

PowerAlgebra.com

5 Assess & Remediate

Assign the Lesson Quiz. Appropriate intervention, practice, or enrichment is automatically generated based on student performance.

Intervention

- **Reteaching** (2 pages) Provides reteaching and practice exercises for the key lesson concepts. Use with struggling students or absent students.
- **English Language Learner Support** Helps students develop and reinforce mathematical vocabulary and key concepts.

All-in-One Resources/Online
Reteaching

1-5 **Reteaching**
Solving Inequalities

As with an equation, the solutions of an inequality are numbers that make it true. The procedure for solving a linear inequality is much like the one for solving linear equations. To isolate the variable on one side of the inequality, perform the same algebraic operation on each side of the inequality symbol.

The **Addition and Subtraction Properties of Inequality** state that adding or subtracting the same number from both sides of the inequality does not change the inequality.

If $a < b$, then $a + c < b + c$.   If $a < b$, then $a - c < b - c$.

The **Multiplication and Division Properties of Inequality** state that multiplying or dividing both sides of the inequality by the same *positive* number does not change the inequality.

If $a < b$ and $c > 0$, then $ac < bc$.   If $a < b$ and $c > 0$, then $\frac{a}{c} < \frac{b}{c}$.

Problem

What is the solution of $3(x + 2) - 5 \leq 21 - x$? Graph the solution.

Justify each line in the solution by naming one of the properties of inequalities.

$3x + 6 - 5 \leq 21 - x$ Distributive Property
$3x + 1 \leq 21 - x$ Simplify.
$4x + 1 \leq 21$ Addition Property of Inequality
$4x \leq 20$ Subtraction Property of Inequality
$x \leq 5$ Division Property of Inequality

To graph the solution, locate the boundary point at $x = 5$. Because the inequality is "*less than or equal to,*" the boundary point is part of the solution set. Therefore, use a closed dot to graph the boundary point. Shade the number line to the left of the boundary point because the inequality is "*less than.*"

Graph the solution on a number line.

Exercises

Solve each inequality. Graph the solution.

1. $2x + 4(x - 2) > 4$ $x > 2$
2. $4 - (2x - 4) \geq 5 - (4x + 3)$ $x \geq -3$

All-in-One Resources/Online
English Language Learner Support

1-5 **Additional Vocabulary Support**
Solving Inequalities

is greater than	is greater than or equal to	is less than	is less than or equal to
>	≥	<	≤

To write an inequality from a sentence, first identify the operation and then identify the inequality.

Example What inequality represents the sentence "6 more than a number is at least 20"?

"more than" means addition   "is at least" means is greater than or equal to

6 more than a number | is at least | 20
$6 + x \geq 20$

Underline the word or words that indicate an operation.

1. the product of 12 and a number
2. 8 less than a number
3. the difference between a number and 24
4. the sum of a number and 7

Circle the word phrase that identifies the inequality to use. Then write the inequality that represents the sentence.

5. The product of 12 and a number is more than 190. $12x > 190$
6. 8 less than a number is at least 34. $x - 8 \geq 34$
7. The difference between a number and 24 is no more than 4. $x - 24 \leq 4$
8. The sum of twice a number and 7 is less than 25. $2x + 7 < 25$

Some word phrases are very similar, but have different meanings.
Example Does the sentence indicate an operation or an inequality?

A number is four greater than 15.   Four is greater than a number.
$x = 4 + 15$ $4 > x$
operation   inequality

Does the sentence indicate an *operation* or an *inequality*?

9. 22 is 7 greater than a number. operation
10. A number is greater than 99. inequality
11. A number is 8 less than another number. operation
12. 50 is less than a number. inequality

Differentiated Remediation *continued*

Available in editable format online.

On-Level

- **Practice** (2 pages) Provides extra practice for each lesson. For simpler practice exercises, use the Form K Practice pages found in the All-in-One Teaching Resources and online.

- **Think About a Plan** Helps students develop specific problem-solving skills and strategies by providing scaffolded guiding questions.
- **Standardized Test Prep** Focuses on all major exercises, all major question types, and helps students prepare for the high-stakes assessments.

Extension

- **Enrichment** Provides students with interesting problems and activities that extend the concepts of the lesson.
- **Activities, Games, and Puzzles** Worksheets that can be used for concepts development, enrichment, and for fun!

Practice and Problem Solving Wkbk/ All-in-One Resources/Online
Practice page 1

1-5 Practice — Form G
Solving Inequalities

Write the inequality that represents the sentence.

1. Four less than a number is greater than −28. $x - 4 > -28$

2. Twice a number is at least 15. $2x \geq 15$

3. A number increased by 7 is less than 5. $x + 7 < 5$

4. The quotient of a number and 8 is at most −6. $\frac{x}{8} \leq -6$

Solve each inequality. Graph the solution.

5. $3(x + 1) + 2 < 11 \; x < 2$
6. $5t - 2(t + 2) \geq 8 \; t \geq 4$
7. $2[(2y - 1) + y] \leq 5(y + 3) \; y \leq 17$
8. $\frac{1}{3}(7a - 1) \leq 2a + 7 \; a \leq 22$
9. $5 - 2(n + 2) \leq 4 + n \; n \geq -1$
10. $-2(w - 7) + 3 > w - 1 \; w < 6$

Solve each problem by writing an inequality.

11. **Geometry** The length of a rectangular yard is 30 meters. The perimeter is at most 90 meters. Describe the width of the yard. at most 15 m

12. **Geometry** A piece of rope 20 feet long is cut from a longer piece that is at least 32 feet long. The remainder is cut into four pieces of equal length. Describe the length of each of the four pieces. at least 3 ft

13. A school principal estimates that no more than 6% of this year's senior class will graduate with honors. If 350 students graduate this year, how many will graduate with honors? no more than 21 students

14. Two sisters drove 144 miles on a camping trip. They averaged at least 32 miles per gallon on the trip. Describe the number of gallons of gas they used. at most 4.5 gal

---

Practice and Problem Solving Wkbk/ All-in-One Resources/Online
Practice page 2

1-5 Practice (continued) — Form G
Solving Inequalities

Is the inequality *always*, *sometimes*, or *never true*?

15. $3(2x + 1) > 5x - (2 - x)$ always true
16. $2(x - 1) \geq x + 7$ sometimes true
17. $7x + 2 \leq 2(2x - 4) + 3x$ never true
18. $5(x - 3) < 2(x - 9)$ sometimes true

Solve each compound inequality. Graph the solution.

19. $3x > -6$ and $2x < 6 \; x > -2$ and $x < 3$
20. $4x \geq -12$ and $7x \leq 7 \; x \geq -3$ and $x \leq 1$
21. $5x > -20$ and $8x \leq 32 \; x > -4$ and $x \leq 4$
22. $6x < -12$ or $5x > 5 \; x < -2$ or $x > 1$
23. $6x \leq -18$ or $2x > 18 \; x \leq -3$ or $x > 9$
24. $2x > 3 - x$ or $2x < x - 3 \; x > 1$ or $x < -3$

Solve each problem by writing and solving a compound inequality.

25. A student believes she can earn between $5200 and $6250 from her summer job. She knows that she will have to buy four new tires for her car at $90 each. She estimates her other expenses while she is working at $660. How much can the student save from her summer wages? between $4180 and $5230

26. Before a chemist can combine a solution with other liquids in a laboratory, the temperature of the solution must be between 39°C and 52°C. The chemist places the solution in a warmer that raises the temperature 6.5°C per hour. If the temperature is originally 0°C, how long will it take to raise the temperature to the necessary range of values? between 6 and 8 h

27. The Science Club advisor expects that between 42 and 49 students will attend the next Science Club field trip. The school allows $5.50 per student for sandwiches and drinks. What is the advisor's budget for food for the trip? between $231 and $269.50

All-in-One Resources/Online
Enrichment

1-5 Enrichment
Solving Inequalities

F	R	I	E	D	R	I	C	H		B	E	S	S	E	L
1	2	3	4	5	6	7	8	9	10	11	12	13	14	15	16

He was the first person to measure the distance to a star successfully. He also discovered that certain mathematical functions play a key role in models of physical phenomena. These functions were named after him.

To find his name, solve each of the following inequalities. Then use the solutions and the table below to determine the position in which to write the associated letter.

Solutions	Position	Solutions	Position	Solutions	Position
$x > 1$	1	$x > \frac{1}{2}$	6	$x < 4$	11
$x < 2$	2	$x > 5$	7	$x < 0$	12
$x > -1$	3	$x < \frac{5}{2}$	8	$x > -\frac{4}{3}$	13
$x > -2$	4	$x > 0$	9	$x > -\frac{1}{2}$	14
all real numbers	5		10	$x > 2$	15
				$x > 3$	16

B $2(x + 1) - (2 - x) < 12 \; x < 4$
C $x + 6 < 16 - x \; x < \frac{5}{2}$
D $3x + 5 + 3(x + 5) > 6x + 15$ all real numbers
E $8x - 2 - 6(x - 3) < 16 \; x < 0$
E $3(x + 2) + 2x > -4 \; x > -2$
E $(3 + x) + (3 - 3x) < x \; x > 2$
F $3x - 5 + (x + 9) > 8 \; x > 1$
H $5x - 3(x - 1) > 3 \; x > 0$
I $5x - 3 - 3(x + \frac{7}{3}) > 0 \; x > 5$
I $2(x + 4) - (5 - x) > 0 \; x > -1$
L $(x + 1) - (1 - x) < (x - 1) - (2 - 2x) \; x > 3$
R $7x - 5 - (-1 - x) > 0 \; x > \frac{1}{2}$
R $3x + 5 + 2(x + 5) < 23 \; x < 2$
S $2(x - 1) < 2 + 2(1 + 7x) \; x > -\frac{1}{2}$
S $3 - x < 5 + 2(x + 1) \; x > -\frac{4}{3}$

Practice and Problem Solving Wkbk/ All-in-One Resources/Online
Think About a Plan

1-5 Think About a Plan
Solving Inequalities

Your math test scores are 68, 78, 90, and 91. What is the lowest score you can earn on the next test and still achieve an average of at least 85?

Understanding the Problem

1. What information do you need to find an average of scores? How do you find an average?
The sum of the scores and the total number of scores; divide the sum of the scores by the total number of scores.

2. How many scores should you include in the average? 5

3. You want to achieve an average that is greater than or equal to what score? 85

Planning the Solution

4. Assign a variable, x.
x = the score on the next test

5. Write an expression for the sum of all of the scores, including the next test.
$327 + x$

6. Write an expression for the average of all of the scores.
$\frac{327 + x}{5}$

7. Write an inequality that can be used to determine the lowest score you can earn on the next test and still achieve an average of at least 85.
$\frac{327 + x}{5} \geq 85$

Getting an Answer

8. Solve your inequality to find the lowest score you can earn on the next test and still achieve an average of at least 85. What score do you need to earn? at least 98

Practice and Problem Solving Wkbk/ All-in-One Resources/Online
Standardized Test Prep

1-5 Standardized Test Prep
Solving Inequalities

Multiple Choice

For Exercises 1–5, choose the correct letter.

1. What is the solution of $4t - (3 + t) \leq t + 7$? B
   Ⓐ $t \leq \frac{5}{2}$ Ⓑ $t \leq 5$ Ⓒ $t \leq 2$ Ⓓ $t \leq 1$

2. What is the solution of $-17 - 2r < 3(r + 1)$? I
   Ⓕ $r > 4$ Ⓖ $r > -20$ Ⓗ $r < -4$ Ⓘ $r > -4$

3. Which graph best represents the solution of $\frac{2}{3}(m + 4) > m + 3$? A

4. What is the solution of the compound inequality $4x < -8$ or $9x > 18$? I
   Ⓕ $x < 2$ or $x > -2$ Ⓗ $x > 2$
   Ⓖ $x < -2$ Ⓘ $x < -2$ or $x > 2$

5. What is the solution of the compound inequality $-2x \leq 6$ and $-3x > -27$? C
   Ⓐ $x \leq -3$ and $x > 9$ Ⓒ $x \geq -3$ and $x < 9$
   Ⓑ $x \geq 3$ and $x < -9$ Ⓓ $x \leq 3$ and $x > -9$

Short Response

6. **Geometry** The lengths of the sides of a triangle are in the ratio 3 : 4 : 5. Describe the length of the longest side if the perimeter is not more than 72 in. Solve the inequality $3x + 4x + 5x \leq 72$ or $12x \leq 72$ or $x \leq 6$. The longest side, 5x, is not more than 5 · 6 = 30 in. [2] All student calculations are correct. [1] minor incorrect calculation [0] no answer given

7. Between 8.5% and 9.4% of the city's population uses the municipal transit system daily. According to the latest census, the city's population is 785,000. How many people use the transit system daily?
[2] between 66,725 and 73,790 people [1] minor incorrect miscalculation of one or both values in the range [0] no answer given

---

Online Teacher Resource Center
Activities, Games, and Puzzles

1-5 Puzzle: What's the Inequality?
Solving Inequalities

To solve this puzzle, each box must be filled in with a math symbol $(x, +, -, <, >)$ or a digit from 0 to 9 to complete an inequality. The clues below give the solution to the inequality you complete. 1-Across has been done for you. The boldfaced "4" and ">" complete the inequality $4x > 4, x > 1$ (See clue below).

ACROSS

1. $x > 1$
3. $x < 7 \; 2x < 14$
5. $x < \frac{11}{3} \; 3x + 1 < 12$
7. $x \geq -\frac{1}{9} \; 11x - 2x \geq -1$
9. $x > \frac{1}{4} \; 9x > x + 2$
10. $x > 3 \; 5x - 5 > 7 + x$

DOWN

2. $x < -\frac{3}{7} \; 4x + 3 < -3x$
3. $x < 4 \; 2x < 8$
4. $x > \frac{1}{2} \; 4x > 2$
5. $x > 3 \; 39 < 13x$
6. $x < 12 \; 2 > x - 10$
8. $x \leq 3 \; x + 2 \leq 5$

Absolute Value Equations and Inequalities

Common Core State Standards
A-SSE.A.1b Interpret complicated expressions by viewing one or more of their parts as a single entity.
A-CED.A.1 Create equations and inequalities in one variable and use them to solve problems.
MP 1, MP 3

Objective To write and solve equations and inequalities involving absolute value

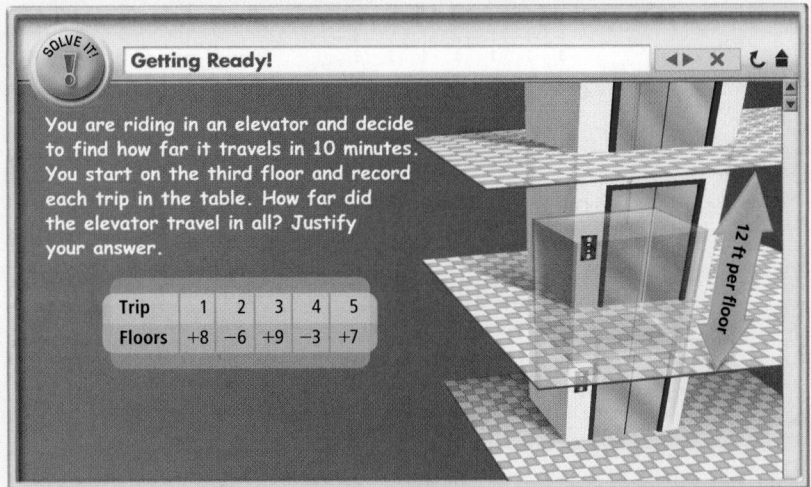

Getting Ready!

You are riding in an elevator and decide to find how far it travels in 10 minutes. You start on the third floor and record each trip in the table. How far did the elevator travel in all? Justify your answer.

Trip	1	2	3	4	5
Floors	+8	−6	+9	−3	+7

12 ft per floor

In the Solve It, signed numbers represent distance and direction. Sometimes, only the size of a number (its *absolute value*), not the direction, is important.

Lesson Vocabulary
• absolute value
• extraneous solution

Essential Understanding An absolute value quantity is nonnegative. Since opposites have the same absolute value, an absolute value equation can have two solutions.

take note

Key Concept Absolute Value

Definition	Numbers	Symbols
The **absolute value** of a real number x, written $|x|$, is its distance from zero on the number line.	$|4| = 4$ $|-4| = 4$	$|x| = x$, if $x \geq 0$ $|x| = -x$, if $x < 0$

An absolute value equation has a variable within the absolute value sign. For example, $|x| = 5$. Here, the value of x can be 5 or −5 since $|5|$ and $|-5|$ both equal 5.

Both 5 and −5 are 5 units from 0.

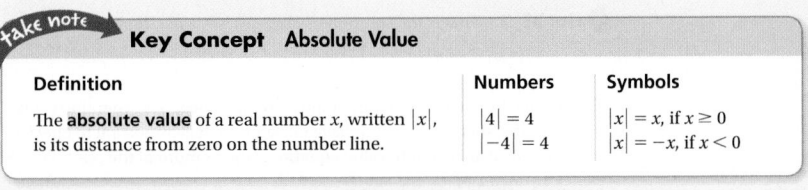

$-6\ -5\ -4\ -3\ -2\ -1\quad 0\quad 1\quad 2\quad 3\quad 4\quad 5\quad 6$

1 Interactive Learning

Solve It!
PURPOSE To use a natural understanding of distance to explore absolute value
PROCESS Students may
• count the total number of floors traveled without respect to direction and then multiply by the height of each floor.
• find the distance traveled in each direction.

FACILITATE

Q Is the distance of the trip affected by the number of the floor where you start your trip? Explain. **[No; traveling 8 floors up is the same distance whether you start on the ground floor or third floor.]**

Q What is the total number of floors traveled upward? **[24]**

Q What is the total number of floors traveled in both directions? **[33]**

Q On which floor does your trip end? **[18]**

Q How far would the elevator travel if it went up n floors and down m floors? **[12(n + m)]**

ANSWER See Solve It in Answers on next page.
CONNECT THE MATH Since distance is positive, students implicitly use absolute value in the Solve It. In the lesson, absolute value is formally defined, and absolute value equations and inequalities are written, solved, and graphed.

2 Guided Instruction

Take Note
Point out that when $x < 0$, the quantity $-x > 0$. Show examples with several values for x.

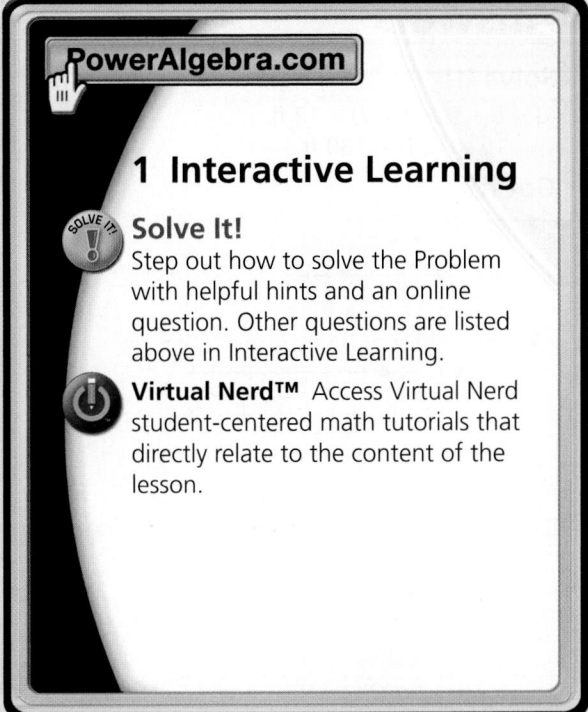

PowerAlgebra.com

1 Interactive Learning

Solve It!
Step out how to solve the Problem with helpful hints and an online question. Other questions are listed above in Interactive Learning.

Virtual Nerd™ Access Virtual Nerd student-centered math tutorials that directly relate to the content of the lesson.

1-6 Preparing to Teach

BIG idea Solving Equations and Inequalities

ESSENTIAL UNDERSTANDINGS
• An absolute value quantity is nonnegative.
• Since opposites have the same absolute value, an absolute value equation can have two solutions.
• Absolute value inequalities can be written as compound inequalities without absolute value signs.

Math Background
To some students, the concept of absolute value may seem artificial. Explain that absolute value is of central importance in mathematics itself, as well as in applied subjects such as statistics.

As a rule, absolute value equations have two solutions, representing two points on a number line that are at the same distance from a certain number. For inequalities, there are two possible situations depending on the sign of the inequality:
• The solution set is a segment, for inequalities of the type $|x| < a$.
• The solution set is two rays, for inequalities of the type $|x| > a$ ($a \geq 0$).

Mathematical Practices
Make sense of problems and persevere in solving them. Students will graph more complicated absolute value inequalities, carefully noting their important features and relationship to regular inequalities and absolute value equations.

Problem 1

Q Why is the equation written as 2 separate equations *without* absolute value signs? **[Answers may vary. Sample: There are two values that have absolute value of 5: 5 and −5.]**

Got It?

Q What is the process for checking your answer? **[Substitute the values you found for *x* in the original equation.]**

Problem 2

In this problem, it is necessary to isolate the absolute value expression first before rewriting the equation as two linear equations.

Q What happens if you set the original expression on the left side equal to 8 and to −8? **[The solutions might not check because you need to isolate the absolute value expression first.]**

Got It?

Q What is the first goal in your solution process? **[Isolate the quantity $|x + 9|$.]**

Q Can you solve $|x| = -5$? Why? **[No; absolute value expressions are never negative.]**

Think

How is solving this equation different from solving a linear equation?
In the absolute value equation, $2x - 1$ can represent two opposite quantities.

Plan

Is there a simpler way to think of this problem?
Solving
$3|x + 2| - 1 = 8$
is similar to solving
$3y - 1 = 8$.

© **Problem 1** Solving an Absolute Value Equation

What is the solution of $|2x - 1| = 5$? Graph the solution.

$$|2x - 1| = 5$$

> Rewrite as two equations.
> $2x - 1$ could be 5 or −5.

$$2x - 1 = 5 \quad \text{or} \quad 2x - 1 = -5$$
$$2x = 6 \qquad\qquad 2x = -4 \qquad \text{Add 1 to each side of both equations.}$$
$$x = 3 \quad \text{or} \quad x = -2 \qquad \text{Divide each side of both equations by 2.}$$

$$\overset{-3\ -2\ -1\ \ 0\ \ 1\ \ 2\ \ 3}{\longleftarrow\!\!+\!\!+\!\!\bullet\!\!+\!\!+\!\!+\!\!\bullet\!\!+\!\!+\!\!\longrightarrow}$$

Check $|2(3) - 1| \overset{?}{=} 5 \qquad\qquad |2(-2) - 1| \overset{?}{=} 5$
$\qquad\qquad |6 - 1| \overset{?}{=} 5 \qquad\qquad\qquad |-4 - 1| \overset{?}{=} 5$
$\qquad\qquad\qquad |5| = 5 \checkmark \qquad\qquad\qquad\qquad |-5| = 5 \checkmark$

✓ **Got It? 1.** What is the solution of $|3x + 2| = 4$? Graph the solution.

© **Problem 2** Solving a Multi-Step Absolute Value Equation

What is the solution of $3|x + 2| - 1 = 8$? Graph the solution.

$$3|x + 2| - 1 = 8$$
$$3|x + 2| = 9 \qquad\qquad\qquad \text{Add 1 to each side.}$$
$$|x + 2| = 3 \qquad\qquad\qquad \text{Divide each side by 3.}$$
$$x + 2 = 3 \quad \text{or} \quad x + 2 = -3 \qquad \text{Rewrite as two equations.}$$
$$x = 1 \quad \text{or} \qquad x = -5 \qquad \text{Subtract 2 from each side of both equations.}$$

$$\overset{-5\ -4\ -3\ -2\ -1\ \ 0\ \ 1\ \ 2\ \ 3}{\longleftarrow\!\!\bullet\!\!+\!\!+\!\!+\!\!+\!\!+\!\!+\!\!\bullet\!\!+\!\!+\!\!\longrightarrow}$$

Check $3|(1) + 2| - 1 \overset{?}{=} 8 \qquad\qquad 3|(-5) + 2| - 1 \overset{?}{=} 8$
$\qquad\qquad 3|3| - 1 \overset{?}{=} 8 \qquad\qquad\qquad 3|-3| - 1 \overset{?}{=} 8$
$\qquad\qquad\qquad 8 = 8 \checkmark \qquad\qquad\qquad\qquad\qquad 8 = 8 \checkmark$

✓ **Got It? 2.** What is the solution of $2|x + 9| + 3 = 7$? Graph the solution.

Distance from 0 on the number line cannot be negative. Therefore, some absolute value equations, such as $|x| = -5$, have no solution. It is important to check the possible solutions of an absolute value equation. One or more of the possible solutions may be *extraneous*.

An **extraneous solution** is a solution derived from an original equation that is *not* a solution of the original equation.

Answers

Solve It!
$(8 - 6 + 9 - 3 + 7) \times 12 \text{ ft} =$
$\qquad 15 \times 12 \text{ ft} = 180 \text{ ft}$

Got It?
1. $\frac{2}{3}$, −2

$$\overset{-3\ -2\ -1\ \ 0\ \ 1}{\longleftarrow\!\!+\!\!\bullet\!\!+\!\!+\!\!+\!\!\bullet\!\!+\!\!\longrightarrow}$$

2. −7, −11

$$\overset{-12\ -10\ -8\ -6\ -4\ -2\ \ 0\ \ 2}{\longleftarrow\!\!+\!\!\bullet\!\!+\!\!\bullet\!\!+\!\!+\!\!+\!\!+\!\!+\!\!\longrightarrow}$$

 PowerAlgebra.com

2 Guided Instruction

© Each Problem is worked out and supported online.

Problem 1
Solving an Absolute Value Equation

Problem 2
Solving a Multi-Step Absolute Value Equation
Animated

Problem 3
Checking for Extraneous Solutions
Animated

Problem 4
Solving the Absolute Value Inequality
$|A| < b$
Animated

Problem 5
Solving the Absolute Value Inequality
$|A| \geq b$

Problem 6
Using an Absolute Value Inequality

Support in Algebra 2 Companion
• Vocabulary
• Key Concepts
• Got It?

Think

Can you solve this the same way as you solved Problem 1?
Yes, let $3x + 2$ equal $4x + 5$ and $-(4x + 5)$.

Problem 3 Checking for Extraneous Solutions

What is the solution of $|3x + 2| = 4x + 5$? Check for extraneous solutions.

$|3x + 2| = 4x + 5$

$3x + 2 = 4x + 5$ or $3x + 2 = -(4x + 5)$ Rewrite as two equations.

$-x = 3$ $3x + 2 = -4x - 5$ Solve each equation.

                           $7x = -7$

$x = -3$ or $x = -1$

Check $|3(-3) + 2| \stackrel{?}{=} 4(-3) + 5$ $|3(-1) + 2| \stackrel{?}{=} 4(-1) + 5$

        $|-9 + 2| \stackrel{?}{=} -12 + 5$ $|-3 + 2| \stackrel{?}{=} -4 + 5$

           $|-7| \neq -7$ ✗ $|-1| = 1$ ✔

Since $x = -3$ does not satisfy the original equation, -3 is an extraneous solution. The only solution to the equation is $x = -1$.

Got It? **3.** What is the solution of $|5x - 2| = 7x + 14$? Check for extraneous solutions.

The solutions of the absolute value inequality $|x| < 5$ include values greater than -5 *and* less than 5. This is the compound inequality $x > -5$ *and* $x < 5$, which you can write as $-5 < x < 5$. So, $|x| < 5$ means x is between -5 and 5.

> The graph of $|x| < 5$ is all values of x between -5 and 5.

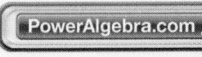

Essential Understanding You can write an absolute value inequality as a compound inequality without absolute value symbols.

Plan

Is this an *and* problem or an *or* problem?
$2x - 1$ is less than 5 and greater than -5. It is an *and* problem.

Problem 4 Solving the Absolute Value Inequality $|A| < b$

What is the solution of $|2x - 1| < 5$? Graph the solution.

$|2x - 1| < 5$

$-5 < 2x - 1 < 5$ $2x - 1$ is between -5 and 5.

$-4 < 2x < 6$ Add 1 to each part.

$-2 < x < 3$ Divide each part by 2.

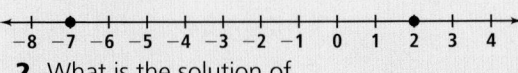

Got It? **4.** What is the solution of $|3x - 4| \leq 8$? Graph the solution.

Problem 3

Q How is the expression outside of the absolute value signs in this problem different from Problem 1 and Problem 2? **[There is an x outside of the absolute value signs.]**

Q If the expression outside the absolute value signs was negative, what would the solutions be? **[There would be no solutions because the absolute value is never negative.]**

Got It?   ERROR PREVENTION

Make sure students use the Opposite of a Sum Property when simplifying $-(7x + 14) = -7x - 14$.

Problem 4   ERROR PREVENTION

Be aware of the placement of the inequality signs. If a student sets up the inequalities as $2x - 1 < 5$ and $2x - 1 < -5$, remind the student that the inequality sign must be flipped in the second example. Review multiplication of inequalities by negative numbers.

                             VISUAL LEARNERS

Q Read $-2 < x < 3$ as x is between -2 and 3. How does the graph confirm this? **[The graph is the segment from -2 to 3, not inclusive of endpoints, so the values of x are between -2 and 3.]**

Got It?

Q How does this inequality compare to the one in Problem 4? **[The solution is like the one in Problem 4, except the boundary points are included in the set of solutions.]**

Additional Problems

1. What is the solution of $|2x + 5| = 9$? Graph the solution.

   ANSWER $-7, 2$

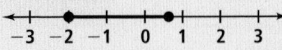

2. What is the solution of $\frac{1}{3}|3x - 6| - 2 = 5$?

   ANSWER $-5, 9$

3. What is the solution of $|-2x + 9| = 3x + 10$?

   ANSWER $-\frac{1}{5}$

4. What is the solution of $|4x + 3| < 5$? Graph the solution.

   ANSWER

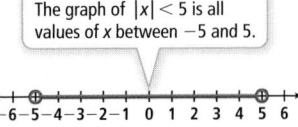

5. What is the solution of $|2x + 6| \geq 10$? Graph the solution.

   ANSWER

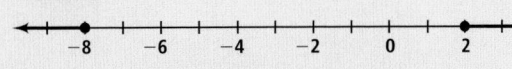

6. You are cutting pieces of wood to make a table. Each piece should be 4.75 ft, but you will use a piece if it is greater than 4.7 ft. and less than 4.8 ft. What absolute value inequality describes the tolerance of the length of wood?

   ANSWER $|x - 4.75| < 0.05$

Answers

Got It? (continued)

3. -1

4. $-\frac{4}{3} \leq x \leq 4$

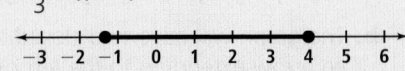

When an absolute value is *less than* a number, the solutions are *between* the number and its opposite. When an absolute value is *more than* a number, the solutions are *outside* of the number and its opposite.

Problem 5

Q What is the smallest positive value in the solution set? The largest negative value? **[1; −5]**

Got It?

Q In 5a, will the graph be two rays or a line segment? **[two rays pointing in opposite directions]**

Q In 5b, how is this inequality different from the one in 5a? How does this affect the graph? **[In 5b the end points are included. The graph will have solid dots.]**

Take Note

Q When $|x| \leq a$ or $|x| \geq a$, how does the graph change? **[For $|x| \leq a$, the graph is a segment. For $|x| \geq a$, the graph is 2 rays.]**

Draw each of the three graphs on the board. Have students describe each graph in words. Reverse the activity by describing a graph in words and having students draw it.

$|x| < 5$ means x is between -5 and 5. So, $|x| > 5$ means x is outside the interval from -5 to 5. You can say $x < -5$ or $x > 5$.

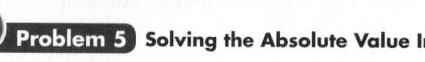 **Problem 5** Solving the Absolute Value Inequality $|A| \geq b$

What is the solution of $|2x + 4| \geq 6$? Graph the solution.

$$|2x + 4| \geq 6$$

$2x + 4 \leq -6$ or	$2x + 4 \geq 6$	Rewrite as a compound inequality.
$2x \leq -10$	$2x \geq 2$	Subtract 4 from each side of both inequalities.
$x \leq -5$ or	$x \geq 1$	Divide each side of both inequalities by 2.

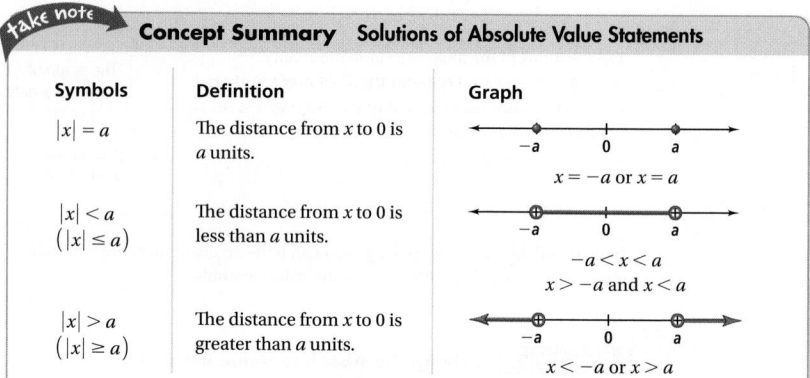

Think

How do you determine the boundary points?
To find the boundary points, find the solutions of the related equation.

Got It? 5. a. What is the solution of $|5x + 10| > 15$? Graph the solution.
  © **b. Reasoning** Without solving $|x - 3| \geq 2$, describe the graph of its solution.

---

take note

Concept Summary   Solutions of Absolute Value Statements

Symbols	Definition	Graph
$|x| = a$	The distance from x to 0 is a units.	$x = -a$ or $x = a$
$|x| < a$ ($|x| \leq a$)	The distance from x to 0 is less than a units.	$-a < x < a$ $x > -a$ and $x < a$
$|x| > a$ ($|x| \geq a$)	The distance from x to 0 is greater than a units.	$x < -a$ or $x > a$

A manufactured item's actual measurements and its target measurements can differ by a certain amount, called *tolerance*. Tolerance is one half the difference of the maximum and minimum acceptable values. You can use absolute value inequalities to describe tolerance.

Answers

Got It? (continued)

5. a. $x < -5$ or $x > 1$

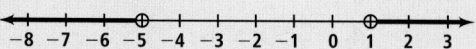

b. The graph will have two closed circles with an arrow extending to the left of one and to the right of the other.

 **Problem 6** Using an Absolute Value Inequality

Car Racing In car racing, a car must meet specific dimensions to enter a race. Officials use a template to ensure these specifications are met. What absolute value inequality describes heights of the model of race car shown within the indicated tolerance?

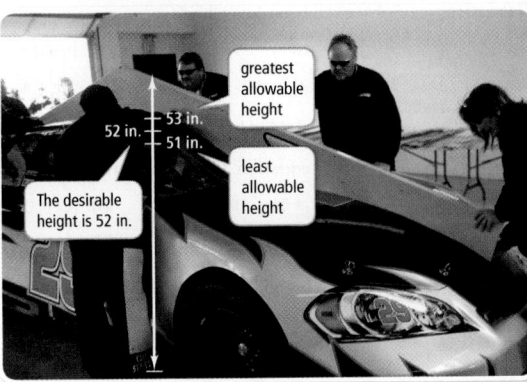

greatest allowable height

53 in.
52 in. — 51 in.

least allowable height

The desirable height is 52 in.

Plan

How does *tolerance* relate to an inequality?
Tolerance allows the height to differ from a desired height by no less and no more than a small amount.

$\frac{53 - 51}{2} = \frac{2}{2} = 1$ Find the tolerance.

$-1 \le h - 52 \le 1$ Use h for the height of the race car. Write a compound inequality.

$|h - 52| \le 1$ Rewrite as an absolute value inequality.

Got It? **6.** Suppose the least allowable height of the race car in Problem 6 was 52 in. and the desirable height was 52.5 in. What absolute value inequality describes heights of the model of race car shown within the indicated tolerance?

Lesson Check

Do you know HOW?

Solve each equation. Check your answers.

1. $|-6x| = 24$

2. $|2x + 8| - 4 = 12$

3. $|x - 2| = 4x + 8$

Solve each inequality. Graph the solution.

4. $|2x + 2| - 5 < 15$

5. $|4x - 6| \ge 10$

Do you UNDERSTAND?  MATHEMATICAL PRACTICES

6. Vocabulary Explain what it means for a solution of an equation to be extraneous.

7. Reasoning When is the absolute value of a number equal to the number itself?

8. Give an example of a compound inequality that has no solution.

9. Compare and Contrast Describe how absolute value equations and inequalities are like linear equations and inequalities and how they differ.

6. $|h - 52.5| \le 0.5$

Lesson Check

1. $-4, 4$

2. $-12, 4$

3. $-\frac{6}{5}$

4. $-11 < x < 9$

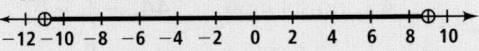

5. $x \le -1$ or $x \ge 4$

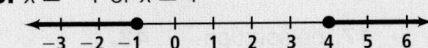

6. A solution of an eq. is extraneous if it is a solution to a derived eq., but is not a solution to the original eq.

7. when the number is positive or 0

8. Answers may vary. Sample: $d < -5$ and $5d > 25$

9. Answers may vary. Sample: An absolute value equation or inequality represents two equations or inequalities; each equation or inequality is solved in the same manner as a linear equation or inequality.

Problem 6
Tolerance measures the allowable distance between a measured value and the accepted value.

Got It?

Q When you know the maximum and minimum allowable values, how can you determine the desirable height? **[You can find the mean or median of the maximum and minimum values.]**

3 Lesson Check

Do You Know HOW?   ERROR INTERVENTION

- For Exercises 1–3, if students have trouble rewriting the absolute value equation as two equations, then revisit Problem 1, or use Additional Problem 1.
- For Exercises 4–5, if students have trouble with graphing, revisit Problem 4 and 5, or use Additional Problems 4 and 5.

Do you UNDERSTAND?

- For Exercise 7, have students find the absolute value of several numbers and compare.
- For Exercise 8, ask students to graph a compound inequality with no solution on a number line, such as the graph of $1 > x > 5$.

Close

Q Why can absolute value equations be written as two different linear equations? **[You can use the definition of absolute value to rewrite linear equations when the argument is positive or negative.]**

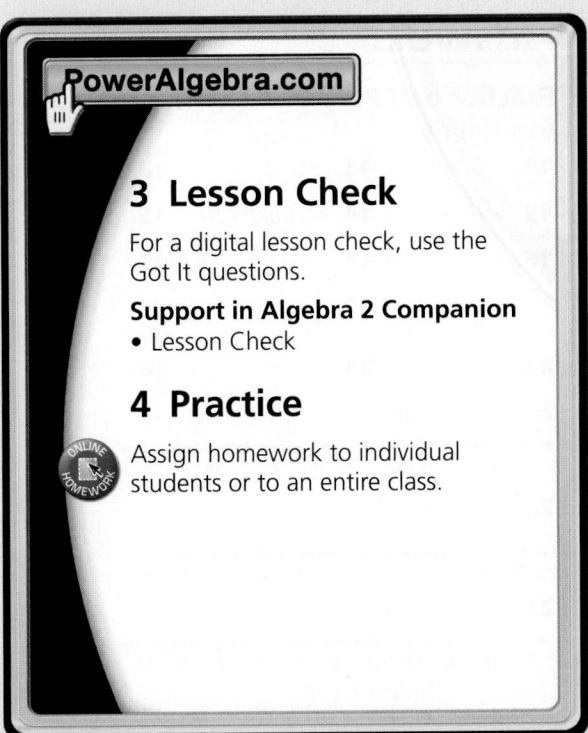

PowerAlgebra.com

3 Lesson Check

For a digital lesson check, use the Got It questions.

Support in Algebra 2 Companion
- Lesson Check

4 Practice

Assign homework to individual students or to an entire class.

4 Practice

ASSIGNMENT GUIDE

Basic: 10–42 all, 48–52 even, 53, 58–66 even, 69, 81

Average: 11–41 odd, 43–81

Advanced: 11–41 odd, 43–89

Standardized Test Prep: 90–93

Mixed Review: 94–102

 Mathematical Practices are supported by exercises with red headings. Here are the Practices supported in this lesson:

MP 1: Make Sense of Problems Ex. 53
MP 3: Communicate Ex. 9, 67, 88, 89
MP 3: Construct Arguments Ex. 7, 68
MP 3: Critique the Reasoning of Others Ex. 81

Applications exercises have blue headings.

EXERCISE 69: Use the Think About a Plan worksheet in the **Practice and Problem Solving Workbook** (also available in the Teaching Resources in print and online) to further support students' development in becoming independent learners.

HOMEWORK QUICK CHECK

To check students' understanding of key skills and concepts, go over Exercises 29, 39, 53, 58, and 69.

Practice and Problem-Solving Exercises

 **Practice** Solve each equation. Check your answers.

See Problems 1 and 2.

10. $|3x| = 18$
11. $|-4x| = 32$
12. $|x - 3| = 9$

13. $2|3x - 2| = 14$
14. $|3x + 4| = -3$
15. $|2x - 3| = -1$

16. $|x + 4| + 3 = 17$
17. $|y - 5| - 2 = 10$
18. $|4 - z| - 10 = 1$

Solve each equation. Check for extraneous solutions.

See Problem 3.

19. $|x - 1| = 5x + 10$
20. $|2z - 3| = 4z - 1$
21. $|3x + 5| = 5x + 2$

22. $|2y - 4| = 12$
23. $3|4w - 1| - 5 = 10$
24. $|2x + 5| = 3x + 4$

Solve each inequality. Graph the solution.

See Problem 4.

25. $3|y - 9| < 27$
26. $|6y - 2| + 4 < 22$
27. $|3x - 6| + 3 < 15$

28. $\frac{1}{4}|x - 3| + 2 < 1$
29. $4|2w + 3| - 7 \le 9$
30. $3|5t - 1| + 9 \le 23$

Solve each inequality. Graph the solution.

See Problem 5.

31. $|x + 3| > 9$
32. $|x - 5| \ge 8$
33. $|y - 3| \ge 12$

34. $|2x + 1| \ge -9$
35. $3|2x - 1| \ge 21$
36. $|3z| - 4 > 8$

Write each compound inequality as an absolute value inequality.

See Problem 6.

37. $1.3 \le h \le 1.5$
38. $50 \le k \le 51$
39. $27.25 \le C \le 27.75$

40. $50 \le b \le 55$
41. $1200 \le m \le 1300$
42. $0.1187 \le d \le 0.1190$

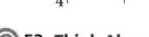 **Apply** Solve each equation.

43. $-|4 - 8b| = 12$
44. $4|3x + 4| = 4x + 8$

45. $|3x - 1| + 10 = 25$
46. $\frac{1}{2}|3c + 5| = 6c + 4$

47. $5|6 - 5x| = 15x - 35$
48. $7|8 - 3h| = 21h - 49$

49. $2|3x - 7| = 10x - 8$
50. $6|2x + 5| = 6x + 24$

51. $\frac{1}{4}|4x + 7| = 8x + 16$
52. $\frac{2}{3}|3x - 6| = 4(x - 2)$

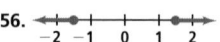 **53. Think About a Plan** The circumference of a basketball for college women must be from 28.5 in. to 29.0 in. What absolute value inequality represents the circumference of the ball?
- What is the tolerance?
- What is the inequality without using absolute value?

Write an absolute value equation or inequality to describe each graph.

54.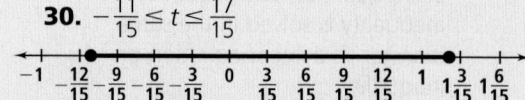
55.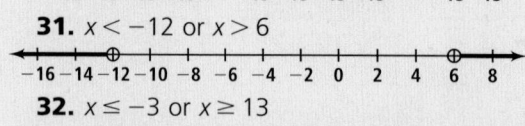
56.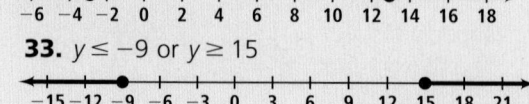

Answers

Practice and Problem-Solving Exercises
(continued)

10. $-6, 6$ **11.** $-8, 8$ **12.** $-6, 12$

13. $-\frac{5}{3}, 3$ **14.** no solution   **15.** no solution

16. $-18, 10$ **17.** $-7, 17$ **18.** $-7, 15$

19. $-\frac{3}{2}$ **20.** $\frac{2}{3}$ **21.** $\frac{3}{2}$

22. $-4, 8$ **23.** $-1, \frac{3}{2}$ **24.** 1

25. $0 < y < 18$

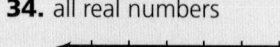

26. $-2\frac{2}{3} < y < 3\frac{1}{3}$

27. $-2 < x < 6$

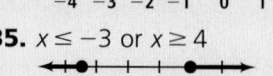

28. no solution   **29.** $-3\frac{1}{2} \le w \le \frac{1}{2}$

30. $-\frac{11}{15} \le t \le \frac{17}{15}$

31. $x < -12$ or $x > 6$

32. $x \le -3$ or $x \ge 13$

33. $y \le -9$ or $y \ge 15$

34. all real numbers

35. $x \le -3$ or $x \ge 4$

36. $z < -4$ or $z > 4$

37. $|h - 1.4| \le 0.1$
38. $|k - 50.5| \le 0.5$
39. $|C - 27.5| \le 0.25$
40. $|b - 52.5| \le 2.5$
41. $|m - 1250| \le 50$
42. $|d - 0.11885| \le 0.00015$

43. no solution   **44.** $-\frac{3}{2}, -1$

45. $-\frac{14}{3}, \frac{16}{3}$ **46.** $-\frac{1}{3}$

47. no solution   **48.** $\frac{5}{2}$

49. $\frac{11}{8}$ **50.** $-1, -3$

51. $-\frac{71}{36}$ **52.** 2

53. $|c - 28.75| \le 0.25$; 0.25; $28.50 \le c \le 29.00$

54. $|x| = 3$ **55.** $|x| < 4$

56. $|x| \ge 1.5$

Solve each inequality. Graph the solutions.

57. $|3x - 4| + 5 \le 27$

58. $|2x + 3| - 6 \ge 7$

59. $-2|x + 4| < 22$

60. $2|4t - 1| + 6 > 20$

61. $|3z + 15| \ge 0$

62. $|-2x + 1| > 2$

63. $\frac{1}{9}|5x - 3| - 3 \ge 2$

64. $\frac{1}{11}|2x - 4| + 10 \le 11$

65. $\left|\frac{x-3}{2}\right| + 2 < 6$

66. $\left|\frac{x+5}{3}\right| - 3 > 6$

67. Writing Describe the differences in the graphs of $|x| < a$ and $|x| > a$, where a is a positive real number.

68. Open-Ended Write an absolute value inequality for which every real number is a solution. Write an absolute value inequality that has no solution.

Write an absolute value inequality to represent each situation.

69. Cooking Suppose you used an oven thermometer while baking and discovered that the oven temperature varied between $+5$ and -5 degrees from the setting. If your oven is set to $350°$, let t be the actual temperature.

70. Time Workers at a hardware store take their morning break no earlier than 10 A.M. and no later than noon. Let c represent the time the workers take their break.

71. Climate A friend is planning a trip to Alaska. He purchased a coat that is recommended for outdoor temperatures from $-15°$F to $45°$F. Let t represent the temperature for which the coat is intended.

Write an absolute value inequality and a compound inequality for each length x with the given tolerance.

72. a length of 36.80 mm with a tolerance of 0.05 mm

73. a length of 9.55 mm with a tolerance of 0.02 mm

74. a length of 100 yd with a tolerance of 4 in.

Is the absolute value inequality or equation *always*, *sometimes*, or *never* true? Explain.

75. $|x| = -6$

76. $-8 > |x|$

77. $|x| = x$

78. $|x| + |x| = 2x$

79. $|x + 2| = x + 2$

80. $(|x|)^2 < x^2$

81. Error Analysis A classmate wrote the solution to the inequality $|-4x + 1| > 3$ as shown. Describe and correct the error.

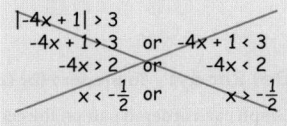

---

57. $-6 \le x \le 8\frac{2}{3}$

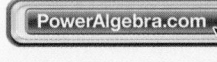

58. $x \le -8$ or $x \ge 5$

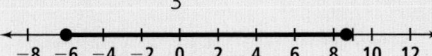

59. all real numbers

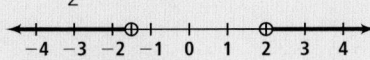

60. $t < -\frac{3}{2}$ or $t > 2$

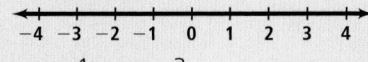

61. all real numbers

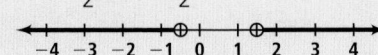

62. $x < -\frac{1}{2}$ or $x > \frac{3}{2}$

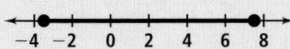

63. $x \le -8.4$ or $x \ge 9.6$

64. $-3.5 \le x \le 7.5$

65. $-5 < x < 11$

66. $x < -32$ or $x > 22$

67. The graph of $|x| < a$ is the set of all points on the number line that lie between a and $-a$. The graph of $|x| > a$ has two parts; the left part consists of the points to the left of $-a$, and the right part consists of the points to the right of a.

68. Answers may vary. Sample: $|x - 1| \ge 0$; $|x| < -5$

69. $|t - 350| \le 5$

70. $|c - 11| \le 1$

71. $|t - 15| \le 30$

72. $|x - 36.80| \le 0.05$; $36.75 \le x \le 36.85$

73. $|x - 9.55| \le 0.02$; $9.53 \le x \le 9.57$

74. x is in inches, $|x - 3600| \le 4$; $3596 \le x \le 3604$

75. never; absolute value is nonnegative

76. never; absolute value is nonnegative

77. sometimes; $|5| = 5$ but $|-5| \ne -5$

78. sometimes; $|-3| + |-3| \ne 2(-3)$

79. sometimes; $|-4 + 2| \ne -4 + 2$

80. never; squaring any number results in a positive result so the two sides will always equal.

81. The "3" in the second set of equations should be "-3."
$$-4x + 1 < -3$$
$$-4x < -4$$
$$x > 1 \text{ not } x > -\frac{1}{2}$$

Answers

Practice and Problem-Solving Exercises
(continued)

82. $-\dfrac{b+c}{a}, \dfrac{b+c}{a}, a \neq 0, b+c \geq 0$

83. $\dfrac{ab+d}{c}, \dfrac{-ab+d}{c}, c \neq 0, ab \geq 0$

84. $\dfrac{ac+d}{ab}, \dfrac{ac-d}{ab}, ab \neq 0, \dfrac{d}{a} \geq 0$

85. $(-6 \leq x \leq -5)$ or $(5 \leq x \leq 6)$

86. $(x \leq -6)$ or $(-5 < x < 5)$ or $(x \geq 6)$

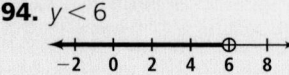

87. $x \geq \dfrac{5}{2}$

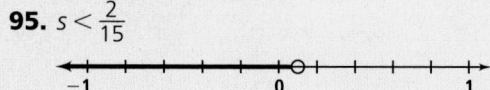

88. $|x+3| > 4$ becomes $x+3 > 4$ or $x+4 < -4$. $x+3$ is outside the interval from -4 to 4 so the solution is an *or* solution. $|x+3| < 4$ becomes $-4 < x+3 < 4$ so the solution is an *and* solution.

89. Use *and* if the absolute value is less than a value and use *or* if the absolute value is greater than a value.

Standardized Test Prep

90. $\dfrac{11}{3}$

91. 0

92. 1.875

93. 0.04

Mixed Review

94. $y < 6$

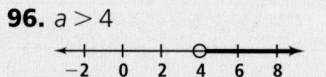

95. $s < \dfrac{2}{15}$

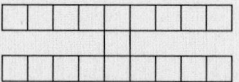

96. $a > 4$

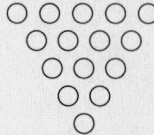

97. Each figure has 4 more squares than the previous figure.

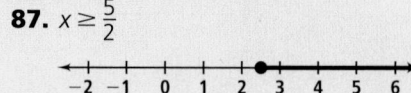

98. Each figure n has n more circles than the previous figure.

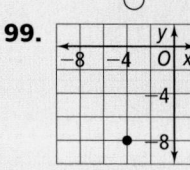

99.

---

48 Chapter 1

Challenge Solve each equation for x.

82. $|ax| - b = c$

83. $|cx - d| = ab$

84. $a|bx - c| = d$

Graph each solution.

85. $|x| \geq 5$ and $|x| \leq 6$

86. $|x| \geq 6$ or $|x| < 5$

87. $|x - 5| \leq x$

88. **Writing** Describe the difference between solving $|x+3| > 4$ and $|x+3| < 4$.

89. **Reasoning** How can you determine whether an absolute value inequality is equivalent to a compound inequality joined by the word *and* or one joined by the word *or*?

Standardized Test Prep

GRIDDED RESPONSE

SAT/ACT

90. What is the positive solution of $|3x + 8| = 19$?

91. If p is an integer, what is the least possible value of p in the following inequality?

$$|3p - 5| \leq 7$$

92. In wood shop, you have to drill a hole that is 2 inches deep into a wood panel. The tolerance for drilling a hole is described by the inequality $|t - 2| \leq 0.125$. What is the shallowest hole allowed?

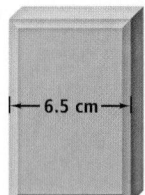

93. The normal thickness of a metal structure is shown. It expands to 6.54 centimeters when heated and shrinks to 6.46 centimeters when cooled down. What is the maximum amount in cm that the thickness of the structure can deviate from its normal thickness?

Mixed Review

Solve each inequality. Graph the solution.

◆ See Lesson 1-5.

94. $5y - 10 < 20$

95. $15(4s + 1) < 23$

96. $4a + 6 > 2a + 14$

Describe each pattern using words. Draw the next figure in each pattern.

◆ See Lesson 1-1.

97.

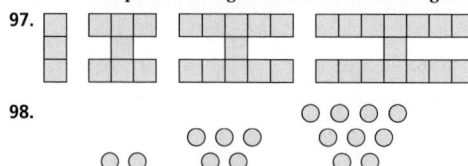

98.

Get Ready! To prepare for Lesson 2-1, do Exercises 99–102.

◆ See p. 977.

Graph each ordered pair on the coordinate plane.

99. $(-4, -8)$

100. $(3, 6)$

101. $(0, 0)$

102. $(-1, 3)$

100.

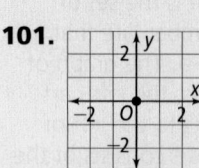

101.

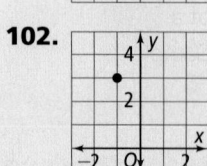

102.

Differentiated Remediation
Available in editable format online.

Additional Instructional Support

Algebra 2 Companion
Students can use the **Algebra 2 Companion** worktext (4 pages) as you teach the lesson. Use the Companion to support

- New Vocabulary
- Key Concepts
- Got It for each Problem
- Lesson Check

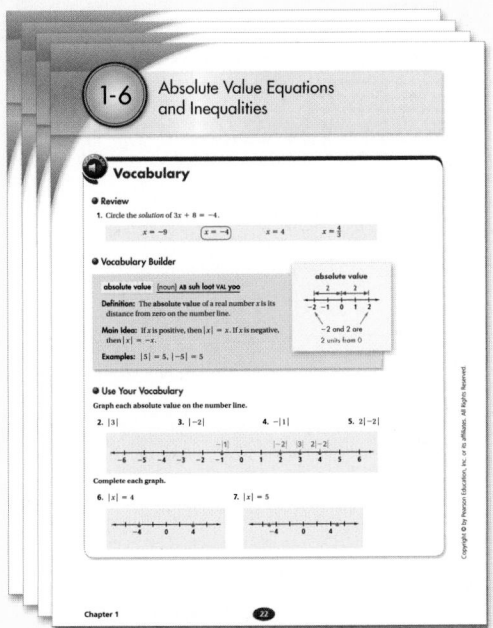

ELL Support

Connect to Prior Knowledge When learning the word *extraneous* highlight *extra*. Since an extraneous solution is not a solution in the original equation, it is *extra*.

Connect to Prior Knowledge Illustrate the difference between a real-life situation where the sign of an answer matters, such as temperature, and a real-life situation where the absolute value is more important, such as distance. Then have small groups of students list more real-life situations modeled either by absolute values or by signed numbers. Have the groups share some of their examples with the class.

5 Assess & Remediate

Lesson Quiz
1. Solve and graph $|3x + 1| = 8$.
2. What is the solution of $3|x - 7| - 2 = 4$?
3. What is the solution of $|2x + 1| = 3x + 4$?
4. Solve and graph $|4x + 1| < 5$.
5. Solve and graph $|3x - 2| \geq 7$.
6. **Do you UNDERSTAND?** You order 1.5 pounds of turkey at a deli. You will accept the turkey if its weight is between 1.54 and 1.46. What absolute value inequality describes the tolerance of the weight of the turkey?

ANSWERS TO LESSON QUIZ

1. $-3, \frac{7}{3}$

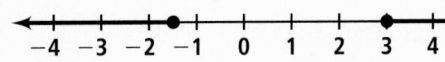
$$-5 \; -4 \; -3 \; -2 \; -1 \; 0 \; 1 \; 2 \; 3 \; 4 \; 5$$

2. 5, 9

3. -1

4. $-\frac{3}{2} < x < 1$

$$-3 \; -2 \; -1 \; 0 \; 1 \; 2 \; 3$$

5. $x \leq -\frac{5}{3}$ or $x \geq 3$

$$-4 \; -3 \; -2 \; -1 \; 0 \; 1 \; 2 \; 3 \; 4$$

6. $|x - 1.5| \leq 0.04$

PRESCRIPTION FOR REMEDIATION
Use the student work on the Lesson Quiz to prescribe a differentiated review assignment:

Points	Differentiated Remediation
0–3	Intervention
4–5	On-level
6	Extension

PowerAlgebra.com

5 Assess & Remediate
Assign the Lesson Quiz. Appropriate intervention, practice, or enrichment is automatically generated based on student performance.

Intervention

- **Reteaching** (2 pages) Provides reteaching and practice exercises for the key lesson concepts. Use with struggling students or absent students.
- **English Language Learner Support** Helps students develop and reinforce mathematical vocabulary and key concepts.

All-in-One Resources/Online
Reteaching

1-6 **Reteaching**
Absolute Value Equations and Inequalities

Solving absolute value equations require solving two equations separately. Recall that for a real number x, $|x|$ is the distance from zero to x on the number line. The equation $|x| = p$ means that either $x = p$ or $x = -p$ because both are p units from 0.

Problem

What is the solution set for the equation $|5x + 1| - 3 = 4$?

The first step in solving an absolute value equation is to isolate the absolute value on one side of the equal sign.

$|5x + 1| - 3 = 4$
$|5x + 1| - 3 + 3 = 4 + 3$ Add 3 to each side.
$|5x + 1| = 7$ Simplify.

Next, rewrite the absolute value as two equations and solve each of them separately.

$5x + 1 = 7$ or $5x + 1 = -7$ Definition of absolute value
$5x = 6$ or $5x = -8$ Addition Property of Equality
$x = \frac{6}{5}$ or $x = -\frac{8}{5}$ Division Property of Equality

Notice that the same operations are performed in the same order on each of the two equations. However, do not try to "simplify" the process by solving a single equation. This leads to errors.

The solutions are $x = \frac{6}{5}$ or $x = -\frac{8}{5}$. Check each solution in the original equation:

Check

$|5 \cdot \frac{6}{5} + 1| - 3 = 4$ $|5 \cdot (-\frac{8}{5}) + 1| - 3 = 4$
$|6 + 1| - 3 = 4$ $|-8 + 1| - 3 = 4$
$4 = 4$ ✓ $4 = 4$ ✓

Exercises

Solve each absolute value equation. Check your work.

1. $|2x - 3| - 4 = 3$ $x = -2$ or $x = 5$ 2. $|3x - 6| + 1 = 13$ $x = 6$ or $x = -2$

All-in-One Resources/Online
English Language Learner Support

1-6 **Additional Vocabulary Support**
Absolute Value Equations and Inequalities

Concept List

| $|x| < 3$ | $|x| > 3$ | $|x| \leq 3$ | $|x| \geq 3$ | $|x| = 3$ |

Choose the concept from the list below that best represents the item in each box.

1. numbers more than 3 units away from zero $|x| > 3$	2. numbers three units away from zero or more than three units away from 0 $|x| \geq 3$	3. $|x| < 3$
4. numbers less than 3 units away from zero $|x| < 3$	5. $|x| > 3$	6. numbers 3 units away from zero $|x| = 3$
7. $|x| \geq 3$	8. numbers three units away from zero or less than three units away from 0 $|x| \leq 3$	9. $|x| \leq 3$

Differentiated Remediation *continued*

Available in editable format online.

On-Level

- **Practice** (2 pages) Provides extra practice for each lesson. For simpler practice exercises, use the Form K Practice pages found in the All-in-One Teaching Resources and online.

- **Think About a Plan** Helps students develop specific problem-solving skills and strategies by providing scaffolded guiding questions.

- **Standardized Test Prep** Focuses on all major exercises, all major question types, and helps students prepare for the high-stakes assessments.

Extension

- **Enrichment** Provides students with interesting problems and activities that extend the concepts of the lesson.

- **Activities, Games, and Puzzles** Worksheets that can be used for concepts development, enrichment, and for fun!

Practice and Problem Solving Wkbk/ All-in-One Resources/Online
Practice page 1

1-6 Practice — Form G
Absolute Value Equations and Inequalities

Solve each equation. Check your answers.

1. $|-3x| = 18$ $x = 6$ or $x = -6$
2. $|5y| = 35$ $y = 7$ or $y = -7$
3. $|t + 5| = 8$ $t = 3$ or $t = -13$
4. $3|z + 7| = 12$ $z = -3$ or $z = -11$
5. $|2x - 1| = 5$ $x = 3$ or $x = -2$
6. $|4 - 2y| + 5 = 9$ $y = 4$ or $y = 0$

Solve each equation. Check for extraneous solutions.

7. $|x + 5| = 3x - 7$ $x = 6$
8. $|2t - 3| = 3t - 2$ $t = 1$
9. $|4w + 3| - 2 = 5w$ $w = 1$ or $w = -\frac{5}{9}$
10. $2|z + 1| - 3 = z - 2$ $z = -1$

Solve each inequality. Graph the solution.

11. $5|y + 3| < 15$ $-6 < y < 0$
12. $|2t - 3| \le 5$ $-1 \le t \le 4$
13. $|4b| - 3 > 9$ $b < -3$ or $b > 3$
14. $3|2w - 1| - 3 \ge 1$ $w \le -\frac{1}{2}$ or $w \ge \frac{5}{6}$
15. $2|4x + 1| - 5 \le 1$ $-1 \le x \le \frac{1}{2}$
16. $|3z - 2| + 5 > 9$ $z < -\frac{2}{3}$ or $z > 2$

Write each compound inequality as an absolute value inequality.

17. $-7.3 \le a \le 7.3$ $|a| \le 7.3$
18. $11 \le m \le 19$ $|m - 15| \le 4$
19. $28.6 \le F \le 29.2$ $|F - 28.9| \le 0.3$
20. $0.0015 \le t \le 0.0018$ $|t - 0.00165| \le 0.00015$

Write an absolute value equation or inequality to describe each graph.

21. $|x| = 6$
22. $|x| > 2.5$

Practice and Problem Solving Wkbk/ All-in-One Resources/Online
Practice page 2

1-6 Practice (continued) — Form G
Absolute Value Equations and Inequalities

Solve each equation.

23. $3|2x - 5| = 9x - 6$ $x = 7$
24. $|4 - 3m| = m + 10$ $m = 7$ or $m = -\frac{3}{2}$
25. $2|4w - 5| = 12w - 18$ $w = 2$
26. $\frac{3}{4}|8t - 12| = 6(t - 1)$ $t = \frac{5}{4}$
27. $|5p + 3| - 4 = 2p$ $p = \frac{1}{3}$ or $p = -1$
28. $|7y - 3| + 1 = 0$ no solution

Solve each inequality. Graph the solution.

29. $-3|2t + 1| < 9$ all real numbers
30. $|-2x + 4| \ge 4$ $x \le 0$ or $x \ge 4$
31. $\left|\frac{z}{3} + 2\right| - 1 < 2$ $-11 < z < 7$
32. $\frac{1}{3}|4z + 5| + 2 > 5$ $z < -\frac{13}{2}$ or $z > 4$

Write an absolute value inequality to represent each situation.

33. To become a potential volunteer donor listed on the National Marrow Donor Program registry, a person must be between the ages of 18 and 60. Let a represent the age of a person on the registry. $|a - 39| \le 21$

34. Two friends are hiking in Death Valley National Park. Their elevation ranges from 228 ft below sea level at Badwater to 690 ft above sea level at Zabriskie Point. Let x represent their elevation. $|x - 231| \le 459$

35. The outdoor temperature ranged between 37°F and 62°F in a 24-hour period. Let t represent the temperature during this time period. $|t - 49.5| \le 12.5$

The diameter of a ball bearing in a wheel assembly must be between 1.758 cm and 1.764 cm.

36. What is the tolerance? 0.003 cm

37. What absolute value inequality represents the diameter of the ball bearing? Let d represent the diameter in cm. $|d - 1.761| < 0.003$

All-in-One Resources/Online
Enrichment

1-6 Enrichment
Absolute Value Equations and Inequalities

When is the distance from six to ten less than the distance from one to two? When the distance is traveled on a word ladder! A word ladder is a sequence of words in which only one letter in each word changes. To find a word ladder beginning with the word ONE and ending with the word TWO, solve each of the following absolute value inequalities. Write the solutions in the form $a < x < b$, where a and b are integers.

Associated with each inequality is a pair of letters. Fill in the word ladder by placing the first letter of the pair on the line numbered by a and the second letter on the line numbered by b.

O	N	E		O	W	E		O	W	L
1	2	3		4	5	6		4	5	6

O	I	L		A	I	L		A	I	R
7	8	9		10	11	12		13	14	15

F	I	R		F	I	N		T	I	N
16	17	18		19	20	21		22	23	24

T	O	N		T	O	O		T	W	O
25	26	27		28	29	30				

OO $|3x - 51| < 39$ $4 < x < 30$
WL $3 < 10 - |11 - 2x|$ $2 < x < 9$
RI $|95 - 5x| + 3 < 23$ $15 < x < 23$
EF $|4x - 38| - 14 < 12$ $3 < x < 16$
IO $|x - 20| < 9$ $11 < x < 29$
II $2 < 5 - |x - 17|$ $14 < x < 20$
WO $|93 - 6x| < 63$ $5 < x < 26$
LL $|2x - 18| + 4 < 10$ $6 < x < 12$
II $|8x - 100| < 36$ $8 < x < 17$
AA $-6 < -|46 - 4x|$ $10 < x < 13$
RF $|4x - 74| + 7 < 9$ $18 < x < 19$
NN $5 < 20 - |225 - 10x|$ $21 < x < 24$
TT $3 + |106 - 4x| < 9$ $25 < x < 28$
ON $20 < 70 - |5x - 85|$ $7 < x < 27$
OT $|92 - 8x| - 40 < 44$ $1 < x < 22$

Practice and Problem Solving Wkbk/ All-in-One Resources/Online
Think About a Plan

1-6 Think About a Plan
Absolute Value Equations and Inequalities

Write an absolute value inequality to represent the situation.

Cooking Suppose you used an oven thermometer while baking and discovered that the oven temperature varied between $+5$ and -5 degrees from the setting. If your oven is set to 350°, let t be the actual temperature.

1. How do you have to think to solve this problem?
   If I subtract the set temperature from the real temperature, the result
   should be between −5° and 5°.

2. Write a compound inequality that represents the actual oven temperature t.
   $345 \le t \le 355$

3. It often helps to draw a picture. Graph this compound inequality on a number line.

4. What is the definition of tolerance?
   Tolerance is the difference between a desired measurement and its
   maximum and minimum allowable values. It equals half of the difference
   between the maximum and minimum values.

5. What is the tolerance of the oven?   5°

6. Use the tolerance to write an inequality without absolute values.
   $-5 \le t - 350 \le 5$

7. Rewrite the inequality as an absolute value inequality.
   $|t - 350| \le 5$

Practice and Problem Solving Wkbk/ All-in-One Resources/Online
Standardized Test Prep

1-6 Standardized Test Prep
Absolute Value Equations and Inequalities

Multiple Choice

For Exercises 1–5, choose the correct letter.

1. What is the solution of $|5t - 3| = 8$? C
   Ⓐ $t = 8$ or $t = -8$ Ⓒ $t = \frac{11}{5}$ or $t = -1$
   Ⓑ $t = 1$ or $t = -\frac{11}{5}$ Ⓓ $t = \frac{8}{5}$ or $t = -\frac{8}{5}$

2. What is the solution of $|3z - 2| \le 8$? F
   Ⓕ $-2 \le z \le \frac{10}{3}$ Ⓗ $z \le -2$ or $z \ge \frac{10}{3}$
   Ⓖ $-\frac{10}{3} \le z \le 2$ Ⓘ $z \le -\frac{10}{3}$ or $z \ge 2$

3. What is the solution of $\frac{1}{2}|2x + 3| - 1 > 1$? B
   Ⓐ $-\frac{7}{2} < x < \frac{1}{2}$ Ⓒ $x > \frac{7}{2}$ or $x < -\frac{1}{2}$
   Ⓑ $x < -\frac{7}{2}$ or $x > \frac{1}{2}$ Ⓓ $x < \frac{1}{2}$ or $x > -\frac{7}{2}$

4. Which absolute value inequality is equivalent to the compound inequality $23 \le T \le 45$? I
   Ⓕ $|T - 11| \le 34$ Ⓖ $|T - 45| \le 22$ Ⓗ $|T - 24| \le 1$ Ⓘ $|T - 34| \le 11$

5. Which is the correct graph for the solution of $|2b + 1| - 3 \le 2$? C

Short Response

6. An employee's monthly earnings at an electronics store are based on a salary plus commissions on her sales. Her earnings can range from $2500 to $3200, depending on her commission. Write a compound inequality to describe E, the amount of her monthly earnings. Then rewrite your inequality as an absolute value inequality.
   $2500 \le E \le 3200, |E - 2850| \le 350$
   [2] correct compound inequality and correct absolute value inequality
   [1] incorrect compound inequality OR incorrect absolute value inequality
   [0] no answer given

Online Teacher Resource Center
Activities, Games, and Puzzles

1-6 Activity: Rolling Out Inequalities
Absolute Value Equations and Inequalities

1. Roll a number cube. Plot the value of the roll on a number line.

2. Roll the number cube again. Using the same number line, plot two different points whose distances from the point in Step 1 are equal to the value of the roll.

3. Describe the points you plotted in Step 2 verbally.
   "I plotted two points on the number line that are [circle one] (*exactly, greater than, less than*) a distance of ⬚ units from ⬚."

4. Describe the two points you plotted in Step 2 mathematically.
   $|x - (1\text{st roll})| = (2\text{nd roll})$
   $x - (1\text{st roll}) = (2\text{nd roll})$ or $x - (1\text{st roll}) = -(2\text{nd roll})$
   $x - ⬚ = ⬚$ or $x - ⬚ = ⬚$
   $x = ⬚$ or $x = ⬚$

5. Roll the number cube a third time. If it is an even number, draw a line segment connecting the points you plotted in Step 2. If it is an odd number, draw two rays on the number line that do not intersect, with endpoints at the points you plotted in Step 2.

6. Describe the points you graphed in Step 5 verbally.
   "I plotted all points on the number line that are [circle one] (*exactly, greater than or equal to, less than or equal to*) a distance of ⬚ units from ⬚."

7. Describe the points you graphed in Step 5 mathematically. Refer to the setup in Step 4 for help.
   Check students' work.

Pull It **All Together**

 ## Completing the Performance Task

Look back at your results from the Apply What You've Learned sections in Lessons 1-2, 1-3, and 1-4. Use the work you did to complete the following.

1. Solve the problem in the Task Description on page 3 by determining how far Cody is from Mia's house when his car runs out of gas. Find all possible distances. Show all your work and explain each step of your solution.

2. **Reflect** Choose one of the Mathematical Practices below and explain how you applied it in your work on the Performance Task.

   MP 1: Make sense of problems and persevere in solving them.

   MP 2: Reason abstractly and quantitatively.

   MP 4: Model with mathematics.

On Your Own

Christine drives her car for her sales job. Her company allows her to drive no more than 50 mi per day.

On Tuesday, Christine drives to a business meeting 15 mi from her house. On her way, she realizes she left her laptop computer at home and must drive back to get it. After attending the business meeting, Christine drives to a client's office 8 mi down the road from the location of the business meeting, as shown in the diagram below. After meeting with her client, Christine drives home, returning by the same road.

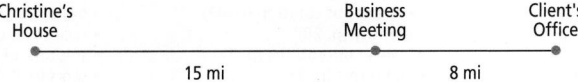

Christine's House	Business Meeting	Client's Office
15 mi	8 mi	

a. Write and simplify an algebraic expression that models the total distance Christine drives by the time she reaches her client's office. Be sure to tell what your variable represents.

b. In order for Christine not to exceed her company's daily mileage limit, what is the greatest distance she can drive before she turns around to go back for her laptop?

 ## Completing the Performance Task

In the Apply What You've Learned sections in Lessons 1-2, 1-3, and 1-4, students considered two cases for where Cody could be when his car runs out of gas, and wrote an equation that models the relationships among distances Mia drives for one of these cases. Now, students use this equation and write a second equation as they complete the task on page 3. Ask students the following questions as they work toward solving the problem.

> **Q** How can you use the work you have done in the chapter to solve the problem? **[Sample: I can use the equation I wrote in Lesson 1-4 to find the distance Cody's car is from the gas station if it runs out of gas between the gas station and the restaurant. Then I will add that distance to 9 mi to find the distance from Mia's house to Cody's car.]**
>
> **Q** How can you find all possible distances Cody could be from Mia's house when he runs out of gas? **[Sample: I can write and solve an equation for the case in which Cody's car runs out of gas between the gas station and the restaurant.]**

FOSTERING MATHEMATICAL DISCOURSE

Have students consider many possible ways to assign variables to the distances in the diagrams they drew to model the problem in the Performance Task. Look at the different equations that arise from different choices for assigning the variable, and have students show that all equations lead them to the same final answers. Advanced students may choose to use two variables and write a system of equations.

ANSWERS

1. 2 mi or 16 mi
2. Check students' work.

On Your Own

This problem is similar to the problem posed on page 3, but now students model a situation with an inequality. Students should strive to solve this problem independently.

ANSWERS

a. $2x + 23$, where x is the number of miles Christine drives before she turns around

b. 2 mi

Essential Questions

BIG idea **Variable**

ESSENTIAL QUESTION How do variables help you model real-world situations?

ANSWER You can use variables to represent variable quantities in real-world situations and in patterns.

BIG idea **Properties**

ESSENTIAL QUESTION How can you use the properties of real numbers to simplify algebraic expressions?

ANSWER The properties that apply to real numbers also apply to variables that represent them.

BIG idea **Solving Equations and Inequalities**

ESSENTIAL QUESTION How do you solve an equation or inequality?

ANSWER You can use properties of numbers and equality (or inequality) to solve an equation (or inequality) by finding increasingly simpler equations (or inequalities) which have the same solution as the original equation (or inequality).

 **Chapter Review**

Connecting **BIG** ideas and Answering Essential Questions

1 Variable
You can use variables to represent variable quantities in real-world situations and in patterns.

Patterns and Expressions (Lesson 1-1)
6, 12, 18, 24, . . . 6n
8, 9, 10, 11, . . . (n + 7)

Algebraic Expressions (Lesson 1-3)
$6n$
$n + 7$
$5x - x = (5 - 1)x$
$a + 0 = a$
$h + k = k + h$

2 Properties
The properties that apply to real numbers also apply to variables that represent them.

Properties of Real Numbers (Lesson 1-2)
$4(6 - 1) = 4(6) - 4(1)$
$23 + 0 = 23$
$5 + 12 = 12 + 5$

3 Solving Equations and Inequalities
You can use properties of numbers and equality (or inequality) to solve an equation (or inequality) by finding increasingly simpler equations (or inequalities) which have the same solution as the original equation (or inequality).

Solving Equations and Inequalities (Lessons 1-4 and 1-5)

$4x - 1 = 5$	$7 > -3h - 2$
$4x = 6$	$9 > -3h$
$x = \frac{3}{2}$	$-3 < h$

Absolute Value Equations and Inequalities (Lesson 1-6)
$|2b + 7| = 15$
$2b + 7 = 15$ or $2b + 7 = -15$
$2b = 8$ | $2b = -22$
$b = 4$ or $b = -11$

Chapter Vocabulary

- absolute value (p. 41)
- additive inverse (p. 14)
- algebraic expression (p. 5)
- coefficient (p. 20)
- compound inequality (p. 36)
- constant (p. 5)
- constant term (p. 20)
- equation (p. 26)
- evaluate (p. 19)
- extraneous solution (p. 42)
- identity (p. 28)
- inverse operations (p. 27)
- like terms (p. 21)
- literal equation (p. 29)
- multiplicative inverse (p. 14)
- numerical expression (p. 5)
- opposite (p. 14)
- reciprocal (p. 14)
- solution of an equation (p. 27)
- term (p. 20)
- variable (p. 5)
- variable quantity (p. 5)

Choose the correct term to complete each sentence.

1. The ? makes an equation true.

2. A number's distance from zero on the number line is its ? .

3. ? is another name for the multiplicative inverse of a number.

4. A pair of inequalities joined by *and* or *or* are called a ? .

Summative Questions

Use the following prompts as you review this chapter with your students. The prompts are designed to assess your students' understanding of the BIG Ideas they have studied.

- The expression $\frac{2}{3}n + 3$ describes a pattern of numbers. To which set of real numbers do the numbers in this pattern belong?
- Which property would you use to start the solution of $3|x + 4| - 2 = 7$?
- Describe the graph of $5 < 2x + 1$. How would the graph change if you reversed the inequality sign?

1-1 Patterns and Expressions

Quick Review

You can represent patterns using words, diagrams, numbers, and **algebraic expressions**. You can identify a pattern by looking for the same type of change between consecutive figures or numbers. It often helps to make a table.

Example

Identify a pattern by making a table of inputs and outputs. Include a process column. 7, 14, 21, 28, 35, . . .

Input	Process Column	Output
1	1 · 7	7
2	2 · 7	14
3	3 · 7	21
⋮	⋮	⋮
n	n · 7	7n

The *n*th output is 7*n*.

Exercises

Identify a pattern and find the next three numbers in the pattern.

5. 5, 10, 15, 20, ...   **6.** 3, 4, 5, 6, ...

Copy and complete the table. Then find the output when the input is *n*.

7.

Input	Output
1	9
2	10
3	11
4	■
⋮	⋮
n	■

8.

Input	Output
1	19
2	38
3	57
4	■
⋮	⋮
n	■

9. Finance If you put $20 in your savings account each week, how much have you saved after *n* weeks?

1-2 Properties of Real Numbers

Quick Review

The natural numbers, whole numbers, integers, rational numbers, and irrational numbers are all subsets of the real numbers.

You can use properties such as the ones listed below to simplify and evaluate expressions.

Commutative Properties	$-3 + 5 = 5 + (-3)$
	$2 \times 9 = 9 \times 2$
Associative Properties	$3 + (5 + 7) = (3 + 5) + 7$
	$4 \times (8 \times 11) = (4 \times 8) \times 11$
Distributive Property	$5(7 + 9) = 5(7) + 5(9)$

Example

Identify the property illustrated by the equation.

$4 \cdot x = x \cdot 4$ Commutative Property of Multiplication

Exercises

Name the subset(s) of real numbers to which each number belongs.

10. 8.1π **11.** -79

12. $\sqrt{121}$ **13.** $12\frac{7}{8}$

Compare the two numbers. Use < or >.

14. $-\sqrt{60}, -8$ **15.** $5, \sqrt{32}$

Name the property of real numbers illustrated by each equation.

16. $\frac{9}{4} \cdot \frac{4}{9} = 1$

17. $\left(8 \cdot \frac{1}{3}\right) \cdot 12 = 8 \cdot \left(\frac{1}{3} \cdot 12\right)$

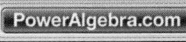
Answers

Chapter Review

1. solution of the equation

2. absolute value

3. reciprocal

4. compound inequality

5. add 5; 25, 30, 35

6. add 1; 7, 8, 9

7. 12; $n + 8$

8. 76; 19n **9.** 20n$

10. irrational numbers

11. rational numbers, integers

12. rational numbers, integers, whole numbers, natural numbers

13. rational numbers

14. $-\sqrt{60} > -8$, or $-8 < -\sqrt{60}$

15. $5 < \sqrt{32}$, or $\sqrt{32} > 5$

16. Inv. Prop. of Mult.

17. Assoc. Prop. of Mult.

Answers

Chapter Review (continued)

18. 114

19. $5b$

20. 11

21. 6

22. $z \le \dfrac{2}{5}$

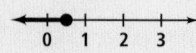

23. $x > 2$

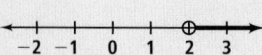

24. no solution

25. $x \le \dfrac{3}{2}$ or $x > 6$

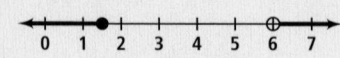

26. 10 cm, 6 cm

27. 1

28. no solution

29. $x = -8$ or $x = -12$

30. no solution

31. $-\dfrac{1}{3} \le x \le \dfrac{5}{3}$

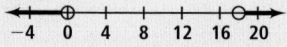

32. $y < 0$ or $y > 18$

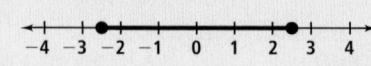

33. $-\dfrac{18}{7} \le x \le \dfrac{18}{7}$

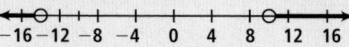

34. $x < -14$ or $x > 10$

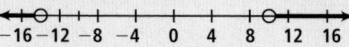

35. $|x - 43.6| \le 0.1$

1-3, 1-4, and 1-5 Expressions, Equations, and Inequalities

Quick Review

You **evaluate** an algebraic expression by substituting numbers for the variables. You simplify an algebraic expression by combining **like terms**. To find the **solution of an equation** or inequality, use the properties of equality or inequality. Some **equations** and inequalities are true for all real numbers, and some have no solution.

Example

Evaluate $3(x - 4) + 2x - x^2$ for $x = 6$.

$3(6 - 4) + 2(6) - 6^2$ Substitute.

$= 3(2) + 2(6) - 6^2$ Simplify inside parentheses.

$= 6 + 12 - 36$ Multiply.

$= 18 - 36$ Add.

$= -18$ Subtract.

Exercises

18. Evaluate $3t(t + 2) - 3t^2$ for $t = 19$.

19. Simplify $-(3a - 2b) - 3(-a - b)$.

Solve each equation. Check your answer.

20. $2x - 5 = 17$ **21.** $3(x + 1) = 9 + 2x$

Solve each inequality. Graph the solution.

22. $4 - 5z \ge 2$

23. $2(5 - 3x) < x - 4(3 - x)$

Solve each compound inequality. Graph the solution.

24. $10 \ge 7 + 3x$ and   **25.** $3 \ge 2x$ or
     $9 - 4x \le 1$ $x - 4 > 2$

Write an equation to solve the problem.

26. Geometry The length and width of a rectangle are in the ratio 5 : 3. The perimeter of the rectangle is 32 cm. Find the length and width.

1-6 Absolute Value Equations and Inequalities

Quick Review

To rewrite an equation or inequality that involves the **absolute value** of an algebraic expression, you must consider both cases of the definition of absolute value.

Example

Solve $|3x - 5| = 4 + 2x$. Check for extraneous solutions.

$3x - 5 = 4 + 2x$ or $3x - 5 = -(4 + 2x)$

                 $3x - 5 = -4 - 2x$

                 $5x = 1$

$x = 9$ or $x = \dfrac{1}{5}$

Check $|3(9) - 5| \overset{?}{=} 4 + 2(9)$ $\left|3\left(\dfrac{1}{5}\right) - 5\right| \overset{?}{=} 4 + 2\left(\dfrac{1}{5}\right)$

$|27 - 5| \overset{?}{=} 22$ $\left|\dfrac{3}{5} - 5\right| \overset{?}{=} 4 + \dfrac{2}{5}$

$|22| = 22$ ✔ $\left|-\dfrac{22}{5}\right| = \dfrac{22}{5}$ ✔

Exercises

Solve each equation. Check for extraneous solutions.

27. $|2x + 8| = 3x + 7$ **28.** $|x - 4| + 3 = 1$

29. $3|x + 10| = 6$ **30.** $2|x - 7| = x - 8$

Solve each inequality. Graph the solution.

31. $|3x - 2| + 4 \le 7$ **32.** $4|y - 9| > 36$

33. $|7x| + 3 \le 21$ **34.** $\dfrac{1}{2}|x + 2| > 6$

35. The specification for a length x is 43.6 cm with a tolerance of 0.1 cm. Write the specification as an absolute value inequality.

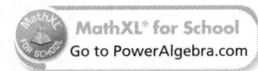
MathXL® for School
Go to PowerAlgebra.com

Do you know HOW?

Evaluate each expression for $x = 5$.

1. $\frac{5}{3}(3x - 6) - (6 - 4x)$

2. $3(x^2 - 4) + 7(x - 2)$

3. $x - 2x + 3x - 4x + 5x$

Simplify each expression.

4. $a^2 + a + a^2$

5. $2x + 3y - 5x + 2y$

6. $5(a - 2b) - 3(a - 2b)$

7. $3[2(x - 3) + 2] + 5(x - 3)$

Solve each equation.

8. $4y - 6 = 2y + 8$

9. $3(2z + 1) = 35$

10. $5(3w - 2) - 7 = 23$

11. $t - 2(3 - 2t) = 2t + 9$

12. $5(s - 12) - 24 = 3(s + 2)$

13. The lateral surface area of a cylinder is given by the formula $S = 2\pi rh$. Solve the equation for r.

14. Savings Briana and her sister Molly both want to buy the same model bicycle. Briana needs $73 more before she can afford the bike. Molly needs $65 more. If they combine their money, they will have just enough to buy one bicycle that they could share. What is the cost of the bicycle?

15. Musical There is only one freshman in the cast of a high school musical. There are 6 sophomores and 11 juniors. One third of the cast are seniors. How many seniors are in the musical?

Determine whether each equation is *always*, *sometimes*, or *never* true.

16. $2x + 7 - x = 3 + x + 4$

17. $5a - 1 - 3a = 2a + 1$

Solve each equation or inequality. Graph the solution.

18. $3x + 17 \geq 5$

19. $25 - 2x < 11$

20. $\frac{3}{8}x < -6$ or $5x > 2$

21. $2 < 10 - 4d < 6$

22. $4 - x = |2 - 3x|$

23. $5|3w + 2| - 3 > 7$

Do you UNDERSTAND?

24. Writing Describe the relationships among these sets of numbers: natural numbers, whole numbers, integers, rational numbers, irrational numbers, and real numbers.

25. Reasoning Justify each step by identifying the property used.

$$t + 5(t + 1) = t + (5t + 5)$$
$$= (t + 5t) + 5$$
$$= (1t + 5t) + 5$$
$$= (1 + 5)t + 5$$
$$= 6t + 5$$

26. Reasoning The first four figures of a pattern are shown.

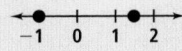

Describe the tenth figure in the pattern.

---

24. Answers may vary. Sample: The natural numbers are the counting numbers (1, 2, 3, . . .); the whole numbers are the natural numbers and zero (0, 1, 2, 3, . . .); the integers are the whole numbers and their opposites (. . . , −3, −2, −1, 0, 1, 2, 3, . . .); the rational numbers are all numbers you can write as a quotient of integers $\frac{a}{b}$, $b \neq 0$; the irrational numbers are decimal representations that neither terminate nor repeat; and the real numbers include all rational numbers and irrational numbers.

25. Distr. Prop.; Assoc. Prop. of Add.; Ident. Prop. of Mult.; Distr. Prop.; add.

26. A triangle formed from 100 smaller triangles arranged in 10 rows.

Chapter Test

1. 29

2. 84

3. 15

4. $2a^2 + a$

5. $-3x + 5y$

6. $2a - 4b$

7. $11x - 27$

8. 7

9. $\frac{16}{3}$

10. $\frac{8}{3}$

11. 5

12. 45

13. $r = \frac{S}{2\pi h}$

14. $138

15. 9 seniors

16. always

17. never

18. $x \geq -4$

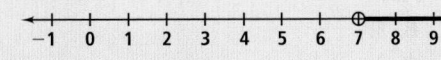

19. $x > 7$

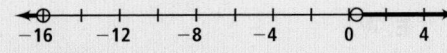

20. $x < -16$ or $x > \frac{2}{5}$

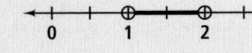

21. $1 < d < 2$

22. $-1, \frac{3}{2}$

23. $w < -\frac{4}{3}$ or $w > 0$

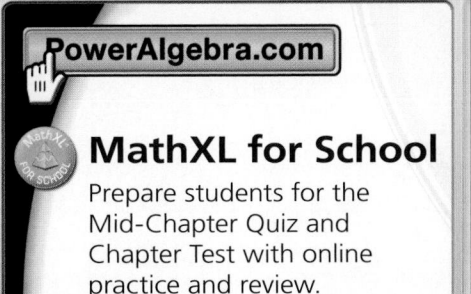

Item Number	Lesson	© Content Standard
1	1-3	*A-SSE.A.1a
2	1-1	*A-SSE.B.3
3	1-6	A-CED.A.1
4	1-5	A-CED.A.1
5	1-3	*A-SSE.A.1a
6	1-5	A-CED.A.1
7	1-6	A-CED.A.1
8	1-6	A-CED.A.1
9	1-1	*A-SSE.B.3
10	1-6	A-CED.A.1
11	1-6	*A-SSE.A.1b
12	1-4	A-CED.A.1
13	1-6	A-CED.A.1
14	1-3	*A-SSE.A.1a
15	1-3	*A-SSE.A.1b
16	1-3	*A-SSE.A.1a
17	1-3	*A-SSE.A.1a
18	1-6	A-CED.A.1
19	1-2	*N-RN.B.3
20	1-4	A-CED.A.4
21	1-4	A-CED.A.4

* Reviews Standard

TIPS FOR SUCCESS

Some questions on tests ask you to write a short response. To get full credit for an answer, you must give the correct answer (including appropriate units, if applicable) and justify your reasoning or show your work. Read the sample question at the right. Then follow the tips to answer it.

TIP 1
Think about the total cost to make a batch of muffins.

Short Response Your school is having a bake sale to raise money for a field trip. The ingredients for each batch of bran muffins cost $3.25, and the cost for the energy to bake them is $.50. You plan to sell each batch for $5.

Write an expression to represent the total amount of money your school will have after selling n batches of muffins. Evaluate your expression for 25 batches. Show your work.

TIP 2
You need to make a profit in the bake sale in order to raise money. Consider the total sales and the cost to make the muffins. What operation do you use to find the profit?

Think It Through
It costs $3.25 + $.50 = $3.75 to bake each batch. The school makes $5 − ($3.75) = $1.25 after selling one batch. So, it makes $1.25n$ after selling n batches. It earns $1.25(25) = $31.25 after selling 25 batches. This answer is complete and earns full credit.

🔊 Vocabulary Builder

As you solve test items, you must understand the meanings of mathematical terms. Match each term with its mathematical meaning.

A. inequality

B. compound inequality

C. extraneous solution

D. expression

E. equation

I. a mathematical sentence that contains $>$, $<$, $\geq$, $\leq$, or $\neq$

II. a solution of an equation derived from an original equation but not a solution of the original equation

III. a pair of inequalities joined by *and* or *or*

IV. a mathematical sentence that contains an equals sign

V. a mathematical phrase that uses numbers, variables, and operational symbols

Selected Response

Read each question. Then write the letter of the correct answer on your paper.

1. A person receives a salary of $600 a month and a 10% commission of all sales made. Which expression can be used to find the person's income when the sales amount is x?

Ⓐ $x + 600$ Ⓒ $10x + 600$
Ⓑ $600 - 0.10x$ Ⓓ $0.10x + 600$

2. Which expression can be used to find the next term of the sequence 1, 4, 9, 16, . . . ?

Ⓕ $2n$ Ⓗ $n^2 + 1$
Ⓖ $n + 3$ Ⓘ n^2

Answers

Common Core Cumulative Standards Review

A. I
B. III
C. II
D. V
E. IV
1. D
2. I

3. Which inequality has a solution that matches the graph below?

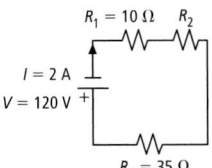

Ⓐ $|x-2|-3 > -2$

Ⓑ $|x-2| < -5$

Ⓒ $|x+2|+3 < 2$

Ⓓ $|x+4|+2 > 1$

4. A worker is taking boxes of nails on an elevator. Each box weighs 54 lb, and the worker weighs 170 lb. The elevator has a weight limit of 2500 lb. Which inequality describes the number of boxes b that he can safely take on each trip?

Ⓕ $54b - 170 \le 2500$

Ⓖ $54b + 170 \le 2500$

Ⓗ $54(b - 170) \le 2500$

Ⓘ $54(b + 170) \le 2500$

5. An electrical circuit is connected in series as shown. The total voltage V can be calculated by using the equation shown, where I is the total current and R is the resistance across the circuit. $\left(Hint: 1A = 1\frac{volt}{ohm} \right)$

$V = I(R_1 + R_2 + R_3)$

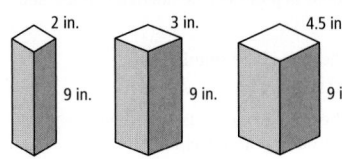

A = amperes
V = volts
Ω = ohms

What is the value of R_2?

Ⓐ 15 Ω   Ⓒ 60 Ω

Ⓑ 45 Ω   Ⓓ 75 Ω

6. Solve $3(x - 2) + 4 \ge -3x + 1$.

Ⓕ $x \ge -3$ Ⓗ $x \ge \frac{3}{2}$

Ⓖ $x \ge \frac{1}{2}$ Ⓘ $x \le 3$

7. You used an oven thermometer while baking and found out that the oven temperature varied between $+7$ degrees and -7 degrees from the setting. If your oven is set to 325°F, let t be the actual temperature. What is the absolute value inequality that represents this situation?

Ⓐ $|t - 325| \ge 7$

Ⓑ $|t - 325| < 7$

Ⓒ $|t - 7| \le 325$

Ⓓ $|t - 325| \le 7$

8. A designer is designing a handbag. The height of the handbag must be between 16 in. and 18 in. The desirable height is 17 in. Which absolute value inequality represents the height of the handbag?

Ⓕ $|h - 16| \le 1$ Ⓗ $|h - 17| \ge 2$

Ⓖ $|h - 17| \le 1$ Ⓘ $|h - 18| \ge 2$

9. A company makes gift boxes in different sizes following the pattern shown below. What is the volume of the fourth gift box to the nearest cubic inch?

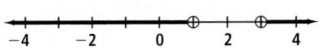

2 in.   3 in.   4.5 in.

9 in.   9 in.   9 in.

Ⓐ 324 in.³

Ⓑ 352 in.³

Ⓒ 376 in.³

Ⓓ 410 in.³

10. How many negative solutions does $2|3x - 6| \le 6$ have?

Ⓕ 0   Ⓗ 2

Ⓖ 1   Ⓘ infinitely many

11. For which value of a does $4 = a + |x - 4|$ have no solution?

Ⓐ -6 Ⓒ 4

Ⓑ 0   Ⓓ 6

3. A
4. G
5. A
6. G
7. D
8. G
9. D
10. F
11. D

Answers

Common Core Cumulative Standards Review (continued)

12. 7.5

13. -4

14. 2.75

15. 5.40

16. 32

17. 24

18. [2] $\dfrac{10.05 - 9.95}{2} = \dfrac{0.1}{2} = 0.05$

$-0.05 \le d - 10 \le 0.05$
$|d - 10| \le 0.05$

    [1] correct tolerance, but incorrect inequality OR a computational error

19. [2] Irrational; the product of a rational nonzero number and an irrational number is always irrational.

    [1] correct answer, without an explanation

20. [4] **a.** $A = 8b + 8$ OR equivalent equation

    b. $b = \dfrac{A - 8}{8}$ OR equivalent equation

    c. 12 ft

    [3] one minor computational error

    [2] two correct answers, but minor computational error on third

    [1] incomplete answer

21. [4] **a.** $V = Bx$; $V = B(2x)$

    b. $x = \dfrac{V}{B}$; $x = \dfrac{V}{2B}$

    c. Answers may vary. Sample: The shorter cylinder has one half the volume of the taller cylinder for all values of x.

    [3] one minor computational error

    [2] two correct answers, but minor computational error on third

    [1] incomplete answer

Constructed Response

12. The graph shows the amount of paint needed (in gallons) to paint the walls (in square feet) of an office building.

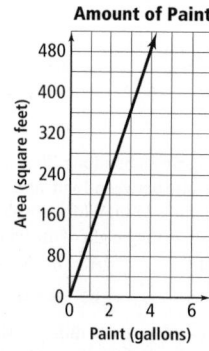

Amount of Paint

The pattern can be represented by $y = 120x$. How many gallons of paint will be needed to paint 900 square feet?

13. What is the sum of the solutions of $|2x + 4| - 6 = 8$?

14. What is the value of $4x^2 + 2x - 1$ when $x = \frac{3}{4}$? Express the answer as a decimal.

15. The cost for taking a taxi is $1.80 plus $.10 per eighth of a mile. What is the cost of a ride that is 4.5 miles long?

16. What is the coefficient of b in the simplified form of the expression $-8(a - 3b) + 2(-a + 4b + 1)$?

17. The expression $21 + 0.5n$ describes the length in inches of a baby n months old. How long is the baby at 6 months?

18. A new 10-lb dumbbell will pass inspection if it is between 9.95 lb and 10.05 lb. What is the tolerance of the weight of the dumbbell? What absolute value inequality describes acceptable weights of the dumbbell within an indicated tolerance? Show all work.

19. Is $7\sqrt{56}$ rational or irrational? Explain.

Extended Response

20. A trapezoidal deck has dimensions as shown.

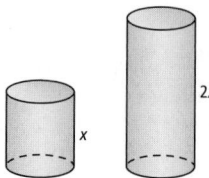

    a. What is a formula for the area of this trapezoid?

    b. Rearrange the formula so that it is solved for b. Show all work.

    c. What is the longer base length if the area is 88 square feet (ft^2)?

21. The two cylinders below have identical bases.

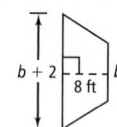

    a. Write an equation for the volume of each cylinder in terms of x.

    b. Solve each equation you wrote in (a) for x. Show all work.

    c. Compare the volume of the shorter cylinder with the volume of the taller cylinder.

Get Ready!

Get Ready!
Assign this diagnostic assessment to determine if students have the prerequisite skills for Chapter 2.

Lesson	Skill
1-3	Simplify Expressions
1-4	Solve Equations
1-6	Solve Absolute Value Inequalities

To remediate students, select from these resources (available for every lesson).
- Online Problems (PowerAlgebra.com)
- Reteaching (All-in-One Teaching Resources)
- Practice (All-in-One Teaching Resources)

Why Students Need These Skills
SIMPLIFYING EXPRESSIONS
Students will simplify equivalent expressions when converting an equation from one form to another.
SOLVING EQUATIONS
Solving equations for one variable prepares students to solve an equation for one variable in terms of another variable. The resulting expression is the function rule for finding the value of one variable given the value of the second.
SOLVING ABSOLUTE VALUE INEQUALITIES
Solving absolute value inequalities in one variable prepares students to solve and graph absolute value inequalities in two variables.

Looking Ahead Vocabulary
DOMAIN Ask students how a person's domain affects their range of interests.
RATE OF CHANGE Ask students to name other common examples of rate of change.
REFLECTION To better understand this, have students sketch a simple figure and its reflection. Have them identify a line of symmetry.
BOUNDARY Ask students how an inequality limits the possible solutions. Ask how they could form a boundary on a plane.

Lesson 1-3 ◆ Simplifying Expressions

Simplify by combining like terms.

1. $7s - s$ **2.** $3a + b + a$ **3.** $xy - y + x$

4. $0.5g + g$ **5.** $4t - (t + 3t)$ **6.** $b - 2(1 + c - b)$

7. $5f - (5d - f)$ **8.** $2(h + 2g) - (g - h)$ **9.** $-(3z - 5) + z$

10. $(2 - d)g - 3d(4 + g)$ **11.** $5v - 3(2 - v)$ **12.** $7t - 3s(2 + t) + s$

Lesson 1-4 ◆ Solving Equations

Solve each equation.

13. $4 + x = -52$ **14.** $-y + 13 = -67$ **15.** $12 = 2 - k$

16. $3x = -72$ **17.** $\frac{h}{5} = 215$ **18.** $64 = 4 + 12g$

19. $5 - 4t = 12$ **20.** $7x - 9 = x$ **21.** $3(w - 8) = 36$

22. $-10p = 2(p - 12)$ **23.** $3(2 - c) = -(c + 4)$ **24.** $7 + b = 11(b - 3)$

Lesson 1-6 ◆ Solving Absolute Value Inequalities

Solve each absolute value inequality. Graph the solution.

25. $|x - 3| < 5$ **26.** $|2a - 1| \geq 2a + 1$ **27.** $|3x + 4| > -4x - 3$

28. $|3x + 1| + 1 > 12$ **29.** $3|d - 4| \leq 13 - d$ **30.** $-\frac{1}{3}|f + 3| + 2 \geq -5$

◆)) Looking Ahead Vocabulary

31. A person's field of study is often called that person's *domain*. If your domain is American history, what topics might you be interested in?

32. When is a person's height likely to show a greater *rate of change*, from 1 to 2 years of age or from 30 to 31 years of age? Explain.

33. When you look in the mirror, you see your *reflection*. How does the image in the mirror differ from the way other people see you? How is it the same?

34. The boundaries of a country determine the limit of the country's land. How does an inequality form a *boundary* on a number line?

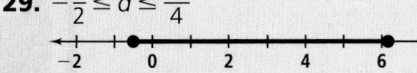

Answers

Get Ready!

1. $6s$ **2.** $4a + b$

3. $xy - y + x$ **4.** $1.5g$

5. 0 **6.** $3b - 2c - 2$

7. $6f - 5d$ **8.** $3h + 3g$

9. $-2z + 5$

10. $2g - 4dg - 12d$

11. $8v - 6$ **12.** $7t - 3st - 5s$

13. -56 **14.** 80

15. -10 **16.** -24

17. 1075 **18.** 5

19. -1.75 **20.** 1.5

21. 20 **22.** 2

23. 5 **24.** 4

25. $-2 < x < 8$

26. $a \leq 0$

27. $x > -1$

28. $x < -4 \text{ or } x > \frac{10}{3}$

29. $-\frac{1}{2} \leq d \leq \frac{25}{4}$

30. $-24 \leq f \leq 18$

31. Answers may vary. Sample: the Civil War, the Great Depression, the Louisiana Purchase

32. Answers may vary. Sample: From 1 to 2 years of age; a person has usually stopped growing by age 30, but a baby is still growing at age 1.

33. Answers may vary. Sample: The image is a reflection, left to right, of what other people see; the size is the same.

34. Answers may vary. Sample: An inequality determines the limit of a value, or a boundary, for the solution on the number line.

Chapter 2 Overview

Chapter 2 expands on students' understandings and skills related to functions, equations, and graphs. In this chapter, students will develop the answers to the Essential Questions as they learn the concepts and skills bulleted below.

BIG idea Equivalence

ESSENTIAL QUESTION Does it matter which form of a linear equation you use?

- Students will identify different forms of linear equations.
- Students will determine which form of a linear equation is most easily found with the given information.
- Students will convert between various forms of linear equations.

BIG idea Function

ESSENTIAL QUESTION How do you use transformations to help graph absolute value functions?

- Students will identify the different kinds of transformations.
- Students will determine whether a transformation changes the location or shape of a graph or both.

BIG idea Modeling

ESSENTIAL QUESTION How can you model data with a linear function?

- Students will make a scatter plot of linear data.
- Students will determine the correlation of linear data.
- Students will use linear regression to find the line of best fit of linear data with a graphing calculator.
- Students will use the correlation coefficient to analyze linear data with a graphing calculator.

© Content Standards

Following are the standards covered in this chapter. Modeling standards are indicated by a star symbol (★).

CONCEPTUAL CATEGORY Functions

Domain Interpreting Functions F-IF

Cluster Interpret functions that arise in applications in terms of the context. (Standards F-IF.B.4★, F-IF.B.6★)
LESSON 2-5

Cluster Analyze functions using different representations. (Standards F-IF.C.7a★, F-IF.C.7b★, F-IF.C.8, F-IF.C.9)
LESSONS 2-4, 2-7

Domain Building Functions F-BF

Cluster Build new functions from existing functions. (Standard F-BF.A.3)
LESSONS 2-6, 2-7

CHAPTER 2 Functions, Equations, and Graphs

Chapter Preview

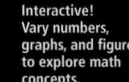 Download videos connecting math to your world.

 Interactive! Vary numbers, graphs, and figures to explore math concepts.

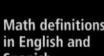 The online Solve It will get you in gear for each lesson.

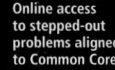 Math definitions in English and Spanish

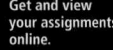 Online access to stepped-out problems aligned to Common Core

 Get and view your assignments online.

Extra practice and review online

Virtual Nerd™ tutorials with built-in support

Vocabulary

English/Spanish Vocabulary Audio Online:

English	Spanish
correlation, p. 92	correlación
direct variation, p. 68	variación directa
domain, p. 61	dominio
function, p. 62	función
linear equation, p. 75	ecuación lineal
range, p. 61	rango
relation, p. 60	relación
slope, p. 74	pendiente

BIG ideas

1 **Equivalence**
Essential Question Does it matter wh form of a linear equation you use?

2 **Function**
Essential Question How do you use transformations to help graph absolute value functions?

3 **Modeling**
Essential Question How can you mod data with a linear function?

 DOMAINS
- Interpreting Functions
- Building Functions
- Creating Equations

 PowerAlgebra.com

Chapter 2 Overview

Use these online assets to engage your students. These include support for the Solve It and step-by-step solutions for Problems.

 Show the student-produced video demonstrating relevant and engaging applications of the new concepts in the chapter.

 Find online definitions for new terms in English and Spanish.

 Start each lesson with an attention-getting Problem. View the Problem online with helpful hints.

Common Core Performance Task

Road Maintenance

A county's Department of Transportation is repainting the lane lines on Main Street. Several streets that intersect Main Street are shown in the diagram below.

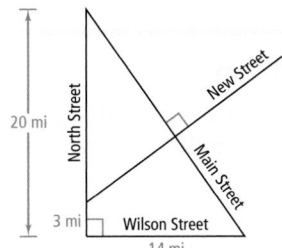

At 1 P.M., the work crew starts at the intersection of New Street and Main Street and moves toward the intersection of Main Street and Wilson Street, painting lane lines at an average speed of 5 mi/h. The work crew will take its afternoon break when it is 3 mi from the intersection of Main Street and Wilson Street.

Task Description
Determine what time the work crew will take its afternoon break.

Connecting the Task to the Math Practices

 **MATHEMATICAL PRACTICES**

As you complete the task, you'll apply these Standards for Mathematical Practice.

• You'll use a coordinate plane to model the streets in the diagram. (MP 4)

• You'll write equations of lines to represent streets, and you will write and interpret a function modeling a distance that changes over time. (MP 2)

 Increase students' depth of knowledge with interactive online activities.

 Show Problems from each lesson solved step by step. Instant replay allows students to go at their own pace when studying online.

 Assign homework to individual students or to an entire class.

 Prepare students for the Mid-Chapter Quiz and Chapter Test with online practice and review.

 Virtual Nerd™ Access Virtual Nerd student-centered math tutorials that directly relate to the content of the lesson.

 ## Overview of the Performance Task

Students will superimpose a coordinate system on a diagram showing the intersections of several streets. They will write equations for the lines representing the streets and find a distance between two intersections. Then they will use this distance to determine what time a work crew reaches a specified point.

Students will work on the Performance Task in the following places in the chapter.

• Lesson 2-3 (p. 80)
• Lesson 2-4 (p. 88)
• Pull it All Together (p. 121)

Introducing the Performance Task

Tell students to read the problem on this page. Do not have them start work on the problem at this time, but ask them the following questions.

Q What do you need to find in order to determine the time the work crew takes its break? **[Sample: I need to find the distance between the intersection of New Street and Main Street and the intersection of Main Street and Wilson Street.]**

Q What is a strategy you could try in order to find the distance between the intersection of New Street and Main Street and the intersection of Main Street and Wilson Street? **[Sample: I could use lines graphed in a coordinate system to represent the streets and find the coordinates of the intersection points. Then I could use the Distance Formula to find the distance.]**

PARCC CLAIMS
Sub-Claim B: Additional and Supporting Content With Connections to Practices
Sub-Claim D: Highlighted Practice MP 4 With Connections to Content

SBAC CLAIMS
Claim 2: Problem Solving
Claim 4: Modeling and Data Analysis

Content Standards (cont')

CONCEPTUAL CATEGORY Algebra
Domain Creating Equations A-CED
Cluster Create equations that describe numbers or relationships. (Standard A-CED-A.2★)
LESSONS 2-2, 2-3, 2-4, 2-5, 2-8

FUNCTIONS, EQUATIONS, AND GRAPHS
Math Background © PROFESSIONAL DEVELOPMENT

The Understanding by Design® methodology was central to the development of the Big Ideas and the Essential Understandings. These will help your students build a structure on which to make connections to prior learning.

UNDERSTANDING PROGRAM ORGANIZATION

Equivalence

BIG idea A single quantity may be represented by many different expressions. The facts about a quantity may be expressed by many different equations (or inequalities).

ESSENTIAL UNDERSTANDINGS

2-3 Consider a line in the coordinate plane. If you move from any point on the line to any other point on the line, the ratio of the vertical change to the horizontal change is constant. That constant ratio describes the slope of the line.

2-4 The slopes of two lines in the same plane indicate how the lines are related.

Function

BIG idea A function is a relationship between variables in which each value of the input variable is associated with a unique value of the output variable. Functions can be represented in a variety of ways, such as graphs, tables, equations, or words. Each representation is particularly useful in certain situations. Some important families of functions are developed through transformations of the simplest form of the function.

ESSENTIAL UNDERSTANDINGS

2-1 A pairing of items from two sets is special if each item from one set pairs with exactly one item from the second set.

2-2 Some quantities are in a relationship where the ratio of corresponding values is constant.

2-6 There are sets of functions, called families, in which each function is a transformation of a special function called the parent.

2-7 Just as the absolute value of x is its distance from 0, the absolute value of $f(x)$, or $|f(x)|$, gives the distance from the line $y = 0$ for each value of $f(x)$.

Modeling

BIG idea Many real-world mathematical problems can be represented algebraically. These representations can lead to algebraic solutions. A function that models a real-world situation can then be used to make estimates or predictions about future occurrences.

ESSENTIAL UNDERSTANDINGS

2-5 Sometimes it is possible to model data from a real-world situation with a linear equation. You can then use the equation to draw conclusions about the situation.

2-8 Graphing an inequality in two variables is similar to graphing a line. The graph of a linear inequality contains all points on one side of the line and may or may not include the points on the line.

Functions

A function is a relation that assigns to every element in one set, called the *domain*, exactly one element in another set, called the *range*.

There are several ways to represent a function.

Ordered Pairs	Graph	Mapping	Table

Ordered Pairs:
(−2, 4)
(−1, 1)
(0, 0)

Mapping:

Domain	Range
−2	4
−1	
1	
2	1

Table:

x	y
−2	4
−1	1
0	0
1	1
2	4

The domain and range of a relation can be determined by examining each representation. For ordered pairs, graphs, and tables, the domain is the set of x-values, and the range is the set of y-values. For mapping diagrams, the domain is the set of input values, and the range is the set of output values.

If any value in the domain corresponds to more than one value in the range, the relation is not a function.

The Vertical Line Test is one way to determine whether a relation is a function. If any vertical line intersects the graph of a relation in more than one point, the relation is not a function.

Function notation represents an output value in terms of an input value. In the examples, x is the independent variable, and y is the dependent variable. Using function notation,

$y = 3x + 2$ is written as $f(x) = 3x + 2$.

In the notation $f(x)$, x is the argument of function f, and y is a function of x.

© Mathematical Practices

Look for and make use of structure. Look for and express regularity in repeated reasoning. Reason abstractly and quantitatively. Students analyze functions and relations using the analytic structure of algebra, the geometric structure of graphs, and the numerical structure of tables and charts. Connections among the various representations are continually reinforced. The familiar applications of direct variation and proportionality are used to motivate linear functions and to set the context for other functions in later chapters.

Linear Models

It is often useful to model data sets with a linear equation.

To model a set of data with a linear equation, it is sometimes helpful to plot the data on a coordinate grid. Then a line can be drawn through the midst of the data passing as close to all of the data points as possible. Such a line is called a trend line. Many trend lines can be drawn, and it may not be possible for a line to pass through all or any of the points.

A line of best fit is the trend line that gives the most accurate model of the data. It is calculated by adding the squares of all vertical distances from the data points to the trend line. The line of best fit is the trend line whose sum of squares is minimum. For example, the line of best fit for the data points P_1, P_2, and P_3 is the line for which $d_1^2 + d_2^2 + d_3^2$ is a minimum.

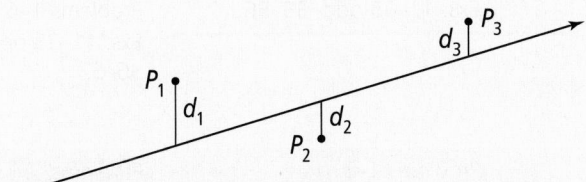

Graphing calculators contain a least-squares function to calculate the line of best fit. Once the line is found, it can be used to make predictions about the data.

Common Errors With Linear Regression

Graphing calculator errors can happen when students do not remember the steps involved. Make a sheet of instructions available until students are comfortable with the steps. Indicate that the calculator will always give the line of best fit, which may be different from any trend line they draw.

ⒸMathematical Practices

Use appropriate tools strategically. Graphing calculators are used as tools for problem solving and additional explorations *after* students have constructed their own connections among the algebraic, numerical, and graphical representations of functions. Linear regression is introduced as a statistical application of linear modeling facilitated by the graphing calculator.

Transformations

Transformations are changes to a function that produce another related function. A family of functions consists of a parent function and all the possible transformations of that function.

A translation is a vertical and/or horizontal displacement. This transformation shifts the graph without changing the graph's orientation or shape.

Translations

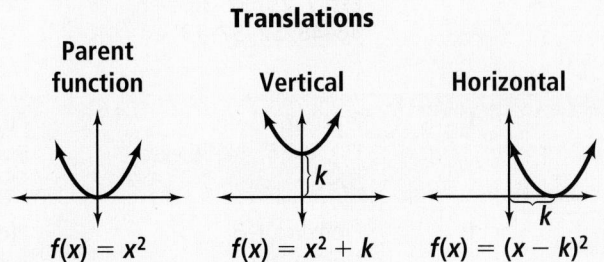

Parent function

Vertical

Horizontal

$f(x) = x^2$ $f(x) = x^2 + k$ $f(x) = (x - k)^2$

A reflection flips the graph of the parent function over a line.

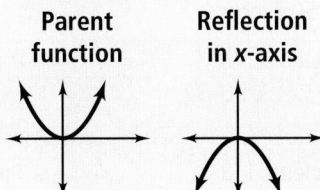

Parent function

Reflection in x-axis

A vertical stretch or compression changes the shape of the graph by multiplying all of the y-values by a factor.

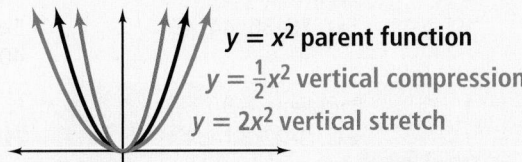

$y = x^2$ **parent function**

$y = \frac{1}{2}x^2$ **vertical compression**

$y = 2x^2$ **vertical stretch**

Common Errors With Transformations

Translation errors occur when students do not know in what direction to translate a graph. Vertical translations are relatively intuitive: $-k$ translates a graph down k units while k translates the graph up k units. However, horizontal translations may confuse students because they are the opposite of what might be expected: $-h$ translates the graph right h units while h translates the graph left h units.

ⒸMathematical Practices

Attend to precision. Construct viable arguments and critique the reasoning of others. Students apply concepts of transformations to reason about the relationships of functions to the parent function.

FUNCTIONS, EQUATIONS, AND GRAPHS
Pacing and Assignment Guide

		TRADITIONAL			BLOCK
Lesson	Teaching Day(s)	Basic	Average	Advanced	Block
2-1	1	Problems 1–4 Exs. 8–16, 40–52	Problems 1–4 Exs. 9–15 odd, 40–52	Problems 1–6 Exs. 9–25 odd, 27–52	**Day 1** Problems 1–6 Exs. 9–25 odd, 27–34, 40–52
	2	Problems 5–6 Exs. 17–32	Problems 5–6 Exs. 17–25 odd, 27–34		
2-2	1	Problems 1–5 Exs. 7–29, 32–36 even, 46–48, 52, 57–73	Problems 1–5 Exs. 7–29 odd, 30–53, 57–73	Problems 1–5 Exs. 7–29 odd, 30–73	**Day 2** Problems 1–5 Exs. 7–29 odd, 30–53, 57–73
2-3	1	Problems 1–4 Exs. 8–36, 44–56 even, 57–59	Problems 1–4 Exs. 9–35 odd, 37–61	Problems 1–4 Exs. 9–35 odd, 37–62	Problems 1–4 Exs. 9–35 odd, 37–61
2-4	1	Problems 1–3 Exs. 10–25	Problems 1–6 Exs. 11–35 odd, 36–52	Problems 1–6 Exs. 11–35 odd, 36–56	**Day 3** Problems 1–6 Exs. 11–35 odd, 36–52
	2	Problems 4–6 Exs. 26–35, 36–44 even, 45, 46–50 even			
2-5	1	Problems 1–3 Exs. 7–18, 20–32	Problems 1–3 Exs. 7–11 odd, 13–18, 20–32	Problems 1–3 Exs. 7–11 odd, 13–32	Problems 1–3 Exs. 7–11 odd, 13–18, 20–32
2-6	1	Problems 1–3 Exs. 10–25, 37–39, 51–58	Problems 1–3 Exs. 11–25 odd, 37–39, 51–58	Problems 1–3 Exs. 11–25 odd, 37–39, 51–58	**Day 4** Problems 1–5 Exs. 11–33 odd, 34–45, 51–58
	2	Problems 4–5 Exs. 26–36, 44, 45	Problems 4–5 Exs. 27–33 odd, 34–36, 40–45	Problems 4–5 Exs. 27–33 odd, 34–36, 40–50	
2-7	1	Problems 1–3 Exs. 8–22, 51–64	Problems 1–3 Exs. 9–21 odd, 51–64	Problems 1–3 Exs. 9–21 odd, 51–64	**Day 5** Problems 1–5 Exs. 9–29 odd, 31–46, 51–64
	2	Problems 4–5 Exs. 23–33, 40–44 even, 45	Problems 4–5 Exs. 23–29 odd, 31–46	Problems 4–5 Exs. 23–29 odd, 31–50	
2-8	1	Problems 1–2 Exs. 8–17, 52–74	Problems 1–2 Exs. 9–17 odd, 52–74	Problems 1–2 Exs. 9–17 odd, 52–74	**Day 6** Problems 1–4 Exs. 9–29 odd, 30–46, 52–74
	2	Problems 3–4 Exs. 18–29, 36–46 even	Problems 3–4 Exs. 19–29 odd, 30–46	Problems 3–4 Exs. 19–29 odd, 30–51	
Review	1	Chapter 2 Review	Chapter 2 Review	Chapter 2 Review	**Day 7** Chapter 2 Review Chapter 2 Test
Assess	1	Chapter 2 Test	Chapter 2 Test	Chapter 2 Test	
Total		**15 Days**	**14 Days**	**13 Days**	**7 Days**

Note: Pacing does not include Concept Bytes and other feature pages.

Resources

	For the Chapter	2-1	2-2	2-3	2-4	2-5	2-6	2-7	2-8
Planning									
Teacher Center Online Planner & Grade Book	I	I	I	I	I	I	I	I	I
Interactive Learning & Guided Instruction									
My Math Video	I								
Solve It!		I M	I M	I M	I M	I M	I M	I M	I M
Student Companion		P M	P M	P M	P M	P M	P M	P M	P M
Vocabulary Support		I P M	I P M	I P M	I P M	I P M	I P M	I P M	I P M
Got It? Support		I P	I P	I P	I P	I P	I P	I P	I P
Dynamic Activity	I								
Online Problems		I	I	I	I	I	I	I	I
Additional Problems		M	M	M	M	M	M	M	M
English Language Learner Support (TR)		E P M	E P M	E P M	E P M	E P M	E P M	E P M	E P M
Activities, Games, and Puzzles		E M	E M	E M	E M	E M	E M	E M	E M
Teaching With TI Technology With CD-ROM				✓ P		✓ P	✓ P	✓ P	✓ P
TI-Nspire™ Support CD-ROM		✓	✓	✓	✓	✓	✓	✓	✓
Lesson Check & Practice									
Student Companion		P M	P M	P M	P M	P M	P M	P M	P M
Lesson Check Support		I P	I P	I P	I P	I P	I P	I P	I P
Practice and Problem Solving Workbook		P	P	P	P	P	P	P	P
Think About a Plan (TR)		E P M	E P M	E P M	E P M	E P M	E P M	E P M	E P M
Practice Form G (TR)		E P M	E P M	E P M	E P M	E P M	E P M	E P M	E P M
Standardized Test Prep (TR)		P M	P M	P M	P M	P M	P M	P M	P M
Practice *Form K* (TR)		E P M	E P M	E P M	E P M	E P M	E P M	E P M	E P M
Extra Practice	E M								
Find the Errors!		M							
Enrichment (TR)		E P M	E P M	E P M	E P M	E P M	E P M	E P M	E P M
Answers and Solutions CD-ROM	✓	✓	✓	✓	✓	✓	✓	✓	✓
Assess & Remediate									
ExamView CD-ROM	✓	✓	✓	✓	✓	✓	✓	✓	✓
Lesson Quiz		I M	I M	I M	I M	I M	I M	I M	I M
Quizzes and Tests *Form G* (TR)	E P M				E P M				E P M
Quizzes and Tests *Form K* (TR)	E P M				E P M				E P M
Reteaching (TR)		E P M	E P M	E P M	E P M	E P M	E P M	E P M	E P M
Performance Tasks (TR)	P M								
Cumulative Review (TR)	P M								
Progress Monitoring Assessments	I P M								

(TR) Available in All-In-One Teaching Resources

1 Interactive Learning

Solve It!

PURPOSE Determine the mapping between the first 12 digits of a bar code and the check digit

PROCESS Students may try various strings of 12 numbers to get the same check digit or change the order of the first 12 digits to get a different check digit.

FACILITATE In a bar code, two digits identify a region, five digits identify the manufacturer, and five digits indicate the product. Digit 13 is a check that the scanner read the first 12 digits correctly.

> **Q** Study the diagram. What calculations are used on the first 12 digits to determine the check digit? **[Multiply the first digit and every other one after that by 1. Multiply the second digit and every other one by 3. Add all these products. Subtract the sum from the next greater multiple of 10.]**
>
> **Q** Could a different set of 12 numbers generate the same check digit, 9? Explain. **[Yes; any set whose sum is 9 less than a multiple of 10 would have 9 as the check digit.]**

ANSWER See Solve It in Answers on next page.
CONNECT THE MATH In the Solve It, students form correspondences between the set of strings of the first 12 digits and the set of possible check digits. After studying relations in the lesson, students will recognize that they can use these two sets to form a function.

2 Guided Instruction

Take Note
Written in set notation, the relation in this Key Concept is $\{(-3, 4), (3, -1), (4, -1), (4, 3)\}$.

© Common Core State Standards
Reviews **F-IF.A.1** Understand that a function . . . assigns to each element of the domain exactly one element of the range. **Also Reviews F-IF.A.2**
MP 1, MP 3, MP 4

Objectives To graph relations
To identify functions

You can use mappings to describe relationships between sets of numbers.

Lesson Vocabulary
- relation
- domain
- range
- function
- vertical-line test
- function rule
- function notation
- independent variable
- dependent variable

Essential Understanding A pairing of items from two sets is special if each item from one set pairs with exactly one item from the second set.

A **relation** is a set of pairs of input and output values. You can represent a relation in four different ways as shown below.

take note

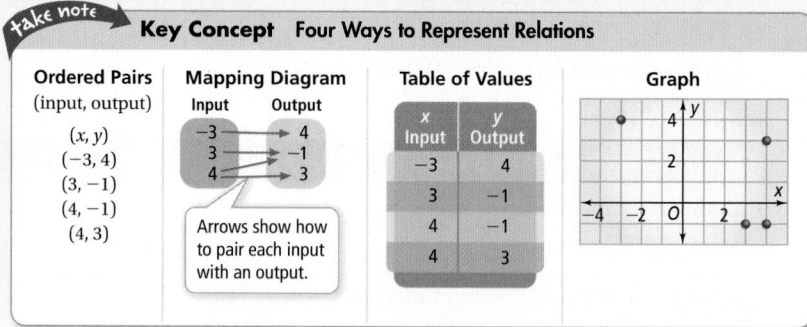

Key Concept   Four Ways to Represent Relations

60   **Chapter 2** Functions, Equations, and Graphs

BIG idea Function
ESSENTIAL UNDERSTANDINGS

- A pairing of items from two sets is special if each item from one set pairs with exactly one item from the second set.
- A relation is a set of pairs of input and output values.
- Relations can be represented with ordered pairs, mapping diagrams, tables of values, and graphs.

Math Background
A relation is set of ordered pairs. Some relations meet a special condition that makes them functions. In a function each item from the domain pairs with exactly one item from the range.
A relation is identified as a function if
- its graph passes the vertical line test,
- its domain values appear only once (in a list of ordered pairs, in a table, or on a mapping diagram), or

- its mapping diagram maps each input to only one output. (This means only one arrow can be drawn from each input value.)

© Mathematical Practices
Make sense of problems and persevere in solving them. Students will find correspondences among four ways to represent numeric relations (ordered pairs, etc.) and also between verbal and algebraic descriptions.

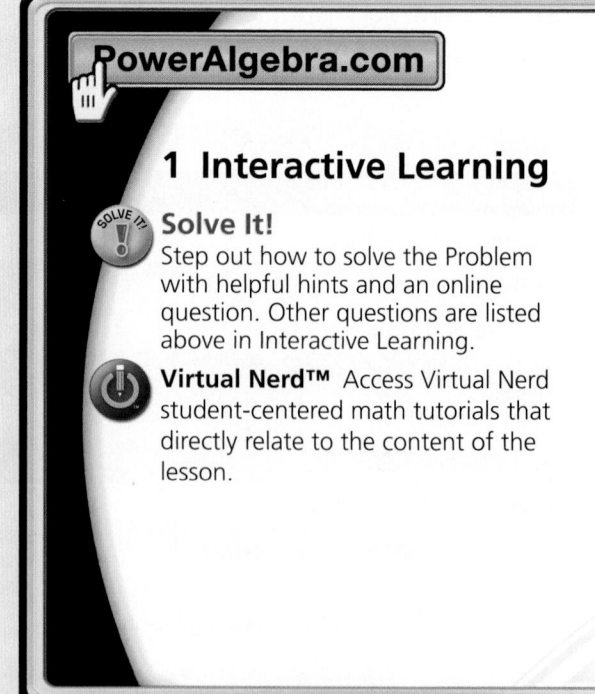

PowerAlgebra.com

1 Interactive Learning

Solve It!
Step out how to solve the Problem with helpful hints and an online question. Other questions are listed above in Interactive Learning.

Virtual Nerd™ Access Virtual Nerd student-centered math tutorials that directly relate to the content of the lesson.

Problem 1 Representing a Relation

Skydiving When skydivers jump out of an airplane, they experience free fall. The photos show various heights of a skydiver at different times during free fall, ignoring air resistance. How can you represent this relation in four different ways?

Think
What is the input? The output?
The input is the time. The output is the height above the ground.

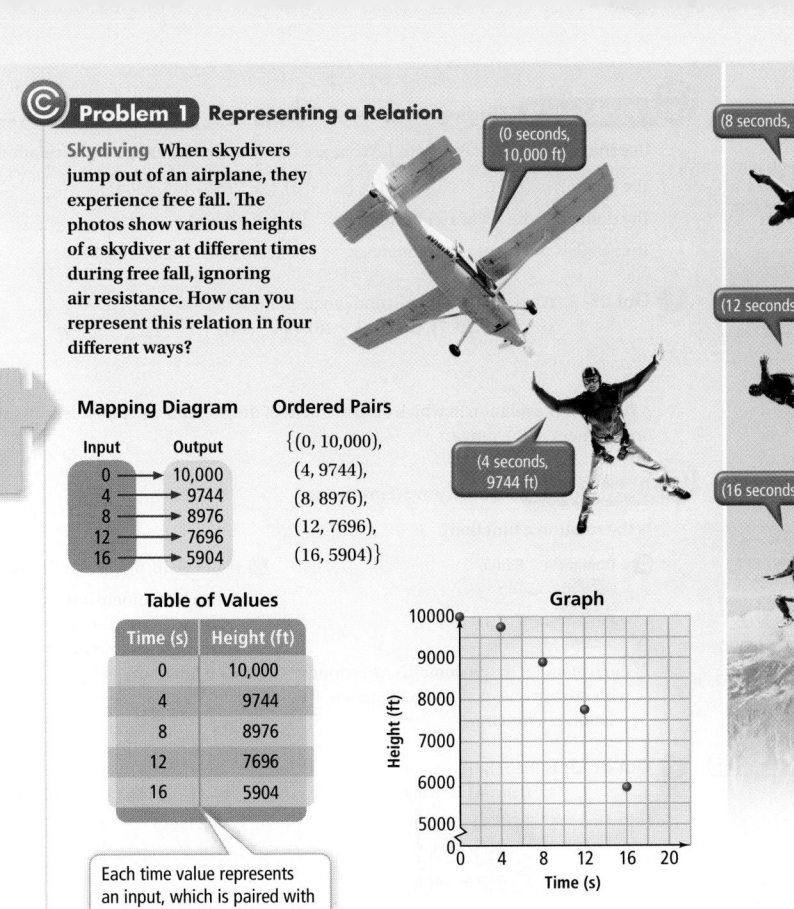

(0 seconds, 10,000 ft)

(8 seconds, 8976 feet)

(12 seconds, 7696 feet)

(4 seconds, 9744 ft)

(16 seconds, 5904 feet)

Mapping Diagram

Input	Output
0	→ 10,000
4	→ 9744
8	→ 8976
12	→ 7696
16	→ 5904

Ordered Pairs

{(0, 10,000),
(4, 9744),
(8, 8976),
(12, 7696),
(16, 5904)}

Table of Values

Time (s)	Height (ft)
0	10,000
4	9744
8	8976
12	7696
16	5904

Each time value represents an input, which is paired with its corresponding output value (height).

Graph

Height (ft) vs Time (s)

✓ **Got It?** **1.** The monthly average water temperature of the Gulf of Mexico in Key West, Florida varies during the year. In January, the average water temperature is 69°F, in February, 70°F, in March, 75°F, and in April, 78°F. How can you represent this relation in four different ways?

The **domain** of a relation is the set of inputs, also called *x*-coordinates, of the ordered pairs. The **range** is the set of outputs, also called *y*-coordinates, of the ordered pairs.

Problem 1 · VISUAL LEARNERS

Q What does each point in the graph represent? Explain. **[An ordered pair; the first coordinate is the number of seconds in the air; the second coordinate is the height in feet at that time.]**

Q Suppose you are given a relation only in table form and you need to graph the relation. How would you do it? **[Answers may vary. Sample: Use the values in the table to form ordered pairs and then graph them.]**

Insert parentheses and commas in a table to show an easy way to see the ordered pairs.

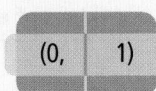

ERROR PREVENTION

Students sometimes misinterpret graphs that show elapsed time versus height, inferring that the graph shows a trajectory, or path of an object. Explain that the points do not show the path of the skydiver.

Got It?

Q What is the first fact given in the problem that contains a value? **[In January, the average water temperature is 69°F.]**

Q What is one way to form ordered pairs of numbers that represent months and temperatures? **[Answers may vary. Sample: Number the months of the year from 1 to 12. Use numbered months and temperature readings to form ordered pairs.]**

Q What are the domain and range for the Got It problem you just solved? **[domain: {1, 2, 3, 4}; range: {69, 70, 75, 78}]**

---

2 Guided Instruction

© Each Problem is worked out and supported online.

Problem 1
Representing a Relation

Problem 2
Finding Domain and Range

Alternative Problem 2
Finding Domain and Range
Animated

Problem 3
Identifying Functions

Problem 4
Using the Vertical-Line Test

Problem 5
Using Function Notation
Animated

Problem 6
Writing and Evaluating a Function
Animated

Support in Algebra 2 Companion
• Vocabulary
• Key Concepts
• Got It?

Answers

Solve It!

Sample: Yes, if the 12 digits are arranged in a different order by switching an even-placed digit and an odd-placed digit, they may generate two different check digits; yes, the sums of the products of the 12 digits can be equal even if the digits and/or products are not the same. This will generate the same check digit.

Got It?

1. Let Jan = 1, Feb = 2, Mar = 3, and Apr = 4.

Input	Output
1	→ 69
2	→ 70
3	→ 75
4	→ 78

{(1, 69), (2, 70), (3, 75), (4, 78)}

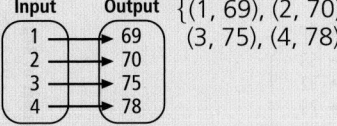

x Month	y Temperature (°F)
1	69
2	70
3	75
4	78

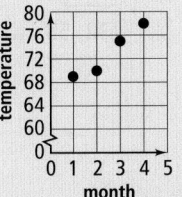

Problem 2
ERROR PREVENTION

Students may mistakenly omit parentheses when writing a relation as ordered pairs or include them when writing a domain or range. Parentheses are used in a relation to indicate ordered pairs but are not used in a domain or range because there are no ordered pairs in a domain or range.

Got It?

Q If you graph these points, will any two of them fall directly above one another? Why? **[No; the *x*-values of each point are different.]**

Problem 3

Q How many ordered pairs are represented in the relation in 3A? Explain. **[3; there are 3 arrows in the mapping diagram.]**

Q If you represent this relation with a mapping diagram, how many arrows would point *from* the domain element 4 in 3B? Explain. **[2; there are 2 ordered pairs that have 4 as the *x*-coordinate.]**

Got It?

Ask the following after solving the problem.

Q What would you change in 3a to make the relation a function? **[Remove either arrow from 2.]**

Q What change would make 3b only a relation, not a function? **[Sample: Change 9 to 14.]**

Here's Why It Works

Q Does the diagram show a relation that is a function? Explain. **[No; two different range elements, y_1 and y_2, correspond to the single domain element x.]**

Think

How could you use the mapping diagram in Problem 1 to find the domain and range?
The *input* corresponds to the domain of the relation. The *output* corresponds to the range.

Ⓒ Problem 2 Finding Domain and Range

Use the relation from Problem 1. What are the domain and range of the relation?

The relation is $\{(0, 10{,}000), (4, 9744), (8, 8976), (12, 7696), (16, 5904)\}$.

The domain is the set of *x*-coordinates. $\{0, 4, 8, 12, 16\}$

The range is the set of *y*-coordinates. $\{10{,}000, 9744, 8976, 7696, 5904\}$

✓ Got It? 2. What are the domain and range of this relation?
$\{(-3, 14), (0, 7), (2, 0), (9, -18), (23, -99)\}$

A **function** is a relation in which each element of the domain corresponds with exactly one element of the range.

Plan

How can you use a mapping diagram to determine whether a relation is a function?
A function has only one arrow from each element of the domain.

Ⓒ Problem 3 Identifying Functions

Is the relation a function?

A Domain   Range

Domain	Range
-3	-2
0	1
4	7

Each element in the domain corresponds with exactly one element in the range. This relation is a function.

B $\{(4, -1), (8, 6), (1, -1), (6, 6), (4, 1)\}$

Each *x*-coordinate must correspond to only one *y*-coordinate. The *x*-coordinate 4 corresponds to -1 and 1. The relation is *not* a function.

Ⓒ ✓ Got It? 3. Is the relation a function?

a. Domain   Range

Domain	Range
2	-3
3	-1
4	3
6	6

b. $\{(-7, 14), (9, -7), (14, 7), (7, 14)\}$

c. Reasoning How does a mapping diagram of a relation that is not a function differ from a mapping diagram of a function?

You can use the *vertical-line test* to determine whether a relation is a function. The **vertical-line test** states that if a vertical line passes through more than one point on the graph of a relation, then the relation is *not* a function.

Here's Why It Works If a vertical line passes through a graph at more than one point, there is more than one value in the range that corresponds to one value in the domain.

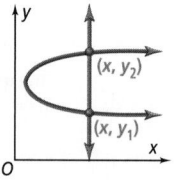

62 Chapter 2 Functions, Equations, and Graphs

Additional Problems

1. In 2000, the 4 most populous states (in millions), were CA (32), TX (21), NY (19), and FL (16). The numbers of U.S. Representatives were CA (53), TX (32), NY (29), and FL (25). How can you represent a relation for these data in 4 different ways?

Pop. in Millions	No. of Reps
32	53
21	32
19	29
16	25

ANSWERS

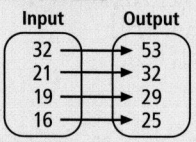

$\{(32, 53), (21, 32), (19, 29), (16, 25)\}$

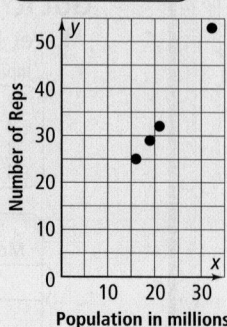

2. What are the domain and range of the relation in Additional Problem 1?

ANSWER
domain: $\{32, 21, 19, 16\}$
range: $\{53, 32, 29, 25\}$

3. Is the relation a function?

a. Domain   Range

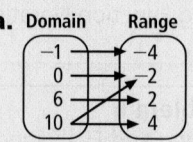

b. $\{(0, 0), (2, 4), (-2, 4), (3, 9), (-3, 9)\}$

ANSWERS a. no   **b.** yes

4. Use the vertical-line test. Which graph(s) represent functions?

A. 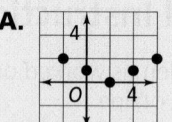   **B.**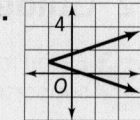

ANSWER graph **A**

5. For $f(x) = -3x + 2$, what is the output for the input -4, 0, and 0.2?

ANSWERS 14, 2, and 1.4

6. A pizza costs \$14; the flat delivery fee is \$1.50. What function rule models the total cost of the number of pizzas delivered? Evaluate for 5 pizzas.

ANSWER $C(p) = 14p + 1.50$; p is number of pizzas; $C(p)$ is total cost; \$71.50.

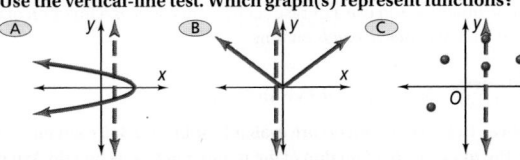

Problem 4 Using the Vertical-Line Test

Use the vertical-line test. Which graph(s) represent functions?

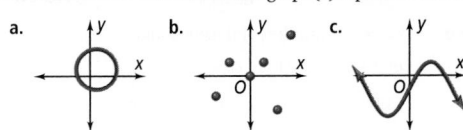

Graphs A and C fail the vertical-line test because for each graph, a vertical line passes through more than one point. They do not represent functions. Graph B does not fail the vertical-line test so it represents a function.

Got It? 4. Use the vertical-line test. Which graph(s) represent functions?

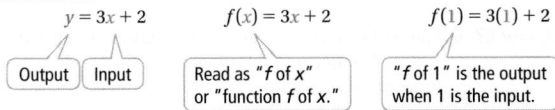

A **function rule** is an equation that represents an output value in terms of an input value. You can write a function rule in **function notation**. Shown below are examples of function rules.

$$y = 3x + 2 \qquad f(x) = 3x + 2 \qquad f(1) = 3(1) + 2$$

Output   Input

Read as "f of x" or "function f of x."

"f of 1" is the output when 1 is the input.

The **independent variable**, x, represents the input of the function. The **dependent variable**, $f(x)$, represents the output of the function. It is called the dependent variable because its value depends on the input value.

Problem 5 Using Function Notation

For $f(x) = -2x + 5$, what is the output for the inputs, $-3, 0,$ and $\frac{1}{4}$?

x Input	Function Rule $f(x) = -2x + 5$	$f(x)$ Output
-3	$f(-3) = -2(-3) + 5$	11
0	$f(0) = -2(0) + 5$	5
$\frac{1}{4}$	$f\left(\frac{1}{4}\right) = -2\left(\frac{1}{4}\right) + 5$	$4\frac{1}{2}$

Got It? 5. For $f(x) = -4x + 1$, what is the output for the given input?
a. -2 b. 0   c. 5

Answers

Got It? (continued)
2. domain: $\{-3, 0, 2, 9, 23\}$, range: $\{-99, -18, 0, 7, 14\}$

3. **a.** no
   b. yes
   c. In a mapping diagram for a relation that is not a function, there is at least one element in the domain that has more than one arrow originating from it. In a mapping diagram for a function, each element in the domain has one arrow originating from it.

4. b and c

5. **a.** 9
   b. 1
   c. -19

Problem 6

Q What are the input and output? **[input: tickets bought; output: total cost]**

Q What does it mean to evaluate the function for 4 tickets? **[Use 4 as an input and find the numerical value of the expression equal to C(4).]**

Got It?

Q How are the operations in this function different from the function in Problem 6? Explain. **[Sample: The function in Problem 6 contains multiplication and addition. This function has no addition since there is no other fee.]**

3 Lesson Check

Do you know HOW? ERROR INTERVENTION

• In Exercise 1, if students list 3 and 4 twice in the domain and −2 twice in the range, remind them to list each element once, no matter how many times it occurs in the ordered pairs.

Do you UNDERSTAND?

• For Exercise 7, draw a horizontal line intersecting a graph in 2 points. Explain that this represents 2 inputs with the same output, which does *not* invalidate a function.

Close

Q What are three methods you can use to determine whether a relation is a function? **[Mapping diagram: only one arrow from each domain element. List of ordered pairs and table of values: no repeated first coordinate. Graph: no vertical line that intersects the graph in more than one point.]**

To model a real-world situation using a function rule, you need to identify the dependent and independent quantities. One way to describe the dependence of a variable quantity is to use a phrase such as, "distance is a function of time." This means that distance *depends* on time.

 Problem 6 Writing and Evaluating a Function

Ticket Price Tickets to a concert are available online for $35 each plus a handling fee of $2.50. The total cost is a function of the number of tickets bought. What function rule models the cost of the concert tickets? Evaluate the function for 4 tickets.

Cost is the dependent quantity and the number of tickets is the independent quantity.

Think

Why is cost the dependent quantity?
Cost is dependent because the cost depends on the number of tickets bought.

Relate	Total cost	is	cost per ticket	times	number of tickets bought	plus	handling fee

Define Let t = number of tickets bought.

Let $C(t)$ = the total cost.

Write	$C(t)$	=	35	·	t	+	2.50

$$C(t) = 35t + 2.50$$
$$C(4) = 35 \cdot 4 + 2.50 \quad \text{Substitute 4 for } t.$$
$$= 142.50 \quad \text{Simplify.}$$

The cost of 4 tickets is $142.50.

Got It? 6. You are buying bottles of a sports drink for a softball team. Each bottle costs $1.19. What function rule models the total cost of a purchase? Evaluate the function for 15 bottles.

Lesson Check

Do you know HOW?

List the domain and range of each relation.

1. $\{(3, -2), (4, 4), (0, -2), (4, 1), (3, 2)\}$

2. $\{(0, 4), (4, 0), (-3, -4), (-4, -3)\}$

Determine whether each relation is a function.

3. $\{(3, -8), (-9, 1), (3, 2), (-4, 1), (-11, -2)\}$

4. $\{(1, 1), (2, 0), (3, 1), (4, 3), (0, 2)\}$

Do you UNDERSTAND?  MATHEMATICAL PRACTICES

5. Vocabulary Can you have a relation that is not a function? Can you have a function that is not a relation? Explain.

6. Error Analysis Your friend writes, "In a function, every vertical line must intersect the graph in exactly one point." Explain your friend's error and rewrite the statement so that it is correct.

7. Reasoning Why is there no horizontal-line test for functions?

3 Lesson Check

For a digital lesson check, use the Got It questions.

Support in Algebra 2 Companion
• Lesson Check

4 Practice

 Assign homework to individual students or to an entire class.

Answers

Got It? (continued)

6. Let x = number of bottles purchased and C = total cost; $C(x) = 1.19x$; $17.85

Lesson Check

1. domain: $\{0, 3, 4\}$,
range: $\{-2, 1, 2, 4\}$

2. domain: $\{-4, -3, 0, 4\}$,
range: $\{-4, -3, 0, 4\}$

3. no

4. yes

5. Yes; a relation is any set of pairs of input and output values. No; a function is a relation in which each element of the domain is paired with exactly one element of the range.

6. *Every* vertical line does not need to intersect a function. Rewrite as: "In a function, every vertical line must intersect the graph in *at most* one point."

7. A horizontal-line test checks the pairing of one element of the range with one or more elements of the domain. A function can have a pairing of one element of the range with *one or more* elements of the domain. A horizontal-line test cannot determine whether a relation is a function.

 Practice

Every year, the Rock and Roll Hall of Fame and Museum inducts legendary musicians and musical acts to the Hall. The table shows the number of inductees for each year.

◀ **See Problems 1 and 2.**

8. Represent the data using each of the following:
   a. a mapping diagram
   b. ordered pairs
   c. a graph on the coordinate plane

9. What are the domain and range of this relation?

Rock and Roll Hall of Fame Inductees

Year	Number of Inductees	Year	Number of Inductees
2001	11	2004	8
2002	8	2005	7
2003	9	2006	6

Source: Rock and Roll Hall of Fame

Determine whether each relation is a function.

◀ **See Problem 3.**

10.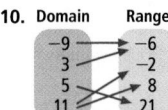

11.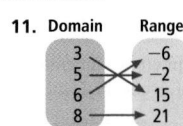

12.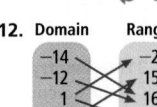

13. $\{(3, -9), (11, 21), (121, 34), (34, 1), (23, 45)\}$

Use the vertical-line test to determine whether each graph represents a function.

◀ **See Problem 4.**

14.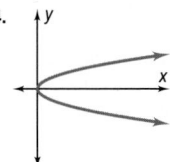

15.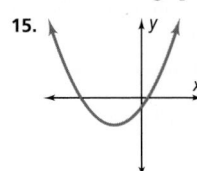

16.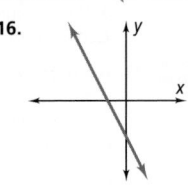

Evaluate each function for the given value of x, and write the input x and output $f(x)$ as an ordered pair.

◀ **See Problem 5.**

17. $f(x) = 17x + 3$ for $x = 4$

18. $f(x) = -\frac{2x+1}{3}$ for $x = -5$

19. $f(x) = 2x - 33$ for $x = 9$

20. $f(x) = -9x - 2$ for $x = 7$

21. $f(x) = \frac{7}{3}x - 9$ for $x = 3$

22. $f(x) = -\frac{12x}{5}$ for $x = -1$

23. $f(x) = 11x - 11$ for $x = -11$

24. $f(x) = \frac{2}{9}x - \frac{9}{2}$ for $x = 9$

Write a function rule to model the cost per month of a long-distance cell phone calling plan. Then evaluate the function for the given number of minutes.

◀ **See Problem 6.**

25. Monthly service fee: $4.52
    Rate: $.12 per minute
    Minutes used: 250

26. Monthly service fee: $3.12
    Rate: $.18 per minute
    Minutes used: 175

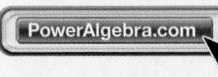
---

4 Practice

ASSIGNMENT GUIDE

Basic: 8–26, 27–32

Average: 9–25 odd, 27–34

Advanced: 9–25 odd, 27–39

Standardized Test Prep: 40–43

Mixed Review: 44–52

© **Mathematical Practices** are supported by exercises with red headings. Here are the Practices supported in this lesson:

MP 1: Make Sense of Problems Ex. 27
MP 3: Construct Arguments Ex. 7, 35
MP 3: Compare Arguments Ex. 34
MP 3: Critique the Reasoning of Others Ex. 6

Applications exercises have blue headings. Exercise 28 supports MP 4: Model.

STEM exercises focus on science or engineering applications.

EXERCISE 28: Use the Think About a Plan worksheet in the **Practice and Problem Solving Workbook** (also available in the Teaching Resources in print and online) to further support students' development in becoming independent learners.

HOMEWORK QUICK CHECK

To check students' understanding of key skills and concepts, go over Exercises 9, 11, 27, 28, and 32.

Practice and Problem-Solving Exercises

8. Let 1 represent 2001, 2 represent 2002, and so forth.

   a.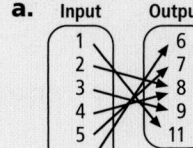

   b. $\{(1, 11), (2, 8), (3, 9), (4, 8), (5, 7), (6, 6)\}$

   c.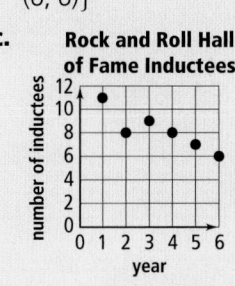

9. domain: $\{1, 2, 3, 4, 5, 6\}$, range: $\{6, 7, 8, 9, 11\}$

10. no

11. yes

12. no

13. yes

14. no

15. yes

16. yes

17. 71; (4, 71)

18. 3; (−5, 3)

19. −15; (9, −15)

20. −65; (7, −65)

21. −2; (3, −2)

22. $\frac{12}{5}$; $\left(-1, \frac{12}{5}\right)$

23. −132; (−11, −132)

24. $-\frac{5}{2}$; $\left(9, -\frac{5}{2}\right)$

25. $C(m) = 4.52 + 0.12m$; $34.52

26. $C(m) = 3.12 + 0.18m$; $34.62

Answers

Practice and Problem-Solving
Exercises (continued)

27. 13.5 cm^2

28. $S(h) = 32 + 16h$; 136 in.^{2}

29. domain: all real numbers, range: $y \geq 0$; yes

30. domain: $-3 \leq x \leq 3$, range: $-1 \leq y \leq 1$; no

31. ≈ 4849 cm^3

32. a. $C(m) = 18 + 0.32m$

   b. $C(m) = 12 + 0.36m$

   c. Proxy

33. a. 109.4

   b. 10.4

   c. $-11.\overline{1}$

   d. $-7.\overline{2}$

34. a. into

   b. into

   c. onto

   d. into

35. $f(x) - g(x) = (3x - 21) - (3x + 21)$
$$= 3x - 21 - 3x - 21 = -42$$

36. Yes; each nonzero x is paired with a unique y.

37. No; each $x > \frac{7}{3}$ is paired with two y values.

38. Yes; each x is paired with a unique y.

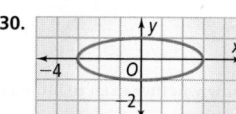 **27. Think About a Plan** A cube is a solid figure with six square faces. If the edges of a cube have length 1.5 cm, what is the surface area of the cube?
- What is the relationship between the length of the edges and the area of each face?
- What is the relationship between the area of one face and the surface area of the whole cube?

28. Geometry Suppose you have a box with a 4×4-in. square base and variable height h. The surface area of this box is a function of its height. Write a function to represent the surface area. Evaluate the function for $h = 6.5$ in.

Find the domain and range of each relation, and determine whether it is a function.

29.

30.

31. Geometry The volume of a sphere is a function of its radius, $V = \frac{4}{3}\pi r^3$. Evaluate the function for the volume of a volleyball with radius 10.5 cm.

32. Car Rental You are considering renting a car from two different rental companies. Proxy car rental company charges \$.32 per mile plus an \$18 surcharge. YourPal rental company charges \$.36 per mile plus a \$12 surcharge.
   a. Write a function that shows the cost of renting a car from Proxy.
   b. Write a function that shows the cost of renting a car from YourPal.
   c. Which company offers the better deal for an 820-mile trip?

STEM 33. Temperature The relation between degrees Fahrenheit F and degrees Celsius C is described by the function $F = \frac{9}{5}C + 32$. In the following ordered pairs, the first element is degrees Celsius and the second element is its equivalent in degrees Fahrenheit. Find the unknown measure in each ordered pair.
   a. $(43, m)$ **b.** $(-12, n)$ **c.** $(p, 12)$ **d.** $(q, 19)$

34. Reasoning Suppose a function pairs items from set A with items from set B. You can say that the function maps *into* set B. If the function uses every item from set B, the function maps *onto* set B. Does each function below map the set of whole numbers *into* or *onto* the set of whole numbers?
   a. Function f doubles every number.
   b. Function g maps every number to 1 more than that number.
   c. Function h maps every number to itself.
   d. Function j maps every number to its square.

Challenge **35. Reasoning** Given the functions $f(x) = 3x - 21$ and $g(x) = 3x + 21$, show that the function $f(x) - g(x)$ is a constant for all the values of x.

Determine whether y is a function of x. Explain.

36. $y = \frac{3}{x} - 11$ **37.** $y^2 = 3x - 7$ **38.** $x^2 = 3y + y$

STEM **39. Chemistry** The time required for a certain chemical reaction is related to the amount of catalyst present during the reaction. The domain of the relation is the number of grains of catalyst, and the range is the number of seconds required for a fixed amount of the chemical to react. The table shows the data from several reactions.

a. Is the relation a function?

b. If the domain and range were interchanged, would the relation be a function? Explain.

Catalyst and Reaction Time

Number of Grains	Number of Seconds
2.0	180
2.5	6
2.7	0.05
2.9	0.001
3.0	6
3.1	15
3.2	37
3.3	176

Standardized Test Prep

SAT/ACT

40. If $f(x) = -3x + 7$ and $g(x) = -7x + 3$, what is the value of $f(-3) - g(3)$?

   Ⓐ 40   Ⓑ 34   Ⓒ 8   Ⓓ −8

41. What is the formula for the volume of a cylinder, $V = \pi r^2 h$, solved for h?

   Ⓕ $h = \frac{r^2}{\pi V}$ Ⓖ $h = \frac{\pi V}{r^2}$ Ⓗ $h = \frac{V}{\pi r^2}$ Ⓘ $h = \frac{\pi r^2}{V}$

42. Which of the following statements are true?

   I. $-(-6) = 6$ and $-(-4) > -4$ III. $5 + 6 = 11$ or $9 - 2 = 11$

   II. $-(-4) < 4$ or $-10 > 10 - 10$ IV. $17 > 2$ or $6 < 9$

   Ⓐ I and II only   Ⓑ I, II, and III only   Ⓒ I, III, and IV only   Ⓓ III and IV only

Short Response

43. What are the numbers 1.9, $\frac{5}{4}$, -1.2, and $\sqrt{3}$ in order from greatest to least?

Mixed Review

Solve each equation or inequality.   ◀ **See Lessons 1-5 and 1-6.**

44. $|3x + 9| = 11$ **45.** $19 + |x - 1| = 33$ **46.** $2 - 3x < 11$

47. $5x - 3 \le 12 - 5x$ **48.** $|2x| + 4 < 7$ **49.** $4x + 6 \ge -6$

Get Ready!   To prepare for Lesson 2-2, do Exercises 50–52.   ◀ **See Lesson 1-4.**

Solve each equation for y.

50. $12y = 3x$ **51.** $-10y = 5x$ **52.** $\frac{3}{4}y = 15x$

 PowerAlgebra.com   **Lesson 2-1** Relations and Functions   **67**

---

39. a. yes

   b. No; 6 would be paired with both 2.5 and 3.

Standardized Test Prep

40. B

41. H

42. C

43. [2] 1.9, $\sqrt{3}$, $\frac{5}{4}$, -1.2

   [1] incorrect placement of one number

Mixed Review

44. $\frac{2}{3}$, $-\frac{20}{3}$

45. -13, 15

46. $x > -3$

47. $x \le \frac{3}{2}$

48. $-\frac{3}{2} < x < \frac{3}{2}$

49. $x \ge -3$

50. $\frac{1}{4}x$

51. $-\frac{1}{2}x$

52. $20x$

Lesson Resources

Differentiated Remediation

Available in editable format online.

Additional Instructional Support

Algebra 2 Companion

Students can use the **Algebra 2 Companion** worktext (4 pages) as you teach the lesson. Use the Companion to support

- New Vocabulary
- Key Concepts
- Got It for each Problem
- Lesson Check

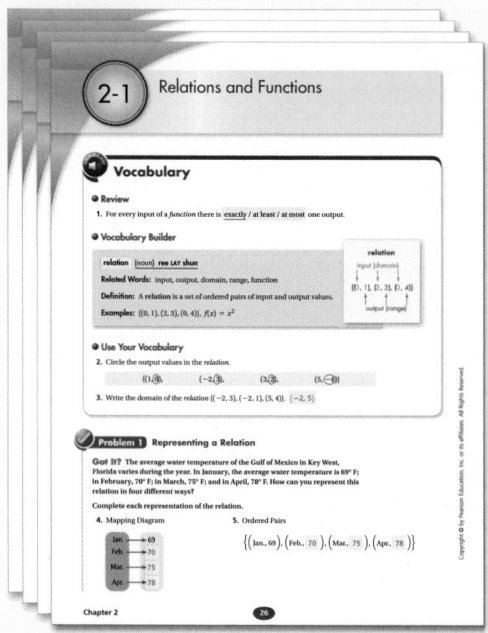

ELL Support

Use Graphic Organizers Have students make a graphic organizer for the bulletin board such as the one shown below to show the domain and range in different situations.

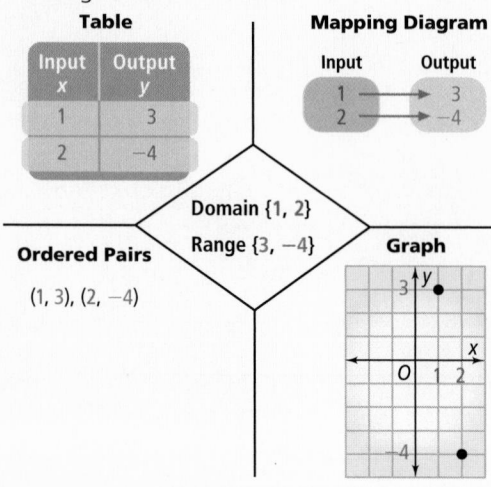

5 Assess & Remediate

Lesson Quiz

1. **Do you UNDERSTAND?** The numbers of tickets sold for a talent show were grade 9: 22; grade 10: 32; grade 11: 41; and grade 12: 30. How can you represent this relation as a mapping diagram?

2. What are the domain and range in Problem 1?

3. **Do you UNDERSTAND?** Is the relation a function? Explain.
   $\{(-2, 3), (-1, 2), (0, 2), (-2, 9)\}$

4. Which graph(s) represent a function?

   a. 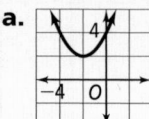   b.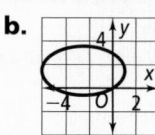

5. Bowling costs $4.50 per game. Shoe rental costs $3.75. The total cost is a function of the number of games. What function rule models the total cost of games and shoe rental? Evaluate the function for 3 games.

ANSWERS TO LESSON QUIZ

1.
Input	Output
9	22
10	32
11	41
12	30

2. domain: $\{9, 10, 11, 12\}$
   range: $\{22, 32, 41, 30\}$

3. No; −2 is paired with two numbers.

4. graph a

5. $C(g) = 4.50g + 3.75$; g is number of games; $C(g)$ is total cost; for 3 games, the cost is $17.25.

PRESCRIPTION FOR REMEDIATION

Use the student work on the Lesson Quiz to prescribe a differentiated review assignment:

Points	Differentiated Remediation
0–2	Intervention
3–4	On-level
5	Extension

PowerAlgebra.com

5 Assess & Remediate

Assign the Lesson Quiz. Appropriate intervention, practice, or enrichment is automatically generated based on student performance.

Intervention

- **Reteaching** (2 pages) Provides reteaching and practice exercises for the key lesson concepts. Use with struggling students or absent students.

- **English Language Learner Support** Helps students develop and reinforce mathematical vocabulary and key concepts.

All-in-One Resources/Online
Reteaching

All-in-One Resources/Online
English Language Learner Support

Differentiated Remediation *continued*

Available in editable format online.

On-Level

- **Practice** (2 pages) Provides extra practice for each lesson. For simpler practice exercises, use the Form K Practice pages found in the All-in-One Teaching Resources and online.

- **Think About a Plan** Helps students develop specific problem-solving skills and strategies by providing scaffolded guiding questions.

- **Standardized Test Prep** Focuses on all major exercises, all major question types, and helps students prepare for the high-stakes assessments.

Extension

- **Enrichment** Provides students with interesting problems and activities that extend the concepts of the lesson.

- **Activities, Games, and Puzzles** Worksheets that can be used for concepts development, enrichment, and for fun!

Practice and Problem Solving Wkbk/All-in-One Resources/Online
Practice page 1

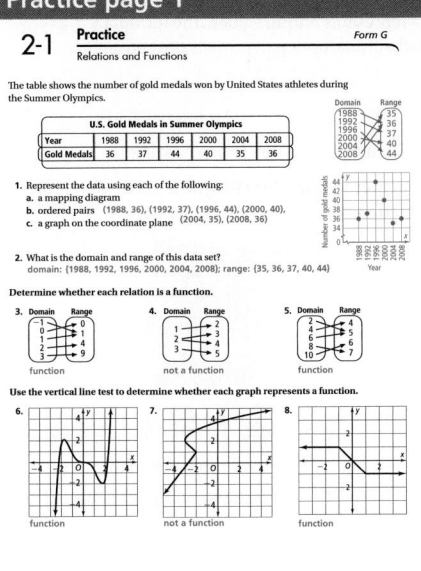

2-1 Practice   Form G
Relations and Functions

The table shows the number of gold medals won by United States athletes during the Summer Olympics.

U.S. Gold Medals in Summer Olympics

Year	1988	1992	1996	2000	2004	2008
Gold Medals	36	37	44	40	35	36

1. Represent the data using each of the following:
   a. a mapping diagram
   b. ordered pairs (1988, 36), (1992, 37), (1996, 44), (2000, 40), (2004, 35), (2008, 36)
   c. a graph on the coordinate plane

2. What is the domain and range of this data set?
   domain: {1988, 1992, 1996, 2000, 2004, 2008}; range: {35, 36, 37, 40, 44}

Determine whether each relation is a function.

3. function 4. not a function 5. function

Use the vertical line test to determine whether each graph represents a function.

6. function 7. not a function 8. function

Practice and Problem Solving Wkbk/All-in-One Resources/Online
Practice page 2

2-1 Practice (continued)   Form G
Relations and Functions

Evaluate each function for the given value of x, and write the input x and the output $f(x)$ as an ordered pair.

9. $f(x) = -3x + 2$ for $x = 3$ (3, −7)
10. $f(x) = \frac{1}{2}x - 1$ for $x = -2$ (−2, −2)
11. $f(x) = 5x - 22$ for $x = 12$ (12, 38)
12. $f(x) = -5x - 3$ for $x = -7$ (−7, 32)
13. $f(x) = \frac{9}{4}x - 15$ for $x = 4$ (4, −6)
14. $f(x) = \frac{5}{3}x - \frac{3}{4}$ for $x = 3$ $(3, 4\frac{1}{4})$

Write a function rule to model the cost of renting a truck for one day. Then evaluate the function for the given number of miles.

15. Daily rental: $19.95
   Rate per mile: $.50 per mile
   Miles traveled: 73 miles
   $f(x) = 0.5x + 19.95$; 56.45

16. Daily rental: $39.95
   Rate per mile: $.60 per mile
   Miles traveled: 48 miles
   $f(x) = 0.6x + 39.95$; 68.75

Find the domain and range of each relation, and determine whether it is a function.

17. domain: {all real numbers}; range: {$y \geq -1$}; function
18. domain: [0, 2]; range: [−2, 2]; not a function

19. The surface area of a sphere is a function of the radius of the sphere: $A = 4\pi r^2$. Evaluate the function for a basketball with a radius of 11.5 cm. 1661.9 cm²

20. The relation between the length of the femur f, the bone from the knee to the hip joint, and the height of an adult woman h is modeled by the function $h(f) = 2.3f + 24$. In the following ordered pairs, the first coordinate is the femur length and the second coordinate is the corresponding height, in inches. Find the unknown measure in each ordered pair.
   a. (13, t) 53.9 in. b. (14.5, p) 57.35 in. c. (m, 56.2) 14 in. d. (n, 72.3) 21 in.

Practice and Problem Solving Wkbk/All-in-One Resources/Online
Think About a Plan

2-1 Think About a Plan
Relations and Functions

Geometry Suppose you have a box with a 4 × 4-in. square base and variable height h. The surface area of this box is a function of its height. Write a function to represent the surface area. Evaluate the function for $h = 6.5$ in.

Understanding the Problem

1. The width of the box is 4 inches. The length of the box is 4 inches. The height of the box is h inches.

2. What is the problem asking you to determine?
   A function that gives the surface area of a box with dimensions 4 in. × 4 in. × h in., and the surface area when $h = 6.5$ in.

Planning the Solution

3. What is the area of the top of the box? What is the area of the bottom of the box? 16 in.²; 16 in.²

4. What is the total area of the top and the bottom of the box? 32 in.²

5. What is the area of each side of the box? $4h$ in.²

6. What is the total area of the sides of the box? $16h$ in.²

Getting an Answer

7. Write a function to represent the surface area of the box. $s(h) = 16h + 32$

8. Evaluate your function for $h = 6.5$ inches. 136 in.²

Practice and Problem Solving Wkbk/All-in-One Resources/Online
Standardized Test Prep

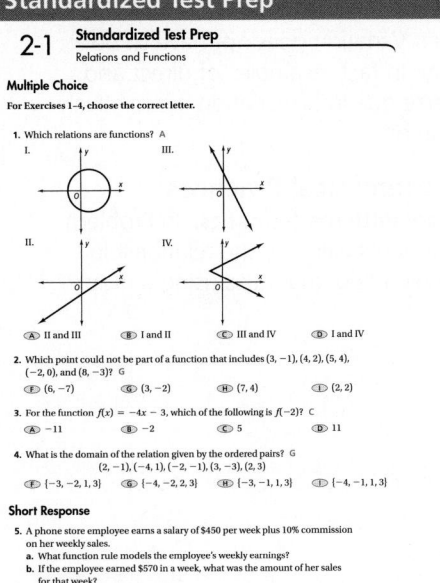

2-1 Standardized Test Prep
Relations and Functions

Multiple Choice

For Exercises 1–4, choose the correct letter.

1. Which relations are functions? A
   I. II. III. IV.
   Ⓐ II and III Ⓑ I and II Ⓒ III and IV Ⓓ I and IV

2. Which point could not be part of a function that includes (3, −1), (4, 2), (5, 4), (−2, 0), and (8, −3)? G
   Ⓕ (6, −7) Ⓖ (3, −2) Ⓗ (7, 4) Ⓘ (2, 2)

3. For the function $f(x) = -4x - 3$, which of the following is $f(-2)$? C
   Ⓐ −11 Ⓑ −2 Ⓒ 5 Ⓓ 11

4. What is the domain of the relation given by the ordered pairs?
   (2, −1), (−4, 1), (−2, −1), (3, −3), (2, 3) G
   Ⓐ {−3, −2, 1, 3} Ⓖ {−4, −2, 2, 3} Ⓗ {−3, −1, 1, 3} Ⓘ {−4, −1, 1, 3}

Short Response

5. A phone store employee earns a salary of $450 per week plus 10% commission on her weekly sales.
   a. What function rule models the employee's weekly earnings?
   b. If the employee earned $570 in a week, what was the amount of her sales for that week?
   [2] a. $f(x) = 0.1x + 450$ b. $1200
   [1] incorrect function rule OR incorrect sales amount
   [0] no answers given

All-in-One Resources/Online
Enrichment

2-1 Enrichment
Relations and Functions

Although relations can be defined on arbitrary sets, we shall confine our attention to relations in the xy-plane. A relation is said to be reflexive if for any real number x in the domain of the relation, the point (x, x) belongs to the relation.

1. How can you tell geometrically whether a relation is reflexive?
   The graph of the relation must contain the line $y = x$.

A relation is said to be symmetric if whenever (x, y) belongs to the relation, (y, x) also belongs to the relation. A relation is asymmetric if whenever (x, y) belongs to the relation, (y, x) does not belong to the relation.

2. What can you say about a relation that is both symmetric and asymmetric?
   The relation is empty.

A relation is said to be transitive if whenever both (x, y) and (y, z) belong to the relation, (x, z) also belongs to the relation. If a relation is reflexive, symmetric, and transitive, it is said to be an equivalence relation.

Decide whether each of the following relations is reflexive, symmetric, asymmetric, transitive, or an equivalence relation.

3. the set of all pairs of real numbers (x, y) such that $x = y$ equivalence relation
4. the set of all pairs of real numbers (x, y) such that $x \geq y$ reflexive, transitive
5. the set of all pairs of real numbers (x, y) such that $x > y$ asymmetric, transitive
6. the set of all pairs of real numbers (x, y) such that $y = 2x$ none
7. the set of all pairs of real numbers (x, y) such that xy is positive   symmetric, transitive
8. the set of all pairs of real numbers (x, y) such that x is an integer   transitive
9. the set of all pairs of real numbers (x, y) such that $xy = 0$ symmetric
10. the set of all pairs of real numbers (x, y) such that $x + y = 1$ symmetric
11. the set of all pairs of real numbers (x, y) such that $x \leq y + 1$ reflexive
12. the set of all pairs of real numbers (x, y) such that $x \neq 0$ when $x = 0$ asymmetric
13. the set of all pairs of real numbers (x, y) such that $xy \neq 0$ symmetric, transitive
14. the set of all pairs of real numbers (x, y) such that $xy < 0$ symmetric
15. the set of all pairs of real numbers (x, y) such that x is an integer and y is not an integer   asymmetric

Online Teacher Resource Center
Activities, Games, and Puzzles

2-1 Activity: Real-Life Relations and Functions
Relations and Functions

This activity should be done in groups of 3 to 5 students, with each group completing the entire sheet.

Relations That Are Not Functions

Here is an ad for a roofing company from a telephone book. Discuss why this is not a function if:
- domain: roofing companies;
- range: telephone numbers.
  Check students' work.

Acme Roofing Co.
(555) 314-1592
(555) 271-8281

Use the spaces below to explain why the following are not functions:
- **Domain:** teachers; **range:** students assigned to each teacher
  Answers may vary. Sample: Any teacher will have more than one student in class.
- **Domain:** all students; **range:** each student's biological parents
  Answers may vary. Sample: Any student has more than one biological parent.

Find two more relations that are not functions, including one that you encountered today. Think about sports, music, science, art, employment, and so on. Discuss how you can express these relations using ordered pairs, a mapping diagram, a table of values, and a graph.

1. Check students' work. 2. Check students' work.

Relations That Are Functions

Here is the cost for mailing a first-class letter at the post office. Discuss why this is a function if:
- domain: letter weight;
- range: mailing cost.
  Check students' work.

First-Class Mail Letter Prices

Weight Up To	Price	Weight Up To	Price
1 oz	$0.42	3 oz	$0.76
2 oz	$0.59	3.5 oz	$0.93

Use the spaces below to explain why the following are functions:
- **Domain:** students; **range:** algebra teacher assigned to each student
  Answers may vary. Sample: Each student will have exactly one algebra teacher.
- **Domain:** all students; **range:** each student's biological mother
  Answers may vary. Sample: Each student will have exactly one biological mother.

Find two more relations that are functions, including one that you encountered today. Think about sports, music, science, art, employment, and so on. Discuss how you could express these functions using ordered pairs, a mapping diagram, a table of values, and a graph.

3. Check students' work. 4. Check students' work.

1 Interactive Learning

Solve It!

PURPOSE To recognize direct variation in a set of nested similar triangles

PROCESS Students may
- see the heights increase in a linear pattern.
- recognize four similar triangles.

FACILITATE

Q What is the length between each pair of adjacent posts along the bottom of the triangle? How do you know? **[2 ft; 8 ft divided into 4 equal intervals equals 2 ft.]**

Q How are the base and height of the large triangle related? **[The height is $\frac{3}{4}$ of the base.]**

Q The base of the smallest triangle is 2 ft. How can you find the height of this triangle? **[2 ft × $\frac{3}{4}$]**

Q When you find the height of a post, will you include the thickness of the wood at the top and bottom of each post? **[Answers may vary.]**

ANSWER See Solve It in Answers on next page.

CONNECT THE MATH The Solve It uses the direct variation principles behind geometric similarity. The lesson formally defines direct variation and prepares students for linear functions.

2 Guided Instruction

Problem 1

Q What is the ratio of y to x in the first row? Is the ratio for the other rows the same? **[2:1; yes]**

Q How is the table in 1B different from the one in 1A? **[Sample: The ratio of y to x in table 1B is not constant for every row.]**

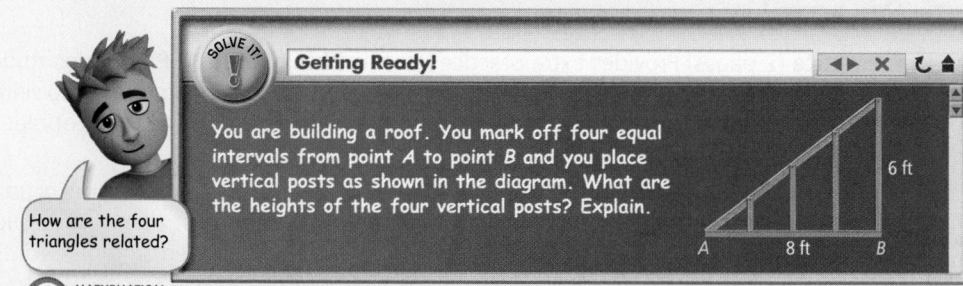

2-2 Direct Variation

Common Core State Standards

A-CED.A.2 Create equations in two or more variables to represent relationships between quantities; graph equations on coordinate axes with labels and scales.
Also F-BF.A.1
MP 1, MP 3, MP 4

Objective To write and interpret direct variation equations

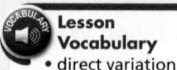

Getting Ready!

You are building a roof. You mark off four equal intervals from point A to point B and you place vertical posts as shown in the diagram. What are the heights of the four vertical posts? Explain.

6 ft

A 8 ft B

How are the four triangles related?

MATHEMATICAL PRACTICES

The post heights in the Solve It satisfy a relationship called *direct variation*.

Lesson Vocabulary
- direct variation
- constant of variation

Essential Understanding Some quantities are in a relationship where the ratio of corresponding values is constant.

You can write a formula for a **direct variation** function as $y = kx$, or $\frac{y}{x} = k$, where $k \neq 0$. x represents input values, and y represents output values. The formula $\frac{y}{x} = k$ says that, except for $(0, 0)$, the ratio of all output-input pairs equals the constant k, the **constant of variation**.

Problem 1 Identifying Direct Variation From Tables

For each function, determine whether y varies directly with x. If so, what is the constant of variation and the function rule?

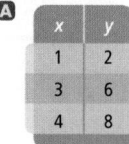

A

x	y
1	2
3	6
4	8

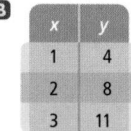

B

x	y
1	4
2	8
3	11

Think

How do you find the constant of variation?
The constant of variation is the ratio of any y-value to the corresponding x-value.

$\frac{y}{x} = \frac{2}{1} = \frac{6}{3} = \frac{8}{4} = 2,$

so y varies directly with x.

The constant of variation is 2.
The function rule is $y = 2x$.

$\frac{y}{x} = \frac{4}{1} = \frac{8}{2} \neq \frac{11}{3}$

so $\frac{y}{x}$ is *not* constant.

y does *not* vary directly with x.

BIG idea Function

ESSENTIAL UNDERSTANDINGS
- Some quantities are in a relationship where the ratio of corresponding values is constant.
- The formula $\frac{y}{x} = k$ says that the ratio of all output-input pairs equals the constant k, the constant of variation.

Math Background

Direct variation functions have equations of the form $y = kx$, where k is the constant of variation. These functions are a subset of the more general linear function $y = ax + b$. The graphs of direct variation functions always pass through the origin. Many types of physical phenomena exhibit direct variation. Examples include rates such as miles per hour, miles per gallon, cost per pound, and so on.

Students will encounter many types of variation relationships in future lessons. Joint variation is briefly touched upon here in the C exercises. Another type is inverse variation. These equations

have the form $y = \frac{k}{x}$. One variable varies directly with the reciprocal of the other. Variation does not have to be linear. In fact, examples of direct and inverse quadratic variation are relatively common.

Mathematical Practices
Model with mathematics. In Problem 4, students will map the relationship between two quantities using a graph.

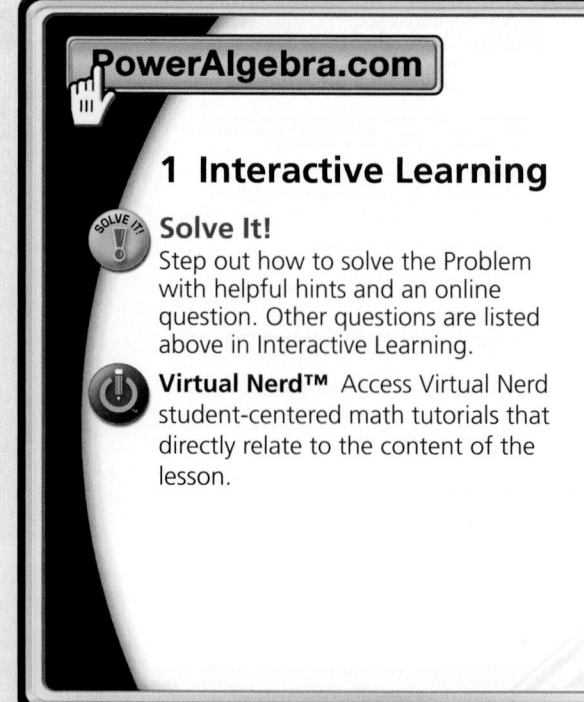

PowerAlgebra.com

1 Interactive Learning

Solve It!
Step out how to solve the Problem with helpful hints and an online question. Other questions are listed above in Interactive Learning.

Virtual Nerd™ Access Virtual Nerd student-centered math tutorials that directly relate to the content of the lesson.

Got It? 1. For each function, determine whether y varies directly with x. If so, what are the constant of variation and the function rule?

a.

x	3	2	1
y	−21	−14	−7

b.

x	2	3	6
y	5	7	13

 Problem 2 Identifying Direct Variation From Equations

For each function, determine whether y varies directly with x. If so, what is the constant of variation?

Ⓐ $3y = 7x$

Divide each side of the equation $3y = 7x$ by 3 to get $y = \frac{7}{3}x$. Since you can write the equation in the form $y = kx$, y varies directly with x. The constant of variation is $\frac{7}{3}$.

Ⓑ $7y = 14x + 7$

Divide each side of the equation $7y = 14x + 7$ by 7 to get $y = 2x + 1$. Since you cannot write the equation in the form $y = kx$, y does not vary directly with x.

Think

How is the form of this function different from the function in part (A)? This function includes a nonzero constant term.

Got It? 2. For each function, determine whether y varies directly with x. If so, what is the constant of variation?

a. $5x + 3y = 0$

b. $y = \frac{x}{9}$

In a direct variation, $\frac{y}{x}$ is the same for all pairs of data where $x \neq 0$. So, $\frac{y_1}{x_1} = \frac{y_2}{x_2}$ is true for the ordered pairs (x_1, y_1) and (x_2, y_2), where neither x_1 nor x_2 is zero.

Problem 3 Using a Proportion to Solve a Direct Variation

Suppose y varies directly with x, and $y = 9$ when $x = -15$. What is y when $x = 21$?

Know	Need	Plan
y varies directly with x. $\frac{y}{x}$ is constant.	The value of y when x is 21.	Use two forms of $\frac{y}{x}$ in a proportion.

$\frac{9}{-15} = \frac{y}{21}$ In a direct variation, $\frac{y}{x}$ is constant.

$9(21) = -15(y)$ Write the cross products.

$\frac{9(21)}{-15} = \frac{-15y}{-15}$ Divide each side by −15.

$-12.6 = y$ Simplify.

So y is −12.6 when x is 21.

Got It? 3. Suppose y varies directly with x, and $y = 15$ when $x = 3$. What is y when $x = 12$?

Got It?   ERROR PREVENTION

Students must check *every* ordered pair given in a table to be sure it shows direct variation. In a direct variation, if the x-values form an arithmetic sequence, so must the y-values.

Problem 2

Q How does the equation in 2B differ from the equation in 2A? **[Answers may vary. Sample: The equation in 2B has the constant 7 added to the right side.]**

Q Can a direct variation function have a nonzero constant term? Explain. **[No; if it did, the ratio of y to x would not be constant.]**

Q How can you use graphing to solve problems of this type? **[Answers may vary. Sample: y varies directly with x if the graph is a line through the origin. The slope equals the constant of variation.]**

Got It?

Q How can you find the constant of variation in a function like $5x + 3y = 0$? **[Solve for y.]**

    EXTENSION

Q Two ordered pairs in a direct variation are $(2, 8)$ and $(5, 20)$. How can you use these to write a proportion? **[The ratio of y to x is constant, so $\frac{8}{20} = \frac{2}{5}$.]**

Problem 3

Q How can you find a missing term in a proportion? **[Find the cross products. Solve for the missing term.]**

Got It?   ERROR PREVENTION

If students confuse x- and y-values, have them organize the values in a table.

---

2 Guided Instruction

 Each Problem is worked out and supported online.

Problem 1
Identifying Direct Variation From Tables
Animated

Problem 2
Identifying Direct Variation From Equations
Animated

Problem 3
Using a Proportion to Solve a Direct Variation

Problem 4
Using Direct Variation to Solve a Problem
Animated

Problem 5
Graphing Direct Variation Equations

Support in Algebra 2 Companion
• Vocabulary
• Key Concepts
• Got It?

Answers

Solve It!
1.5 ft, 3 ft, 4.5 ft, 6 ft; The vertical posts form similar triangles, so you can use proportions to find their lengths.

Got It?
1. a. yes; −7, $y = -7x$
   b. no
2. a. yes; $-\frac{5}{3}$
   b. yes; $\frac{1}{9}$
3. 60

Problem 4

Q How do you know commission varies directly with sales? **[Answers may vary. Sample: because the ratio of $\frac{c}{s}$ is constant.]**

Got It?

Q What are two different ways to solve 4a? **[Answers may vary. Sample: Solve the proportion $\frac{200}{50} = \frac{y}{70}$; or solve $200 = k(50)$ for k, write the equation $y = kx$, substitute $x = 70$, and solve for y.]**

Problem 5

Q Why is every point on the line in each graph part of a direct variation function? **[For every point, the ratio of y to x equals the constant of variation k.]**

Q Suppose a student graphs a set of points from a table, and they do not lie on a line. What can the student conclude? **[The points are not part of a direct variation function.]**

Q Suppose the data points in a table form the line $y = \frac{1}{2}x + 2$. Is the function a direct variation? Explain. **[No; answers may vary. Sample: A direct variation must go through the origin. This equation has a y-intercept of 2.]**

Got It?

Q What point do all graphs of direct variation have in common? **[(0, 0)]**

Think

Could you use the method in Problem 3 to solve this problem? Yes; you could solve this problem by using the proportion $\frac{c_1}{s_1} = \frac{c_2}{s_2}$.

 Problem 4 Using Direct Variation to Solve a Problem

A salesperson's commission varies directly with sales. For $1000 in sales, the commission is $85. What is the commission for $2300 in sales?

Step 1 Use $y = kx$ to find k.

Let $c =$ commission.
Let $s =$ sales.

$$c = k(s)$$

Commission varies directly with sales, so it is the dependent variable.

$$85 = k(1000)$$
$$0.085 = k$$

Step 2 Write the direct variation for the situation and find the commission when sales = $2300.

$c = k(s)$	
$c = 0.085(s)$	Write the direct variation using k.
$c = 0.085(2300)$	Substitute 2300 for s.
$c = 195.5$	Simplify.

The commission for $2300 in sales is $195.50.

Got It? 4. a. The number of Calories varies directly with the mass of cheese. If 50 grams of cheese contain 200 Calories, how many Calories are in 70 grams of cheese?

b. Reasoning If y^2 varies directly with x^2, does that mean y must vary directly with x? Explain.

The graph of a direct variation function is always a line through the origin.

Problem 5 Graphing Direct Variation Equations

What is the graph of each direct variation equation?

Think

What x-values should you use to make a table of values? The constant of variation is a fraction. Use multiples of the denominator for x. This ensures integer values for y.

Ⓐ $y = \frac{3}{4}x$

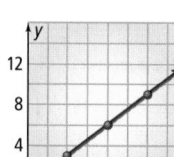

Ⓑ $y = -2x$

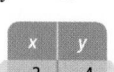

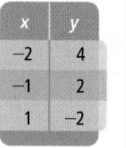

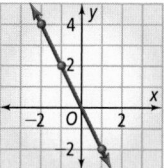

Got It? 5. What is the graph of each direct variation equation?

a. $y = -\frac{2}{3}x$ **b.** $y = 3x$

Additional Problems

1. For each function, determine whether y varies directly with x. If so, what is the constant of variation and the function rule?

a.

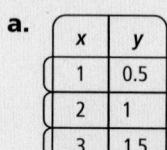

x	y
1	0.5
2	1
3	1.5

b.

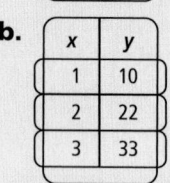

x	y
1	10
2	22
3	33

ANSWERS

a. yes; $k = 0.5$; $y = 0.5x$

b. no; $\frac{y}{x}$ is not constant

2. For each function, determine whether y varies directly with x. If so, what is the constant of variation?

a. $y + 2 = x - 2$

b. $\frac{y}{6} = x$

ANSWERS

a. no; $\frac{y}{x}$ is not constant

b. yes; $k = 6$

3. Suppose y varies directly with x, and $y = -4$ when $x = 25$. What is x when $y = 10$?

ANSWER -62.5

4. The cost of buying fancy nuts varies directly with the weight. If 8.5 kg of nuts cost $47.60, how much do 20 kg cost?

ANSWER $112

5. What is the graph of each direct variation equation?

a. $y = \frac{x}{5}$

b. $y = -4x$

ANSWERS

a.

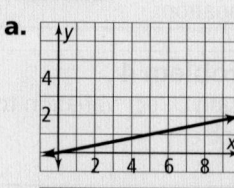

b.

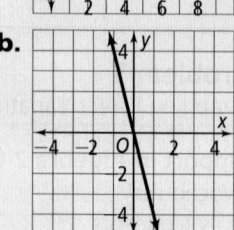

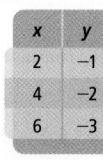

Lesson Check

Do you know HOW?

1. Write a function rule for the direct variation in the table.

x	y
2	−1
4	−2
6	−3

Identify the constant of variation.

2. $y = \frac{3}{2}x$

3. $4y − 5x = 0$

Do you UNDERSTAND?

4. **Vocabulary** Explain what it means for two variables to be directly related.

5. **Reasoning** Explain why the graph of a direct variation function always passes through the origin.

6. Give an example of a function that represents a direct variation.

Practice and Problem-Solving Exercises

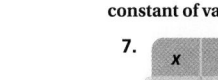 For each function, determine whether y varies directly with x. If so, find the constant of variation and write the function rule.

◀ See Problem 1.

7.
x	y
2	14
3	21
5	35

8.
x	y
27	9
30	10
60	20

9.
x	y
11	22
16	32
7	42

10.
x	y
3	9
4	10
5	11

Determine whether y varies directly with x. If so, find the constant of variation.

◀ See Problem 2.

11. $y = 12x$
12. $y = 6x$
13. $y = −2x$
14. $y = 4x + 1$

15. $y = 4x − 3$
16. $y = −5x$
17. $y − 6x = 0$
18. $y + 3 = −3x$

For Exercises 19–24, y varies directly with x.

◀ See Problem 3.

19. If $y = 4$ when $x = −2$, find x when $y = 6$.
20. If $y = 6$ when $x = 2$, find x when $y = 12$.

21. If $y = 7$ when $x = 2$, find x when $y = 3$.
22. If $y = 5$ when $x = −3$, find x when $y = −1$.

23. If $y = −7$ when $x = −3$, find y when $x = 9$.
24. If $y = 25$ when $x = 15$, find y when $x = 6$.

25. **Distance** For a given speed, the distance traveled varies directly with the time. Kate's school is 5 miles away from her home and it takes her 10 minutes to reach the school. If Josh lives 2 miles from school and travels at the same speed as Kate, how long will it take him to reach the school?

◀ See Problem 4.

26. **Conservation** A dripping faucet wastes a cup of water if it drips for three minutes. The amount of water wasted varies directly with the amount of time the faucet drips. How long will it take for the faucet to waste $4\frac{1}{2}$ cups of water?

3 Lesson Check

Do you know HOW?

- In Exercise 1, students may name the ratio of y to x or write the direct variation function.

Do you UNDERSTAND?

- For Exercise 5, discuss what students can conclude if the graph of a line does not pass through the origin. [For $y = ax + b$, $b \neq 0$, the ratio of y and x cannot be constant.]

Close

Q What are some different ways of representing a direct variation function? **[as a table of ordered pairs, as an equation, by stating the constant of variation]**

Q What does it mean for the ratio of two variables to be constant? **[If you divide one variable by the other, you will always get a nonzero constant.]**

Q What must be true of $Ax + By + C = 0$ for the equation to represent a direct variation? What would the constant of variation be? **[C must equal 0, and A and B must be nonzero; $k = \frac{A}{B}$.]**

Answers

Got It? (continued)

4. **a.** 280

b. No; if $y^2 = kx^2$ then $y = \pm\sqrt{k}x$. So $\frac{y}{x}$ could be $+\sqrt{k}$ for one pair of values and $−\sqrt{k}$ for another pair. Then y would not vary directly with x.

5. **a.**
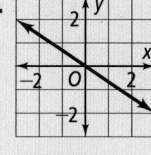

b.

Lesson Check

1. $y = −\frac{1}{2}x$ 2. $\frac{3}{2}$ 3. $\frac{5}{4}$

4. Answers may vary. Sample: Two variables are directly related when the ratio of the output to the input is a constant value.

5. For a direct variation, $y = kx$ where k is the constant of variation. If $x = 0$, then $y = 0$ and the graph of $y = kx$ passes through the origin.

6. Check students' work.

Practice and Problem-Solving Exercises

7. yes; 7, $y = 7x$ 8. yes; $\frac{1}{3}$, $y = \frac{1}{3}x$

9. no 10. no 11. yes; 12

12. yes; 6 13. yes; −2 14. no

15. no 16. yes; −5 17. yes; 6

18. no 19. −3 20. 4

21. $\frac{6}{7}$ 22. $\frac{3}{5}$ 23. 21

24. 10 25. 4 min 26. 13.5 min

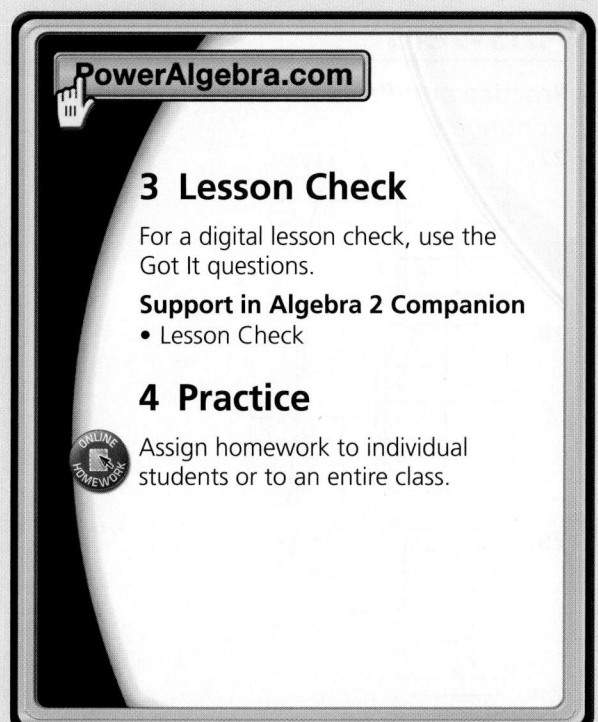

4 Practice

ASSIGNMENT GUIDE
Basic: 7–29 all, 32–36 even, 46–48, 52

Average: 7–29 odd, 30–53

Advanced: 7–29 odd, 30–56

Standardized Test Prep: 57–61

Mixed Review: 62–73

 Mathematical Practices are supported by exercises with red headings. Here are the Practices supported in this lesson:

MP 1: Make Sense of Problems Ex. 34

MP 3: Communicate Ex. 53

MP 3: Construct Arguments Ex. 5, 47, 56

MP 3: Compare Arguments Ex. 48–50

MP 3: Critique the Reasoning of Others Ex. 51

Applications exercises have blue headings. Exercise 51 supports MP 4: Model.

EXERCISE 52: Use the Think About a Plan worksheet in the **Practice and Problem Solving Workbook** (also available in the Teaching Resources in print and online) to further support students' development in becoming independent learners.

HOMEWORK QUICK CHECK
To check students' understanding of key skills and concepts, go over Exercises 7, 19, 34, 47, and 52.

Make a table of x- and y-values and use it to graph the direct variation equation.

◀ **See Problem 5.**

27. $x = \left(-\frac{1}{3}\right)y$ **28.** $y = -9x$ **29.** $x = y$

B Apply

Determine whether y varies directly with x. If so, find the constant of variation and write the function rule.

30.

x	y
1	−2
3	−8
5	14

31.

x	y
9	6
12	8
15	10

32.

x	y
4	1
6	2
8	3

33.

x	y
23	24
55	56
66	67

© **34. Think About a Plan** Suppose you make a 4-minute local call using a calling card and are charged 7.6 cents. The cost of a local call varies directly with the length of the call. How much more will it cost to make a 30-minute local call?
• Which quantity is the dependent quantity?
• How does the word "more" affect the method needed to solve the problem?

Write and graph a direct variation equation that passes through each point.

35. $(1, 2)$ **36.** $(-3, -7)$ **37.** $(2, -9)$ **38.** $(-0.1, 50)$

39. $(-5, -3)$ **40.** $(9, -1)$ **41.** $(7, 2)$ **42.** $(-3, 14)$

For Exercises 43–46, y varies directly with x.

43. If $y = \frac{1}{2}$ when $x = 4$, find y when $x = 5$. **44.** If $y = \frac{3}{4}$ when $x = \frac{1}{2}$, find y when $x = 3$.

45. If $y = \frac{5}{3}$ when $x = \frac{3}{4}$, find x when $y = \frac{1}{2}$. **46.** If $y = -\frac{5}{8}$ when $x = \frac{3}{2}$, find x when $y = \frac{2}{5}$.

© **47. Reasoning** Explain why you cannot answer the following question.
If $y = 0$ when $x = 0$, what is x when $y = 13$?

© **Open-Ended** Choose a value of k within the given range. Then write and graph a direct variation function using your value for k.

48. $0 < k < 1$ **49.** $3 < k < 4.5$ **50.** $-1 < k < -\frac{1}{2}$

© **51. Error Analysis** Identify the error in the statement shown at the right.

52. Sports The number of rotations of a bicycle wheel varies directly with the number of pedal strokes. Suppose that in the bicycle's lowest gear, 6 pedal strokes move the cyclist about 357 in. In the same gear, how many pedal strokes are needed to move 100 ft?

> If y varies directly with x², and y = 2 when x = 4, then y = 3 when x = 9.

© **53. Writing** Suppose you use the origin to test whether a linear equation is a direct variation function. Does this method work? Support your answer with an example.

Answers

Practice and Problem-Solving Exercises (continued)

27.

x	y
−1	3
1	−3
2	−6

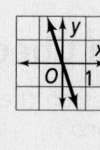

28.

x	y
−1	9
1	−9
2	−18

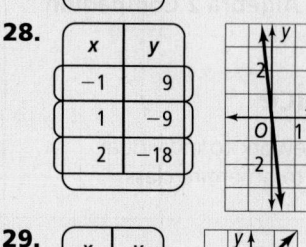

29.

x	y
−1	−1
1	1
2	2

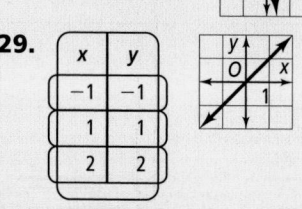

30. no **31.** yes; $k = \frac{2}{3}$, $y = \frac{2}{3}x$

32. no **33.** no

34. 49.4 cents

35. $y = 2x$ **36.** $y = \frac{7}{3}x$

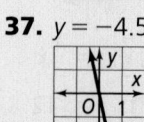

37. $y = -4.5x$

38. $y = -500x$

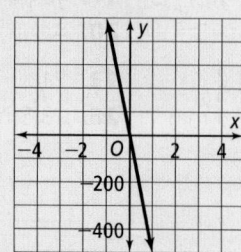

39. $y = \frac{3}{5}x$ **40.** $y = -\frac{x}{9}$

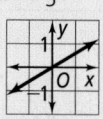 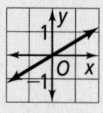

41. $y = \frac{2}{7}x$ **42.** $y = -\frac{14}{3}x$

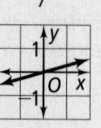 

43. 0.625

44. 4.5

45. 0.225

46. −0.96

47. Every direct variation includes the point (0, 0), so x cannot be determined because k could be any value.

48. Answers may vary. Sample: $y = 0.5x$

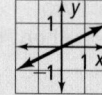

Challenge In Exercises 54–55, *y* varies directly with *x*. Explain your answer.

54. If *x* is doubled, what happens to *y*?

55. If *x* is divided by 7, what happens to *y*?

56. If *z* varies directly with the product of *x* and *y* ($z = kxy$), then *z* is said to vary jointly with *x* and *y*.

    a. Geometry The area of a triangle varies jointly with its base and height. What is the constant of variation?

    b. Suppose *q* varies jointly with *v* and *s*, and *q* = 24 when *v* = 2 and *s* = 3. Find *q* when *v* = 4 and *s* = 2.

    c. Reasoning Suppose *z* varies jointly with *x* and *y*, and *x* varies directly with *w*. Show that *z* varies jointly with *w* and *y*.

Standardized Test Prep

SAT/ACT

                                                            GRIDDED RESPONSE

57. A speed of 75 mi/h is equal to a speed of 110 ft/s. To the nearest mile per hour, what is the speed of an aircraft traveling at a speed of 1600 ft/s?

58. What number is a solution to both $|x - 3| = 2$ and $|9 - x| = 8$?

59. If $f(x) = 7 - 3x$ and $g(x) = 3x - 7$, what is the value of $f(1) + g(1)$?

60. Look at the pattern. How many circles are in the 6th figure of this pattern?

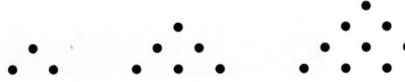

61. What is the solution of $4(x - 5) + x = 8x - 10 - x$?

Mixed Review

Graph each relation. Find the domain and range.   ◆ See Lesson 2-1.

62. $\{(0, 1), (1, -3), (-2, -3), (3, -3)\}$

63. $\{(4, 0), (7, 0), (4, -1), (7, -1)\}$

64. $\{(1, -2), (2, -1), (4, 1), (5, 2)\}$

65. $\{(1, 7), (2, 8), (3, 9), (4, 10)\}$

Identify a pattern and find the next three numbers in the pattern.   ◆ See Lesson 1-1.

66. 8, 16, 24, 32, . . .

67. 5, 3, 1, −1, . . .

68. 144, 132, 120, 108, . . .

69. 30, 45, 60, 75, . . .

Get Ready! To prepare for Lesson 2-3, do Exercises 70–73.

Evaluate each expression for *x* = −2, 0, 1, and 4.   ◆ See Lesson 1-3.

70. $\frac{2}{3}x + 7$ **71.** $\frac{3}{5}x - 2$ **72.** $3x + 1$ **73.** $\frac{1}{2}x - 8$

63.

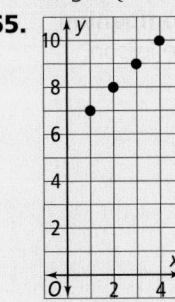

domain: $\{4, 7\}$; range: $\{0, -1\}$

64.

domain: $\{1, 2, 4, 5\}$;
range: $\{-2, -1, 1, 2\}$

65.

domain: $\{1, 2, 3, 4\}$;
range: $\{7, 8, 9, 10\}$

66. 8*n*; 40, 48, 56

67. $7 - 2n$; −3, −5, −7

68. $12(13 - n)$; 96, 84, 72

69. $15(n + 1)$; 90, 105, 120

70. $\frac{17}{3}$; 7; $\frac{23}{3}$, $\frac{29}{3}$

71. −3.2; −2; −1.4; 0.4

72. −5; 1; 4; 13

73. −9; −8; −7.5; −6

---

49. Answers may vary. Sample: $y = 3.2x$

50. Answers may vary. Sample: $y = -\frac{3}{4}x$

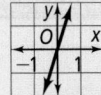

51. Answers may vary. Sample: If *y* varies directly with x^2, and *y* = 2 when *x* = 4, then $y = \frac{81}{8}$ when *x* = 9.

52. about 20 strokes

53. Answers may vary. Sample: No; the line *y* = 0 passes through the origin, but is not a direct variation.

54. *y* is doubled; $y = kx$, so if *x* is doubled, $y = k(2x)$ or twice the original value of *y*.

55. *y* is divided by 7; $y = kx$, so if *x* is divided by 7, $y = k\left(\frac{x}{7}\right)$ or $\frac{1}{7}$ the original value of *y*.

56. a. $\frac{1}{2}$

    b. 32

    c. $z = kxy$, and $x = k_1 w$, so $z = kk_1 wy$, and *z* varies jointly with *w* and *y*.

Standardized Test Prep

57. 1091

58. 1

59. 0

60. 21

61. −5

Mixed Review

62.

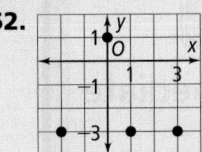

domain: $\{-2, 0, 1, 3\}$;
range: $\{-3, 1\}$

2-2 Lesson Resources

Differentiated Remediation

Additional Instructional Support

Algebra 2 Companion

Students can use the **Algebra 2 Companion** worktext (4 pages) as you teach the lesson. Use the Companion to support

- New Vocabulary
- Key Concepts
- Got It for each Problem
- Lesson Check

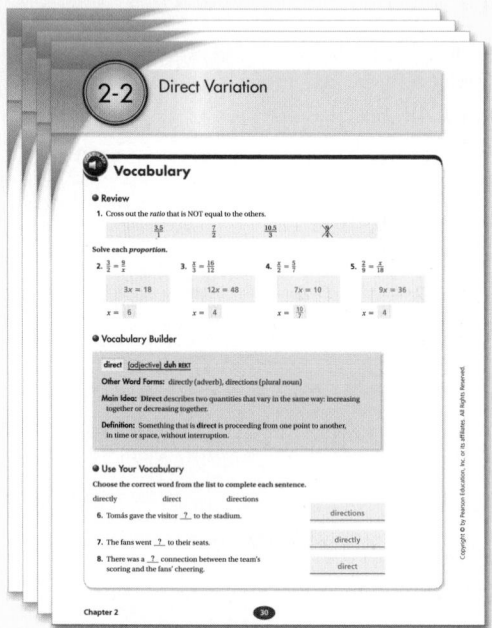

ELL Support

Connect to Prior Knowledge Have groups of students graph a linear equation such as $y = 2x + 1$ and write a step-by-step description of how they make the graph. Next, have the groups graph a related inequality such as $y > 2x + 1$ and write a step-by-step description of that process. Ask each group to contrast the processes of graphing an equation and graphing an inequality.

Next have students make a poster which explains the process of graphing inequalities. Students should include illustrations, examples, and familiar phrases and expressions in their poster.

5 Assess & Remediate

Lesson Quiz

1. Does y vary directly with x? If so, what is the constant of variation and the function rule?

x	y
2	5
5	12.5
10	25

2. Determine whether y varies directly with x in $6x - 3 = 2y - 3$. If so, what is the constant of variation?

3. y varies directly with x, and $y = 24$ when $x = -15$. What is x when $y = 16$?

4. Do you UNDERSTAND? You have a set of nested boxes whose lengths vary directly with their widths. One box is 2.5 in. wide and 5.5 in. long. A second box is 3 in. wide. How long is it?

5. What is the graph of $y = -1.5x$?

ANSWERS TO LESSON QUIZ

1. yes; $k = 2.5$; $y = 2.5x$

2. yes; $k = 3$

3. -10

4. 6.6 in.

5.

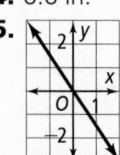

PRESCRIPTION FOR REMEDIATION

Use the student work on the Lesson Quiz to prescribe a differentiated review assignment:

Points	Differentiated Remediation
0–2	Intervention
3–4	On-level
5	Extension

PowerAlgebra.com

5 Assess & Remediate

Assign the Lesson Quiz. Appropriate intervention, practice, or enrichment is automatically generated based on student performance.

Intervention

- **Reteaching** (2 pages) Provides reteaching and practice exercises for the key lesson concepts. Use with struggling students or absent students.

- **English Language Learner Support** Helps students develop and reinforce mathematical vocabulary and key concepts.

All-in-One Resources/Online
Reteaching

2-2 Reteaching
Direct Variation

A direct variation is a function of the form,

$$y = kx \text{ or } \frac{y}{x} = k, \text{ where } k \neq 0.$$

Represent the input values as x and represent the output values as y. The ratio of any output-input pair is equal to k, the constant of variation.

Problem

For each function, determine whether y varies directly with x. If so, what is the constant of variation?

Identify direct variation from a table.	Identify direct variation from an equation
a.	b. $2y = 5x - 3$
	Try to put the equation in the form $y = kx$.
	$2y = 5x - 3$
	$\frac{2y}{2} = \frac{5x}{2} - \frac{3}{2}$ Divide both sides by 2.
	$y = \frac{5}{2}x - \frac{3}{2}$ Simplify.

Exercises

For each function, determine whether y varies directly with x. If so, find the constant of variation.

1. yes; 2 **2.** no **3.** yes; -2

4. $y = 4x + 1$ no **5.** $5y = -4x$ yes; $-\frac{4}{5}$ **6.** $3y + 4x = 0$ yes; $-\frac{4}{3}$

7. $2y = 4x - 5$ no **8.** $3y = 15x$ yes; 5 **9.** $34y - 17x = 0$ yes; $\frac{1}{2}$

All-in-One Resources/Online
English Language Learner Support

2-2 Additional Vocabulary Support
Direct Variation

A clerk's weekly salary varies directly with the number of hours he works. For 12 h of work, the clerk earns $114. How much will he earn for 19 h of work? The steps to solve this problem were written on the note cards below, but they got mixed up.

Use the note cards to write the steps in order.

1. First, salary varies directly with hours worked, so $\frac{salary}{hours\ worked}$ is constant

2. Second, let s = the salary and h = the number of hours worked

3. Third, use the proportion $\frac{s_1}{h_1} = \frac{s_2}{h_2}$ to model the situation

4. Next, substitute $s_1 = 114$, $h_1 = 12$, and $h_2 = 19$

5. Then, write the cross products

6. Finally, solve for s_2

Differentiated Remediation *continued*

Available in editable format online.

On-Level

- **Practice** (2 pages) Provides extra practice for each lesson. For simpler practice exercises, use the Form K Practice pages found in the All-in-One Teaching Resources and online.

- **Think About a Plan** Helps students develop specific problem-solving skills and strategies by providing scaffolded guiding questions.

- **Standardized Test Prep** Focuses on all major exercises, all major question types, and helps students prepare for the high-stakes assessments.

Extension

- **Enrichment** Provides students with interesting problems and activities that extend the concepts of the lesson.

- **Activities, Games, and Puzzles** Worksheets that can be used for concepts development, enrichment, and for fun!

Practice and Problem Solving Wkbk/ All-in-One Resources/Online
Practice page 1

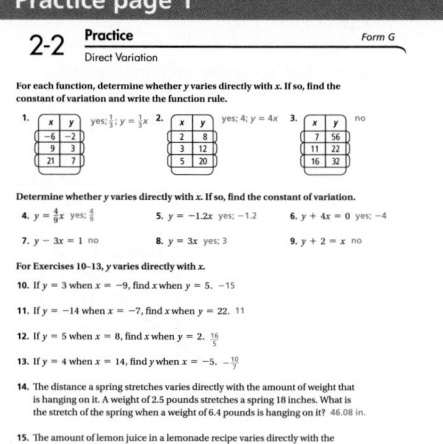

Practice and Problem Solving Wkbk/ All-in-One Resources/Online
Practice page 2

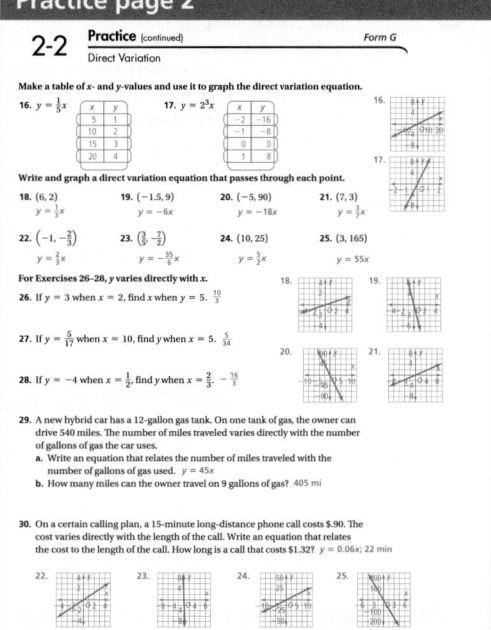

All-in-One Resources/Online
Enrichment

2-2 Enrichment
Direct Variation

Direct Variation: Drawing Conclusions

The charts below show the amount of commission each salesperson received on a given real estate sale.

Jones's Sales	Commission		Ortiz's Sales	Commission
$125,000	$4,375		$ 75,000	$ 6,750
$ 80,000	$2,800		$ 66,400	$ 5,976
$ 60,000	$2,100		$182,000	$16,380

O'Hara's Sales	Commission		D'Angelo's Sales	Commission
$250,000	$15,000		$124,000	$3,720
$405,500	$18,110		$ 42,000	$ 840
$635,000	$22,700		$ 89,100	$1,782

1. Determine which salespeople received a straight commission. (A straight commission is a constant percent received based on sales.) What percentage does each receive?
Jones: 3.5%; Ortiz: 9%

In Exercises 2–4, determine whether y varies directly with x. For each function that is a direct variation, find the constant of variation.

2a. $y = 4x$ b. $\frac{y}{x} = -\frac{4}{3}$ c. $y + x = 7$ d. $3y = \frac{x}{10}$
direct variation; 4   direct variation; $-\frac{4}{3}$ not direct variation   direct variation; $\frac{1}{30}$

3a. $y = 3 - x$ b. $y = -3x$ c. $y = x + 3$ d. $y = 3x + 1$
not direct variation   direct variation; -3 not direct variation   not direct variation

4a. $y = 2x$ b. $4y - 5x = 0$ c. $x + y = 2$ d. $\frac{3y}{x} = 11$
direct variation; 2   direct variation; $\frac{5}{4}$ not direct variation   direct variation; $\frac{11}{3}$

Solve.

5. If y is directly proportional to x^3 and x is doubled, what happens to y? y is multiplied by 8.

6. Suppose y varies directly with x and you are given a value of x. What do you need to know in order to find the corresponding value of y? the value of the constant of variation

7. In an electric circuit, the voltage varies directly as the electric current, measured in amperes. If the voltage is 75 volts when the current is 15 amps, find the voltage when the current is 10 amps. 50 volts

Practice and Problem Solving Wkbk/ All-in-One Resources/Online
Think About a Plan

2-2 Think About a Plan
Direct Variation

Sports The number of rotations of a bicycle wheel varies directly with the number of pedal strokes. Suppose that in the bicycle's lowest gear, 6 pedal strokes move the cyclist about 357 in. In the same gear, how many pedal strokes are needed to move 100 ft?

Know

1. The number of _rotations of a bicycle wheel_ varies directly with the number of _pedal strokes_.

2. 6 pedal strokes move the cyclist 357 in.
There are 12 in. in a foot.

Need

3. To solve the problem I need to:
Find the constant of variation by solving for k in $d = kp$, convert 100 ft to inches,
and then use the constant of variation to find the number of pedal strokes needed to
move 100 ft.

Plan

4. Write an equation of direct variation to model the situation. Find the constant of variation. $357 = k \cdot 6$; $k = 59.5$

5. Substitute for one variable and the constant of variation in the equation of direct variation. $100 \cdot 12 = 59.5 \, p$

6. What does the solution mean?
About 20 pedal strokes are needed to move the cyclist 100 ft.

7. Is the solution reasonable? Explain.
Yes; 100 ft is 1200 in., which is between 3 and 4 times 357 in.; 20 pedal strokes
is between 3 and 4 times 6 pedal strokes.

Practice and Problem Solving Wkbk/ All-in-One Resources/Online
Standardized Test Prep

2-2 Standardized Test Prep
Direct Variation

Multiple Choice

For Exercises 1–5, choose the correct letter.

1. If y varies directly with x and y is 18 when x is 6, which of the following represents this situation? B
   Ⓐ $y = 24x$ Ⓑ $y = 3x$ Ⓒ $y = 12x$ Ⓓ $y = \frac{1}{3}x$

2. Which function best represents the relationship between the quantities in the table? H

x	y
6	4
12	8
21	14
30	20

   Ⓕ $x = \frac{2}{3}y - 2$ Ⓖ $x = \frac{2}{3}y + 2$ Ⓗ $y = \frac{2}{3}x$ Ⓘ $y = \frac{3}{2}x$

3. If y varies directly with x and y is 9 when x is 3, what is x when y is -1? B
   Ⓐ -1 Ⓑ $-\frac{3}{8}$ Ⓒ 1 Ⓓ $\frac{8}{9}$

4. Which equation of direct variation has $(24, -8)$ as a solution? I
   Ⓕ $y = \frac{1}{3}x$ Ⓖ $y = -3x$ Ⓗ $y = 3x$ Ⓘ $y = -\frac{1}{3}x$

5. Which equation does NOT represent a direct variation? C
   Ⓐ $y - 4x = 0$ Ⓑ $\frac{y}{x} = \frac{3}{4}$ Ⓒ $y - 4 = \frac{1}{4}x$ Ⓓ $4y = -\frac{1}{4}x$

Short Response

6. You can download a 5 MB file in 2 seconds. The time t it takes to download a file varies directly with the size s of the file. Write an equation of direct variation to represent the situation. How long will it take you to download a 3 MB file?
[2] $t = \frac{2}{5}s$; 1.2 s
[1] incorrect equation OR incorrect time
[0] no answers given

Online Teacher Resource Center
Activities, Games, and Puzzles

2-2 Puzzle: Constant of Variation
Direct Variation

Begin by answering the questions below. Write your simplified answers next to the exercise.

For Exercises 1–16, y varies directly with x. Find the constant of variation.

1. $y = -8x$ -8
2. $y = 2x$ 2
3. $y + 3x = 0$ -3
4. $y - 13x = 0$ 13
5. $9x - y = 0$ 9
6. $x - y = 0$ 1
7. $\frac{1}{2}y = x$ 7
8. $\frac{1}{3}y = x$ 3
9. $\frac{1}{2}y + x = 0$ -2
10. $\frac{1}{2}y - x = 0$ 2
11. $y + x = 2x$ 1
12. $y - x = -2x$ -1
13. $2y - 7x = y + 6x$ 13
14. $3y + x = 2y - 3x$ -4
15. $2y - 5x = 7x$ 6
16. $4y + 19x = y - 5x$ -8

For Exercises 17–23, y varies directly with x.

17. If $y = 12$ when $x = 6$, find x when $y = -2$. -1
18. If $y = 6$ when $x = -2$, find x when $y = -39$. 13
19. If $y = 4$ when $x = 8$, find x when $y = \frac{3}{2}$. 3
20. If $y = -7$ when $x = 4$, find y when $x = \frac{7}{2}$. -2
21. If $y = \frac{3}{4}$ when $x = \frac{1}{2}$, find x when $y = -\frac{18}{4}$. -3
22. If $y = 1.2$ when $x = 4$, find x when $y = 3.9$. 13
23. If $y = 3.9$ when $x = 3$, find x when $y = -2.6$. -2

The answers correspond to letters as shown in the table below.

−1	1	−2	2	−3	3	−4	4	−5	5	−6	6	−7
O	E	T	H	A	S	L	V	U	J	D	Y	X

7	−8	8	−9	9	−10	10	−11	11	−12	12	−13	13
I	C	Q	P	G	R	M	B	K	W	Z	F	N

Decode each answer and place its corresponding letter in the appropriate space below. If your answers are correct, then you will uncover an important quote.

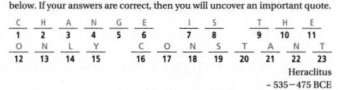

C	H	A	N	G	E		I	S		T	H	E
1	2	3	4	5	6		7	8		9	10	11
O	N	L	Y		C	O	N	S	T	A	N	T
12	13	14	15		16	17	18	19	20	21	22	23

Heraclitus
~ 535 − 475 BCE

1 Interactive Learning

Solve It!

PURPOSE To recognize that in moving along a line, the vertical change is proportional to the horizontal change

PROCESS Students may recognize two similar triangles and find the ratios to solve for H in terms of h or replace the variables with numerical values and find the ratio.

FACILITATE

Q Notice that H and h each represent the side of a different triangle. How are these triangles related? **[They are similar.]**

Q What proportion do these similar triangles give you? $[\frac{h}{OB} = \frac{H}{OA}]$

Q So, what is H in terms of h? $[H = h\frac{OA}{OB}]$

Q How does rotating the line change the triangles? **[They are larger but still similar.]**

Q What is the new H in terms of the new h? **[The heights change but the proportion stays the same; $H = h\frac{OA}{OB}$]**

ANSWER See Solve It in Answers on next page.

CONNECT THE MATH In the Solve It, students show that the vertical change is proportional to horizontal change. In the lesson, they will find the slope of a line, which is the ratio of vertical change to horizontal change.

2 Guided Instruction

Take Note

If students find the subscripted variables confusing or intimidating, present the slope formula using (a, b) and (c, d) as the two given points.

2-3 Linear Functions and Slope-Intercept Form

© Common Core State Standards
A-CED.A.2 Create equations in two or more variables to represent relationships between quantities; graph equations on coordinate axes with labels and scales.
Also F-IF.B.4, F-LE.B.5
MP 1, MP 3, MP 4

Objectives To graph linear equations
To write equations of lines

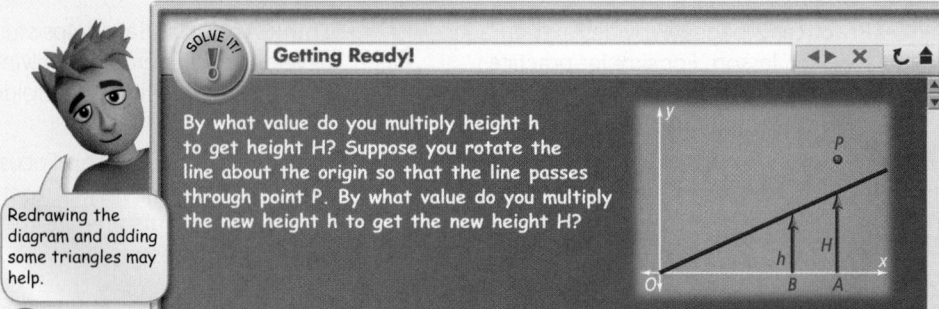

Redrawing the diagram and adding some triangles may help.

Getting Ready!

By what value do you multiply height h to get height H? Suppose you rotate the line about the origin so that the line passes through point P. By what value do you multiply the new height h to get the new height H?

© MATHEMATICAL PRACTICES

Lesson Vocabulary

• slope
• linear function
• linear equation
• y-intercept
• x-intercept
• slope-intercept form

You can describe movement in a coordinate plane by describing how far you need to move vertically and how far you need to move horizontally to get from one point to another point.

Essential Understanding Consider a nonvertical line in the coordinate plane. If you move from any point on the line to any other point on the line, the ratio of the vertical change to the horizontal change is constant. That constant ratio is the slope of the line.

The **slope** of a nonvertical line is the ratio of the vertical change to the horizontal change between two points. You can calculate slope by finding the ratio of the difference in the y-coordinates to the difference in the x-coordinates for any two points on the line.

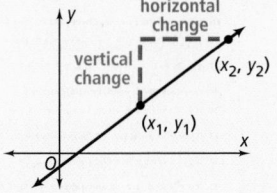

take note

Key Concept Slope

The slope of a nonvertical line through points (x_1, y_1) and (x_2, y_2) is the ratio of the vertical change to the corresponding horizontal change.

$$\text{slope} = \frac{\text{vertical change (rise)}}{\text{horizontal change (run)}} = \frac{y_2 - y_1}{x_2 - x_1}, \text{ where } x_2 - x_1 \neq 0$$

2-3 Preparing to Teach

BIG idea Equivalence

ESSENTIAL UNDERSTANDINGS

• Moving from any point on a nonvertical line in the coordinate plane to any other point on the line, the ratio of the vertical change to the horizontal change is constant. That constant ratio describes the slope of the line.

• Slope can be calculated by finding the ratio of the difference in the y-coordinates to the difference in the x-coordinates for any two points on the line.

Math Background

Although any two-variable equation can be graphed on a coordinate grid by plotting ordered pairs, there are often more efficient ways. The first step is to recognize the general shape of a graph from its equation. For example, the graph of $y = 3x^2 - 2$ is a parabola and $y = |x - 2|$ is V-shaped. Graphs of linear equations are straight lines. There are various forms for these equations:

standard forms: $Ax + By + C = 0$
$\qquad\qquad\qquad Ax + By = C$

slope-intercept form: $y = mx + b$

point-slope form: $y - y_1 = m(x - x_1)$

two-point form:
$$y - y_1 = \frac{y_2 - y_1}{x_2 - x_1}(x - x_1)$$

intercept form: $\frac{x}{a} + \frac{y}{b} = 1$

© Mathematical Practices

Make sense of problems and persevere in solving them. With a knowledge of direct variation, students will construct and graph linear equations as well as explain correspondences between graphs and equations.

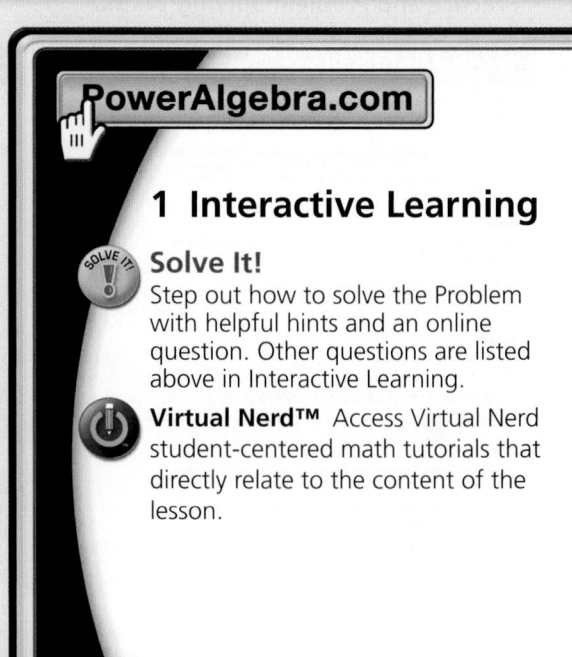

PowerAlgebra.com

1 Interactive Learning

Solve It!
Step out how to solve the Problem with helpful hints and an online question. Other questions are listed above in Interactive Learning.

Virtual Nerd™ Access Virtual Nerd student-centered math tutorials that directly relate to the content of the lesson.

Problem 1 Finding Slope

What is the slope of the line that passes through the given points?

A $(-3, 7)$ and $(-2, 4)$

$$m = \frac{y_2 - y_1}{x_2 - x_1} = \frac{4 - 7}{-2 - (-3)} = \frac{-3}{1}$$

The slope of the line that passes through $(-3, 7)$ and $(-2, 4)$ is $\frac{-3}{1}$ or -3.

B $(3, 1)$ and $(-4, 1)$

$$m = \frac{y_2 - y_1}{x_2 - x_1} = \frac{1 - 1}{-4 - 3} = \frac{0}{-7} = 0$$

The slope of the line that passes through $(3, 1)$ and $(-4, 1)$ is $\frac{0}{-7}$ or 0.

C $(7, -3)$ and $(7, 1)$

$$m = \frac{y_2 - y_1}{x_2 - x_1} = \frac{1 - (-3)}{7 - 7} = \frac{4}{0}$$

Division by zero is undefined, so slope is undefined for the line that passes through $(7, -3)$ and $(7, 1)$.

Think

Does it matter which point you choose for (x_1, y_1)?

No; you can choose either point for (x_1, y_1).

Got It? 1. What is the slope of the line that passes through the given points?
   a. $(5, 4)$ and $(8, 1)$ **b.** $(2, 2)$ and $(-2, -2)$ **c.** $(9, 3)$ and $(9, -4)$
   d. Reasoning Use the slope formula to show in part (a) that it does not matter which point you choose for (x_1, y_1).

take note

Concept Summary Slope of a Line

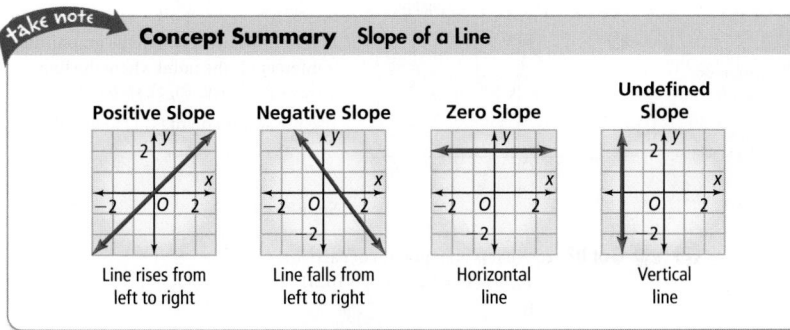

Positive Slope	Negative Slope	Zero Slope	Undefined Slope
Line rises from left to right	Line falls from left to right	Horizontal line	Vertical line

A function whose graph is a line is a **linear function**. You can represent a linear function with a **linear equation**, such as $y = 6x - 4$. A solution of a linear equation is any ordered pair (x, y) that makes the equation true.

---

2 Guided Instruction

 Each Problem is worked out and supported online.

Problem 1
Finding Slope

Problem 2
Writing Linear Equations
Animated

Problem 3
Writing Equations in Slope-Intercept Form

Alternative Problem 3
Writing Equations in Slope-Intercept Form
Animated

Problem 4
Graphing a Linear Equation
Animated

Support in Algebra 2 Companion
• Vocabulary
• Key Concepts
• Got It?

Problem 1

Sometimes $\frac{y_1 - y_2}{x_1 - x_2}$ is easier to compute than $\frac{y_2 - y_1}{x_2 - x_1}$. Either order of the coordinates will give the correct answer.

Q What values do you use in the numerator of the slope fraction? in the denominator? **[y-coordinates; x-coordinates]**

Q How can you use graphing to check your answers? **[Plot the two points and draw the line connecting them. Find the slope by counting the squares for the vertical change and horizontal change.]**

Got It?

Make sure all students can find slope from two points. If necessary, provide remedial practice finding slope using (0, 0) and one other point.

Take Note

Q Why should you look at graphs from left to right? **[If you look at a graph from right to left, it will appear to have the opposite slope than when you look at it from left to right.]**

Q Why is the slope of a vertical line undefined? **[Every point on a vertical line has the same x-coordinate, so the slope ratio results in division by a horizontal change of zero.]**

Answers

Solve It!

$\frac{A}{B}, \frac{A}{B}$

Got It?

1. a. -1
   b. 1
   c. undefined
   d. $\frac{1 - 4}{8 - 5} = \frac{-3}{3} = -1 = \frac{3}{-3} = \frac{4 - 1}{5 - 8}$

Take Note

Why is the letter m used to indicate the slope? It may be from the word *modulas*, but nobody knows for sure.

Q Why is a direct variation a special form of a linear function? **[Answers may vary. Sample: The general form of a direct variation $y = kx$ is a special case of slope-intercept form $y = mx + b$ where the slope is the constant of variation and the y-intercept is (0, 0).]**

Problem 2
Students write equations for lines using either the slope and y-intercept or a line in the coordinate plane.

Q In 2A, how do you know what to substitute for b? **[The y-intercept is (0, b) in slope-intercept form. Here, the y-intercept is (0, −3), so $b = -3$.]**

Q In 2B, how can you find the slope between (0, 4) and (1, 1) without using the slope formula? **[Count the units from (0, 4) to (1, 1). The vertical change is −3; the horizontal change is 1.]**

Got It?
Have a volunteer explain how to use a graphing calculator to check the answer to 2a.

A special form of a linear equation is called *slope-intercept form*.

An *intercept* of a line is a point where a line crosses an axis. The **y-intercept** of a nonvertical line is the point at which the line crosses the y-axis. The **x-intercept** of a nonhorizontal line is the point at which the line crosses the x-axis.

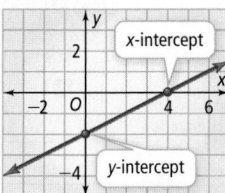

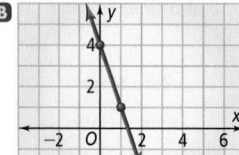 **Key Concept** Slope-Intercept Form

The **slope-intercept form** of an equation of a line is $y = mx + b$, where m is the slope of the line and (0, b) is the y-intercept.

 Problem 2 Writing Linear Equations

What is an equation of each line?

A $m = \frac{1}{5}$ and the y-intercept is (0, −3)

$y = mx + b$ Use the slope-intercept form.

$y = \frac{1}{5}x + (-3)$ Substitute $m = \frac{1}{5}$ and $b = -3$.

$y = \frac{1}{5}x - 3$ Simplify.

B 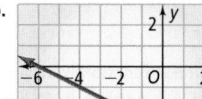 Look at the line shown in the graph. The y-intercept is the point where the line crosses the y-axis, (0, 4), so $b = 4$.

Use the second point (1, 1) to find the slope.

$m = \frac{y_2 - y_1}{x_2 - x_1} = \frac{1 - 4}{1 - 0} = -3$.

So, $y = -3x + 4$.

Plan
What information do you need from the graph?
You need the y-intercept and another point to find the slope.

Got It? **2.** What is an equation of each line?

   a. $m = 6$, y-intercept is (0, 5)

   b.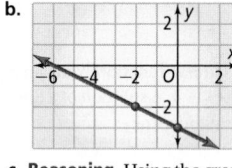

   c. Reasoning Using the graph from part (b), do you get a different equation if you use (−6, 0) and the y-intercept to find the slope of the line? Explain.

Additional Problems

1. What is the slope of the line that passes through the given points?

  a. (−10, 2) and (4, −5)

  b. (6, −1) and (5, −1)

  c. (−2, 5) and (−2, −3)

ANSWERS

  a. $-\frac{1}{2}$

  b. 0

  c. undefined

2. What is an equation of each line?

  a. slope $= -3$, y-intercept is (0, 5)

b.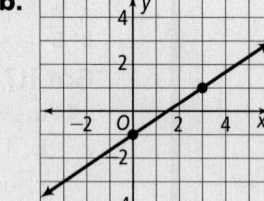

ANSWERS

  a. $y = -3x + 5$

  b. $y = \frac{2}{3}x - 1$

3. Write the equation in slope-intercept form. What are the slope and y-intercept?

  a. $2x + 3y - 15 = 0$

  b. $12 = 10y - 3x$

ANSWERS

  a. $y = -\frac{2}{3}x + 5$, slope $= -\frac{2}{3}$, y-intercept is (0, 5)

  b. $y = \frac{3}{10}x + \frac{6}{5}$, slope $= \frac{3}{10}$, y-intercept is $\left(0, \frac{6}{5}\right)$

4. What is the graph of $24 = 4x - 3y$?

ANSWER

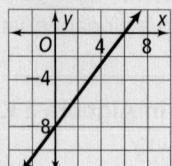

You can rewrite a linear equation in slope–intercept form by solving for y.

 Problem 3 Writing Equations in Slope-Intercept Form

Write the equation in slope-intercept form. What are the slope and y-intercept?

Ⓐ $5x - 4y = 16$

$\quad -4y = -5x + 16$ Subtract $5x$ from each side.

$\quad \dfrac{-4y}{-4} = \dfrac{-5x}{-4} + \dfrac{16}{-4}$ Divide each side by -4.

$\quad y = \dfrac{5}{4}x - 4$ Compare the equation with $y = mx + b$

The slope $m = \dfrac{5}{4}$. The y-intercept is $(0, -4)$.

Ⓑ $-\dfrac{3}{4}x + \dfrac{1}{2}y = -1$

$\quad \dfrac{1}{2}y = \dfrac{3}{4}x - 1$ Add $\dfrac{3}{4}x$ to each side.

$\quad y = \dfrac{3}{2}x - 2$ Multiply each side by 2.

The slope $m = \dfrac{3}{2}$. The y-intercept is $(0, -2)$.

Think

Is there another way to solve this problem?
Yes; clear the fractions by multiplying all terms by 4, the LCM of the denominators.

 Got It? **3.** Write the equation in slope-intercept form. What are the slope and y-intercept?
    a. $3x + 2y = 18$ **b.** $-7x - 5y = 35$

 Problem 4 Graphing a Linear Equation

What is the graph of $-2x + y = 1$?

Know	**Need**	**Plan**
• The equation of a line	Two points to draw the line	• Write the equation in slope-intercept form. • Plot the y-intercept. • Use the slope to find a second point. • Draw a line through the two points.

Write the equation in slope-intercept form.

$\quad -2x + y = 1$

$\quad\quad\quad y = 2x + 1$

The slope is 2 and the y-intercept is $(0, 1)$.

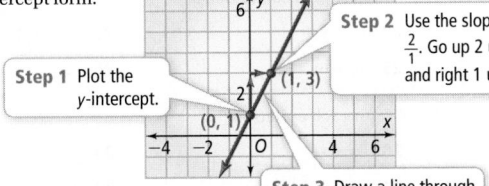

Step 1 Plot the y-intercept.

Step 2 Use the slope $\dfrac{2}{1}$. Go up 2 units and right 1 unit.

Step 3 Draw a line through the two points.

Got It? **4.** What is the graph of $4x - 7y = 14$?

Problem 3

Q In 3A, suppose a student got the answer $y = \dfrac{5}{4}x + 16$. What mistake was made? **[The student did not divide 16 by -4.]**

Q In 3A, suppose a student got the answer $y = \dfrac{5}{4}x + 4$. What mistake was made? **[16 divided by -4 is -4, not 4.]**

Got It?   ERROR PREVENTION

Q When you rewrite an equation in slope-intercept form, you are solving for a variable. Which variable? **[y]**

Problem 4

Q What is another ratio equivalent to the slope 2? **[Answers may vary. Samples: $\dfrac{4}{2}$ or $\dfrac{-2}{-1}$]**

Q What happens if you use your alternative ratio to measure the vertical and horizontal change from $(0, 1)$? **[You end up at another point on the same line.]**

Got It?   EXTENSION

Write $4x - 7y = 14$. Cover the y-term.
Q When $y = 0$, what is x? **[$\dfrac{7}{2}$]**
Then cover the x-term.
Q When $x = 0$, what is y? **[-2]**
Q What two points on the line does this give you? **[$\left(\dfrac{7}{2}, 0\right)$ and $(0, -2)$]**
Q What are these points called? **[x-intercept, y-intercept]**

Answers

Got It? (continued)

2. a. $y = 6x + 5$

    b. $y = -\dfrac{1}{2}x - 3$

    c. No; any two points on a line can be used to calculate the slope.

3. a. $y = -\dfrac{3}{2}x + 9$; $-\dfrac{3}{2}$; $(0, 9)$

    b. $y = -\dfrac{7}{5}x - 7$; $-\dfrac{7}{5}$; $(0, -7)$

4. $y = \dfrac{4}{7}x - 2$

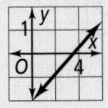

3 Lesson Check

Do you know HOW?

- For Exercises 1 and 2, remind students to first isolate the *y*-term and then divide both sides by the coefficient of that term.

Do you UNDERSTAND?

- For Exercise 5, write the words *intercept* and *interception* on the board. Have students use dictionaries or online sources to find definitions for each word. As a class, brainstorm a list of usages.

Close

> **Q** If you have 3 points, how can you use the slope formula to determine whether the points are collinear? **[Calculate the slope between any 2 pairs. If the slope between both pairs is the same, all 3 points are collinear; otherwise they are not.]**

 Lesson Check

Do you know HOW?

Write each equation in slope-intercept form.

1. $x - 2y + 3 = 1$

2. $-4x + 3y = 1$

What is the slope of the line passing through the following points?

3. $(2, 4)$ and $(4, 2)$

4. $(-1, -3)$ and $(3, 1)$

Do you UNDERSTAND?  MATHEMATICAL PRACTICES

5. **Vocabulary** What is a *y*-intercept? How is a *y*-intercept different from an *x*-intercept?

6. Explain why the slope of a vertical line is called "undefined."

7. **Error Analysis** A classmate found the slope between two points. What error did she make?

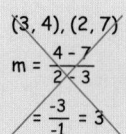

 **Practice and Problem-Solving Exercises** 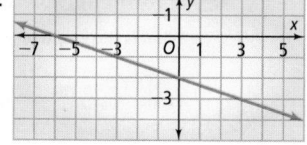 MATHEMATICAL PRACTICES

A **Practice** Find the slope of the line through each pair of points. ◆ See Problem 1.

8. $(1, 6)$ and $(8, -1)$ 9. $(-3, 9)$ and $(0, 3)$ 10. $(0, 0)$ and $(2, 6)$

11. $(-4, -3)$ and $(7, 1)$ 12. $(-2, -1)$ and $(8, -3)$ 13. $(1, 2)$ and $(2, 3)$

14. $(2, 7)$ and $(-3, 11)$ 15. $(-3, 5)$ and $(4, 5)$ 16. $(-5, -7)$ and $(0, 10)$

Write an equation for each line. ◆ See Problem 2.

17. $m = 3$ and the *y*-intercept is $(0, 2)$.

19. $m = \frac{5}{6}$ and the *y*-intercept is $(0, 12)$.

20. $m = 0$ and the *y*-intercept is $(0, -2)$.

21. $m = -5$ and the *y*-intercept is $(0, -7)$.

18.

Write each equation in slope-intercept form. Then find the slope and *y*-intercept of each line. ◆ See Problem 3.

22. $5x + y = 4$ 23. $-3x + 2y = 7$ 24. $-\frac{1}{2}x - y = \frac{3}{4}$

25. $8x + 6y = 5$ 26. $9x - 2y = 10$ 27. $y = 7$

Graph each equation. ◆ See Problem 4.

28. $y = 2x$ 29. $y = -3x - 1$ 30. $y = 3x - 2$

31. $y = -4x + 5$ 32. $5x - 2y = -4$ 33. $-2x + 5y = -10$

34. $y - 3 = -2x$ 35. $y + 4 = -3x$ 36. $-y + 5 = -2x$

PowerAlgebra.com

3 Lesson Check

For a digital lesson check, use the Got It questions.

Support in Algebra 2 Companion
- Lesson Check

4 Practice

Assign homework to individual students or to an entire class.

Answers

Lesson Check

1. $y = \frac{1}{2}x + 1$

2. $y = \frac{4}{3}x + \frac{1}{3}$

3. -1

4. 1

5. The *y*-intercept of a line is the point at which the line crosses the *y*-axis. The *x*-intercept is the point at which the line crosses the *x*-axis.

6. Since division by zero is undefined, the slope of a vertical line that passes through (a, b) and (a, c), $\frac{c - b}{0}$, is undefined.

7. She subtracted the *x*-coordinates in the wrong order. The *x*- and *y*-coordinates of each point must be subtracted consistently.

Practice and Problem-Solving Exercises

8. -1 9. -2 10. 3 11. $\frac{4}{11}$

12. $-\frac{1}{5}$ 13. 1 14. $-\frac{4}{5}$ 15. 0

16. $\frac{17}{5}$ 17. $y = 3x + 2$

18. $y = -\frac{x}{3} - 2$ 19. $y = \frac{5}{6}x + 12$

20. $y = -2$

21. $y = -5x - 7$

22. $y = -5x + 4$; -5, $(0, 4)$

23. $y = \frac{3}{2}x + \frac{7}{2}$; $\frac{3}{2}$, $\left(0, \frac{7}{2}\right)$

24. $y = -\frac{1}{2}x - \frac{3}{4}$; $-\frac{1}{2}$, $\left(0, -\frac{3}{4}\right)$

25. $y = -\frac{4}{3}x + \frac{5}{6}$; $-\frac{4}{3}$, $\left(0, \frac{5}{6}\right)$

26. $y = \frac{9}{2}x - 5$; $\frac{9}{2}$, $\left(0, -5\right)$

27. $y = 7$; 0, $(0, 7)$

Graph each equation.

37. $y = -\frac{1}{2}x - \frac{3}{2}$ **38.** $y = -2x + 3$ **39.** $y = -x + 7$

40. $3y - 2x = -12$ **41.** $4x + 5y = 20$ **42.** $4x - 3y = -6$

43. $\frac{2}{3}x + \frac{y}{3} = -\frac{1}{3}$ **44.** $x = 5$ **45.** $2.4 = -3.6x - 0.4y$

46. Think About a Plan Suppose the equation $y = 12 + 10x$ models the amount of money in your wallet, where y is the total in dollars and x is the number of weeks from today. If you graphed this equation, what would the slope represent in the situation? Explain.
- Is the equation in slope-intercept form?
- What units make sense for the slope?

Find the slope and y-intercept of each line.

47. 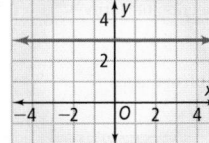   **48.** 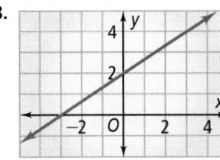   **49.**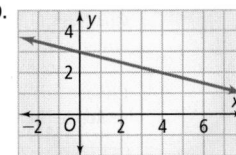

Find the slope and y-intercept of each line.

50. $y = 0.4 - 0.8x$ **51.** $x = -3$ **52.** $y = 0$

53. $-\frac{1}{3}x - \frac{2}{3}y = \frac{5}{3}$ **54.** $-Ax + By = -C$ **55.** $\frac{A}{D}x + \frac{B}{D}y = \frac{C}{D}$

56. The equation $d = 4 - \frac{1}{15}t$ represents your distance from home d for each minute you walk t.
 a. If you graphed this equation, what would the slope represent? What would the constant term 4 represent? Explain.
 b. Are you walking towards or away from your home? Explain.

57. Reasoning Use the graph to find the slope between the following points on the line.
 a. P and Q **b.** Q and S
 c. S and P **d.** R and Q
 e. Make a conjecture based on your answers to parts (a)-(d).

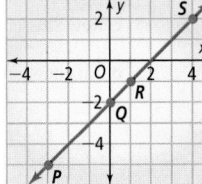

58. Error Analysis A classmate says that the graph of $3y - 2x = 5$ has a slope of 2. What mistake did he make?

Find the slope of the line through each pair of points.

59. $\left(\frac{3}{2}, -\frac{1}{2}\right)$ and $\left(-\frac{2}{3}, \frac{1}{3}\right)$ **60.** $\left(-\frac{1}{2}, -\frac{1}{2}\right)$ and $(-3, -4)$ **61.** $\left(0, -\frac{1}{2}\right)$ and $\left(\frac{7}{5}, 10\right)$

4 Practice

ASSIGNMENT GUIDE

Basic: 8–36 all, 44–56 even, 57–59

Average: 9–35 odd, 37–61

Advanced: 9–35 odd, 37–62

Ⓒ Mathematical Practices are supported by exercises with red headings. Here are the Practices supported in this lesson:

MP 1: Make Sense of Problems Ex. 46, 57
MP 3: Critique the Reasoning of Others Ex. 7, 58

Applications exercises have blue headings. Exercise 65 supports MP 4: Model.

EXERCISE 56: Use the Think About a Plan worksheet in the **Practice and Problem Solving Workbook** (also available in the Teaching Resources in print and online) to further support students' development in becoming independent learners.

HOMEWORK QUICK CHECK

To check students' understanding of key skills and concepts, go over Exercises 23, 29, 46, 56, and 57.

---

28. 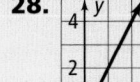   **29.** 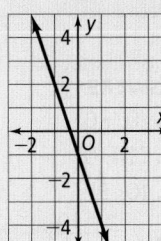   **34.** 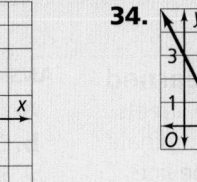   **35.** 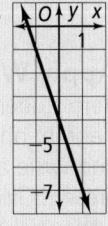   **40.** 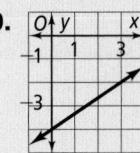   **41.**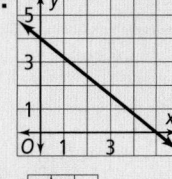

30. 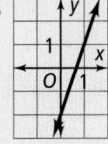   **31.** 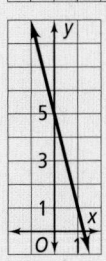   **36.** 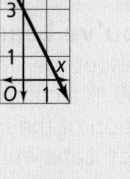   **37.**   **42.** 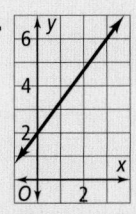   **43.**

38. 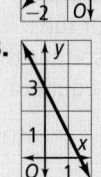   **44.**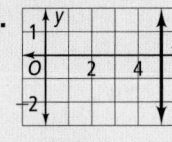

32. 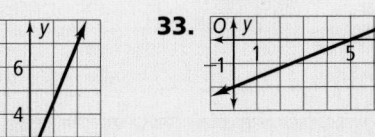   **33.**   **39.** 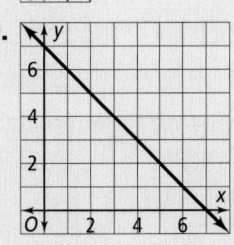   **45.**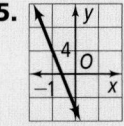

46–61. See next page.

Answers

Practice and Problem-Solving Exercises (continued)

46. The slope represents the amount of money you put in your wallet each week.

47. 0; (0, 3)

48. $\frac{2}{3}$; (0, 2)

49. $-\frac{1}{4}$; (0, 3)

50. -0.8; (0, 0.4)

51. undefined slope; no y-intercept

52. 0; (0, 0)

53. $-\frac{1}{2}$; $\left(0, -\frac{5}{2}\right)$

54. $\frac{A}{B}$; $\left(0, -\frac{C}{B}\right)$

55. $-\frac{A}{B}$; $\left(0, \frac{C}{B}\right)$

56. a. the rate at which you walk; the distance away from home when you start walking; the slope is the same as the change in distance divided by the change in time, which is the rate at which you walk. When you start walking, you have been walking for $t = 0$ minutes, so $d = 4$ is your distance from home when you start to walk.

b. towards your home; the slope is negative and the distance (y-value) decreases as the time (x-value) increases.

57. a. 1   **b.** 1   **c.** 1   **d.** 1

e. Any two points on a line can be used to find the slope of the line.

58. He did not isolate y first and then find the coefficient of x. The slope is $\frac{2}{3}$.

59. $-\frac{5}{13}$ **60.** $\frac{7}{5}$ **61.** $\frac{15}{2}$

62. a. $y = \frac{1}{2}x + 4$

b. $y = -3x + 4$

c. $y = -4x + 9$

 **Challenge**

62. You can find the equation of a line through two points even if one point is not the y-intercept.

- Find the slope m of the line passing through the two points.
- Using either point, substitute for x, y, and m into $y = mx + b$.
- Solve for b and rewrite $y = mx + b$ for the values of m and b.

Write an equation in slope-intercept form for the line passing through each pair of points.

a. (2, 5) and (6, 7)   **b.** (-4, 16) and (3, -5)   **c.** (-2, 17) and (2, 1)

 Apply What You've Learned

 MATHEMATICAL PRACTICES
MP 4

Look back at the information on page 59 about the work crew that is painting lane lines on Main Street. Copy the diagram of the streets and place it in Quadrant 1 of a coordinate plane, with the origin at the intersection of North Street and Wilson Street.

Choose from the following coordinates and equations to complete the sentences below. Explain your reasoning.

| (0, 14) | (14, 0) | (0, 20) | (20, 0) | (0, 3) |

| (3, 0) | (0, 17) | (14, 20) | $y = -\frac{10}{7}x + 17$ | $y = \frac{7}{10}x + 17$ |

| $y = \frac{10}{7}x + 20$ | $y = -\frac{10}{7}x + 20$ | $y = -\frac{7}{10}x + 20$ | $y = \frac{7}{10}x + 20$ | $y = -\frac{7}{10}x + 17$ |

a. North Street and Main Street intersect at __?__ .

b. Wilson Street and Main Street intersect at __?__ .

c. New Street intersects North Street at __?__ .

d. An equation of the line that represents Main Street is __?__ .

 Apply What You've Learned

Here students represent the streets in the diagram on page 59 in a coordinate plane, and write an equation of the line that represents Main Street. Later in the chapter, they will write the equation of a line perpendicular to Main Street.

Mathematical Practices

Students **model** the location of the streets on a coordinate plane so that they can represent the streets with equations. (MP 4)

ANSWERS

a. (0, 20)

b. (14, 0)

c. (0, 3)

d. $y = -\frac{10}{7}x + 20$

2-3 **Lesson Resources**

Additional Instructional Support

Algebra 2 Companion

Students can use the **Algebra 2 Companion** worktext (4 pages) as you teach the lesson. Use the Companion to support

- New Vocabulary
- Key Concepts
- Got It for each Problem
- Lesson Check

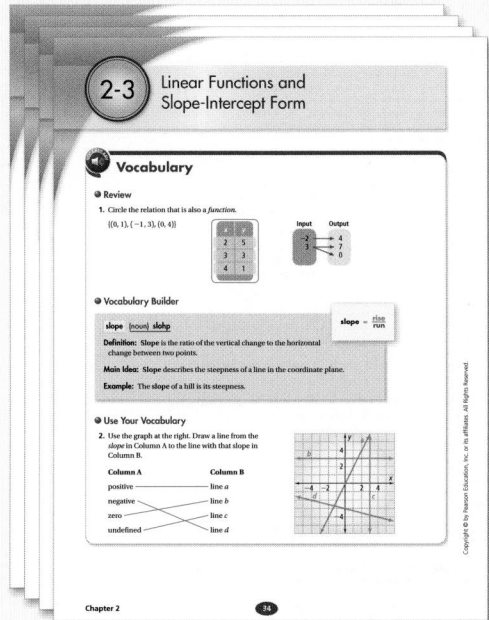

ELL Support

Focus on Communication Divide the class into groups of three. Each student draws a line in a labeled coordinate plane and passes it to the second student. The second student writes the coordinates of the x- and y-intercepts and passes the graph to the third student, who determines whether the slope is positive, negative, zero, or undefined, and labels the line. The students discuss whether they agree with the labels and then switch groups to play again.

5 Assess & Remediate

Lesson Quiz

1. What is the slope of the line that passes through $(-2, 3)$ and $(4, -5)$?
2. What is an equation of the line with slope 4 and y-intercept at $(0, -3)$?
3. Write the equation $12 - y = 2x - 5$ in slope-intercept form. What are the slope and y-intercept?
4. What is the graph of $5x = 2y - 20$?
5. **Do you UNDERSTAND?** Can a horizontal line have an x-intercept? What if the line passes through the origin? Explain.

ANSWERS TO LESSON QUIZ

1. $-\frac{4}{3}$
2. $y = 4x - 3$
3. $y = -2x + 17$, $m = -2$, y-intercept $(0, 17)$
4.

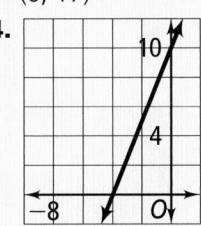

5. A horizontal line cannot have an x-intercept. Even if the horizontal line is the x-axis itself, it will not have an x-intercept, because the x-intercept is defined as the point at which a line *crosses* the x-axis.

PRESCRIPTION FOR REMEDIATION

Use the student work on the Lesson Quiz to prescribe a differentiated review assignment:

Points	Differentiated Remediation
0–2	Intervention
3–4	On-level
5	Extension

PowerAlgebra.com

5 Assess & Remediate

Assign the Lesson Quiz. Appropriate intervention, practice, or enrichment is automatically generated based on student performance.

Differentiated Remediation

Available in editable format online.

Intervention

- **Reteaching** (2 pages) Provides reteaching and practice exercises for the key lesson concepts. Use with struggling students or absent students.
- **English Language Learner Support** Helps students develop and reinforce mathematical vocabulary and key concepts.

All-in-One Resources/Online
Reteaching

2-3 Reteaching
Linear Functions and Slope-Intercept Form

You can use the slope-intercept form to write equations of lines.

- The slope-intercept formula is $y = mx + b$, where m represents the slope of the line, and b represents its y-intercept. The y-intercept is the point at which the line crosses the y-axis.
- The slope of a horizontal line is always zero, and the slope of a vertical line is always undefined.

Problem

What is the equation of the line that contains the point $(3, -1)$ and has a slope of $-\frac{4}{3}$?

$-1 = \left(-\frac{4}{3}\right)(3) + b$ To find b, substitute the values $-\frac{4}{3}$ for m, 3 for x, and -1 for y into the slope-intercept formula.

$-1 = -4 + b$ Multiply.

$3 = b$ Add 4 to each side and simplify.

$y = -\frac{4}{3}x + 3$ Substitute $-\frac{4}{3}$ for m and 3 for b into the slope-intercept formula.

Exercises

Write an equation for each line.

1. $m = 4$; contains $(3, 2)$ $y = 4x - 10$
2. $m = -2$; contains $(4, 7)$ $y = -2x + 15$
3. $m = 0$; contains $(3, 0)$ $y = 0$
4. $m = -1$; contains $(-5, -2)$ $y = -x - 7$
5. $m = 3$; contains $(-2, -4)$ $y = 3x + 2$
6. $m = 0$; contains $(0, -7)$ $y = -7$
7. $m = 8$; contains $(5, 0)$ $y = 8x - 40$
8. $m = -1$; contains $(0, 7)$ $y = -x + 7$
9. $m = 0$; contains $(3, 8)$ $y = 8$
10. $m = 4$; contains $(2, 5)$ $y = 4x - 3$
11. $m = 7$; contains $(3, 2)$ $y = 7x - 19$
12. $m = -1$; contains $(2, -6)$ $y = -x - 4$
13. $y = 2x + 3$
14. $y = -x - 2$
15. $y = \frac{2}{3}x + 2$

All-in-One Resources/Online
English Language Learner Support

2-3 Additional Vocabulary Support
Linear Functions and Slope-Intercept Form

Read the steps and notes in the example at the left, and answer the questions below.

Exercise Write the equation in slope-intercept form. What is the slope and y-intercept? $3x - 4y = 20$	
$3x - 4y = 20$	Solve the equation for y.
$-4y = -3x + 20$	Subtract 3x from each side.
$y = \frac{3}{4}x - 5$	Divide each side by -4.
The slope is $\frac{3}{4}$.	The coefficient of x is the slope.
The y-intercept is $(0, -5)$.	The constant is the y-intercept.

1. Read the exercise. What process are you going to use to solve the problem?
   Answers may vary. Sample: Solve the equation for y.
2. What is the slope-intercept form of a line?
   $y = mx + b$
3. Why subtract 3x from both sides?
   to isolate the term with y
4. Which part of the slope-intercept form of a line tells you what the slope of the line is?
   m (the coefficient of x)
5. Which part of the slope-intercept form of a line tells you what the y-intercept is?
   b (the constant)
6. Why is the x-coordinate of the y-intercept always zero?
   Answers may vary. Sample: All points on the y-axis have x-coordinates of 0.

Differentiated Remediation *continued*

Available in editable format online.

On-Level

- **Practice** (2 pages) Provides extra practice for each lesson. For simpler practice exercises, use the Form K Practice pages found in the All-in-One Teaching Resources and online.

- **Think About a Plan** Helps students develop specific problem-solving skills and strategies by providing scaffolded guiding questions.

- **Standardized Test Prep** Focuses on all major exercises, all major question types, and helps students prepare for the high-stakes assessments.

Extension

- **Enrichment** Provides students with interesting problems and activities that extend the concepts of the lesson.

- **Activities, Games, and Puzzles** Worksheets that can be used for concepts development, enrichment, and for fun!

Practice and Problem Solving Wkbk/All-in-One Resources/Online
Practice page 1

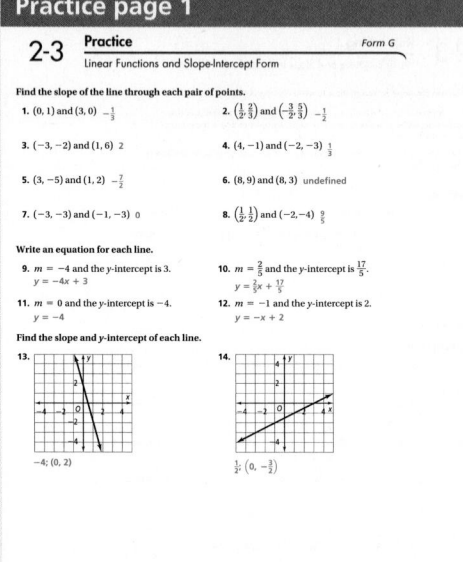

2-3 Practice — Form G
Linear Functions and Slope-Intercept Form

Find the slope of the line through each pair of points.

1. (0, 1) and (3, 0) $-\frac{1}{3}$
2. $\left(\frac{1}{2}, \frac{2}{3}\right)$ and $\left(-\frac{3}{2}, \frac{5}{3}\right)$ $-\frac{1}{2}$
3. (−3, −2) and (1, 6) 2
4. (4, −1) and (−2, −1) $\frac{1}{3}$
5. (3, −5) and (1, 2) $-\frac{7}{2}$
6. (8, 9) and (8, 3) undefined
7. (−3, −3) and (−1, −3) 0
8. $\left(\frac{1}{2}, \frac{1}{2}\right)$ and (−2, −4) $\frac{9}{5}$

Write an equation for each line.

9. $m = -4$ and the y-intercept is 3.
  $y = -4x + 3$
10. $m = \frac{2}{5}$ and the y-intercept is $\frac{17}{5}$.
  $y = \frac{2}{5}x + \frac{17}{5}$
11. $m = 0$ and the y-intercept is −4.
  $y = -4$
12. $m = -1$ and the y-intercept is 2.
  $y = -x + 2$

Find the slope and y-intercept of each line.

13. −4; (0, 2)
14. $\frac{1}{2}$; $\left(0, -\frac{3}{2}\right)$

Practice and Problem Solving Wkbk/All-in-One Resources/Online
Practice page 2

2-3 Practice (continued) — Form G
Linear Functions and Slope-Intercept Form

Find the slope and y-intercept of each line.

15. $3x - 4y = 12$ $\frac{3}{4}$; (0, −3)
16. $y = -2$ 0; (0, −2)
17. $f(x) = \frac{6}{4}x + 7$ $\frac{5}{4}$; (0, 7)
18. $x = 5$ undefined; none
19. $4x - 3y = -6$ $\frac{4}{3}$; (0, 2)
20. $g(x) = -3x - 17.5$ −3; (0, −17.5)

Graph each equation.

21. $4x + 3y = 12$
22. $\frac{x}{3} - \frac{y}{6} = 1$
23. $y = -\frac{3}{2}x + \frac{1}{2}$

Find the slope and y-intercept of each line.

24. $-\frac{1}{2}$; (0, −1)
25. $\frac{2}{3}$; $\left(0, -\frac{2}{3}\right)$
26. 2; (0, −2)

27. The equation $e = 1200 + 11t$ represents your elevation e in feet for each minute t you hike from a trailhead.
  a. If you graphed this equation, what would the slope represent? Explain.
  b. Are you hiking uphill or downhill? Explain.
  Uphill; the slope is positive, so the elevation is increasing.

  a. The slope represents the gain or loss in elevation per minute. The slope is 11, so for each minute of hiking, elevation increases by 11 feet.

Practice and Problem Solving Wkbk/All-in-One Resources/Online
Think About a Plan

2-3 Think About a Plan
Linear Functions and Slope-Intercept Form

The equation $d = 4 - \frac{1}{15}t$ represents your distance (in miles) from home d for each minute of your walk t.

a. If you graphed this equation, what would the slope represent? Explain.
b. Are you walking towards or away from your home? Explain.

1. What does d represent?
  your distance from home in miles

2. What does t represent?
  the number of minutes you spend walking

3. Is the equation in slope-intercept form? If not, write the equation in slope-intercept form.
  no; $d = -\frac{1}{15}t + 4$

4. What units make sense for the slope? Explain.
  mi/min; slope is the ratio of the change in distance to the change in time (in minutes), and it is reasonable to walk 1 mi in 15 min, or 4 mi/hr.

5. What does the slope represent? Explain.
  The constant rate by which your distance from home changes; you walk at a rate of 1 mi per 15 min towards home.

6. Is your distance from home increasing or decreasing?
  decreasing

Practice and Problem Solving Wkbk/All-in-One Resources/Online
Standardized Test Prep

2-3 Standardized Test Prep
Linear Functions and Slope-Intercept Form

Multiple Choice

For Exercises 1–5, choose the correct letter.

1. For the linear equation $5x - y = 2$, which of the following has a value of 5? A
  Ⓐ the slope Ⓑ the x-intercept Ⓒ the y-intercept Ⓓ the origin

2. What is true about the line that passes through the points (3, −7) and (3, 2)? H
  Ⓕ It is horizontal. Ⓗ It is vertical.
  Ⓖ It rises from left to right. Ⓘ It falls from left to right.

3. What is the slope-intercept form of $3x + 2y = 1$? B
  Ⓐ $y = \frac{3}{2}x - \frac{1}{2}$ Ⓑ $y = -\frac{3}{2}x + \frac{1}{2}$ Ⓒ $y = -\frac{2}{3}x + \frac{1}{2}$ Ⓓ $y = \frac{3}{2}x - \frac{1}{2}$

4. What is the y-intercept of the graph of $5x - 9y = 45$? H
  Ⓕ −9 Ⓖ −5 Ⓘ 5

5. Which of the following is a graph of $4x = -\frac{1}{2}y - 1$? C
  Ⓐ Ⓑ Ⓒ Ⓓ

Short Response

Write the equation in slope-intercept form. What are the slope and the y-intercept?

6. $\frac{1}{2}x + \frac{3}{2}y - 1 = 0$
  [2] $y = -\frac{1}{3}x + \frac{2}{3}$; $-\frac{1}{3}$; $\frac{2}{3}$
  [1] incorrect equation OR incorrect slope OR incorrect y-intercept
  [0] no answers given

All-in-One Resources/Online
Enrichment

2-3 Enrichment
Linear Functions and Slope-Intercept Form

Explicit, Implicit, and Parametric Equations of Lines

When a function $y = f(x)$ is written so that you can directly compute the value of y given any value of x, the function is said to be defined explicitly. If you have to do algebraic manipulations to find the value of y, the function is said to be defined implicitly. For example, the equation $2y + 6x = 16$ implicitly defines y as a function of x. Given $x = 1$, you would have to solve the equation $2y + 6 = 16$ to find the corresponding value of y.

1. How could you write the equation $2y + 6x = 16$ expressing y explicitly as a function of x? $y = -3x + 8$

Another way to define a function involves using another variable or parameter—for example, $x = 2t + 1$ and $y = 5 - 6t$. When both x and y are written as explicit functions of another variable (in this case t), they are said to be defined parametrically in terms of that variable.

2. The graph of such parametric equations can be constructed by plotting values of x and corresponding y to each value of t. Here, if $t = 1$, then $x = 3$ and $y = -1$. What point on the graph corresponds to $t = 1$? (3, −1)

3. What point corresponds to $t = 2$? (5, −7)

This technique has an important physical interpretation. If you think of the parameter t as time, the graph can be viewed as being traced out by a "moving point" that occupies a specific location at time t.

4. In the example, as time changes from $t = 1$ to $t = 2$, the "moving point" travels between which two points? (3, −1); (5, −7)

5. Sometimes it is possible to go from a parametric representation to an explicit one. In the example above, solve for t as a function of x. $t = \frac{x-1}{2}$

6. Substitute this value for t into the equation for y. When simplified, what equation results? $y = -3x + 8$

7. What kind of equation is this? linear

8. What is the slope of the line? What is the y-intercept? −3; (0, 8)

9. Write the pair of parametric equations, $x = -2t - 6$ and $y = 8t - 1$, as an explicit function of y in terms of x. $y = -4x - 25$

10. Write the pair of parametric equations, $x = 2t + 5$ and $y = 3 - 2t$, as an explicit function of y in terms of x. $y = -x + 8$

Online Teacher Resource Center
Activities, Games, and Puzzles

2-3 Game: Risk and Reward
Linear Functions and Slope-Intercept Form

Provide the host with the following questions and answers.

	Vocabulary (Define)	Find the Slope of the Line	Find the y-Intercept of the Line	Express in Slope-Intercept Form	Review
10 pts	y-intercept of a line See below.	$y = 2x + 1$ Answer: 2	$y = 4x - 5$ Answer: (0, −5)	$m = -5$ and the y-intercept is 1 Answer: $y = -5x + 1$	Solve $3x + 2 = 5x - 6$. Answer: $x = 4$
20 pts	x-intercept of a line See below.	$y + 3x = 5$ Answer: −3	through (1, 3) and (0, 4) Answer: (0, 4)	$m = 0$ and the y-intercept is −4 Answer: $y = -4$	Solve $|x - 1| < 3$. Answer: $-2 < x < 4$
30 pts	linear function See below.	$2y - 5x = 1$ Answer: $\frac{5}{2}$	$3x - 2y = -6$ Answer: (0, 3)	$9x + 6y = -18$ Answer: $y = -\frac{3}{2}x - 3$	Solve $|x + 2| \geq 2$. Answer: $x \leq -4$ or $x \geq 0$
40 pts	slope See below.	$\frac{2}{3}x = \frac{3}{8}y - 3$ Answer: $\frac{8}{9}$	$x = 3y + \frac{7}{2}$ Answer: $\left(0, -\frac{7}{21}\right)$	$0.2x - 0.6y = 1.2$ Answer: $y = \frac{1}{3}x - 2$	Solve $r = \frac{s}{2\pi h}$ for h. Answer: $h = \frac{s}{2\pi r}$
50 pts	slope-intercept form See below.	through $\left(\frac{2}{3}, -\frac{2}{3}\right)$ and $\left(-\frac{1}{2}, -\frac{3}{4}\right)$ Answer: $\frac{1}{54}$	$-\frac{2}{3}x - \frac{3}{2}y - 3 = 1$ Answer: $\left(0, -\frac{13}{3}\right)$	$\frac{1}{2}x = \frac{5}{6}y + \frac{3}{4}$ Answer: $y = \frac{3}{5}x - \frac{9}{10}$	Evaluate $f(x) = -9x + 2$ for $x = -\frac{2}{3}$. Answer: 8

Row 1. the point at which the line crosses the y-axis
Row 2. the point at which the line crosses the x-axis
Row 3. a function whose graph is a line
Row 4. the ratio of the vertical change to the horizontal change between points
Row 5. $y = mx + b$, where $m =$ slope and (0, b) = y-intercept

2-4 More About Linear Equations

Common Core State Standards
F-IF.C.9 Compare properties of two functions each represented in a different way...Also F-IF.A.2, F-IF.C.8, A-CED.A.2, F-LE.B.5
MP 1, MP 3, MP 7

Objective To write an equation of a line given its slope and a point on the line

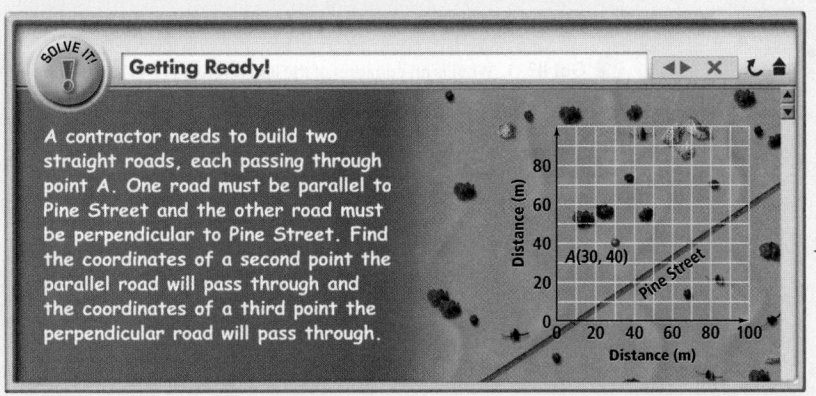

SOLVE IT!

Getting Ready!

A contractor needs to build two straight roads, each passing through point A. One road must be parallel to Pine Street and the other road must be perpendicular to Pine Street. Find the coordinates of a second point the parallel road will pass through and the coordinates of a third point the perpendicular road will pass through.

Lesson Vocabulary
• point-slope form
• standard form of a linear equation
• parallel lines
• perpendicular lines

If you travel along a line that is parallel to a given line, you will stay the same distance from the given line. If you travel along a line that is perpendicular to a given line, you will travel either toward or away from the given line along the most direct path.

Essential Understanding The slopes of two lines in the same plane indicate how the lines are related.

Given the slope and y-intercept, you can write the equation of a line in slope-intercept form. You can also write the equation of a line in *point-slope form*.

take note

Key Concept   Point-Slope Form

The equation of a line in **point-slope form** through point (x_1, y_1) with slope m:
$$y - y_1 = m(x - x_1)$$

Here's Why It Works By substituting the general point (x, y), for (x_2, y_2) in the slope formula, you can rewrite the slope formula in point-slope form.

$$m = \frac{y_2 - y_1}{x_2 - x_1} = \frac{y - y_1}{x - x_1}$$
$$m(x - x_1) = \frac{y - y_1}{x - x_1}(x - x_1)$$
$$m(x - x_1) = y - y_1$$
$$y - y_1 = m(x - x_1)$$

PowerAlgebra.com | Lesson 2-4 More About Linear Equations | **81**

2-4 Preparing to Teach

BIG idea Equivalence

ESSENTIAL UNDERSTANDINGS
• The slopes of two lines in the same plane indicate how the lines are related.
• Linear functions can be represented by either the slope-intercept, point-slope, or standard form. One version can be transformed to another as needed.

Math Background
Students know how to compare lines with different slopes: a line of slope 2 is steeper than one with slope $\frac{1}{2}$.

In this lesson, students compare the slopes of parallel and perpendicular lines. Important properties of these lines include:
• Parallel lines are equidistant.
• Parallel lines have the same slope but different y-intercepts.

• The shortest distance between a point and a line is the perpendicular distance.
• The slopes of perpendicular lines are negative reciprocals of each other.

Mathematical Practices
Look for and make use of structure.
In Problems 1 and 2, students will find linear equations to be composed of a slope and a point of intersection, and will determine the function of a line this way. Students will also flexibly use basic operations to change a linear equation into standard form.

---

1 Interactive Learning

Solve It!

PURPOSE Find the coordinates of points that satisfy conditions of parallel and perpendicular lines
PROCESS Students may
• sketch lines parallel or perpendicular and choose a point on that line.
• count the units vertically and horizontally from A to find a point on the parallel line.

FACILITATE
Q How could you draw the one line through A that is parallel to Pine Street? **[Answers may vary. Sample: From A, count up and to the right the same as the distance between any two points on Pine Street and plot a point. Draw the line through A and that point.]**
Q How could you use the corner of a sheet of paper to find the coordinates of a point on the perpendicular line? **[Use the corner to approximate a right angle, and follow the side of the page to find a point.]**

ANSWER See Solve It in Answers on next page.
CONNECT THE MATH In the Solve It, students apply previous knowledge about perpendicular and parallel lines. The lesson compares the slopes of perpendicular and parallel lines.

2 Guided Instruction

Take Note
Show that if m represents the slope, then $m = \frac{y - y_1}{x - x_1}$, so $y - y_1 = m(x - x_1)$.

Here's Why it Works
In the equation, x_1 and y_1 represent the coordinates of a given point on the line.

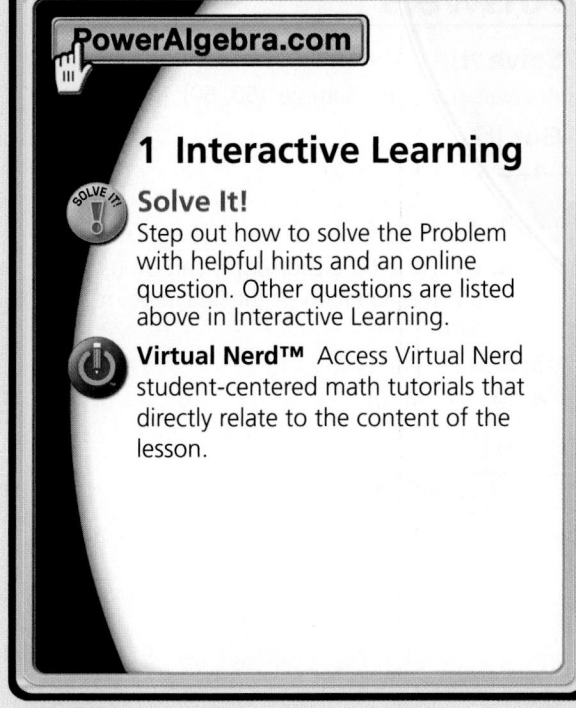

PowerAlgebra.com

1 Interactive Learning

Solve It!
Step out how to solve the Problem with helpful hints and an online question. Other questions are listed above in Interactive Learning.

Virtual Nerd™ Access Virtual Nerd student-centered math tutorials that directly relate to the content of the lesson.

Problem 1
Sketch a graph of a line through $(-5, 2)$. Label any other point on the line (x, y) using a magnet or tape. Move (x, y) to a different location on the line to reinforce the idea that it represents *any* point on the line.

Got It?
ERROR PREVENTION
Remind students to be careful with signs.

$$y - y_1 = m(x - x_1)$$
$$y - (-1) = -3(x - 7)$$
$$y + 1 = -3x + 21$$

Problem 2
When calculating slope, either point can be selected for (x_1, y_1) or (x_2, y_2).

> **Q** If $(x_1, y_1) = (5, 8)$ and $(x_2, y_2) = (3, 2)$, how would you calculate the slope?
> $[m = \frac{y_2 - y_1}{x_2 - x_1} = \frac{2 - 8}{3 - 5} = \frac{-6}{-2} = 3]$

The **Think** note refers to substituting for (x_1, y_1) later in the solution process.

Got It?

> **Q** Write the equation for 2a in slope-intercept form. Then do the same for 2b. How do the equations compare? **[They are equivalent: $y = \frac{7}{5}x + 7$.]**

Take Note

> **Q** What variable is used for the coefficient of x? for y? for the constant term? **[A; B; C]**
> **Q** What types of numbers are A, B, and C? **[They must be real numbers.]**

Is slope-intercept or point-slope form more helpful for writing this equation?
Since the slope and a point (not the y-intercept) are given, point-slope form is more helpful.

© **Problem 1** Writing an Equation Given a Point and the Slope

A line passes through $(-5, 2)$ with slope $\frac{3}{5}$. What is an equation of the line?

$$y - y_1 = m(x - x_1) \quad \text{Use point-slope form.}$$
$$y - 2 = \frac{3}{5}[x - (-5)] \quad \text{Substitute } m = \frac{3}{5} \text{ and } (x_1, y_1) = (-5, 2).$$
$$y - 2 = \frac{3}{5}(x + 5) \quad \text{Simplify.}$$

An equation for the line is $y - 2 = \frac{3}{5}(x + 5)$.

✓ **Got It? 1.** What is an equation of the line through $(7, -1)$ with slope -3?

© **Problem 2** Writing an Equation Given Two Points

A line passes through $(3, 2)$ and $(5, 8)$. What is an equation of the line in point-slope form?

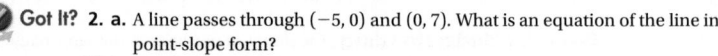
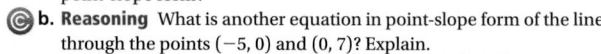

Know	Need	Plan
Two points	An equation written in point-slope form	Substitute the slope and either point in the point-slope form.

Does it matter which point you substitute into point-slope form?
No; you can choose either point as (x_1, y_1).

Let $(x_1, y_1) = (3, 2)$ and $(x_2, y_2) = (5, 8)$.

$$m = \frac{8 - 2}{5 - 3} = \frac{6}{2} = 3 \quad \text{Substitute into the slope formula and simplify.}$$
$$y - 2 = 3(x - 3) \quad \text{Substitute into point-slope form.}$$

✓ **Got It? 2. a.** A line passes through $(-5, 0)$ and $(0, 7)$. What is an equation of the line in point-slope form?
  © **b. Reasoning** What is another equation in point-slope form of the line through the points $(-5, 0)$ and $(0, 7)$? Explain.

Another form of the equation of a line is *standard form*, in which the sum of the x and y terms are set equal to a constant. When possible, you write the coefficients of x and y and the constant term as integers.

take note **Key Concept** Standard Form of a Linear Equation

A **standard form of a linear equation** is $Ax + By = C$, where A, B, and C are real numbers and A and B are not *both* zero.

Answers

Solve It!
Answers may vary. Sample: $(60, 60)$; $(50, 10)$

Got It?
1. $y + 1 = -3(x - 7)$

2. **a.** $y - 7 = \frac{7}{5}x$

   b. $y = \frac{7}{5}(x + 5)$; either point can be used to put the equation of the line in point-slope form.

3. $-91x + 10y = 36$

4. $(0, -2)$, $(4, 0)$;

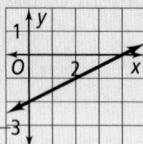

PowerAlgebra.com

2 Guided Instruction

© Each Problem is worked out and supported online.

Problem 1
Writing an Equation Given a Point and the Slope

Problem 2
Writing an Equation Given Two Points
Animated

Problem 3
Writing an Equation in Standard Form

Alternative Problem 3
Writing an Equation in Standard Form
Animated

Problem 4
Graphing an Equation Using Intercepts

Problem 5
Drawing and Interpreting a Linear Graph

Problem 6
Writing Equations of Parallel and Perpendicular Lines
Animated

Support in Algebra 2 Companion
• Vocabulary
• Key Concepts
• Got It?

Think

How can you rewrite the equation using only integer values?
Multiply each side of the equation by the least common denominator of all fraction coefficients.

© **Problem 3** Writing an Equation in Standard Form

What is an equation of the line $y = \frac{3}{4}x - 5$ in standard form? Use integer coefficients.

$$y = \frac{3}{4}x - 5$$

$$-\frac{3}{4}x + y = -5 \qquad \text{Subtract } \frac{3}{4}x \text{ from each side.}$$

$$-3x + 4y = -20 \qquad \text{Multiply each side by 4.}$$

✓ **Got It?** 3. What is an equation of the line $y = 9.1x + 3.6$ in standard form?

take note

Concept Summary Writing Equations of Lines

Slope-Intercept Form	Point-Slope Form	Standard Form
$y = mx + b$	$y - y_1 = m(x - x_1)$	$Ax + By = C$
Use this form when you know the slope and the y-intercept.	Use this form when you know the slope and a point, or when you know two points.	A, B, and C are real numbers. A and B cannot both be zero.

You can graph an equation in standard form quickly by determining the x- and y-intercepts and then drawing the line through them.

Think

Why set $x = 0$ to find the y-intercept?
The x-coordinate of any point on the y-axis is zero.

© **Problem 4** Graphing an Equation Using Intercepts

What are the intercepts of $3x + 5y = 15$? Graph the equation.

Set $x = 0$ to find the y-intercept.

$$3(0) + 5y = 15$$
$$5y = 15$$
$$y = 3$$

Set $y = 0$ to find the x-intercept.

$$3x + 5(0) = 15$$
$$3x = 15$$
$$x = 5$$

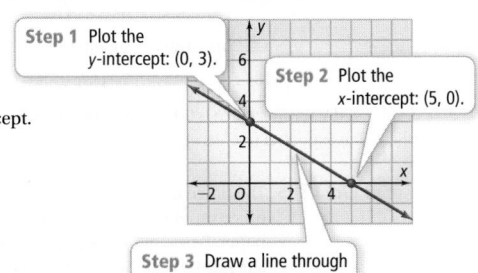

Step 1 Plot the y-intercept: (0, 3).

Step 2 Plot the x-intercept: (5, 0).

Step 3 Draw a line through the intercepts.

✓ **Got It?** 4. What are the intercepts of $2x - 4y = 8$? Graph the equation.

PowerAlgebra.com | Lesson 2-4 More About Linear Equations | 83

Problem 3

Q Is it necessary to subtract $\frac{3}{4}x$ as the first step? Explain. **[No; you could multiply each side by 4 first and then subtract 3x.]**

Got It? ERROR PREVENTION

Q How could you write this in standard form with integer coefficients? **[Multiply each side by 10.]**

Take Note

Q In standard form, what kind of line do you get if either A or B is zero? **[If $A = 0$, the line is horizontal; if $B = 0$, the line is vertical.]**

Problem 4 TACTILE LEARNERS

Because substituting $x = 0$ or $y = 0$ eliminates a term of the equation, tactile learners may prefer to cover the term with their finger and write the resulting equation with one variable.

Got It? SYNTHESIZING

Q In Problem 4, the standard form of the equation is $3x + 5y = 15$. Do the coefficients have the same sign or opposite signs? Is the graph's slope positive or negative? **[the same sign; negative]**

Q In this problem the standard equation is $2x - 4y = 8$. Do the coefficients have the same sign or opposite signs? Is the graph's slope positive or negative? **[opposite signs; positive]**

Q What generalization can you make about a graph's slope? **[Answers may vary. Sample: In standard form, if the coefficients have the same sign, the slope of the graph is negative. If opposite, the slope is positive.]**

Additional Problems

1. A line passes through $(-1, 3)$ with slope $-\frac{2}{3}$. What is an equation of the line?

ANSWER $y - 3 = -\frac{2}{3}(x + 1)$

2. A line passes through $(5, 1)$ and $(7, 9)$. What is an equation of the line in point-slope form?

ANSWER $y - 1 = 4(x - 5)$ or $y - 9 = 4(x - 7)$

3. What is an equation of the line $y = \frac{2}{5}x - 3$ in standard form? Use integer coefficients.

ANSWER $-2x + 5y = -15$ or $2x - 5y = 15$

4. What are the intercepts of $4x + 3y = 12$? Graph the equation.

ANSWERS $(3, 0)$ and $(0, 4)$

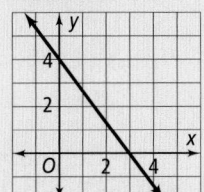

5. The cost of a taxi ride depends on the distance traveled. You paid $8.50 for a 3-mile ride, while your friend paid $18.50 for an 8-mile ride.

a. What graph models the situation?

b. What is an equation of the line in standard form?

ANSWERS

a. Taxicab Costs

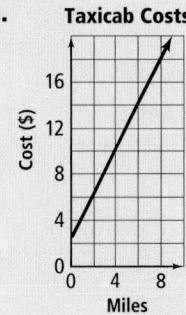

b. $2x - y = -2.50$ or $-2x + y = 2.50$, where x is distance in miles and y is cost in dollars

6. What is the equation of each line in slope-intercept form?

a. the line parallel to $y = 5x - 4$ through $(-2, 1)$

b. the line perpendicular to $y = -2x + \frac{3}{4}$ with the same y-intercept as $x + 3y = 12$.

ANSWERS

a. $y = 5x + 11$

b. $y = \frac{1}{2}x + 4$

Lesson 2-4 **83**

Problem 5

Q Which of the equations is in slope-intercept form in 5B? **[$y = 4.5x - 180$]**

Q What is the slope? What does it represent in this problem? **[4.5; the change in the number of chirps per 1°F]**

Note that the domain only includes temperatures at or above 40°F since crickets do not chirp at temperatures lower than 40°F.

Q For 5C, does it matter which equation you use? Explain. **[No; answers may vary. Sample: You could use either the standard form or slope-intercept form since they are equivalent.]**

Got It?

Students may graph the function of packs *used* per number of days, plotting (0, 0) and (80, 140). In order to answer 5c, it makes more sense to find the function of packs *left* per number of days, plotting (0, 140) and (80, 0)

Q What do the x-values represent? y-values? **[number of days; packs left]**

Q The office manager ordered 140 packs of paper. What point represents this situation? Why? **[(0, 140); before any days have passed, the office has 140 packs of paper.]**

Q When the office runs out of paper, what point represents this situation? Explain. **[(80, 0); after 80 days pass, there will be 0 packs of paper left.]**

 Problem 5 Drawing and Interpreting a Linear Graph **STEM**

Biology The number of times a cricket chirps per minute depends on the temperature. The number of chirps in 2 seconds for two temperatures are shown at the bottom right.

A What graph models the situation?

First, find the number of chirps per minute.

40°F: 30(0) = 0
93°F: 30(8) = 240

Let x = temperature in degrees Fahrenheit.
Let y = number of times a cricket chirps.

Plot (40,0) and (93, 240).
Draw a line through the points.

Think

How can you find the number of chirps in a minute given the number of chirps in 2 seconds?
There are 60 seconds in 1 minute. Multiply the number of chirps in 2 seconds by $\frac{60}{2}$ or 30.

Cricket Chirping

[graph: Chirps per Minute vs Temperature (°F)]

B What is an equation of the line in standard form?

$m = \frac{240 - 0}{93 - 40}$	Use the slope formula $m = \frac{y_2 - y_1}{x_2 - x_1}$.
$= \frac{240}{53} \approx 4.5$	Subtract and simplify.
$y - y_1 = m(x - x_1)$	Use point-slope form.
$y - 0 = 4.5(x - 40)$	Substitute one of the points: (40, 0).
$y = 4.5x - 180$	Simplify.
$4.5x - y = 180$	Write in standard form.

C If the temperature is 70°F, how many times would a cricket be expected to chirp in one minute?

Let $x = 70$.

$y = 4.5x - 180$	Use an equation from part (b).
$y = 4.5(70) - 180$	Substitute.
$y = 135$	Simplify.

If the temperature is 70°F, the cricket would be expected to chirp 135 times in one minute.

0 chirps

40.0ᶠ

2 seconds

93.0ᶠ

8 chirps

✓ **Got It? 5.** The office manager of a small office ordered 140 packs of printer paper. Based on average daily use, she knows that the paper will last about 80 days.
a. What graph represents this situation?
b. What is the equation of the line in standard form?
c. How many packs of printer paper should the manager expect to have after 30 days?

Answers

Got It? (continued)

5. a.

Packs of Paper Left

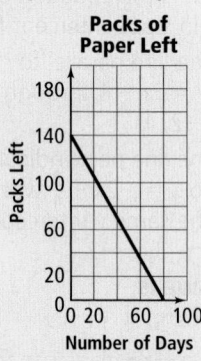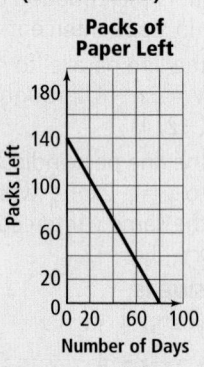

[graph: Packs Left vs Number of Days]

b. $7x + 4y = 560$

c. 87.5

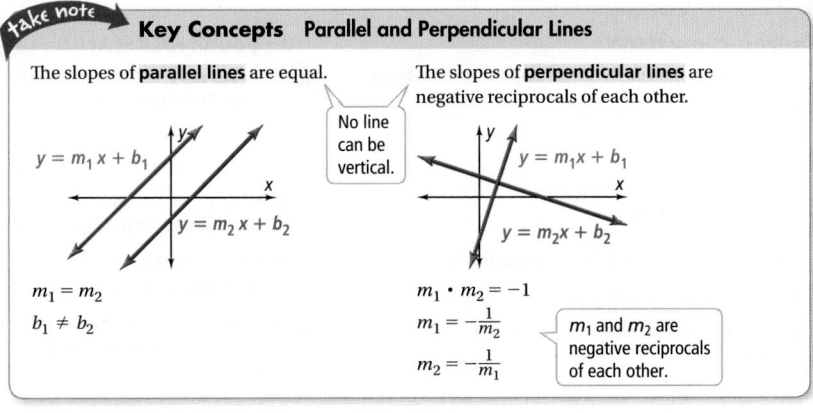

take note   Key Concepts   Parallel and Perpendicular Lines

The slopes of **parallel lines** are equal.

No line can be vertical.

$y = m_1x + b_1$

$y = m_2x + b_2$

$m_1 = m_2$
$b_1 \neq b_2$

The slopes of **perpendicular lines** are negative reciprocals of each other.

$y = m_1x + b_1$

$y = m_2x + b_2$

$m_1 \cdot m_2 = -1$
$m_1 = -\frac{1}{m_2}$
$m_2 = -\frac{1}{m_1}$

m_1 and m_2 are negative reciprocals of each other.

Ⓒ Problem 6 Writing Equations of Parallel and Perpendicular Lines

What is the equation of each line in slope-intercept form?

Ⓐ **the line parallel to $y = 6x - 2$ through $(1, -3)$**

Identify the slope, use point-slope form, and rewrite in slope-intercept form.

$m = 6$	Parallel lines have the same slope. The slope of the line with equation $y = 6x - 2$ is 6.
$y - y_1 = m(x - x_1)$	Point-slope form
$y - (-3) = 6(x - 1)$	Substitute 6 for m and $(1, -3)$ for (x_1, y_1).
$y + 3 = 6x - 6$	Distributive Property
$y = 6x - 9$	Write in slope-intercept form.

Ⓑ **the line perpendicular to $y = -4x + \frac{2}{3}$ through $(8, 5)$**

Identify the slope, use point-slope form, and rewrite in slope-intercept form.

$m = -\frac{1}{-4} = \frac{1}{4}$	The slopes of perpendicular lines are negative reciprocals.
$y - y_1 = m(x - x_1)$	Point-slope form
$y - 5 = \frac{1}{4}(x - 8)$	Substitute $\frac{1}{4}$ for m and $(8, 5)$ for (x_1, y_1).
$y - 5 = \frac{1}{4}x - 2$	Distributive Property
$y = \frac{1}{4}x + 3$	Write in slope-intercept form.

✓ **Got It?** **6.** What is the equation of each line in slope-intercept form?
  a. the line parallel to $4x + 2y = 7$ through $(4, -2)$
  b. the line perpendicular to $y = \frac{2}{3}x - 1$ through $(0, 6)$

PowerAlgebra.com   Lesson 2-4   More About Linear Equations   85

Take Note

Q When would you start with point-slope form rather than slope-intercept form? **[when the information given is a point and a slope]**

Q Notice that the y-intercepts of two parallel lines must be different. Can the y-intercepts of two perpendicular lines be the same? Explain your answer. **[Yes; the lines can intersect on the y-axis.]**

Draw a sketch to illustrate this point, having a student (or students) working at the board.

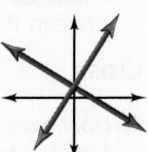

Problem 6   ERROR PREVENTION

Have students graph $y = 6x - 2$ and $y = 6x - 9$ to visually check that the lines are parallel.

If students have difficulty with 6B because there are 3 equations involved, have them graph the 3 equations.

Got It?

Q Do you have to use point-slope form to solve these types of problems? Explain. **[No; you could use slope-intercept form $y = mx + b$; substitute the slope and one point for x and y, and solve for b; then write the equation $y = mx + b$ with the values of m and b substituted.]**

---

6. a. $y = -2x + 6$

  b. $y = -\frac{3}{2}x + 6$

3 Lesson Check

Do you know HOW? ERROR INTERVENTION
- For Exercises 4–5, if students are confused about which form to use, have them review Problem 6. They are now being asked to find equations in standard form, which they can derive from slope-intercept form.

Do you UNDERSTAND?
- For Exercise 6, have students list the differences between the various forms of the linear equation.

Close

> **Q** How does the format of the equation identify its form? **[Standard form has both variables on one side of the equation, slope-intercept form has *y* alone on one side of the equation, and point-slope form has *y* and a *y*-value on one side of the equation.]**

 Lesson Check

Do you know HOW?
Write an equation of each line in slope-intercept form.

1. slope -3; through $(1, -4)$
2. slope $\frac{1}{2}$; through $(2, 3)$
3. What are the intercepts of $3x + y = 6$? Graph the equation.

Write an equation of each line in standard form.

4. the line parallel to $y = -3x + 4$ through $(0, -1)$
5. the line perpendicular to $-2x + 3y = 9$ through $(-1, -3)$

Do you UNDERSTAND?  MATHEMATICAL PRACTICES

6. **Vocabulary** Tell whether each equation is in slope-intercept, point-slope, or standard form.
   a. $y + 2 = -2(x - 1)$ b. $y = -\frac{1}{4}x + 9$
   c. $-x - 2y = 1$ d. $y - 3 = 4x$

7. Which form would you use to write the equation of a line if you knew its slope and x-intercept? Explain.

8. If the intercepts of a line are $(a, 0)$ and $(0, b)$, what is the slope of the line?

9. **Error Analysis** Your friend says the line $y = -2x + 3$ is perpendicular to the line $x + 2y = 8$. Do you agree? Explain.

 Practice and Problem-Solving Exercises  MATHEMATICAL PRACTICES

 Practice   Write an equation of each line.   ◀ See Problem 1.

10. slope $= 3$; through $(1, 5)$ 11. slope $= \frac{5}{6}$; through $(22, 12)$ 12. slope $= -\frac{3}{5}$; through $(-4, 0)$

13. slope $= 0$; through $(4, -2)$ 14. slope $= -1$; through $(-3, 5)$ 15. slope $= 5$; through $(0, 2)$

Write in point-slope form an equation of the line through each pair of points.   ◀ See Problem 2.

16. $(-10, 3)$ and $(-2, -5)$ 17. $(1, 0)$ and $(5, 5)$ 18. $(-4, 10)$ and $(-6, 15)$

19. $(0, -1)$ and $(3, -5)$ 20. $(7, 11)$ and $(13, 17)$ 21. $(1, 9)$ and $(6, 2)$

Write an equation of each line in standard form with integer coefficients.   ◀ See Problem 3.

22. $y = \frac{1}{2}x - 2$ 23. $y = -7x - 9$ 24. $y = -\frac{3}{5}x + 3$ 25. $y = 4.2x + 7.9$

Find the intercepts and graph each line.   ◀ See Problem 4.

26. $x - 4y = -4$ 27. $2x + 5y = -10$ 28. $-3x + 2y = 6$ 29. $5x + 7y = 14$

Write and graph an equation to represent each situation.   ◀ See Problem 5.

30. You put 15 gallons of gasoline in your car. You know that this amount of gasoline will allow you to drive about 450 miles.

31. A meal plan lets students buy $20 meal cards. Each meal card lasts about 8 days.

Write the equation of the line through each point. Use slope-intercept form.   ◀ See Problem 6.

32. $(1, -1)$; parallel to $y = \frac{2}{5}x - 3$ 33. $(-3, 1)$; perpendicular to $y = -\frac{2}{5}x - 4$

34. $(-7, 10)$; parallel to $2x - 3y = -3$ 35. $(-2, 1)$; perpendicular to $3x + y = 1$

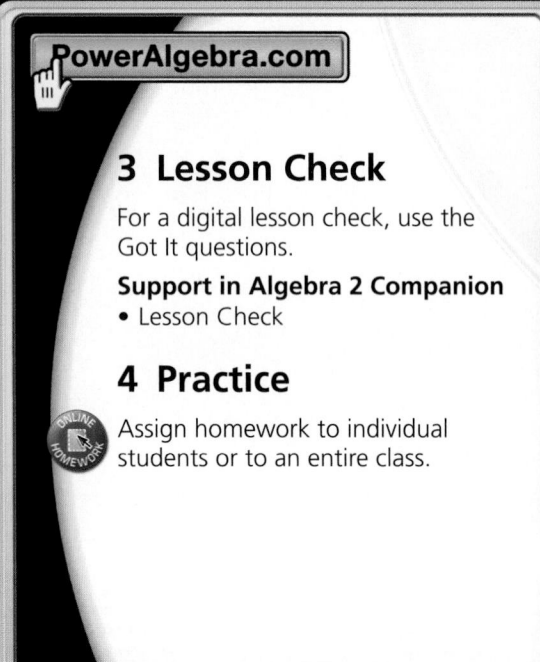

PowerAlgebra.com

3 Lesson Check

For a digital lesson check, use the Got It questions.

Support in Algebra 2 Companion
- Lesson Check

4 Practice

Assign homework to individual students or to an entire class.

Answers

Lesson Check

1. $y = -3x - 1$ 2. $y = \frac{1}{2}x + 2$

3. $(0, 6), (2, 0)$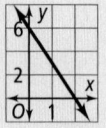

4. $3x + y = -1$ 5. $3x + 2y = -9$

6. a. point-slope   b. slope-intercept
   c. standard   d. point-slope

7. Point-slope form; since the x-intercept is the point where y is zero, you know the point on the line, $(x, 0)$, and you know the slope.

8. $-\frac{b}{a}$

9. No; one line has a slope of -2 and the other line has a slope of $-\frac{1}{2}$. $-\frac{1}{2}$ is the reciprocal of -2, not the *negative* reciprocal.

Practice and Problem-Solving Exercises

10. $y - 5 = 3(x - 1)$

11. $y - 12 = \frac{5}{6}(x - 22)$

12. $y = -\frac{3}{5}(x + 4)$

13. $y + 2 = 0$

14. $y - 5 = -(x + 3)$

15. $y - 2 = 5x$

16. Sample: $y - 3 = -(x + 10)$ or $y + 5 = -(x + 2)$

17. Sample: $y = \frac{5}{4}(x - 1)$ or $y - 5 = \frac{5}{4}(x - 5)$

18. Sample: $y - 10 = -\frac{5}{2}(x + 4)$ or $y - 15 = -\frac{5}{2}(x + 6)$

19. Sample: $y + 1 = -\frac{4}{3}x$ or $y + 5 = -\frac{4}{3}(x - 3)$

20. Sample: $y - 11 = x - 7$ or $y - 17 = x - 13$

Apply

Graph each equation.

36. $3x + 5y = 12$

37. $y = \frac{2}{3}x + 4$

38. $x + 3 = 0$

39. $3y - x = -6$

40. $y + 3 = 3$

41. $2x - \frac{3}{2}y = -3$

Write an equation of the line through each pair of points. Use point-slope form.

42. $\left(\frac{3}{2}, -\frac{1}{2}\right)$ and $\left(-\frac{2}{3}, \frac{1}{3}\right)$

43. $\left(-\frac{1}{2}, -\frac{1}{2}\right)$ and $(-3, -4)$

44. $\left(0, \frac{1}{2}\right)$ and $\left(\frac{5}{7}, 0\right)$

 45. Think About a Plan Write an equation for the line shown here. Each interval is 1 unit.
- What do you know from the graph?
- Which form of the equation of a line could you use with the information you have?

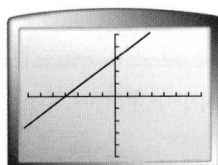

Write an equation for each line. Each interval is 1 unit.

46.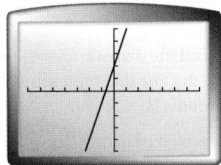

47.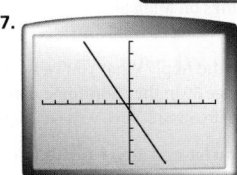

48. The equation $5x - 2y = -6$ and the table each represent linear functions. Which has the greater slope? Explain.

x	-2	-1	0	1	2
y	1	3	5	7	9

49. a. Write the point-slope form of the line that passes through $A(-3, 12)$ and $B(9, -4)$. Use point A in the equation.
b. Write the point-slope form of the same line using point B in the equation.
c. Rewrite each equation in standard form. What do you notice?

Write an equation for each line. Then graph the line.

50. $m = 0$, through $(5, -1)$

51. $m = -\frac{3}{2}$, through $(0, -1)$

52. Reasoning Suppose lines ℓ_1 and ℓ_2 intersect at the origin. Also, ℓ_1 has slope $\frac{y}{x}$ ($x > 0, y > 0$) and ℓ_2 has slope $-\frac{x}{y}$. Then ℓ_1 contains (x, y) and ℓ_2 contains $(-y, x)$.
a. Explain why the two right triangles are congruent.
b. Complete each equation about the angle measures a, b, c, and d.
$a = \blacksquare$ $c = \blacksquare$
$a + c = \blacksquare$ $b + d = \blacksquare$
c. What must be true about $a + b$? Why?
d. What must be true about ℓ_1 and ℓ_2? Why?

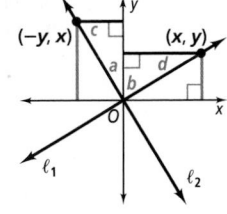

ASSIGNMENT GUIDE

Basic: 10–35 all, 36–44 even, 45, 46–50 even

Average: 11–35 odd, 36–52

Advanced: 11–35 odd, 36–56

© **Mathematical Practices** are supported by exercises with red headings. Here are the Practices supported in this lesson:

MP 1: Make Sense of Problems Ex. 45

MP 3: Construct Arguments Ex. 52

MP 3: Critique the Reasoning of Others Ex. 9

Applications exercises have blue headings.

EXERCISE 49: Use the Think About a Plan worksheet in the **Practice and Problem Solving Workbook** (also available in the Teaching Resources in print and online) to further support students' development in becoming independent learners.

HOMEWORK QUICK CHECK

To check students' understanding of key skills and concepts, go over Exercises 27, 31, 33, 45, and 49.

---

21. Sample: $y - 9 = -\frac{7}{5}(x - 1)$ or $y - 2 = -\frac{7}{5}(x - 6)$

22. $-x + 2y = -4$

23. $7x + y = -9$

24. $3x + 5y = 15$

25. $-42x + 10y = 79$

26. $(0, 1), (-4, 0)$

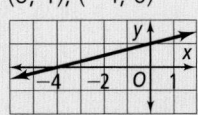

27. $(0, -2), (-5, 0)$

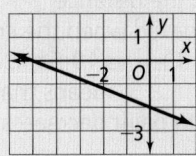

28. $(0, 3), (-2, 0)$ **29.** $(0, 2), \left(\frac{14}{5}, 0\right)$

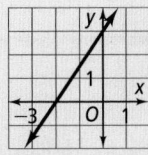 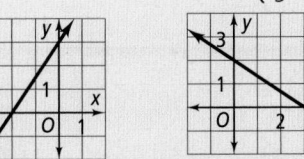

30. $y = -\frac{1}{30}x + 15$

Gas Mileage

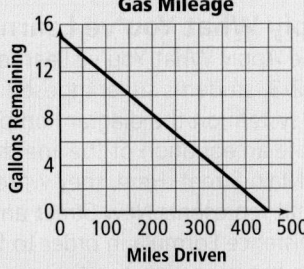

31. $y = -2.5x + 20$

Meal Cards

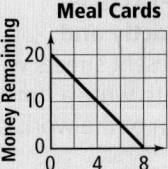

32. $y = \frac{2}{5}x - \frac{7}{5}$

33. $y = \frac{5}{2}x + \frac{17}{2}$

34. $y = \frac{2}{3}x + \frac{44}{3}$

35. $y = \frac{1}{3}x + \frac{5}{3}$

36.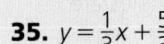

37.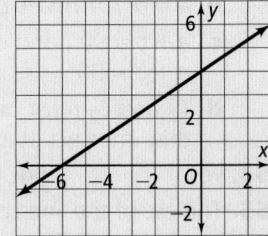

38.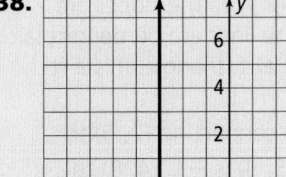

39.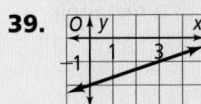

40–52. See next page.

Answers

Practice and Problem-Solving Exercises (continued)

40. 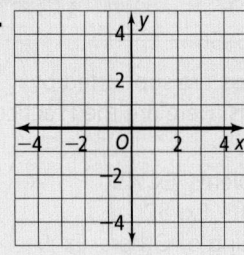 **41.**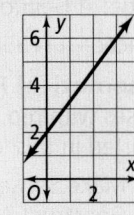

42. $y - \frac{1}{3} = -\frac{5}{13}\left(x + \frac{2}{3}\right)$ or
$y + \frac{1}{2} = -\frac{5}{13}\left(x - \frac{3}{2}\right)$

43. $y + 4 = \frac{7}{5}(x + 3)$ or
$y + \frac{1}{2} = \frac{7}{5}\left(x + \frac{1}{2}\right)$

44. $y - \frac{1}{2} = -\frac{7}{10}x$ or $y = -\frac{7}{10}\left(x - \frac{5}{7}\right)$

45. $y = \frac{3}{4}x + 3$ **46.** $y = 3x + 2$

47. $y = -\frac{3}{2}x - \frac{1}{2}$

48. The equation's slope is $2\frac{1}{2}$, while the table's slope is 2; the equation has the greater slope.

49. a. $y - 12 = -\frac{4}{3}(x + 3)$

   b. $y + 4 = -\frac{4}{3}(x - 9)$

   c. They have the same standard form:
   $4x + 3y = 24$.

50. $y = -1$ **51.** $y = -\frac{3}{2}x - 1$

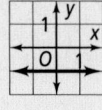   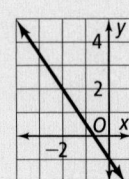

52. a. The rt. triangles have the same length legs (x and y) as the congruent rt. angle, so by SAS congruence the triangles are congruent.

   b. $a = d$; $c = b$; $a + c = 90°$; $b + d = 90°$

   c. $a + c = 90°$, and $c = b$, therefore $a + b = 90°$

   d. ℓ_1 and ℓ_2 must be perpendicular because they intersect at a rt. angle.

53. yes   **54.** no

55. The eq. of the line connecting (1, 3) to (−2, 6) is $y = -x + 4$. The eq. of the line connecting (1, 3) to (3, 5) is $y = x + 2$. The slopes are neg. reciprocals so the lines are perpendicular. Therefore, by def. of a rt. triangle, it is a rt. triangle.

56. The slope of the line connecting (2, 5) to (4, 8) is $\frac{3}{2}$, (2, 5) to (5, 3) is $-\frac{2}{3}$, (4, 8) to (7, 6) is $-\frac{2}{3}$, and (5, 3) to (7, 6) is $\frac{3}{2}$. Since the adjacent sides' slopes are neg. reciprocals, they are perpendicular. By the def. of a rectangle, it is a rectangle.

Challenge Points that are on the same line are *collinear*. Use the definition of slope to determine whether the given points are collinear.

53. $(-2, 6), (0, 2), (1, 0)$ **54.** $(3, -5), (-3, 3), (0, 2)$

55. Geometry Prove that the triangle with vertices $(3, 5)$, $(-2, 6)$, and $(1, 3)$ is a right triangle.

56. Geometry Prove that the quadrilateral with vertices $(2, 5)$, $(4, 8)$, $(7, 6)$, and $(5, 3)$ is a rectangle.

Apply What You've Learned

MATHEMATICAL PRACTICES
MP 2

Look back at the information on page 59 about the work crew that is painting lane lines on Main Street. Note that the diagram on page 59 shows that New Street and Main Street intersect at a right angle.

   a. In the Apply What You've Learned in Lesson 2-3, you placed the diagram shown on page 59 in the coordinate plane and wrote an equation of the line that represents Main Street. Now, write an equation of the line that represents New Street.

   b. You have written equations in x and y for two lines that each contain the intersection point of Main Street and New Street. How can you use these two equations to write an equation that involves only x?

   c. Solve the equation you wrote in part (b). Round your answer to the nearest tenth of a mile.

   d. The solution you found in part (d) is the x-coordinate of the intersection point of Main Street and New Street. Find the y-coordinate. Round your answer to the nearest tenth of a mile.

   e. Find the distance from the intersection of Main Street and New Street to the intersection of Main Street and Wilson Road. Round your answer to the nearest tenth of a mile. (*Hint:* Use the Distance Formula.)

   f. Let d represent the distance, in miles, along Main Street that the work crew still needs to paint. Find a function rule that expresses d in terms of the time t, in hours, since 1 P.M. Interpret each coefficient or constant in the function rule in terms of the problem situation.

Apply What You've Learned

In the Apply What You've Learned for Lesson 2-3, students superimposed a coordinate system on the diagram on page 59 and wrote an equation of the line that represents Main Street. Here, they write an equation that represents New Street and recall the Distance Formula in order to find the distance between two points.

Mathematical Practices

Students **reason abstractly and quantitatively** to represent streets with equations of lines, and to write a function that models the location of the work crew over time. (MP 2)

ANSWERS

a. $y = \frac{7}{10}x + 3$

b. Set the two expressions for y equal to each other to get the equation $-\frac{10}{7}x + 20 = \frac{7}{10}x + 3$.

c. about 8.0 mi

d. about 8.6 mi

e. about 10.5 mi

f. $d(t) = 10.5 - 5t$; the constant term, 10.5, means that the distance remaining to be paved when the crew starts working at 1 P.M. is 10.5 mi, and the coefficient of t, −5, means that the distance left to paint decreases at a rate of 5 mi/h.

Additional Instructional Support

Algebra 2 Companion

Students can use the **Algebra 2 Companion** worktext (4 pages) as you teach the lesson. Use the Companion to support

- New Vocabulary
- Key Concepts
- Got It for each Problem
- Lesson Check

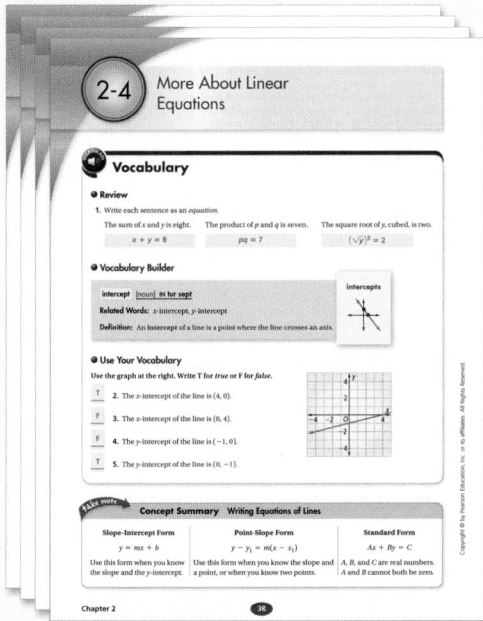

ELL Support

Use Graphic Organizers Sketch and have students copy the following graphic organizer. Students should finish filling out the table by rewriting each equation in the two other forms.

Point-Slope	Standard	Slope-Intercept
$y - 1 = 2(x + 5)$		
	$2x - 5y = 18$	
		$y = mx + b$

5 Assess & Remediate

Lesson Quiz

1. A line passes through $(2, -1)$ with slope 3. What is the equation of the line in point-slope form?

2. A line passes through $(3, 5)$ and $(6, 14)$. What is the equation of the line in point-slope form?

3. What is the equation of the line $y = -0.25x + 1$ in standard form? Use integer coefficients.

4. What are the intercepts of $4x - 5y = -20$?

5. Do you UNDERSTAND? You sell sporting goods. Your wages depend on the value of your sales. One week you sold \$3,500 in sporting goods, earning \$950. Another week you sold \$2,800 in sporting goods, earning \$810. Write an equation of the line in standard form.

6. What is the equation of each line in slope-intercept form?

  a. parallel to $y = 3x + 1$ through $(4, -1)$

  b. perpendicular to $y = 3x - 4$ with the same y-intercept as $-x + 5y = 10$.

ANSWERS TO LESSON QUIZ

1. $y + 1 = 3(x - 2)$

2. $y - 5 = 3(x - 3)$ or $y - 14 = 3(x - 6)$

3. Answers may vary. Sample: $x + 4y = 4$

4. $(-5, 0)$ and $(0, 4)$

5. $-x + 5y = 1250$ or $x - 5y = -1250$, where x is sales and y is wages

6. a. $y = 3x - 13$

  b. $y = -\frac{1}{3}x + 2$

PRESCRIPTION FOR REMEDIATION

Use the student work on the Lesson Quiz to prescribe a differentiated review assignment:

Points	Differentiated Remediation
0–3	Intervention
4–5	On-level
6	Extension

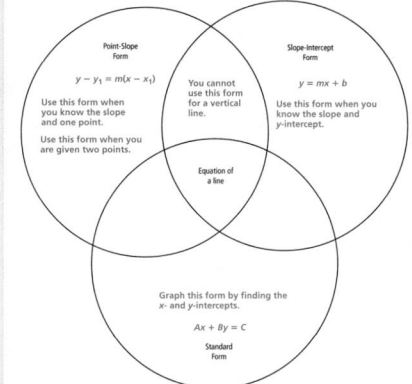

PowerAlgebra.com

5 Assess & Remediate

Assign the Lesson Quiz. Appropriate intervention, practice, or enrichment is automatically generated based on student performance.

Differentiated Remediation

Available in editable format online.

Intervention

- **Reteaching** (2 pages) Provides reteaching and practice exercises for the key lesson concepts. Use with struggling students or absent students.

- **English Language Learner Support** Helps students develop and reinforce mathematical vocabulary and key concepts.

All-in-One Resources/Online
Reteaching

2-4 **Reteaching**
More About Linear Equations

You can use the point-slope form to write equations of lines if you are given two points on the line. The point-slope form of a linear equation is:

$$y - y_1 = m(x - x_1)$$

Problem

What is the point-slope form of an equation of the line through $(3, 4)$ and $(5, -2)$?

Find the slope. Substitute for each variable using the coordinates of the given points.

Let $(x_1, y_1) = (3, 4)$ and $(x_2, y_2) = (5, -2)$.   Identify each point.

So $x_1 = 3, y_1 = 4, x_2 = 5$, and $y_2 = -2$.   Identify $x_1, y_1, x_2,$ and y_2.

$m = \frac{y_2 - y_1}{x_2 - x_1} = \frac{-2 - 4}{5 - 3} = \frac{-6}{2} = -3$ Substitute the x- and y-values and simplify.

The slope is -3.

Write the equation of the line in point-slope form. Substitute one point and the slope into the point-slope formula. It does not matter which point is substituted into the point-slope formula.

Let $(x_1, y_1) = (3, 4)$.   Use either of the points as (x_1, y_1).

So $x_1 = 3, y_1 = 4$, and $m = -3$.   Identify the values of x_1, y_1, and m.

$y - y_1 = m(x - x_1)$ Write the point-slope form.

$y - 4 = -3(x - 3)$ Substitute the values of x_1, y_1, and m.

An equation for the line in point-slope form is $y - 4 = -3(x - 3)$.

Exercises

Using point-slope form, write an equation of the line through each pair of points.

1. $(6, -7)$ and $(4, -1)$ $y + 7 = -3(x - 6)$ **2.** $(3, 5)$ and $(0, 7)$ $y - 5 = -\frac{2}{3}(x - 3)$

3. $(-1, 3)$ and $(2, 6)$ $y - 3 = x + 1$ **4.** $(-1, -2)$ and $(0, 1)$ $y + 2 = x + 1$

5. $(-2, -5)$ and $(8, -3)$ $y + 5 = \frac{1}{5}(x + 2)$ **6.** $(-1, 3)$ and $(-7, -6)$ $y - 3 = \frac{3}{2}(x + 1)$

7. $(-3, 8)$ and $(-2, 4)$ $y - 8 = -4(x + 3)$ **8.** $(0, -2)$ and $(9, 3)$ $y + 2 = \frac{5}{9}x$

All-in-One Resources/Online
English Language Learner Support

2-4 **Additional Vocabulary Support**
More About Linear Equations

1. Write each equation in the correct location in the circles below.

$y = mx + b$ $y - y_1 = m(x - x_1)$ $Ax + By = C$

2. Each sentence below describes one or more of the equations. Write each sentence in the correct location in the circles below.

- Use this form when you know the slope and one point.
- Graph this form by finding the x- and y-intercepts.
- You cannot use this form for a vertical line.
- Use this form when you know the slope and y-intercept.
- Use this form when you are given two points.

Differentiated Remediation *continued*

Available in editable format online.

On-Level

- **Practice** (2 pages) Provides extra practice for each lesson. For simpler practice exercises, use the Form K Practice pages found in the All-in-One Teaching Resources and online.

- **Think About a Plan** Helps students develop specific problem-solving skills and strategies by providing scaffolded guiding questions.

- **Standardized Test Prep** Focuses on all major exercises, all major question types, and helps students prepare for the high-stakes assessments.

Extension

- **Enrichment** Provides students with interesting problems and activities that extend the concepts of the lesson.

- **Activities, Games, and Puzzles** Worksheets that can be used for concepts development, enrichment, and for fun!

Practice and Problem Solving Wkbk/All-in-One Resources/Online
Practice page 1

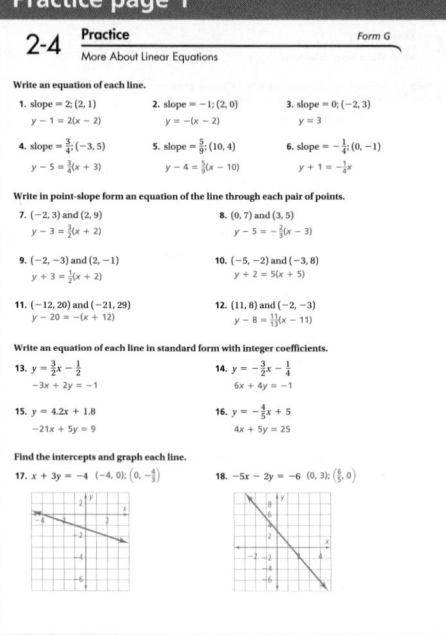

Practice and Problem Solving Wkbk/All-in-One Resources/Online
Practice page 2

All-in-One Resources/Online
Enrichment

Practice and Problem Solving Wkbk/All-in-One Resources/Online
Think About a Plan

Practice and Problem Solving Wkbk/All-in-One Resources/Online
Standardized Test Prep

Online Teacher Resource Center
Activities, Games, and Puzzles

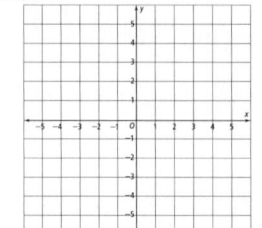

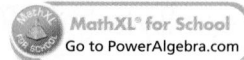
Do you know HOW?

Determine whether each relation is a function.

1.

x	y
3	7
4	2
3	2
5	1

2.

x	y
1	1
2	2
3	3
4	4

Find the *x*- and *y*-intercepts of each line.

3. $x - 3y = 9$

4. $y = 7x + 5$

5. $y = 6x$

6. $-4x + y = 10$

Write the equation of each line in slope-intercept form and identify the slope.

7. $2x - y = 9$

8. $4x = 2 + y$

9. $5y = -3x - 10$

10. $4x + 6y = 12$

Write an equation of each line in standard form with integer coefficients.

11. the line through $(2, 3)$ and $(4, 5)$

12. the line through $(-4, 6)$ and $(2, -2)$

13. the line through $(-4, 2)$ with slope 3

14. the line through $(1, 2)$ with slope $\frac{4}{5}$

15. a line through $(3, 1)$ with slope 0

16. a line with slope of $\frac{2}{3}$ and *y*-intercept $(0, 5)$

17. $2y = -4x - 12$

18. $\frac{2}{3}x + 3 = 6y - 15$

Write an equation of each line in point-slope form.

19. $(-4, 2)$ and $(-3, 5)$

20. $(0, 0)$ and $(-4, -5)$

21. $(-4, -3)$ and $(2, 7)$

Graph each equation.

22. $2y = 4x + 8$

23. $2x - 3y = 6$

24. $4y - x = 16$

For each function, determine whether *y* varies directly with *x*. If so, identify the constant of variation.

25. $2y = 3x$

26. $4y - 7x = 0$

27. $y + \frac{3}{4}x = 12$

Do you UNDERSTAND?

28. a. A group of friends is going to the movies. Each ticket costs $8.00. Write an equation to model the total cost of the group's tickets.

  b. Graph the equation. Explain what the *x*- and *y*-intercepts represent.

  c. What would be the cost for 12 tickets?

  d. Writing Could the domain include fractions? Explain.

29. Which line is perpendicular to $3x + 2y = 6$?

  Ⓐ $4x - 6y = 3$ Ⓒ $2x + 3y = 12$

  Ⓑ $y = -\frac{3}{2}x + 4$ Ⓓ $y = \frac{3}{2}x + 1$

30. Reasoning Why is the slope of a vertical line undefined?

31. Suppose $m = 25 - 0.15n$ describes the amount of money remaining on a $25 phone card *m*, as a function of the number of minutes of calls you make *n*. What are a reasonable domain and range?

24.

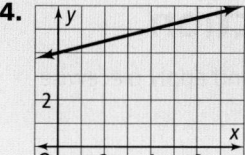

25. yes; $\frac{3}{2}$

26. yes; $\frac{7}{4}$

27. no

28. a. $y = 8x$ where $x =$ number of tickets

  b.

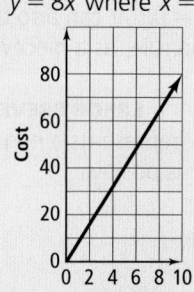

  Both intercepts are zero when no one has bought any tickets

  c. $96

  d. No; the number of tickets must be a whole number.

29. A

30. The change in *x* is 0 in a vertical line, so the slope formula has a 0 in the denominator and is undefined.

31. domain: all real numbers 0 to $166\frac{2}{3}$; range: all real numbers 0 to 25

Answers

1. no

2. yes

3. $(9, 0)$, $(0, -3)$

4. $\left(-\frac{5}{7}, 0\right)$, $(0, 5)$

5. $(0, 0)$

6. $\left(-\frac{5}{2}, 0\right)$, $(0, 10)$

7. $y = 2x - 9$; 2

8. $y = 4x - 2$; 4

9. $y = -\frac{3}{5}x - 2$; $-\frac{3}{5}$

10. $y = -\frac{2}{3}x + 2$; $-\frac{2}{3}$

11. $-x + y = 1$

12. $4x + 3y = 2$

13. $-3x + y = 14$

14. $-4x + 5y = 6$

15. $y = 1$

16. $-2x + 3y = 15$

17. $2x + y = -6$

18. $x - 9y = -27$

19. $y - 2 = 3(x + 4)$ or $y - 5 = 3(x + 3)$

20. $y = \frac{5}{4}x$ or $y + 5 = \frac{5}{4}(x + 4)$

21. $y - 7 = \frac{5}{3}(x - 2)$ or $y + 3 = \frac{5}{3}(x + 4)$

22.

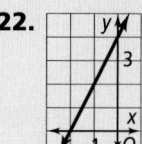

23.

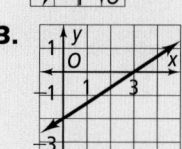

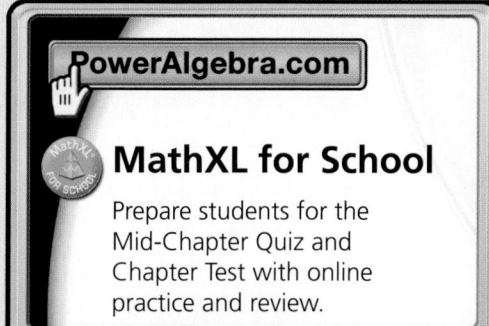

Guided Instruction

PURPOSE To graph, write, and apply piecewise functions

PROCESS Students will

- graph the absolute value function and the greatest integer function.
- write a piecewise function rule for a graph.
- identify characteristics of piecewise functions.
- use a piecewise function to solve a problem.

DISCUSS The absolute value function can be written using one rule: $f(x) = |x|$. It can also be written using more than one rule, as a piecewise function.

ERROR PREVENTION

Students may think that $-x$ represents a negative number. If x is negative, $-x$ is positive.

Example 1

1. $f(x) = \begin{cases} -x, & \text{if } x \leq 0 \\ x, & \text{if } x > 0 \end{cases}$

2. $f(x) = \begin{cases} -x, & \text{if } x < 0 \\ x, & \text{if } x > 0 \end{cases}$

Q Consider the functions above. Which function is identical to the absolute value function? Explain. **[1; it assigns the same function values as the absolute value function to all x-values. Function 2 is different, since it does not assign any function value to x = 0.]**

Example 2

Q Is there a gap in the function? Explain. **[No; the second part of the function is directly above the first part where x = 2. Also, you can tell that there is no gap in the domain by looking at the function; 2 is included.]**

Ⓒ Mathematical Practices This Concept Byte supports students in becoming proficient in using appropriate tools, Mathematical Practice 5.

 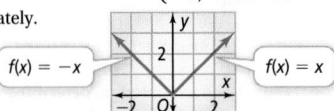
Ⓒ Common Core State Standards
F-IF.C.7b Graph . . . piecewise-defined functions, including step functions and absolute value functions.
MP 5

Recall from Lesson 1-6 that $|x|$, the absolute value of x, is the distance of x from zero. When $x \geq 0$, $|x| = x$. When $x < 0$, $|x| = -x$. The absolute value function is an example of a *piecewise function*. A **piecewise function** has different rules for different parts of its domain.

Example 1

Graph the absolute value function $f(x) = \begin{cases} x, & \text{for } x \geq 0 \\ -x, & \text{for } x < 0 \end{cases}$.

Graph each piece separately.

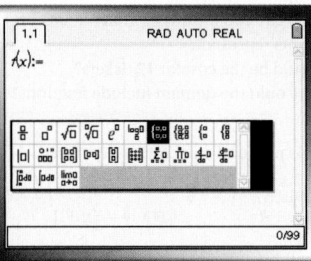

$f(x) = -x$ $f(x) = x$

Example 2

Use a graphing calculator to graph the function $f(x) = \begin{cases} -2x + 3, & \text{if } x < 2 \\ x - 1, & \text{if } x \geq 2 \end{cases}$.

Define the function $f(x)$. Use the brackets from the math expression templates to enter the piecewise function.

Enter the rules for the two branches. Set $f_1(x) = f(x)$ and graph.

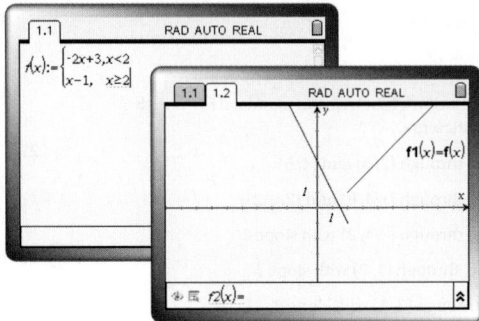

Step functions are piecewise functions. A **step function** pairs every number in an interval with a single value. The graph of a step function can look like the steps of a staircase. One step function is the **greatest integer function** $y = [x]$, where $[x]$ represents the greatest integer less than or equal to x.

Example 3

What is the graph of the function $f(x) = [x]$?

Each piece of the graph is a horizontal segment that is missing its right endpoint. The open circle indicates that the right endpoint is not part of the graph.

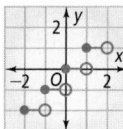

Given a piecewise function in one form, you can represent it in each of the other forms, including a table, graph, algebraic function, or verbal statement.

Example 4

Media Postage You want to mail a book that weighs 2.5 lb. The table lists postage for a book weighing up to 3 lb. Define and graph the media-postage function. How much will you pay in postage?

Media Postage

Weight (lb)	Price ($)
$x \le 1$	2.23
$1 < x \le 2$	2.58
$2 < x \le 3$	2.93

$$f(x) = \begin{cases} 2.23, & \text{for } 0 < x \le 1 \\ 2.58, & \text{for } 1 < x \le 2 \\ 2.93, & \text{for } 2 < x \le 3 \end{cases}$$

Since $2 < 2.5 \le 3$, you will pay $2.93.

Example 5

What piecewise function represents the graph?

Piece 1 When $x \le -2$, the rule is $f(x) = 2x + 6$.

Piece 2 When $-2 < x \le 0$, the rule is $f(x) = -2x - 2$.

Piece 3 When $x > 0$, the rule is $f(x) = 3x - 2$.

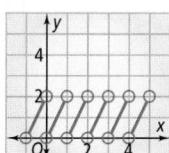

$$f(x) = \begin{cases} 2x + 6, & \text{for } x \le -2 \\ -2x - 2, & \text{for } -2 < x \le 0 \\ 3x - 2, & \text{for } x > 0 \end{cases}$$

Exercises

1. Graph the sign function. $f(x) = \begin{cases} -1, & \text{for } x < 0 \\ 0, & \text{for } x = 0 \\ 1, & \text{for } x > 0 \end{cases}$

2. Graph the function $f(x) = $ the least integer greater than x.
3. What piecewise function represents the graph at the right?
4. **Postage** In 2008, first-class letter postage was $.42 for up to one ounce and $.17 for each additional ounce up to 3.5 oz. Graph this postage function.

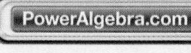

Example 3   VISUAL LEARNERS

Copy, complete, and extend this table.

x	-2	-1.9	-1.1	-1	-0.9
$[x]$	-2	-2	-2	-1	-1

Example 4   ERROR PREVENTION

Q Does this graph show the entire function? That is, does it show all function values for its entire domain? Explain. **[Yes; the domain is the set of all x-values between 0 and 3, and the graph shows all function values for all those x-values.]**

Q Does the graph in Example 3 show the entire function? Explain. **[No; the domain is the set of all real numbers, and the graph shows function values for only some x-values.]**

Example 5

Q Name two points that appear to be on the leftmost piece. **[(−3, 0) and (−2, 2)]**

Q How can you write an equation using two points on the line? **[Use point-slope form.]**

Exercises

Q For Exercise 1, what is the graph of $y = 1$? $y = -1$? **[the horizontal line 1 unit above the x-axis; the horizontal line 1 unit below the x-axis]** Use these lines and (0, 0) to draw the graph.

For Exercise 3, pay close attention to whether the endpoints are solid or not. This determines whether or not the endpoint is included in that part of the function. For Exercise 4, notice that the segments in this piecewise function are not the same length.

Answers

Exercises

1.

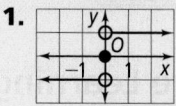

2.

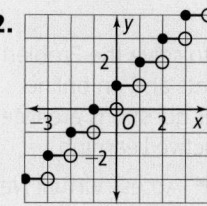

3. $f(x) = \begin{cases} 2x + 2, & -1 < x < 0 \\ 2x, & 0 < x < 1 \\ 2x - 2, & 1 < x < 2 \\ 2x - 4, & 2 < x < 3 \\ 2x - 6, & 3 < x < 4 \\ 2x - 8, & 4 < x < 5 \end{cases}$

4.

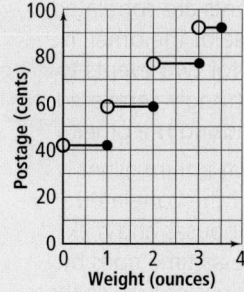

1 Interactive Learning

Solve It!

PURPOSE To use a scatter plot to estimate an unknown quantity

PROCESS Students may

- estimate the hourly rate modeled by each point, find the mean, and divide $200 by that mean.
- identify (6, 120) as a point in the graph and reason that 6 : 120 = 1 : 20 = 10 : 200.

FACILITATE

Q The leftmost point in the graph is (5, 90). What hourly rate does it represent? Explain. **[$18 per hour; 90 ÷ 5 = 18]**

Q Did you earn money at the same rate each day? Explain. **[No; answers may vary. Sample: If you earned the same rate per hour, the data would form a direct variation and the points would be on a line.]**

Q How could you use an hourly rate to solve the problem? **[Answers may vary. Sample: Find the mean of the hourly rates in the graph and divide $200 by the mean.]**

ANSWER See Solve It in Answers on next page.

CONNECT THE MATH In the Solve It, students estimate an unknown quantity using rates, means, or proportional reasoning. In the lesson, they will make similar scatter plots and use trend lines to estimate unknown quantities.

Using Linear Models

Common Core State Standards

F-IF.B.4 For a function that models a relationship between two quantities, interpret key features of graphs . . . and sketch graphs showing key features . . .
Also A-CED.A.2, F-IF.B.6
MP 1, MP 3, MP 4, MP 5

Objectives To write linear equations that model real-world data
To make predictions from linear models

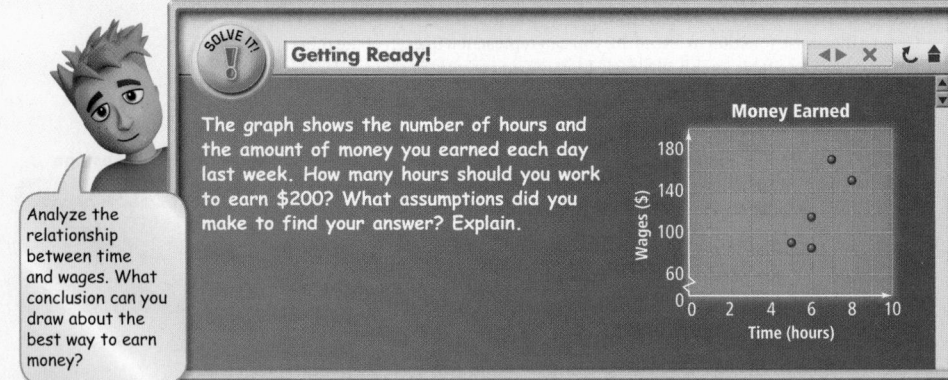

Analyze the relationship between time and wages. What conclusion can you draw about the best way to earn money?

Getting Ready!

The graph shows the number of hours and the amount of money you earned each day last week. How many hours should you work to earn $200? What assumptions did you make to find your answer? Explain.

MATHEMATICAL PRACTICES Graphs of data pairs for a real-world situation rarely fall in a line. Their arrangement, however, can suggest a relationship that you can model with a linear function.

Essential Understanding Sometimes it is possible to model data from a real-world situation with a linear equation. You can then use the equation to draw conclusions about the situation.

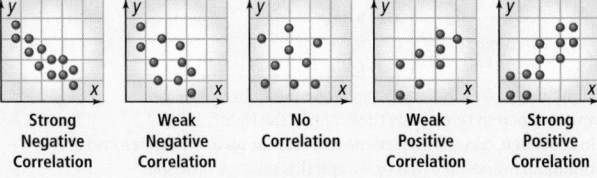

Lesson Vocabulary
- scatter plot
- correlation
- line of best fit
- correlation coefficient

A **scatter plot** is a graph that relates two sets of data by plotting the data as ordered pairs. You can use a scatter plot to determine the strength of the relationship, or **correlation**, between data sets. The closer the data points fall along a line,

- the stronger the relationship and
- the stronger the positive or negative correlation

between the two variables.

Strong Negative Correlation   Weak Negative Correlation   No Correlation   Weak Positive Correlation   Strong Positive Correlation

---

BIG idea Modeling

ESSENTIAL UNDERSTANDINGS

- Sometimes it is possible to model data from a real-world situation with a linear equation. The equation can then be used to draw conclusions about the situation.
- The equation of a trend line, or line of best fit, can be used to model data that cluster in a linear pattern.
- A scatter plot is a graph that relates two sets of data by plotting the data as ordered pairs. A scatter plot can be used to determine the strength of the relationship, or correlation between data sets.

Math Background

When data from a real-world situation can be written as a set of ordered pairs, you can use various types of regression equations as models. The idea of correlation is addressed throughout the lesson. It is a common mistake to conclude

that because two events are correlated, one must be the cause of the other. It is possible, however, for two events to be correlated, even strongly correlated, without one event causing the other.

It may be the case that a third event is the common cause of the correlated events. For example, houses and milk do seem to cost more as time goes by. However, time itself does not *cause* these prices to go up; rather, other factors like inflation and demand, which change over time, are the causes.

Mathematical Practices

Use appropriate tools strategically.
In Problem 3, students will use a calculator to determine the line of best fit and its possible error.

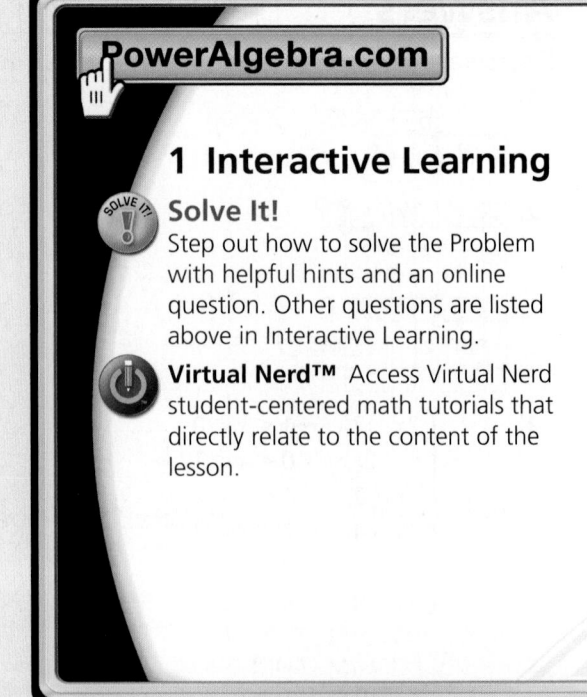

PowerAlgebra.com

1 Interactive Learning

Solve It!
Step out how to solve the Problem with helpful hints and an online question. Other questions are listed above in Interactive Learning.

Virtual Nerd™ Access Virtual Nerd student-centered math tutorials that directly relate to the content of the lesson.

Problem 1 Using a Scatter Plot

Utilities The table lists average monthly temperatures and electricity costs for a Texas home in 2008. The table displays the values rounded to the nearest whole number. Make a scatter plot. How would you describe the correlation?

Average Temperatures and Electricity Costs

Month	Average Temp. (°F)	Electricity Bill ($)	Month	Average Temp. (°F)	Electricity Bill ($)
January	61	150	July	84	255
February	58	139	August	85	245
March	67	172	September	81	210
April	75	205	October	76	183
May	79	170	November	65	132
June	83	234	December	58	110

Plan

Which variable is the independent variable?
Temperature does not depend on the electric bill, so temperature is the independent variable.

Step 1 Make a scatter plot.

Step 2 Describe the correlation.

As the temperature increases, the electricity cost also increases. The points are relatively tightly clustered around a line. There is a strong positive correlation between temperature and electricity cost.

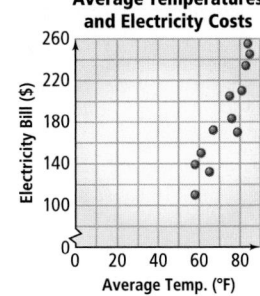

Average Temperatures and Electricity Costs

Got It? **1. a.** The table shows the numbers of hours students spent online the day before a test and the scores on the test. Make a scatter plot. How would you describe the correlation?

b. Reasoning Using the graph from Problem 1, how much would you expect to pay for electricity if the average temperature was 70°F? Explain.

Computer Use and Test Scores

Number of Hours Online	0	0	1	1	1.5	1.75	2	2	3	4	4.5	5
Test score	100	94	98	88	92	89	75	70	78	72	57	60

A *trend line* is a line that approximates the relationship between the variables, or data sets, of a scatter plot. You can use a trend line to make predictions from the data. In a previous lesson you learned how to use two points to write the equation of a line to model a real-world problem. You can use this method to write the equation of a trend line.

2 Guided Instruction

Each Problem is worked out and supported online.

Problem 1
Using a Scatter Plot
Animated

Problem 2
Writing the Equation of a Trend Line
Animated

Problem 3
Finding the Line of Best Fit
Animated

Support in Algebra 2 Companion
• Vocabulary
• Key Concepts
• Got It?

2 Guided Instruction

Problem 1

Q What quantities form each ordered pair? **[average temperature and electricity cost]**

Q Which quantity should you represent on each axis? Explain. **[Answers may vary. Sample: Represent temperature on the horizontal axis and cost on the vertical axis because the independent quantity is represented on the horizontal axis and the dependent quantity is represented on the vertical axis. In this case, the amount of electricity used probably depends on the temperature.]**

Q What ordered pair corresponds to January? **[(61, 150)]**

Q How many ordered pairs should be graphed? Explain. **[12; there are 12 months represented by the data.]**

Got It?

Q What scale will you use on the horizontal axis? Explain. **[Answers may vary. Sample: 0 to 5 because the hours range from 0 to 5.]**

Q What scale will you use on the vertical axis? Explain. **[Answers may vary. Sample: 0 to 100 because the highest test score is 100.]**

Answers

Solve It!

about 10; based on the graph, you can assume that you generally earn more money the more hours you work.

Got It?

1. a. strong negative correlation

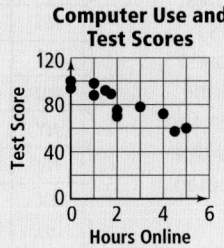

Computer Use and Test Scores

b. about $170

Problem 2

Q Why do you think letting the *x*-values represent the number of years since 1940 is a good idea? **[Answers may vary. Sample: Doing so allows you to begin the scale on the *x*-axis at 0 without having a lot of unused distance on the axis.]**

Q Look at the graph and table of values. What are the coordinates of the leftmost point, and what do they represent? **[(0, 23,100)]; the median home price in Florida in 1940 was $23,100.]**

For Step 2, suggest the following way to sketch a trend line: Sketch a line that follows the pattern of the points with approximately the same number of points above it as below it.

In Step 3, two points must be chosen to use in finding an equation of the trend line. Point out that any two points on the line may be chosen; they need not be actual data points.

Got It?

Q How will you define the variable *x*? **[Let *x* = number of years since 1940.]**

Q In which year(s) did the median home price vary the most from your trend line? Was the median price higher or lower than the trend? Explain. **[Answers may vary. Sample: On a graphing calculator with a true regression line, the median price in 1970 is the lowest below the trend by almost $40,000, and 1990 is the highest above the trend by almost $50,000.]**

Problem 2 Writing the Equation of a Trend Line

Finance The table shows the median home prices in Florida. What is the equation of a trend line that models a relationship between time and home prices? Use the equation to predict the median home price in 2020.

Florida Median Home Prices							
Year	1940	1950	1960	1970	1980	1990	2000
Median Price ($)	23,100	40,100	58,100	57,600	89,300	98,500	105,500

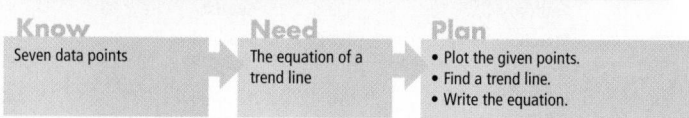

Know	Need	Plan
Seven data points	The equation of a trend line	• Plot the given points. • Find a trend line. • Write the equation.

Step 1 Make a scatter plot. Let $x = 0$ correspond to 1940.

Step 2 Sketch a trend line.

Step 3 Choose two points on the trend line, (10, 40,000) and (55, 110,000). Use slope-intercept form to write an equation for the line.
$$y = 1556x + 24,440$$

Step 4 Use the equation to predict the median home price in 2020.
$$y = 1556(80) + 24,440 = 148,920$$
Based on the trend line, the median home price in 2020 will be around $149,000.

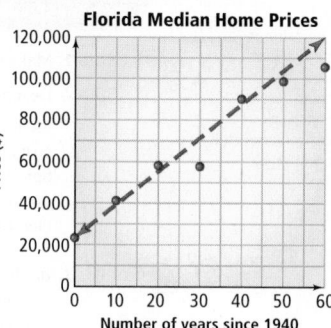

Got It? 2. The table shows median home prices in California. What is an equation for a trend line that models the relationship between time and home prices?

California Median Home Prices							
Year	1940	1950	1960	1970	1980	1990	2000
Median Price ($)	36,700	57,900	74,400	88,700	167,300	249,800	211,500

The trend line that gives the most accurate model of related data is the **line of best fit**. One method for finding a line of best fit is *linear regression*. You can use the **LinReg** function on your graphing calculator to find the line of best fit. The **correlation coefficient**, *r*, indicates the strength of the correlation. The closer *r* is to 1 or −1, the more closely the data resembles a line and the more accurate your model is likely to be.

Additional Problems

1. The table lists the percent of persons 25 years or older with at least a Bachelor's degree and the median household income for 12 states in 2000. Percents are rounded to the nearest whole percent; incomes are rounded to the nearest thousand dollars. Describe the correlation between the percentage of adults with a college degree and median income.

ANSWER There is a weak positive correlation between level of education and income.

State	Adults With at Least BS/BA	Income
AK	25%	$52,000
AL	19%	$34,000
CA	27%	$47,000
FL	22%	$39,000
MS	17%	$31,000
MT	24%	$33,000
ND	22%	$35,000
NY	27%	$43,000
NV	18%	$45,000
TX	23%	$40,00
WA	28%	$46,000
WV	15%	$30,000

2. The table shows the median home prices in New Jersey. What is an equation of a trend line that models a relationship between time and home prices? Use that equation to predict the median home price in 2020.

ANSWERS Sample:
$y = 2061x + 47,100$
x = the years since 1940
y = price;
$211,980

Year	Median Price ($)
1940	47,100
1950	63,100
1960	76,900
1970	89,900
1980	119,200
1990	207,400
2000	170,800

Problem 3 Finding the Line of Best Fit

Food You research the average cost of whole milk for several recent years to look for trends. The table shows your data.

Cost of Whole Milk						
Year	1998	2000	2002	2004	2006	2008
Average cost for one gallon ($)	2.65	2.89	3.00	3.01	3.20	3.77

Source: U.S. Department of Agriculture

Ⓐ What is the equation for the line of best fit? How accurate is your line of best fit?

Step 1
Use the **STAT** feature to enter the data in your graphing calculator. Enter the x-values (year) in **L1** and the y-values (price) in **L2**. Let 1997 = year 0.

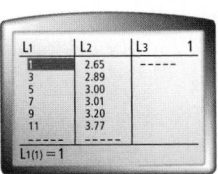

Step 2
Use **LinReg** to find the linear regression line of best fit for the data.

$$y = 0.09x + 2.53$$

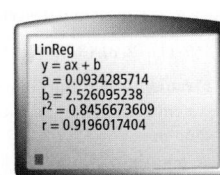

The correlation coefficient, r, is approximately 0.92. Since r is close to 1, the line of best fit is quite accurate.

Ⓑ Based on your linear model, how much would you expect to pay for a gallon of whole milk in 2020?

$y = 0.09x + 2.53$ Use the line of best fit.

$y = 0.09(23) + 2.53$ Substitute 23 for x.

$y = 4.60$

In 2020, you would expect to pay about $4.60 for a gallon of whole milk.

Got It? 3. The table lists the cost of 2% milk. Use a scatter plot to find the equation of the line of best fit. Based on your linear model, how much would you expect to pay for a gallon of 2% milk in 2025?

Cost of 2% Milk						
Year	1998	2000	2002	2004	2006	2008
Average cost for one gallon ($)	2.57	2.83	2.93	2.93	3.10	3.71

Source: U.S. Department of Agriculture

Think
What factors could affect the accuracy of your prediction?
Predictions based on strongly correlated data are likely to be more reliable than predictions based on weakly correlated data.

PowerAlgebra.com   Lesson 2-5   Using Linear Models   95

Problem 3

Q Look at Step 2 in 3A. In the context of the problem, what does the value 0.09 in the equation represent? **[It represents an increase of $0.09 per year in the cost of a gallon of milk.]**

Q Is this representation exact? Explain. **[No; it is based on the regression equation, which is a model, so it provides only an estimate.]**

Q What was the actual average yearly increase in the cost of a gallon of milk from 1998 to 2008? Explain. **[About $0.11: ($3.72 − $2.65) ÷ 10 = $0.107**

For Step 2 of 3A, if the values for r and r^2 do not appear on the TI-83 or TI-84 calculator screen, press **2nd** CATALOG, then scroll down to Diagnostic On, press **enter** and then press **enter** again.

Got It?

Q Compare this data with Problem 3. How do you expect the equations to compare? Explain. **[Answers may vary. Sample: They will be very similar because the years are the same and the costs are very close.]**

Q Why is comparing the equations useful? **[Answers may vary. Sample: It is a way to check the reasonableness of the equation.]**

---

3. You research the cost of movie tickets for recent years to look for trends. The table shows your data.

Year	Average Cost of Movie Ticket
1995	4.35
1997	4.59
1999	5.06
2001	5.65
2003	6.03
2005	6.41
2007	6.88

a. What is the equation for the line of best fit? How accurate is your line of best fit?

b. Based on your linear model, how much would you expect to pay for a movie ticket in 2025?

ANSWERS

a. $y = 0.22x + 4.26$, where x is the years since 1995 and y is the average movie ticket cost. Since $r = 0.997$, which is close to 1, the line of best fit is quite accurate.

b. $10.86

Answers

Got It? (continued)

2. $y = 3500x + 25,000$

3. $y = 0.09x + 2.44$, where 1997 is year 0; $4.96

Lesson 2-5   95

3 Lesson Check

Do you know HOW?

- For Exercises 1–2, if students have difficulty choosing appropriate scales for the axes or estimating when graphing some of the ordered pairs, ask them to look at the domain and range of the given values.
- For Exercise 3, either make a scatter plot with paper and pencil or do a linear regression on a calculator and use the value of r.

Do you UNDERSTAND?

- For Exercise 5, if students have difficulty understanding the line of best fit, try graphing some points on a coordinate plane and using a piece of spaghetti to help students see the line of best fit.

Close

> **Q** What is a scatter plot? **[a graph that relates two sets of data by plotting the data as ordered pairs]**
>
> **Q** How is the line of best fit related to a trend line? **[A line of best fit is a special trend line that was calculated by a standard procedure. Trend lines are visual estimates, so not all are accurate enough to be a line of best fit.]**
>
> **Q** How can you write an equation of a trend line? **[Use two points on the trend line along with the point-slope form.]**

 Lesson Check

Do you know HOW?

Make a scatter plot of each set of points and describe the correlation.

1. $\{(1.2, 1), (2.5, 6), (2.5, 7.5), (4.1, 11), (7.9, 19)\}$

2. $\{(1, 55), (2, 38), (3, 54), (4, 37), (5, 53), (6, 40), (7, 53), (8, 36)\}$

3. Make a scatter plot for the following set of points. Describe the correlation and sketch a trend line. $\{(2, 58), (6, 105), (8, 88), (8, 118), (12, 117), (16, 137), (20, 157), (20, 169)\}$

Do you UNDERSTAND?  MATHEMATICAL PRACTICES

4. **Writing** How can you determine whether two variables x and y for a real-life situation are correlated?

5. Do you think a trend line on a graph is always the same as the line of best fit? Why or why not?

6. **Compare and Contrast** What is the difference between a positive correlation and a negative correlation? How might you relate positive correlation with direct variation?

Practice and Problem-Solving Exercises  MATHEMATICAL PRACTICES

A Practice   Make a scatter plot and describe the correlation.   ◀ See Problem 1.

7. $\{(0, 11), (2, 8), (3, 7), (7, 2), (8, 0)\}$

8. **Manufacturing** The table shows the numbering system used in Europe and the United States for shoe sizes.

Shoe Sizes						
U.S. Size	1	3	5	7	9	11
European Size	31	34	36	39	41	44

Write the equation of a trend line.   ◀ See Problem 2.

9. $\{(-10, 3), (-5, 1), (-1, -4), (3, -7), (12, -12)\}$

10. $\{(-15, 8), (-8, 7), (-3, 0), (0, 0), (7, -3)\}$

11. The table shows the number of hours you studied before your eight math tests and your percent score on each test.

Studying Hours and Test Score								
Number of Hours	8	5	12	10	2	9	11	14
Score (%)	75	62	80	85	35	70	82	95

12. **a. Food Production** The table below shows pork production in China from 2000 to 2007. Use a calculator to find the line of best fit.   ◀ See Problem 3.
    b. Use your linear model to predict how many metric tons of pork will be produced in 2025.
    c. Use your linear model to predict when production is likely to reach 100,000 metric tons.

Pork Production in China								
Year	2000	2001	2002	2003	2004	2005	2006	2007
Production (metric tons)	40,475	42,010	43,413	45,331	47,177	50,254	52,407	54,491

Source: USDA Foreign Agricultural Service GAIN Report

---

3 Lesson Check

For a digital lesson check, use the Got It questions.

Support in Algebra 2 Companion
- Lesson Check

4 Practice

Assign homework to individual students or to an entire class.

Answers

Lesson Check

1. strong positive correlation

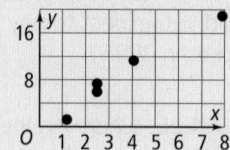

2. no correlation

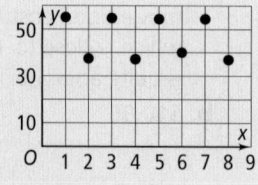

3. strong positive correlation

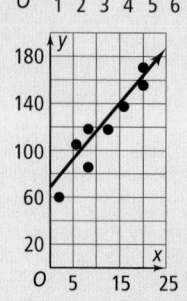

4. Plot the data points in a scatter plot to determine the correlation. The closer the data points fall along a line with a positive or negative slope, the stronger the correlation.

5. No; answers may vary. Sample: A trend line is determined by using two pts. close to the line drawn through the data sets of the scatter plot. The line of best fit is the most accurate of the trend lines because it uses all the data pts.

6. The slope of the trend line or line of best fit is positive for data pts. with positive correlation and negative for data pts. with negative correlation. The constant of variation for a direct variation is positive for data pts. with positive correlation.

B Apply © **13. Think About a Plan** The table shows the relationship between the production and the export of rice in Vietnam from 1985 to 2005.

Rice Production and Export					
Production (1000 tonnes)	15,875	19,225	24,964	32,554	35,600
Export (1000 tonnes)	59	1624	1988	3400	5100

Source: International Rice Research Institute

How much rice would you expect Vietnam to export in 2015 if the production that year is 42,250,000 tonnes?
- How can you use a scatter plot to find a linear model?
- How can you use your model to make a prediction?

© **14. Nutrition** The table shows the relationship between Calories and fat in various fast-food hamburgers.

Fast Food Calories									
Restaurant	A	B	C	D	E	F	G	H	I
Number of Calories	720	530	510	500	305	410	440	320	598
Grams of fat	46	30	27	26	13	20	25	13	26

   a. Find the line of best fit for the relationship between Calories and fat.
   b. How much fat would you expect a 330-Calorie hamburger to have?
   c. Error Analysis Which estimate is *not* reasonable: 10 g of fat for a 200-Calorie hamburger or 36 g of fat for a 660-Calorie hamburger? Explain.

© **Reasoning** For any correlation, people often assume that change in one quantity *causes* change in the second quantity. This is not always true. For each situation, do you think that change in the first quantity causes change in the second quantity? What else may have affected the change in the second quantity?

   15. number of miles driven and fuel expenses

   16. the size of a car's engine and the number of passengers it is designed for

   17. a person's age and the number of cassette tapes he or she owns

© **18. Data Analysis** The table shows population and licensed driver statistics from a recent year.
   a. Make a scatter plot.
   b. Draw a trend line.
   c. The population of Michigan was approximately 10 million that year. About how many licensed drivers lived in Michigan that year?
   d. Writing Is the correlation between population and number of licensed drivers strong or weak? Explain.

Licensed Drivers

State	Population (millions)	Number of Drivers (millions)
Arkansas	2.8	2.0
Illinois	12.8	8.1
Kansas	2.8	2.0
Massachusetts	6.4	4.7
Pennsylvania	12.4	8.5
Texas	23.5	14.9

4 Practice

ASSIGNMENT GUIDE
Basic: 7–12 all, 13–18

Average: 7–11 odd, 13–18

Advanced: 7–11 odd, 13–19

Standardized Test Prep: 20–23

Mixed Review: 24–32

© **Mathematical Practices** are supported by exercises with red headings. Here are the Practices supported in this lesson:

MP 1: Make Sense of Problems Ex.13
MP 3: Communicate Ex. 4, 18
MP 3: Construct Arguments Ex. 6, 15–17
MP 4: Model with Mathematics Ex.14, 18

Applications exercises have blue headings. Exercises 8, 12, 14, and 19 support MP 4: Model.

EXERCISE 18: Use the Think About a Plan worksheet in the **Practice and Problem Solving Workbook** (also available in the Teaching Resources in print and online) to further support students' development in becoming independent learners.

HOMEWORK QUICK CHECK
To check students' understanding of key skills and concepts, go over Exercises 7, 11, 13, 14, and 18.

Practice and Problem-Solving Exercises

7. strong negative correlation

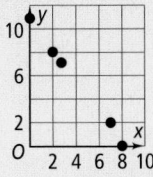

8. strong positive correlation

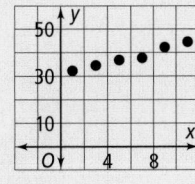

9. Sample: $y = -0.7x - 4$

10. not possible

11. Sample: $y = 4.47x + 33.31$

12. a. Sample:
   Let 2000 = year 0
   $y = 2053.17x + 39,758.67$
   b. about 91,090 tons
   c. in the year 2030

13. 6,055,359 tonnes

14. a. Sample: $y = 0.0714x - 9.2682$
   b. 14.3 g
   c. 200 Cal; a 200-Cal hamburger has about 5 g of fat.

15. yes

16. No. Check students' answer.

17. No. Check students' answer.

18. a.

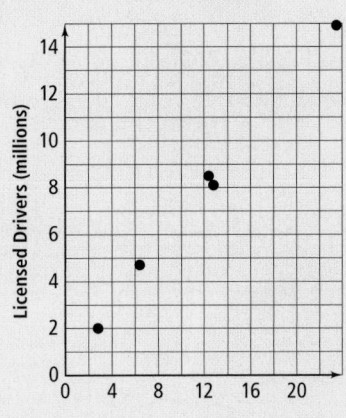

b.

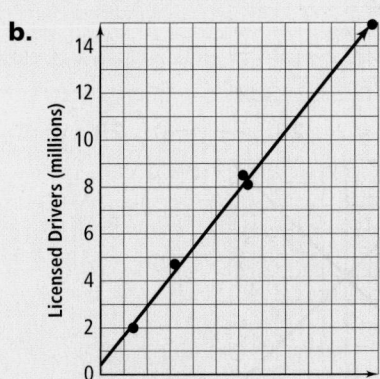

   c. about 6.5 million
   d. Strong; the pts. fall close to a straight line.

Answers

Practice and Problem-Solving Exercises (continued)

19. a.

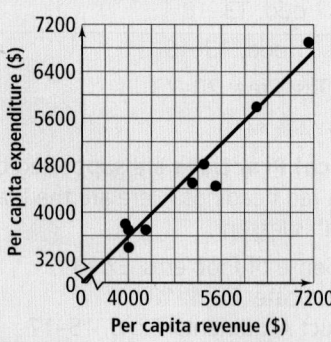

b. about $2506   **c.** about $5610

d. Answers may vary. Sample: Yes; expenditure would be predicted to be between $5300 and $5400.

Standardized Test Prep

20. C   **21.** G   **22.** B

23. [2] $(y - 1) = \frac{2}{3}(x + 1)$

$$(-3 - 1) = \frac{2}{3}(a + 1)$$

$$-4 = \frac{2}{3}a + \frac{2}{3}$$

$$\frac{-14}{3} = \frac{2}{3}a$$

$$-7 = a$$

[1] a computational error

Mixed Review

24. 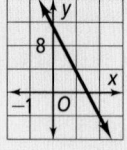   **25.**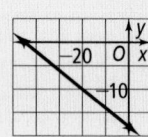

26.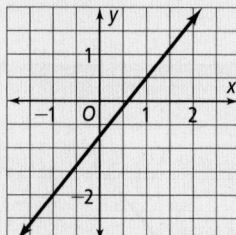

27. $-2x + y = 2$ **28.** $x + y = 0$ **29.** $y = 2$

30.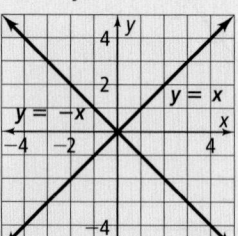

31.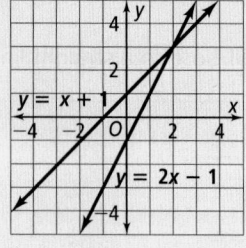

 **Challenge**

19. Social Studies The table shows per capita revenues and expenditures for selected states for a recent year.

  a. Show the data on a scatter plot. Draw a trend line.

  b. If a state collected revenue of $3000 per capita, how much would you expect it to spend per capita?

  c. Ohio spent $5142 per capita during that year. According to your model, how much did it collect in taxes per capita?

  d. In that same year, New Jersey collected $5825 per capita in taxes and spent $5348 per capita. Does this information follow the trend? Explain.

Per Capita Revenue and Expenditure

State	Per Capita Revenue ($)	Per Capita Expenditure ($)
Arizona	4144	3789
Georgia	3904	3834
Maryland	5109	4557
Mississippi	5292	4871
New Mexico	6205	5793
Nevada	4345	3723
New York	7081	6891
Texas	4030	3442
Utah	5439	4459

Standardized Test Prep

SAT/ACT

20. What is the equation of the line shown in the graph?

  Ⓐ $y = -2x + 2$ Ⓒ $y = 2x + 1$

  Ⓑ $y = 2x$ Ⓓ $y = 2x + 2$

21. Shauna drove 75 miles in 3 hours at a constant speed. How many miles did she drive in 2 hours?

  Ⓕ 25 miles   Ⓖ 50 miles   Ⓗ 75 miles   Ⓘ 100 miles

22. Which equation does NOT represent a direct variation?

  Ⓐ $y = x$ Ⓒ $2x - y = 0$

  Ⓑ $2x - y = 5$ Ⓓ $2x - 5y = 0$

Short Response

23. The line $(y - 1) = \frac{2}{3}(x + 1)$ contains point $(a, -3)$. What is the value of a? Show your work.

Mixed Review

Graph the following linear equations.   ◀ See Lesson 2-3.

24. $y = -7.5x + 11$ **25.** $-\frac{2}{9}x - \frac{5}{9}y = 10$ **26.** $5x - 4y = 3$

Write the equation of each line in standard form.   ◀ See Lesson 2-4.

27. slope $= 2$; $(2, 6)$ **28.** slope $= -1$; $(-3, 3)$ **29.** slope $= 0$; $(0, 2)$

Get Ready! To prepare for Lesson 2-6, do Exercises 30–32.

Graph each pair of functions on the same coordinate plane.   ◀ See Lesson 2-3.

30. $y = -x$; $y = x$ **31.** $y = x + 1$; $y = 2x - 1$ **32.** $y = -\frac{1}{4}x$; $y = -\frac{1}{4}x + 2$

32.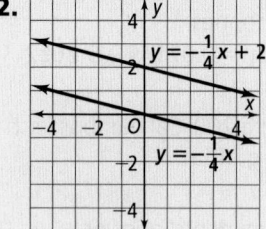

2-5 Lesson Resources

Additional Instructional Support

Algebra 2 Companion

Students can use the **Algebra 2 Companion** worktext (4 pages) as you teach the lesson. Use the Companion to support

- New Vocabulary
- Key Concepts
- Got It for each Problem
- Lesson Check

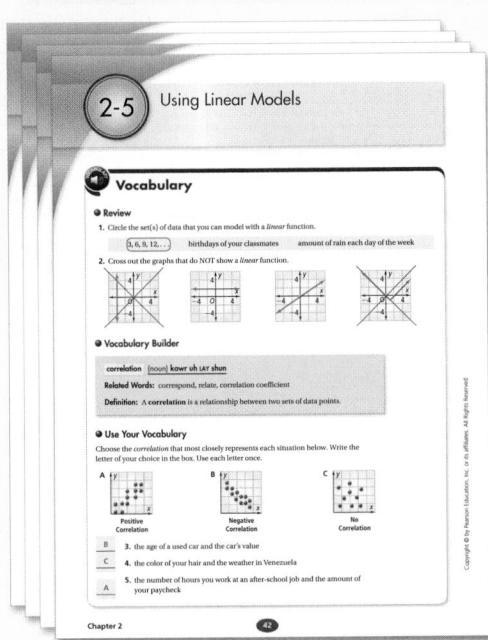

ELL Support

Use Manipulatives Have groups of students select two variables whose relationship can be tested in the classroom. For instance, they might investigate the correlation between the number of pages in a book and its weight or the number of faces and number of edges of polyhedra. The group should predict the correlation they expect to find and explain their reasoning.

Groups should next test as many cases as possible and make a scatter plot of their data. Each group should find a line of best fit for their data and report how the results of their research matches with their predictions.

5 Assess & Remediate

Lesson Quiz

1. The table shows how much Kim earned. What is the equation of a trend line that models a relationship between time and Kim's annual salary?

Year	Annual Salary ($)
1996	42,000
1998	47,500
2000	48,900
2002	55,000
2004	60,000

2. Using the table in **1**, predict Kim's salary in 2025.

3. **Do you UNDERSTAND?** The table shows the cost of the lunch special for selected years since a diner opened. What is an equation for the line of best fit? How accurate is the line of best fit?

Year	Cost ($)
1997	6.95
1999	7.95
2001	8.00
2003	8.00
2005	9.25
2007	9.50

ANSWERS TO LESSON QUIZ

1. $y = 2500x + 40,000$; x is years since 1996; y is annual salary.

2. Kim's salary in 2025 should be $112,500.

3. $y = 0.24x + 6.85$; x is years since 1996; y is cost of the lunch special. Since $r = .94$, which is close to 1, the line of best fit is quite accurate.

PRESCRIPTION FOR REMEDIATION

Use the student work on the Lesson Quiz to prescribe a differentiated review assignment:

Points	Differentiated Remediation
0–1	Intervention
2	On-level
3	Extension

PowerAlgebra.com

5 Assess & Remediate

Assign the Lesson Quiz. Appropriate intervention, practice, or enrichment is automatically generated based on student performance.

Differentiated Remediation

Available in editable format online.

Intervention

- **Reteaching** (2 pages) Provides reteaching and practice exercises for the key lesson concepts. Use with struggling students or absent students.

- **English Language Learner Support** Helps students develop and reinforce mathematical vocabulary and key concepts.

All-in-One Resources/Online

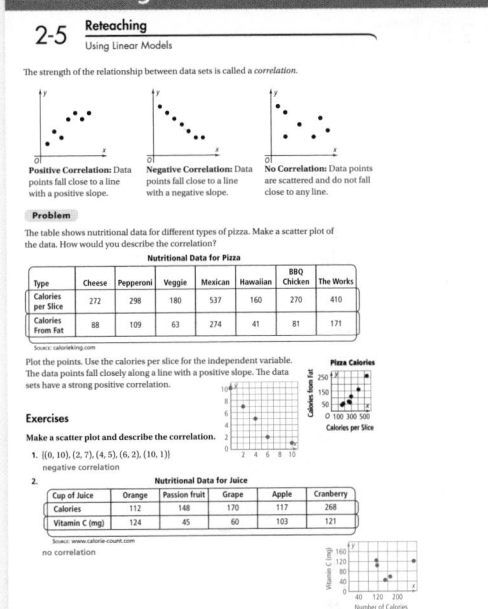

Differentiated Remediation *continued*

Available in editable format online.

On-Level

- **Practice** (2 pages) Provides extra practice for each lesson. For simpler practice exercises, use the Form K Practice pages found in the All-in-One Teaching Resources and online.

- **Think About a Plan** Helps students develop specific problem-solving skills and strategies by providing scaffolded guiding questions.

- **Standardized Test Prep** Focuses on all major exercises, all major question types, and helps students prepare for the high-stakes assessments.

Extension

- **Enrichment** Provides students with interesting problems and activities that extend the concepts of the lesson.

- **Activities, Games, and Puzzles** Worksheets that can be used for concepts development, enrichment, and for fun!

Practice and Problem Solving Wkbk/ All-in-One Resources/Online
Practice page 1

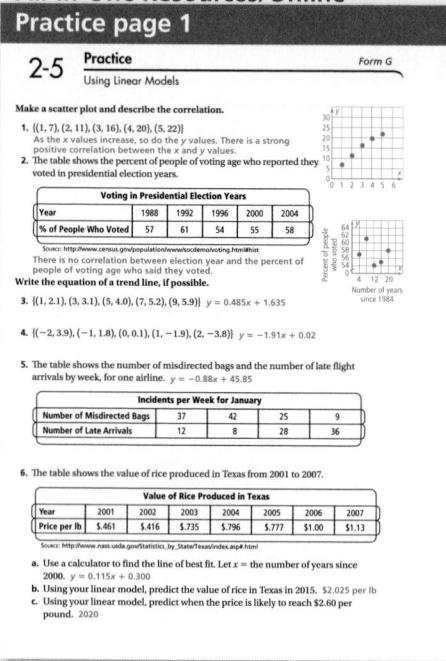

2-5 Practice — Form G
Using Linear Models

Make a scatter plot and describe the correlation.

1. {(1, 7), (2, 11), (3, 16), (4, 20), (5, 22)}
As the *x* values increase, so do the *y* values. There is a strong positive correlation between the *x* and *y* values.

2. The table shows the percent of people of voting age who reported they voted in presidential election years.

Voting in Presidential Election Years

Year	1988	1992	1996	2000	2004
% of People Who Voted	57	61	54	55	58

Source: http://www.census.gov/population/www/socdemo/voting.html#hist

There is no correlation between election year and the percent of people of voting age who said they voted.

Write the equation of a trend line, if possible.

3. {(1, 2.1), (3, 3.1), (5, 4.0), (7, 5.2), (9, 5.9)} $y = 0.485x + 1.635$

4. {(−2, 3.9), (−1, 1.8), (0, 0.1), (1, −1.9), (2, −3.8)} $y = -1.91x + 0.02$

5. The table shows the number of misdirected bags and the number of late flight arrivals by week for one airline. Let $x = -0.88x + 45.85$

Incidents per Week for January

Number of Misdirected Bags	37	42	25	9
Number of Late Arrivals	12	8	28	36

6. The table shows the value of rice produced in Texas from 2001 to 2007.

Value of Rice Produced in Texas

Year	2001	2002	2003	2004	2005	2006	2007
Price per lb	$.461	$.416	$.735	$.796	$.777	$1.00	$1.13

Source: http://www.nass.usda.gov/Statistics_by_State/Texas/index.asp#.html

a. Use a calculator to find the line of best fit. Let $x =$ the number of years since 2000. $y = 0.115x + 0.300$

b. Using your linear model, predict the value of rice in Texas in 2015. $2.025 per lb

c. Using your linear model, predict when the price is likely to reach $2.60 per pound. 2020

Practice and Problem Solving Wkbk/ All-in-One Resources/Online
Practice page 2

2-5 Practice (continued) — Form G
Using Linear Models

7. The table shows the percent of the population not covered by health insurance in selected states for the years 1997 and 2006.

Percent of Population Not Covered by Health Insurance

State	Idaho	Illinois	Michigan	Montana	New York
1997	17.7	12.4	11.6	19.5	17.5
2006	15.4	14	10.5	17.1	14

Source: www.census.gov

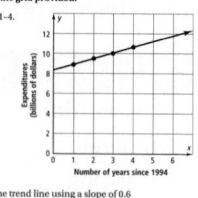

a. Which variable should be the independent variable? the 1997 percent
b. Make a scatter plot. Use a calculator to find the line of best fit. $y = 0.59x + 4.99$
c. In Wyoming, 15.5% of the population was not covered by health insurance in 1997. Use the equation from part (c) to predict the percent of the population that was not covered in 2006. 14.14%
d. **Writing** The actual percent for Wyoming in 2006 was 14.6%. Is the line of best fit accurate? Explain. Yes; the prediction was 14.1% and the actual was 14.6%; the correlation coefficient is 0.85, so the line of best fit is fairly accurate.

8. The table shows the numbers of countries that participated in the Winter Olympics from 1984 to 2006.

Winter Olympic Participation

Year	1984	1988	1992	1994	1998	2002	2006
Number of Countries	49	57	64	67	72	77	80

Source: www.infoplease.com

a. Make a scatter plot. Let $x =$ the number of years since 1980.
b. Use a calculator to find the line of best fit and write the equation for the line.
c. Predict the number of participating countries in 2022. $y = 1.41x + 45.68$ about 105

9. The table shows the price per box of fresh Florida oranges from 2001 to 2006.

Florida Oranges

Year	2001	2002	2003	2004	2005	2006
Price per Box	$6.39	$6.99	$7.78	$6.07	$9.27	$8.40

Source: http://www.nass.usda.gov/Data_and_Statistics/Quick_Stats/

a. Make a scatter plot and find the trend line. Let $x =$ the number of years since 2000.
b. In 2007, the price per box of fresh oranges was $16. Does this information follow the trend? Explain.
c. **Reasoning** Is a model invalid if new data does not fit its predictions? Explain.
[a] $y = 0.43x + 5.97$ [b] No; using the equation for the line of best fit, the price of oranges per box should be $8.98, not $16. [c] No; even if the linear model fits the data well, predictions outside the range of the given values can vary greatly from the model.

All-in-One Resources/Online
Enrichment

2-5 Enrichment
Using Linear Models

When a cake is first removed from the oven, its temperature is 350°F. After 3 hours, its temperature is approximately 75°F, the temperature of the kitchen.

1. Use the information above to write two ordered pairs (x, y), where *x* represents the time (in hours) since the cake was removed from the oven and *y* represents the temperature (in degrees Fahrenheit) of the cake at that time. (0, 350), (3, 75)

2. Find the slope of the line through the two points identified in Exercise 1. $-\frac{275}{3}$

3. Write in slope-intercept form the equation of the line through the two points in Exercise 1. $y = -\frac{275}{3}x + 350$

4. Use the equation from Exercise 3 to estimate the temperature of the cake after 1 hour, after 2 hours, and after 4 hours. ≈258°F; ≈167°F; ≈−17°F

5. Suppose that the actual temperature of the cake is about 116°F after 1 hour, about 81°F after 2 hours, and about 75°F after 4 hours. Compare these temperatures to your answer from Exercise 4. Does the equation from Exercise 3 model the temperature of the cake accurately? no

What happened? Linear equations are not appropriate for modeling every situation. The linear model assumes that the temperature of the cake decreases by the same number of degrees during each hour. Notice how the model fails after 4 hours, when the temperature of the cake is below room temperature, an impossibility.

The problem is that the temperature of the cake does not decrease by a constant number of degrees each hour. Its temperature decreases by a percent of the difference between its temperature and room temperature during each hour.

6. What is the difference between the temperature of the cake and room temperature when the cake is removed from the oven? 275°F

7. Find 85% of the difference you found in Exercise 6. 233.75°F

8. Subtract your answer for Exercise 7 from 350°F. How does this number compare to the temperature after 1 hour given in Exercise 5? 116.25°F; very close

---

Practice and Problem Solving Wkbk/ All-in-One Resources/Online
Think About a Plan

2-5 Think About a Plan
Using Linear Models

Data Analysis The table shows population and licensed driver statistics from a recent year.

a. Make a scatter plot.
b. Draw a trend line.
c. The population of Michigan was approximately 10 million that year. About how many licensed drivers lived in Michigan that year?
d. **Writing** Is the correlation between population and number of licensed drivers strong or weak? Explain.

Licensed Drivers

State	Population (millions)	Number of Drivers (millions)
Arkansas	2.7	1.9
Illinois	12.4	7.7
Kansas	2.7	1.8
Massachusetts	6.4	4.4
Pennsylvania	12.3	8.3
Texas	20.9	12.8

Know

1. The independent variable should be _population, in millions_

2. Points to plot: _(2.7, 1.9), (12.4, 7.7), (2.7, 1.8), (6.4, 4.4), (12.3, 8.3), (20.9, 12.8)_

Need

3. To solve the problems, I need to _make a scatter plot; draw a trend line;_
use the trend line to find the number of licensed drivers if the population is
10 million; find the strength of the correlation.

Plan

4. Make the scatter plot.

5. Draw a trend line on the scatter plot.

6. How do you find the equation of the trend line? Write the equation.
Use two data points to write the point-slope form of the equation. Answers may vary.
Sample: $y = 0.61x + 0.36$

7. About how many licensed drivers lived in Michigan that year? about 6.5 million

8. What is correlation? Is the correlation between population and licensed drivers strong or weak? Explain.
Correlation is the strength of the relationship, or how close the data points are to the trend line; the correlation is strong; the points fall very close to the trend line.

Practice and Problem Solving Wkbk/ All-in-One Resources/Online
Standardized Test Prep

2-5 Standardized Test Prep
Using Linear Models

Gridded Response

Solve each exercise and enter your answer in the grid provided.

Use the table and the scatter plot for Exercises 1–4.

U.S. Health Expenditures Drug and Other Medical Nondurables

Year	Expenditures (billions of dollars)
1995	8.9
1996	9.4
1997	10.0
1998	10.6

Source: The World Almanac and Book of Facts, 2001

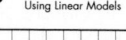

1. What is the *y*-intercept of the trend line if the trend line using a slope of 0.6 and the point (1, 8.9)?

2. During what year did the U.S. spend $10 billion in health expenditures?

3. Using the points for 1995 and 1997, what is the slope of the trend line? Round to the nearest hundredth.

4. Use the equation $y = 0.6x + 8.3$, where $x = 0$ is 1994. About how many billion dollars would the U.S. have spent on health expenditures in the year 2001, rounded to the nearest tenth?

Answers

1.    2.   3.   4.

Online Teacher Resource Center
Activities, Games, and Puzzles

2-5 Activity: Making a Scatter Plot
Using Linear Models

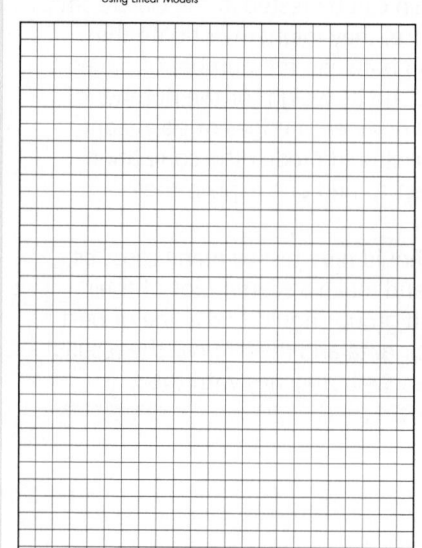

2-6 Families of Functions

Common Core State Standards
F-BF.B.3 Identify the effect on the graph of replacing
$f(x)$ by $f(x) + k$, $k\,f(x)$, $f(kx)$, and $f(x + k)$ for specific
values of k (both positive and negative) find the value of
k given the graphs.
MP 1, MP 3, MP 7

Objective To analyze transformations of functions

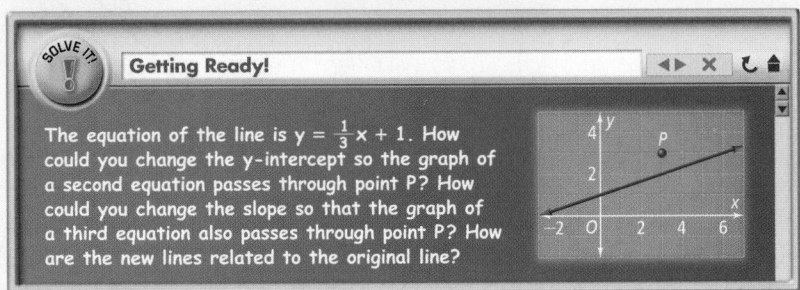

Getting Ready!

The equation of the line is $y = \frac{1}{3}x + 1$. How could you change the y-intercept so the graph of a second equation passes through point P? How could you change the slope so that the graph of a third equation also passes through point P? How are the new lines related to the original line?

Lesson Vocabulary
• parent function
• transformation
• translation
• reflection
• vertical stretch
• vertical compression

Different nonvertical lines have different slopes, or y-intercepts, or both. They are graphs of different linear functions. For two such lines, you can think of one as a *transformation* of the other.

Essential Understanding There are sets of functions, called *families*, in which each function is a transformation of a special function called the *parent*.

The linear functions form a family of functions. Each linear function is a transformation of the function $y = x$. The function $y = x$ is the *parent* linear function.

A **parent function** is the simplest form in a set of functions that form a family. Each function in the family is a **transformation** of the parent function.

One type of transformation is a **translation**. A translation shifts the graph of the parent function horizontally, vertically, or both without changing shape or orientation. For a positive constant k and a parent function $f(x)$, $f(x) \pm k$ is a vertical translation. For a positive constant h, $f(x \pm h)$ is a horizontal translation.

Adding k to the outputs shifts the graph up.

Subtracting h from the inputs shifts the graph right.

Vertical Translation

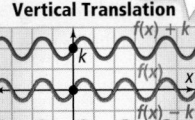

Horizontal Translation

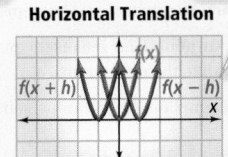

1 Interactive Learning

Solve It!

PURPOSE To determine how changing the y-intercept or slope affects the graph of a line

PROCESS Students may
• realize that if you move the line directly up 1 unit, it will go through (3, 3).
• plot a point at (0, 1) and find the slope of the line that connects (0, 1) and (3, 3).

FACILITATE

Q What happens when you change the y-intercept? **[The line moves up or down.]**

Q How must the graph move to pass through P? How does this affect the y-intercept? **[The graph must move up one unit, so the y-intercept will increase by 1.]**

Q What happens when you change m? **[The line pivots clockwise or counterclockwise on (0, 1).]**

Q What point stays on the line when you change m? **[(0, 1)]**

Q How can you find the new slope? **[Find the slope of the line though (0, 1) and P.]**

ANSWER See Solve It in Answers on next page.

CONNECT THE MATH In the Solve It, students use visual clues to determine how to change a function so that its graph goes through a desired point. The lesson illustrates how changing a function changes the graph of that function and vice versa.

2-6 Preparing to Teach

BIG idea Function

ESSENTIAL UNDERSTANDINGS
• There are sets of functions, called *families*, in which each function is a transformation of a special function called the *parent*.
• A parent function is the simplest form of a set of functions that form a family. Each function in the family is a transformation of the parent function.

Math Background

This lesson shows how to sketch families of functions by performing transformations. The basic, or parent, linear function is $y = x$. The parent quadratic function is $y = x^2$. Learning how to transform these simpler functions will help students later when working with logarithmic and trigonometric functions.

Be aware of students who think all transformations are translations. Translations are a type of transformations. Rigid transformations (also called isometries) do not change the shape, only the location. The three types are translations, reflections, and rotations. Non-rigid transformations include stretches, compressions, and dilations. An example of a stretch is the graph $y = 2x^2$ when compared to the parent graph $y = x^2$.

Mathematical Practices

Look for and make use of structure.
Students will break down various complicated transformations of graphs and functions into simpler basic calculations.

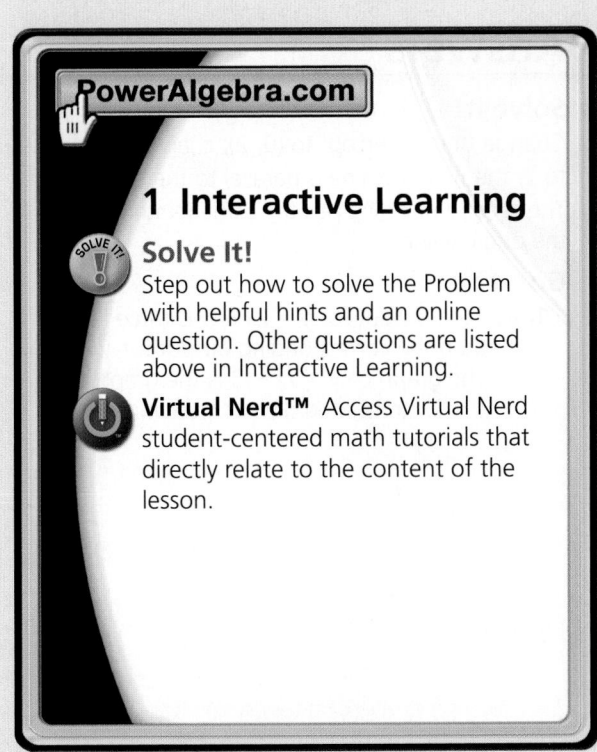

PowerAlgebra.com

1 Interactive Learning

Solve It!
Step out how to solve the Problem with helpful hints and an online question. Other questions are listed above in Interactive Learning.

Virtual Nerd™ Access Virtual Nerd student-centered math tutorials that directly relate to the content of the lesson.

2 Guided Instruction

Problem 1
TACTILE LEARNERS

A translation can be thought of as a slide or shift. Have students lay their pencils on the line $y = x$ and then slide their pencils straight down until they align with $y = x - 2$.

> **Q** How can you determine whether the graph of a function is translated up or down? **[It is translated up when a positive value is added to the function and down when a positive value is subtracted.]**

Got It?

> **Q** How can you tell whether the lines are parallel? **[The slopes are the same.]**
>
> **Q** If you made a table for the functions in 1a, what would you notice? **[Corresponding y-values would differ by 3.]**

Problem 2
SYNTHESIZING

> **Q** What would negative x-values model in this situation? **[the number of hours before noon]**
>
> **Q** How can you determine whether the graph of a function is translated left or right? **[It is translated left when a positive value is added to the input variable and right when a positive value is subtracted from it.]**

Got It?

> **Q** Why is $f(x + 30)$ incorrect? **[Since the scale is in hours, 30 min must be converted to 0.5h.]**

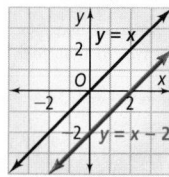 **Problem 1** Vertical Translation

A How are the functions $y = x$ and $y = x - 2$ related? How are their graphs related?

Make a table of values.

x	y = x	y = x − 2
−2	−2	−4
−1	−1	−3
0	0	−2
1	1	−1
2	2	0

Draw their graphs.

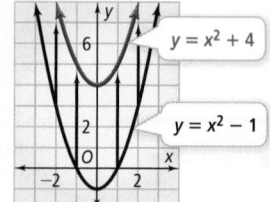

Each output for $y = x - 2$ is two less than the corresponding output for $y = x$.

The graph of $y = x - 2$ is the graph of $y = x$ translated down two units.

B What is the graph of $y = x^2 - 1$ translated up 5 units?

Translate the graph of $y = x^2 - 1$ up 5 units to get the blue parabola. The equation of the blue parabola is $y = x^2 + 4$.

Check Every value in the $y = x^2 + 4$ column is 5 greater than the corresponding value in the $y = x^2 - 1$ column.

x	y = x² − 1	y = x² + 4
−2	3	8
−1	0	5
0	−1	4
1	0	5
2	3	8

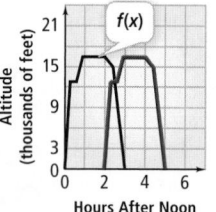

✔ **Got It?** **1. a.** How are the functions $y = 2x$ and $y = 2x - 3$ related? How are their graphs related?
  b. What is the graph of $y = 3x$ translated up 2 units?

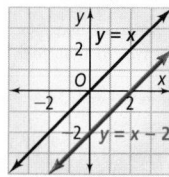 **Problem 2** Horizontal Translation

The graph shows the projected altitude $f(x)$ of an airplane scheduled to depart an airport at noon. If the plane leaves two hours late, what function represents this transformation?

A two-hour delay means the plane leaves at 2 P.M. This shifts the graph to the right 2 units.

The function $f(x - 2)$ represents this transformation.

✔ **Got It?** **2.** Suppose the flight leaves 30 minutes early. What function represents this transformation?

Airplane Altitude

Answers

Solve It!

Change the y-intercept to (0, 2); change the slope to $\frac{2}{3}$; the first new line is parallel to the original line. The second new line has the same y-intercept as the original line.

Got It?

1. a. Each output for $y = 2x - 3$ is three less than the corresponding output for $y = 2x$. The graph of $y = 2x - 3$ is the graph of $y = 2x$ translated down three units.

b.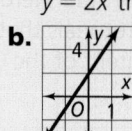

2. $f\left(x + \frac{1}{2}\right)$

3. $h(x) = -3x - 3$

PowerAlgebra.com

2 Guided Instruction

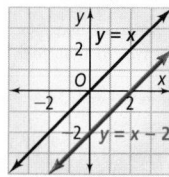 Each Problem is worked out and supported online.

Problem 1
Vertical Translation

Alternative Problem 1
Vertical Translation
Animated

Problem 2
Horizontal Translation

Problem 3
Reflecting a Function Algebraically
Animated

Alternative Problem 3
Reflecting a Function Algebraically

Problem 4
Stretching and Compressing a Function
Animated

Problem 5
Combining Transformations

Support in Algebra 2 Companion
• Vocabulary
• Key Concepts
• Got It?

A **reflection** flips the graph of a function across a line, such as the x- or y-axis. Each point on the graph of the reflected function is the same distance from the line of reflection as its corresponding point on the graph of the original function.

When you reflect a graph in the y-axis, the x-values change signs and the y-values stay the same.

When you reflect a graph in the x-axis, the x-values stay the same and the y-values change signs.

For a function f(x), the reflection in the y-axis is f(−x) and the reflection in the x-axis is −f(x).

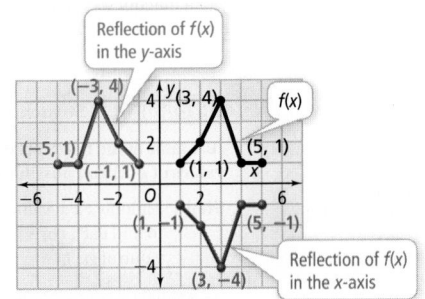
Reflection of f(x) in the y-axis
Reflection of f(x) in the x-axis

Ⓒ **Problem 3** Reflecting a Function Algebraically

Let g(x) be the reflection of f(x) = 3x + 3 in the y-axis. What is a function rule for g(x)?

Think

For a reflection in the y-axis, change the sign of x.

Evaluate f(−x) and simplify.

You can check by graphing f(x) and g(x).

Write

g(x) = f(−x)

g(x) = f(−x)
= 3(−x) + 3
g(x) = −3x + 3

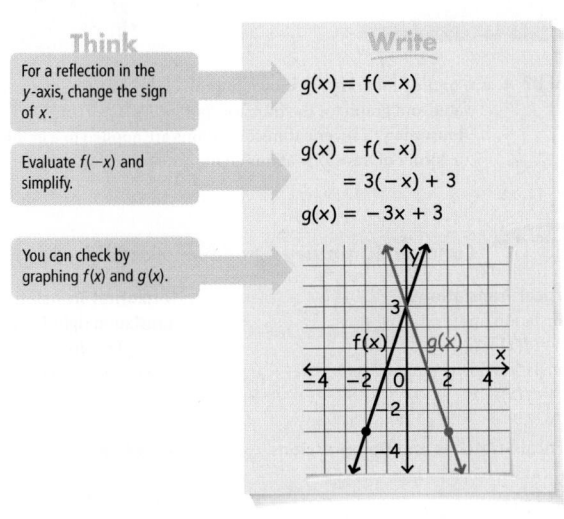

🗸 **Got It?** 3. Let h(x) be the reflection of f(x) = 3x + 3 in the x-axis. What is a function rule for h(x)?

Additional Problems

1. a. How are the functions y = x and y = x + 4 related? How are their graphs related?

b. What is the graph of y = −x² translated down 3 units?

ANSWER

a. Each output for y = x + 4 is 4 more than the corresponding output for y = x. The graph of y = x + 4 is the graph of y = x translated up four units.

b.
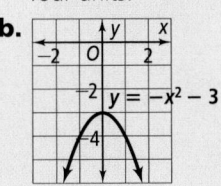

2. The graph shows the distance f(x) you will hike if you leave at 8 A.M. If you leave at 10 A.M., what function represents the transformation?

Hiking Plan
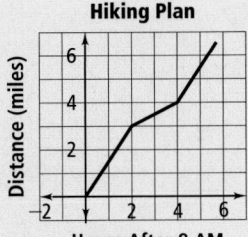
Distance (miles)
Hours After 8 AM

ANSWER f(x − 2)

3. Let g(x) be the reflection of f(x) = 2x − 7 in the x-axis. What is the function rule for g(x)?

ANSWER g(x) = −2x + 7

4. The function f(x) is shown below. What is the graph of h(x) = 0.5 f(x)?

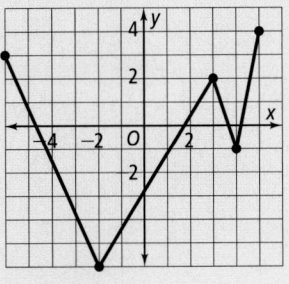

ANSWER
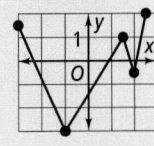

5. a. The function f(x) = 8x. The graph of g(x) is f(x) vertically compressed by a factor of .5 and reflected in the x-axis. What is the function rule for g(x)?

b. What transformations change the graph of f(x) to the graph of g(x)?
f(x) = x³
g(x) = (x + 4)³ − 1

ANSWER

a. g(x) = −4x

b. a horizontal translation left 4 units and a vertical translation down one unit

A vertical stretch pulls away from the *x*-axis. A vertical compression pushes towards the *x*-axis.

Problem 4

Q For which points will the output values for both functions be the same? Why? **[The points that are on the *x*-axis, because the *y*-values are 0, and anything multiplied by 0 is 0.]**

Q How many such points are in this graph? **[3]**

Q Why can you see these points in the graph but not in the table? **[because the table does not include those specific input values]**

Got It?

Q How you could you sketch the graph of *h*(*x*) without making a table of values? **[Draw the same graph $\frac{1}{3}$ the distance from either side of the *x*-axis.]**

Take Note
The option *a* < 0 is not listed for vertical stretches and compressions. This would be the same as a vertical stretch of the absolute value of *a*, followed by a reflection in the *x*-axis.

A **vertical stretch** multiplies all *y*-values of a function by the same factor greater than 1. A **vertical compression** reduces all *y*-values of a function by the same factor between 0 and 1. For a function *f*(*x*) and a constant *a*, *y* = *af*(*x*) is a vertical stretch when *a* > 1 and a vertical compression when 0 < *a* < 1.

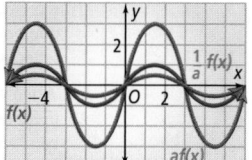

 Problem 4 Stretching and Compressing a Function

The table at the right represents the function *f*(*x*). What are corresponding values of *g*(*x*) and possible graphs for the transformation *g*(*x*) = 3*f*(*x*)?

x	f(x)
−5	2
−2	2
0	−3
3	1
5	−2

Think
Is this a vertical stretch or compression?
3 is greater than 1, so this is a vertical stretch.

Step 1 Multiply each value of *f*(*x*) by 3 to find each corresponding value of *g*(*x*).

x	f(x)	3f(x)	g(x)
−5	2	3(2)	6
−2	2	3(2)	6
0	−3	3(−3)	−9
3	1	3(1)	3
5	−2	3(−2)	−6

Step 2 Use the values from the table in Step 1. Draw simple graphs for *f*(*x*) and *g*(*x*).

Got It? 4. a. For the function *f*(*x*) shown in Problem 4, what are the corresponding table and graph for the transformation *h*(*x*) = $\frac{1}{3}$*f*(*x*)?

b. Reasoning If several transformations are applied to a graph, will changing the order of transformations change the resulting graph? Explain.

Concept Summary   Transformations of *f*(*x*)

Vertical Translations
Translation up *k* units, *k* > 0
  y = *f*(*x*) + *k*
Translation down *k* units, *k* > 0
  y = *f*(*x*) − *k*

Horizontal Translations
Translation right *h* units, *h* > 0
  y = *f*(*x* − *h*)
Translation left *h* units, *h* > 0
  y = *f*(*x* + *h*)

Vertical Stretches and Compressions
Vertical stretch, *a* > 1
  y = *a f*(*x*)
Vertical compression, 0 < *a* < 1
  y = *a f*(*x*)

Reflections
In the *x*-axis
  y = −*f*(*x*)
In the *y*-axis
  y = *f*(−*x*)

Answers

Got It? (continued)
4. a.

x	y
−5	$\frac{2}{3}$
−2	$\frac{2}{3}$
0	−1
3	$\frac{1}{3}$
5	−$\frac{2}{3}$

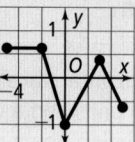

b. Sometimes; answers may vary. Sample: switching the order of a horizontal translation and a reflection in the *y*-axis will change the resulting graph, but switching the order of a horizontal and vert. translation will not.

Problem 5 **Combining Transformations**

A The graph of $g(x)$ is the graph of $f(x) = 4x$ compressed vertically by the factor $\frac{1}{2}$ and then reflected in the y-axis. What is a function rule for $g(x)$?

$\frac{1}{2}(4x) = 2x$ Compress $f(x)$.

$2(-x) = -2x$ Reflect the new function in the y-axis.

The function rule is $g(x) = -2x$.

B What transformations change the graph of $f(x)$ to the graph of $g(x)$?

$f(x) = 2x^2$ $g(x) = 6x^2 - 1$

$g(x) = 6x^2 - 1$

$\quad = 3(2x^2) - 1$

$\quad = 3(f(x)) - 1$

The graph of $g(x)$ is the graph of $f(x)$ stretched vertically by a factor of 3 and then translated down 1 unit.

Think

How can you write $g(x)$ in terms of $f(x)$?
Factor out 3 from the $6x^2$ term.

 Got It? 5. a. The graph of $g(x)$ is the graph of $f(x) = x$ stretched vertically by a factor of 2 and then translated down 3 units. What is the function rule for $g(x)$?

b. What transformations change the graph of $f(x) = x^2$ to the graph of $g(x) = (x + 4)^2 - 2$?

Lesson Check

Do you know HOW?

Describe the transformation of the parent function $f(x)$.

1. $g(x) = f(x) + 6$ **2.** $h(x) = 0.25f(x)$

3. $j(x) = f(x - 4)$ **4.** $k(x) = f(-x)$

The graph of $f(x) = -2x$ is shown. Describe and graph each transformation.

5. $g(x) = f(x + 1) - 2$

6. $h(x) = 2f(x) + 1$

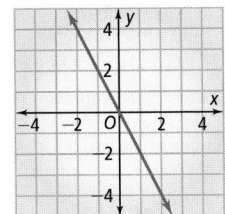

Do you UNDERSTAND?  MATHEMATICAL PRACTICES

 **7. Compare and Contrast** The graph shows $f(x) = 0.5x - 1$.

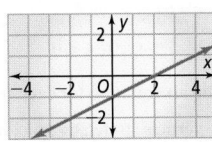

Graph $g(x)$ by translating $f(x)$ up 2 units and then stretching it vertically by the factor 2. Graph $h(x)$ by stretching $f(x)$ vertically by the factor 2 and then translating it up 2 units. Compare the graphs of $g(x)$ and $h(x)$.

 8. Reasoning Can you give an example of a function for which a horizontal translation gives the same resulting graph as a vertical translation? Explain.

9. Find a new function $g(x)$ transformed from $f(x) = -x - 2$ such that $g(x)$ is perpendicular to $f(x)$.

Problem 5

Q What are the values of a and h in the function $g(x)$ in 5A? **[−2 and 0]**

Got It?

Q Without first finding the function rule, what are the values of a and k in the function $g(x)$ in 3a? **[2, −3]**

3 Lesson Check

Do you know HOW?   ERROR INTERVENTION

• For Exercise 3, if students describe the transformation as a horizontal translation left, show an alternate rule, which fits the mental match of positive/right and negative/left: for $f(x - h)$, h moves left when h is negative (show the double negative becoming a positive) and right when h is positive.

Do you UNDERSTAND?

• For Exercise 9, slopes of perpendicular lines are opposite reciprocals. Refer to the Take Note chart to help determine what transformations need to be performed.

Close

Q In which transformations are you changing the input values? **[horizontal translations and reflections in the y-axis]**

Q In which transformations are you changing the output values? **[vertical translations, reflections in the x-axis, and vertical stretches and compressions]**

---

5. a. $g(x) = 2x - 3$

b. $g(x) = f(x + 4) - 2$; translated left 4 units and translated down 2 units

Lesson Check

1. translated 6 units up

2. compressed vertically by a factor of 0.25

3. translated 4 units to the rt.

4. reflected over y-axis

5. translated 1 unit to the left and 2 units down

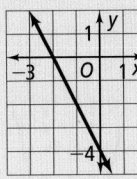

6. stretched vertically by a factor of 2 and translated 1 unit up

7. $g(x)$ is the graph of $h(x)$ translated 2 units up

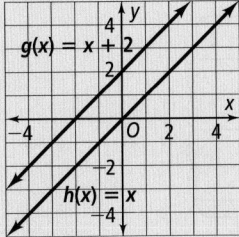

8. Answers may vary. Sample: $f(x) = x$, $f(x - 2) = f(x) - 2$

9. $f(x) = -x - 2$; $g(x) = f(-x) = x - 2$

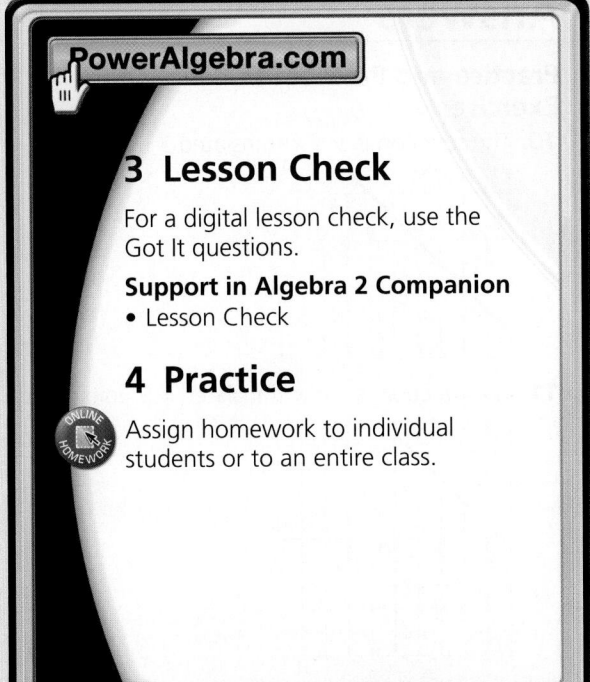

PowerAlgebra.com

3 Lesson Check

For a digital lesson check, use the Got It questions.

Support in Algebra 2 Companion
• Lesson Check

4 Practice

Assign homework to individual students or to an entire class.

4 Practice

ASSIGNMENT GUIDE

Basic: 10–33 all, 34–39, 44, 45

Average: 11–33 odd, 34–45

Advanced: 11–33 odd, 34–50

Standardized Test Prep: 51–54

Mixed Review: 55–58

Mathematical Practices are supported by exercises with red headings. Here are the Practices supported in this lesson:

MP 1: Make Sense of Problems Ex. 34

MP 3: Communicate Ex. 39, 40

MP 3: Construct Arguments Ex. 7, 8

MP 3: Critique the Reasoning of Others Ex. 45

Applications exercises have blue headings.

EXERCISE 35: Use the Think About a Plan worksheet in the **Practice and Problem Solving Workbook** (also available in the Teaching Resources in print and online) to further support students' development in becoming independent learners.

HOMEWORK QUICK CHECK

To check students' understanding of key skills and concepts, go over Exercises 17, 33, 34, 35, and 45.

Practice and Problem-Solving Exercises MATHEMATICAL PRACTICES

A Practice How is each function related to $y = x$? Graph the function by translating the parent function. ◀ See Problem 1.

10. $y = x - 3$　　**11.** $y = x + 4.5$　　**12.** $y = x + 1.5$

Make a table of values for $f(x)$ after the given translation.

13. 3 units up

x	f(x)
−2	3
0	1
1	−2
3	−1

14. 1 unit down

x	f(x)
−1	1
0	0
2	−4
3	2

15. 4 units up

x	f(x)
−3	1
−1	−2
1	0
4	3

Write an equation for each vertical translation of $y = f(x)$.

16. $\frac{2}{3}$ unit down　　**17.** 4 units up　　**18.** 2 units up

For each function, identify the horizontal translation of the parent function, $f(x) = x^2$. Then graph the function. ◀ See Problems 2 and 3.

19. $y = (x - 4)^2$　　**20.** $y = (x + 1)^2$　　**21.** $y = (x + 3)^2$

22. The graph of the function $f(x)$ is shown at the right.
　　a. Make a table of values for $f(x)$ and $f(x + 3)$.
　　b. Graph $f(x)$ and $f(x + 3)$ on the same coordinate grid.

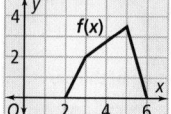

Write the function rule for each function reflected in the given axis.

23. $f(x) = x + 1$; x-axis　　**24.** $f(x) = 3x$; y-axis　　**25.** $f(x) = 2x - 4$; x-axis

Write an equation for each transformation of $y = x$. ◀ See Problem 4.

26. vertical stretch by a factor of 4　　**27.** vertical stretch by a factor of 2

28. vertical compression by a factor of $\frac{1}{2}$　　**29.** vertical compression by a factor of $\frac{1}{4}$

Write the function rule $g(x)$ after the given transformations of the graph of $f(x) = 4x$. ◀ See Problem 5.

30. translation up 5 units; reflection in the x-axis

31. reflection in the y-axis; vertical compression by a factor of $\frac{1}{8}$

Describe the transformations of $f(x)$ that produce $g(x)$.

32. $f(x) = \frac{x}{2}$; $g(x) = -2x + 4$　　　**33.** $f(x) = 3x$; $g(x) = \left(\frac{3x}{4} - 2\right)$

Answers

Practice and Problem-Solving Exercises

10. The function is $y = x$ translated 3 units down.

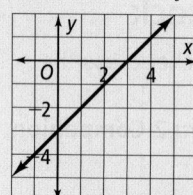

11. The function is $y = x$ translated 4.5 units up.

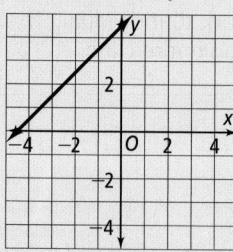

12. The function is $y = x$ translated 1.5 units up.

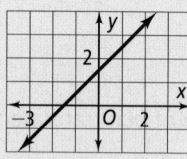

13.

x	f(x) + 3
−2	6
0	4
1	1
3	2

14.

x	f(x) − 1
−1	0
0	−1
2	−5
3	1

15.

x	f(x) + 4
−3	5
−1	2
1	4
4	7

16. $y = f(x) - \frac{2}{3}$

17. $y = f(x) + 4$　　**18.** $y = f(x) + 2$

19. translated rt. 4 units

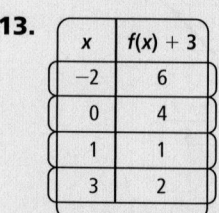 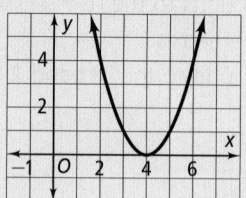

20. translated left 1 unit

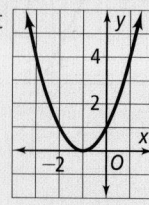

Ⓒ **34. Think About a Plan** Suppose you are playing with a yo-yo during a school talent show. The string is 3 ft long and you hold your hand 4 ft above the stage. The stage is 3.5 ft above the floor of the auditorium. Make a graph of the yo-yo's distance from the auditorium floor with respect to time during the show.
• How could you graph the position of the yo-yo with respect to the stage, if you let time $t = 0$ when you start your routine?
• How could you transform this graph to show the position with respect to the auditorium floor?

35. If someone started to take a video of your yo-yo routine when you were introduced, 10 seconds before you actually started, what transformation would you have to make to your graph to match their video?

Write the equations for $f(x)$ and $g(x)$. Then identify the reflection that transforms the graph of $f(x)$ to the graph of $g(x)$.

36. 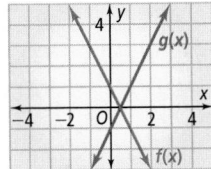   **37.** 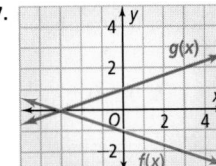   **38.**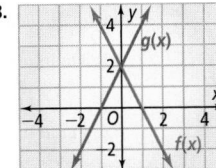

Ⓒ **39. Open-Ended** Draw a figure in Quadrant I. Use a translation to move your figure into Quadrant III. Describe your translation.

Ⓒ **40. Writing** The graph of $f(x)$ is shown at the right. Suppose each transformation of $f(x)$ results in the given functions.
   i. vertical translation; $g(x)$
   ii. reflection in the x-axis; $h(x)$
   iii. vertical stretch; $k(x)$,
   iv. horizontal translation; $m(x)$
   a. Describe how the domain and range of the four new functions compare with the domain and range of $f(x)$.
Ⓒ **b. Reasoning** Do you think these effects on the domain and range of the original function hold true for all functions? Explain.

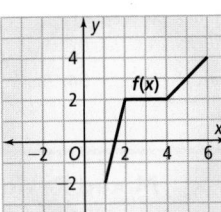

Graph each pair of functions on the same coordinate plane. Describe a transformation that changes $f(x)$ to $g(x)$.

41. $f(x) = x + 1; g(x) = x - 5$

42. $f(x) = -x + 3; g(x) = x - 4$

43. $f(x) = x - 3; g(x) = x + 1$

44. $f(x) = -x - 1; g(x) = -x + 2$

Ⓒ **45. Error Analysis** Your friend wrote the transformations shown to describe how to change the graph of $f(x) = x^2$ to the graph of $g(x) = 2(x + 1)^2 - 3$. Explain the error and give the correct transformations.

• ~~shift vertically 1 unit up~~
• ~~shift horizontally 2 units right~~
• ~~shift vertically 3 units down~~

21. translated left 3 units

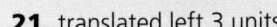
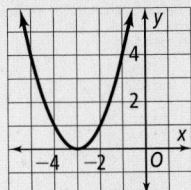

22. a.

x	$f(x)$
2	0
3	2
5	3.5
6	0

x	$f(x + 3)$
-1	0
0	2
2	3.5
3	0

b.

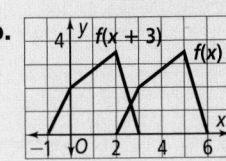

23. $g(x) = -x - 1$ **24.** $g(x) = -3x$
25. $g(x) = -2x + 4$ **26.** $y = 4x$

27. $y = 2x$ **28.** $y = \frac{1}{2}x$
29. $y = \frac{1}{4}x$ **30.** $g(x) = -4x - 5$
31. $g(x) = -0.5x$
32. vertically stretched by a factor of 4, reflected over the x-axis, and translated up 4 units
33. vertically compressed by a factor of $\frac{1}{4}$ and translated down 2 units

34.

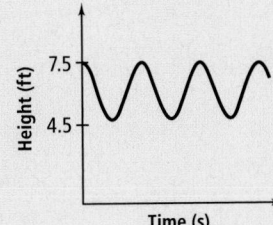

35. translate to the right 10 s
36. $f(x) = -2x + 1; g(x) = 2x - 1;$ $g(x) = -f(x)$

37. $f(x) = -\frac{1}{3}x - 1; g(x) = \frac{1}{3}x + 1;$ $g(x) = -f(x)$

38. $f(x) = -2x + 2; g(x) = 2x + 2; g(x) = f(-x)$
39. Check students' work.
40. a. The functions $g(x)$, $h(x)$, and $k(x)$ have the same domain as the function $f(x)$, but different ranges, and the function $m(x)$ has the same range as $f(x)$ but a different domain.

b. Yes; the transformations in (i), (ii), and (iii) affect only the vert. position of a function, which determines the range. The transformation in (iv) affects only the horizontal position, which determines the domain.

41. translated 6 units down

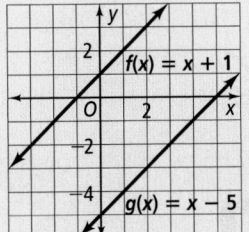

42. translated 7 units down, then reflected over the y-axis; or reflected over the x-axis, then translated 1 unit down

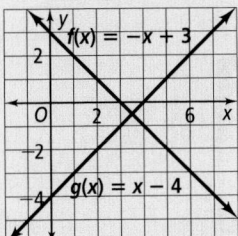

43. translated 4 units up

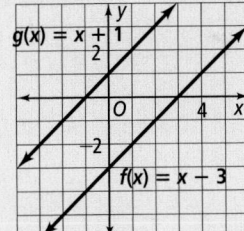

44. translated 3 units up

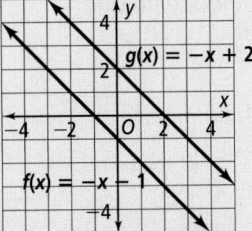

45. The first two steps are incorrect; the transformations should be: shift 1 unit left, vertically stretch by a factor of 2, and shift 3 units down.

Answers

Practice and Problem-Solving Exercises (continued)

46.

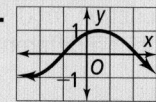

47.

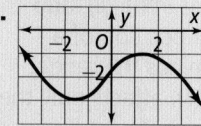

48.

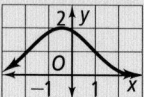

49.

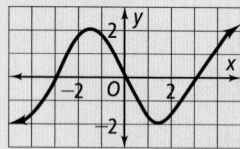

50.

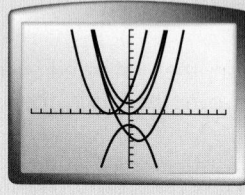

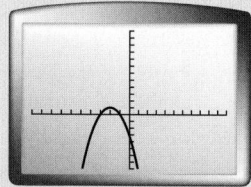

Standardized Test Prep

51. D

52. F

53. A

54. [2] $y = kx$

$772 = k\,(40)$

$19.3 = k$

$y = (19.3)(100)$

$y = 1930\ g$

[1] appropriate method, with one computational error

Mixed Review

55. $y = -15.82x + 914.59$

56. $-2, 8$

57. $-12, 11$

58. $-3, \dfrac{21}{5}$

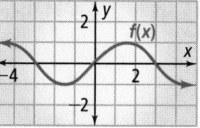

46. $f(x + 1)$

47. $f(x) - 2$

48. $f(x + 2) + 1$

49. $-2f(x)$

50. Graph all of the following functions in the same viewing window. After you enter each new function, view its graph.

    i. $y = x^2$ ii. $y = x^2 + 2$ iii. $y = (x + 2)^2$ iv. $y = (x - 1)^2 - 4$ v. $y = -x^2 - 2$

Based on your results, make a sketch of the graph of $f(x) = -(x + 2)^2 + 1$ and check your prediction on your calculator.

Standardized Test Prep

SAT/ACT

What is an equation for each vertical translation of $y = 2x - 1$?

51. 3 units down

  Ⓐ $y = 2x - 7$ Ⓑ $y = 2x + 2$ Ⓒ $y = 2x + 5$ Ⓓ $y = 2x - 4$

52. $\dfrac{3}{5}$ units up

  Ⓕ $y = 2x - \dfrac{2}{5}$ Ⓖ $y = 2x - \dfrac{11}{5}$ Ⓗ $y = 2x - \dfrac{8}{5}$ Ⓘ $y = 2x + \dfrac{1}{5}$

53. What is the slope of the line in the graph at the right?

  Ⓐ $-\dfrac{5}{2}$ Ⓒ $\dfrac{2}{5}$

  Ⓑ $-\dfrac{2}{5}$ Ⓓ $\dfrac{5}{2}$

Short Response

54. The weight of a gold bar varies directly with its volume. If a 40 cm³ bar weighs 772 grams, how much will a 100 cm³ bar weigh?

Mixed Review

55. A musician's manager keeps track of the ticket prices and the attendance at recent performances. Use a graphing calculator to determine the equation of the line of best fit for the given data.   ◀ **See Lesson 2-5.**

Ticket Prices($)	41.00	41.50	42.00	43.00	43.50	44.00	44.50	45.00	45.00	47.00
Number Sold	256	276	250	241	210	235	195	194	205	180

Get Ready!   **To prepare for Lesson 2-7, do Exercises 56–58.**

Solve each absolute value equation.   ◀ **See Lesson 1-6.**

56. $|x - 3| + 2 = 7$ **57.** $|2x + 1| - 14 = 9$ **58.** $\dfrac{1}{3}|5x - 3| = 6$

Differentiated Remediation

Available in editable format online.

Additional Instructional Support

Algebra 2 Companion

Students can use the **Algebra 2 Companion** worktext (4 pages) as you teach the lesson. Use the Companion to support

- New Vocabulary
- Key Concepts
- Got It for each Problem
- Lesson Check

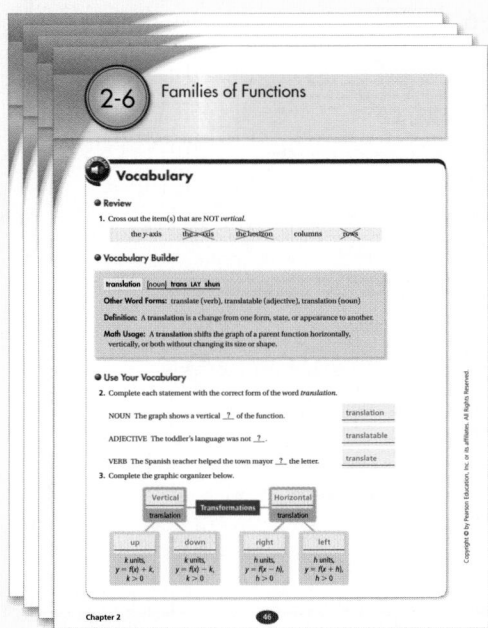

ELL Support

Use Graphic Organizers Make a table that connects the different ways of describing transformations. Headings could be Words, Geometry, Graphs, and Functions. Students can identify a transformation in words and then describe it the remaining three ways. For example,

- Words: translate right 2 units
- Geometry: graph of the points (x, y) and $(x + 2, y)$
- Graph: graph of two parabolas, one 2 units to the right of the other
- Function: $f(x) = x^2$ and $g(x) = (x - 2)^2$

5 Assess & Remediate

Lesson Quiz

1. How are the functions $y = 2x^2$ and $y = 2x^2 + 7$ related? How are their graphs related?

2. **Do you UNDERSTAND?** The graph shows how many words you have written for a paper. What function models the progress if you had begun an hour earlier?

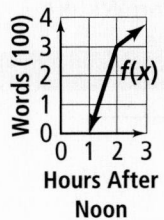

Hours After Noon

3. Let $g(x)$ be the reflection of $f(x) = -4x - 1$ in the x-axis. What is a function rule for $g(x)$?

4. What transformations change the graph of $f(x) = -x$ to the graph of $g(x) = -0.1(x - 6)$?

ANSWERS TO LESSON QUIZ

1. Each output for $y = 2x^2 + 7$ is 7 greater than the corresponding output of $y = 2x^2$. The graph of $y = 2x^2 + 7$ is the graph of $y = 2x^2$ translated up 7 units.

2. $f(x + 1)$

3. $g(x) = 4x + 1$

4. vertical compression by a factor of 0.1 and a horizontal translation 6 units right

PRESCRIPTION FOR REMEDIATION

Use the student work on the Lesson Quiz to prescribe a differentiated review assignment:

Points	Differentiated Remediation
0–2	Intervention
3	On-level
4	Extension

Intervention

- **Reteaching** (2 pages) Provides reteaching and practice exercises for the key lesson concepts. Use with struggling students or absent students.

- **English Language Learner Support** Helps students develop and reinforce mathematical vocabulary and key concepts.

All-in-One Resources/Online
Reteaching

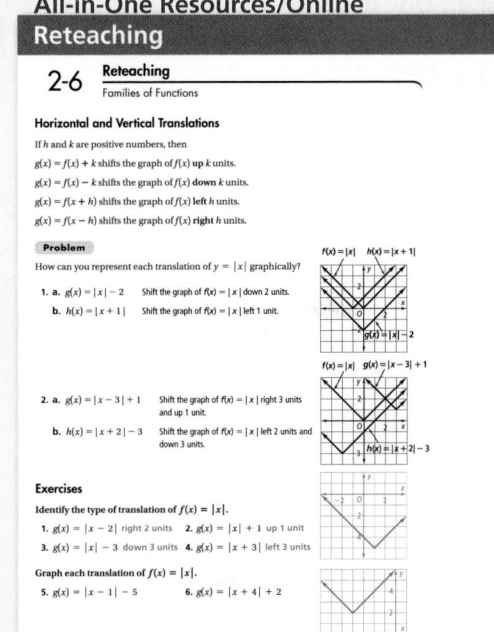

All-in-One Resources/Online
English Language Learner Support

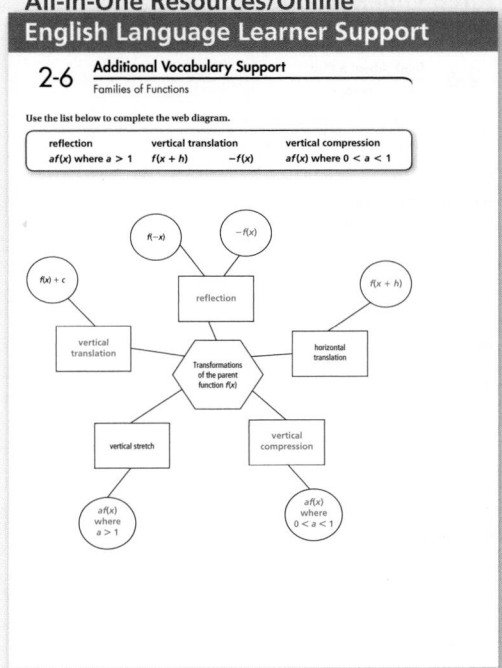

Differentiated Remediation _continued_

Available in editable format online.

On-Level

- **Practice** (2 pages) Provides extra practice for each lesson. For simpler practice exercises, use the Form K Practice pages found in the All-in-One Teaching Resources and online.

- **Think About a Plan** Helps students develop specific problem-solving skills and strategies by providing scaffolded guiding questions.

- **Standardized Test Prep** Focuses on all major exercises, all major question types, and helps students prepare for the high-stakes assessments.

Extension

- **Enrichment** Provides students with interesting problems and activities that extend the concepts of the lesson.

- **Activities, Games, and Puzzles** Worksheets that can be used for concepts development, enrichment, and for fun!

Practice and Problem Solving Wkbk/ All-in-One Resources/Online
Practice page 1

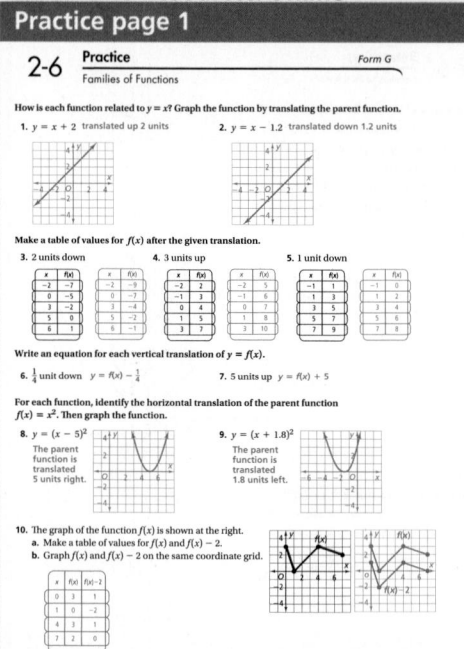

Practice and Problem Solving Wkbk/ All-in-One Resources/Online
Practice page 2

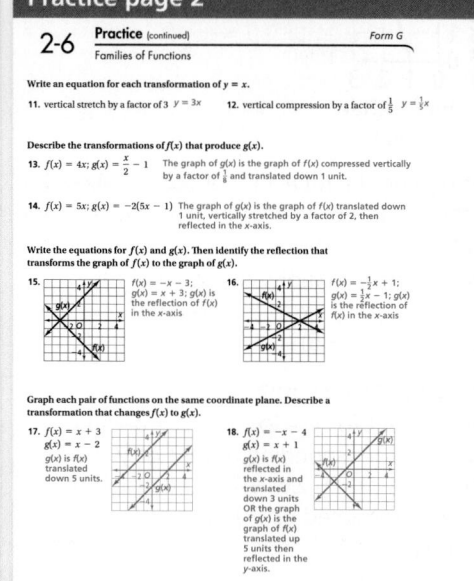

All-in-One Resources/Online
Enrichment

Practice and Problem Solving Wkbk/ All-in-One Resources/Online
Think About a Plan

Practice and Problem Solving Wkbk/ All-in-One Resources/Online
Standardized Test Prep

Online Teacher Resource Center
Activities, Games, and Puzzles

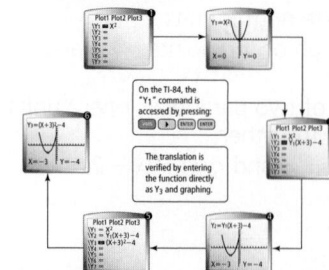

2-7 Absolute Value Functions and Graphs

Common Core State Standards
F-BF.B.3 Identify the effect on the graph of replacing $f(x)$ by $f(x) + k$, $k\,f(x)$, $f(kx)$, and $f(x + k)$ for specific values of k . . . find the value of k given the graphs. **Also** F-IF.C.7b
MP 1, MP 3, MP 5

Objective To graph absolute value functions

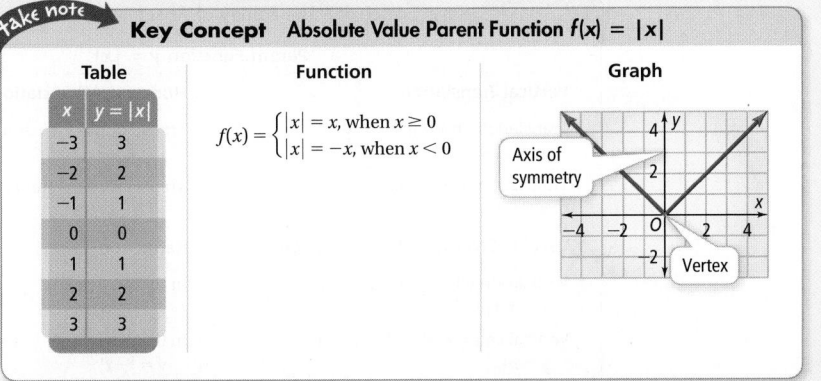

Getting Ready!

You jog at a constant speed. Your jogging route takes you across the county line. Suppose you graph your distance from the county line with respect to time. What would the graph look like? Explain.

ENTERING Jefferson County

> **Think about how the distance changes before and after you cross the county line. Can a distance ever be negative?**

MATHEMATICAL PRACTICES

There is a family of functions related to the one you represented in the Solve It.

Essential Understanding Just as the absolute value of x is its distance from 0, the absolute value of $f(x)$, or $|f(x)|$, gives the distance from the line $y = 0$ for each value of $f(x)$.

The simplest example of an **absolute value function** is $f(x) = |x|$. The graph of the absolute value of a linear function in two variables is V-shaped and symmetric about a vertical line called the **axis of symmetry**. Such a graph has either a single maximum point or a single minimum point, called the **vertex**.

Lesson Vocabulary
• absolute value function
• axis of symmetry
• vertex

take note

Key Concept   Absolute Value Parent Function $f(x) = |x|$

Table	Function	Graph

Table

x	$y = \lvert x \rvert$
−3	3
−2	2
−1	1
0	0
1	1
2	2
3	3

Function

$$f(x) = \begin{cases} |x| = x, & \text{when } x \geq 0 \\ |x| = -x, & \text{when } x < 0 \end{cases}$$

Graph

Axis of symmetry

Vertex

---

1 Interactive Learning

Solve It!

PURPOSE To represent a physical situation with an absolute value graph

PROCESS Students may try assigning arbitrary numerical values or realize the graph has two linear parts.

FACILITATE

Q Where do you start? Explain. **[(0, p); the time starts at $x = 0$, when you are a positive distance p from the county line.]**

Q Is the slope from (0, p) to (q, 0) positive or negative? Explain. **[Negative; the distance between you and the county line is decreasing.]**

Q Assume the x-intercept is (q, 0). What does this point mean in terms of the problem situation? **[This is when you reach the county line.]**

Q Is the slope from (q, 0) rightward positive or negative? Explain. **[Positive; the distance between you and the county line is increasing.]**

Q Is this graph symmetric? If so, where is the axis of symmetry? Explain. **[Yes; since you are jogging at a constant speed, $x = q$, where q is the time at which you get to the county line.]**

ANSWER See Solve It in Answers on next page.
CONNECT THE MATH The Solve It models an absolute value graph in a realistic situation. In the lesson, students will identify different parts of absolute value graphs and graph transformations of the absolute value parent function.

2 Guided Instruction

Take Note
Absolute value graphs are not linear. They are, however, composed of two linear parts.

2-7 Preparing to Teach

BIG idea Function
ESSENTIAL UNDERSTANDINGS
• Just as the absolute value of x is its distance from 0, the absolute value of $f(x)$, or $|f(x)|$, gives the distance from the line $y = 0$ for each value of $f(x)$.
• The simplest example of an absolute value function is $f(x) = |x|$.
• The values of a, b, and k, in the form $y = a|x - h| + k$ determine how the parent function $y = |x|$ can be transformed.

Math Background
Students can apply translations, stretches, compressions, and reflections to any parent function $f(x)$. The absolute value function is a particularly good parent function to use for these transformations since it has an easily recognizable V shape.

This lesson discusses vertical stretches and compressions (those in which all y-coordinates are multiplied by a common factor). You may also wish to have students explore horizontal stretches and compressions (those in which the x-coordinates are multiplied by a common factor). Making tables of ordered pairs can help students analyze the effects of the transformations on each coordinate.

Mathematical Practices
Make sense of problems and persevere in solving them. In Problem 2, students will make conjectures about the form of an absolute value function and its graph, focusing on basic translations.

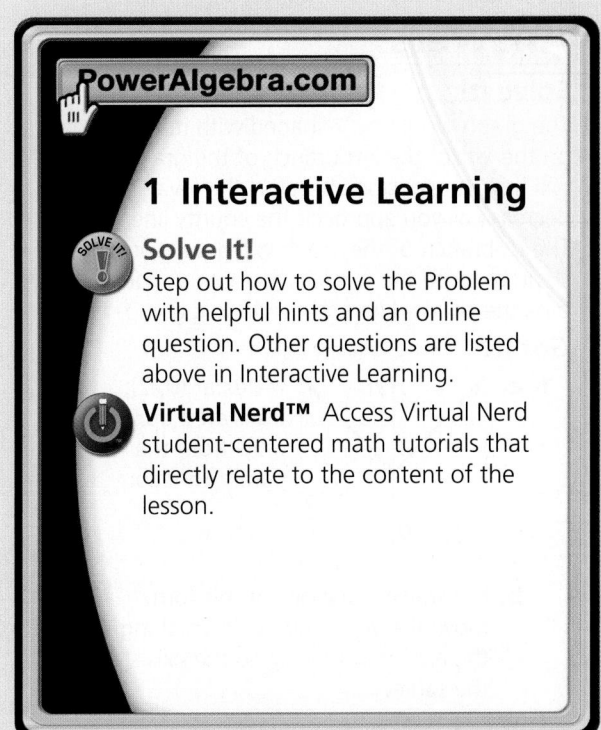

PowerAlgebra.com

1 Interactive Learning

Solve It!
Step out how to solve the Problem with helpful hints and an online question. Other questions are listed above in Interactive Learning.

Virtual Nerd™ Access Virtual Nerd student-centered math tutorials that directly relate to the content of the lesson.

Problem 1

Q What part of the graph is part of the line $y = x - 4$? of the line $y = -x - 4$? **[the part to the right of the *y*-axis; the part to the left of the *y*-axis]**

Q As the parent function $y = |x|$ is translated 4 units down, what happens to the *y*-coordinate of the vertex? to the *x*-coordinate? **[It changes from 0 to −4; it stays the same.]**

Q Why can the graph of an absolute value function have more than one *x*-intercept? **[There can be two different values for *x* that will make *y* equal 0.]**

Got It?   VISUAL LEARNERS

Some students may not be able to compare the graph with the parent function unless they draw both graphs on the same grid. Have them use different colors to distinguish the functions clearly.

Q What kinds of transformations affect the axis of symmetry? **[Transformations that change the *x*-value of the vertex, such as a horizontal translation, change the axis of symmetry.]**

Take Note

Sketch examples of the graphs for $k = 2$ and -2, $h = 2$ and -2, and $a = 2$, -2, $\frac{1}{2}$ and $-\frac{1}{2}$.

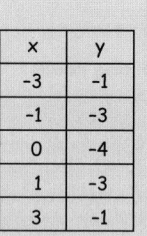 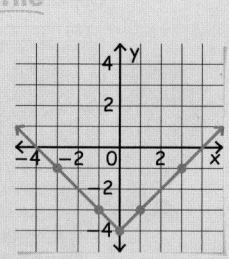

Problem 1 Graphing an Absolute Value Function

What is the graph of the absolute value function $y = |x| - 4$? How is this graph different from the graph of the parent function $f(x) = |x|$?

Think

Make a table of values and graph the function.

x	y
-3	-1
-1	-3
0	-4
1	-3
3	-1

Write

Use the location of the vertex to see how the graph has been translated. The parent function was not multiplied by a number, so the graph wasn't stretched, compressed, or reflected.

Since the vertex is at $(0, -4)$, you translated the graph of $y = |x|$ down 4 units.

 Got It? 1. a. What is the graph of the function $y = |x| + 2$? How is this graph different from the parent function?
b. Reasoning Do transformations of the form $y = |x| + k$ affect the axis of symmetry? Explain.

The transformations you studied in Lesson 2-6 also apply to absolute value functions.

take note

Key Concept The Family of Absolute Value Functions

Parent Function $y = |x|$

Vertical Translation	**Horizontal Translation**
Translation up k units, $k > 0$ $y = |x| + k$	Translation right h units, $h > 0$ $y = |x - h|$
Translation down k units, $k > 0$ $y = |x| - k$	Translation left h units, $h > 0$ $y = |x + h|$
Vertical Stretch and Compression	**Reflection**
Vertical stretch, $a > 1$ $y = a|x|$	In the *x*-axis $y = -|x|$
Vertical compression, $0 < a < 1$ $y = a|x|$	In the *y*-axis $y = |-x|$

Answers

Solve It!

The graph would be V-shaped with its vertex on the *x*-axis: the left branch of the graph will have a neg. slope because the *y*-values decrease as you approach the county line. The rt. branch of the graph will have a pos. slope because the *y*-values increase as you pass the county line and continue jogging.

Got It?

1. a. 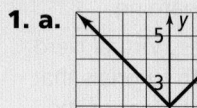 vertex at (0, 2); translated up 2 units from the parent function

b. No; transformations of this form move the vertex up or down along the axis of symmetry, so the axis stays the same.

PowerAlgebra.com

2 Guided Instruction

Each Problem is worked out and supported online.

Problem 1
Graphing an Absolute Value Function

Problem 2
Combining Translations

Alternative Problem 2
Combining Translations Animated
Animated

Problem 3
Vertical Stretch and Compression
Animated

Problem 4
Identifying Transformations

Problem 5
Writing an Absolute Value Function
Animated

Support in Algebra 2 Companion
• Vocabulary
• Key Concepts
• Got It?

Problem 2 Combining Translations

Multiple Choice Which of the following is the graph of $y = |x + 2| + 3$?

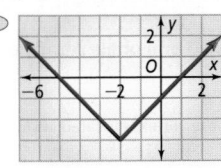
Ⓐ

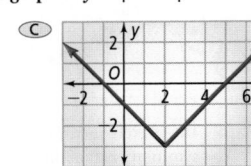
Ⓒ

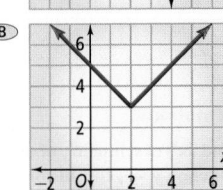
Ⓑ

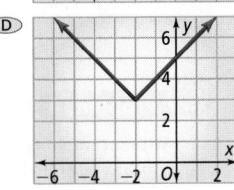
Ⓓ

Think

Can you eliminate any answers after this comparison?
Only choices A and D show translations of $y = |x|$ to the left.

Compare $y = |x + 2| + 3$ to each form, $y = |x + h|$ and $y = |x| + k$.

$y = |x + h|$ The parent function, $y = |x|$, is translated left 2 units.

$y = |x| + k$ The parent function, $y = |x|$, is translated up 3 units.

The parent function $y = |x|$ is translated left 2 units and up 3 units. The vertex will be at $(-2, 3)$. The correct choice is D.

✓ Got It? 2. What is the graph of the function $y = |x - 2| + 1$?

The right branch of the graph of $y = |x|$ has slope 1. The graph of $y = a|x|$, $a > 0$, is a stretch or compression of the graph of $y = |x|$. Its right branch has slope a. The graph of $y = -a|x|$ is a reflection of $y = a|x|$ in the x-axis and its right branch has slope $-a$.

Problem 3 Vertical Stretch and Compression

What is the graph of $y = \frac{1}{2}|x|$?

The graph is a vertical compression of the graph of $f(x) = |x|$ by the factor $\frac{1}{2}$. Graph the right branch and use symmetry to graph the left branch.

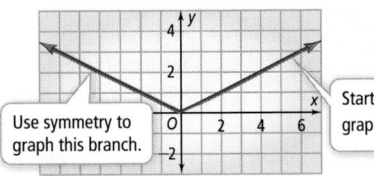

Use symmetry to graph this branch.

Starting at $(0, 0)$, graph $y = \frac{1}{2}x$.

✓ Got It? 3. What is the graph of each function?
  a. $y = 2|x|$ **b.** $y = -\frac{2}{3}|x|$

Problem 2

Q What absolute value functions are shown in the other three graphs? **[A: $y = |x + 2| - 3$; B: $y = |x - 2| + 3$; C: $y = |x - 2| - 3$]**

Got It? SYNTHESIZING

Q Does the order in which you identify the vertical and horizontal translations matter? Explain. **[No; answers may vary. Sample: As long as you correctly identify the vertical change as the y-coordinate of the vertex and the horizontal change as the x-coordinate, the order in which you identify them is not important.]**

Problem 3

Q How are the equations $y = |x|$ and $y = \frac{1}{2}|x|$ different? **[In the second equation, the absolute value term is multiplied by $\frac{1}{2}$.]**

Q What is the difference between a vertical stretch and a vertical compression? **[In a stretch, each y-coordinate is multiplied by a number whose value is greater than 1. In a compression, the value of the factor is between 0 and 1.]**

Got It? SYNTHESIZING

Q What characteristic of the equation results in the V shape opening downward? **[when the sign of the coefficient of the absolute value term is negative]**

Additional Problems

1. What is the graph of the absolute value function $y = |x| + 3$? How is this graph different from the parent function $f(x) = |x|$?

ANSWER It is translated up 3 units.

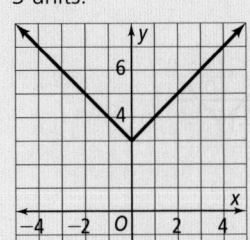

2. Which of the following is the graph of $y = |x + 3| - 1$?

a.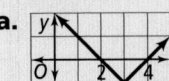

b.

c.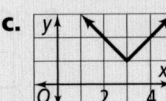

d.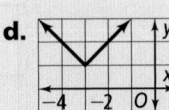

ANSWER b

3. What is the graph of $y = -\frac{1}{4}|x|$? What are the transformations of the parent function?

ANSWER Vertical compression by the factor $\frac{1}{4}$ and reflection in the x-axis.

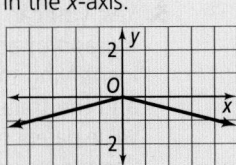

4. Compare $y = -2|x + 2| + 3$ with the parent function. Without graphing, what are the vertex, axis of symmetry, and transformations of the parent function?

ANSWER vertex $(-2, 3)$; axis of symmetry $x = -2$; translated 2 units left, vertically stretched by the factor 2, reflected in x-axis and translated 3 units up

5. What is the equation of the absolute value function?

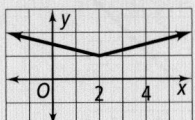

ANSWER $y = \frac{1}{4}|x - 2| + 1$

Got It 2–3. See next page.

Take Note

An absolute value function of the form $a|x| + k$, with no horizontal translation, is not changed by being reflected in the y-axis.

Problem 4

Q Can the y-value of this function ever be less than 4? Explain. **[No; the minimum value of $3|x - 2|$ is 0 because the absolute value factor can never be negative, so the minimum value of $3|x - 2| + 4$ is 4.]**

Q Describe the y-coordinates of two points that are an equal distance from the axis of symmetry. **[The y-coordinates are equal.]**

Got It?   ERROR PREVENTION

Make sure students use order of operations when describing order of transformations to avoid unintentionally changing the vertex.

Problem 5

Q What is the slope of the right branch of the graph in terms of the function? **[the stretch or compression factor a]**

Q What is the vertex in terms of the function? **[(h, k)]**

Q Does it matter in what order you perform the steps of this solution? Explain. **[Sample: No; you could find the slope of the right branch and the coordinates of the vertex in either order since one result does not affect the other.]**

Got It?

Q What two parts of the graph do you need to identify to write the equation? **[the slope of the right branch a and vertex (h, k)]**

You can combine the equations for stretches and compressions with the equations for translations to write a general form for absolute value functions.

 **take note**

> **Key Concept**   **General Form of the Absolute Value Function**
>
> $y = a|x - h| + k$
>
> The stretch or compression factor is $|a|$, the vertex is located at (h, k), and the axis of symmetry is the line $x = h$.

 Problem 4   Identifying Transformations

Without graphing, what are the vertex and axis of symmetry of the graph of $y = 3|x - 2| + 4$? How is the parent function $y = |x|$ transformed?

Compare $y = 3|x - 2| + 4$ with the general form $y = a|x - h| + k$.

    $a = 3, h = 2,$ and $k = 4$.

The vertex is $(2, 4)$ and the axis of symmetry is $x = 2$.

The parent function $y = |x|$ is translated 2 units to the right, vertically stretched by the factor 3, and translated 4 units up.

Check Check by graphing the equation on a graphing calculator.

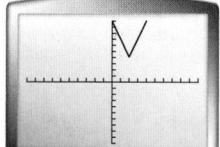

Plan
To what should you compare $y = 3|x - 2| + 4$?
Compare it to the general form, $y = a|x - h| + k$.

✓ **Got It?**   **4.** What are the vertex and axis of symmetry of $y = -2|x - 1| - 3$? How is $y = |x|$ transformed?

 Problem 5   Writing an Absolute Value Function

What is the equation of the absolute value function?

Step 1   Identify the vertex.
    The vertex is at $(-1, 4)$, so $h = -1$ and $k = 4$.

Step 2   Identify a.
    The slope of the branch to the right of the vertex is $-\frac{1}{3}$, so $a = -\frac{1}{3}$.

Step 3   Write the equation.
    Substitute the values of a, h, and k into the general form $y = a|x - h| + k$. The equation that describes the graph is $y = -\frac{1}{3}|x + 1| + 4$.

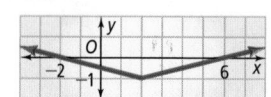

Think
What does the graph tell you about a?
The upside-down V suggests that $a < 0$.

✓ **Got It?**   **5.** What is the equation of the absolute value function?

110   **Chapter 2**   Functions, Equations, and Graphs

Answers

Got It? (continued)

2.
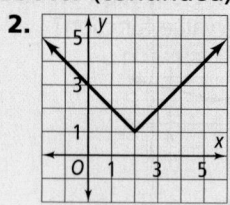

3. a. 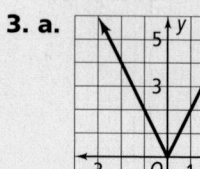   **b.**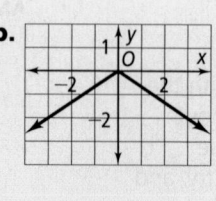

4. $(1, -3)$; $x = 1$; translated 1 unit to the rt., vertically stretched by a factor of 2, then reflected over the x-axis and translated down 3 units

5. $y = \frac{1}{4}|x - 2| - 1$

Lesson Check

1. $(-4, -3)$; $x = -4$

2. $(-3, 9)$; $x = -3$

3. vert. stretch   **4.** vert. stretch

5. Yes; you can determine the position of a graph of an absolute value function by identifying the vertex, axis of symmetry and the transformation of the absolute value parent function. Answers may vary. Sample: $y = -\frac{1}{2}|x + 3| - 5$; vertex $(-3, -5)$; axis of symmetry, $x = -3$; translated 3 units to the left, vertically compressed by a factor of $\frac{1}{2}$, then reflected over the x-axis and translated down 5 units.

6. Sample: $y = |x + 1| - 2$ and $y = -|x + 1| - 2$

7. $y = |x|$ is the same as $y = x$ when $x \geq 0$ and is the reflection of $y = x$ across the x-axis when $x < 0$.

Practice and Problem-Solving Exercises

8.

x	y
-2	3
-1	2
0	1
1	2
2	3

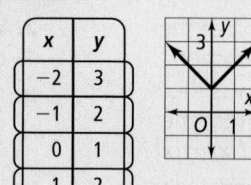

9.

x	y
-2	1
-1	0
0	-1
1	0
2	1

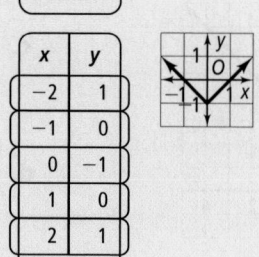

Lesson Check

Do you know HOW?

Find the vertex and the axis of symmetry of the graph of each function.

1. $y = 2|x + 4| - 3$ **2.** $y = |-x - 3| + 9$

Determine if each function is a vertical stretch or vertical compression of the parent function $y = |x|$.

3. $y = -\frac{7}{2}|x|$ **4.** $y = \frac{3}{2}|x|$

Do you UNDERSTAND?  MATHEMATICAL PRACTICES

5. Is it true that without making a graph of an absolute value function, you can describe its position in the coordinate plane? Explain with an example.

6. Write two absolute value functions such that they have a common vertex in Quadrant III and one is the reflection of the other in a horizontal line.

7. Compare and Contrast How is the graph of $y = x$ different from the graph of $y = |x|$?

Practice and Problem-Solving Exercises  MATHEMATICAL PRACTICES

Ⓐ Practice

Make a table of values for each equation. Then graph the equation.   ◀ See Problems 1 and 2.

8. $y = |x| + 1$ **9.** $y = |x| - 1$ **10.** $y = |x| - 3$

11. $y = |x + 2|$ **12.** $y = |x + 4|$ **13.** $y = |x + 5|$

14. $y = |x - 1| + 3$ **15.** $y = |x + 6| - 1$ **16.** $y = |x - 5| + 4$

Graph each equation. Then describe the transformation from the parent function $f(x) = |x|$.   ◀ See Problem 3.

17. $y = 3|x|$ **18.** $y = -\frac{1}{2}|x|$ **19.** $y = -2|x|$

20. $y = \frac{1}{3}|x|$ **21.** $y = \frac{3}{2}|x|$ **22.** $y = -\frac{3}{4}|x|$

Without graphing, identify the vertex, axis of symmetry, and transformations from the parent function $f(x) = |x|$.   ◀ See Problem 4.

23. $y = |x + 2| - 4$ **24.** $y = \frac{3}{2}|x - 6|$ **25.** $y = 3|x + 6|$

26. $y = 4 - |x + 2|$ **27.** $y = -|x - 5|$ **28.** $y = |x - 2| - 6$

Write an absolute value equation for each graph.   ◀ See Problem 5.

29.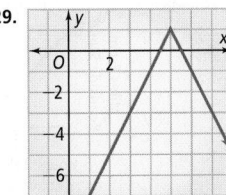

30.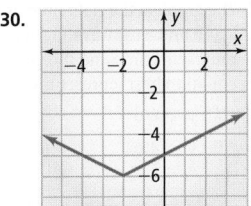

---

3 Lesson Check

Do you know HOW?

- For Exercise 1, encourage students to rewrite the equation in the form $y = a|x - h| + k$.
- In Exercises 3–4, point out that just because a number is written as a fraction, it is not necessarily less than 1. The sign of the coefficient of the absolute value expression does not affect the answer because the question asks only if each function is a stretch or compression. If students have difficulty, revisit Problem 2.

Do you UNDERSTAND?

- For Exercise 5, giving the location of the vertex is not enough to describe the position; you also need to specify the slopes of both sides of the graph.
- For Exercise 6, make sure students know which quadrant is Quadrant III.

Close

Q The absolute value of a quantity is always nonnegative. How can an absolute value graph extend below the x-axis? **[If the absolute value term is multiplied by a negative number, the graph is reflected across the x-axis, or if the graph is translated down k units, the vertex will be below the x-axis.]**

Q For what values in its domain is an absolute value function linear? **[for $x \geq x$-coordinate of the vertex; for $x \leq x$-coordinate of the vertex]**

10.

x	y
-2	-1
-1	-2
0	-3
1	-2
2	-1

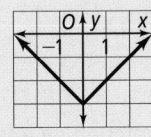

12.

x	y
-6	2
-5	1
-4	0
-3	1
-2	2

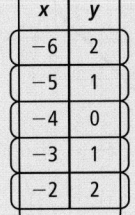

11.

x	y
-4	2
-3	1
-2	0
-1	1
0	2

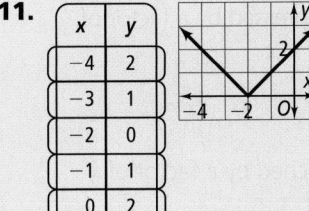

13.

x	y
-7	2
-6	1
-5	0
-4	1
-3	2

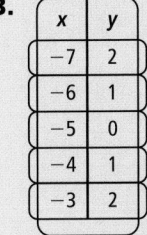

14–30. See pages 112–113.

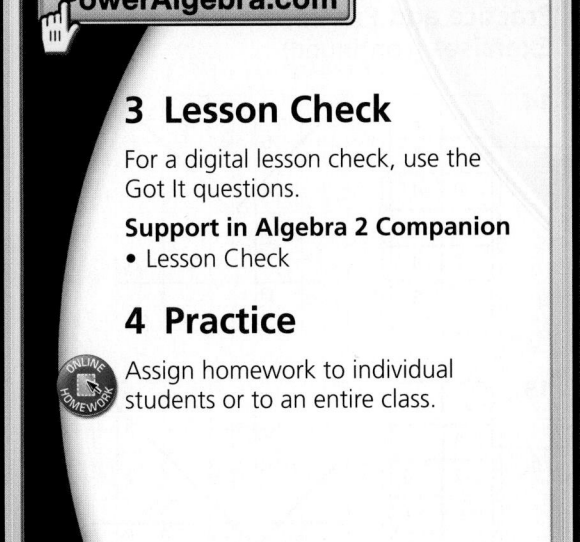

PowerAlgebra.com

3 Lesson Check

For a digital lesson check, use the Got It questions.

Support in Algebra 2 Companion
- Lesson Check

4 Practice

Assign homework to individual students or to an entire class.

4 Practice

ASSIGNMENT GUIDE

Basic: 8–30 all, 31–33, 40–44 even, 45

Average: 9–29 odd, 31–46

Advanced: 9–29 odd, 31–50

Standardized Test Prep: 51–54

Mixed Review: 55–64

 Mathematical Practices are supported by exercises with red headings. Here are the Practices supported in this lesson:

MP 1: Make Sense of Problems Ex. 31

MP 3: Communicate Ex. 34, 45

MP 3: Construct Arguments Ex. 7, 35

MP 3: Critique the Reasoning of Others Ex. 33

MP 5: Use Appropriate Tools Ex. 46

Applications exercises have blue headings.

EXERCISE 32: Use the Think About a Plan worksheet in the **Practice and Problem Solving Workbook** (also available in the Teaching Resources in print and online) to further support students' development in becoming independent learners.

HOMEWORK QUICK CHECK

To check students' understanding of key skills and concepts, go over Exercises 23, 29, 31, 32, and 33.

B Apply

31. Think About a Plan Graph $y = -2|x + 3| + 4$. List the x- and y-intercepts, if any.
- What is the vertex?
- What does y equal at the x-intercept(s)? What does x equal at the y-intercept(s)?

32. Graph $y = 4|x - 3| + 1$. List the vertex and the x- and y-intercepts, if any.

33. Error Analysis A classmate says that the graphs of $y = -3|x|$ and $y = |-3x|$ are identical. Graph each function and explain why your classmate is not correct.

34. Graph each pair of equations on the same coordinate grid.
  a. $y = 2|x + 1|$; $y = |2x + 1|$ b. $y = 5|x - 2|$; $y = |5x - 2|$
  c. **Reasoning** Explain why each pair of graphs in parts (a) and (b) are different.

35. The graphs of the absolute value functions $f(x)$ and $g(x)$ are given.
  a. Describe a series of transformations that you can use to transform $f(x)$ into $g(x)$.
  b. **Reasoning** If you change the order of the transformations you found in part(a), could you still transform $f(x)$ into $g(x)$? Explain.

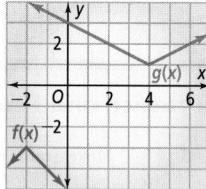

Graph each absolute value equation.

36. $y = \left|-\frac{1}{4}x - 1\right|$ **37.** $y = \left|\frac{5}{2}x - 2\right|$ **38.** $y = \left|\frac{3}{2}x + 2\right|$

39. $y = |3x - 6| + 1$ **40.** $y = -|x - 3|$ **41.** $y = |2x + 6|$

42. $y = 2|x + 2| - 3$ **43.** $y = 6 - |3x|$ **44.** $y = 6 - |3x + 1|$

45. a. Graph the equations $f(x) = -\frac{1}{2}|x - 3|$ and $g(x) = \left|-\frac{1}{2}(x - 3)\right|$ on the same set of axes.
  b. **Writing** Describe the similarities and differences in the graphs.

46. a. Use a graphing calculator. Graph $y_1 = k|x|$ and $y_2 = |kx|$ for some positive value of k.
  b. Graph $y_1 = k|x|$ and $y_2 = |kx|$ for some negative value of k.
  c. What conclusion can you make about the graphs of $y_1 = k|x|$ and $y_2 = |kx|$?

C Challenge **Graph each absolute value equation.**

47. $y = |3x| - \frac{x}{3}$ **48.** $y = \frac{1}{2}|x| + 4|x - 1|$ **49.** $y = |2x| + |x - 4|$

50. The graph at the right models the distance between a roadside stand and a car traveling at a constant speed. The x-axis represents time and the y-axis represents distance. Which equation best represents the relation shown in the graph?

Ⓐ $y = |60x|$ Ⓒ $y = |x| + 60$

Ⓑ $y = |40x|$ Ⓓ $y = |x| + 40$

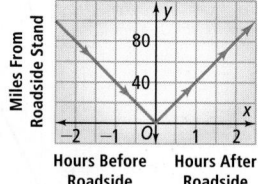

Answers

Practice and Problem-Solving Exercises (continued)

14.

x	y
−1	5
0	4
1	3
2	4
3	5

15.

x	y
−8	1
−7	0
−6	−1
−5	0
−4	1

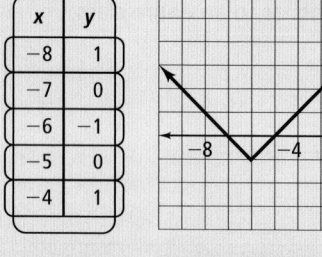

16.

x	y
3	6
4	5
5	4
6	5
7	6

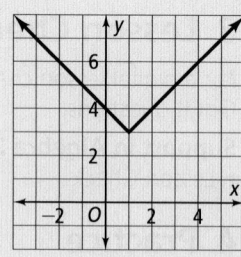

17.

vertically stretched by a factor of 3

18.

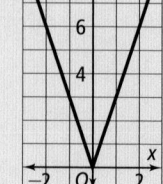

vertically compressed by a factor of $\frac{1}{2}$ and reflected across the x-axis

19.

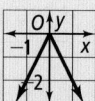

vertically stretched by a factor of 2 and reflected across the x-axis

20.

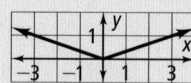

vertically compressed by a factor of $\frac{1}{3}$

21.

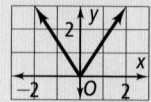

vertically stretched by a factor of $\frac{3}{2}$

22.

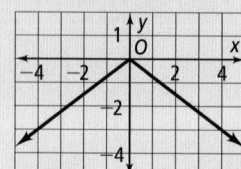

vertically compressed by a factor of $\frac{3}{4}$, reflected across the x-axis

SAT/ACT

51. The graph shows which equation?

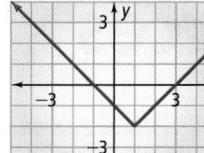

   (A) $y = |3x - 1| + 2$ (C) $y = |x - 1| - 2$

   (B) $y = |x - 1| + 2$ (D) $y = |3x - 3| - 2$

52. How are the graphs of $y = 2x$ and $y = 2x + 2$ related?

   (F) The graph of $y = 2x + 2$ is the graph of $y = 2x$ translated down two units.

   (G) The graph of $y = 2x + 2$ is the graph of $y = 2x$ translated up two units.

   (H) The graph of $y = 2x + 2$ is the graph of $y = 2x$ translated to the left two units.

   (I) The graph of $y = 2x + 2$ is the graph of $y = 2x$ translated to the right two units.

53. What is the equation of a line parallel to $y = x$ that passes through the point $(0, 1)$?

   (A) $y = x + 1$ (C) $y = x - 1$

   (B) $y = 2x + 2$ (D) $y = -x$

Short Response

54. Is $|y| = x$ a function? Explain.

Mixed Review

Write an equation for each transformation of the graph of $y = x + 2$.   ◀ See Lesson 2-6.

55. 2 units up, 3 units right

56. vertical compression by a factor of $\frac{1}{2}$, reflection in the y-axis

Write the function rule for each function reflected in the given axis.

57. $f(x) = x - 7$; y-axis   **58.** $f(x) = 2x - 6$; y-axis   **59.** $f(x) = 4 + x$; x-axis

Find a trend line for each scatter plot. Write the equation for each trend line.   ◀ See Lesson 2-5.

60. 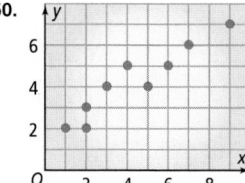   **61.**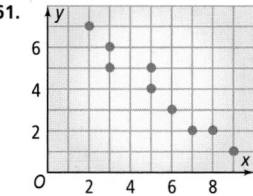

Get Ready!   To prepare for Lesson 2-8, do Exercises 62–64.

Solve each inequality. Graph the solution on a number line.   ◀ See Lesson 1-5.

62. $12p \le 15$ **63.** $4 + t > 17$ **64.** $5 - 2t \ge 11$

23. $(-2, -4)$; $x = -2$; translate 2 units to the left and 4 units down

24. $(0, 0)$; $x = 0$; vertically stretch by a factor of $\frac{3}{2}$

25. $(-6, 0)$; $x = -6$; translate 6 units to the left and vertically stretch by a factor of 3

26. $(-2, 4)$; $x = -2$; reflect across the x-axis, translate 2 units to the left and 4 units up

27. $(5, 0)$; $x = 5$; translate 5 units to the rt. and reflect across the x-axis

28. $(2, -6)$; $x = 2$; translate 2 units to the rt. and 6 units down

29. $y = -2|x - 5| + 1$

30. $y = 0.5|x + 2| - 6$

31. 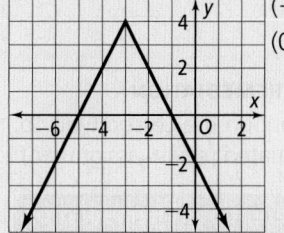 $(-5, 0)$, $(-1, 0)$, $(0, -2)$

32. 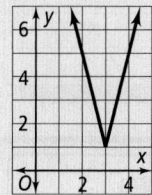 $(3, 1)$; no x-intercept; $(0, 13)$

33. 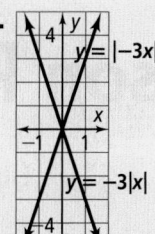 The graphs are not identical; one is the reflection across the x-axis of the other.

34. a.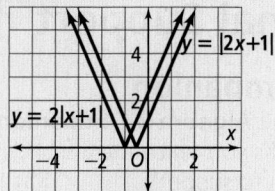

    b.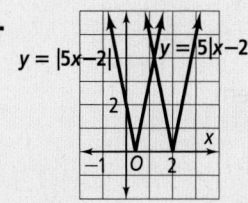

    c. The absolute value bars act as grouping symbols, like parentheses.

35. a. Answers may vary. Sample: reflection across the x-axis, vert. compression by a factor of $\frac{1}{2}$, translation down $\frac{1}{2}$ unit, translation rt. 6 units

    b. Yes; changing the order of the transformations may or may not change the result.

36.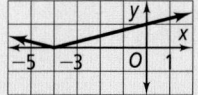

37.    **38.**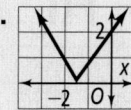

39. 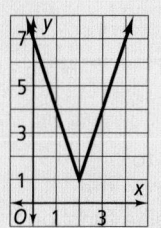   **40.**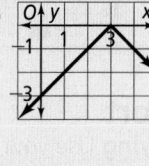

41. 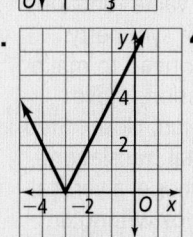   **42.**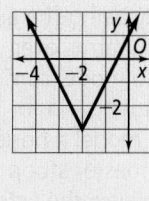

43. 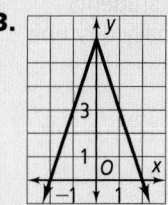   **44.**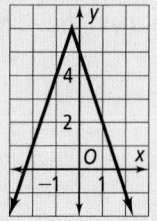

45–64. See back of book.

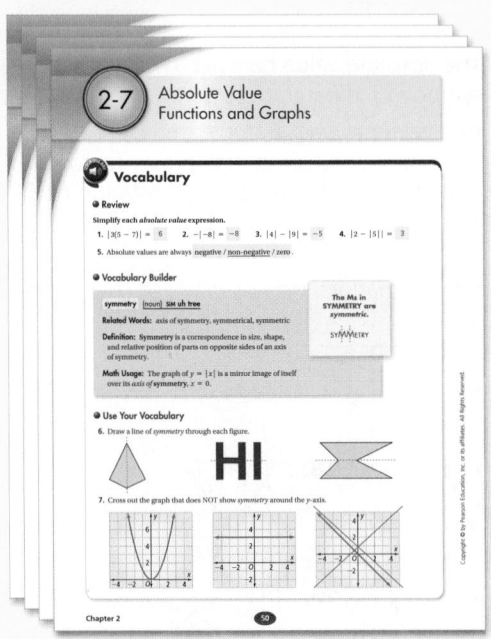

2-7 Lesson Resources

Differentiated Remediation
Available in editable format online.

Additional Instructional Support

Algebra 2 Companion
Students can use the **Algebra 2 Companion** worktext (4 pages) as you teach the lesson. Use the Companion to support

- New Vocabulary
- Key Concepts
- Got It for each Problem
- Lesson Check

ELL Support
Use Role Playing Use your arms to demonstrate as you verbally describe the transformations of an absolute value function, with your body being the axis of symmetry. Stretch out your arms over your head to make the V shape. To model compression, move arms further apart, and for stretch, closer. Step to one side to model a horizontal translation, and stand on toes or stoop to model a vertical translation. Reverse the activity by writing an equation on the board and having students model it with their bodies and verbally describe their actions.

5 Assess & Remediate

Lesson Quiz
1. How is the graph of $y = |x| - 1$ different from the parent function $f(x) = |x|$?
2. What is the graph of $y = |x - 3| + 1$?
3. What is the graph of $y = 3|x|$?
4. **Do you UNDERSTAND?** Compare $y = \frac{1}{3}|x - 2| - 5$ with the parent function. Without graphing, what are the vertex, axis of symmetry, and transformations of the parent function?
5. What is the equation of the absolute value function?

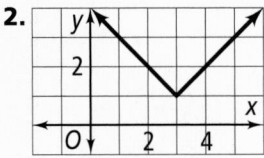

ANSWERS TO LESSON QUIZ
1. It is translated down 1 unit.

2.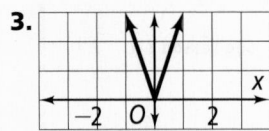

3.

4. $a = \frac{1}{3}$, $h = 2$, $k = -5$; vertex: $(2, -5)$; axis of symmetry: $x = 2$; translated 2 units right, vertically compressed by the factor $\frac{1}{3}$, and translated 5 units down.

5. $y = \frac{1}{2}|x + 1| + 1$

PRESCRIPTION FOR REMEDIATION
Use the student work on the Lesson Quiz to prescribe a differentiated review assignment:

Points	Differentiated Remediation
0–2	Intervention
3–4	On-level
5	Extension

PowerAlgebra.com

5 Assess & Remediate
Assign the Lesson Quiz. Appropriate intervention, practice, or enrichment is automatically generated based on student performance.

Intervention
- **Reteaching** (2 pages) Provides reteaching and practice exercises for the key lesson concepts. Use with struggling students or absent students.
- **English Language Learner Support** Helps students develop and reinforce mathematical vocabulary and key concepts.

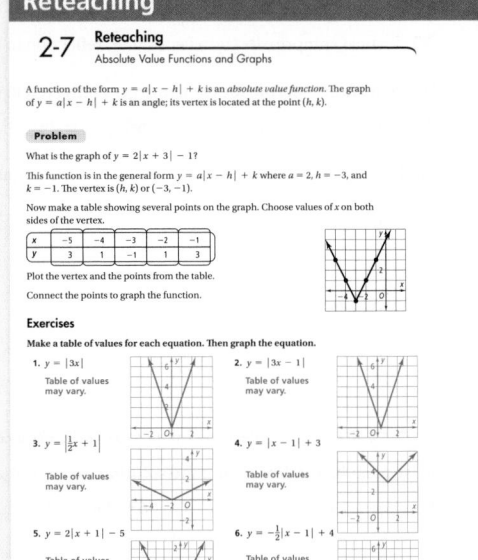

Differentiated Remediation *continued*

Available in editable format online.

On-Level

- **Practice** (2 pages) Provides extra practice for each lesson. For simpler practice exercises, use the Form K Practice pages found in the All-in-One Teaching Resources and online.

- **Think About a Plan** Helps students develop specific problem-solving skills and strategies by providing scaffolded guiding questions.

- **Standardized Test Prep** Focuses on all major exercises, all major question types, and helps students prepare for the high-stakes assessments.

Extension

- **Enrichment** Provides students with interesting problems and activities that extend the concepts of the lesson.

- **Activities, Games, and Puzzles** Worksheets that can be used for concepts development, enrichment, and for fun!

Practice and Problem Solving Wkbk/All-in-One Resources/Online
Practice page 1

2-7 Practice — Form G
Absolute Value Functions and Graphs

Graph each equation.

1. $y = |x| - 2$
2. $y = |x| + 3$
3. $y = |x| - 5$
4. $y = |x| - 4$
5. $y = |x - 3| + 1$
6. $y = |x + 1| - 4$

Graph each equation. Then describe the transformation from the parent function $f(x) = |x|$.

7. $y = 2|x|$ — vertical stretch of the parent function by a factor of 2
8. $y = \frac{1}{4}|x|$ — vertical compression of the parent function by a factor of $\frac{1}{4}$
9. $y = -3|x|$ — vertical stretch of the parent function by a factor of 3, reflected in the x-axis

Without graphing, identify the vertex, axis of symmetry, and transformations from the parent function $f(x) = |x|$.

10. $y = |x - 4|$ (4, 0); $x = 4$; translation of the parent function 4 units to the right
11. $y = -3|x| - 2$ (0, −2); $x = 0$; vertical stretch of the parent function by a factor of 3, reflected in the x-axis, and translated 2 units down
12. $y = -|3x| + 4$ (0, 4); $x = 0$; vertical stretch of the parent function by a factor of 3, reflected in the x-axis, and translated 4 units up
13. $y = 5 - |x - 1|$ (1, 5); $x = 1$; translated 1 unit right, reflected in the x-axis, and translated 5 units up

---

Practice and Problem Solving Wkbk/All-in-One Resources/Online
Practice page 2

2-7 Practice [continued] — Form G
Absolute Value Functions and Graphs

14. Graph $y = -|x - 4| + 5$. List the vertex and the x- and y-intercepts, if any.
vertex: (4, 5); x-intercepts: (−1, 0), (9, 0); y-intercept: (0, 1)

Graph each absolute value equation.

15. $y = |3 - x|$
16. $y = 3 - |x + 1|$
17. $y = -|-x - 2|$
18. $y = -|x| + 2$
19. $y = |3x - 1| - 2$
20. $y = \left|\frac{3}{4}x + 1\right|$
21. $y = \frac{1}{3}|2x - 9|$
22. $y = |x + 1| - 3$
23. $y = -\frac{1}{2}|2x - 4|$

24. a. Graph the equations $y = 2|x + 4| - 1$ and $y = \frac{1}{2}|x - 4| - 1$ on the same set of axes.
b. **Writing** Describe the similarities and differences in the graphs.
The first equation is a stretch of $y = |x|$ by a factor of 2 and the second equation is a compression of $y = |x|$ by a factor of $\frac{1}{2}$. The first equation is also translated left 4 units and down 1 unit. The second equation is also translated right 4 units and up 1 unit.

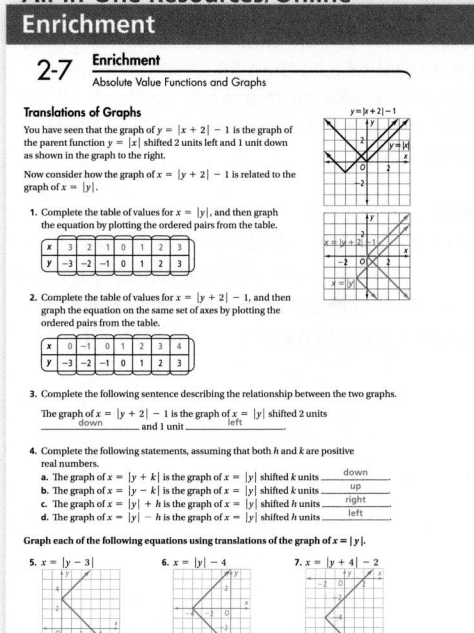

All-in-One Resources/Online
Enrichment

2-7 Enrichment
Absolute Value Functions and Graphs

Translations of Graphs
You have seen that the graph of $y = |x + 2| - 1$ is the graph of the parent function $y = |x|$ shifted 2 units left and 1 unit down as shown in the graph to the right.

Now consider how the graph of $x = |y + 2| - 1$ is related to the graph of $x = |y|$.

1. Complete the table of values for $x = |y|$, and then graph the equation by plotting the ordered pairs from the table.

x	3	2	1	0	1	2	3
y	−3	−2	−1	0	1	2	3

2. Complete the table of values for $x = |y + 2| - 1$, and then graph the equation on the same set of axes by plotting the ordered pairs from the table.

x	0	−1	0	1	2	3	4
y	−3	−2	−1	0	1	2	3

3. Complete the following sentence describing the relationship between the two graphs.
The graph of $x = |y + 2| - 1$ is the graph of $x = |y|$ shifted 2 units ___down___ and 1 unit ___left___.

4. Complete the following statements, assuming that both h and k are positive real numbers.
a. The graph of $x = |y + k|$ is the graph of $x = |y|$ shifted k units ___down___
b. The graph of $x = |y - k|$ is the graph of $x = |y|$ shifted k units ___up___
c. The graph of $x = |y| + h$ is the graph of $x = |y|$ shifted h units ___right___
d. The graph of $x = |y| - h$ is the graph of $x = |y|$ shifted h units ___left___

Graph each of the following equations using translations of the graph of $x = |y|$.

5. $x = |y - 3|$
6. $x = |y| - 4$
7. $x = |y + 4| - 2$

Practice and Problem Solving Wkbk/All-in-One Resources/Online
Think About a Plan

2-7 Think About a Plan
Absolute Value Functions and Graphs

Graph $y = 4|x - 3| + 1$. List the vertex and the x- and y-intercepts, if any.

Understanding the Problem

1. What is the problem asking you to determine?
the graph of $y = 4|x - 3| + 1$, an absolute value function, and its vertex and x- and y-intercepts

2. What is the parent function for the function $y = 4|x - 3| + 1$? $y = |x|$

Planning the Solution

3. What do you know about the function $y = 4|x - 3| + 1$?
The graph requires multiple transformations of the parent function.

4. Graph the parent function.

5. What transformations do you need to apply to the parent function to graph this function?
Translate right 3 units; stretch vertically by a factor of 4; translate up 1 unit

Getting an Answer

6. What is the vertex of the function? ___(3, 1)___

7. What are the x- and y-intercepts of the function?
no x-intercepts; y-intercept: (0, 13)

8. Graph the function.

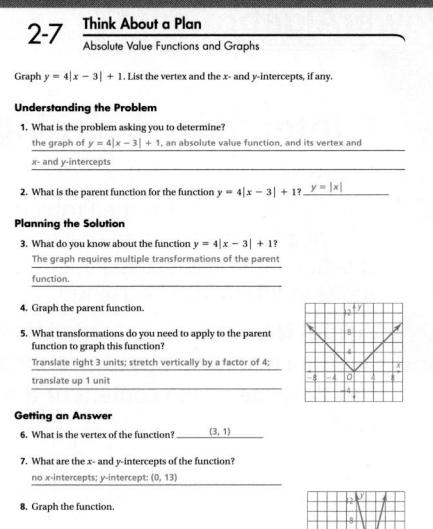

Practice and Problem Solving Wkbk/All-in-One Resources/Online
Standardized Test Prep

2-7 Standardized Test Prep
Absolute Value Functions and Graphs

Multiple Choice

For Exercises 1–3, choose the correct letter.

1. Which equation has the graph shown at the right? D
   A. $y = -\frac{1}{2}|x|$
   B. $y = 2|x|$
   C. $y = \frac{1}{2}|x|$
   D. $y = -2|x|$

2. Which statement about the graph of the function $y = -\frac{1}{3}|x + 2| - 5$ is true? I
   F. the vertex is at (2, −5)
   G. the vertex is at (2, 5)
   H. the vertex is at (−2, 5)
   I. the vertex is at (−2, −5)

3. The graph of which equation is the graph of $f(x) = |x|$ reflected in the x-axis, translated 2 units left, vertically compressed by a factor of $\frac{1}{3}$, and translated up 4 units? B
   A. $y = 3|x - 2| + 4$
   B. $y = -\frac{1}{3}|x + 2| + 4$
   C. $y = -3|x + 2| + 4$
   D. $y = -\frac{1}{3}|x - 2| + 4$

Extended Response

4. Determine the parent function of $y = -|x + 4| - 1$. Describe the graph of $y = -|x + 4| - 1$ as three transformations of the parent function. Then graph the parent function and each translation.
[4] $f(x) = |x|$; the graph of $y = -|x + 4| - 1$ is the parent function $f(x) = |x|$ translated 4 units left, reflected in the x-axis and translated down 1 unit
[3] correct parent function, but with one error in describing and graphing the transformations
[2] incorrect parent function OR multiple errors in describing and graphing the transformations
[1] incorrect parent function AND incorrect description of all transformations OR missing graph
[0] no answers given

Online Teacher Resource Center
Activities, Games, and Puzzles

2-7 Game: Bounce and Hit
Absolute Value Functions and Graphs

This is a game for two players. Each player secretly places a point, or *flag*, on the grid at the bottom of the page. Then players take turns trying to hit the opponent's flag with the graphs of absolute value functions. Your teacher will decide if a graphing calculator can be used.

Rules: The flag must have integer coordinates and be on the interior of the grid; neither coordinate of the flag can be −5 or 5. *Do not* allow your opponent to see your flag! With a coin flip, decide which player begins. When it is your turn:

- Try to find an absolute value function whose graph goes through your opponent's flag. The graph of the function must have its vertex on the grid. Announce it to your opponent.
- You want the vertex of the function to have an x-coordinate smaller than the flag's; that is, the vertex must be to the *left* of the flag. Think of the graph as the path of a ball bouncing from left to right—the hit must occur *after* the bounce.
- Your opponent checks your function and announces one of the four possibilities:

Misses Above (vertex *above* point; *no hit*) **Misses Below** (vertex *below* point; *no hit*) **Hits On The Fly** (vertex to *right* of point; *no hit*) **Hits On The Bounce** (vertex to *left* of point; hit!)

- Take turns until someone hits the opponent's flag "on the bounce." Check students' work.

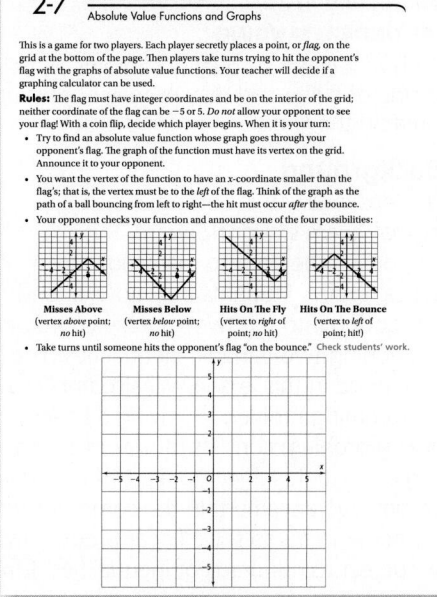

1 Interactive Learning

Solve It!

PURPOSE To use prior knowledge to write a two-variable inequality

PROCESS Students may
- assign variables and write the inequality.
- use trial and error to generate values of the variables that satisfy the inequality.

FACILITATE

Q What items can be bought with the gift card? **[CDs and books]**

Q Assign variables. Let x = number of CDs and y = number of books. What inequality models the situation? **[$5.25x + 3y \le 50$]**

Q What values of x and y make the inequality true? **[Answers may vary. Sample: $x = 8$ and $y = 2$]**

Q How do you know whether you chose the combination that uses as much of the card as possible? **[There are many combinations that give a total of less than 50. With trial and error, it can take quite a while to check all the possibilities, unless you find one that costs exactly $50.]**

ANSWER See Solve It in Answers on next page.

CONNECT THE MATH Students use the Solve It's context to solve a two-variable inequality by trial and error. In this lesson, students will solve two-variable inequalities by graphing.

© **Common Core State Standards**
A-CED.A.2 Create equations in two or more variables to represent relationships between quantities; graph equations on coordinate axes with labels and scales.
Also F-IF.C.7b
MP 1, MP 3, MP 4, MP 5, MP 7

Objective To graph two-variable inequalities

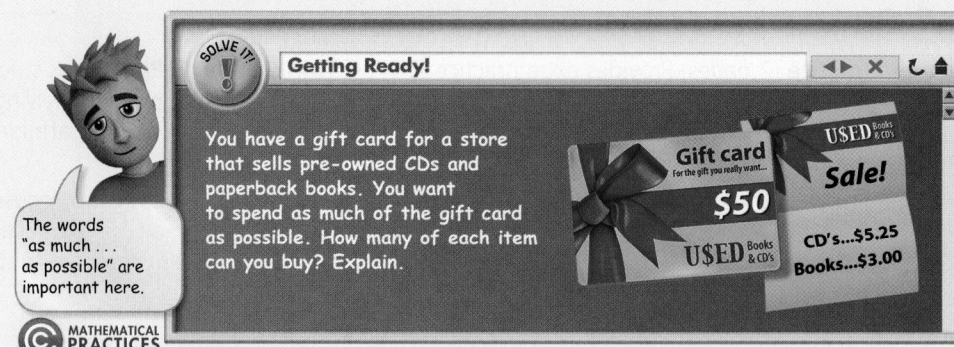

The words "as much . . . as possible" are important here.

© MATHEMATICAL PRACTICES

Getting Ready!

You have a gift card for a store that sells pre-owned CDs and paperback books. You want to spend as much of the gift card as possible. How many of each item can you buy? Explain.

Gift card — For the gift you really want... **$50** — U$ED Books & CD's

U$ED Books & CD's — Sale! — CD's...$5.25 — Books...$3.00

In some situations you need to compare quantities. You can use inequalities for situations that involve these relationships: *less than, less than or equal to, greater than,* and *greater than or equal to*.

Essential Understanding Graphing an inequality in two variables is similar to graphing a line. The graph of a linear inequality contains all points on one side of the line and may or may not include the points on the line.

A **linear inequality** is an inequality in two variables whose graph is a region of the coordinate plane bounded by a line. This line is the **boundary** of the graph. The boundary separates the coordinate plane into two **half-planes**, one of which consists of solutions of the inequality.

VOCABULARY **Lesson Vocabulary**
- linear inequality
- boundary
- half-plane
- test point

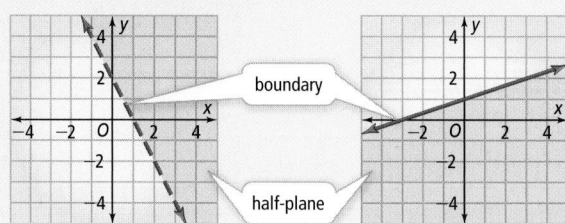

boundary

half-plane

2-8 Preparing to Teach

BIG idea Modeling

ESSENTIAL UNDERSTANDING
- The graph of a linear inequality contains all points on one side of a line and may or may not include the points on the line.

Math Background

While the steps involved in solving a linear inequality may seem straightforward, this knowledge opens the door to many advanced mathematical topics. Students may now extend their investigation into the two-variable coordinate plane by graphing two-variable inequalities. The principles learned in this lesson will also apply to linear programming problems. Solving a linear programming problem consists of maximizing or minimizing a function subject to a list of constraints or inequalities. Advancement in the computer field allows mathematicians to solve linear programming problems subject to hundreds of inequalities. Many economic, labor, and business problems can be solved using linear programming techniques.

© Mathematical Practices

Look for and make use of structure. In graphing two-variable inequalities, students will see a complicated graph as composed of two elements: a solid or dashed line (representing a linear equation) and a shaded region. Students will also be able to check their answers through substitution.

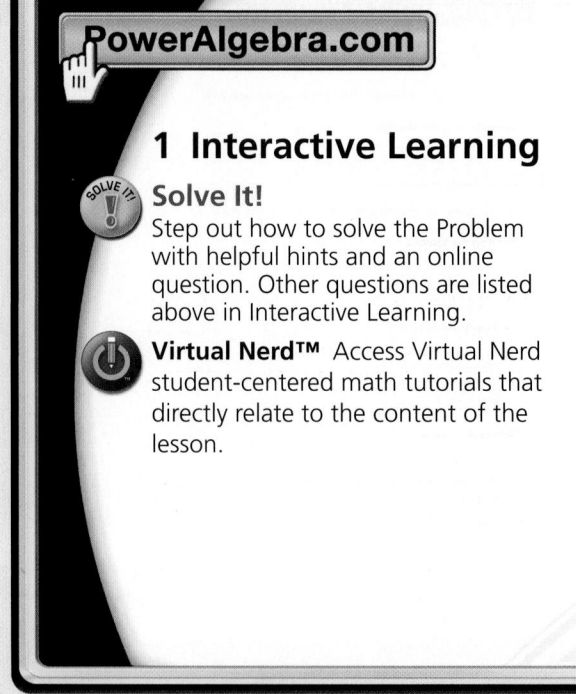

PowerAlgebra.com

1 Interactive Learning

Solve It! Step out how to solve the Problem with helpful hints and an online question. Other questions are listed above in Interactive Learning.

Virtual Nerd™ Access Virtual Nerd student-centered math tutorials that directly relate to the content of the lesson.

To determine which half-plane to shade, pick a **test point** that is *not* on the boundary. Check whether that point satisfies the inequality. If it does, shade the half-plane that includes the test point. If not, shade the other half-plane. The origin, (0, 0), is usually an easy test point as long as it is not on the boundary.

 Problem 1 Graphing Linear Inequalities

What is the graph of each inequality?

A $y > 3x - 1$

Step 1
Graph the boundary line $y = 3x - 1$. Use a dashed boundary line because the inequality is *greater than*, and the points on the line do not satisfy the inequality.

Step 2
Choose a test point, (0, 0). Substitute $x = 0$ and $y = 0$ into $y > 3x - 1$.
$$0 > 3(0) - 1$$
$$0 > -1$$
Since $0 > -1$ is true, shade the half plane that includes (0, 0).

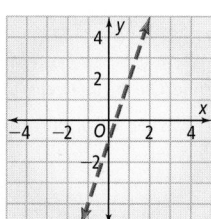

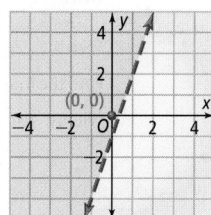

B $y \le 3x - 1$

The boundary line is again $y = 3x - 1$, but it is solid because the inequality is less than or *equal to*.

Shade the region opposite the region shaded above (for >) because the inequality is *less than* or equal to.

You can also check the point (0, 0).
$$0 \le 3(0) - 1$$
$$0 \le -1$$
Since $0 \le -1$ is false, (0, 0) is not part of the solution.

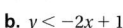

 Got It? **1.** What is the graph of each inequality?
    a. $y \ge -2x + 1$ **b.** $y < -2x + 1$

You can also inspect inequalities solved for y, such as $y > mx + b$ to determine which half-plane describes the solution. Since y describes vertical position, the solution of $y > mx + b$ will be *above* the boundary line. The solution of $y < mx + b$ will be *below* the boundary line.

PowerAlgebra.com   Lesson 2-8   Two-Variable Inequalities   **115**

Plan
Can you use the graph of $y > 3x - 1$ to help graph $y \le 3x - 1$?
If you shaded above the line for $y > 3x - 1$, then shade below the line for $y \le 3x - 1$.

---

2 Guided Instruction

Problem 1   SYNTHESIZING

To obtain the boundary line, write the inequality as an equation. Use a test point to determine which half-plane contains the solutions, and shade that half-plane.

Q Can you use (0, −1) as a test point? Explain. **[No; (0, −1) lies on the boundary line $y = 3x - 1$.]**

Q Why is it helpful to plot the test point on the graph? **[The test point determines where to shade and where not to shade.]**

Got It?   ERROR PREVENTION

Q What is the difference between 1a and 1b? **[Answers may vary. Sample: The inequality is changed from ≥ to <.]**

Q How will the change affect the graphs? Explain. **[The inequality symbol determines whether the boundary line is included in the solutions and which half-plane contains the solutions, so the boundary line will change from solid to dashed, and the shaded half-plane will change from one side of the boundary line to the other.]**

     EXTENSION

Q What would a graph of $y \ne -2x + 1$ look like? **[A dashed boundary line with both half planes shaded; the only excluded solutions are those on the line itself.]**

---

2 Guided Instruction

 Each Problem is worked out and supported online.

Problem 1
Graphing a Linear Inequality

Problem 2
Using a Linear Inequality
          Animated

Problem 3
Graphing an Absolute Value Inequality

Problem 4
Writing an Inequality Based on a Graph
          Animated

Alternative Problem 4
Writing an Inequality Based on a Graph
          Animated

Support in Algebra 2 Companion
• Vocabulary
• Key Concepts
• Got It?

Answers

Solve It!
You can buy 6 CDs and 6 books or 2 CDs and 13 books. In both cases you will spend $49.50.

Got It?

1. a.
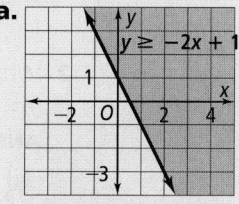

b.
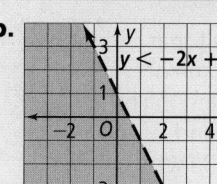

Problem 2

Students may use other techniques to graph the boundary line such as changing the equation to slope-intercept form.

Q What words in the paragraph suggest an inequality? **[more than]**

Q How is the type of inequality determined? **[The phrase "do not want to spend more than \$15" suggests ≤.]**

Q Is $3x + 5y \leq 60$ the only inequality that could be used to solve this problem? Explain. **[Answers may vary. Samples: No; you could let $x =$ number of large rides and $y =$ number of small rides and use $5x + 3y \leq 60$; or you could convert number of tickets per ride to cost per ride and use $0.75x + 1.25y \leq 15$.]**

Q What is another example of a discrete variable? **[Answers may vary. Sample: number of people at the fair]**

Got It?

Q How is this different from Problem 2? **[The only difference is the amount of money you may spend.]**

Q If you double the money you spend, do you double the number of discrete ordered-pair solutions? Explain. **[Answers may vary. Sample: No; doubling the amount doubles both the base and height of the triangular solution region, so the number of solutions increases by a factor greater than 2 (though in most cases less than 4).]**

© **Problem 2** Using a Linear Inequality

Entertainment The map shows the number of tickets needed for small or large rides at the fair. You do not want to spend more than \$15 on tickets. How many small or large rides can you ride?

You can buy 60 tickets with \$15.

Think

What are the unknowns?
The unknowns are the number of small rides and the number of large rides you can get on.

Relate | the number of tickets for small rides | plus | the number of tickets for large rides | is less than or equal to | 60

Define Let x = the number of small rides.

Let y = the number of large rides.

Write $3x$ + $5y$ ≤ 60

Step 1

Find the intercepts of the boundary line. Use the intercepts to graph the boundary line.

When $y = 0$, $3x + 5(0) = 60$.
$$3x = 60$$
$$x = 20$$

When $x = 0$, $3(0) + 5y = 60$.
$$5y = 60$$
$$y = 12$$

Graph the line that connects the intercepts $(20, 0)$ and $(0, 12)$. Since the inequality is ≤, use a solid boundary line.

Step 2

The region above the boundary line represents combinations of rides that require more than 60 tickets. You purchased a *finite* number of tickets, 60, so you will not be able to go on an infinite number of rides. Shade the region below the boundary line.

The number of small rides x and the number of large rides y are whole numbers. In math, such a situation is called *discrete*. All points with whole number coordinates in the shaded region represent possible combinations of small and large rides.

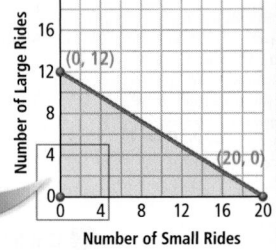

Rides at the Fair

© ✓ **Got It? 2. a.** Suppose that you decide to spend no more than \$30 for tickets. What are the possible combinations of small and large rides that you can ride now? Use a graph to find your answer.

b. Reasoning Why did the graph of the solution in Problem 2 only include Quadrant I?

116 **Chapter 2** Functions, Equations, and Graphs

Additional Problems

1. What is the graph of $y > 2x - 3$?

ANSWER

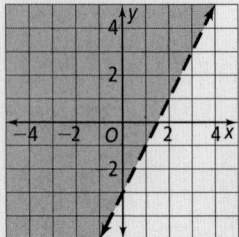

2. You put up a new shelf that is 1 ft wide to store some of your books and trophies. Each book takes up 1 inch and each trophy takes up 3 inches. What is a graph showing how many books and how many trophies will fit on the shelf?

ANSWER

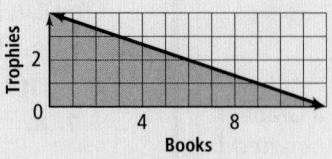

3. What is the graph of $y \leq |x - 2| + 1$?

ANSWER

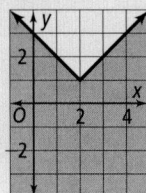

4. What inequality does this graph represent?

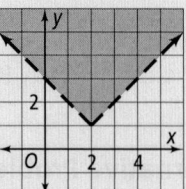

ANSWER $y > |x - 2| + 1$

Got It? (continued)

2. a.

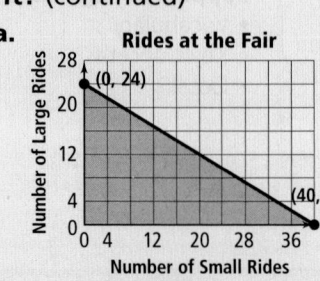

Rides at the Fair

b. The number of rides cannot be neg.

3.

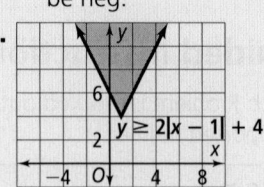

$y \geq 2|x - 1| + 4$

4. a. $y > -|x + 4| + 3$

b. No; when you solve the ineq. for y, you multiply both sides by -1. This changes the ineq. sign from $>$ to $<$.

You can graph two-variable absolute value inequalities in the same way that you graph linear inequalities.

 Problem 3 Graphing an Absolute Value Inequality

What is the graph of $1 - y < |x + 2|$?

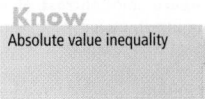 

Know	Need	Plan
Absolute value inequality	Boundary	• Solve the inequality for y. • Graph the related equation. • Shade the solution.

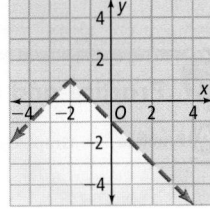

$1 - y < |x + 2|$

$-y < |x + 2| - 1$ Subtract 1 from each side.

$y > -|x + 2| + 1$ Multiply both sides by -1.

The graph of $y = -|x + 2| + 1$ is the graph of $y = |x|$, reflected in the x-axis and translated left 2 units and up 1 unit.

Since the inequality is solved for y and $y > -|x + 2| + 1$, shade the region above the boundary.

✔ **Got It? 3.** What is the graph of $y - 4 \geq 2|x - 1|$?

You can use the transformations discussed in previous lessons to help draw the boundary graphs more quickly. You can also use them to write an inequality based on a graph.

 Problem 4 Writing an Inequality Based on a Graph

What inequality does this graph represent?

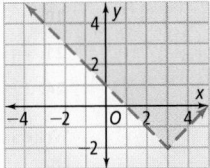

The boundary is the graph of the absolute value function $y = |x|$, translated. The vertex of $y = |x|$ is translated to $(3, -2)$, so the boundary is the graph of $y = |x - 3| - 2$.

The solution is shaded above the boundary, so the inequality is either $>$ or $\geq$. Since the boundary is a dashed line, the correct inequality is $y > |x - 3| - 2$.

© ✔ **Got It? 4. a.** What inequality does this graph represent?

b. Reasoning You can tell from looking at the inequality $y > 5x - 3$ to shade above the boundary line to represent the solution. Can you use the same technique to show the solution of an inequality like $2x - y > 1$? Explain.

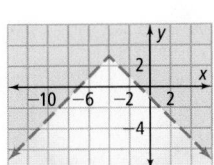

Answers

Practice and Problem-Solving Exercises (continued)

17. a. $y \geq 20x$ if $x \leq 6$; $y \geq 15x$ if $x > 6$
b.

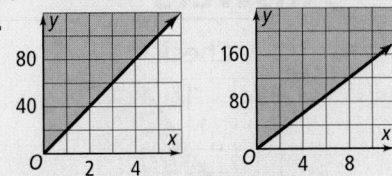

11. 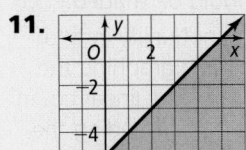   **12.**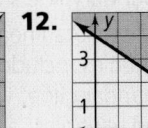

18. 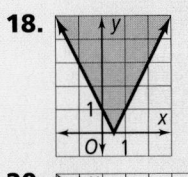   **19.**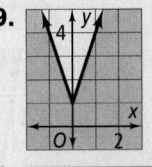

13. 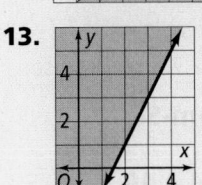   **14.**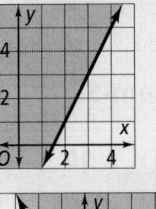

20. 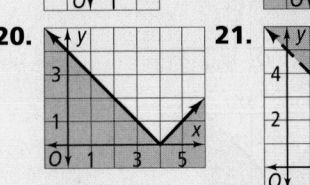   **21.**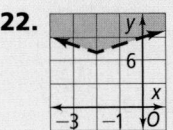

15. 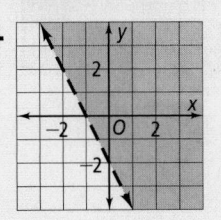   **16.**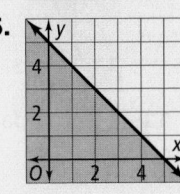

22. 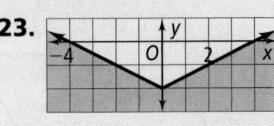   **23.**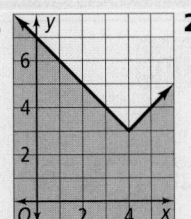

24.   **25.**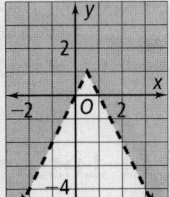

26.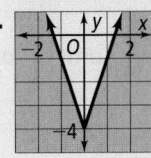

27. $y < -x - 2$ **28.** $5x + 3y \leq 9$

29. $2y \geq |2x + 6|$

Lesson 2-8 117

3 Lesson Check

Do you know HOW?   ERROR INTERVENTION

- For Exercises 1–4, if students shade the wrong half-planes, remind them that the inequality sign relates to above or below the boundary line, and determines which half-plane to shade.

Do you UNDERSTAND? ERROR INTERVENTION

- For Exercise 6, suggest students make a list of the steps for graphing a linear inequality in two variables and another list of steps for graphing the linear equation in two variables, and then compare the lists.

Close

> **Q** What are the differences between solving linear equations in two variables and solving linear inequalities in two variables? **[The graph of a linear equation is a line; all solutions are on that line. The graph of a linear inequality includes the linear equation solution (called the boundary line) as well as a set of points that make up a half-plane. The boundary line may or may not be included in the solution of the inequality.]**

Lesson Check

Do you know HOW?

What is the graph of each inequality?

1. $9y \le 12x$

2. $7x + y \ge 8$

What is the graph of each absolute value inequality?

3. $y \le |x + 1|$

4. $y \ge |2x - 3|$

Do you UNDERSTAND?

5. Do the points on the boundary line of the graph of an inequality help determine the shaded area of the graph? Explain.

6. **Compare and Contrast** How is graphing a linear inequality in two variables different from graphing a linear equation in two variables?

7. **Reasoning** Is the ordered pair $\left(\frac{3}{4}, 0\right)$ a solution of $3x + y > 3$? Explain.

Practice and Problem-Solving Exercises   MATHEMATICAL PRACTICES

A Practice

Graph each inequality.   ◀ See Problem 1.

8. $y > 2x + 1$	9. $y < 3$	10. $x \le 0$
11. $y \le x - 5$	12. $2x + 3y \ge 12$	13. $2y \ge 4x - 6$
14. $3x - 2y \le 9$	15. $-y < 2x + 2$	16. $5 - y \ge x$

17. **Cooking** The time needed to roast a chicken depends on its weight. Allow at least 20 min/lb for a chicken weighing as much as 6 lb. Allow at least 15 min/lb for a chicken weighing more than 6 lb.   ◀ See Problem 2.
    a. Write two inequalities to represent the time needed to roast a chicken.
    b. Graph the inequalities.

Graph each absolute value inequality.   ◀ See Problem 3.

18. $y \ge |2x - 1|$	19. $y \le |3x| + 1$	20. $y \le |4 - x|$
21. $y > |-x + 4| + 1$	22. $y - 7 > |x + 2|$	23. $y + 2 \le \left|\frac{1}{2}x\right|$
24. $3 - y \ge -|x - 4|$	25. $1 - y < |2x - 3|$	26. $y + 3 \le |3x| - 1$

Write an inequality for each graph. The equation for the boundary line is given.   ◀ See Problem 4.

27. $y = -x - 2$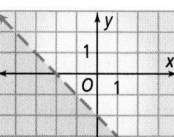

28. $5x + 3y = 9$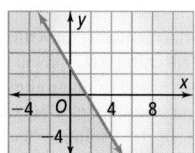

29. $2y = |2x + 6|$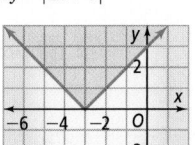

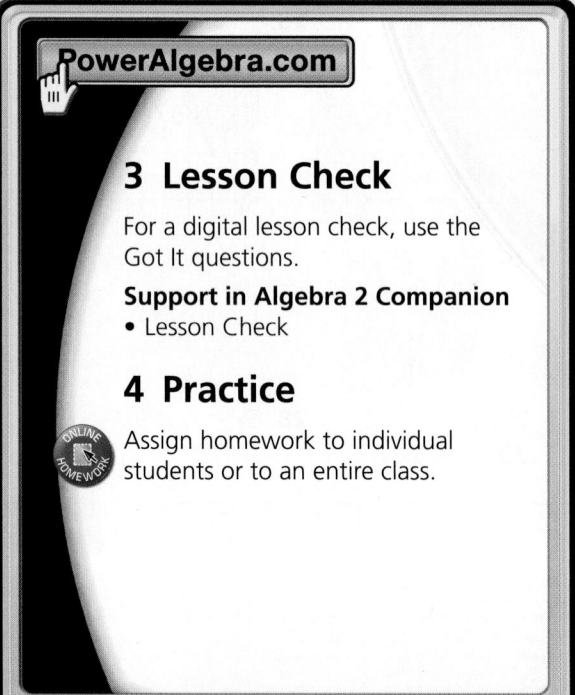

3 Lesson Check

For a digital lesson check, use the Got It questions.

Support in Algebra 2 Companion
- Lesson Check

4 Practice

Assign homework to individual students or to an entire class.

Answers

Lesson Check

1.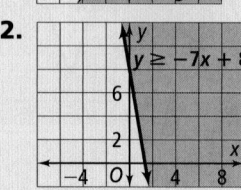

2.

3.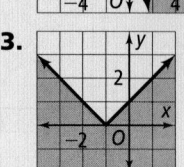

4.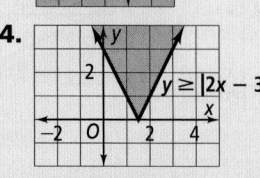

5. No; points on the boundary line distinguish between shaded and non-shaded areas, but do not give any information as to which side of the boundary line should be shaded.

6. Graphing a linear inequality in two variables includes first graphing the boundary line, which is a linear eq. in two variables, and then shading the half-plane.

7. No; $\left(\frac{3}{4}, 0\right)$ does not satisfy the inequality because $2.25 > 3$ is false.

Practice and Problem-Solving Exercises

8. 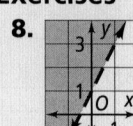   9. 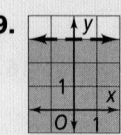   10.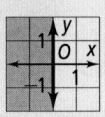

11–29.   See page 117.

Graph each inequality on a coordinate plane.

30. $5x - 2y \geq -10$ **31.** $2x - 5y < -10$ **32.** $\frac{3}{4}x + \frac{2}{3}y > \frac{5}{2}$ **33.** $3(x - 2) + 2y \leq 6$

34. $|x - 1| > y + 7$ **35.** $y - |2x| \leq 21$ **36.** $\frac{2}{3}x + 2 \leq \frac{2}{9}y$ **37.** $0.25y - 1.5x \geq -4$

38. Think About a Plan The graph at the right relates the number of hours you spend on the phone to the number of hours you spend studying per week. Describe the domain for this situation. Write an inequality for the graph.
- What is the least amount of time you can spend on the phone per week? What is the most?
- What is the least amount of time you can spend studying per week? What is the most?
- What is the greatest amount of time you can spend either on the phone or studying per week?

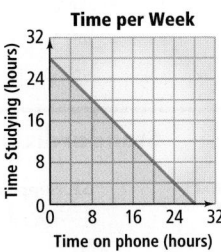

Time per Week

Write an inequality for each graph.

39. 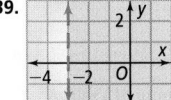 **40.** 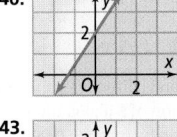 **41.**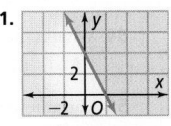

42. 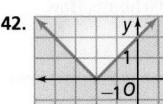 **43.** 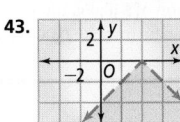 **44.**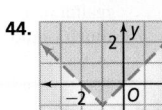

45. Which graph best represents the solution of the inequality $y \geq 2|x - 1| - 2$?

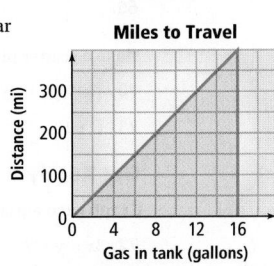

46. The graph at the right relates the amount of gas in the tank of your car to the distance you can drive.
  a. Describe the domain for this situation.
  b. Why does the graph stop?
  c. Why is only the first quadrant shown?
  d. Reasoning Would every point in the solution region be a solution?
  e. Write an inequality for the graph.
  f. What does the coefficient of x represent?

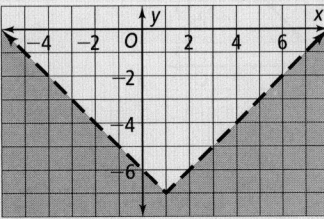

Miles to Travel

---

4 Practice

ASSIGNMENT GUIDE

Basic: 8–29 all, 36–46 even

Average: 9–29 odd, 30–46

Advanced: 9–29 odd, 30–51

Standardized Test Prep: 52–55

Mixed Review: 56–74

Mathematical Practices are supported by exercises with red headings. Here are the Practices supported in this lesson:

MP 1: Make Sense of Problems Ex. 38
MP 3: Communicate Ex. 47
MP 3: Construct Arguments Ex. 6, 7
MP 4: Model with Mathematics Ex. 46
MP 5: Use Appropriate Tools Ex. 48–51

Applications exercises have blue headings. Exercise 17 supports MP 4: Model.

EXERCISE 46: Use the Think About a Plan worksheet in the **Practice and Problem Solving Workbook** (also available in the Teaching Resources in print and online) to further support students' development in becoming independent learners.

HOMEWORK QUICK CHECK

To check students' understanding of key skills and concepts, go over Exercises 17, 19, 38, 44, and 46.

30.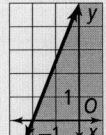

31.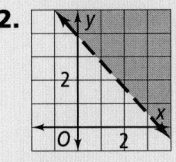

32.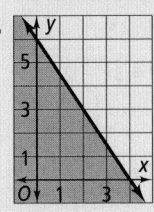

33.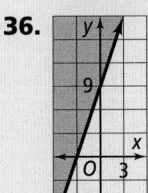

34.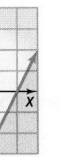

35.

36. **37.**

38. domain: $0 \leq x \leq 28$; $y \leq -x + 28$

39. $x > -3$ **40.** $y \leq \frac{3}{2}x + 2$

41. $y \geq -2x + 4$ **42.** $y \leq |x + 2|$

43. $y < -|x - 4|$

44. $y > |x + 1| - 1$

45. C

46. a. domain: $0 \leq x \leq 16$

  b. There is a limit to the number of gallons in your car's gas tank.

  c. You can't have a negative number of gallons of gas in your tank, nor can you drive a negative number of miles.

  d. Yes; you can use a fraction of a gallon, and you can drive a fraction of a mile.

  e. $y \leq 25x$

  f. the number of miles you can drive per gallon

Answers

Practice and Problem-Solving
Exercises (continued)

47. when the origin lies on the boundary line

48.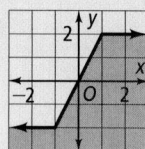

49.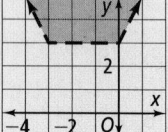

50.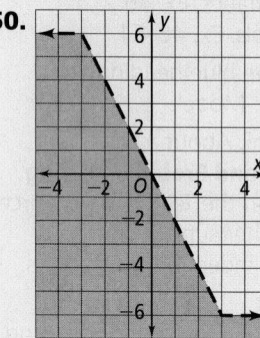

51.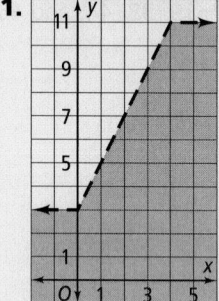

Standardized Test Prep

52. B

53. I

54. D

55. **[4]** let c = amnt. of a commission,
let s = amnt. of a sale
$c = ks$
($48,000) = k($800,000)
.06 = k
c = .06 ($650,000) = $39,000
(OR sltn. by another appropriate method)
[3] appropriate method, with one computational error
[2] correct value for k
[1] no work shown

Mixed Review

56.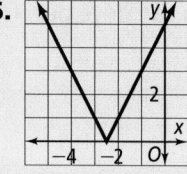

57.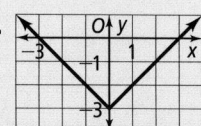

C Challenge

47. Writing When you graph an inequality, you can often use the point (0, 0) to test which side of the boundary line to shade. Describe a situation in which you could not use (0, 0) as a test point.

 **Graphing Calculator** Graph each inequality on a graphing calculator. Then sketch the graph.

48. $y \le |x + 1| - |x - 1|$

49. $y > |x| + |x + 3|$

50. $y < |x - 3| - |x + 3|$

51. $y < 7 - |x - 4| + |x|$

Standardized Test Prep

SAT/ACT

52. Suppose y varies directly with x. If x is 30 when y is 10, what is x when y is 9?

Ⓐ 3 　　 Ⓑ 27 　　 Ⓒ 29 　　 Ⓓ $\frac{300}{9}$

53. Which equation represents a line with slope -2 and y-intercept 3?

Ⓕ $3y = x - 2$ 　　 Ⓖ $3y = -2x + 1$ 　　 Ⓗ $y = 2x - 3$ 　　 Ⓘ $y = -2x + 3$

54. What is the vertex of $y = |x| - 5$?

Ⓐ $(5, 0)$ 　　 Ⓑ $(-5, 0)$ 　　 Ⓒ $(0, 5)$ 　　 Ⓓ $(0, -5)$

Extended Response

55. The amount of a commission is directly proportional to the amount of a sale. A realtor received a commission of $48,000 on the sale of an $800,000 house. How much would the commission be on a $650,000 house?

Mixed Review

Graph each function by translating its parent function.　　◆ See Lesson 2-7.

56. $y = |2x + 5|$ 　　 **57.** $y = |x| - 3$ 　　 **58.** $f(x) = |x + 6|$

59. $f(x) = |x| - 2$ 　　 **60.** $y = |x + 2|$ 　　 **61.** $y = |x - 1| + 5$

Determine whether y varies directly with x. If so, find the constant of variation.　　◆ See Lesson 2-2.

62. $y = x + 1$ 　　 **63.** $y = 100x$ 　　 **64.** $5x + y = 0$ 　　 **65.** $y - 2 = 2x$

66. $x = \frac{y}{3}$ 　　 **67.** $-4 = y - x$ 　　 **68.** $y = -10x$ 　　 **69.** $xy = 1$

Make a scatter plot and describe the correlation.　　◆ See Lesson 2-5.

70. $\{(0, 6), (1, 4), (2, 4), (4, 1), (5, 0)\}$

71. $\{(-10, 5), (-5, -5), (-2, 0), (0, 3), (5, -2)\}$

Get Ready! To prepare for Lesson 3-1, do Exercises 72–74.

Graph each equation. Use one coordinate plane for all three graphs.　　◆ See Lesson 2-3.

72. $3x - y = 2$ 　　 **73.** $3x - y = -2$ 　　 **74.** $x + 3y = -2$

58.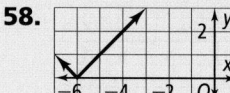

59.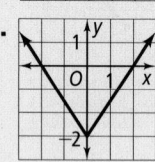

60.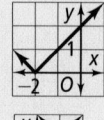

61.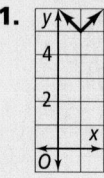

62. no 　　 **63.** yes; 100

64. yes; -5 　　 **65.** no

66. yes; 3 　　 **67.** no

68. yes; -10 　　 **69.** no

70. strong neg. correlation

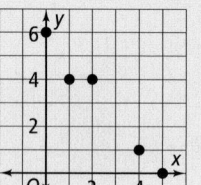

71. no correlation

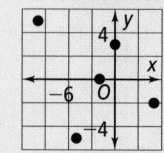

72–74.

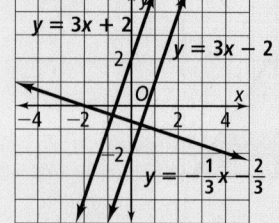

Additional Instructional Support

Algebra 2 Companion

Students can use the **Algebra 2 Companion** worktext (4 pages) as you teach the lesson. Use the Companion to support

- New Vocabulary
- Key Concepts
- Got It for each Problem
- Lesson Check

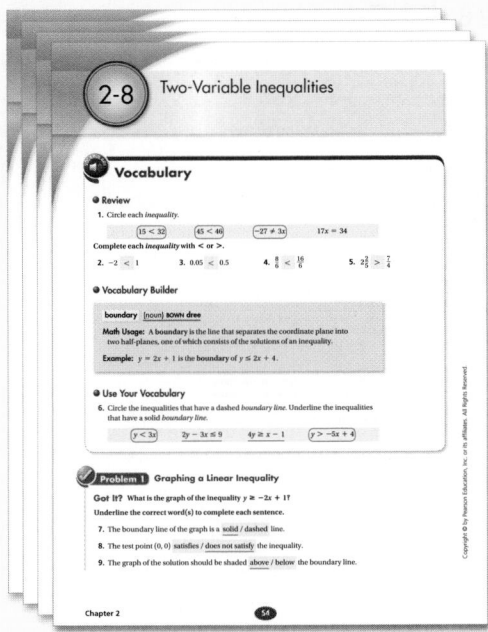

ELL Support

Focus on Language Draw a linear inequality on the board and have students identify each element. Ask students to identify the *boundary*, and a *half-plane*. Ask students if they can think of other examples of boundaries. Ask why it is called a *linear* inequality.

5 Assess & Remediate

Lesson Quiz

1. What is the graph of $y \le 5x + 2$?
2. **Do you UNDERSTAND?** At a local carnival, a hot dog costs $1.50 and water costs $0.80. You want to buy food and water for yourself and your friends but do not want to spend more than $20. What inequality represents how many hot dogs and how much water you can buy?
3. What is the graph of $-y > |x - 1| + 4$?
4. What inequality does this graph represent?

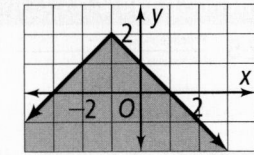

ANSWERS TO LESSON QUIZ

1.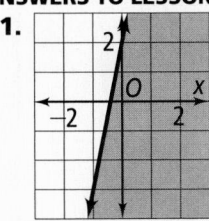

2. $0.8x + 1.5y \le 20$ or $1.5x + 0.8y \le 20$

3.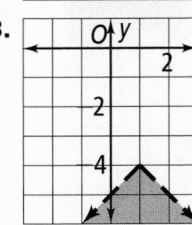

4. $y \le -|x + 1| + 2$

PRESCRIPTION FOR REMEDIATION

Use the student work on the Lesson Quiz to prescribe a differentiated review assignment:

Points	Differentiated Remediation
0–1	Intervention
2–3	On-level
4	Extension

PowerAlgebra.com

5 Assess & Remediate

Assign the Lesson Quiz. Appropriate intervention, practice, or enrichment is automatically generated based on student performance.

Differentiated Remediation

Available in editable format online.

Intervention

- **Reteaching** (2 pages) Provides reteaching and practice exercises for the key lesson concepts. Use with struggling students or absent students.
- **English Language Learner Support** Helps students develop and reinforce mathematical vocabulary and key concepts.

All-in-One Resources/Online
Reteaching

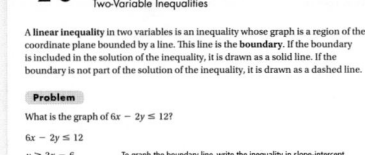

All-in-One Resources/Online
English Language Learner Support

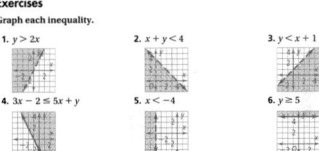

Differentiated Remediation continued

Available in editable format online.

On-Level

- **Practice** (2 pages) Provides extra practice for each lesson. For simpler practice exercises, use the Form K Practice pages found in the All-in-One Teaching Resources and online.

- **Think About a Plan** Helps students develop specific problem-solving skills and strategies by providing scaffolded guiding questions.

- **Standardized Test Prep** Focuses on all major exercises, all major question types, and helps students prepare for the high-stakes assessments.

Extension

- **Enrichment** Provides students with interesting problems and activities that extend the concepts of the lesson.

- **Activities, Games, and Puzzles** Worksheets that can be used for concepts development, enrichment, and for fun!

Practice and Problem Solving Wkbk/All-in-One Resources/Online
Practice page 1

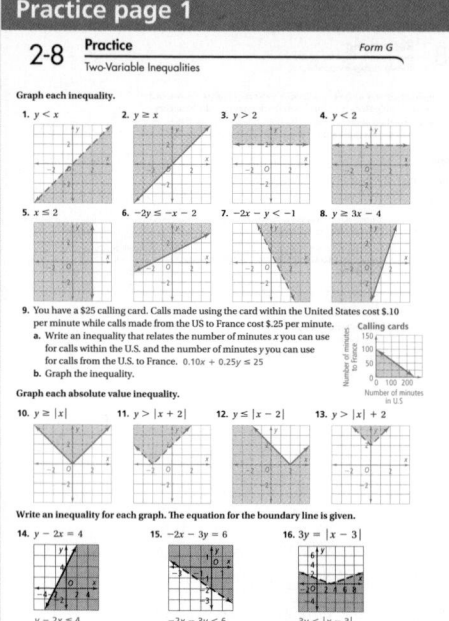

Practice and Problem Solving Wkbk/All-in-One Resources/Online
Practice page 2

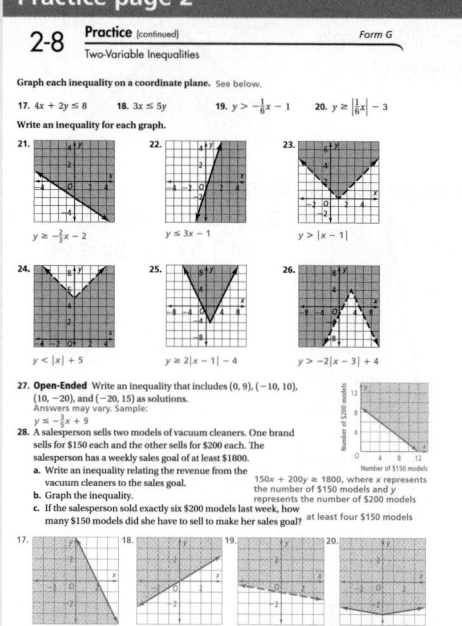
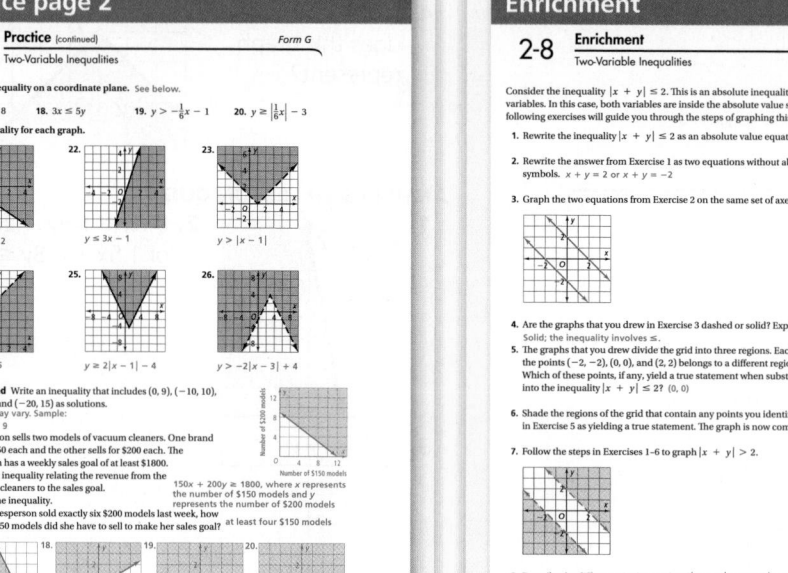

All-in-One Resources/Online
Enrichment

Practice and Problem Solving Wkbk/All-in-One Resources/Online
Think About a Plan

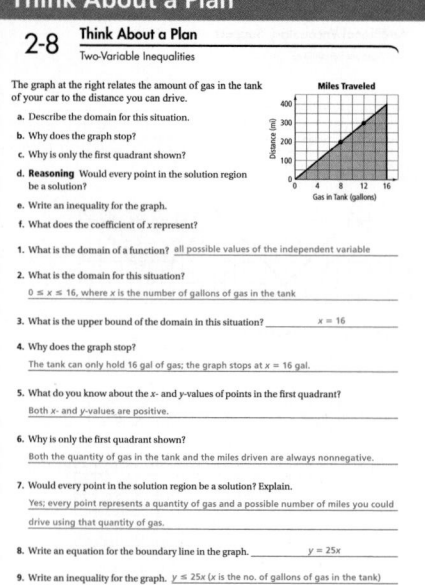

Practice and Problem Solving Wkbk/All-in-One Resources/Online
Standardized Test Prep

Online Teacher Resource Center
Activities, Games, and Puzzles

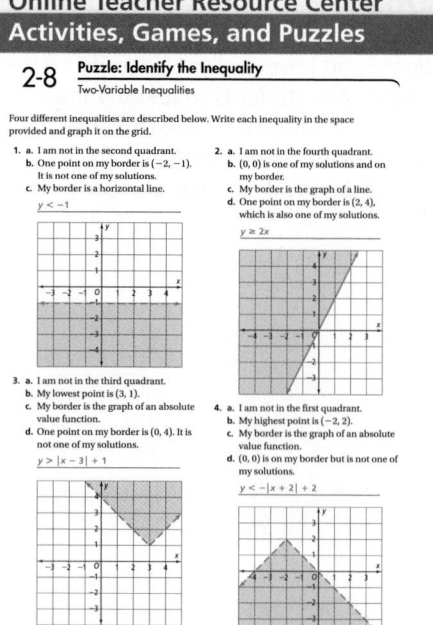

Pull It **All Together**

Completing the Performance Task

Look back at your results from the Apply What You've Learned sections in Lessons 2-3 and 2-4. Use the work you did to complete the following.

> To solve these problems, you will pull together concepts about equivalence, linear functions and modeling. Show your work and justify your reasoning.

1. Solve the problem in the Task Description on page 59 by determining what time the work crew will take its afternoon break. Show all your work and explain each step of your solution.

2. Reflect Choose one of the Mathematical Practices below and explain how you applied it in your work on the Performance Task.

MP 2: Reason abstractly and quantitatively.

MP 4: Model with mathematics.

On Your Own

The diagram from page 59 is shown again below. The county's Department of Transportation is planning the construction of another road, to be called Oak Street. Oak Street will begin at North Street, 30 miles north of Wilson Street. *Note:* North Street continues north, beyond its intersection with Main Street. Oak Street will be parallel to Main Street.

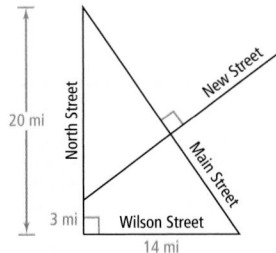

Determine how far the intersection of Oak Street and New Street will be from the intersection of Main Street and New Street.

Overview of the Performance Task

In the Apply What You've Learned sections in Lessons 2-3 and 2-4, students represented the diagram on page 59 with a coordinate system and found the coordinates of the intersection point of the lines representing Main Street and New Street. They also found the distance the work crew must paint before taking a break, and wrote a function that models the distance left to paint in terms of the time the crew has been painting. Here, students use their function to complete the Performance Task. Ask students the following question as they work toward solving the problem.

Q How can you use the work you have done in the chapter to solve the problem? **[Sample: I can substitute 3 for $d(t)$ in the function rule I wrote in Lesson 2-4, and solve for t to find the length of time the crew works before they reach the point that is 3 mi from the intersection of Main Street and Wilson Street.]**

FOSTERING MATHEMATICAL DISCOURSE

Have students discuss alternative methods for finding the distance from the intersection of Main Street and Wilson Street to the intersection of New Street and Main Street to solve the problem in the Performance Task. Some students may suggest using similar triangles or the Pythagorean Theorem, without superimposing a coordinate system on the diagram.

ANSWERS

1. 2:30 P.M.

2. Check students' work.

On Your Own

This problem is similar to the problem posed on page 59, but now students work with parallel streets. Students should strive to solve this problem independently.

ANSWER

about 5.7 mi

Essential Questions

BIG idea Equivalence
ESSENTIAL QUESTION Does it matter which form of a linear equation you use?

ANSWER You can use either slope-intercept, point-slope, or standard form to represent linear functions. (You can transform one version to another as needed.)

BIG idea Functions
ESSENTIAL QUESTION How do you use transformations to help graph absolute value functions?

ANSWER You can use the values of a, h, and k in the form $y = a|x - h| + k$ to determine how the parent function $y = |x|$ has been transformed.

BIG idea Modeling
ESSENTIAL QUESTION How can you model data with a linear function?

ANSWER You can use the equation of a trend line or line of best fit to model data that cluster in a linear pattern.

---

(2) Chapter Review

Connecting BIG ideas and Answering the Essential Questions

1 Equivalence
You can use either slope-intercept, point-slope, or standard form to represent linear functions. (You can transform one version to another as needed.)

Slope-Intercept Form (Lesson 2-3)
$y = mx + b$
$y = 2x - 1$
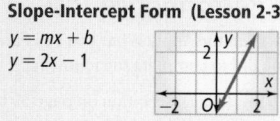

More Linear Equations (Lesson 2-4)
$y - y_1 = m(x - x_1)$ $Ax + By = C$
$y - 5 = 2(x - 3)$ $2x - y = 1$

2 Function
You can use the values of a, h, and k in the form $y = a|x - h| + k$ to determine how the parent function $y = |x|$ has been transformed.

Families of Functions (Lesson 2-6)
$f(x) + k$ vertical translation
$f(x - h)$ horizontal translation
$af(x)$ stretch or compression
$-f(x)$ reflection in the x-axis
$f(-x)$ reflection in the y-axis

Absolute Value Functions and Graphs (Lesson 2-7)
Parent: $y = |x|$
General form:
$y = a|x - h| + k$
vertex: (h, k)
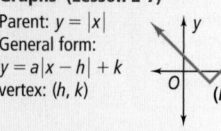

3 Modeling
You can use the equation of a trend line or line of best fit to model data that cluster in a linear pattern.

Using Linear Models (Lesson 2-5)
Positive correlation   Trend Line
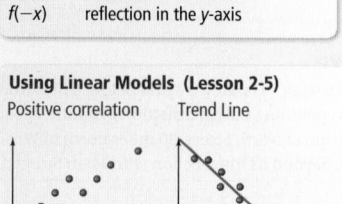

Chapter Vocabulary

- absolute value function (p. 107)
- axis of symmetry (p. 107)
- boundary (p. 114)
- constant of variation (p. 68)
- correlation (p. 92)
- correlation coefficient (p. 94)
- dependent variable (p. 63)
- direct variation (p. 68)
- domain (p. 61)
- function (p. 62)
- function notation (p. 63)
- function rule (p. 63)
- half-plane (p. 114)
- independent variable (p. 63)
- line of best fit (p. 94)
- linear equation (p. 75)
- linear function (p. 75)
- linear inequality (p. 114)
- parallel lines (p. 85)
- parent function (p. 99)
- perpendicular lines (p. 85)
- point-slope form (p. 81)
- range (p. 61)
- reflection (p. 101)
- relation (p. 60)
- scatter plot (p. 92)
- slope (p. 74)
- slope-intercept form (p. 76)
- standard form of a linear equation (p. 82)
- test point (p. 115)
- transformation (p. 99)
- translation (p. 99)
- vertex (p. 107)
- vertical compression (p. 102)
- vertical stretch (p. 102)
- vertical-line test (p. 62)
- x-intercept (p. 76)
- y-intercept (p. 76)

Choose the correct term to complete each sentence.

1. The graph of a function is (*always*/*sometimes*) a line.

2. The equation $y - 5 = 3(x + 2)$ is in (*point-slope*/*slope-intercept*) form.

Summative Questions

Use the following prompts as you review this chapter with your students. The prompts are designed to help you assess your students' understanding of the Big Ideas they have studied.

- A data set can be modeled by a direct variation function. What type of correlation might a scatter plot of this data show?
- What does the slope of the line of best fit of a scatter plot tell you about the correlation?
- How does a translation change a graph? reflection? vertical stretch or compression?
- How does a horizontal translation change the axis of symmetry of the graph of an absolute value function? How does a vertical translation change the axis of symmetry?
- What information does the slope-intercept form of a linear function give you about the graph of the function?

2-1 Relations and Functions

Quick Review

A **relation** is a set of ordered pairs. The **domain** of a relation is the set of x-coordinates. The **range** is the set of y-coordinates. When each element of the domain is paired with exactly one element of the range, the relation is a **function**.

Example

Determine whether the relation is a function. Find the domain and range.

$$\{(5, 0), (8, 1), (1, 3), (5, 2), (3, 8)\}$$

In this relation, the x-coordinate 5 is paired with both 0 and 2. This relation is not a function.

The domain is the set of x-coordinates, which is $\{5, 8, 1, 3\}$.

The range is the set of y-coordinates, which is $\{0, 1, 3, 2, 8\}$.

Exercises

Determine whether each relation is a function. Find the domain and range.

3. $\{(10, 2), (-10, 2), (6, 4), (5, 3), (-6, 7)\}$

4. $\{(4, 5), (1, 5), (3, 8), (4, 6), (10, 12)\}$

5. 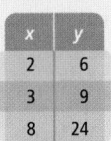   **6.**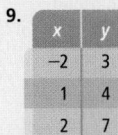

For each function, find $f(-2), f(-0.5)$, and $f(3)$.

7. $f(x) = -x + 4$ **8.** $f(x) = \frac{3}{8}x - 3$

2-2 Direct Variation

Quick Review

A linear equation of the form $y = kx$, $k \neq 0$, represents **direct variation**. The **constant of variation** is k. You can use proportions to solve direct variation problems.

Example

In the table, determine whether y varies directly with x. If so, what is the constant of variation and the function rule?

x	y
2	6
3	9
8	24

$\frac{6}{2} = \frac{9}{3} = \frac{24}{8} = 3$, so y varies directly with x, and the constant of variation is 3.

The function rule is $y = 3x$.

Exercises

For each function, determine whether y varies directly with x. If so, find the constant of variation and write the function rule.

9. 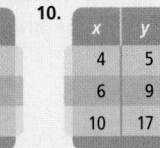 **10.** **11.**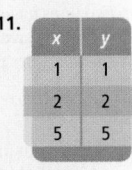

x	y
-2	3
1	4
2	7

x	y
4	5
6	9
10	17

x	y
1	1
2	2
5	5

For each function, y varies directly with x. Find each constant of variation. Then find the value of y when $x = -0.3$.

12. $y = 2$ when $x = -\frac{1}{2}$ **13.** $y = \frac{2}{3}$ when $x = 0.2$

14. $y = 7$ when $x = 2$ **15.** $y = 4$ when $x = -3$

Answers

Chapter Review

1. sometimes

2. point-slope

3. yes; domain: $\{-10, -6, 5, 6, 10\}$, range: $\{2, 3, 4, 7\}$

4. no; domain: $\{1, 3, 4, 10\}$, range: $\{5, 6, 8, 12\}$

5. no; domain:
$\left\{-2, -\frac{3}{2}, -1, \frac{1}{2}, 1, 2, 3\right\}$,
range: $\left\{-\frac{7}{2}, -\frac{1}{2}, 0, \frac{1}{2}, \frac{3}{2}, 2, \frac{5}{2}\right\}$

6. yes; domain:
$\left\{-2, -1, \frac{1}{2}, 3\right\}$, range: $\{2\}$

7. 6, 4.5, 1

8. $-3\frac{3}{4}, -3\frac{3}{16}, -1\frac{7}{8}$

9. no

10. no

11. yes; 1; $y = x$

12. -4; 1.2

13. $\frac{10}{3}$; -1

14. $\frac{7}{2}$; $-1\frac{1}{20}$

15. $-\frac{4}{3}$; 0.4

Answers

Chapter Review (continued)

16. $-\frac{2}{5}$

17. $\frac{7}{6}$

18. $\frac{2}{3}$

19. $-\frac{4}{9}$

20. $y = -3x + 4$

21. $y = \frac{1}{2}x + 6$

22. $y = 2x - \frac{3}{2}$

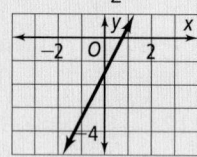

23. $y = \frac{2}{3}x + 3$

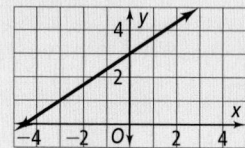

24. $y = -x + 5$

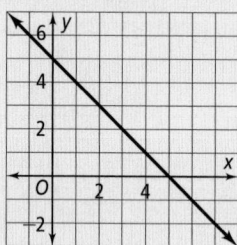

25. $y = -\frac{1}{3}x + \frac{5}{3}$

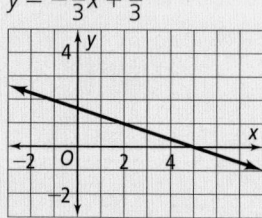

26. $y = -3(x - 4)$; $3x + y = 12$

27. $y + 1 = 5(x - 1)$; $5x - y = 6$

28. $y + 7 = -\frac{7}{3}(x - 3)$; $7x + 3y = 0$

29. $y - 3 = 2(x - 2)$; $2x - y = 1$

30. a. $y = -\frac{1}{2}x + 7$

   b. $y = 2x - 13$

   c. $y = -\frac{1}{2}x + 7$

   $y = 2x - 13$

   $y = -\frac{1}{2}x + 3$

2-3 Linear Functions and Slope-Intercept Form

Quick Review

The graph of a **linear function** is a line. You can represent a linear function with a **linear equation**. Given two points on a line, the **slope** of the line is the ratio of the change in the *y*-coordinates to the change in the corresponding *x*-coordinates. The slope is the coefficient of *x* when you write a linear equation in **slope-intercept form**.

Example

What is the slope of the line that passes through (3, 5) and (−1, −2)?

$m = \frac{y_2 - y_1}{x_2 - x_1}$ Find the difference between the coordinates.

$= \frac{5 - (-2)}{3 - (-1)} = \frac{7}{4}$ Simplify.

Exercises

Identify the slope of the line that passes through the given points.

16. (1, 3) and (6, 1)   **17.** (4, 4) and (−2, −3)

18. (3, 2) and (−3, −2)   **19.** (5, 2) and (−4, 6)

Write an equation for each line in slope-intercept form.

20. slope = −3 and the *y*-intercept is (0, 4)

21. slope = $\frac{1}{2}$ and the *y*-intercept is (0, 6)

Rewrite each equation in slope-intercept form. Graph each line.

22. $4x - 2y = 3$ **23.** $-4x + 6y = 18$

24. $3y + 3x = 15$ **25.** $3y + x = 5$

2-4 More About Linear Equations

Quick Review

You write the equation of a line in **point-slope form** when you have a point and the slope or when you have two points. The **standard form** of an equation has both variables and no constants on the left side.

When two lines have the same slope, they are **parallel**. When two lines have slopes that are negative reciprocals of each other, they are **perpendicular**.

Example

Write an equation in standard form for the line with a slope of 2, going through (1, 6).

$y - 6 = 2(x - 1)$ Write the equation in point-slope form, substituting the given point and slope.

$y = 2x - 2 + 6$ Simplify.

$-2x + y = 4$ Write in standard form.

Exercises

Write an equation for each line in point-slope form and then convert it to standard form.

26. slope = −3, through (4, 0)

27. slope = 5, through (1, −1)

28. through (0, 0) and (3, −7)

29. through (2, 3) and (3, 5)

30. a. Write an equation of the line parallel to $x + 2y = 6$ through (8, 3).

   b. Write an equation of the line perpendicular to $x + 2y = 6$ through (8, 3).

   c. Graph the three lines on the same coordinate plane.

2-5 Using Linear Models

Quick Review

You can use a **scatter plot** to show relationships between data sets. You can make predictions using a trend line, which approximates the relationship between two data sets. The most accurate trend line is a **line of best fit**.

Example

Draw a scatter plot of the data. Is a linear model reasonable? If so, predict the value of y when $x = 9$.

$\{(0, 6), (1, 7), (2, 5), (3, 4), (4, 2), (5, 1)\}$

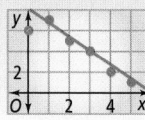

The points are close to the line $y = -\frac{4}{3}x + 8$, so a linear model is reasonable. When $x = 9$,

$y = -\frac{4}{3}(9) + 8$

$\quad = -4$

Exercises

Draw a scatter plot of each set of data. Decide whether a linear model is reasonable. If so, describe the correlation. Then draw a trend line and write its equation. Predict the value of y when x is 15.

31. $\{(3, 5), (4, 7), (5, 9), (7, 10), (8, 10), (9, 11), (10, 13)\}$

32. $\{(6, 15.5), (7, 14.0), (8, 13.0), (9, 12.5), (10, 12.0), (11, 11.5), (12, 10.0)\}$

33.

x	0	3	6	9	12
y	17.5	35.4	50.5	60.6	66.3

2-6 Families of Functions

Quick Review

A **parent function** is the simplest form of a function in a family of functions. Each member is a **transformation** of the parent function.

Translations shift the graph horizontally, vertically, or both. A **reflection** flips the graph over a line of symmetry. **Vertical stretches** and **compressions** change the shape of the graph by a factor.

Example

Write the equation of the transformation of the graph of $f(x) = x^2$ translated 3 units up, vertically stretched by a factor of 6, and reflected across the y-axis.

$y = x^2 + 3$ Translated 3 units up.

$y = 6(x^2 + 3)$ Vertically stretched.

$y = 6(-x)^2 + 18$ Reflected across the y-axis.

$y = 6x^2 + 18$

Exercises

Write the equation for the transformation of the graph of $y = f(x)$.

34. translated 2 units left, 7 units down

35. translated 5 units right, reflected across the x-axis

36. translated 3 units up, reflected across the y-axis

Describe the transformation(s) of the parent function $f(x)$.

37. $g(x) = f(x) - 4$

38. $h(x) = 12f(x) + 2$

39. $k(x) = -2f(-x)$

31.

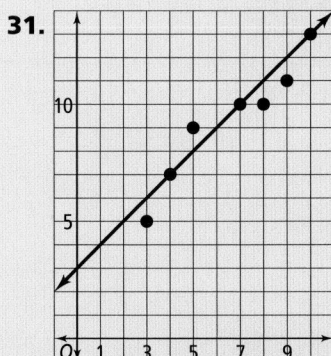

Strong pos. correlation; answers may vary. Sample: $y = x + 3$; 18

32.

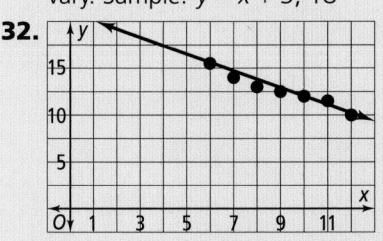

Strong neg. correlation; answers may vary. Sample: $y = -0.9x + 21$; 7.5

33.

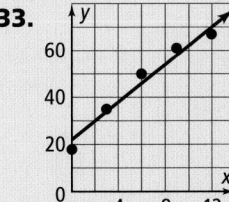

Strong pos. correlation; answers may vary. Sample:

$y = 4x + 22$; 82

34. $y = f(x + 2) - 7$

35. $y = -f(x - 5)$

36. $y = f(-x) + 3$

37. translated 4 units down

38. vertically stretched by a factor of 12, translated 2 units up

39. vertically stretched by a factor of 2, reflected across the y-axis, reflected across the x-axis

Answers

Chapter Review (continued)

40. $y = |x - 2| + 4$

41. $y = |x + 3|$

42. $y = |x - 5| + 2$

43. $y = |x - 4| + 1$

44.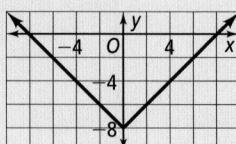

45.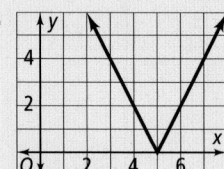

46.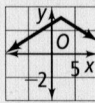

47.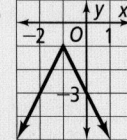

48. $(4, 0)$; $x = 4$

49. $(0, 2)$; $x = 0$

50.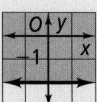

51.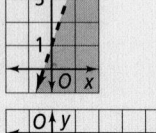

52.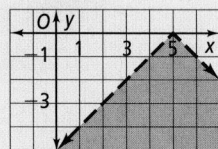

53.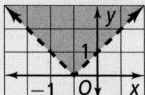

54. a. Answers may vary. Sample: $x + 3y \le 15$

 b. Answers may vary. Sample: domain: $\{0, 1, 2, 3, 4, 5, 6, 7, 8, 9, 10, 11, 12, 13, 14, 15\}$, range: $\{0, 1, 2, 3, 4, 5\}$

 c.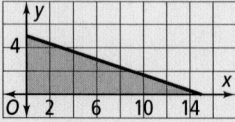

55. Answers may vary. Sample: $y \le -|x| - 1$

2-7 Absolute Value Functions and Graphs

Quick Review

The **absolute value function** $y = |x|$ is the **parent function** for the family of functions of the form $y = a|x - h| + k$. The maximum or minimum point of the graph is the vertex of the graph.

$y = 2|x + 3| + 1$
$a = 2, h = -3, k = 1$
- Vertex is at $(-3, 1)$
- Translated left 3 units
- Stretched by a factor of 2
- Translated up 1 unit

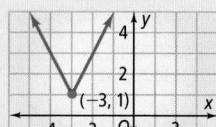

Example

Write an equation for the translation of the graph $y = |x|$ up 5 units.

Because the graph is translated up, k is positive, so the equation of the translated graph is $y = |x| + 5$.

Exercises

Write an equation for each translation of the graph of $y = |x|$.

40. up 4 units, right 2 units
41. vertex $(-3, 0)$
42. vertex $(5, 2)$
43. vertex $(4, 1)$

Graph each function.

44. $f(x) = |x| - 8$
45. $f(x) = 2|x - 5|$
46. $y = -\frac{1}{4}|x - 2| + 3$
47. $y = -2|x + 1| - 1$

Without graphing, identify the vertex and axis of symmetry of each function.

48. $y = 2|x - 4|$
49. $y = -|x| + 2$

2-8 Two Variable Inequalities

Quick Review

An inequality describes a region of the coordinate plane that has a **boundary**. To graph an inequality involving two variables, first graph the boundary. Then determine which side of the boundary contains the solutions. Points on a dashed boundary are not solutions. Points on a solid boundary are solutions.

Example

Graph the inequality $y \ge 2x + 3$.

Graph the solid boundary line $y = 2x + 3$.

Since y is *greater than* $2x + 3$, shade above the boundary.

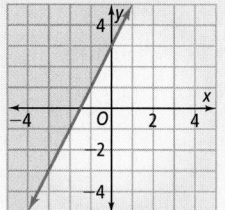

Exercises

Graph each inequality.

50. $y \ge -2$
51. $y < 3x + 1$
52. $y < -|x - 5|$
53. $y > |2x + 1|$

54. Transportation An air cargo plane can transport as many as 15 regular shipping containers. One super-size container takes up the space of 3 regular containers.
 a. Write an inequality to model the number of regular and super-size containers the plane can transport.
 b. Describe the domain and range.
 c. Graph the inequality you wrote in part (a).

55. Open-Ended Write an absolute value inequality with a solid boundary that only has solutions below the x-axis.

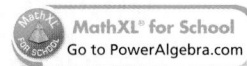
MathXL® for School
Go to PowerAlgebra.com

Do you know HOW?

Find the domain and range. Graph each relation.

1. $\{(0, 0), (1, -1), (2, -4), (3, -9), (4, -16)\}$

2. $\{(3, 2), (4, 3), (5, 4), (6, 5), (7, 6)\}$

Determine whether each relation is a function.

3.
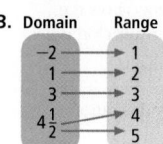
Domain   Range

4.
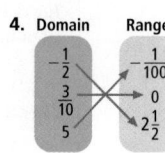
Domain   Range

Suppose $f(x) = 2x - 5$ and $g(x) = |-3x - 1|$.
Find each value.

5. $f(3)$ **6.** $f(1) + g(2)$ **7.** $g(0)$

8. $g(2) - f(0)$ **9.** $f(-1) - g(3)$ **10.** $2g(-4)$

Find the slope of each line.

11. through $(3, 5)$, parallel to $y = 5x - 1$

12. through $(-0.5, 0.5)$, perpendicular to $y = -2x - 4$

Write an equation of the line in standard form with the given slope through the given point.

13. slope $= -3$, $(0, 0)$ **14.** slope $= \frac{2}{5}$, $(6, 7)$

15. slope $= 4$, $(-2, -5)$ **16.** slope $= -0.5$, $(0, 6)$

Write an equation of the line in point-slope form through each pair of points.

17. $(0, 0)$ and $(-4, 7)$ **18.** $(-1, -6)$ and $(-2, 10)$

19. $(3, 0)$ and $(-1, -2)$ **20.** $(9, 5)$ and $(8, 2)$

For each direct variation, find the constant of variation. Then find the value of y when $x = -0.5$.

21. $y = 4$ when $x = 0.5$ **22.** $y = 2$ when $x = 3$

Write an equation of the line with the given slope and y-intercept. Use slope-intercept form. Then rewrite each equation in standard form.

23. $m = 3$, $b = -7$ **24.** $m = -6$, $b = 9$

25. $m = \frac{1}{4}$, $b = 11$ **26.** $m = -\frac{1}{2}$, $b = 4$

Graph each inequality.

27. $y \geq x + 7$ **28.** $y > 2|x + 3| - 3$

29. $4x - 3y < 2$ **30.** $y \leq -\frac{1}{2}|x + 2| - 3$

Do you UNDERSTAND?

31. Open-Ended Graph a relation that is *not* a function. Find its domain and range.

32. Writing Explain how point-slope form is related to the formula for slope.

Describe each transformation of the parent function $y = |x|$. Then, graph each function.

33. $y = |x| - 4$ **34.** $y = |x - 1| - 5$

35. $y = -|x + 4| + 3$ **36.** $y = 2|x + 1|$

37. Recreation The table displays the amounts the Jackson family spent on vacations during the years 2000–2009.

Family Vacations

Year	Cost	Year	Cost
2000	$1750	2005	$2750
2001	$1750	2006	$3200
2002	$2000	2007	$2900
2003	$2200	2008	$3100
2004	$2700	2009	$3300

a. Make a scatter plot of the data.
b. Draw a trend line. Write its equation.
c. Estimate the amount the Jackson family will spend on vacations in 2015.
d. Writing Explain how to use a trend line to make a prediction.

27.
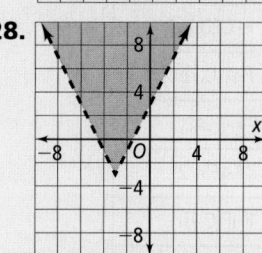

28.
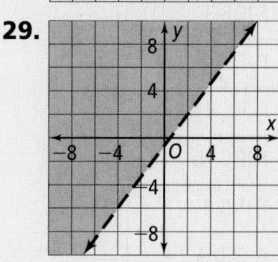

29.
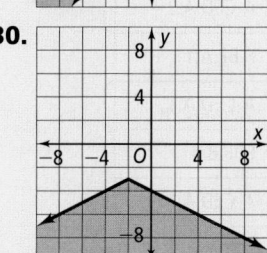

30.
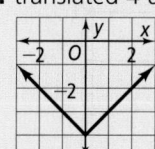

31. Check students' work.

32. The slope m of the line through pts. (x, y) and (x_1, y_1) is given by the formula $m = \frac{y - y_1}{x - x_1}$. Multiplying both sides of this eq. by the denominator $(x - x_1)$ gives the point-slope form of the eq. of a line: $y - y_1 = m(x - x_1)$.

33. translated 4 units down

34–37. See next page.

Answers

Chapter Test

1. domain: $\{0, 1, 2, 3, 4\}$,
range: $\{-16, -9, -4, -1, 0\}$

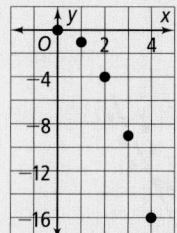

2. domain: $\{3, 4, 5, 6, 7\}$,
range: $\{2, 3, 4, 5, 6\}$

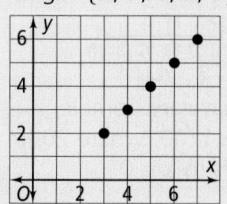

3. no **4.** yes **5.** 1

6. 4 **7.** 1 **8.** 12
9. -17 **10.** 22 **11.** 5
12. $\frac{1}{2}$ **13.** $3x + y = 0$
14. $2x - 5y = -23$
15. $4x - y = -3$
16. $x + 2y = 12$
17. $y = -\frac{7x}{4}$ or $y - 7 = \frac{-7}{4}(x + 4)$
18. $y + 6 = -16(x + 1)$ or $y - 10 = -16(x + 2)$
19. $y = \frac{1}{2}(x - 3)$ or $y + 2 = \frac{1}{2}(x + 1)$
20. $y - 2 = 3(x - 8)$ or $y - 5 = 3(x - 9)$
21. 8; -4 **22.** $\frac{2}{3}$; $-\frac{1}{3}$
23. $y = 3x - 7$; $3x - y = 7$
24. $y = -6x + 9$; $6x + y = 9$
25. $y = \frac{1}{4}x + 11$; $-x + 4y = 44$
26. $y = -\frac{1}{2}x + 4$; $x + 2y = 8$

Item Number	Lesson	© Content Standard
1	2-8	F-IF.C.7b
2	1-6	*A-SSE.A.1b
3	1-6	A-CED.A.1
4	1-6	A-CED.A.1
5	2-8	F-IF.C.7b
6	2-1	*F-IF.A.1
7	2-1	*F-IF.A.2
8	2-7	F-IF.C.7b
9	2-7	F-IF.B.3
10	2-5	F-IF.B.4
11	p. 90	F-IF.C.7b
12	p. 90	F-IF.C.7b
13	2-3	F-IF.B.4
14	2-2	A-CED.A.2
15	2-2	F-BF.A.1
16	1-4	A-CED.A.1
17	2-3	F-IF.B.4
18	1-4	A-CED.A.1
19	1-4	A-CED.A.1
20	1-3	*A-SSE.A.1a
21	1-6	A-CED.A.1
22	1-6	A-CED.A.1
23	1-4	A-CED.A.1
24	2-3	F-IF.B.4
25	2-1	*F-IF.A.2
26	2-3	F-IF.B.4
27	2-2	F-BF.A.1
28	2-1	*F-IF.A.2
29	2-8	F-IF.C.7b
30	2-2	F-BF.A.1
31	2-1	*F-IF.A.2
32	2-4	A-CED.A.2
33	1-2	*N-RN.B.3
34	2-4	F-IF.C.7

* Reviews standard

TIPS FOR SUCCESS

Some problems require you to use direct variation to solve for an unknown quantity. Read the question at the right. Then follow the tips to answer the sample question.

TIP 1

Some problems give more information than you need. Decide what information you need to answer the question.

A salad dressing recipe calls for $1\frac{1}{3}$ cups of buttermilk, 1 egg, $\frac{1}{2}$ cup of orange juice, and 1 tablespoon of lemon juice. Dan plans to use 2 cups of buttermilk instead. How much orange juice should he use?

Ⓐ $\frac{3}{8}$ cup

Ⓑ $\frac{3}{4}$ cup

Ⓒ $1\frac{1}{6}$ cup

Ⓓ $1\frac{1}{3}$ cup

TIP 2

Use some of the information to find k, the constant of variation in $y = kx$.

Think It Through

The ratio that shows how the amount of buttermilk changes is $k = \frac{2}{1\frac{1}{3}}$.

You can simplify this ratio.

$$2 \div \frac{4}{3} = \frac{2}{1} \cdot \frac{3}{4} = \frac{3}{2}$$

Use $k = \frac{3}{2}$ in the direct variation equation $y = \frac{3}{2}x$.

Let x represent the original amount of orange juice.

$$y = \frac{3}{2}x = \frac{3}{2} \cdot \frac{1}{2} = \frac{3}{4}$$

The correct answer is B.

 **Vocabulary Builder**

As you solve test items, you must understand the meanings of mathematical terms. Match each term with its mathematical meaning.

A. linear function

B. direct variation

C. range

D. translation

I. the set of all outputs, or y-coordinates, of a relation

II. a transformation that shifts a graph horizontally, vertically, or both

III. a function that can be written in the form $y = mx + b$

IV. a function that can be written in the form $y = kx$, $k \neq 0$

Selected Response

Read each question. Then write the letter of the correct answer on your paper.

1. Which of the following absolute value inequalities has no solutions in Quadrant IV?

Ⓐ $y + 2 \geq |x - 3|$ Ⓒ $y - 1 > |2x + 6|$

Ⓑ $y > 3 - |5 - x|$ Ⓓ $y \leq |4x| - 7$

2. For which value of b would the equation $3|x - 2| = bx - 6$ have infinitely many solutions?

Ⓕ -6 Ⓗ -3

Ⓖ 3 Ⓘ 6

128 Chapter 2 Common Core Cumulative Standards Review

Answers

Chapter Test (continued)

34. translated 1 unit to the rt. and 5 units down

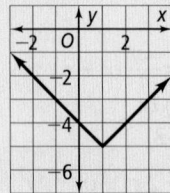

35. translated 4 units to the left, reflected vertically across the x-axis, then translated up 3 units

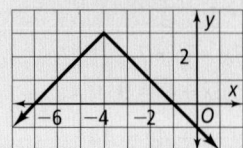

36. translated 1 unit to the left and vertically stretched by a factor of 2

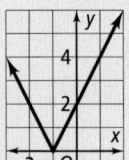

37. a–b.

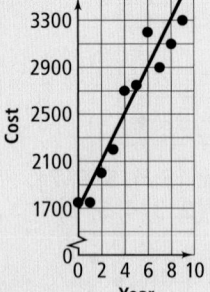

Answers may vary. Sample: $y = 200x + 1700$, where 2000 corresponds to $x = 0$.

c. $4700

d. Check students' work.

3. A meteorologist predicts the daily high and low temperatures as 91°F and 69°F. If t represents the temperature, then this situation can be described with the inequality $69 \le t \le 91$. Which of the following absolute value inequalities is an equivalent way of expressing this?

Ⓐ $69 \le |t| \le 91$

Ⓑ $|t - 80| \le 11$

Ⓒ $|t - 69| \le 91$

Ⓓ $|t - 11| \le 80$

4. Which inequality has a solution that matches the graph below?

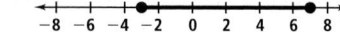

Ⓕ $|x - 2| - 3 \ge 2$

Ⓖ $|x - 2| - 3 \le 2$

Ⓗ $|x - 3| + 2 \ge 7$

Ⓘ $|x - 3| + 2 \le 7$

5. Which inequality best describes the graph?

Ⓐ $y \le \frac{1}{2}|x + 1| - 1$

Ⓑ $y \ge \frac{1}{2}|x - 1| - 1$

Ⓒ $y \le \frac{1}{2}|x - 1| - 1$

Ⓓ $y \ge \frac{1}{2}|x + 1| - 1$

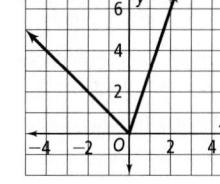

6. Which relation is a function?

Ⓕ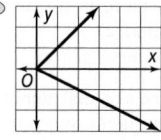

Ⓗ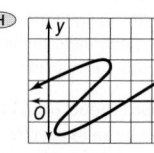

Ⓖ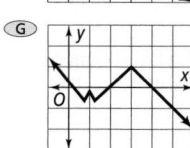

Ⓘ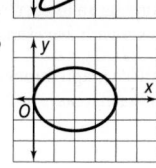

7. For $f(x) = 2x - 3$ find $f\left(-\frac{1}{4}\right)$.

Ⓐ $-\frac{3}{2}$ Ⓑ -2 Ⓒ $2\frac{1}{2}$ Ⓓ $-\frac{7}{2}$

8. Which equation is graphed?

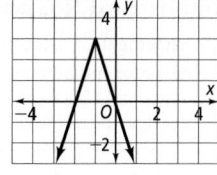

Ⓕ $y = -3|x + 1| + 3$

Ⓖ $y = 3|x + 1| + 3$

Ⓗ $y = -3|x - 1| + 3$

Ⓘ $y = 3|x + 1| - 3$

9. Which describes the translation of $y = |x - 3| + 5$?

Ⓐ $y = |x|$ translated 3 units left and 5 units up

Ⓑ $y = |x|$ translated 3 units right and 5 units up

Ⓒ $y = |x|$ translated 5 units left and 3 units up

Ⓓ $y = |x|$ translated 5 units right and 3 units up

10. If a rate of speed r is constant, then distance, rate, and time are related by the direct variation equation $d = rt$, where d represents distance and t represents time. If $r = 30$ miles per hour, which of the following best describes the graph of $d = rt$?

Ⓕ A straight line through the point $(0, 0)$

Ⓖ A straight line through the point $(0, 30)$

Ⓗ A parabola through the point $(0, 0)$

Ⓘ A parabola through the point $(0, 30)$

11. Which function has the graph shown?

Ⓐ $f(x) = \begin{cases} -x, & x < 0 \\ 3x, & x \ge 0 \end{cases}$

Ⓑ $f(x) = \begin{cases} x, & x < 0 \\ -3x, & x \ge 0 \end{cases}$

Ⓒ $f(x) = \begin{cases} x, & x > 0 \\ -3x, & x \le 0 \end{cases}$

Ⓓ $f(x) = \begin{cases} -x, & x > 0 \\ 3x, & x \le 0 \end{cases}$

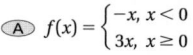

12. Which equation has the same graph as

$f(x) = \begin{cases} \frac{1}{3}x, & x > 6 \\ -\frac{1}{3}x + 4, & x \le 6 \end{cases}$?

Ⓕ $f(x) = -\frac{1}{3}|x - 6| + 4$

Ⓖ $f(x) = \frac{1}{3}x$

Ⓗ $f(x) = \frac{1}{3}|x - 6| + 2$

Ⓘ $f(x) = -\frac{1}{3}x + 10$

PowerAlgebra.com

Answers

Common Core Cumulative Standards Review

A. III

B. IV

C. I

D. II

1. C

2. G

3. B

4. G

5. C

6. G

7. D

8. F

9. B

10. F

11. A

12. H

Answers

Common Core Cumulative Standards Review (continued)

13. $\frac{2}{25}$

14. 2.25

15. 0

16. $12

17. 4

18. −14

19. $63.75

20. 27

21. 0

22. 16

23. 8

24. $\frac{3}{2}$

25. 15

26. −4

27. [2] yes; 58; $d = 58t$

[1] partial correct answer

28. [2] $f(-3) = \frac{2}{5}(-3) - 2 = -3\frac{1}{5}$

$f(0) = \frac{2}{5}(0) - 2 = -2$

$f(1) = \frac{2}{5}(1) - 2 = -1\frac{3}{5}$

[1] computational error

29. [2]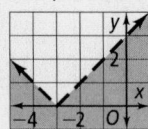

the parent function is $y = |x|$, and $y = |x + 3|$ is $y = |x|$ shifted 3 units to the left.

[1] correct graph, incorrect description of the translation

30. [2] $y = kx$

$(2) = k(-2)$

$-1 = k$

$y = (-1)x$

$(3) = (-1)x$

$-3 = x$ (OR another appropriate method)

[1] computational error

31. [2] domain: $\{-3, -2, -1, 0\}$

range: $\{-1, 0, 2, 3\}$

[1] partial correct answer

32. [4] **a.** $y - 6 = 2(x + 2) = 2x + 4$

$y = 2x + 10$ (OR equivalent eq.)

b. $y - 1 = -\frac{1}{2}(x - 1) = -\frac{1}{2}x + \frac{1}{2}$

$y = -\frac{1}{2}x + \frac{3}{2}$ (OR equivalent eq.)

c.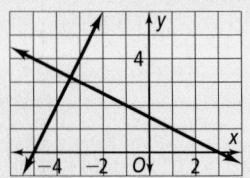

Constructed Response

13. What is the slope of the line $5y + 3 = \frac{2}{5}x$?

14. A recipe for custard sauce calls for 6 egg yolks, $\frac{2}{3}$ cup of sugar, and $1\frac{1}{2}$ cups of hot milk. Chelsea needs more sauce than the recipe yields. She plans to use 1 cup of sugar. How many cups of hot milk should she use?

15. What is the y-coordinate of the point through which the graph of every direct variation passes?

16. Six members of the math club will participate in a regional competition. A processing fee of $15 is added to the registration cost. If the math coach sends in a check for $87, how much does he pay for each registration?

17. What is the y-coordinate of the y-intercept of the line $4x + 3y = 12$?

18. If $4(x + 2) - 2(x - 10) = 0$, what is the value of x?

19. Mr. Wong traveled 45 miles on a business trip. The cost to rent a car is $30.00 plus $.75 per mile. How much did Mr. Wong pay for the car rental?

20. In the expression $38 + 27y$, which number is a coefficient?

21. What is the greatest integer solution of $|-2x - 5| - 3 \le 2$?

22. What is the sum of the solutions of $3|y - 4| = 9$ and $|y - 4| = 3$?

23. What is the value of x in the equation $6(x - 4) = 3x$?

24. What is the slope of the line represented by the function $3x - 2y = -12$?

25. What is $f(-3)$ for the function $f(x) = -3x + 6$?

26. What is the y-coordinate of the y-intercept of the line?

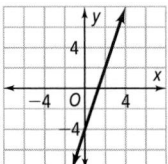

27. Matt drove at a steady speed during the first morning of his road trip. The table shows data about his driving.

Time Driving (hours) t	Total Distance (miles) d
1.5	87
2.25	130.5
3	174

Determine whether distance d varies directly with time t. If so, what are the constant of variation and the function rule?

28. Find $f(-3)$, $f(0)$, and $f(1)$ for the function $f(x) = \frac{2}{5}x - 2$.

29. Graph $y < |x + 3|$. Identify the parent function of the boundary and describe the translation.

30. Suppose y varies directly with x, and $y = 2$ when $x = -2$. Find the constant of variation. Then find the value of x when $y = 3$.

31. The points $(-3, 2)$, $(-1, 3)$, $(0, 0)$, $(-2, -1)$ represent a function. What are the domain and range?

Extended Response

32. a. Write an equation of the line through $(-2, 6)$ with slope 2.

b. Write an equation of the line through $(1, 1)$ and perpendicular to the line in part (a).

c. Graph the two lines on the same set of axes.

33. Will the product of an integer and a natural number always be an integer? Why or why not? Justify your answer with two examples.

34. Sketch a graph through the point $(1, 1)$ such that as an x-value increases by 2, the y-value decreases by 3.

---

[3] appropriate method, but with one computational error

[2] incorrect eq. of the perpendicular ln., graph drawn correctly given previous results

[1] correct equations, no graph

33. [4] Yes; the product of an integer and an integer is always an integer. Since the set of natural numbers is a subset of integers, the product of an integer and a natural number will always be an integer. For example: the number 1 is a natural number. 1 multiplied by any integer will always be that integer because 1 is the mult. ident. Also, 0 is an integer. 0 multiplied by any natural number is always 0. (OR equivalent explanation)

[3] incomplete explanation OR only one example provided

[2] correct explanation, but without examples provided

[1] two examples provided, no explanation

34. [4]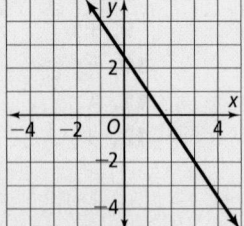

[3] sketch of a line that passes through $(1, 1)$ but slope is $\frac{3}{2}$ rather than $-\frac{3}{2}$

[2] sketch of a line that passes through $(1, 1)$ but slope is neither $\frac{3}{2}$ nor $-\frac{3}{2}$

[1] plotted the point $(1, 1)$

Get Ready!

Lesson 1-3 ◆ **Evaluating Algebraic Expressions**

Evaluate each expression for the given values of the variables.

1. $9t + 6(2v - t) - 7v$; $t = 1$ and $v = 5$

2. $11(a + 2b) + 2(a - 2b)$; $a = -3$ and $b = 4$

3. $\frac{3}{5}d + \frac{1}{10}h - \frac{7}{10}d - \frac{4}{5}h$; $d = 5$ and $h = 10$

4. $12\left(\frac{3}{4}x - \frac{1}{2}y\right) - 6\left(\frac{1}{2}x - \frac{3}{4}y\right)$; $x = 2$ and $y = -2$

Lesson 2-3 ◆ **Writing Linear Equations in Slope-Intercept Form**

Write the equation of each line in slope-intercept form.

5. $2x - 4y = 10$ **6.** $3y + 9 = -6x$ **7.** $y - 5x = 16$ **8.** $-7 - y = -3x$

9. $\frac{x}{6} - \frac{5}{12}y = \frac{5}{8}$ **10.** $4x = y - 11$ **11.** $2y = -12x - 16$ **12.** $\frac{y}{9} + \frac{x}{3} = 2$

Lesson 2-3 ◆ **Graphing Linear Equations**

Graph each equation.

13. $3x = y - 1$ **14.** $x - 5y = 10$ **15.** $12 + 2y = 3x$ **16.** $y = 4x$

Lesson 2-8 ◆ **Graphing Inequalities**

Graph each inequality.

17. $4y \le 24x$ **18.** $y \ge 2|x - 1.5|$ **19.** $x + 5y \ge 20$ **20.** $y > |x + 6| - 2$

Looking Ahead Vocabulary

21. A *system* of mountains is a group of mountains that share similar geographic and geological features. What are some mountain systems in the United States?

22. Two things are *consistent* if they are in agreement with each other. What does it mean for your actions to be consistent with your words?

23. How many books does Jeff own if he has more than 14 books? Describe the number of books that Jeff owns if you add the *constraint* that he owns fewer than his sister, who owns 19 books.

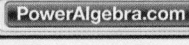

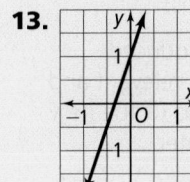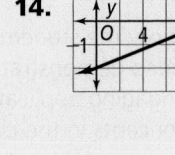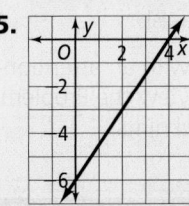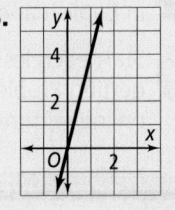

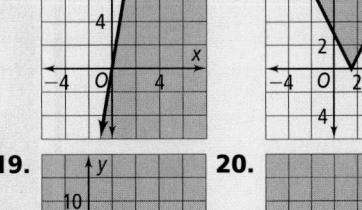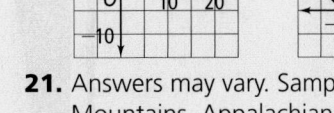

 PowerAlgebra.com   Chapter 3   Linear Systems   **131**

Get Ready!

Assign this diagnostic assessment to determine if students have the prerequisite skills for Chapter 3.

Lesson	Skill
1-3	Evaluate Algebraic Expressions
2-3	Write Linear Equations in Slope-Intercept Form
2-3	Graph Linear Equations
2-8	Graph Inequalities

To remediate students, select from these resources (available for every lesson).
• Online Problems (PowerAlgebra.com)
• Reteaching (All-in-One Teaching Resources)
• Practice (All-in-One Teaching Resources)

Why Students Need These Skills

EVALUATING ALGEBRAIC EXPRESSIONS
To check whether a solution is correct, students will need to evaluate the expressions on both sides of the equation for the values of the variables to make sure they are equivalent.

WRITING LINEAR EQUATIONS IN SLOPE-INTERCEPT FORM
Students will need to rewrite the equations in a system of linear equations in slope-intercept form when making a table. This form makes it easy to find y, given a value of x.

GRAPHING LINEAR EQUATIONS
Graphing is one way to find the solution to a system of linear equations.

GRAPHING INEQUALITIES
To find the feasible region of a linear programming problem, students will need to graph the given constraints, which are inequalities.

Looking Ahead Vocabulary

SYSTEM Ask students what a system of equations might be, based on the mountain definition.

CONSISTENT Ask students what it would mean if their actions were *not* consistent with their words.

CONSTRAINT Ask students how the constraint affects the possible number of books that Jeff owns. Ask students for some more examples of constraints that act as limitations or restrictions.

Answers

Get Ready!

1. 28   **2.** 33   **3.** $-\frac{15}{2}$ **4.** 15

5. $y = \frac{1}{2}x - \frac{5}{2}$ **6.** $y = -2x - 3$

7. $y = 5x + 16$ **8.** $y = 3x - 7$

9. $y = \frac{2}{5}x - \frac{3}{2}$ **10.** $y = 4x + 11$

11. $y = -6x - 8$ **12.** $y = -3x + 18$

13.   **14.**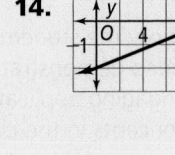

15.   **16.**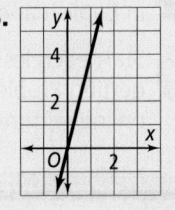

17.   **18.**

19.   **20.**

21. Answers may vary. Samples: Rocky Mountains, Appalachian Mountains

22. Answers may vary. Sample: Your actions are consistent with your words when your actions show what you are saying. For example, if you say you are happy and you are laughing or smiling.

23. 15 books or more; 15 books or more but less than 19, i.e., 15, 16, 17, or 18 books

Chapter 3 Overview

Chapter 3 expands on students' understandings and skills related to functions, equations, and graphs. In this chapter, students will develop the answers to the Essential Questions as they learn the concepts and skills bulleted below.

BIG idea Function

ESSENTIAL QUESTION How does representing functions graphically help you solve a system of equations?

- Students will solve a system of linear equations by graphing the equations to find the point(s) of intersection.

BIG idea Equivalence

ESSENTIAL QUESTION How does writing equivalent equations help you solve a system of equations?

- Students will use substitution and elimination methods to write equivalent equations until they get an equation with only one variable.

BIG idea Solving Equations and Inequalities

ESSENTIAL QUESTION How are the properties of equality used in the matrix solution of a system of equations?

- Students will use the Addition Property of Equality to add rows of matrices and the Multiplication Property of Equality to multiply rows by a constant.
- Students will use row operations to get reduced row echelon form, which gives the solution.

 **Content Standards**

Following are the standards covered in this chapter. Modeling standards are indicated by a star symbol (★).

CONCEPTUAL CATEGORY Algebra

Domain Creating Equations A-CED

Cluster Create equations that describe numbers or relationships.
(Standards A-CED.A.2★, A-CED.A.3★)
LESSONS 3-1, 3-4, CB 3-4

Domain Reasoning with Equations and Inequalities A-REI

Cluster Solve systems of equations.
(Standards A-REI.C.5, A-REI.C.6, A-REI.C.8)
LESSONS 3-2, 3-5, 3-6, CB 3-5

Cluster Represent and solve equations and inequalities graphically.
(Standards A-REI.D.11★, A-REI.D.12)
LESSONS 3-1, 3-3

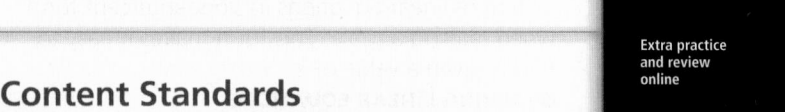

CHAPTER
3

Linear Systems

Download videos connecting math to your world.

Interactive! Vary numbers, graphs, and figures to explore math concepts.

The online Solve It will get you in gear for each lesson.

Math definitions in English and Spanish

Online access to stepped-out problems aligned to Common Core

Get and view your assignments online.

Extra practice and review online

Virtual Nerd™ tutorials with built-in support

Chapter Preview

3-1 Solving Systems Using Tables and Graphs
3-2 Solving Systems Algebraically
3-3 Systems of Inequalities
3-4 Linear Programming
3-5 Systems With Three Variables
3-6 Solving Systems Using Matrices

Vocabulary

English/Spanish Vocabulary Audio Online:

English	Spanish
dependent system, p. 137	sistema dependiente
equivalent systems, p. 144	sistemas equivalentes
independent system, p. 137	sistema independiente
linear system, p. 134	sistema lineal
matrix, p. 174	matriz
matrix element, p. 174	elemento matricial
row operation, p. 176	operación de filas
system of equations, p. 134	sistema de ecuaciones

BIG ideas

1 Function
Essential Question How does representing functions graphically help you solve a system of equations?

2 Equivalence
Essential Question How does writing equivalent equations help you solve a system of equations?

3 Solving Equations and Inequalities
Essential Question How are the properties of equality used in the matrix solution of a system of equations?

 DOMAINS
- Creating Equations
- Reasoning with Equations and Inequalities

 PowerAlgebra.com

Chapter 3 Overview

Use these online assets to engage your students. These include support for the Solve It and step-by-step solutions for Problems.

 Show the student-produced video demonstrating relevant and engaging applications of the new concepts in the chapter.

 Find online definitions for new terms in English and Spanish.

 Start each lesson with an attention-getting Problem. View the Problem online with helpful hints.

Common Core Performance Task

Planning a Triathlon

Sophia is in charge of planning an annual triathlon in her city. The triathlon will consist of three distinct sections, as described below.

Section 1: A swim across a part of Sunset Lake

Section 2: A bicycle ride through the new city park

Section 3: A run through downtown that ends at City Hall

The organizing committee for the triathlon asks Sophia to follow these criteria:

- Elite athletes should be able to finish in 2 hours.
- The distance of the swim is $\frac{1}{5}$ the distance of the run.
- The entire course covers a distance of 28 miles.

Sophia does some research on top triathlon finish times. She finds that, on average, elite athletes are able to swim at about 3 mi/h, bicycle at about 20 mi/h, and run at about 10 mi/h. Sophia needs to determine a triathlon course based on these rates.

Task Description

Plan the triathlon by determining the distance for each part of the course.

Connecting the Task to the Math Practices

MATHEMATICAL PRACTICES

As you complete the task, you'll apply several Standards for Mathematical Practice.

- You'll use a table and a graph to solve a related problem. (MP 5)
- You'll reason abstractly to write algebraic representations of parts of the triathlon. (MP 2)
- You'll use a system of linear equations to model the three criteria for the triathlon. (MP 4)

Overview of the Performance Task

Students will write a system of equations to model the problem situation. They will then solve the system of equations and interpret the results.

Students will work on the Performance Task in the following places in the chapter.

- Lesson 3-1 (p. 141)
- Lesson 3-2 (p. 148)
- Lesson 3-5 (p. 173)
- Pull It All Together (p. 182)

Introducing the Performance Task

Tell students to read the problem on this page. Do not have them start work on the problem at this time, but ask them the following questions.

> **Q** What is a strategy you could use in order to solve the problem? **[Sample: I can create an equation for each of the criteria and use these equations to find the distance of each part of the course.]**
>
> **Q** How many variables are there in this problem? Explain. **[Sample: There are three variables: the distances for the swim, the bicycle ride, and the run.]**

PARCC CLAIMS

Sub-Claim A: Major Content with Connections to Practices

Sub-Claim D: Highlighted Practice MP 4 with Connections to Content

SBAC CLAIMS

Claim 1: Concepts and Procedures

Claim 4: Modeling and Data Analysis

Increase students' depth of knowledge with interactive online activities.

Show Problems from each lesson solved step by step. Instant replay allows students to go at their own pace when studying online.

Assign homework to individual students or to an entire class.

Prepare students for the Mid-Chapter Quiz and Chapter Test with online practice and review.

Virtual Nerd™ Access Virtual Nerd student-centered math tutorials that directly relate to the content of the lesson.

LINEAR SYSTEMS
Math Background © PROFESSIONAL DEVELOPMENT

The Understanding by Design® methodology was central to the development of the Big Ideas and the Essential Understandings. These will help your students build a structure on which to make connections to prior learning.

Function

BIG idea A function is a relationship between variables in which each value of the input variable is associated with a unique value of the output variable. Functions can be represented in a variety of ways, such as graphs, tables, equations, or words. Each representation is particularly useful in certain situations. Some important families of functions are developed through transformations of the simplest form of the function.

ESSENTIAL UNDERSTANDINGS

3–1 To solve a system of equations, find a set of values that replace the variables in the equations and make each equation true.

3–3 You can solve a system of inequalities in more than one way. Graphing the solution is usually the most appropriate method. The solution is the set of all points that are solutions of each inequality in the system.

3–4 Some real-world problems involve multiple linear relationships. Linear programming accounts for all of these linear relationships and gives the solution to the problem.

Equivalence

BIG idea A single quantity may be represented by many different expressions. The facts about a quantity may be expressed by many different equations (or inequalities).

ESSENTIAL UNDERSTANDINGS

3–2 You can solve a system of equations by writing equivalent systems until the value on one variable is clear. Then substitute to find the value(s) of the other variable.

3–5 To solve systems of three equations in three variables, you can use some of the same algebraic methods you used to solve systems of two equations in two variables.

Solving Equations & Inequalities

BIG idea Solving an equation is the process of rewriting the equation to make what it says about its variable(s) as simple as possible. Properties of numbers and equality can be used to transform an equation (or inequality) into equivalent, simpler equations (or inequalities) in order to find solutions. Useful information about equations and inequalities (including solutions) can be found by analyzing graphs or tables. The numbers and types of solutions vary predictably, based on the type of equation.

ESSENTIAL UNDERSTANDINGS

3–1 to 3–3, 3–5 See above.

3–6 You can use a matrix to represent and solve a system of equations without writing the variables.

Solving Systems of Linear Equations

A solution to a system of linear equations is an ordered pair that makes all of the equations true. A system of linear equations can be solved by graphing or by algebraic methods.

Solving by graphing requires graphing each equation. It gives a visual representation of the solution of the system.
- Parallel lines indicate no solution.
- Intersecting lines indicate one solution—the point of intersection.
- Coinciding lines indicate infinitely many solutions—all the points on the line.

Solving by algebraic methods requires writing equivalent systems until the value of one variable is found. Use substitution to find the value(s) of the other variables.

Substitution is most often used when it is simple to isolate one of the variables. Solve $\begin{cases} y - x = 3 \\ 3y + 2x = 4 \end{cases}$.

$y = x + 3$ Solve the first equation for y.
$3(x + 3) + 2x = 4$ Substitute the expression for y into
$x = -1$ the second equation. Solve for x.

Substituting into either equation yields $y = 2$.

Elimination uses the Addition Property of Equality to solve systems. Write equivalent systems (if necessary) and use additive inverses to eliminate one of the variables. Solve for the other variable, and then substitute to find a solution.

$$\begin{cases} y - x = 3 \\ 3y + 2x = 4 \end{cases} \rightarrow \begin{matrix} 2[y - x = 3] \\ 3y + 2x = 4 \end{matrix} \rightarrow \begin{matrix} 2y - 2x = 6 \\ \underline{3y + 2x = 4} \end{matrix}$$

Add the equations to get $5y = 10$ so $y = 2$. Substituting into one of the original equations yields $x = -1$. The solution is $(-1, 2)$.

Common Errors With Solving Systems of Linear Equations

Graphing errors can occur when graphs are not drawn carefully. Errors include
- incorrect sign on the slope
- incorrectly graphed ordered pairs
- straight edge not used to draw lines.

Algebraic errors in substitution or elimination include
- solving for a variable and substituting the value back into the same equation rather than into the other equation
- failing to multiply through the entire equation when writing equivalent systems

© Mathematical Practices

Look for and make use of structure. Reason abstractly and quantitatively. Linear systems are analyzed algebraically, graphically, and numerically, with continual emphasis on the connections among the various representations.

Solving Systems of Inequalities

Graphing and tables can be used to solve systems of inequalities. The lines are boundary lines and may or may not be included in the solution. The shaded area for each inequality is determined, and the overlap area is the solution set of the system. Note that instead of the solution being a single ordered pair, the solution is the area where both inequalities are true.

For the system $\begin{cases} y \geq x + 3 \\ y < -2x - 4 \end{cases}$

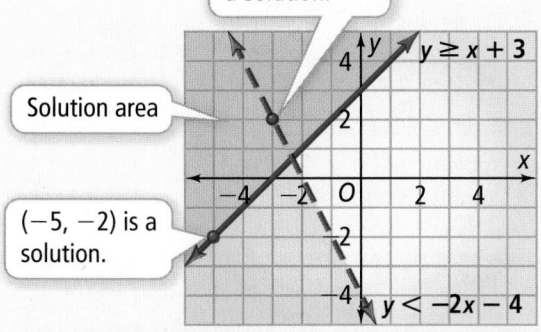

(−3, 2) is NOT a solution.

Solution area

(−5, −2) is a solution.

$y \geq x + 3$

$y < -2x - 4$

Linear programming is a type of inequality system used for solving many real-world problems. It consists of an objective function that needs to be maximized or minimized as well as several constraints represented by linear inequalities. Most real world problems solved by linear programming contain many variables. The solution area for this type of system is usually closed and is referred to as the feasible region. Like the solution area, the feasible region contains all points that satisfy all constraints. If there is a maximum or minimum value for the objective function, it will occur at one of the vertices of the feasible region.

© Mathematical Practices

Model with mathematics. Make sense of problems and persevere in solving them. Look for and express regularity in repeated reasoning. Multiple linear equations are presented in a variety of real-world contexts in which students can appreciate the need for finding simultaneous solutions. Linear programming problems motivate the study of simultaneous linear inequalities.

Solving Systems With 3 Variables

The graph of a linear equation in three variables is a plane. The graph of a solution of a system of three linear equations in three variables will be
- planes intersecting in one common point (one solution),
- planes intersecting along a common line (infinitely many solutions), or
- no point lying in all three planes (no solution).

Elimination, substitution, and matrix operations are used to solve any linear system if the number of variables is less than or equal to the number of equations in the system. Thus, two equations are needed to solve a system with two variables, three equations are needed to solve a system with three variables, and so on.

Elimination and substitution are used to combine any two of the equations into one equation with two variables. Then the unused linear equation is added to either of the original equations to obtain an equation with the same two variables.

To solve $\begin{cases} -6x - y - 3z = 10 \\ -x - y + 4z = 0 \\ x - y - z = -4 \end{cases}$, add the bottom two

equations to eliminate x, resulting in $-2y + 3z = -4$. The top equation was not used, so add it to either remaining equation to eliminate x. Multiplying the bottom equation by 6 and adding it to the top equation yields $-7y - 9z = -14$. Use substitution or elimination to find $y = 2$. By substitution, $z = 0$ and $x = -2$.

Matrices are helpful for representing and solving linear systems because it is not necessary to write the variables. The above system is represented by a matrix as

$A = \begin{bmatrix} -6 & -1 & -3 & | & 10 \\ -1 & -1 & 4 & | & 0 \\ 1 & -1 & -1 & | & -4 \end{bmatrix}$. Using row operations to get

Reduced Row Echelon Form yields $\begin{bmatrix} -2 \\ 2 \\ 0 \end{bmatrix}$ in the last

column, indicating that $x = -2$, $y = 2$, and $z = 0$.

© Mathematical Practices

Use appropriate tools strategically. Graphing calculators are used as tools for problem solving and additional explorations *after* students have solved simultaneous linear equations on their own. Technology enables students to succeed with problems that are structurally simple to model, but computationally tedious to solve.

LINEAR SYSTEMS
Pacing and Assignment Guide

		TRADITIONAL			BLOCK
Lesson	**Teaching Day(s)**	**Basic**	**Average**	**Advanced**	**Block**
3-1	1	Problems 1–2 Exs. 7–14, 53–56	Problems 1–2 Exs. 7–13 odd, 53–56	Problems 1–2 Exs. 7–13 odd, 53–56	**Day 1** Problems 1–4 Exs. 7–27 odd, 29–47, 53–56
	2	Problems 3–4 Exs. 15–28, 30–36 even, 38–43	Problems 3–4 Exs. 15–27 odd, 29–47	Problems 3–4 Exs. 15–27 odd, 29–52	
3-2	1	Problems 1–3 Exs. 10–30	Problems 1–3 Exs. 11–29 odd	Problems 1–3 Exs. 11–29 odd	**Day 2** Problems 1–5 Exs. 11–41 odd, 43–61
	2	Problems 4–5 Exs. 31–43, 53–57	Problems 4–5 Exs. 31–41 odd, 43–61	Problems 4–5 Exs. 31–41 odd, 43–66	
3-3	1	Problems 1–4 Exs. 8–34, 36–44 even, 59–72	Problems 1–4 Exs. 9–31 odd, 32–54, 59–72	Problems 1–4 Exs. 9–31 odd, 32–72	**Day 3** Problems 1–4 Exs. 9–29 odd, 31–54, 59–72
3-4	1	Problems 1–2 Exs. 10–19, 25–37	Problems 1–2 Exs. 11–13 odd, 14–22, 25–37	Problems 1–2 Exs. 11–13 odd, 14–37	Problems 1–2 Exs. 11–13 odd, 14–22, 25–37
3-5	1	Problems 1–2 Exs. 9–20	Problems 1–2 Exs. 9–19 odd	Problems 1–2 Exs. 9–19 odd	**Day 4** Problems 1–4 Exs. 9–29 odd, 31–42
	2	Problems 3–4 Exs. 21–31, 32–42 even	Problems 3–4 Exs. 21–29 odd, 31–42	Problems 3–4 Exs. 21–29 odd, 31–45	
3-6	1	Problems 1–3 Exs. 8–23, 48–58	Problems 1–3 Exs. 9–23 odd, 48–58	Problems 1–3 Exs. 9–23 odd, 48–58	**Day 5** Problems 1–5 Exs. 9–29 odd, 30–41, 48–58
	2	Problems 4–5 Exs. 24–32, 39–41	Problems 4–5 Exs. 25–29 odd, 30–41	Problems 4–5 Exs. 25–29 odd, 30–47	
Review	1	Chapter 3 Review	Chapter 3 Review	Chapter 3 Review	**Day 6** Chapter 3 Review Chapter 3 Test
Assess	1	Chapter 3 Test	Chapter 3 Test	Chapter 3 Test	
Total		**12 Days**	**12 Days**	**12 Days**	**6 Days**

Note: Pacing does not include Concept Bytes and other feature pages.

Resources

	For the Chapter	3-1	3-2	3-3	3-4	3-5	3-6
Planning							
Teacher Center Online Planner & Grade Book	I	I	I	I	I	I	I
Interactive Learning & Guided Instruction							
My Math Video	I						
Solve It!		I M	I M	I M	I M	I M	I M
Student Companion		P M	P M	P M	P M	P M	
Vocabulary Support		I P M	I P M	I P M	I P M	I P M	I P M
Got It? Support		I P	I P	I P	I P	I P	I P
Dynamic Activity	I						
Online Problems		I	I	I	I	I	I
Additional Problems		M	M	M	M	M	M
English Language Learner Support (TR)		E P M	E P M	E P M	E P M	E P M	E P M
Activities, Games, and Puzzles		E M	E M	E M	E M	E M	E M
Teaching With TI Technology With CD-ROM				✓ P	✓ P		
TI-Nspire™ Support CD-ROM		✓	✓	✓	✓	✓	✓
Lesson Check & Practice							
Student Companion		P M	P M	P M	P M	P M	P M
Lesson Check Support		I P	I P	I P	I P	I P	I P
Practice and Problem Solving Workbook		P	P	P	P	P	P
Think About a Plan (TR)		E P M	E P M	E P M	E P M	E P M	E P M
Practice Form G (TR)		E P M	E P M	E P M	E P M	E P M	E P M
Standardized Test Prep (TR)		P M	P M	P M	P M	P M	P M
Practice *Form K* (TR)		E P M	E P M	E P M	E P M	E P M	E P M
Extra Practice	E M						
Find the Errors!	M						
Enrichment (TR)		E P M	E P M	E P M	E P M	E P M	E P M
Answers and Solutions CD-ROM	✓	✓	✓	✓	✓	✓	✓
Assess & Remediate							
ExamView CD-ROM	✓	✓	✓	✓	✓	✓	✓
Lesson Quiz		I M	I M	I M	I M	I M	I M
Quizzes and Tests *Form G* (TR)	E P M			E P M			E P M
Quizzes and Tests *Form K* (TR)	E P M			E P M			E P M
Reteaching (TR)		E P M	E P M	E P M	E P M	E P M	E P M
Performance Tasks (TR)	P M						
Cumulative Review (TR)	P M						
Progress Monitoring Assessments	I P M						

(TR) Available in All-In-One Teaching Resources

1 Interactive Learning

Solve It!
PURPOSE To find the intersection of two lines
PROCESS Students may
- copy the graph and extend the lines to find the point of intersection.
- write the equations of the lines.

FACILITATE
Q Copy the graph and draw lines through the red and blue dots. What are the x-intercepts of the lines? **[red: (25, 0); blue: (30, 0)]**

Q What is the slope of the red line? Why does it make sense? **[− 1; one more bike means one less trike, so the slope is $\frac{-1}{1} = -1$.]**

Q What does the point of intersection represent? **[an ordered pair of the number of bikes and trikes that sum to 25 and have 60 wheels]**

Q Do you need to know the equations of the lines to answer the question? Explain. **[No; you can find the solution graphically.]**

ANSWER See Solve It in Answers on next page.
CONNECT THE MATH In the Solve It, students find the intersection of two lines. In the lesson, students will solve systems of linear equations by using tables and graphs.`

2 Guided Instruction

Problem 1   ERROR PREVENTION

Q Why should you check the intersection point you read from the graph by trying the values in both equations? **[You may have graphed incorrectly or misread the graph.]**

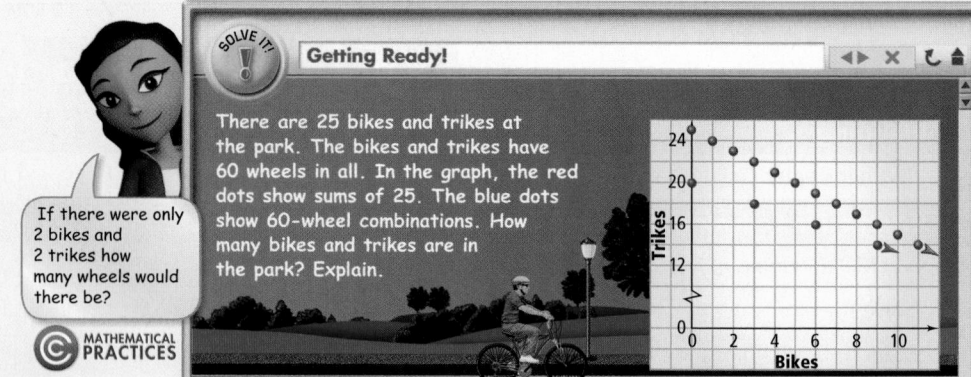

3-1 Solving Systems Using Tables and Graphs

Common Core State Standards
A-CED.A.2 Create equations in two or more variables to represent relationships between quantities; graph equations on coordinate axes with labels and scales. Also A-REI.C.6, A-CED.D.11, A-CED.A.3
MP 1, MP 2, MP 3, MP 4, MP 5

Objective To solve a linear system using a graph or a table

Getting Ready!

There are 25 bikes and trikes at the park. The bikes and trikes have 60 wheels in all. In the graph, the red dots show sums of 25. The blue dots show 60-wheel combinations. How many bikes and trikes are in the park? Explain.

If there were only 2 bikes and 2 trikes how many wheels would there be?

Lesson Vocabulary
- system of equations
- linear system
- solution of a system
- inconsistent system
- consistent system
- independent system
- dependent system

When you have two or more related unknowns, you may be able to represent their relationship with a **system of equations**—a set of two or more equations.

Essential Understanding To solve a system of equations, find a set of values that replace the variables in the equations and make each equation true.

A **linear system** consists of linear equations. A **solution of a system** is a set of values for the variables that makes all the equations true. You can solve a system of equations graphically or by using tables.

Think
How can you use a graph to find the solution of a system? Find the point where the two lines intersect.

> **Problem 1** Using a Graph or Table to Solve a System
>
> What is the solution of the system? $\begin{cases} -3x + 2y = 8 \\ x + 2y = -8 \end{cases}$
>
> **Method 1** Graph the equations. The point of intersection appears to be $(-4, -2)$.
>
> Check by substituting the values into both equations.
>
> $\qquad -3x + 2y = 8 \qquad\qquad x + 2y = -8$
>
> $-3(-4) + 2(-2) = 8 \checkmark \qquad -4 + 2(-2) = -8 \checkmark$
>
> Both equations are true so $(-4, -2)$ is the solution of the system.

BIG idea Solving Equations and Inequalities

ESSENTIAL UNDERSTANDINGS
- A system of equations is solved by finding a set of values that replace the variables in the equations and make each equation true.
- A point of intersection (x, y) of the graphs of the functions f and g is a solution of the system $y = f(x)$, $y = g(x)$.

Math Background
Linear systems of two equations can be analyzed using the nature of the solutions.

One solution
- consistent—independent
- 2 lines intersect at one point
- the slopes of the lines are not equal
- the y-intercepts may or may not be equal

Infinitely many solutions
- consistent—dependent
- 2 lines coincide
- the slopes of the lines are equal
- the y-intercepts are equal

No solution
- inconsistent
- 2 parallel lines
- the slopes of the lines are equal
- the y-intercepts are not equal

Mathematical Practices
Use appropriate tools strategically.
In Problem 3, students will use a graphing calculator to determine the lines of best fit and their intersection. They will find that graphing calculators can help to visualize results of a situation and can make predictions about the data.

PowerAlgebra.com

1 Interactive Learning

Solve It!
Step out how to solve the Problem with helpful hints and an online question. Other questions are listed above in Interactive Learning.

Virtual Nerd™ Access Virtual Nerd student-centered math tutorials that directly relate to the content of the lesson.

Method 2 Use a table. Write the equations in slope-intercept form.

$$-3x + 2y = 8 \qquad\qquad x + 2y = -8$$
$$2y = 3x + 8 \qquad\qquad 2y = -x - 8$$
$$y_1 = \frac{3}{2}x + 4 \qquad\qquad y_2 = -\frac{1}{2}x - 4$$

X	Y1	Y2
−5	−3.5	−1.5
−4	−2	−2
−3	−.5	−2.5
−2	1	−3
−1	2.5	−3.5
0	4	−4
1	5.5	−4.5

X = −4

Enter the equations in the **Y=** screen as **Y1** and **Y2**.
View the table. Adjust the x-values until you see $y_1 = y_2$.

When $x = -4$, both y_1 and y_2 equal -2. So, $(-4, -2)$ is the solution of the system.

 Got It? **1.** What is the solution of the system? $\begin{cases} x - 2y = 4 \\ 3x + \ y = 5 \end{cases}$

© **Problem 2** Using a Table to Solve a Problem **STEM**

Biology The diagrams show the birth lengths and growth rates of two species of shark. If the growth rates stay the same, at what age would a Spiny Dogfish and a Greenland shark be the same length?

GREENLAND SHARK

Growth rate: 0.75 cm/yr
Birth length: 37 cm

SPINY DOGFISH SHARK

Growth rate: 1.5 cm/yr
Birth length: 22 cm

Step 1 Define the variables and write the equation for the length of each shark.

Let x = age in years.
Let y = length in centimeters.

Length of Greenland: $y_1 = 0.75x + 37$
Length of Spiny Dogfish: $y_2 = 1.5x + 22$

Step 2 Use the table to solve the problem.
List x-values until the corresponding y-values match.

The sharks will be the same length when they are 20 years old.

Think

How can you use slope-intercept form to write each equation?
Use the growth rate for m and the length at birth for b.

Shark Length in cm

Age	Greenland	Spiny Dogfish
x	$y_1 = 0.75x + 37$	$y_2 = 1.5x + 22$
15	48.25	44.5
16	49	46
⋮	⋮	⋮
20	52	52

©  **Got It?** **2. a.** If the growth rates continue, how long will each shark be when it is 25 years old?

b. Reasoning Explain why growth rates for these sharks may not continue indefinitely.

Q In Method 2, why do you put the equations in slope-intercept form? **[So you can efficiently find y-values for each value of x.]**

Got It?
Have students solve this system by both methods to show that both methods are valid and that the answer will be the same.

Problem 2

Step 1

Q Why is the slope of the linear equation of the Spiny Dogfish's length 1.5? **[Every two years, the spiny dogfish grows 3 cm, which is 1.5 cm per year.]**

Q Why is the y-intercept of the equation of the Greenland's length 37? **[This is the length of the shark when it is born at age zero.]**

Step 2

Q How can you choose x-values to use in a table when you are looking for a solution? **[As the difference between the y-values approaches zero, you get closer to the solution.]**

ERROR PREVENTION
Remind students that the slope is a ratio. When it is written as a single number, it is understood that the second value in the ratio is 1. A slope of 1.5 is the ratio 1.5 : 1.

Got It?
If students have trouble with 2b, ask them how much they expect to grow in height when they are thirty years old.

---

2 Guided Instruction

 Each Problem is worked out and supported in the Student Online Center.

Problem 1
Using a Graph or Table to Solve a System
Animated

Alternative Problem 1
Using a Graph or Table to Solve a System
Animated

Problem 2
Using a Table to Solve a Problem

Problem 3
Using Linear Regression

Problem 4
Classifying a System Without Graphing
Animated

Alternative Problem 4
Classifying a System Without Graphing

Support in Algebra 2 Companion
• Vocabulary
• Key Concepts
• Got It?

Answers

Solve It!
15 bikes and 10 trikes

Got It?
1. $(2, -1)$
2. a. Spiny Dogfish: 59.5 cm; Greenland: 55.75 cm
   b. Each species of shark has a maximum total length; growth rates decrease with increase in age.

Problem 3

Students may prefer to use the actual years, 1950 to 2000, instead of the number of years after 1950, 0 to 50.

> **Q** How accurate do you think your prediction is? **[Answers may vary. Sample: Not very accurate because a population grows exponentially, not linearly.]**

ERROR PREVENTION

Remind students to add the *x*-value of the point of intersection to 1950 to find the year the populations will be equal. If students are having trouble using the calculator to find the regression equation and are getting a DIM MISMATCH error message, have them check that there are no stray values in any of the columns.

EXTENSION

Show students how to do an exponential regression (ExpReg). Graph these exponential models and find the predicted intersection. [about 21.9 million in 2008]

EXTENSION

In the problem, students perform *extrapolation* by making a prediction outside the domain and range of the given data. Prediction within the domain and range, or between the given data, is called *interpolation*. The Got It uses interpolation.

Got It?

> **Q** What is different about Detroit's population? How is this reflected in the line of best fit? **[Detroit's population is declining instead of growing. Detroit's line of best fit has a negative slope.]**

© Problem 3 Using Linear Regression

Population The table shows the populations of the New York City and Los Angeles metropolitan regions from the census reports for 1950 through 2000. Assuming these linear trends continue, when will the populations of these regions be equal? What will that population be?

Populations of New York City and Los Angeles Metropolitan Regions (1950–2000)

	1950	1960	1970	1980	1990	2000
New York City	12,911,994	14,759,429	16,178,700	16,121,297	18,087,251	21,199,865
Los Angeles	4,367,911	6,742,696	7,032,075	11,497,568	14,531,529	16,373,645

SOURCE: U.S. Census Bureau

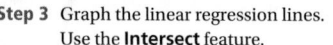

Know	Need	Plan
Population data for two regions	The point in time when their populations will be the same	• Use a calculator to find linear regression models. • Plot the models. • Find the point of intersection.

Enter all the numbers as millions, rounded to the nearest hundred thousand. For example, enter 12,911,994 as 12.9.

Step 1 Enter the data into lists on your calculator.
 L1: number of years since 1950
 L2: New York City populations
 L3: Los Angeles populations

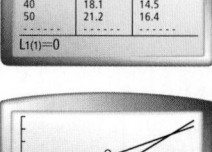

Step 2 Use **LinReg(ax + b)** to find lines of best fit.
 Use **L1** and **L2** for New York City.
 Use **L1** and **L3** for Los Angeles.

Step 3 Graph the linear regression lines.
 Use the **Intersect** feature.

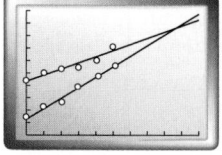

Think

What does *x* represent?
The *x*-value is the number of years *since* the zero year.

The *x*-value of the point of intersection is about 87, which represents the year 2037. The data suggest that the populations of the New York City and Los Angeles metropolitan regions will each be about 25.6 million in 2037.

Got It? **3.** The table shows the populations of the San Diego and Detroit metropolitan regions. When were the populations of these regions equal? What was that population?

Populations of San Diego and Detroit Metropolitan Regions (1950–2000)

	1950	1960	1970	1980	1990	2000
San Diego	334,387	573,224	696,769	875,538	1,110,549	1,223,400
Detroit	1,849,568	1,670,144	1,511,482	1,203,339	1,027,974	951,270

SOURCE: U.S. Census Bureau

Additional Problems

1. What is the solution of the system?
$$\begin{cases} 2x - y = -1 \\ \frac{1}{2}x - 2 = y \end{cases}$$
ANSWER $(-2, -3)$

2. You want to buy a camera. A film camera costs $89.98, and each photo costs $0.24. A digital camera costs $124.48, and each photo costs $0.09. After how many photos will the overall cost of the cameras be the same? What will that cost be?

ANSWER 230 photos; $145.18

3. The enrollments for two high schools are given in the table. If the trends continue, when can the schools expect to

have the same enrollment? What will the enrollment be?

Year	School A	School B
2005	628	432
2006	632	436
2007	627	461
2008	621	477
2009	615	488
2010	612	498

ANSWER In 2016, the enrollment will be about 589 students.

4. Determine without graphing whether the system is independent, dependent, or inconsistent.
$$\begin{cases} 3x - 4y = 6 \\ 6x + 3 = 8y \end{cases}$$
ANSWER inconsistent

You can classify a system of two linear equations by the number of solutions.

A **consistent system** has at least one solution.

An **inconsistent system** has no solution.

Consistent system
Inconsistent system

Independent — An **independent system** has one solution.

Dependent — A **dependent system** has infinitely many solutions.

The graphs for an inconsistent system are parallel lines. So, there are no solutions. For a dependent system, the two equations represent the same line.

Concept Summary Graphical Solutions of Linear Systems

Intersecting Lines	Coinciding Lines	Parallel Lines
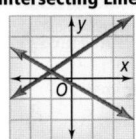	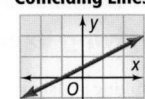	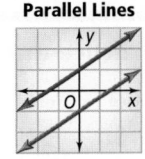
one solution	infinitely many solutions	no solution
Consistent	Consistent	Inconsistent
Independent	Dependent	

 Problem 4 Classifying a System Without Graphing

Without graphing, is the system *independent*, *dependent*, **or** *inconsistent*?

$$\begin{cases} 4y - 2x = 6 \\ 8y = 4x - 12 \end{cases}$$

Rewrite each equation in slope-intercept form. Compare slopes and y-intercepts.

$4y - 2x = 6$ $\qquad\qquad$ $8y = 4x - 12$

$y = \frac{1}{2}x + \frac{3}{2}$ $\qquad\qquad$ $y = \frac{1}{2}x - \frac{3}{2}$

$m = \frac{1}{2}$; y-intercept is $\frac{3}{2}$ $\qquad$ $m = \frac{1}{2}$; y-intercept is $-\frac{3}{2}$

The slopes are equal and the y-intercepts are different. The lines are different but parallel. The system is inconsistent.

 **Got It?** 4. Without graphing, is each system *independent*, *dependent*, or *inconsistent*?

a. $\begin{cases} -3x + y = 4 \\ x - \frac{1}{3}y = 1 \end{cases}$
b. $\begin{cases} 2x + 3y = 1 \\ 4x + y = -3 \end{cases}$
c. $\begin{cases} y = 2x - 3 \\ 6x - 3y = 9 \end{cases}$

PowerAlgebra.com Lesson 3-1 Solving Systems Using Tables and Graphs **137**

Take Note

Q How do the slopes of parallel lines compare? **[They are the same.]**

Q How do the slopes of coinciding lines compare? **[They are the same.]**

Q How can you tell whether the graphs of two linear equations with the same slope will be coinciding lines or parallel lines? **[Compute the *y*-intercepts. If the *y*-intercepts are different, the lines are parallel. If the *y*-intercepts are the same, the lines coincide.]**

EXTENSION

For linear systems in standard form $ax + by = c$, if the equations are linear multiples of each other, then the system is dependent.

Example: $\begin{cases} 3x - 2y = 5 \\ -6x + 4y = -10 \end{cases}$

If the coefficients are the same linear multiples but the constants are not, then the system is inconsistent. Example: $\begin{cases} 3x - 2y = 5 \\ -6x + 4y = 15 \end{cases}$

If the coefficients are not of the same multiple, then the system is independent.

Example: $\begin{cases} 3x - 2y = 5 \\ -6x - 4y = -10 \end{cases}$

Problem 4

Q What condition indicates an independent system? **[the equations have different slopes]**

Q What conditions indicate a dependent system? **[when the equations have the same slope and the same *y*-intercept]**

Got It?
Students can check their answers by graphing.

Answers

Got It? (continued)

3. in the yr 1990; about 1,100,000

4. a. inconsistent

　b. independent

　c. dependent

3 Lesson Check

Do you know HOW?

- For Exercises 1 and 2, students sometimes accidentally drop the negative sign in front of the y. To avoid this, have students put a 1 in front of the y.
- For Exercise 3, students may have trouble defining the variables. Have students identify that they are looking for the number of pens and the number of pencils.

Do you UNDERSTAND? ERROR INTERVENTION

- For Exercise 4, if students have trouble identifying the conditions that make a system of equations independent and inconsistent, refer to Problem 4 and the text preceding it.
- For Exercise 6, suggest writing an example system and graphing the system to illustrate that the negative reciprocal slopes mean that the lines are perpendicular.

Close

> **Q** What does it mean to find the solution to a system of equations? **[Find the values for the variables that make all equations true.]**
>
> **Q** From this lesson, what two methods can you use to find a solution to a system of equations? **[graphing and making a table]**
>
> **Q** How can you determine whether a system is independent, dependent, or inconsistent? **[Use a graph or the coefficients and constants of the equations to determine the number of solutions.]**

Lesson Check

Do you know HOW?

Solve each system of equations by graphing. Check your solution.

1. $\begin{cases} y = x - 1 \\ y = -x + 3 \end{cases}$
2. $\begin{cases} 2x + y = 4 \\ x - y = 2 \end{cases}$

3. You bought a total of 6 pens and pencils for $4. If each pen costs $1 and each pencil costs $.50, how many pens and pencils did you buy?

Do you UNDERSTAND?

4. **Vocabulary** Is it possible for a system of equations to be both independent and inconsistent? Explain.

5. **Open-Ended** Write a system of linear equations that has no solution.

6. **Reasoning** In a system of linear equations, the slope of one line is the negative reciprocal of the slope of the other line. Is this system *independent*, *dependent*, or *inconsistent*? Explain.

Practice and Problem-Solving Exercises

A Practice

Solve each system by graphing or using a table. Check your answers. ◀ See Problem 1.

7. $\begin{cases} y = x - 2 \\ y = -2x + 7 \end{cases}$
8. $\begin{cases} y = -x + 3 \\ y = \frac{3}{2}x - 2 \end{cases}$
9. $\begin{cases} 2x + 4y = 12 \\ x + y = 2 \end{cases}$

10. $\begin{cases} x = -3 \\ y = 5 \end{cases}$
11. $\begin{cases} 2x - 2y = 4 \\ y - x = 6 \end{cases}$
12. $\begin{cases} 3x + y = 5 \\ x - y = 7 \end{cases}$

Write and solve a system of equations for each situation. Check your answers. ◀ See Problem 2.

13. A store sells small notebooks for $8 and large notebooks for $10. If you buy 6 notebooks and spend $56, how many of each size notebook did you buy?

14. A shop has one-pound bags of peanuts for $2 and three-pound bags of peanuts for $5.50. If you buy 5 bags and spend $17, how many of each size bag did you buy?

Graphing Calculator Find linear models for each set of data. In what year will the two quantities be equal? ◀ See Problem 3.

15.

U.S. Life Expectancy at Birth (1970–2000)

Year	1970	1975	1980	1985	1990	1995	2000
Men (years)	67.1	68.8	70.0	71.1	71.8	72.5	74.3
Women (years)	74.7	76.6	77.4	78.2	78.8	78.9	79.7

SOURCE: U.S. Census Bureau

16.

Annual U.S. Consumption of Vegetables

Year	1980	1985	1990	1995	1998	1999	2000
Broccoli (lb/person)	1.5	2.6	3.4	4.3	5.1	6.5	6.1
Cucumbers (lb/person)	3.9	4.4	4.7	5.6	6.5	6.8	6.4

SOURCE: U.S. Census Bureau

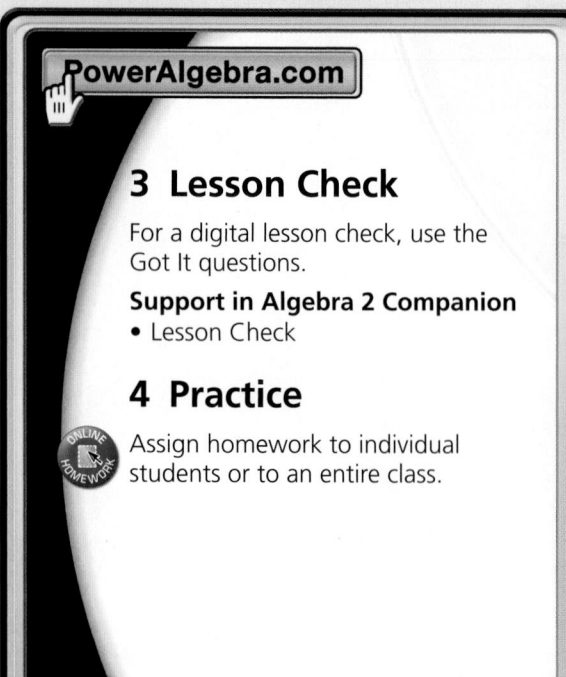

PowerAlgebra.com

3 Lesson Check

For a digital lesson check, use the Got It questions.

Support in Algebra 2 Companion
- Lesson Check

4 Practice

Assign homework to individual students or to an entire class.

Answers

Lesson Check

1. (2, 1)

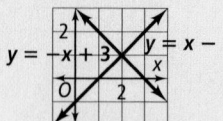

$y = -x + 3$ $y = x - 1$

2. (2, 0)

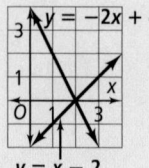

$y = -2x + 4$

$y = x - 2$

3. 2 pens; 4 pencils

4. No; an independent system has a unique solution whereas an inconsistent system has no solution.

5. Answers may vary. Sample:
$\begin{cases} y = 2x + 1 \\ y = 2x - 3 \end{cases}$

6. Independent; if the slope of one equation is the negative reciprocal of the slope of the other equation, the lines are perpendicular and intersect at a unique point.

Practice and Problem-Solving Exercises

7–12. How solutions are determined may vary (graphing or using a table).

7. (3, 1)

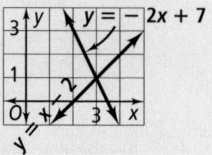

$y = -2x + 7$

8. (2, 1)

$y = -x + 3$ $y = \frac{3}{2}x - 2$

Without graphing, classify each system as *independent*, *dependent*, or *inconsistent*.

◀ See Problem 4.

17. $\begin{cases} 7x - y = 6 \\ -7x + y = -6 \end{cases}$

18. $\begin{cases} -3x + y = 4 \\ x - \frac{1}{3}y = 1 \end{cases}$

19. $\begin{cases} 4x + 8y = 12 \\ x + 2y = -3 \end{cases}$

20. $\begin{cases} y = 2x - 1 \\ y = -2x + 5 \end{cases}$

21. $\begin{cases} x = 6 \\ y = -2 \end{cases}$

22. $\begin{cases} 2y = 5x + 6 \\ -10x + 4y = 8 \end{cases}$

23. $\begin{cases} x - 3y = 2 \\ 4x - 12y = 8 \end{cases}$

24. $\begin{cases} y - x = 0 \\ y = -x \end{cases}$

25. $\begin{cases} 2y - x = 4 \\ \frac{1}{2}x + y = 2 \end{cases}$

26. $\begin{cases} x + 4y = 12 \\ 2x - 8y = 4 \end{cases}$

27. $\begin{cases} 4x + 8y = -6 \\ 6x + 12y = -9 \end{cases}$

28. $\begin{cases} 4y - 2x = 6 \\ 8y = 4x - 12 \end{cases}$

B Apply

Graph and solve each system.

29. $\begin{cases} 3 = 4y + x \\ 4y = -x + 3 \end{cases}$

30. $\begin{cases} y = \frac{1}{2}x + \frac{1}{2} \\ y = \frac{1}{4}x + \frac{3}{2} \end{cases}$

31. $\begin{cases} 3x + 6y - 12 = 0 \\ x + 2y = 8 \end{cases}$

32. $\begin{cases} 3x = -5y + 4 \\ 250 + 150x = 300y \end{cases}$

33. $\begin{cases} y = -\frac{1}{2}x + 8 \\ y = 2x - 6 \end{cases}$

34. $\begin{cases} x + 3y = 6 \\ 6y + 2x = 12 \end{cases}$

Without graphing, classify each system as *independent*, *dependent*, or *inconsistent*.

35. $\begin{cases} 3x - 2y = 8 \\ 4y = 6x - 5 \end{cases}$

36. $\begin{cases} 2x + 8y = 6 \\ x = -4y + 3 \end{cases}$

37. $\begin{cases} 3m = -5n + 4 \\ n - \frac{6}{5} = -\frac{3}{5}m \end{cases}$

ⒸⒸ 38. **Reasoning** Find the solution of the system of equations $f(x) = 3x - 1$ and $g(x) = |x - 3|$. Explain why the x-coordinates of the points where the graphs of the equations $y = f(x)$ and $y = g(x)$ intersect are solutions of $3x - 1 = |x - 3|$.

ⒸⒸ 39. **Think About a Plan** You and a friend are both reading a book. You read 2 pages each minute and have already read 55 pages. Your friend reads 3 pages each minute and has already read 35 pages. Graph and solve a system of equations to find when the two of you will have read the same number of pages. Since the number of pages you have read depends on how long you have been reading, let x represent the number of minutes it takes to read y pages.
   • How can you describe the relationship between x and y for you?
   • How can you describe the relationship between x and y for your friend?
   • How can a graph help you solve this problem?

ⒸⒸ 40. **Sports** You can choose between two tennis courts at two university campuses to learn how to play tennis. One campus charges $25 per hour. The other campus charges $20 per hour plus a one-time registration fee of $10.
   a. Write a system of equations to represent the cost c for h hours of court use at each campus.
   🖩 **b. Graphing Calculator** Find the number of hours for which the costs are the same.
   c. Reasoning If you want to practice for a total of 10 hours, which university campus should you choose? Explain.

9. $(-2, 4)$

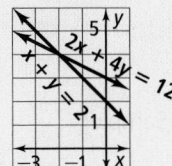

10. $(-3, 5)$

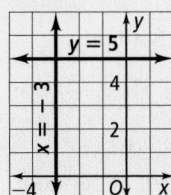

11. no solution

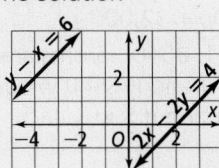

12. $(3, -4)$

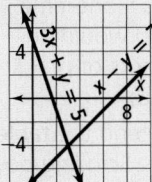

13. 2 small; 4 large

14. 3 one-pound bags; 2 three-pound bags

15. Models may vary. Sample: Use 0 for 1970.
$\begin{cases} y = 0.22x + 67.5 \\ y = 0.15x + 75.507 \end{cases}$
Around 2085, the quantities will be equal.

16. Models may vary. Sample: Use 0 for 1980.
$\begin{cases} y = 0.232x + 1.328 \\ y = 0.145x + 3.673 \end{cases}$
Around 2007, the quantities were equal.

4 Practice

ASSIGNMENT GUIDE
Basic: 7–28, 30–36 even, 38–43
Average: 7–27 odd, 29–47
Advanced: 7–27 odd, 29–52
Standardized Test Prep: 53–56

Ⓒ **Mathematical Practices** are supported by exercises with red headings. Here are the Practices supported in this lesson:

MP 1: Make Sense of Problems Ex. 39
MP 2: Reason Abstractly Ex. 48, 49
MP 2: Reason Quantitatively Ex. 40
MP 3: Communicate Ex. 43
MP 3: Construct Arguments Ex. 5, 6, 42, 51
MP 3: Compare Arguments Ex. 44–47
MP 3: Critique the Reasoning of Others Ex. 41
MP 4: Model with Mathematics Ex. 52
MP 5: Use Appropriate Tools Ex. 15, 16

Applications exercises have blue headings. Exercise 52 supports MP 4: Model.

EXERCISE 40: Use the Think About a Plan worksheet in the **Practice and Problem Solving Workbook** (also available in the Teaching Resources in print and online) to further support students' development in becoming independent learners.

HOMEWORK QUICK CHECK
To check students' understanding of key skills and concepts, go over Exercises 13, 23, 39, 40, and 42.

17. dependent   18. inconsistent
19. inconsistent   20. independent
21. independent   22. inconsistent
23. dependent   24. independent
25. independent   26. independent
27. dependent   28. inconsistent
29. infinitely many solutions

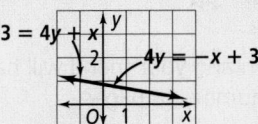

30. $\left(4, \frac{5}{2}\right)$

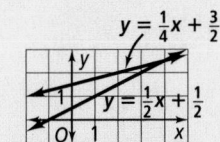

31–40. See next page.

Answers

Practice and Problem-Solving Exercises
(continued)

31. no solution

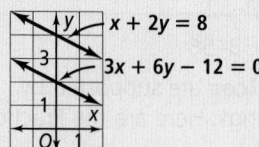

32. $\left(-\dfrac{1}{33}, \dfrac{9}{11}\right)$

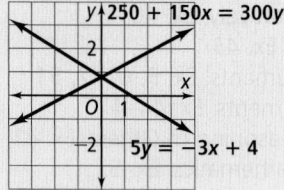

33. $\left(\dfrac{28}{5}, \dfrac{26}{5}\right)$

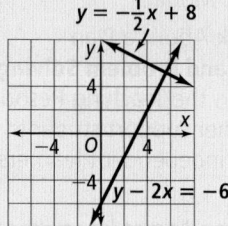

34. infinitely many solutions

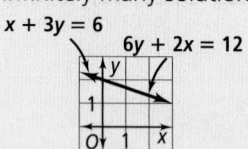

35. inconsistent

36. dependent

37. inconsistent

38. (1, 2); since (1, 2) is a solution of both equations, $f(1) = 2$ and $g(1) = 2$. So, at $x = 1$, $f(x) = g(x)$.

39.

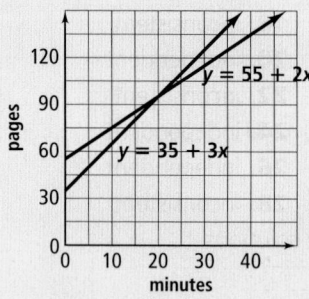

After 20 min you and your friend will have read the same number of pages.

40. a. $\begin{cases} c = 25h \\ c = 20h + 10 \end{cases}$

b.

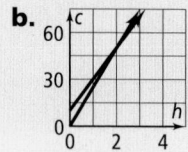

The cost would be the same for 2 hours of instruction.

---

41. Error Analysis Your friend used a graphing calculator to solve a system of linear equations, shown below. After using the **TABLE** feature, your friend says that the system has no solution. Explain what your friend did wrong. What is the solution of the system?

X	Y₁	Y₂
-4	14	10
-3	12	8.5
-2	10	7
-1	8	5.5
0	6	4
1	4	2.5
2	2	1

X=2

$$2x + y = 6 \qquad 3x + 2y = 8$$
$$y = 6 - 2x \qquad y = \dfrac{8 - 3x}{2}$$

42. Reasoning Is it possible for an inconsistent linear system to contain two lines with the same y-intercept? Explain.

43. Writing Summarize the possible relationships for the y-intercepts, slopes, and number of solutions in a system of two linear equations in two variables.

Reasoning Determine whether each statement is *always*, *sometimes*, or *never* true for the following system.

$$\begin{cases} y = x + 3 \\ y = mx + b \end{cases}$$

44. If $m = 1$, the system has no solution.

45. If $b = 3$, the system has exactly one solution.

46. If $m \neq 1$, the system has no solution.

47. If $m \neq 1$ and $b = 2$, the system has infinitely many solutions.

Challenge

Open-Ended Write a second equation for each system so that the system will have the indicated number of solutions.

48. infinite number of solutions
$$\begin{cases} \dfrac{x}{4} + \dfrac{y}{3} = 1 \\ \underline{} \end{cases}$$

49. no solutions
$$\begin{cases} 5x + 2y = 10 \\ \underline{} \end{cases}$$

50. Write a system of linear equations with the solution set $\{(x, y) \mid y = 5x + 2\}$.

51. Reasoning What relationship exists between the equations in a dependent system?

52. Economics Research shows that in a certain market only 2000 widgets can be sold at \$8 each, but if the price is reduced to \$3, then 10,000 can be sold.
a. Let p represent price and n represent the number of widgets. Identify the independent and dependent variables.
b. Write a linear equation that relates price and the quantity demanded. This type of equation is called a *demand* equation.
c. A shop can make 2000 widgets for \$5 each and 20,000 widgets for \$2 each. Use this information to write a linear equation that relates price and the quantity supplied. This type of equation is called a *supply* equation.
d. Find the equilibrium point where supply is equal to demand. Explain the meaning of the coordinates of this point within the context of the exercise.

140   Chapter 3   Linear Systems

c. The campus that charges \$20 per hour plus a one-time registration of \$10 would be cheaper for 10 hours of practice (\$210 versus \$250).

41. My friend did not extend the table of values far enough. Scrolling down will show that when $x = 4$ then $y_1 = y_2 = -2$, so the system has a solution, (4, −2).

42. No; they would be the same line, and the system would be dependent and consistent.

43. An independent system has one solution. The slopes are different, but the y-intercepts could be the same. An inconsistent system has no solution. The slopes are the same and the y-intercepts are different. A dependent system has an infinite number of solutions. The slopes and y-intercepts are the same.

44. sometimes

45. sometimes

46. never

47. never

48. Answers may vary. Sample: $3x + 4y = 12$

49. Answers may vary. Sample: $5x + 2y = 5$

50. Answers may vary. Sample:
$$\begin{cases} -10x + 2y = 4 \\ 5x - y = -2 \end{cases}$$

51. They are equivalent eqs.

52. a. p: independent; n: dependent
b. $n = -1600p + 14,800$
c. $n = -6000p + 32,000$
d. About (3.91, 8540); profits are maximized if about 8540 widgets are sold for about \$3.91 each.

SAT/ACT

53. Which graph shows the solution of the following system? $\begin{cases} 4x + y = 1 \\ x + 4y = -11 \end{cases}$

Ⓐ 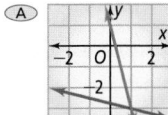 Ⓑ 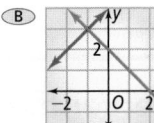 Ⓒ 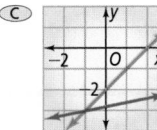 Ⓓ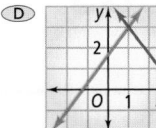

54. Which is the equation of a line that is perpendicular to the line in the graph?

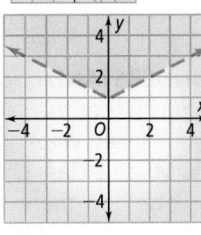

Ⓕ $y = -3x + 2$　　Ⓗ $y = -\frac{1}{3}x - 4$

Ⓖ $y = \frac{1}{3}x + 5$　　Ⓘ $y = 3x - 1$

55. Which inequality represents the graph at the right?

Ⓐ $y \geq \frac{1}{2}|x| + 1$　　Ⓒ $y > \frac{1}{2}|x| + 1$

Ⓑ $y \leq \frac{1}{2}|x| + 1$　　Ⓓ $y < \frac{1}{2}|x| + 1$

Extended Response

56. Amy ordered prints of a total of 6 photographs in two different sizes, 5×7 and 4×6, from an online site. She paid $7.50 for her order. The cost of a 5×7 print is $1.75 and the cost of a 4×6 print is $.25. Explain how to solve a system of equations using tables to find the number of 4×6 prints Amy ordered.

Apply What You've Learned

MATHEMATICAL PRACTICES
MP 5

William and Maggie are competing in a triathlon like the one described on page 133. Maggie begins the bicycle portion of the triathlon half an hour ahead of William, and rides at a rate of 12 mi/h. William rides at a rate of 18 mi/h.

a. If the bicycle portion of the race is long enough, can William catch up with Maggie? Explain your answer.

b. Use a table to find how much time it takes William to catch up with Maggie.

c. Write a system of equations to model William's and Maggie's bicycle portions of the triathlon.

d. Graph the system of equations.

e. Does your graph give the same amount of time for William to catch up with Maggie as the table from part (b)? Explain how each tool is used to find the amount of time.

f. After how many miles will William catch up with Maggie?

Standardized Test Prep

53. A

54. G

55. C

56. [4] Write the eqs. in slope-intercept form. Let x = number of 5×7 prints, let y = number of 4×6 prints:
$$x + y = 6$$
$$y = -x + 6$$
$$1.75x + 0.25y = 7.5$$
$$y = -7x + 30$$
Enter the eqs. in your calc. and view the table. Adjust the x-values until you see $y_1 = y_2$. When $x = 4$, $y_1 = y_2 = 2$. So Amy ordered two 4×6 prints.

[3] error made entering eqs. in calc., OR computational error

[2] correct number of 4×6 prints, incomplete explanation

[1] correct number of 4×6 prints, without an explanation, OR solved by another method

---

Apply What You've Learned

Here students will write and solve a system of equations in two variables to model part of a triathlon. Later in the chapter, they will write a system of equations in three variables to represent the triathlon described on page 133.

ⓒ Mathematical Practices

Students understand how to **use appropriate tools strategically** by solving a problem with a table and with a graph. (MP 5)

ANSWERS

a. Yes; William is riding faster than Maggie.

b. 1 h; check students' tables.

c. Let x represent the time, in hours, that William rides his bicycle.
Maggie: $y = 12(x + 0.5)$
William: $y = 18x$

d.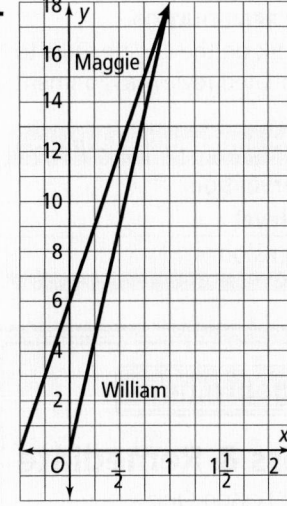

e. Yes; check students' work.

f. William will catch up with Maggie at 18 mi.

Lesson Resources

Additional Instructional Support

Algebra 2 Companion

Students can use the **Algebra 2 Companion** worktext (4 pages) as you teach the lesson. Use the Companion to support

• New Vocabulary
• Key Concepts
• Got It for each Problem
• Lesson Check

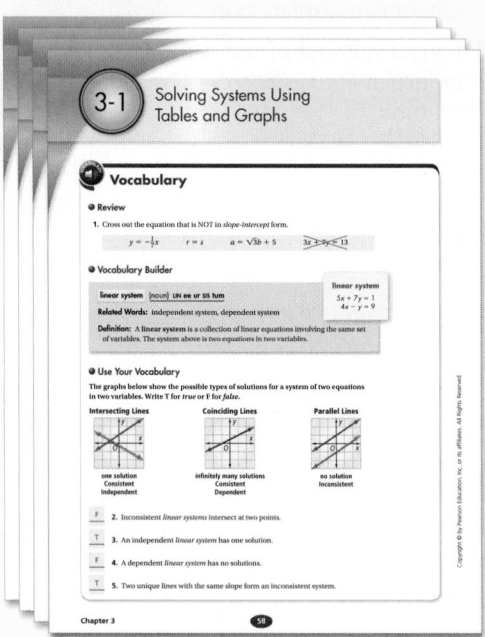

3-1 Solving Systems Using Tables and Graphs

ELL Support

Use Multiple Representation In Problem 1, place the table and the graph side by side, and indicate each point on the graph and in the table, emphasizing that the coordinates of the point the equations share are the solution.

Assess Understanding Give each student nine 3 × 5 cards. Have them do the following
• Write each of the following types of linear systems on a card: Consistent Independent, Consistent Dependent, Inconsistent.
• Use three cards to draw an example of each type of linear system.
• Write a description of each type on the final three cards.

Students should shuffle their cards and trade with a neighbor. Each person tries to make 3 matches with their new set of cards. Then check answers with the person who made the cards.

5 Assess & Remediate

Lesson Quiz

1. What is the solution of the system?
$$\begin{cases} x - 2y = -7 \\ 2x + y = 6 \end{cases}$$

2. Do you UNDERSTAND? You and a friend start a typing class at the same time. You measure your speed weekly in words per minute (WPM) on a class chart. If the trend continues, after how many weeks can you expect to type as quickly as your friend? What will that WPM be?

Weeks	0	1	2	3
Your WPM	13	16	19	22
Your Friend's WPM	20	22	24	26

3. Use linear regression on your calculator for the points (1.0, 2.6), (2.3, 2.8), (3.1, 3.1), (4.8, 4.7), (5.6, 5.1), (6.3, 5.3). Where does this line intersect $x = 0$?

4. Without graphing, is the system of equations independent, dependent, or inconsistent?
$$\begin{cases} 2x + y = 6 \\ 12 - y = 4x \end{cases}$$

ANSWERS TO LESSON QUIZ

1. (1, 4)
2. 7 weeks; 34 WPM
3. (0, 1.7)
4. independent

PRESCRIPTION FOR REMEDIATION

Use the student work on the Lesson Quiz to prescribe a differentiated review assignment:

Points	Differentiated Remediation
0–2	Intervention
3	On-level
4	Extension

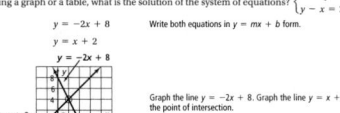

5 Assess & Remediate

Assign the Lesson Quiz. Appropriate intervention, practice, or enrichment is automatically generated based on student performance.

Intervention

• **Reteaching** (2 pages) Provides reteaching and practice exercises for the key lesson concepts. Use with struggling students or absent students.

• **English Language Learner Support** Helps students develop and reinforce mathematical vocabulary and key concepts.

All-in-One Resources/Online
Reteaching

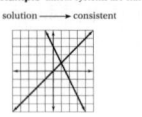

3-1 **Reteaching**
Solving Systems Using Tables and Graphs

All-in-One Resources/Online
English Language Learner Support

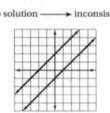

3-1 **Additional Vocabulary Support**
Solving Systems Using Tables and Graphs

Differentiated Remediation *continued*

On-Level

- **Practice** (2 pages) Provides extra practice for each lesson. For simpler practice exercises, use the Form K Practice pages found in the All-in-One Teaching Resources and online.

- **Think About a Plan** Helps students develop specific problem-solving skills and strategies by providing scaffolded guiding questions.

- **Standardized Test Prep** Focuses on all major exercises, all major question types, and helps students prepare for the high-stakes assessments.

Extension

- **Enrichment** Provides students with interesting problems and activities that extend the concepts of the lesson.

- **Activities, Games, and Puzzles** Worksheets that can be used for concepts development, enrichment, and for fun!

Practice and Problem Solving Wkbk/All-in-One Resources/Online
Practice page 1

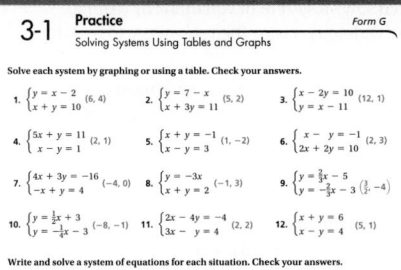

Practice and Problem Solving Wkbk/All-in-One Resources/Online
Practice page 2

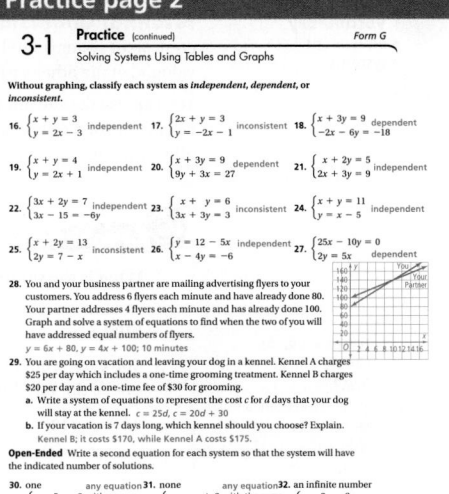

All-in-One Resources/Online
Enrichment

Practice and Problem Solving Wkbk/All-in-One Resources/Online
Think About a Plan

Practice and Problem Solving Wkbk/All-in-One Resources/Online
Standardized Test Prep

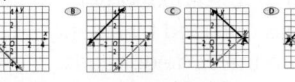

Online Teacher Resource Center
Activities, Games, and Puzzles

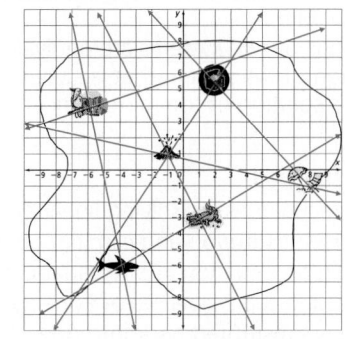

1 Interactive Learning

Solve It!

PURPOSE To use a system of equations to compare two jobs

PROCESS Students may
- make a table of sales and wages.
- write two expressions for the wages in terms of sales, set them equal, and solve.
- solve the system by graphing.

FACILITATE

Q What do you want to find? **[the sales that result in equal wages at both stores]**

Q Use x for sales made. What expressions model the daily amount you can earn at each store? **[$35 + 0.10x$, $10 + 0.18x$]**

Q How can you use these expressions to solve the problem? **[Write an equation setting the expressions equal, and solve for x.]**

Q Why might it be difficult to solve this problem by graphing? **[Answers may vary. Samples: Decimals in the x-terms make graphing difficult. The numbers involved are large.]**

ANSWERS See Solve It in Answers on next page.

CONNECT THE MATH The Solve It is more easily solved using algebra than graphing. In this lesson students will learn algebraic strategies for solving this type of problem.

2 Guided Instruction

Problem 1

The original system $\begin{cases} 3x + 4y = 12 \\ 2x + y = 10 \end{cases}$ is equivalent

to the system in Step 2: $\begin{cases} 3x + 4y = 12 \\ x + 5.6 \end{cases}$.

BIG idea Equivalence

ESSENTIAL UNDERSTANDINGS
- A system of equations can be solved by writing equivalent systems until the value of one variable is clear, then substituting to find the value(s) of the other variable.
- If the equations of two systems are equivalent, then a solution of the system that is easier to solve is also a solution of the more difficult system.

Math Background

Two algebraic techniques for solving linear systems of equations are substitution and elimination. Both strategies obtain an equation in one variable that can be solved using the Properties of Equality. The resulting value is substituted back into one of the original equations to find the value of the other variable.

3-2 Solving Systems Algebraically

© **Common Core State Standards**
A-REI.C.6 Solve systems of linear equations exactly and approximately (e.g., with graphs), focusing on pairs of linear equations in two variables. **Also A-REI.C.5, A-CED.A.2**
MP 1, MP 2, MP 3

Objective To solve linear systems algebraically

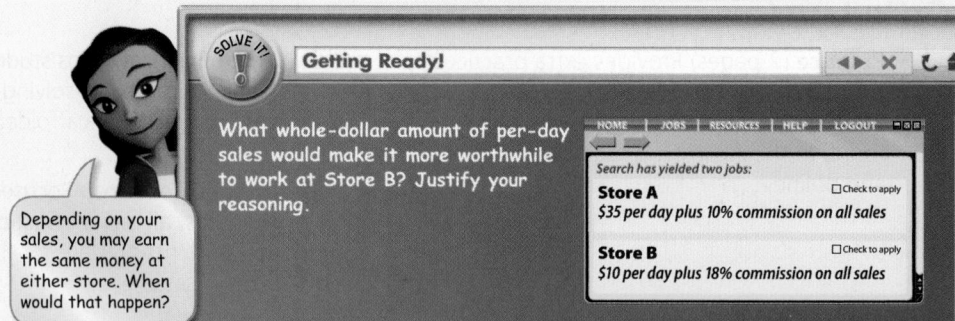

Getting Ready!

What whole-dollar amount of per-day sales would make it more worthwhile to work at Store B? Justify your reasoning.

Depending on your sales, you may earn the same money at either store. When would that happen?

Search has yielded two jobs:

Store A ☐ Check to apply
$35 per day plus 10% commission on all sales

Store B ☐ Check to apply
$10 per day plus 18% commission on all sales

© **MATHEMATICAL PRACTICES**

Lesson Vocabulary
- equivalent systems

When you try to solve a system of equations by graphing, the coordinates of the point of intersection may not be obvious.

Essential Understanding You can solve a system of equations by writing equivalent systems until the value of one variable is clear. Then substitute to find the value(s) of the other variable(s).

You can use the substitution method to solve a system of equations when it is easy to isolate one of the variables. After isolating the variable, substitute for that variable in the other equation. Then solve for the other variable.

© **Problem 1** Solving by Substitution

What is the solution of the system of equations? $\begin{cases} 3x + 4y = 12 \\ 2x + y = 10 \end{cases}$

Think
Which variable should you solve for first?
In the second equation, the coefficient of y is 1. It is the easiest variable to isolate.

Step 1
Solve one equation for one of the variables.
$$2x + y = 10$$
$$y = -2x + 10$$

Step 2
Substitute the expression for y in the other equation. Solve for x.
$$3x + 4y = 12$$
$$3x + 4(-2x + 10) = 12$$
$$3x - 8x + 40 = 12$$
$$x = 5.6$$

Step 3
Substitute the value for x into one of the original equations. Solve for y.
$$2x + y = 10$$
$$2(5.6) + y = 10$$
$$11.2 + y = 10$$
$$y = -1.2$$

The solution is $(5.6, -1.2)$.

For substitution, the equation in one variable is obtained by solving for one variable in terms of the second. Then, substitute the literal expression for the first variable into the other equation and solve for the second variable. Substitution works well when
- one equation is already solved for one variable.
- the coefficient of one or more variables is 1 or -1.

For elimination, the equation in one variable is obtained by adding or subtracting the two equations, eliminating one variable.

Elimination works well when the coefficients of one variable are the same or inverses.

© **Mathematical Practices**
Reason abstractly and quantitatively.
Problem 4 challenges students to flexibly use the properties of operations to solve an equivalent linear system.

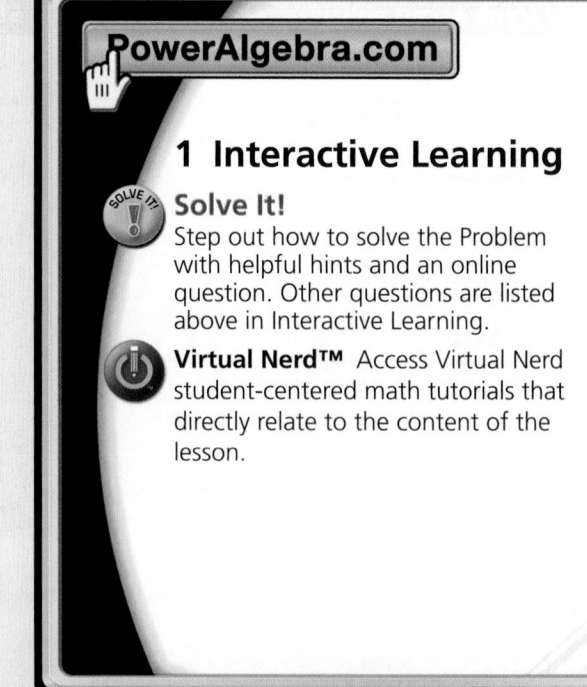

PowerAlgebra.com

1 Interactive Learning

Solve It!
Step out how to solve the Problem with helpful hints and an online question. Other questions are listed above in Interactive Learning.

Virtual Nerd™ Access Virtual Nerd student-centered math tutorials that directly relate to the content of the lesson.

Got It? 1. What is the solution of the system of equations? $\begin{cases} x + 3y = 5 \\ -2x - 4y = -5 \end{cases}$

 Problem 2 Using Substitution to Solve a Problem

Music A music store offers piano lessons at a discount for customers buying new pianos. The costs for lessons and a one-time fee for materials (including music books, CDs, software, etc.) are shown in the advertisement. What is the cost of each lesson and the one-time fee for materials?

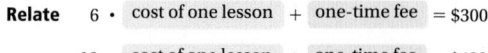

6 Lessons: $300 12 Lessons: $480

(Prices include one-time fee)

Relate 6 · [cost of one lesson] + [one-time fee] = $300

12 · [cost of one lesson] + [one-time fee] = $480

Define Let c = the cost of one lesson.

Let f = the one-time fee.

Write $\begin{cases} 6 \cdot c + f = 300 \\ 12 \cdot c + f = 480 \end{cases}$

$6c + f = 300$ — Choose one equation. Solve for f in terms of c.

$f = 300 - 6c$

$12c + (300 - 6c) = 480$ — Substitute the expression for f into the other equation, $12c + f = 480$. Solve for c.

$c = 30$

$6(30) + f = 300$ — Substitute the value of c into one of the equations. Solve for f.

$f = 120$

Think

Which equation should you use to find f?
Use the equation with numbers that are easier to work with.

Check Substitute $c = 30$ and $f = 120$ in the original equations.

$6c + f = 300$ $12c + f = 480$

$6(30) + 120 \stackrel{?}{=} 300$ $12(30) + 120 \stackrel{?}{=} 480$

$180 + 120 \stackrel{?}{=} 300$ $360 + 120 \stackrel{?}{=} 480$

$300 = 300$ ✔ $480 = 480$ ✔

The cost of each lesson is $30. The one-time fee for materials is $120.

 Got It? 2. An online music company offers 15 downloads for $19.75 and 40 downloads for $43.50. Each price includes the same one-time registration fee. What is the cost of each download and the registration fee?

You can use the Addition Property of Equality to solve a system of equations. If you add a pair of additive inverses or subtract identical terms, you can eliminate a variable.

Got It?

Q Which variable is easier to use in the substitution method? **[Answers may vary. Sample: The x in the first equation is easier to use because its coefficient is 1.]**

Problem 2
The substitution method is often used when one variable has the coefficient 1 in either equation.

Q What ordered pair is the solution to this system? **[(30, 120)]**

Q Could you solve this problem by graphing by hand? Explain. **[Answers may vary. Sample: Yes; since 6, 12, 300, and 480 are all multiples of 2, 3, and 6, it would not be too difficult with appropriate scaling.]**

Q What is a linear equation for the cost of piano lessons? Let x be the number of lessons and y be the total cost. **[$y = 30x + 120$]**

Got It?   ERROR PREVENTION
Students may have trouble identifying the variables. Point out that the question at the end of the problem refers to the two variable quantities that you need to find.

Q How would the equations be different if there was no registration fee? **[There would be only one variable.]**

---

2 Guided Instruction

 Each Problem is worked out and supported in the Student Online Center.

Problem 1
Solving by Substitution
Animated

Problem 2
Using Substitution to Solve a Problem
Animated

Problem 3
Solving by Elimination
Animated

Problem 4
Solving an Equivalent System

Problem 5
Solving Systems Without Unique Solutions

Support in Algebra 2 Companion
• Vocabulary
• Key Concepts
• Got It?

Answers

Solve It!
Per-day sales of $313 or greater;
store A: $35 + 0.1s$
store B: $10 + 0.18s$
$35 + 0.1s < 10 + 0.18s$
$s > 312.5$

Got It?
1. $(-2.5, 2.5)$

2. $.95 per download; $5.50 one-time registration fee

Problem 3

Q What variable is eliminated when you add the two equations? Why? **[x, because 4x + (−4x) = 0 by the Inverse Property of Addition.]**

Q How can you check the solution? **[Answers may vary. Sample: Substitute the values into both of the original equations. Both equations must result in true statements.]**

Q How would you solve this problem if both coefficients of x were positive 4? **[Subtract the equations instead of adding them to eliminate x.]**

Got It?   SYNTHESIZING

Q If you solved the first equation for 8y, how could you use the substitution method to find the solution? **[Substitute that value for 8y in the second equation. Be sure to include the subtraction sign.]**

Problem 4

Q What happens when you use substitution to solve the system? **[Answers may vary. Sample: The substitution requires fractions or decimals.]**

Q Why might graphing also work well to solve this system? **[Answers may vary. Sample: The solution (−5, 2) has integer coordinates.]**

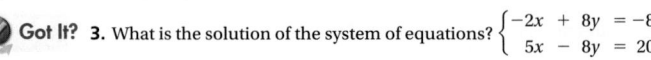

Problem 3 Solving by Elimination

What is the solution of the system of equations? $\begin{cases} 4x + 2y = 9 \\ -4x + 3y = 16 \end{cases}$

Think

How can you use the Addition Property of Equality?
Since $-4x + 3y$ is equal to 16, you can add the same value to each side of $4x + 2y = 9$.

$4x + 2y = 9$

$\underline{-4x + 3y = 16}$ — One equation has 4x and the other has $-4x$. Add to eliminate the variable x.

$5y = 25$

$y = 5$ Solve for y.

$4x + 2y = 9$ Choose one of the original equations.

$4x + 2(5) = 9$ Substitute for y.

$4x = -1$ Solve for x.

$x = -\frac{1}{4}$

The solution is $\left(-\frac{1}{4}, 5\right)$.

Got It? 3. What is the solution of the system of equations? $\begin{cases} -2x + 8y = -8 \\ 5x - 8y = 20 \end{cases}$

When you multiply each side of one or both equations in a system by the same nonzero number, the new system and the original system have the same solutions. The two systems are called **equivalent systems**. You can use this method to make additive inverses.

Problem 4 Solving an Equivalent System

What is the solution of the system of equations? $\begin{array}{c} ① \\ ② \end{array} \begin{cases} 2x + 7y = 4 \\ 3x + 5y = -5 \end{cases}$

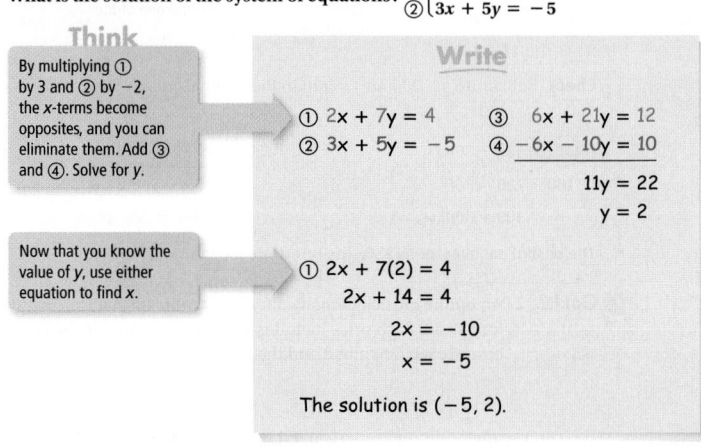

Think

By multiplying ① by 3 and ② by −2, the x-terms become opposites, and you can eliminate them. Add ③ and ④. Solve for y.

Now that you know the value of y, use either equation to find x.

Write

① 2x + 7y = 4   ③ 6x + 21y = 12
② 3x + 5y = −5   ④ −6x − 10y = 10

11y = 22
y = 2

① 2x + 7(2) = 4
2x + 14 = 4
2x = −10
x = −5

The solution is (−5, 2).

Additional Problems

1. What is the solution of the system of equations?
$\begin{cases} 5x - 3y = -1 \\ x + y = 3 \end{cases}$
ANSWER (1, 2)

2. You are in charge of ordering labels for a small business. A company that makes custom labels charges a yearly fee plus a cost per label. You paid $375 last year for 300 labels. This year you ordered 1,000 labels and paid $725. What are the yearly fee and cost per label, assuming the prices did not change?
ANSWER $225 yearly fee, $0.50 per label

3. What is the solution of the system of equations?
$\begin{cases} 2x - 3y = 14 \\ 4x + 3y = 46 \end{cases}$
ANSWER (10, 2)

4. What is the solution of the system of equations?
$\begin{cases} 7x + 5y = 2 \\ 8x - 9y = 17 \end{cases}$
ANSWER (1, −1)

5. What are the solutions of the following systems?
a. $\begin{cases} 6x + 4y = 2 \\ 3x + 2y = -1 \end{cases}$
ANSWER no solution

b. $\begin{cases} 6x - 3y = 15 \\ -8x + 4y = -20 \end{cases}$
ANSWER infinitely many solutions

Got It? 4. a. What is the solution of this system of equations? $\begin{cases} 3x + 7y = 15 \\ 5x + 2y = -4 \end{cases}$

b. Reasoning In Problem 4, you found that $y = 2$. Substitute this value into equation ② instead of equation ①. Do you still get the same value for x? Explain why.

Solving a system algebraically does not always provide a unique solution. Sometimes you get infinitely many solutions. Sometimes you get no solutions.

 Problem 5 Solving Systems Without Unique Solutions

Think
How are the two equations in this system related?
Multiplying both sides of the first equation by −1 results in the second equation.

What are the solutions of the following systems? Explain.

A $\begin{cases} -3x + y = -5 \\ 3x - y = 5 \end{cases}$
$0 = 0$

B $\begin{cases} 4x - 6y = 6 \\ -4x + 6y = 10 \end{cases}$
$0 = 16$

Elimination gives an equation that is always true. The two equations in the system represent the same line. This is a dependent system with infinitely many solutions.

Elimination gives an equation that is always false. The two equations in the system represent parallel lines. This is an inconsistent system. It has no solutions.

 Got It? 5. What are the solutions of the following systems? Explain.

a. $\begin{cases} -x + y = -2 \\ 2x - 2y = 0 \end{cases}$

b. $\begin{cases} 4x + y = 6 \\ 12x + 3y = 18 \end{cases}$

Lesson Check

Do you know HOW?

Solve each system by substitution.

1. $\begin{cases} 3x + 5y = 13 \\ 2x + y = 4 \end{cases}$

2. $\begin{cases} 2x - 3y = 6 \\ x + y = -12 \end{cases}$

Solve each system by elimination.

3. $\begin{cases} 2x + 3y = 7 \\ -2x + 5y = 1 \end{cases}$

4. $\begin{cases} x + 2y = -1 \\ x - y = 8 \end{cases}$

5. $\begin{cases} x - y = -4 \\ 3x + 2y = 7 \end{cases}$

6. $\begin{cases} 3x + 4y = 10 \\ 2x + 3y = 7 \end{cases}$

Do you UNDERSTAND?  **MATHEMATICAL PRACTICES**

7. Vocabulary Give an example of two equivalent systems.

8. Compare and Contrast Explain how the substitution method of solving a system of equations differs from the elimination method.

9. Writing A café sells a regular cup of coffee for $1 and a large cup for $1.50. Melissa and her friends buy 5 cups of coffee and spend a total of $6. Explain how to write and solve a system of equations to find the number of large cups of coffee they bought.

Got It?

Q Does it matter which variable you solve for first? **[No; either way you get the same solution.]**

Problem 5

Q What are the three possible types of solutions for a system of two equations? **[one solution, no solution, infinitely many solutions]**

Got It?
Another way to solve these is to solve each equation for y. Compare the slopes and y-intercepts to determine whether the lines are parallel, intersecting, or coinciding.

3 Lesson Check

Do you know HOW?
- For Exercises 1 and 2, encourage students to determine which variable is the easiest to use.

Do you UNDERSTAND?
- In Exercise 7, encourage students to use equations with two variables rather than one.
- For Exercise 9, if students have trouble identifying the variables, review Problem 2.

Close

Q Why might you use different methods for solving a system of equations? **[Answers may vary. Samples: Graphing only works well if the coefficients and constants are small in magnitude and integral. Substitution works best if one of the equations can easily be solved for one of the variables. Elimination is efficient if a variable can be easily eliminated.]**

Answers

Got It? (continued)

3. $(4, 0)$

4. a. $(-2, 3)$

b. Yes; the solution $(-5, 2)$ is a solution to both eqs. in the system, so substituting $y = 2$ into either equation will result in $x = -5$.

5. a. no solution; The eq. is always false.

b. infinite number of solutions; The eq. is always true.

Lesson Check

1. $(1, 2)$ **2.** $(-6, -6)$

3. $(2, 1)$ **4.** $(5, -3)$

5. $\left(-\frac{1}{5}, \frac{19}{5}\right)$ **6.** $(2, 1)$

7. Answers may vary. Sample:
$\begin{cases} 4x - 3y = -2 \\ 3x - 2y = -1 \end{cases}$
$\begin{cases} -8x + 6y = 4 \\ 9x - 6y = -3 \end{cases}$

8. In the substitution method of solving a system of equations, you first solve one equation for one of the variables. Then substitute for this variable in the other equation and solve for the other variable. In the elimination method, you create an equivalent system of equations that contain a pair of additive inverses so that you can eliminate one variable and solve for the remaining variable.

9. Let r = number of regular cups of coffee and c = number of large cups of coffee. First, $r + c = 5$ because a total of 5 cups of coffee were purchased. Second, $r + 1.5c = 6$ because each regular cup of coffee is $1, each large cup is $1.50, and the total spent is $6. Then, solve the system of equations using elimination by subtracting the first equation from the second to eliminate r and solve for c. $c = 2$; 2 large cups

---

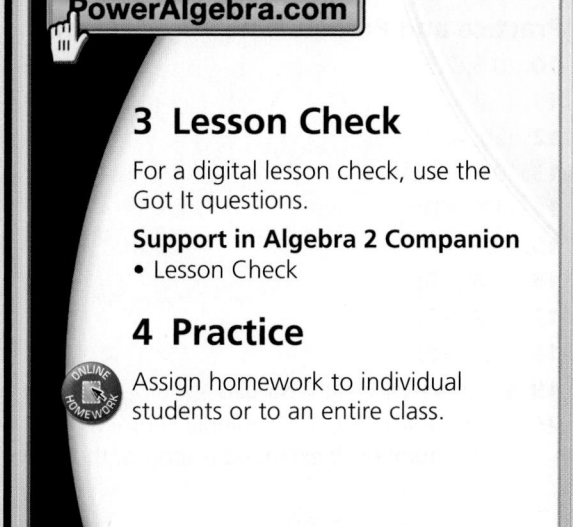

PowerAlgebra.com

3 Lesson Check

For a digital lesson check, use the Got It questions.

Support in Algebra 2 Companion
- Lesson Check

4 Practice

Assign homework to individual students or to an entire class.

4 Practice

ASSIGNMENT GUIDE

Basic: 10–43, 53–57

Average: 11–41 odd, 43–61

Advanced: 11–41 odd, 43–66

 Mathematical Practices are supported by exercises with red headings. Here are the Practices supported in this lesson:

MP 1: Make Sense of Problems Ex. 43

MP 3: Communicate Ex. 9, 57

MP 3: Compare Arguments Ex. 8

MP 3: Critique the Reasoning of Others Ex. 53

Applications exercises have blue headings.

STEM exercises focus on science or engineering applications.

EXERCISE 56: Use the Think About a Plan worksheet in the **Practice and Problem Solving Workbook** (also available in the Teaching Resources in print and online) to further support students' development in becoming independent learners.

HOMEWORK QUICK CHECK

To check students' understanding of key skills and concepts, go over Exercises 19, 33, 43, 56, and 57.

 Practice and Problem-Solving Exercises  MATHEMATICAL PRACTICES

 **Practice** Solve each system by substitution. Check your answers. ◀ See Problem 1.

10. $\begin{cases} 4x + 2y = 7 \\ y = 5x \end{cases}$
11. $\begin{cases} 3c + 2d = 2 \\ d = 4 \end{cases}$
12. $\begin{cases} x + 12y = 68 \\ x = 8y - 12 \end{cases}$

13. $\begin{cases} 4p + 2q = 8 \\ q = 2p + 1 \end{cases}$
14. $\begin{cases} x + 3y = 7 \\ 2x - 4y = 24 \end{cases}$
15. $\begin{cases} x + 6y = 2 \\ 5x + 4y = 36 \end{cases}$

16. $\begin{cases} t = 2r + 3 \\ 5r - 4t = 6 \end{cases}$
17. $\begin{cases} y = 2x - 1 \\ 3x - y = -1 \end{cases}$
18. $\begin{cases} r + s = -12 \\ 4r - 6s = 12 \end{cases}$

19. **Money** A student has some \$1 bills and \$5 bills in his wallet. He has a total of 15 bills that are worth \$47. How many of each type of bill does he have? ◀ See Problem 2.

20. A student took 60 minutes to answer a combination of 20 multiple-choice and extended-response questions. She took 2 minutes to answer each multiple-choice question and 6 minutes to answer each extended-response question.
    a. Write a system of equations to model the relationship between the number of multiple choice questions m and the number of extended-response questions r.
    b. How many of each type of question was on the test?

21. **Transportation** A youth group with 26 members is going skiing. Each of the five chaperones will drive a van or sedan. The vans can seat seven people, and the sedans can seat five people. Assuming there are no empty seats, how many of each type of vehicle could transport all 31 people to the ski area in one trip?

Solve each system by elimination. ◀ See Problem 3.

22. $\begin{cases} x + y = 12 \\ x - y = 2 \end{cases}$
23. $\begin{cases} x + 2y = 10 \\ x + y = 6 \end{cases}$
24. $\begin{cases} 3a + 4b = 9 \\ -3a - 2b = -3 \end{cases}$

25. $\begin{cases} 4x + 2y = 4 \\ 6x + 2y = 8 \end{cases}$
26. $\begin{cases} 2w + 5y = -24 \\ 3w - 5y = 14 \end{cases}$
27. $\begin{cases} 3u + 3v = 15 \\ -2u + 3v = -5 \end{cases}$

28. $\begin{cases} 3x + 2y = 6 \\ 3x + 3 = y \end{cases}$
29. $\begin{cases} 5x - y = 4 \\ 2x - y = 1 \end{cases}$
30. $\begin{cases} 2r + s = 3 \\ 4r - s = 9 \end{cases}$

Solve each system by elimination. ◀ See Problems 4 and 5.

31. $\begin{cases} 4x - 6y = -26 \\ -2x + 3y = 13 \end{cases}$
32. $\begin{cases} 9a - 3d = 3 \\ -3a + d = -1 \end{cases}$
33. $\begin{cases} 2a + 3b = 12 \\ 5a - b = 13 \end{cases}$

34. $\begin{cases} 2x - 3y = 6 \\ 6x - 9y = 9 \end{cases}$
35. $\begin{cases} 20x + 5y = 120 \\ 10x + 7.5y = 80 \end{cases}$
36. $\begin{cases} 6x - 2y = 11 \\ -9x + 3y = 16 \end{cases}$

37. $\begin{cases} 2x - 3y = -1 \\ 3x + 4y = 8 \end{cases}$
38. $\begin{cases} 5x - 2y = -19 \\ 2x + 3y = 0 \end{cases}$
39. $\begin{cases} r + 3s = 7 \\ 2r - s = 7 \end{cases}$

40. $\begin{cases} y = 4 - x \\ 3x + y = 6 \end{cases}$
41. $\begin{cases} 3x + 2y = 10 \\ 6x + 4y = 15 \end{cases}$
42. $\begin{cases} 3m + 4n = -13 \\ 5m + 6n = -19 \end{cases}$

146 Chapter 3 Linear Systems

Answers

Practice and Problem-Solving Exercises

10. $(0.5, 2.5)$

11. $(-2, 4)$

12. $(20, 4)$

13. $(0.75, 2.5)$

14. $(10, -1)$

15. $(8, -1)$

16. $(-6, -9)$

17. $(-2, -5)$

18. $(-6, -6)$

19. seven \$1-bills; eight \$5-bills

20. a. Let m = number of multiple choice and r = number of extended response, then
$$\begin{cases} m + r = 20 \\ 2m + 6r = 60 \end{cases}$$
    b. 15 multiple choice; 5 extended response

21. 3 vans and 2 sedans

22. $(7, 5)$

23. $(2, 4)$

24. $(-1, 3)$

25. $(2, -2)$

26. $(-2, -4)$

27. $(4, 1)$

28. $(0, 3)$

29. $(1, 1)$

30. $(2, -1)$

31. infinite number of solutions; $\{(x, y) | -2x + 3y = 13\}$

32. infinite number of solutions; $\{(a, d) | -3a + d = -1\}$

33. $(3, 2)$

34. no solution

35. $(5, 4)$

36. no solution

37. $\left(\frac{20}{17}, \frac{19}{17}\right)$

38. $(-3, 2)$

39. $(4, 1)$

40. $(1, 3)$

41. no solution

42. $(1, -4)$

146 Chapter 3

B Apply

43. Think About a Plan Suppose you have a part-time job delivering packages. Your employer pays you a flat rate of $9.50 per hour. You discover that a competitor pays employees $2 per hour plus $3 per delivery. How many deliveries would the competitor's employees have to make in four hours to earn the same pay you earn in a four-hour shift?
- How can you write a system of equations to model this situation?
- Which method should you use to solve the system?
- How can you interpret the solution in the context of the problem?

Solve each system.

44. $\begin{cases} 5x + y = 0 \\ 5x + 2y = 30 \end{cases}$

45. $\begin{cases} 2m = -4n - 4 \\ 3m + 5n = -3 \end{cases}$

46. $\begin{cases} 7x + 2y = -8 \\ 8y = 4x \end{cases}$

47. $\begin{cases} 2m + 4n = 10 \\ 3m + 5n = 11 \end{cases}$

48. $\begin{cases} -6 = 3x - 6y \\ 4x = 4 + 5y \end{cases}$

49. $\begin{cases} \frac{x}{3} + \frac{4y}{3} = 300 \\ 3x - 4y = 300 \end{cases}$

50. $\begin{cases} 0.02a - 1.5b = 4 \\ 0.5b - 0.02a = 1.8 \end{cases}$

51. $\begin{cases} 4y = 2x \\ 2x + y = \frac{x}{2} + 1 \end{cases}$

52. $\begin{cases} \frac{1}{2}x + \frac{2}{3}y = 1 \\ \frac{3}{4}x - \frac{1}{3}y = 2 \end{cases}$

53. Error Analysis Identify and correct the error shown in finding the solution of $\begin{cases} 3x - 4y = 14 \\ x + y = -7 \end{cases}$ using substitution.

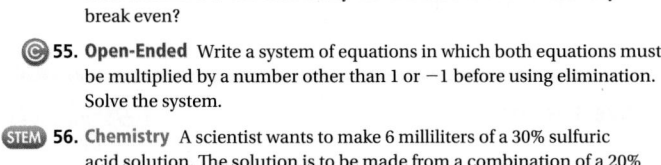

$x + y = -7$
$y = -7 - x$

$3x - 4y = 14$
$3x - 4(-7 - x) = 14$
$3x - 28 - 4x = 14$
$-x - 28 = 14$
$x = -42$

$y = -7 - (-42)$
$y = 35$

54. Break-Even Point Jenny's Bakery sells carrot muffins at $2 each. The electricity to run the oven is $120 per day and the cost of making one carrot muffin is $1.40. How many muffins need to be sold each day to break even?

55. Open-Ended Write a system of equations in which both equations must be multiplied by a number other than 1 or −1 before using elimination. Solve the system.

STEM 56. Chemistry A scientist wants to make 6 milliliters of a 30% sulfuric acid solution. The solution is to be made from a combination of a 20% sulfuric acid solution and a 50% sulfuric acid solution. How many milliliters of each solution must be combined to make the 30% solution?

57. Writing Explain how you decide whether to use substitution or elimination to solve a system.

58. The equation $3x - 4y = 2$ and which equation below form a system with no solutions?

Ⓐ $2y = 1.5x - 2$ Ⓒ $3x + 4y = 2$

Ⓑ $2y = 1.5x - 1$ Ⓓ $4y - 3x = -2$

For each system, choose the method of solving that seems easier to use. Explain why you made each choice. Solve each system.

59. $\begin{cases} 3x - y = 5 \\ y = 4x + 2 \end{cases}$

60. $\begin{cases} 2x - 3y = 4 \\ 2x - 5y = -6 \end{cases}$

61. $\begin{cases} 6x - 3y = 3 \\ 5x - 5y = 10 \end{cases}$

---

43. 10 deliveries

44. $(-6, 30)$

45. $(4, -3)$

46. $\left(-1, -\frac{1}{2}\right)$

47. $(-3, 4)$

48. $(6, 4)$

49. $(300, 150)$

50. $(-235, -5.8)$

51. $(0.5, 0.25)$

52. $\left(\frac{5}{2}, -\frac{3}{8}\right)$

53. Error in 5th line:
$-4(-7 - x) = 28 + 4x$ **not**
$-28 - 4x$; Lines 5–9 should be:
$3x + 28 + 4x = 14$; $7x = -14$;
$x = -2$; $y = -7 - (-2)$; $y = -5$

54. 200 muffins

55. Answers may vary. Sample:
$\begin{cases} -3x + 4y = 12 \\ 5x - 3y = 13 \end{cases}$; $(8, 9)$

56. 4 ml of 20% sulfuric acid solution and 2 ml of 50% sulfuric acid solution

57. In determining whether to use substitution or elimination to solve an equation, look at the equations to determine if one is solved or can be easily solved for a particular variable. If that is the case, substitution can easily be used. Otherwise, elimination might be easier.

58. A

59. Substitution; the second equation is solved for y; $(-7, -26)$

60. Elimination; $2x$ would be eliminated from the system if the equations were subtracted; $(9\frac{1}{2}, 5)$

61. Elimination; substitution would be difficult since no coefficient is 1 in the original system. Dividing the first equation by 3 and dividing the second equation by 5 results in an equivalent system where y would be eliminated from the system if the equations were subtracted; $(-1, -3)$

Answers

Practice and Problem-Solving Exercises
(continued)

62. 2875 votes

63. yes; −40 degrees

64. −2

65. 0

66. 8

Standardized Test Prep

67. 2

68. 5

69. 6

70. 2

71. 4

 **Challenge** **62. Entertainment** In the final round of a singing competition, the audience voted for one of the two finalists, Luke or Sean. Luke received 25% more votes than Sean received. Altogether, the two finalists received 5175 votes. How many votes did Luke receive?

 63. Weather The equation $F = \frac{9}{5}C + 32$ relates temperatures on the Celsius and Fahrenheit scales. Does any temperature have the same number reading on both scales? If so, what is the number?

Find the value of a that makes each system a dependent system.

64. $\begin{cases} y = 3x + a \\ 3x - y = 2 \end{cases}$

65. $\begin{cases} 3y = 2x \\ 6y - a - 4x = 0 \end{cases}$

66. $\begin{cases} y = \frac{x}{2} + 4 \\ 2y - x = a \end{cases}$

Standardized Test Prep

GRIDDED RESPONSE

 SAT/ACT

67. What is the slope of the line at the right?

68. What is the x-value of the solution of $\begin{cases} x + y = 7 \\ 3x - 2y = 11 \end{cases}$?

69. Solve $9(x + 7) - 6(x - 3) = 99$. What is the value of x?

70. Georgia has only dimes and quarters in her bag. She has a total of 18 coins that are worth \$3. How many more dimes than quarters does she have?

71. The graph of $g(x)$ is a horizontal translation of $f(x) = 2|x + 1| + 3$, 5 units to the right. What is the x-value of the vertex of $g(x)$?

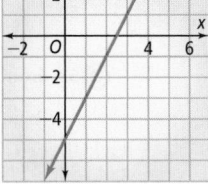

 Apply What You've Learned

MATHEMATICAL PRACTICES
MP 2

In the Apply What You've Learned in Lesson 3-1, you created a system of equations and solved the system graphically. Now, you will start to create a system of three linear equations to represent the criteria in the problem on page 133.

a. Write an equation that models the distances of all parts of the triathlon.

b. Write an equation modeling the relationship between the distances of the swim and the run of the triathlon.

c. Use substitution to write a new equation that models the distance of all parts of the triathlon, and solve it for the distance for the bicycle ride.

 **Apply What You've Learned**
In the Apply What You've Learned for Lesson 3-1, students solved a system of equations in two variables. Now, they will begin to create a system of equations in three variables to model the triathlon described on page 133.

© **Mathematical Practices**
Students will **reason abstractly** as they create linear equations to model the problem. (MP 2)

ANSWERS

a. Let x, y, and z represent the distances for the swim, bicycle ride, and run, respectively.
$x + y + z = 28$

b. $x = \frac{1}{5}z$, or $5x = z$

c. Answers may vary. Sample:
$$x + y + 5x = 28$$
$$6x + y = 28$$
$$y = 28 - 6x$$

Lesson Resources

Additional Instructional Support

Algebra 2 Companion

Students can use the **Algebra 2 Companion** worktext (4 pages) as you teach the lesson. Use the Companion to support

- New Vocabulary
- Key Concepts
- Got It for each Problem
- Lesson Check

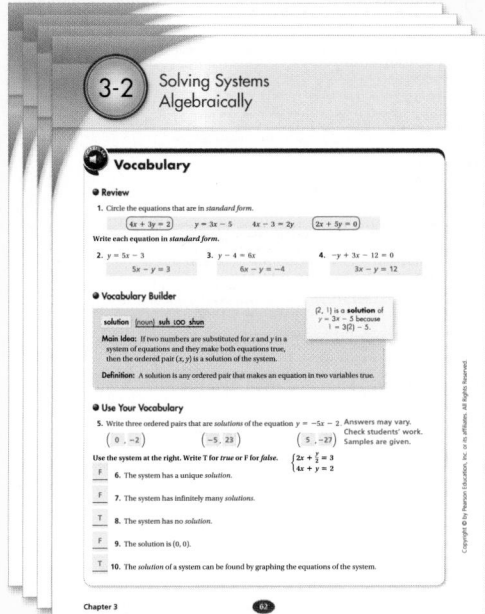

ELL Support

Connect to Prior Knowledge Draw a line on the board. Have a volunteer come up and draw an intersecting line. Have the class identify the relationship between the pair of lines and the number of solutions of the system. Repeat for parallel lines and coinciding lines.

Focus on Communication Write a series of systems of equations on the board. Model a statement for students explaining how you would approach the first problem. For example, say: I would use the substitution method because I can quickly solve for the variable x. Have each student explain how to do a problem. After each answer, ask if anyone has another idea.

5 Assess & Remediate

Lesson Quiz

1. Solve $\begin{cases} x - 2y = 0 \\ 4x - 3y = 15 \end{cases}$.

2. **Do you UNDERSTAND?** You and your friend are saving for a vacation. You start with the same amount and save for the same number of weeks. You save $75 per week, and your friend saves $50 per week. When the vacation time comes, you have $950, and your friend has $800. How much did you start with, and for how many weeks did you save?

3. Solve $\begin{cases} -3x + 7y = -15 \\ 3x - 7y = 20 \end{cases}$.

4. Solve $\begin{cases} 2x - 3y = -1 \\ 3x + 4y = 24 \end{cases}$.

5. Solve $\begin{cases} 2x + 2y = 4 \\ x + y = 2 \end{cases}$.

ANSWERS TO LESSON QUIZ

1. (6, 3)
2. $500, 6 weeks
3. no solution
4. (4, 3)
5. infinitely many solutions

PRESCRIPTION FOR REMEDIATION
Use the student work on the Lesson Quiz to prescribe a differentiated review assignment:

Points	Differentiated Remediation
0–2	Intervention
3–4	On-level
5	Extension

PowerAlgebra.com

5 Assess & Remediate

Assign the Lesson Quiz. Appropriate intervention, practice, or enrichment is automatically generated based on student performance.

Intervention

- **Reteaching** (2 pages) Provides reteaching and practice exercises for the key lesson concepts. Use with struggling students or absent students.

- **English Language Learner Support** Helps students develop and reinforce mathematical vocabulary and key concepts.

All-in-One Resources/Online
Reteaching

All-in-One Resources/Online
English Language Learner Support

Differentiated Remediation *continued*

On-Level

- **Practice** (2 pages) Provides extra practice for each lesson. For simpler practice exercises, use the Form K Practice pages found in the All-in-One Teaching Resources and online.

- **Think About a Plan** Helps students develop specific problem-solving skills and strategies by providing scaffolded guiding questions.

- **Standardized Test Prep** Focuses on all major exercises, all major question types, and helps students prepare for the high-stakes assessments.

Extension

- **Enrichment** Provides students with interesting problems and activities that extend the concepts of the lesson.

- **Activities, Games, and Puzzles** Worksheets that can be used for concepts development, enrichment, and for fun!

Practice and Problem Solving Wkbk/All-in-One Resources/Online
Practice page 1

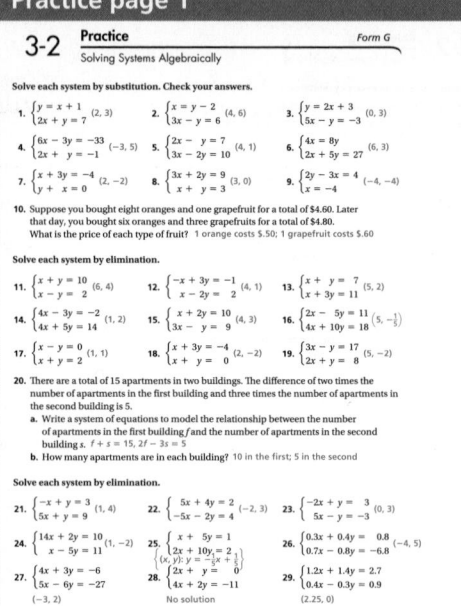

3-2 Practice — Form G
Solving Systems Algebraically

Practice and Problem Solving Wkbk/All-in-One Resources/Online
Practice page 2

3-2 Practice (continued) — Form G
Solving Systems Algebraically

All-in-One Resources/Online
Enrichment

3-2 Enrichment
Solving Systems Algebraically

Practice and Problem Solving Wkbk/All-in-One Resources/Online
Think About a Plan

3-2 Think About a Plan
Solving Systems Algebraically

Practice and Problem Solving Wkbk/All-in-One Resources/Online
Standardized Test Prep

3-2 Standardized Test Prep
Solving Systems Algebraically

Online Teacher Resource Center
Activities, Games, and Puzzles

3-2 Game: Risk and Reward
Solving Systems Algebraically

Common Core State Standards

A-REI.D.12 Graph . . . the solution set to a system of linear inequalities in two variables as the intersection of the corresponding half-planes. **Also A-REI.C.6, A-CED.A.3**

MP 1, MP 2, MP 3, MP 4, MP 7

Objective To solve systems of linear inequalities

Would using your calculator speed up the process here? You'll need a plan first.

MATHEMATICAL PRACTICES

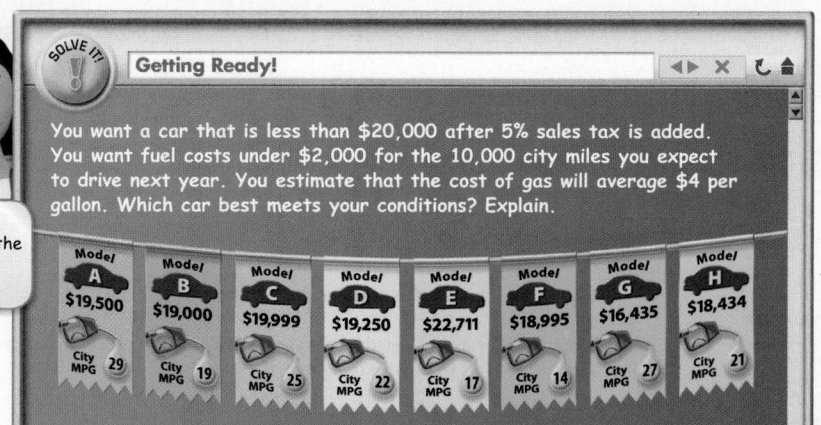

Getting Ready!

You want a car that is less than $20,000 after 5% sales tax is added. You want fuel costs under $2,000 for the 10,000 city miles you expect to drive next year. You estimate that the cost of gas will average $4 per gallon. Which car best meets your conditions? Explain.

Model A	Model B	Model C	Model D	Model E	Model F	Model G	Model H
$19,500	$19,000	$19,999	$19,250	$22,711	$18,995	$16,435	$18,434
City MPG 29	City MPG 19	City MPG 25	City MPG 22	City MPG 17	City MPG 14	City MPG 27	City MPG 21

An inequality and a system of inequalities can each have many solutions. A solution of a system of inequalities is a solution for each inequality in the system.

Essential Understanding You can solve a system of inequalities in more than one way. Graphing the solution is usually the most appropriate method. The solution is the set of all points that are solutions of each inequality in the system.

Plan

Which inequality should you use to build a table?
The first inequality has an infinite number of whole number solutions. The second one has a finite number of solutions. Use the second inequality.

Problem 1 Solving a System by Using a Table

Assume that g and m are whole numbers. What is the solution of the system of inequalities? $\begin{cases} g + m \geq 6 \\ 5g + 2m \leq 20 \end{cases}$

Make a table of values for g and m that satisfy the second inequality. The values for g and m must be whole numbers.

If $g = 0$, then $5(0) + 2m \leq 20$, and $m \leq 10$.
If $m = 0$, then $5g + 2(0) \leq 20$, and $g \leq 4$.

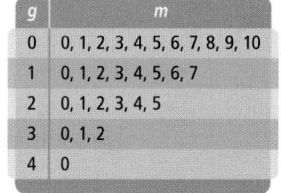

g	m
0	0, 1, 2, 3, 4, 5, 6, 7, 8, 9, 10
1	0, 1, 2, 3, 4, 5, 6, 7
2	0, 1, 2, 3, 4, 5
3	0, 1, 2
4	0

1 Interactive Learning

Solve It!

PURPOSE To solve a problem with constraints by using elimination

PROCESS Students may determine the cars that satisfy the constraints and then choose the cheapest.

FACILITATE

Q Which cars cost under $20,000 with tax? **[B, F, G, H]**

Q How can you determine the cost of driving 10,000 miles for a car? **[Divide 10,000 by the MPG, and multiply the quotient by the cost of a gallon of gas.]**

Q Which remaining cars cost less than $2000 to drive 10,000 miles? **[C, G, H]**

Q Which is the cheapest car? **[C]**

ANSWER See Solve It in Answers on next page.

CONNECT THE MATH The Solve It can be solved using a system of inequalities with the following constraints: total price less than $20,000 and fuel costs less than $2000. Students will use this method to solve similar problems in the lesson.

2 Guided Instruction

Problem 1   EXTENSION

Q How would the solution be different if the constraint $g + m \geq 6$ was removed? **[All of the pairs of values in the table would be solutions.]**

3-3
Preparing to Teach

BIG ideas **Function**
Solving Equations and Inequalities

ESSENTIAL UNDERSTANDINGS

• A system of inequalities can be solved in more than one way. Graphing is usually the most appropriate method to solve a system of inequalities.

• The solution is the set of all points that are solutions of each inequality in the system.

Math Background

This lesson extends what students know about graphing inequalities and systems of equations to solving systems of inequalities.

A system of two linear inequalities divides the plane into 4 parts:

• points that satisfy one inequality but not the other

• points that satisfy the other inequality but not the first

• points that satisfy both inequalities

• points that satisfy neither of the inequalities

The solution of a system of linear inequalities is the section of the plane where the points satisfy both inequalities: the intersection of each of the corresponding half-plane solutions. The solution may or may not include parts of the boundaries of the graph, depending on the inequality.

If a system has whole number solutions, it can also be solved (with a few more calculations) with a table, as shown in Problem 1.

Mathematical Practices

Look for and make use of structure.
Students will see a complicated solution to a system of inequalities as being composed of simple boundaries and a shaded region.

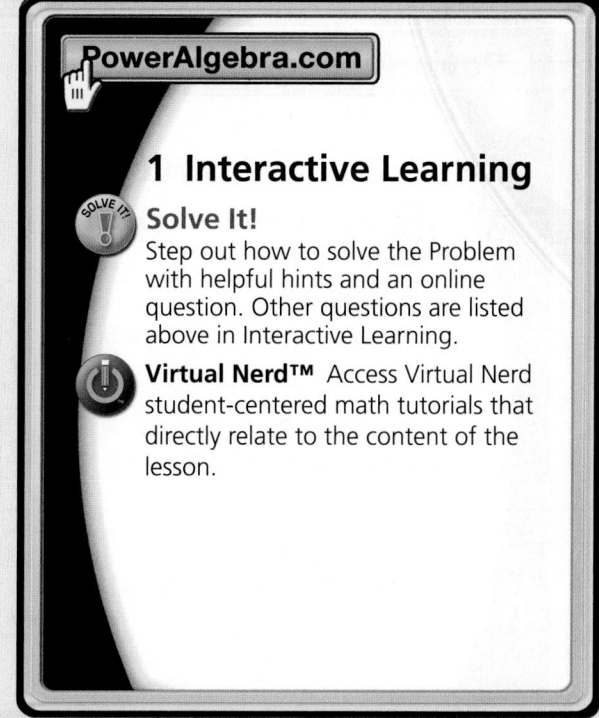

PowerAlgebra.com

1 Interactive Learning

Solve It!
Step out how to solve the Problem with helpful hints and an online question. Other questions are listed above in Interactive Learning.

Virtual Nerd™ Access Virtual Nerd student-centered math tutorials that directly relate to the content of the lesson.

Got It?

Q How would the solution be different if x and y were any real numbers? **[There would be infinitely many solutions, since there are infinitely many real numbers that satisfy the constraints.]**

Problem 2   VISUALIZE

Q In the third graph, which inequalities does the blue region satisfy? yellow region? green region? white region? **[first inequality; second inequality; both inequalities; neither inequality]**

Got It?   EXTENSION

Q One way to graph $x + 2y = 4$ is to first solve for y. What is another way? **[Answers may vary. Sample: Graph the intercepts (0, 2) and (4, 0).]**

Q How is the shading of the graph of $-y \geq -x - 1$ different from the graph of $y \geq x + 1$? **[When you multiply both sides of the inequality by -1, the inequality sign flips and the signs change, giving $y \leq x + 1$, so the shading is below the graphed line for the first inequality. For the second inequality, the shading is above the graphed line.]**

In the table, highlight each pair of values that satisfies the first inequality. The highlighted pairs are the solutions of both inequalities.

g	m
0	0, 1, 2, 3, 4, 5, 6, 7, 8, 9, 10
1	0, 1, 2, 3, 4, 5, 6, 7
2	0, 1, 2, 3, 4, 5
3	0, 1, 2
4	0

 Got It? 1. Assume that x and y are whole numbers. What is the solution of the system of inequalities?
$$\begin{cases} x + y > 4 \\ 3x + 7y \leq 21 \end{cases}$$

You can solve a system of linear inequalities by graphing. Recall that when the variables of a linear inequality represent real numbers, a graphed solution consists of a half-plane and possibly its boundary line. Thus, for two inequalities, the solution is the overlap of the two half-planes.

Ⓒ Problem 2   **Solving a System by Graphing**

What is the solution of the system of inequalities? $\begin{cases} 2x - y \geq -3 \\ y \geq -\frac{1}{2}x + 1 \end{cases}$

Graph each inequality. Rewrite $2x - y \geq -3$ in slope-intercept form as $y \leq 2x + 3$. The overlap is the solution of the system.

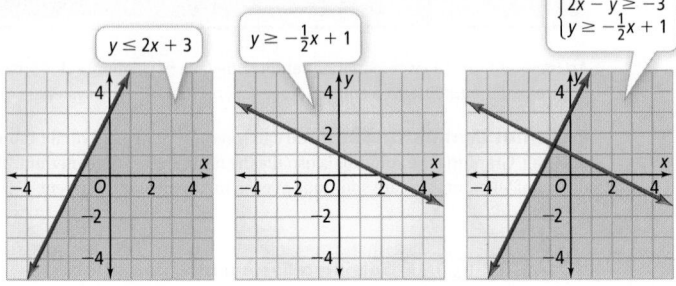

Plan

How can you be sure to shade the correct half-planes?
If the inequality is in slope-intercept form, shade above the boundary if $y >$ or $y \geq$ and shade below the boundary if $y <$ or $y \leq$. If not, use a test point.

Check   Pick a point in the overlap region, such as $(0, 2)$, and check it in both inequalities of the system.

$$2x - y \geq -3 \qquad\qquad y \geq \frac{1}{2}x + 1$$
$$2(0) - 2 \geq -3 \qquad\qquad 2 \geq \frac{1}{2}(0) + 1$$
$$-2 \geq -3 ✔ \qquad\qquad 2 \geq 1 ✔$$

 Got It? 2. What is the solution of the system of inequalities? $\begin{cases} x + 2y \leq 4 \\ y \geq -x - 1 \end{cases}$

 PowerAlgebra.com

2 Guided Instruction

Ⓒ Each Problem is worked out and supported online.

Problem 1
Solving a System by Using a Table
Animated

Problem 2
Solving a System by Graphing
Animated

Problem 3
Using a System of Inequalities
Animated

Problem 4
Solving a Linear/Absolute-Value System

Support in Algebra 2 Companion
• Vocabulary
• Key Concepts
• Got It?

Answers

Solve It!
Model G; the price after taxes will be about \$17,257 and fuel costs for the year will be about \$1481.

Got It?
1. (4, 1), (5, 0), (6, 0), (7, 0)

2.

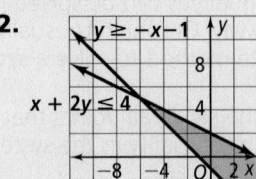

3. 5 meats and no vegetables; 4 meats and 1 or 2 vegetables; 3 meats and 2, 3, or 4 vegetables; 2 meats and 3, 4, 5, or 6 vegetables; 1 meat and 4–8 vegetables; no meat 5–10 vegetables

Sometimes, you can model a real situation with a system of linear inequalities. Solutions to real-world problems are often whole numbers, so only certain points in the region of overlap will solve the problem.

 **Problem 3** Using a System of Inequalities

Fundraising Your city's cultural center is sponsoring a concert to raise at least $30,000 for the city's Youth Services. Tickets are $20 for balcony seats and $30 for orchestra seats. If the center has 500 orchestra seats, how many of each type of seat must they sell?

Know	Need	Plan
Must raise at least $30,000. There are at most 500 orchestra seats.	The possible sales of balcony and orchestra seats	• Model the problem with a system of inequalities. • Graph the inequalities on your calculator.

Relate $20 \cdot$ balcony seats $+ 30 \cdot$ orchestra seats $\geq 30{,}000$

orchestra seats ≤ 500

Define Let x = the number of balcony seats sold.

Let y = the number of orchestra seats sold.

Write $20 \cdot x + 30 \cdot y \geq 30{,}000$

$y \leq 500$

Rewrite $20x + 30y \geq 30{,}000$ in slope intercept form as $y \geq -\frac{2}{3}x + 1000$.

The system of inequalities is $\begin{cases} y \geq -\frac{2}{3}x + 1000 \\ y \leq 500 \end{cases}$.

Use your graphing calculator to graph the inequalities.

The solution is the overlap.

Test a point. If the cultural center sells 900 balcony and 450 orchestra tickets, will the Youth Services meet its goal?

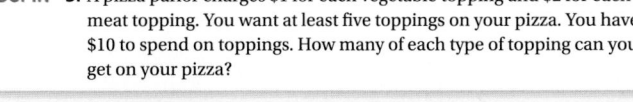

$20(900) + 30(450) \overset{?}{\geq} 30{,}000 \qquad 450 \overset{?}{\leq} 500$

$18{,}000 + 13{,}250 \overset{?}{\geq} 30{,}000 \qquad 450 \leq 500$ ✔

$31{,}250 \geq 30{,}000$ ✔

Because the number of seats must be a whole number, only the points in the overlap that represent whole numbers are solutions.

 Got It? 3. A pizza parlor charges $1 for each vegetable topping and $2 for each meat topping. You want at least five toppings on your pizza. You have $10 to spend on toppings. How many of each type of topping can you get on your pizza?

Think

What do points in the overlap represent? The points represent combinations of balcony and orchestra seats that have a total value of at least $30,000.

 PowerAlgebra.com | **Lesson 3-3** Systems of Inequalities | **151**

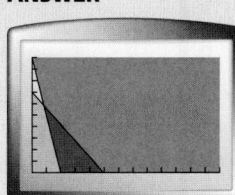

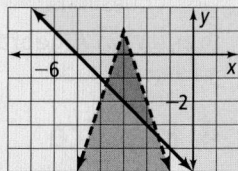

Problem 3

Q Why might this problem be difficult to solve by hand? How could you make it easier? **[Answers may vary. Sample: The numbers are large. To make it easier, you could graph the dollars by thousands and seats by hundreds.]**

Q Are all of the points on the boundary solutions? Explain your answer. **[No; only the points with whole-number values are solutions.]**

Q Generally speaking, what values of x will result in whole numbers? **[multiples of 3]**

Q If 600 balcony seats were sold, would the Cultural Center meet their goal? Explain. **[No; even if they sell all 500 orchestra seats, they will make only $27,000 and not reach their $30,000 goal.]**

Got It?

Q What will the variables represent? **[the number of vegetable toppings and the number of meat toppings]**

Q What is the system of inequalities? **[Let v = vegetable toppings and m = meat toppings. $\begin{cases} v + 2m \leq 10 \\ v + m \geq 5 \end{cases}$]**

Additional Problems

1. Assume that x and y are whole numbers. What is the solution of the system of inequalities?

$\begin{cases} x + y \geq 5 \\ 2x + 3y \leq 15 \end{cases}$

ANSWER $(0, 5)$, $(1, 4)$, $(2, 3)$, $(3, 2)$, $(3, 3)$, $(4, 1)$, $(4, 2)$, $(5, 0)$, $(5, 1)$, $(6, 0)$, $(6, 1)$, $(7, 0)$

2. What is the solution of the system of inequalities?

$\begin{cases} y - 3x \leq -4 \\ y \geq x - 3 \end{cases}$

ANSWER

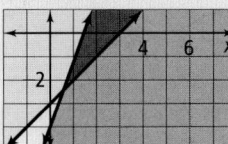

3. Tickets to a concert cost $70, or $20 with a student discount. Ticket sales must exceed $500,000 for the group to perform. If 20,000 seats are available, how many of each type must be sold? Show the solution on your calculator.

ANSWER

4. What is the solution of the system of inequalities?

$\begin{cases} y < -3|x + 3| + 1 \\ y \geq -x - 5 \end{cases}$

ANSWER

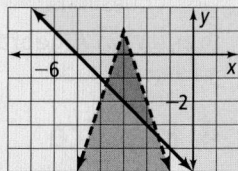

Problem 4

Q Why do two rays and one line bound the overlap when there are only two inequalities? **[The absolute value inequality is equivalent to two linear inequalities.]**

Q How would the graph be different if the inequalities were $y < 3$ and $y > |x - 1|$? **[The line and the absolute value graph would be dashed and would not be included in the solutions.]**

Got It?
ERROR PREVENTION

If students have trouble graphing the transformations of the absolute value function, review Lesson 2-7. Some students may benefit from rewriting the inequality as $y > 2|x - 1| + 0$.

3 Lesson Check

Do you know HOW?
• For Exercises 1–2, if students are unsure how to graph the solution, review Problem 2.

Do you UNDERSTAND? ERROR INTERVENTION
• For Exercise 6, if students talk about the number of solutions, encourage them to also compare the *graphs* of the solutions.

Close

Q How does graphing a system of inequalities on the same coordinate plane help you see which points satisfy both inequalities? **[You can see the overlap, as well as the regions that satisfy only one or neither inequality.]**

A system of inequalities can include nonlinear inequalities. You can also solve these systems graphically.

Problem 4 Solving a Linear/Absolute-Value System

What is the solution of the system of inequalities? $\begin{cases} y \le 3 \\ y \ge |x - 1| \end{cases}$

Graph each inequality.

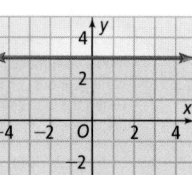 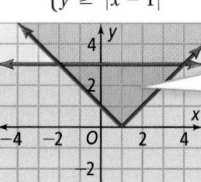

$y \le 3$ $\qquad$ $y \ge |x - 1|$ $\qquad$ $\begin{cases} y \le 3 \\ y \ge |x - 1| \end{cases}$

Think
Why is the shape of the overlap different from that of a system of linear inequalities?
The overlap is not formed by 2 half-planes so it is more varied in shape.

The region of represents the

Got It? **4.** What is the solution of the system of inequalities? $\begin{cases} y < -\frac{1}{3}x + 1 \\ y > 2|x - 1| \end{cases}$

Lesson Check

Do you know HOW?

Solve each system of inequalities by graphing.

1. $\begin{cases} x + y \ge 2 \\ 2x + y \le 5 \end{cases}$

2. $\begin{cases} y > x \\ y < x + 1 \end{cases}$

3. $\begin{cases} y \ge -3x - 1 \\ y < x + 2 \end{cases}$

4. You spend no more than 3 hours each day watching TV and playing football. You play football for at least 1 hour each day. What are the possible numbers of hours you can spend on each activity in one day?

Do you UNDERSTAND? MATHEMATICAL PRACTICES

5. **Reasoning** Is the solution of a system of linear inequalities the union or intersection of the solutions of the two inequalities? Justify your answer.

6. **Compare and Contrast** Explain how the graphical solution of a system of inequalities is different from the graphical solution of a system of equations.

7. **Error Analysis** Describe and correct the error made in solving this system of inequalities.
$\begin{cases} y < \frac{1}{2}x - 1 \\ y > -3x + 3 \end{cases}$

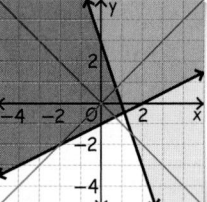

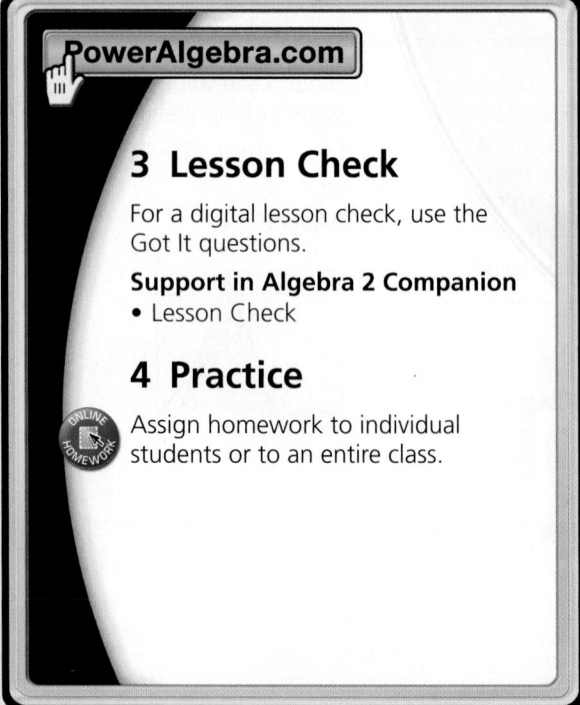

3 Lesson Check

For a digital lesson check, use the Got It questions.

Support in Algebra 2 Companion
• Lesson Check

4 Practice

Assign homework to individual students or to an entire class.

Answers

Got It? (continued)

4. $y > 2|x - 1|$

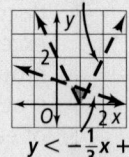

$y < -\frac{1}{3}x + 1$

Lesson Check

1.

$2x + y \le 5$

$x + y \ge 2$

2. $y < x + 1$; $y > x$ $\qquad$ **3.** $y < x + 2$; $y \ge -3x - 1$

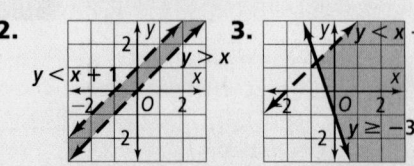

---

4. 0 h TV and 1, 2, or 3 h football; 1 h TV and 1 or 2 h football; or 2 h TV and 1 h football

5. Intersection; the solution of two inequalities is the over-lap or the intersection of the graphs of the individual inequalities.

6. The graphical solution of a system of inequalities consists of the overlap or intersection of the individual half-planes and corresponding boundary lines (either dotted or solid). The graphical solution of a system of equations includes only the intersection of the lines, not the half-planes.

7. For each inequality, the wrong half-plane has been shaded. The half-plane below $y = \frac{1}{2}x - 1$ should be shaded and the half-plane above $y = -3x + 3$ should be shaded. Also, both boundary lines should be dashed because the inequalities are $<$ and $>$.

Practice and Problem-Solving Exercises  MATHEMATICAL PRACTICES

 A Practice   Find all whole number solutions of each system using a table.   ◀ See Problem 1.

8. $\begin{cases} y + 3x \le 8 \\ y - 3 > 2x \end{cases}$

9. $\begin{cases} x + y < 8 \\ 3x \le y + 6 \end{cases}$

10. $\begin{cases} y \ge x + 2 \\ 3y < -6x + 6 \end{cases}$

Solve each system of inequalities by graphing.   ◀ See Problem 2.

11. $\begin{cases} y \le 2x + 2 \\ y < -x + 1 \end{cases}$

12. $\begin{cases} y > -2 \\ x < 1 \end{cases}$

13. $\begin{cases} y \le 3 \\ y \le \frac{1}{2}x + 1 \end{cases}$

14. $\begin{cases} y \le 3x + 1 \\ -6x + 2y > 5 \end{cases}$

15. $\begin{cases} x + 2y \le 10 \\ x + y \le 3 \end{cases}$

16. $\begin{cases} -x - y \le 2 \\ y - 2x > 1 \end{cases}$

17. $\begin{cases} y > -2x \\ 2x - y \ge 2 \end{cases}$

18. $\begin{cases} c \ge d - 3 \\ c < \frac{1}{2}d + 3 \end{cases}$

19. $\begin{cases} 2x + y < 1 \\ y > -2x + 3 \end{cases}$

20. You want to decorate a party hall with a total of at least 40 red and yellow balloons, with a minimum of 25 yellow balloons. Write and graph a system of inequalities to model the situation.   ◀ See Problem 3.

21. A gardener wants to plant at least 50 tulips and rose plants in a garden, but no more than 20 rose plants. Write and graph a system of inequalities to model the situation.

Solve each system of inequalities by graphing.   ◀ See Problem 4.

22. $\begin{cases} y > 4 \\ y < |x - 1| \end{cases}$

23. $\begin{cases} y < -\frac{1}{3}x + 1 \\ y > |2x - 1| \end{cases}$

24. $\begin{cases} y > x - 2 \\ y \ge |x + 2| \end{cases}$

25. $\begin{cases} y \le -\frac{4}{3}x \\ y \ge -|x| \end{cases}$

26. $\begin{cases} 3y < -x - 1 \\ y \le |x + 1| \end{cases}$

27. $\begin{cases} y > -2 \\ y \le -|x - 3| \end{cases}$

28. $\begin{cases} -2y < 4x + 2 \\ y > |2x + 1| \end{cases}$

29. $\begin{cases} -x \ge 4 - y \\ y \ge |3x - 6| \end{cases}$

30. $\begin{cases} y \le x - 4 \\ y > |x - 6| \end{cases}$

 B Apply   **31. Think About a Plan** The food pyramid suggests that you eat 4–6 servings of fruits and vegetables a day for a healthy diet. It also says that the number of servings of vegetables should be greater than the number of servings of fruits. Find the number of servings of fruits and vegetables that could make a healthy diet. Use whole numbers only.
- How can you write two inequalities that model the information in the problem?
- How can you use a graph to find combinations of fruits and vegetable servings that may help in having a healthy diet?

32. **College Admissions** An entrance exam has two sections, a verbal section and a mathematics section. You can score a maximum of 1600 points. For admission, the school of your choice requires a math score of at least 600. Write a system of inequalities to model scores that meet the school's requirements. Then solve the system by graphing.

---

4 Practice

ASSIGNMENT GUIDE

Basic: 8–34, 36–44 even

Average: 9–31 odd, 32–54

Advanced: 9–31 odd, 32–58

Standardized Test Prep: 59–62

Mixed Review: 63–72

Mathematical Practices are supported by exercises with red headings. Here are the Practices supported in this lesson:

MP 1: Make Sense of Problems Ex. 31
MP 2: Reason Abstractly Ex. 33
MP 3: Communicate Ex. 34
MP 3: Construct Arguments Ex. 5
MP 3: Compare Arguments Ex. 6
MP 3: Critique the Reasoning of Others Ex. 7

Applications exercises have blue headings. Exercise 32 supports MP 4: Model.

EXERCISE 32: Use the Think About a Plan worksheet in the **Practice and Problem Solving Workbook** (also available in the Teaching Resources in print and online) to further support students' development in becoming independent learners.

HOMEWORK QUICK CHECK

To check students' understanding of key skills and concepts, go over Exercises 21, 27, 31, 32, and 34.

Practice and Problem-Solving Exercises

8. (0, 4), (0, 5), (0, 6), (0, 7), (0, 8)

9. (0, 0), (0, 1), (0, 2), (0, 3), (0, 4), (0, 5), (0, 6), (0, 7), (1, 0), (1, 1), (1, 2), (1, 3), (1, 4), (1,5), (1, 6), (2, 0), (2, 1), (2, 2), (2, 3), (2, 4), (2, 5), (3, 3), (3, 4)

10. no solution

11.

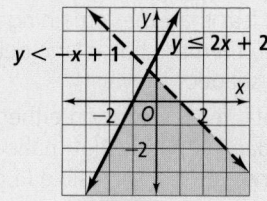

$y < -x + 1$ $y \le 2x + 2$

12.

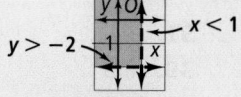

$y > -2$ $x < 1$

13.

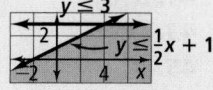

$y \le 3$ $y \le \frac{1}{2}x + 1$

14. no solution

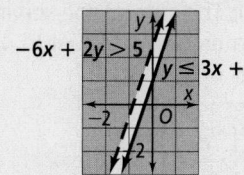

$-6x + 2y > 5$ $y \le 3x + 1$

15.

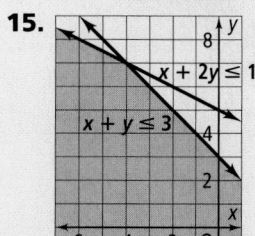

$x + 2y \le 10$ $x + y \le 3$

16. $-x - y \le 2$ $y - 2x > 1$

17.

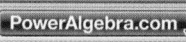

$y > -2x$ $-2x + y \le -2$

18.

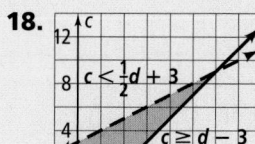

$c < \frac{1}{2}d + 3$ $c \ge d - 3$

19. no solution

20. Let y = number of yellow balloons and r = number of red balloons.

$r + y \ge 40$

$y \ge 25$

Because the number of balloons must be a whole number, only the points in the overlap that represent whole numbers are solutions of the problem; i.e., (0, 40), (0, 41), (1, 39), (1, 40), (2, 38), etc.

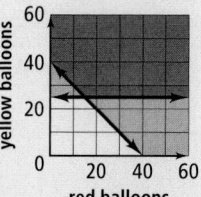

21–32. See next page.

Lesson 3-3   153

Answers

Practice and Problem-Solving Exercises
(continued)

21. Let r = number of rose plants and
t = number of tulip plants.
$t + r \geq 50$
$\quad\quad r \leq 20$
Because the number of plants must be a whole number, only the points in the overlap that represent whole numbers are solutions of the problem.

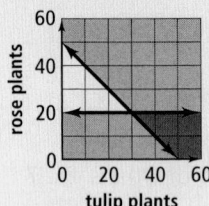

22.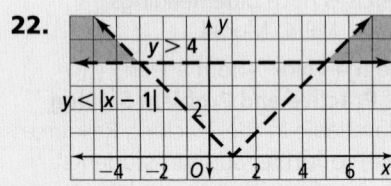

23.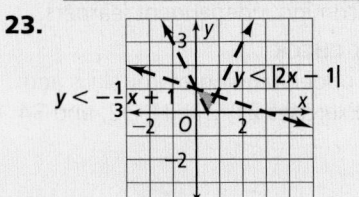

24. $y \geq |x + 2|$ 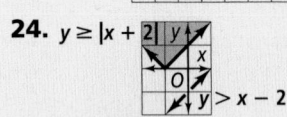 $y > x - 2$

25.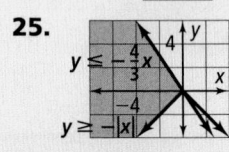
$y \leq -\frac{4}{3}x$
$y \geq -|x|$

26.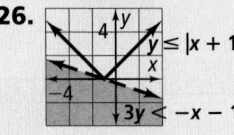
$y \leq |x + 1|$
$3y < -x - 1$

27.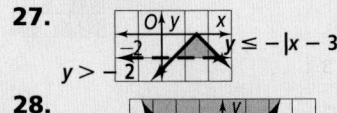
$y \leq -|x - 3|$
$y > -2$

28.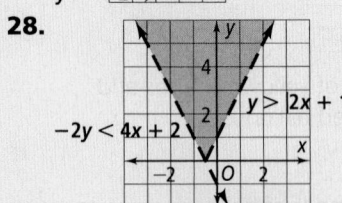
$-2y < 4x + 2$
$y > |2x + 1|$

29.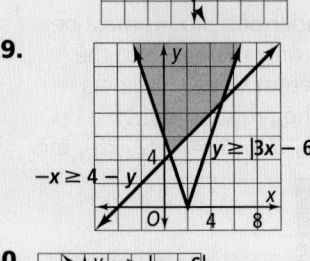
$-x \geq 4 - y$
$y \geq |3x - 6|$

30.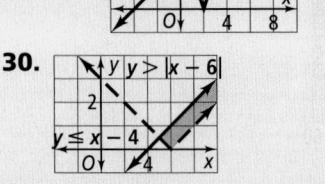
$y > |x - 6|$
$y \leq x - 4$

---

35. Given a system of two linear inequalities, explain how you can pick test points in the plane to determine where to shade the solution set.

In Exercises 36–45, identify the inequalities A, B, and C for which the given ordered pair is a solution.

A. $x + y \leq 2$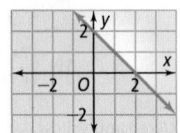

B. $y \leq \frac{3}{2}x - 1$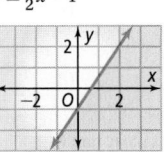

C. $y > -\frac{1}{3}x - 2$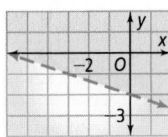

36. $(0, 0)$ **37.** $(-2, -5)$ **38.** $(-2, 0)$ **39.** $(0, -2)$ **40.** $(-15, 15)$

41. $(3, 2)$ **42.** $(2, 0)$ **43.** $(-6, 0)$ **44.** $(4, -1)$ **45.** $(-8, -11)$

Solve each system of inequalities by graphing.

46. $\begin{cases} x + y < 8 \\ x \geq 0 \\ y \geq 0 \end{cases}$ **47.** $\begin{cases} 2y - 4x \leq 0 \\ x \geq 0 \\ y \geq 0 \end{cases}$ **48.** $\begin{cases} y \geq -2x + 4 \\ x > -3 \\ y \geq 1 \end{cases}$

49. $\begin{cases} y \leq \frac{2}{3}x + 2 \\ y \geq |x| + 2 \end{cases}$ **50.** $\begin{cases} y < x - 1 \\ y > -|x - 2| + 1 \end{cases}$ **51.** $\begin{cases} 2x + y \leq 3 \\ y > |x + 3| - 2 \end{cases}$

52. $\begin{cases} y < |x - 1| + 2 \\ x \geq 0 \end{cases}$ **53.** $\begin{cases} y > |x - 1| + 1 \\ y \leq -|x - 3| + 4 \end{cases}$ **54.** $\begin{cases} y \leq |x| - 2 \\ y \leq |x| + 2 \end{cases}$

Challenge   **Geometry** Write a system of inequalities to describe each shaded figure.

55.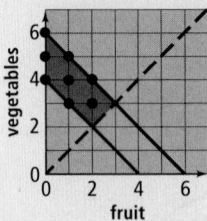

56.

57.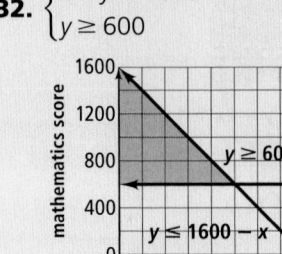

58. a. Graph the "bowtie" inequality, $|y| \leq |x|$.
    b. Write a system of inequalities to describe the graph shown at the right.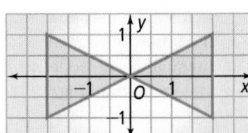

---

31. $(0, 4)$, $(0, 5)$, $(0, 6)$, $(1, 3)$, $(1, 4)$, $(1, 5)$, $(2, 3,)$, $(2, 4)$; The sum of the servings must be greater than or equal to 4 and less than or equal to 6.

32. $\begin{cases} x + y \leq 1600 \\ y \geq 600 \end{cases}$

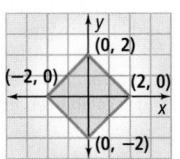

33. Answers may vary. Sample: $\begin{cases} x < 5 \\ y \geq 1 \end{cases}$

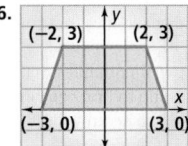

34. Answers may vary. Sample: If the isolated variable, y, is greater than the remaining expression, the half-plane above the boundary is shaded. If the variable is less than the remaining expression, then the half-plane below the line is shaded.

35. Use test pts. that are not on either of the boundary lines and that make the calculations as easy as possible (e.g., the origin).

36. A, C   **37.** A, B

38. A, C   **39.** A, B

40. A, C   **41.** B, C

42. A, B, C   **43.** A

44. B, C   **45.** A

Standardized Test Prep

59. Which system of inequalities is shown in the graph?

Ⓐ $\begin{cases} x \geq 4 \\ 3x - 2y > 5 \end{cases}$ Ⓒ $\begin{cases} x < 4 \\ 3x - 2y \geq 5 \end{cases}$

Ⓑ $\begin{cases} x > 4 \\ 3x - 2y \leq 5 \end{cases}$ Ⓓ $\begin{cases} x \leq 4 \\ 3x - 2y < 5 \end{cases}$

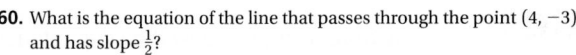

60. What is the equation of the line that passes through the point $(4, -3)$ and has slope $\frac{1}{2}$?

Ⓕ $y = \frac{1}{2}x + 3$ Ⓗ $y = \frac{1}{2}x - 5$

Ⓖ $y = \frac{1}{2}x - 1$ Ⓘ $y = x - \frac{1}{2}$

61. Which equation is a vertical translation of $y = -5x$?

Ⓐ $y = -\frac{5}{2}x$ Ⓒ $y = -10x$

Ⓑ $y = -5x + 2$ Ⓓ $y = 5x - 2$

62. The cost of renting a pool at an aquatic center is either $30 per hour or $20 per hour with a $40 non-refundable deposit. For how many hours is the cost of renting a pool the same for both plans?

Mixed Review

Solve each system by elimination or substitution. ◆ **See Lesson 3-2.**

63. $\begin{cases} y = 3x + 1 \\ 2x - y = 8 \end{cases}$ **64.** $\begin{cases} 3x + y = 4 \\ 2x - 4y = 7 \end{cases}$

65. $\begin{cases} -x + 5y = 3 \\ 2x - 10y = 4 \end{cases}$ **66.** $\begin{cases} 2x + 4y = -8 \\ -5x + 4y = 6 \end{cases}$

67. $\begin{cases} y - 3 = x \\ 4x + y = -2 \end{cases}$ **68.** $\begin{cases} 2 = 4y - 3x \\ 5x = 2y - 3 \end{cases}$

Get Ready! To prepare for Lesson 3-4, do Exercises 69–72.

Write an ordered pair that is a solution of each system of inequalities. ◆ **See Lesson 3-3.**

69. $\begin{cases} x + y > 2 \\ 3x + 2y \leq 6 \end{cases}$ **70.** $\begin{cases} 2y > 4 \\ 3x + 4y \leq 14 \end{cases}$

71. $\begin{cases} x \geq 2 \\ 5x + 2y \leq 9 \end{cases}$ **72.** $\begin{cases} x + 3y < 6 \\ y < x \end{cases}$

46.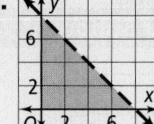

47.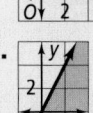

48.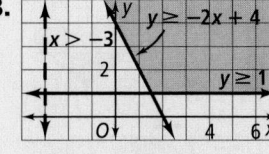
$x > -3$, $y \geq -2x + 4$, $y \geq 1$

49.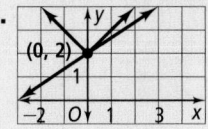
$(0, 2)$

50.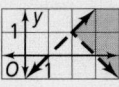

51.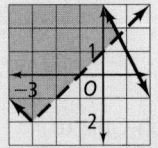

52.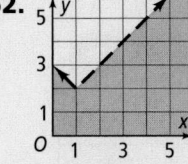

53.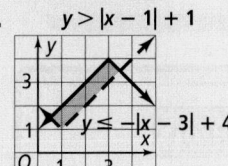
$y > |x - 1| + 1$
$y \leq -|x - 3| + 4$

54.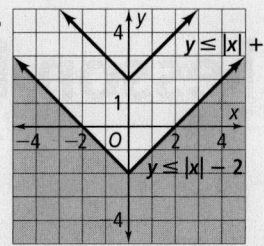
$y \leq |x| + 2$
$y \leq |x| - 2$

55. $\begin{cases} y \geq |x| - 2 \\ y \leq -|x| + 2 \end{cases}$

56. $\begin{cases} y \leq 3 \\ y \geq 0 \\ y \leq 3x + 9 \\ y \leq -3x + 9 \end{cases}$

57. $\begin{cases} y \leq 4 \\ y \geq 0 \\ y \leq 2x \\ y \geq 2x - 8 \end{cases}$

58. a.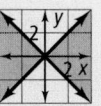

b. Answers may vary. Sample:
$\begin{cases} |y| \leq \frac{1}{2}|x| \\ |x| \leq 2 \end{cases}$

Standardized Test Prep

59. C

60. H

61. B

62. **[2]** let x = number of hours

$30x = 20x + 40$

$-20x = -20x$

$10x = 40$

$x = 4$

[1] one computational error, OR correct answer, without work shown

Mixed Review

63. $(-9, -26)$

64. $\left(\frac{23}{14}, -\frac{13}{14}\right)$

65. no solution

66. $(-2, -1)$

67. $(-1, 2)$

68. $\left(-\frac{4}{7}, \frac{1}{14}\right)$

69–72. Answers may vary. Samples are given for each exercise.

69. $(0, 3)$

70. $(0, 3)$

71. $(2, -1)$

72. $(1, -1)$

Differentiated Remediation
Available in editable format online.

Additional Instructional Support

Algebra 2 Companion
Students can use the **Algebra 2 Companion** worktext (4 pages) as you teach the lesson. Use the Companion to support

- New Vocabulary
- Key Concepts
- Got It for each Problem
- Lesson Check

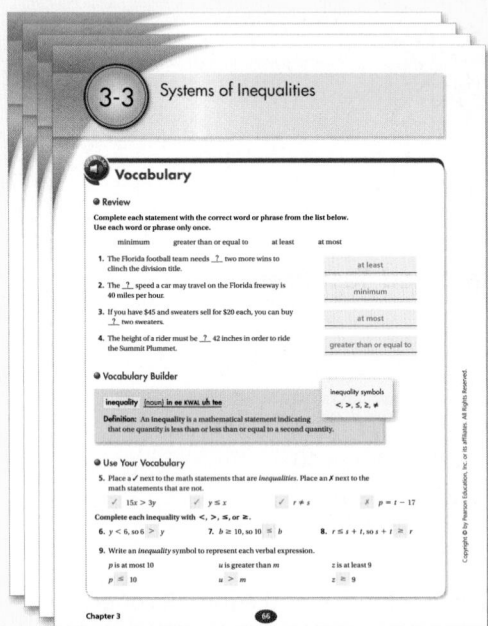

ELL Support
Use Graphic Organizers Match terms and phrases with inequality symbols by making a table of each symbol, words that describe it, and descriptions of the corresponding graph. For example,
Symbol: $<$
Words: less than, up to
Graph: dashed boundary with shading below

Assess Understanding Give pairs of students a real-world problem. Have them use the Know/Need/Plan method modeled on page 151. Before they graph their equations, check that they have properly defined the variables and written the correct inequalities.

5 Assess & Remediate

Lesson Quiz

1. Graph the solution of the system of inequalities. $\begin{cases} x + 2y \geq -6 \\ y \geq x + 5 \end{cases}$

2. Do you UNDERSTAND? Tickets for a dance are sold for \$5 to seniors and \$7 to juniors. The dance hall can hold 560 students. How many of each type of ticket must be sold to raise at least \$3,500?

3. Graph the solution of the system of inequalities. $\begin{cases} y \leq |x + 2| \\ y \geq 1 \end{cases}$

ANSWERS TO LESSON QUIZ

1.

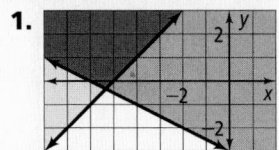

2. Let x = number of juniors
y = number of seniors
x and y are integers greater than or equal to 0.
The system of inequalities is
$x + y \leq 560$
$7x + 5y \geq 3500$
At least 350 juniors and at most 210 seniors must attend. Samples: (350, 210), (400, 140), (400, 160), (430, 130), (430, 100), (430, 98). Check that the sales equal or exceed \$3500.

3.

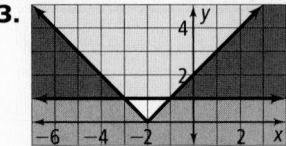

PRESCRIPTION FOR REMEDIATION
Use the student work on the Lesson Quiz to prescribe a differentiated review assignment:

Points	Differentiated Remediation
0–1	Intervention
2	On-level
3	Extension

PowerAlgebra.com

5 Assess & Remediate
Assign the Lesson Quiz. Appropriate intervention, practice, or enrichment is automatically generated based on student performance.

Intervention

- **Reteaching** (2 pages) Provides reteaching and practice exercises for the key lesson concepts. Use with struggling students or absent students.

- **English Language Learner Support** Helps students develop and reinforce mathematical vocabulary and key concepts.

All-in-One Resources/Online
Reteaching

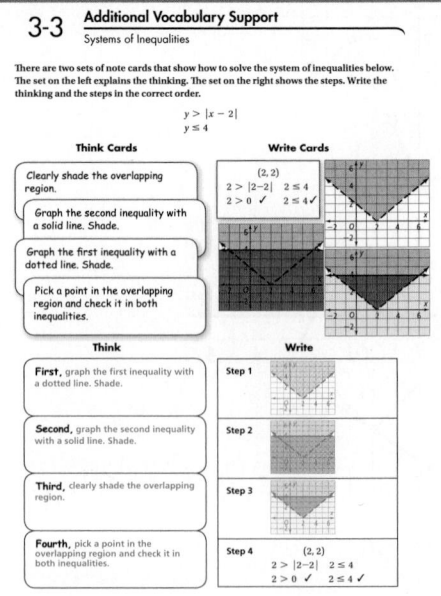

All-in-One Resources/Online
English Language Learner Support

Differentiated Remediation *continued*

Available in editable format online.

On-Level

- **Practice** (2 pages) Provides extra practice for each lesson. For simpler practice exercises, use the Form K Practice pages found in the All-in-One Teaching Resources and online.

- **Think About a Plan** Helps students develop specific problem-solving skills and strategies by providing scaffolded guiding questions.

- **Standardized Test Prep** Focuses on all major exercises, all major question types, and helps students prepare for the high-stakes assessments.

Extension

- **Enrichment** Provides students with interesting problems and activities that extend the concepts of the lesson.

- **Activities, Games, and Puzzles** Worksheets that can be used for concepts development, enrichment, and for fun!

Practice and Problem Solving Wkbk/ All-in-One Resources/Online
Practice page 1

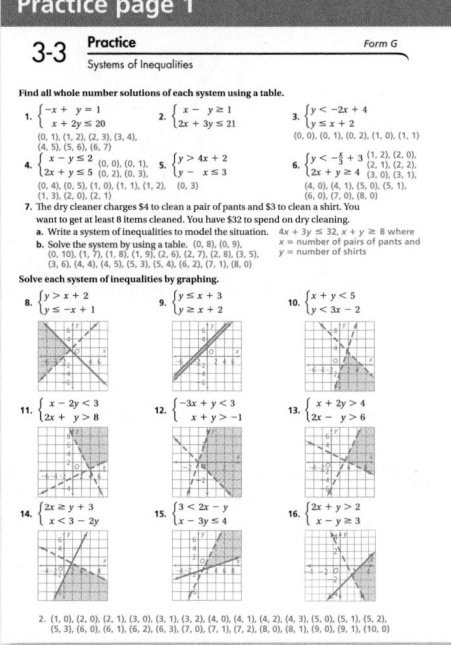

Practice and Problem Solving Wkbk/ All-in-One Resources/Online
Practice page 2

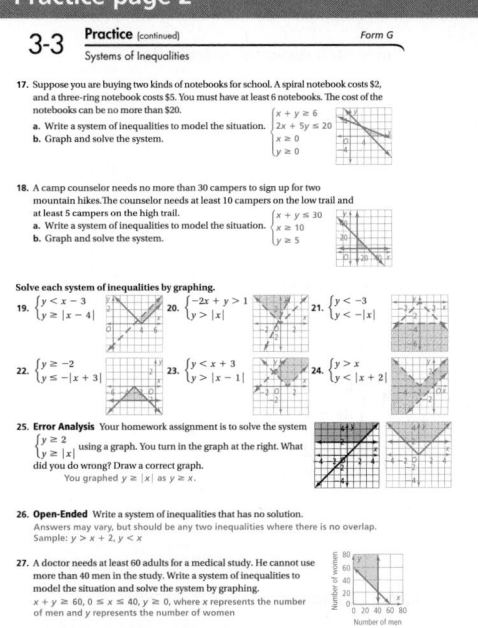

All-in-One Resources/Online
Enrichment

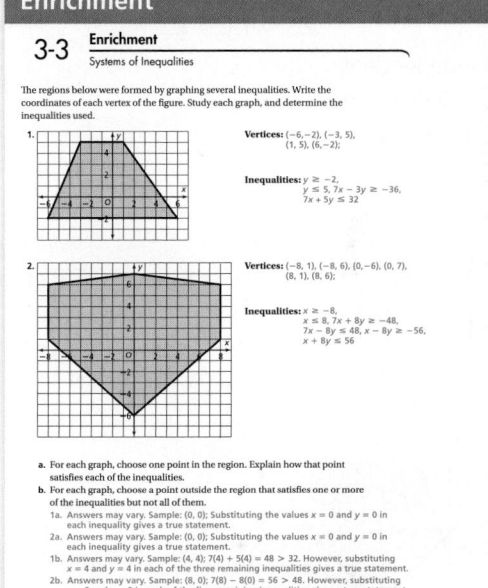

Practice and Problem Solving Wkbk/ All-in-One Resources/Online
Think About a Plan

Practice and Problem Solving Wkbk/ All-in-One Resources/Online
Standardized Test Prep

Online Teacher Resource Center
Activities, Games, and Puzzles

Answers

1. (3, 1)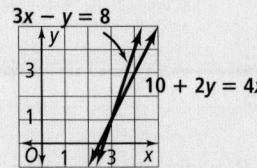

2. (1, −3)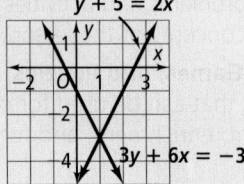

3. (1, 4)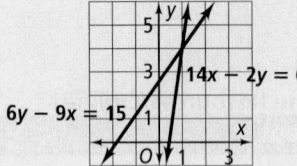

4. independent

5. independent

6. inconsistent

7. (2, 3)

8. (−3, 0)

9. $\left(-2, \dfrac{1}{2}\right)$

10. $\left(-3, -\dfrac{23}{4}\right)$

11. (−1, −2)

12. $\left(\dfrac{5}{2}, 2\right)$

13.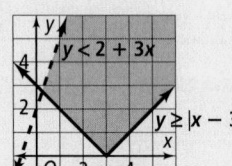

14.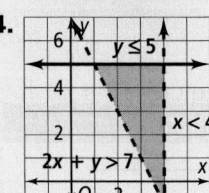

15. D

16. $\begin{cases} y \geq -2x + 1 \\ y \geq 1.5x - 6 \end{cases}$

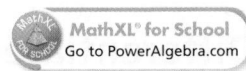
Do you know HOW?

Solve each system by graphing.

1. $\begin{cases} 3x - y = 8 \\ 10 + 2y = 4x \end{cases}$

2. $\begin{cases} y + 5 = 2x \\ 3y + 6x = -3 \end{cases}$

3. $\begin{cases} 14x - 2y = 6 \\ 6y - 9x = 15 \end{cases}$

Without graphing, classify each system as *independent*, *dependent*, or *inconsistent*.

4. $\begin{cases} 3y + 2x = 12 \\ 36 - 9y = -6x \end{cases}$

5. $\begin{cases} -2y = 20 - 2x \\ 3y - 6x = -30 \end{cases}$

6. $\begin{cases} 15x = 10y - 20 \\ 18 + 9x = 6y \end{cases}$

Solve each system by substitution.

7. $\begin{cases} 5m - n = 7 \\ 3 + 3n = 6m \end{cases}$

8. $\begin{cases} 4y - 6 = 2x \\ y - 3x = 9 \end{cases}$

9. $\begin{cases} 3u + 8 = 4v \\ 24v = 6 - 3u \end{cases}$

Solve each system by elimination.

10. $\begin{cases} 5c - 4t = 8 \\ 14 + 4t = 3c \end{cases}$

11. $\begin{cases} 8y + 10 = 6x \\ 8y - 4x = -12 \end{cases}$

12. $\begin{cases} 11 - 2c = 3d \\ 2c - 7d = -9 \end{cases}$

Graph the solutions to each of the following systems.

13. $\begin{cases} y < 2 + 3x \\ y \geq |x - 3| \end{cases}$

14. $\begin{cases} 2x + y > 7 \\ x < 4 \\ y \leq 5 \end{cases}$

Do you UNDERSTAND?

15. Which equation below combines with the equation $-4x + 6y = 3$ to form a system with an infinite number of solutions?

Ⓐ $0.5 + x = 1.5y$

Ⓑ $0.75 + 2x = 1.5y$

Ⓒ $0.5 + 2x = 1.5y$

Ⓓ $0.75 + x = 1.5y$

16. Write a system of inequalities to describe the shaded region.

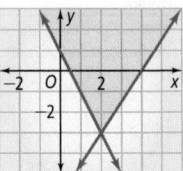

17. An ordinary refrigerator costs $503 and has an estimated annual operating cost of $92. An energy-efficient model costs $615 with an estimated annual operating cost of $64. Write a system of equations to represent this situation.
   a. What is the solution of the system?
   b. What does the solution mean?
   c. Which model would you choose for your family? Why?

Ⓒ **18. Writing** Explain how to classify a linear system as independent, dependent, or inconsistent without graphing.

---

17. a. (4, 871)

   b. The solution means that in four years the costs to own and operate the refrigerators are the same for both models.

   c. Answers may vary. Sample: I would choose the energy-efficient model if I didn't plan on moving within 4 years.

18. Use *y*-intercepts, slopes, and the number of solutions to classify a linear system as independent, dependent, or inconsistent without graphing. An independent system has one solution. The slopes are different, but the *y*-intercepts could be the same. An inconsistent system has no solution. The slopes are the same and the *y*-intercepts are different. A dependent system has an infinite number of solutions. The slopes and *y*-intercepts are the same.

3-4 Linear Programming

Common Core State Standards
A-CED.A.3 Represent constraints by equations or inequalities, and by systems of equations and/or inequalities, and interpret solutions as viable or nonviable options in a modeling context.
MP 1, MP 3, MP 4

Objective To solve problems using linear programming

Getting Ready!

You want to spend no more than $40 for at most 15 tomato plants. You want to maximize the pounds of tomatoes you'll get. How many of each plant should you buy? Justify your answer.

Roma Tomato Plants
Guaranteed tomato yield 8 lb/plant $2 each

Cherry Tomato Plants
Guaranteed tomato yield 10 lb/plant $3 each

Maybe I should buy only cherry tomato plants. They yield more than roma plants. On the other hand . . .

MATHEMATICAL PRACTICES

Lesson Vocabulary
• constraint
• linear programming
• feasible region
• objective function

In the Solve It, you maximized your tomato production given some limits, or **constraints**. **Linear programming** is a method for finding a minimum or maximum value of some quantity, given a set of constraints.

Essential Understanding Some real-world problems involve multiple linear relationships. Linear programming accounts for all of these linear relationships and gives the solution to the problem.

The constraints in a linear programming situation form a system of inequalities, like the one at the right. The graph of the system is the **feasible region**. It contains all the points that satisfy all the constraints.

$$\begin{cases} x \ge 2 \\ y \ge 3 \\ y \le 6 \\ x + y \le 10 \end{cases}$$

Feasible Region

The quantity you are trying to maximize or minimize is modeled with an **objective function**. Often this quantity is cost or profit. Suppose the objective function is $C = 2x + y$.

Graphs of the objective function for various values of C are parallel lines. Lines closer to the origin represent smaller values of C.

The graphs of the equations $7 = 2x + y$ and $17 = 2x + y$ intersect the feasible region at $(2, 3)$ and $(7, 3)$. These vertices of the feasible region represent the least and the greatest values for the objective function.

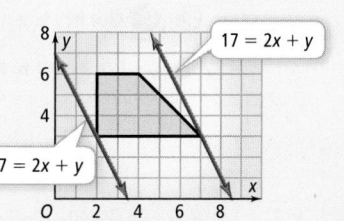

$17 = 2x + y$

$7 = 2x + y$

1 Interactive Learning

Solve It!
PURPOSE To introduce the concept of linear programming in a real-world situation with intuitive constraints
PROCESS Students may
• write and graph each inequality and the function to maximize.
• compare the number of plants versus the yield of tomatoes.

FACILITATE
Q What quantities do the variables represent in this problem? **[number of roma tomato plants and number of cherry tomato plants]**
Q What inequality symbolizes what you can afford to spend? **[$2x + 3y \le 40$ where x is the number of roma plants and y is the number of cherry plants]**
Q What happens if you buy only one type of plant? **[If you buy all roma you get 15 plants and 120 pounds of tomatoes, and if you buy all cherry you get 13 plants and 130 pounds of tomatoes.]**

ANSWER See Solve It in Answers on next page.
CONNECT THE MATH In the Solve It, students find the feasible region and maximize a quantity given constraints on the variables. In this lesson, the formal technique of linear programming is introduced.

3-4 Preparing to Teach

BIG idea Function

ESSENTIAL UNDERSTANDINGS
• Some real-world problems involve multiple linear relationships. Linear programming accounts for all of these linear relationships and gives the solution to the problem.
• The feasible region contains all the points that satisfy all the constraints.

Math Background
This lesson extends students' ability to solve systems of linear inequalities and introduces them to optimization (finding the maximum or minimum value of a function).

An objective function is used in linear programming to model some quantity that we wish to maximize or minimize. An objective function may be used to *maximize* quantities such as profit or items produced or to *minimize* quantities such as cost or time.

While the objective functions in the lesson would not generally have a maximum or minimum value, they may when the region given by the inequalities restricts the domain. An example of a restriction on a domain is as follows. If one variable represented a number of people, that variable could not be negative.

As in the previous lesson, the most reasonable method to determine the common solutions of a set of inequalities is graphing.

Mathematical Practices
Make sense of problems and persevere in solving them. Students will analyze constraints with inequalities and graph them.

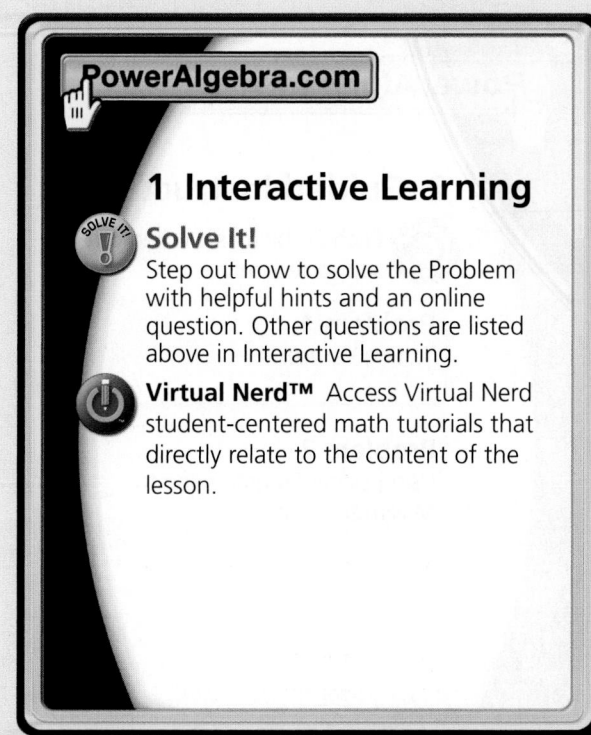

PowerAlgebra.com

1 Interactive Learning

Solve It!
Step out how to solve the Problem with helpful hints and an online question. Other questions are listed above in Interactive Learning.

Virtual Nerd™ Access Virtual Nerd student-centered math tutorials that directly relate to the content of the lesson.

2 Guided Instruction

Take Note

ERROR PREVENTION

Not every objective function has a maximum and/or minimum on a feasible region. This occurs if the region is not bounded.

Problem 1

To find the vertices of the feasible region, the constraints must all be graphed on the same grid.

Q After graphing in Step 1, what do you notice about the multiple-choice answers? Explain. **[They are vertices of the feasible region, so they can maximize the objective function.]**

Q Is there another way to solve this problem? Explain. **[Answers may vary. Sample: Yes; without graphing, you could substitute each given pair into $P = 2x + y$ and see which gives the greatest value of P. Then you would have to make sure it is a vertex of the feasible region.]**

Q If this were not a multiple-choice question, could you solve it without graphing? **[No; if you are not given the answers to choose from, you would have to graph to find the vertices.]**

Got It?

VISUAL LEARNERS

Q What is the maximum value of P in the feasible region? **[7.5]**

 Key Concept Vertex Principle of Linear Programming

If there is a maximum or a minimum value of the linear objective function, it occurs at one or more vertices of the feasible region.

You can solve a problem using linear programming by testing in the objective function all of the vertices of the feasible region.

Problem 1 Testing Vertices

Multiple Choice What point in the feasible region maximizes P for the objective function $P = 2x + y$?

Constraints $\begin{cases} x + 2y \le 5 \\ x - y \le 2 \\ x \ge 0 \\ y \ge 0 \end{cases}$

Ⓐ (2, 0) Ⓑ (0, 0) Ⓒ (3, 1) Ⓓ (0, 2.5)

Think

What quadrant will the feasible region be in?
The constraints $x \ge 0$ and $y \ge 0$ indicate the first quadrant.

Step 1
Graph the inequalities.

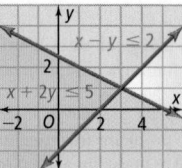

Step 2
Form the feasible region.

The intersections of the boundaries are the vertices of the feasible region.

Step 3
Find the coordinates of each vertex.

$Q(0, 0)$
$R(0, 2.5)$
$S(3, 1)$
$T(2, 0)$

Step 4
Evaluate P at each vertex.

$P = 2(0) + 0 = 0$
$P = 2(0) + 2.5 = 2.5$
$P = 2(3) + 1 = 7$ ⟵ Maximum Value
$P = 2(2) + 0 = 4$

P has a maximum value of 7 when $x = 3$ and $y = 1$. The correct choice is C.

Got It? **1. a.** Use the constraints in Problem 1 with the objective function $P = x + 3y$. What values of x and y maximize P?

b. Reasoning Can an objective function $P = ax + by + c$ have (the same) maximum value at all four vertex points Q, R, S, and T? At points R and S only? Explain using examples.

 PowerAlgebra.com

2 Guided Instruction

Each Problem is worked out and supported online.

Problem 1
Testing Vertices
Animated

Problem 2
Using Linear Programming to Maximize Profit
Animated

Support in Algebra 2 Companion
- Vocabulary
- Key Concepts
- Got It?

Answers

Solve It!

10 cherry tomato plants, 5 roma tomato plants

Got It?

1. a. P has a maximum value of 7.5 at (0, 2.5).

b. Answers may vary. Sample: $P = 5$ has same (maximum) value at all four vertex points. $P = x + 2y$ has maximum value 5 at R and S.

2. 100 T-shirts and 10 sweatshirts

 **Problem 2** Using Linear Programming to Maximize Profit

Business You are screen-printing T-shirts and sweatshirts to sell at the Polk County Blues Festival and are working with the following constraints.

- You have at most 20 hours to make shirts.
- You want to spend no more than $600 on supplies.
- You want to have at least 50 items to sell.

1-Color T-shirt
Takes 10 minutes to make
Supplies cost $4
Profit $6

3-Color Sweatshirt
Takes 30 minutes to make
Supplies cost $20
Profit $20

How many T-shirts and how many sweatshirts should you make to maximize your profit? How much is the maximum profit?

Organize the information in a table.

Write the constraints and the objective function.

Constraints: $\begin{cases} 10x + 30y \le 1200 \\ x + y \ge 50 \\ 4x + 20y \le 600 \\ x \ge 0 \\ y \ge 0 \end{cases}$

	T-Shirts, x	Sweatshirts, y	Total
Minutes	10x	30y	1200
Number	x	y	50
Cost	4x	20y	600
Profit	6x	20y	6x + 20y

Objective Function: $P = 6x + 20y$

 Think

How do you find the coordinates of the vertices if they are hard to read off the graph?
Solve the system of equations related to the lines that intersect to form the vertex.

Step 1

Graph the constraints to form the feasible region.

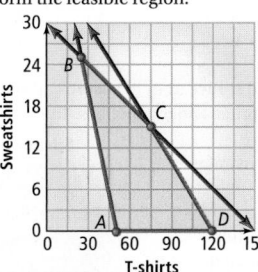

Step 2

Find the coordinates of each vertex.

A(50, 0)

B(25, 25)

C(75, 15)

D(120, 0)

Step 3

Evaluate P.

$P = 6(50) + 20(0) = 300$

$P = 6(25) + 20(25) = 650$

$P = 6(75) + 20(15) = 750$

$P = 6(120) + 20(0) = 720$

You can maximize your profit by selling 75 T-shirts and 15 sweatshirts. The maximum profit is $750.

✔ **Got It? 2.** If it took you 20 minutes to make a sweatshirt, how many of each type of shirt should you make to maximize your profit?

Problem 2

Q What does the 1200 in the constraint $10x + 30y \le 1200$ represent? **[It represents the 20 hours you have to make shirts; 20 hours equals 1200 minutes.]**

Q Why are $x \ge 0$ and $y \ge 0$ included as constraints? **[Since x represents the number of T-shirts and y represents the number of sweatshirts, they cannot be negative.]**

Q Where does the objective function $P = 6x + 20y$ come from? **[Your goal is to maximize the profit, so the objective function is the total profit as a function of the number of T-shirts and the number of sweatshirts made.]**

Q The number of T-shirts x and the number of sweatshirts y can only be whole numbers. What type of function is the objective function $P = 6x + 20y$? **[a discrete function]**

Got It?

Q Which constraint is different from one in Problem 2? What is the new constraint? Explain. **[The constraint $10x + 30y \le 1200$ must change to $10x + 20y \le 1200$ because the time needed to make a sweatshirt changed from 30 minutes to 20 minutes.]**

Q How does the new constraint affect the feasible region? **[The intersection with the constraint $4x + 20y \le 600$ changes so vertex C changes from (75, 15) to (100, 10).]**

Additional Problems

1. What point in the feasible region minimizes P for the objective function $P = 5x - y$?

Constraints $\begin{cases} x + y \le 1 \\ 4x + y \ge -2 \\ x \le 0 \end{cases}$

a. $(-1, 2)$ **c.** $(0, 1)$
b. $(0, -2)$ **d.** $(-0.5, 0)$

ANSWER a

2. You are making your summer movie plans and are working with the following constraints:

- It costs $8 to go to the movies at night.
- It costs $5 to go to a matinee.
- You want to go to at least as many night shows as matinees.
- You want to spend at most $42.

What is the greatest number of movies you can see?

ANSWER 6; 3 night movies and 3 matinees or 4 night movies and 2 matinees

3 Lesson Check

Do you know HOW? ERROR INTERVENTION

- For Exercises 1–4, if students have trouble graphing the inequalities, revisit Problem 1 or Additional Problem 1, or review Lesson 2-8.

Do you UNDERSTAND? ERROR INTERVENTION

- For Exercises 7–9, if students have difficulty with the definition of *feasible region*, relate the graphical definition to the set of solutions common to each inequality given by the constraints. Explain that the feasible region is the overlap, and the constraints are the linear inequalities.

Close

> **Q** If the feasible region is a triangle, how can you find the minimum value of the objective function? **[Evaluate the objective function at the three vertices, and choose the point that gives the least value.]**
>
> **Q** If the maximum of an objective function occurs at $(-2, 3)$, can $x \geq 0$ be one of the constraints? Explain. **[No; since $(-2, 3)$ is a vertex, the feasible region is not restricted to nonnegative x-values.]**

 Lesson Check

Do you know HOW?

Graph each system of inequalities.

1. $\begin{cases} x + y \leq 6 \\ x \geq 0 \\ y \geq 0 \end{cases}$
   2. $\begin{cases} 2x - y \leq 4 \\ x \geq 0 \\ y \geq 0 \end{cases}$

3. $\begin{cases} x + 2y \leq 10 \\ x \geq 1 \\ y \geq 2 \end{cases}$
   4. $\begin{cases} 2x + 3y \leq 18 \\ 0 \leq x \leq 5 \\ 0 \leq y \leq 4 \end{cases}$

Graph each system of constraints. Then name the vertices of the feasible region.

5. $\begin{cases} x \leq 5 \\ y \leq 4 \\ x \geq 0 \\ y \geq 0 \end{cases}$
   6. $\begin{cases} x + y \leq 8 \\ y \geq 5 \\ x \geq 0 \end{cases}$

Do you UNDERSTAND?  MATHEMATICAL PRACTICES

7. **Vocabulary** Explain why the inequalities of a linear programming problem are called constraints. *Hint*: Use the definition of *constraint* as part of your answer.

8. **Compare and Contrast** What are some similarities between solving a linear programming problem and solving a system of linear inequalities? What are some differences?

9. **Open-Ended** Write a system of constraints whose graphs determine a trapezoid. Write an objective function and evaluate it at each vertex.

Practice and Problem-Solving Exercises MATHEMATICAL PRACTICES

Practice Graph each system of constraints. Name all vertices. Then find the values of x and y that maximize or minimize the objective function. ◀ See Problem 1.

10. $\begin{cases} x + y \leq 8 \\ 2x + y \leq 10 \\ x \geq 0 \\ y \geq 0 \end{cases}$

    Maximum for
    $N = 100x + 40y$

11. $\begin{cases} x + 2y \geq 8 \\ x \geq 2 \\ y \geq 0 \end{cases}$

    Minimum for
    $C = x + 3y$

12. $\begin{cases} 2 \leq x \leq 6 \\ 1 \leq y \leq 5 \\ x + y \leq 8 \end{cases}$

    Maximum for
    $P = 3x + 2y$

13. **Air Quality** A city wants to plant maple and spruce trees to absorb carbon dioxide It has $2100 to spend on planting spruce and maple trees. The city has 45,000 ft² available for planting. ◀ See Problem 2.

    a. Use the data from the table. Write the constraints for the situation.
    b. Write the objective function.
    c. Graph the feasible region and find the vertices.
    d. How many of each tree should the city plant to maximize carbon dioxide absorption?

Spruce and Maple Tree Data

	Spruce	Maple
Planting Cost	$30	$40
Area Required	600 ft²	900 ft²
Carbon Dioxide Absorption	650 lb/yr	300 lb/yr

Source: Auburn University and Anderson Associates

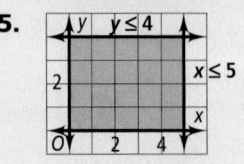 **PowerAlgebra.com**

3 Lesson Check

For a digital lesson check, use the Got It questions.

Support in Algebra 2 Companion
- Lesson Check

4 Practice

Assign homework to individual students or to an entire class.

Answers

Lesson Check

1.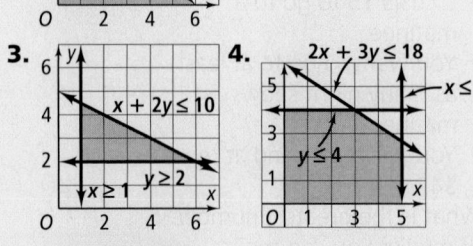
2.
3.
4.

5. (0, 0), (0, 4), (5, 0), (5, 4)

6. (0, 8), (3, 5), (0, 5)

7. Constraints are limits or restrictions on the variables in the objective function in a linear programming problem. These constraints are written as linear inequalities.

8. Linear programming is an extension of solving linear inequalities. For each, you are given constraints represented by linear inequalities that are graphed. All the points in the overlapping region are solutions, but linear programming problems are usually looking for maximum or minimum values of some quantity modeled with an objective function.

B Apply

C 14. Think About a Plan A biologist is developing two new strains of bacteria. Each sample of Type I bacteria produces four new viable bacteria, and each sample of Type II produces three new viable bacteria. Altogether, at least 240 new viable bacteria must be produced. At least 30, but not more than 60, of the original samples must be Type I. Not more than 70 of the original samples can be Type II. A sample of Type I costs $5 and a sample of Type II costs $7. How many samples of Type II bacteria should the biologist use to minimize the cost?
- What are the unknowns?
- What constraints do you get from each condition in the problem?
- Are there any implicit constraints?

C 15. Error Analysis Your friend is trying to find the maximum value of $P = -x + 3y$ subject to the following constraints.

$$\begin{cases} y \le -2x + 6 \\ y \le x + 3 \\ x \ge 0, y \ge 0 \end{cases}$$

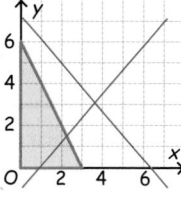

What error did your friend make? What is the correct solution?

16. Cooking Baking a tray of corn muffins takes 4 cups of milk and 3 cups of wheat flour. Baking a tray of bran muffins takes 2 cups of milk and 3 cups of wheat flour. A baker has 16 cups of milk and 15 cups of wheat flour. He makes $3 profit per tray of corn muffins and $2 profit per tray of bran muffins. How many trays of each type of muffin should the baker make to maximize his profit?

Graph each system of constraints. Name all vertices. Then find the values of x and y that maximize or minimize the objective function. Find the maximum or minimum value.

17. $\begin{cases} 3x + y \le 7 \\ x + 2y \le 9 \\ x \ge 0, y \ge 0 \end{cases}$
Maximum for
$P = 2x + y$

18. $\begin{cases} 25 \le x \le 75 \\ y \le 110 \\ 8x + 6y \ge 720 \end{cases}$
Minimum for
$C = 8x + 5y$

19. $\begin{cases} x + y \le 11 \\ 2y \ge x \\ x \ge 0, y \ge 0 \end{cases}$
Maximum for
$P = 3x + 2y$

20. $\begin{cases} 2x + y \le 300 \\ x + y \le 200 \\ x \ge 0, y \ge 0 \end{cases}$
Maximum for
$P = x + 2y$

21. $\begin{cases} 5x + y \ge 10 \\ x + y \le 6 \\ x + 4y \ge 12 \\ x \ge 0, y \ge 0 \end{cases}$
Minimum for
$C = 10{,}000x + 20{,}000y$

22. $\begin{cases} 6 \le x + y \le 13 \\ x \ge 3 \\ y \ge 1 \end{cases}$
Maximum for
$P = 4x + 3y$

4 Practice

ASSIGNMENT GUIDE
Basic: 10–19
Average: 11–13 odd, 14–22
Advanced: 11–13 odd, 14–24
Standardized Test Prep: 25–27
Mixed Review: 28–37

C Mathematical Practices are supported by exercises with red headings. Here are the Practices supported in this lesson:

MP 1: Make Sense of Problems Ex. 14
MP 3: Reason Abstractly Ex. 9, 24
MP 3: Compare Arguments Ex. 8
MP 3: Critique the Reasoning of Others Ex. 15

Applications exercises have blue headings. Exercises 13 and 16 support MP 4: Model.

EXERCISE 16: Use the Think About a Plan worksheet in the **Practice and Problem Solving Workbook** (also available in the Teaching Resources in print and online) to further support students' development in becoming independent learners.

HOMEWORK QUICK CHECK
To check students' understanding of key skills and concepts, go over Exercises 11, 13, 14, 15, and 16.

---

9. Answers may vary. Sample:
$\begin{cases} y \le x \\ y \le -x + 4 \\ 0 \le y \le 1 \end{cases}$
$P = 2x + 3y$, $P(0, 0) = 0$, $P(1, 1) = 5$, $P(3, 1) = 9$, $P(4, 0) = 8$; maximum value of P is 9 at $(3, 1)$

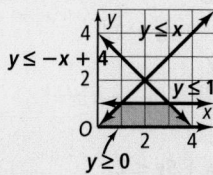

Practice and Problem-Solving Exercises

10.
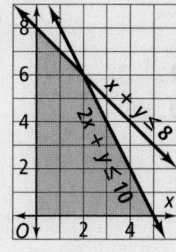
vertices: (0, 0), (5, 0), (2, 6), (0, 8); maximized at (5, 0)

11. 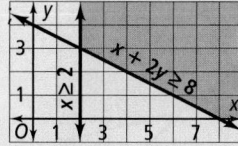 vertices: (8, 0), (2, 3); minimized at (8, 0)

12. vertices: (2, 1), (6, 1), (6, 2), (2, 5), (3, 5); maximized at (6, 2)

13. Let s = number of spruce trees and m = number of maple trees.

a. $\begin{cases} 30s + 40m \le 2100 \\ 600s + 900m \le 45{,}000 \\ s \ge 0, m \ge 0 \end{cases}$

b. $P = 650s + 300m$

c. 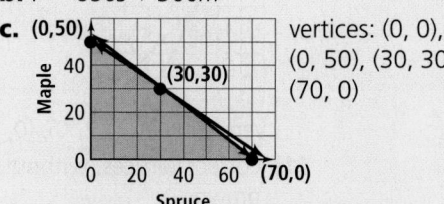 vertices: (0, 0), (0, 50), (30, 30), (70, 0)

d. 70 spruce trees and 0 maple trees

14. Let x = number of Type I samples and y = number of Type II samples;

$\begin{cases} 4x + 3y \ge 240 \\ 30 \le x \le 60 \\ y \le 70 \\ x \ge 0 \\ y \ge 0 \end{cases}$

$C = 5x + 7y$
The implicit constraints are $x \ge 0$, $y \ge 0$; $C = 300$ and is minimized at (60, 0); the biologist should use 0 Type II bacteria.

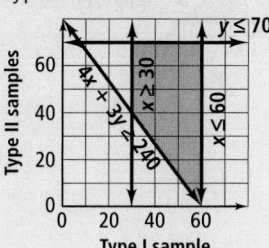

15–22. See next page.

Answers

Practice and Problem-Solving Exercises
(continued)

15. He is not considering the constraint $y \le x + 3$; maximized when $P = 11$ at $(1, 4)$.

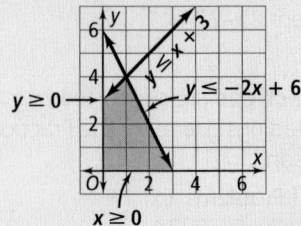

16. 3 trays of corn muffins and 2 trays of bran muffins

17. 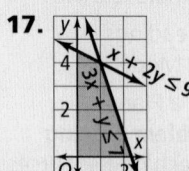 vertices: $(0, 0)$, $(1, 4)$, $(0, 4.5)$, $\left(\frac{7}{3}, 0\right)$; maximized when $P = 6$ at $(1, 4)$

18. 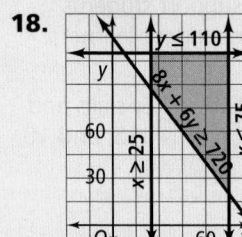 vertices: $(75, 20)$, $(75, 110)$, $(25, 110)$, $\left(25, 86\frac{2}{3}\right)$, minimized when $C = 633\frac{1}{3}$ at $\left(25, 86\frac{2}{3}\right)$.

19. 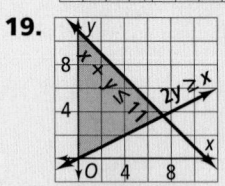 vertices: $(0, 0)$, $\left(7\frac{1}{3}, 3\frac{2}{3}\right)$, $(0, 11)$; maximized when $P = 29\frac{1}{3}$ at $\left(7\frac{1}{3}, 3\frac{2}{3}\right)$.

20. 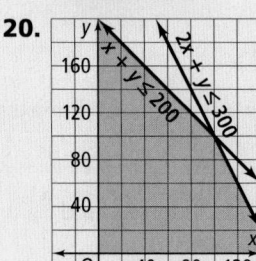 vertices: $(0, 0)$, $(150, 0)$, $(100, 100)$, $(0, 200)$; maximized when $P = 400$ at $(0, 200)$.

21. 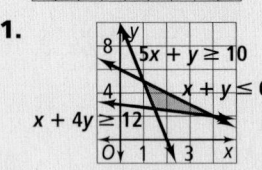 vertices: $\left(\frac{28}{19}, \frac{50}{19}\right)$, $(4, 2)$, $(1, 5)$; minimized when $C = 67{,}370$ at $\left(\frac{28}{19}, \frac{50}{19}\right)$

22. 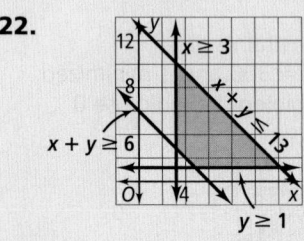 vertices: $(3, 3)$, $(3, 10)$, $(5, 1)$, $(12, 1)$; maximized when $P = 51$ at $(12, 1)$

---

23. A vertex of a feasible region does not always have whole-number coordinates. Sometimes you may need to round coordinates to find the solution. Using the objective function and the constraints at the right, find the whole-number values of x and y that minimize C. Then find C for those values of x and y.

$$C = 6x + 9y$$
$$\begin{cases} x + 2y \ge 50 \\ 2x + y \ge 60 \\ x \ge 0, y \ge 0 \end{cases}$$

24. Reasoning Sometimes two corners of a graph both yield the maximum profit. In this case, many other points may also yield the maximum profit. Evaluate the profit formula $P = x + 2y$ for the graph shown. Find four points that yield the maximum profit.

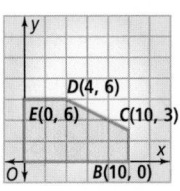

Standardized Test Prep

SAT/ACT

25. Solve the equation $\frac{1}{2}(a + b) = c$ for b.

Ⓐ $b = \frac{1}{2}c - a$ Ⓑ $b = 2a - c$ Ⓒ $b = 2c - a$ Ⓓ $b = 2ca$

26. Which is the graph of $y \le |x - 3|$?

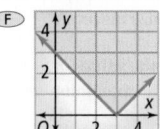 Ⓕ   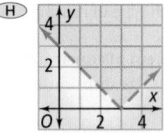 Ⓗ   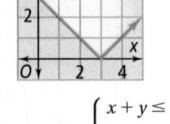 Ⓘ

Short Response

27. What are the vertices of the feasible region bounded by the constraints at the right?

$$\begin{cases} x + y \le 3 \\ 2x + y \le 4 \\ x \ge 0, y \ge 0 \end{cases}$$

Mixed Review

Solve each system of inequalities by graphing.   ◀ See Lesson 3-3.

28. $\begin{cases} y < -2x + 8 \\ 3y \ge 4x - 6 \end{cases}$ **29.** $\begin{cases} x - 2y \ge 11 \\ 5x + 4y < 27 \end{cases}$ **30.** $\begin{cases} 2x + 6y > 12 \\ 3x + 9y \le 27 \end{cases}$

Evaluate each expression for $a = 3$ and $b = -5$.   ◀ See Lesson 1-3.

31. $2a + b$ **32.** $-4 + 2ab$ **33.** $3(a - b)$ **34.** $b(2b - a)$

Get Ready! To prepare for Lesson 3-5, do Exercises 35–37.

Find the x- and y-intercepts of the graph of each linear equation.   ◀ See Lesson 2-4.

35. $y = 2x + 6$ **36.** $2x + 9y = 36$ **37.** $y = x - 1$

23.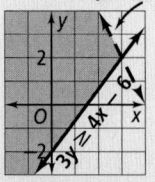

vertices: $(0, 60)$, $\left(23\frac{1}{3}, 13\frac{1}{3}\right)$, $(50, 0)$; minimized when $x = 23\frac{1}{3}$ and $y = 13\frac{1}{3}$; Round to $(23, 14)$ and $(24, 13)$; $(24, 13)$ gives a minimum cost of $261

24. Answers may vary. Sample: $(4, 6)$, $(6, 5)$, $(9, 3.5)$, $(10, 3)$

25. C   **26.** I

27. [2]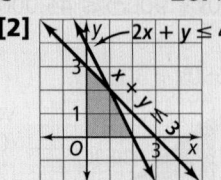

vertices: $(0, 0)$, $(2, 0)$, $(0, 3)$, $(1, 2)$

[1] correct vertices, without graph drawn

28.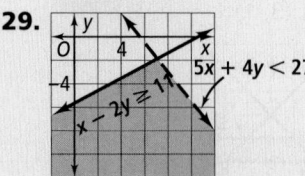

29.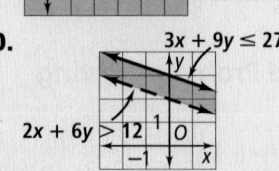

30.

$3x + 9y \le 27$

$2x + 6y > 12$

31. 1   **32.** -34

33. 24   **34.** 65

35. $(0, 6)$, $(-3, 0)$

36. $(0, 4)$, $(18, 0)$

37. $(0, -1)$, $(1, 0)$

Additional Instructional Support

Algebra 2 Companion

Students can use the **Algebra 2 Companion** worktext (4 pages) as you teach the lesson. Use the Companion to support

- New Vocabulary
- Key Concepts
- Got It for each Problem
- Lesson Check

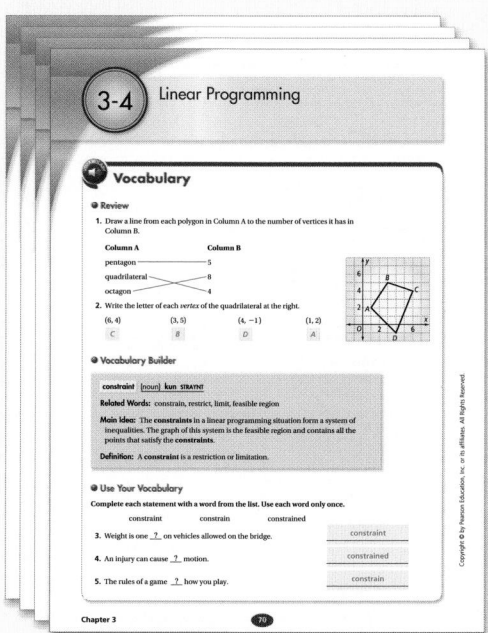

ELL Support

Focus on Communication State the steps you would take to solve a linear programming problem. In Problem 2, state that you are looking for information about the two types of shirts to describe inequalities. Write the variables that you define and the objective function. Have students plan and solve one of the practice word problems with you.

Focus on Language Copy the feasible region at the top of page 162 on the board. Give each student a different objective function. Have them find the maximum and minimum values. Then they should say the following sentence and fill in the blanks: For the objective function ____, the minimum value is ____ and the maximum value is ____. Draw another polygonal feasible region and repeat.

5 Assess & Remediate

Lesson Quiz

1. What point in the feasible region maximizes P for the objective function $P = 2x + 3y$?

Constraints $\begin{cases} 2x + y \le 15 \\ x + 3y \le 20 \\ x \ge 0, \, y \ge 0 \end{cases}$

  a. $(0, 6\frac{2}{3})$ **b.** $(5, 5)$

  c. $(0, 0)$ **d.** $(7.5, 0)$

2. **Do you UNDERSTAND?** You are painting pictures to sell and are working with the following constraints:

- It takes 3 h to paint a small picture.
- It takes 5 h to paint a large picture.
- You want to spend no more than 48 h painting.
- You sell the small pictures for $12.
- You sell large pictures for $22.
- You want to sell at least one picture of each size.

How many of each picture size should you paint to maximize your earnings?

ANSWERS TO LESSON QUIZ

1. b
2. 1 small picture, 9 large pictures

PRESCRIPTION FOR REMEDIATION

Use the student work on the Lesson Quiz to prescribe a differentiated review assignment:

Points	Differentiated Remediation
0	Intervention
1	On-level
2	Extension

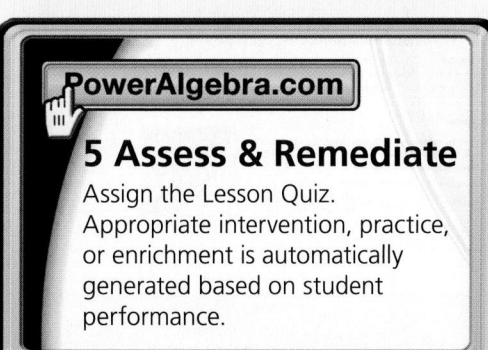

5 Assess & Remediate

Assign the Lesson Quiz. Appropriate intervention, practice, or enrichment is automatically generated based on student performance.

Intervention

- **Reteaching** (2 pages) Provides reteaching and practice exercises for the key lesson concepts. Use with struggling students or absent students.
- **English Language Learner Support** Helps students develop and reinforce mathematical vocabulary and key concepts.

All-in-One Resources/Online
Reteaching

3-4 Reteaching — Linear Programming

Problem

What point in the feasible region maximizes P for the objective function $P = 10x + 15y$? What point minimizes P?

Constraints $\begin{cases} x + y \le 16 \\ 3x + 6y \le 60 \\ x \ge 0 \\ y \ge 0 \end{cases}$

Step 1 Graph the constraints and shade the feasible region.

Step 2 Find the coordinates for each vertex of the region.

VERTEX
$A\,(0, 0)$
$B\,(16, 0)$
$C\,(12, 4)$
$D\,(0, 10)$

Step 3 Evaluate P at each vertex.

$P = 10x + 15y$

$P = 10(0) + 15(0) = 0$
$P = 10(16) + 15(0) = 160$
$P = 10(12) + 15(4) = 180$
$P = 10(0) + 15(10) = 150$

The maximum value of the objective function is 180. It occurs when $x = 12$ and $y = 4$.
The minimum value of the objective function is 0. It occurs when $x = 0$ and $y = 0$.

Exercises

Graph each system of constraints. Name all vertices. Then find the values of x and y that maximize or minimize the objective function.

All-in-One Resources/Online
English Language Learner Support

3-4 Additional Vocabulary Support — Linear Programming

Choose the word from the list that best matches each sentence.

| constraints | feasible region | linear programming | objective function | vertices |

1. The limits or restrictions are also called ___constraints___.
2. ___Linear programming___ is a method for finding a minimum or maximum value of some quantity, given a set of constraints.
3. On a graph, the ___feasible region___ contains all of the points that satisfy the constraints.
4. The ___objective function___ models a quantity that is related to the constraint variables.
5. The ___vertices___ of the feasible region are the points where the least and greatest values for the objective function occur.

Use a word from the list above to complete each sentence.

6. The inequalities $x - 2y \le 4$ and $2x + y \le 6$ are the ___constraints___.
7. The equation $P = 5x + 10y$ is an example of an ___objective function___ where P stands for profit.
8. The intersections of the constraint graphs are the ___vertices___ of the feasible region.
9. You have to graph the inequalities to find the ___feasible region___ for a linear programming problem.

Vertex is the singular form of vertices. Vertex means one of the vertices.

Multiple Choice

10. Which of the following is a vertex of the feasible region on the graph at the right? C
  Ⓐ (5, 4)   Ⓒ (2, 7)
  Ⓑ (3, 6)   Ⓓ (1, 1)

11. How many constraints were graphed to form the feasible region on the graph? H
  Ⓕ 2   Ⓖ 3   Ⓗ 4   Ⓘ 5

Differentiated Remediation *continued*

On-Level

- **Practice** (2 pages) Provides extra practice for each lesson. For simpler practice exercises, use the Form K Practice pages found in the All-in-One Teaching Resources and online.

- **Think About a Plan** Helps students develop specific problem-solving skills and strategies by providing scaffolded guiding questions.

- **Standardized Test Prep** Focuses on all major exercises, all major question types, and helps students prepare for the high-stakes assessments.

Extension

- **Enrichment** Provides students with interesting problems and activities that extend the concepts of the lesson.

- **Activities, Games, and Puzzles** Worksheets that can be used for concepts development, enrichment, and for fun!

Practice and Problem Solving Wkbk/All-in-One Resources/Online
Practice page 1

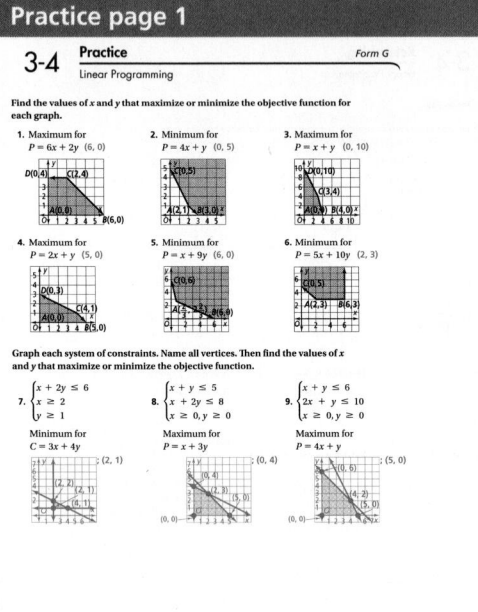

Practice and Problem Solving Wkbk/All-in-One Resources/Online
Practice page 2

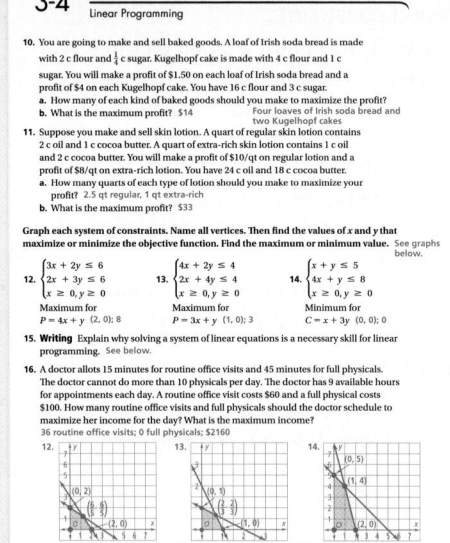

All-in-One Resources/Online
Enrichment

Practice and Problem Solving Wkbk/All-in-One Resources/Online
Think About a Plan

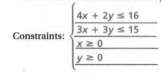

Practice and Problem Solving Wkbk/All-in-One Resources/Online
Standardized Test Prep

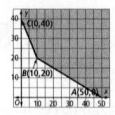

Online Teacher Resource Center
Activities, Games, and Puzzles

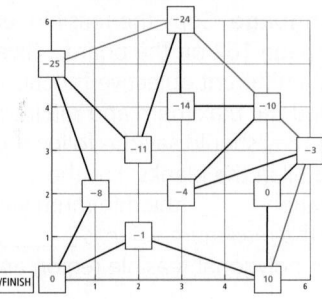

Concept Byte

For Use With Lesson 3-4

TECHNOLOGY

Linear Programming

Common Core State Standards

A-CED.A.3 Represent constraints by equations or inequalities, and by systems of equations and/or inequalities, and interpret solutions as viable or nonviable options in a modeling context.

MP 5

You can solve linear programming problems using your graphing calculator.

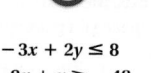

Activity

Find the values of x and y that will maximize the objective function $P = 13x + 2y$ for the constraints at the right. What is the value of P at this maximum point?

$$\begin{cases} -3x + 2y \le 8 \\ -8x + y \ge -48 \\ x \ge 0, y \ge 0 \end{cases}$$

Step 1 Rewrite the first two inequalities to isolate y. Enter the inequalities.

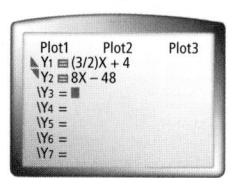

Step 2 Use the **VALUE** option of **CALC** to find the upper left vertex. Press 0 `enter`.

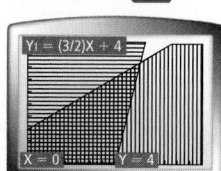

Step 3 Enter the objective function on the home screen. Press `enter` for the value of P at the vertex.

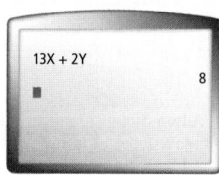

Step 4 Use the **INTERSECT** option of **CALC** to find the upper right vertex. Go to the home screen and press `enter` for the value of P.

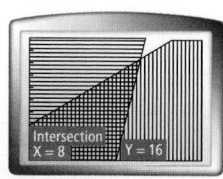

Step 5 Use the **ZERO** option of **CALC** to find the lower right vertex. Go to the home screen and press `enter` for the value of P. The objective function has a value of 0 when the vertex is at the origin. The maximum value of P is 136.

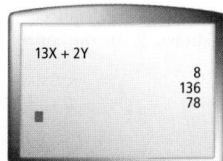

Exercises

Find the values of x and y that maximize or minimize the objective function.

1. $\begin{cases} 4x + 3y \ge 30 \\ x + 3y \ge 21 \\ x \ge 0, y \ge 0 \end{cases}$
Minimum for
$C = 5x + 8y$

2. $\begin{cases} 3x + 5y \ge 35 \\ 2x + y \le 14 \\ x \ge 0, y \ge 0 \end{cases}$
Maximum for
$P = 3x + 2y$

3. $\begin{cases} x + y \ge 8 \\ x + 5y \ge 20 \\ x \ge 0, y \ge 2 \end{cases}$
Minimum for
$C = 3x + 4y$

4. $\begin{cases} x + 2y \le 24 \\ 3x + 2y \le 34 \\ 3x + y \le 29 \\ x \ge 0 \end{cases}$
Maximum for
$P = 2x + 3y$

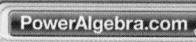
Guided Instruction

PURPOSE To use a graphing calculator to solve a linear programming problem

PROCESS Students will
- graph the constraints.
- use the calculator to find the vertices and evaluate the objective function at each vertex.

DISCUSS Graphing calculators can be used to find the feasible region and its vertices. This can be a helpful tool when the coordinates of the vertices are not integers.
- To graph the constraints, you must first solve each for y.
- The coordinate of the vertices given by the calculator may be rounded.

Q What functions of the calculator would be useful to solve linear programming problems? **[Answers may vary. Sample: GRAPH to graph the constraint functions, CALC to find the vertices]**

Activity

Q What quadrant(s) do you have to look at for the graph? Why? **[Quadrant I, since x and y are nonnegative by the constraints.]**

Exercises   ERROR PREVENTION

The intersection of a constraint and the x- or y-axis may not be a vertex of the feasible region. It will be a vertex if the constraints include $x \ge 0$ or $y \ge 0$.

Mathematical Practices This Concept Byte supports students in becoming proficient in using appropriate tools, Mathematical Practice 5.

Answers

1. $x = 3, y = 6; C = 63$

2. $x = 5, y = 4; P = 23$

3. $x = 5, y = 3; C = 27$

4. $x = 5, y = 9.5; P = 38.5$

Guided Instruction

PURPOSE To graph in coordinate space
PROCESS Students will
- identify coordinates of points in coordinate space.
- graph three-variable equations in coordinate space.
- graph pairs of three-variable equations in coordinate space and describe their intersections.

DISCUSS Draw the familiar two-dimensional coordinate system on the board, labeling the axes *x* and *y*. Make a transparency of Quadrant I and place it over Quadrant I on the board. Then erase the *x* and *y* on the board. Turn the transparency so that its *x*-axis and *y*-axis look like the second diagram. The *x*-axis protrudes from the board. Label the vertical axis *z*, the third label in a three-dimensional coordinate system. Next, use a yard stick or similar object to show the position of the *x*-axis through the origin and perpendicular to the plane of the board.

Activity 1
Students will need a yardstick, meter stick, or tape measure for this activity.

> **Q** What represents the *xy* plane in the picture? **[the floor]** What plane is represented by the wall that contains the board? **[the *yz* plane]**
>
> **Q** Suppose distance is measured in centimeters and the corner of a desk has coordinates (220, 183, 72). Describe how to get to that desk corner from the origin. **[Travel 220 cm along the *x*-axis, then 183 cm parallel to the *y*-axis, then 72 cm up.]**

Ⓒ **Mathematical Practices** This Concept Byte supports students in modeling with mathematics, Mathematical Practice 4.

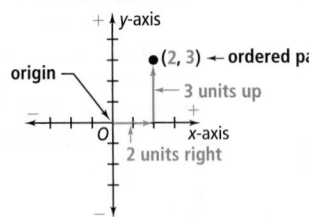

Concept Byte
For Use With Lesson 3-5
ACTIVITY

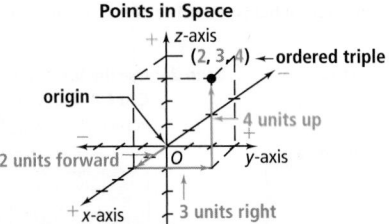

Graphs in Three Dimensions

Ⓒ **Common Core State Standards**
Extends A-REI.C.6 Solve systems of linear equations exactly and approximately (e.g., with graphs), focusing on pairs of linear equations in two variables.
MP 4

To describe positions in space, you need a three-dimensional coordinate system. You have learned to graph on an *xy*-coordinate plane using ordered pairs. Adding a third axis, the *z*-axis, to the *xy*-coordinate plane creates **coordinate space**. In coordinate space you graph points using **ordered triples** of the form (*x*, *y*, *z*).

Points in a Plane

origin

(2, 3) ← ordered pair
3 units up
O
x-axis
2 units right

A two-dimensional coordinate system allows you to graph points in a plane.

Points in Space

z-axis
(2, 3, 4) ← ordered triple
origin
4 units up
2 units forward
O
y-axis
x-axis
3 units right

A three-dimensional coordinate system allows you to graph points in space.

In the coordinate plane, point (2, 3) is two units right and three units up from the origin. In coordinate space, point (2, 3, 4) is two units forward, three units right, and four units up.

Activity 1

Define one corner of your classroom as the origin of a three-dimensional coordinate system like the classroom shown. Write the coordinates of each item in your coordinate system.

1. each corner of your classroom
2. each corner of your desk
3. one corner of the blackboard
4. the clock
5. the waste-paper basket
6. Pick 3 items in your classroom and write the coordinates of each.

Answers

1–6. Check students' work.

Activity 2

7.

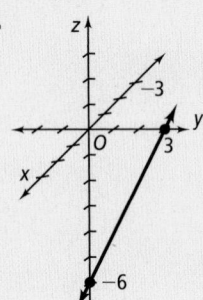

8.

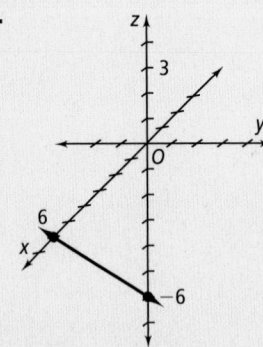

9.

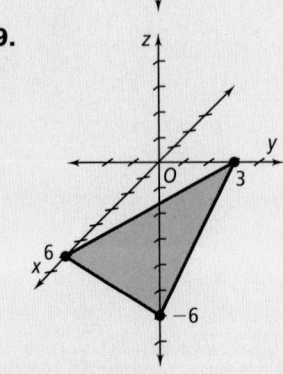

Activity 3

10.

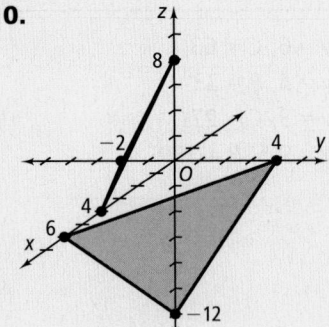

11. line

An equation in two variables represents a line in a plane. An equation in three variables represents a plane in space.

Activity 2

Given the following equation in three variables, draw the plane in a coordinate space. $x + 2y - z = 6$

7. Let $x = 0$. Graph the resulting equation in the yz plane.

8. Let $y = 0$. Graph the resulting equation in the xz plane.

From geometry you know that two lines determine a plane.

9. Sketch the plane $x + 2y - z = 6$.
   (If you need help, find a third line by letting $z = 0$ and then graph the resulting equation in the xy plane.)

Activity 3

Two equations in three variables represent two planes in space.

10. Draw the two planes determined by the following equations:
    $2x + 3y - z = 12$
    $2x - 4y + z = 8$

11. Describe the intersection of the two planes above.

Exercises

Find the coordinates of each point in the diagram.

12. A 13. B 14. C

15. D 16. E 17. F

Sketch the graph of each equation.

18. $x - y - 4z = 8$ 19. $x + y + z = 2$

20. $-3x + 5y + 10z = 15$ 21. $6x + 6y - 12z = 36$

Graph the following pairs of equations in the same coordinate space and describe their intersection, if any.

22. $-x + 3y + z = 6$ 23. $-2x - 3y + 5z = 7$
    $-3x + 5y - 2z = 60$ $2x - 3y - 4z = -4$

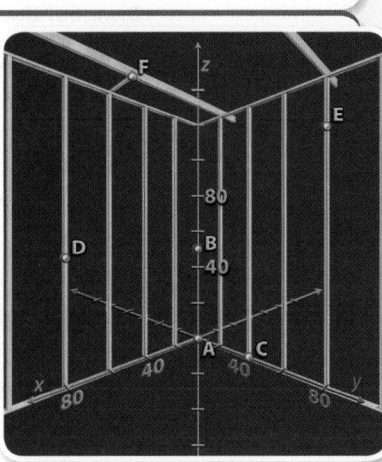

Activity 2

Q In Problem 7, you let $x = 0$. What equation will you graph? **[$2y - z = 6$]**

Q What is a method to graph this equation? **[Answers may vary. Sample: Graph the y- and z-intercepts, and draw the line through them.]**

Q What is the y-intercept, expressed as an ordered pair in the form (y, z)? **[(3, 0)]**

Q What is the z-intercept, expressed as an ordered pair in the form (y, z)? **[(0, −6)]**

Q Now, recall that $x = 0$. What are the y- and z-intercepts, expressed as ordered triples in the form (x, y, z)? **[(0, 3, 0) and (0, 0, −6)]**

Students can use the same method to draw the line in Problem 8 and the third line mentioned in the hint for Problem 9.

Activity 3

For Problem 11, show a model of two intersecting planes, such as two books, two index cards, two walls coming together in the room, or the flat palms of your two hands.

Q If two planes intersect, what does the intersection form? **[a line]**

Exercises

Q For Exercise 1, what are the coordinates of point A? Explain. **[(0, 0, 0); A is the origin.]**

Q For Exercises 2–6, what number is a coordinate of every point? Explain. **[0; B is on the z-axis, C is on the y-axis, D is in the xz-plane, E is in the yz-plane, and F is in the xz-plane.]**

Exercises

12. $(0, 0, 0)$ 13. $(0, 0, 50)$

14. $(0, 40, 0)$ 15. $(60, 0, 50)$

16. $(0, 80, 100)$ 17. $(60, 30, 100)$

18.
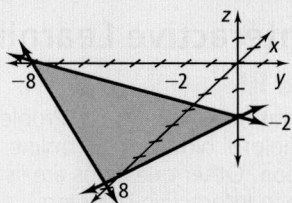

19.
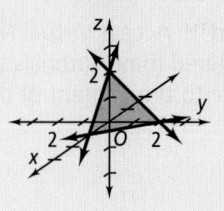

20.
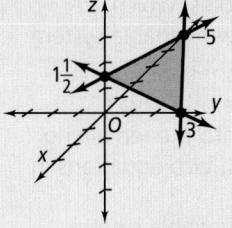

21.
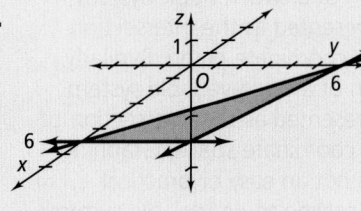

22.
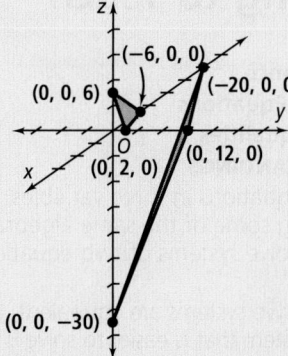

line

23.
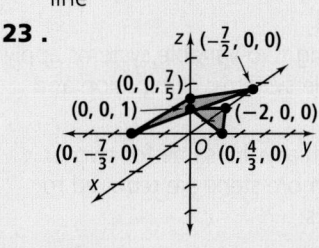

line

1 Interactive Learning

Solve It!

PURPOSE To find unknown weights by relating them to each other and to a known weight

PROCESS Students may
- write two-variable equations and solve using substitution.
- use guess-and-check.

FACILITATE

Q Let A, B, and C represent the weights. What equation can you write that contains a known weight? **[$B + C = 10$]**

Q What equation does the first diagram suggest? **[$2A = B$]**

Q What equation does the second diagram suggest? **[$3A = C$]**

Q How can you write an equation that you can solve to get an answer? **[Answers may vary. Sample: Rewrite the equation $B + C = 10$, substituting $2A$ for B and $3A$ for C.]**

Q If you rewrite the equation, substituting $2A$ for B and $3A$ for C, what equation do you get? **[$2A + 3A = 10$]**

ANSWER See Solve It in Answers on next page.

CONNECT THE MATH In the Solve It, students use relationships that can be represented by three equations, each containing two variables. In the lesson, they will solve systems of three equations, each containing as many as three variables.

3-5 Systems With Three Variables

Common Core State Standards

Extends A-REI.C.6 Solve systems of linear equations exactly and approximately (e.g., with graphs), focusing on pairs of linear equations in two variables.
MP 1, MP 3

Objectives To solve systems in three variables using elimination
To solve systems in three variables using substitution

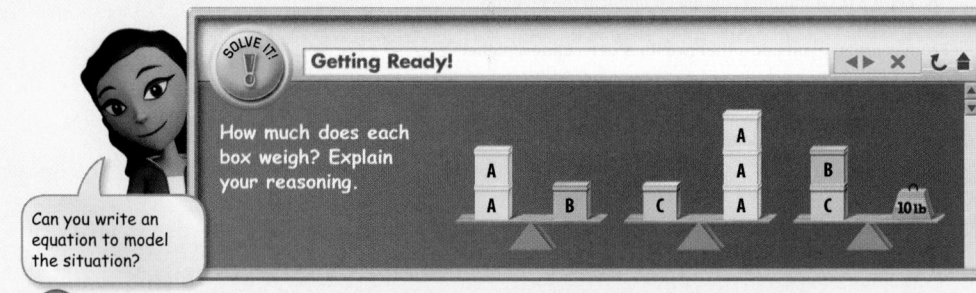

Getting Ready!

How much does each box weigh? Explain your reasoning.

Can you write an equation to model the situation?

MATHEMATICAL PRACTICES You can represent three relationships involving three unknowns with a system of equations.

Essential Understanding To solve systems of three equations in three variables, you can use some of the same algebraic methods you used to solve systems of two equations in two variables.

You can represent systems of equations in three variables as graphs in three dimensions. The graph of an equation of the form $Ax + By + Cz = D$, where A, B, and C are not all zero, is a plane. You can show the solutions of a three-variable system graphically as the intersection of planes.

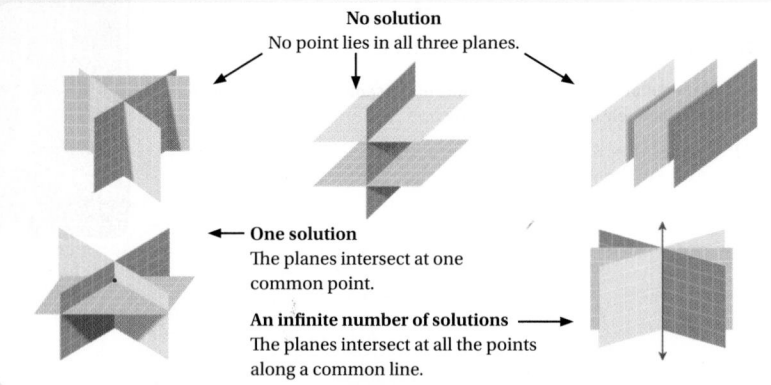

No solution
No point lies in all three planes.

One solution
The planes intersect at one common point.

An infinite number of solutions
The planes intersect at all the points along a common line.

3-5 Preparing to Teach

BIG ideas Equivalence
Solving Equations and Inequalities

ESSENTIAL UNDERSTANDINGS
- Systems of three equations in three variables can be solved using some of the same algebraic methods used to solve systems of two equations in two variables.
- If the equations of two systems are equivalent, then a solution of the system that is easier to solve is also a solution of the more difficult system.

Math Background
Two methods for solving two-variable systems apply to solving three-variable systems: elimination and substitution.

The methods are essentially the same for two or three variables; a few more steps are required to solve for three variables.

For elimination, use two equations at a time to eliminate one variable. This will result in two

equations in two variables, which are solved like any other two-variable system.

Similarly for substitution: solve for one variable in terms of the other two. Substitute that value into the remaining two equations, yielding two equations in two variables.

The solution of a two-variable system can be represented as the intersection of lines in a coordinate plane. Similarly, the solution of a three-variable system can be represented as the intersection of *planes* in a coordinate space. Graphing, however, is not an easy or practical method of solving three-variable systems.

Mathematical Practices
Make sense of problems and persevere in solving them. Students will learn two methods of solving three-variable systems and will identify correspondences between the two approaches.

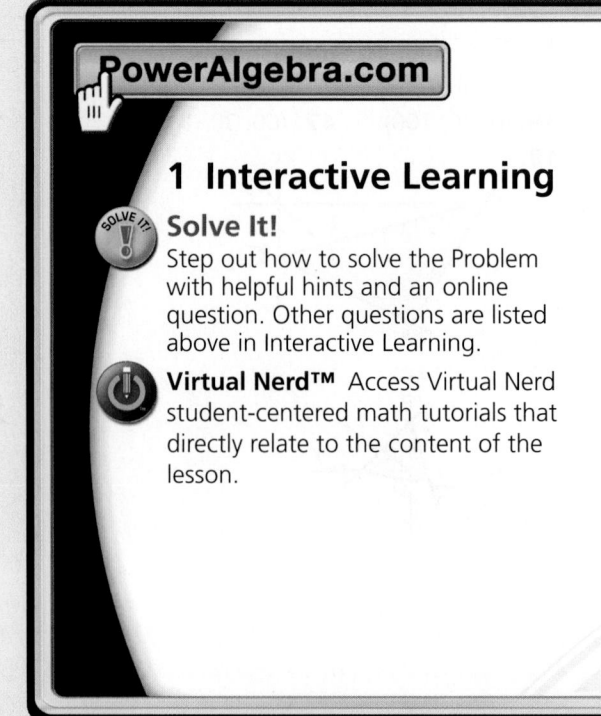

PowerAlgebra.com

1 Interactive Learning

Solve It!
Step out how to solve the Problem with helpful hints and an online question. Other questions are listed above in Interactive Learning.

Virtual Nerd™ Access Virtual Nerd student-centered math tutorials that directly relate to the content of the lesson.

You can use the elimination and substitution methods to solve a system of three equations in three variables by working with the equations in pairs. You will use one of the equations *twice*. When one point represents the solution of a system of equations in three variables, write it as an ordered triple (x, y, z).

 Problem 1 Solving a System Using Elimination

What is the solution of the system? Use elimination. The equations are numbered to make the procedure easy to follow.

$$\begin{array}{r} ① \quad 2x - y + z = 4 \\ ② \quad x + 3y - z = 11 \\ ③ \quad 4x + y - z = 14 \end{array}$$

Think

Which variable do you eliminate first?
Eliminate the variable for which the process requires the fewest steps.

Step 1 Pair the equations to eliminate z. Then you will have two equations in x and y.

Add.

$$\begin{array}{r} ① \quad 2x - y + z = 4 \\ ② \quad x + 3y - z = 11 \\ \hline ④ \quad 3x + 2y = 15 \end{array}$$

Subtract.

$$\begin{array}{r} ② \quad x + 3y - z = 11 \\ ③ \quad 4x + y - z = 14 \\ \hline ⑤ \quad -3x + 2y = -3 \end{array}$$

Step 2 Write the two new equations as a system. Solve for x and y.

Add and solve for y.

$$\begin{array}{r} ④ \quad 3x + 2y = 15 \\ ⑤ \quad -3x + 2y = -3 \\ \hline 4y = 12 \\ y = 3 \end{array}$$

Substitute $y = 3$ and solve for x.

$$\begin{array}{r} ④ \quad 3x + 2y = 15 \\ 3x + 2(3) = 15 \\ 3x = 9 \\ x = 3 \end{array}$$

Think

Does it matter which equation you substitute into to find z?
No, you can substitute into any of the original three equations.

Step 3 Solve for z. Substitute the values of x and y into one of the original equations.

$$\begin{array}{rl} ① \quad 2x - y + z = 4 & \text{Use equation ①.} \\ 2(3) - 3 + z = 4 & \text{Substitute.} \\ 6 - 3 + z = 4 & \text{Simplify.} \\ z = 1 & \text{Solve for } z. \end{array}$$

Step 4 Write the solution as an ordered triple. The solution is $(3, 3, 1)$.

 Got It? **1.** What is the solution of the system? Use elimination. Check your answer in all three original equations.

$$\begin{cases} x - y + z = -1 \\ x + y + 3z = -3 \\ 2x - y + 2z = 0 \end{cases}$$

You can apply the method in Problem 1 to most systems of three equations in three variables. You may need to multiply in one, two, or all three equations by one, two, or three nonzero numbers. Your goal is to obtain a system—equivalent to the original system—with coefficients that allow for the easy elimination of variables.

2 Guided Instruction

Problem 1

Q Why do you think z was chosen as the variable to eliminate? **[The only z-coefficients are 1 and −1, so it is easy to eliminate z by adding or subtracting.]**

Q Look at the subtraction in Step 1. What would be the result if equations 2 and 3 were reversed? **[All the signs in equation 5 would be opposite; z would still be eliminated.]**

Q In Step 2, the value of y is substituted into equation 4. Could the value of y be substituted into a different equation to solve for x? Explain. **[Yes; it could be substituted into equation 5 because it also has x and y.]**

EXTENSION

Students can substitute the values of x and y into the original equations 2 or 3 to verify that they get the same result for z. They can check the solution by substituting the values of x, y, and z into all three equations in the original system.

Got It?

Q What variable will you eliminate first? Explain. **[Answers may vary. Sample: y because the only y-coefficients are 1 and −1.]**

2 Guided Instruction

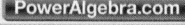 Each Problem is worked out and supported in the Student Online Center.

Problem 1
Solving a System Using Elimination

Animated

Problem 2
Solving an Equivalent System

Animated

Problem 3
Solving a System Using Substitution

Animated

Problem 4
Solving a Real-World Problem

Support in Algebra 2 Companion
• Vocabulary
• Key Concepts
• Got It?

Answers

Solve It!
A: 2 lb, B: 4 lb, C: 6 lb
$B + C = 10$
$C = 3A$
$B = 2A$
Therefore, $2A + 3A = 10$ and $A = 2$.
Use substitution to find the weights of each box.

Got It?
1. $(4, 2, -3)$

Problem 2

Q Look at the given system. Does it seem that there is clearly one best choice of a variable that should be eliminated first? Explain your reasoning. **[Answers may vary. Sample: No; x and y seem to be equally good choices because the process to eliminate x would have about the same number of steps as the process to eliminate y. The x-coefficients are 1, 2, and -1. The y-coefficients are 1, 1, and -2.]**

Q Which variable *is* eliminated first, and how is it accomplished? **[y; both sides of equation 1 are multiplied by -1, and then addition is used on the resulting equation and equation 2.]**

Q Can you think of another method that would eliminate y just as quickly? **[Answers may vary. Sample: Use subtraction on equations 1 and 2.]**

Got It?

Q For 2a, which variable will you eliminate first, and how will you start? **[Answers may vary. Sample: x; use equations 1 and 2. Multiply equation 1 by -2. Then add.]**

 **Problem 2** Solving an Equivalent System

What is the solution of the system? Use elimination.

① $x + y + 2z = 3$
② $2x + y + 3z = 7$
③ $-x - 2y + z = 10$

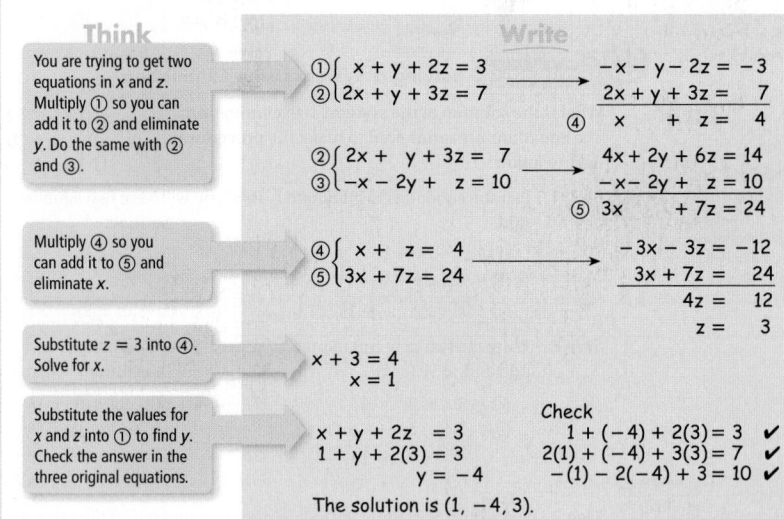

Think

You are trying to get two equations in x and z. Multiply ① so you can add it to ② and eliminate y. Do the same with ② and ③.

Multiply ④ so you can add it to ⑤ and eliminate x.

Substitute $z = 3$ into ④. Solve for x.

Substitute the values for x and z into ① to find y. Check the answer in the three original equations.

Write

① $x + y + 2z = 3$
② $2x + y + 3z = 7$

$\quad -x - y - 2z = -3$
$\quad \underline{2x + y + 3z = 7}$
④ $\quad x + z = 4$

② $2x + y + 3z = 7$
③ $-x - 2y + z = 10$

$\quad 4x + 2y + 6z = 14$
$\quad \underline{-x - 2y + z = 10}$
⑤ $\quad 3x + 7z = 24$

④ $x + z = 4$
⑤ $3x + 7z = 24$

$\quad -3x - 3z = -12$
$\quad \underline{3x + 7z = 24}$
$\quad 4z = 12$
$\quad z = 3$

$x + 3 = 4$
$ x = 1$

$x + y + 2z = 3$
$1 + y + 2(3) = 3$
$ y = -4$

Check
$1 + (-4) + 2(3) = 3$ ✔
$2(1) + (-4) + 3(3) = 7$ ✔
$-(1) - 2(-4) + 3 = 10$ ✔

The solution is $(1, -4, 3)$.

Got It? 2. **a.** What is the solution of the system? Use elimination.
  b. **Reasoning** Could you have used elimination in another way? Explain.

$x - 2y + 3z = 12$
$2x - y - 2z = 5$
$2x + 2y - z = 4$

Here is a graphical representation of the solution of Problem 2. The graphs are enclosed in a 10-by-10-by-10 cube with the origin of the coordinate axes at the center.

The graphs of equations ①, ②, and ③, are planes ①, ②, and ③, respectively.

Each pair of planes intersects in a line. The three lines intersect in $(1, -4, 3)$, the solution of the system.

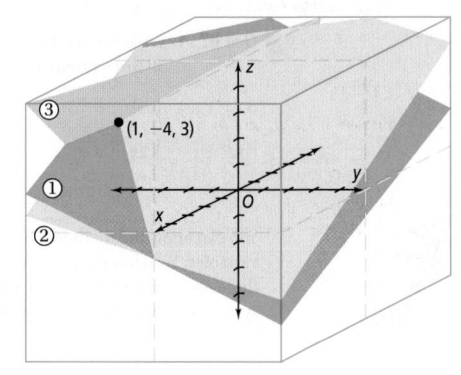

Additional Problems

1. What is the solution of the system? Use elimination.

$3x + y - z = 1$
$x + 2y + z = 4$
$3x - y - z = 3$

ANSWER $(2, -1, 4)$

2. What is the solution of the system? Use elimination.

$x + y + 2z = -7$
$3x + y - 2z = 7$
$-x - 3y + z = -9$

ANSWER $(-1, 2, -4)$

3. What is the x-value of the solution of the system?

$x - 2y + z = 1$
$2x + z = 9$
$-3x + y = -3$

ANSWER 2

4. You are an office supply distributor and budget $7200 for 80 office chairs. You can buy leather chairs for $125 each, mesh chairs for $100 each, and fabric chairs for $75 each. If you want to have 3 times as many fabric chairs as leather chairs, how many of each type should you buy?

ANSWER 16 leather chairs, 16 mesh chairs, 48 fabric chairs

You can also use substitution to solve a system of three equations. Substitution is the best method to use when you can easily solve one of the equations for a single variable.

 Problem 3 Solving a System Using Substitution

Multiple Choice What is the x-value in the solution of the system?

$$\begin{cases} ① & 2x + 3y - 2z = -1 \\ ② & x + 5y = 9 \\ ③ & 4z - 5x = 4 \end{cases}$$

Ⓐ 1   Ⓒ 6

Ⓑ 4   Ⓓ 10

Step 1 Choose equation ②. Solve for x.

② $x + 5y = 9$
      $x = 9 - 5y$

Step 2 Substitute the expression for x into equations ① and ③ and simplify.

① $2x + 3y - 2z = -1$ ③ $4z - 5x = 4$
    $2(9 - 5y) + 3y - 2z = -1$ $4z - 5(9 - 5y) = 4$
    $18 - 10y + 3y - 2z = -1$ $4z - 45 + 25y = 4$
        $18 - 7y - 2z = -1$ $4z + 25y = 49$
④ $-7y - 2z = -19$ ⑤ $25y + 4z = 49$

Step 3 Write the two new equations as a system. Solve for y and z.

$$\begin{cases} ④ & -7y - 2z = -19 \\ ⑤ & 25y + 4z = 49 \end{cases}$$

    $-14y - 4z = -38$ Multiply by 2.
     $\underline{25y + 4z = 49}$ Then add.
          $11y = 11$
           $y = 1$

④ $-7y - 2z = -19$
   $-7(1) - 2z = -19$ Substitute the value of y into ④.
       $-2z = -12$
         $z = 6$

Step 4 Use one of the original equations to solve for x.

② $x + 5y = 9$
   $x + 5(1) = 9$ Substitute the value of y into ②.
      $x = 4$

The solution of the system is $(4, 1, 6)$, and $x = 4$.

The correct answer is B.

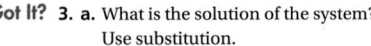 **Got It? 3. a.** What is the solution of the system? Use substitution.

$$\begin{cases} x - 2y + z = -4 \\ -4x + y - 2z = 1 \\ 2x + 2y - z = 10 \end{cases}$$

     b. Reasoning In Problem 3, was it necessary to find the value of z to solve the problem? Explain.

Problem 3

Q Problems 1 and 2 on the previous pages both used a method called elimination. Was the Substitution Property of Equality used in those problems? Explain. **[Yes; answers may vary. Sample: In Problem 2, the value of z was substituted into equation 4, and then the values of x and z were substituted into equation 1.]**

Q Look at equations 4 and 5 in Step 3. Would you use substitution to solve for y? **[Answers may vary. Sample: No; you could not easily solve for z in terms of y in either equation.]**

Q Could you have solved this problem using elimination? Would it have been a better method? Explain. **[Answers may vary. Samples: Yes; this problem could be solved using elimination. No; since none of variables have the same or inverse coefficients in at least two of the three equations, you would have to multiply the equations by constants in order to eliminate a variable.]**

Got It?   SYNTHESIS

Q What process could you use to solve this system of equations? **[Answers may vary. Sample: Solve equation 2 for y and equation 3 for z and substitute both into equation 1 and solve for x.]**

Answers

Got It? (continued)

2. a. $(4, -1, 2)$

   b. Answers may vary. Sample: Yes; you can choose to eliminate either x, y, or z resulting in a system of equations in 2 variables.

3. a. $(2, 1, -4)$

   b. No; in Step 1 we solved for x in terms of y only. Therefore, once we found the value of y we could have substituted that value into the equation we wrote in Step 1 and solved for x without ever finding the z-value.

Problem 4

Q You will *budget* $6000 to restock 200 shirts. What does it mean to *budget* an amount of money in this situation? **[Answers may vary. Samples: plan to spend, set aside]**

Q You will budget $6000 to *restock* 200 shirts. What does it mean to *restock* a number of shirts in this situation? **[Answers may vary. Samples: replace, buy]**

Q Look at the system of equations in the Write section. Which method do you think is best to solve this system: elimination or substitution? Explain your choice. **[Answers may vary. Sample: A combination of substitution and elimination. Use z = 2y to substitute for z in both equation 1 and equation 3, but then use elimination to solve the resulting equations in x and y.]**

Got It?

Make sure students use the following system.

$$\begin{cases} x + y + z = 200 \\ x = y \\ 12x + 24y + 36z = 5400 \end{cases}$$

Q Why is equation 1 the same in Problem 4 and the Got It? **[You are still buying a total of 200 shirts.]**

 Problem 4 Solving a Real-World Problem

Business You manage a clothing store and budget $6000 to restock 200 shirts. You can buy T-shirts for $12 each, polo shirts for $24 each, and rugby shirts for $36 each. If you want to have twice as many rugby shirts as polo shirts, how many of each type of shirt should you buy?

Relate   T-shirts + polo shirts + rugby shirts = 200

rugby shirts = 2 · polo shirts

12 · T-shirts + 24 · polo shirts + 36 · rugby shirts = 6000

Think
How many unknowns are there?
There are three unknowns: the number of each type of shirt.

Define   Let x = the number of T-shirts.
Let y = the number of polo shirts.
Let z = the number of rugby shirts.

Write   ① $\begin{cases} x + y + z = 200 \\ ② \quad z = 2 \cdot y \\ ③ \quad 12 \cdot x + 24 \cdot y + 36 \cdot z = 6000 \end{cases}$

Step 1 Since 12 is a common factor of all the terms in equation ③, write a simpler equivalent equation.

③ $\begin{cases} 12x + 24y + 36z = 6000 \\ ④ \quad x + 2y + 3z = 500 \qquad \text{Divide by 12.} \end{cases}$

Step 2 Substitute 2y for z in equations ① and ④. Simplify to find equations ⑤ and ⑥.

① $x + y + z = 200$ ④ $x + 2y + 3z = 500$
$x + y + (2y) = 200$ $x + 2y + 3(2y) = 500$
⑤ $x + 3y = 200$ ⑥ $x + 8y = 500$

Step 3 Write ⑤ and ⑥ as a system. Solve for x and y.

⑤ $\begin{cases} x + 3y = 200 \\ ⑥ \quad x + 8y = 500 \end{cases}$ $\begin{aligned} -x - 3y &= -200 \quad \text{Multiply by } -1. \\ x + 8y &= 500 \quad \text{Then add.} \\ \hline 5y &= 300 \\ y &= 60 \end{aligned}$

⑤ $x + 3y = 200$
$x + 3(60) = 200$ Substitute the value of y into ⑤.
$x = 20$

Step 4 Substitute the value of y in ② and solve for z.

② $z = 2y$
$z = 2(60) = 120$

You should buy 20 T-shirts, 60 polo shirts, and 120 rugby shirts.

✓ **Got It? 4.** Suppose you want to have the same number of T-shirts as polo shirts. Buying 200 shirts with a budget of $5400, how many of each shirt should you buy?

Answers

Got It? (continued)

4. 50 T-shirts, 50 polo shirts, and 100 rugby shirts

Lesson Check

Do you know HOW?

Solve each system.

1. $\begin{cases} 2y - 3z = 0 \\ x + 3y = -4 \\ 3x + 4y = 3 \end{cases}$

2. $\begin{cases} 3x + y - 2z = 22 \\ x + 5y + z = 4 \\ x = -3z \end{cases}$

3. $\begin{cases} 2x + 3y - 2z = 1 \\ -x - y + 2z = 5 \\ 3x + 2y - 3z = -6 \end{cases}$

4. $\begin{cases} 2x - y + z = -2 \\ x + 3y - z = 10 \\ x + 2z = -8 \end{cases}$

Do you UNDERSTAND?  MATHEMATICAL PRACTICES

5. **Reasoning** How do you decide whether substitution is the best method to solve a system in three variables?

6. **Error Analysis** A classmate says that the system consisting of $x = 0$, $y = 0$, and $z = 0$ has no solution. Explain the student's error.

7. **Writing** How many solutions does this system have? Explain your answer in terms of intersecting planes. (*Hint:* Is the system dependent? inconsistent?)

① $\begin{cases} 2x - 3y + z = 5 \\ ② \quad 2x - 3y + z = -2 \\ ③ \quad -4x + 6y - 2z = 10 \end{cases}$

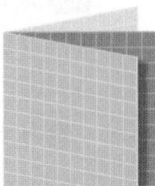

8. The graph of a system is shown. How many solutions does this system have? Explain.

Practice and Problem-Solving Exercises  MATHEMATICAL PRACTICES

 Practice   Solve each system by elimination. Check your answers.   ◆ **See Problems 1 and 2.**

9. $\begin{cases} x - y + z = -1 \\ x + y + 3z = -3 \\ 2x - y + 2z = 0 \end{cases}$

10. $\begin{cases} x - y - 2z = 4 \\ -x + 2y + z = 1 \\ -x + y - 3z = 11 \end{cases}$

11. $\begin{cases} -2x + y - z = 2 \\ -x - 3y + z = -10 \\ 3x + 6z = -24 \end{cases}$

12. $\begin{cases} a + b + c = -3 \\ 3b - c = 4 \\ 2a - b - 2c = -5 \end{cases}$

13. $\begin{cases} 6q - r + 2s = 8 \\ 2q + 3r - s = -9 \\ 4q + 2r + 5s = 1 \end{cases}$

14. $\begin{cases} x - y + 2z = -7 \\ y + z = 1 \\ x = 2y + 3z \end{cases}$

15. $\begin{cases} 3x + 3y + 6z = 9 \\ 2x + y + 3z = 7 \\ x + 2y - z = -10 \end{cases}$

16. $\begin{cases} 3x - y + z = 3 \\ x + y + 2z = 4 \\ x + 2y + z = 4 \end{cases}$

17. $\begin{cases} x - 2y + 3z = 12 \\ 2x - y - 2z = 5 \\ 2x + 2y - z = 4 \end{cases}$

18. $\begin{cases} x + 2y = 2 \\ 2x + 3y - z = -9 \\ 4x + 2y + 5z = 1 \end{cases}$

19. $\begin{cases} 3x + 2y + 2z = -2 \\ 2x + y - z = -2 \\ x - 3y + z = 0 \end{cases}$

20. $\begin{cases} x + 4y - 5z = -7 \\ 3x + 2y + 3z = 7 \\ 2x + y + 5z = 8 \end{cases}$

---

3 Lesson Check

Do you know HOW?

- For Exercise 1, if students have trouble choosing a method, explain that either will work. If they choose elimination, they may want to multiply equation 2 by -3. If they choose substitution, they may want to solve equation 2 for x.

Do you UNDERSTAND?

- For Exercise 5, if students have trouble coming up with ideas, suggest that students reread the paragraph preceding Problem 3.

Close

Q How can you represent the solutions of a three-variable system of equations graphically? **[as the intersection of planes]**

Q How can you decide whether to use elimination or substitution to solve a three-variable system? **[Choose whichever makes it easier to reduce the system to two equations with two variables and then to find the value of one of the variables.]**

Lesson Check

1. $(5, -3, -2)$
2. $(6, 0, -2)$
3. $(0, 3, 4)$
4. $(2, 1, -5)$
5. Answers may vary. Sample: Substitution is the best method to use when one of the equations can be solved easily for one variable.
6. Answers may vary. Sample: $(0, 0, 0)$ is a unique solution to a system of three variables. The planes intersect at one common point. When a system has no solution, no point lies in all three planes.
7. No solution since no point lies in all three planes. The three planes are parallel.
8. infinitely many solutions

Practice and Problem-Solving Exercises

9. $(4, 2, -3)$
10. $(0, 2, -3)$
11. $(2, 1, -5)$
12. $(-3, 1, -1)$
13. $\left(\frac{1}{2}, -3, 1\right)$
14. $(0, 3, -2)$
15. $(1, -4, 3)$
16. $(1, 1, 1)$
17. $(4, -1, 2)$
18. $\left(-\frac{122}{11}, \frac{72}{11}, \frac{71}{11}\right)$
19. $\left(-\frac{10}{13}, -\frac{2}{13}, \frac{4}{13}\right)$
20. $(2, -1, 1)$

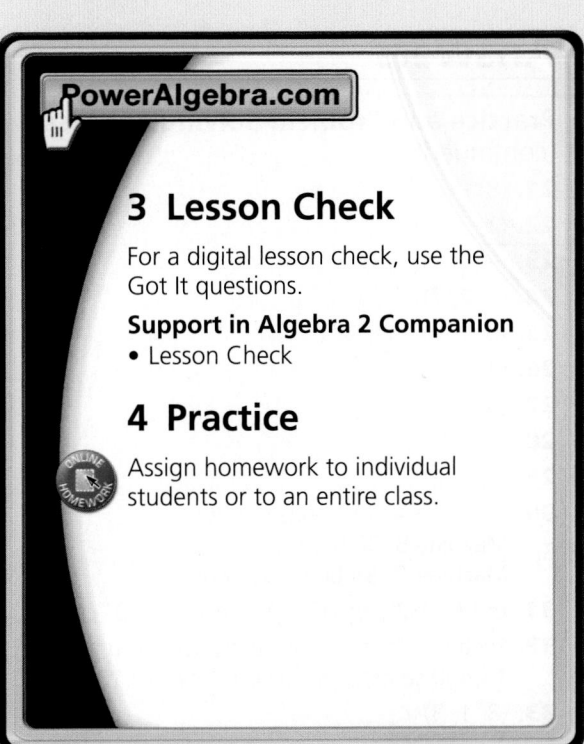

PowerAlgebra.com

3 Lesson Check

For a digital lesson check, use the Got It questions.

Support in Algebra 2 Companion
- Lesson Check

4 Practice

Assign homework to individual students or to an entire class.

4 Practice

ASSIGNMENT GUIDE

Basic: 9–31, 32–42 even

Average: 9–29 odd, 31–42

Advanced: 9–29 odd, 31–45

Ⓒ **Mathematical Practices** are supported by exercises with red headings. Here are the Practices supported in this lesson:

MP 1: Make Sense of Problems Ex. 31

MP 3: Communicate Ex. 7

MP 3: Compare Arguments Ex. 5

MP 3: Critique the Reasoning of Others Ex. 6

Applications exercises have blue headings.

STEM exercises focus on science or engineering applications.

EXERCISE 32: Use the Think About a Plan worksheet in the **Practice and Problem Solving Workbook** (also available in the Teaching Resources in print and online) to further support students' development in becoming independent learners.

HOMEWORK QUICK CHECK

To check students' understanding of key skills and concepts, go over Exercises 9, 23, 31, 32, and 38.

Solve each system by substitution. Check your answers. ◀ **See Problems 3 and 4.**

21. $\begin{cases} x + 2y + 3z = 6 \\ y + 2z = 0 \\ z = 2 \end{cases}$

22. $\begin{cases} 3a + b + c = 7 \\ a + 3b - c = 13 \\ b = 2a - 1 \end{cases}$

23. $\begin{cases} 5r - 4s - 3t = 3 \\ t = s + r \\ r = 3s + 1 \end{cases}$

24. $\begin{cases} 13 = 3x - y \\ 4y - 3x + 2z = -3 \\ z = 2x - 4y \end{cases}$

25. $\begin{cases} x + 3y - z = -4 \\ 2x - y + 2z = 13 \\ 3x - 2y - z = -9 \end{cases}$

26. $\begin{cases} x - 4y + z = 6 \\ 2x + 5y - z = 7 \\ 2x - y - z = 1 \end{cases}$

27. $\begin{cases} x - y + 2z = 7 \\ 2x + y + z = 8 \\ x - z = 5 \end{cases}$

28. $\begin{cases} x + y + z = 2 \\ x + 2z = 5 \\ 2x + y - z = -1 \end{cases}$

29. $\begin{cases} 5x - y + z = 4 \\ x + 2y - z = 5 \\ 2x + 3y - 3z = 5 \end{cases}$

STEM 30. **Manufacturing** In a factory there are three machines, A, B, and C. When all three machines are working, they produce 287 bolts per hour. When only machines A and C are working, they produce 197 bolts per hour. When only machines A and B are working, they produce 202 bolts per hour. How many bolts can each machine produce per hour?

Ⓑ **Apply** Ⓒ 31. **Think About a Plan** In triangle PQR, the measure of angle Q is three times the measure of angle P. The measure of angle R is 20° more than the measure of angle P. Find the measure of each angle.
- What are the unknowns in this problem?
- What system of equations represents this situation?
- Which method of solving looks easier for this problem?

32. **Sports** A stadium has 49,000 seats. Seats sell for $25 in Section A, $20 in Section B, and $15 in Section C. The number of seats in Section A equals the total number of seats in Sections B and C. Suppose the stadium takes in $1,052,000 from each sold-out event. How many seats does each section hold?

Solve each system using any method.

33. $\begin{cases} x - 3y + 2z = 11 \\ -x + 4y + 3z = 5 \\ 2x - 2y - 4z = 2 \end{cases}$

34. $\begin{cases} x + 2y + z = 4 \\ 2x - y + 4z = -8 \\ -3x + y - 2z = -1 \end{cases}$

35. $\begin{cases} 4x - y + 2z = -6 \\ -2x + 3y - z = 8 \\ 2y + 3z = -5 \end{cases}$

36. $\begin{cases} 4a + 2b + c = 2 \\ 5a - 3b + 2c = 17 \\ a - 5b = 3 \end{cases}$

37. $\begin{cases} 4x - 2y + 5z = 6 \\ 3x + 3y + 8z = 4 \\ x - 5y - 3z = 5 \end{cases}$

38. $\begin{cases} 2\ell + 2w + h = 72 \\ \ell = 3w \\ h = 2w \end{cases}$

39. $\begin{cases} 6x + y - 4z = -8 \\ \frac{y}{4} - \frac{z}{6} = 0 \\ 2x - z = -2 \end{cases}$

40. $\begin{cases} 4y + 2x = 6 - 3z \\ x + z - 2y = -5 \\ x - 2z = 3y - 7 \end{cases}$

41. $\begin{cases} 4x - y + z = -5 \\ -x + y - z = 5 \\ 2x - z - 1 = y \end{cases}$

42. **Finance** A worker received a $10,000 bonus and decided to split it among three different accounts. He placed part in a savings account paying 4.5% per year, twice as much in government bonds paying 5%, and the rest in a mutual fund that returned 4%. His income from these investments after one year was $455. How much did the worker place in each account?

Answers

Practice and Problem-Solving Exercises
(continued)

21. $(8, -4, 2)$

22. $(2, 3, -2)$

23. $(-2, -1, -3)$

24. $(5, 2, 2)$

25. $(0, 1, 7)$

26. $(4, 1, 6)$

27. $(5, -2, 0)$

28. $(1, -1, 2)$

29. $(1, 3, 2)$

30. Machine A: 112 bolts per hour; Machine B: 90 bolts per hour; Machine C: 85 bolts per hour

31. $m\angle P = 32°$; $m\angle Q = 96°$; $m\angle R = 52°$

32. Section A has 24,500 seats; Section B has 14,400 seats; and Section C has 10,100 seats.

33. $(8, 1, 3)$

34. $(3, 2, -3)$

35. $\left(\frac{1}{2}, 2, -3\right)$

36. $(-2, -1, 12)$

37. no solution

38. $(21.6, 7.2, 14.4)$

39. $(2, 4, 6)$

40. $(-1, 2, 0)$

41. $(0, 2, -3)$

42. He placed $2200 in the savings account, $4400 in government bonds, and $3400 in the mutual fund.

 **Challenge**

43. Open-Ended Write your own system with three variables. Begin by choosing the solution. Then write three equations that are true for your solution. Use elimination to solve the system.

44. Geometry Refer to the regular five-pointed star at the right. Write and solve a system of three equations to find the measure of each labeled angle.

45. Geometry In the regular polyhedron described below, all faces are congruent polygons. Use a system of three linear equations to find the numbers of vertices, edges, and faces.

Every face has five edges and every edge is shared by two faces. Every face has five vertices and every vertex is shared by three faces. The sum of the number of vertices and faces is two more than the number of edges.

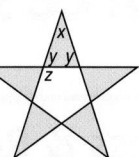

Apply What You've Learned

 **MATHEMATICAL PRACTICES**
MP 4

In the Apply What You've Learned section in Lesson 3-2, you represented some of the criteria given on page 133 using equations in three variables. Now, you will create another equation needed to solve the problem. Choose from the following words and equations to complete the sentences below.

multiply	substitution	three
a graph	divide	two
$\frac{x}{3} + \frac{y}{20} + \frac{z}{10} = 2$	elimination	$x + y + z = 28$

a. If a distance traveled is given in *miles*, then you should ? by the rate in *miles per hour* to find the time traveled in *hours*.

b. To create a system of equations in three variables that you can solve, you need to write at least ? equations.

c. The equation ? models the time in hours each section of the triathlon takes an elite athlete to complete.

---

43. Answers may vary. Sample: Solution is (1, 2, 3).
$$\begin{cases} x + y + z = 6 \\ 2x - y + 2z = 6 \\ 3x + 3y + z = 12 \end{cases}$$

44. $\begin{cases} x + 2y = 180 \\ y + z = 180 \\ 5z = 540 \end{cases}$

Solution is $x = 36$, $y = 72$, $z = 108$

45. Let *E*, *F*, and *V* represent the number of edges, faces, and vertices, respectively. From the first statement, $E = \frac{5}{2}F$. From the second statement, $V = \frac{5}{3}F$. From the third statement, $V + F = E + 2$. Solving this system of 3 equations yields $E = 30$, $F = 12$, and $V = 20$.

 Apply What You've Learned
In the Apply What You've Learned section in Lesson 3-2, students represented two of the criteria given on page 133 using equations in three variables. Now, they will create the third equation needed to solve the problem.

 Mathematical Practices
Students complete their **model** of the situation by identifying the equation that represents the time for an elite athlete to complete the triathlon. (MP 4)

ANSWERS
a. divide
b. three
c. $\frac{x}{3} + \frac{y}{20} + \frac{z}{10} = 2$

Lesson Resources

Differentiated Remediation

Additional Instructional Support

Algebra 2 Companion

Students can use the **Algebra 2 Companion** worktext (4 pages) as you teach the lesson. Use the Companion to support

- New Vocabulary
- Key Concepts
- Got It for each Problem
- Lesson Check

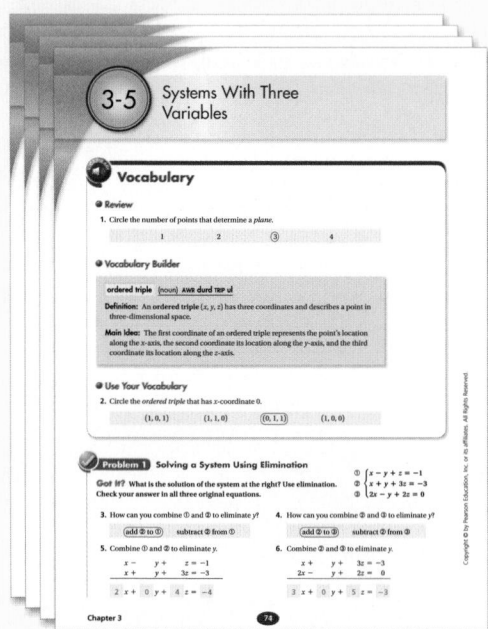

ELL Support

Focus on Communication Write the system below on a transparency including 1s for "missing" coefficients. Place another transparency on top to write on. Draw an oval to enclose the *x*-column and state the numbers. Move the oval from column to column, stating the coefficients in each column. Ask which coefficients add up to zero. Keep the oval on the *z*-column and say: 1 and −1 are opposites. I will eliminate *z*.

$$2x - 1y + 1z = 4$$
$$1x + 3y - 1z = 11$$
$$4x + 2y - 1z = 14$$

5 Assess & Remediate

Lesson Quiz

1. What is the solution of the system? Use elimination.

$$\begin{cases} x + y - 3z = -8 \\ -x - 2y + z = 4 \\ -x + y + 4z = 7 \end{cases}$$

2. What is the solution of the system? Use elimination.

$$\begin{cases} 2x + 2y + z = 7 \\ -x - y + z = -5 \\ x + 3y - 4z = 12 \end{cases}$$

3. What is the *x*-value in the solution of the system?

$$\begin{cases} x - 3y + 2z = 14 \\ 3x - 2z = 7 \\ 2x - y = 9 \end{cases}$$

4. Do you UNDERSTAND? You manage a health food store and budget $80 to buy ingredients to make 30 pounds of trail mix. Peanuts cost $2.50 per pound, raisins cost $2.00 per pound, and granola costs $4.00 per pound. If you use twice as many pounds of peanuts as raisins, how many pounds of each ingredient should you buy?

ANSWERS TO LESSON QUIZ

1. $(3, -2, 3)$

2. $(2, 2, -1)$

3. 3

4. 16 lb of peanuts, 8 lb of raisins, 6 lb of granola

PRESCRIPTION FOR REMEDIATION

Use the student work on the Lesson Quiz to prescribe a differentiated review assignment:

Points	Differentiated Remediation
0–2	Intervention
3	On-level
4	Extension

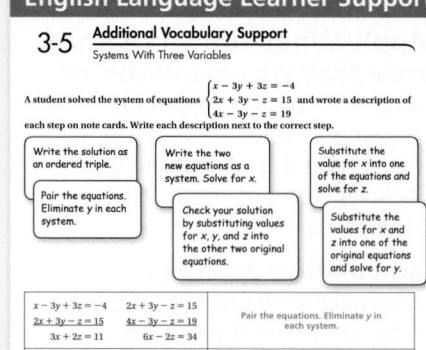

PowerAlgebra.com

5 Assess & Remediate

Assign the Lesson Quiz. Appropriate intervention, practice, or enrichment is automatically generated based on student performance.

Intervention

- **Reteaching** (2 pages) Provides reteaching and practice exercises for the key lesson concepts. Use with struggling students or absent students.
- **English Language Learner Support** Helps students develop and reinforce mathematical vocabulary and key concepts.

All-in-One Resources/Online
Reteaching

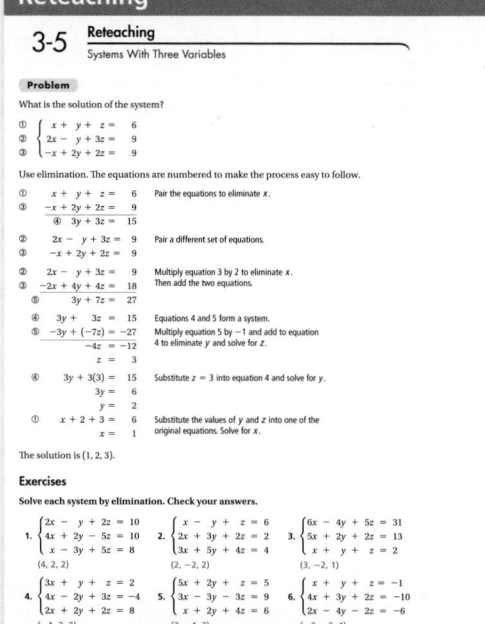

Differentiated Remediation *continued*

On-Level

- **Practice** (2 pages) Provides extra practice for each lesson. For simpler practice exercises, use the Form K Practice pages found in the All-in-One Teaching Resources and online.

- **Think About a Plan** Helps students develop specific problem-solving skills and strategies by providing scaffolded guiding questions.

- **Standardized Test Prep** Focuses on all major exercises, all major question types, and helps students prepare for the high-stakes assessments.

Extension

- **Enrichment** Provides students with interesting problems and activities that extend the concepts of the lesson.

- **Activities, Games, and Puzzles** Worksheets that can be used for concepts development, enrichment, and for fun!

Practice and Problem Solving Wkbk/All-in-One Resources/Online
Practice page 1

3-5 Practice *Form G*
Systems With Three Variables

Solve each system by elimination. Check your answers.

Practice and Problem Solving Wkbk/All-in-One Resources/Online
Practice page 2

3-5 Practice (continued) *Form G*
Systems With Three Variables

Write and solve a system of equations for each problem.

All-in-One Resources/Online
Enrichment

3-5 Enrichment
Systems With Three Variables

The Italian Navigator Has Landed

The above phrase was one of the most important coded messages that has ever been sent. It referred to the fact that a team of physicists had managed to achieve the first successful controlled nuclear chain reaction. The physicist who directed these efforts was an accomplished theorist and experimenter, whose work in producing artificial radioactive elements won him the Nobel Prize in Physics in 1938.

E	N	R	I	C	O			F	E	R	M	I
1	2	3	4	5	6	7	8	9	10	11	12

First solve each of the following sets of equations. For each letter with a value between 1 and 12, write that letter in its corresponding location in the puzzle.

Practice and Problem Solving Wkbk/All-in-One Resources/Online
Think About a Plan

3-5 Think About a Plan
Systems With Three Variables

Sports A stadium has 49,000 seats. Seats sell for $25 in Section A, $20 in Section B, and $15 in Section C. The number of seats in Section A equals the total number of seats in Sections B and C. Suppose the stadium takes in $1,052,000 from each sold-out event. How many seats does each section hold?

Understanding the Problem

1. Define a variable for each unknown in this problem.
Let $x =$ the number of seats in Section A
Let $y =$ the number of seats in Section B
Let $z =$ the number of seats in Section C

2. What system of equations represents this situation?
$x + y + z = 49,000$
$x = y + z$
$25x + 20y + 15z = 1,052,000$

Planning the Solution

3. Can you write a simpler equivalent equation for one of the equations in your system? If so, write the equivalent equation.
yes; $5x + 4y + 3z = 210,400$

4. What method of solving looks easier for this problem? Explain.
Answers may vary. Sample: Substitution; one of the equations is already solved for x.

Getting an Answer

5. Solve the system of equations.
$(24,500, 14,400, 10,100)$

6. How can you interpret the solution in the context of the problem?
Section A holds 24,500 seats, Section B holds 14,400 seats, and Section C holds 10,100 seats.

Practice and Problem Solving Wkbk/All-in-One Resources/Online
Standardized Test Prep

3-5 Standardized Test Prep
Systems With Three Variables

Gridded Response

Solve each exercise and enter your answer in the grid provided.

1. A change machine contains nickels, dimes, and quarters. There are 75 coins in the machine, and the value of the coins is $7.25. There are 5 times as many nickels as dimes. How many quarters are in the machine?

2. The sum of three numbers is 23. The first number is equal to twice the second number minus 7. The third number is equal to one more than the sum of the first and second numbers. What is the first number?

3. A fish's tail weighs 9 lb. Its head weighs as much as its tail plus half its body. Its body weighs as much as its head and tail. How many pounds does the fish weigh?

4. You are training for a triathlon. In your training routine each week, you bike 5 times as far as you run and you run 4 times as far as you swim. One week you trained a total of 200 miles. How many miles did you swim that week?

5. Three multiplied by the first number is equal to the second number plus 4. The second number is equal to one plus two multiplied by the third number. The third number is one less than the first number. What is the sum of all three numbers?

Answers

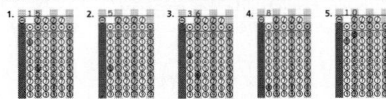

Online Teacher Resource Center
Activities, Games, and Puzzles

3-5 Activity: Writing Systems
Systems With Three Variables

This activity is for groups of three students. Your teacher will determine whether you can use your calculator.

Activity

- Each group makes four systems of equations with three variables.

Rules

- All equations must have integer coefficients between -6 and 6.
- Not all coefficients can be 1 or -1.
- At most, one coefficient can be 0.
- No equation is a constant multiple of the other.

Phase 1
Each group member writes one equation according to the rules above. The group works together to solve the system that the three equations form.

Check students' work.

Phase 2
Each group member writes one equation according to the rules above. Each member works separately to solve the system that the three equations form.

Check students' work.

Phase 3
The group members write one equation according to the rules above. Then the group finds two more equations to make a system of three equations that has an infinite number of solutions. The two additional equations may violate one of the rules above.

Check students' work.

Phase 4
Two group members each write one equation according to the rules above. Then the group finds a third equation to make a system of three equations that has no solution.

Check students' work.

1 Interactive Learning

Solve It!

PURPOSE To prepare students to use matrices to solve a system of linear equations

PROCESS Students may

- use Rule 1 to obtain a 1 in row 2, column 2.
- replace the eights in column 2 by using the 1 from the previous step and both rules.
- obtain a 1 in row 3, column 3 using Rule 1.
- replace the 2 in column 3 by using the 1 from the previous step and both rules.

FACILITATE

Q Examine the game array. What numbers from Figure 1 must you change to match Figure 2? **[You must change all of the numbers in column 2, and the numbers in rows 1 and 3 of column 3.]**

Q Examine column 2. What math operation would be used to change a 4 to a 1? **[Multiply 4 by its reciprocal, $\frac{1}{4}$ (Rule 1).]**

Q How would we use that 1 to change the eights to zeros? **[Multiply row 2 by -8 and add the result to row 1 and then row 3 (Rule 2).]**

Q What steps would you use on column 3 to change it to a 0,0,1? **[Multiply row 3 by $\frac{1}{2}$ (Rule 1), then multiply row 3 by -2 and add the result to row 1 (Rule 2).]**

ANSWER See Solve It in Answers on next page.

CONNECT THE MATH In the Solve It, the "Game Rules" used to solve the puzzle are actually matrix row operations. In the lesson, students use row operations to solve systems of linear equations expressed as matrices.

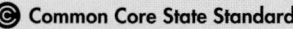

Common Core State Standards

A-REI.C.8 Represent a system of linear equations as a single matrix equation in a vector variable.

MP 1, MP 2, MP 3, MP 5

Objectives To represent a system of linear equations with a matrix
To solve a system of linear equations using matrices

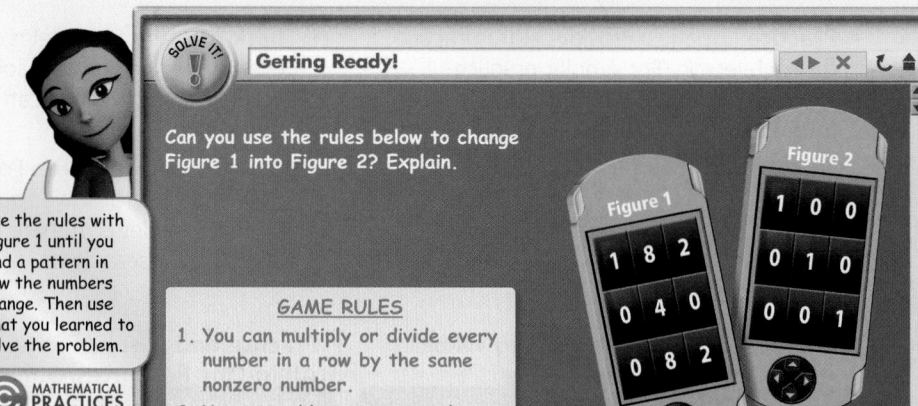

Use the rules with Figure 1 until you find a pattern in how the numbers change. Then use what you learned to solve the problem.

MATHEMATICAL PRACTICES

Lesson Vocabulary
- matrix
- matrix element
- row operation

An array of numbers, such as each of those suggested by the tile arrangements in the Solve It, is a matrix.

Essential Understanding You can use a *matrix* to represent and solve a system of equations without writing the variables.

A **matrix** is a rectangular array of numbers. You usually display the array within brackets. The dimensions of a matrix are the numbers of rows and columns in the array.

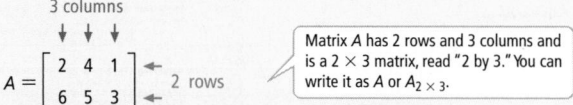

3 columns

$$A = \begin{bmatrix} 2 & 4 & 1 \\ 6 & 5 & 3 \end{bmatrix} \leftarrow 2 \text{ rows}$$

Matrix A has 2 rows and 3 columns and is a 2×3 matrix, read "2 by 3." You can write it as A or $A_{2 \times 3}$.

Each number in a matrix is a **matrix element**. You can identify a matrix element by its row and column numbers. In matrix A, a_{12} is the element in row 1 and column 2. a_{12} is the element 4.

3-6 Preparing to Teach

BIG idea Solving Equations and Inequalities

ESSENTIAL UNDERSTANDINGS

- Matrices can be used to represent and solve a system of equations without writing the variables.
- The matrix row operations of adding rows and multiplying by a constant are equivalent to the addition and multiplication properties of equality.

Math Background

Students have solved systems of linear equations by graphing and by applying the algebraic methods of substitution and elimination. In this lesson, students solve systems of equations using matrices.

Students must recognize that they are solving systems of equations when they use matrix operations. It may help if you relate the row operations to the steps in substitution and elimination.

Matrices have many applications including data storage and computer programming; solving systems of equations is one of these applications.

Emphasize that the order of the elements is important and that every row and column must have an entry. All coefficients are represented in the matrix, including zeros and ones.

Mathematical Practices

Reason abstractly and quantitatively.
Students will flexibly use the basic operations in solving systems using matrices. They will also look for general methods and shortcuts to matrix calculations.

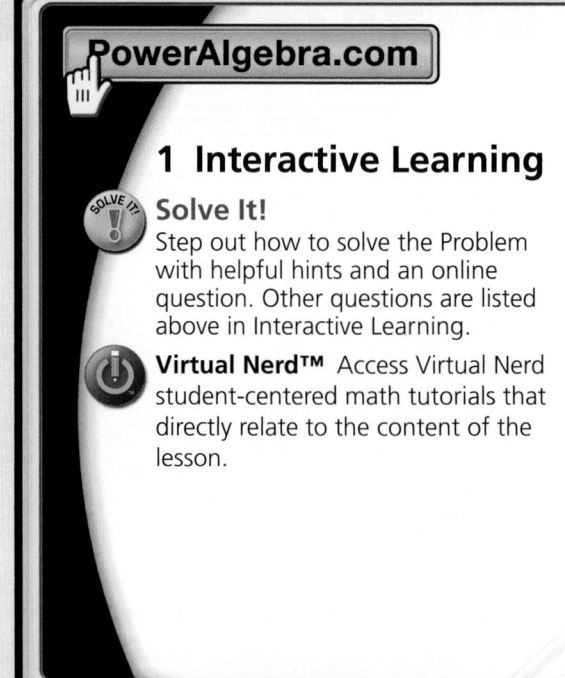

PowerAlgebra.com

1 Interactive Learning

Solve It!
Step out how to solve the Problem with helpful hints and an online question. Other questions are listed above in Interactive Learning.

Virtual Nerd™ Access Virtual Nerd student-centered math tutorials that directly relate to the content of the lesson.

Think

Does the order of the subscript in a_{23} matter?

Yes. a_{23} and a_{32} are different elements.

Problem 1 Identifying a Matrix Element

GRIDDED RESPONSE

What is element a_{23} in matrix A?

$$A = \begin{bmatrix} 4 & -9 & 17 & 1 \\ 0 & 5 & 8 & 6 \\ -3 & -2 & 10 & 0 \end{bmatrix}$$

A_{23} is in Row 2 and Column 3.

a_{23} is 8.

Got It? 1. What is element a_{13} in matrix A?

You can represent a system of equations efficiently with a matrix. Each matrix row represents an equation. The last matrix column shows the constants to the right of the equal signs. Each of the other columns shows the coefficients of one of the variables.

System of Equations

$$\begin{array}{rcrcr} x & + & 3y & = & 7 \\ 3x & + & y & = & -8 \end{array}$$

x-coefficients   *y*-coefficients   constants

Matrix

$$\begin{bmatrix} 1 & 3 & 7 \\ 3 & 1 & -8 \end{bmatrix}$$

The 1's are coefficients of x and y.

Draw a vertical bar to replace the equal signs and separate the coefficients from the constants.

Think

Why is the order of elements important in a matrix?

Different orders of elements could correspond to different systems of equations.

Problem 2 Representing Systems With Matrices

How can you represent the system of equations with a matrix?

A $\begin{cases} 2x + y = 9 \\ x - 6y = -1 \end{cases}$

The matrix $\begin{bmatrix} 2 & 1 & 9 \\ 1 & -6 & -1 \end{bmatrix}$ represents the system above.

B $\begin{cases} x - 3y + z = 6 \\ x + 3z = 12 \\ y = -5x + 1 \end{cases}$

Step 1 Write each equation in the same variable order. Line up the variables. Leave space where a coefficient is 0.

$$\begin{cases} x - 3y + z = 6 \\ x \quad\quad + 3z = 12 \\ 5x + y \quad\quad = 1 \end{cases}$$

Step 2 Write the matrix using the coefficients and constants. Notice the 1's and 0's.

$$\begin{bmatrix} 1 & -3 & 1 & 6 \\ 1 & 0 & 3 & 12 \\ 5 & 1 & 0 & 1 \end{bmatrix}$$

PowerAlgebra.com   **Lesson 3-6** Solving Systems Using Matrices   **175**

---

2 Guided Instruction

Problem 1   SYNTHESIZING

The notation is used to identify a particular element in a matrix.

Q Which is listed first: row or column? **[Row always comes before column.]**

Got It?   EXTENSION

Ask students to identify all remaining matrix elements by their positions.

Problem 2   ERROR PREVENTION

Students must be able to write a system of equations in matrix form in order to solve the system by matrices.

Q Why must a zero be included in a matrix that represents an equation that is missing a variable? Explain. **[A zero means that a coefficient is zero. If the zero was not included, the matrix would be missing a number.]**

Q Does the matrix $\begin{bmatrix} 1 & -6 & -1 \\ 2 & 1 & 9 \end{bmatrix}$ represent the system in 2A? Why or why not? **[Yes. The rows represent equations. It does not matter which row is first.]**

---

2 Guided Instruction

Each Problem is worked out and supported in the Student Online Center.

Problem 1
Identifying a Matrix Element

Problem 2
Representing a System With a Matrix
Animated

Problem 3
Writing a System from a Matrix
Animated

Problem 4
Solving a System Using a Matrix
Animated

Problem 5
Using a Calculator to Solve a Linear System

Support in Algebra 2 Companion
• Vocabulary
• Key Concepts
• Got It?

Answers

Solve It!

Yes; multiply row 3 by −1. and add it to row 1. Multiply row 2 by 2 and add it to row 3. Divide row 2 by 8 and row 3 by −2.

Got It?

1. 17

Got It?

ERROR PREVENTION

Make sure the students write the third equation in 2b in standard form. A space must be left where a coefficient is zero in the second and third equations. Once the new system is written, represent it as a matrix.

Problem 3

SYNTHESIZING

Students must be comfortable with representing matrices as systems and understand that matrices can represent many things, such as an inventory of different products at several different retail stores.

Q What does each row represent? **[Each row represents a linear equation.]**

Q What does each column represent? **[The columns before the | represent the coefficients of the variables. The column after | represents the constants.]**

Got It?

ERROR PREVENTION

Before you write the linear system, count the columns to determine the number of variables. Insert variables in alphabetical order, taking note of any zeros.

Take Note

SYNTHESIZING

The row operations are the only legal operations that can be used to change a matrix to the indicated form.

 Got It? 2. How can you represent the system of equations with a matrix?

a. $\begin{cases} -4x - 2y = 7 \\ 3x + y = -5 \end{cases}$

b. $\begin{cases} 4x - y + 2z = 1 \\ y + 5z = 20 \\ 2x = -y + 7 \end{cases}$

Problem 3 Writing a System From a Matrix

What linear system of equations does this matrix represent? $\begin{bmatrix} 5 & 2 & | & 7 \\ 0 & 1 & | & 9 \end{bmatrix}$

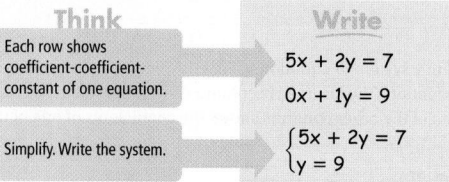

Think

Each row shows coefficient-coefficient-constant of one equation.

Write

$5x + 2y = 7$
$0x + 1y = 9$

Simplify. Write the system.

$\begin{cases} 5x + 2y = 7 \\ y = 9 \end{cases}$

Got It? 3. What linear system does $\begin{bmatrix} 2 & 0 & | & 6 \\ 5 & -2 & | & 1 \end{bmatrix}$ represent?

You can use a matrix that represents a system of equations to solve the system. In this way, you do not have to write the variables. To solve the system using the matrix, use the steps for solving by elimination. Each step is a **row operation**.

Your goal is to use row operations to get a matrix in the form $\begin{bmatrix} 1 & 0 & | & a \\ 0 & 1 & | & b \end{bmatrix}$ or $\begin{bmatrix} 1 & 0 & 0 & | & a \\ 0 & 1 & 0 & | & b \\ 0 & 0 & 1 & | & c \end{bmatrix}$

Notice that the first matrix represents the system $x = a, y = b$, which then will be the solution of a system of two equations in two unknowns. The second matrix represents the system $x = a, y = b$, and $z = c$.

take note

| **Key Concept** | **Row Operations** |

Switch any two rows. $\begin{bmatrix} 2 & -1 & 3 \\ 3 & 2 & 5 \end{bmatrix}$ becomes $\begin{bmatrix} 3 & 2 & 5 \\ 2 & -1 & 3 \end{bmatrix}$

Multiply a row by a constant. $\begin{bmatrix} 3 & 2 & 5 \\ 2 & -1 & 3 \end{bmatrix}$ becomes $\begin{bmatrix} 3 & 2 & 5 \\ 2 \cdot 2 & -1 \cdot 2 & 3 \cdot 2 \end{bmatrix} = \begin{bmatrix} 3 & 2 & 5 \\ 4 & -2 & 6 \end{bmatrix}$

Add one row to another. $\begin{bmatrix} 3 & 2 & 5 \\ 4 & -2 & 6 \end{bmatrix}$ becomes $\begin{bmatrix} 3+4 & 2-2 & 5+6 \\ 4 & -2 & 6 \end{bmatrix} = \begin{bmatrix} 7 & 0 & 11 \\ 4 & -2 & 6 \end{bmatrix}$

Combine any of these steps.

Additional Problems

1. What is m_{12} in matrix M?

$M = \begin{bmatrix} 8 & 7 & 4 \\ 2 & 0 & 5 \end{bmatrix}$

ANSWER 7

2. How do you represent the system of equations

$\begin{cases} 6x - y = 12 \\ -x + 10y = 1 \end{cases}$ with a matrix?

ANSWER $\begin{bmatrix} 6 & -1 & | & 12 \\ -1 & 10 & | & 1 \end{bmatrix}$

3. What linear system of equations does this matrix represent?

$\begin{bmatrix} -2 & 4 & 9 & | & 0 \\ -1 & 3 & 0 & | & 7 \\ 5 & 1 & 9 & | & 8 \end{bmatrix}$

ANSWER

$\begin{cases} -2x + 4y + 9z = 0 \\ -x + 3y = 7 \\ 5x + y + 9z = 8 \end{cases}$

4. What is the solution of this system?

$\begin{cases} x + 2y = 16 \\ 3x + y = 8 \end{cases}$

ANSWER $(0, 8)$

5. What is the solution of this system of equations? Use your calculator.

$\begin{cases} 3a + 2b - c = 7 \\ 2a - c = 5 \\ a - 4b + c = -4 \end{cases}$

ANSWER $\left(1, \frac{1}{2}, -3\right)$

Think

How is solving a system using row operations similar to using elimination?
You use the same steps but the variables don't appear in the matrices.

Problem 4 Solving a System Using a Matrix

What is the solution of the system? $\begin{cases} x + 4y = -1 \\ 2x + 5y = 4 \end{cases}$

$\begin{bmatrix} 1 & 4 & | & -1 \\ 2 & 5 & | & 4 \end{bmatrix}$

Write the matrix for the system.

$\begin{array}{r} -2 \ (1 \quad 4 \quad -1) \\ + \quad 2 \quad 5 \quad 4 \\ \hline 0 \quad -3 \quad 6 \end{array}$

Multiply Row 1 by -2. Add to Row 2. Replace Row 2 with the sum. Write the new matrix.

$\begin{bmatrix} 1 & 4 & | & -1 \\ 0 & -3 & | & 6 \end{bmatrix}$

$-\frac{1}{3} \ (0 \quad -3 \quad 6) = 0 \quad 1 \quad -2$

Multiply Row 2 by $-\frac{1}{3}$. Write the new matrix.

$\begin{bmatrix} 1 & 4 & | & -1 \\ 0 & 1 & | & -2 \end{bmatrix}$

$\begin{array}{r} 1 \quad 4 \quad -1 \\ + -4 \ (0 \quad 1 \quad -2) \\ \hline 1 \quad 0 \quad 7 \end{array}$

Multiply Row 2 by -4. Add to Row 1. Replace Row 1 with the sum. Write the new matrix.

$\begin{bmatrix} 1 & 0 & | & 7 \\ 0 & 1 & | & -2 \end{bmatrix}$

The solution to the system is $(7, -2)$.

Check

		Use the original equations.
$x + 4y = -1$	$2x + 5y = 4$	
$7 + 4(-2) \overset{?}{=} -1$	$2(7) + 5(-2) \overset{?}{=} 4$	Substitute.
$7 + (-8) \overset{?}{=} -1$	$14 + (-10) \overset{?}{=} 4$	Multiply.
$-1 = -1$ ✔	$4 = 4$ ✔	Simplify.

Got It? **4. a.** What is the solution of the system? $\begin{cases} 9x - 2y = 5 \\ 3x + 7y = 17 \end{cases}$

b. Reasoning Which method is more similar to solving a system using row operations: *elimination* or *substitution*? Justify your reasoning.

Matrices that represent the solution of a system are in *reduced row echelon form*. Many calculators have a **rref** (reduced row echelon form) function for working with matrices. This function will do all the row operations for you. You can use **rref** to solve a system of equations.

Problem 4 SYNTHESIZING

Q What is the reasoning behind the first row operation? **[The goal is to get a zero in the first column, second row. When you add the rows after multiplying, the -2 and 2 cancel, yielding a zero in the right place.]**

Q Why can't you multiply a row by 0? **[Multiplying by 0 makes every element in the row 0, eliminating the equation.]**

Q When would it be to your advantage to switch rows? Give an example. **[Answers may vary.**

Sample: Switching rows in $\begin{bmatrix} 0 & 5 & | & 2 \\ 1 & 0 & | & 3 \end{bmatrix}$ produces

$\begin{bmatrix} 1 & 0 & | & 3 \\ 0 & 5 & | & 2 \end{bmatrix}$. It saves time because the first column now contains 1 and 0 in the correct order.]

Got It?

Q What do the matrix row operations have in common with elimination? **[Answers may vary. Sample: In row operations, you can multiply a row by a constant and add rows together. In elimination, you can multiply the coefficients of an equation by a constant and add the coefficients in both equations.]**

Answers

Got It? (continued)

2. a. $\begin{bmatrix} -4 & -2 & | & 7 \\ 3 & 1 & | & -5 \end{bmatrix}$

b. $\begin{bmatrix} 4 & -1 & 2 & | & 1 \\ 0 & 1 & 5 & | & 20 \\ 2 & 1 & 0 & | & 7 \end{bmatrix}$

3. $\begin{cases} 2x = 6 \\ 5x - 2y = 1 \end{cases}$

4. a. $(1, 2)$

b. elimination; you use the same steps to solve

Problem 5
SYNTHESIZING

Students use the calculator matrix method to solve a system of equations.

Q Why is this a 3 × 4 matrix when entered in the calculator? **[The system has 3 equations, which means the matrix has 3 rows. The system has 4 columns because there are 3 variables and 1 column of constants.]**

EXTENSION

Q What is an example of a system of two linear equations with two variables that has no solution? **[Answers may vary. Sample:** $\begin{cases} x + y = 1 \\ x + y = 2 \end{cases}$**]**

Q What happens when you try to solve this as a matrix? **[You get a row that represents a false equation, such as 0 + 0 = 1.]**

Q What is an example of a system of two linear equations in two variables that has infinitely many solutions? **[**$\begin{cases} x + y = 1 \\ x + y = 1 \end{cases}$**]**

Q What happens when you try to solve this as a matrix? **[You get a row that represents an equation that is always true, such as 0 + 0 = 0.]**

Got It?
ELL SUPPORT

Make a list of all of the calculator matrix steps. Check off each step as it is completed.

What is the solution of the system of equations? $\begin{cases} 2a + 3b - c = 1 \\ -4a + 9b + 2c = 8 \\ -2a + 2c = 3 \end{cases}$

Think

How do you enter missing variables into a matrix?
If a variable is not present in an equation, enter its coefficient as 0 in the matrix.

Step 1 Enter the system into a calculator as a matrix.

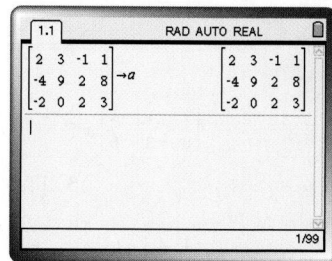

Step 2 Apply the **rref()** function to the matrix. Put the matrix elements in fraction form if some are not integers.

Step 3 List the solution.

The solution of the system is $a = \frac{1}{2}$, $b = \frac{2}{3}$, $c = 2$.

Check

$2a + 3b - c = 1$	$-4a + 9b + 2c = 8$	$-2a + 2c = 3$
$2\left(\frac{1}{2}\right) + 3\left(\frac{2}{3}\right) - 2 \stackrel{?}{=} 1$	$-4\left(\frac{1}{2}\right) + 9\left(\frac{2}{3}\right) + 2(2) \stackrel{?}{=} 8$	$-2\left(\frac{1}{2}\right) + 2(2) \stackrel{?}{=} 3$
$1 + 2 - 2 \stackrel{?}{=} 1$	$-2 + 6 + 4 \stackrel{?}{=} 8$	$-1 + 4 \stackrel{?}{=} 3$
$1 = 1$ ✔	$8 = 8$ ✔	$3 = 3$ ✔

 Got It? **5.** What is the solution of the system of equations?
$\begin{cases} a + 4b + 6c = 21 \\ 2a - 2b + c = 4 \\ -8b + c = -1 \end{cases}$

Answers

Got It? (continued)

5. $\left(1, \frac{1}{2}, 3\right)$

Lesson Check

1. 2×1

2. 2×4

3. $\begin{bmatrix} 3 & 5 & | & 0 \\ 1 & 1 & | & 2 \end{bmatrix}$

4. $\begin{bmatrix} 1 & 3 & -1 & | & 2 \\ 1 & 0 & 2 & | & 8 \\ 0 & 2 & -1 & | & 1 \end{bmatrix}$

5. 16

6. a_{21} is 0, the element in row 2, column 1. a_{12} is −9, the element in row 1 and column 2.

7. Answers may vary. Sample: The entry fee to a school play is $2 for adults. Jamie paid a total of $8 for 4 student entry fees and 2 adult entry fees. What is the student entry fee?

Lesson Check

Do you know HOW?

State the dimensions of each matrix.

1. $\begin{bmatrix} 2 \\ 5 \end{bmatrix}$

2. $\begin{bmatrix} 6 & 9 & 0 & 3 \\ 4 & 6 & 2 & 7 \end{bmatrix}$

Write a matrix to represent each system.

3. $\begin{cases} 3a + 5b = 0 \\ a + b = 2 \end{cases}$

4. $\begin{cases} x + 3y - z = 2 \\ x + 2z = 8 \\ 2y - z = 1 \end{cases}$

Do you UNDERSTAND?  MATHEMATICAL PRACTICES

5. How many elements are in a 4×4 matrix?

6. Writing Using Matrix A in Problem 1, describe the difference in identifying element a_{21} and element a_{12}.

7. Open-Ended Write a situation that can be modeled by the matrix. $\begin{bmatrix} 4 & 2 & 8 \\ 0 & 1 & 2 \end{bmatrix}$

Practice and Problem-Solving Exercises  MATHEMATICAL PRACTICES

A Practice

Identify the indicated element. $A = \begin{bmatrix} 3 & 12 & 6 \\ 1 & 0 & 9 \\ 8 & 7 & 4 \end{bmatrix}$ ◀ See Problem 1.

8. a_{32} **9.** a_{21} **10.** a_{13} **11.** a_{31}

Write a matrix to represent each system.   ◀ See Problem 2.

12. $\begin{cases} x + 2y = 11 \\ 2x + 3y = 18 \end{cases}$

13. $\begin{cases} 3x + 2y = 16 \\ y = 5 \end{cases}$

14. $\begin{cases} 2a - 3b = 6 \\ a + b = 2 \end{cases}$

15. $\begin{cases} r - s + t = 150 \\ 2r + t = 425 \\ s + 3t = 0 \end{cases}$

16. $\begin{cases} y = 3x - 7 \\ x = 2 \end{cases}$

17. $\begin{cases} x - y + z = 0 \\ x - 2y - z = 5 \\ 2x - y + 2z = 8 \end{cases}$

Write the system of equations represented by each matrix.   ◀ See Problem 3.

18. $\begin{bmatrix} 1 & 0 & 4 \\ 0 & 1 & -6 \end{bmatrix}$

19. $\begin{bmatrix} 5 & 1 & -3 \\ -2 & 2 & 4 \end{bmatrix}$

20. $\begin{bmatrix} -1 & 2 & -6 \\ 1 & 1 & 7 \end{bmatrix}$

21. $\begin{bmatrix} 2 & 1 & 1 & 1 \\ 1 & 1 & 1 & 2 \\ 1 & -1 & 1 & -2 \end{bmatrix}$

22. $\begin{bmatrix} 0 & 1 & 2 & 4 \\ -2 & 3 & 6 & 9 \\ 1 & 0 & 1 & 3 \end{bmatrix}$

23. $\begin{bmatrix} 5 & 2 & 1 & 5 \\ 4 & 1 & 2 & 8 \\ 1 & 3 & -6 & 2 \end{bmatrix}$

Solve the system of equations using a matrix.   ◀ See Problems 4 and 5.

24. $\begin{cases} x + 3y = 5 \\ x + 4y = 6 \end{cases}$

25. $\begin{cases} p - 3q = -1 \\ -5p + 16q = 5 \end{cases}$

26. $\begin{cases} 300x - y = 130 \\ 200x + y = 120 \end{cases}$

27. $\begin{cases} x + 3y = 22 \\ 2x - y = 2 \end{cases}$

28. $\begin{cases} x + 3y = 6 \\ 2x + 4y = 12 \end{cases}$

29. $\begin{cases} x + y = 5 \\ -2x + 4y = 8 \end{cases}$

---

3 Lesson Check

Do you know HOW?   **ERROR INTERVENTION**

- For Exercise 4, if students forget to place the zeros where the coefficient is zero, review Problem 2B.

Do you UNDERSTAND?

- For Exercise 7, if students have trouble coming up with ideas, have them first try writing the matrix as a linear system.

Close

> **Q** Why use matrices to solve systems of equations? **[Answers may vary. Sample: The matrix method can be used for any size system. Row operations can be done quickly. Calculators can be used for large systems.]**

Practice and Problem-Solving Exercises

8. 7   **9.** 1
10. 6   **11.** 8

12. $\begin{bmatrix} 1 & 2 & 11 \\ 2 & 3 & 18 \end{bmatrix}$ **13.** $\begin{bmatrix} 3 & 2 & 16 \\ 0 & 1 & 5 \end{bmatrix}$

14. $\begin{bmatrix} 2 & -3 & 6 \\ 1 & 1 & 2 \end{bmatrix}$

15. $\begin{bmatrix} 1 & -1 & 1 & 150 \\ 2 & 0 & 1 & 425 \\ 0 & 1 & 3 & 0 \end{bmatrix}$

16. $\begin{bmatrix} -3 & 1 & -7 \\ 1 & 0 & 2 \end{bmatrix}$

17. $\begin{bmatrix} 1 & -1 & 1 & 0 \\ 1 & -2 & -1 & 5 \\ 2 & -1 & 2 & 8 \end{bmatrix}$

18. $\begin{cases} x = 4 \\ y = -6 \end{cases}$

19. $\begin{cases} 5x + y = -3 \\ -2x + 2y = 4 \end{cases}$

20. $\begin{cases} -x + 2y = -6 \\ x + y = 7 \end{cases}$

21. $\begin{cases} 2x + y + z = 1 \\ x + y + z = 2 \\ x - y + z = -2 \end{cases}$

22. $\begin{cases} y + 2z = 4 \\ -2x + 3y + 6z = 9 \\ x + z = 3 \end{cases}$

23. $\begin{cases} 5x + 2y + z = 5 \\ 4x + y + 2z = 8 \\ x + 3y - 6z = 2 \end{cases}$

24. $(2, 1)$ **25.** $(-1, 0)$
26. $\left(\frac{1}{2}, 20\right)$ **27.** $(4, 6)$
28. $(6, 0)$ **29.** $(2, 3)$

3 Lesson Check

For a digital lesson check, use the Got It questions.

Support in Algebra 2 Companion
- Lesson Check

4 Practice

Assign homework to individual students or to an entire class.

4 Practice

ASSIGNMENT GUIDE

Basic: 8–32, 39–41

Average: 9–29 odd, 30–41

Advanced: 9–29 odd, 30–47

Standardized Test Prep: 48–50

Mixed Review: 51–58

© **Mathematical Practices** are supported by exercises with red headings. Here are the Practices supported in this lesson:

MP 1: Make Sense of Problems Ex. 31

MP 2: Reason Abstractly Ex. 7, 42–44

MP 3: Communicate Ex. 6, 38

MP 3: Critique the Reasoning of Others Ex. 40

MP 5: Use Appropriate Tools Ex. 32–37

Applications exercises have blue headings.

EXERCISE 41: Use the Think About a Plan worksheet in the **Practice and Problem Solving Workbook** (also available in the Teaching Resources in print and online) to further support students' development in becoming independent learners.

HOMEWORK QUICK CHECK

To check students' understanding of key skills and concepts, go over Exercises 15, 25, 31, 40, and 41.

B Apply

30. Business A manufacturer sells pencils and erasers in packages. The price of a package of five erasers and two pencils is \$.23. The price of a package of seven erasers and five pencils is \$.41. Write a system of equations to represent this situation. Then write a matrix to represent the system.

© **31. Think About a Plan** Last year your town invested a total of \$25,000 into two separate funds. The return on one fund was 4% and the return on the other was 6%. If the town earned a total of \$1300 in interest, how much money was invested in each fund?
- What variables will you use? What will they represent?
- What equations can you write to model this situation?
- How can you use a matrix to solve this system?

 Graphing Calculator Solve each system.

32. $\begin{cases} x + y + z = 2 \\ 2y - 2z = 2 \\ x - 3z = 1 \end{cases}$

33. $\begin{cases} x - y + z = 3 \\ x + 3z = 6 \\ y - 2z = -1 \end{cases}$

34. $\begin{cases} x + y + z = -1 \\ 3x + 4y - z = 8 \\ 6x + 8y - 2z = 16 \end{cases}$

35. $\begin{cases} x - y + 3z = 9 \\ x + 2z = 3 \\ 2x + 2y + z = 10 \end{cases}$

36. $\begin{cases} 2x + 3y + z = 13 \\ 5x - 2y - 4z = 7 \\ 4x + 5y + 3z = 25 \end{cases}$

37. $\begin{cases} -2w + x + y = 0 \\ -w + 2x - y + z = 1 \\ -2w + 3x + 3y + 2z = 6 \\ w + x + 2y + z = 5 \end{cases}$

© **38. Snacks** Suppose you want to fill nine 1-lb tins with a snack mix. You have \$15 and plan to buy almonds for \$2.45 per lb, hazelnuts for \$1.85 per lb, and raisins for \$.80 per lb. You want the mix to contain an equal amount of almonds and hazelnuts and twice as much of the nuts as the raisins by weight.
   a. Writing Explain how each equation to the right relates to the problem. What does each variable represent?
   b. Solve the system.
   c. How many of each ingredient should you buy?

$\begin{cases} x + y + z = 9 \\ 2.45x + 1.85y + 0.8z = 15 \\ x + y = 2z \end{cases}$

39. Geometry The coordinates (x, y) of a point in a plane are the solution of the system $\begin{cases} 2x + 3y = 13 \\ 5x + 7y = 31 \end{cases}$. Find the coordinates of the point.

© **40. Error Analysis** A classmate writes the matrix at the right to represent a system and says that the solution is $x = 2, y = 0$. Explain your classmate's error and describe how to correct it.

$\begin{bmatrix} 1 & 0 & 2 \\ 0 & 0 & 0 \end{bmatrix}$

41. Paint A hardware store mixes paints in a ratio of two parts red to six parts yellow to make two gallons of pumpkin orange. A ratio of five parts red to three parts yellow makes two gallons of pepper red. A gallon of pumpkin orange sells for \$25, and a gallon of pepper red sells for \$28. Find the cost of 1 quart of red paint and the cost of 1 quart of yellow paint.

180 **Chapter 3** Linear Systems

Answers

Practice and Problem-Solving Exercises (continued)

30. $\begin{cases} 5e + 2p = 0.23 \\ 7e + 5p = 0.41 \end{cases}$

$\begin{bmatrix} 5 & 2 & | & 0.23 \\ 7 & 5 & | & 0.41 \end{bmatrix}$

31. \$10,000 at 4% and \$15,000 at 6%
Let x = amount invested at 4% and y = amount invested at 6%.

$\begin{cases} x + y = 25,000 \\ 0.04x + 0.06y = 1300 \end{cases}$

$\begin{bmatrix} 1 & 1 & | & 25000 \\ 0.04 & 0.06 & | & 1300 \end{bmatrix} = \begin{bmatrix} 1 & 0 & | & 10000 \\ 0 & 1 & | & 15000 \end{bmatrix}$

32. $(1, 1, 0)$

33. $(3, 1, 1)$

34. no unique solution

35. $(35, -22, -16)$

36. $(3, 2, 1)$

37. $(1, 1, 1, 1)$

38. a. Let x = weight of almonds at \$2.45/lb, y = weight of hazelnuts at \$1.85/lb and z = weight of raisins at \$0.80/lb

$x + y + z = 9$; the total weight of the nuts and raisins is 9 lbs

$2.45x + 1.85y + 0.80z = 15$; the total cost of the nuts and raisins is \$15

$x + y = 2z$; twice as much of the nuts as the raisins by weight or the total weight of the nuts is equal to twice the weight of the raisins

b. $(2.5, 3.5, 3)$

c. 2.5 lbs almonds, 3.5 lbs hazelnuts, and 3 lbs raisins

39. $(2, 3)$

40. Your classmate thinks there is one solution of the system. There are infinitely many solutions since the matrix represents the system $\begin{cases} x + 0y = 2 \\ 0x + 0y = 0 \end{cases}$. Every ordered pair that has 2 as its x-coordinate is a solution.

41. 1 qt. of red paint: \$7.75; 1 qt. of yellow paint: \$5.75

Challenge Open-Ended Complete each system for the given number of solutions.

42. infinitely many

$$\begin{cases} x + y = 7 \\ 2x + 2y = \blacksquare \end{cases}$$

43. one solution

$$\begin{cases} x + y + z = 7 \\ y + z = \blacksquare \\ z = \blacksquare \end{cases}$$

44. no solution

$$\begin{cases} x + y + z = 7 \\ y + z = \blacksquare \\ y + z = \blacksquare \end{cases}$$

Solve the system of equations using a matrix. (Hint: Start by substituting $m = \frac{1}{x}$ and $n = \frac{1}{y}$.)

45.
$$\begin{cases} \frac{4}{x} + \frac{1}{y} = 1 \\ \frac{8}{x} + \frac{4}{y} = 3 \end{cases}$$

46.
$$\begin{cases} \frac{4}{x} - \frac{2}{y} = 1 \\ \frac{10}{x} + \frac{20}{y} = 0 \end{cases}$$

47.
$$\begin{cases} \frac{7}{x} + \frac{3}{y} = 5 \\ \frac{2}{x} + \frac{1}{y} = -1 \end{cases}$$

Standardized Test Prep

SAT/ACT

48. Which equation represents a line with a slope of $\frac{1}{2}$ and a y-intercept of $\frac{3}{4}$?

Ⓐ $y = \frac{1}{2}x - \frac{3}{4}$ Ⓑ $y = \frac{3}{4}x - \frac{1}{2}$ Ⓒ $y = \frac{1}{2}x + \frac{3}{4}$ Ⓓ $y = \frac{3}{4}x + \frac{1}{2}$

49. Which graph best represents the solution of the inequality $y \le 2|x - 1| - 4$?

Ⓕ 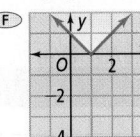   Ⓖ 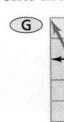   Ⓗ 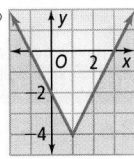   Ⓘ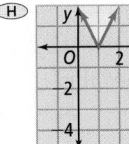

Short Response

50. At what point do the graphs of the equations $y = 7x - 3$ and $-6x + y = 2$ intersect?

Mixed Review

Solve each inequality. Graph the solution.   ◀ **See Lesson 1-5.**

51. $12 \ge 2(4x + 1) + 22$ **52.** $2x - (3x + 5) \le 30$ **53.** $4x + 5 - 3x \le 2x + 1$

Solve each equation. Check your answers.   ◀ **See Lesson 1-6.**

54. $|2y - 3| = 12$ **55.** $|4x| = 40$ **56.** $|2y - 4| = 16$

Get Ready! To prepare for Lesson 4-1, do Exercises 57 and 58.

Write an equation for each transformation of $y = x$.   ◀ **See Lesson 2-6.**

57. vertical stretch by a factor of 2.   **58.** vertical compression by a factor of $\frac{1}{3}$

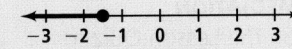

42. 14

43. Answers may vary. Sample: 0; 0

44. Answers may vary. Sample: 0; 1

45. (8, 2)

46. (5, −10)

47. $\left(\frac{1}{8}, -\frac{1}{17} \right)$

Standardized Test Prep

48. C

49. G

50. [2]
$$y = 7x - 3$$
$$\underline{-6x + y = 2}$$
$$6x = 7x - 5$$
$$-x = -5$$
$$x = 5$$
$$y = 7(5) - 3 = 32$$
$$(5, 32)$$

[1] computational error

Mixed Review

51. $x \le -\frac{3}{2}$;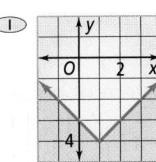

52. $x \ge -35$;

53. $x \ge 4$;

54. $\frac{15}{2}, -\frac{9}{2}$

55. 10, −10

56. 10, −6

57. $y = 2x$

58. $y = \frac{1}{3}x$

Additional Instructional Support

Algebra 2 Companion

Students can use the **Algebra 2 Companion** worktext (4 pages) as you teach the lesson. Use the Companion to support

- New Vocabulary
- Key Concepts
- Got It for each Problem
- Lesson Check

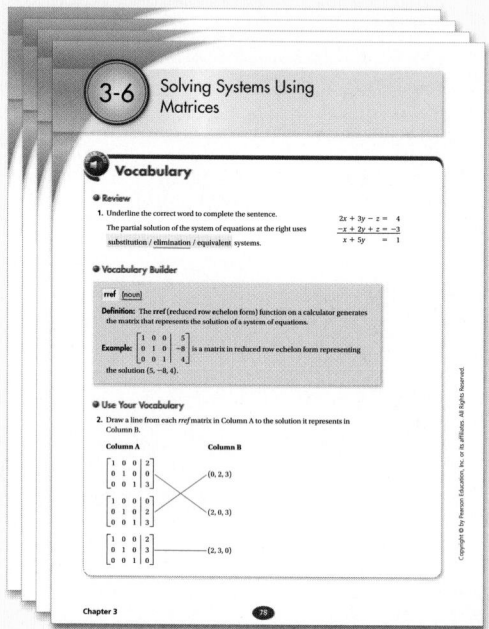

ELL Support

Connect to Prior Knowledge When writing linear systems as matrices, have students assign variables to each column. The last column can be named c to represent the constants. Place an equals sign over the bar separating the constants from the coefficients.

$$\begin{array}{ccc|c} x & y & z & = c \end{array}$$
$$\begin{bmatrix} 1 & 2 & 3 & | & 4 \\ 5 & 6 & 7 & | & 8 \\ 9 & 0 & 1 & | & 2 \end{bmatrix}$$

5 Assess & Remediate

Lesson Quiz

1. What is m_{34} in matrix M?

$$M = \begin{bmatrix} 3 & 4 & 7 & 1 \\ 0 & 2 & 6 & 8 \\ -9 & 5 & 0 & 16 \end{bmatrix}$$

2. Represent the system with a matrix.
$$\begin{cases} 2x + 3y + 5z = 9 \\ -x + 4z = 10 \\ -6x + z - 12 = y \end{cases}$$

3. What linear system of equations does this matrix represent? $\begin{bmatrix} 1 & 4 & | & 8 \\ -3 & 9 & | & 0 \end{bmatrix}$

4. Do you UNDERSTAND? You perform row operations and the result is the matrix
$$\begin{bmatrix} 1 & 0 & 0 & | & 3 \\ 0 & 1 & 0 & | & 2 \\ 0 & 0 & 0 & | & 4 \end{bmatrix}.$$
What is the solution to this system?

5. What is the solution of this system of equations? Use your calculator.
$$\begin{cases} a + 2b - c = 9 \\ 3a - b + 5c = -2 \\ -a + c = -3 \end{cases}$$

ANSWERS TO LESSON QUIZ

1. 16

2. $\begin{bmatrix} 2 & 3 & 5 & | & 9 \\ -1 & 0 & 4 & | & 10 \\ 6 & 1 & -1 & | & -12 \end{bmatrix}$

3. $\begin{cases} x + 4y = 8 \\ -3x + 9y = 0 \end{cases}$

4. no solution

5. $(2, 3, -1)$

PRESCRIPTION FOR REMEDIATION

Use the student work on the Lesson Quiz to prescribe a differentiated review assignment:

Points	Differentiated Remediation
0–2	Intervention
3–4	On-level
5	Extension

PowerAlgebra.com

5 Assess & Remediate

Assign the Lesson Quiz. Appropriate intervention, practice, or enrichment is automatically generated based on student performance.

Intervention

- **Reteaching** (2 pages) Provides reteaching and practice exercises for the key lesson concepts. Use with struggling students or absent students.

- **English Language Learner Support** Helps students develop and reinforce mathematical vocabulary and key concepts.

All-in-One Resources/Online
Reteaching

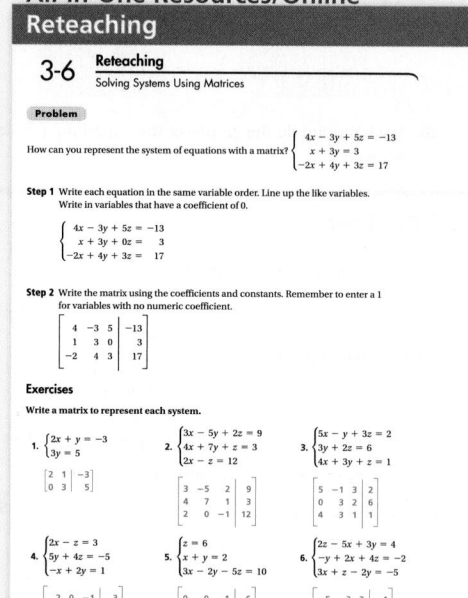

All-in-One Resources/Online
English Language Learner Support

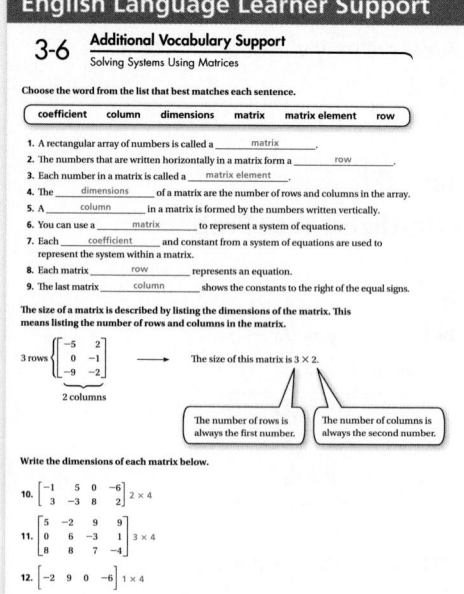

Differentiated Remediation *continued*

On-Level

- **Practice** (2 pages) Provides extra practice for each lesson. For simpler practice exercises, use the Form K Practice pages found in the All-in-One Teaching Resources and online.

- **Think About a Plan** Helps students develop specific problem-solving skills and strategies by providing scaffolded guiding questions.

- **Standardized Test Prep** Focuses on all major exercises, all major question types, and helps students prepare for the high-stakes assessments.

Extension

- **Enrichment** Provides students with interesting problems and activities that extend the concepts of the lesson.

- **Activities, Games, and Puzzles** Worksheets that can be used for concepts development, enrichment, and for fun!

Practice and Problem Solving Wkbk/ All-in-One Resources/Online
Practice page 1

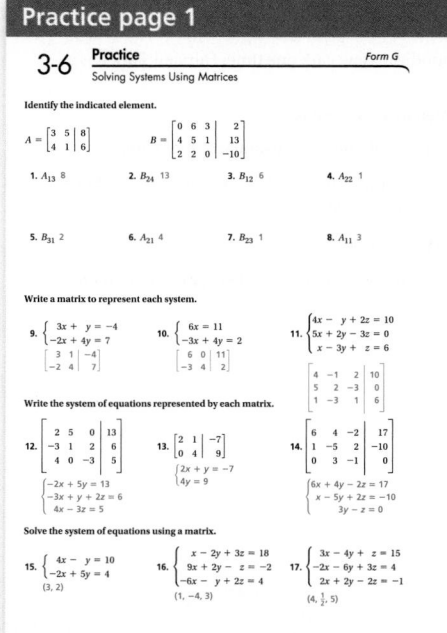

Practice and Problem Solving Wkbk/ All-in-One Resources/Online
Practice page 2

All-in-One Resources/Online
Enrichment

Practice and Problem Solving Wkbk/ All-in-One Resources/Online
Think About a Plan

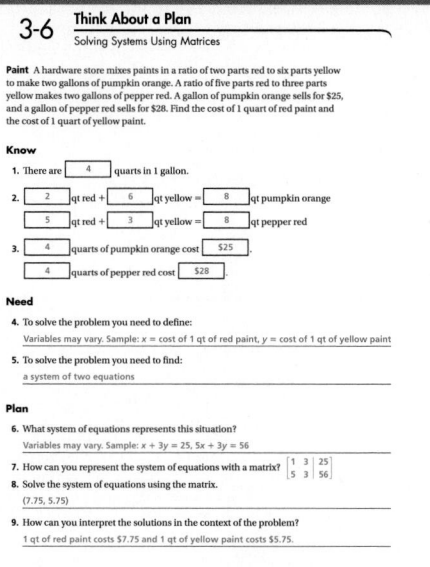

Practice and Problem Solving Wkbk/ All-in-One Resources/Online
Standardized Test Prep

Online Teacher Resource Center
Activities, Games, and Puzzles

Completing the Performance Task

In the Apply What You've Learned sections in Lessons 3-1, 3-2, and 3-5 students wrote systems of equations in two and three variables. Now, they can use their system of equations in three variables to complete the Performance Task on page 133. Ask students the following questions as they work toward solving the problem.

Q How can you use the work you have done in the chapter to solve the problem? **[Sample: I can use substitution with the three equations I wrote in Lessons 3-2 and 3-5 to find the distance of each part of the triathlon.]**

Q How can you check that your answer is reasonable? **[Sample: I can add the distances of the three parts and make sure that their sum is 28 miles.]**

FOSTERING MATHEMATICAL DISCOURSE

Have students exchange solutions and critique each other's reasoning.

ANSWERS

1. The swimming part is $1\frac{1}{8}$ mi, the bicycling part is $21\frac{1}{4}$ mi, and the running part is $5\frac{5}{8}$ mi.
2. Check students' work.

On Your Own

This problem is similar to the problem posed on page 133, but now students use different criteria to plan a new triathlon. Students should strive to solve this problem independently.

ANSWERS

a. The swimming portion is 0.8 mi, the bicycling portion is 16 mi, and the running portion is 4.2 mi.

b. 1.8 h, or 1 h 48 min

Pull It **All Together**

Completing the Performance Task

Look back at your results from the Apply What You've Learned sections in Lessons 3-1, 3-2, and 3-5. Use the work you did to complete the following.

1. Solve the problem in the Task Description on page 133 by determining the distance for each part of the course. Show all your work and explain each step of your solution.

2. Reflect Choose one of the Mathematical Practices below and explain how you applied it in your work on the Performance Task.

> MP 2: Reason abstractly and quantitatively.
>
> MP 4: Model with mathematics.
>
> MP 5: Use appropriate tools strategically.

To solve these problems, you will pull together concepts and skills related to solving a system of linear equations.

On Your Own

Manny is planning a triathlon for his athletic club. The director of the club asks Manny to follow these criteria when creating his plan.

- The run needs to go completely around Fairview Park one time. Fairview Park has a perimeter of 4.2 miles.
- The entire triathlon should cover a distance of 21 miles.
- The bicycle part of the triathlon should be 20 times the distance of the swim.

Manny finds that, on average, the members of his athletic club are able to swim about 2 mi/h, bicycle about 20 mi/h, and run about 7 mi/h.

a. What are the distances of each part of the triathlon?

b. On average, how long will it take a member of Manny's athletic club to complete the course?

3 Chapter Review

Connecting BIG ideas and Answering the Essential Questions

1 Function
Find a point of intersection (x, y) of the graphs of functions f and g and you have found a solution of the system $y = f(x)$, $y = g(x)$.

Solving Systems Using Tables and Graphs (Lesson 3-1)
$$\begin{cases} y = -2x + 3 \\ y = 2x - 1 \end{cases}$$
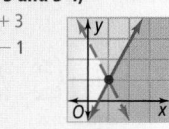
The solution is $(1, 1)$.

Systems of Inequalities and Linear Programming (Lessons 3-3 and 3-4)
$$\begin{cases} y > -2x + 3 \\ y \leq 2x - 1 \end{cases}$$

2 Equivalence
If the equations of two systems are equivalent, then a solution of the system that is easier to solve is also a solution of the more difficult system.

Solving Systems Algebraically (Lesson 3-2)
$$\begin{cases} -y = -x + 2 \\ 3y = 2x - 2 \end{cases} \quad \begin{aligned} -2y &= -2x + 4 \\ \underline{3y} &= \underline{2x - 2} \\ y &= 2 \end{aligned}$$
$3(2) = 2x - 2 \quad \rightarrow \quad x = 4$
The solution is $x = 4$, $y = 2$.

Systems With Three Variables (Lesson 3-5)
$$\begin{cases} -2x + y + z = -3 \\ 2x - y + z = -1 \\ -2x, -y - z = -1 \end{cases}$$
$x = 1$, $y = 1$, $z = -2$

3 Solving Equations and Inequalities
The matrix row operations of adding rows and multiplying a row by a constant are equivalent to addition and multiplication properties of equality.

Solving Systems Using Matrices (Lesson 3-6)
$$\begin{bmatrix} -2 & 3 & | & 1 \\ 2 & -1 & | & 1 \end{bmatrix}$$
$$\begin{bmatrix} 1 & 0 & | & 1 \\ 0 & 1 & | & 1 \end{bmatrix} \rightarrow x = 1, y = 1$$

Chapter Vocabulary

- consistent system (p. 137)
- constraint (p. 157)
- dependent system (p. 137)
- equivalent systems (p. 144)
- feasible region (p. 157)
- inconsistent system (p. 137)
- independent system (p. 137)
- linear programming (p. 157)
- linear system (p. 134)
- matrix (p. 174)
- matrix element (p. 174)
- objective function (p. 157)
- row operation (p. 176)
- solution of a system (p. 134)
- system of equations (p. 134)

Fill in the blank.

1. A consistent system with exactly one solution is a(n) _____.

2. _____ is a method for finding a minimum or maximum value, given a system of limits called _____.

Essential Questions

BIG idea Function
ESSENTIAL QUESTION How does representing functions graphically help you solve a system of equations?
ANSWER Find a point of intersection (x, y) of the graphs of functions f and g and you have found a solution of the system $y = f(x)$, $y = g(x)$

BIG idea Equivalence
ESSENTIAL QUESTION How does writing equivalent equations help you solve a system of equations?
ANSWER If the equations of two systems are equivalent, then a solution of the system that is easier to solve is also a solution of the more difficult system.

BIG idea Solving Equations and Inequalities
ESSENTIAL QUESTION How are the properties of equality used in the matrix solution of a system of equations?
ANSWER The matrix row operations of adding rows and multiplying a row by a constant are equivalent to addition and multiplication properties of equality.

Answers

1. independent system
2. Linear programming; constraints

Summative Questions

Use the following prompts as you review this chapter with your students. The prompts are designed to help you assess your students' understanding of the Big Ideas they have studied.

- What do you look for to determine whether to use elimination, substitution, or a matrix to solve a linear system?
- In a linear programming problem, what determines the feasible region?
- What are the three different kinds of systems? How many solutions does each have?
- How does the graph of a solution to a system of inequalities compare to the graph of the solutions of a single inequality?
- Are these systems equivalent?
$$\begin{cases} 2x - 2y = 4 \\ 2x + 4y = 7 \end{cases} \text{ and } \begin{cases} 2x - 2y = 4 \\ 2x + 8y = 14 \end{cases}$$
What determines whether two systems are equivalent?

Answers

3. independent; $(-1, -4)$

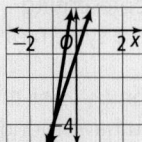

4. dependent

5. inconsistent

6. dependent

7. independent; $(-4, 6)$

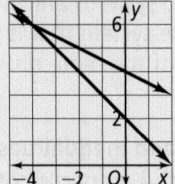

8. independent; $(1, 0)$

9. 3 pens

10. $(-1, -2)$

11. $(0, -5)$

12. $(-2, 3)$

13. inconsistent; no solution

14. 1 serving of roast beef and 2 servings of mashed potatoes

3-1 Solving Systems Using Tables and Graphs

Quick Review

A **system of equations** has two or more equations. Points of intersection are solutions. A **linear system** has linear equations. A **consistent system** can be **dependent**, with infinitely many solutions, or **independent**, with one solution. An **inconsistent system** has no solution.

Example

Solve the system $\begin{cases} 3x + 2y = 4 \\ 2x - 4y = 8 \end{cases}$

Graph the equations.

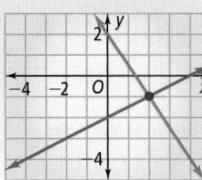

The only solution, where the lines intersect, is $(2, -1)$.

Exercises

Without graphing, classify each system of equations as *independent*, *dependent*, or *inconsistent*. Solve independent systems by graphing.

3. $\begin{cases} 6x - 2y = 2 \\ 2 + 6x = y \end{cases}$

4. $\begin{cases} 5 - y = 2x \\ 6x - 15 = -3y \end{cases}$

5. $\begin{cases} 6y + 2x = 8 \\ 12y + 4x = 4 \end{cases}$

6. $\begin{cases} 1.5 + 3x = 0.5y \\ 6 - 2y = -12x \end{cases}$

7. $\begin{cases} 2 - 0.25x = 0.5y \\ -1.5y = 1.5x - 3 \end{cases}$

8. $\begin{cases} 1 + y = x \\ x + y = 1 \end{cases}$

9. For \$7.52, you purchased 8 pens and highlighters from a local bookstore. Each highlighter cost \$1.09 and each pen cost \$.69. How many pens did you buy?

3-2 Solving Systems Algebraically

Quick Review

To solve an independent system by substitution, solve one equation for a variable. Then substitute that expression into the other equation and solve for the remaining variable. To solve by elimination, add two equations with additive inverses as coefficients to eliminate one variable and solve for the other. In both cases you solve for one of the variables and use substitution to solve for the remaining variable.

Example

Solve $\begin{cases} 10 - y = 4x \\ x = 4 + 0.5y \end{cases}$ by substitution.

Substitute for x: $10 - y = 4(4 + 0.5y) = 16 + 2y$.

Solve for y: $y = -2$.

Substitute into the first equation:

$10 - (-2) = 4x$.

Solve for x: $x = 3$. The solution is $(3, -2)$.

Exercises

Solve each system by substitution.

10. $\begin{cases} x - 2y = 3 \\ 3x + y = -5 \end{cases}$

11. $\begin{cases} 14x - 35 = 7y \\ -25 - 6x = 5y \end{cases}$

Solve each system by elimination.

12. $\begin{cases} 11 - 5y = 2x \\ 5y + 3 = -9x \end{cases}$

13. $\begin{cases} 2x + 3y = 4 \\ 4x + 6y = 9 \end{cases}$

14. Roast beef has 25 g of protein and 11 g of calcium per serving. A serving of mashed potatoes has 2 g of protein and 25 g of calcium. How many servings of each are needed to supply exactly 29 g of protein and 61 g of calcium?

3-3 Systems of Inequalities

Quick Review

To solve a system of inequalities by graphing, first graph the boundaries for each inequality. Then shade the region(s) of the plane containing solutions valid for both inequalities.

Example

Solve the system of inequalities by graphing.

$$\begin{cases} y > -3 \\ y \le -|x-1| \end{cases}$$

Graph both inequalities and shade the region valid for both inequalities.

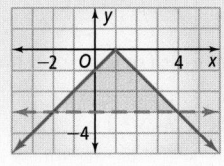

Exercises

Solve each system of inequalities by graphing.

15. $\begin{cases} y < 4x \\ 3x + y \ge 5 \end{cases}$ **16.** $\begin{cases} y < |2x - 4| \\ x + 5y \ge -1 \end{cases}$

17. $\begin{cases} y \le |x + 2| - 3 \\ y \ge 1 + \frac{1}{4}x \end{cases}$ **18.** $\begin{cases} 2x + 3y > 6 \\ x \le -1 \\ y \ge 4 \end{cases}$

19. For a community breakfast there should be at least three times as much regular coffee as decaffeinated coffee. A total of ten gallons is sufficient for the breakfast. Write and graph a system of inequalities to model the problem.

3-4 Linear Programming

Quick Review

Linear programming is used to find a minimum or maximum of an **objective function**, given **constraints** as linear inequalities. The maximum or minimum occurs at a vertex of the **feasible region**, which contains the solutions to the system of constraints.

Example

Graph the system of constraints and name the vertices.

Objective function: $P = 2x + y$

$$\begin{cases} x \le 8 \\ y \le 5 \\ x \ge 0, y \ge 0 \end{cases}$$

Graph the inequalities and shade the area satisfying all inequalities.

The vertices of the feasible region are (0, 0), (0, 5), (8, 5), and (8, 0).

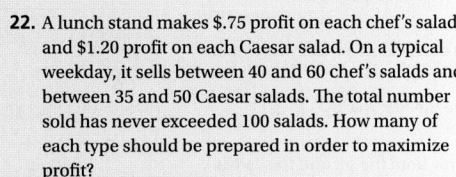

Evaluate the objective function at each vertex:

$2(0) + 0 = 0$	$2(0) + 5 = 5$
$2(8) + 5 = 21$	$2(8) + 0 = 16$

The maximum value occurs at (8, 5).

Exercises

Graph the system of constraints. Name the vertices. Then find the values of x and y that maximize or minimize the objective function.

20. $\begin{cases} x \ge 2 \\ y \ge 0 \\ 3x + 2y \ge 12 \end{cases}$ **21.** $\begin{cases} 3x + 2y \le 12 \\ x + y \le 5 \\ x \ge 0, y \ge 0 \end{cases}$

Minimum for $C = x + 5y$ Maximum for $P = 3x + 5y$

22. A lunch stand makes $.75 profit on each chef's salad and $1.20 profit on each Caesar salad. On a typical weekday, it sells between 40 and 60 chef's salads and between 35 and 50 Caesar salads. The total number sold has never exceeded 100 salads. How many of each type should be prepared in order to maximize profit?

20. vertices: (4, 0) and (2, 3); $C = 4$ is minimized at (4, 0).

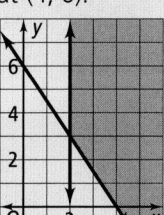

21. vertices: (0, 0), (4, 0), (2, 3), (0, 5); $P = 25$ is maximized at (0, 5).

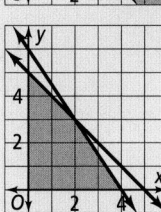

22. 50 chef's salads and 50 Caesar salads

15.
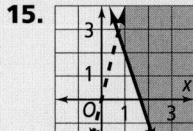

16.
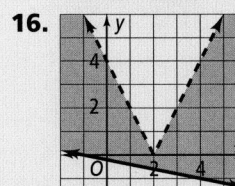

17.
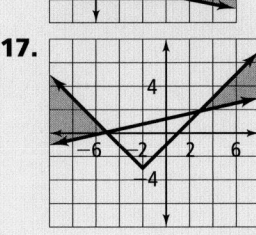

18.
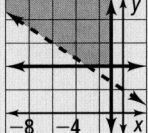

19. Let r = amount of regular coffee and d = amount of decaffeinated coffee

$$\begin{cases} r + d \le 10 \\ r \ge 3d, r \ge 0, d \ge 0 \end{cases}$$

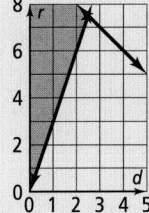

Answers

23. $(1, 3, -2)$

24. $(-4, 1, -5)$

25. $(6, 0, -2)$

26. no solution

27. $\left(\dfrac{1}{2}, \dfrac{1}{4}\right)$

28. $(1, -1)$

29. $(2, -4, 6)$

30. $(5, 2, -3)$

3-5 Systems With Three Variables

Quick Review

To solve a system of three equations, either pair two equations and eliminate the same variable from both equations, using one equation twice, or choose an equation, solve for one variable, and substitute the expression for that variable into the other two equations. Then, solve the remaining system.

Example

Solve by elimination.
$$\text{①} \begin{cases} x + y + z = 10 \\ \text{②}\ 2x - y + z = 9 \\ \text{③}\ -3x + 2y + 2z = 5 \end{cases}$$

Add equations ① and ② to eliminate y. ④ $3x + 2z = 19$

Add 2 times ② to ③ to eliminate y. ⑤ $x + 4z = 23$

Add -3 times ⑤ to ④ to eliminate x. $z = 5$

Substitute $z = 5$ into ⑤. $x = 3$

Substitute $z = 5$ and $x = 3$ into ① or ②. $y = 2$

The solution to the system is $(3, 2, 5)$.

Exercises

Solve each system by elimination.

23. $\begin{cases} x + y - 2z = 8 \\ 5x - 3y + z = -6 \\ -2x - y + 4z = -13 \end{cases}$

24. $\begin{cases} -x + y + 2z = -5 \\ 5x + 4y - 4z = 4 \\ x - 3y - 2z = 3 \end{cases}$

Solve each system by substitution.

25. $\begin{cases} 3x + y - 2z = 22 \\ x + 5y + z = 4 \\ x = -3z \end{cases}$

26. $\begin{cases} x + 2y + z = 14 \\ y = z + 1 \\ x = -3z + 6 \end{cases}$

3-6 Solving Systems Using Matrices

Quick Review

A **matrix** can represent a system of equations where each row stands for a different equation. The columns contain the coefficients of the variables and the constants.

Example

Solve using a matrix. $\begin{cases} 6x + 3y = -15 \\ 2x + 4y = 10 \end{cases}$

Enter coefficients as matrix elements $\begin{bmatrix} 6 & 3 & | & -15 \\ 2 & 4 & | & 10 \end{bmatrix}$.

Divide the first row by 3 to get $\begin{bmatrix} 2 & 1 & | & -5 \\ 2 & 4 & | & 10 \end{bmatrix}$. Subtract the

first row from the second row to get $\begin{bmatrix} 2 & 1 & | & -5 \\ 0 & 3 & | & 15 \end{bmatrix}$. Multiply

the second row by $\frac{1}{3}$ to get $\begin{bmatrix} 2 & 1 & | & -5 \\ 0 & 1 & | & 5 \end{bmatrix}$. Subtract the second

row from the first row to get $\begin{bmatrix} 2 & 0 & | & -10 \\ 0 & 1 & | & 5 \end{bmatrix}$. Divide the first row

by 2 to get $\begin{bmatrix} 1 & 0 & | & -5 \\ 0 & 1 & | & 5 \end{bmatrix}$. The solution to the system is $(-5, 5)$.

Exercises

Solve each system using a matrix.

27. $\begin{cases} 4x - 12y = -1 \\ 6x + 4y = 4 \end{cases}$

28. $\begin{cases} 7x + 2y = 5 \\ 13x + 14y = -1 \end{cases}$

29. $\begin{cases} -5x + 3y + 4z = 2 \\ 3x - y - z = 4 \\ x - 6y - 5z = -4 \end{cases}$

30. $\begin{cases} x + y + z = 4 \\ 2x - y + z = 5 \\ x + y - 2z = 13 \end{cases}$

 **MathXL® for School**
Go to PowerAlgebra.com

Do you know HOW?

Without graphing, classify each system. Then find the solution to each system using a graph.

1. $\begin{cases} y = 5x - 2 \\ y = x + 4 \end{cases}$

2. $\begin{cases} 3x + 2y = 9 \\ 3x + 2y = 4 \end{cases}$

Solve the system by substitution.

3. $\begin{cases} 0.3x - y = 0 \\ y = 2 + 0.25x \end{cases}$

Solve the system by elimination.

4. $\begin{cases} 4x - 2y = 3 \\ y - 2x = -\frac{3}{2} \end{cases}$

5. $\begin{cases} 3x + 4y = 9 \\ 2x + y = 6 \end{cases}$

Graph the solution of each system.

6. $\begin{cases} 2x + y < 3 \\ x < y + 3 \end{cases}$

7. $\begin{cases} |x + 3| > y \\ y > 2x - 1 \end{cases}$

Graph the system of constraints. Identify all vertices. Then find the values of x and y that maximize or minimize the objective function.

8. $\begin{cases} x \le 5 \\ y \le 4 \\ x \ge 0 \\ y \ge 0 \end{cases}$

Maximum for $P = 2x + y$

Solve each system.

9. $\begin{cases} x - y + z = 0 \\ 3x - 2y + 6z = 9 \\ -x + y - 2z = -2 \end{cases}$

10. $\begin{cases} 2x + y + z = 8 \\ x + 2y - z = -5 \\ z = 2x - y \end{cases}$

Do you UNDERSTAND?

Write a matrix that represents the system. Then solve the system. Tell what method you used and why.

11. $\begin{cases} -a + 4b + 2c = -8 \\ 3a + b - 4c = 9 \\ b = -1 \end{cases}$

12. **Sales** A pizza shop makes $1.50 on each small pizza and $2.15 on each large pizza. On a typical Friday, it sells between 70 and 90 small pizzas and between 100 and 140 large pizzas. The shop can make no more than 210 pizzas in a day. How many of each size pizza must be sold in order to maximize profit?

13. **Investing** Your teacher invested $5000 in three funds. After a year they had $5450. The growth fund had a return rate of 12%, the income fund had a return rate of 8%, and the money market fund had a return rate of 5%. Your teacher invested twice as much in the income fund as in the money market fund. How much money was invested in each fund?

© 14. **Writing** Describe how to identify situations in which substitution may be the best method for solving a system of equations.

© 15. **Open-Ended** Write a system of constraints whose graph is a parallelogram.

---

10. $(2, -1, 5)$

11. $\begin{bmatrix} -1 & 4 & 2 & | & -8 \\ 3 & 1 & -4 & | & 9 \\ 0 & 1 & 0 & | & -1 \end{bmatrix}$;

$(2, -1, -1)$; Check students' work

12. 70 small; 140 large

13. She invested $2000 in the growth fund, $2000 in the income fund, and $1000 in the money market fund.

14. Substitution is used when an equation is easily solved for one of the variables.

15. Check students' work.

Answers

1. independent; $\left(\frac{3}{2}, \frac{11}{2}\right)$

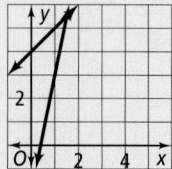

2. inconsistent

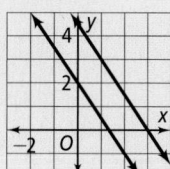

3. $(40, 12)$

4. infinitely many solutions

5. $(3, 0)$

6.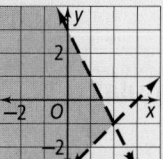

7.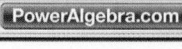

8.

vertices: $(0, 0)$, $(5, 0)$, $(5, 4)$, $(0, 4)$; maximum $P = 14$ at $(5, 4)$.

9. $(1, 3, 2)$

Item Number	Lesson	© Content Standard
1	3-2	A-REI.C.6
2	2-7	F-IF.C.7b
3	1-6	A-CED.A.1
4	3-2	A-REI.C.6
5	1-6	A-CED.A.1
6	3-1	A-REI.C.6
7	1-4	A-CED.A.4
8	2-4	A-CED.A.2
9	2-7	F-BF.B.3
10	2-2	A-CED.A.2
11	3-2	A-CED.A.2
12	1-6	A-CED.A.1
13	2-6	F-BF.B.3
14	3-2	A-REI.C.6
15	2-3	F-IF.B.4
16	2-4	F-IF.C.8
17	3-2	A-REI.C.6
18	3-3	A-REI.D.12
19	2-1	*F-IF.A.2
20	3-1	A-REI.D.11
21	2-4	A-CED.A.2
22	3-3	A-REI.D.12
23	2-5	F-IF.B.6

*Reviews standard

3 Common Core Cumulative Standards Review

ASSESSMENT

TIPS FOR SUCCESS

Some problems require the selection of an appropriate representation (concrete, pictorial, graphical, verbal, or symbolic) to find a solution.

TIP 1
Make a drawing.

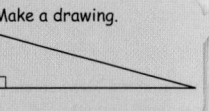

One angle of a right triangle measures 90°. The measure of the second angle is 5 times the measure of the third. What are the measures of these angles?

Ⓐ 30° and 60°

Ⓑ 30° and 150°

Ⓒ 15° and 75°

Ⓓ 20° and 100°

TIP 2
Write a system:
$x + y + 90 = 180$
$x = 5y$

Think It Through
A triangle can have only one right angle, so the other two angles must each have a measure less than 90°. Use x and y to represent the unknown angles.

$x = 5y$
$5y + y + 90 = 180$
$6y + 90 = 180$
$6y = 90$
$y = 15, x = 75$

The correct answer is C.

Vocabulary Builder

As you solve test items, you must understand the meanings of mathematical terms. Match each term with its mathematical meaning.

A. equivalent systems

B. absolute value

C. system of equations

D. linear inequality

I. a number's distance from zero on a number line

II. an inequality in two variables whose graph is a region of the half-plane

III. a set of two or more equations that use the same variables

IV. systems that have the same solution(s)

Selected Response

Read each question. Then write the letter of the correct answer on your paper.

1. Which of the following is true about the given system?
$$\begin{cases} -4y = 12 - 8x \\ y = 2x - 3 \end{cases}$$

The system has
Ⓐ zero solutions.
Ⓑ exactly one solution.
Ⓒ two solutions.
Ⓓ infinitely many solutions.

Answers

Common Core Cumulative Standards Review

A. IV

B. I

C. III

D. II

1. D

2. Which is the graph of $y = -|x - 2| + 1$?

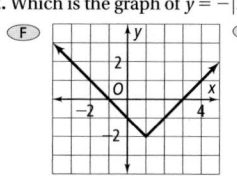
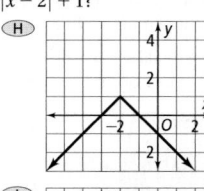
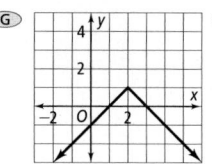
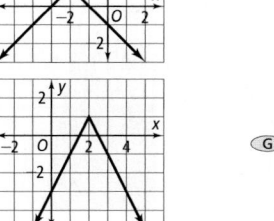

3. Which graph represents the solution of the inequality $|3x + 12| \geq 3$?

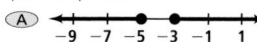

(A)

(B)

(C)

(D)

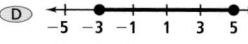

4. Josea wants to solve the system using substitution.

$$\begin{cases} x = -2y + 4 \\ 2x - 3y = 5 \end{cases}$$

Which of the following is the best way for Josea to proceed?

(F) Solve the first equation for y, then substitute into the second equation.

(G) Solve the second equation for y, then substitute into the first equation.

(H) Substitute $-2y + 4$ for x in the second equation.

(I) Substitute $-2y + 4$ for y in the second equation.

5. A board must be cut so that its length is 40.50 cm. The tolerance is 0.25 cm. Which inequality describes the allowable lengths for the board?

(A) $|x - 0.25| \leq 40.50$

(B) $|x + 0.25| \leq 40.50$

(C) $|x - 40.50| \leq 0.25$

(D) $|x - 0.25| \leq 40.75$

6. Which graph shows the solution to the given system?

$$\begin{cases} \frac{1}{2}x - y = 1 \\ x = 3 \end{cases}$$

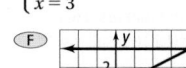
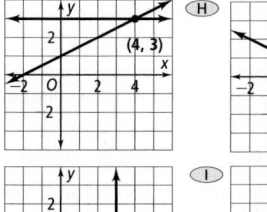
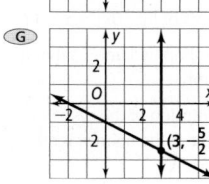
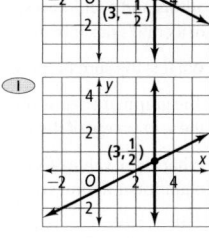

7. The formula for the area of a trapezoid is $A = \frac{h}{2}(b_1 + b_2)$. Solve this equation for b_2.

(A) $b_2 = \frac{2A}{hb_1}$

(B) $b_2 = \frac{2A}{h} - b_1$

(C) $b_2 = \frac{2A}{h - b_1}$

(D) $b_2 = \frac{2A}{h + b_1}$

8. What is the equation of the line that passes through $(-2, 4)$ and $(2, 7)$?

(F) $y - 7 = \frac{3}{4}(x + 2)$

(G) $y + 7 = \frac{3}{4}(x - 2)$

(H) $y - 7 = \frac{3}{4}(x - 2)$

(I) $y - 2 = \frac{3}{4}(x - 7)$

9. Which of the following describes the translation of $y = |x|$ to $y = |x + 2| - 1$?

(A) $y = |x|$ translated 2 units to the left and 1 unit down

(B) $y = |x|$ translated 2 units to the right and 1 unit down

(C) $y = |x|$ translated 1 unit to the left and 2 units down

(D) $y = |x|$ translated 1 unit to the right and 2 units down

2. G

3. A

4. H

5. C

6. I

7. B

8. H

9. A

Answers

Common Core Cumulative Standards Review (continued)

10. 20

11. 5

12. 4

13. −2

14. −1.1

15. $\frac{1}{6}$

16. 8

17. **[2]** let r = number of reg. mix-ins, let p = number of premium mix-ins

$r + p \geq 4 \qquad 0.5r + 1p \leq 2.5$
$\quad p \geq 4 - r \qquad\quad p \leq -0.5r + 2.5$

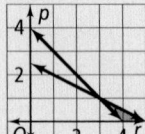

you can get 3 reg. and 1 premium mix-in, or 4 reg. mix-ins, or 5 reg. mix-ins.

[1] correct answer, without work shown

18. **[2]** $(-3, 2)$

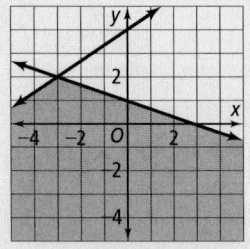

[1] one minor computational error

19. **[2]** $f(-4) = 1$, $f(0) = 2$, $f(3) = 2\frac{3}{4}$

[1] one minor computational error

20. **[2]** You can graph $f(x)$ and $g(x)$. The x-coordinate of the point of intersection is the solution to the equation $-|3x| + 6 = 2x + 1$.

[1] partially correct answer

21. **[2]** slope of line $m = 3$, slope of line perpendicular to $m = -\frac{1}{3}$. Write eq. of line in point-slope form:

$y - (-2) = -\frac{1}{3}(x - 3)$
$\quad y + 2 = -\frac{1}{3}x + 1$
$\qquad y = -\frac{1}{3}x - 1$

[1] one computational error

22. **[2]** **a.** C

   b. A

   c. D

   d. B

[1] one incorrect answer

Constructed Response

10. The nutrition label on a package of crackers shows there are 80 Calories in 16 grams of crackers. How many grams are in a package labeled 100 Calories?

11. A family with 4 adults and 3 children spends $47 for movie tickets at the theater. Another family with 2 adults and 4 children spends $36. What is the price of a child's ticket in dollars?

12. What is the sum of the solutions of $|5 - 3x| = x + 1$?

13. The graph of $y = x$ is translated up two units. What is the x-intercept of the new graph?

14. What is the value of x in the solution of the system of equations? Round your answer to the nearest tenth.

$\begin{cases} 5x = -3y - 7 \\ 5y = -4x - 7 \end{cases}$

15. What is the slope of the line $3y - 4 = \frac{1}{2}x$?

16. The line $(y - 2) = \frac{2}{7}(x - 1)$ contains point $(a, 4)$. What is the value of a?

17. An ice cream shop has regular mix-ins for $.50 each and premium mix-ins for $1 each. You have $2.50 to spend on mix-ins, and you want at least 4 mix-ins. How many of each type of mix-in can you get in your ice cream?

18. Solve the following system by graphing.

$\begin{cases} y < \frac{1}{3}x + 1 \\ y \leq \frac{2}{3}x + 4 \end{cases}$

19. Find $f(-4)$, $f(0)$, and $f(3)$ for the function $f(x) = \frac{1}{4}x + 2$.

20. How can you use the graphs of $f(x) = -|3x| + 6$ and $g(x) = 2x + 1$ to find the solutions of $-|3x| + 6 = 2x + 1$?

21. The equation of line m is $y = 3x - 1$. What is the equation of a line that goes through the point $(3, -2)$ and is perpendicular to line m? Show your work.

---

22. The graph below shows the boundaries for the system of linear inequalities.

$\begin{cases} y \leq 0.5x + 5 \\ y \leq -5x - 6 \end{cases}$

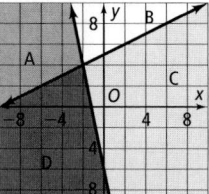

   a. Of the shaded areas A, B, C and D, which area represents a solution to the first inequality but not the second?

   b. Which represents a solution to the second inequality but not the first?

   c. Which represents a solution to both inequalities?

   d. Which represents a solution to neither inequality?

Extended Response

23. Jenna is trying to break her school's record for doing the most push-ups in ten minutes. The current record holder did 350 push-ups in ten minutes. The table shows the number of push-ups Jenna completed in the first 6 minutes.

   a. Draw a scatter plot and find the line of best fit.

   b. Will Jenna beat the current record? Justify your reasoning.

Time (min)	1	2	3	4	5	6
Number of push-ups	37	70	99	132	169	207

23. **[4]** **a.**

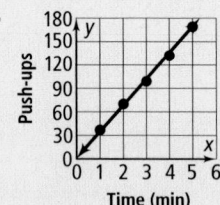

$y = 34x + 1$ (OR another reasonable trend line)

   b. No; $y = 34(10) + 1 = 341$, Jenna will only do 341 push-ups in 10 min, and the record is 350.

[3] incomplete explanation for part (b)

[2] only part (a) answered correctly

[1] correct answers, without work shown

Get Ready!

Lesson 1-4 ◆ Solving Linear Equations

Solve each equation. Check your answer.

1. $9x - 16 = 8 + 5x$

2. $4(y + 2) + 1 = -5(3 - 2y)$

Lesson 1-6 ◆ Solving Absolute Value Inequalities

Solve each inequality. Graph the solution.

3. $|6x - 12| + 6 < 30$

4. $6|4y - 2| \geq 42$

Lesson 2-3 ◆ Writing and Graphing Equations in Slope-Intercept Form

Graph the line passing through the given points. Then write its equation in slope-intercept form.

5. $(1, -1)$ and $(3, 17)$

6. $(2, 9)$ and $(6, 11)$

Lesson 2-6 ◆ Identifying Translations

Identify each horizontal and vertical translation of the parent function $y = |x|$.

7. $y = |x - 4| + 2$

8. $y = |x + 10| - 3$

Lesson 3-2 ◆ Solving Systems of Equations

Solve each system of equations by substitution.

9. $\begin{cases} 2x + 6y = 14 \\ 4x - 8y = 48 \end{cases}$

10. $\begin{cases} x + 2y = -18 \\ 2x - 4y = 12 \end{cases}$

 Looking Ahead Vocabulary

11. A *form* is a document with blank spaces to fill in. What types of forms might you use?

12. Something is *imaginary* if it has no factual reality. What are some examples of imaginary items?

13. Many items have a specific *function*, or purpose for use. What is the function of a pencil?

Get Ready!

Assign this diagnostic assessment to determine if students have the prerequisite skills for Chapter 4.

Lesson	Skill
1-4	Solve Linear Equations
1-6	Solve Absolute Value Inequalities
2-3	Write and Graph Linear Equations in Slope-Intercept Form
2-6	Identify Translations
3-2	Solve Systems of Equations

To remediate students, select from these resources (available for every lesson).
- Online Problems (PowerAlgebra.com)
- Reteaching (All-in-One Teaching Resources)
- Practice (All-in-One Teaching Resources)

Why Students Need These Skills

SOLVING LINEAR EQUATIONS
Solving linear equations is extended to solving quadratic equations.

SOLVING ABSOLUTE VALUE INEQUALITIES
Students will need to solve absolute value equations when solving systems of inequalities.

WRITING AND GRAPHING EQUATIONS IN SLOPE-INTERCEPT FORM
Writing and graphing equations in slope-intercept form prepares students for writing and graphing quadratic equations in vertex form.

IDENTIFYING TRANSLATIONS
Identifying translations of the absolute value parent functions corresponds to finding translations of the quadratic function.

SOLVING SYSTEMS OF EQUATIONS
Solving systems of linear equations prepares students to solve systems of quadratic equations using the same techniques.

Looking Ahead Vocabulary

FORM When comparing the form of an equation to a document, the blank spaces to be filled in correspond to the constant values in the equation.

IMAGINARY Ask students why these imaginary items are important regardless of having no factual reality.

FUNCTION Students may list several specific functions for a pencil, such as writing and erasing.

Answers

Get Ready!

1. 6

2. 4

3. $-2 < x < 6$

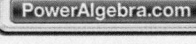

4. $y \leq -\dfrac{5}{4}$ or $y \geq \dfrac{9}{4}$

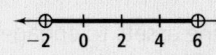

5. $y = 9x - 10$

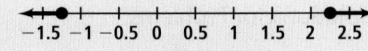

6. $y = \dfrac{1}{2}x + 8$

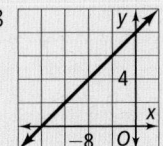

7. translated 4 units to the right and 2 units up

8. translated 10 units to the left and 3 units down

9. $(10, -1)$

10. $(-6, -6)$

11. Answers may vary. Sample: application forms, registration forms, tests

12. Answers may vary. Sample: monsters, ghosts, tooth fairy

13. writing

Chapter 4 Overview

Chapter 4 expands on students' understandings and skills related to functions, equations, and graphs. In this chapter, students will develop the answers to the Essential Questions as they learn the concepts and skills bulleted below.

BIG idea Equivalence

ESSENTIAL QUESTION What are the advantages of a quadratic function in vertex form? in standard form?

- Students will identify the vertex, line of symmetry, maximum or minimum, domain, range, and translations of a quadratic function.
- Students will graph quadratic functions with and without graphing calculators.
- Students will use quadratic functions as models.

BIG idea Function

ESSENTIAL QUESTION How is any quadratic function related to the parent quadratic function $y = x^2$?

- Students will graph transformations of the parent quadratic function $y = x^2$.
- Students will compare translations to the parent quadratic function.

BIG idea Solving Equations and Inequalities

ESSENTIAL QUESTION How are the real solutions of a quadratic equation related to the graph of the related quadratic function?

- Students will identify the x-intercepts of the graphs of related quadratic functions.

© Content Standards

Following are the standards covered in this chapter. Modeling standards are indicated by a star symbol (★).

CONCEPTUAL CATEGORY Numbers and Quantity

Domain The Complex Number System N-CN
Cluster Perform arithmetic operations with complex numbers. (Standards N-CN.A.1, N-CN.A.2)
LESSON 4-8

Cluster Use complex numbers in polynomial identities and equations.
(Standards N-CN.C.7, N-CN.C.8)
LESSON 4-8

CONCEPTUAL CATEGORY Functions

Domain Interpreting Functions F-IF
Cluster Interpret functions that arise in applications in terms of the context.
(Standards F-IF.B.4, F-IF.B.5★, F-IF.B.6★)
LESSONS 4-1, 4-2, 4-3

Domain Building Functions F.BF
Cluster Build new functions from existing functions. (Standards F-BF.B.1★, F-BF.B.3★)
LESSON 4-1

CONCEPTUAL CATEGORY Algebra

Domain Seeing Structure in Expressions A-SSE
Cluster Interpret the structure of expressions.
(Standards A-SSE.A.1a★, A-SSE.A.1b★, A-SSE.A.2)
LESSON 4-4

Cluster Write expressions in equivalent forms to solve problems. (Standard A-SSE.B.3a)
LESSON 4-5

CHAPTER 4

Quadratic Functions and Equations

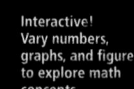 Download videos connecting math to your world.

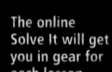 Interactive! Vary numbers, graphs, and figures to explore math concepts.

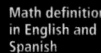 The online Solve It will get you in gear for each lesson.

Math definitions in English and Spanish

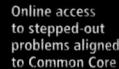 Online access to stepped-out problems aligned to Common Core

Get and view your assignments online.

 Extra practice and review online

Virtual Nerd™ tutorials with built-in support

Chapter Preview

4-1 Quadratic Functions and Transformations
4-2 Standard Form of a Quadratic Function
4-3 Modeling With Quadratic Functions
4-4 Factoring Quadratic Expressions
4-5 Quadratic Equations
4-6 Completing the Square
4-7 The Quadratic Formula
4-8 Complex Numbers
4-9 Quadratic Systems

Vocabulary

English/Spanish Vocabulary Audio Online:

English	Spanish
axis of symmetry, p. 194	eje de simetría
complex number, p. 249	números complejos
discriminant, p. 242	discriminante
greatest common factor, p. 218	máximo factor común de una expresión
imaginary number, p. 249	número imaginario
parabola, p. 194	parábola
Quadratic Formula, p. 240	fórmula cuadrática
quadratic function, p. 194	función cuadrática
standard form, p. 202	forma normal
vertex form, p. 194	forma del vértice
zero of a function, p. 226	cero de una función

BIG ideas

1 **Equivalence**
Essential Question What are the advantages of a quadratic function in vertex form? In standard form?

2 **Function**
Essential Question How is any quadratic function related to the parent quadratic function $y = x^2$?

3 **Solving Equations and Inequalities**
Essential Question How are the real solutions of a quadratic equation related to the graph of the related quadratic function?

© **DOMAINS**
- Interpreting Functions
- Creating Equations
- The Complex Number System

PowerAlgebra.com

Chapter 4 Overview

Use these online assets to engage your students. These include support for the Solve It and step-by-step solutions for Problems.

 Show the student-produced video demonstrating relevant and engaging applications of the new concepts in the chapter.

 Find online definitions for new terms in English and Spanish.

 Start each lesson with an attention-getting Problem. View the Problem online with helpful hints.

Common Core Performance Task

Maximizing Profit

Victor runs a small sandwich shop. He plans to sell a new brand of chips, which he is able to buy at a cost of $.30 per bag. Victor needs to decide the price he will charge customers for a bag of chips.

Another sandwich shop sells the same brand of chips. The shop owner tells Victor that the number of bags of chips she sold increased when she lowered her selling price. The table below shows her data.

Average Weekly Sales of Chips

Number of Bags Sold	Selling Price per Bag
150	$1.00
190	$.90
250	$.75
350	$.50

Victor wants to price the bags of chips so that he maximizes his profit.

Task Description

Find all possible prices Victor can charge for a bag of chips in order to make a profit, and determine the price he should charge to maximize his profit.

Connecting the Task to the Math Practices

MATHEMATICAL PRACTICES

As you complete the task, you'll apply several Standards for Mathematical Practice.

- You'll model the situation with functions for selling price, cost, revenue, and profit. (MP 4)
- You'll use connections between the profit function's equation and its graph to give you information about the situation. (MP 1)
- You'll find the zeros of the profit function and interpret them in terms of the situation. (MP 2)

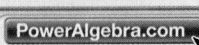
 Increase students' depth of knowledge with interactive online activities.

 Show Problems from each lesson solved step by step. Instant replay allows students to go at their own pace when studying online.

 Assign homework to individual students or to an entire class.

 Prepare students for the Mid-Chapter Quiz and Chapter Test with online practice and review.

 Virtual Nerd™ Access Virtual Nerd student-centered math tutorials that directly relate to the content of the lesson.

 Overview of the Performance Task
Students will use linear functions to build a quadratic function model for profit. They will find and interpret the maximum point and the zeros of the profit function and relate them to the selling price of a product.

Students will work on the Performance Task in the following places in the chapter.

- Lesson 4-2 (p. 208)
- Lesson 4-3 (p. 214)
- Lesson 4-5 (p. 231)
- Pull It All Together (p. 266)

Introducing the Performance Task

Tell students to read the problem on this page. Do not have them start work on the problem at this time, but ask them the following questions.

> **Q** What is a strategy you could try in order to solve the problem? **[Sample: I could write a profit function, and then look for *x*-values that make the *y*-values positive, and for the *x*-value that corresponds to the maximum *y*-value.]**

> **Q** How is the profit Victor earns on the sale of one bag of chips related to his cost and selling price for the bag of chips? **[The profit is the difference between the selling price and the cost.]**

PARCC CLAIMS

Sub-Claim A: Major Content With Connections to Practices
Sub-Claim D: Highlighted Practice MP 4 With Connections to Content

SBAC CLAIMS

Claim 2: Problem Solving
Claim 4: Modeling and Data Analysis

Content Standards (cont')

Domain Arithmetic with Polynomials and Rational Expressions A-APR

Cluster Understand the relationship between zeros and factors of polynomials. (Standard A-APR.B.3)
LESSON 4-5

Domain Creating Equations A-CED

Cluster Create equations that describe numbers or relationships. (Standards A-CED.A.1★, A-CED.A.2★, A-CED.A.3★)
LESSONS 4-1, 4-2, 4-5, 4-9

Domain Reasoning with Equations and Inequalities A-REI

Cluster Solve systems of equations. (Standard A-REI.C.7)
LESSON 4-9

Cluster Represent and solve equations and inequalities graphically. (Standard A-REI.D.11★)
LESSON 4-9

QUADRATIC FUNCTIONS AND EQUATIONS
Math Background

© PROFESSIONAL DEVELOPMENT

The Understanding by Design® methodology was central to the development of the Big Ideas and the Essential Understandings. These will help your students build a structure on which to make connections to prior learning.

Equivalence

BIG idea A single quantity may be represented by many different expressions. The facts about a quantity may be expressed by many different equations (or inequalities).

ESSENTIAL UNDERSTANDINGS

4-1 The graph of any quadratic function is a transformation of the graph of the parent quadratic function, $y = x^2$.

4-2 For any quadratic function $f(x) = ax^2 + bx + c$, the values of a, b, and c provide key information about its graph.

4-3 Three noncollinear points, no two of which are in line vertically, are on the graph of exactly one quadratic function.

4-9 You can solve systems involving quadratic equations using methods similar to the ones used to solve systems of linear equations.

Function

BIG idea A function is a relationship between variables in which each value of the input variable is associated with a unique value of the output variable. Functions can be represented in a variety of ways, such as graphs, tables, equations, or words. Each representation is particularly useful in certain situations. Some important families of functions are developed through transformations of the simplest form of the function.

ESSENTIAL UNDERSTANDINGS

4-1 to 4-3 & 4-9 See above.

4-5 To find the zeros of a quadratic function $y = ax^2 + bx + c$, solve the related quadratic equation $0 = ax^2 + bx + c$.

Solving Equations & Inequalities

BIG idea Solving an equation is the process of rewriting the equation to make what it says about its variable(s) as simple as possible. Properties of numbers and equality can be used to transform an equation (or inequality) into equivalent, simpler equations (or inequalities) in order to find solutions. Useful information about equations and inequalities (including solutions) can be found by analyzing graphs or tables.

ESSENTIAL UNDERSTANDINGS

4-4 You can factor many quadratic trinomials $(ax^2 + bx + c)$ into products of two binomials.

4-5 & 4-9 See above.

4-6 Completing a perfect square trinomial allows you to factor the completed trinomial as the square of a binomial.

4-7 You can solve a quadratic equation $ax^2 + bx + c = 0$ in more than one way. In general, you can find a formula that gives values of x in terms of a, b, and c.

4-8 A basis for the complex numbers is a number whose square is -1. Every quadratic equation has complex number solutions (that sometimes are real numbers).

Describing and Graphing Quadratic Functions

The features used to describe a quadratic function can be determined by using a graphing calculator or analyzing the function in vertex or standard form.

Standard Form $y = ax^2 + bx + c$
- calculator friendly
- features found using simple formulas

Vertex Form $y = a(x - h)^2 + k$
- vertex and maximum or minimum can be read directly from equation
- shows how graph is transformed from the parent function

	Standard Form	Vertex Form
	$y = ax^2 + bx + c$	$y = a(x - h)^2 + k$
axis of symmetry	$x = \frac{-b}{2a}$	$x = h$
vertex	$\left(\frac{-b}{2a}, f\left(\frac{-b}{2a}\right)\right)$	(h, k)
y-intercept	$(0, c)$	$(0, a(x - h)^2 + k)$
maximum or minimum	$f\left(\frac{-b}{2a}\right)$	k

Graphing Calculator

The axis of symmetry, minimum or maximum, vertex, y-intercept, domain, and range can be found using the trace key or the table of a graphing calculator.

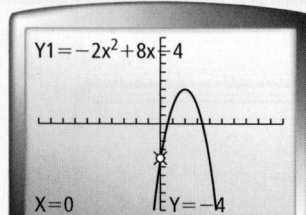
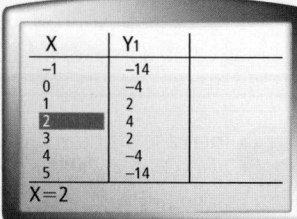

© Mathematical Practices

Look for and make use of structure. Reason abstractly and quantitatively. Quadratic functions are analyzed algebraically, graphically, and numerically, with continual emphasis on the connections among the various representations. Quadratic functions are introduced not only as a logical next step after linear functions, but also as a family of functions obtained by transformations of the basic function $y = x^2$. The quadratic formula is proved using the technique of completing the square.

Finding Zeros of Quadratic Functions

The zeros of quadratic functions are equivalent to the x-intercepts of the graph of the function or the solutions of the quadratic equation. The zeros can be found by graphing, factoring, completing the square, or using the quadratic formula.

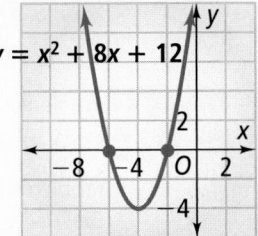

$y = x^2 + 8x + 12$

Factoring

Factor the quadratic function, set the equation equal to zero and solve for x.

$y = x^2 + 8x + 12$
$0 = (x + 6)(x + 2)$
$x = -6$ and $x = -2$

Completing the Square

Gather the x-terms on one side, and add $\left(\frac{b}{2}\right)^2$ to both sides.

$$x^2 + 8x = -12$$
$$x^2 + 8x + 16 = -12 + 16$$
$$(x + 4)^2 = 4$$
$$x + 4 = \pm 2$$
$$x = -6 \text{ or } -2$$

Quadratic Formula

The solutions of any quadratic equation can be found using the quadratic formula

$$x = \frac{-b \pm \sqrt{b^2 - 4ac}}{2a}.$$

The discriminant $b^2 - 4ac$ is used to determine the number and types of solutions.
- discriminant > 0, then 2 real solutions
- discriminant $= 0$, then 1 real solution (double root)
- discriminant < 0, then no real solutions

Common Errors When Finding Zeros of Quadratic Functions

Factoring and Completing the Square Errors

Many errors are due to algebraic mistakes. Encourage students to substitute the solutions back into the original equation to check their answers.

Quadratic Formula Errors

Mistakes occur when students use graphing calculators to solve the quadratic formula because they fail to use parentheses correctly. Encourage students to first find the discriminant to describe and check their solutions.

ⓒ Mathematical Practices

Model with mathematics. Make sense of problems and persevere in solving them. Students use quadratic equations to model a variety of real-world contexts. Students develop a variety of tools to solve quadratic equations.

Complex Numbers

A complex number has a real part and an imaginary part. Complex numbers can be written in the form $a + bi$ where a and b are real numbers.
- If $a = 0$ and $b \neq 0$, then the number is a pure imaginary number.
- If $b = 0$ and $a \neq 0$, then the number is a real number.
- If $a \neq 0$ and $b \neq 0$, then the number is a complex number with a real and imaginary part.

Imaginary Numbers

The square root of a negative number is an imaginary number. Imaginary numbers are indicated by i. By definition, $i = \sqrt{-1}$ or $i^2 = -1$.

Operations with Complex Numbers

Complex numbers can be added, subtracted, multiplied, or divided. The rules are similar to the rules for operations with binomials.

Complex Conjugates

The product of complex conjugates is a real number. Use complex conjugates to simplify quotients of complex numbers and rationalize denominators.

$$\frac{3}{3 + i} = \frac{3}{3 + i}\left(\frac{3 - i}{3 - i}\right)$$
$$= \frac{3(3 - i)}{(3 + i)(3 - i)}$$
$$= \frac{9 - 3i}{10}$$
$$= \frac{9}{10} - \frac{3i}{10}$$

Graphing Quadratic Functions with No Real Solutions

The graph of a quadratic function with no real solutions has no x-intercepts.

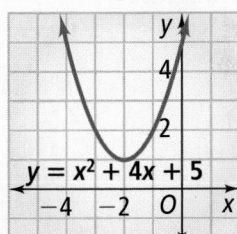

$y = x^2 + 4x + 5$

Common Errors When Using Complex Numbers

Simplifying Have students rewrite the problem using -1 to help them simplify. For example, $\sqrt{-9} = \sqrt{-1} \cdot \sqrt{9} = i(3)$ or $3i$.

Operations Suggest to students that they treat i using the same rules as they do for variables, reminding them that $i^2 = -1$.

Complex Conjugates Point out that multiplying complex conjugates is similar to multiplying binomials whose product is a difference of squares. For example,

$(x + 2)(x - 2) = x^2 - 4$
$(2 + i)(2 - i) = 4 - i^2 = 5$

ⓒ Mathematical Practices

Construct viable arguments and critique the reasoning of others. Attend to precision. Students extend their understanding of quadratics to include complex numbers. They develop the necessary vocabulary to communicate mathematically about complex numbers.

QUADRATIC FUNCTIONS AND EQUATIONS
Pacing and Assignment Guide

Lesson	Teaching Day(s)	TRADITIONAL Basic	Average	Advanced	BLOCK Block
4-1	1	Problems 1–3 Exs. 7–28, 66–75	Problems 1–3 Exs. 7–27 odd, 66–75	Problems 1–3 Exs. 7–27 odd, 66–75	**Day 1** Problems 1–5 Exs. 7–37 odd, 38–54, 66–75
	2	Problems 4–5; Exs. 29–39, 41–53 odd, 54	Problems 4–5 Exs. 29–37 odd, 38–54	Problems 4–5 Exs. 29–37 odd, 38–65	
4-2	1	Problems 1–2 Exs. 8–25	Problems 1–2 Exs. 9–25 odd	Problems 1–2 Exs. 9–25 odd	**Day 2** Problems 1–4 Exs. 9–31 odd, 33–48
	2	Problems 3–4 Exs. 26–32, 35–38, 40–46 even	Problems 3–4 Exs. 27–31 odd, 33–48	Problems 3–4 Exs. 27–31 odd, 33–53	
4-3	1	Problems 1–2 Exs. 7–13	Problems 1–2 Exs. 7–13 odd	Problems 1–2 Exs. 7–13 odd	**Day 3** Problems 1–3 Exs. 7–17 odd, 18–27
	2	Problem 3 Exs. 14–17, 21–25	Problem 3 Exs. 15, 18–26	Problem 3 Exs. 15, 18–30	
4-4	1	Problems 1–3 Exs. 14–46, 95–102	Problems 1–3 Exs. 15–45 odd, 95–102	Problems 1–3 Exs. 15–45 odd, 95–102	**Day 4** Problems 1–5 Exs. 15–55 odd, 56–82, 95–102
	2	Problems 4–5; Exs. 47–58, 71–74, 79, 82	Problems 4–5 Exs. 47–55 odd, 56–82	Problems 4–5 Exs. 47–55 odd, 56–94	
4-5	1	Problems 1–2 Exs. 9–26, 60–63	Problems 1–2 Exs. 9–25 odd, 60–63	Problems 1–2 Exs. 9–25 odd, 60–63	**Day 5** Problems 1–4 Exs. 9–35 odd, 37–56, 60–63
	2	Problems 3–4 Exs. 27–36, 37–43, 55	Problems 3–4 Exs. 27–35 odd, 37–56	Problems 3–4 Exs. 27–35 odd, 37–59	
4-6	1	Problems 1–3 Exs. 12–27, 86–100	Problems 1–3 Exs. 13–27 odd, 86–100	Problems 1–3 Exs. 13–27 odd, 86–100	**Day 6** Problems 1–6 Exs. 29–51 odd, 52–75, 86–100
	2	Problems 4–6; Exs. 28–51, 52, 54, 62, 64, 75	Problems 4–6 Exs. 29–51 odd, 52–75	Problems 4–6 Exs. 29–51 odd, 52–85	
4-7	1	Problems 1–2 Exs. 11–24, 78–90	Problems 1–2 Exs. 11–23 odd, 78–90	Problems 1–2 Exs. 11–23 odd, 78–90	**Day 7** Problems 1–4 Exs. 11–37 odd, 39–69, 78–90
	2	Problems 3–4 Exs. 25–42, 57–59, 67	Problems 3–4 Exs. 25–37 odd, 39–69	Problems 3–4 Exs. 25–37 odd, 39–77	
4-8	1	Problems 1–4 Exs. 8–26, 73–89	Problems 1–4 Exs. 9–25 odd, 73–89	Problems 1–4 Exs. 9–25 odd, 73–89	**Day 8** Problems 1–7 Exs. 9–43 odd, 45–69, 73–89
	2	Problems 5–7 Exs. 27–46, 48, 50, 56, 57	Problems 5–7 Exs. 27–43 odd, 45–69	Problems 5–7 Exs. 27–43 odd, 45–72	
4-9	1	Problems 1–2 Exs. 8–19, 62–77	Problems 1–2 Exs. 9–19 odd, 62–77	Problems 1–2 Exs. 9–19 odd, 62–77	**Day 9** Problems 1–4 Exs. 9–27 odd, 29–55, 62–77
	2	Problems 3–4 Exs. 20–31, 39–41, 47	Problems 3–4 Exs. 21–27 odd, 29–55	Problems 3–4 Exs. 21–27 odd, 29–61	
Review	1	Chapter 4 Review	Chapter 4 Review	Chapter 4 Review	**Day 10** Chapter 4 Review Chapter 4 Test
Assess	1	Chapter 4 Test	Chapter 4 Test	Chapter 4 Test	
Total		**20 Days**	**20 Days**	**20 Days**	**10 Days**

Note: Pacing does not include Concept Bytes and other feature pages.

Resources

KEY
I = Interactive asset at PowerAlgebra.com
E = Editable master at PowerAlgebra.com
P = Available in Print
M = Master at PowerAlgebra.com
✓ = CD-ROM

	For the Chapter	4-1	4-2	4-3	4-4	4-5	4-6	4-7	4-8	4-9
Planning										
Teacher Center Online Planner & Grade Book	I	I	I	I	I	I	I	I	I	I
Interactive Learning & Guided Instruction										
My Math Video	I									
Solve It!		I M	I M	I M	I M	I M	I M	I M	I M	I M
Student Companion		P M	P M	P M	P M	P M	P M	P M	P M	P M
Vocabulary Support		I P M	I P M	I P M	I P M	I P M	I P M	I P M	I P M	I P M
Got It? Support		I P	I P	I P	I P	I P	I P	I P	I P	I P
Dynamic Activity	I									
Online Problems		I	I	I	I	I	I	I	I	I
Additional Problems		M	M	M	M	M	M	M	M	M
English Language Learner Support (TR)		E P M	E P M	E P M	E P M	E P M	E P M	E P M	E P M	E P M
Activities, Games, and Puzzles		E M	E M	E M	E M	E M	E M	E M	E M	E M
Teaching With TI Technology With CD-ROM		✓ P	✓ P			✓ P		✓ P		
TI-Nspire™ Support CD-ROM		✓	✓	✓	✓	✓	✓	✓	✓	✓
Lesson Check & Practice										
Student Companion		P M	P M	P M	P M	P M	P M	P M	P M	P M
Lesson Check Support		I P	I P	I P	I P	I P	I P	I P	I P	I P
Practice and Problem Solving Workbook		P	P	P	P	P	P	P	P	P
Think About a Plan (TR)		E P M	E P M	E P M	E P M	E P M	E P M	E P M	E P M	E P M
Practice Form G (TR)		E P M	E P M	E P M	E P M	E P M	E P M	E P M	E P M	E P M
Standardized Test Prep (TR)		P M	P M	P M	P M	P M	P M	P M	P M	P M
Practice Form K (TR)		E P M	E P M	E P M	E P M	E P M	E P M	E P M	E P M	E P M
Extra Practice	E M									
Find the Errors!	M									
Enrichment (TR)		E P M	E P M	E P M	E P M	E P M	E P M	E P M	E P M	E P M
Answers and Solutions CD-ROM	✓	✓	✓	✓	✓	✓	✓	✓	✓	✓
Assess & Remediate										
ExamView CD-ROM	✓	✓	✓	✓	✓	✓	✓	✓	✓	✓
Lesson Quiz		I M	I M	I M	I M	I M	I M	I M	I M	I M
Quizzes and Tests Form G (TR)	E P M				E P M					E P M
Quizzes and Tests Form K (TR)	E P M				E P M					E P M
Reteaching (TR)		E P M	E P M	E P M	E P M	E P M	E P M	E P M	E P M	E P M
Performance Tasks (TR)	P M									
Cumulative Review (TR)	P M									
Progress Monitoring Assessments	I P M									

(TR) Available in All-In-One Teaching Resources

1 Interactive Learning

Solve It!

PURPOSE To identify features of a parabola and translate it

PROCESS Students may
- sketch the path of the jump onto paper and shift it so the highest part is over the fence.
- count the horizontal distance between the start and highest part of the jump.

FACILITATE

Q How can you calculate the horizontal distance between the start of the jump and the highest part? $[x_2 - x_1 = 2 - 0 = 2]$

Q What are the coordinates of the top of the fence? $[(4.5, 1)]$

Q What equation could you solve to find the start of a jump over the fence? $[4.5 - x = 2]$

ANSWER See Solve It in Answers on next page.
CONNECT THE MATH In the Solve It, students find the vertex, axis of symmetry, and points on a parabola and apply a translation. In the lesson, students will use these elements to identify and graph quadratic functions.

2 Guided Instruction

Take Note

Q How can you use vertex form to verify the axis of symmetry and vertex of $f(x) = x^2$? $[h = 0,$ so the axis of symmetry is $x = h = 0$; $k = 0$, so the vertex is $(h, k) = (0, 0).]$

Q What is $f(x) = x^2$ in vertex form? $[f(x) = 1(x - 0)^2 + 0]$

Common Core State Standards
F-BF.B.3 Identify the effect on the graph of replacing $f(x)$ by $f(x) + k$, $k f(x)$, $f(kx)$, and $f(x + k)$ for specific values of k . . . find the value of k given the graphs. **Also** A-CED.A.1, F-IF.B.4, F-IF.B.6
MP 1, MP 2, MP 3, MP 4, MP 7

Objective To identify and graph quadratic functions

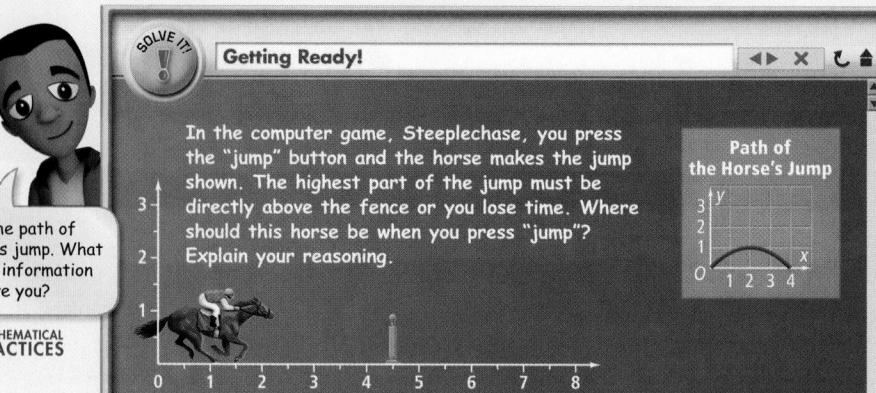

Analyze the path of the horse's jump. What additional information does it give you?

MATHEMATICAL PRACTICES

In the Solve It, you used the *parabolic* shape of the horse's jump. A **parabola** is the graph of a **quadratic function**, which you can write in the form $f(x) = ax^2 + bx + c$, where $a \neq 0$.

Essential Understanding The graph of any quadratic function is a transformation of the graph of the parent quadratic function, $y = x^2$.

The **vertex form** of a quadratic function is $f(x) = a(x - h)^2 + k$, where $a \neq 0$. The **axis of symmetry** is a line that divides the parabola into two mirror images. The equation of the axis of symmetry is $x = h$. The **vertex of the parabola** is (h, k), the intersection of the parabola and its axis of symmetry.

Lesson Vocabulary
- parabola
- quadratic function
- vertex form
- axis of symmetry
- vertex of the parabola
- minimum value
- maximum value

take note

Key Concept The Parent Quadratic Function

The parent quadratic function is $f(x) = x^2$. Its graph is the parabola shown. The axis of symmetry is $x = 0$. The vertex is $(0, 0)$.

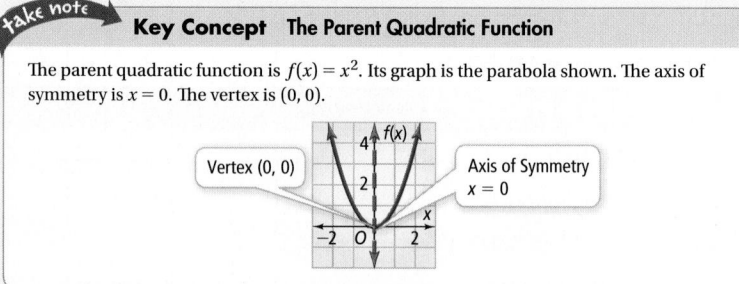

Vertex $(0, 0)$

Axis of Symmetry $x = 0$

4-1 Preparing to Teach

BIG ideas Function
Equivalence

ESSENTIAL UNDERSTANDINGS
- The graph of any quadratic function is a transformation of the graph of the parent quadratic function, $y = x^2$.
- The vertex form of a quadratic function is $f(x) = a(x - h)^2 + k$, where $a \neq 0$.
- The axis of symmetry is a line that divides the parabola into two mirror images.
- The vertex of the parabola is (h, k), the intersection of the parabola and its axis of symmetry.

Math Background

When considering transformations, students may wonder whether they can transform the graph of a quadratic function so that the parabola opens leftward or rightward. The graph can be transformed this way, for example, by a reflection in $y = x$. Suggest that students draw the graph and check to see whether the graph represents

a function. Except for the vertex, two values in the range are paired with each value in the domain. Only parabolas that open upward or downward are functions of x.

Note the comparisons between the transformations of the quadratic function $y = x^2$ and the transformations of the absolute value function in Lesson 2-7. However, be aware that students sometimes confuse absolute value graphs with parabolas. If this happens, help them determine the degree of the function. Absolute value functions, like linear functions, have the variable in the first degree.

Mathematical Practices
Make sense of problems and persevere in solving them. Students will graph quadratic functions and label important features such as the vertex and axis of symmetry.

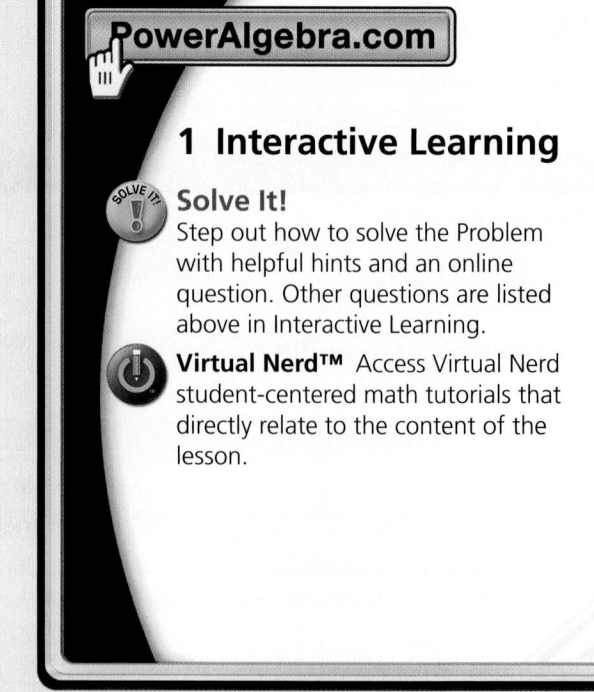

PowerAlgebra.com

1 Interactive Learning

Solve It!
Step out how to solve the Problem with helpful hints and an online question. Other questions are listed above in Interactive Learning.

Virtual Nerd™ Access Virtual Nerd student-centered math tutorials that directly relate to the content of the lesson.

Plan

How do you choose points to plot?
Choose the vertex and two points on one side of the axis of symmetry that give integer values of $f(x)$.

© **Problem 1** Graphing a Function of the Form $f(x) = ax^2$

What is the graph of $f(x) = \frac{1}{2}x^2$?

Step 1 Plot the vertex $(0, 0)$. Draw the axis of symmetry, $x = 0$.

Step 2 Find and plot two points on one side of the axis of symmetry.

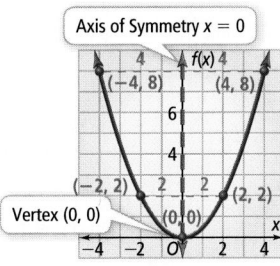

x	$f(x) = \frac{1}{2}x^2$	$(x, f(x))$
0	$\frac{1}{2}(0)^2 = 0$	$(0, 0)$
2	$\frac{1}{2}(2)^2 = 2$	$(2, 2)$
4	$\frac{1}{2}(4)^2 = 8$	$(4, 8)$

Axis of Symmetry $x = 0$

$(-4, 8)$ $f(x)$ $(4, 8)$

$(-2, 2)$ $(2, 2)$

Vertex $(0, 0)$

Step 3 Plot the corresponding points on the other side of the axis of symmetry.

Step 4 Sketch the curve.

© ✓ **Got It?** **1. a.** What is the graph of $f(x) = -\frac{1}{3}x^2$?

b. Reasoning What can you say about the graph of the function $f(x) = ax^2$ if a is a negative number? Explain.

Graphs of $y = ax^2$ and $y = -ax^2$ are reflections of each other across the x-axis. Increasing $|a|$ stretches the graph vertically and narrows it horizontally. Decreasing $|a|$ compresses the graph vertically and widens it horizontally.

Key Concept Reflection, Stretch, and Compression

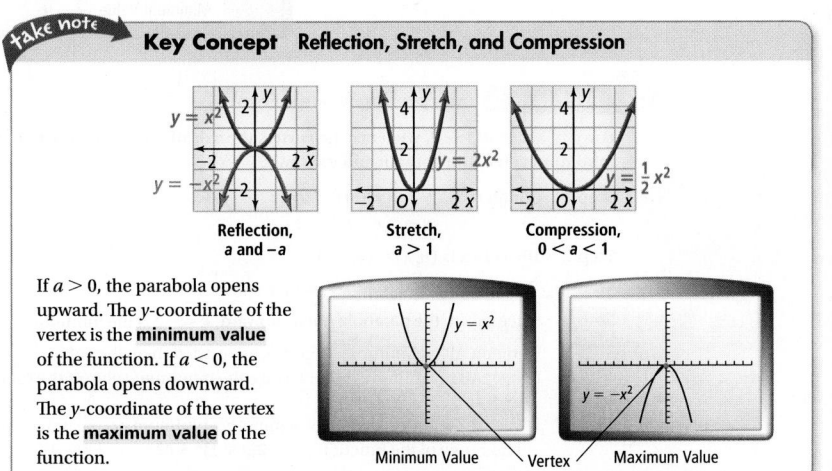

$y = x^2$

$y = -x^2$

$y = 2x^2$

$y = \frac{1}{2}x^2$

Reflection, a and $-a$

Stretch, $a > 1$

Compression, $0 < a < 1$

If $a > 0$, the parabola opens upward. The y-coordinate of the vertex is the **minimum value** of the function. If $a < 0$, the parabola opens downward. The y-coordinate of the vertex is the **maximum value** of the function.

$y = x^2$

Minimum Value   Vertex   Maximum Value

$y = -x^2$

Problem 1 — EXTENSION

An alternate strategy is to think of $f(x) = x^2$ as the relation between x-values and their squares: $(-1, 1), (0, 0), (1, 1), (2, 4)$. Then $f(x) = \frac{1}{2}x^2$ is the relation between x-values and *half* of their squares: $(-1, 0.5), (0, 0), (1, 0.5), (2, 2)$.

Q Why is it preferable to use two points on each side of the axis? **[Two points help determine the curvature of the parabola.]**

Got It?

Q What is the vertex of $f(x) = ax^2$? What is the greatest value of $f(x)$ for $a < 0$? **[(0, 0); 0]**

Take Note — ELL SUPPORT

The terms *stretch, compression, minimum,* and *maximum* are challenging, since each word can be used in different contexts and has several synonyms. Focus on the mathematical meanings by creating a graphic organizer with several examples of meanings of each term. If time allows, use word webs to raise students' comfort with alternate meanings and synonyms such as *mirror image* for *reflection* or *shrink* for *compression*.

Q For the parabola in the Solve It, what can you say about a? **[a < 0, because the parabola opens downward and has a maximum.]**

ERROR PREVENTION

Explain that a stretch moves each y-value higher as if the parabola were stretched up. Do not allow students to describe the transformation as the process that makes the parabola thinner.

---

2 Guided Instruction

© Each Problem is worked out and supported online.

Problem 1
Graphing a Function of the Form $f(x) = ax^2$

Problem 2
Graphing Translations of $f(x) = x^2$
Animated

Problem 3
Interpreting Vertex Form

Problem 4
Using Vertex Form
Animated

Problem 5
Writing a Quadratic Function in Vertex Form
Animated

Support in Algebra 2 Companion
• Vocabulary
• Key Concepts
• Got It?

Answers

Solve It!
2 units before the fence, or at 2.5; the horse is at its highest pt. 2 units after beginning the jump.

Got It?

1. a.

b. If a is a negative number, the parabola will open downward. There will be a maximum value for y at the vertex of the parabola.

Problem 2 — EXTENSION

Q What function $p(x)$ translates the graph of $f(x)$ up 5 units? **[$p(x) = x^2 + 5$]**

Q What function $q(x)$ translates the graph of $f(x)$ left 4 units? **[$q(x) = (x + 4)^2$]**

Q What function $n(x)$ translates the graph of $h(x) = (x - 4)^2$ right 5 units? **[$n(x) = (x - 9)^2$]**

Got It? — ERROR PREVENTION

Be aware of students who interpret the $+1$ in 2b as a translation of the vertex one unit to the right on the x-axis.

Q How can you write 2b in vertex form?
[$h(x) = 1[x - (-1)]^2 + 0$]

Problem 3

This problem is the first to show the combined effects of all three constants, a, h, and k, in a single quadratic function. You may need to briefly review the definitions of domain and range.

Q Do all quadratic functions have a domain of all real numbers? **[Answers may vary. Sample: No; some real-world quadratic models have restricted domains; for example, the function that models the path of the jump in the Solve It is restricted to x-values between 0 and 4.]**

Got It? — EXTENSION

Q Assuming $f(x) = a(x - h)^2 + k$ has an unrestricted domain, what is the range in terms of a, h, and k? **[If $a > 0$, then the range is all real numbers $\geq k$; if $a < 0$, then the range is all real numbers $\leq k$.]**

 Problem 2 Graphing Translations of $f(x) = x^2$

Graph each function. How is each graph a translation of $f(x) = x^2$?

Think

How does $g(x)$ differ from $f(x)$?
For each value of x, the value of $g(x)$ is 5 less than the value of $f(x)$.

Ⓐ $g(x) = x^2 - 5$

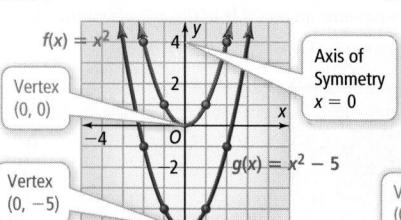

Translate the graph of f down 5 units to get the graph of $g(x) = x^2 - 5$.

Ⓑ $h(x) = (x - 4)^2$

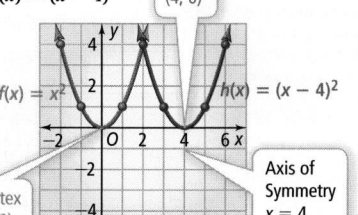

Translate the graph of f to the right 4 units to get the graph of $h(x) = (x - 4)^2$.

 Got It? 2. Graph each function. How is it a translation of $f(x) = x^2$?
a. $g(x) = x^2 + 3$ b. $h(x) = (x + 1)^2$

The vertex form, $f(x) = a(x - h)^2 + k$, gives you information about the graph of f without drawing the graph. If $a > 0$, k is the minimum value of the function. If $a < 0$, k is the maximum value.

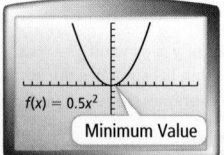

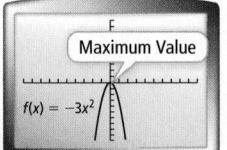

 Problem 3 Interpreting Vertex Form

For $y = 3(x - 4)^2 - 2$, what are the vertex, the axis of symmetry, the maximum or minimum value, the domain and the range?

Plan

How do you use vertex form?
Compare
$y = 3(x - 4)^2 - 2$
to vertex form
$y = a(x - h)^2 + k$
to find values for a, h, and k.

Step 1 Compare: $y = 3(x - 4)^2 - 2$
$y = a(x - h)^2 + k$

Step 2 The vertex is $(h, k) = (4, -2)$.

Step 3 The axis of symmetry is $x = h$, or $x = 4$.

Step 4 Since $a > 0$, the parabola opens upward. $k = -2$ is the minimum value.

Step 5 Domain: All real numbers. There is no restriction on the value of x.
Range: All real numbers ≥ -2, since the minimum value of the function is -2.

 Got It? 3. What are the vertex, axis of symmetry, minimum or maximum, and domain and range of the function $y = -2(x + 1)^2 + 4$?

Additional Problems

1. What is the graph of $f(x) = -\frac{1}{4}x^2$?

ANSWER

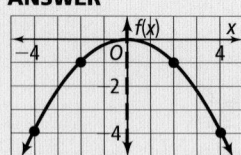

2. Graph each function. How is each graph a translation of $f(x) = x^2$?
a. $g(x) = (x - 3)^2$
b. $h(x) = x^2 + 1$

ANSWER

a.
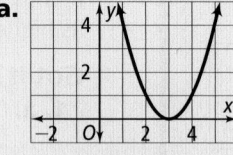

b.
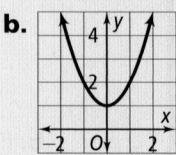

Translate $f(x) = x^2$ right 3 units to get $g(x) = (x - 3)^2$.
Translate $f(x) = x^2$ up 1 unit to get $h(x) = x^2 + 1$.

3. For $y = \frac{1}{2}(x - 3)^2 - 5$, what are the vertex, the axis of symmetry, the minimum or maximum value, the domain, and the range?

ANSWER The vertex is $(3, -5)$; the axis of symmetry is $x = 3$; $k = -5$ is the minimum value; the domain is all real numbers; and the range is all real numbers ≥ -5.

4. What is the graph of $f(x) = -3(x + 5)^2 + 2$?

ANSWER

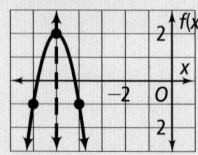

5. The arch of the Sidney Harbor Bridge is approximately 500 meters long and 85 meters high. What quadratic function models the curve of the arch? Assume the arch starts at $(0, 0)$.

ANSWER
$f(x) = -\frac{17}{12,500}(x - 250)^2 + 85$

You can use the vertex form of a quadratic function, $f(x) = a(x - h)^2 + k$, to transform the graph of the parent function $f(x) = x^2$.
- Stretch or compress the graph of $f(x) = x^2$ vertically by the factor $|a|$.
- If $a < 0$, reflect the graph across the x-axis.
- Shift the graph $|h|$ units horizontally and $|k|$ units vertically.

take note — Key Concept Translation of the Parabola

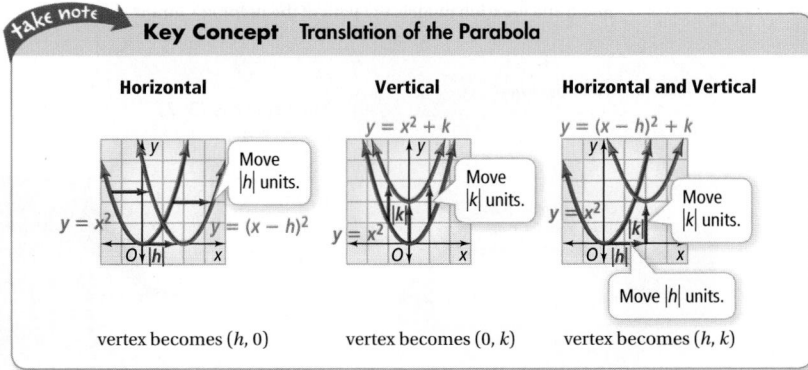

Horizontal	Vertical	Horizontal and Vertical
vertex becomes $(h, 0)$	vertex becomes $(0, k)$	vertex becomes (h, k)

Problem 4 Using Vertex Form

A What is the graph of $f(x) = -2(x - 1)^2 + 3$?

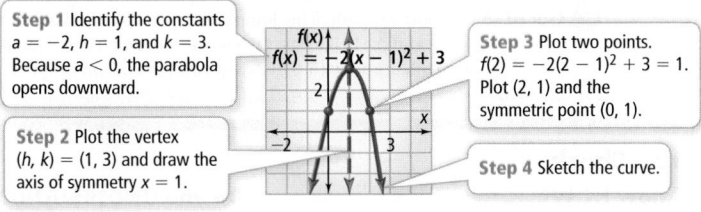

Step 1 Identify the constants $a = -2$, $h = 1$, and $k = 3$. Because $a < 0$, the parabola opens downward.

Step 2 Plot the vertex $(h, k) = (1, 3)$ and draw the axis of symmetry $x = 1$.

Step 3 Plot two points. $f(2) = -2(2 - 1)^2 + 3 = 1$. Plot $(2, 1)$ and the symmetric point $(0, 1)$.

Step 4 Sketch the curve.

B **Multiple Choice** What steps transform the graph of $y = x^2$ to $y = -2(x + 1)^2 + 3$?

Ⓐ Reflect across the x-axis, stretch by the factor 2, translate 1 unit to the right and 3 units up.

Ⓑ Stretch by the factor 2, translate 1 unit to the right and 3 units up.

Ⓒ Reflect across the x-axis, translate 1 unit to the left and 3 units up.

Ⓓ Stretch by the factor 2, reflect across the x-axis, translate 1 unit to the left and 3 units up.

The correct choice is D.

Got It? **4.** What steps transform the graph of $y = x^2$ to $y = 2(x + 2)^2 - 5$?

PowerAlgebra.com | **Lesson 4-1** Quadratic Functions and Transformations | **197**

Take Note   SYNTHESIZING

Have students compare and contrast translations of quadratic functions with translations of absolute value functions from Lesson 2-7. Note that they will do this in the future with other types of functions. The effects on the graphs and function equations are identical; only the shapes of the curves are different. The same can be said for the effects of reflections, stretches, and compressions.

Problem 4

Q Identify the steps to transform the graph of $y = x^2$ to the graph in 4A. How does this transformation compare to the transformation in 4B? **[stretch by the factor 2, reflect across the x-axis, translate 1 unit to the right and 3 units up; answers may vary. Sample: The only difference is that the horizontal translation is 1 unit to the left instead of 1 unit to the right.]**

Q Why is the vertex form the easiest form to graph a parabola? **[It isolates two of the most important features of the parabola: the maximum or minimum point and the direction it opens.]**

Got It?

Q In what order should the steps be taken? **[Sample: First stretch or compression, then reflection and then translation.]**

Q In which quadrant is the vertex located? **[Quadrant III]**

Answers

Got It? (continued)

2. a. translated 3 units up

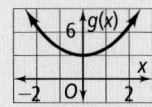

b. translated 1 unit to the left

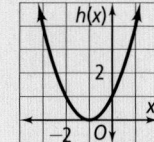

3. vertex: $(-1, 4)$; axis of symmetry: $x = -1$; maximum: 4; domain: all real numbers, range: $y \leq 4$

4. stretch by the factor 2, translate 2 units to the left and 5 units down

5. $f(x) = -\frac{2}{9}(x - 2)^2 + 7$

Lesson Check

1.

2. minimum

3. $y = -2(x - 0)^2 + 35$

4. when $a > 0$

5. No; a must be > 0 or < 0.

6. $y = (x + 6)^2$ is the graph of $y = x^2$ translated 6 units to the left and has a minimum at $(-6, 0)$; $y = (x - 6)^2 + 7$ is the graph of $y = x^2$ translated 6 units to the right and 7 units up, with a minimum at $(6, 7)$.

Practice and Problem-Solving Exercises

7.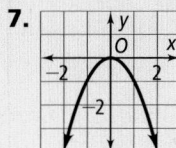

8.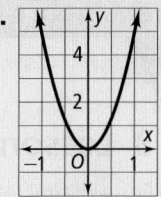

9.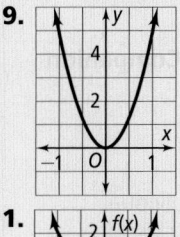

10.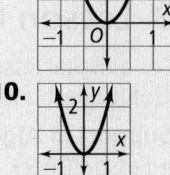

11.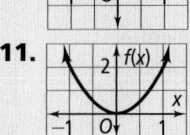

12.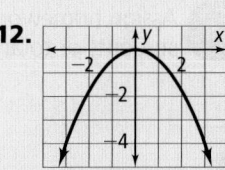

13.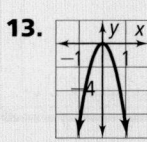

14.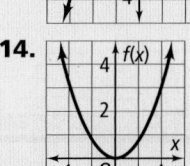

Problem 5

Unlike Problems 1–4 that went from function to graph, this problem goes from graph to function.

Q How can you tell from the picture that a is negative? **[The path of the jump opens downward.]**

Q What is the least information you need to write the equation? **[the vertex and one other point]**

Got It?

ERROR PREVENTION

Suggest students sketch the path so they see the vertex is (2, 7). Be aware of students simplifying $5 = a(5 - 2)^2 + 7$ as $5 = a(25 - 4) + 7$, which would give an answer of $a = -\frac{2}{21}$.

3 Lesson Check

Do you know HOW?

- For Exercise 3, if students say the equation is already in vertex form, confirm understanding by asking for the values of a, h, and k.

Do you UNDERSTAND?

- For Exercise 4, review the definition of vertex form on page 194. Explain that the constant linear function results when $a = 0$.

Close

Q How can you use a quadratic function written in vertex form to describe the graph of the parabola? **[The absolute value of a in vertex form gives a stretch or compression of the parent function; the sign of a gives the direction the parabola opens; h gives the axis of symmetry; and (h, k) is the vertex.]**

You can use the vertex form of a quadratic function to model a real-world situation.

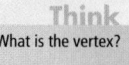 **Problem 5** Writing a Quadratic Function in Vertex Form

Nature The picture shows the jump of a dolphin. What quadratic function models the path of the dolphin's jump?

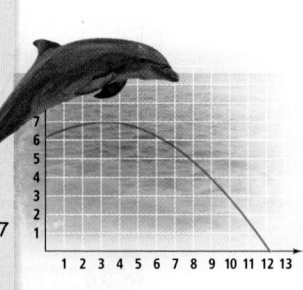

Think	Write
What is the vertex?	The vertex is $(3, 7)$. $h = 3, k = 7$
Choose another point, $(9, 4)$, from the path. Substitute in the vertex form. Solve for a.	$f(x) = a(x - h)^2 + k$ $4 = a(9 - 3)^2 + 7$ $4 = 36a + 7$ $-3 = 36a$ $a = -\frac{1}{12}$
Substitute in the vertex form.	$f(x) = -\frac{1}{12}(x - 3)^2 + 7$ models the path of the dolphin's jump.

Got It? 5. Suppose the path of the jump changes so that the axis of symmetry becomes $x = 2$ and the height stays the same. If the path of the jump also passes through the point $(5, 5)$, what quadratic function would model this path?

Lesson Check

Do you know HOW?

1. Graph the function $f(x) = -3x^2$.

2. Determine whether the function $f(x) = 0.25 (2x - 15)^2 + 150$ has a maximum or a minimum value.

3. Rewrite $y = -2x^2 + 35$ in vertex form.

Do you UNDERSTAND? **MATHEMATICAL PRACTICES**

4. Vocabulary When does the graph of a quadratic function have a minimum value?

5. Reasoning Is $y = 0(x - 4)^2 + 3$ a quadratic function? Explain.

6. Compare and Contrast Describe the differences between the graphs of $y = (x + 6)^2$ and $y = (x - 6)^2 + 7$.

---

3 Lesson Check

For a digital lesson check, use the Got It questions.

Support in Algebra 2 Companion
- Lesson Check

4 Practice

ONLINE HOMEWORK

Assign homework to individual students or to an entire class.

Answers

Got It? (continued)

5. See page 197.

Lesson Check

1–6. See page 197.

Practice and Problem-Solving Exercises (continued)

7–14. See page 197.

15. translated 3 units up

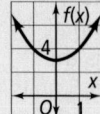

16. translated 2 units to the right

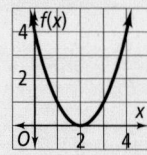

17. translated 6 units down

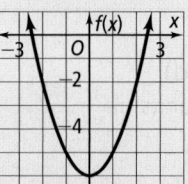

18. translated 3 units to the left

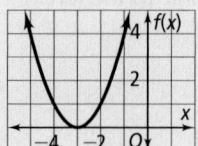

Practice and Problem-Solving Exercises  MATHEMATICAL PRACTICES

A Practice

Graph each function. ◀ **See Problem 1.**

7. $y = -x^2$
8. $f(x) = 5x^2$
9. $y = \frac{2}{5}x^2$
10. $y = 2x^2$

11. $f(x) = 2\frac{1}{4}x^2$
12. $y = -\frac{4}{9}x^2$
13. $y = -7x^2$
14. $f(x) = 3\frac{2}{5}x^2$

Graph each function. Describe how it was translated from $f(x) = x^2$. ◀ **See Problem 2.**

15. $f(x) = x^2 + 3$
16. $f(x) = (x - 2)^2$
17. $f(x) = x^2 - 6$
18. $f(x) = (x + 3)^2$

19. $f(x) = x^2 - 9$
20. $f(x) = (x + 5)^2$
21. $f(x) = x^2 + 1.5$
22. $f(x) = (x - 2.5)^2$

Identify the vertex, the axis of symmetry, the maximum or minimum value, and the domain and the range of each function. ◀ **See Problem 3.**

23. $y = -1.5(x + 20)^2$
24. $f(x) = 0.1(x - 3.2)^2$
25. $f(x) = 24(x + 5.5)^2$

26. $y = 0.0035(x + 1)^2 - 1$
27. $f(x) = -(x - 4)^2 - 25$
28. $y = (x - 125)^2 + 125$

Graph each function. Identify the axis of symmetry. ◀ **See Problem 4.**

29. $f(x) = (x - 1)^2 + 2$
30. $y = (x + 3)^2 - 4$
31. $f(x) = 2(x - 2)^2 + 5$

32. $y = -3(x + 7)^2 - 8$
33. $y = -(x - 1)^2 + 4$
34. $f(x) = -(x - 7)^2 + 10$

Write a quadratic function to model each graph. ◀ **See Problem 5.**

35.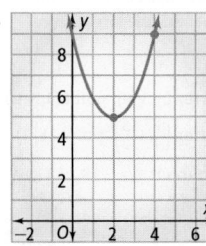
36.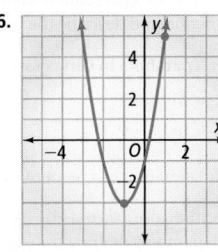
37.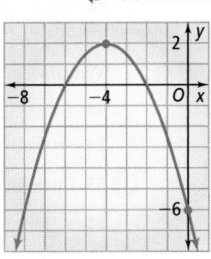

B Apply

38. **Think About a Plan** A gardener is putting a wire fence along the edge of his garden to keep animals from eating his plants. If he has 20 meters of fence, what is the largest rectangular area he can enclose?
- To find the area of a rectangle, what two quantities do you need? Choose one to be your variable and write the other in terms of this variable.
- How can a graph help you solve this problem?
- What quadratic function represents the area of the garden?

STEM **39.** **Manufacturing** The equation for the cost in dollars of producing computer chips is $C = 0.000015x^2 - 0.03x + 35$, where x is the number of chips produced. Find the number of chips that minimizes the cost. What is the cost for that number of chips?

PowerAlgebra.com | **Lesson 4-1** Quadratic Functions and Transformations | **199**

---

4 Practice

ASSIGNMENT GUIDE
Basic: 7–39 all, 41–53 odd, 54
Average: 7–37 odd, 38–54
Advanced: 7–37 odd, 38–65
Standardized Test Prep: 66–69
Mixed Review: 70–75

© **Mathematical Practices** are supported by exercises with red headings. Here are the Practices supported in this lesson:

MP 1: Make Sense of Problems Ex. 38
MP 2: Reason Abstractly Ex. 5, 53
MP 3: Communicate Ex. 6
MP 7: Look for Patterns Ex. 47

Applications exercises have blue headings. Exercise 39 supports MP 4: Model.

STEM exercises focus on science or engineering applications.

EXERCISE 48: Use the Think About a Plan worksheet in the **Practice and Problem Solving Workbook** (also available in the Teaching Resources in print and online) to further support students' development in becoming independent learners.

HOMEWORK QUICK CHECK
To check students' understanding of key skills and concepts, go over Exercises 15, 23, 38, 39, and 48.

---

19. translated 9 units down

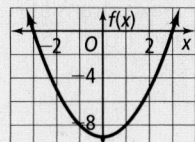

20. translated 5 units to the left

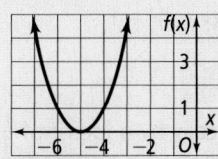

21. translated 1.5 units up

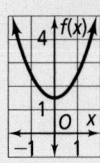

22. translated 2.5 units to the right

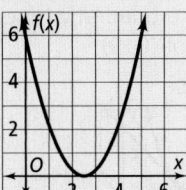

23. vertex: $(-20, 0)$; axis of symmetry: $x = -20$; maximum: 0; domain: all real numbers, range: $y \le 0$

24. vertex: $(3.2, 0)$; axis of symmetry: $x = 3.2$; minimum: 0; domain: all real numbers, range: $y \ge 0$

25. vertex: $(-5.5, 0)$; axis of symmetry: $x = -5.5$; minimum: 0; domain: all real numbers, range: $y \ge 0$

26. vertex: $(-1, -1)$; axis of symmetry: $x = -1$; minimum: -1; domain: all real numbers, range: $y \ge -1$

27. vertex: $(4, -25)$; axis of symmetry: $x = 4$; maximum: -25; domain: all real numbers, range: $y \le -25$

28. vertex: $(125, 125)$; axis of symmetry: $x = 125$; minimum: 125; domain: all real numbers, range: $y \ge 125$

29. $x = 1$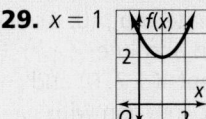

30. $x = -3$ **31.** $x = 2$

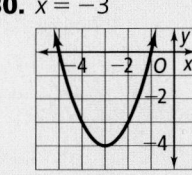

32. $x = -7$ **33.** $x = 1$

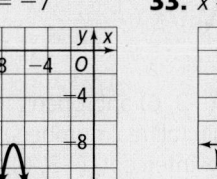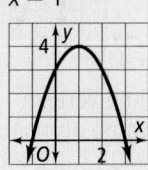

34–39. See next page.

Lesson 4-1 **199**

Answers

Practice and Problem-Solving
Exercises (continued)

34. $x = 7$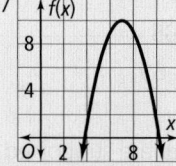

35. $y = (x - 2)^2 + 5$

36. $y = 2(x + 1)^2 - 3$

37. $y = -\frac{1}{2}(x + 4)^2 + 2$

38. 25 m² **39.** 1000 chips; $20

40. similar: same vertex (2, 1) and open downward, same domain (all real numbers), same range ($y \le 1$), same x-intercepts, (1, 0), (3, 0); different: $y = -|x - 2| + 1$ is an absolute value function with y-intercept (0, −1) and $y = -(x - 2)^2 + 1$ is a quadratic function with y-intercept of (0, −3).

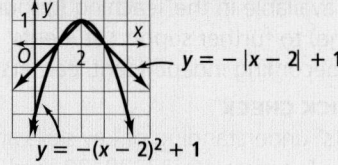

41. similar: same vertex (−1, −2) and open upward, same domain (all real numbers), same range ($y \ge -2$), same y-intercept, (0, 1); different: $y = 3|x + 1| - 2$ is an absolute value function with x-intercepts $\left(-\frac{1}{3}, 0\right)$ and $\left(-\frac{5}{3}, 0\right)$, and $y = 3(x + 1)^2 - 2$ is a quadratic function with x-intercepts $\left(-1 \pm \sqrt{\frac{2}{3}}, 0\right)$

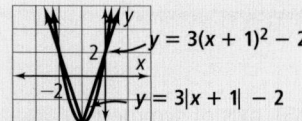

42. similar: same vertex (0, 4) and open downward, same domain (all real numbers), same range ($y \le 4$), same y-intercept, (0, 4); different: $y = -2|x| + 4$ is an absolute value function with x-intercepts (± 2, 0) and $y = -2(x)^2 + 4$ is a quadratic function with x-intercepts ($\pm\sqrt{2}$, 0)

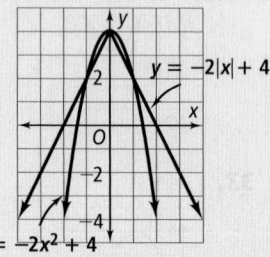

43. similar: same vertex (−3, 0) and open upward, same domain (all real numbers), same range ($y \ge 0$), same x-intercept, (−3, 0); different: $y = |x + 3|$ is an absolute value

---

In Chapter 2, you graphed absolute value functions as transformations of their parent function $y = |x|$. Similarly, you can graph a quadratic function as a transformation of the parent function $y = x^2$. Graph the following pairs of functions on the same set of axes. Determine how they are similar and how they are different.

40. $y = -|x - 2| + 1; y = -(x - 2)^2 + 1$

41. $y = 3|x + 1| - 2; y = 3(x + 1)^2 - 2$

42. $y = -2|x| + 4; y = -2x^2 + 4$

43. $y = |x + 3|; y = (x + 3)^2$

Describe how to transform the parent function $y = x^2$ to the graph of each function below. Graph both functions on the same axes.

44. $y = -2(x - 1)^2$ **45.** $y = -2(x + 1)^2 + 1$ **46.** $y = -0.25x^2 + 3$

47. You can find the rate of change for an interval between two points of a function by finding the slope between the points. Use the graph to find the y-value for each x-value. Then find the rate of change for each interval.

   a. (0, ■) and (1, ■)
   b. (1, ■) and (2, ■)
   c. (2, ■) and (3, ■)
   d. Reasoning. What do you notice about the rate of change as the interval gets further away from the vertex?
   e. Would your answer to part (d) change if the intervals were on the left side of the graph? Explain.

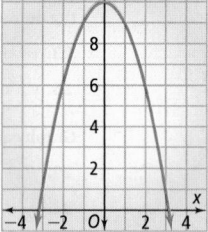

48. Write a quadratic function to represent the areas of all rectangles with a perimeter of 36 ft. Graph the function and describe the rectangle that has the largest area.

Write the equation of each parabola in vertex form.

49. vertex (1, 2), point (2, −5) **50.** vertex (−3, 6), point (1, −2)

51. vertex (0, 5), point (1, −2) **52.** vertex $\left(\frac{1}{4}, -\frac{3}{2}\right)$, point (1, 3)

53. Open-Ended Write an equation of a parabola symmetric about $x = -10$.

54. a. Technology Determine the axis of symmetry for each parabola defined by the spreadsheet values at the right.
   b. How could you use the spreadsheet columns to verify that the axes of symmetry are correct?
   c. What functions in vertex form model the data?
   Check that the axes of symmetry are correct.

	A	B
	X1	Y1
1		
2	1	−35
3	2	−15
4	3	−3
5	4	1
6	5	−3

	A	B
	X2	Y2
1		
2	1	10
3	2	2
4	3	2
5	4	10
6	5	26

---

function with y-intercept (0, 3), and $y = (x + 3)^2$ is a quadratic function with y-intercept (0, 9)

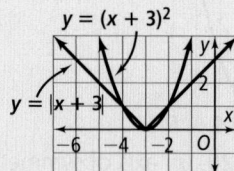

44. stretch vertically by a factor of 2, reflect across the x-axis, and translate 1 unit to the right

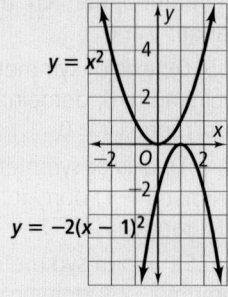

45. stretch vertically by a factor of 2, reflect across the x-axis, translate 1 unit to the left and 1 unit up

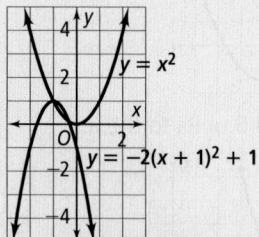

46. compress vertically by a factor of $\frac{1}{4}$, reflect across the x-axis and translate 3 units up

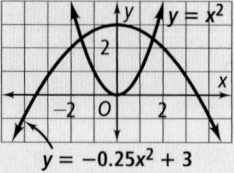

Challenge

Determine *a* and *k* so the given points are on the graph of the function.

55. $(0, 1), (2, 1); y = a(x - 1)^2 + k$

56. $(-3, 2), (0, 11); y = a(x + 2)^2 + k$

57. $(1, 11), (2, -19); y = a(x + 1)^2 + k$

58. $(-2, 6), (3, 1); y = a(x - 3)^2 + k$

59. a. In the function $y = ax^2 + bx + c$, c represents the y-intercept. Find the value of the y-intercept in the function $y = a(x - h)^2 + k$.
   b. Under what conditions does k represent the y-intercept?

Find the quadratic function $y = a(x - h)^2$ whose graph passes through the given points.

60. $(-2, 1)$ and $(2, 1)$

61. $(-5, 2)$ and $(-1, 2)$

62. $(-1, -4)$ and $(7, -4)$

63. $(2, -1)$ and $(4, 0)$

64. $(-2, 18)$ and $(1, 0)$

65. $(1, -64)$ and $(-3, 0)$

Standardized Test Prep

66. One parabola at the right has the equation $y = (x - 4)^2 + 2$. Which equation represents the second parabola?

Ⓐ $y = -(x - 4)^2 + 2$

Ⓑ $y = (-x - 4)^2 + 2$

Ⓒ $y = (x + 4)^2 - 2$

Ⓓ $y = -(x + 4)^2 - 2$

67. Which system has the unique solution $(1, 4)$?

Ⓕ $\begin{cases} y = x - 3 \\ x + y = 5 \end{cases}$

Ⓖ $\begin{cases} y = -x + 5 \\ x - y = -3 \end{cases}$

Ⓗ $\begin{cases} x + y = 5 \\ y = -x + 3 \end{cases}$

Ⓘ $\begin{cases} -x + y = 3 \\ 2x - 2y = -6 \end{cases}$

68. What is the formula for the surface area of a right circular cylinder, $S = 2\pi rh + 2\pi r^2$, solved for h?

Ⓐ $h = \dfrac{S}{4\pi r}$

Ⓑ $h = \dfrac{S}{2\pi r^2}$

Ⓒ $h = \dfrac{S}{2\pi r} - r$

Ⓓ $h = r - \dfrac{S}{2\pi r}$

69. An athletic club has 225 feet of fencing to enclose a tennis court. What quadratic function can be used to find the maximum area of the tennis court? Find the maximum area, and the lengths of the sides of the resulting fence.

Mixed Review

Solve each system of equations using a matrix. ◆ See Lesson 3-6.

70. $\begin{cases} 3x - y = 7 \\ 2x + 2y = 10 \end{cases}$

71. $\begin{cases} 2x + 5y = 10 \\ -3x + y = 36 \end{cases}$

72. $\begin{cases} 3x + y - 2z = -3 \\ x - 3y - z = -2 \\ 2x + 2y + 3z = 11 \end{cases}$

Get Ready! **To prepare for Lesson 4-2, do Exercises 73–75.**

Find the vertex of the graph of each function. ◆ See Lesson 2-7.

73. $y = -2|x|$

74. $y = |-x - 1|$

75. $y = 5|x - 5|$

---

58. Answers may vary. Sample:
$a = \dfrac{1}{5}, k = 1; y = \dfrac{1}{5}(x - 3)^2 + 1$

59. a. $ah^2 + k$ **b.** when $h = 0$

60. $y = \dfrac{1}{4}x^2$

61. $y = \dfrac{1}{2}(x + 3)^2$

62. $y = -\dfrac{1}{4}(x - 3)^2$

63. $y = -\dfrac{1}{4}(x - 4)^2$

64. $y = 2(x - 1)^2$

65. $y = -4(x + 3)^2$

Standardized Test Prep

66. A   **67.** G   **68.** C

69. [2]
$$2x + 2y = 225$$
$$2y = 225 - 2x$$
$$y = \frac{225}{2} - x$$
$$A = xy = x\left(\frac{225}{2} - x\right)$$
$$A = -x^2 + 112.5x$$

Graph the function. There is a max. at about $(56.25, 3164.06)$, so the max. area is about 3164.06 ft^2 and the length of each side is 56.25 ft.

[1] correct area, incorrect length of each side OR a computational error

Mixed Review

70. $(3, 2)$ **71.** $(-10, 6)$ **72.** $(1, 0, 3)$

73. $(0, 0)$ **74.** $(-1, 0)$ **75.** $(5, 0)$

---

47. a. $10; 9; -1$

   b. $9; 6; -3$

   c. $6; 1; -5$

   d. The rate of change decreases at a greater rate.

   e. Yes; the rates of change increase as you move away from the origin on the negative x-axis.

48. $y = 18x - x^2$ or $y = -(x - 9)^2 + 81$. The rectangle with the largest area will be 9 ft long and 9 feet wide.

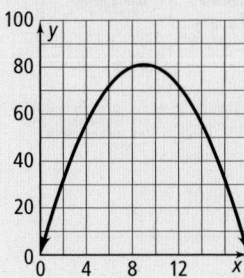

49. $y = -7(x - 1)^2 + 2$

50. $y = -\dfrac{1}{2}(x + 3)^2 + 6$

51. $y = -7x^2 + 5$

52. $y = 8\left(x - \dfrac{1}{4}\right)^2 - \dfrac{3}{2}$

53. Answers may vary. Sample:
$y = (x + 10)^2 - 4$

54. a. $(x_1, y_1): x = 4; (x_2, y_2): x = 2.5$

   b. Expand the spreadsheet to have an equal number of values on each side of the axis of symmetry.

   c. $(x_1, y_1): y = -4(x - 4)^2 + 1;$ $(x_2, y_2): y = 4(x - 2.5)^2 + 1$

55. Answers may vary. Sample:
$k = -2, a = 3; y = 3(x - 1)^2 - 2$

56. Answers may vary. Sample:
$a = 3, k = -1; y = 3(x + 2)^2 - 1$

57. Answers may vary. Sample:
$a = -6, k = 35; y = -6(x + 1)^2 + 35$

4-1 Lesson Resources

Differentiated Remediation

Additional Instructional Support

Algebra 2 Companion

Students can use the **Algebra 2 Companion** worktext (4 pages) as you teach the lesson. Use the Companion to support

- New Vocabulary
- Key Concepts
- Got It for each Problem
- Lesson Check

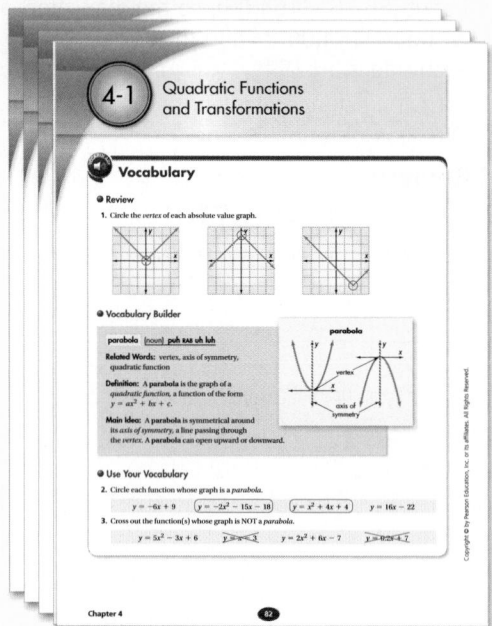

ELL Support

Use Manipulatives Demonstrate translations with rubber stamps. Draw a parabola on a transparency, and move it around the coordinate plane. Model transformations with Silly Putty by making an impression or taking an image from a piece of newspaper and then stretching or compressing the image on the putty. Show students a picture of a fractal or some other artwork, and have them identify the transformations within it in words, using vocabulary terms.

5 Assess & Remediate

Lesson Quiz

1. What are the vertex, the axis of symmetry, the minimum or the maximum, the domain, and the range of $y = -5(x + 2)^2 - 8$?

2. What is the graph of $f(x) = \frac{1}{3}(x - 4)^2 - 1$?

3. **Do you UNDERSTAND?** A frog leaps 2 feet. The highest point in the jump is 6 inches. Assume the frog starts at (0, 0). What quadratic function models the path of the jump? Specify the units you use.

ANSWERS TO LESSON QUIZ

1. The vertex is $(-2, -8)$; the axis of symmetry is $x = -2$; $k = -8$ is the maximum value; the domain is all real numbers; the range is all real numbers ≤ -8.

2.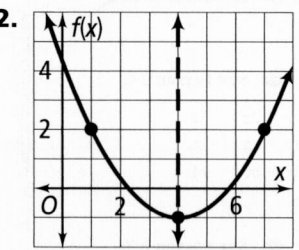

3. Samples: $f(x) = -\frac{1}{24}(x - 12)^2 + 6$ (inches) or $f(x) = -\frac{1}{2}(x - 1)^2 + \frac{1}{2}$ (feet)

PRESCRIPTION FOR REMEDIATION

Use the student work on the Lesson Quiz to prescribe a differentiated review assignment:

Points	Differentiated Remediation
0–1	Intervention
2	On-level
3	Extension

PowerAlgebra.com

5 Assess & Remediate

Assign the Lesson Quiz. Appropriate intervention, practice, or enrichment is automatically generated based on student performance.

Intervention

- **Reteaching** (2 pages) Provides reteaching and practice exercises for the key lesson concepts. Use with struggling students or absent students.

- **English Language Learner Support** Helps students develop and reinforce mathematical vocabulary and key concepts.

All-in-One Resources/Online
Reteaching

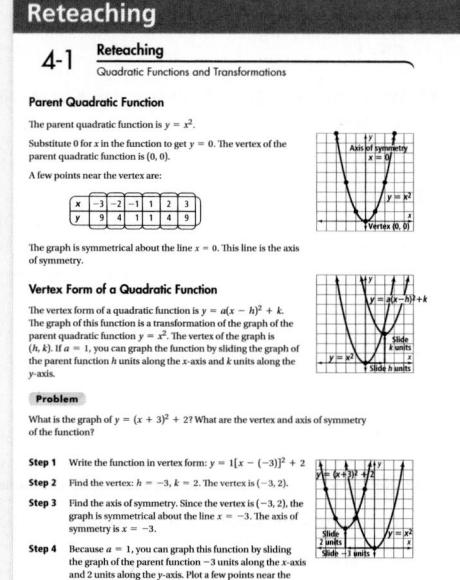

All-in-One Resources/Online
English Language Learner Support

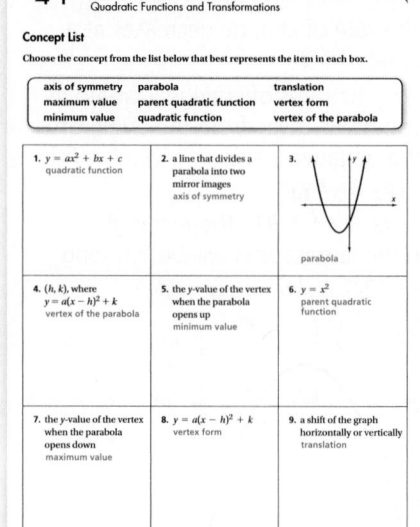

Differentiated Remediation *continued*

On-Level

- **Practice** (2 pages) Provides extra practice for each lesson. For simpler practice exercises, use the Form K Practice pages found in the All-in-One Teaching Resources and online.

- **Think About a Plan** Helps students develop specific problem-solving skills and strategies by providing scaffolded guiding questions.

- **Standardized Test Prep** Focuses on all major exercises, all major question types, and helps students prepare for the high-stakes assessments.

Extension

- **Enrichment** Provides students with interesting problems and activities that extend the concepts of the lesson.

- **Activities, Games, and Puzzles** Worksheets that can be used for concepts development, enrichment, and for fun!

Practice and Problem Solving Wkbk/ All-in-One Resources/Online
Practice page 1

4-1 **Practice**   *Form G*
Quadratic Functions and Transformations

Graph each function.

1. $y = 3x^2$ 2. $f(x) = -5x^2$ 3. $y = \frac{8}{3}x^2$

4. $f(x) = -\frac{5}{6}x^2$ 5. $f(x) = \frac{87}{10}x^2$ 6. $f(x) = \frac{4}{5}x^2$

Graph each function. Describe how it was translated from $f(x) = x^2$.

7. $f(x) = x^2 + 4$ up 4 units
8. $f(x) = (x - 3)^2$ right 3 units

Identify the vertex, axis of symmetry, the maximum or minimum value, and the domain and the range of each function.

9. $y = (x - 2)^2 + 3$ vertex: (2, 3); axis of symmetry: $x = 2$; minimum value: 3; domain: all real numbers; range: all real numbers ≥ 3
10. $f(x) = -0.2(x + 3)^2 + 2$ vertex: (-3, 2); axis of symmetry: $x = -3$; maximum value: 2; domain: all real numbers; range: all real numbers ≤ 2

Graph each function. Identify the axis of symmetry.

11. $y = (x + 2)^2 - 1$ $x = -2$
12. $y = -4(x - 3)^2 + 2$ $x = 3$

Write a quadratic function to model each graph.

13. $y = (x - 2)^2 + 3$ 14. $y = 2(x + 3)^2 - 1$

Practice and Problem Solving Wkbk/ All-in-One Resources/Online
Think About a Plan

4-1 **Think About a Plan**
Quadratic Functions and Transformations

Write a quadratic function to represent the areas of all rectangles with a perimeter of 36 ft. Graph the function and describe the rectangle that has the largest area.

1. Write an equation that represents the area of a rectangle with a perimeter of 36 ft. Let x = width and y = length.
$2x + 2y = 36$

2. Solve your equation for y.
$y = 18 - x$

3. Write a quadratic function for the area of the rectangle.
$A = \boxed{x} \cdot \boxed{y}$
$= \boxed{x} \cdot \boxed{(18 - x)}$
$= \boxed{18x - x^2}$

4. Graph the quadratic function you wrote.

5. What point on the graph has a coordinate that represents the largest area?
the maximum of the graph: the vertex

6. How can you find the coordinates of this point? What are the coordinates?
Answers may vary. Sample: Read the x-coordinate of the vertex from the graph and then substitute that value into the quadratic function to get the y-value; (9, 81).

7. Describe the rectangle that has the largest area. What is its area?
The rectangle that has the largest area is a square with length 9 ft; 81 ft²

Practice and Problem Solving Wkbk/ All-in-One Resources/Online
Practice page 2

4-1 **Practice** *(continued)*   *Form G*
Quadratic Functions and Transformations

Describe how to transform the parent function $y = x^2$ to the graph of each function below. Graph both functions on the same axes.

15. $y = 3(x + 2)^2$
Translate 2 units to the left; stretch vertically by the factor 3.
16. $y = -(x + 5)^2 + 1$
Translate 5 units to the left; reflect across the x-axis; translate 1 unit up.

17. $y = \frac{1}{2}(x + 4)^2 - 2$
Translate 4 units to the left; shrink vertically by the factor $\frac{1}{2}$; translate 2 units down.
18. $y = -0.08(x - 0.04)^2 + 1.2$
Translate 0.04 units to the right; shrink vertically by a factor of 0.08; reflect across the x-axis; translate 1.2 units up.

Write the equation of each parabola in vertex form.

19. vertex (3, −2), point (2, 3) $y = 5(x - 3)^2 - 2$
20. vertex $\left(\frac{1}{2}, 1\right)$, point (2, −8) $y = -4\left(x - \frac{1}{2}\right)^2 + 1$
21. vertex (−4, −24), point (−5, −25) $y = -(x + 4)^2 - 24$
22. vertex (−12.5, 35.5), point (1, 400) $y = 2(x + 12.5)^2 + 35.5$

23. The amount of cloth used to make four curtains is given by the function $A = -4x^2 + 40x$, where x is the width of one curtain in feet and A is the total area in square feet. Find the width that maximizes the area of the curtains. What is the maximum area?
5 ft; 100 ft²

24. The diagram shows the path of a model rocket launched from the ground. It reaches a maximum altitude of 384 ft when it is above a location 16 ft from the launch site. What quadratic function models the height of the rocket?
$f(x) = -1.5(x - 16)^2 + 384$

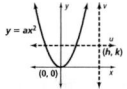

25. To make an enclosure for chickens, a rectangular area will be fenced next to a house. Only three sides will need to be fenced. There is 120 ft of fencing material.
a. What quadratic function represents the area of the rectangular enclosure, where x is the distance from the house? $A = -2x^2 + 120x$
b. What dimensions will maximize the area of the enclosure? 30 ft × 60 ft

Practice and Problem Solving Wkbk/ All-in-One Resources/Online
Standardized Test Prep

4-1 **Standardized Test Prep**
Quadratic Functions and Transformations

Multiple Choice

For Exercises 1–4, choose the correct letter.

1. What is the vertex of the function $y = 3(x - 7)^2 + 4$? D
   A. $(-7, -4)$ B. $(-7, 4)$ C. $(7, -4)$ D. $(7, 4)$

2. Which is the graph of the function $f(x) = -2(x + 3)^2 + 5$? F

3. Which of the following best describes how to transform $y = x^2$ to the graph of $y = 4(x - 2.5)^2 - 3$? C
   A. Translate 2.5 units left, stretch by a factor of 4, translate 3 units down.
   B. Translate 3 units right and 2.5 units down, stretch by a factor of 4.
   C. Translate 2.5 units right, stretch by a factor of 4, translate 3 units down.
   D. Stretch by a factor of 4, translate 2.5 units left and 3 units down.

4. What is the equation of the parabola with vertex (−4, 6) passing through the point (−2, −2)? F
   F. $y = -2(x + 4)^2 - 6$ H. $y = 2(x + 4)^2 + 6$
   G. $y = 2(x - 4)^2 - 6$ I. $y = -2(x + 4)^2 + 6$

Short Response

5. A baseball is hit so that its height above ground is given by the equation $h = -16t^2 + 96t + 4$, where h is the height in feet and t is the time in seconds after it is hit. Show your work.
a. How long does it take the baseball to reach its highest point?
b. How high will it go?
[2] a. 3 s; b. 148 ft
[1] incorrect time to highest point OR incorrect final height OR correct time and distance, but no work shown
[0] incorrect answers and no work shown OR no answers given

All-in-One Resources/Online
Enrichment

4-1 **Enrichment**
Quadratic Functions and Transformations

Parabolas in Other Coordinate Systems

1. What are the coordinates of the vertex of the parabola $y = ax^2$? (0, 0)

2. How do you determine whether the vertex is a maximum or a minimum? If $a > 0$, vertex is a minimum; if $a < 0$, vertex is a maximum.

3. What is the equation of the axis of symmetry? $x = 0$

Suppose you choose any point (h, k). Through (h, k), draw two lines, one parallel to the x-axis and one parallel to the y-axis. Let the line parallel to the x-axis be called the u-axis, and let the line parallel to the y-axis be called the v-axis. You have now established a new coordinate system—the u-v system.

4. In the x-y system, what are the coordinates of the origin of the u-v system? (h, k)

5. In the u-v system, what are the coordinates of the vertex of the parabola $y = ax^2$? What is the equation of its axis of symmetry? $(-h, -k)$; $u = -h$

Suppose point P has coordinates (x, y) in the x-y system and coordinates (u, v) in the u-v system.

6. Write an equation expressing the relationship between u and x. $x = u + h$

7. Write an equation expressing the relationship between v and y. $y = v + k$

8. Use these relationships to write an equation of the parabola $y = ax^2$ in terms of u and v. $v + k = a(u + h)^2$

9. Expand and simplify your equation to express v as a quadratic function of u. $v = au^2 + 2ahu + ah^2 - k$
If we let $b = 2ah$ and $c = ah^2 - k$, the parabola represented by the quadratic equation $v = au^2 + bu + c$ in the u-v system is equivalent to the parabola $y = ax^2$ in the x-y system.

10. In the u-v system, express the coordinates of the vertex of this parabola in terms of a, b, and c. What is the equation of its axis of symmetry? $\left(-\frac{b}{2a}, c - \frac{b^2}{4a}\right)$; $u = -\frac{b}{2a}$

Online Teacher Resource Center
Activities, Games, and Puzzles

4-1 **Activity: Sharing Vertices**
Quadratic Functions and Transformations

This is an activity that can be done alone or in groups of two or three students. Your teacher may discuss each group's results once everyone has finished.

- Twelve different quadratic functions are given below.
- Your job is to find 4 sets of 3 functions that have the same vertex.
- Fill in your results at the bottom of the page and then check each set using a graphing calculator.

By graphing the following three functions, you can see that they share a common vertex (1, −2). Thus, they form a set.

Example Set
Vertex: (1, −2)
$y = x^2 - 2x - 1$
$y = \frac{1}{4}x^2 - \frac{1}{2}x - \frac{7}{4}$
$y = 3x^2 - 6x + 1$

1. $y = x^2 + 6x + 11$ 2. $y = x^2 - 4x + 1$ 3. $y = -3x^2 + 12x - 9$
4. $y = -\frac{1}{4}x^2 - \frac{3}{2}x - \frac{17}{4}$ 5. $y = -3x^2 - 18x - 29$ 6. $y = \frac{1}{4}x^2 + \frac{3}{2}x + \frac{17}{4}$
7. $y = \frac{1}{4}x^2 - x - 2$ 8. $y = -x^2 + 4x - 1$ 9. $y = -\frac{1}{4}x^2 + x + 2$
10. $y = -x^2 - 6x - 11$ 11. $y = 3x^2 + 18x + 29$ 12. $y = 3x^2 - 12x + 9$

Set A	Set B	Set C	Set D
Vertex: (−3, 2)	Vertex: (−3, −2)	Vertex: (2, 3)	Vertex: (2, −3)
1. $y = x^2 + 6x + 11$	4. $y = -\frac{1}{4}x^2 - \frac{3}{2}x - \frac{17}{4}$	3. $y = -3x^2 + 12x - 9$	2. $y = x^2 - 4x + 1$
6. $y = \frac{1}{4}x^2 + \frac{3}{2}x + \frac{17}{4}$	5. $y = -3x^2 - 18x - 29$	8. $y = -x^2 + 4x - 1$	7. $y = \frac{1}{4}x^2 - x - 2$
11. $y = 3x^2 + 18x + 29$	10. $y = -x^2 - 6x - 11$	9. $y = -\frac{1}{4}x^2 + x + 2$	12. $y = 3x^2 - 12x + 9$

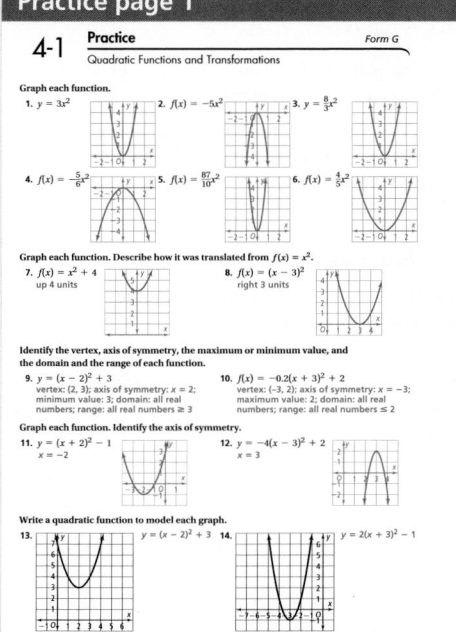

1 Interactive Learning

Solve It!

PURPOSE To use a quadratic model to determine the y-coordinate of the vertex of a parabola

PROCESS Students may
- graph the equation on a calculator and determine the maximum value of the function.
- estimate the x-coordinate of the vertex and use it to find the height.

FACILITATE

Q What point on the curve represents the maximum height of the ball? Explain. **[The vertex; it is the turning point.]**

Q How do you find the vertex? **[Answers may vary. Sample: Graph the given equation on a calculator, and use the max function. The x- and y-values are the coordinates of the vertex.]**

ANSWER See Solve It in Answers on next page.

CONNECT THE MATH In the Solve It, students used the standard form of a quadratic function. In this lesson, they will use the properties of a quadratic function in standard form to model and graph parabolas.

2 Guided Instruction

Problem 1   ERROR PREVENTION

Q What does $x = -2$ represent? **[-2 is the x-coordinate of the vertex, and $x = -2$ is the equation of the axis of symmetry.]**

Q What point can you use to find the range and the maximum or minimum of the parabola? **[the vertex]**

BIG ideas **Function**
        Equivalence

ESSENTIAL UNDERSTANDINGS
- Any quadratic function is a stretch, compression, reflection, and/or a translation of $y = x^2$.
- The standard form of a quadratic function is $f(x) = ax^2 + bx + c$, where $a \neq 0$.
- For any quadratic function $f(x) = ax^2 + bx + c$, the values of a, b, and c provide key information about its graph.
- Standard form is "calculator ready" and a transformation of $y = x^2$.

Math Background

$f(x) = ax^2 + bx + c$ is the standard form of a quadratic function. It is the form calculators use and the easiest model to find with systems of equations. Note that if $a = 0$, the function is linear rather than quadratic, so the graph is a line rather than a parabola. The values of a, b, and c provide

the following information about the graph:
- whether the graph opens upward or downward
- the coordinates of the vertex
- the axis of symmetry
- the y-intercept.

This lesson examines the connection between standard form and vertex form.

Mathematical Practices
Make sense of problems and persevere in solving them. In graphing quadratic equations in standard form, students will convert the equation into the simpler vertex form to gain insight on why $h = \frac{-b}{2a}$.

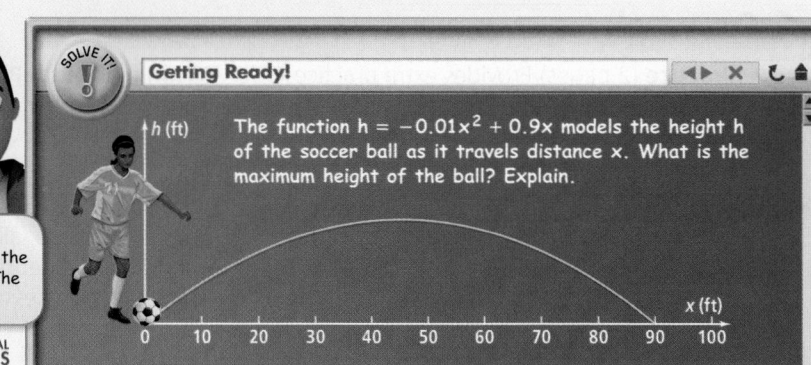

4-2

Standard Form of a Quadratic Function

Common Core State Standards
A-CED.A.2 Create equations in two or more variables . . . graph equations on coordinate axes with labels and scales. **Also F-IF.B.4, F-IF.B.6, F-IF.C.8, F-IF.C.9**
MP 1, MP 3, MP 4

Objective To graph quadratic functions written in standard form

Getting Ready!

The function $h = -0.01x^2 + 0.9x$ models the height h of the soccer ball as it travels distance x. What is the maximum height of the ball? Explain.

What useful information does the graph give you? The equation?

Lesson Vocabulary
- standard form

In Lesson 4-1, you worked with quadratic functions written in vertex form. Now you will use quadratic functions in *standard form*. The **standard form** of a quadratic function is $f(x) = ax^2 + bx + c$, where $a \neq 0$.

Essential Understanding For any quadratic function $f(x) = ax^2 + bx + c$, the values of a, b, and c provide key information about its graph.

You can find information about the graph of a quadratic function (such as the vertex) easily from the vertex form. Such information is "hidden" in standard form. However, standard form is easier to enter into a graphing calculator.

Problem 1 Finding the Features of a Quadratic Function

Graphing Calculator What are the vertex, the axis of symmetry, the maximum or minimum value, and the range of $y = 2x^2 + 8x - 2$?

Plan

How can you use a calculator to find the features of a quadratic function in standard form?
Graph the function. Then use the **CALC** and **TABLE** features.

Range: $y \geq -10$.

Minimum $x = -2$ $y = -10$

The vertex is $(-2, -10)$.

Notice the symmetry of y values.

X	Y1
-5	8
-4	-2
-3	-8
-2	-10
-1	-8
0	-2
1	8

-10 is the minimum value.

Axis of symmetry is $x = -2$.

202   Chapter 4   Quadratic Functions and Equations

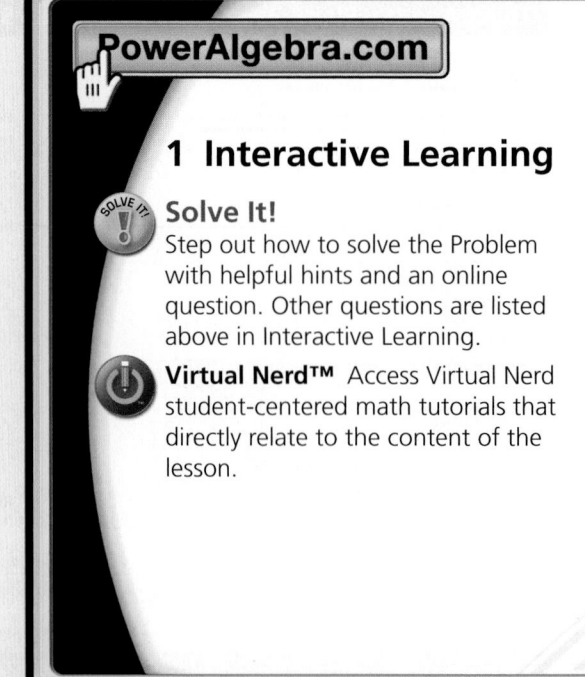

PowerAlgebra.com

1 Interactive Learning

Solve It!
Step out how to solve the Problem with helpful hints and an online question. Other questions are listed above in Interactive Learning.

Virtual Nerd™ Access Virtual Nerd student-centered math tutorials that directly relate to the content of the lesson.

✓ **Got It?** **1.** What are the vertex, axis of symmetry, maximum or minimum value, and range of $y = -3x^2 - 4x + 6$?

You can find information about the quadratic function $f(x) = ax^2 + bx + c$ from the coefficients a and b, and from the constant term c.

take note
Properties Quadratic Function in Standard Form

- The graph of $f(x) = ax^2 + bx + c$, $a \neq 0$, is a parabola.
- If $a > 0$, the parabola opens upward. If $a < 0$, the parabola opens downward.
- The axis of symmetry is the line $x = -\frac{b}{2a}$.
- The x-coordinate of the vertex is $-\frac{b}{2a}$. The y-coordinate of the vertex is the y-value of the function for $x = -\frac{b}{2a}$, or $y = f\left(-\frac{b}{2a}\right)$.
- The y-intercept is $(0, c)$.

$y = ax^2 + bx + c, a > 0$ $y = ax^2 + bx + c, a < 0$

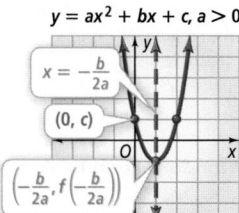 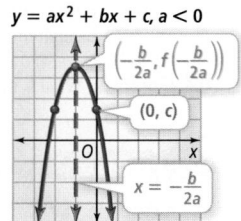

Here's Why It Works You can expand the vertex form of a quadratic function to determine properties of the graph of a quadratic function written in standard form.

$$f(x) = a(x - h)^2 + k$$
$$= a(x^2 - 2hx + h^2) + k$$
$$= ax^2 - 2ahx + ah^2 + k$$
$$= ax^2 + (-2ah)x + (ah^2 + k)$$

Compare to the standard form, $f(x) = ax^2 + bx + c$.

$a = a$ a in standard form is the same as a in vertex form.

$b = -2ah$

$-\frac{b}{2a} = h$ Solve for h.

Since, $h = -\frac{b}{2a}$, the axis of symmetry is $x = -\frac{b}{2a}$ and the vertex is

$(h, k) = \left(-\frac{b}{2a}, f\left(-\frac{b}{2a}\right)\right)$.

 PowerAlgebra.com   Lesson 4-2 Standard Form of a Quadratic Function   **203**

Got It?   SYNTHESIZING

Q Does this parabola contain a maximum or minimum value? Explain your reasoning. **[maximum; because the parabola opens downward]**

Take Note   ELL SUPPORT

Students may benefit from making a checklist for graphing quadratic functions using standard form. Have them design their own list to best meet their needs and to learn while making it.

For example, for the function $f(x) = ax^2 + bx + c$

[ ] $a \neq 0$

[ ] If $a > 0$, the parabola opens upward.

[ ] If $a < 0$, the parabola opens downward.

[ ] the axis of symmetry $x = \frac{-b}{2a}$

[ ] the vertex $\left(\frac{-b}{2a}, f\left(\frac{-b}{2a}\right)\right)$

[ ] the y-intercept $(0, c)$

Here's Why It Works

Although equivalent, different forms of equations present information differently. Have students list the steps for graphing using vertex form and using standard form.

---

2 Guided Instruction

© Each Problem is worked out and supported online.

Problem 1
Finding the Features of a Quadratic Function

Problem 2
Graphing a Function of the Form $y = ax^2 + bx + c$
Animated

Problem 3
Converting Standard Form to Vertex Form
Animated

Problem 4
Interpreting a Quadratic Graph

Alternative Problem 4
Interpreting a Quadratic Graph
Animated

Support in Algebra 2 Companion
- Vocabulary
- Key Concepts
- Got It?

Answers

Solve It!
20.25 ft; graph and trace the function until the vertex is located. The y-coordinate of this point is the maximum height the ball will attain.

Got It?
1. vertex: $\left(-\frac{2}{3}, 7\frac{1}{3}\right)$; axis of symmetry: $x = -\frac{2}{3}$; maximum: $7\frac{1}{3}$; range: $y \leq 7\frac{1}{3}$

Lesson 4-2 203

Q Why is it helpful to sketch the axis of symmetry? **[You can use reflection to find points on the curve on the opposite side of the axis.]**

Q Is $(0, c)$ always the y-intercept? Explain. **[Yes; using standard form $y = ax^2 + bx + c$, substitute $x = 0$, which gives you $y = c$.]**

Q Can you always use the y-intercept and its reflection to find the second and third points? Explain. **[No, not when the vertex is on the y-axis.]**

Got It?

Students may write the equation $x = -\frac{b}{2a}$ on their paper for each problem. By the end of the problem set, they will know the equation.

Problem 3   SYNTHESIZING

Students relate vertex form from a previous lesson to standard form.

Q What values do we know that will be used in this problem? **[Sample: a and b because they are used to find the vertex]**

Q What values must be found to write the equation in vertex form? **[h and k]**

Q How do you find k? **[k represents the y-coordinate of the vertex. Substitute the x-coordinate of the vertex in the standard form to solve for y.]**

Got It?   ERROR PREVENTION

To eliminate arithmetic errors, use a calculator to simplify the equation after substitution.

 **Problem 2** Graphing a Function of the Form $y = ax^2 + bx + c$

What is the graph of $y = x^2 + 2x + 3$?

Step 1   Identify a, b, and c.
$a = 1$, $b = 2$, $c = 3$

Step 2   The axis of symmetry is $x = -\frac{b}{2a}$.
$$x = -\frac{2}{2(1)}$$
Lightly sketch the line $x = -1$.

Step 3   The x-coordinate of the vertex is also $-\frac{b}{2a}$, or -1.
The y-coordinate is
$y = (-1)^2 + 2(-1) + 3 = 2$.
Plot the vertex $(-1, 2)$.

Step 4   Since $c = 3$, the y-intercept is $(0, 3)$. The reflection of $(0, 3)$ across $x = -1$ is $(-2, 3)$. Plot both points.

Step 5 $a > 0$ confirms that the graph opens upward. Draw a smooth curve through the points you found in Steps 3 and 4.

Think
How can you use the axis of symmetry?
The entire curve on one side of the axis is the mirror image of the curve on the other side.

✔ **Got It? 2.** What is the graph of $y = -2x^2 + 2x - 5$?

 Problem 3 Converting Standard Form to Vertex Form

What is the vertex form of $y = 2x^2 + 10x + 7$?

$y = 2x^2 + 10x + 7$	Identify a and b.
$x = -\dfrac{b}{2a}$	Find the x-coordinate of the vertex.
$\quad = -\dfrac{10}{2(2)}$	
$\quad = -2.5$	
$y = 2(-2.5)^2 + 10(-2.5) + 7$	Substitute $x = -2.5$ into the equation.
$\quad = -5.5$	

The vertex is $(-2.5, -5.5)$.

$y = a(x - h)^2 + k$	Write the vertex form.
$y = 2[x - (-2.5)]^2 + (-5.5)$	Substitute $a = 2$, $h = -2.5$, $k = -5.5$.
$y = 2(x + 2.5)^2 - 5.5$	Simplify.

The vertex form is $y = 2(x + 2.5)^2 - 5.5$.

Plan
How do you find h, k, and a?
Find the vertex. This gives you h and k. The value for a is the same in both forms.

✔ **Got It? 3.** What is the vertex form of $y = -x^2 + 4x - 5$?

Additional Problems

1. What are the vertex, axis of symmetry, maximum or minimum value, and range of $y = -x^2 + 6x + 3$?

ANSWER $(3, 12)$; $x = 3$; max: 12; range: $y \leq 12$

2. What is the graph of $y = 4x^2 - 16x + 10$?

ANSWER

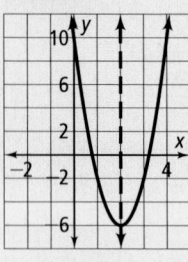

3. What is the vertex form of $y = 2x^2 - 3x + 2$?

ANSWER
$y = 2(x - 0.75)^2 + 0.875$

4. A model for the performance of a stock is $P = -3d^2 + 50d$ where d represents the days of trading and P is the price per share. What is the maximum price per share of the stock?

ANSWER $208.33

Answers

Got It? (continued)

2.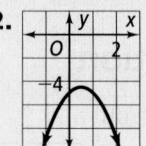

3. $y = -(x - 2)^2 - 1$

4. a. 4 ft
    b. because the y-intercept is $(0, 0)$

 **Problem 4** Interpreting a Quadratic Graph STEM

Bridges The New River Gorge Bridge in West Virginia is the world's largest steel single arch bridge. You can model the arch with the function $y = -0.000498x^2 + 0.847x$, where x and y are in feet. How high above the river is the arch? How long is the section of bridge above the arch?

Length of bridge above arch

Height of arch

516 ft

Problem 4 SYNTHESIZING

Q What do you have to find first to determine the bridge height? Explain. **[The vertex; answers may vary. Sample: The vertex gives the height and half the length of the arch.]**

Q What quantities are added to find the height of the bridge above the river? Explain your reasoning. **[The y-coordinate of the vertex and 516; answers may vary. Sample: The y-coordinate of the vertex represents the height of the arch, and 516 is the vertical distance from the lowest part of river to the bottom of the arch.]**

Q What quantity is used to find the length of the bridge above the arch? Explain. **[The x-coordinate of the vertex. Since the vertex is in the middle of the bridge, 2x represents the entire horizontal distance between the x-intercepts of the arch.]**

Think

How can you tell that the quadratic function has a maximum value? Since $a < 0$, the graph of the function opens down. The function has a maximum value.

Know	Need	Plan
A function that models the arch and the vertical distance from the base of the supports to the water	The height of the arch above the support base and the length of the bridge above the arch	Find the vertex. The y-coordinate is the height of the arch above the support base. The x-coordinate is half the distance between the supports.

Step 1 Find the vertex of the arch.

$$x = -\frac{b}{2a} = -\frac{0.847}{2(-0.000498)} \approx 850$$

$$y = -0.000498(850)^2 + 0.847(850) \approx 360$$

The vertex is about (850, 360).

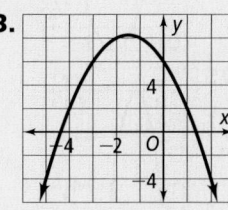

(850, 360)

The height is 360 ft.

$x = 850$

Step 2 Find the height of the arch above its supports.

The y-coordinate of the vertex is the height of the arch above its supports. The arch is about 360 ft above its supports.

Step 3 Find the height of the arch above the river.

The arch is about 360 ft + 516 ft = 876 ft above the river.

Step 4 Find the length of the bridge above the arch.

The x-coordinate of the vertex is half the length of the bridge above the arch. The length of that part of the bridge is about 850 ft + 850 ft = 1700 ft long.

Got It? **4. a.** The Zhaozhou Bridge in China is the one of the oldest known arch bridges, dating to A.D. 605. You can model the support arch with the function $f(x) = -0.001075x^2 + 0.131148x$, where x and y are measured in feet. How high is the arch above its supports?

b. Reasoning Why does the model in part (a) not have a constant term?

Got It? SYNTHESIZING

Q Why might you want to solve this problem using a graphing calculator? **[Answers may vary. Sample: The numbers are decimals.]**

Q Where does the bridge start? **[on the ground at (0, 0)]**

PowerAlgebra.com | Lesson 4-2 Standard Form of a Quadratic Function | 205

Lesson Check

1. vertex: (0, −4); axis of symmetry: $x = 0$; minimum: −4

2.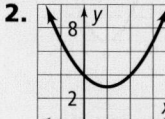

3.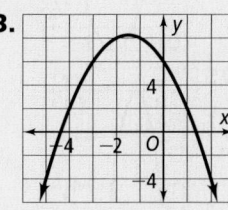

4. $y = (x − 1)^2 + 8$

5. $y = -\left(x - \frac{3}{2}\right)^2 + \frac{5}{4}$

6. Error in calculation of x. The correct calculation is:

$$x = \frac{-(-4)}{2(2)} = 1$$

$$y = 2(1) - 4(1) - 3$$
$$= 2 - 4 - 3$$
$$= -5$$

Vertex: (1, −5)

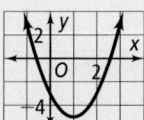

7. The vertex of a function written in vertex form can easily be determined. It is (h, k) where $f(x) = a(x − h)^2 + k$. The vertex of a function in standard form is $\left(\frac{-b}{2a}, f\left(\frac{-b}{2a}\right)\right)$ where $f(x) = ax^2 + bx + c$.

Practice and Problem-Solving Exercises

8. vertex: (−1, 0); axis of symmetry: $x = -1$; minimum: 0; range: $y \geq 0$

9. vertex: (1, 2); axis of symmetry: $x = 1$; maximum: 2; range: $y \leq 2$

10. vertex: (−2, −3); axis of symmetry: $x = -2$; minimum: 3; range: $y \geq -3$

11. vertex: (1, 6); axis of symmetry: $x = 1$; maximum: 6; range: $y \leq 6$

12. vertex: $\left(\frac{2}{3}, -3\frac{1}{3}\right)$; axis of symmetry: $x = \frac{2}{3}$; minimum: $-3\frac{1}{3}$; range: $y \geq -3\frac{1}{3}$

13. vertex: $\left(-\frac{3}{4}, 5\frac{1}{8}\right)$; axis of symmetry: $x = -\frac{3}{4}$; maximum: $5\frac{1}{8}$; range: $y \leq 5\frac{1}{8}$

14. vertex: $\left(\frac{3}{2}, -\frac{3}{2}\right)$; axis of symmetry: $x = \frac{3}{2}$; minimum: $-\frac{3}{2}$; range: $y \geq -\frac{3}{2}$

15. vertex: $\left(-\frac{1}{2}, \frac{1}{4}\right)$; axis of symmetry: $x = -\frac{1}{2}$; maximum: $\frac{1}{4}$; range: $y \leq \frac{1}{4}$

16. vertex: (0, 5); axis of symmetry: $x = 0$; minimum: 5; range: $y \geq 5$

3 Lesson Check

Do you know HOW?
- For Exercise 1, if students have trouble identifying the parts of a parabola, have them review Problem 1 and make a list.
- For Exercises 2–3, if students have trouble graphing, suggest they start by graphing the axes of symmetry.

Do you UNDERSTAND?
- For Exercise 7, if students have trouble comparing standard form with vertex form, suggest they use an actual function in both forms and compare the steps needed to find the vertex.

Close

Q How can you graph a quadratic function written in standard form? **[First find the axis of symmetry and vertex from $x = -\frac{b}{2a}$. See if $a > 0$ or $a < 0$. Find the y-intercept.]**

Q What form provides easier access to the y-intercept and any y-values given an x-value? **[standard form]**

 **Lesson Check**

Do you know HOW?

1. Identify the vertex, axis of symmetry, and the maximum or minimum value of the parabola at the right.

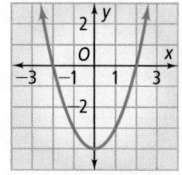

Graph each function.

2. $y = x^2 - 2x + 4$

3. $y = -x^2 - 3x + 6$

Write each function in vertex form.

4. $y = x^2 - 2x + 9$

5. $y = -x^2 + 3x - 1$

Do you UNDERSTAND?  MATHEMATICAL PRACTICES

6. **Error Analysis** A student graphed the function $y = 2x^2 - 4x - 3$. Find and correct the error.

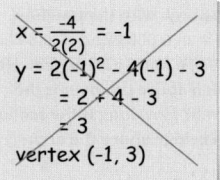

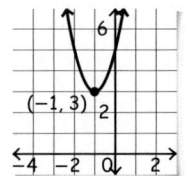

7. **Compare and Contrast** Explain the difference between finding the vertex of a function written in vertex form and finding the vertex of a function written in standard form.

 Practice and Problem-Solving Exercises  MATHEMATICAL PRACTICES

 Practice Identify the vertex, the axis of symmetry, the maximum or minimum value, and the range of each parabola. ◆ See Problem 1.

8. $y = x^2 + 2x + 1$ 9. $y = -x^2 + 2x + 1$ 10. $y = x^2 + 4x + 1$

11. $y = -x^2 + 2x + 5$ 12. $y = 3x^2 - 4x - 2$ 13. $y = -2x^2 - 3x + 4$

14. $y = 2x^2 - 6x + 3$ 15. $y = -x^2 - x$ 16. $y = 2x^2 + 5$

Graph each function. ◆ See Problem 2.

17. $y = x^2 + 6x + 9$ 18. $y = -x^2 - 3x + 6$ 19. $y = 2x^2 + 4x$

20. $y = 4x^2 - 12x + 9$ 21. $y = -6x^2 - 12x - 1$ 22. $y = -\frac{3}{4}x^2 + 6x + 6$

23. $y = 3x^2 - 12x + 10$ 24. $y = \frac{1}{2}x^2 + 2x - 8$ 25. $y = -4x^2 - 24x - 36$

Write each function in vertex form. ◆ See Problem 3.

26. $y = x^2 - 4x + 6$ 27. $y = x^2 + 2x + 5$

28. $y = 4x^2 + 7x$ 29. $y = 2x^2 - 5x + 12$

30. $y = -2x^2 + 8x + 3$ 31. $y = \frac{9}{4}x^2 + 3x - 1$

32. **Economics** A model for a company's revenue from selling a software package is $R = -2.5p^2 + 500p$, where p is the price in dollars of the software. What price will maximize revenue? Find the maximum revenue. ◆ See Problem 4.

PowerAlgebra.com

3 Lesson Check
For a digital lesson check, use the Got It questions.

Support in Algebra 2 Companion
- Lesson Check

4 Practice
Assign homework to individual students or to an entire class.

Answers

1–16. See page 205.

17.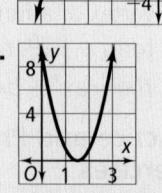

18.

19.

20.

21.

22.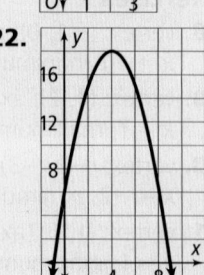

23.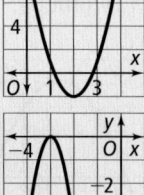

24.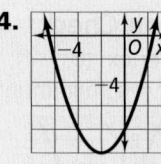

25.

26. $y = (x - 2)^2 + 2$

27. $y = (x + 1)^2 + 4$

28. $y = 4\left(x + \frac{7}{8}\right)^2 - \frac{49}{16}$

29. $y = 2\left(x - \frac{5}{4}\right)^2 + \frac{71}{8}$

30. $y = -2(x - 2)^2 + 11$

31. $y = \frac{9}{4}\left(x + \frac{2}{3}\right)^2 - 2$

32. 100; $25,000$

Sketch each parabola using the given information.

33. vertex $(3, 6)$, y-intercept 2

34. vertex $(-1, -4)$, y-intercept 3

35. vertex $(0, 5)$, point $(1, -2)$

36. vertex $(2, 3)$, point $(6, 9)$

37. Think About a Plan Suppose you work for a packaging company and are designing a box that has a rectangular bottom with a perimeter of 36 cm. The box must be 4 cm high. What dimensions give the maximum volume?
• How can you model the volume of the box with a quadratic function?
• What information can you get from the function to find the maximum volume?

38. Landscaping A town is planning a playground. It wants to fence in a rectangular space using an existing wall. What is the greatest area it can fence in using 100 ft of donated fencing?

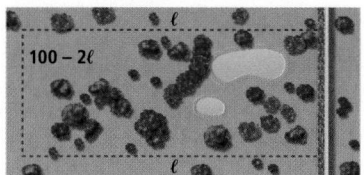

For each function, the vertex of the function's graph is given. Find the unknown coefficients.

39. $y = x^2 + bx + c$; $(3, -4)$

40. $y = -3x^2 + bx + c$; $(1, 0)$

41. $y = ax^2 + 10x + c$; $(-5, -27)$

42. $y = c - ax^2 - 2x$; $(-1, 3)$

STEM 43. Physics The height of a projectile fired straight up in the air with an initial velocity of 64 ft/s is $h = 64t - 16t^2$, where h is height in feet and t is time in seconds. The table represents the data for another projectile. Which projectile goes higher? How much higher?

Time (t)	Height (h)
0.5	20
1	32
1.5	36
2	32

44. A student says that the graph of $y = ax^2 + bx + c$ gets wider as a increases.
a. Error Analysis Use examples to show that the student is wrong.
b. Writing Summarize the relationship between $|a|$ and the width of the graph of $y = ax^2 + bx + c$.

For each function, find the y-intercept.

45. $y = (x - 1)^2 + 2$

46. $y = -3(x + 2)^2 - 4$

47. $y = -\frac{2}{3}(x - 9)^2$

48. Use the functions $f(x) = 4x + 3$ and $g(x) = \frac{1}{2}x^2 + 2$ to answer parts (a)–(c).
a. Which function has a greater rate of change from $x = 0$ to $x = 1$?
b. Which function has a greater rate of change from $x = 2$ and $x = 3$?
c. Does $g(x)$ ever have a greater rate of change than $f(x)$? Explain.

ASSIGNMENT GUIDE
Basic: 8–32 all, 35–38, 40–46 even
Average: 9–31 odd, 33–48
Advanced: 9–31 odd, 33–53

Mathematical Practices are supported by exercises with red headings. Here are the Practices supported in this lesson:

MP 1: Make Sense of Problems Ex. 37
MP 3: Communicate Ex. 7, 44b
MP 3: Critique the Reasoning of Others Ex. 6, 44a

Applications exercises have blue headings. Exercises 32 and 38 support MP 4: Model.

STEM exercises focus on science or engineering applications.

EXERCISE 38: Use the Think About a Plan worksheet in the **Practice and Problem Solving Workbook** (also available in the Teaching Resources in print and online) to further support students' development in becoming independent learners.

HOMEWORK QUICK CHECK
To check students' understanding of key skills and concepts, go over Exercises 9, 27, 37, 38, and 43.

33.
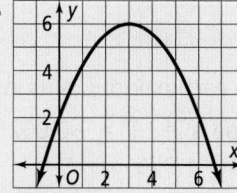

34.
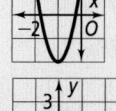

35.
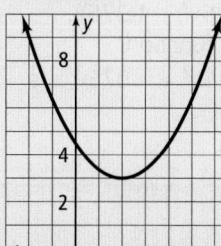

36.

37. 4 cm × 9 cm × 9 cm

38. 1250 ft²

39. $b = -6$; $c = 5$

40. $b = 6$; $c = -3$

41. $a = 1$; $c = -2$

42. $a = 1$; $c = 2$

43. a. The projectile represented by the equation goes higher by 28 feet.
b. equation: $t = 0.27$ s and $t = 3.73$ s; table: $t = 0.38$ s and $t = 2.62$ s

44. a. Check students' work.
b. Answers may vary. Sample: The widths of the graphs of $y = ax^2 + bx + c$ and $y = -ax^2 + bx + c$ are the same. As $|a|$ increases, the widths of $y = ax^2 + bx + c$ and $y = -ax^2 + bx + c$ decrease.

45. $(0, 3)$

46. $(0, -16)$

47. $(0, -54)$

48. a. $f(x)$
b. $f(x)$
c. Yes; the rate of change for $g(x)$ increases as x increases and will eventually have a greater rate of change than $f(x)$, which has a constant rate of change.

Answers

49. $a = -6, b = 24$
50. $a = 1, b = 2$
51. $a = 3, b = -12$
52. $a = -\dfrac{2}{9}, b = -\dfrac{4}{3}$
53.

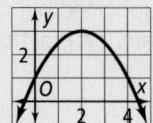

For each function, the vertex of the function's graph is given. Find a and b.

49. $y = ax^2 + bx - 27; (2, -3)$ **50.** $y = ax^2 + bx + 5; (-1, 4)$

51. $y = ax^2 + bx + 8; (2, -4)$ **52.** $y = ax^2 + bx; (-3, 2)$

53. Sketch the parabola with an axis of symmetry $x = 2$, y-intercept 1, and point $(3, 2.5)$.

Apply What You've Learned

MATHEMATICAL PRACTICES
MP 4

Look back at the information about the sandwich shops and at the table of data on page 193.

a. Victor plans to use the other shop owner's data to determine the relationship between the number of bags sold, x, and the selling price, s. Does the other shop owner's data set appear to be linear? Explain.

b. Write an equation that models the data in the table. This is Victor's selling-price function.

You can use the following relationship to construct a function that models Victor's profit from selling x bags of chips.

$$\text{Profit} = \text{Revenue} - \text{Cost}$$
$$P(x) = R(x) - C(x)$$

c. Write an equation for Victor's cost function $C(x)$.

d. Victor's revenue will be the selling price times the number of bags sold. Use your result from part (b) to write and simplify an equation for Victor's revenue function $R(x)$.

e. Use your results from parts (c) and (d) to write an equation for Victor's profit function $P(x)$.

f. You have now written four functions. Which functions are linear functions and which are quadratic functions?

Apply What You've Learned

Here students use the information and table given on page 193 to generate four functions related to the problem of determining the selling price that will maximize Victor's profit. Later in the chapter, they will look at characteristics of the graph of the profit function, including the vertex and the zeros.

Mathematical Practices

Students **model with mathematics** by writing equations of functions for selling price, cost, revenue, and profit. (MP 4)

ANSWERS

a. Yes; between each pair of points in the table, the slope is $\dfrac{s_2 - s_1}{x_2 - x_1} = -0.0025$.

b. $s = -0.0025x + 1.375$

c. $C(x) = 0.3x$

d. $R(x) = -0.0025x^2 + 1.375x$

e. $P(x) = -0.0025x^2 + 1.075x$

f. The selling-price function, $s = -0.0025x + 1.375$, and the cost function, $C(x) = 0.3x$, are linear. The revenue function, $R(x) = -0.0025x^2 + 1.375x$, and the profit function, $P(x) = -0.0025x^2 + 1.075x$, are quadratic.

Lesson Resources

Additional Instructional Support

Algebra 2 Companion

Students can use the **Algebra 2 Companion** worktext (4 pages) as you teach the lesson. Use the Companion to support

- New Vocabulary
- Key Concepts
- Got It for each Problem
- Lesson Check

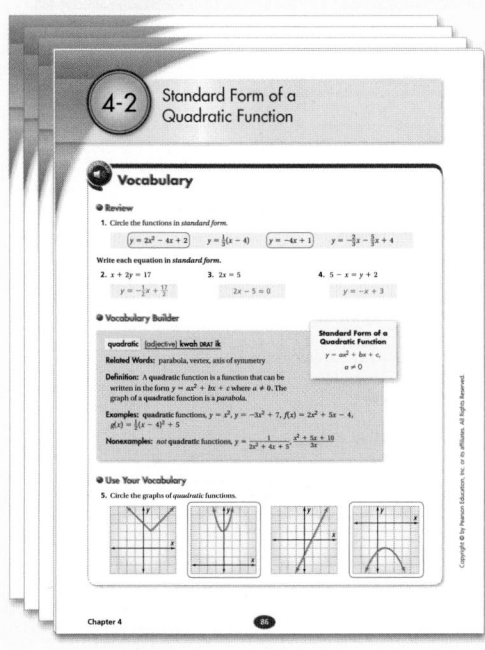

ELL Support

Focus on Language Ask students what they know about the word *standard*. What are some common uses? [Standard deviation, standard English, standard time, standard methods, standard definitions, standard styles, educational standards, standard measurement, etc.] Thinking about these uses, what is the meaning of standard? [Usual, common, normal, familiar, basis of comparison, etc.] The standard form relates to a common form for all polynomial functions, including the linear function. The vertex form is a special form only for quadratics.

5 Assess & Remediate

Lesson Quiz

1. What are the vertex, axis of symmetry, maximum or minimum value, and range of $y = 3x^2 + 6x - 1$?

2. What is the graph of $y = x^2 + 8x + 4$?

3. Write $y = -5x^2 + x + 1$ in vertex form.

4. Do you UNDERSTAND?

A parabolic arch sculpture is on top of a city bank. A model of the arch is $y = -0.005x^2 + 0.3x$ where x and y are in feet.

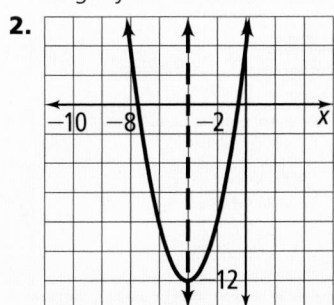

a. What is the distance from the highest point of the arch to the ground?

b. What is the width of the bank building?

ANSWERS TO LESSON QUIZ

1. $(-1, -4)$; $x = -1$; min: -4; range: $y \geq -4$

2.

3. $y = -5(x - 0.1)^2 + 1.05$

4. a. 34.5 feet   **b.** 60 feet

PRESCRIPTION FOR REMEDIATION

Use the student work on the Lesson Quiz to prescribe a differentiated review assignment:

Points	Differentiated Remediation
0–2	Intervention
3	On-level
4	Extension

PowerAlgebra.com

5 Assess & Remediate

Assign the Lesson Quiz. Appropriate intervention, practice, or enrichment is automatically generated based on student performance.

Intervention

- **Reteaching** (2 pages) Provides reteaching and practice exercises for the key lesson concepts. Use with struggling students or absent students.

- **English Language Learner Support** Helps students develop and reinforce mathematical vocabulary and key concepts.

All-in-One Resources/Online
Reteaching

All-in-One Resources/Online
English Language Learner Support

Differentiated Remediation *continued*

On-Level

- **Practice** (2 pages) Provides extra practice for each lesson. For simpler practice exercises, use the Form K Practice pages found in the All-in-One Teaching Resources and online.

- **Think About a Plan** Helps students develop specific problem-solving skills and strategies by providing scaffolded guiding questions.

- **Standardized Test Prep** Focuses on all major exercises, all major question types, and helps students prepare for the high-stakes assessments.

Extension

- **Enrichment** Provides students with interesting problems and activities that extend the concepts of the lesson.

- **Activities, Games, and Puzzles** Worksheets that can be used for concepts development, enrichment, and for fun!

Practice and Problem Solving Wkbk/All-in-One Resources/Online
Practice page 1

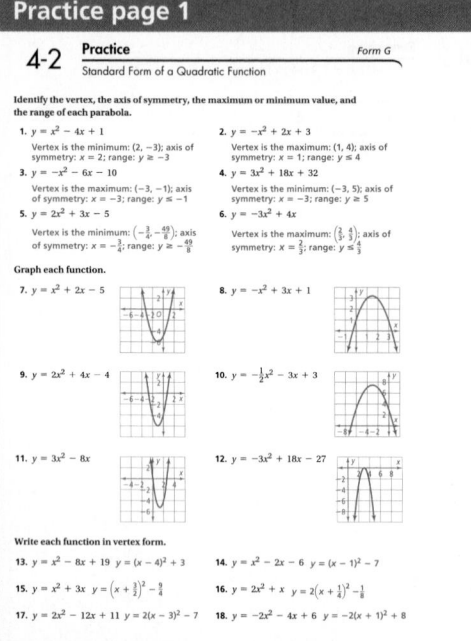

Practice and Problem Solving Wkbk/All-in-One Resources/Online
Practice page 2

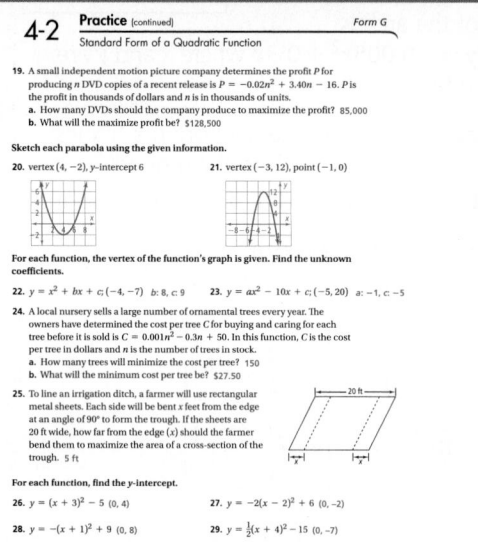

All-in-One Resources/Online
Enrichment

Practice and Problem Solving Wkbk/All-in-One Resources/Online
Think About a Plan

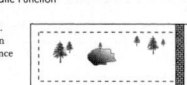

Practice and Problem Solving Wkbk/All-in-One Resources/Online
Standardized Test Prep

Online Teacher Resource Center
Activities, Games, and Puzzles

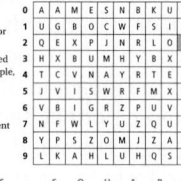

4-3 Modeling With Quadratic Functions

Common Core State Standards
F-IF.B.5 Relate the domain of a function to its graph and, where applicable, to the quantitative relationship it describes. **Also F-IF.B.4**
MP 1, MP 3, MP 4

Objective To model data with quadratic functions

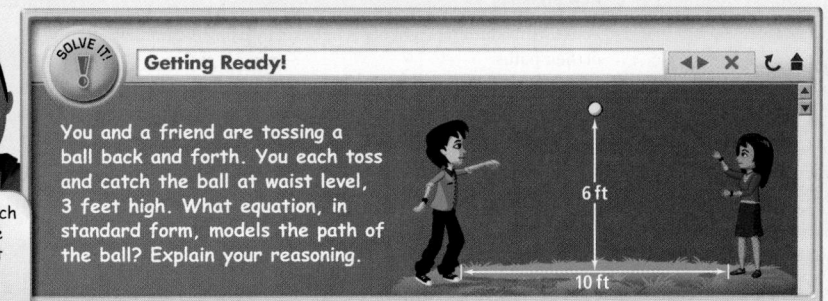

Getting Ready!

You and a friend are tossing a ball back and forth. You each toss and catch the ball at waist level, 3 feet high. What equation, in standard form, models the path of the ball? Explain your reasoning.

6 ft

10 ft

Try making a sketch of the path of the ball based on what you know about projectile motion.

MATHEMATICAL PRACTICES

When you know the vertex and a point on a parabola, you can use vertex form to write an equation of the parabola. If you do not know the vertex, you can use standard form and any three points of the parabola to find an equation.

Essential Understanding Three noncollinear points, no two of which are in line vertically, are on the graph of exactly one quadratic function.

Plan

How do you use the 3 given points?
Use them to write a system of 3 equations. Solve the system to get a, b, and c.

Problem 1 Writing an Equation of a Parabola

A parabola contains the points $(0, 0)$, $(-1, -2)$, and $(1, 6)$. What is the equation of this parabola in standard form?

Substitute the (x, y) values into $y = ax^2 + bx + c$ to write a system of equations.

Use $(0, 0)$.	Use $(-1, -2)$.	Use $(1, 6)$.
$y = ax^2 + bx + c$	$y = ax^2 + bx + c$	$y = ax^2 + bx + c$
$0 = a(0)^2 + b(0) + c$	$-2 = a(-1)^2 + b(-1) + c$	$6 = a(1)^2 + b(1) + c$
$0 = c$	$-2 = a - b + c$	$6 = a + b + c$

Since $c = 0$, the resulting system has two variables. $\begin{cases} a - b = -2 \\ a + b = 6 \end{cases}$ Use elimination. $a = 2$ and $b = 4$.

Substitute $a = 2$, $b = 4$, and $c = 0$ into standard form: $y = 2x^2 + 4x + 0$.

$y = 2x^2 + 4x$ is the equation of the parabola that contains the given points.

✓ **Got It? 1.** What is the equation of a parabola containing the points $(0, 0)$, $(1, -2)$, and $(-1, -4)$?

---

1 Interactive Learning

Solve It!
PURPOSE To introduce the idea that three points determine a quadratic function
PROCESS Students may place a coordinate system on the diagram and use vertex form of a quadratic function.

FACILITATE
Q How can you model the path with a parabola that has vertex $(0, 3)$? **[Sample: Assume the y-axis goes through the vertex and the x-axis is at waist level.]**

ANSWER See Solve It in Answers on next page.
CONNECT THE MATH In the Solve It, students use what they know about vertex form and standard form to write an equation of a parabola. In the lesson, they will use standard form and systems of equations to write equations of parabolas.

2 Guided Instruction

Problem 1

Q Use $y = ax^2 + bx + c$. Graph the three given points. What sign should you expect for a? Explain. **[Positive; because the parabola opens upward]**
Q How do you know you only need three points? **[You need one point to find each constant: a, b, and c.]**

Got It?

Q Graph the points. What can you conclude about a and c? Explain. **[The parabola opens downward, so a < 0; the y-intercept is 0, so c = 0.]**

4-3 Preparing to Teach

BIG ideas Function
          Equivalence
ESSENTIAL UNDERSTANDINGS
• Any quadratic function is possibly a stretch, compression, reflection, and/or a translation of $y = x^2$.
• Three noncollinear points, no two of which are in line vertically, are on the graph of exactly one quadratic function.
• Standard form is "calculator ready".

Math Background

Students should know that two points determine a line. The Essential Understanding extends this property. Since the points are on *exactly one* quadratic function, the three points *determine* this function. In the lesson, students will use the three points to write and solve a system of linear equations. This same method will be used to find a quadratic model for a real-world situation.

Be aware that a *quadratic model* can apply to a data set that contains more than three points. A quadratic model for three points is an exact fit, while a model for more than three points may be only an approximation. However, in some cases, a quadratic function *is* the exact fit for more than three data points. See the Lesson Check Exercises 2–3 for examples.

Once students have grasped this concept, you may wish to challenge them by asking how many points determine the graph of a cubic or higher-degree polynomial function.

Mathematical Practices

Model with mathematics. In Problem 2, students will use a parabola as a model for trajectory and solve an everyday physics situation.

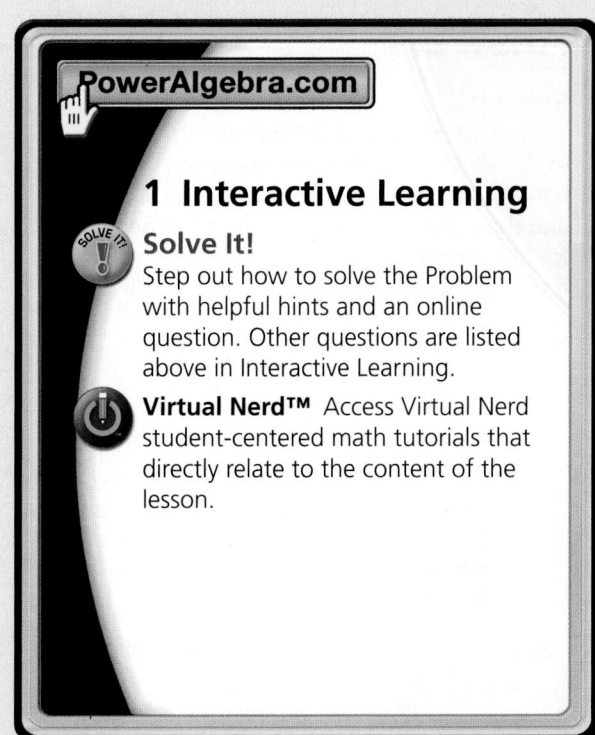

PowerAlgebra.com

1 Interactive Learning

Solve It!
Step out how to solve the Problem with helpful hints and an online question. Other questions are listed above in Interactive Learning.

Virtual Nerd™ Access Virtual Nerd student-centered math tutorials that directly relate to the content of the lesson.

Problem 2

Q What is the initial height of Rocket 1?
[**1 ft because h(0) = 1**]

Q Is the vertex of Rocket 1 a maximum or minimum point? How can you tell? [**Maximum; the coefficient of the squared term is negative so the parabola opens downward.**]

Q At what time *t* did Rocket 2 reach its maximum height? [***t* = 6**]

Got It?

Q What do the zeros of the function represent? [**the time at which the height was 0 feet**]

Q How can you determine how long Rocket 1 was in the air? [**Replace *h* with 0 and solve for *t*. Then find the difference of the times.**]

Q How can you determine how long Rocket 2 was in the air? [**Look at the graph to find the zeros of the function.**]

Q How many times during the flight of Rocket 2 was the height 0? [**twice, once at *t* = 0 and once at *t* = 12**]

 **Problem 2** Comparing Quadratic Models

Physics Campers at an aerospace camp launch rockets on the last day of camp. The path of Rocket 1 is modeled by the equation $h = -16t^2 + 150t + 1$ where *t* is time in seconds and *h* is the distance from the ground. The path of Rocket 2 is modeled by the graph at the right. Which rocket flew higher?

Find the maximum height of each rocket by using the models of their paths.

Think

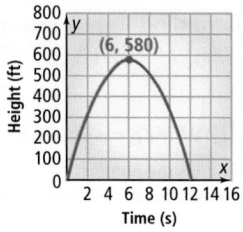

What property of the quadratic tells you how high the rocket flew?
The parabolas model the rockets' paths, so the maximums of each parabola describe how high the rockets flew.

Rocket 1

The maximum height of Rocket 1 is at the vertex of the parabola.

$$-\frac{b}{2a}, f\left(-\frac{b}{2a}\right)$$ Use the vertex formula.

$$-\frac{150}{2(-16)}, f\left(-\frac{150}{2(-16)}\right)$$ $a = -16, b = 150$

$(4.7, 352.6)$ Simplify.

The maximum height of Rocket 1 is 352.6 feet.

Rocket 2

The maximum height of Rocket 2 is at the vertex of the parabola.

You can use the graph to find the approximate maximum height of the rocket.

The maximum height of Rocket 2 is at about 580 feet.

Rocket 2 flew higher than Rocket 1.

 Got It? 2. a. Which rocket stayed in the air longer?
  b. What is the reasonable domain and range for each quadratic model?
  c. Reasoning Describe what the domains tell you about each of the models and why the domains for the models are different.

Answers

Solve It!

$y = -0.12x^2 + 1.2x + 3$, You catch the ball at $(0, 3)$, and the vertex is the maximum, midway between you and your friend. Use the vertex $(5, 6)$ and the point $(0, 3)$ in the vertex form and solve for *a*. Then convert the vertex form to the standard form by squaring the binomial and simplifying.

Got It?

1. $y = -3x^2 + x$

2. a. Rocket 2

  b. Rocket 1: D: $0 \le t \le 9.4$, R: $0 \le h \le 352.6$; Rocket 2: D: $0 \le t \le 12$, R: $0 \le h \le 580$

  c. The domains tell you how many seconds the rockets were in the air. The domains are different because the rockets were in the air for different amounts of time.

3. $y = -0.329x^2 + 9.798x + 15.571$; 88.5°F at 2:53 P.M.

 PowerAlgebra.com

2 Guided Instruction

Each Problem is worked out and supported online.

Problem 1
Writing an Equation of a Parabola
Animated

Problem 2
Comparing Quadratic Models

Problem 3
Using a Quadratic Regression
Animated

Support in Algebra 2 Companion
• Vocabulary
• Key Concepts
• Got It?

When more than three data points suggest a quadratic function, you can use the quadratic regression feature of a graphing calculator to find a quadratic model.

© **Problem 3** Using Quadratic Regression

The table shows a meteorologist's predicted temperatures for an October day in Sacramento, California.

Sacramento, CA

Time	Predicted Temperature (°F)
8 A.M.	52
10 A.M.	64
12 P.M.	72
2 P.M.	78
4 P.M.	81
6 P.M.	76

A What is a quadratic model for this data?

Think

How do you write times using a 24-hour clock?
Add 12 to the number of hours past noon. So, 2 P.M. is 14:00 in the 24-hour clock.

Step 1 Enter the data. Use the 24-hour clock to represent times after noon.

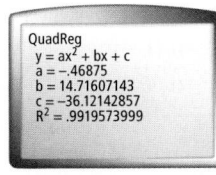

Step 2 Use **QuadReg**.

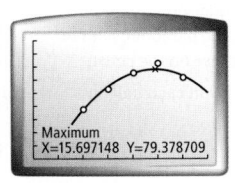

QuadReg
$y = ax^2 + bx + c$
$a = -.46875$
$b = 14.71607143$
$c = -36.12142857$
$R^2 = .9919573999$

Step 3 Graph the data and the function.

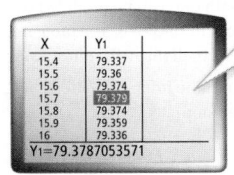

A quadratic model is reasonable.

A quadratic model for temperature is $y = -0.469x^2 + 14.716x - 36.121$.

B Use your model to predict the high temperature for the day. At what time does the high temperature occur?

Use the **Maximum** feature or tables.

Maximum
X=15.697148 Y=79.378709

X	Y1
15.4	79.337
15.5	79.36
15.6	79.374
15.7	79.379
15.8	79.374
15.9	79.359
16	79.336

Y1=79.3787053571

16 represents 4 P.M. The maximum occurs at approximately 15.7, or about 3:42 P.M.

Predict the high temperature for the day to be 79.4°F at about 3:42 P.M.

✓ **Got It?** **3.** The table shows a meteorologist's predicted temperatures for a summer day in Denver, Colorado. What is a quadratic model for this data? Predict the high temperature for the day. At what time does the high temperature occur?

Denver, CO

Time	Predicted Temperature (°F)
6 A.M.	63
9 A.M.	76
12 P.M.	86
3 P.M.	89
6 P.M.	85
9 P.M.	76

Problem 3

Q Are the calculated *y*-values equal to the Predicted Temperature values in the table? Explain why or why not. **[No; answers may vary. Sample: The *y*-values in the calculator table are values of the quadratic model for the data. The model is a function that approximates the data; it is not an exact fit.]**

Q What is the value of R^2 rounded to three decimal places? What does this answer indicate? Explain. **[0.992; answers may vary. Sample: It indicates that the model is a very close fit for the data because the value of R^2 is close to 1.]**

Got It?

Q Using the model, what is your predicted high temperature? Justify your prediction. **[88.4°F; answers may vary. Sample: It is approximately the highest temperature value of the quadratic model. Although the predicted temperature for 3 P.M. is 89 degrees, it did not fit the model.]**

Q Which is an actual data point: (14.87, 88.4) or (15, 89)? Does that mean 89°F is the actual high temperature? Explain. **[(15, 89); no 89°F is a temperature predicted by a meteorologist.]**

Additional Problems

1. A parabola contains the points (0, 0), (−1, 1), and (1, 5). What is the equation of this parabola in standard form?

ANSWER $y = 3x^2 + 2x$

2. Refer to Problem 2. Campers launched a third rocket which can be modeled by the equation $h = -16t^2 + 160t + 1$.
  a. Did Rocket 1 or Rocket 3 fly higher?
  b. Did Rocket 2 or Rocket 3 stay in the air longer?

ANSWERS
a. Rocket 3
b. Rocket 2

3. The table shows a meteorologist's predicted temperatures for a fall day in Baltimore, Maryland.

Time	Predicted Temperature (°F)
8 A.M.	52
11 A.M.	59
2 P.M.	63
5 P.M.	63
8 P.M.	58
11 P.M.	56

a. What is a quadratic model for this data? (Round numerical values to the nearest hundredth.)

b. Use your model to predict the high temperature for the day. At what time does the predicted high temperature occur?

ANSWERS
a. $y = -0.16x^2 + 5.14x + 21.60$
b. 62.9°F at about 4 P.M.

3 Lesson Check

Do you know HOW?

- For Exercises 2–3, students will need to choose three of the given points to work with. Then, after finding the function, they will need to verify that *all* the given points satisfy that function.

Do you UNDERSTAND?

- If students have trouble with Exercise 5, revisit Problem 2.

Close

> **Q** How can you write a quadratic function whose graph passes through three known points? [**Substitute the (x, y) values into $y = ax^2 + bx + c$ to write a system of equations, and then solve the system for a, b, and c.**]
>
> **Q** How can you write a quadratic function that models data consisting of more than three points? [**Use quadratic regression.**]

Lesson Check

Do you know HOW?

Find a quadratic function that includes each set of values.

1. $(1, 0), (2, -3), (3, -10)$

2.

x	-2	-1	0	1	2
y	3.5	3.5	7.5	15.5	27.5

3.

x	-2	-1	0	1
y	-41.5	-25.5	-13.5	-5.5

Do you UNDERSTAND?

4. Compare and Contrast How do you know whether to perform a linear regression or a quadratic regression for a given set of data?

5. Reasoning Explain how you can determine which of the quadratic functions in Exercise 1 and Exercise 2 attains the greatest values.

6. Error Analysis Your classmate says he can write the equation of a quadratic function that passes through the points $(3, 4)$, $(5, -2)$, and $(3, 0)$. Explain his error.

Practice and Problem-Solving Exercises

A Practice Find an equation in standard form of the parabola passing through the points. ◆ See Problem 1.

7. $(1, -2), (2, -2), (3, -4)$ **8.** $(1, -2), (2, -4), (3, -4)$ **9.** $(-1, 6), (1, 4), (2, 9)$

10. $(1, 1), (-1, -3), (-3, 1)$ **11.** $(3, -6), (1, -2), (6, 3)$ **12.** $(-2, 9), (-4, 5), (1, 0)$

13.

x	f(x)
-1	-1
1	3
2	8

14.

x	f(x)
-1	17
1	17
2	8

15.

x	f(x)
-1	-4
1	-2
2	-4

16. A player throws a basketball toward a hoop. The basketball follows a parabolic path that can be modeled by the equation $y = -0.125x^2 + 1.84x + 6$. The table models the parabolic path of another basketball thrown from somewhere else on the court.

If the center of the hoop is located at (12, 10), will each ball pass through the hoop?

◆ See Problems 2 and 3.

x	y
2	10
4	12
10	12

STEM 17. Physics A man throws a ball off the top of a building and records the height of the ball at different times, as shown in the table.
  a. Find a quadratic model for the data.
  b. Use the model to estimate the height of the ball at 2.5 seconds.
  c. What is the ball's maximum height?

Height of a Ball

Time (s)	Height (ft)
0	46
1	63
2	48
3	1

---

3 Lesson Check

For a digital lesson check, use the Got It questions.

Support in Algebra 2 Companion
- Lesson Check

4 Practice

Assign homework to individual students or to an entire class.

Answers

Lesson Check

1. $y = -2x^2 + 3x - 1$

2. $y = 2x^2 + 6x + 7.5$

3. $y = -2x^2 + 10x - 13.5$

4. Answers may vary. Sample: A rough plot of the data will indicate whether the data are collinear (linear regression) or non-collinear where the data follows a curve (quadratic regression).

5. A parabola that opens up always attains greater values than one that opens down.

6. y is not a function of x since for one value of x, "3," there are 2 values of y, "4" and "0."

Practice and Problem-Solving Exercises

7. $y = -x^2 + 3x - 4$

8. $y = x^2 - 5x + 2$

9. $y = 2x^2 - x + 3$

10. $y = x^2 + 2x - 2$

11. $y = x^2 - 6x + 3$

12. $y = -x^2 - 4x + 5$

13. $y = x^2 + 2x$

14. $y = -3x^2 + 20$

15. $y = -x^2 + x - 2$

16. Yes, both balls will pass through the hoop.

17. a. $y = -16x^2 + 33x + 46$, where x is the number of seconds after release and y is the height in ft

  b. 28.5 ft

  c. about 63 ft

Determine whether a quadratic model exists for each set of values. If so, write the model.

18. $f(-2) = 16, f(0) = 0, f(1) = 4$

19. $f(0) = 5, f(2) = 3, f(-1) = 0$

20. $f(-1) = -4, f(1) = -2, f(2) = -1$

21. $f(-2) = 7, f(0) = 1, f(2) = 0$

22. a. Geometry Copy and complete the table. It shows the total number of segments whose endpoints are chosen from x points, no three of which are collinear.

Number of points, x	2	3	▓	▓
Number of segments, y	1	3	▓	▓

b. Write a quadratic model for the data.

c. Predict the number of segments that can be drawn using 10 points.

© 23. Think About a Plan The table shows the height of a column of water as it drains from its container. Use a quadratic model of this data to estimate the water level at 30 seconds.
- What system of equations can you use to solve this problem?
- How can you determine if your answer is reasonable?

Water Levels

Elapsed Time (s)	Water Level (mm)
0	120
20	83
40	50

24. A parabola contains the points $(-1, 8)$, $(0, 4)$, and $(1, 2)$. Name another point also on the parabola.

25. a. Postal Rates Find a quadratic model for the data. Use 1981 as year 0.

Price of First-Class Stamp							
Year	1981	1991	1995	1999	2001	2006	2007	2008
Price (cents)	18	29	32	33	34	39	41	42

SOURCE: United States Postal Service

b. Describe a reasonable domain and range for your model. (*Hint*: This is a discrete, real situation.)

© c. Estimation Estimate when first-class postage was 37 cents.

d. Use your model to predict when first-class postage will be 50 cents. Explain why your prediction may not be valid.

26. Road Safety The table and graph below give the stopping distances of an automobile for dry and wet road conditions.

Speed (mi/h)	0	20	30	40	50
Stopping Distance on Dry Roadway (ft)	0	40	75	120	175

a. Find a quadratic model for the stopping distance of an automobile for each type of road condition.

© b. Writing Use your models to compare the stopping distance of an automobile traveling at 65 mph on dry and wet road conditions.

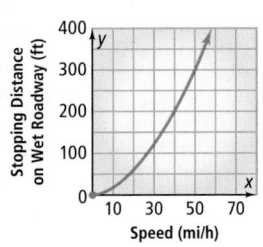

---

18. yes; $y = 4x^2$

19. yes; $y = -2x^2 + 3x + 5$

20. no

21. yes; $y = 0.625x^2 - 1.75x + 1$

22. a. x: 4, 5; y: 6, 10

b. $y = \frac{1}{2}x^2 - \frac{1}{2}x$

c. 45 segments

23. $y = 0.005x^2 - 1.95x + 120$; 66 mm

24. Answers may vary. Sample: (2, 2)

25. a. $y = -0.00357x^2 + 0.930x + 18.586$

b. Answers may vary. Sample: domain: integers from 0 to 27; range: whole numbers from 18 to 42

c. the year 2004

d. The year 2021; the year is outside the domain of the data pts.

26. a. Dry: $y = 0.05x^2 + x$; Wet: $0.01x^2 + x$

b. The stopping distance on a wet roadway, 487.5 ft, is 211.25 ft more than the stopping distance on a dry roadway, 276.25 ft.

© Mathematical Practices are supported by exercises with red headings. Here are the Practices supported in this lesson:

MP 1: Make Sense of Problems Ex. 23

MP 3: Communicate Ex. 26b

MP 3: Construct Arguments Ex. 27

MP 3: Critique the Reasoning of Others Ex. 6

Applications exercises have blue headings. Exercises 22 and 25 support MP 4: Model.

STEM exercises focus on science or engineering applications.

EXERCISE 25: Use the Think About a Plan worksheet in the **Practice and Problem Solving Workbook** (also available in the Teaching Resources in print and online) to further support students' development in becoming independent learners.

HOMEWORK QUICK CHECK

To check students' understanding of key skills and concepts, go over Exercises 7, 17, 22, 23, and 25.

Answers

Practice and Problem-Solving Exercises (continued)

27. a. (3, 5)

  b. 3 pts.; answers may vary. Sample: you substitute x- and y-values into $y = ax^2 + bx + c$ to set up and solve a linear system to find the values of a, b, and c.

28. a. You can find how high the arrow was when it was released.

  b. The negative intercept tells you how much earlier you would have to shoot the arrow from height zero for its height to be described by the same function. The positive intercept tells you how many seconds after the release the arrow will take to hit the ground.

 **Challenge**   **27. a.** A parabola contains the points $(0, -4)$, $(2, 4)$, and $(4, 4)$. Find the vertex.

 b. Reasoning What is the minimum number of data points you need to find a single quadratic model for a data set? Explain.

28. A model for the height of an arrow shot into the air is $h(t) = -16t^2 + 72t + 5$, where t is time and h is height. Without graphing, answer the following questions.

  a. What can you learn by finding the graph's intercept with the h-axis?

  b. What can you learn by finding the graph's intercept(s) with the t-axis?

Apply What You've Learned

 **MATHEMATICAL PRACTICES**
MP 1

Look back at the information about Victor's sandwich shop on page 193 and at the equations you wrote in the Apply What You've Learned in Lesson 4-2.

From your work in Lesson 4-2, you know that the following function models Victor's profit for selling x bags of chips at selling price s.

$$P(x) = -0.0025x^2 + 1.075x$$

Select all of the following that are true about the function $y = P(x)$ and its graph. Explain your reasoning.

  A. The graph is a parabola that opens up and the function has a maximum value.

  B. The graph is a parabola that opens down and the function has a maximum value.

  C. The graph is a parabola that opens up and the function has a minimum value.

  D. The equation of the axis of symmetry is $y = 215$.

  E. The x-coordinate of the vertex is 215.

  F. The x-coordinate of the vertex is -215.

  G. The x-coordinate of the vertex is 430.

  H. The x-coordinate of the vertex represents the number of bags of chips Victor should sell to maximize his profit.

  I. The y-coordinate of the vertex represents the number of bags of chips Victor should sell to maximize his profit.

  J. The y-coordinate of the vertex represents the price Victor should charge for a bag of chips in order to maximize his profit.

Apply What You've Learned

In the Apply What You've Learned for Lesson 4-2, students generated four functions, including a profit function, from the information given on page 193. Here, they analyze the equation of the profit function to identify the vertex of the graph and interpret the x- and y-coordinates of the vertex in terms of the situation. Later in the chapter, students will find the zeros of the profit function.

Mathematical Practices

Students **make sense of the problem** as they recognize and explain correspondences between the profit function's equation, its graph, and the real-world situation. (MP 1)

ANSWERS

Choices B, E, and H are all true.

Additional Instructional Support

Algebra 2 Companion

Students can use the **Algebra 2 Companion** worktext (4 pages) as you teach the lesson. Use the Companion to support

- New Vocabulary
- Key Concepts
- Got It for each Problem
- Lesson Check

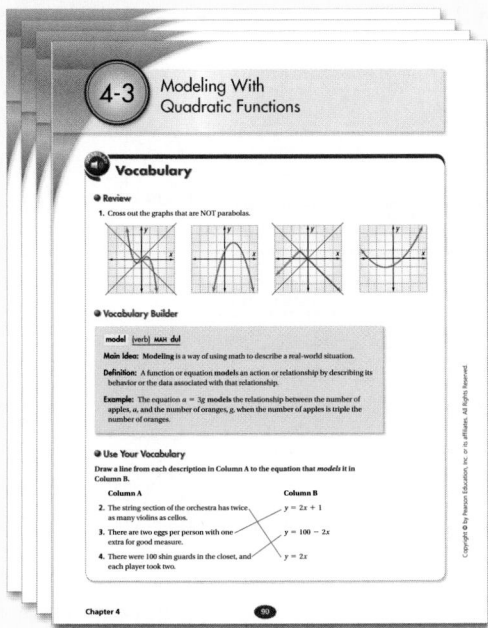

ELL Support

Focus on Language Read the Essential Understanding aloud. You may also want to have students read it aloud. Use the following activity to have students explain the meaning in their own words. Draw three collinear points on the board and elicit why they do *not* satisfy all the stated conditions. Draw three noncollinear points, but with two of them in line vertically, and elicit why *they* do not satisfy all the stated conditions. Draw three noncollinear points with no two of them in line vertically, and elicit why *they do* satisfy all the stated conditions. Sketch a parabola-shaped curve through the points. Then draw several sets of points that satisfy the stated conditions and have student volunteers sketch parabola-shaped curves through them.

5 Assess & Remediate

Lesson Quiz

1. Write in standard form the equation of the parabola that contains the points $(0, 0)$, $(-1, -5)$, and $(2, -2)$.

2. You throw a ball toward a trashcan. The ball follows a parabolic path through $(10, 10)$, $(14, 10)$, and $(20, 7)$. Will the ball pass through the center at $(0, 3)$?

3. Do you UNDERSTAND? The table shows predicted temperatures for a fall day in Orlando, Florida.

Time	Predicted Temperature (°F)
8 A.M.	74
11 A.M.	81
2 P.M.	83
5 P.M.	81
8 P.M.	77
11 P.M.	74

a. Find a quadratic model for the data.

b. Use your model to predict the high temperature for the day. At what time does the high temperature occur?

ANSWERS TO LESSON QUIZ

1. $y = -2x^2 + 3x$

2. Yes

3. a. $y = -0.15x^2 + 4.42x + 48.98$

b. 81.5°F at about 3 P.M.

PRESCRIPTION FOR REMEDIATION

Use the student work on the Lesson Quiz to prescribe a differentiated review assignment:

Points	Differentiated Remediation
0–1	Intervention
2	On-level
3	Extension

PowerAlgebra.com

5 Assess & Remediate

Assign the Lesson Quiz. Appropriate intervention, practice, or enrichment is automatically generated based on student performance.

Intervention

- **Reteaching** (2 pages) Provides reteaching and practice exercises for the key lesson concepts. Use with struggling students or absent students.

- **English Language Learner Support** Helps students develop and reinforce mathematical vocabulary and key concepts.

All-in-One Resources/Online
Reteaching

4-3 Reteaching
Modeling With Quadratic Functions

Three non-collinear points, no two of which are in line vertically, are on the graph of exactly one quadratic function.

Problem

A parabola contains the points $(0, -2)$, $(-1, 5)$, and $(2, 2)$. What is the equation of this parabola in standard form?

If the parabola $y = ax^2 + bx + c$ passes through the point (x, y), the coordinates of the point must satisfy the equation of the parabola. Substitute the (x, y) values into $y = ax^2 + bx + c$ to write a system of equations.

First, use the point $(0, -2)$. $y = ax^2 + bx + c$ Write the standard form.
$-2 = a(0)^2 + b(0) + c$ Substitute.
$-2 = c$ Simplify.

Use the point $(-1, 5)$ next. $5 = a(-1)^2 + b(-1) + c$ Substitute.
$5 = a - b + c$ Simplify.

Finally, use the point $(2, 2)$. $2 = a(2)^2 + b(2) + c$ Substitute.
$2 = 4a + 2b + c$ Simplify.

Because $c = -2$, the resulting system has two variables. Simplify the equations above.
$$a - b = 7$$
$$4a + 2b = 4$$

Use elimination to solve the system and obtain $a = 3$, $b = -4$, and $c = -2$. Substitute these values into the standard form $y = ax^2 + bx + c$.

The equation of the parabola that contains the given points is $y = 3x^2 - 4x - 2$.

Exercises

Find an equation in standard form of the parabola passing through the given points.

1. $(0, -1), (1, 5), (-1, -5)$ $y = x^2 + 5x - 1$ **2.** $(0, 4), (-1, 9), (2, 0)$ $y = x^2 - 4x + 4$

3. $(0, 1), (1, 4), (3, 22)$ $y = 2x^2 + x + 1$ **4.** $(1, -1), (-2, 20), (2, 0)$ $y = 2x^2 - 5x + 2$

5. $(-1, -5), (0, -1), (2, 1)$ $y = -x^2 + 3x - 1$ **6.** $(1, 3), (-2, -3), (-1, 3)$ $y = -2x^2 + 5$

All-in-One Resources/Online
English Language Learner Support

4-3 Additional Vocabulary Support
Modeling With Quadratic Functions

A football player kicks a football and records the height of the ball at different times. When kicked, at 0 seconds, the ball was 2 ft above the ground. One second later the ball was 28 ft above the ground, and 2 seconds after being kicked the ball was 20 ft above the ground. When will the ball hit the ground?

You wrote these steps to solve the problem on note cards, but they got mixed up.

Substitute the x and y values into the standard form of a quadratic function.	Use the quadratic model to determine when the ball hits the ground.
Solve the system of three linear equations.	Substitute the values of a, b, and c into the standard form of a quadratic function.

Use the note cards to write the steps in order.

1. First, substitute the x- and y-values into the standard form of a quadratic function

2. Second, solve the system of three linear equations

3. Next, substitute the values of a, b, and c into the standard form of a quadratic function

4. Finally, use the quadratic model to determine when the ball hits the ground

Differentiated Remediation *continued*

On-Level

- **Practice** (2 pages) Provides extra practice for each lesson. For simpler practice exercises, use the Form K Practice pages found in the All-in-One Teaching Resources and online.

- **Think About a Plan** Helps students develop specific problem-solving skills and strategies by providing scaffolded guiding questions.

- **Standardized Test Prep** Focuses on all major exercises, all major question types, and helps students prepare for the high-stakes assessments.

Extension

- **Enrichment** Provides students with interesting problems and activities that extend the concepts of the lesson.

- **Activities, Games, and Puzzles** Worksheets that can be used for concepts development, enrichment, and for fun!

Practice and Problem Solving Wkbk/All-in-One Resources/Online
Practice page 1

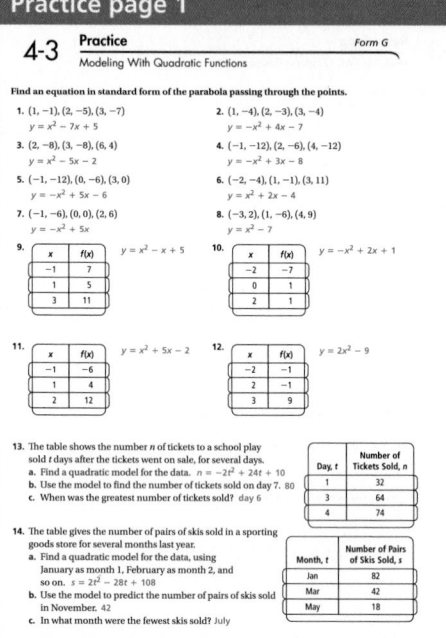

Practice and Problem Solving Wkbk/All-in-One Resources/Online
Practice page 2

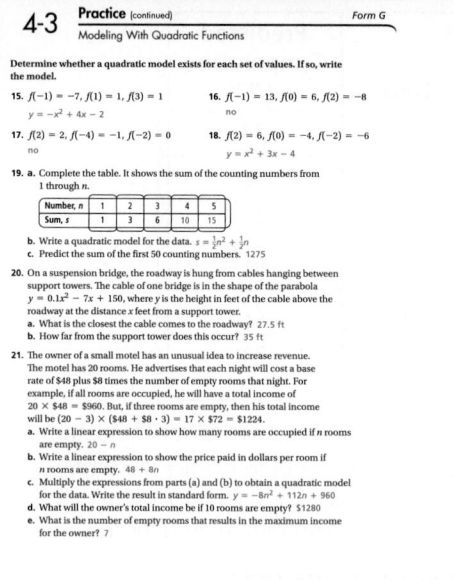

All-in-One Resources/Online
Enrichment

4-3 Enrichment
Modeling With Quadratic Functions

Baseballs in Flight

When baseballs are shot out of a cannon, their flight through the air depends on both the angle at which the cannon is set and the initial velocity of the baseball.

The equation $y = 0.5x - 0.01x^2$ represents the parabolic flight of a certain baseball shot at an angle of 26° with the horizon and at an initial velocity of 25 meters per second. In this equation, y is the height of the baseball, in meters, and x is the horizontal distance traveled, in meters. The graph of the equation is shown to the right.

1. Given that the points (10, 4) and (40, 4) lie on the parabola, at what x-coordinate must the vertex lie? $x = 25$

2. Use the equation and your answer to question 1 to find the maximum height of the baseball. 6.25 m

3. Use the point (0, 0) and the location of the vertex to find the total horizontal distance that the baseball will travel. 50 m

When the angle of the cannon is decreased, the baseball will travel in a different flight. The parabolic flight of the baseball is shown to the right, with the vertex labeled.

4. What is the total horizontal distance that this baseball will travel? 25 m

Using the same angle, the initial velocity of the baseball is increased to produce the graph of the flight shown to the right. The point shown represents the total horizontal distance the baseball will travel.

5. How far will the baseball travel horizontally before it reaches its maximum height? 25 m

Note: Sources: Gustafson, R. David. *Concepts of intermediate algebra: an early functions approach.* Pacific Grove, Calif.: Brooks/Cole Pub. Co., 1996.

Practice and Problem Solving Wkbk/All-in-One Resources/Online
Think About a Plan

4-3 Think About a Plan
Modeling With Quadratic Functions

a. Postal Rates Find a quadratic model for the data. Use 1981 as year 0.

Price of First-Class Stamp							
Year	1981	1991	1995	1999	2001	2006	2007	2008
Price (cents)	18	29	32	33	34	39	41	42

b. Describe a reasonable domain and range for your model. (*Hint:* This is a discrete, real situation.)
c. **Estimation** Estimate when first-class postage was 37 cents.
d. Use your model to predict when first-class postage will be 50 cents. Explain why your prediction may not be valid.

1. How can you find the x-coordinates of the data points?
   Subtract 1981 from each year.

2. What calculator function finds a quadratic model for data? QuadReg

3. Find a quadratic model for the data. $y = \boxed{-0.0036} x^2 + \boxed{0.930} x + \boxed{18.586}$

4. What does the domain of your model represent? What set of numbers would be a reasonable domain?
   Years since 1981; answers may vary. Sample: positive integers

5. What does the range of your model represent? What set of numbers would be a reasonable domain?
   Cost of first-class stamp, in cents; answers may vary. Sample: positive integers

6. How can you find the x-value that produces a given y-value?
   Answers may vary. Sample: Graph the function on a calculator and use the TRACE function.

7. Estimate the year when first-class postage was 37 cents. 2002

8. Predict the year when first-class postage will be 50 cents. 2021

9. Why might your prediction not be valid?
   Answers may vary. Sample: Many factors influence postal rates, such as inflation, fuel costs, and demand for postal services.

Practice and Problem Solving Wkbk/All-in-One Resources/Online
Standardized Test Prep

4-3 Standardized Test Prep
Modeling With Quadratic Functions

Multiple Choice

For Exercises 1–5, choose the correct letter.

1. Which parabola passes through the points $(1, -2)$, $(4, 1)$, and $(5, -2)$? B
   - (A) $y = -x^2 + x - 3$
   - (B) $y = -x^2 + 6x - 7$
   - (C) $y = x^2 - 4x + 1$
   - (D) $y = x^2 - 4x - 1$

2. Which parabola passes through the points in the table at the right? I

x	f(x)
-1	2
2	-4
4	2

   - (F) $y = -x^2 - x + 2$
   - (G) $y = \frac{1}{2}x^2 - \frac{3}{2}x - 1$
   - (H) $y = 2x^2 - 4x - 4$
   - (I) $y = x^2 - 3x - 2$

3. A baseball coach records the height at every second of a ball thrown in the air. Some of the data appears in the table below.

Time (s)	0	1	3
Height (ft)	0	64	96

   Which equation is a quadratic model for the data? A
   - (A) $h = -16t^2 + 80t$
   - (B) $h = -48t^2 + 112t$
   - (C) $h = -32t^2 + 80t$
   - (D) $h = -16t^2 + 64t$

4. Use the table in Exercise 3. What is the height of the ball at 2.5 s? H
   - (F) 80 ft
   - (G) 88 ft
   - (H) 100 ft
   - (I) 112 ft

5. Which of the following sets of values cannot be modeled with a quadratic function? C
   - (A) $(2, 3), (0, -1), (3, 2)$
   - (B) $f(2) = 7, f(-1) = -2, f(0) = 3$
   - (C) $(2, -7), (-1, 5), (3, -11)$
   - (D) $f(2) = -6, f(0) = -2, f(-1) = 3$

Short Response

6. The accountant for a small company studied the amount spent on advertising and the company's profit for several years. He made the table below. What is a quadratic model for the data? Show your work.

Advertising (Hundreds of Dollars)	1	2	3
Profit (Dollars)	269	386	501

   [2] $y = -x^2 + 120x + 150$
   [1] correct method but computational errors OR correct model but no work shown
   [0] incorrect answers and no work shown OR no answers given

---

Online Teacher Resource Center
Activities, Games, and Puzzles

4-3 Activity: Flight Path
Modeling With Quadratic Functions

This is an activity for groups of two to four students. You will need a graphing calculator.

A spacecraft is going to a distant planet to collect and transmit data to the scientists at mission control. The figure below represents an overhead view of a region of interest on the surface of the planet. The five stars in the figure mark specific locations from which scientists want to receive data.

The spacecraft will take a flight path that must be parabolic and passes over exactly three of the targeted areas. There are ten different flight paths that pass over three of the points. Find the ten equations that model these flight paths. Round your answers to the nearest hundredth.

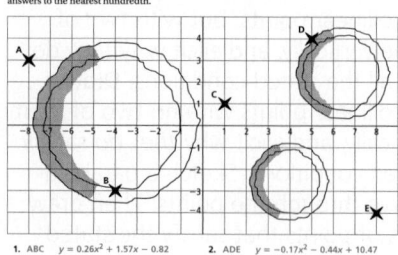

1. ABC $y = 0.26x^2 + 1.57x - 0.82$
2. ADE $y = -0.17x^2 - 0.44x + 10.47$
3. ABD $y = 0.18x^2 + 0.60x - 3.39$
4. BCD $y = -0.01x^2 + 0.78x + 0.22$
5. ABE $y = 0.09x^2 - 0.44x - 6.17$
6. BCE $y = -0.13x^2 + 0.42x + 0.70$
7. ACD $y = 0.07x^2 + 0.30x + 0.62$
8. BDE $y = -0.29x^2 + 1.06x + 5.85$
9. ACE $y = -0.03x^2 - 0.44x + 1.47$
10. CDE $y = -0.49x^2 + 3.68x - 2.19$

Identifying Quadratic Data

Common Core State Standards
F-IF.B.6 Calculate and interpret the average rate of change of a function . . . Estimate the rate of change from a graph.
MP 7

You can identify perfect quadratic data when x-values are evenly spaced using the pattern in the differences between y-values.

Example

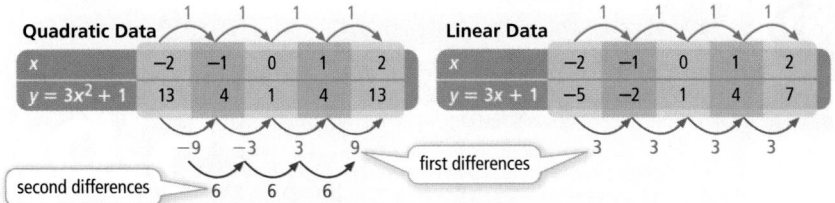

For linear data, the *first* differences of adjacent y-values are constant.
For quadratic data, the *second* differences are constant and not equal to 0.

Exercises

Determine if each data set represents perfect quadratic data.

1.

x	1	2	3	4	5	6	7
y	6	12	22	36	54	76	102

2.

x	−2	−1	0	1	2	3	4
y	−8	−1	0	1	8	27	64

3. **Reasoning** Can you use the method above to determine if a data set represents perfect linear or quadratic data if the x-values are *not* evenly spaced? Explain.

4. Recall that the average rate of change over any interval of a function is the slope of the line segment joining the endpoints of the interval.

x	−4	−2	0	2	4
y	16	4	0	4	16

   a. The table indicates points on a quadratic function. Use the table to find the average rate of change between the vertex and each of the other points in the table.

   b. As one of the endpoints gets further away from the vertex, what do you notice about the average rate of change?

Guided Instruction

PURPOSE To determine whether a data set represents perfect quadratic data

PROCESS Students find first and second differences of adjacent y-values to see whether a data set represents perfect quadratic data.

DISCUSS

Q What subtraction statement shows how to find the first first difference? the first second difference? **[4 − 13 = −9; −3 − (−9) = 6]**

Q What does *adjacent* mean? **[Answers may vary. Samples: consecutive, next to]**

Q The first differences are those of adjacent y-values. What are the second? **[differences of adjacent first differences]**

Q Could you use this method if each x in the table was not 1 unit from the previous x-values? Explain. **[Yes; as long as the x-values are evenly spaced.]**

Complete the table and find first and second differences to reinforce that x-values only need to be evenly spaced.

x	−4	−2	0	2	4
$y = 3x^2 + 1$	■	■	■	■	■

Exercises   **VISUAL LEARNERS**

Have students copy the tables so they can draw the curves and write the differences.

ERROR PREVENTION

In the second table in the Example, the second differences are all 0, which is constant. For data to be quadratic, the second differences must be a *nonzero* constant.

Mathematical Practices This Concept Byte supports students in looking for and making use of structure, Mathematical Practice 7.

Answers

1. yes

2. no

3. No; when x-values are not evenly spaced, linear or quadratic data will not necessarily have constant 1st or 2nd differences, and data that is neither linear nor quadratic may have constant 1st or 2nd differences.

4. a. between −4 and 0: −4
   between −2 and 0: −2
   between 0 and 2: 2
   between 0 and 4: 4

   b. The average rate of change is greater as the endpoints get farther away from the vertex.

1 Interactive Learning

Solve It!

PURPOSE To identify factors of a number that have a given sum

PROCESS Students may

- write a linear equation to model each clue, and solve them as a system of equations.
- make tables with one row for factor pairs and one row for the sum of each pair.

FACILITATE

Q Can the two numbers on the cards be negative? Explain. **[Yes; the problem only says that the cards have numbers; it does not specify positive numbers.]**

Q What are all the pairs of numbers that have the product 5? **[1 and 5; −1 and −5]**

Q Which pair has a sum of 6? **[1 and 5]**

Q Does this mean that 1 and 5 are the only possible numbers that could be on your two cards? Explain. **[No; the two numbers can also have a product of 6 and a sum of 5, for example, 2 × 3 and 2 + 3.]**

ANSWER See Solve It in Answers on next page.

CONNECT THE MATH To solve the puzzle in the Solve It, students found sums and products of factors of given numbers. In this lesson, students use sums of factors to write equivalent quadratic expressions.

Factoring Quadratic Expressions

Common Core State Standards
A-SSE.A.2 Use the structure of an expression to identify ways to rewrite it.
MP 1, MP 3, MP 4

Objectives To find common and binomial factors of quadratic expressions
To factor special quadratic expressions

Getting Ready!

In a game, you see the two cards shown. You get two other cards with numbers. You win if
1. the product of your two numbers equals the number on one card shown, AND
2. the sum of your two numbers equals the number on the other card shown.
What should your two cards be for you to win the game? Is there more than one answer? Explain.

If you have cards numbered 1 to 50, could you play the game with any two cards?

MATHEMATICAL PRACTICES

Factors of a given number are numbers that have a product equal to the given number. Factors of a given expression are expressions that have a product equal to the given expression. **Factoring** is rewriting an expression as a product of its factors.

Essential Understanding You can factor many quadratic trinomials $(ax^2 + bx + c)$ into products of two binomials.

You can use the Distributive Property or the FOIL method to multiply two binomials. You can use FOIL in reverse to help you factor.

Lesson Vocabulary
- factoring
- greatest common factor (GCF) of an expression
- perfect square trinomial
- difference of two squares

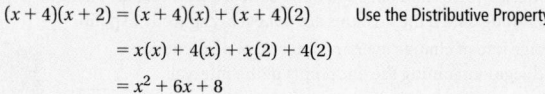

$$(x + 4)(x + 2) = (x + 4)(x) + (x + 4)(2) \quad \text{Use the Distributive Property.}$$
$$= x(x) + 4(x) + x(2) + 4(2)$$
$$= x^2 + 6x + 8$$

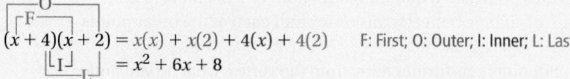

$$(x + 4)(x + 2) = x(x) + x(2) + 4(x) + 4(2) \quad \text{F: First; O: Outer; I: Inner; L: Last}$$
$$= x^2 + 6x + 8$$

To factor $x^2 + 6x + 8$, think of FOIL in reverse. Find two binomials for which the first terms have the product x^2, the products of the outer and inner terms have the sum $6x$, and the last terms have the product 8.

$$x^2 + 6x + 8 = (x + 4)(x + 2)$$

When you factor, a table of the different possible factors of the constant term may be helpful.

Preparing to Teach

BIG idea Solving Equations and Inequalities

ESSENTIAL UNDERSTANDINGS

- Many quadratic trinomials $(ax^2 + bx + c)$ can be factored into products of two binomials.
- The Distributive Property or FOIL method can be used to multiply two binomials. FOIL can be used in reverse to factor.

Math Background

Students who are accustomed to factoring numbers are sometimes confused by the concept of factoring expressions. Point out the similarity between factoring numbers and factoring expressions. When you factor a number, you find pairs of numbers whose products are the original number. When you factor a quadratic expression, you find a pair of expressions whose product is the original expression.

Factoring is one way to solve quadratic equations. In this lesson, students will use the Distributive Property and the FOIL method. Factoring expressions is a skill that comes with practice. Allow students ample time to make sure they go through all the steps properly.

Mathematical Practices
Make sense of problems and persevere in solving them. Students will check their answers when factoring quadratic expressions using the Distributive Property.

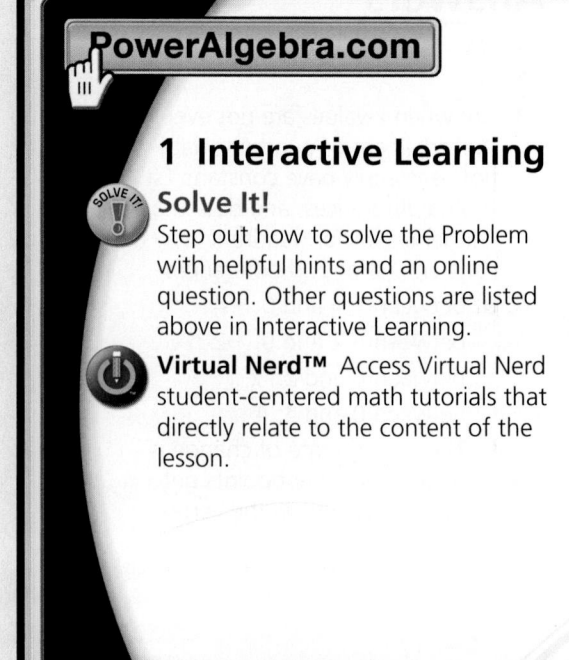

PowerAlgebra.com

1 Interactive Learning

Solve It!
Step out how to solve the Problem with helpful hints and an online question. Other questions are listed above in Interactive Learning.

Virtual Nerd™ Access Virtual Nerd student-centered math tutorials that directly relate to the content of the lesson.

 **Problem 1** Factoring $ax^2 + bx + c$ when $a = \pm 1$

What is the expression in factored form?

A $x^2 + 9x + 20$

Plan

How can you *make a table* to find factors?
Use the first row to list sets of factors of the constant. Use the second row to find the sum of each set of factors.

Step 1 Find factors of 20 with sum 9.
Since both 20 and 9 are positive, both factors are positive.

Factors of 20	1, 20	2, 10	4, 5
Sum of factors	21	12	9

Step 2 Use the factors you found. Write the expression as the product of two binomials.

$x^2 + 9x + 20 = (x + 4)(x + 5)$ Use the factors 4 and 5.

B $x^2 + 14x - 72$

Step 1 Find factors of -72 with sum 14.

Since $c < 0$, one factor is positive and the other is negative.
Since $b > 0$, the factor with greater absolute value is positive.

Factors of –72	–1, 72	–2, 36	–3, 24	–4, 18	–6, 12	–8, 9
Sum of factors	71	34	21	14	6	1

Step 2 Use the factors you found, -4 and 18. Write
$x^2 + 14x - 72 = (x - 4)(x + 18)$.

C $-x^2 + 13x - 12$

Step 1 Rewrite the expression to show a trinomial with leading coefficient 1.

$-(x^2 - 13x + 12)$ Factor out -1.

Step 2 Find factors of 12 with sum -13.

Since $c > 0$, both factors have the same sign.
Since $b < 0$, both factors must be negative.

Think

Will factoring out -1 change the answer?
No; because the final factored expression will include -1 as a factor.

Factors of 12	–1, –12	–2, –6	–3, –4
Sum of factors	–13	–8	–7

Step 3 Use the factors you found, -1 and -12. Write
$-x^2 + 13x - 12 = -(x^2 - 13x + 12) = -(x - 1)(x - 12)$.

 Got It? 1. What is the expression in factored form?
   a. $x^2 + 14x + 40$ **b.** $x^2 - 11x + 30$ **c.** $-x^2 + 14x + 32$

2 Guided Instruction

Problem 1
VISUAL LEARNERS

In 1A, students factor quadratic expressions when $a = 1$ and $c > 0$. Use algebra tiles to model the factorization.

Q In 1B, how do you know that the first term in each binomial factor is x? **[The first terms have the product x^2.]**

Q In 1B, why are -4 and 18 used for the outer and inner terms? **[They are the only factors of -72 that have a sum of 14.]**

Q In 1C, if you did not factor out -1, what would be the first term in each binomial factor? Explain. **[x and $-x$; they must have a product of $-x^2$.]**

Got It?
ELL SUPPORT

Students can make a list describing the signs of factors depending on the signs of b and c. Use this to help find factors quickly or as a check.

Signs of Factors

If a is not 1, factor it out first.		
b	c	Factors
$+$	$+$	$+, +$
$-$	$-$	$+, -$ [The factor with the greater absolute value is $-$]
$+$	$-$	$+, -$ [The factor with the greater absolute value is $+$]
$-$	$+$	$-, -$

EXTENSION

Ask students to show examples for each combination of signs.

2 Guided Instruction

 Each Problem is worked out and supported online.

Problem 1
Factoring $ax^2 + bx + c$ when $a = \pm 1$

Problem 2
Finding Common Factors

Problem 3
Factoring $ax^2 + bx + c$ when $|a| \neq 1$
Animated

Problem 4
Factoring a Perfect Square Trinomial
Animated

Problem 5
Factoring a Difference of Two Squares
Animated

Support in Algebra 2 Companion
• Vocabulary
• Key Concepts
• Got It?

Answers

Solve It!
One card should be a 2, the other card should be a 3; yes; one card could be a 5 and the other card could be a 1.

Got It?
1. a. $(x + 10)(x + 4)$
   b. $(x - 5)(x - 6)$
   c. $-(x + 2)(x - 16)$

Problem 2

Checking for a GCF to factor out is the first step when factoring any quadratic expression.

> **Q** If the expression were $6n^2 + 9$, what GCF would you factor out? If it were $6n^3 + 9n^2$? **[3; $3n^2$]**
>
> **Q** How do you know when you are finished factoring common terms out of an expression? **[The factoring is finished when the GCF is 1.]**

Got It?

ERROR PREVENTION

Students sometimes incorrectly factor the trinomial in 2b as $9(x - 2)(x + 1)$. Use the Distributive Property to show that this factorization in incorrect.

EXTENSION

> **Q** When the signs of the constants in the factor binomials are reversed, how does the trinomial change? **[The sign of the middle term in the trinomial is reversed.]**

Problem 3

The only common factors of the terms in this trinomial are 1 and −1, so the GCF cannot be used to factor it.

> **Q** In 3A Step 3, why is $11x$ rewritten as $3x + 8x$? **[3 and 8 are factors of 24 with a sum of 11.]**
>
> **Q** Would this method work if you switched the order of $3x$ and $8x$? Explain. **[Yes; $2x^2 + 8x + 3x + 12 = 2x(x + 4) + 3(x + 4) = (2x + 3)(x + 4)$.]**

The **greatest common factor (GCF) of an expression** is a common factor of the terms in the expression. It is the common factor with the greatest coefficient and the greatest exponent. You can factor any expression that has a GCF not equal to 1.

 Problem 2 Finding Common Factors

What is the expression in factored form?

Ⓐ $6n^2 + 9n$

$$6n^2 + 9n = 3n(2n) + 3n(3) \qquad \text{Factor out the GCF, } 3n.$$
$$= 3n(2n + 3) \qquad \text{Use the Distributive Property.}$$

Ⓑ $4x^2 + 20x - 56$

$$4x^2 + 20x - 56 = 4(x^2) + 4(5x) - 4(14) \qquad \text{Factor out the GCF, 4.}$$
$$= 4(x^2 + 5x - 14) \qquad \text{Use the Distributive Property.}$$
$$= 4(x - 2)(x + 7) \qquad \text{Factor the trinomial.}$$

✔ Got It? 2. What is the expression in factored form?

     a. $7n^2 - 21$ **b.** $9x^2 + 9x - 18$ **c.** $4x^2 + 8x + 12$

To factor a quadratic trinomial of the form $ax^2 + bx + c$ where $a \neq 1$, and there is no common factor, rewrite the middle term, bx, as two terms. The coefficients of these two terms will be factors of ac that have sum b.

 Problem 3 Factoring $ax^2 + bx + c$ when $|a| \neq 1$

What is the expression in factored form?

Ⓐ $2x^2 + 11x + 12$

Step 1 Since there is no common factor, find ac.

$$ac = 2(12) = 24$$

Step 2 Since both b and ac are positive, find positive factors of 24 that have sum 11.

Factors of 24	1, 24	2, 12	3, 8	4, 6
Sum of factors	25	14	11	10

Step 3 Factor the trinomial as follows.

$$2x^2 + 11x + 12$$
$$2x^2 + 3x + 8x + 12 \qquad \text{Rewrite } bx. \text{ Since } ac = 24, \text{ try 3 and 8 as coefficients of } x.$$
$$x(2x + 3) + 4(2x + 3) \qquad \text{Find a common factor for the first two terms and another common factor for the last two terms.}$$
$$(x + 4)(2x + 3) \qquad \text{Rewrite using the Distributive Property.}$$

Plan

Should you factor out a number, a variable, or both?
Both; the two terms have numerical and variable common factors.

Think

How should you make your table in this case?
Use the first row to list sets of factors of ac. Use the second row as before, to find the sum of each set of factors.

Additional Problems

1. What is the expression in factored form? $x^2 + 7x + 6$

     ANSWER $(x + 1)(x + 6)$

2. What is the expression in factored form? $4x^2 - 28x$

     ANSWER $4x(x - 7)$

3. What is the expression in factored form? $2x^2 + 5x - 12$

     ANSWER $(2x - 3)(x + 4)$

4. What is $x^2 - 12x + 36$ in factored form?

     ANSWER $(x - 6)^2$

5. What is $81x^2 - 100$ in factored form?

     ANSWER $(9x + 10)(9x - 10)$

Ⓑ $4x^2 - 4x - 3$

Step 1 Since there is no common factor, rewrite bx as the sum of two terms with coefficients that are factors of ac, and have sum b.

$ac = 4(-3) = -12$

Step 2 Since $ac = -12 < 0$, find factors of ac with opposite signs. Since $b < 0$, the factor with greater absolute value is negative.

Factors of –12	1, –12	2, –6	3, –4
Sum of factors	–11	–4	–1

Step 3 Factor the trinomial as follows.

$4x^2 - 4x - 3$

$4x^2 + 2x - 6x - 3$ Rewrite bx using $b = 2 - 6$.

$2x(2x + 1) - 3(2x + 1)$ Find a common factor for the first two terms and another common factor for the last two terms.

$(2x - 3)(2x + 1)$ Rewrite using the Distributive Property.

Check $(2x - 3)(2x + 1) = 4x^2 + 2x - 6x - 3$

$= 4x^2 - 4x - 3$ ✔

Got It? **3.** What is the expression in factored form? Check your answers.

a. $4x^2 + 7x + 3$ **b.** $2x^2 - 7x + 6$

c. Reasoning Can you factor the expression $2x^2 + 2x + 2$ into a product of two binomials? Explain.

A **perfect square trinomial** is a trinomial that is the square of a binomial. For example, $x^2 + 10x + 25 = (x + 5)^2$ is a perfect square trinomial.

If $ax^2 + bx + c$ is a perfect square trinomial, then ax^2 and c are squares of the terms of the binomial and thus are both positive. bx is twice the product of the terms of the binomial. b is negative if the binomial terms have opposite signs.

Here is another way to represent the two forms of a perfect square trinomial.

Key Concept   **Factoring Perfect Square Trinomials**

$a^2 + 2ab + b^2 = (a + b)^2$ $a^2 - 2ab + b^2 = (a - b)^2$

VISUAL LEARNERS

Students sometimes confuse terms when checking a factorization. Use a box to organize the process. Write each binomial in a row with one term in each column:

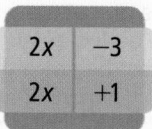

- Multiply down each column:
  $2x(2x) = 4x^2$
  $-3(+1) = -3$
- Multiply diagonally in both directions:
  $2x(+1) = 2x$
  $2x(-3) = -6x$
- Add all the products: $4x^2 - 4x - 3$

Got It?   **EXTENSION**

Q For 3c, what is the correct terminology to explain how the expression can be factored? **[Answers may vary. Sample: It can be factored as a product of one monomial and one trinomial: $2(x^2 + x + 1)$.]**

Take Note

The factoring methods used in previous sections can also be used to factor perfect square trinomials. For example:

$x^2 + 10x + 25$
$= x^2 + 5x + 5x + 25$
$= x(x + 5) + 5(x + 5)$
$= (x + 5)(x + 5)$
$= (x + 5)^2$.

Answers

Got It? (continued)

2. a. $7(n^2 - 3)$

    b. $9(x + 2)(x - 1)$

    c. $4(x^2 + 2x + 3)$

3. a. $(x + 1)(4x + 3)$

    b. $(x - 2)(2x - 3)$

    c. No; $2x^2 + 2x + 2 = 2(x^2 + x + 1)$, there are no real factors of a and c whose product is 1 and whose sum is 1.

Problem 4

Q How do the terms $4x^2$ and 36 help you identify it as a perfect square trinomial? **[Both terms are squares.]**

Q What must be true of the term $-24x$ for this expression to be a perfect square trinomial? **[Its absolute value must be twice the product of the square roots of $4x^2$ and 36 ($2x$ and 6).]**

Got It?

A trinomial $ax^2 + bx + c$ is a perfect square only if
- both ax^2 and c are squares,
- both ax^2 and c are positive, AND
- $|b| = 2\sqrt{a} \cdot \sqrt{c}$.

Take Note

A binomial is a difference of squares only if
- both ax^2 and c are squares, AND
- ax^2 and c have opposite signs.

Problem 5

As long as the terms of a binomial have opposite signs, their order does not affect whether or not the expression is a difference of two squares.

Q Is $-25x^2 + 49$ a difference of two squares? Explain. **[yes; $49 - 25x^2 = (7 - 5x)(7 + 5x)$]**

Got It? EXTENSION

Q What are a and b in this problem? **[$4x$ and 9]**

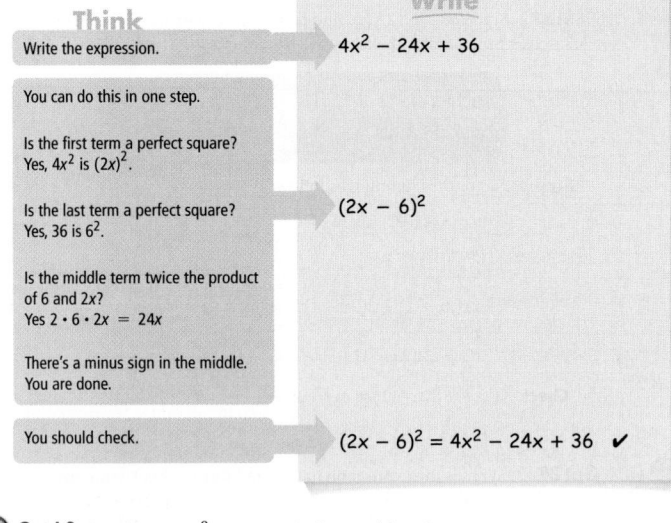

Problem 4 Factoring a Perfect Square Trinomial

What is $4x^2 - 24x + 36$ in factored form?

Think	Write
Write the expression.	$4x^2 - 24x + 36$
You can do this in one step.	
Is the first term a perfect square? Yes, $4x^2$ is $(2x)^2$.	
Is the last term a perfect square? Yes, 36 is 6^2.	$(2x - 6)^2$
Is the middle term twice the product of 6 and $2x$? Yes $2 \cdot 6 \cdot 2x = 24x$	
There's a minus sign in the middle. You are done.	
You should check.	$(2x - 6)^2 = 4x^2 - 24x + 36$ ✔

Got It? 4. What is $64x^2 - 16x + 1$ in factored form?

The expression $a^2 - b^2$ is the **difference of two squares**. There is a pattern to its factors.

 take note

Key Concept Factoring a Difference of Two Squares

$$a^2 - b^2 = (a + b)(a - b)$$

Think

How can a binomial be the product of two binomials? If the outer and inner products of the binomials are opposites, their sum is zero.

Problem 5 Factoring a Difference of Two Squares

What is $25x^2 - 49$ in factored form?

$25x^2 - 49 = (5x)^2 - 7^2$ Write as the difference of two squares.

$= (5x + 7)(5x - 7)$ Use the pattern for factoring a difference of two squares.

Got It? 5. What is $16x^2 - 81$ in factored form?

Answers

Got It? (continued)

4. $(8x - 1)^2$

5. $(4x - 9)(4x + 9)$

Lesson Check

1. $(x + 4)(x + 2)$

2. $(x - 12)(x - 1)$

3. $(x - 9)(x + 9)$

4. $(5y - 6)(5y + 6)$

5. $(y - 3)^2$ **6.** $(2x - 1)^2$

7. $5x$ **8.** $4a^2$

9. 6   **10.** $7h$

11. No; the middle term is not twice the product of the square root of the end terms.

12. For $a \neq 1$, look for two factors whose sum is b and whose product is ac. For $a = 1$, look for two factors whose sum is b and whose product is c.

13. $a^2 - 2ab + b^2 - 25$ Group the first 3 terms.

$= \left(a^2 - 2ab + b^2\right) - 25$

$= (a - b)^2 - 5^2$

$= (a - b - 5)(a - b + 5)$

Lesson Check

Do you know HOW?

Factor each expression.

1. $x^2 + 6x + 8$ **2.** $x^2 - 13x + 12$

3. $x^2 - 81$ **4.** $25y^2 - 36$

5. $y^2 - 6y + 9$ **6.** $4x^2 - 4x + 1$

Find the GCF of each expression.

7. $15x^2 - 25x$ **8.** $4a^3 + 8a^2$

9. $18b^2 - 12b + 24$ **10.** $21h^3 + 35h^2 - 28h$

Do you UNDERSTAND?

11. Vocabulary Is $4b^2 - 26b + 169$ a perfect square trinomial? Explain.

12. Compare and Contrast How is factoring a trinomial $ax^2 + bx + c$ when $a \neq 1$ different from factoring a trinomial when $a = 1$? How is it similar?

13. Reasoning Explain how to rewrite the expression $a^2 - 2ab + b^2 - 25$ as the product of two trinomial factors. (*Hint:* Group the first three terms. What type of expression is this?)

Practice and Problem-Solving Exercises

Ⓐ Practice   Factor each expression.   **See Problem 1.**

14. $x^2 + 3x + 2$ **15.** $x^2 + 5x + 6$ **16.** $x^2 + 7x + 10$

17. $x^2 + 10x + 16$ **18.** $y^2 + 15y + 36$ **19.** $x^2 + 22x + 40$

20. $x^2 - 3x + 2$ **21.** $-x^2 + 13x - 12$ **22.** $-r^2 + 11r - 18$

23. $x^2 - 10x + 24$ **24.** $d^2 - 12d + 27$ **25.** $x^2 - 13x + 36$

26. $x^2 - 5x - 14$ **27.** $-x^2 - x + 20$ **28.** $-x^2 + 3x + 40$

29. $c^2 + 2c - 63$ **30.** $x^2 + 10x - 75$ **31.** $-t^2 + 7t + 44$

Find the GCF of each expression. Then factor the expression.   **See Problem 2.**

32. $3a^2 + 9$ **33.** $25b^2 - 20b$ **34.** $x^2 - 2x$

35. $5t^2 - 5t - 10$ **36.** $14y^2 + 7y - 21$ **37.** $27p^2 - 9p + 18$

Factor each expression.   **See Problem 3.**

38. $3x^2 + 31x + 36$ **39.** $2x^2 - 19x + 24$ **40.** $5r^2 + 23r + 26$

41. $2m^2 - 11m + 15$ **42.** $5t^2 + 28t + 32$ **43.** $2x^2 - 27x + 36$

44. $3x^2 + 7x - 20$ **45.** $5y^2 + 12y - 32$ **46.** $7x^2 - 8x - 12$

Factor each expression that can be factored. For an expression that cannot be factored into a product of two binomials, explain why.   **See Problems 4 and 5.**

47. $x^2 + 2x + 1$ **48.** $t^2 - 14t + 49$ **49.** $k^2 - 18k + 81$

50. $4z^2 - 20z + 25$ **51.** $4x^2 + 16x + 8$ **52.** $81z^2 + 36z + 4$

53. $x^2 - 4$ **54.** $25a^2 - 120a + 144$ **55.** $81y^2 + 49$

---

3 Lesson Check

Do you know HOW?

- If students give the answers for Exercises 3 and 4 as $(x - 9)^2$ and $(5y - 6)^2$, refer them to Problem 5.
- For Exercise 6, suggest factoring out 4 from the expression: $4(x^2 - x + \frac{1}{4})$. If necessary, remind students that $-\frac{1}{2}(-\frac{1}{2}) = \frac{1}{4}$.
- For Exercises 7–10, have students factor out the GCF for each expression. Then challenge them to explain why each expression cannot be simplified further (other than by substituting a value for the variable).

Do you UNDERSTAND?

- For Exercise 12, if students have trouble explaining their thinking, suggest that they use two example trinomials in their explanations.
- For Exercise 13, after students group the first three terms and recognize that they can be factored as $(a - b)^2$, suggest that they replace $(a - b)$ with a new variable. This should help students see that $(a - b)^2 - 25$ can be factored as a difference of squares.

Close

> **Q** What is the purpose of factoring quadratic expressions? **[Answers may vary. Samples: to simplify an expression to identify values for its variable(s); to solve quadratic equations; to solve problems that can be modeled with parabolas]**

Practice and Problem-Solving Exercises

14. $(x + 1)(x + 2)$ **15.** $(x + 2)(x + 3)$

16. $(x + 2)(x + 5)$ **17.** $(x + 2)(x + 8)$

18. $(y + 3)(y + 12)$

19. $(x + 2)(x + 20)$

20. $(x - 1)(x - 2)$

21. $-(x - 1)(x - 12)$

22. $-(r - 2)(r - 9)$

23. $(x - 4)(x - 6)$ **24.** $(d - 3)(d - 9)$

25. $(x - 4)(x - 9)$ **26.** $(x - 7)(x + 2)$

27. $-(x - 4)(x + 5)$

28. $-(x - 8)(x + 5)$

29. $(c - 7)(c + 9)$

30. $(x - 5)(x + 15)$

31. $-(t - 11)(t + 4)$

32. $3; 3(a^2 + 3)$

33. $5b; 5b(5b - 4)$

34. $x; x(x - 2)$

35. $5; 5(t + 1)(t - 2)$

36. $7; 7(2y + 3)(y - 1)$

37. $9; 9(3p^2 - p + 2)$

38. $(3x + 4)(x + 9)$

39. $(x - 8)(2x - 3)$

40. $(r + 2)(5r + 13)$

41. $(m - 3)(2m - 5)$

42. $(t + 4)(5t + 8)$

43. $(x - 12)(2x - 3)$

44. $(x + 4)(3x - 5)$

45. $(y + 4)(5y - 8)$

46. $(x - 2)(7x + 6)$

47. $(x + 1)^2$ **48.** $(t - 7)^2$

49. $(k - 9)^2$ **50.** $(2z - 5)^2$

51. Cannot be factored; 8 is not a perfect square and there are no positive factors of 32 that have a sum of 16.

52. $(9z + 2)^2$

53. $(x - 2)(x + 2)$

54. $(5a - 12)^2$

55. Cannot be factored; this is a sum of squares, not a difference of squares.

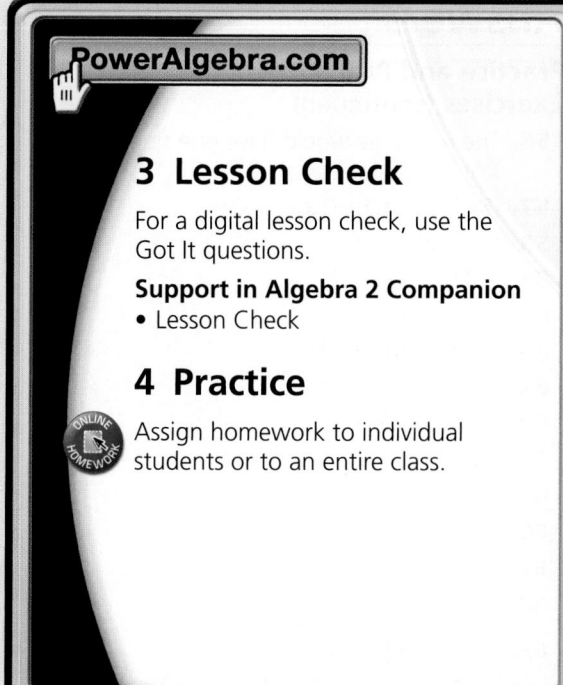

PowerAlgebra.com

3 Lesson Check

For a digital lesson check, use the Got It questions.

Support in Algebra 2 Companion
- Lesson Check

4 Practice

Assign homework to individual students or to an entire class.

4 Practice

ASSIGNMENT GUIDE

Basic: 14–58 all, 71–74, 79, 82

Average: 15–55 odd, 56–82

Advanced: 15–55 odd, 56–94

Standardized Test Prep: 95–97

Mixed Review: 98–102

Ⓒ **Mathematical Practices** are supported by exercises with red headings. Here are the Practices supported in this lesson:

MP 1: Make Sense of Problems Ex. 56

MP 3: Communicate Ex.12, 13, 82

MP 3: Construct Arguments Ex. 81, 89

MP 3: Critique the Reasoning of Others Ex. 71

Applications exercises have blue headings
Exercise 80 supports MP 4: Model.

EXERCISE 72: Use the Think About a Plan worksheet in the **Practice and Problem Solving Workbook** (also available in the Teaching Resources in print and online) to further support students' development in becoming independent learners.

HOMEWORK QUICK CHECK

To check students' understanding of key skills and concepts, go over Exercises 33, 39, 56, 57, and 72.

Ⓑ **Apply**

Ⓒ **56. Think About a Plan** Suppose you cut a small square from a square sheet of cardboard. Find the sides of one rectangle whose area is equal to the area of the remaining part.
- How can you represent the remaining part as a combination of rectangles with known sides?
- Can you factor the resulting expression?

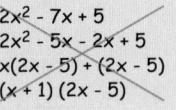

57. The area in square centimeters of a square area rug is $25x^2 - 10x + 1$. What are the dimensions of the rug in terms of x?

Factor each expression completely.

58. $9x^2 - 36$ **59.** $18z^2 - 8$ **60.** $4n^2 - 20n + 24$

61. $64t^2 - 16$ **62.** $12x^2 + 36x + 27$ **63.** $3y^2 + 24y + 45$

64. $2a^2 - 16a + 32$ **65.** $3x^2 - 24x - 27$ **66.** $-x^2 + 5x - 4$

67. $4x^2 - 22x + 10$ **68.** $-6z^2 - 600$ **69.** $-\frac{1}{16}s^2 + 1$

70. a. Multiply $(a + b)(a - b)(a^2 + b^2)$.
　　b. Use your result from part (a) to completely factor $81x^4 - 256y^4$.

Ⓒ **71. Error Analysis** Your friend attempted to factor an expression as shown. Find the error in your friend's work. Then factor the expression correctly.

$2x^2 - 7x + 5$
$2x^2 - 5x - 2x + 5$
$x(2x - 5) + (2x - 5)$
$(x + 1)(2x - 5)$

72. Agriculture The area in square feet of a rectangular field is $x^2 - 120x + 3500$. The width, in feet, is $x - 50$. What is the length, in feet?

Find the GCF of each expression. Then factor the expression.

73. $y^2 - y$ **74.** $ab^2 - b$ **75.** $10x^2 - 90$

76. $3t^2 - 24t$ **77.** $2x^2 - 74x + 12$ **78.** $x^2y^2 + xy$

79. What is the factored form of $4x^2 + 15x - 4$?
　Ⓐ $(2x + 2)(2x - 2)$ 　Ⓒ $(4x + 1)(x - 4)$
　Ⓑ $(2x - 4)(2x + 1)$ 　Ⓓ $(4x - 1)(x + 4)$

80. Geometry What is the volume of the shaded pipe with outer radius R, inner radius r, and height h as shown? Express your answer in completely factored form.

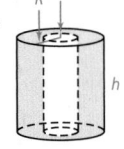

Ⓒ **81. Open-Ended** Write a quadratic trinomial that you can factor, where $a \neq 1$, $ac > 0$, and $b < 0$. Factor the expression.

Ⓒ **82. Writing** Explain how to factor $3x^2 + 6x - 72$ completely.

Ⓒ **Challenge** **Factor each expression completely.**

83. $0.25t^2 - 0.16$ **84.** $8100x^2 - 10,000$

85. $(x + 3)^2 + 3(x + 3) - 54$ **86.** $(x - 2)^2 - 15(x - 2) + 56$

87. $6(x + 5)^2 - 5(x + 5) + 1$ **88.** $3(2a - 3)^2 + 17(2a - 3) + 10$

Answers

Practice and Problem-Solving Exercises (continued)

56. The rectangle would have one side equal to x and one side equal to $x + 2y$.

57. $(5x - 1)$ cm by $(5x - 1)$ cm

58. $9(x + 2)(x - 2)$

59. $2(3z + 2)(3z - 2)$

60. $4(n - 3)(n - 2)$

61. $16(2t + 1)(2t - 1)$

62. $3(2x + 3)^2$

63. $3(y + 5)(y + 3)$

64. $2(a - 4)^2$

65. $3(x + 1)(x - 9)$

66. $-(x - 1)(x - 4)$

67. $2(x - 5)(2x - 1)$

68. $-6(z^2 + 100)$

69. $-\left(\frac{1}{4}s - 1\right)\left(\frac{1}{4}s + 1\right)$

70. a. $a^4 - b^4$
　　b. $(3x + 4y)(3x - 4y)(9x^2 + 16y^2)$

71. The third line should be $x(2x - 5) - (2x - 5)$, and the final line should be $(x - 1)(2x - 5)$.

72. $(x - 70)$ ft

73. y; $y(y - 1)$

74. b; $b(ab - 1)$

75. 10; $10(x - 3)(x + 3)$

76. $3t$; $3t(t - 8)$

77. 2; $2(x^2 - 37x + 6)$

78. xy; $xy(xy + 1)$

79. D

80. $\pi h (R + r)(R - r)$

81. Check students' work.

82. Factor 3 from the terms to get $3(x^2 + 2x - 24)$. Look for numbers whose product is -24 and whose sum is 2. The numbers -4 and 6 work. The complete factorization is $3(x - 4)(x + 6)$.

83. $(0.5t + 0.4)(0.5t - 0.4)$

84. $100(9x - 10)(9x + 10)$

85. $(x + 12)(x - 3)$

86. $(x - 10)(x - 9)$

87. $(2x + 9)(3x + 14)$

88. $2(a + 1)(6a - 7)$

89. Reasoning Explain how to factor $4x^4 + 24x^3 + 32x^2$.

Factor each expression completely.

90. $\frac{1}{16}x^4 - y^4$

91. $16x^4 - 625y^4$

92. $243a^5 - 3a$

93. When the expression $x^2 + bx - 24$ is factored completely, the difference of the factors is 11. Find both factors if it is known that b is negative.

94. Prove that $n^3 - n$ is divisible by 3 for all positive integer values of n.
(*Hint:* Factor the expression completely.)

Standardized Test Prep

SAT/ACT

95. How can you write $(m - 5)(m + 4) + 8$ as a product of two binomials?

Ⓐ $(m - 1)(m + 8)$ Ⓒ $(m + 8)(m + 8)$

Ⓑ $(m - 4)(m + 3)$ Ⓓ $(m - 5)(8m + 32)$

96. The graph of a quadratic function has vertex $(7, 6)$. What is the axis of symmetry?

Ⓕ $x = 6$ Ⓖ $y = 6$ Ⓗ $x = 7$ Ⓘ $y = 7$

Extended Response

97. Suppose you hit a baseball and its flight takes a parabolic path. The height of the ball at certain times appears in the table below.

Time (s)	0.5	0.75	1	1.25
Height (ft)	10	10.5	9	5.5

a. Find a quadratic model for the ball's height as a function of time.
b. Write the quadratic function in factored form.

Mixed Review

98. Find a quadratic model for the values in the table.

x	0	5	10	15	20
y	17	39	54	61	61

◀ See Lesson 4-3.

99. Coins The combined mass of a penny, a nickel, and a dime is 9.8 g. Ten nickels and three pennies have the same mass as 25 dimes. Fifty dimes have the same mass as 18 nickels and 10 pennies. Write and solve a system of equations to find the mass of each type of coin.

◀ See Lesson 3-6.

Get Ready! To prepare for Lesson 4-5, do Exercises 100–102.

Graph each function.

◀ See Lesson 4-2.

100. $y = x^2 - 2x - 5$

101. $y = x^2 - 4x + 4$

102. $y = -x^2 - 3x + 8$

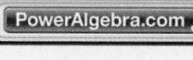

Mixed Review

98. $y = -0.149x^2 + 5.171x + 16.971$

99. penny: 2.5 g, nickel: 5 g, dime: 2.3 g

100.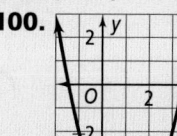

101.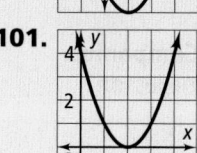

102.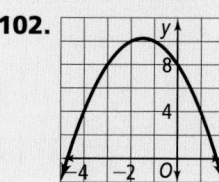

89. Factor the GCF, $4x^2$, from the terms to get $4x^2(x^2 + 6x + 8)$. Look for numbers whose product is 8 and whose sum is 6. The numbers 4 and 2 work. The complete factorization is $4x^2(x + 4)(x + 2)$.

90. $\left(\frac{1}{2}x - y\right)\left(\frac{1}{2}x + y\right)\left(\frac{1}{4}x^2 + y^2\right)$

91. $(2x - 5y)(2x + 5y)\left(4x^2 + 25y^2\right)$

92. $3a(3a - 1)(3a + 1)(9a^2 + 1)$

93. $(x - 8)(x + 3)$

94. Factor the expression completely to get $(n - 1)\,n(n + 1)$. The number 3 must go into exactly one of any three consecutive numbers.

Standardized Test Prep

95. B

96. H

97. [4] a. By entering the given lists into a graphing calculator and then calculating the quadratic regression, you get $h = -16t^2 + 22t + 3$ as the quadratic model for the ball's height as a function of time.

b. $h = -16t^2 + 22t + 3$
$h = -[8t(2t - 3) + 1(2t - 3)]$
$h = -(2t - 3)(8t + 1)$

[3] computational error

[2] incorrect function, factored correctly OR correct function, factored incorrectly

[1] correct answers, without work shown

Additional Instructional Support

Algebra 2 Companion

Students can use the **Algebra 2 Companion** worktext (4 pages) as you teach the lesson. Use the Companion to support

- New Vocabulary
- Key Concepts
- Got It for each Problem
- Lesson Check

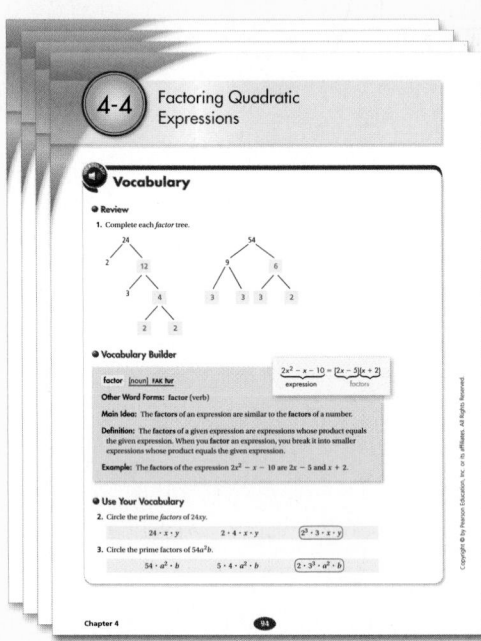

ELL Support

Focus on Language Write *binomial* and *trinomial* on the board. Underline the prefixes *bi-* and *tri-*. Explain that *bi-* means "two" and *tri-* means "three." A binomial has 2 terms, and a trinomial has 3 terms. Show pictures of a bicycle and a tricycle and use the number of wheels each has to help students understand the meaning and use of the two prefixes.

Ask students for examples of quadratic trinomials and binomials. Then have them make word cards for new terms. They should put familiar terms and illustrations on their cards.

5 Assess & Remediate

Lesson Quiz

1. **Do you UNDERSTAND?** What is the expression in factored form? $x^2 + 7x + 10$
2. What is the expression in factored form? $3x^2 + 21x + 18$
3. What is the expression in factored form? $3x^2 + 4x - 15$
4. What is $x^2 - 14x + 49$ in factored form?
5. What is $16x^2 - 25$ in factored form?

ANSWERS TO LESSON QUIZ

1. $(x + 5)(x + 2)$
2. $3(x + 6)(x + 1)$
3. $(3x - 5)(x + 3)$
4. $(x - 7)^2$
5. $(4x - 5)(4x + 5)$

PRESCRIPTION FOR REMEDIATION
Use the student work on the Lesson Quiz to prescribe a differentiated review assignment:

Points	Differentiated Remediation
0–2	Intervention
3–4	On-level
5	Extension

PowerAlgebra.com

5 Assess & Remediate

Assign the Lesson Quiz. Appropriate intervention, practice, or enrichment is automatically generated based on student performance.

Intervention

- **Reteaching** (2 pages) Provides reteaching and practice exercises for the key lesson concepts. Use with struggling students or absent students.
- **English Language Learner Support** Helps students develop and reinforce mathematical vocabulary and key concepts.

All-in-One Resources/Online
Reteaching

4-4 Reteaching
Factoring Quadratic Expressions

Problem
What is $6x^2 - 5x - 4$ in factored form?

$a = 6, b = -5,$ and c; they are the coefficients of each term.
$ac = -24$ and $b = -5$ We are looking for factors with product ac and sum b.

Factors of −24	1, −24	−1, 24	2, −12	−2, 12	3, −8	−3, 8	4, −6	−4, 6
Sum of factors	−23	23	−10	10	−5	5	−2	2

The factors 3 and −8 are the combination whose sum is −5.

$6x^2 + 3x - 8x - 4$ Rewrite the middle term using the factors you found.
$3x(2x + 1) - 4(2x + 1)$ Find common factors by grouping the terms in pairs.
$(3x - 4)(2x + 1)$ Rewrite using the Distributive Property.

Check $(3x - 4)(2x + 1)$ You can check your answer by multiplying the factors together.
$6x^2 + 3x - 8x - 4$
$6x^2 - 5x - 4$
Remember that not all quadratic expressions are factorable.

Exercises

Factor each expression.

1. $x^2 + 6x + 8$ $(x + 4)(x + 2)$
2. $x^2 - 4x + 3$ $(x - 3)(x - 1)$
3. $2x^2 - 6x + 4$ $2(x - 2)(x - 1)$
4. $2x^2 - 11x + 5$ $(2x - 1)(x - 5)$
5. $2x^2 - 7x - 4$ $(2x + 1)(x - 4)$
6. $4x^2 + 16x + 15$ $(2x + 5)(2x + 3)$
7. $x^2 - 5x - 14$ $(x + 2)(x - 7)$
8. $7x^2 - 19x - 6$ $(7x + 2)(x - 3)$
9. $x^2 - x - 72$ $(x - 9)(x + 8)$
10. $2x^2 + 9x + 7$ $(2x + 7)(x + 1)$
11. $x^2 + 12x + 32$ $(x + 4)(x + 8)$
12. $4x^2 - 28x + 49$ $(2x - 7)(2x - 7)$
13. $x^2 - 3x - 10$ $(x - 5)(x + 2)$
14. $2x^2 + 9x + 4$ $(2x + 1)(x + 4)$
15. $9x^2 - 6x + 1$ $(3x - 1)(3x - 1)$
16. $x^2 - 10x + 9$ $(x - 1)(x - 9)$
17. $x^2 + 4x - 12$ $(x + 6)(x - 2)$
18. $x^2 + 7x + 10$ $(x + 5)(x + 2)$
19. $x^2 - 8x + 12$ $(x - 6)(x - 2)$
20. $2x^2 - 5x - 3$ $(2x + 1)(x - 3)$
21. $x^2 - 6x + 5$ $(x - 1)(x - 5)$
22. $3x^2 + 2x - 8$ $(3x - 4)(x + 2)$

All-in-One Resources/Online
English Language Learner Support

4-4 Additional Vocabulary Support
Factoring Quadratic Expressions

Choose the word from the list that best matches each sentence.

factoring	greatest common factor	perfect square trinomial	difference of two squares

1. the expression $a^2 - b^2$ difference of two squares
2. rewriting an expression as a product of its factors   factoring
3. a trinomial that is the square of a binomial   perfect square trinomial
4. a common factor of each term in the expression   greatest common factor

Choose the word from the list that best matches each sentence.

factoring	greatest common factor	perfect square trinomial	difference of two squares

5. 10 is the ___greatest common factor___ of the expression $20x^2 - 50$.
6. An example of a ___perfect square trinomial___ is $x^2 - 8x + 16$.
7. When ___factoring___ $x^2 + 8x + 15$, find numbers with product 15 and sum 8.
8. The ___difference of two squares___ will always be a binomial.

Multiple Choice

9. Which of the following is a perfect square trinomial? B
   Ⓐ $2x - 7$ Ⓑ $9x^2 - 6x + 1$ Ⓒ $4x^2 - 25$ Ⓓ $9x^2 - 4x$
10. Which of the following is a difference of perfect squares? H
   Ⓕ $2x - 7$ Ⓖ $9x^2 - 6x + 1$ Ⓗ $4x^2 - 25$ Ⓘ $9x^2 - 4x$

Differentiated Remediation *continued*

On-Level

- **Practice** (2 pages) Provides extra practice for each lesson. For simpler practice exercises, use the Form K Practice pages found in the All-in-One Teaching Resources and online.

- **Think About a Plan** Helps students develop specific problem-solving skills and strategies by providing scaffolded guiding questions.

- **Standardized Test Prep** Focuses on all major exercises, all major question types, and helps students prepare for the high-stakes assessments.

Extension

- **Enrichment** Provides students with interesting problems and activities that extend the concepts of the lesson.

- **Activities, Games, and Puzzles** Worksheets that can be used for concepts development, enrichment, and for fun!

Practice and Problem Solving Wkbk/All-in-One Resources/Online
Practice page 1

4-4 Practice Form G
Factoring Quadratic Expressions

Factor each expression.

1. $x^2 + 11x + 28$ $(x + 7)(x + 4)$
2. $x^2 + 11x + 24$ $(x + 8)(x + 3)$
3. $s^2 + 13s + 42$ $(s + 7)(s + 6)$
4. $x^2 - 10x + 21$ $(x - 7)(x - 3)$
5. $y^2 - 8y + 15$ $(y - 5)(y - 3)$
6. $x^2 - 12x + 32$ $(x - 8)(x - 4)$
7. $-x^2 + 9x - 18$ $-(x - 6)(x - 3)$
8. $-w^2 + 12w - 35$ $-(w - 7)(w - 5)$
9. $-t^2 - 3t + 54$ $-(t + 9)(t - 6)$
10. $x^2 - 7x - 60$ $(x - 12)(x + 5)$

Find the GCF of each expression. Then factor the expression.

11. $6x^2 - 9$ $3(2x^2 - 3)$
12. $16m^2 + 8m$ $8m(2m + 1)$
13. $2a^2 + 22a + 60$ $2(a + 6)(a + 5)$
14. $5x^2 + 25x - 70$ $5(x + 7)(x - 2)$
15. $\frac{1}{3}x^2 + \frac{1}{3}x - 4$ $\frac{1}{3}(x - 3)(x + 4)$
16. $-7x^2 + 7x + 14$ $-7(x + 1)(x - 2)$

Factor each expression.

17. $5x^2 - 17x + 6$ $(x - 3)(5x - 2)$
18. $3x^2 + 10x + 8$ $(x + 2)(3x + 4)$
19. $2b^2 - 9b - 5$ $(2b + 1)(b - 5)$
20. $z^2 + 12z + 36$ $(z + 6)^2$
21. $9x^2 - 6x + 1$ $(3x - 1)^2$
22. $4k^2 + 12k + 9$ $(2k + 3)^2$
23. $n^2 - 49$ $(n - 7)(n + 7)$
24. $2x^2 - 50$ $2(x - 5)(x + 5)$

25. The area of a rectangular field is $x^2 - x - 72$ m^2. The length of the field is $x + 8$ m. What is the width of the field in meters? $x - 9$

Practice and Problem Solving Wkbk/All-in-One Resources/Online
Practice page 2

4-4 Practice (continued) Form G
Factoring Quadratic Expressions

26. The product of two integers is $w^2 - 3w - 40$, where w is a whole number. Write expressions for each of the two integers in terms of w. $w - 8, w + 5$

27. John is j years old. The product of his younger brother's and older sister's ages is $j^2 - 2j - 15$. How old are John's brother and sister in terms of John's age? brother: $j - 5$; sister: $j + 3$

Factor each expression completely.

28. $2x^2 + 9x + 10$ $(2x + 5)(x + 2)$
29. $6y^2 - 5y + 1$ $(2y - 1)(3y - 1)$
30. $3x^2 + 8x - 3$ $(x + 3)(3x - 1)$
31. $4x^2 - 7x - 15$ $(4x + 5)(x - 3)$
32. $12t^2 + 10t - 12$ $2(2t + 3)(3t - 2)$
33. $-10x^2 + x + 24$ $-(5x + 7)(2x - 3)$
34. $-4k^2 + 2k + 30$ $-2(2k + 5)(k - 3)$
35. $\frac{1}{2}x^2 + \frac{1}{2}x - 10$ $\frac{1}{2}(x + 5)(x - 4)$
36. $x^2 - 16x + 64$ $(x - 8)^2$
37. $m^2 + 22m + 121$ $(m + 11)^2$
38. $16x^2 - 40x + 25$ $(4x - 5)^2$
39. $36x^2 + 12x + 1$ $(6x + 1)^2$
40. $-2x^2 - 32x - 128$ $-2(x + 8)^2$
41. $-25p^2 + 30p - 9$ $-(5p - 3)^2$
42. $r^2 - 144$ $(r + 12)(r - 12)$
43. $\frac{1}{4}x^2 - \frac{1}{4}$ $\frac{1}{4}(x + 1)(x - 1)$
44. $-7x^2 + 175$ $-7(x + 5)(x - 5)$
45. $-\frac{1}{25}x^2 + 1$ $-\frac{1}{25}(x + 5)(x - 5)$

46. The radius of the outer circle in the illustration is R. The radius of the inner circle is r.
a. Write an expression for the area of the outer circle. πR^2
b. Write an expression for the area of the inner circle. πr^2
c. Write an expression representing the area of the ring, the shaded region in the illustration. Do not simplify. $\pi R^2 - \pi r^2$
d. Factor the expression in part (c). $\pi(R + r)(R - r)$

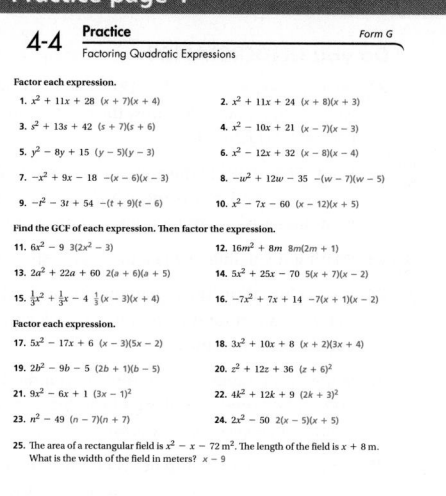

All-in-One Resources/Online
Enrichment

4-4 Enrichment
Factoring Quadratic Expressions

To factor a quadratic expression of the form $ax^2 + bx + c$, break the middle term of the expression into two terms and use common factors to complete the factoring.

$$2x^2 - 3x - 5$$
$$2x^2 + 2x - 5x - 5 \quad \text{Rewrite } -3x \text{ as } 2x - 5x.$$
$$2x(x + 1) - 5(x + 1) \quad \text{Factor the first two terms. Then factor the third and fourth terms.}$$
$$(2x - 5)(x + 1) \quad \text{Rewrite the expression using the Distributive Property.}$$

This same method can be used to factor polynomials with more than three terms.

1. Rewrite $x^3 + 3x^2 + 4x + 12$ by finding a common factor for the first two terms and another for the last two terms. $x^2(x + 3) + 4(x + 3)$
2. Factor $x^3 + 3x^2 + 4x + 12$ using the Distributive Property. $(x^2 + 4)(x + 3)$

Use this method to factor the polynomials below.

3. $3x^2 + xy - 12x - 4y$ $(x - 4)(3x + y)$
4. $a^3 - 2a^2 + 5a - 10$ $(a^2 + 5)(a - 2)$
5. $x^4 + 2x^3 - 2x - 4$ $(x^3 - 2)(x + 2)$
6. $b^3 + 3b^2 - 2b - 6$ $(b^2 - 2)(b + 3)$
7. $m^3 + 4m^2 - 9m - 36$ $(m + 4)(m - 3)(m + 3)$
8. $c^4 - c^2d^2 + c^2d - d^3$ $(c^2 + d)(c - d)(c + d)$

Practice and Problem Solving Wkbk/All-in-One Resources/Online
Think About a Plan

4-4 Think About a Plan
Factoring Quadratic Expressions

Agriculture The area in square feet of a rectangular field is $x^2 - 120x + 3500$. The width, in feet, is $x - 50$. What is the length, in feet?

Know

1. The area of the field equals the [length] times the [width].
2. The area of the field is $x^2 - 120x + 3500$ ft^2.
3. The width of the field is [$x - 50$] ft.

Need

4. To solve the problem I need to:
   rewrite the expression for the area of the field as a product of its factors

Plan

5. One factor is [$x - 50$].
6. What is the coefficient of the first term of the other factor? 1
   How do you know?
   The coefficient of the trinomial is 1.
7. What is the sign of the second term of the other factor? [negative]
   How do you know?
   The second terms of the two factors must have the same sign because the third term of the trinomial is positive. The second term of the first factor is negative.
8. The product of 50 and [70] is 3500.
9. The sum of 50 and [70] is 120.
10. The other factor is [$x - 70$].
11. What is the length of the rectangular field, in feet? $x - 70$

Practice and Problem Solving Wkbk/All-in-One Resources/Online
Standardized Test Prep

4-4 Standardized Test Prep
Factoring Quadratic Expressions

Multiple Choice

For Exercises 1–6, choose the correct letter.

1. What is the complete factorization of $2x^2 + x - 15$? B
   A. $(x - 5)(2x - 3)$
   B. $(x - 3)(2x + 5)$
   C. $(x + 3)(2x - 5)$
   D. $(x + 5)(2x - 3)$

2. What is the complete factorization of $-x^2 + 3x + 28$? I
   F. $(x - 4)(x - 7)$
   G. $-(x - 4)(x + 7)$
   H. $-(x + 4)(x + 7)$
   I. $-(x - 7)(x + 4)$

3. What is the complete factorization of $6x^2 + 9x - 6$? A
   A. $3(2x - 1)(x + 2)$
   B. $(3x + 2)(2x - 3)$
   C. $3(x - 2)(2x + 1)$
   D. $3(x - 2)(2x - 1)$

4. What is the complete factorization of $16x^2 - 56x + 49$? G
   F. $(4x - 7)(4x + 7)$
   G. $(4x - 7)^2$
   H. $(4x + 7)^2$
   I. $16(x - 7)^2$

5. What is the complete factorization of $5x^2 - 20$? C
   A. $(5x - 4)(x + 5)$
   B. $5(x + 4)(x - 4)$
   C. $5(x + 2)(x - 2)$
   D. $5(x - 2)^2$

6. What is the complete factorization of $x^2 - 14x + 24$? I
   F. $(x - 8)(x - 3)$
   G. $(x - 4)(x - 6)$
   H. $(x + 2)(x - 12)$
   I. $(x - 12)(x - 2)$

Short Response

7. The area in square meters of a rectangular parking lot is $x^2 - 95x + 2100$. The width in meters is $x - 60$. What is the length of the parking lot in meters? Show your work.
   [2] $x - 35$
   [1] correct method but an error in finding the length OR correct length but no work shown
   [0] incorrect answer and no work shown OR no answer given

Online Teacher Resource Center
Activities, Games, and Puzzles

4-4 Game: Factor This!
Factoring Quadratic Expressions

Game Play

This is a game for four students separated into two teams. Each team begins by secretly developing eight factorable polynomial expressions and writing them in standard form at the bottom of the page. Teams exchange pages and attempt to factor the opponent's functions. Then they write the factored form next to each function.

Rules

You must have two of each of the following types of polynomials.
A. the binomial factors have all integer coefficients and terms, and the leading coefficient equals 1
   Example: $(x + 2)(x - 7) = x^2 - 5x - 14$
B. the binomial factors have all integer coefficients and terms, and one of the factors has leading coefficient *not* equal to 1
   Example: $(2x + 1)(x - 3) = 2x^2 - 5x - 3$
C. the binomial factors have all integer coefficients and terms, and both of the factors have leading coefficients *not* equal to 1
   Example: $(3x - 2)(2x - 9) = 6x^2 - 31x + 18$
D. the binomial factors have fractional coefficients and terms, and one of the factors has leading coefficient equal to 1 and all numerators equal 1
   Example: $\left(x - \frac{1}{7}\right)\left(\frac{1}{3}x + \frac{1}{5}\right) = \frac{1}{3}x^2 + \frac{16}{105}x - \frac{1}{35}$

For each factor, all integer coefficients and terms must be between -10 and 10, and fractions must have numerators equal to 1 and denominators between -7 and 7.

The team that earns the most points wins.

Scoring
Correctly factoring:
- Type A — 1 point each
- Type B — 2 points each
- Type C — 3 points each
- Type D — 4 points each

Other:
- Stumping your opponent — 1 point per function
- Correctly identifying the opponent's function as unfactorable — 5 points

1. Check students' work.   2.
3.   4.
5.   6.
7.   8.

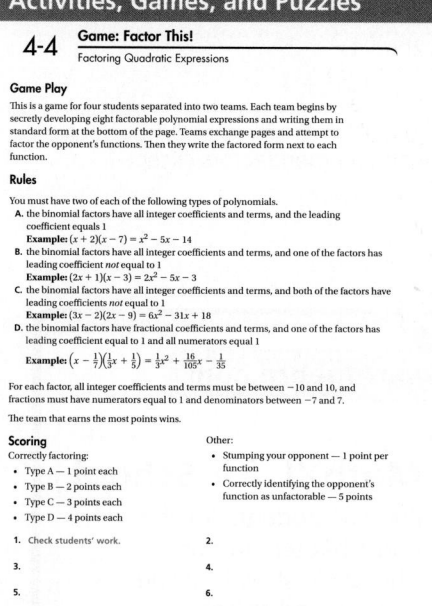

Answers

Mid-Chapter Quiz

1.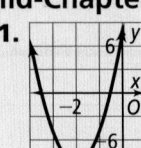

2.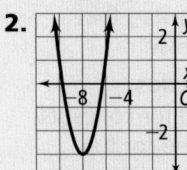

3.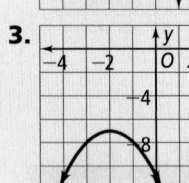

4.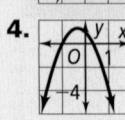

5. axis of symmetry: $x = 3$; maximum: 14; domain: all real numbers, range: $y \leq 14$

6. axis of symmetry: $x = 6$; minimum: 7; domain: all real numbers, range: $y \geq 7$

7. axis of symmetry: $x = -2$; maximum: 1; domain: all real numbers, range: $y \leq 1$

8. axis of symmetry: $x = 1$; minimum: -4; domain: all real numbers, range: $y \geq -4$

9. $y = -3(x + 1)^2 - 5$; vertex: $(-1, -5)$; axis of symmetry: $x = -1$

10. $-2(m^2 - 8)$

11. $-x(x - 3)$

12. $(y - 12)(y - 1)$

13. $(k - 8)(k + 3)$

14. $(2y - 3)(2y + 3)$

15. $(n - 5)^2$

16. $(2x + 3)(x + 2)$

17. $y = x^2 + 6x + 3$

18. $y = 5x^2 - 10x$

19. $y = 2(x - 1)^2 - 2$

20. $y = -(x + 2)^2 + 4$

21. $3x^2(x - 6)(x + 2)$; $3x^2$, x^2, and $x + 2$ have no common factors except 1.

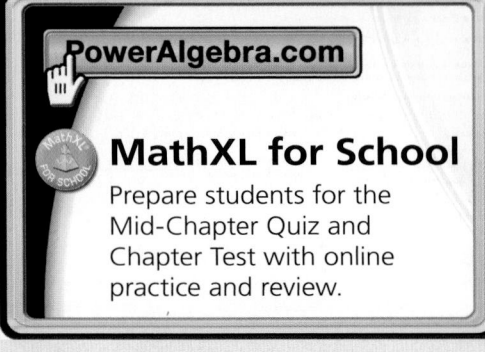

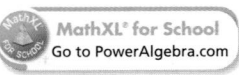
Do you know HOW?

Graph each function.

1. $y = 4x^2 + 16x + 7$

2. $y = (x + 8)^2 - 3$

3. $y = -(x + 2)^2 - 7$

4. $y = -3x^2 - 2x + 1$

Identify the axis of symmetry, maximum or minimum value, and the domain and range of each function.

5. $y = -x^2 + 6x + 5$

6. $y = \frac{1}{2}(x - 6)^2 + 7$

7. $y = -3(x + 2)^2 + 1$

8. $y = 4x^2 - 8x$

9. Rewrite the equation $y = -3x^2 - 6x - 8$ in vertex form. Identify the vertex and the axis of symmetry of the graph.

Write each expression in factored form.

10. $16 - 2m^2$

11. $-x^2 + 3x$

12. $y^2 - 13y + 12$

13. $k^2 - 5k - 24$

14. $4y^2 - 9$

15. $-10n + 25 + n^2$

16. $2x^2 + 7x + 6$

Find a quadratic model in standard form for each set of values.

17. $(0, 3)$, $(1, 10)$, $(2, 19)$

18. $(0, 0)$, $(1, -5)$, $(2, 0)$

Write the equation of each parabola in vertex form.

19.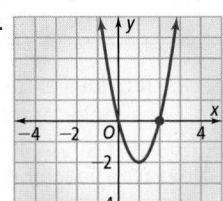

20.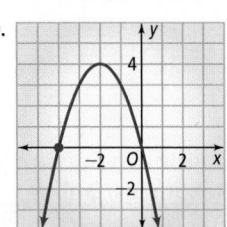

Do you UNDERSTAND?

21. Write the expression $3x^4 - 12x^3 - 36x^2$ in factored form. Explain how you know the expression is completely factored.

22. Open-Ended Write the equation of a parabola with a vertex at $(3, 2)$. Name the axis of symmetry and the coordinates of two other points on the graph.

23. Writing Explain how to factor $25x^2 - 30x + 9$.

24. Reasoning Write the equations of two parabolas that have a common vertex and are reflections of each other across the x-axis.

25. Write the equation of a parabola in standard form and explain how to convert it to vertex form. How would you reverse the process?

26. What is the relationship between the x-intercepts of the graph of a quadratic function and the x-coordinate of the vertex of that graph? Explain how you determined your answer.

---

22. $y = a(x - 3)^2 + 2$; axis of symmetry: $x = 3$; answers may vary. Sample: if $a = -1$, then $(5, -2)$, $(1, -2)$

23. $25x^2 - 30x + 9$ is a perfect square trinomial. The first term is $(5x)^2$. The last term is 3^2. The middle term is negative and twice the product of $5x$ and 3: $(5x - 3)^2$

24. Answers may vary. Sample: $y = 2x^2$ and $y = -2x^2$

25. Standard form: $y = ax^2 + bx + c$; find the x-coordinate of the vertex: $x = -\frac{b}{2a}$; find the y-coordinate of the vertex by finding y when $x = -\frac{b}{2a}$. Now that the vertex is known, write the eq. in vertex form. If the vertex is (h, k) write: $y = a(x - h)^2 + k$. To reverse the process from vertex form to standard form, expand the squared binomial and simplify the eq.

26. If there are two x-intercepts, the x-coordinate of the vertex is the midpt. between the two x-intercepts. Explanations may vary. Sample: The vertex lies on the axis of symmetry, so the x-coordinate of the vertex must be halfway between the x-intercepts.

© **Common Core State Standards**
Prepares for N-RN.A.2 Rewrite expressions involving radicals and rational exponents using the properties of exponents.

A radical symbol $\sqrt{}$ indicates a square root. In general, $\sqrt{x^2} = |x|$ for all real numbers x.

Square Roots

Multiplication Property of Square Roots	Division Property of Square Roots
For any numbers $a \geq 0$ and $b \geq 0$,	For any numbers $a \geq 0$ and $b > 0$,
$\sqrt{ab} = \sqrt{a} \cdot \sqrt{b}.$	$\sqrt{\dfrac{a}{b}} = \dfrac{\sqrt{a}}{\sqrt{b}}.$

Example

Simplify each expression.

Ⓐ $\sqrt{50}$

$\sqrt{50} = \sqrt{25} \cdot \sqrt{2}$ Multiplication Property of Square Roots

$\quad = 5\sqrt{2}$ Simplify.

Ⓑ $\sqrt{\dfrac{5}{11}}$

$\sqrt{\dfrac{5}{11}} = \dfrac{\sqrt{5}}{\sqrt{11}}$ Division Property of Square Roots

$\quad = \dfrac{\sqrt{5}}{\sqrt{11}} \cdot \dfrac{\sqrt{11}}{\sqrt{11}}$ Multiply both the numerator and denominator by $\sqrt{11}$.

$\quad = \dfrac{\sqrt{55}}{\sqrt{121}}$ Multiplication Property of Square Roots

$\quad = \dfrac{\sqrt{55}}{11}$ Simplify.

Exercises

Simplify each radical expression.

1. $\sqrt{18}$
2. $\sqrt{75}$
3. $-\sqrt{32}$
4. $\sqrt{\dfrac{-5}{7}}$

5. $-\sqrt{\dfrac{7}{13}}$
6. $\sqrt{\dfrac{3}{15}}$
7. $-\sqrt{200}$
8. $5\sqrt{320}$

9. $(2\sqrt{27})^2$
10. $-\sqrt{10^4}$
11. $\sqrt{x^2 y^2}$
12. $\sqrt{\dfrac{8}{x^2}}$

13. $-\sqrt{\dfrac{7x^3}{5x}}$
14. $\sqrt{\dfrac{(-3)^4}{12}}$
15. $\sqrt{\dfrac{200}{28}}$
16. $\sqrt{120x}$

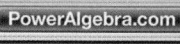
Guided Instruction

Example
Students may wonder why $\dfrac{\sqrt{55}}{11}$ is considered simplified form for $\sqrt{\dfrac{5}{11}}$, noticing that it does not look simpler. Explain that it is both easier and more accurate to evaluate a radical expression if you do not have to divide by an endless decimal. To avoid such cumbersome divisions, it is customary to write radical expressions in a form that has no radicals in the denominator. (In Chapter 6, students will learn that this is called *rationalizing the denominator*.) Ask the students to compare the process of evaluating $\dfrac{\sqrt{3}}{\sqrt{10}}$ with the process of evaluating $\dfrac{\sqrt{3}}{10}$.

Q When can you use the Multiplication Property of Square Roots to simplify a radical? **[when the radicand can be factored]**

Q After applying the Division Property of Square Roots to a radical with a fractional radicand, how can you simplify it? **[Multiply both the numerator and denominator by a radical that makes the denominator a perfect square and simplify.]**

Exercises   ERROR INTERVENTION
Students may think the simplified form of $\sqrt{x^2 y^2}$ is xy. Assign numeric values to x and y to show why $\sqrt{x^2 y^2} \neq xy$, such as $x = -3$ and $y = 4$. Elicit that $\sqrt{x^2 y^2} = \sqrt{x^2} \cdot \sqrt{y^2} = |x| \cdot |y| = |xy|$.

Answers

Algebra Review
1. $3\sqrt{2}$
2. $5\sqrt{3}$
3. $-4\sqrt{2}$
4. You cannot take the square root of a neg. no.
5. $\dfrac{-\sqrt{91}}{13}$
6. $\dfrac{\sqrt{5}}{5}$
7. $-10\sqrt{2}$
8. $40\sqrt{5}$
9. 108
10. -100
11. $|xy|$
12. $\dfrac{2\sqrt{2}}{|x|}$
13. $\dfrac{-|x|\sqrt{35}}{5}$
14. $\dfrac{3\sqrt{3}}{2}$
15. $\dfrac{5\sqrt{14}}{7}$
16. $2\sqrt{30x}$

1 Interactive Learning

Solve It!
PURPOSE To find an *x*-intercept of a parabola
PROCESS Students may
- use the ZERO function on a calculator.
- use symmetry, addition, and subtraction.

FACILITATE
Q What is the vertex of the parabola? **[(6.4, 12.96)]**
Q What property of symmetry does a parabola have? **[A parabola is symmetric about the vertical line through its vertex.]**
Q What is the horizontal distance from *A* to the axis of symmetry? Explain. **[6.4 − (−8) = 14.4]**
Q How can you find the *x*-coordinate of *C*? **[Answers may vary. Sample: 6.4 + 14.4]**

ANSWER See Solve It in Answers on next page.
CONNECT THE MATH Students use either an equation or symmetry to find an *x*-intercept of a parabola. In the lesson, they learn that an *x*-intercept is a zero of a function and find zeros of quadratic functions by solving related equations.

2 Guided Instruction

Take Note

Q Is it possible that both *a* and *b* are 0? Explain. **[Yes; 0 · 0 = 0.]**

Problem 1

Q What are all the factor pairs of 6? **[(1)(6), (−1)(−6), (2)(3), (−2)(−3)]**
Q Which pair has the sum −5? **[−2 and −3]**

Common Core State Standards
A-CED.A.1 Create equations and inequalities in one variable and use them to solve problems. **Also** A-SSE.A.1a, A-APR.B.3, A-SSE.B.3a
MP 1, MP 2, MP 3, MP 4, MP 5, MP 8

Objectives To solve quadratic equations by factoring
To solve quadratic equations by graphing

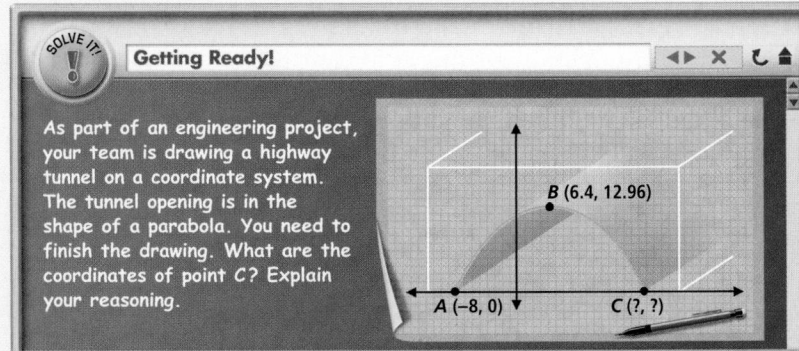

Getting Ready!

As part of an engineering project, your team is drawing a highway tunnel on a coordinate system. The tunnel opening is in the shape of a parabola. You need to finish the drawing. What are the coordinates of point *C*? Explain your reasoning.

B (6.4, 12.96)
A (−8, 0)   *C* (?, ?)

Lesson Vocabulary
- zero of a function
- Zero-Product Property

Wherever the graph of a function $f(x)$ intersects the *x*-axis, $f(x) = 0$. A value of *x* for which $f(x) = 0$ is a **zero of the function**.

Essential Understanding To find the zeros of a quadratic function $y = ax^2 + bx + c$, solve the related quadratic equation $0 = ax^2 + bx + c$.

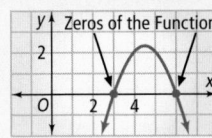
Zeros of the Function

You can solve some quadratic equations in standard form by factoring the quadratic expression and using the **Zero-Product Property**.

Property Zero-Product Property

If $ab = 0$, then $a = 0$ or $b = 0$.

Think
What do you know about the factors of $x^2 - bx + c$?
The product of their constant terms is *c*. The sum is −*b*.

Problem 1 Solving a Quadratic Equation by Factoring

What are the solutions of the quadratic equation $x^2 - 5x + 6 = 0$?

$$(x - 2)(x - 3) = 0 \quad \text{Factor the quadratic expression.}$$
$$x - 2 = 0 \quad \text{or} \quad x - 3 = 0 \quad \text{Use the Zero-Product Property.}$$
$$x = 2 \quad \text{or} \quad x = 3 \quad \text{Solve for } x.$$

The solutions are $x = 2$ and $x = 3$.

BIG ideas Solving Equations and Inequalities
Function

ESSENTIAL UNDERSTANDINGS
- The zeros of a quadratic function $y = ax^2 + bx + c$ can be found by solving the related quadratic equation $0 = ax^2 + bx + c$.
- Some quadratic equations in standard form can be solved by factoring the quadratic expression and using the Zero-Product Property.
- The real solutions of a quadratic equation show the zeros of the related quadratic function and the *x*-intercepts of its graph.

Math Background
The zeros of a quadratic function are equivalent to the *x*-intercepts of the graph of the function (where *y* is 0). Thus, finding the zeros of the quadratic function is a way of solving the related quadratic equation set equal to 0.

The following are equivalent:
- the zeros of a quadratic function
- the *x*-intercepts of the graph of the function
- the solutions of the related quadratic equation set equal to zero.

To solve a quadratic equation by factoring, you rely on the Zero-Product Property. Elicit that *a* and *b* represent any number or expression. The Zero-Product Property makes sense because for any product to be 0, one or both factors must be zero. Here is a quick proof by contradiction:

Assume $a, b \neq 0$.

$a \cdot b = 0$ Since $b \neq 0$, divide both sides by b

$a = 0$ Contradiction

Mathematical Practices
Use appropriate tools strategically.
Students will use a graphing calculator to find the zeros of a quadratic equation.

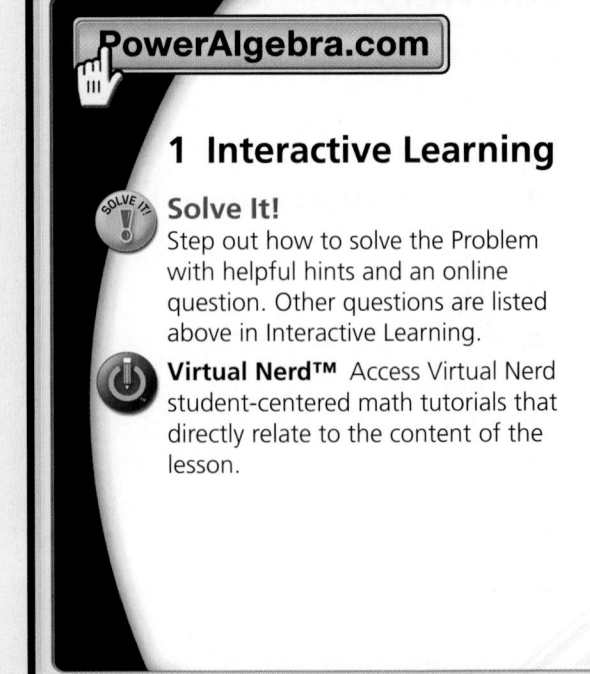

PowerAlgebra.com

1 Interactive Learning

Solve It!
Step out how to solve the Problem with helpful hints and an online question. Other questions are listed above in Interactive Learning.

Virtual Nerd™ Access Virtual Nerd student-centered math tutorials that directly relate to the content of the lesson.

Got It? **1.** What are the solutions of the quadratic equation $x^2 - 7x = -12$?

© Problem 2 Solving a Quadratic Equation With Tables

What are the solutions of the quadratic equation $5x^2 + 30x + 14 = 2 - 2x$?

$5x^2 + 30x + 14 = 2 - 2x$

$5x^2 + 32x + 12 = 0$ Rewrite in standard form.

Use your calculator's **TABLE** feature to find the zeros.

Think
What should you look for in the calculator table?
Look for x-values for which $y = 0$.

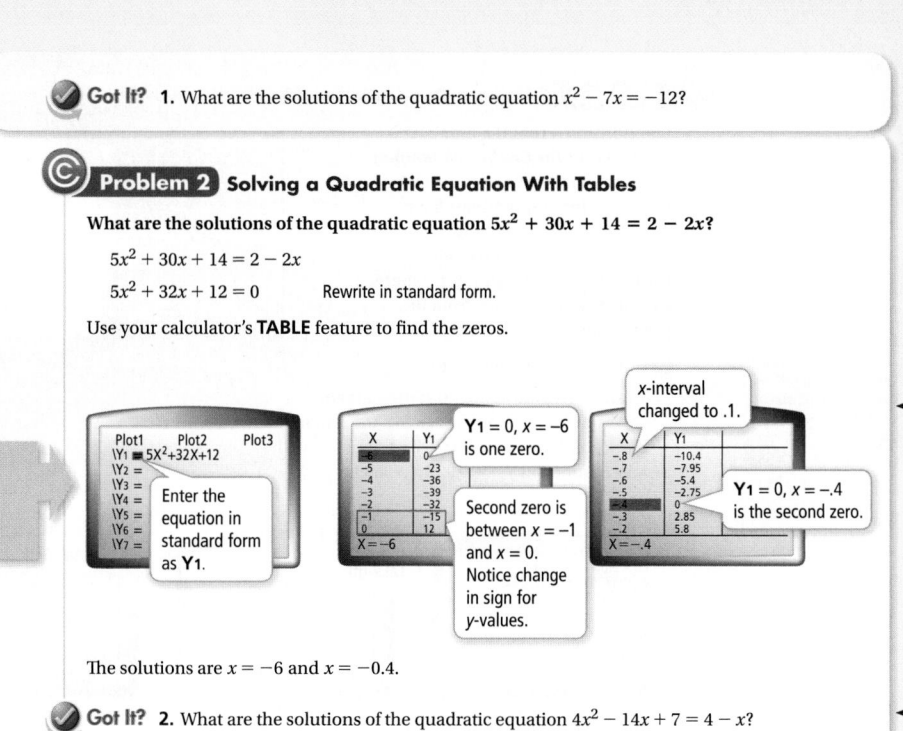

The solutions are $x = -6$ and $x = -0.4$.

Got It? **2.** What are the solutions of the quadratic equation $4x^2 - 14x + 7 = 4 - x$?

© Problem 3 Solving a Quadratic Equation by Graphing

What are the solutions of the quadratic equation $2x^2 + 7x = 15$?

$2x^2 + 7x = 15$

$2x^2 + 7x - 15 = 0$ Rewrite in standard form.

Plan
How can you use a graph to find the solutions?
Find the zeros of the related quadratic function.

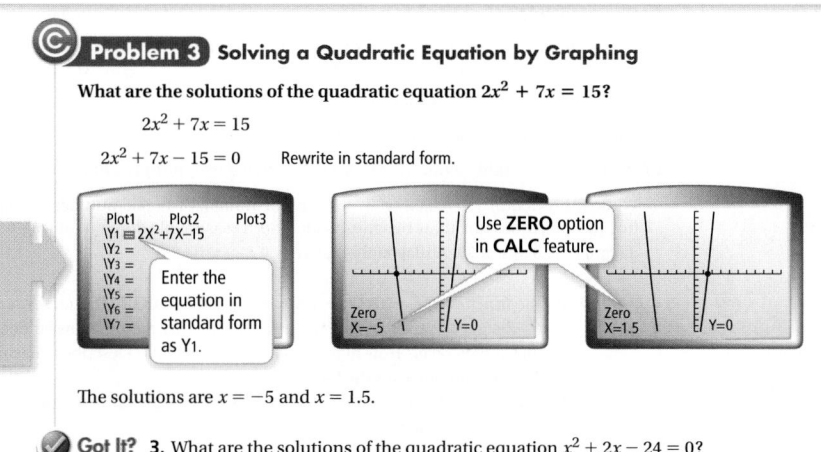

The solutions are $x = -5$ and $x = 1.5$.

Got It? **3.** What are the solutions of the quadratic equation $x^2 + 2x - 24 = 0$?

Got It?   **ERROR PREVENTION**

Students sometimes think -4 and -3 are solutions of $(x - 4)(x - 3) = 0$. Remind them to use the Zero-Product Property and then solve the two resulting equations.

Problem 2

Q What is the related quadratic equation for the quadratic function y_1? **[$5x^2 + 32x + 12 = 0$]**

Q How is that equation related to the original equation in the problem? **[It is equivalent.]**

Q What are the zeros of the function y_1? Explain. **[-6 and -0.4; the zeros of a function are equivalent to the solutions of the related equation.]**

Got It?   **SYNTHESIZING**

Students will not be able to find the noninteger zero by using 0.1 for the x-interval.

Q Between what x-values is the noninteger zero? Explain. **[0.2 and 0.3 because the y-values change sign]**

Q How can you find the noninteger zero? **[Change the x-interval to 0.01.]**

Problem 3

An alternate method is to enter the left side of the equation in y_1 and the right side in y_2. Then find the intersection point.

Got It?   **EXTENSION**

Students sometimes think they can find zeros by simply looking at a graph. To show why a better option is needed, have them find the solutions of $x^2 + 1.1x - 11.6 = 0$. **[2.9 and -4]**

---

2 Guided Instruction

© Each Problem is worked out and supported online.

Problem 1
Solving a Quadratic Equation by Factoring
Animated

Problem 2
Solving a Quadratic Equation With Tables
Animated

Problem 3
Solving a Quadratic Equation by Graphing

Problem 4
Using a Quadratic Equation
Animated

Support in Algebra 2 Companion
• Vocabulary
• Key Concepts
• Got It?

Answers

Solve It!
(20.8, 0); the vertex of the parabola is (6.4, 12.96) so the parabola is symmetric over the line $x = 6.4$.

Got It?
  1. 3, 4
  2. 3, $\frac{1}{4}$
  3. -6, 4

Problem 4

Quadratic functions are models for many problems involving distance and movement. However, the function graphs do not necessarily show the path of the movement. The function graph in this problem models the actual path of a moving object.

> **Q** In 4B, why does the maximum value of $f(x)$ occur midway between the zeros? **[Answers may vary. Sample: A quadratic function graph is symmetric about the vertical line through its vertex.]**
>
> **Q** How does the shape of the calculator graph compare to the shape of the actual frog jump? **[Answers may vary. Sample: The scales on the axes are different, so the shape of the graph makes the jump appear higher than it really was.]**

Use the ZSquare option of the ZOOM feature to see the undistorted graph.

> **Q** In 4C, the function $y = -0.029x^2 + 0.59x$ has a domain of all real numbers. What is its range? Explain. **[All real numbers less than or equal to 3.0, since 3.0 is approximately the maximum value of the function, and there is no minimum value.]**
>
> **Q** What is the difference between the domain and range of the situational model? **[The domain is positive numbers less than 30, while the range is positive numbers less than 5.]**

Got It?

An alternate method to find how high the soccer ball goes is to use the MAXIMUM option of the CALC feature.

Problem 4 Using a Quadratic Equation

Competition From the time Mark Twain wrote *The Celebrated Jumping Frog of Calaveras County* in 1865, frog-jumping competitions have been growing in popularity. The graph shows a function modeling the height of one frog's jump, where x is the distance, in feet, from the jump's start.

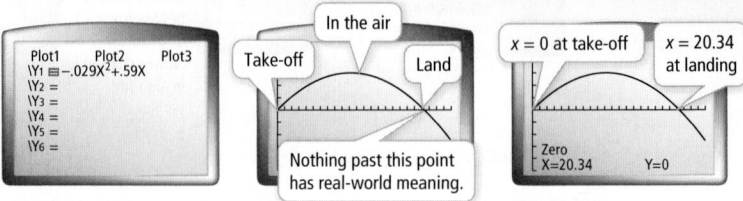

Think

How can you use a graphing calculator to determine the distance?
Graph the function and locate the point where the graph crosses the x-axis.

A How far did the frog jump?

The height of the jump is 0 at the start and end of the jump. Find the zeros of the function. Use a graphing calculator to find the zeros of the related function $y = -0.029x^2 + 0.59x$.

The frog jumped about 20.34 ft.

B How high did the frog jump?

The maximum height of the jump is the maximum value of the function. This occurs midway, at 10.17 ft from the start. Find y for $x = 10.17$.

$$y = -0.029(10.17)^2 + 0.59(10.17) \approx 3.0$$

The frog jumped to a height of about 3.0 ft.

C What is a reasonable domain and range for such a frog-jumping function?

While the function $y = -0.029x^2 + 0.59x$ has a domain of all real numbers, actual frog jumping does not allow negative values. So, a reasonable domain for frog-jumping distances is $0 \le x \le 30$. A reasonable range is $0 \le y \le 5$.

Got It? **4. a.** The function $y = -0.03x^2 + 1.60x$ models the path of a kicked soccer ball. The height is y, the distance is x, and the units are meters. How far does the soccer ball travel? How high does the soccer ball go? Describe a reasonable domain and range for the function.

b. Reasoning Are all domains and ranges reasonable for real-world situations? Explain.

228   Chapter 4   Quadratic Functions and Equations

Additional Problems

1. What are the solutions of the quadratic equation $x^2 + 3x - 18 = 0$?

ANSWER 3 and −6

2. What are the solutions of the quadratic equation $10x^2 + 2x - 46 = x - 4$?

ANSWER 2 and −2.1

3. What are the solutions of the quadratic equation $5x^2 - 8 = 18x$?

ANSWER −0.4 and 4

4. The function $f(x) = -0.002x^2 + 0.77x$ models the path of a baseball, where $f(x)$ gives the height of the ball and x gives the distance from where it is hit in feet.

a. How far does the ball travel before hitting the ground?

b. How high does the ball go?

c. What is a reasonable domain and range for such a function?

ANSWERS

a. 385 ft

b. about 74 ft

c. Answers may vary. Sample: domain: $0 \le x \le 500$, range: $0 \le y \le 100$

Lesson Check

Do you know HOW?

Solve each equation by factoring.

1. $x^2 - 9 = 0$

2. $x^2 + 13x = -36$

3. $3x^2 - x - 2 = 0$

Solve by graphing.

4. $x^2 - 3x = 6$

5. $2x^2 - x = 11$

Do you UNDERSTAND?  MATHEMATICAL PRACTICES

6. **Vocabulary** If 5 is a zero of the function $y = x^2 + bx - 20$, what is the value of b? Explain.

7. **Compare and Contrast** When is it easier to solve a quadratic equation by factoring than to solve it using a table?

8. **Reasoning** Using tables, how might you recognize that a quadratic equation likely has exactly one solution? no solutions?

Practice and Problem-Solving Exercises  MATHEMATICAL PRACTICES

A **Practice**   Solve each equation by factoring. Check your answers.   ◀ **See Problem 1.**

9. $x^2 + 6x + 8 = 0$

10. $x^2 + 18 = 9x$

11. $2x^2 - x = 3$

12. $x^2 - 10x + 25 = 0$

13. $2x^2 + 6x = -4$

14. $3x^2 = 16x + 12$

15. $x^2 - 4x = 0$

16. $6x^2 + 4x = 0$

17. $2x^2 = 8x$

Graphing Calculator Solve each equation using tables. Give each answer to at most two decimal places.   ◀ **See Problem 2.**

18. $x^2 + 5x + 3 = 0$

19. $x^2 - 11x + 24 = 0$

20. $x^2 - 7x = 11$

21. $2x^2 - x = 2$

22. $x^2 - 16x = 36$

23. $x^2 + 6x = 40$

24. $4x^2 = x + 3$

25. $5x^2 + x = 4$

26. $10x^2 + 3 = 11x$

Graphing Calculator Solve each equation by graphing. Give each answer to at most two decimal places.   ◀ **See Problem 3.**

27. $6x^2 = -19x - 15$

28. $3x^2 - 5x - 4 = 0$

29. $5x^2 - 7x - 3 = 8$

30. $6x^2 + 31x = 12$

31. $1 = 4x^2 + 3x$

32. $\frac{1}{2}x^2 - x = 8$

33. $x^2 = 4x + 8$

34. $x^2 + 4x = 6$

35. $2x^2 - 2x - 5 = 0$

STEM 36. Physics The function $h = -16t^2 + 1700$ gives an object's height h, in feet, at t seconds.   ◀ **See Problem 4.**
   a. What does the constant 1700 tell you about the height of the object?
   b. What does the coefficient of t^2 tell you about the direction the object is moving?
   c. When will the object be 1000 ft above the ground?
   d. When will the object be 940 ft above the ground?
   e. What are a reasonable domain and range for the function h?

---

3 Lesson Check

Do you know HOW?
- If students have trouble with Exercise 2, remind them to get 0 on one side of the equation.
- If students have trouble finding the actual factors for Exercises 1–3, they should revisit Lesson 4-4.

Do you UNDERSTAND?
- If students have trouble with Exercise 6, remind them that (5, 0) makes the equation true.

Close

Q What equation can you solve to find the zeros of $f(x) = 0.5x^2 + x - 1$? **[the related equation, $0.5x^2 + x - 1 = 0$]**

Q What is the first step in solving $3x^2 - 1 = 4x$? **[Put the equation in standard form by adding $-4x$ to both sides.]**

Q If $(3, -0.4)$ and $(3.6, 2)$ are on a parabola, where is a zero of the function? Explain. **[It is between 3 and 3.6. The two y-values have different signs, so there must be a point between them where the y-value passes through zero.]**

Answers

Got It? (continued)

4. **a.** $53\frac{1}{3}$ m; $21\frac{1}{3}$ m; answers may vary. Sample: domain: $0 \le x \le 60$, range: $0 \le y \le 30$

   b. No; domains and ranges are constrained by real-world limits.

Lesson Check

1. 3, −3
2. −4, −9
3. $-\frac{2}{3}$, 1
4. 4.372, −1.372
5. 2.608, −2.108
6. −1; since $y = 0$ when $x = 5$, substitute these values into the equation to find b.
7. when the coefficients are integers and a recognizable pattern of factoring is evident
8. One solution: when the table's range consists of zero and all positive numbers or zero and all negative numbers

   No solution: when the table does not include zero and the y-values are either all positive or all negative numbers

Practice and Problem-Solving Exercises

9. −4, −2   10. 3, 6   11. $-1, \frac{3}{2}$
12. 5   13. −2, −1   14. $-\frac{2}{3}$, 6
15. 0, 4   16. $-\frac{2}{3}$, 0   17. 0, 4
18. −4.30, −0.70   19. 3, 8
20. −1.32, 8.32   21. −0.78, 1.28
22. 18, −2   23. 4, −10   24. 1, −0.75
25. 0.8, −1   26. 0.5, 0.6
27. −1.67, −1.5   28. −0.59, 2.26
29. −0.94, 2.34   30. −5.53, 0.36
31. −1, 0.25   32. −3.12, 5.12
33. −1.46, 5.46   34. −5.16, 1.16
35. −1.16, 2.16
36. **a.** The initial height of the object is 1700 ft.

   b. The object is accelerating down.

   c. about 6.61 s

   d. about 6.89 s

   e. domain: $0 \le t \le 10.4$, range: $0 \le h \le 1700$

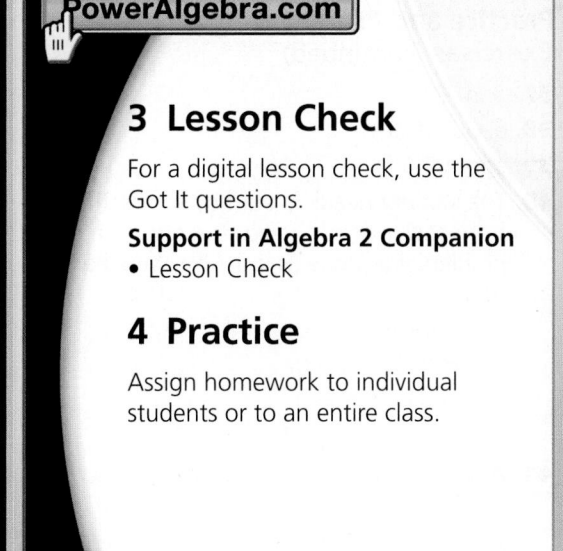

3 Lesson Check

For a digital lesson check, use the Got It questions.

Support in Algebra 2 Companion
- Lesson Check

4 Practice

Assign homework to individual students or to an entire class.

4 Practice

Basic: 9–36 all, 37–43, 55

Average: 9–35 odd, 37–56

Advanced: 9–35 odd, 37–59

Standardized Test Prep: 90–93

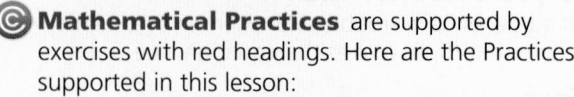 **Mathematical Practices** are supported by exercises with red headings. Here are the Practices supported in this lesson:

MP 1: Make Sense of Problems Ex. 37

MP 2: Reason Abstractly Ex. 41

MP 3: Construct Arguments Ex. 7, 8

MP 3: Critique the Reasoning of Others Ex. 40

MP 8: Use Repeated Reasoning Ex. 54–56

Applications exercises have blue headings.

Exercise 39 supports MP 4: Model.

STEM exercises focus on science or engineering applications.

EXERCISE 39: Use the Think About a Plan worksheet in the **Practice and Problem Solving Workbook** (also available in the Teaching Resources in print and online) to further support students' development in becoming independent learners.

HOMEWORK QUICK CHECK

To check students' understanding of key skills and concepts, go over Exercises 11, 27, 37, 39, and 40.

B Apply

G 37. Think About a Plan Suppose you want to put a frame around the painting shown at the right. The frame will be the same width around the entire painting. You have 276 in.² of framing material. How wide should the frame be?
- What does 276 in.² represent in this situation?
- How can you write the dimensions of the frame using two binomials?

16 in.

24 in.

38. The period of a pendulum is the time the pendulum takes to swing back and forth. The function $L = 0.81t^2$ relates the length L in feet of a pendulum to the time t in seconds that it takes to swing back and forth. A convention center has a pendulum that is 90 feet long. Find the period.

39. Landscaping Suppose you have an outdoor pool measuring 25 ft by 10 ft. You want to add a cement walkway around the pool. If the walkway will be 1 ft thick and you have 304 ft³ of cement, how wide should the walkway be?

G 40. Error Analysis A classmate solves the quadratic equation as shown. Find and correct the error. What are the correct solutions?

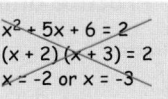
$x^2 + 5x + 6 = 2$
$(x + 2)(x + 3) = 2$
$x = -2$ or $x = -3$

G 41. Open-Ended Write an equation with the given solutions.
a. 3 and 5   b. −3 and 2   c. −1 and −6

Solve each equation by factoring, using tables, or by graphing. If necessary, round your answer to the nearest hundredth.

42. $x^2 + 2x = 6 - 6x$ **43.** $6x^2 + 13x + 6 = 0$ **44.** $2x^2 + x - 28 = 0$

45. $2x^2 + 8x = 5x + 20$ **46.** $3x^2 + 7x = 9$ **47.** $2x^2 - 6x = 8$

48. $(x + 3)^2 = 9$ **49.** $x^2 + 4x = 0$ **50.** $x^2 = 8x - 7$

51. $x^2 - 3x = 6$ **52.** $4x^2 + 5x = 4$ **53.** $7x - 3x^2 = -10$

G Reasoning The graphs of each pair of functions intersect. Find their points of intersection without using a calculator. (*Hint:* Solve as a system using substitution.)

54. $y = x^2$
$y = -\frac{1}{2}x^2 + \frac{3}{2}x + 3$

55. $y = x^2 - 2$
$y = 3x^2 - 4x - 2$

56. $y = -x^2 + x + 4$
$y = 2x^2 - 6$

C Challenge

57. The equation $x^2 - 10x + 24 = 0$ can be written in factored form as $(x - 4)(x - 6) = 0$. How can you use this fact to find the vertex of the graph of $y = x^2 - 10x + 24$?

58. a. Let $a > 0$. Use algebraic or arithmetic ideas to explain why the lowest point on the graph of $y = a(x - h)^2 + k$ must occur when $x = h$.
b. Suppose that the function in part (a) is $y = a(x - h)^3 + k$. Is your reasoning still valid? Explain.

Answers

Practice and Problem-Solving Exercises (continued)

37. 3 in.

38. about 10.5 s

39. about 3.6 ft

40. The student needs to start by subtracting 2 from each side of the eq. The error is that the problem was done as if the eq. were equal to 0.
$x^2 + 5x + 6 - 2 = 0$
$x^2 + 5x + 4 = 0$
$(x + 1)(x + 4) = 0$
$x = -1, -4$

41. Answers may vary. Samples are given:
a. $x^2 - 8x + 15 = 0$
b. $x^2 + x - 6 = 0$
c. $x^2 + 7x + 6 = 0$

42. −8.69, 0.69

43. $-\frac{3}{2}, -\frac{2}{3}$

44. −4, 3.5   **45.** $-4, \frac{5}{2}$

46. −3.25, 0.92

47. −1, 4   **48.** −6, 0

49. −4, 0   **50.** 1, 7

51. 4.37, −1.37

52. −1.8, 0.55

53. $-1, \frac{10}{3}$

54. (−1, 1), (2, 4)

55. (0, −2), (2, 2)

56. $\left(-\frac{5}{3}, -\frac{4}{9}\right)$, (2, 2)

57. Solve $(x - 4)(x - 6) = 0$ to find that the zeros of $y = x^2 - 10x + 24$ are 4 and 6. Average 4 and 6 to get 5. This is the x-coordinate of the vertex. Substitute 5 for x in $x^2 - 10x + 24$ to find that −1 is the y-coordinate of the vertex. The vertex is (5, −1).

58. a. Answers may vary. Sample: If $x \neq h$, then $x - h$ will be nonzero, $(x - h)^2$ will be positive, and $a(x - h)^2$ will be positive. Adding a positive to k will always result in a number greater than k. So the pt. (h, k) is the lowest pt. when $x = h$ on the graph of $y = (x - h)^2 + k$.
b. No; $(x - h)^3$ can be negative.

STEM **59. Physics** When serving in tennis, a player tosses the tennis ball vertically in the air. The height h of the ball after t seconds is given by the quadratic function $h(t) = -5t^2 + 7t$ (the height is measured in meters from the point of the toss).

   a. How high in the air does the ball go?

   b. Assume that the player hits the ball on its way down when it's 0.6 m above the point of the toss. For how many seconds is the ball in the air between the toss and the serve?

Standardized Test Prep

SAT/ACT

60. What are the solutions of the equation $6x^2 + 9x - 15 = 0$?

   Ⓐ $1, -15$ Ⓑ $1, -\frac{5}{2}$ Ⓒ $-1, -5$ Ⓓ $3, \frac{5}{2}$

61. The vertex of a parabola is $(3, 2)$. A second point on the parabola is $(1, 7)$. Which point is also on the parabola?

   Ⓕ $(-1, 7)$ Ⓖ $(3, 7)$ Ⓗ $(5, 7)$ Ⓘ $(3, -2)$

62. For which quadratic function is -3 the constant term?

   Ⓐ $y = (3x + 1)(-x - 3)$ Ⓒ $f(x) = (x - 3)(x - 3)$

   Ⓑ $y = x^2 - 3x + 3$ Ⓓ $g(x) = -3x^2 + 3x + 9$

Short Response

63. What transformations are needed to go from the parent function $f(x) = x^2$ to the new function $g(x) = -3x^2 + 2$? Graph $g(x)$.

Apply What You've Learned

MATHEMATICAL PRACTICES MP 2

Look back at the information about Victor's sandwich shop on page 193 and at the equations you wrote in the Apply What You've Learned in Lesson 4-2. Your equations should be equivalent to the ones shown below.

   $s = -0.0025x + 1.375$, where x is the number of bags sold at selling price s

   $C(x) = 0.3x$

   $R(x) = -0.0025x^2 + 1.375x$

   $P(x) = -0.0025x^2 + 1.075x$

a. Write the function $P(x) = -0.0025x^2 + 1.075x$ in factored form, and use the factored form to find the zeros of $P(x)$.

b. What information do the zeros you found in part (a) give you about the graph of $P(x) = -0.0025x^2 + 1.075x$?

c. What information do the zeros you found in part (a) give you about Victor's profit?

d. Use the revenue and cost equations you wrote in the Apply What You Learned in Lesson 4-2. For each zero z of the profit function, what should be true about $C(z)$ and $R(z)$? Why? To confirm your answer, evaluate $C(z)$ and $R(z)$ for each zero z.

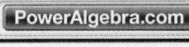

---

59. a. 2.45m

   b. ≈ 1.3 s

Standardized Test Prep

60. B

61. H

62. A

63. **[2]** reflection across the *x*-axis, followed by a vertical translation 2 units up, and stretched by a factor of 3

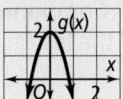

   [1] correct transformations, with one error in graph

 Apply What You've Learned

In the Apply What You've Learned for Lesson 4-2 and Lesson 4-3, students wrote a profit function from the information given on page 193 and then interpreted the coordinates of the vertex of the function's graph. Here, they find and interpret the zeros of the profit function.

Ⓒ **Mathematical Practices**

Students **reason abstractly and quantitatively** to find the zeros of the profit function and analyze the information the zeros give about the function's graph and about the real-world situation. (MP 2)

ANSWERS

   a. $P(x) = -0.0025x(x - 430)$; 0 and 430

   b. The graph crosses the x-axis at $(0, 0)$ and $(430, 0)$.

   c. Victor's profit will be \$0 if he sells 0 bags of chips or if he sells 430 bags of chips.

   d. $C(z) = R(z)$; profit is revenue minus cost, so for the profit to be zero, the revenue produced by x bags of chips must be the same as Victor's cost to buy the x bags of chips; $C(0) = R(0) = \$0$ and $C(430) = R(430) = \$129$.

Instructional Support

Algebra 2 Companion

Students can use the **Algebra 2 Companion** worktext (4 pages) as you teach the lesson. Use the Companion to support

- New Vocabulary
- Key Concepts
- Got It for each Problem
- Lesson Check

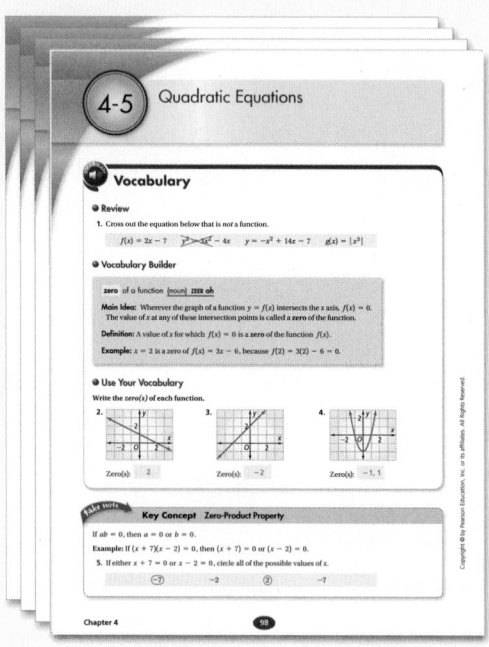

ELL Support

Use Graphic Organizers Make the following reference display for the board or bulletin board.

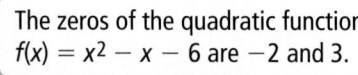

The zeros of the quadratic function $f(x) = x^2 - x - 6$ are -2 and 3.

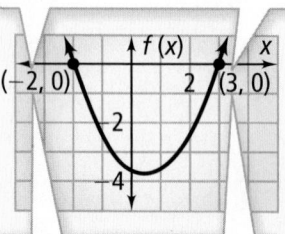

The solutions, or roots, of the related quadratic equation $x^2 - x - 6 = 0$ are $x = -2$ and $x = 3$.

5 Assess & Remediate

Lesson Quiz

1. Solve $x^2 - 8x + 12 = 0$.

2. Solve $5x^2 - 4x - 7 = 1 - x$.

3. Solve $2x^2 + x = 10$.

4. Do you UNDERSTAND? The function $f(x) = -0.002x^2 + 0.66x$ models the path of a softball that is hit for a home run, where $f(x)$ gives the height of the ball and x gives the distance from where it is hit in feet.

    a. How far does the ball travel before hitting the ground?

    b. How high does the ball go?

    c. What is a reasonable domain and range for a home run modeling function?

ANSWERS TO LESSON QUIZ

1. 6 and 2

2. -1 and 1.6

3. -2.5 and 2

4. a. 330 ft

    b. approximately 54.45 ft

    c. Answers may vary. Sample: domain: $0 \le x \le 330$, range: $0 \le y \le 54.45$

PRESCRIPTION FOR REMEDIATION

Use the student work on the Lesson Quiz to prescribe a differentiated review assignment:

Points	Differentiated Remediation
0–2	Intervention
3	On-level
4	Extension

PowerAlgebra.com

5 Assess & Remediate

Assign the Lesson Quiz. Appropriate intervention, practice, or enrichment is automatically generated based on student performance.

Intervention

- **Reteaching** (2 pages) Provides reteaching and practice exercises for the key lesson concepts. Use with struggling students or absent students.

- **English Language Learner Support** Helps students develop and reinforce mathematical vocabulary and key concepts.

All-in-One Resources/Online
Reteaching

4-5 **Reteaching**
Quadratic Equations

There are several ways to solve quadratic equations. If you can factor the quadratic expression in a quadratic equation written in standard form, you can use the Zero-Product Property.

If $ab = 0$ then $a = 0$ or $b = 0$.

Problem

What are the solutions of the quadratic equation $2x^2 + x = 15$?

$2x^2 + x = 15$	Write the equation.
$2x^2 + x - 15 = 0$	Rewrite in standard form, $ax^2 + bx + c = 0$.
$(2x - 5)(x + 3) = 0$	Factor the quadratic expression (the nonzero side).
$2x - 5 = 0$ or $x + 3 = 0$	Use the Zero-Product Property.
$2x = 5$ or $x = -3$	Solve for x.
$x = \frac{5}{2}$ or $x = -3$	

Check the solutions:

$x = \frac{5}{2}: 2\left(\frac{5}{2}\right)^2 + \left(\frac{5}{2}\right) \stackrel{?}{=} 15$ $x = -3: 2(-3)^2 + (-3) \stackrel{?}{=} 15$

$\frac{25}{2} + \frac{5}{2} \stackrel{?}{=} 15$ $18 - 3 \stackrel{?}{=} 15$

$15 = 15$ $15 = 15$

Both solutions check. The solutions are $x = \frac{5}{2}$ and $x = -3$.

Exercises

Solve each equation by factoring. Check your answers.

1. $x^2 - 10x + 16 = 0$ 2, 8   **2.** $x^2 + 2x = 63$ -9, 7   **3.** $x^2 + 9x = 22$ -11, 2

4. $x^2 - 24x + 144 = 0$ 12   **5.** $2x^2 = 7x + 4$ $-\frac{1}{2}$, 4   **6.** $2x^2 = -5x + 12$ $-4, \frac{3}{2}$

7. $x^2 - 7x = -12$ 3, 4   **8.** $2x^2 + 10x = 0$ -5, 0   **9.** $x^2 + x = 2$ -2, 1

10. $3x^2 - 5x + 2 = 0$ $\frac{2}{3}$, 1   **11.** $x^2 = -5x - 6$ -3, -2   **12.** $x^2 + x = 20$ -5, 4

All-in-One Resources/Online
English Language Learner Support

4-5 **Additional Vocabulary Support**
Quadratic Equations

Problem

What are the solutions of the quadratic equation $2x^2 - 4x = 6$?

Explain	Work	Justify
First, write the equation.	$2x^2 - 4x = 6$	Original equation
Second, subtract 6 from each side to set equal to 0.	$2x^2 - 4x - 6 = 0$	Subtraction Property of Equality
Next, factor out the GCF, 2.	$2(x^2 - 2x - 3) = 0$	Distributive Property
Then, factor the trinomial.	$2(x - 3)(x + 1) = 0$	Factor the quadratic expression
Then, use the Zero-Product Property.	$x - 3 = 0$ or $x + 1 = 0$	Zero-Product Property
Finally, solve for x.	$x = 3$ or $x = -1$	Addition Property of Equality

Solution 3 or −1

Exercise

What are the solutions of the quadratic equation $3x^2 - 6x = -3$?

Explain	Work	Justify
First, write the equation.	$3x^2 - 6x = -3$	Original equation
Second, add 3 to each side to set equal to 0.	$3x^2 - 6x + 3 = 0$	Addition Property of Equality
Next, factor out the GCF, 3.	$3(x^2 - 2x + 1) = 0$	Distributive Property
Then, factor the trinomial.	$3(x - 1)(x - 1) = 0$	Factor the quadratic expression
Then, use the Zero-Product Property.	$x - 1 = 0$ or $x - 1 = 0$	Zero-Product Property
Finally, solve for x.	$x = 1$	Addition Property of Equality

Solution 1

Differentiated Remediation *continued*

On-Level

- **Practice** (2 pages) Provides extra practice for each lesson. For simpler practice exercises, use the Form K Practice pages found in the All-in-One Teaching Resources and online.
- **Think About a Plan** Helps students develop specific problem-solving skills and strategies by providing scaffolded guiding questions.
- **Standardized Test Prep** Focuses on all major exercises, all major question types, and helps students prepare for the high-stakes assessments.

Practice and Problem Solving Wkbk/ All-in-One Resources/Online

Practice page 1

4-5 Practice — Quadratic Equations — *Form G*

Solve each equation by factoring. Check your answers.

1. $x^2 - 2x - 24 = 0$ $-4, 6$
2. $3x^2 = x + 4$ $-1, \frac{4}{3}$
3. $x^2 - 6x + 9 = 0$ 3
4. $3x^2 + 45 = 24x$ $3, 5$
5. $4x^2 + 6x = 0$ $-\frac{3}{2}, 0$
6. $7x^2 = 21x$ $0, 3$
7. $(x + 2)^2 = 49$ $-9, 5$
8. $x + 3 = 24x^2$ $-\frac{1}{3}, \frac{3}{8}$

Solve each equation using tables. Give each answer to at most two decimal places.

9. $5x^2 + 7x - 6 = 0$ $-2, 0.6$
10. $x^2 - 2x = 1$ $-0.41, 2.41$
11. $2x^2 - x = 5$ $-1.35, 1.85$
12. $x^2 - 4x + 2 = 0$ $0.59, 3.41$
13. $3x^2 + 7x = 1$ $-2.47, 0.14$
14. $2x^2 - 3x = 15$ $-2.09, 3.59$

Solve each equation by graphing. Give each answer to at most two decimal places.

15. $10x^2 = 4 - 3x$ $-0.8, 0.5$
16. $3x^2 + 2x = 2$ $-1.22, 0.55$
17. $4x^2 - x = 6$ $-1.11, 1.36$
18. $4x^2 + 3x = 6 - 2x$ $-2, 0.75$
19. $x^2 + 4 = 6x$ $0.76, 5.24$
20. $5 - x = \frac{1}{2}x^2$ $-4.32, 2.32$
21. A woman drops a front door key to her husband from their apartment window several stories above the ground. The function $h = -16t^2 + 64$ gives the height h of the key in feet, t seconds after she releases it.
    a. How long does it take the key to reach the ground? 2 s
    b. What are the reasonable domain and range for the function h? $0 \le t \le 2$; $0 \le h \le 64$

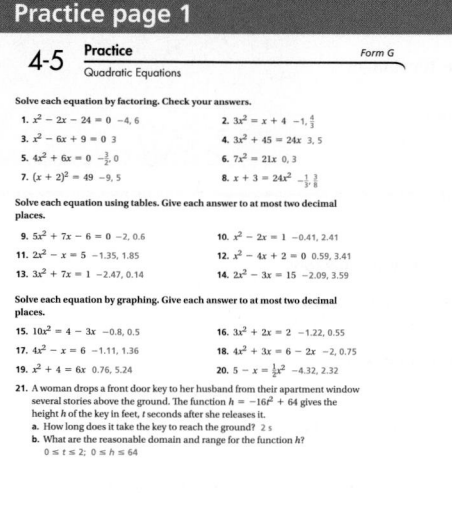

Practice and Problem Solving Wkbk/ All-in-One Resources/Online

Practice page 2

4-5 Practice (continued) — Quadratic Equations — *Form G*

22. The function $C = 75x + 2600$ gives the cost, in dollars, for a small company to manufacture x items. The function $R = 225x - x^2$ gives the revenue, also in dollars, for selling x items. How many items should the company produce so that the cost and revenue are equal? 20 or 130
23. The function $a = 2.4t - 0.1t^2$ gives the amount a, in micromilligrams (mmg), of a drug in a patient's bloodstream t hours after being ingested in tablet form. When is the amount of the drug equal to 8 mmg? (*Hint:* Multiply the equation you write by 10 before solving.) 4 h; 20 h
24. You use a rectangular piece of cardboard measuring 20 in. by 30 in. to construct a box. You cut squares with sides x in. from each corner of the piece of cardboard and then fold up the sides to form the bottom.

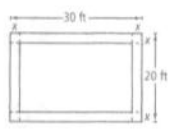

    a. Write a function A representing the area of the base of the box in terms of x. $A = (30 - 2x)(20 - 2x) = 4x^2 - 100x + 600$
    b. What is a reasonable domain for the function A? $0 < x < 10$
    c. Write an equation if the area of the base must be 416 in.^{2}. $4x^2 - 100x + 600 = 416$
    d. Solve the equation in part (c) for values of x in the reasonable domain. 2
    e. What are the dimensions of the base of the box? 26 in. by 16 in.

Solve each equation by factoring, using tables, or by graphing. If necessary, round your answer to the nearest hundredth.

25. $9x^2 = 49$ $-\frac{7}{3}, \frac{7}{3}$
26. $x^2 + 10x + 17 = 0$ $-7.83, -2.17$
27. $4x^2 + 1 = 8x$ $0.13, 1.87$
28. $5x^2 - 2x - 7 = 0$ $-1, \frac{7}{5}$
29. $4(x^2 - x) = 19$ $-1.74, 2.74$
30. $25x^2 + 20x + 4 = 0$ $-\frac{2}{5}$
31. $3x^2 = 4x + 32$ $-\frac{8}{3}, 4$
32. $x^2 - 5x - 12 = 0$ $-1.77, 6.77$

Practice and Problem Solving Wkbk/ All-in-One Resources/Online

Think About a Plan

4-5 Think About a Plan — Quadratic Equations

Landscaping Suppose you have an outdoor pool measuring 25 ft by 10 ft. You want to add a cement walkway around the pool. If the walkway will be 1 ft thick and you have 304 ft^3 of cement, how wide should the walkway be?

Understanding the Problem

1. Draw a diagram of the pool and the walkway. Let x = the width of the walkway in feet.

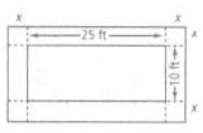

2. If you lay the pieces of walkway end to end, what is the total length of the walkway? $4x + 70$
3. What is the thickness of the walkway? 1 ft
4. What is the problem asking you to determine?
   The width of a walkway that is $(4x + 70)$ ft long and 1 ft thick, that has volume 304 ft^3.

Planning the Solution

5. Write a quadratic equation to model the volume of the walkway. $V = 4x^2 + 70x$
6. What method can you use to find the solutions of your quadratic equation?
   Answers may vary. Sample: Substitute 304 for V in the equation. Subtract 304 from each side to set it equal to zero. Graph $y = 4x^2 + 70x - 304$ on a graphing calculator and use the ZERO option in the CALC feature to solve for x.

Getting an Answer

7. How many solutions of your quadratic equation do you need to find? Explain.
   One; only one solution is positive, and a negative solution does not make sense.
8. How wide should the walkway be? about 3.6 ft

Practice and Problem Solving Wkbk/ All-in-One Resources/Online

Standardized Test Prep

4-5 Standardized Test Prep — Quadratic Equations

Gridded Response

Solve each exercise and enter your answer in the grid provided.

1. What is the positive solution of the equation $x^2 = 2x + 35$? Solve by factoring.
2. What is the positive solution of the equation $5x^2 + 2x - 16 = 0$? Solve by factoring.
3. What is the positive solution of the equation $x^2 - 3x = 1$? Solve by using a table or by graphing. If necessary, round your answer to the nearest hundredth.
4. What is the positive solution of the equation $3x^2 - 5x - 7 = 0$? Solve by using a table or by graphing. If necessary, round your answer to the nearest hundredth.
5. What is the positive solution of the equation $\frac{1}{2}x^2 - 3x = 5$? Solve by using a table or by graphing. If necessary, round your answer to the nearest hundredth.

Answers

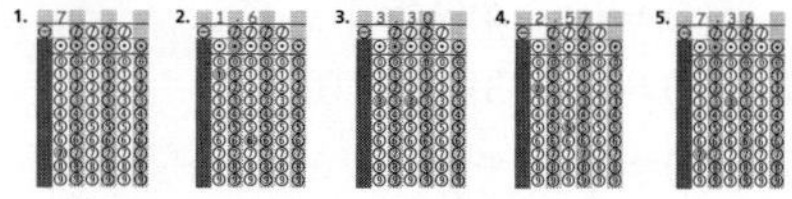

Extension

- **Enrichment** Provides students with interesting problems and activities that extend the concepts of the lesson.
- **Activities, Games, and Puzzles** Worksheets that can be used for concepts development, enrichment, and for fun!

All-in-One Resources/Online

Enrichment

4-5 Enrichment — Quadratic Equations

Fencing Costs

Solve each of the following problems by using a quadratic equation.

1. The area of a rectangular field is 1200 m^2. Two parallel sides are fenced with aluminum at \$20/m. The remaining two sides are fenced with steel at \$10/m. The total cost of the fencing is \$2200.
   a. What is the length of each side fenced with aluminum? 40 m, or 15 m
   b. What is the length of each side fenced with steel? 30 m, or 80 m, respectively
2. The perimeter of a rectangular field is 140 yards. The land sells for \$10/yd^2 and the total cost of the land is \$12,000. What are the dimensions of the field? 30 yd by 40 yd
3. The area of a rectangular field is 875 m^2. Two adjacent sides of the field are fenced with wood costing \$5/m. The remaining two sides are fenced with steel costing \$10/m. The total cost of the fencing is \$900. What are the dimensions of the field? 25 m by 35 m
4. The area of a field shaped like a right triangle is 600 m^2. The legs of the field are fenced with steel at \$10/m, while the hypotenuse is fenced with aluminum at \$20/m. The perimeter of the field is 120 m. The total cost of the fencing is \$1700.
   a. What is the length of each side fenced with steel? 30 m, 40 m
   b. What is the length of the side fenced with aluminum? 50 m
5. The area of a field shaped like a right triangle is 750 yd^2. One leg of the field is fenced with wood costing \$5/yd. The remainder of the perimeter of the field is fenced with steel costing \$10/yd. The perimeter of the field is 150 yd. The total cost of the fencing is \$1200.
   a. What is the length of the leg fenced with wood? 60 yd
   b. What is the length of the leg fenced with steel? 25 yd
6. The area of a rectangular field is 1000 yd^2. Two parallel sides are fenced with aluminum at \$15/yd. One of the remaining sides is fenced with steel at \$10/yd, and all but 10 yd of the remaining side is fenced with wood costing \$5/yd. The remaining 10 yd are left unfenced. The total cost of the fencing is \$1525.
   a. What is the length of the side fenced with steel? 25 yd or 80 yd
   b. What is the length of each side fenced with aluminum? 40 yd, or $12\frac{1}{2}$ yd, respectively.
7. Two rectangular fields with identical shapes and areas are to be fenced side by side. The total area enclosed is 1200 yd^2. The shared side is fenced with wood costing \$5/yd. The remaining perimeter of the two joined fields is fenced with aluminum at \$15/yd. The total cost of the fencing is \$2250.
   a. What is the length of the shared side? 30 yd, or $34\frac{2}{7}$ yd
   b. What is the length of each side fenced with aluminum? 30 yd and 20 yd, or $34\frac{2}{7}$ yd and $17\frac{1}{2}$ yd, respectively

Online Teacher Resource Center

Activities, Games, and Puzzles

4-5 Puzzle: Dominoes — Quadratic Equations

Complete this puzzle with a partner.

Materials

- Twenty-four small index cards
- Transparent tape

Goal

- Find the solutions to the 24 quadratic equations given below.
- Make a card for each equation, writing the two solutions and the equation number, as shown in the example below.
- Tape the index cards together end to end to form the longest string possible. You can only tape together two cards when they share at least one solution (when the ends match).

Longest possible string uses all twenty-four cards. Answers may vary. Sample: 18, 1, 8, 15, 22, 5, 12, 19, 2, 9, 16, 23, 6, 13, 20, 3, 10, 17, 24, 7, 14, 21, 4, 11.

Example

$x^2 + x - 6 = 0 \rightarrow (x + 3)(x - 2) = 0 \rightarrow x = -3$ or $x = 2$

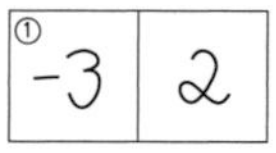

1. $x^2 + x - 6 = 0$ — $(x + 3)(x - 2) = 0; x = -3, 2$
2. $x^2 - 4x - 5 = 0$ — $(x + 1)(x - 5) = 0; x = -1, 5$
3. $x^2 - 25 = 0$ — $(x + 5)(x - 5) = 0; x = -5, 5$
4. $2x^2 + 3x - 5 = 0$ — $(2x + 5)(x - 1) = 0; x = -\frac{5}{2}, 1$
5. $2x^2 + 7x - 4 = 0$ — $(2x - 1)(x + 4) = 0; x = \frac{1}{2}, -4$
6. $5x^2 - 31x + 6 = 0$ — $(x - 6)(5x - 1) = 0; x = 6, \frac{1}{5}$
7. $x^2 + 2x - 24 = 0$ — $(x - 4)(x + 6) = 0; x = 4, -6$
8. $x^2 - 9x + 14 = 0$ — $(x - 2)(x - 7) = 0; x = 2, 7$
9. $3x^2 - 11x - 20 = 0$ — $(x - 5)(3x + 4) = 0; x = 5, -\frac{4}{3}$
10. $2x^2 - 11x + 5 = 0$ — $(x - 5)(2x - 1) = 0; x = 5, \frac{1}{2}$
11. $x^2 - 2x + 1 = 0$ — $(x - 1)^2 = 0; x = 1$
12. $x^2 - 4x - 32 = 0$ — $(x + 4)(x - 8) = 0; x = -4, 8$
13. $5x^2 - x = 0$ — $(5x - 1)(x) = 0; x = \frac{1}{5}, 0$
14. $3x^2 + 20x + 12 = 0$ — $(x + 6)(3x + 2) = 0; x = -6, -\frac{2}{3}$
15. $x^2 - 7x = 0$ — $(x - 7)(x) = 0; x = 7, 0$
16. $6x^2 - x - 12 = 0$ — $(3x + 4)(2x - 3) = 0; x = -\frac{4}{3}, \frac{3}{2}$
17. $6x^2 + 3x - 3 = 0$ — $3(2x - 1)(x + 1) = 0; x = \frac{1}{2}, -1$
18. $x^2 + 2x - 3 = 0$ — $(x - 1)(x + 3) = 0; x = 1, -3$
19. $x^2 - 7x - 8 = 0$ — $(x - 8)(x + 1) = 0; x = 8, -1$
20. $3x^2 + 15x = 0$ — $3(x)(x + 5) = 0; x = 0, -5$
21. $6x^2 + 19x + 10 = 0$ — $(3x + 2)(2x + 5) = 0; x = -\frac{2}{3}, -\frac{5}{2}$
22. $2x^2 - x = 0$ — $(x)(2x - 1) = 0; x = 0, \frac{1}{2}$
23. $2x^2 - 15x + 18 = 0$ — $(2x - 3)(x - 6) = 0; x = \frac{3}{2}, 6$
24. $x^2 - 3x - 4 = 0$ — $(x + 1)(x - 4) = 0; x = -1, 4$

Guided Instruction

PURPOSE To write a quadratic function, given its zeros, or a quadratic equation, given its roots

PROCESS Students will
- write a quadratic function, given its zeros, or a quadratic equation, given its roots, in factored and standard form.
- find the sum and product of the roots of a quadratic equation in standard form.

DISCUSS Students expand what they know about zeros of linear functions to discover and apply properties of zeros of quadratic functions.

Activity 1

Q What basic function satisfies 1a? **[Answers may vary. Sample: $f(x) = x - 3$]**

Q Are there any other nonzero linear functions that have a zero at $x = 3$? Explain. **[Yes; answers may vary. Sample: If you multiply $x - 3$ by any number, the new function will still have a zero at $x = 3$.]**

Q For Exercise 7, how could you write the equation in standard form so that a, b, and c are integers? **[Multiply each term by 2.]**

Activity 2 ERROR PREVENTION

Since standard form of a quadratic equation is $ax^2 + bx + c = 0$, the use of a and b in the table may confuse students. To write $(x - a)(x - b)$ in standard form, just multiply the binomials.

Exercises ERROR PREVENTION

For Exercise 10, watch for $x + 6 = 0$ or $x^2 - 6 = 0$. Suggest checking by substituting -6 into the equation. Refer to Questions 3–7 in Activity 1. Suggest the same process, using -6 and -6 as the pair.

Mathematical Practices This Concept Byte supports students in using repeated reasoning, Mathematical Practice 8.

Chapter 4

Concept Byte
For Use With Lesson 4-5

Writing Equations From Roots

Common Core State Standards
A-CED.A.2 Create equations in two or more variables to represent relationships between quantities; graph equations on coordinate axes with labels and scales.
MP 8

A **root** of an equation is a value that makes the equation true. You can use the Zero-Product Property to write a quadratic function from its zeros or a quadratic equation from its roots.

Activity 1

1. a. Write a nonzero linear function $f(x)$ that has a zero at $x = 3$.
  b. Write a nonzero linear function $g(x)$ that has a zero at $x = 4$.

2. a. For f and g from Exercise 1, write the product function $h(x) = f(x) \cdot g(x)$.
  b. What kind of function is $h(x)$?   **c.** Solve the equation $h(x) = 0$.

Mental Math Write a quadratic equation with each pair of values as roots.

3. 5 and 3   **4.** 2.5 and 4   **5.** -4 and 4   **6.** 5 and 10   **7.** $\frac{3}{2}$ and -2

You can also use zeros or roots to write quadratic expressions in standard form.

Activity 2

8. a. Copy and complete the table. Write the product $(x - a)(x - b)$ in standard form for each pair a and b.
  b. Is there a pattern in the table? Explain.

9. a. If you know the roots, you can write a quadratic function or equation in standard form. Explain how.
  b. Demonstrate your method for each pair of values in Exercises 3–7.

a	b	$a + b$	ab	$(x - a)(x - b)$
4	5	9	20	$x^2 - 9x + 20$
-4	5	1	-20	
4	-5			
-4	-5			
-9	-1			
-2	7			

Exercises

10. Explain how to write a quadratic equation that has -6 as its only root.

11. Describe the family of quadratic functions that have zeros at r and s. Sketch several members of the family in the coordinate plane.

Find the sum and product of the roots for each quadratic equation.

12. $2x^2 + 3x - 2 = 0$ **13.** $x^2 - 2x + 1 = 0$ **14.** $x^2 - 5x + 6 = 0$

Given the sum and product of the roots, write a quadratic equation in standard form.

15. sum $= -3$, product $= -18$ **16.** sum $= 4$, product $= 3$ **17.** sum $= 2$, product $= \frac{3}{4}$

Concept Byte Writing Equations From Roots

Answers

Concept Byte

1. Answers may vary. Samples:
  a. $f(x) = x - 3$
  b. $g(x) = 2x - 8$

2. Answers may vary. Samples:
  a. $h(x) = (x - 3)(2x - 8)$
  b. quadratic
  c. 3, 4

3. $f(x) = (x - 5)(x - 3)$

4. $f(x) = (x - 2.5)(x - 4)$

5. $f(x) = (x - 4)(x - (-4))$ or
  $f(x) = (x - 4)(x + 4)$

6. $f(x) = (x - 5)(x - 10)$

7. $f(x) = \left(x - \frac{3}{2}\right)(x - (-2))$ or
  $f(x) = \left(x - \frac{3}{2}\right)(x + 2)$

8. a. $a + b$: $-1, -9, -10, 5$;
  ab: $-20, 20, 9, -14$;
  $(x - a)(x - b)$: $x^2 - x - 20$,
  $x^2 + x - 20, x^2 + 9x + 20$,
  $x^2 + 10x + 9, x^2 - 5x - 14$

b. Yes; the sum of the numbers is the opposite of the coefficients of the x-term; the product is the constant term.

9. a. For roots a and b, the constant term is ab and the x-coefficient is $-(a + b)$. The x^2-coefficient is 1.

b. $x^2 - 8x + 15$; $x^2 - 6.5x + 10$;
  $x^2 - 16$; $x^2 - 15x + 50$;
  $x^2 + \frac{1}{2}x - 3$

10. If a quadratic function has only one root, then the corresponding quadratic expression is a perfect square. The eq. is $(x + 6)^2 = 0$.

11. $y = a(x - r)(x - s)$, $a \neq 0$; check students' sketches.

12. sum: $-\frac{3}{2}$; product: -1

13. sum: 2; product: 1

14. sum: 5; product: 6

15. $x^2 + 3x - 18 = 0$

16. $x^2 - 4x + 3 = 0$

17. $x^2 - 2x + \frac{3}{4} = 0$ or
  $4x^2 - 8x + 3 = 0$

4-6 Completing the Square

Objectives To solve equations by completing the square
To rewrite functions by completing the square

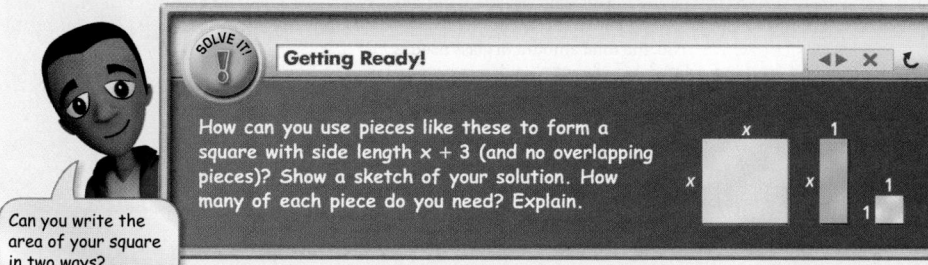

Can you write the area of your square in two ways?

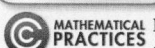

Forming a square with model pieces provides a useful geometric image for completing a square algebraically.

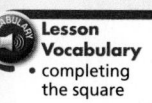

Lesson Vocabulary
• completing the square

Essential Understanding Completing a perfect square trinomial allows you to factor the completed trinomial as the square of a binomial.

You can solve an equation that contains a perfect square by finding square roots. The simplest of this type of equation has the form $ax^2 = c$.

Plan
How is solving this equation like solving a linear equation?
You isolate the variable term.

Problem 1 Solving by Finding Square Roots

What is the solution of each equation?

A $4x^2 + 10 = 46$

$4x^2 = 36$ ← Rewrite in $ax^2 = c$ form. →

$\frac{4x^2}{4} = \frac{36}{4}$ ← Isolate x^2. →

$x^2 = 9$

$x = \pm 3$ ← Find square roots. →

B $3x^2 - 5 = 25$

$3x^2 = 30$

$\frac{3x^2}{3} = \frac{30}{3}$

$x^2 = 10$

$x = \pm \sqrt{10}$

 Got It? 1. What is the solution of each equation?

a. $7x^2 - 10 = 25$ **b.** $2x^2 + 9 = 13$

---

1 Interactive Learning

Solve It!
PURPOSE To build a model of a perfect square
PROCESS Students may
• arrange pieces by trial-and-error to get a square with the necessary side lengths.
• first draw a square with side length $x + 3$, and then fill the interior with pieces.

FACILITATE

Q Use two pieces to form a rectangle. What are its dimensions? **[Samples: a rectangle along a large square; x by $x + 1$]**

Q If each side of the square is $x + 3$, what is the area of the square? Explain. **[$A = s^2 = (x + 3)^2 = x^2 + 6x + 9$]**

ANSWER See Solve It in Answers on next page.
CONNECT THE MATH In the Solve It, students model a perfect square expression. In the lesson, students will solve quadratic equations by algebraically forming perfect squares and finding square roots.

2 Guided Instruction

Problem 1

Q Why is there a $\pm$, and will it always be needed? **[When you take the square root there are two solutions: a positive and a negative. The $\pm$ gives both solutions, so you should always use it.]**

Got It? EXTENSION

Q What happens if you try to solve $3x^2 + 16 = 1$? **[Answers may vary. Sample: You get $x = \pm\sqrt{-5}$, but no real number squared gives -5, so the equation does not have a real number solution.]**

4-6 Preparing to Teach

BIG idea Solving Equations and Inequalities

ESSENTIAL UNDERSTANDINGS
• Completing a perfect square trinomial allows the completed trinomial to be factored as the square of a binomial.
• An equation that contains a perfect square can be solved by finding square roots. The simplest of this type of equation has the form $ax^2 = c$.
• The real solutions of a quadratic equation show the zeros of the related quadratic function and the x-intercepts of its graph.

Math Background
Factoring, tables, and graphs give exact rational solutions or rational approximations. This lesson introduces two methods that may give exact irrational solutions:
• solving by finding square roots
• completing the square.

Both methods rely on isolating a perfect square variable expression on one side of the equation and finding square roots of both sides of the equation. When the isolated constant is positive but not a perfect square, the solutions are irrational. By adding a constant, you can turn *any* quadratic expression into a perfect square trinomial.

Note that completing the square yields the vertex form of a parabola.

Mathematical Practices
Make sense of problems and persevere in solving them. Students will plan a pathway to a solution by completing the squares of quadratic equations and then solving for x.

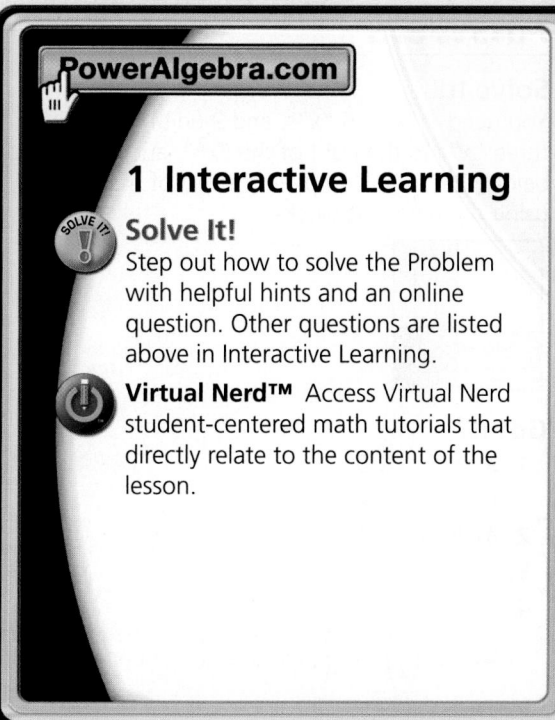

PowerAlgebra.com

1 Interactive Learning

Solve It!
Step out how to solve the Problem with helpful hints and an online question. Other questions are listed above in Interactive Learning.

Virtual Nerd™ Access Virtual Nerd student-centered math tutorials that directly relate to the content of the lesson.

Problem 2

Q What is another way to find the area of the rectangular part? **[Answers may vary. Sample: Sum the area of two squares: $x^2 + x^2$.]**

Q How do you evaluate $\sqrt{\dfrac{2766}{2 + \frac{\pi}{8}}}$ on a calculator?

[Answers may vary. Sample: Enter $\sqrt{(2766/(2 + \pi/8))}$]

Got It?

Q If x represents the shorter side of this window, what expression represents the length of the longer side? **[1.6x]**

Q Why are the final answers not $\pm$ a constant as in Problem 1? **[Length cannot be negative so only the positive solutions are needed.]**

Problem 3

Q If the leading coefficient of a quadratic trinomial is 1, how do you recognize whether it is a perfect square trinomial? **[Answers may vary. Sample: For $x^2 + bx + c$ to be a perfect square, c must be the square of half of b.]**

Q What happens if the constant on the right side is not a perfect square? **[Answers may vary. Sample: The solutions are irrational.]**

Got It?   ERROR PREVENTION

Watch that students take the square root of *both* sides of the equation rather than just the side with the perfect square trinomial. Also draw attention to the $\pm$.

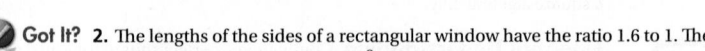

Problem 2 Determining Dimensions STEM

Architecture While designing a house, an architect used windows like the one shown here. What are the dimensions of the window if it has 2766 square inches of glass?

Step 1 Find the area of the window.

The area of the rectangular part is $(2x)(x) = 2x^2$ in.^{2}.

The area of the semicircular part is

$\frac{1}{2}\pi r^2 = \frac{1}{2}\pi\left(\frac{x}{2}\right)^2 = \frac{1}{2}\pi\frac{x^2}{4} = \frac{\pi}{8}x^2$ in.^{2}.

So, the total amount of glass used is
$2x^2 + \frac{\pi}{8}x^2 = 2766$ in.^{2}.

Step 2 Solve for x.

$\left(2 + \dfrac{\pi}{8}\right)x^2 = 2766$	Write the equation in $ax^2 = c$ form.
$x^2 = \dfrac{2766}{2 + \frac{\pi}{8}}$	Isolate x^2.
$x \approx \pm 34$	Find square roots. Use a calculator.

Length cannot be negative. So the rectangular portion of the window is 34 in. wide by 68 in. long. The semicircular top has a radius of 17 in.

Think

Is the answer reasonable?
Yes; the rectangular part is about $30 \times 70 = 2100$ in.^{2}. This leaves enough glass for the semicircle.

✔ **Got It? 2.** The lengths of the sides of a rectangular window have the ratio 1.6 to 1. The area of the window is 2822.4 in.^{2}. What are the window dimensions?

Sometimes an equation shows a perfect square trinomial equal to a constant. To solve, factor the perfect square trinomial into the square of a binomial. Then find square roots.

Problem 3 Solving a Perfect Square Trinomial Equation

What is the solution of $x^2 + 4x + 4 = 25$?

Think	Write
Factor the perfect square trinomial.	$x^2 + 4x + 4 = 25$
	$(x + 2)^2 = 25$
Find square roots.	$x + 2 = \pm 5$
Rewrite as two equations.	$x + 2 = 5 \text{ or } x + 2 = -5$
Solve for x.	$x = 3 \text{ or } x = -7$

✔ **Got It? 3.** What is the solution of $x^2 - 14x + 49 = 25$?

Answers

Solve It!
You need 1 "x^2", 6 "x"s, and 9 unit blocks. Line three "x"s to the right of the "x^2", and three "x"s below the "x^2". Complete the rest of the square using the nine unit blocks.

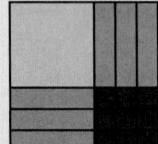

Got It?
1. a. $\sqrt{5}, -\sqrt{5}$
  b. $\sqrt{2}, -\sqrt{2}$
2. 42 in. $\times$ 67.2 in.
3. 2, 12
4. a. 9
  b. No; $\left(\dfrac{b}{2}\right)^2 = \dfrac{b^2}{4}$, which is a function of b.

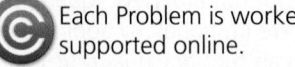

⌐ **PowerAlgebra.com**

2 Guided Instruction

© Each Problem is worked out and supported online.

Problem 1
Solving by Finding Square Roots

Problem 2
Determining Dimensions
Animated

Problem 3
Solving a Perfect Square Trinomial Equation

Problem 4
Completing the Square

Problem 5
Solving by Completing the Square
Animated

Problem 6
Writing in Vertex Form
Animated

Support in Algebra 2 Companion
• Vocabulary
• Key Concepts
• Got It?

If $x^2 + bx$ is not part of a perfect square trinomial, you can use the coefficient b to find a constant c so that $x^2 + bx + c$ is a perfect square. When you do this, you are **completing the square**. The diagram models this process.

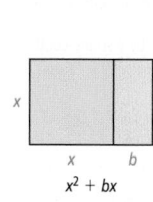 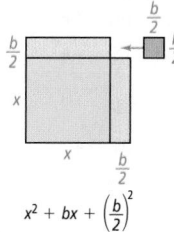 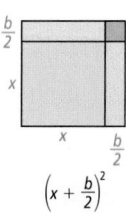

$x^2 + bx$ $x^2 + bx + \left(\frac{b}{2}\right)^2$ $\left(x + \frac{b}{2}\right)^2$

---

take note

Key Concept   **Completing the Square**

You can form a perfect square trinomial from $x^2 + bx$ by adding $\left(\frac{b}{2}\right)^2$.

$$x^2 + bx + \left(\frac{b}{2}\right)^2 = \left(x + \frac{b}{2}\right)^2$$

© **Problem 4**   **Completing the Square**

Think

Why do you want a perfect square trinomial?
You can factor a perfect square trinomial into the square of a binomial.

What value completes the square for $x^2 - 10x$? Justify your answer.

$x^2 - 10x$ Identify b; $b = -10$

$\left(\frac{b}{2}\right)^2 = \left(\frac{-10}{2}\right)^2 = (-5)^2 = 25$ Find $\left(\frac{b}{2}\right)^2$.

$x^2 - 10x + 25$ Add the value of $\left(\frac{b}{2}\right)^2$ to complete the square.

$x^2 - 10x + 25 = (x - 5)^2$ Rewrite as the square of a binomial.

© ✓ **Got It?**   **4. a.** What value completes the square for $x^2 + 6x$?
     b. Reasoning Is it possible for more than one value to complete the square for an expression? Explain.

---

take note

Key Concept   **Solving an Equation by Completing the Square**

1. Rewrite the equation in the form $x^2 + bx = c$. To do this, get all terms with the variable on one side of the equation and the constant on the other side. Divide all the terms of the equation by the coefficient of x^2 if it is not 1.

2. Complete the square by adding $\left(\frac{b}{2}\right)^2$ to each side of the equation.

3. Factor the trinomial.

4. Find square roots.

5. Solve for x.

PowerAlgebra.com   Lesson 4-6   Completing the Square   **235**

Additional Problems

1. What is the solution of each equation?
   a. $3x^2 + 5 = 20$
   b. $8x^2 - 3 = 29$
   ANSWERS
   a. $\pm\sqrt{5}$
   b. ± 2

2. The total area of three congruent circles is 500 cm². Find the approximate radius of each circle.
   ANSWER about 7.3 cm

3. What is the solution of $x^2 + 12x + 36 = 9$?
   ANSWER -3 or -9

4. What value completes the square for $x^2 + 14x$? Justify your answer.
   ANSWER 49;
   $x^2 + 14x + 49 = (x + 7)^2$

5. What is the solution of $3x^2 + 18x - 3 = 0$?
   ANSWER $-3 \pm \sqrt{10}$

6. What is $y = x^2 - 10x + 4$ in vertex form? Name the vertex and y-intercept.
   ANSWER $y = (x - 5)^2 - 21$;
   vertex $(5, -21)$;
   y-intercept $(0, 4)$

Problem 5

Q Why is 4 added to each side of the equation? **[Sample: On the left side, it completes the square; it is added on the right to keep the equation unchanged.]**

Q If you solve a quadratic equation by completing the square and the solutions are integers, what does that indicate? **[Sample: You could also solve by factoring.]**

Q What could you do if the "*a*" value does not divide evenly into each term of the quadratic equation? **[You divide by "*a*" anyway to get $x^2 + \frac{b}{a}x + \frac{c}{a}$, then take $\frac{b}{2a}$ and square it. Add and subtract $\frac{b^2}{4a^2}$.]**

Got It?   ERROR PREVENTION

Q How do you get all *x* terms alone on the left side? **[Subtract *x* from each side, and subtract 3 from each side, in either order.]**

Problem 6   SYNTHESIZING

This problem connects concepts of Lessons 4-1 and 4-2 by converting standard to vertex form.

Q What is $y = ax^2 + bx + c$ in vertex form?
$$y = a\left(x + \frac{b}{2a}\right)^2 + \frac{4ac - b^2}{4a}$$

Got It?

This is the first Problem or Got It that features an odd value of *b*. Be aware of students who may struggle with the fractions or decimals involved in completing the square.

Think

Is there a way to check without a calculator?
Yes; you can check that your solutions are reasonable by estimating.

Plan

What should be your first step?
Complete the square.

 Problem 5 Solving by Completing the Square

What is the solution of $3x^2 - 12x + 6 = 0$?

$$3x^2 - 12x + 6 = 0$$

$3x^2 - 12x = -6$	Rewrite. Get all terms with *x* on one side of the equation.
$\frac{3x^2}{3} - \frac{12x}{3} = \frac{-6}{3}$	Divide each side by 3 so the coefficient of x^2 will be 1.
$x^2 - 4x = -2$	Simplify.
$\left(\frac{b}{2}\right)^2 = \left(\frac{-4}{2}\right)^2 = (-2)^2 = 4$	Find $\left(\frac{b}{2}\right)^2 = 4$.
$x^2 - 4x + 4 = -2 + 4$	Add 4 to each side.
$(x - 2)^2 = 2$	Factor the trinomial.
$x - 2 = \pm\sqrt{2}$	Find square roots.
$x = 2 \pm \sqrt{2}$	Solve for *x*.

Check your results on your calculator. Replace *x* in the original equation with $2 + \sqrt{2}$ and $2 - \sqrt{2}$.

Got It? 5. What is the solution of $2x^2 - x + 3 = x + 9$?

You can complete a square to change a quadratic function to vertex form.

 Problem 6 Writing in Vertex Form

What is $y = x^2 + 4x - 6$ in vertex form? Name the vertex and *y*-intercept.

$y = x^2 + 4x - 6$	
$y = x^2 + 4x + 2^2 - 6 - 2^2$	Add $\left(\frac{4}{2}\right)^2 = 2^2$ to complete the square. Also, subtract 2^2 to leave the function unchanged.
$y = (x + 2)^2 - 6 - 2^2$	Factor the perfect square trinomial.
$y = (x + 2)^2 - 10$	Simplify.

The vertex is $(-2, -10)$. The *y*-intercept is $(0, -6)$.

Check with a graphing calculator.

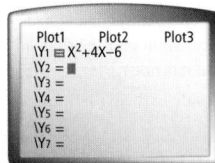 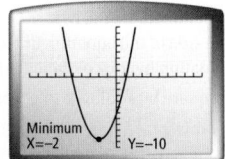 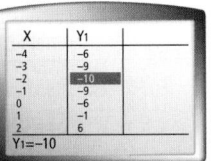

Got It? 6. What is $y = x^2 + 3x - 6$ in vertex form? Name the vertex and *y*-intercept.

Answers

Got It? (continued)

5. $\frac{1}{2} \pm \frac{\sqrt{13}}{2}$

6. $y = \left(x + \frac{3}{2}\right)^2 - \frac{33}{4}$;
vertex: $\left(-\frac{3}{2}, -\frac{33}{4}\right)$;
y-intercept: $(0, -6)$

Lesson Check

1. $6, -6$

2. $3, -3$

3. 1

4. 25

5. 4

6. 36

7. 2500

8. 256

9. First, you rewrite the eq. to get all terms with *x* on one side. Then, you find $\left(\frac{b}{2}\right)^2$ and add it

to both sides of the eq. Then, you factor the resulting trinomial.

10. $x^2 + 12x + 5 = 3$

$x^2 + 12x = -2$	Rewrite to get all terms with *x* on one side of the eq.
$\left(\frac{12}{2}\right)^2 = 6^2 = 36$	Find $\left(\frac{b}{2}\right)^2 = 36$.
$x^2 + 12x + 36$ $= -2 + 36$	Add 36 to each side.
$(x + 6)^2 = 34$	Factor the trinomial.

11. Your friend should also have subtracted 49;
$(x^2 - 14x + 49) + 36 - 49$
$= (x - 7)^2 - 13$

Lesson Check

Do you know HOW?

Solve each equation by finding square roots.

1. $2x^2 = 72$ **2.** $6x^2 = 54$

Complete the square.

3. $x^2 + 2x + \blacksquare$ **4.** $x^2 + 10x + \blacksquare$

5. $x^2 - 4x + \blacksquare$ **6.** $x^2 + 12x + \blacksquare$

7. $x^2 + 100x + \blacksquare$ **8.** $x^2 - 32x + \blacksquare$

Do you UNDERSTAND?  MATHEMATICAL PRACTICES

9. Vocabulary Explain the process of completing the square.

10. How can you rewrite the equation $x^2 + 12x + 5 = 3$ so the left side of the equation is in the form $(x + a)^2$?

11. Error Analysis Your friend completed the square and wrote the expression shown. Explain your friend's error and write the expression correctly.

$$x^2 - 14x + 36$$
$$x^2 - 14x + 49 + 36$$
$$(x - 7)^2 + 36$$

Practice and Problem-Solving Exercises  MATHEMATICAL PRACTICES

Ⓐ Practice

Solve each equation by finding square roots.   ◀ See Problem 1.

12. $5x^2 = 80$ **13.** $x^2 - 4 = 0$ **14.** $2x^2 = 32$

15. $9x^2 = 25$ **16.** $3x^2 - 15 = 0$ **17.** $5x^2 - 40 = 0$

18. Fitness A rectangular swimming pool is 6 ft deep. One side of the pool is 2.5 times longer than the other. The amount of water needed to fill the swimming pool is 2160 cubic feet. Find the dimensions of the pool.   ◀ See Problem 2.

Solve each equation.   ◀ See Problem 3.

19. $x^2 + 6x + 9 = 1$ **20.** $x^2 - 4x + 4 = 100$ **21.** $x^2 - 2x + 1 = 4$

22. $x^2 + 8x + 16 = \frac{16}{9}$ **23.** $4x^2 + 4x + 1 = 49$ **24.** $x^2 - 12x + 36 = 25$

25. $25x^2 + 10x + 1 = 9$ **26.** $x^2 - 30x + 225 = 400$ **27.** $9x^2 + 24x + 16 = 36$

Complete the square.   ◀ See Problem 4.

28. $x^2 + 18x + \blacksquare$ **29.** $x^2 - x + \blacksquare$ **30.** $x^2 - 24x + \blacksquare$

31. $x^2 + 20x + \blacksquare$ **32.** $m^2 - 3m + \blacksquare$ **33.** $x^2 + 4x + \blacksquare$

Solve each quadratic equation by completing the square.   ◀ See Problem 5.

34. $x^2 + 6x - 3 = 0$ **35.** $x^2 - 12x + 7 = 0$ **36.** $x^2 + 4x + 2 = 0$

37. $x^2 - 2x = 5$ **38.** $x^2 + 8x = 11$ **39.** $x^2 + 12 = 10x$

40. $x^2 - 3x = x - 1$ **41.** $x^2 + 2 = 6x + 4$ **42.** $2x^2 + 2x - 5 = x^2$

43. $4x^2 + 10x - 3 = 0$ **44.** $9x^2 - 12x - 2 = 0$ **45.** $25x^2 + 30x = 12$

Practice and Problem-Solving Exercises

12. $4, -4$ **13.** $2, -2$

14. $4, -4$ **15.** $\frac{5}{3}, -\frac{5}{3}$

16. $\sqrt{5}, -\sqrt{5}$

17. $2\sqrt{2}, -2\sqrt{2}$

18. $12\text{ ft} \times 30\text{ ft} \times 6\text{ ft}$

19. $-4, -2$

20. $-8, 12$ **21.** $-1, 3$

22. $-\frac{16}{3}, -\frac{8}{3}$

23. $-4, 3$

24. $1, 11$

25. $-\frac{4}{5}, \frac{2}{5}$

26. $35, -5$

27. $-\frac{10}{3}, \frac{2}{3}$

28. 81

29. $\frac{1}{4}$

30. 144

31. 100

32. $\frac{9}{4}$

33. 4

34. $-3 \pm 2\sqrt{3}$

35. $6 \pm \sqrt{29}$

36. $-2 \pm \sqrt{2}$

37. $1 \pm \sqrt{6}$

38. $-4 \pm 3\sqrt{3}$

39. $5 \pm \sqrt{13}$

40. $2 \pm \sqrt{3}$

41. $3 \pm \sqrt{11}$

42. $-1 \pm \sqrt{6}$

43. $-\frac{5}{4} \pm \frac{1}{4}\sqrt{37}$

44. $\frac{2}{3} \pm \frac{\sqrt{6}}{3}$

45. $-\frac{3}{5} \pm \frac{\sqrt{21}}{5}$

---

3 Lesson Check

Do you know HOW?

- If students solve Exercises 1 and 2 by rewriting in standard form and factoring (as in Lesson 4-5), then suggest they also try finding square roots as in Problem 1.

Do you UNDERSTAND?

- For Exercise 11, if students overlook the error, then have them look at the red numbers in Problem 6.

Close

Q How does completing the square help solve any quadratic equation? **[Answers may vary. Sample: Completing the square creates a perfect square trinomial that factors as the square of a binomial; the quadratic equation is solved by finding square roots.]**

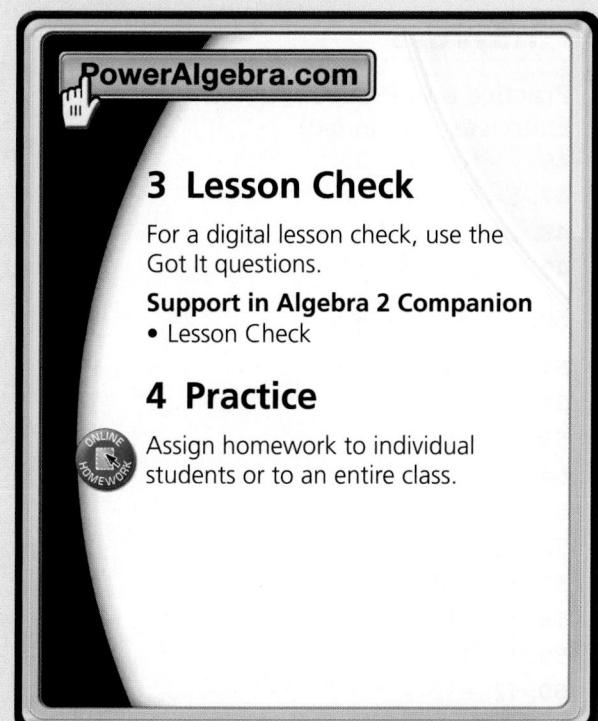

PowerAlgebra.com

3 Lesson Check

For a digital lesson check, use the Got It questions.

Support in Algebra 2 Companion
- Lesson Check

4 Practice

Assign homework to individual students or to an entire class.

4 Practice

ASSIGNMENT GUIDE

Basic: 12–51 all, 52–56 even, 62–66 even, 75

Average: 13–51 odd, 52–75

Advanced: 13–51 odd, 52–85

Standardized Test Prep: 86–89

Mixed Review: 90–100

Ⓒ **Mathematical Practices** are supported by exercises with red headings. Here are the Practices supported in this lesson:

MP 1: Make Sense of Problems Ex. 52
MP 3: Critique the Reasoning of Others Ex. 11

Applications exercises have blue headings. Exercises 18 and 62 support MP 4: Model.

EXERCISE 62: Use the Think About a Plan worksheet in the **Practice and Problem Solving Workbook** (also available in the Teaching Resources in print and online) to further support students' development in becoming independent learners.

HOMEWORK QUICK CHECK

To check students' understanding of key skills and concepts, go over Exercises 13, 35, 52, 62, and 75.

Rewrite each equation in vertex form. ◆ **See Problem 6.**

46. $y = x^2 + 4x + 1$ **47.** $y = 2x^2 - 8x + 1$ **48.** $y = -x^2 - 2x + 3$

49. $y = x^2 + 4x - 7$ **50.** $y = 2x^2 - 6x - 1$ **51.** $y = -x^2 + 4x - 1$

Ⓑ **Apply** Ⓒ **52. Think About a Plan** The area of the rectangle shown is 80 square inches. What is the value of x?
- How can you write an equation to represent 80 in terms of x?
- How can you find the value of x by completing the square?

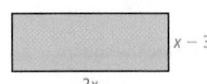
$x - 3$
$2x$

Find the value of k that would make the left side of each equation a perfect square trinomial.

53. $x^2 + kx + 25 = 0$ **54.** $x^2 - kx + 100 = 0$ **55.** $x^2 - kx + 121 = 0$

56. $x^2 + kx + 64 = 0$ **57.** $x^2 - kx + 81 = 0$ **58.** $25x^2 - kx + 1 = 0$

59. $x^2 + kx + \frac{1}{4} = 0$ **60.** $9x^2 - kx + 4 = 0$ **61.** $36x^2 - kx + 49 = 0$

62. Geometry The table shows some possible dimensions of rectangles with a perimeter of 100 units. Copy and complete the table.
  a. Plot the points (width, area). Find a model for the data set.
  b. What is another point in the data set? Use it to verify your model.
  c. What is a reasonable domain for this function? Explain.
  d. Find the maximum possible area. What dimensions yield this area?
  e. Find a function for area in terms of width without using the table. Do you get the same model as in part (a)? Explain.

Width	Length	Area
1	49	49
2	48	▪
3	▪	▪
4	▪	▪
5	▪	▪

Solve each quadratic equation by completing the square.

63. $x^2 + 5x - 3 = 0$ **64.** $x^2 + 3x = 2$

65. $x^2 - x = 5$ **66.** $x^2 + x - 1 = 0$

67. $3x^2 - 4x = 2$ **68.** $5x^2 - x = 4$

69. $x^2 + \frac{3}{4}x = \frac{1}{2}$ **70.** $2x^2 - \frac{1}{2}x = \frac{1}{8}$

71. $3x^2 + x = \frac{2}{3}$ **72.** $-x^2 + 2x + 4 = 0$

73. $-x^2 - 6x = 2$ **74.** $-0.25x^2 - 0.6x + 0.3 = 0$

75. Football The quadratic function $h = -0.01x^2 + 1.18x + 2$ models the height of a punted football. The horizontal distance in feet from the point of impact with the kicker's foot is x, and h is the height of the ball in feet.
  a. Write the function in vertex form. What is the maximum height of the punt?
  b. The nearest defensive player is 5 ft horizontally from the point of impact. How high must the player reach to block the punt?
  c. Suppose the ball was not blocked but continued on its path. How far down the field would the ball go before it hit the ground?

Answers

Practice and Problem-Solving Exercises (continued)

46. $y = (x + 2)^2 - 3$

47. $y = 2(x - 2)^2 - 7$

48. $y = -(x + 1)^2 + 4$

49. $y = (x + 2)^2 - 11$

50. $y = 2\left(x - \frac{3}{2}\right)^2 - \frac{11}{2}$

51. $y = -(x - 2)^2 + 3$

52. 8 in.

53. 10, −10

54. 20, −20

55. 22, −22

56. 16, −16

57. 18, −18

58. 10, −10

59. 1, −1

60. 12, −12

61. 84, −84

62.

Width	Length	Area
1	49	49
2	48	96
3	47	141
4	46	184
5	45	225

a.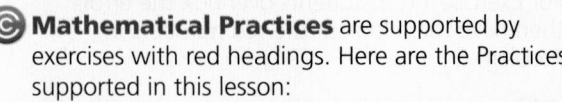
$A = -w^2 + 50w$

b. Check students' work.

c. $0 < w < 50$; since the perimeter is 100, the width would have to be less than 50. Also, width can't be negative so it would have to be greater than 0.

d. 625 units^2; 25 units x 25 units

e. $A = w(50 - w)$; yes; the eqs. are equivalent.

63. $\frac{-5 \pm \sqrt{37}}{2}$ **64.** $\frac{-3 \pm \sqrt{17}}{2}$

65. $\frac{1 \pm \sqrt{21}}{2}$ **66.** $\frac{1 \pm \sqrt{5}}{2}$

67. $\frac{2 \pm \sqrt{10}}{3}$ **68.** $1, -\frac{4}{5}$

69. $\frac{-3 \pm \sqrt{41}}{8}$ **70.** $\frac{1 \pm \sqrt{5}}{8}$

71. $\frac{1}{3}, -\frac{2}{3}$ **72.** $1 \pm \sqrt{5}$

73. $-3 \pm \sqrt{7}$ **74.** $\frac{-6 \pm \sqrt{66}}{5}$

75. a. $-0.01(x - 59)^2 + 36.81$; 36.81 ft

b. 7.65 ft

c. about 120 ft

Solve for x in terms of a.

76. $2x^2 - ax = 6a^2$ **77.** $3x^2 + ax = a^2$ **78.** $2a^2x^2 - 8ax = -6$

79. $4a^2x^2 + 8ax + 3 = 0$ **80.** $3x^2 + ax^2 = 9x + 9a$ **81.** $6a^2x^2 - 11ax = 10$

82. Solve $x^2 = (6\sqrt{2})x + 7$ by completing the square.

Rewrite each equation in vertex form. Then find the vertex of the graph.

83. $y = -4x^2 - 5x + 3$ **84.** $y = \frac{1}{2}x^2 - 5x + 12$ **85.** $y = -\frac{1}{5}x^2 + \frac{4}{5}x + \frac{11}{5}$

Standardized Test Prep

SAT/ACT

86. The graph of which inequality has its vertex at $\left(2\frac{1}{2}, -5\right)$?

  Ⓐ $y < |2x - 5| + 5$ Ⓒ $y > |2x + 5| - 5$

  Ⓑ $y < |2x + 5| - 5$ Ⓓ $y > |2x - 5| - 5$

87. Which number is a solution of $|9 - x| = 9 + x$?

  Ⓕ -3 Ⓖ 0 Ⓗ 3 Ⓘ 6

88. Joanne tosses an apple seed on the ground. It travels along a parabola with the equation $y = -x^2 + 4$. Assume the seed was thrown from a height of 4 ft. How many feet away from Joanne will the apple seed land?

  Ⓐ 1 ft   Ⓑ 2 ft   Ⓒ 4 ft   Ⓓ 8 ft

Extended Response

89. List the steps for solving the equation $x^2 - 9 = -8x$ by the completing the square method. Explain each step.

Mixed Review

Solve each equation by factoring. Check your answers.   ◀ See Lesson 4-5.

90. $2x^2 - 3x + 1 = 0$ **91.** $x^2 - 4 = -3x$ **92.** $16 + 22x = 3x^2$

Determine whether a quadratic model exists for each set of values. If so, write the model.   ◀ See Lesson 4-3.

93. $(-4, 3), (-3, 3), (-2, 4)$ **94.** $\left(-1, \frac{1}{2}\right), (0, 2), (2, 2)$ **95.** $(0, 2), (1, 0), (2, 4)$

Solve each system by elimination.   ◀ See Lesson 3-2.

96. $\begin{cases} 2x + y = 4 \\ 3x - y = 6 \end{cases}$ **97.** $\begin{cases} 2x + y = 7 \\ -2x + 5y = -1 \end{cases}$ **98.** $\begin{cases} 2x + 4y = 10 \\ 3x + 5y = 14 \end{cases}$

Get Ready!   **To prepare for Lesson 4-7, do Exercises 99–100.**

Evaluate each expression for the given values of the variables.   ◀ See Lesson 1-3.

99. $b^2 - 4ac$; $a = 1, b = 6, c = 3$ **100.** $b^2 - 4ac$; $a = -5, b = 2, c = 4$

---

76. $-\frac{3a}{2}, 2a$

77. $\frac{-a \pm a\sqrt{13}}{6}$

78. $\frac{3}{a}, \frac{1}{a}, a \neq 0$

79. $-\frac{3}{2a}, -\frac{1}{2a}, a \neq 0$

80. $3, \frac{-3a}{a + 3}, a \neq -3$

81. $-\frac{2}{3a}, \frac{5}{2a}, a \neq 0$

82. $-5 + 3\sqrt{2}, 5 + 3\sqrt{2}$

83. $y = -4\left(x + \frac{5}{8}\right)^2 + \frac{73}{16}; \left(-\frac{5}{8}, \frac{73}{16}\right)$

84. $y = \frac{1}{2}(x - 5)^2 - \frac{1}{2}; \left(5, -\frac{1}{2}\right)$

85. $y = -\frac{1}{5}(x - 2)^2 + 3; (2, 3)$

Standardized Test Prep

86. D

87. G

88. B

89. **[4]** $x^2 - 9 = -8x$

$x^2 + 8x = 9$	Move the variables to the left side and the constant to the right by using the Add. Prop. of Eq.
$\left(\frac{8}{2}\right)^2 = 4^2 = 16$	Find $\left(\frac{b}{2}\right)^2 = 16$.
$x^2 + 8x + 16 = 9 + 16$	Add 16 to each side.
$(x + 4)^2 = 25$	Factor left side. Simplify right side.
$x + 4 = \pm 5$	Take the square root of each side.
$x = -4 \pm 5$	Add -4 to each side.
$x = -9, 1$	Simplify.

[3] computational error

[2] steps are listed, without explanations

[1] eq. is solved correctly, without work shown

Mixed Review

90. $\frac{1}{2}, 1$

91. $-4, 1$

92. $8, -\frac{2}{3}$

93. yes; $y = \frac{1}{2}x^2 + \frac{7}{2}x + 9$

94. yes; $y = -\frac{1}{2}x^2 + x + 2$

95. yes; $y = 3x^2 - 5x + 2$

96. $(2, 0)$

97. $(3, 1)$

98. $(3, 1)$

99. 24

100. 84

Lesson Resources

Differentiated Remediation

Additional Instructional Support

Algebra 2 Companion

Students can use the **Algebra 2 Companion** worktext (4 pages) as you teach the lesson. Use the Companion to support

- New Vocabulary
- Key Concepts
- Got It for each Problem
- Lesson Check

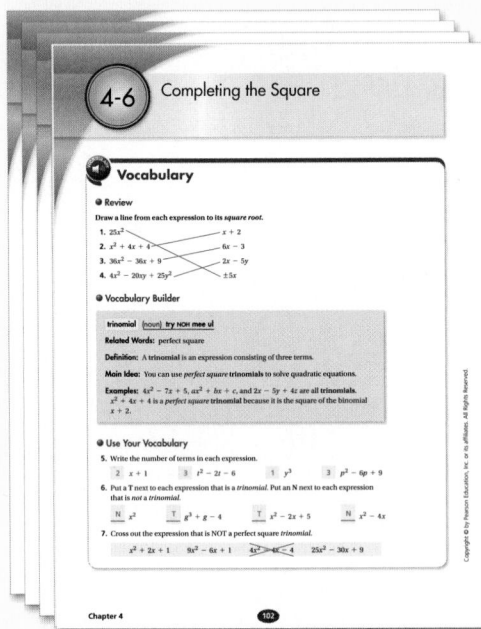

ELL Support

Use Manipulatives Let students use algebra tiles (or photocopied cut-outs of the pieces shown in the Solve It) to model completing the square when $a = 1$ and b is even. In Problem 4, for example, students can arrange one large square (x^2) and 10 rectangles ($10x$) into the best possible square. (To model the fact that $10x$ is negative, students can flip the rectangles over to the *opposite* sides.) Then students can see that 25 unit squares are needed to literally complete the square.

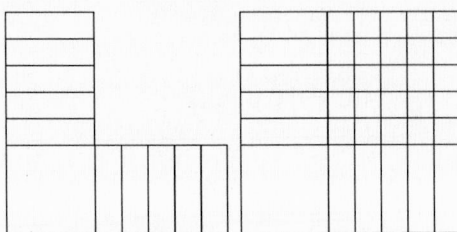

Give students different equations to model. Have them sketch it and describe how their model can be used to solve the problem.

5 Assess & Remediate

Lesson Quiz

1. What is the solution of $6x^2 = 42$?

2. A rectangle is constructed on a semicircle so that the length equals the diameter. The rectangle is 3 times as long as it is wide. The total area of this figure is 750 in.^{2}. Find the approximate dimensions of the rectangle.

3. What is the solution of $x^2 - 14x + 49 = 4$?

4. Complete the square: $x^2 - 8x + \square$.

5. Solve $x^2 - 10x + 22 = 0$.

6. **Do you UNDERSTAND?** Explain the process of rewriting $y = x^2 + 2x + 26$ in vertex form.

ANSWERS TO LESSON QUIZ

1. $\pm \sqrt{7}$

2. about 10.7 in. by 32.1 in.

3. 5 or 9

4. 16

5. $5 \pm \sqrt{3}$

6. Answers may vary. Sample: Complete the square by adding 1, which is the square of half of 2; keep the equation unchanged by also subtracting 1, $y = x^2 + 2x + 1 + 26 - 1$; rewrite the perfect square trinomial as the square of a binomial and add the constants, $y = (x + 1)^2 + 25$.

PRESCRIPTION FOR REMEDIATION

Use the student work on the Lesson Quiz to prescribe a differentiated review assignment:

Points	Differentiated Remediation
0–2	Intervention
3–5	On-level
6	Extension

PowerAlgebra.com

5 Assess & Remediate

Assign the Lesson Quiz. Appropriate intervention, practice, or enrichment is automatically generated based on student performance.

Intervention

- **Reteaching** (2 pages) Provides reteaching and practice exercises for the key lesson concepts. Use with struggling students or absent students.

- **English Language Learner Support** Helps students develop and reinforce mathematical vocabulary and key concepts.

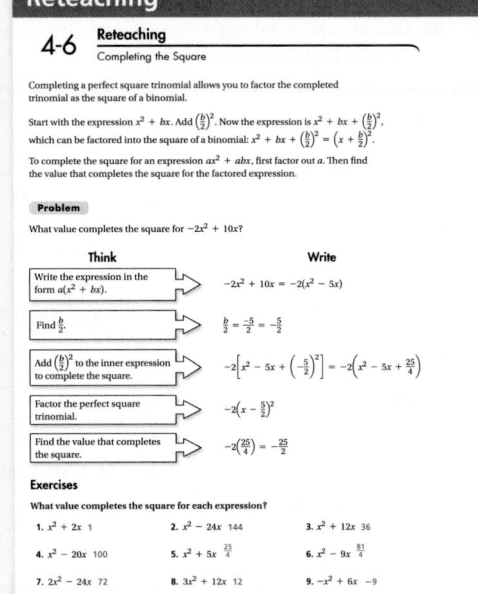

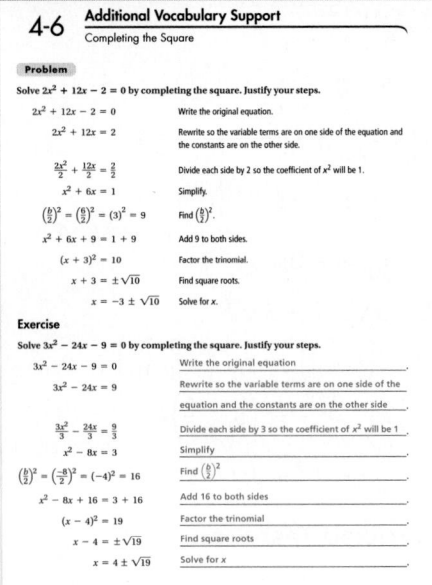

Differentiated Remediation *continued*

On-Level

- **Practice** (2 pages) Provides extra practice for each lesson. For simpler practice exercises, use the Form K Practice pages found in the All-in-One Teaching Resources and online.

- **Think About a Plan** Helps students develop specific problem-solving skills and strategies by providing scaffolded guiding questions.
- **Standardized Test Prep** Focuses on all major exercises, all major question types, and helps students prepare for the high-stakes assessments.

Extension

- **Enrichment** Provides students with interesting problems and activities that extend the concepts of the lesson.
- **Activities, Games, and Puzzles** Worksheets that can be used for concepts development, enrichment, and for fun!

Practice and Problem Solving Wkbk/All-in-One Resources/Online
Practice page 1

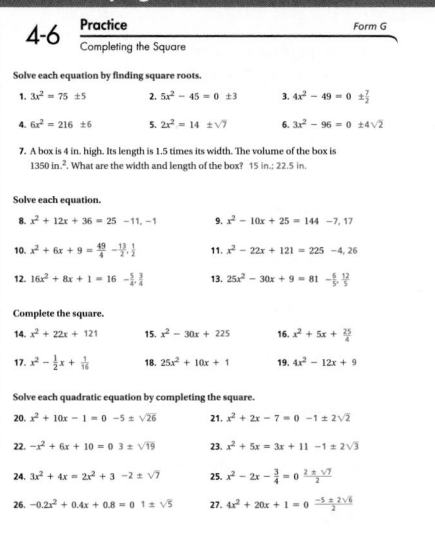

Practice and Problem Solving Wkbk/All-in-One Resources/Online
Practice page 2

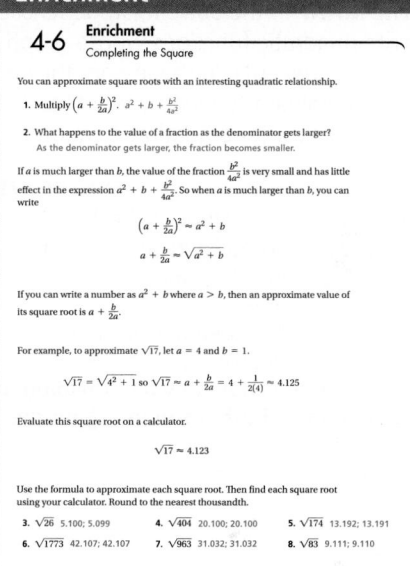

All-in-One Resources/Online
Enrichment

(Enrichment worksheet 4-6: Completing the Square)

Practice and Problem Solving Wkbk/All-in-One Resources/Online
Think About a Plan

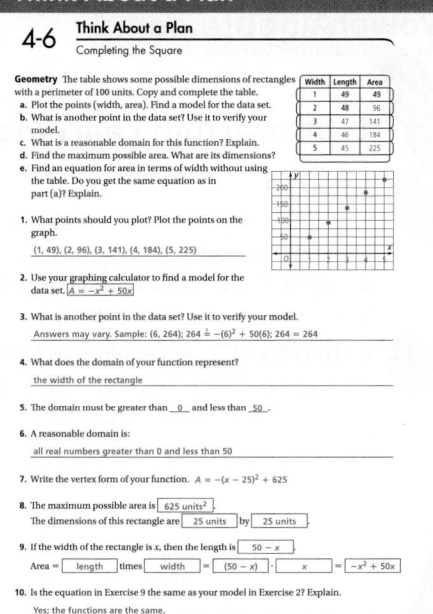

Practice and Problem Solving Wkbk/All-in-One Resources/Online
Standardized Test Prep

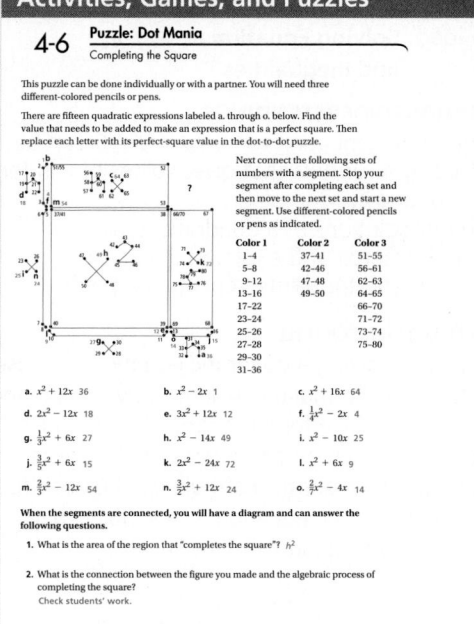

Online Teacher Resource Center
Activities, Games, and Puzzles

(Puzzle: Dot Mania 4-6: Completing the Square)

Solve It!

PURPOSE To write quadratic functions whose graphs have 2, 1, or 0 *x*-intercepts

PROCESS Students may

- pick the vertex point and use one of the endpoints to find an equation in vertex form.
- pick any third point and use a system of three equations or quadratic regression to find an equation in standard form.

FACILITATE

Q If the smile crosses the *x*-axis twice, what coordinates do you estimate for intercepts? [**Answers may vary. Sample: (3, 0), (5, 0)**]

Q What is the axis of symmetry of the smile? Explain. [***x* = 4; fold the face in half on that line.**]

ANSWER See Solve It in Answers on next page.
CONNECT THE MATH In the Solve It, students use points to write quadratic functions whose graphs have 2, 1, or 0 *x*-intercepts. In the lesson, they will evaluate the discriminant to identify whether 2, 1, or 0 real solutions exist for a quadratic equation.

SYNTHESIZING

Refer to page 235 and the steps in the Take Note section while presenting this derivation. Steps 1 and 2 are reversed in this derivation.

Q Why can you divide by *a* before rewriting so all terms with a variable are on one side? [**Subtracting *c* then dividing by *a* or dividing by *a* then subtracting $\frac{c}{a}$ both result in $-\frac{c}{a}$ on the right.**]

4-7 The Quadratic Formula

© **Common Core State Standards**
Reviews A-REI.B.4b Solve quadratic equations by . . . the quadratic formula . . .
MP 1, MP 2, MP 3, MP 4, MP 8

Objectives To solve quadratic equations using the Quadratic Formula
To determine the number of solutions by using the discriminant

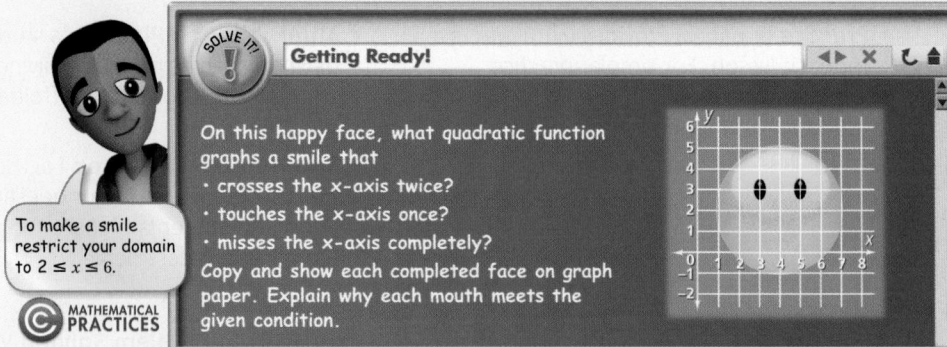

To make a smile restrict your domain to $2 \le x \le 6$.

© MATHEMATICAL PRACTICES

Getting Ready!

On this happy face, what quadratic function graphs a smile that
- crosses the x-axis twice?
- touches the x-axis once?
- misses the x-axis completely?

Copy and show each completed face on graph paper. Explain why each mouth meets the given condition.

Another way to solve a quadratic equation $ax^2 + bx + c = 0$ is by completing a square and then factoring.

Lesson Vocabulary
- Quadratic Formula
- discriminant

Essential Understanding You can solve a quadratic equation $ax^2 + bx + c = 0$ in more than one way. In general, you can find a formula that gives values of *x* in terms of *a*, *b*, and *c*.

Here's how to solve $ax^2 + bx + c = 0$ to get the *Quadratic Formula*.

$$ax^2 + bx + c = 0$$

$$x^2 + \frac{b}{a}x + \frac{c}{a} = 0 \qquad \text{Divide each side by } a.$$

$$x^2 + \frac{b}{a}x = -\frac{c}{a} \qquad \text{Rewrite so all terms containing } x \text{ are on one side.}$$

$$x^2 + \frac{b}{a}x + \left(\frac{b}{2a}\right)^2 = \left(\frac{b}{2a}\right)^2 - \frac{c}{a} \qquad \text{Complete the square.}$$

$$\left(x + \frac{b}{2a}\right)^2 = \frac{b^2 - 4ac}{4a^2} \qquad \text{Factor the perfect square trinomial. Also, simplify.}$$

$$x + \frac{b}{2a} = \pm \sqrt{\frac{b^2 - 4ac}{4a^2}} \qquad \text{Find square roots.}$$

$$x = -\frac{b}{2a} \pm \frac{\sqrt{b^2 - 4ac}}{2a} \qquad \text{Solve for } x. \text{ Also, simplify the radical.}$$

$$x = \frac{-b \pm \sqrt{b^2 - 4ac}}{2a} \qquad \text{Simplify.}$$

240 Chapter 4 Quadratic Functions and Equations

4-7 Preparing to Teach

BIG idea Solving Equations and Inequalities

ESSENTIAL UNDERSTANDINGS

- A quadratic equation $ax^2 + bx + c = 0$ can be solved by a formula that gives values of *x* in terms of *a*, *b*, and *c*.
- The real solutions of a quadratic equation show the zeros of the related quadratic function and the *x*-intercepts of its graph.

Math Background

One way of solving a quadratic equation is to use the Quadratic Formula. It is derived by completing the square to solve for *x* in terms of *a*, *b*, and *c* in the literal equation $ax^2 + bx + c = 0$. Unlike factoring, the Quadratic Formula can be used to solve any quadratic equation. It is simpler than completing the square in many cases.

Students sometimes get caught up in the computation and lose sight that they are solving quadratic equations. Emphasize the algebraic and graphical connections between solutions, zeroes, and *x*-intercepts. Students should be able to visualize a parabola when solving a quadratic equation and use the discriminant to determine how the parabola intersects the *x*-axis.

© **Mathematical Practices**
Look for and express regularity in repeated reasoning. Students will use the Quadratic Formula as a shortcut to solving quadratic equations.

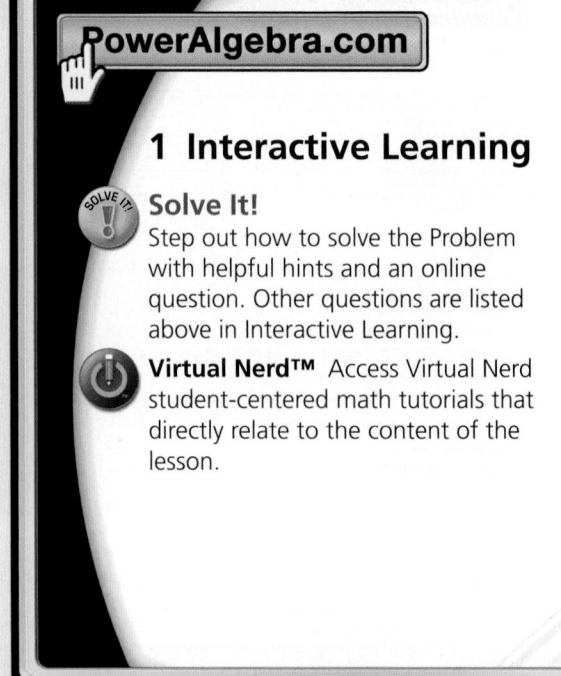

PowerAlgebra.com

1 Interactive Learning

Solve It!
Step out how to solve the Problem with helpful hints and an online question. Other questions are listed above in Interactive Learning.

Virtual Nerd™ Access Virtual Nerd student-centered math tutorials that directly relate to the content of the lesson.

Key Concept The Quadratic Formula

To solve the quadratic equation $ax^2 + bx + c = 0$, use the **Quadratic Formula**.

$$x = \frac{-b \pm \sqrt{b^2 - 4ac}}{2a}$$

 Problem 1 Using the Quadratic Formula

What are the solutions? Use the Quadratic Formula.

A $2x^2 - x = 4$

$2x^2 - x = 4$	
$2x^2 - x - 4 = 0$	Write in standard form.
$a = 2, b = -1, c = -4$	Find the values of a, b, and c.
$x = \dfrac{-b \pm \sqrt{b^2 - 4ac}}{2a}$	Write the Quadratic Formula.
$= \dfrac{-(-1) \pm \sqrt{(-1)^2 - 4(2)(-4)}}{2(2)}$	Substitute for a, b, and c.
$= \dfrac{1 \pm \sqrt{33}}{4}$	Simplify.
$= \dfrac{1 + \sqrt{33}}{4}$ or $\dfrac{1 - \sqrt{33}}{4}$	

Check Use a graphing calculator to graph
$y = 2x^2 - x - 4$. The x-intercepts are about
$-1.186 \approx \frac{1 - \sqrt{33}}{4}$ and $1.686 \approx \frac{1 + \sqrt{33}}{4}$, as
expected.

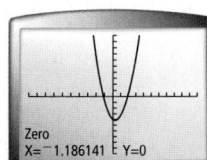

Zero
X = -1.186141 Y = 0

B $x^2 + 6x + 9 = 0$

$x^2 + 6x + 9 = 0$	
$a = 1, b = 6, c = 9$	Find the values of a, b, and c.
$x = \dfrac{-6 \pm \sqrt{6^2 - 4(1)(9)}}{2(1)}$	Substitute into $\dfrac{-b \pm \sqrt{b^2 - 4ac}}{2a}$.
$= \dfrac{-6 \pm \sqrt{36 - 36}}{2}$	Simplify.
$= \dfrac{-6 \pm \sqrt{0}}{2}$	
$= -3$	

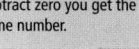 **Got It?** **1.** What are the solutions? Use the Quadratic Formula.

　　a. $x^2 + 4x = -4$　　　　　　　　**b.** $x^2 + 4x - 3 = 0$

Plan

Should you write the equation in standard form?
Yes; write the equation in standard form to identify a, b, and c.

Think

Why is there only one solution?
Because if you add or subtract zero you get the same number.

---

2 Guided Instruction

Take Note SYNTHESIZING

The Quadratic Formula solves any quadratic equation, including those that cannot be solved by factoring.

Problem 1 ERROR PREVENTION

Students must write the quadratic equation in standard form before using the Quadratic Formula. Be sure students use the correct order of operations when simplifying the expressions.

> **Q** Why are there two solutions to 1A? **[Answers may vary. Sample: The graph of the related function intersects the x-axis twice.]**
>
> **Q** For 1B, what would a graph of the related function look like? **[Answers may vary. Sample: The parabola touches but does not cross the x-axis.]**
>
> **Q** If the solution(s) are integers, what does that indicate about the quadratic equation? **[Answers may vary. Sample: The equation could also be solved by factoring.]**

Got It? ERROR PREVENTION

Some students may solve 1a by factoring. For 1b, watch that students reduce the square root and common factors in all terms.

> **Q** For 1a, what must you do before applying the Quadratic Formula? **[Rewrite the equation in standard form.]**

---

2 Guided Instruction

 Each Problem is worked out and supported online.

Problem 1
Using the Quadratic Formula
Animated

Problem 2
Applying the Quadratic Formula
Animated

Problem 3
Using the Discriminant

Problem 4
Using the Discriminant to Solve a Problem
Animated

Support in Algebra 2 Companion
• Vocabulary
• Key Concepts
• Got It?

Answers

Solve It!
Answers may vary. Sample:
$y = 0.375x^2 - 3x + 5.5$
crosses the x-axis twice
because it has two real roots;

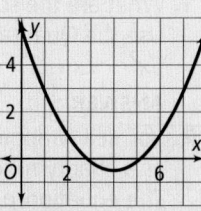

$y = 0.25(x - 4)^2$ touches the
x-axis once because the vertex
is the only root;

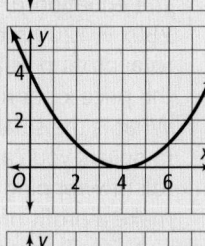

$y = 0.125(x - 4)^2 + 0.5$
misses the x-axis completely
because it has no real roots.

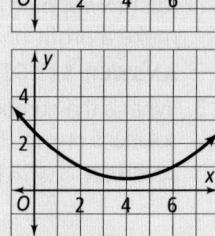

Problem 2

Students solve a real-world problem by applying the Quadratic Formula to a quadratic model. This is the first example students see where the value of a is negative.

> **Q** Why was 200 substituted into the equation? **[The variable p represents profit, and the desired profit is $200.]**
>
> **Q** If the band sells the CDs for the smallest price of $15.28, will the profit be exactly $200? [Answers may vary. Samples: No, because 15.28 was a rounded value; if you substitute 15.28 into the original equation for profit, $p \approx 199.96$.]**

Got It?

> **Q** How does this problem differ from Problem 2? **[You need to substitute 100 for p.]**

Take Note   ERROR PREVENTION

Emphasize that the discriminant is the expression *under* the radical symbol. The symbol itself is not part of the discriminant.

> **Q** In terms of a, b, and c, when is the discriminant zero? **[The discriminant is zero when b^2 is equal to $4ac$.]**

Problem 2 Applying the Quadratic Formula   GRIDDED RESPONSE

Fundraising Your school's jazz band is selling CDs as a fundraiser. The total profit p depends on the amount x that your band charges for each CD. The equation $p = -x^2 + 48x - 300$ models the profit of the fundraiser. What is the least amount, in dollars, you can charge for a CD to make a profit of $200?

$$p = -x^2 + 48x - 300$$
$$200 = -x^2 + 48x - 300 \qquad \text{Substitute 200 for } p.$$
$$0 = -x^2 + 48x - 500 \qquad \text{Write the equation in standard form.}$$
$$a = -1, b = 48, c = -500 \qquad \text{Find the values of } a, b, \text{ and } c.$$
$$x = \frac{-48 \pm \sqrt{48^2 - 4(-1)(-500)}}{2(-1)} \qquad \text{Substitute into } \frac{-b \pm \sqrt{b^2 - 4ac}}{2a}.$$
$$x = \frac{-48 \pm \sqrt{304}}{-2} \qquad \text{Simplify.}$$
$$x \approx 15.282 \text{ or } x \approx 32.717 \qquad \text{Use a calculator.}$$

The least amount you can charge is $15.29 for each CD to make a profit of $200.

The answer is 15.29.

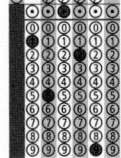

 Think

Does it make sense that two different prices can yield the same profit? Yes. You can generate a given profit either by selling many CDs at a low price, or fewer CDs at a high price.

Got It? **2. a.** In Problem 2, what is the least amount you can charge for each CD to make a $100 profit?
   b. Reasoning Would a negative profit make sense in this problem? Explain.

A quadratic equation can have two real solutions ($x^2 = 4$), one real solution ($x^2 = 0$), or no real solutions ($x^2 = -4$). In the Quadratic Formula, the value under the radical symbol, $b^2 - 4ac$, tells you how many real-number solutions exist.

In Problem 1(a), $b^2 - 4ac > 0$ and there are two real solutions. In Problem 1(b), $b^2 - 4ac = 0$ and there is only one real solution.

> **take note**   **Key Concept Discriminant**
>
> The **discriminant** of a quadratic equation in the form $ax^2 + bx + c = 0$ is the value of the expression $b^2 - 4ac$.
>
> $$x = \frac{-b \pm \sqrt{b^2 - 4ac}}{2a} \leftarrow \text{discriminant}$$

Additional Problems

1. What are the solutions? Use the Quadratic Formula.
$5x^2 - 2x = 2$
ANSWER $\frac{1}{5} \pm \frac{\sqrt{11}}{5}$

2. You sell wrapping paper as a charity fundraiser. The equation $p = -6x^2 + 280x - 1200$ models the total profit p as a function of the price x per roll of paper. What is the smallest amount in dollars you can charge per roll of wrapping paper to make a profit of $1500?
ANSWER $13.62

3. What is the number of real solutions of $-x^2 + 14x = 49$?
ANSWER one real solution

4. A rocket is launched from the ground with an initial vertical velocity of 150 ft/s. The function $h = -16t^2 + 150t$ models the height in feet of the rocket at time t in seconds. Will the rocket reach a height of 300 ft? Explain your answer.
ANSWER Yes; the discriminant is positive, so there are two real solutions for time t when the rocket's height is 300 ft.

Answers

Got It?

1. a. -2
   b. $-2 \pm \sqrt{7}$

2. a. $10.74
   b. Yes; a neg. profit means more money was spent than earned.

Discriminants and Solutions of Quadratic Equations		
Value of the Discriminant	**Number of Solutions for $ax^2 + bx + c = 0$**	**x-intercepts of Graph of Related Function $y = ax^2 + bx + c$**
$b^2 - 4ac > 0$	two real solutions	two x-intercepts
$b^2 - 4ac = 0$	one real solution	one x-intercept
$b^2 - 4ac < 0$	no real solutions	no x-intercepts

© **Problem 3** Using the Discriminant

What is the number of real solutions of $-2x^2 - 3x + 5 = 0$?

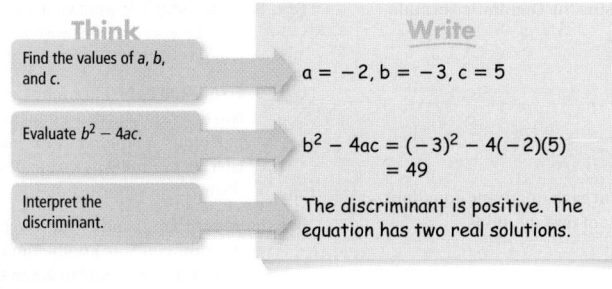

Think	Write
Find the values of a, b, and c.	$a = -2, b = -3, c = 5$
Evaluate $b^2 - 4ac$.	$b^2 - 4ac = (-3)^2 - 4(-2)(5)$ $= 49$
Interpret the discriminant.	The discriminant is positive. The equation has two real solutions.

✓ **Got It?** **3.** What is the number of real solutions of each equation?
   a. $2x^2 - 3x + 7 = 0$ **b.** $x^2 = 6x + 5$

ELL SUPPORT

This table connects the discriminant, solutions, and x-intercepts.

Q How could you paraphrase the entries in the first column? **[Answers may vary. Samples: discriminant is positive, discriminant is zero, and discriminant is negative]**

Q What is the root word for *discriminant*? **[*discriminate* (which means to distinguish)]**

VISUAL LEARNERS

Some students think that "no real solutions" means an equation is entirely nonsensical. Highlight the last row of this table and point out that the graph of the corresponding quadratic function *does* exist; it simply has no x-intercepts.

Problem 3

Q In terms of the Quadratic Formula, why are there two real solutions? **[Answers may vary. Sample: In the Quadratic Formula, the square root follows $\pm$; that means the Quadratic Formula will contain $\pm \sqrt{49}$ or ± 7, and two real values can be calculated.]**

Q What would the graph of $y = -2x^2 - 3x + 5$ look like? **[The parabola opens downward and intersects the x-axis twice.]**

Got It?   **ERROR PREVENTION**

Q How can you check your work? **[Answers may vary. Sample: Graph the related function using a calculator, and check the number of x-intercepts.]**

3. a. no real solutions
   b. two real solutions

Problem 4

Q Why use the discriminant here instead of the Quadratic Formula? **[Answers may vary. Sample: You only need to know whether a real solution exists, not its actual value.]**

Q What would a positive discriminant mean here? **[The ball reaches 115 ft twice on its path.]**

Q If the ball's maximum height were 115 ft, what would happen to the discriminant? **[It would be zero since the maximum occurs once.]**

Got It?

Q How does this height compare to 115 ft? **[higher]**

Q Why does it help to compare the heights? **[Answers may vary. Sample: The ball never reaches 115 ft, so it never reaches higher.]**

3 Lesson Check

Do you know HOW?   ERROR INTERVENTION

- For Exercises 1–4, to avoid sign errors, suggest students circle each coefficient, including the leading + or −.

Do you UNDERSTAND?

- For Exercises 8 and 10, if students unsuccessfully use trial-and-error, refer them to page 243 to help them find an equation.

Close

Q Is the Quadratic Formula the best way to solve a quadratic equation? **[Answers may vary. Sample: The Quadratic Formula solves any quadratic equation, but other methods might be easier for certain equations.]**

 Problem 4 Using the Discriminant to Solve a Problem STEM

Projectile Motion You hit a golf ball into the air from a height of 1 in. above the ground with an initial vertical velocity of 85 ft/s. The function $h = -16t^2 + 85t + \frac{1}{12}$ models the height, in feet, of the ball at time t, in seconds. Will the ball reach a height of 115 ft?

Plan

What value should you substitute for h?
You are trying to determine whether the ball will reach 115 ft. Replace h with 115.

$h = -16t^2 + 85t + \frac{1}{12}$

$115 = -16t^2 + 85t + \frac{1}{12}$ Substitute 115 for h.

$0 = -16t^2 + 85t - 114\frac{11}{12}$ Write the equation in standard form.

$a = -16, b = 85, c = -114\frac{11}{12}$ Find the values of a, b, and c.

$b^2 - 4ac = 85^2 - 4(-16)\left(-114\frac{11}{12}\right)$ Evaluate the discriminant.

$= 7225 - 7354\frac{2}{3}$ Simplify.

$= -129\frac{2}{3}$

The discriminant is negative. The equation $115 = -16t^2 + 85t + \frac{1}{12}$ has no real solutions. The golf ball will not reach a height of 115 feet.

Got It? **4. Reasoning** Without solving an equation, will the golf ball in Problem 4 reach a height of 110 ft? Explain.

Lesson Check

Do you know HOW?

Solve each equation using the Quadratic Formula.

1. $x^2 - 5x - 7 = 0$

2. $x^2 + 3x - 13 = 0$

3. $2x^2 - 5x - 3 = 0$

4. $3x^2 - 4x + 3 = 0$

Find the discriminant of each quadratic equation. Determine the number of real solutions.

5. $-x^2 + 2x - 9 = 0$

6. $x^2 + 17x + 4 = 0$

7. $x^2 - 6x + 9 = 0$

Do you UNDERSTAND? MATHEMATICAL PRACTICES

8. Reasoning For what values of k does the equation $x^2 + kx + 9 = 0$ have one real solution? two real solutions?

9. Error Analysis Your friend concluded that because two discriminants are equal, the solutions to the two equations are the same. Explain your friend's error. Give an example of two quadratic equations that disprove this conclusion.

10. Reasoning If one quadratic equation has a positive discriminant, and another quadratic equation has a discriminant equal to 0, can the two quadratic equations share a solution? Explain why or why not. If so, give two quadratic equations that meet this criterion.

3 Lesson Check

For a digital lesson check, use the Got It questions.
Support in Algebra 2 Companion
- Lesson Check

4 Practice

 Assign homework to individual students or to an entire class.

Answers

Got It? (continued)

4. Yes;

$b^2 - 4ac = (85)^2 - 4(-16)\left(-109\frac{11}{12}\right)$

$= 190\frac{1}{3}.$

The discriminant is positive. So the eq. has two real solutions.

Lesson Check

1. $\dfrac{5 \pm \sqrt{53}}{2}$

2. $\dfrac{-3 \pm \sqrt{61}}{2}$

3. $3, -\dfrac{1}{2}$

4. no real solutions

5. −32; no real solutions

6. 273; two real solutions

7. 0; one real solution

8. $k = \pm 6$ for one real solution; $k > 6$ or $k < -6$ for two real solutions

9. Answers may vary. Sample: The discriminants of eqs. with one real solution are all zero and thus equal, but the solutions may or may not be equal. An example is $x^2 - 8x + 16$ and $x^2 - 4x + 4$. Each has a discriminant of zero, but the solutions are 4 and 2.

10. Yes; the eqs. can share common factors such as for $x^2 + 2x - 8$ where the discriminant is 36 and the solutions are 2 and −4, and $x^2 - 4x + 4$ where the discriminant is zero and the solution is 2.

Practice and Problem-Solving Exercises  MATHEMATICAL PRACTICES

A Practice

Solve each equation using the Quadratic Formula. ◀ See Problem 1.

11. $x^2 - 4x + 3 = 0$ **12.** $x^2 + 8x + 12 = 0$ **13.** $2x^2 + 5x = 7$

14. $3x^2 + 2x - 1 = 0$ **15.** $x^2 + 10x = -25$ **16.** $2x^2 - 5 = -3x$

17. $x^2 = 3x - 1$ **18.** $6x - 5 = -x^2$ **19.** $3x^2 = 2(2x + 1)$

20. $2x(x - 1) = 3$ **21.** $x(x - 5) = -4$ **22.** $12x + 9x^2 = 5$

23. Fundraising Your class is selling boxes of flower seeds as a fundraiser. The total ◀ See Problem 2.
profit p depends on the amount x that your class charges for each box of seeds. The
equation $p = -0.5x^2 + 25x - 150$ models the profit of the fundraiser. What's the
smallest amount, in dollars, that you can charge and make a profit of at least $125?

24. Baking Your local bakery sells more bagels when it reduces prices, but then its
profit changes. The function $y = -1000x^2 + 1100x - 2.5$ models the bakery's
daily profit in dollars, from selling bagels, where x is the price of a bagel in dollars.
What's the highest price the bakery can charge, in dollars, and make a profit of at
least $200?

Evaluate the discriminant for each equation. Determine the number of real ◀ See Problem 3.
solutions.

25. $x^2 + 4x + 5 = 0$ **26.** $x^2 - 4x - 5 = 0$ **27.** $-4x^2 + 20x - 25 = 0$

28. $-2x^2 + x - 28 = 0$ **29.** $2x^2 + 7x - 15 = 0$ **30.** $6x^2 - 2x + 5 = 0$

31. $-2x^2 + 7x = 6$ **32.** $x^2 - 12x + 36 = 0$ **33.** $x^2 + 8x = -16$

34. $3x^2 + x = -3$ **35.** $x + 2 = -3x^2$ **36.** $12x(x + 1) = -3$

37. Business The weekly revenue for a company is $r = -3p^2 + 60p + 1060$, ◀ See Problem 4.
where p is the price of the company's product. Use the discriminant to find
whether there is a price for which the weekly revenue would be $1500.

STEM **38. Physics** The equation $h = 80t - 16t^2$ models the height h in feet reached in t
seconds by an object propelled straight up from the ground at a speed of 80 ft/s.
Use the discriminant to find whether the object will ever reach a height of 90 ft.

B Apply

39. Think About a Plan The area of a rectangle is 36 in.^{2}. The perimeter of the
rectangle is 36 in. What are the dimensions of the rectangle to the nearest
hundredth of an inch?
• How can you write an equation using one variable to find the dimensions of
the rectangle?
• How can the discriminant of the equation help you solve the problem?

40. Writing Summarize how to use the discriminant to analyze the types of solutions
of a quadratic equation.

Practice and Problem-Solving Exercises

11. 1, 3

12. −6, −2

13. $-\frac{7}{2}$, 1

14. $-1, \frac{1}{3}$

15. −5

16. $-\frac{5}{2}$, 1

17. $\frac{3 \pm \sqrt{5}}{2}$

18. $-3 \pm \sqrt{14}$

19. $\frac{2 \pm \sqrt{10}}{3}$

20. $\frac{1 \pm \sqrt{7}}{2}$

21. 1, 4

22. $-\frac{5}{3}, \frac{1}{3}$

23. $16.34

24. $.86

25. −4; no real solutions

26. 36; two

27. 0; one

28. −223; no real solutions

29. 169; two

30. −116; no real solutions

31. 1; two

32. 0; one

33. 0; one

34. −35; no real solutions

35. −23; no real solutions

36. 0; one

37. no

38. yes

39. 2.29 in. × 15.71 in.

40. Answers may vary. Sample: Assume
the coefficients are real numbers. If the
discriminant is negative, then there is no
real solution. If the discriminant is zero, then
there is one real solution. If the discriminant is
positive, then there are two real solutions.

---

4 Practice

ASSIGNMENT GUIDE
Basic: 11–38 all, 39–42, 57–59, 67
Average: 11–37 odd, 39–69
Advanced: 11–37 odd, 39–77
Standardized Test Prep: 78–81
Mixed Review: 82–90

Mathematical Practices are supported by
exercises with red headings. Here are the Practices
supported in this lesson:

MP 1: Make Sense of Problems Ex. 39
MP 2: Reason Abstractly Ex. 67
MP 3: Communicate Ex. 10, 40
MP 3: Construct Arguments Ex. 8, 10
MP 3: Critique the Reasoning of Others Ex. 9

Applications exercises have blue headings.
Exercises 56 and 57 support MP 4: Model.

STEM exercises focus on science or engineering
applications.

EXERCISE 57: Use the Think About a Plan
worksheet in the **Practice and Problem Solving
Workbook** (also available in the Teaching Resources
in print and online) to further support students'
development in becoming independent learners.

HOMEWORK QUICK CHECK
To check students' understanding of key skills and
concepts, go over Exercises 13, 23, 39, 57, and 67.

Answers

Practice and Problem-Solving Exercises (continued)

41. $-\frac{1}{6}$, 1

42. -1.24, 1.38

43. -2.49, 0.89

44. -2.90, 1.90

45. -0.19, 2.69

46. -0.81, 0.31

47. 1, 10

48. 0, 42

49. $-\frac{3}{2}$, $\frac{1}{2}$

50. -3.45, 1.45

51. -1.70, 4.70

52. -7, 7

53. -8.47, 0.47

54. $-\frac{1}{2}$, $\frac{3}{2}$

55. 1.47, -7.47

56. a. Answers may vary. Sample: Graph $y = 0.4409x^2 - 5.1724x + 99.0321$ and $y = 100$. The x-coordinate of the point where they intersect is the year when 100 million tons were released in the air. The graph of $y = 0.4409x^2 - 5.1724x + 99.0321$ is above the graph of $y = 100$ when more than 100 million tons were released.

b. Write $y = 0.4409x^2 - 5.1724x + 99.0321 > 100$. Subtract 100 from both sides to get $y = 0.4409x^2 - 5.1724x - 0.9679 < 0$. Use the Quadratic Formula to solve.

c. Check students' work.

57. about 1.89 s

58. two

59. one

60. none

61. two

62. two

63. two

64. two

65. two

66. none

67. a. k such that $|k| < 12$

b. 12 or -12

c. k such that $|k| > 12$

68. a. II

b. III

c. I

69. a. $x^2 = 100\pi$

b. 17.72 cm

Solve each equation using any method. When necessary, round real solutions to the nearest hundredth.

41. $6x^2 - 5x - 1 = 0$

42. $7x^2 - x - 12 = 0$

43. $5x^2 + 8x - 11 = 0$

44. $4x^2 + 4x = 22$

45. $2x^2 - 1 = 5x$

46. $2x^2 + x = \frac{1}{2}$

47. $x^2 = 11x - 10$

48. $5x^2 = 210x$

49. $4x^2 + 4x = 3$

50. $2x^2 + 4x = 10$

51. $x^2 - 3x - 8 = 0$

52. $-3x^2 + 147 = 0$

53. $x^2 + 8x = 4$

54. $4x^2 - 4x - 3 = 0$

55. $x^2 = 11 - 6x$

STEM 56. Air Pollution The function $y = 0.4409x^2 - 5.1724x + 99.0321$ models the emissions of carbon monoxide in the United States since 1987, where y represents the amount of carbon monoxide released in a year in millions of tons, and $x = 0$ represents the year 1987.

a. How can you use a graph to estimate the year in which more than 100 million tons of carbon monoxide were released into the air?

b. How can you use the Quadratic Formula to estimate the year in which more than 100 million tons of carbon monoxide were released into the air?

c. Which method do you prefer? Explain why.

57. Sports A diver dives from a 10 m springboard. The equation $f(t) = -4.9t^2 + 4t + 10$ models her height above the pool at time t in seconds. At what time does she enter the water?

Without graphing, determine how many x-intercepts each function has.

58. $y = -2x^2 + 3x - 1$

59. $y = 0.25x^2 + 2x + 4$

60. $y = x^2 + 3x + 5$

61. $y = -x^2 + 3x + 10$

62. $y = 3x^2 - 10x + 6$

63. $y = 10x^2 + 13x - 3$

64. $y = x^2 + 17x - 2$

65. $y = -5x^2 - 4x + 3$

66. $y = 7x^2 - 2x + 9$

© 67. Reasoning Determine the value(s) of k for which $3x^2 + kx + 12 = 0$ has each type of solution.

a. no real solutions

b. exactly one real solution

c. two real solutions

68. Use the discriminant to match each function with its graph.

a. $f(x) = x^2 - 4x + 2$

b. $f(x) = x^2 - 4x + 4$

c. $f(x) = x^2 - 4x + 6$

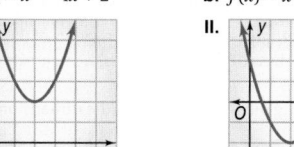

I.   **II.**   **III.**

69. a. Geometry Write an equation to find the dimensions of a square that has the same area as a circle with a radius of 10 cm.

b. Find the length of a side of the square, to the nearest hundredth centimeter.

Write a quadratic equation with the given solutions.

70. $\frac{3 + \sqrt{5}}{2}, \frac{3 - \sqrt{5}}{2}$

71. $\frac{-5 + \sqrt{13}}{2}, \frac{-5 - \sqrt{13}}{2}$

72. $\frac{-5 + \sqrt{17}}{4}, \frac{-5 - \sqrt{17}}{4}$

Solve each equation.

73. $|5 - 2x^2| = 5$

74. $|x^2 - 4x| = 3$

75. $|x^2 + 4x + 3| = 8$

76. Use the Quadratic Formula to prove each statement.
   a. The sum of the solutions of the quadratic equation $ax^2 + bx + c = 0$ is $-\frac{b}{a}$.
   b. The product of the solutions of the quadratic equation $ax^2 + bx + c = 0$ is $\frac{c}{a}$.

77. Explain the meaning of the value $\frac{\sqrt{b^2 - 4ac}}{2a}$ in terms of the graph of the standard quadratic function $y = ax^2 + bx + c$.

Standardized Test Prep

GRIDDED RESPONSE

78. How many different real solutions are there for $2x^2 - 3x + 5 = 0$?

79. What is the y-value of the y-intercept of the quadratic function $y = 2(x + 2)^2 - 5$?

80. What is the x-value in the solution to the system $\begin{cases} 3x + y = -7 \\ 2x - 2y = -10 \end{cases}$?

81. The graph of the system of inequalities $\begin{cases} y \le \frac{1}{2}x + 3 \\ y \ge 6x - 30 \\ x \ge 0 \\ y \ge 0 \end{cases}$ is shown at the right.

What is the maximum value of the function $P = 3x - 4y$ for the (x, y) pairs in the bounded region shown?

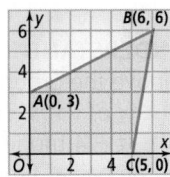

Mixed Review

Solve each equation by completing the square.

See Lesson 4-6.

82. $x^2 - 8x - 20 = 0$

83. $2y^2 = 4y - 1$

84. $x^2 - 3x - 8 = 0$

Simplify by combining like terms.

See Lesson 1-3.

85. $z^2 + 8z^2 - 2z + 5z$

86. $4k - x - 3k + 5x$

87. $4y - (2y + 3x) - 5x$

Get Ready! To prepare for Lesson 4-8, do Exercises 88–90.

See p. 981.

Simplify each expression.

88. $\sqrt{(-2)^2 + 8^2}$

89. $\sqrt{3^2 + 4^2}$

90. $\sqrt{5^2 + (-12)^2}$

Standardized Test Prep

78. 0

79. 3

80. −3

81. 15

Mixed Review

82. −2, 10

83. $\frac{2 \pm \sqrt{2}}{2}$

84. $\frac{3 \pm \sqrt{41}}{2}$

85. $9z^2 + 3z$

86. $4x + k$

87. $2y - 8x$

88. $2\sqrt{17}$

89. 5

90. 13

---

70. Answers may vary. Sample:
$x^2 - 3x + 1 = 0$

71. Answers may vary. Sample:
$x^2 + 5x + 3 = 0$

72. Answers may vary. Sample:
$2x^2 + 5x + 1 = 0$

73. $0, \pm\sqrt{5}$

74. $1, 3, 2 \pm 7$

75. $-5, 1$

76. a. $-\frac{b}{2a} + \frac{\sqrt{b^2 - 4ac}}{2a} + \left(-\frac{b}{2a}\right) - \frac{\sqrt{b^2 - 4ac}}{2a}$

$= \frac{(-2b)}{2a} = -\frac{b}{a}$

b. $\left(-\frac{b}{2a} + \frac{\sqrt{b^2 - 4ac}}{2a}\right) \times \left(-\frac{b}{2a} - \frac{\sqrt{b^2 - 4ac}}{2a}\right)$

$= \left(-\frac{b}{2a}\right)^2 - \left(\frac{\sqrt{b^2 - 4ac}}{2a}\right)^2$

$= \frac{(4ac)}{4a^2} = \frac{c}{a}$

77. The absolute value of $\frac{\sqrt{b^2 - 4ac}}{2a}$ is the distance from the axis of symmetry to the x-intercepts, if the discriminant is nonnegative.

Additional Instructional Support

Algebra 2 Companion

Students can use the **Algebra 2 Companion** worktext (4 pages) as you teach the lesson. Use the Companion to support

- New Vocabulary
- Key Concepts
- Got It for each Problem
- Lesson Check

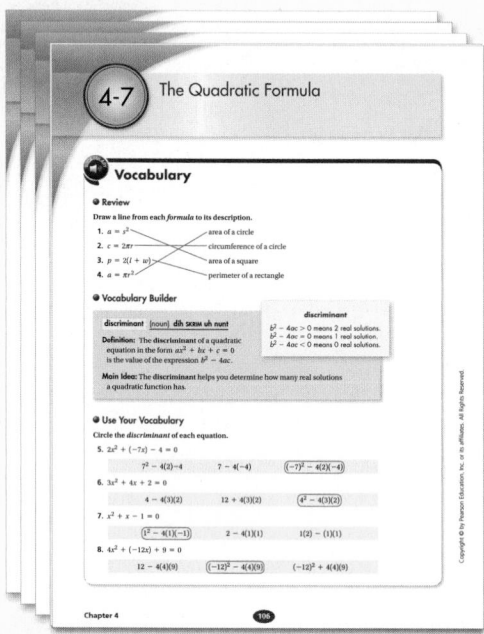

ELL Support

Use Manipulatives Colored pencils and corresponding colored sticky notes are useful when students first practice the Quadratic Formula in Problem 1. Let students use colored pencils to write a "shell" of the formula with colored blanks.

$$x = \frac{-\boxed{b} \pm \sqrt{\boxed{b}^2 - 4 \cdot \boxed{a} \cdot \boxed{c}}}{2 \cdot \boxed{a}}.$$

After writing each equation in standard form and identifying the values of a, b, and c, have students copy the values onto color-coded sticky notes (e.g., blue for a, red for b, and green for c). Students fill each blank in the formula with an appropriate note. Then, as the expression is simplified, students can use larger yellow sticky notes to cover and replace parts of the formula.

5 Assess & Remediate

Lesson Quiz

1. Solve $2x^2 + 3x = 6$ using the Quadratic Formula.

2. The equation $p = -5x^2 + 100x - 250$ models the profit p in dollars from selling pizzas, where x is the price per pizza in dollars. What is the highest price you can charge per pizza to profit $100?

3. Use the discriminant to determine the number of real solutions of $3x^2 - x = -1$.

4. **Do you UNDERSTAND?** You hit a ball from 4 ft above the ground with an initial vertical velocity of v ft/s. The function $h = -16t^2 + vt + 4$ models the height h in feet of the ball at time t in seconds. Explain how to find the initial velocity for which the ball reaches a maximum height of 40 ft.

ANSWERS TO LESSON QUIZ

1. $\dfrac{-3}{4} \pm \dfrac{\sqrt{57}}{4}$

2. $15.48

3. discriminant $= -11$; no real solutions

4. Answers may vary. Sample: The maximum or minimum of a quadratic function occurs only once; if the ball reaches a maximum height of 40 ft, then $40 = -16t^2 + vt + 4$, or $0 = -16t^2 + vt - 36$, has one real solution and the discriminant is zero; solve $v^2 - 4(-16)(-36) = 0$ or $v = \pm 48$. The positive initial velocity is 48 ft/s.

PRESCRIPTION FOR REMEDIATION

Use the student work on the Lesson Quiz to prescribe a differentiated review assignment:

Points	Differentiated Remediation
0–2	Intervention
3	On-level
4	Extension

PowerAlgebra.com

5 Assess & Remediate

Assign the Lesson Quiz. Appropriate intervention, practice, or enrichment is automatically generated based on student performance.

Intervention

- **Reteaching** (2 pages) Provides reteaching and practice exercises for the key lesson concepts. Use with struggling students or absent students.

- **English Language Learner Support** Helps students develop and reinforce mathematical vocabulary and key concepts.

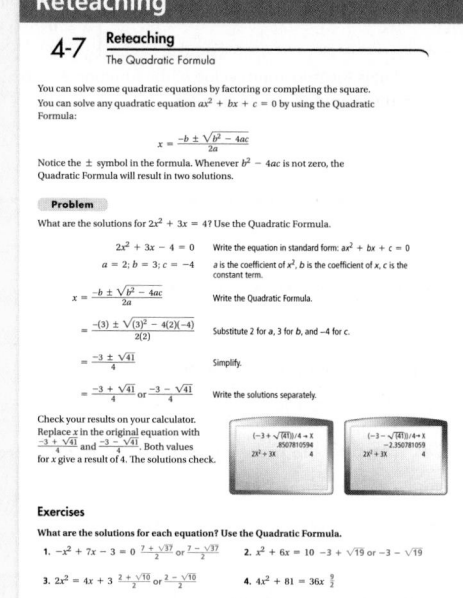

Differentiated Remediation *continued*

On-Level

- **Practice** (2 pages) Provides extra practice for each lesson. For simpler practice exercises, use the Form K Practice pages found in the All-in-One Teaching Resources and online.

- **Think About a Plan** Helps students develop specific problem-solving skills and strategies by providing scaffolded guiding questions.

- **Standardized Test Prep** Focuses on all major exercises, all major question types, and helps students prepare for the high-stakes assessments.

Extension

- **Enrichment** Provides students with interesting problems and activities that extend the concepts of the lesson.

- **Activities, Games, and Puzzles** Worksheets that can be used for concepts development, enrichment, and for fun!

Practice and Problem Solving Wkbk/ All-in-One Resources/Online
Practice page 1

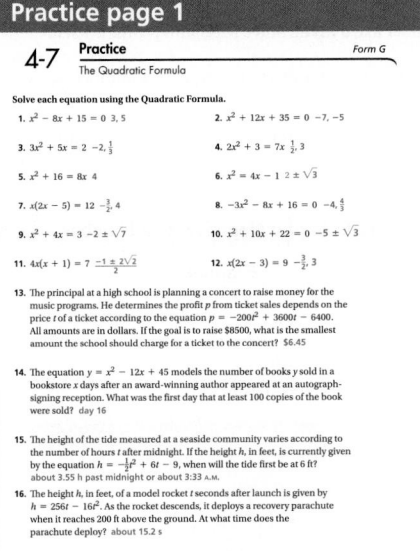

Practice and Problem Solving Wkbk/ All-in-One Resources/Online
Practice page 2

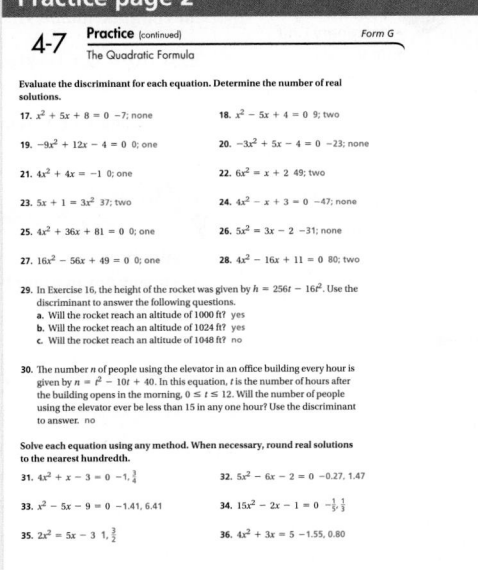

All-in-One Resources/Online
Enrichment

Practice and Problem Solving Wkbk/ All-in-One Resources/Online
Think About a Plan

Practice and Problem Solving Wkbk/ All-in-One Resources/Online
Standardized Test Prep

Online Teacher Resource Center
Activities, Games, and Puzzles

1 Interactive Learning

Solve It!

PURPOSE To explore a function that simulates a cycle of powers for -1 or $i = \sqrt{-1}$

PROCESS Students may make and complete a table that only uses powers of a, replace the powers of a with appropriate powers of b, c, and d, and identify the pattern of reducing the powers.

ANSWER See Solve It in Answers on next page.
CONNECT THE MATH In the Solve It, students identify a pattern of powers using the base a. In this lesson, students will apply the properties of powers of i.

2 Guided Instruction

Take Note   SYNTHEZISING

Q Why must a be a positive number? **[Sample: show by counterexample. Let $a = -1$. Then, $\sqrt{-(-1)} = \sqrt{-1 \cdot -1} = \sqrt{-1} \cdot \sqrt{-1} = i \cdot i = -1$. However, $\sqrt{-(-1)} = \sqrt{1} = 1$, which is a contradiction.]**

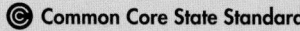

4-8 Complex Numbers

Common Core State Standards
N-CN.A.1 Know there is a complex number i such that $i^2 = -1$, and every complex number has the form $a = bi$ with a and b real. **Also N-CN.A.2, N-CN.C.7, N-CN.C.8**
MP 1, MP 2, MP 3, MP 6

Objectives To identify, graph, and perform operations with complex numbers
To find complex number solutions of quadratic equations

SOLVE IT

Getting Ready!

Here is a partially-completed multiplication table.
If you know that

$a \cdot a = a^2 = b$, $a \cdot b = a \cdot a^2 = a^3 = c$,
$a^4 = d$, and $a^5 = a$,

how would you complete the table? What is a^{99}? Explain your reasoning.

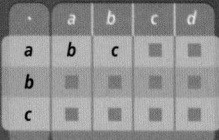

Once you find the pattern in the boxes, finding a^{99} becomes simple.

MATHEMATICAL PRACTICES

Lesson Vocabulary
- imaginary unit
- imaginary number
- complex number
- pure imaginary number
- complex number plane
- absolute value of a complex number
- complex conjugates

In Chapter 1, you learned about different subsets of real numbers. The set of real numbers is itself a subset of a larger set of numbers, the *complex numbers*. Curiously, the complex numbers include a number like a in the Solve It. Its fifth power is itself.

Essential Understanding The complex numbers are based on a number whose square is -1.

The **imaginary unit** i is the complex number whose square is -1. So, $i^2 = -1$, and $i = \sqrt{-1}$.

| Key Concept | Square Root of a Negative Real Number |

Algebra
For any positive number a,
$\sqrt{-a} = \sqrt{-1 \cdot a} = \sqrt{-1} \cdot \sqrt{a} = i\sqrt{a}$.

Example
$\sqrt{-5} = i\sqrt{5}$

Note that $(\sqrt{-5})^2 = (i\sqrt{5})^2 = i^2(\sqrt{5})^2 = -1 \cdot 5 = -5$ (not 5).

4-8 Preparing to Teach

BIG idea Solving Equations and Inequalities

ESSENTIAL UNDERSTANDINGS
- Every quadratic equation has complex number solutions (that sometimes are real numbers).
- The imaginary unit is the complex number whose square is -1. So $i^2 = -1$ and $i = \sqrt{-1}$.
- The real solutions of a quadratic equation show the zeros of the related quadratic function and the x-intercepts of its graph.

Math Background

The set of complex numbers includes imaginary and real numbers, as shown in Lesson 1-2. Thus, every quadratic equation has solutions, and some may be imaginary.

Be aware of the common misconception that imaginary numbers do not really exist. Imaginary numbers were introduced to solve quadratic equations of the form $x^2 + k = 0$, where $k > 0$. The imaginary unit i is a number, not a variable, and is defined as $\sqrt{-1}$. In general, you cannot order complex numbers, since they cannot be graphed on the real number line.

Complex numbers have numerous applications in many fields including engineering, science, physics, and computer graphics.

Mathematical Practices

Attend to precision. Students will use a clear definition of the imaginary unit and explicitly utilize it in their answers.

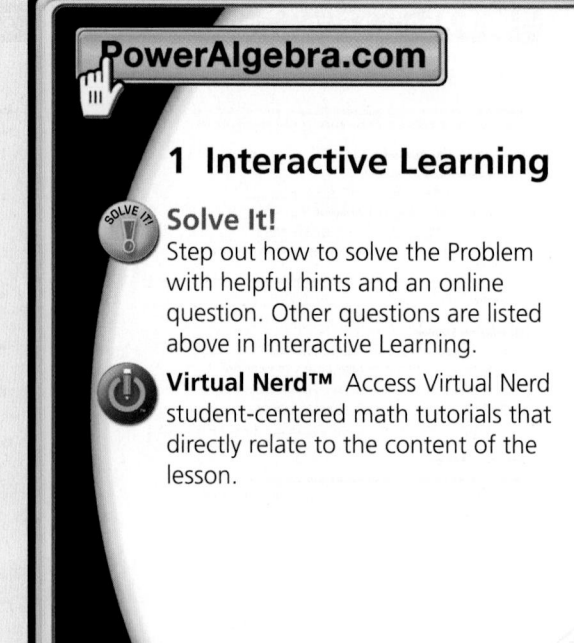

PowerAlgebra.com

1 Interactive Learning

Solve It!
Step out how to solve the Problem with helpful hints and an online question. Other questions are listed above in Interactive Learning.

Virtual Nerd™ Access Virtual Nerd student-centered math tutorials that directly relate to the content of the lesson.

Think

Is $\sqrt{-18}$ a real number?
No. There is no real number that when multiplied by itself gives -18. You must use the imaginary unit i to write $\sqrt{-18}$.

Problem 1 Simplifying a Number Using i

How do you write $\sqrt{-18}$ by using the imaginary unit i?

$\sqrt{-18} = \sqrt{-1 \cdot 18}$

$\quad = \sqrt{-1} \cdot \sqrt{18}$ Multiplication Property of Square Roots

$\quad = i \cdot \sqrt{18}$ Definition of i

$\quad = i \cdot 3\sqrt{2}$ Simplify.

$\quad = 3i\sqrt{2}$

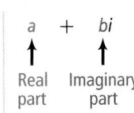 **Got It?** 1. How do you write each number in parts (a)–(c) by using the imaginary unit i?

a. $\sqrt{-12}$ **b.** $\sqrt{-25}$ **c.** $\sqrt{-7}$

d. Reasoning Explain why $\sqrt{-64} \neq -\sqrt{64}$.

An **imaginary number** is any number of the form $a + bi$, where a and b are real numbers and $b \neq 0$. Imaginary numbers and real numbers together make up the set of *complex numbers*.

take note

Key Concept Complex Numbers

You can write a **complex number** in the form $a + bi$, where a and b are real numbers.

If $b = 0$, the number $a + bi$ is a real number.

If $a = 0$ and $b \neq 0$, the number $a + bi$ is a **pure imaginary number**.

$$\underset{\uparrow}{a} \; + \; \underset{\uparrow}{bi}$$
Real part   Imaginary part

Complex Numbers ($a + bi$)

Real Numbers ($a + 0i$)	Imaginary Numbers ($a + bi$, $b \neq 0$)
	Pure Imaginary Numbers ($0 + bi$, $b \neq 0$)

In the **complex number plane**, the point (a, b) represents the complex number $a + bi$. To graph a complex number, locate the real part on the horizontal axis and the imaginary part on the vertical axis.

The **absolute value of a complex number** is its distance from the origin in the complex plane.

$$|a + bi| = \sqrt{a^2 + b^2}$$

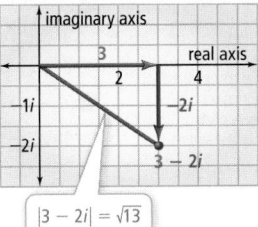

$|3 - 2i| = \sqrt{13}$

Problem 1

By convention, i is written before the radical.

Q Why is it better to write $i\sqrt{18}$ rather than $\sqrt{18}i$? **[so that you do not mistakenly think that the i is under the radical]**

Q How do you know that both ways are equivalent? **[because of the Commutative Property of Multiplication]**

Got It?

Q For 1d, consider $\sqrt{-64} = \sqrt{-1 \cdot 64}$. Can you move -1 outside of the radical? Explain. **[No; since $\sqrt{-1}$ does not equal -1, you cannot move it outside of the radical.]**

Take Note

Complex numbers and imaginary numbers are not synonymous; the set of complex numbers consists of both real and imaginary numbers.

Q How is the absolute value of a complex number like the absolute value of a real number? **[Answers may vary. Sample: They both represent the distance from the point to the origin.]**

Q Where does the formula $\sqrt{a^2 + b^2}$ come from? **[The distance formula is the distance from the origin to (a, b) derived using the Pythagorean Theorem.]**

2 Guided Instruction

 Each Problem is worked out and supported online.

Problem 1
Simplifying a Number Using i

Problem 2
Graphing in the Complex Number Plane

Problem 3
Adding and Subtracting Complex Numbers

Alternative Problem 3
Adding and Subtracting Complex Numbers
Animated

Problem 4
Multiplying Complex Numbers

Problem 5
Dividing Complex Numbers
Animated

Problem 6
Factoring Using Complex Conjugates

Problem 7
Finding Imaginary Solutions
Animated

Answers

Solve It!

·	a	b	c	d
a	b	c	d	a
b	c	d	a	b
c	d	a	b	c

$a^{99} = c$; $99 \div 4 = 24$ with a remainder of 3, and $a^3 = c$.

Got It?

1. **a.** $2i\sqrt{3}$

   b. $5i$

   c. $i\sqrt{7}$

   d. $8i \neq -8$

Problem 2
VISUAL LEARNERS

Q What determines the horizontal position of a complex number? **[the real part]**

Q What determines the vertical position of a complex number? **[the imaginary part]**

Got It?

Q What type of numbers lie on the imaginary axis? **[pure imaginary numbers]**

Q What type of numbers lie on the real axis? **[real numbers]**

Q If $a + bi$ lies in Quadrant II, then is a positive or negative? b? **[negative; positive]**

Problem 3

Q Is it possible to add two complex numbers and get a real number? Explain. **[Yes; real numbers are a subset of complex numbers. If the imaginary parts of the complex numbers are additive inverses, the sum is real. For example, $4 - 2i + 3 + 2i = 7$.]**

Q Is it possible to add two real numbers and get an imaginary number? Explain. **[No; the set of real numbers is closed under addition.]**

Got It?
ERROR PREVENTION

When subtracting imaginary numbers, the subtraction sign must be distributed over both the real and imaginary parts.

Q Are the numbers in 3d additive inverses? Explain. **[No; the sum is $18i$, not 0.]**

 Problem 2 Graphing in the Complex Number Plane

What are the graph and absolute value of each number?

Ⓐ $-5 + 3i$

$$|-5 + 3i| = \sqrt{(-5)^2 + 3^2}$$
$$= \sqrt{34}$$

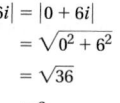 **Think**

Where is a pure imaginary number in the complex plane?
The real part of a pure imaginary number is 0. The number must be on the imaginary axis.

Ⓑ $6i$

$$|6i| = |0 + 6i|$$
$$= \sqrt{0^2 + 6^2}$$
$$= \sqrt{36}$$
$$= 6$$

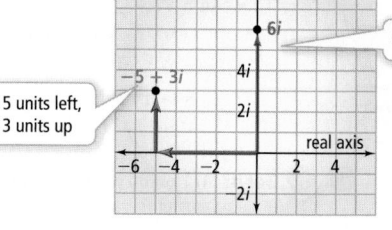

5 units left, 3 units up

6 units up

Got It? **2.** What are the graph and absolute value of each number?
a. $5 - i$ **b.** $-3 - 2i$ **c.** $1 + 4i$

Essential Understanding You can define operations on the set of complex numbers so that when you restrict the operations to the subset of real numbers, you get the familiar operations on the real numbers.

To add or subtract complex numbers, combine the real parts and the imaginary parts separately. If the sum of two complex numbers is 0, or $0 + 0i$, then each number is the opposite, or additive inverse, of the other. The associative and commutative properties apply to complex numbers as well.

© **Problem 3** Adding and Subtracting Complex Numbers

What is each sum or difference?

Plan

How is adding complex numbers similar to adding algebraic expressions?
Adding the real parts and imaginary parts separately is like adding like terms.

Ⓐ $(4 - 3i) + (-4 + 3i)$

$4 + (-4) + (-3i) + 3i$ Use the commutative and associative properties.

$0 + 0 = 0$ $4 - 3i$ and $-4 + 3i$ are additive inverses.

Ⓑ $(5 - 3i) - (-2 + 4i)$

$5 - 3i + 2 - 4i$ To subtract, add the opposite.

$5 + 2 - 3i - 4i$ Use the commutative and associative properties.

$7 - 7i$ Simplify.

Got It? **3.** What is each sum or difference?
a. $(7 - 2i) + (-3 + i)$ **b.** $(1 + 5i) - (3 - 2i)$
c. $(8 + 6i) - (8 - 6i)$ **d.** $(-3 + 9i) + (3 + 9i)$

Additional Problems

1. How do you write $\sqrt{-24}$ using the imaginary unit i?

ANSWER $2i\sqrt{6}$

2. What are the graph and absolute value of each complex number?

a. $1 - 3i$

b. $-4 + i$

ANSWERS

a. $\sqrt{10}$

b. $\sqrt{17}$

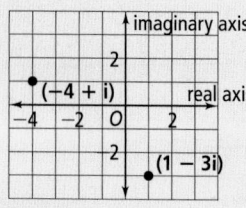

3. What is each sum or difference?

a. $(2 + i) + (-3 + 3i)$

b. $(5 + i) + (5 - i)$

c. $(-6 - 2i) - (4 + 2i)$

ANSWERS

a. $-1 + 4i$

b. 10

c. $-10 - 4i$

4. What is each product?

a. $-i(4 - 8i)$

b. $(5 - 7i)(-4 - 3i)$

ANSWERS

a. $-8 - 4i$

b. $-41 + 13i$

5. What is each quotient?

a. $\dfrac{7i}{8 + i}$

b. $\dfrac{5 + 2i}{3 - 2i}$

ANSWERS

a. $\dfrac{7}{65} + \dfrac{56}{65}i$

b. $\dfrac{11}{13} + \dfrac{16}{13}i$

6. What is the factored form of $3x^2 + 12$?

ANSWER $3(x + 2i)(x - 2i)$

7. What are the solutions of $-x^2 + 4x - 5 = 0$?

ANSWER $2 + i, 2 - i$

You multiply complex numbers $a + bi$ and $c + di$ as you would multiply binomials. For imaginary parts bi and di, $(bi)(di) = bd(i)^2 = bd(-1) = -bd$.

© Problem 4 Multiplying Complex Numbers

What is each product?

A $(3i)(-5 + 2i)$

$-15i + 6i^2$ Distributive Property

$-15i + 6(-1)$ Substitute -1 for i^2.

$-6 - 15i$ Simplify.

Think

How do you multiply two binomials?
Multiply each term of one binomial by each term of the other binomial.

B $(4 + 3i)(-1 - 2i)$

$-4 - 8i - 3i - 6i^2$

$-4 - 8i - 3i - 6(-1)$ [Substitute -1 for i^2.]

$2 - 11i$

C $(-6 + i)(-6 - i)$

$36 + 6i - 6i - i^2$

$36 + 6i - 6i - (-1)$

37

✔ **Got It? 4.** What is each product?

    a. $(7i)(3i)$ **b.** $(2 - 3i)(4 + 5i)$ **c.** $(-4 + 5i)(-4 - 5i)$

In Problem 4(c), the product is a real number. Number pairs of the form $a + bi$ and $a - bi$ are **complex conjugates**. The product of complex conjugates is a real number.

$$(a + bi)(a - bi) = a^2 - (bi)^2 = a^2 - b^2i^2 = a^2 - b^2(-1) = a^2 + b^2$$

You can use complex conjugates to simplify quotients of complex numbers.

© Problem 5 Dividing Complex Numbers

What is each quotient?

Plan

What is the goal?
Write the quotient in the form $a + bi$.

A $\dfrac{9 + 12i}{3i}$

$\dfrac{9 + 12i}{3i} \cdot \dfrac{-3i}{-3i}$ [Multiply numerator and denominator by the complex conjugate of the denominator.]

$\dfrac{-27i - 36i^2}{-9i^2}$

$\dfrac{-27i - 36(-1)}{-9(-1)}$ [Substitute -1 for i^2.]

$\dfrac{36 - 27i}{9}$

$4 - 3i$

B $\dfrac{2 + 3i}{1 - 4i}$

$\dfrac{2 + 3i}{1 - 4i} \cdot \dfrac{1 + 4i}{1 + 4i}$

$\dfrac{2 + 8i + 3i + 12i^2}{1 + 4i - 4i - 16i^2}$

$\dfrac{2 + 8i + 3i + 12(-1)}{1 + 4i - 4i - 16(-1)}$

$\dfrac{-10 + 11i}{17}$

$-\dfrac{10}{17} + \dfrac{11}{17}i$

✔ **Got It? 5.** What is each quotient?

    a. $\dfrac{5 - 2i}{3 + 4i}$ **b.** $\dfrac{4 - i}{6i}$ **c.** $\dfrac{8 - 7i}{8 + 7i}$

Problem 4

Q Is it possible to multiply two imaginary numbers and get a real number? Explain. **[Yes; the set of imaginary numbers is not closed under multiplication. For example, $i \cdot i = -1$, a real number.]**

Q What is the absolute value of each complex number in 4C? How does it compare to the product? [Each absolute value is $\sqrt{37}$, and the product is 37, which is the absolute value squared.]**

Q How are the numbers in 4C related? **[Answers may vary. Sample: They are factors of a difference of two squares.]**

Got It?

Q What method of multiplying binomials can you use to multiply complex numbers? **[Answers may vary. Sample: FOIL]**

Problem 5

Q Why is $\dfrac{-10 + 11i}{17}$ rewritten as $-\dfrac{10}{17} + \dfrac{11i}{17}$? **[because $-\dfrac{10}{17} + \dfrac{11i}{17}$ is in $a + bi$ form]**

Q Could you solve 5A by multiplying the fraction by $\dfrac{i}{i}$? Explain. **[Yes; i would be eliminated from the denominator.]**

Q Could you do the same for 5B? Explain. **[No; the denominator would still be a complex number.]**

Got It?

Q What is the complex conjugate of $6i$? Explain. **[$-6i$; $6i = 0 + 6i$, so the conjugate is $0 - 6i = -6i$.]**

Answers

Got It? (continued)

2. a. 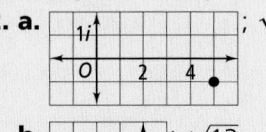 $; \sqrt{26}$

    b. 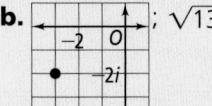 $; \sqrt{13}$

    c.  $; \sqrt{17}$

3. a. $4 - i$

    b. $-2 + 7i$

    c. $12i$

    d. $18i$

4. a. -21

    b. $23 - 2i$

    c. 41

5. a. $\dfrac{7}{25} - \dfrac{26}{25}i$

    b. $-\dfrac{1}{6} - \dfrac{2}{3}i$

    c. $\dfrac{15}{113} - \dfrac{112}{113}i$

Problem 6

> **Q** Why should you first factor out the greatest common factor? **[It can be easier to identify the form of the polynomial after factoring out the greatest common factor.]**
> **Q** What are the factors of $x^2 - 16$? **[$(x + 4)(x - 4)$]**
> **Q** Can $x^2 + 16$ be factored using real numbers? **[no]**
> **Q** What type of numbers do you need to use to factor $x^2 + 16$? **[imaginary numbers]**

Got It?

> **Q** How can you check your answer? **[Multiply the factors and compare the product to the original expression.]**

Problem 7

> **Q** What is a quick way to identify whether a quadratic equation has complex solutions? **[Determine whether the discriminant of the quadratic formula is positive or negative.]**
> **Q** Why does the number of real solutions not affect the y-intercept? **[The y-intercept of a quadratic function is always the function's value at $x = 0$.]**
> **Q** What would be a good way to check whether the answer is reasonable? **[Answers may vary. Sample: Graph the associated function and see whether it has any real solutions.]**

Got It?

> **Q** If you know the solutions are imaginary, why does it make sense that the graph does not cross the x-axis? **[because x-intercepts occur at real number solutions]**

 Problem 6 Factoring Using Complex Conjugates

What is the factored form of $2x^2 + 32$?

$2x^2 + 32$	
$2(x^2 + 16)$	Factor out the GCF.
$2(x + 4i)(x - 4i)$	Use $a^2 + b^2 = (a + bi)(a - bi)$ to factor $(x^2 + 16)$.

Think
Is the expression factorable using real numbers?
No. Look for factors using complex numbers.

Check

$2(x^2 + 4xi - 4xi - 16i^2)$	Multiply the binomials.
$2(x^2 - 16(-1))$	$i^2 = -1$
$2(x^2 + 16)$	Simplify within the binomial.
$2x^2 + 32$	Multiply.

✔ **Got It?** **6.** What are the factored forms of each expression?
a. $5x^2 + 20$ **b.** $x^2 + 81$

Essential Understanding Every quadratic equation has complex number solutions (that sometimes are real numbers).

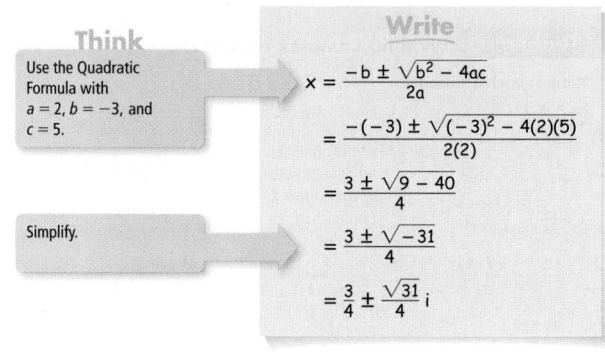

 Problem 7 Finding Imaginary Solutions

What are the solutions of $2x^2 - 3x + 5 = 0$?

Think
Use the Quadratic Formula with $a = 2$, $b = -3$, and $c = 5$.

Write

$$x = \frac{-b \pm \sqrt{b^2 - 4ac}}{2a}$$

$$= \frac{-(-3) \pm \sqrt{(-3)^2 - 4(2)(5)}}{2(2)}$$

$$= \frac{3 \pm \sqrt{9 - 40}}{4}$$

Simplify.

$$= \frac{3 \pm \sqrt{-31}}{4}$$

$$= \frac{3}{4} \pm \frac{\sqrt{31}}{4} i$$

✔ **Got It?** **7.** What are the solutions of each equation?
a. $3x^2 - x + 2 = 0$ **b.** $x^2 - 4x + 5 = 0$

Answers

Got It? (continued)

6. a. $5(x + 2i)(x - 2i)$
  b. $(x + 9i)(x - 9i)$

7. a. $\frac{1}{6} \pm \frac{i\sqrt{23}}{6}$
  b. $2 \pm i$

Lesson Check

1. $5i\sqrt{3}$ **2.** 5
3. $(x + 4i)(x - 4i)$ **4.** $7 - 3i$
5. $13 - 6i$
6. The add. inv. of a complex number, $a + bi$, is the opposite of the complex number, or $-a - bi$. The complex conjugate of a complex number, $a + bi$, is the real part plus the opposite of the imaginary part of the complex number, or $a - bi$.

7. error in the sign of the last term of the first line, which carries through to the end of the calculation; the line should be: " . . . $= 16 + 28i - 28i - 49i^2$
  $= 16 + 49$
  $= 65$."

Lesson Check

Do you know HOW?

1. Simplify $\sqrt{-75}$ by using the imaginary number i.

2. Find the absolute value of $4 - 3i$.

3. Find the complex factors of $x^2 + 16$. Check your answers.

Simplify each expression.

4. $(4 - 2i) - (-3 + i)$

5. $(2 + i)(4 - 5i)$

Do you UNDERSTAND?

6. Vocabulary Explain the difference between the additive inverse of a complex number and a complex conjugate.

7. Error Analysis Describe and correct the error made in simplifying the expression $(4 - 7i)(4 + 7i)$.

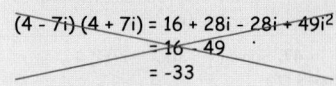
$$(4 - 7i)(4 + 7i) = 16 + 28i - 28i + 49i^2$$
$$= 16 - 49$$
$$= -33$$

Practice and Problem-Solving Exercises

 Practice

Simplify each number by using the imaginary number i. **◄ See Problem 1.**

8. $\sqrt{-4}$ **9.** $\sqrt{-7}$ **10.** $\sqrt{-15}$ **11.** $\sqrt{-81}$ **12.** $\sqrt{-50}$

Plot each complex number and find its absolute value. **◄ See Problem 2.**

13. $2i$ **14.** $5 + 12i$ **15.** $2 - 2i$ **16.** $1 - 4i$ **17.** $3 - 6i$

Simplify each expression. **◄ See Problems 3 and 4.**

18. $(2 + 4i) + (4 - i)$ **19.** $(-3 - 5i) + (4 - 2i)$ **20.** $(7 + 9i) + (-5i)$

21. $(12 + 5i) - (2 - i)$ **22.** $(-6 - 7i) - (1 + 3i)$ **23.** $(8 + i)(2 + 7i)$

24. $(-6 - 5i)(1 + 3i)$ **25.** $(-6i)^2$ **26.** $(9 + 4i)^2$

Write each quotient as a complex number. **◄ See Problem 5.**

27. $\frac{3 - 2i}{5i}$ **28.** $\frac{-2i}{1 + i}$ **29.** $\frac{4 - 3i}{-1 - 4i}$

30. $\frac{i + 2}{i - 2}$ **31.** $\frac{4}{2 - 3i}$ **32.** $\frac{3 + 2i}{(1 + i)^2}$

Find the factored forms of each expression. Check your answer. **◄ See Problem 6.**

33. $x^2 + 25$ **34.** $x^2 + 1$ **35.** $3s^2 + 75$

36. $x^2 + \frac{1}{4}$ **37.** $4b^2 + 1$ **38.** $-9x^2 - 100$

Find all solutions to each quadratic equation. **◄ See Problem 7.**

39. $x^2 + 2x + 3 = 0$ **40.** $-3x^2 + x - 3 = 0$ **41.** $2x^2 - 4x + 7 = 0$

42. $x^2 - 2x + 2 = 0$ **43.** $x^2 + 5 = 4x$ **44.** $2x(x - 3) = -5$

---

3 Lesson Check

Do you know HOW?   ERROR INTERVENTION

- For Exercise 2, if students have difficulty with the definition of absolute value of complex numbers, compare it to the absolute value of a real number by drawing a graph and showing that absolute value is the distance from the origin. If needed, revisit Problem 2, or use Additional Problem 2.

Do you UNDERSTAND?

- In Exercise 7, students should see that the negative sign is not correctly distributed. If they have trouble understanding multiplication of complex numbers, compare it to multiplying binomials, and show more examples. If needed, revisit Problem 4, or use Additional Problem 4.

Close

Q Is the square of a complex number always a real number? Explain. **[No; only the square of a pure imaginary number is always a real number.]**

Q How could you simplify i^5? **[Use the rules of exponents; $i^5 = (i^4)i = (1)i = i$.]**

Practice and Problem-Solving Exercises

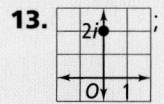

8. $2i$ **9.** $i\sqrt{7}$

10. $i\sqrt{15}$ **11.** $9i$ **12.** $5i\sqrt{2}$

13. 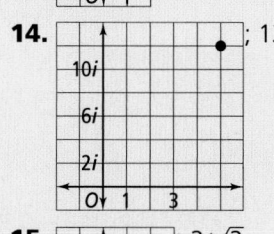 ; 2

14. 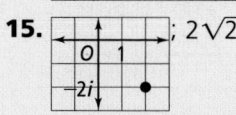 ; 13

15. 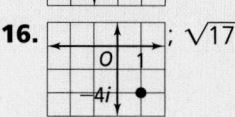 ; $2\sqrt{2}$

16. ; $\sqrt{17}$

17. 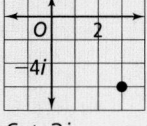 ; $3\sqrt{5}$

18. $6 + 3i$ **19.** $1 - 7i$
20. $7 + 4i$ **21.** $10 + 6i$
22. $-7 - 10i$ **23.** $9 + 58i$
24. $9 - 23i$ **25.** -36
26. $65 + 72i$ **27.** $-\frac{2}{5} - \frac{3}{5}i$
28. $-1 - i$ **29.** $\frac{8}{17} + \frac{19}{17}i$
30. $-\frac{3}{5} - \frac{4}{5}i$ **31.** $\frac{8}{13} + \frac{12}{13}i$
32. $1 - \frac{3}{2}i$ **33.** $(x + 5i)(x - 5i)$
34. $(x + i)(x - i)$ **35.** $3(s + 5i)(s - 5i)$
36. $(x + \frac{1}{2}i)(x - \frac{1}{2}i)$ **37.** $(2b + i)(2b - i)$
38. $-(3x + 10i)(3x - 10i)$
39. $-1 \pm i\sqrt{2}$
40. $\frac{1}{6} \pm \frac{i\sqrt{35}}{6}$ **41.** $1 \pm i\frac{\sqrt{10}}{2}$
42. $1 \pm i$ **43.** $2 \pm i$
44. $\frac{3}{2} \pm \frac{i}{2}$

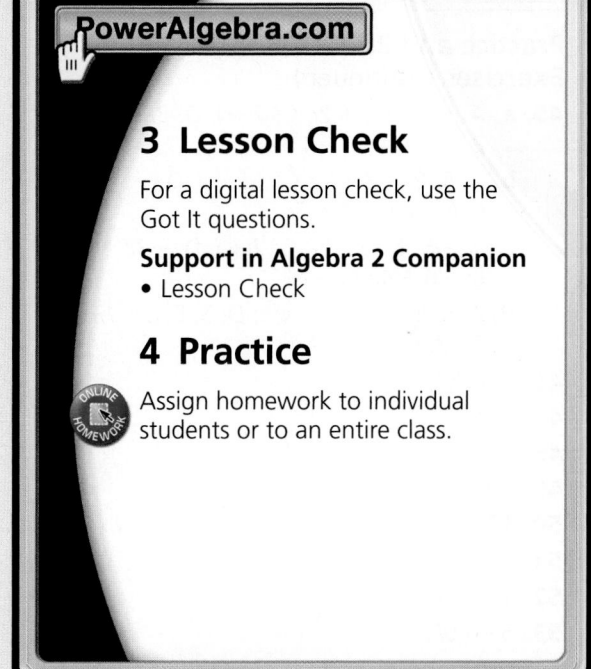

PowerAlgebra.com

3 Lesson Check

For a digital lesson check, use the Got It questions.

Support in Algebra 2 Companion
- Lesson Check

4 Practice

Assign homework to individual students or to an entire class.

4 Practice

ASSIGNMENT GUIDE

Basic: 8–44 all, 45, 46–50 even, 56, 57

Average: 9–43 odd, 45–69

Advanced: 9–43 odd, 45–72

Standardized Test Prep: 73–76

Mixed Review: 77–89

 Mathematical Practices are supported by exercises with red headings. Here are the Practices supported in this lesson:

MP 1: Make Sense of Problems Ex. 46

MP 2: Reason Abstractly Ex. 56

MP 3: Communicate Ex. 72

MP 3: Construct Arguments Ex. 72

MP 3: Critique the Reasoning of Others Ex. 7

Applications exercises have blue headings.

EXERCISE 57: Use the Think About a Plan worksheet in the **Practice and Problem Solving Workbook** (also available in the Teaching Resources in print and online) to further support students' development in becoming independent learners.

HOMEWORK QUICK CHECK

To check students' understanding of key skills and concepts, go over Exercises 27, 39, 46, 56, and 57.

B Apply

45. a. Name the complex number represented by each point on the graph at the right.
  b. Find the additive inverse of each number.
  c. Find the complex conjugate of each number.
  d. Find the absolute value of each number.

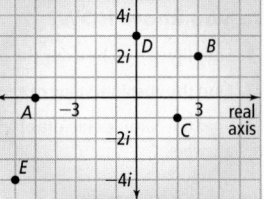

46. Think About a Plan In the complex number plane, what geometric figure describes the complex numbers with absolute value 10?
  • What does the absolute value of a complex number represent?
  • How can you use the complex number plane to solve this problem?

47. Solve $(x + 3i)(x - 3i) = 34$.

Simplify each expression.

48. $(8i)(4i)(-9i)$

49. $(2 + \sqrt{-1}) + (-3 + \sqrt{-16})$

50. $(4 + \sqrt{-9}) + (6 - \sqrt{-49})$

51. $(10 + \sqrt{-9}) - (2 + \sqrt{-25})$

52. $(8 - \sqrt{-1}) - (-3 + \sqrt{-16})$

53. $2i(5 - 3i)$

54. $-5(1 + 2i) + 3i(3 - 4i)$

55. $(3 + \sqrt{-4})(4 + \sqrt{-1})$

56. Open-Ended In the equation $x^2 - 6x + c = 0$, find values of c that will give:
  a. two real solutions   **b.** two imaginary solutions   **c.** one real solution

57. A student wrote the numbers 1, 5, $1 + 3i$, and $4 + 3i$ to represent the vertices of a quadrilateral in the complex number plane. What type of quadrilateral has these vertices?

The multiplicative inverse of a complex number z is $\frac{1}{z}$ where $z \neq 0$. Find the multiplicative inverse, or reciprocal, of each complex number. Then use complex conjugates to simplify. Check each answer by multiplying it by the original number.

58. $2 + 5i$

59. $8 - 12i$

60. $a + bi$

Find the sum and product of the roots of each equation.

61. $x^2 - 2x + 3 = 0$

62. $5x^2 + 2x + 1 = 0$

63. $-2x^2 + 3x - 3 = 0$

For $ax^2 + bx + c = 0$, the sum of the roots is $-\frac{b}{a}$ and the product of the roots is $\frac{c}{a}$. Find a quadratic equation for each pair of roots. Assume $a = 1$.

64. $-6i$ and $6i$

65. $2 + 5i$ and $2 - 5i$

66. $4 - 3i$ and $4 + 3i$

Two complex numbers $a + bi$ and $c + di$ are equal when $a = c$ and $b = d$. Solve each equation for x and y.

67. $2x + 3yi = -14 + 9i$

68. $3x + 19i = 16 - 8yi$

69. $-14 - 3i = 2x + yi$

Answers

Practice and Problem-Solving Exercises (continued)

45. a. A: -5; B: $3 + 2i$; C: $2 - i$; D: $3i$;
  E: $-6 - 4i$; F: $-1 + 5i$

  b. A: 5; B: $-3 - 2i$; C: $-2 + i$; D: $-3i$;
  E: $6 + 4i$; F: $1 - 5i$

  c. A: -5; B: $3 - 2i$; C: $2 + i$; D: $-3i$;
  E: $-6 + 4i$; F: $-1 - 5i$

  d. A: 5; B: $\sqrt{13}$; C: $\sqrt{5}$; D: 3; E: $2\sqrt{13}$;
  F: $\sqrt{26}$

46. a circle

47. $-5, 5$

48. $288i$

49. $-1 + 5i$

50. $10 - 4i$

51. $8 - 2i$

52. $11 - 5i$

53. $6 + 10i$

54. $7 - i$

55. $10 + 11i$

56. a. $c < 9$
  b. $c > 9$
  c. $c = 9$

57. trapezoid

58. $\frac{2}{29} - \frac{5}{29}i$

59. $\frac{1}{26} + \frac{3}{52}i$

60. $\frac{a}{a^2 + b^2} - \frac{bi}{a^2 + b^2}$

61. sum: 2, product: 3

62. sum: $-\frac{2}{5}$, product: $\frac{1}{5}$

63. sum: $\frac{3}{2}$, product: $\frac{3}{2}$

64. Answers may vary. Sample:
  $x^2 + 36 = 0$

65. Answers may vary. Sample:
  $x^2 - 4x + 29 = 0$

66. Answers may vary. Sample:
  $x^2 - 8x + 25 = 0$

67. $x = -7, y = 3$

68. $x = \frac{16}{3}, y = -\frac{19}{8}$

69. $x = -7, y = -3$

 **Challenge**

70. Show that the product of any complex number $a + bi$ and its complex conjugate is a real number.

71. For what real values of x and y is $(x + yi)^2$ an imaginary number?

 72. Reasoning True or false: The conjugate of the additive inverse of a complex number is equal to the additive inverse of the conjugate of that complex number. Explain your answer.

Standardized Test Prep

SAT/ACT

73. How can you rewrite the expression $(8 - 5i)^2$ in the form $a + bi$?

Ⓐ $39 + 80i$ Ⓑ $39 - 80i$ Ⓒ $69 + 80i$ Ⓓ $69 - 80i$

74. How many solutions does the quadratic equation $4x^2 - 12x + 9 = 0$ have?

Ⓕ two real solutions   Ⓗ two imaginary solutions
Ⓖ one real solution   Ⓘ one imaginary solution

75. What are the solutions of $3x^2 - 2x - 4 = 0$?

Ⓐ $\dfrac{1 \pm \sqrt{13}}{3}$ Ⓑ $\dfrac{1 \pm i\sqrt{11}}{3}$ Ⓒ $\dfrac{-1 \pm \sqrt{13}}{3}$ Ⓓ $\dfrac{-1 \pm i\sqrt{11}}{3}$

Short Response

76. Using factoring, what are all four solutions to $x^4 - 16 = 0$? Show your work.

Mixed Review

Solve each equation using the Quadratic Formula.   ◀ See Lesson 4-7.

77. $2x^2 + 3x - 4 = 0$ **78.** $4x^2 + x = 1$ **79.** $x^2 = -7x - 8$

Graph each function. Identify the axis of symmetry.   ◀ See Lesson 4-1.

80. $y = -2(x + 1)^2 - 3$ **81.** $y = \frac{1}{2}(x - 4)^2 + 1$ **82.** $y = 3(x - 1)^2 - 5$

Write an equation for each line.   ◀ See Lesson 2-3.

83. $m = 3$ and the y-intercept is -4 **84.** $m = -0.5$ and the y-intercept is -2

85. $m = -7$ and the y-intercept is 10   **86.** $m = 2$ and the y-intercept is 8

Get Ready! To prepare for Lesson 4-9, do Exercises 87–89.   ◀ See Lesson 3-3.

Solve each system of inequalities by graphing.

87. $\begin{cases} y < 2x + 4 \\ y \geq |x - 3| + 2 \end{cases}$ **88.** $\begin{cases} y > -x \\ y < -|x + 1| \end{cases}$ **89.** $\begin{cases} y \leq |x| + 2 \\ y \geq -\frac{1}{2}x + 4 \end{cases}$

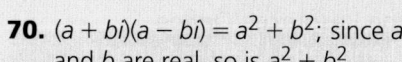
83. $y = 3x - 4$
84. $y = -0.5x - 2$
85. $y = -7x + 10$
86. $y = 2x + 8$
87.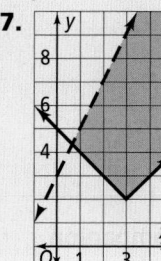

88.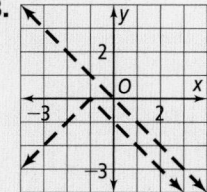

no solution

89.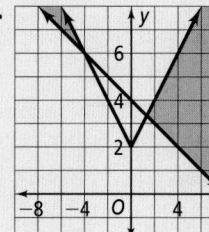

---

70. $(a + bi)(a - bi) = a^2 + b^2$; since a and b are real, so is $a^2 + b^2$.

71. all nonzero numbers x and y such that $|x| = |y|$

72. True; the add. inv. of $a + bi$ is $-a - bi$ and the conjugate of $-a - bi$ is $-a + bi$. The conjugate of $a + bi$ is $a - bi$ and the add. inv. of $a - bi$ is $-a + bi$.

Standardized Test Prep

73. B   **74.** G   **75.** A

76. [2] $\pm 2, \pm 2i$;

$$x^4 - 16 = (x^2 - 4)(x^2 + 4)$$
$$= (x - 2)(x + 2)(x^2 + 4)$$
$$x - 2 = 0, x + 2 = 0,$$
$$x^2 + 4 = 0$$
$$x = 2 \quad x = -2 \quad x = \pm 2i$$

[1] appropriate method, with one computational error

Mixed Review

77. $\dfrac{-3 \pm \sqrt{41}}{4}$

78. $\dfrac{-1 \pm \sqrt{17}}{8}$

79. $\dfrac{-7 \pm \sqrt{17}}{2}$

80. 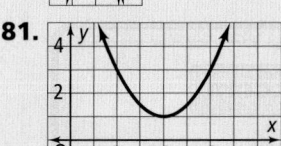 ; axis of symmetry: $x = -1$

81. ; axis of symmetry: $x = 4$

82. 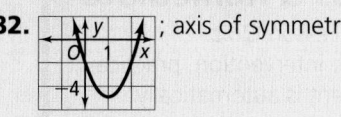 ; axis of symmetry: $x = 1$

Lesson 4-8 255

4-8 Lesson Resources

Differentiated Remediation

Additional Instructional Support

Algebra 2 Companion

Students can use the **Algebra 2 Companion** worktext (4 pages) as you teach the lesson. Use the Companion to support

- New Vocabulary
- Key Concepts
- Got It for each Problem
- Lesson Check

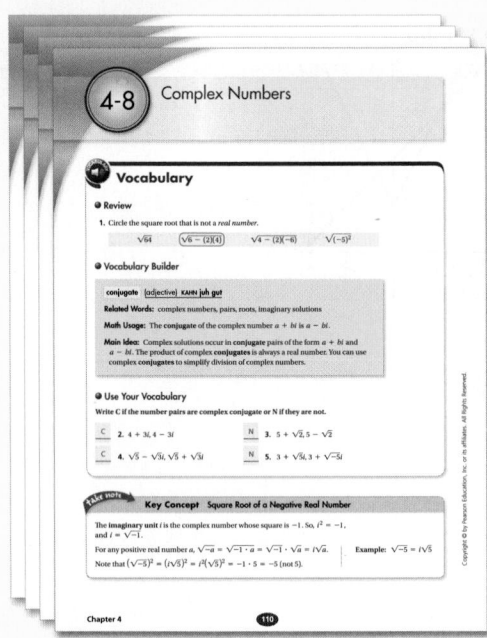

ELL Support

Connect to Prior Knowledge Go back to the table in Lesson 4-7 on page 243. Point out the last example, where the discriminant is less than zero. The table tells you that there are no real solutions. Ask students what that means in terms of complex solutions. [There will be 2 complex solutions.]

Point out the graphs in the table. Real solutions only occur where the graph crosses the x-axis. Unlike real solutions, complex solutions cannot be identified on the parabola. However, you can still use the graph to determine that there are no real solutions and then know that there are complex solutions.

5 Assess & Remediate

Lesson Quiz

1. **Do you UNDERSTAND?** How do you write $\sqrt{-20}$ using the imaginary unit i?
2. What are the graph and absolute value of $2 + 2i$?
3. What is the sum $(7 + 2i) + (5 - 3i)$?
4. What is the product $(-2 + 5i)(-1 + 4i)$?
5. What is the quotient $\dfrac{7 + 4i}{2 - 3i}$?
6. What is the factored form of $2x^2 + 18$?
7. Find the solutions of $6x^2 + 4x = -11$.

ANSWERS TO LESSON QUIZ

1. $2i\sqrt{5}$
2. $2\sqrt{2}$

   (2 + 2i) graphed on imaginary axis at (2, 2); real axis labeled 2, 4, 6

3. $12 - i$
4. $-18 - 13i$
5. $\dfrac{2}{13} + \dfrac{29}{13}i$
6. $2(x + 3i)(x - 3i)$
7. $-\dfrac{1}{3} \pm \dfrac{i\sqrt{62}}{6}$

PRESCRIPTION FOR REMEDIATION

Use the student work on the Lesson Quiz to prescribe a differentiated review assignment:

Points	Differentiated Remediation
0–2	Intervention
3–6	On-level
7	Extension

PowerAlgebra.com

5 Assess & Remediate

Assign the Lesson Quiz. Appropriate intervention, practice, or enrichment is automatically generated based on student performance.

Intervention

- **Reteaching** (2 pages) Provides reteaching and practice exercises for the key lesson concepts. Use with struggling students or absent students.
- **English Language Learner Support** Helps students develop and reinforce mathematical vocabulary and key concepts.

All-in-One Resources/Online
Reteaching

4-8 Reteaching
Complex Numbers

- A *complex number* consists of a real part and an imaginary part. It is written in the form $a + bi$, where a and b are real numbers.
- $i = \sqrt{-1}$ and $i^2 = (\sqrt{-1})(\sqrt{-1}) = -1$
- When adding or subtracting complex numbers, combine the real parts and then combine the imaginary parts.
- When multiplying complex numbers, use the Distributive Property or FOIL.

Problem
What is $(3 - i) + (2 + 3i)$?

$(3 - i) + (2 + 3i)$
$= \boxed{3} - \boxed{i} + \boxed{2} + \boxed{3i}$ Circle real parts. Put a square around imaginary parts.
$= (3 + 2) + (-1 + 3)i$ Combine.
$= 5 + 2i$ Simplify.

Problem
What is the product $(7 - 3i)(-4 + 9i)$?
Use FOIL to multiply:

$(7 - 3i)(-4 + 9i) = 7(-4) + 7(9i) + (-3i)(-4) + (-3i)(9i)$
$(7 - 3i)(-4 + 9i) = -28 + 63i + 12i - 27i^2$
First $= 7(-4)$ $\qquad = -28 + 75i - 27i^2$
Outer $= 7(9i)$ $\quad$ You can simplify the expression by substituting -1 for i^2.
Inner $= (-3i)(-4)$ $\quad (7 - 3i)(-4 + 9i) = -28 + 75i - 27(-1)$
Last $= (-3i)(9i)$ $\qquad = -1 + 75i$

Exercises
Simplify each expression.

1. $2i + (-4 - 2i)$ $\quad$ 2. $(3 + i)(2 + i)$ $\quad$ 3. $(4 + 3i)(1 + 2i)$
-4 $\qquad\qquad$ $5 + 5i$ $\qquad\qquad$ $-2 + 11i$

4. $3(1 - 2i)$ $\quad$ 5. $3(4 - i)$ $\quad$ 6. $3 - (-2 + 3i) + (-5 + i)$
$6 + 3i$ $\qquad\qquad$ $3 + 12i$ $\qquad\qquad$ $-2i$

7. $4i(6 - 2i)$ $\quad$ 8. $(5 + 6i) + (-2 + 4i)$ $\quad$ 9. $9(11 + 5i)$
$8 + 24i$ $\qquad\qquad$ $3 + 10i$ $\qquad\qquad$ $99 + 45i$

All-in-One Resources/Online
English Language Learner Support

4-8 Additional Vocabulary Support
Complex Numbers

Complete the vocabulary chart by filling in the missing information.

Word or Word Phrase	Definition	Picture or Example
imaginary unit	The *imaginary unit i* is a complex number whose square is -1.	$i = \sqrt{-1}$
pure imaginary number	A *pure imaginary number* is of the form $a + bi$, where $a = 0$ and $b \neq 0$.	1. Answers may vary. Sample: $5i$
complex number	2. any number of the form $a + bi$ where a and b are real numbers	$7 - 4i$
complex number plane	In the *complex number plane*, the point (a, b) represents the complex number $a + bi$. To graph, locate the real part on the horizontal axis and the imaginary part on the vertical axis.	3. (imaginary/real axis graph)
absolute value of a complex number	4. Answers may vary. Sample: The absolute value of a complex number is its distance from the origin in the complex number plane.	$\|8 + 6i\| = \sqrt{8^2 + 6^2} = 10$
complex conjugates	number pairs of the form $a + bi$ and $a - bi$	5. Answers may vary. Sample: $-3 + 4i$ and $-3 - 4i$

Differentiated Remediation *continued*

On-Level

- **Practice** (2 pages) Provides extra practice for each lesson. For simpler practice exercises, use the Form K Practice pages found in the All-in-One Teaching Resources and online.

- **Think About a Plan** Helps students develop specific problem-solving skills and strategies by providing scaffolded guiding questions.

- **Standardized Test Prep** Focuses on all major exercises, all major question types, and helps students prepare for the high-stakes assessments.

Extension

- **Enrichment** Provides students with interesting problems and activities that extend the concepts of the lesson.

- **Activities, Games, and Puzzles** Worksheets that can be used for concepts development, enrichment, and for fun!

Practice and Problem Solving Wkbk/All-in-One Resources/Online
Practice page 1

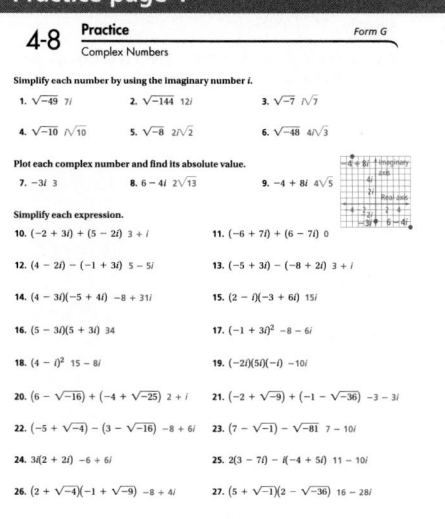

Practice and Problem Solving Wkbk/All-in-One Resources/Online
Practice page 2

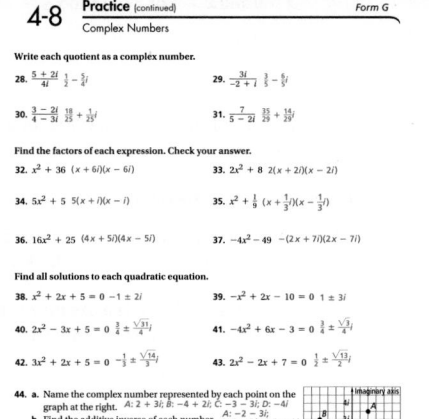

All-in-One Resources/Online
Enrichment

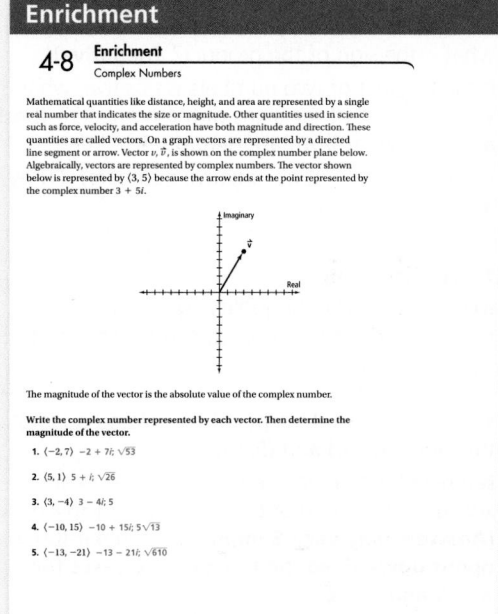

Practice and Problem Solving Wkbk/All-in-One Resources/Online
Think About a Plan

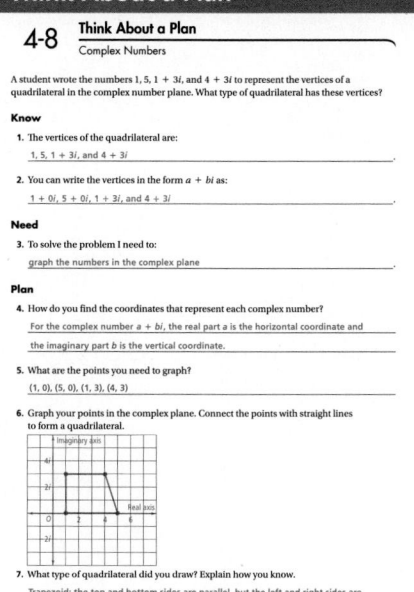

Practice and Problem Solving Wkbk/All-in-One Resources/Online
Standardized Test Prep

Online Teacher Resource Center
Activities, Games, and Puzzles

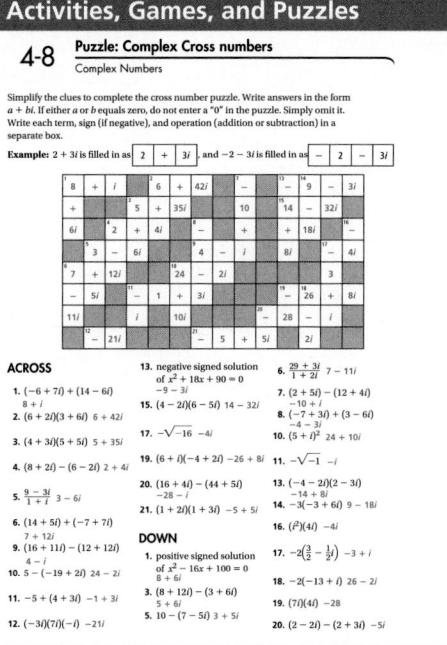

Guided Instruction

PURPOSE To investigate and use different methods to solve quadratic inequalities

PROCESS Students will solve quadratic inequalities by
- factoring.
- using a table for the related function.
- graphing the related quadratic function.
- solving the related quadratic equation.

DISCUSS

Q What do the *x*-intercepts of a parabola represent? **[The *x*-values for which the related function equals zero.]**

Q What do all points above the *x*-axis have in common? **[The *y*-value is positive.]**

Example 1

Q If one factor is positive and the other is negative, what is the sign of the product? **[negative]**

Q If the product of two numbers is positive, what do you know about the signs of the numbers? **[both are positive or both are negative]**

Q What is true about all negative numbers? **[They are less than zero.]**

Activity

To solve a quadratic inequality by using a table, you must have a table of solutions for the related quadratic function.

Q What are the *x*-intercepts of the related quadratic function? **[(1, 0) and (5, 0)]**

Q Is it possible that any negative *y*-values exist for *x*-values less than 0 or greater than 6? Explain. **[Answers may vary. Sample: No; the parabola opens upward, so the function increases for $x \le 0$ and $x \ge 6$.]**

© **Mathematical Practices** This Concept Byte supports students in constructing arguments, Mathematical Practice 3.

© **Common Core State Standards**
A-APR.B.3 Identify zeros of polynomials when suitable factorizations are available, and use the zeros to construct a rough graph of the function defined by the polynomial.
MP 3

To solve some quadratic inequalities, relate the quadratic expression to 0 and factor. To determine the sign of each factor, use what you know about multiplying positive and negative numbers.

Example 1

Solve each inequality algebraically.

a. $2x^2 - 14x < 0$

$2x(x - 7) < 0$	Factor.
$2x > 0$ and $(x - 7) < 0$, or $2x < 0$ and $(x - 7) > 0$	The product is negative, so the two factors must have *different* signs.
$x > 0$ and $x < 7$, or $x < 0$ and $x > 7$	Simplify.
$0 < x < 7$	No value can be both greater than 7 *and* less than 0.

b. $2x^2 - 14x > 0$

$2x(x - 7) > 0$	Factor.
$2x > 0$ and $(x - 7) > 0$, or $2x < 0$ and $(x - 7) < 0$	The product is positive, so the two factors must have the *same* signs.
$x > 0$ and $x > 7$, or $x < 0$ and $x < 7$	Simplify.
$x > 7$ or $x < 0$	A value that is greater than both 0 *and* 7 is always greater than 7. A value that is less than both 0 *and* 7 is always less than 0.

You can use a table to solve inequalities by analyzing the values of *y* around 0.

Activity

Use a table to find the solutions of $x^2 - 6x + 5 < 0$.

1. What happens to the value of *y* when $0 \le x \le 6$?
2. Does this make sense when you think of the shape of the graph of $y = x^2 - 6x + 5$? Explain.
3. What *x*-values in the table make the inequality $x^2 - 6x + 5 < 0$ true?
4. What are the solutions of $x^2 - 6x + 5 < 0$?

x	y
0	5
1	0
2	-3
3	-4
4	-3
5	0
6	5

You can determine the solution of a quadratic inequality based on how many times and where the graph of the related function crosses the *x*-axis. The graph could open upward or downward, and could intersect the *x*-axis at 0, 1, or 2 points.

Answers

Activity

1. Values range from positive to zero to negative and then back to zero and positive.
2. Yes; the shape is a parabola that dips below the *x*-axis and then comes back up.
3. 2, 3, 4
4. $1 < x < 5$

You can solve inequalities of the form $ax^2 + bx + c > 0$ or $ax^2 + bx + c < 0$ by graphing the corresponding function and seeing where the graph is above or below the x-axis.

Example 2

Find the solution sets for $\frac{1}{4}(x - 2)^2 - 1 > 0$ and $\frac{1}{4}(x - 2)^2 - 1 < 0$.

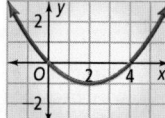

The solution set for $\frac{1}{4}(x - 2)^2 - 1 > 0$ is all x-values of points on the parabola that lie above the x-axis.

$$x < 0 \text{ or } x > 4$$

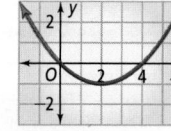

The solution set for $\frac{1}{4}(x - 2)^2 - 1 < 0$ is all x-values of points on the parabola that lie below the x-axis.

$$0 < x < 4$$

Example 3

Solve $-2x^2 - 8x - 6 < 0$.

Think: Since the coefficient of x^2 is less than zero, the graph of $y = -2x^2 - 8x - 6$ opens downward.

Solve: Find where $-2x^2 - 8x - 6$ equals 0.

$$-2x^2 - 8x - 6 = 0$$
$$-2(x^2 + 4x + 3) = 0$$
$$-2(x + 3)(x + 1) = 0$$
$$x = -3 \text{ or } x = -1$$

The graph of $y = -2x^2 - 8x - 6$ opens down and crosses the x-axis at $x = -3$ and $x = -1$. The solution of $-2x^2 - 8x - 6 < 0$ is $x < -3$ or $x > -1$.

Exercises

5. Solve each inequality. Graph your solution on a number line.
   a. $x^2 < 36$
   b. $x^2 - 9 > 0$
   c. $x^2 < -4$
   d. $x^2 - 3x - 18 > 0$

6. How can you use the graph of $y = 3x - 4$ to solve the linear inequality $3x - 4 < 0$? Graph the solution.

7. How can you solve the absolute value inequality $|-3x + 4| > 0$?

8. Example 2 shows two possible graphs for a quadratic inequality. What other possibilities are there?

9. Describe the graphs of possible solutions of $ax^3 + bx^2 + cx + d > 0$.

PowerAlgebra.com · Concept Byte · Quadratic Inequalities · 257

Example 2

The previous activity alluded to the graphical connection between solutions of a quadratic function and solutions of a quadratic inequality. This example solidifies that connection by finding when the y-values of a parabola are positive or negative.

Q Are the x-intercepts part of either solution? Why or why not? **[No; the x-intercepts represent $\frac{1}{4}(x - 2)^2 - 1 = 0$, so they are not part of the solution sets of the strict inequalities.]**

Q Will $ax^2 + bx + c < 0$ always have a solution? Explain. **[No; a parabola entirely above the x-axis never has negative y-values.]**

Example 3

This method is related to the tabular method in the Activity. Both require finding the zeros of the quadratic function. However, while the Activity uses the table to determine the sign of the function around the zeros, Example 3 uses prior knowledge about the direction of a parabola based on the leading coefficient.

Q Without actually making one, what would a table of values for $y = -2x^2 - 8x - 6$ look like? **[Answers may vary. Sample: The y-values would be zero for $x = -3$ and $x = -1$, negative for $x < -3$ or $x > -1$ and positive for $-3 < x < -1$.]**

Q Why does it matter whether the graph opens upward or downward? **[Answers may vary. Sample: Assuming the graph intersects the x-axis, the direction in which the graph opens determines where y is positive or negative.]**

---

5. a. $-6 < x < 6$

b. $x > 3$ or $x < -3$

c. no solution

d. $x < -3$ or $x > 6$

6. Graph $y = 3x - 4$ and shade the x-values for which the line is below the x-axis.

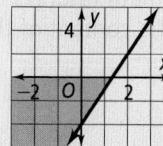

7. Absolute value is always nonnegative, thus $|-3x + 4| > 0$ for all values of x, $x \neq \frac{4}{3}$.

8. intersects the x-axis at one point:

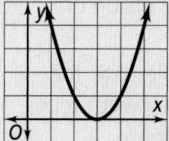

does not intersect the x-axis:

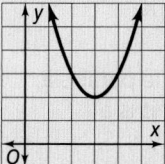

9. Graphs of solutions of $ax^3 + bx^2 + cx + d > 0$ could be: for $a > 0$, $x > n$ or $n < x < m$ and $x > k$; for $a < 0$, $x < n$, or $x < n$ and $n < x < m$, or $x < n$ and $m < x < k$, where n, m, and k are real solutions of the equation $ax^3 + bx^2 + cx + d = 0$ with $n < m < k$.

1 Interactive Learning

Solve It!
PURPOSE To use inequalities to define a region bounded by quadratic functions
PROCESS Students may
- write a system of inequalities of two of the three functions from Lesson 4-7 Solve It.
- solve a simpler problem by finding a linear function for the top "lip" of the mouth.

FACILITATE
Q What points must the functions share? Why? **[The functions must share (2, 1) and (6, 1) because they are the corners of the mouth.]**

Q Are the "lips" part of the inside of the mouth? Explain. **[Answers may vary. Sample: Yes; the lips form the boundary of the inside.]**

Q Do you need to restrict the domain? Explain. **[Answers may vary. Sample: No; the intersection of the inequalities already restricts $2 \le x \le 6$.]**

ANSWER See Solve It in Answers on next page.
CONNECT THE MATH In the Solve it, students combine their knowledge of inequalities and graphs of quadratic functions to describe a region bounded by parabolas. In this lesson, students solve quadratic systems by graphing or substitution.

2 Guided Instruction

Take Note
VISUAL LEARNERS
The number of solutions of a Linear-Quadratic system indicates the number of points of intersection in the graphs of the functions.

© Common Core State Standards
A-CED.A.3 Represent constraints by equations or inequalities, and by systems of equations and/or inequalities, and interpret solutions as viable or nonviable options in a modeling context. **Also** A-REI.C.7, A-REI.D.11
MP 1, MP 2, MP 3, MP 4

Objectives To solve and graph systems of linear and quadratic equations
To solve and graph systems of quadratic inequalities

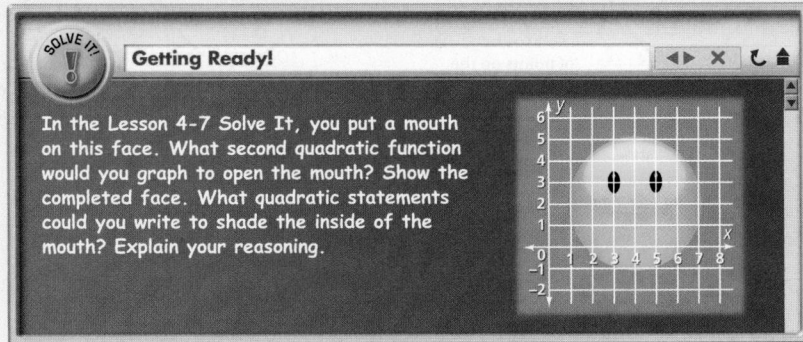

Getting Ready!

In the Lesson 4-7 Solve It, you put a mouth on this face. What second quadratic function would you graph to open the mouth? Show the completed face. What quadratic statements could you write to shade the inside of the mouth? Explain your reasoning.

By drawing a second parabola in the Solve It, you created a quadratic system.

Essential Understanding You can solve systems involving quadratic equations using methods similar to the ones used to solve systems of linear equations.

The points where the graphs of the equations intersect represent the solutions of a system.

take note

Key Concept **Solutions of a Linear-Quadratic System**

A system of one quadratic equation and one linear equation can have two solutions, one solution, or no solution.

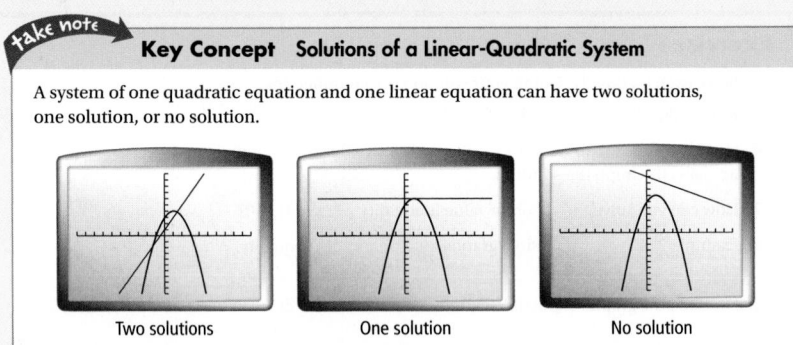

Two solutions   One solution   No solution

258   **Chapter 4** Quadratic Functions and Equations

BIG ideas Equivalence
Function
Solving Equations
and Inequalities

ESSENTIAL UNDERSTANDINGS
- Systems involving quadratic equations can be solved using methods similar to the ones used to solve systems of linear equations.
- Any quadratic function is a stretch, compression, reflection, and/or a translation of $y = x^2$.
- The points where the graphs of the equations intersect represent the solutions of a system.

Math Background
Students are familiar with solving systems of linear equations and inequalities. In this lesson, they will solve nonlinear systems of equations and inequalities. The methods used to solve nonlinear systems are the same methods used to solve linear systems: substitution, elimination, and graphing.

Students often shade inequalities incorrectly when solving by graphing. Like linear inequalities,

students should use a test point to determine whether to shade inside or outside of the parabola.

For students who still struggle with the graphing aspect, teach these basic steps:
1. Use the inequality symbol to determine whether the graph should have a dotted or solid line.
2. Graph the parabola.
3. Choose a point inside the parabola, and determine whether it is a solution of the inequality.
4. If the point is a solution, shade inside the parabola; otherwise shade outside the parabola.

© Mathematical Practices
Construct viable arguments and critique the reasoning of others. Students will draw on knowledge from Lesson 1-6 to solve systems of quadratic inequalities.

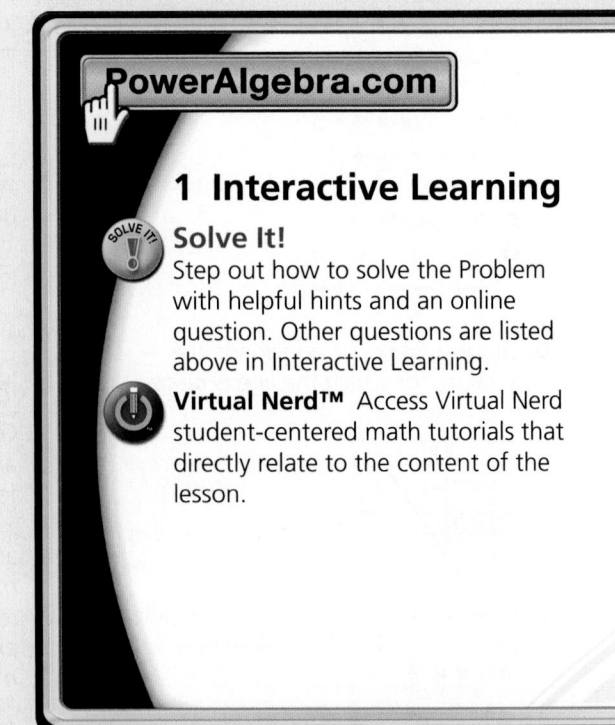

PowerAlgebra.com

1 Interactive Learning

Solve It!
Step out how to solve the Problem with helpful hints and an online question. Other questions are listed above in Interactive Learning.

Virtual Nerd™ Access Virtual Nerd student-centered math tutorials that directly relate to the content of the lesson.

Problem 1 Solving a Linear-Quadratic System by Graphing

Multiple Choice Which numbers are *y*-values of the solutions of the system of equations? $\begin{cases} y = -x^2 + 5x + 6 \\ y = x + 6 \end{cases}$

   Ⓐ 4 only   Ⓑ 6 only   Ⓒ 4 and 6   Ⓓ 6 and 10

Graph the equations. Find their intersections.

The solutions appear to be (0, 6) and (4, 10).

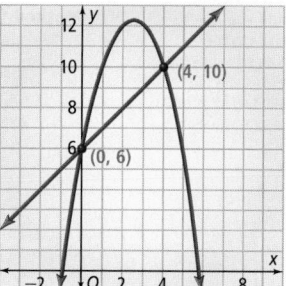

Check

$$y = -x^2 + 5x + 6 \qquad y = x + 6$$
$$6 \overset{?}{=} -(0)^2 + 5(0) + 6 \qquad 6 \overset{?}{=} 0 + 6$$
$$6 = 6 ✔ \qquad 6 = 6 ✔$$

$$y = -x^2 + 5x + 6 \qquad y = x + 6$$
$$10 \overset{?}{=} -(4)^2 + 5(4) + 6 \qquad 10 \overset{?}{=} 4 + 6$$
$$10 = 10 ✔ \qquad 10 = 10 ✔$$

The *y*-values of the solutions are 6 and 10, choice D.

Got It? 1. What is the solution of the system? $\begin{cases} y = x^2 + 6x + 9 \\ y = x + 3 \end{cases}$

Plan

How can you graph these two equations?
Use slope-intercept form to graph the linear equation. Make a table of values to graph the quadratic equation.

Problem 2 Solving a Linear-Quadratic System Using Substitution

What is the solution of the system of equations? $\begin{cases} y = -x^2 - x + 6 \\ y = x + 3 \end{cases}$

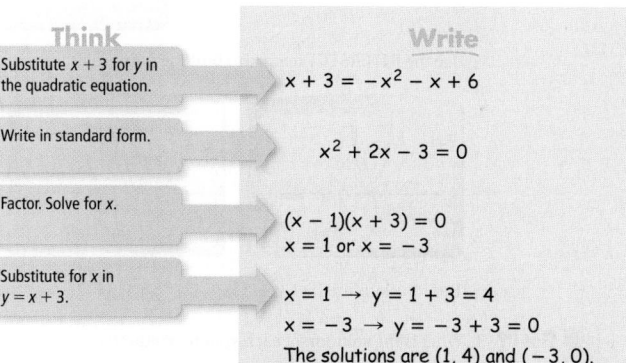

Think

Substitute *x* + 3 for *y* in the quadratic equation.

Write in standard form.

Factor. Solve for *x*.

Substitute for *x* in *y* = *x* + 3.

Write

$$x + 3 = -x^2 - x + 6$$

$$x^2 + 2x - 3 = 0$$

$$(x - 1)(x + 3) = 0$$
$$x = 1 \text{ or } x = -3$$

$$x = 1 \rightarrow y = 1 + 3 = 4$$
$$x = -3 \rightarrow y = -3 + 3 = 0$$

The solutions are (1, 4) and (−3, 0).

Got It? 2. What is the solution of the system? $\begin{cases} y = -x^2 - 3x + 10 \\ y = x + 5 \end{cases}$

Problem 1

Q What are the *x*-values of the solutions? **[0 and 4]**

Q What does it mean algebraically for a point to be the intersection of the graphs of two functions? **[The coordinates are a solution to both equations.]**

Q Can you solve any linear-quadratic systems by graphing? Explain. **[Answers may vary. Sample: No; if the intersection points do not fall on the grid, you could only estimate.]**

Got It?

A graphing calculator could also be used to find the intersections.

Q How many times do the graphs intersect? **[twice]**

Problem 2

Q If the linear equation had been in $ax + by + c = 0$ form, what would have been a good first step and why? **[Solve the equation for *y* so you could easily set the two equations equal to each other by substitution.]**

Q Does it matter which equation you substitute the *x*-values into? Explain. **[No; the solutions need to satisfy both equations.]**

Got It?

Q Without graphing how can you tell how many times the functions intersect? **[Sample: The *y*-intercept of the parabola is above the *y*-intercept of the line and the parabola opens downward, so they intersect at two points.]**

2 Guided Instruction

 Each Problem is worked out and supported online.

Problem 1
Solving a Linear-Quadratic System by Graphing
      Animated

Problem 2
Solving a Linear-Quadratic System Using Substitution
      Animated

Problem 3
Solving a Quadratic System of Equations
      Animated

Problem 4
Solving a Quadratic System of Inequalities

Support in Algebra 2 Companion
• Vocabulary
• Key Concepts
• Got It?

Answers

Solve It!
$y = -0.25(x - 4)^2 + 2$ will open the mouth.
To shade the inside of the mouth, write:
$y \geq 0.25(x - 4)^2$ and $y \leq -0.25(x - 4)^2 + 2$.

Got It?
1. (−3, 0), (−2, 1)
2. (−5, 0), (1, 6)

Problem 3

A system of two quadratic equations could also be solved by graphing or using substitution.

Q Why would adding the two equations together to eliminate x^2 not be useful? **[There are still two variables; neither x nor y is eliminated.]**

Q If you use the elimination method, which variable would you eliminate? **[Eliminate y, so you are left with an equation in only one variable.]**

Q Does each method produce the same solutions? Explain why. **[Yes; the points of intersection are conceptually equivalent to the algebraic solutions.]**

EXTENSION

Q A linear-quadratic system can have 2, 1, or no solutions. What are the possibilities for a quadratic-quadratic system? **[There can be infinitely many, 2, 1, or 0 solutions.]**

Got It?

Q Why do the numbers of solutions in 3a and 3b differ? **[Answers may vary. Sample: Between 3a and 3b, the function $y = -x^2 + 5$ is translated down 10 units to become $y = -x^2 - 5$, so the parabolas no longer intersect.]**

SYNTHESIZING

If time allows, have students solve Problem 3 or Got It 3a by the elimination method to verify that it produces the same solutions.

You can solve quadratic-quadratic systems using the same methods you used for linear-quadratic systems.

© **Problem 3** Solving a Quadratic System of Equations

What is the solution of the system? $\begin{cases} y = -x^2 - x + 12 \\ y = x^2 + 7x + 12 \end{cases}$

Plan

Which variable should you substitute for?
You can substitute for either variable, but substituting for y results in a simple equation.

Method 1 Use substitution.

Substitute $y = -x^2 - x + 12$ for y in the second equation. Solve for x.

$-x^2 - x + 12 = x^2 + 7x + 12$	Substitute for y.
$-2x^2 - 8x = 0$	Write in standard form.
$-2x(x + 4) = 0$	Factor.
$x = 0 \text{ or } x = -4$	Solve for x.

Substitute each value of x into either equation. Solve for y.

$y = x^2 + 7x + 12$ $y = x^2 + 7x + 12$

$y = (0)^2 + 7(0) + 12$ $y = (-4)^2 + 7(-4) + 12$

$y = 0 + 0 + 12 = 12$ $y = 16 - 28 + 12 = 0$

The solutions are $(0, 12)$ and $(-4, 0)$.

Method 2 Graph the equations.

Use a graphing calculator.
Define functions Y_1 and Y_2.

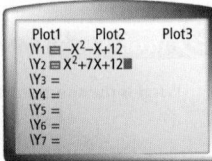

Use the **INTERSECT** feature to find the points of intersection.

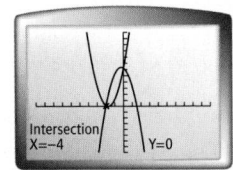 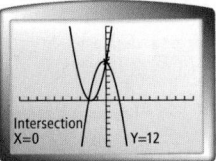

The solutions are $(-4, 0)$ and $(0, 12)$.

 Got It? 3. What is the solution of each system of equations?

a. $\begin{cases} y = x^2 - 4x + 5 \\ y = -x^2 + 5 \end{cases}$ **b.** $\begin{cases} y = x^2 - 4x + 5 \\ y = -x^2 - 5 \end{cases}$

Additional Problems

1. What is the solution of the system?
$\begin{cases} y = x^2 - 2x + 1 \\ y = x - 3 \end{cases}$

ANSWER no solution

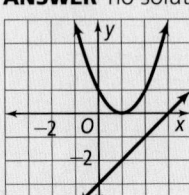

2. What is the solution of the system?
$\begin{cases} y = x^2 + 3x + 9 \\ y = -3x + 4 \end{cases}$

ANSWER $(-5, 19)$ and $(-1, 7)$

3. What is the solution of the system?
$\begin{cases} y = x^2 + 9x + 7 \\ y = -x^2 + 3x + 7 \end{cases}$

ANSWER $(-3, -11)$ and $(0, 7)$

4. What is the solution to this system of inequalities?
$\begin{cases} y \geq x^2 + 5x - 8 \\ y < -x^2 + 3x + 4 \end{cases}$

ANSWER

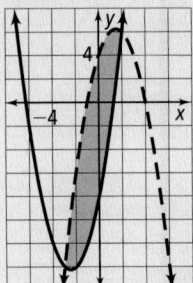

Answers

Got It? (continued)

3. a. $(0, 5), (2, 1)$

   b. no solution

4. a.

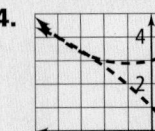

   b. infinite, one, or none

Lesson Check

1. $(1, 2), (2, 3)$

2. $(1, -1), (2, 0)$

3. $(2, -5), \left(-\frac{4}{3}, \frac{25}{9}\right)$

4.

5.

6. For each system of eqs., linear or quadratic, to solve the system you need to find the pt. (or pts.) of intersection or, in the case of inequalities, the regions of intersection. A linear system of eqs. can have one, infinite, or no solutions, whereas a quadratic system of eqs. can have one, two, infinite, or no solutions.

You can use the techniques for solving a linear system of inequalities to solve a quadratic system of inequalities.

Plan

How can you find the solution?
Graph each inequality and find the region where the graphs overlap.

Problem 4 Solving a Quadratic System of Inequalities

What is the solution of the system of inequalities? $\begin{cases} y < -x^2 - 9x - 2 \\ y > x^2 - 2 \end{cases}$

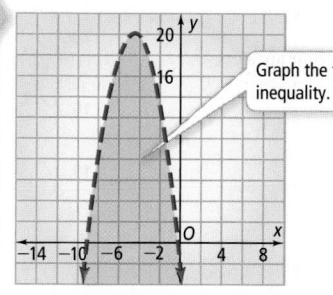

Graph the first inequality.

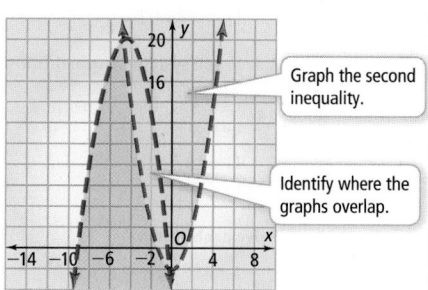

Graph the second inequality.

Identify where the graphs overlap.

The solution of this system is the region where the graphs overlap. The region contains no boundary points.

Got It? 4. a. What is the solution of this system of inequalities? $\begin{cases} y \le -x^2 - 4x + 3 \\ y > x^2 + 3 \end{cases}$

    b. **Reasoning** How many solutions can a system of inequalities have?

Lesson Check

Do you know HOW?

Solve each system by substitution.

1. $\begin{cases} y = x^2 - 2x + 3 \\ y = x + 1 \end{cases}$

2. $\begin{cases} y = 2x^2 - 5x + 2 \\ y = x - 2 \end{cases}$

3. $\begin{cases} y = x^2 - 3x - 3 \\ y = -2x^2 - x + 5 \end{cases}$

Solve each system by graphing.

4. $\begin{cases} y > 2x^2 + x + 3 \\ y < -x^2 - 4x + 1 \end{cases}$

5. $\begin{cases} y > -3x^2 - 6x + 1 \\ y < -2x^2 - 3x + 5 \end{cases}$

Do you UNDERSTAND? MATHEMATICAL PRACTICES

6. **Compare and Contrast** How are solving systems of two linear equations or inequalities and solving systems of two quadratic equations or inequalities alike? How are they different?

7. **Reasoning** How many points of intersection can graphs of the following types of functions have? Draw graphs to justify your answers.
    a. a linear function and a quadratic function
    b. two quadratic functions
    c. a quadratic function and an absolute value function (*Hint:* Graph $y = x^2$ and $y = |x|$ together. Can you transform one of the graphs slightly to increase the number of intersections?)

Problem 4

Q What is the domain of the solution? **[−4.5 < x < 0]**
Q What is the range of the solution? **[−2 < y < 18.25]**
Q Will two quadratic inequalities always intersect? Why? **[No. A quadratic inequality opening upward with a positive minimum, shaded inside, will not intersect with a quadratic inequality opening downward with a negative maximum, shaded inside.]**

Got It? ERROR PREVENTION

Q Does the region contain any boundary points? Explain. **[Yes; the first inequality is not strict, so that parabola is included for −2 < x < 0.]**

3 Lesson Check

Do you know HOW? ERROR INTERVENTION

• Exercise 4 has a very narrow region of overlap. If students assume that there is no solution, then suggest they graph the parabolas on a calculator and zoom in on the intersection.

Do you UNDERSTAND? TACTILE LEARNERS

• For Exercise 7, if students have difficulty visualizing intersections, have them sketch the curves on patty paper and explore different ways to position one curve on top of another.

Close

Q How are linear systems similar to, yet different from, quadratic systems? **[Answers may vary. Sample: Both kinds of systems are similar because they can be solved by graphing or substitution; they are different because only a quadratic system can have exactly two solutions.]**

Answers

c. four, three, two, one, or zero

7. a. two, one, or zero

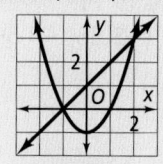

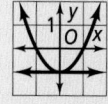

b. two, one, or zero

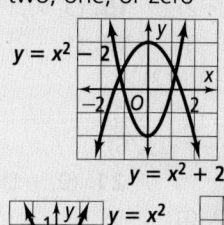

$y = x^2 - 2$

$y = x^2 + 2$

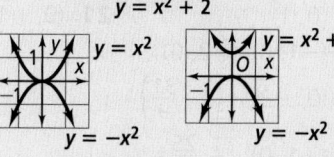

$y = x^2$ $y = x^2 + 1$

$y = -x^2$ $y = -x^2$

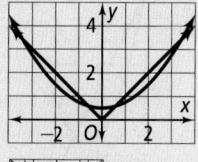

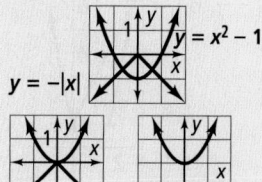

$y = x^2 - 1$

$y = -|x|$

4 Practice

ASSIGNMENT GUIDE

Basic: 8–28 all, 29–31, 39–41, 47

Average: 9–27 odd, 29–55

Advanced: 9–27 odd, 29–61

Standardized Test Prep: 62–65

Mixed Review: 66–77

 Mathematical Practices are supported by exercises with red headings. Here are the Practices supported in this lesson:

MP 1: Make Sense of Problems Ex. 29

MP 2: Reason Abstractly Ex. 52

MP 3: Communicate Ex. 6, 30

MP 3: Construct Arguments Ex. 30

MP 3: Compare Arguments Ex. 7

MP 3: Critique the Reasoning of Others Ex. 40

Applications exercises have blue headings. Exercise 47 supports MP 4: Model.

EXERCISE 47: Use the Think About a Plan worksheet in the **Practice and Problem Solving Workbook** (also available in the Teaching Resources in print and online) to further support students' development in becoming independent learners.

HOMEWORK QUICK CHECK

To check students' understanding of key skills and concepts, go over Exercises 9, 15, 29, 40, and 47.

A Practice

Solve each system by graphing. Check your answers.   ◀ See Problem 1.

8. $\begin{cases} y = -x^2 + 2x + 1 \\ y = 2x + 1 \end{cases}$

9. $\begin{cases} y = x^2 - 2x + 1 \\ y = 2x + 1 \end{cases}$

10. $\begin{cases} y = x^2 - x + 3 \\ y = -2x + 5 \end{cases}$

11. $\begin{cases} y = 2x^2 + 3x + 1 \\ y = -2x + 1 \end{cases}$

12. $\begin{cases} y = -x^2 - 3x + 2 \\ y = x + 6 \end{cases}$

13. $\begin{cases} y = -x^2 - 2x - 2 \\ y = x - 4 \end{cases}$

Solve each system by substitution. Check your answers.   ◀ See Problem 2.

14. $\begin{cases} y = x^2 + 4x + 1 \\ y = x + 1 \end{cases}$

15. $\begin{cases} y = -x^2 + 2x + 10 \\ y = x + 4 \end{cases}$

16. $\begin{cases} y = -x^2 + x - 1 \\ y = -x - 1 \end{cases}$

17. $\begin{cases} y = 2x^2 - 3x - 1 \\ y = x - 3 \end{cases}$

18. $\begin{cases} y = x^2 - 3x - 20 \\ y = -x - 5 \end{cases}$

19. $\begin{cases} y = -x^2 - 5x - 1 \\ y = x + 2 \end{cases}$

Solve each system.   ◀ See Problem 3.

20. $\begin{cases} y = x^2 + 5x + 1 \\ y = x^2 + 2x + 1 \end{cases}$

21. $\begin{cases} y = x^2 - 2x - 1 \\ y = -x^2 - 2x - 1 \end{cases}$

22. $\begin{cases} y = -x^2 - 3x - 2 \\ y = x^2 + 3x + 2 \end{cases}$

23. $\begin{cases} y = -x^2 - x - 3 \\ y = 2x^2 - 2x - 3 \end{cases}$

24. $\begin{cases} y = -3x^2 - x + 2 \\ y = x^2 + 2x + 1 \end{cases}$

25. $\begin{cases} y = x^2 + 2x + 1 \\ y = x^2 + 2x - 1 \end{cases}$

Solve each system by graphing.   ◀ See Problem 4.

26. $\begin{cases} y > x^2 + 2x \\ y > x^2 - 1 \end{cases}$

27. $\begin{cases} y > x^2 - 3x \\ y < 2x^2 - 3x \end{cases}$

28. $\begin{cases} y < -x^2 - 3x \\ y > x^2 - 1 \end{cases}$

B Apply

© **29. Think About a Plan** A manufacturer is making cardboard boxes by cutting out four equal squares from the corners of the rectangular piece of cardboard and then folding the remaining part into a box. The length of the cardboard piece is 1 in. longer than its width. The manufacturer can cut out either 3 × 3 in. squares, or 4 × 4 in. squares. Find the dimensions of the cardboard for which the volume of the boxes produced by both methods will be the same.
- How can you represent the volume of the box using one variable?
- What system of equations can you write?
- Which method can you use to solve the system?

© **30. Open-Ended** Can you solve the system of equations shown by graphing? Justify your answer. Can you solve this system using another method? If so, solve the system and explain why you chose that method. $\begin{cases} x = y^2 + 2y + 1 \\ y = x - 4 \end{cases}$

Solve each system by substitution.

31. $\begin{cases} x + y = 3 \\ y = x^2 - 8x - 9 \end{cases}$

32. $\begin{cases} y - 2x = x + 5 \\ y + 1 = x^2 + 5x + 3 \end{cases}$

33. $\begin{cases} y - \frac{1}{2}x^2 = 1 + 3x \\ y + \frac{1}{2}x^2 = x \end{cases}$

34. $\begin{cases} x + y - 2 = 0 \\ x^2 + y - 8 = 0 \end{cases}$

35. $\begin{cases} x^2 - y = x + 4 \\ x - 1 = y + 3 \end{cases}$

36. $\begin{cases} 2y = y - x^2 + 1 \\ y = x^2 - 5x - 2 \end{cases}$

Answers

Practice and Problem-Solving Exercises (continued)

8. (0, 1);

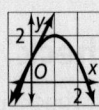

9. (0, 1), (4, 9);

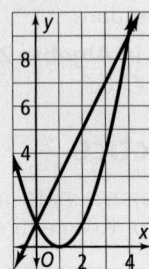

10. (−2, 9), (1, 3);

11. (0, 1), $\left(-\frac{5}{2}, 6\right)$;

12. (−2, 4);

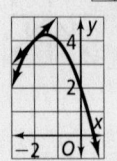

13. $\left(\dfrac{-3 + \sqrt{17}}{2}, \dfrac{-11 + \sqrt{17}}{2}\right),$ $\left(\dfrac{-3 - \sqrt{17}}{2}, \dfrac{-11 - \sqrt{17}}{2}\right)$
$\approx (0.56, -3.44), (-3.56, -7.56)$

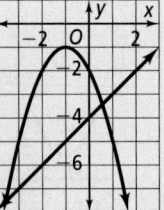

14. (0, 1), (−3, −2)   15. (3, 7), (−2, 2)

16. (0, −1), (2, −3)   17. (1, −2)

18. (5, −10), (−3, −2)

19. $(-3 + \sqrt{6}, -1 + \sqrt{6}),$ $(-3 - \sqrt{6}, -1 - \sqrt{6})$

20. (0, 1)   21. (0, −1)

22. (−1, 0), (−2, 0)

23. (0, −3), $\left(\dfrac{1}{3}, -\dfrac{31}{9}\right)$

24. (−1, 0), $\left(\dfrac{1}{4}, \dfrac{25}{16}\right)$

Graph the solution to each set of inequalities.

37. $\begin{cases} y < -3x^2 + 1 \\ y > x^2 - x - 5 \end{cases}$

38. $\begin{cases} y < 3x^2 + 2x + 1 \\ y > 2x^2 - x + 1 \end{cases}$

39. $\begin{cases} y > x^2 - 5x + 4 \\ y > x^2 + 3x + 2 \end{cases}$

40. **Error Analysis** A classmate graphed the system of inequalities and concluded that because the shaded regions do not intersect, there are no solutions to the system. Describe and correct the error.
$\begin{cases} y \le x^2 - 4x + 6 \\ y \ge x^2 - 4x + 2 \end{cases}$

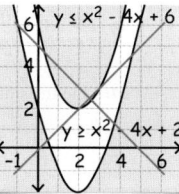

Solve each system.

41. $\begin{cases} y = 3x^2 - 2x - 1 \\ y = x - 1 \end{cases}$

42. $\begin{cases} y = -x^2 + x - 5 \\ y = x - 5 \end{cases}$

43. $\begin{cases} y = x^2 - 3x - 2 \\ y = 4x + 28 \end{cases}$

44. $\begin{cases} y = \frac{1}{2}x^2 + 4x + 4 \\ y = -4x + 12\frac{1}{2} \end{cases}$

45. $\begin{cases} y = -\frac{3}{4}x^2 - 4x \\ y = 3x + 8 \end{cases}$

46. $\begin{cases} y = -\frac{1}{4}x^2 + x + 1 \\ y = x - 4 \end{cases}$

47. **Business** A company's weekly revenue R is given by the formula $R = -p^2 + 30p$, where p is the price of the company's product. The company is considering hiring a distributor, which will cost the company $4p + 25$ per week.
   a. Use a system of equations to find the values of the price p for which the product will still remain profitable if they hire this distributor.
   b. Which value of p will maximize the profit after including the distributor cost?

Solve each system.

48. $\begin{cases} y = 5x^2 + 9x + 4 \\ y = -5x + 3 \end{cases}$

49. $\begin{cases} y = -7x^2 - 9x + 6 \\ y = \frac{1}{2}x + 11 \end{cases}$

50. $\begin{cases} y = x^2 + 3x + 6 \\ y = -x + 2 \end{cases}$

51. $\begin{cases} y = -4x^2 + 7x + 1 \\ y = 3x + 2 \end{cases}$

52. **Reasoning** Sketch the graphs of $y = 2x^2 + 4x - 5$ and $y = x^2 + 2x - 3$. Change these equations into inequalities so the system has solutions that comprise:
   a. two non-overlapping regions   **b.** one bounded region

Solve the systems by graphing. For each system indicate one point in the solution set.

53. $\begin{cases} y < x^2 - 1 \\ y > 3x^2 - 3 \end{cases}$

54. $\begin{cases} y > x^2 \\ y < -x^2 + 1 \end{cases}$

55. $\begin{cases} y > (x - 3)^2 + 4 \\ y < -(x - 3)^2 + 5 \end{cases}$

Challenge

56. Find a value of a for which the line $y = x + a$ separates the parabolas $y = x^2 - 3x + 2$ and $y = -x^2 + 8x - 15$.

---

40. The solution of the system is the common area (shaded) on the graph. So, yes, there are solutions, even though the graphs of the parabolas do not intersect.

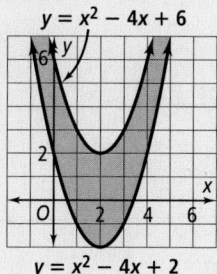

$y = x^2 - 4x + 6$

$y = x^2 - 4x + 2$

41. $(0, -1)$, $(1, 0)$

42. $(0, -5)$

43. $(10, 68)$, $(-3, 16)$

44. $(-17, 80.5)$, $(1, 8.5)$

45. $(-8, -16)$, $\left(-\frac{4}{3}, 4\right)$

46. $(4.47, 0.47)$, $(-4.47, -8.47)$

47. **a.** $0 < p < 25$ **b.** 13

48. $\left(\frac{-7 + 2\sqrt{11}}{5}, 10 - 2\sqrt{11}\right)$,
    $\left(\frac{-7 - 2\sqrt{11}}{5}, 10 + 2\sqrt{11}\right)$
    $\approx (-0.0734, 3.3668)$, $(-2.7266, 16.6332)$

49. no solution

50. $(-2, 4)$ 51. $\left(\frac{1}{2}, \frac{7}{2}\right)$

52.

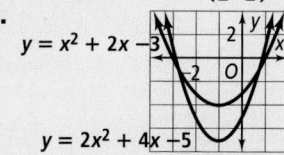

$y = x^2 + 2x - 3$

$y = 2x^2 + 4x - 5$

a.

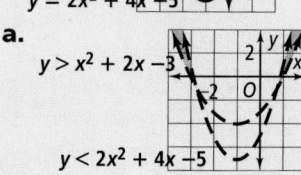

$y > x^2 + 2x - 3$

$y < 2x^2 + 4x - 5$

b.

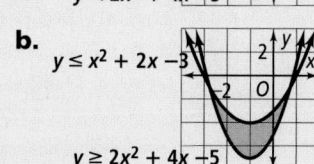

$y \le x^2 + 2x - 3$

$y \ge 2x^2 + 4x - 5$

53. 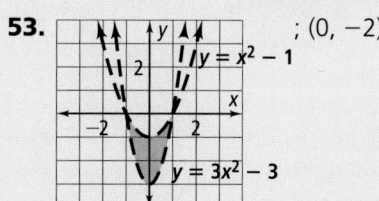 ; $(0, -2)$

$y = x^2 - 1$

$y = 3x^2 - 3$

54. 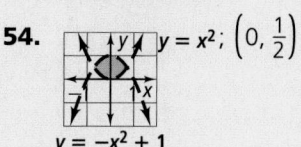 $y = x^2$; $\left(0, \frac{1}{2}\right)$

$y = -x^2 + 1$

55. 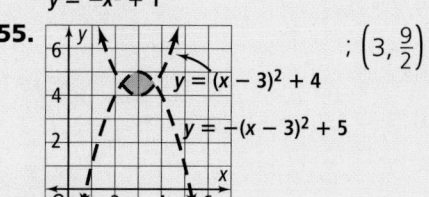 ; $\left(3, \frac{9}{2}\right)$

$y = (x - 3)^2 + 4$

$y = -(x - 3)^2 + 5$

56. Answers may vary. Sample: -2.5

---

25. no solution

26.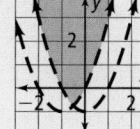

Then graph $y = -1 + \sqrt{x}$ and $y = -1 - \sqrt{x}$ along with the second equation.

31. $(8.42, -5.42)$, $(-1.42, 4.42)$

32. $(-3, -4)$, $(1, 8)$

33. $\left(-1, -\frac{3}{2}\right)$

34. $(3, -1)$, $(-2, 4)$

35. $(0, -4)$, $(2, -2)$

36. $(3, -8)$, $(-0.5, 0.75)$

27.

28.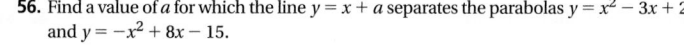

29. width = 20.45 in. and length = 21.45 in.; or width = 6.55 in. and length = 7.55 in.

30. The system can be solved by graphing or substitution: $(5.30, 1.30)$, $(1.70, -2.30)$. To solve graphically, solve the first equation for y: $y = -1 \pm \sqrt{x}$.

37.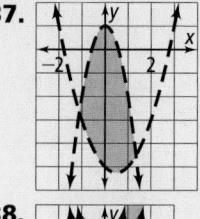

38.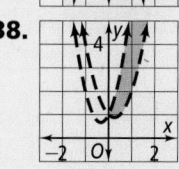

39.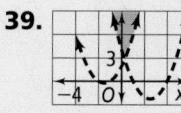

Answers

Practice and Problem-Solving Exercises (continued)

57. never; $x^2 + c \neq x^2 + d$

58. always; $(0, c)$

59. always; $\left(\dfrac{-a-b}{2}, \dfrac{a^2 - 2ab + b^2}{2}\right)$

60. sometimes; for example, no solution if $a > 0, c > 0, b < 0, d < 0$

61. $\sqrt{5} - 1$ units

Standardized Test Prep

62. C

63. F

64. C

65. [2] $x = \dfrac{-b \pm \sqrt{b^2 - 4ac}}{2a}$

$x = \dfrac{-(5) \pm \sqrt{(5)^2 - 4(-3)(4)}}{2(-3)}$

$x = \dfrac{5 \pm \sqrt{73}}{6}$

[1] appropriate method, with one computational error

Mixed Review

66. $-4 + 3i$

67. $7 + 7i$

68. $3 + 3i$

69. $-1, -\dfrac{3}{2}$

70. $1, 3$

71. $\dfrac{3}{5}$

72. $y = -(k-2)^2 + 10$

73. $y = (x+3)^2 - 8$

74. $y = 2(n-2)^2 - 11$

75. $11q$

76. $2a^2b + ab^2$

77. $-y^2 + 2y$

Determine whether the following systems *always, sometimes,* or *never* have solutions. (Assume that different letters refer to unequal constants.) Explain.

57. $\begin{cases} y = x^2 + c \\ y = x^2 + d \end{cases}$

58. $\begin{cases} y = ax^2 + c \\ y = bx^2 + c \end{cases}$

59. $\begin{cases} y = (x + a)^2 \\ y = (x + b)^2 \end{cases}$

60. $\begin{cases} y = a(x + m)^2 + c \\ y = b(x + n)^2 + d \end{cases}$

61. Find the side of the square with vertical and horizontal sides inscribed in the region representing the solution of the system $\begin{cases} y \leq -x^2 + 1 \\ y \geq x^2 - 1 \end{cases}$.

Standardized Test Prep

SAT/ACT

62. How many solutions does the system have? $\begin{cases} y = -\frac{1}{4}x^2 - 2x \\ y = x^2 + \frac{3}{4} \end{cases}$

Ⓐ 0   Ⓑ 1   Ⓒ 2   Ⓓ 3

63. Which expression is equivalent to $(-3 + 2i)(2 - 3i)$?

Ⓕ $13i$ Ⓖ 12 Ⓗ $12 + 13i$ Ⓘ -12

64. Which expression is equivalent to $(2 - 7i) \div (2i)^3$?

Ⓐ $\frac{7}{8} - \frac{1}{4}i$ Ⓑ $\frac{1}{4} - \frac{7}{8}i$ Ⓒ $\frac{7}{8} + \frac{1}{4}i$ Ⓓ $\frac{1}{4} + \frac{7}{8}i$

Short Response

65. Solve the equation $-3x^2 + 5x + 4 = 0$. Show your work.

Mixed Review

Find the sum or difference.   ◀ See Lesson 4-8.

66. $(1 - i) + (-5 + 4i)$ **67.** $(3 + 4i) - (-4 - 3i)$ **68.** $(1 + i) + (2 + 2i)$

Solve each equation using the Quadratic Formula.   ◀ See Lesson 4-7.

69. $2m^2 + 5m + 3 = 0$ **70.** $p^2 - 4p + 3 = 0$ **71.** $25x^2 - 30x + 9 = 0$

Rewrite each equation in vertex form.   ◀ See Lesson 4-6.

72. $y = -k^2 + 4k + 6$ **73.** $y = x^2 + 6x + 1$ **74.** $y = 2n^2 - 8n - 3$

Get Ready!   **To prepare for Lesson 5-1, do Exercises 75–77.**

Simplify by combining like terms.   ◀ See Lesson 1-3.

75. $3q + 9q - q$ **76.** $-2ab^2 + 2a^2b + 3ab^2$ **77.** $-4y^2 + 2y + 3y^2$

Lesson Resources

Differentiated Remediation

Additional Instructional Support

Algebra 2 Companion

Students can use the **Algebra 2 Companion** worktext (4 pages) as you teach the lesson. Use the Companion to support

- New Vocabulary
- Key Concepts
- Got It for each Problem
- Lesson Check

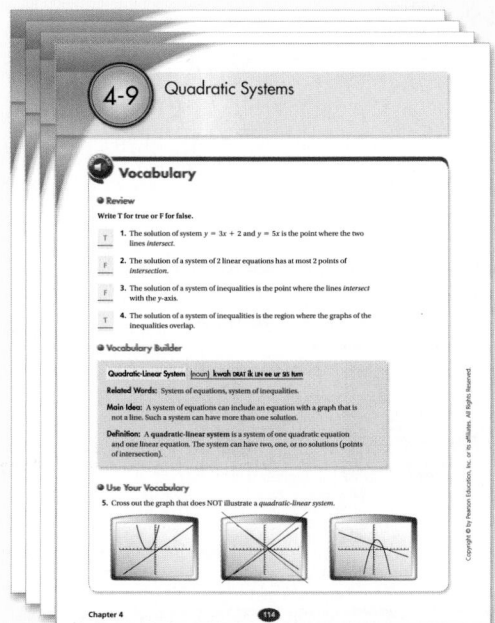

ELL Support

Use Manipulatives Sketch a line on 2 transparencies and a parabola on 2 more transparencies.

First, review the number of real solutions of a system of 2 linear equations. Demonstrate the number of intersections (solutions) for each: none (parallel lines), 1, or infinitely many (the lines coincide).

Then, show a line and a parabola. It is possible that they do not intersect at all, at 1 point, or at 2 points. They will not, however, intersect at infinitely many points.

Finally, show the 2 parabolas. Demonstrate where they intersect at no points, 1 point, 2 points, and infinitely many points.

5 Assess & Remediate

Lesson Quiz

1. Do you UNDERSTAND? How many solutions can a linear-quadratic system have? Explain what the number of solutions means about a graph of the system.

2. Solve and check: $\begin{cases} y = x^2 - 6x + 12 \\ y = x + 2 \end{cases}$

3. Solve and check: $\begin{cases} y = x^2 - 3x + 6 \\ y = -x^2 + 7x + 6 \end{cases}$

4. Solve: $\begin{cases} y > x^2 - x + 1 \\ y < -x^2 + x + 5 \end{cases}$

ANSWERS TO LESSON QUIZ

1. Answers may vary. Samples: There can be 2, 1, or no solutions. 2 solutions means the line intersects the parabola twice; 1 solution means a line intersects the parabola once; no solution means the line never intersects the parabola.

2. (2, 4) and (5, 7)

3. (0, 6) and (5, 16)

4.

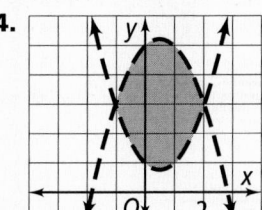

PRESCRIPTION FOR REMEDIATION

Use the student work on the Lesson Quiz to prescribe a differentiated review assignment:

Points	Differentiated Remediation
0–2	Intervention
3	On-level
4	Extension

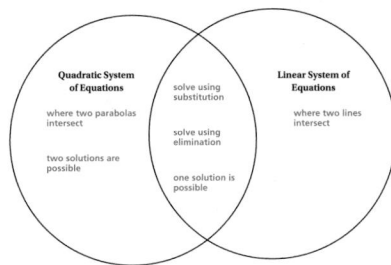

PowerAlgebra.com

5 Assess & Remediate

Assign the Lesson Quiz. Appropriate intervention, practice, or enrichment is automatically generated based on student performance.

Intervention

- **Reteaching** (2 pages) Provides reteaching and practice exercises for the key lesson concepts. Use with struggling students or absent students.

- **English Language Learner Support** Helps students develop and reinforce mathematical vocabulary and key concepts.

All-in-One Resources/Online
Reteaching

All-in-One Resources/Online
English Language Learner Support

Differentiated Remediation *continued*

On-Level

- **Practice** (2 pages) Provides extra practice for each lesson. For simpler practice exercises, use the Form K Practice pages found in the All-in-One Teaching Resources and online.

- **Think About a Plan** Helps students develop specific problem-solving skills and strategies by providing scaffolded guiding questions.
- **Standardized Test Prep** Focuses on all major exercises, all major question types, and helps students prepare for the high-stakes assessments.

Extension

- **Enrichment** Provides students with interesting problems and activities that extend the concepts of the lesson.
- **Activities, Games, and Puzzles** Worksheets that can be used for concepts development, enrichment, and for fun!

Practice and Problem Solving Wkbk/All-in-One Resources/Online
Practice page 1

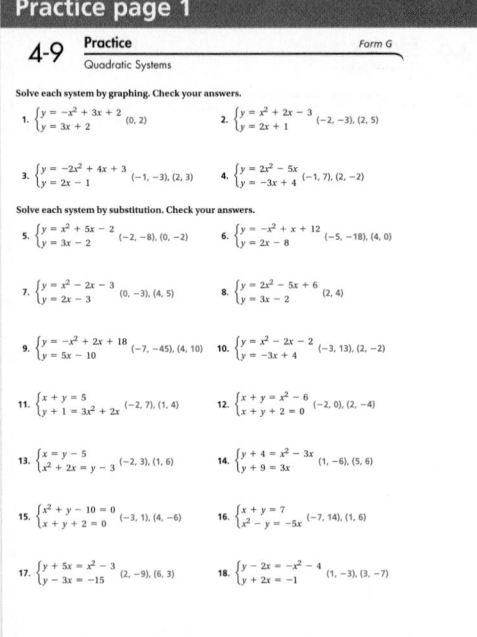

Practice and Problem Solving Wkbk/All-in-One Resources/Online
Practice page 2

All-in-One Resources/Online
Enrichment

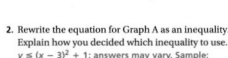
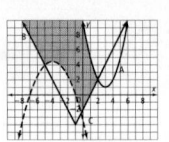
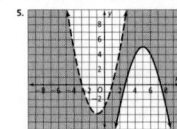
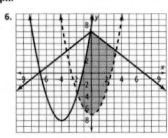

Practice and Problem Solving Wkbk/All-in-One Resources/Online
Think About a Plan

Practice and Problem Solving Wkbk/All-in-One Resources/Online
Standardized Test Prep

Online Teacher Resource Center
Activities, Games, and Puzzles

Powers of Complex Numbers

Common Core State Standards

Extends N-CN.A.2 Use the relation $i^2 = -1$ and the commutative, associative, and distributive properties to add, subtract, and multiply . . .

MP 5

You can use the rules for multiplying complex numbers to find powers of complex numbers.

Example 1

Compute and graph $(2i)^n$, for $n = 0, 1, 2,$ and 3.

n	$(2i)^n$
0	$(2i)^0 = 1$
1	$(2i)^1 = 2i$
2	$(2i)^2 = 4i^2 = 4(-1) = -4$
3	$(2i)^3 = 8i^3 = 8(i^2 \cdot i) = 8(-1 \cdot i) = -8i$

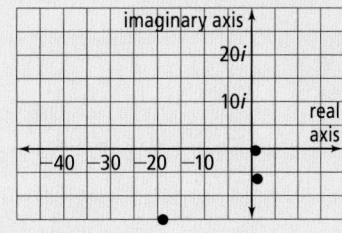

Example 2

Compute and graph $(2 - 3i)^n$, for $n = 0, 1, 2,$ and 3.

n	$(2 - 3i)^n$
0	$(2 - 3i)^0 = 1$
1	$(2 - 3i)^1 = 2 - 3i$
2	$(2 - 3i)^2 = 4 - 6i - 6i + 9i^2 = 4 - 12i + 9(-1) = -5 - 12i$
3	$(2 - 3i)^3 = -10 - 24i + 15i + 36i^2 = -10 - 9i + 36(-1) = -46 - 9i$

Exercises

1. Based on the graph in Example 1, predict the location of $(2i)^5$.

2. Compute and graph $(-3i)^n$ for $n = 0, 1, 2,$ and 3.

3. **a.** Connect the points from the graph in Example 1 with a smooth curve. Estimate $(2i)^{\frac{1}{2}}$.
   b. Use a graphing calculator to compute $(2i)^{\frac{1}{2}}$. Does it fall on the curve? Was it close to your estimate?

4. Use a graphing calculator to find values of $(2 - 3i)^n$ for $n = 0.5, 1.5,$ and 2.5. Copy the graph and add these points.

5. Compute and graph $(3 - 4i)^n$ for $n = 0, 1, 2,$ and 3.

PowerAlgebra.com | Concept Byte Powers of Complex Numbers | **265**

Answers

Exercises

1. $0 + 32i$

2.

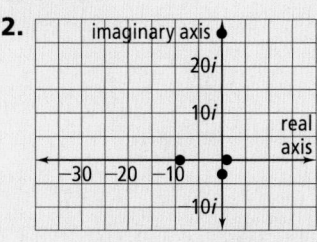

$(1 + 0i, 0 - 3i, -9 + 0i, 0 + 27i)$

3. a. $1 + i$
   b. $1 + i$; yes

4. $n = 0.5, 1.674 - 0.896i$
$n = 1.5, 0.6604 - 6.8144i$
$n = 2.5, -19.1225 - 15.6099i$

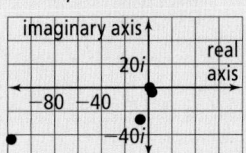

5. $n = 0, 1$
$n = 1, 3 - 4i$
$n = 2, -7 - 24i$
$n = 3, -117 - 44i$

Guided Instruction

PURPOSE To investigate powers of complex numbers

PROCESS Students will

- use repeated multiplication to algebraically evaluate powers of complex numbers.
- use a calculator to evaluate fractional powers of complex numbers.
- graph powers of a complex number.

DISCUSS   **VISUAL LEARNERS**

The graph of a complex number raised to successively higher powers circles around the origin in a rapidly expanding pattern.

Q How can you evaluate the square of a complex number? **[Answers may vary. Sample: Write as a product of binomials and use FOIL.]**

Example 1

Q In what direction does the curve move around the origin? **[counterclockwise]**

Q Which powers are on the imaginary axis? real axis? **[odd powers; even powers]**

VISUAL

Compare the graphs to reinforce the difference between pure imaginary and complex numbers.

Example 2

Q Do any of the positive integer powers lie on the axes? Explain. **[No; the positive integer values are neither real numbers nor pure imaginary numbers.]**

Exercises

Q For Exercise 4, do the powers lie on the graph where you would expect them to be—between the integer powers? Explain. **[Answers may vary. Sample: Yes; they lie on the spiral curve.]**

Mathematical Practices This Concept Byte supports students in using appropriate tools, Mathematical Practice 5.

Completing the Performance Task

In the Apply What You've Learned sections in Lessons 4-2, 4-3, and 4-5, students wrote and analyzed four functions based on information from page 193. Here, students use information from the profit function and the selling-price function to complete the Performance Task. Ask students the following questions as they work toward solving the problem.

Q How can you use the work you have done in the chapter to solve the problem? **[Sample: To find the lowest and highest prices that will give Victor a profit, I can evaluate the selling-price function that I wrote in Lesson 4-2 at the profit function's zeros, which I found in Lesson 4-5. To find the price that will maximize Victor's profit, I can evaluate the selling-price function at the x-coordinate of the profit function's vertex, which I found in Lesson 4-3.]**

Q How can you use a graph of the profit function $y = P(x)$ to identify all the x-values for which Victor earns a profit? **[Sample: Identify points on the graph that are above the x-axis. Those points have positive y-values, indicating a profit.]**

FOSTERING MATHEMATICAL DISCOURSE

Have students discuss alternative methods for solving the problem in the Performance Task, including writing the cost, revenue, and profit functions in terms of the variable s (selling price) instead of x (number of bags sold at price s).

ANSWERS

1. Victor can make a profit with a selling price from $.31 to $1.37 per bag; he will maximize his profit with a selling price of $.84 per bag.

2. Check students' work.

On Your Own

This problem is similar to the problem posed on page 193, but now students must find the maximum profit in addition to finding the selling price that gives the maximum profit. Students should strive to solve this problem independently.

ANSWERS

a. Victor can charge at most $7.99.

b. Victor's maximum weekly profit from sandwiches is $1056.25 at a selling price of $4.75.

Pull It **All Together**

Completing the Performance Task

Look back at your results from the Apply What You've Learned sections in Lessons 4-2, 4-3, and 4-5. Use the work you did to complete the following.

To solve these problems, you will pull together many concepts and skills related to solving quadratic equations. Be sure to show your work and justify your reasoning.

1. Solve the problem in the Task Description on page 193 by finding all possible prices Victor can charge for a bag of chips in order to make a profit, and determining the price he should charge to maximize his profit. Show all your work and explain each step of your solution.

2. Reflect Choose one of the Mathematical Practices below and explain how you applied it in your work on the Performance Task.

MP 1: Make sense of problems and persevere in solving them.

MP 2: Reason abstractly and quantitatively.

MP 4: Model with mathematics.

On Your Own

At his sandwich shop, Victor charges customers $5.00 for a sandwich, and sells an average of 300 sandwiches per week. He wonders if lowering his selling price will increase his sandwich sales. One week, Victor offers sandwiches at $3.00 instead of $5.00. That week, he sells 500 sandwiches.

Victor's cost per sandwich is $1.50. He assumes a linear relationship between the selling price per sandwich and the number of sandwiches sold per week.

a. Determine the greatest price Victor can charge and still make a profit.

b. Determine Victor's maximum weekly profit from sandwich sales and the selling price that gives him that profit.

 **Chapter Review**

Connecting **BIG** ideas and Answering the Essential Questions

1 Equivalence
Vertex form of a quadratic function shows the vertex of the parabola. Standard form is "calculator ready." Both forms give additional information.

2 Function
Any quadratic function is possibly a stretch or compression, a reflection, and a translation of $y = x^2$.

3 Solving Equations and Inequalities
The real solutions of a quadratic equation show the zeros of the related quadratic function and the x-intercepts of its graph.

The Different Forms of a Quadratic Function (Lessons 4-1 and 4-2)
$y = 2(x - 1)^2 + 3$ has vertex $(1, 3)$ and opens upward $(2 > 0)$.
$y = -2x^2 + 4x + 1$ has vertex with x-coordinate $-\frac{4}{2(-2)} = 1$ and opens downward $(-2 < 0)$.
Each has axis of symmetry $x = 1$.
Each is a stretch of $y = x^2$ by the factor 2.

Helpful Aids for Solving Quadratic Equations (Lessons 4-4, 4-6, 4-8)
Factor a quadratic: $-16x^2 + 12x + 4$
$\qquad = -4(4x + 1)(x - 1)$
Complete the square: $x^2 + 4x + 1$
$= x^2 + 4x + \left(\frac{4}{2}\right)^2 + 1 - \left(\frac{4}{2}\right)^2$
$= (x + 2)^2 - 3$
Complex numbers: $x^2 + 1 = (x + i)(x - i)$
$\qquad$ where $i = \sqrt{-1}$.

Modeling With Quadratics (Lessons 4-3 and 4-9)
$y = -16x^2 + 12x + 4$ can model the height y in feet reached by the coin tossed by the referee before the game. x represents time in seconds.

Solving Quadratic Equations (Lessons 4-5, 4-7)
$-16x^2 + 12x + 4 = 0 \quad \rightarrow$
$-4(4x + 1)(x - 1) = 0 \quad \rightarrow$
$x = -\frac{1}{4}$ or $x = 1$.
$-2x^2 + 4x + 1 = 0 \quad \rightarrow$
$x = \frac{-4 \pm \sqrt{4^2 - 4(-2)(1)}}{2(-2)} \quad \rightarrow$
$x = 1 + \frac{\sqrt{6}}{2}$ or $x = 1 - \frac{\sqrt{6}}{2}$.

Chapter Vocabulary

- absolute value of a complex number (p. 249)
- axis of symmetry (p. 194)
- completing the square (p. 235)
- complex conjugate (p. 251)
- complex number (p. 249)
- complex number plane (p. 249)
- difference of two squares (p. 220)
- discriminant (p. 242)
- factoring (p. 216)
- greatest common factor (p. 218)
- imaginary number (p. 249)
- imaginary unit (p. 248)
- maximum value (p. 195)
- minimum value (p. 195)
- parabola (p. 194)
- perfect square trinomial (p. 219)
- pure imaginary number (p. 249)
- quadratic formula (p. 240)
- quadratic function (p. 194)
- standard form (p. 202)
- vertex form (p. 194)
- vertex of the parabola (p. 194)
- zero of a function (p. 226)
- zero product property (p. 226)

Choose the correct term to complete each sentence.

1. To solve an equation by factoring, the equation should first be written in (standard form/vertex form).

2. The value of $b^2 - 4ac$ for the equation $ax^2 + bx + c = 0$ is called the (discriminant/difference of two squares).

3. The number $a + bi$, where $b = 0$, is an example of a(n) (imaginary/complex) number.

Essential Questions

BIG idea **Equivalence**
ESSENTIAL QUESTION What are the advantages of a quadratic function in vertex form? in standard form?
ANSWER Vertex form of a quadratic function shows the vertex of the parabola. Standard form is "calculator ready." Both forms give additional information.

BIG idea **Function**
ESSENTIAL QUESTION How is any quadratic function related to the parent quadratic function $y = x^2$?
ANSWER Any quadratic function is possibly a stretch or compression, a reflection, and/or a translation of $y = x^2$.

BIG idea **Solving Equations**
ESSENTIAL QUESTION How are the real solutions of a quadratic equation related to the graph of the related quadratic function?
ANSWER The real solutions of a quadratic equation show the zeros of the related quadratic function and the x-intercepts of its graph.

Answers

Chapter Review
1. standard
2. discriminant
3. complex

Summative Questions

Use the following prompts as you review this chapter with your students. The prompts are designed to help you assess your students' understanding of the Big Ideas they have studied.

- Compare and contrast vertex and standard form of a quadratic function. What information does each form give you? Which would you use to graph the function?
- Why might you factor a quadratic equation? What does the Zero-Product Property tell you about the factors?
- What information does the discriminant give you about the number and type of solutions to a quadratic equation?
- When is a complex number the solution to a quadratic equation?
- Compare and contrast factoring, completing the square, and using the Quadratic Formula to solve a quadratic equation. Under what circumstances would you use each one?

Answers

Chapter Review (continued)

4. vertex: $(-2, -6)$; axis of symmetry: $x = -2$; minimum: -6; domain: all real numbers; range: $y \geq -6$

5. vertex: $(3, 2)$; axis of symmetry: $x = 3$; maximum: 2; domain: all real numbers; range: $y \leq 2$

6. vertex: $(1, 5)$; axis of symmetry: $x = 1$; minimum: 5; domain: all real numbers; range: $y \geq 5$

7. vertex: $(-9, -4)$; axis of symmetry: $x = -9$; minimum: -4; domain: all real numbers; range: $y \geq -4$

8. 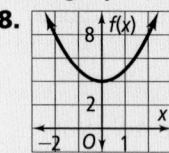 translation 4 units up

9. 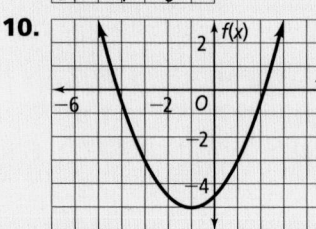 translation 9 units to the right and 2 units up

10. vert. compression by a factor of $\frac{1}{2}$, translation 1 unit to the left and 5 units down

11. $y = 2(x - 2)^2 + 1$

12. $y = \left(-\frac{1}{3}\right)(x + 5)^2 + 4$

4-1 Quadratic Functions and Transformations

Quick Review

You can write every **quadratic function** in the form $f(x) = ax^2 + bx + c$, where $a \neq 0$. A **parabola** is the graph of a quadratic function. Every parabola has a vertex and an axis of symmetry. Shown below is the graph of the quadratic parent function $f(x) = x^2$.

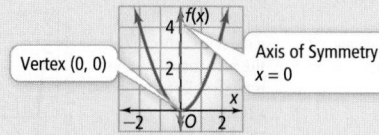

The **vertex form** of a quadratic function is $f(x) = a(x - h)^2 + k$, where $a \neq 0$. The vertex of the parabola formed by a quadratic function is (h, k).

If $a > 0$, k is the **minimum value** of the function.

If $a < 0$, k is the **maximum value** of the function. The axis of symmetry is given by $x = h$.

Example

What is the vertex, axis of symmetry, maximum or minimum, and domain and range of the function $f(x) = 5(x - 7)^2 + 2$?

$a = 5, h = 7, k = 2$	Identify a, h, and k.
vertex: $(7, 2)$	Find the vertex: (h, k).
axis of symmetry: $x = 7$	The axis of symmetry is at $x = h$.
$k = 2$ is a minimum	Since $a > 0$, k is a minimum.
domain: all real numbers	There are no restrictions on x.
range: $y \geq 2$.	Since the minimum is 2, $y \geq 2$.

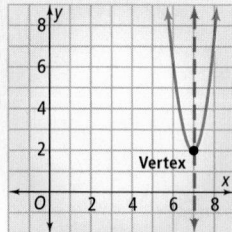

Exercises

Identify the vertex, axis of symmetry, maximum or minimum, and domain and range of each function.

4. $f(x) = 4(x + 2)^2 - 6$

5. $f(x) = -(x - 3)^2 + 2$

6. $f(x) = 10(x - 1)^2 + 5$

7. $f(x) = 2(x + 9)^2 - 4$

Graph each function. Describe each transformation of the parent function $f(x) = x^2$.

8. $f(x) = x^2 + 4$

9. $f(x) = (x - 9)^2 + 2$

10. $f(x) = \frac{1}{2}(x + 1)^2 - 5$

Write the equation of each parabola in vertex form.

11.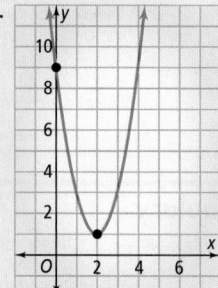

12.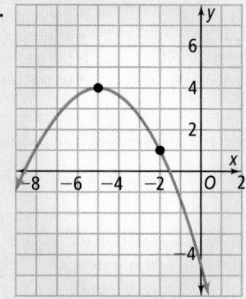

4-2 Standard Form of a Quadratic Function

Quick Review

The **standard form** of a quadratic function is $f(x) = ax^2 + bx + c$, where $a \neq 0$. When $a > 0$, the parabola opens up. When $a < 0$, the parabola opens down.

The axis of symmetry is the line $x = -\frac{b}{2a}$. The vertex is $\left(-\frac{b}{2a}, f\left(-\frac{b}{2a}\right)\right)$, and the y-intercept is $(0, c)$.

Example

What are the vertex, the axis of symmetry and y-intercept of the graph of the function $f(x) = x^2 - 6x + 8$?

axis of symmetry: $x = -\left(\frac{-6}{2(1)}\right) = 3$

vertex: $(3, -1)$

y-intercept: $(0, 8)$

Exercises

Graph each function.

13. $f(x) = x^2 + 6x + 5$ **14.** $f(x) = x^2 - 7x - 18$

15. $f(x) = x^2 - 7x + 12$ **16.** $f(x) = x^2 - 9$

Write each function in vertex form.

17. $f(x) = 4x^2 - 8x + 2$ **18.** $f(x) = x^2 - 8x + 12$

19. $f(x) = 8x^2 + 8x - 12$ **20.** $f(x) = -2x^2 - 6x + 10$

21. Physics The equation $h = -16t^2 + 32t + 9$ gives the height of a ball, h, in feet above the ground, at t seconds after the ball is thrown upward. How many seconds after the ball is thrown will it reach its maximum height? What is its maximum height?

4-3 Modeling With Quadratic Functions

Quick Review

You can use quadratic functions to model real world data. You can find a quadratic function to model data that passes through any three non-collinear points given that no two of the points lie on a vertical line.

Example

Find the equation of the parabola that passes through the points $(-2, 8)$, $(0, -2)$, and $(1, 2)$.

$y = ax^2 + bx + c$ — Use the standard form of a quadratic function.

$\begin{cases} 8 = a(-2)^2 + b(-2) + c \\ -2 = a(0)^2 + b(0) + c \\ 2 = a(1)^2 + b(1) + c \end{cases}$ — Substitute the (x, y) values to write a system of equations.

$\begin{cases} 4a - 2b + c = 8 \\ c = -2 \\ a + b + c = 2 \end{cases}$

$a = 3, b = 1, c = -2$ — Solve the system of equations. Substitute a, b, and c to find the quadratic function.

$y = 3x^2 + x - 2$

Exercises

Find the equation of the parabola that passes through each set of points.

22. $(0, 5), (2, -3), (-1, 12)$

23. $(2, 0), (3, -2), (1, -2)$

24. $(4, 10), (0, -18), (-2, -20)$

25. $(0, -7), (7, -14), (-3, -19)$

26. Track and Field The table shows the height of a javelin as it is thrown and travels across a horizontal distance. Use your calculator to find a quadratic model to represent the path of the javelin.

Distance (m)	Height (m)
5	2
18	5
33	8
55	6
68	4
74	3

PowerAlgebra.com | Chapter 4   Chapter Review | 269

13.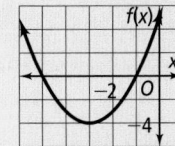

16.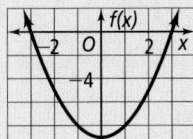

14.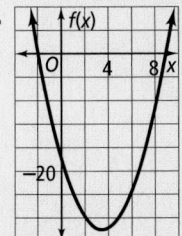

15.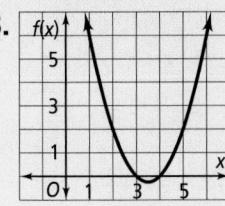

17. $f(x) = 4(x - 1)^2 - 2$

18. $f(x) = (x - 4)^2 - 4$

19. $f(x) = 8\left(x + \frac{1}{2}\right)^2 - 14$

20. $f(x) = -2\left(x + \frac{3}{2}\right)^2 + \frac{29}{2}$

21. 1s; 25 ft

22. $y = x^2 - 6x + 5$

23. $y = -2x^2 + 8x - 8$

24. $y = x^2 + 3x - 18$

25. $y = -0.5x^2 + 2.5x - 7$

26. $y = -0.0043x^2 + 0.3521x + 0.3691$

Answers

Chapter Review (continued)

27. $(x - 6)(x - 2)$

28. $(3x - 4)(x + 5)$

29. $-2(2x - 1)(x - 3)$

30. $(x + 10)(x + 4)$

31. $(x - 7)^2$

32. $(3x + 5)^2$

33. $4(3x - 2)(3x + 2)$

34. $(5x - 2)(5x + 2)$

35. $6x$; $6x(x - 4)$

36. 7; $-7(2x^2 + 7)$

37. $-2, 6$

38. $-2, \frac{7}{2}$

39. $-4, 2$

40. $-9, 2$

41. $1, -2.6$;

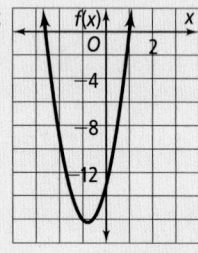

42. $1.345, -3.345$;

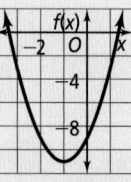

43. $1.618, -0.618$;

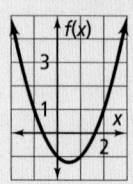

44. $3.236, -1.236$;

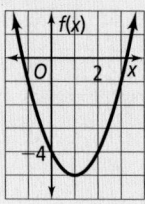

45. $2, 4$

46. no real solutions

47. $4.56, 0.44$

48. $2, 4$

4-4 Factoring Quadratic Expressions

Quick Review

To factor an expression of the form $ax^2 + bx + c$, when $a \neq 1$, you find numbers that have the product ac and sum b. You can also factor an expression using the FOIL method in reverse or by finding the greatest common factor (GCF).

Example

Factor the expression $5x^2 + 13x + 6$.

$ac = (5)(6) = 30$	Find ac.
$30 = 1 \cdot 30 = 2 \cdot 15 = 3 \cdot 10 = 5 \cdot 6$	Find the factors of ac.
$b = 13 = 3 + 10$	Find two factors that sum to b.
$5x^2 + 10x + 3x + 6$	Rewrite bx.
$5x(x + 2) + 3(x + 2)$	Find the common factors.
$(5x + 3)(x + 2)$	Rewrite using the Distributive Property.

Exercises

Factor each expression.

27. $x^2 - 8x + 12$

28. $3x^2 + 11x - 20$

29. $-4x^2 + 14x - 6$

30. $x^2 + 14x + 40$

Factor each perfect square trinomial.

31. $x^2 - 14x + 49$

32. $9x^2 + 30x + 25$

Factor each difference of two squares.

33. $36x^2 - 16$

34. $25x^2 - 4$

Find the GCF of each expression. Then factor each expression.

35. $6x^2 - 24x$

36. $-14x^2 - 49$

4-5 Solving Quadratic Equations

Quick Review

The **zeros** of a quadratic function are the solutions of the related quadratic equation. You can find the zeros from a table or from the x-intercepts of the parabola that is the graph of the function. You can also find them by **factoring** the **standard form of a quadratic equation**, $ax^2 + bx + c = 0$, and using the **Zero-Product Property**.

Example

Solve $2x^2 + 6x = 8$ by factoring.

$2x^2 + 6x - 8 = 0$	Rewrite the equation in standard form.
$2(x^2 + 3x - 4) = 0$	Factor out the GCF, 2.
$2(x + 4)(x - 1) = 0$	Factor the quadratic expression.
$2(x + 4) = 0$ or $x - 1 = 0$	Use the Zero-Product Property.
$x = -4$ or $x = 1$	Solve.

Exercises

Solve each equation by factoring.

37. $x^2 = 4x + 12$

38. $2x^2 - 3x - 14 = 0$

39. $x^2 + 2x = 8$

40. $x^2 + 7x = 18$

Solve each equation by graphing.

41. $5x^2 + 8x - 13 = 0$

42. $9 - 4x = 2x^2$

43. $x^2 - x = 1$

44. $x^2 - 2x - 4 = 0$

Solve each equation by using a table.

45. $x^2 - 6x + 8 = 0$

46. $9x - 14 = 3x^2$

47. $x^2 - 5x + 2 = 0$

48. $2x^2 - 12x = -16$

4-6 Completing the Square

Quick Review

If you cannot solve a quadratic equation by factoring, you can use **completing the square**. You write one side as a perfect square trinomial and then take square roots. You can also convert a quadratic function from standard form to vertex form by completing the square.

Example

Solve $x^2 + 6x - 7 = 0$ by completing the square.

$x^2 + 6x = 7$	Rewrite the equation so the constant is by itself.
$\left(\frac{b}{2}\right)^2 = \left(\frac{6}{2}\right)^2 = 3^2 = 9$	Find $\left(\frac{b}{2}\right)^2$.
$x^2 + 6x + 9 = 7 + 9$	Add $\left(\frac{b}{2}\right)^2$ to each side.
$(x + 3)^2 = 16$	Factor and simplify.
$x + 3 = \pm 4$	Take the square root of each side.
$x = 1$ or $x = -7$	Solve for x.

Exercises

Solve each equation by finding square roots.

49. $4x^2 = 16$

50. $4x^2 - 20 = 0$

51. $5x^2 - 45 = 0$

52. $3x^2 = 36$

What values complete each square?

53. $x^2 - 6x$

54. $x^2 + 3x$

Solve each equation by completing the square.

55. $x^2 + 8x + 6 = 0$

56. $x^2 - 10x = 13$

57. $9x^2 + 6x + 1 = 4$

58. $x^2 - 2x + 4 = 0$

59. $x^2 + 3x = -25$

60. $4x^2 - x - 3 = 0$

4-7 The Quadratic Formula

Quick Review

You can solve a quadratic equation in the form $ax^2 + bx + c = 0$ by using the **Quadratic Formula**, $x = \frac{-b \pm \sqrt{b^2 - 4ac}}{2a}$. The **discriminant** of a quadratic equation in standard form is the value of the expression $b^2 - 4ac$. You can use it to find the quantity and type of solutions of a quadratic equation.

Example

Use the Quadratic Formula to solve $2x^2 - 6x = -3$.

$2x^2 - 6x + 3 = 0$	Write the equation in standard form.
$a = 2, b = -6, c = 3$	Identify a, b, and c.
$x = \frac{-(-6) \pm \sqrt{(-6)^2 - 4(2)(3)}}{2(2)}$	Substitute a, b, and c into the quadratic formula.
$x = \frac{6 \pm \sqrt{12}}{4} = \frac{3 \pm \sqrt{3}}{2}$	Simplify.

Exercises

Solve each equation using the quadratic formula.

61. $3x^2 + 5x = 8$

62. $x^2 = 6x - 9$

63. $x(x - 3) = 4$

64. $5x^2 - 7x - 3 = 0$

Determine the discriminant of each equation. How many real solutions does each equation have?

65. $4x^2 - 2x = 10$

66. $x^2 - 5x + 7 = 0$

67. $3x^2 + 3 = 6x$

68. $7 - 3x = 8x^2$

69. Gardening Margaret is planning a rectangular garden. Its length is 4 ft less than twice its width. Its area is 170 ft². What are the dimensions of the garden?

49. ± 2

50. $\pm \sqrt{5}$

51. ± 3

52. $\pm 2\sqrt{3}$

53. 9

54. $\frac{9}{4}$

55. $-4 \pm \sqrt{10}$

56. $5 \pm \sqrt{38}$

57. $-1, \frac{1}{3}$

58. $1 \pm i\sqrt{3}$

59. $\frac{-3}{2} \pm \frac{i\sqrt{91}}{2}$

60. $1, -\frac{3}{4}$

61. $1, -\frac{8}{3}$

62. 3

63. $4, -1$

64. $1.744, -0.344$

65. 164; two

66. -3; none

67. 0; one

68. 233; two

69. $10.2736 \text{ ft} \times 16.5472 \text{ ft}$

Answers

Chapter Review (continued)

70. $2i\sqrt{6}$

71. $-3 + i\sqrt{2}$

72. $-50 + 40i$

73. $6 + 4i\sqrt{6}$

74. $3 + 9i$

75. $13 + 20i$

76. $21 - 25i$

77. $-12 - 15i$

78. $-3 - 2i$

79. $-\frac{1}{2} - \frac{1}{2}i$

80. $\pm 3i$

81. $\frac{1}{5} \pm \frac{2}{5}i$

82. $2 \pm i\sqrt{6}$

83. $\frac{-4}{7} \pm \frac{i\sqrt{26}}{7}$

84. $(7, -6), (-2, 12)$

85. $(5, -27), (-2, 8)$

86. $(-5, 37), (3, -27)$;

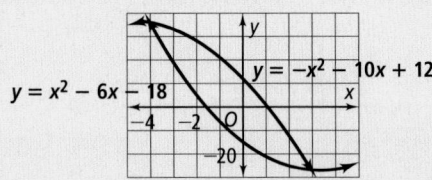

87. $(6.32, 15.64), (-3.32, -3.64)$;

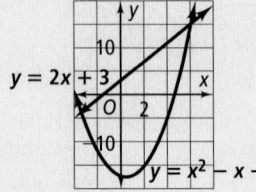

88.

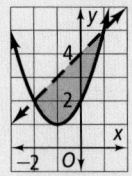

89.

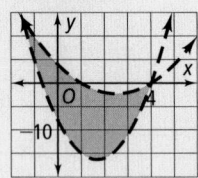

4-8 Complex Numbers

Quick Review

A **complex number** is written in the form $a + bi$, where a and b are real numbers, and i is equal to $\sqrt{-1}$. If $b = 0$, $a + bi$ is a real number. If $b \neq 0$, $a + bi$ is an **imaginary number**. You can use the Quadratic Formula or completing the square to find the imaginary solutions of quadratic equations.

Example

Use the Quadratic Formula to solve $3x^2 - 4x + 2 = 0$.

$x = \dfrac{-(-4) \pm \sqrt{(-4)^2 - 4(3)(2)}}{2(3)}$ Enter a, b, and c into the quadratic formula.

$x = \dfrac{4 \pm \sqrt{16 - 24}}{6} = \dfrac{4 \pm \sqrt{-8}}{6}$ Simplify.

$x = \dfrac{2}{3} \pm \dfrac{\sqrt{2}}{3}i$ Write the solutions.

Exercises

Simplify each expression using the imaginary unit i.

70. $\sqrt{-24}$ **71.** $\sqrt{-2} - 3$

72. $(4 + \sqrt{-25})(\sqrt{-100})$ **73.** $2\sqrt{-24} + 6$

Simplify each expression.

74. $(9 + 7i) - (6 - 2i)$ **75.** $(3 + 11i) + (10 + 9i)$

76. $(1 - 9i)(3 + 2i)$ **77.** $(3i)^2 - 3(1 + 5i)$

78. $\dfrac{4 - 6i}{2i}$ **79.** $\dfrac{2 - 3i}{1 + 5i}$

Solve each equation.

80. $x^2 + 9 = 0$ **81.** $5x^2 - 2x + 1 = 0$

82. $-x^2 + 4x = 10$ **83.** $7x^2 + 8x = -6$

4-9 Quadratic Systems

Quick Review

A system of quadratic equations can be solved by substitution or by graphing. You can use these methods to solve a linear–quadratic system or a quadratic–quadratic system. Use graphing to solve a quadratic system of inequalities.

Example

Use substitution to solve $\begin{cases} y = 2x^2 + 2x - 10 \\ y = x^2 + 5x - 6 \end{cases}$.

$2x^2 + 2x - 10 = x^2 + 5x - 6$ Substitute for y.

$x^2 - 3x - 4 = 0$ Rewrite in standard form.

$(x + 1)(x - 4) = 0$ Factor.

$x = -1 \text{ or } x = 4$ Solve for x.

$y = (-1)^2 + 5(-1) - 6 = -10$ Substitute for x then solve for y.

$y = (4)^2 + 5(4) - 6 = 30$

$(-1, -10) \text{ and } (4, 30)$ Write solutions as ordered pairs.

Exercises

Solve each system by substitution.

84. $\begin{cases} y = x^2 - 7x - 6 \\ y = 8 - 2x \end{cases}$

85. $\begin{cases} y = -x^2 - 2x + 8 \\ y = x^2 - 8x - 12 \end{cases}$

Solve each system by graphing.

86. $\begin{cases} y = -x^2 - 10x + 12 \\ y = x^2 - 6x - 18 \end{cases}$

87. $\begin{cases} y = x^2 - x - 18 \\ y = 2x + 3 \end{cases}$

Solve each system of inequalities.

88. $\begin{cases} y < x + 4 \\ y \geq x^2 + 2x + 2 \end{cases}$

89. $\begin{cases} y > 3x^2 - 10x - 8 \\ y < x^2 - 5x + 4 \end{cases}$

Do you know HOW?

Sketch a graph of the quadratic function with the given vertex and through the given point. Then write the equation of the parabola in vertex form and describe how the function was transformed from the parent function $y = x^2$.

1. vertex $(0, 0)$, point $(-3, 3)$

2. vertex $(1, 5)$, point $(2, 1)$

Graph each quadratic function. Identify the axis of symmetry, the vertex, and the domain and the range of each function.

3. $y = x^2 - 7$

4. $y = x^2 + 2x + 6$

5. $y = -x^2 + 5x - 3$

Simplify each expression.

6. $\sqrt{-16}$

7. $4\sqrt{-9} - 2$

8. $(2 + 3i)(8 - 5i)$

9. $(-3 + 2i) - (6 + i)$

10. $\frac{4 + 2i}{2 - i}$

Factor each expression completely.

11. $2y^2 - 8y$

12. $3x^2 + 8x - 3$

13. $9w^2 - 30w + 25$

Solve each quadratic equation.

14. $x^2 - 25 = 0$

15. $x^2 - 2x + 3 = 0$

16. $x^2 - 8x = -6$

Solve the following systems of equations.

17. $\begin{cases} y = 3x^2 - x + 1 \\ y = 3x^2 + x - 1 \end{cases}$

18. $\begin{cases} y = -x^2 + 2x - 3 \\ y = 4x - 3 \end{cases}$

Solve the following systems of inequalities.

19. $\begin{cases} y > 2x^2 + 5x + 1 \\ y < -2x^2 - 5x - 1 \end{cases}$

20. $\begin{cases} y < x^2 - x + 2 \\ y > x^2 - 1 \end{cases}$

Evaluate the discriminant of each equation. How many real and imaginary solutions does each have?

21. $x^2 + 6x - 7 = 0$

22. $3x^2 - x + 3 = 0$

23. $-4x^2 - 4x + 1 = 0$

Do you UNDERSTAND?

24. Writing Compare graphing a number on the complex plane to graphing a point on the coordinate plane. How are they similar? How are they different?

25. Open-Ended Sketch the graph of a quadratic function $f(x) = ax^2 + bx + c$ that has no real zeros. How does this relate to the solutions of the related equation $ax^2 + bx + c = 0$?

STEM 26. Physics A model for the path of a toy rocket is given by $h = 68t - 4.9t^2$, where h is the altitude in meters and t is the time in seconds. Explain how to find both the maximum altitude of the rocket and how long it takes to reach that altitude.

27. How many solutions are possible for:
  a. a system of two quadratic equations?
  b. a system of two quadratic inequalities?
  Explain your answers.

5.
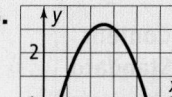
axis of symmetry: $x = \frac{5}{2}$; vertex $\left(\frac{5}{2}, \frac{13}{4}\right)$;
domain: all real numbers, range: $y \le \frac{13}{4}$

6. $4i$

7. $-2 + 12i$

8. $31 + 14i$

9. $-9 + i$

10. $\frac{6}{5} + \frac{8}{5}i$

11. $2y(y - 4)$

12. $(3x - 1)(x + 3)$

13. $(3w - 5)^2$

14. ± 5

15. $1 \pm i\sqrt{2}$

16. $4 \pm \sqrt{10}$

17. $(1, 3)$

18. $(0, -3), (-2, -11)$

19.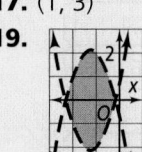

20.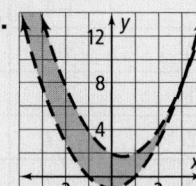

21. 64; two real

22. -35; two imaginary

23. 32; two real

24. Answers may vary. Sample: In the coordinate plane you graph ordered pairs (a, b); in the complex plane you graph complex numbers $a + bi$. For both you find a on the horizontal axis and you find b on the vertical axis.

25. Answers may vary. Sample: Below is the graph $y = -x^2 - 4x - 6$. There will only be imaginary solutions to the equation: $-x^2 - 4x - 6 = 0$.
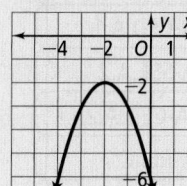

26. To find the maximum altitude of the rocket (235.92 m), either look at a table or graph the function and trace to locate the vertex. The h-value of the vertex is the maximum altitude of the rocket. The t-value of the vertex (6.939 s) is the amount of time the rocket takes to reach that altitude.

27. a. zero, one, or two solutions
  b. zero, one, or an infinite number of solutions

Answers

Chapter Test

1.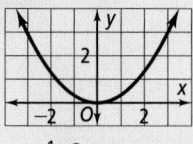
$y = \frac{1}{3}x^2$, vertically compressed by a factor of $\frac{1}{3}$

2.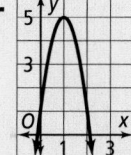
$y = -4(x - 1)^2 + 5$, reflected across the x-axis, vertically stretched by a factor of 4, translated 1 unit to the right and 5 units up

3.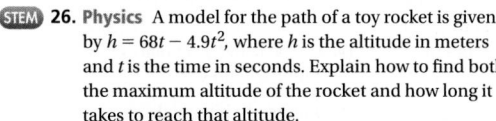
axis of symmetry: $x = 0$; vertex $(0, -7)$; domain: all real numbers, range: $y \ge -7$

4.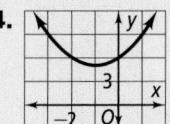
axis of symmetry: $x = -1$; vertex $(-1, 5)$; domain: all real numbers, range: $y \ge 5$

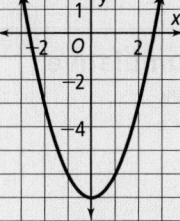

Item Number	Lesson	© Content Standard
1	4-6	*A-REI.B.4b
2	3-2	A-REI.C.6
3	4-5	*A-APR.B.3
4	4-8	N-CN.C.7
5	1-6	A-CED.A.1
6	4-1	F-BF.B.3
7	4-2	F-IF.B.4
8	4-1	F-IF.B.4
9	1-4	A-CED.A.4
10	3-2	A-REI.C.6
11	3-3	A-REI.D.12
12	2-7	F-BF.B.3
13	4-7	*A-REI.B.4b
14	3-2	A-REI.C.6
15	3-2	A-CED.A.2
16	1-6	A-CED.A.1
17	2-2	A-CED.A.2
18	1-4	A-CED.A.1
19	1-3	*A-SSE.A.1a
20	4-8	N-CN.A.2
21	4-8	N-CN.C.7
22	4-8	N-CN.A.2
23	1-6	A-CED.A.1
24	4-4	A-SSE.A.2
25	3-2	A-CED.A.2
26	4-9	A-REI.C.7
27	3-2	A-CED.A.2
28	4-2	A-CED.A.2
29	2-8	F-BF.B.3
30	1-6	A-CED.A.1
31	3-4	A-CED.A.3

* Reviews standard

TIPS FOR SUCCESS

Some questions on tests require that you model a word problem with a quadratic function.

TIP 1

To identify the function, use what you already know. You know that the perimeter of a rectangle is $2(\ell + w)$ and the area is $\ell \cdot w$.

Roy has a 400 foot roll of wire. He wants to use it to fence in a rectangular area. What is the maximum area of the enclosed space?

  Ⓐ 20,000 square feet

  Ⓑ 10,000 square feet

  Ⓒ 200 square feet

  Ⓓ 100 square feet

TIP 2

Use the information from the problem. The perimeter is 400, so $2(\ell + w) = 400$. Solve for w: $w = 200 - \ell$.

Think It Through

Substitute for w in the area formula:
$$A = f(\ell) = \ell \cdot (200 - \ell)$$
$$= -\ell^2 + 200\ell.$$

The maximum value is the y-coordinate of the vertex, $f\left(-\frac{b}{2a}\right) = f(100) = 10,000$. So, the maximum area Roy can enclose is 10,000 square feet.

The correct answer is B.

Vocabulary Builder

As you solve test items, you must understand the meanings of mathematical terms. Match each term with its mathematical meaning.

A. axis of symmetry

B. discriminant

C. imaginary number

D. Zero-Product Property

E. parabola

F. perfect square trinomial

G. completing the square

I. value of $b^2 - 4ac$ for the equation $ax^2 + bx + c = 0$

II. If $ab = 0$, then $a = 0$ or $b = 0$.

III. line that divides a parabola into two parts that are mirror images

IV. $a + bi$, a and b are real numbers and $b \neq 0$

V. square of a binomial

VI. process of finding the last term to make a perfect square trinomial

VII. graph of a quadratic function

Selected Response

Read each question. Then write the letter of the correct answer on your paper.

1. Which equation is equivalent to $x^2 + 24x + 100 = -46$?

  Ⓐ $(x + 12)^2 = -2$

  Ⓑ $(x - 12)^2 = -2$

  Ⓒ $(x - 12)^2 = 2$

  Ⓓ $(x + 12)^2 = 2$

2. What is the solution of the following system of equations?

$$2x - y = 4$$
$$3x + y = 1$$

  Ⓕ $(-1, 2)$

  Ⓖ $(1, -2)$

  Ⓗ $(2, 1)$

  Ⓘ $(-2, 1)$

Answers

Common Core Cumulative Standards Review

A. III

B. I

C. IV

D. II

E. VII

F. V

G. VI

1. A

2. G

3. What are the factors of the quadratic function graphed below?

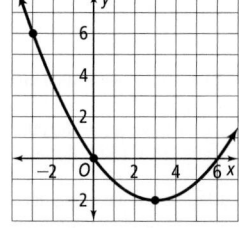

- Ⓐ $(x + 3)$ and $(x + 2)$
- Ⓑ x and $(x - 6)$
- Ⓒ x and $(x + 6)$
- Ⓓ $(x - 3)$ and $(x + 2)$

4. Which equation has $-1 \pm i$ as its solution?

- Ⓕ $x^2 - 2x - 2 = 0$
- Ⓖ $2x^2 - 2x - 1 = 0$
- Ⓗ $2x^2 + 2x + 1 = 0$
- Ⓘ $x^2 + 2x + 2 = 0$

5. What are the solutions of $|3x - 5| = 2$?

- Ⓐ $x = -1$ and $x = \frac{7}{3}$
- Ⓑ $x = 1$ and $x = \frac{7}{3}$
- Ⓒ $x = 1$ and $x = \frac{1}{5}$
- Ⓓ $x = -1$ and $x = \frac{1}{5}$

6. What is the transformation of the graph of $y = (x + 3)^2 - 2$ from its parent function $y = x^2$?

- Ⓕ 3 units left and 2 units down
- Ⓖ 3 units right and 2 units up
- Ⓗ 6 units right and 2 units up
- Ⓘ 2 units left and 3 units down

7. What is the axis of symmetry for the graph of the quadratic equation $y = -3x^2 - 12 + 12x$?

- Ⓐ $x = -2$
- Ⓑ $x = 2$
- Ⓒ $x = 12$
- Ⓓ $x = -12$

8. What are the domain and range of the function graphed below?

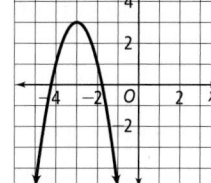

- Ⓕ Domain: All real numbers
  Range: All real numbers ≤ 3
- Ⓖ Domain: All real numbers
  Range: All real numbers ≥ 3
- Ⓗ Domain: All real numbers between -5 and -1
  Range: All real numbers ≤ 3
- Ⓘ Domain: All real numbers between -5 and -1
  Range: All real numbers ≥ 3

9. The formula for the total surface area of a regular right pentagonal prism is $A = ap + pH$. Solve this equation for p.

- Ⓐ $p = \frac{a + H}{A}$
- Ⓒ $p = A - \frac{a}{H}$
- Ⓑ $p = \frac{A}{a + H}$
- Ⓓ $p = \frac{H - a}{A}$

10. What is the solution of $\begin{cases} -y = 3x - 1 \\ 2y = -x - 2 \end{cases}$?

- Ⓕ $x = 20, y = -11$
- Ⓗ $x = -20, y = 11$
- Ⓖ $x = \frac{4}{5}, y = -\frac{7}{5}$
- Ⓘ $x = -\frac{4}{5}, y = \frac{7}{5}$

11. Which system of inequalities is graphed below?

- Ⓐ $\begin{cases} y \leq -1 \\ y + x \geq 2 \end{cases}$
- Ⓑ $\begin{cases} y \geq -1 \\ y + x \leq 2 \end{cases}$
- Ⓒ $\begin{cases} y < 1 \\ y + x > -2 \end{cases}$
- Ⓓ $\begin{cases} y > 1 \\ y + x < -2 \end{cases}$

12. What is the vertex of $y = -2|x + 4| - 5$?

- Ⓕ $(-2, -5)$
- Ⓗ $(4, -5)$
- Ⓖ $(-4, -5)$
- Ⓘ $(2, -5)$

3. B
4. I
5. B
6. F
7. B
8. F
9. B
10. G
11. B
12. G

Answers

Common Core Cumulative Standards Review (continued)

13. 1.67   **14.** 7   **15.** 15

16. 1   **17.** $-\frac{4}{5}$ **18.** 5.6

19. 5.48   **20.** -8 **21.** 0

22. 25

23. 0

24. 5

25. 18

26. **[2]** (2, 0) and (-2, 4)

     [1] one minor computational error

27. **[2]** Let s = rate of the swimmer and let c = rate of the current:

$$s + c = \frac{1000}{15}$$

$$s - c = \frac{1000}{30}$$

$$2s = \frac{3000}{30} \quad \text{Add the eqs.}$$

$$s = \frac{3000}{60}$$

$$s - c = \frac{1000}{30}$$

$$\left(\frac{3000}{60}\right) - c = \frac{1000}{30}$$

$$c = \frac{1000}{60} = \frac{50}{3} \text{ m/h}$$

(OR another appropriate method)

     [1] computational error OR correct solution, without work shown

28. **[2]** $(w + 3)(2w - 1)$ OR $2w^2 + 5w - 3$

     [1] one minor computational error

29. **[2]** Rewrite the inequality as $y < 2|x - 3| - 4$.
This is a transformation of the parent function $y = |x|$. Vertically stretch by a factor of 2, translate 3 units to the right and 4 units down. Shade the region below the graph.

     [1] parent funcion not named

30. **[4]** $\frac{64 + 51}{2} = 57.5$ cm

$$\frac{64 - 51}{2} = 6.5 \text{ cm}$$

$$|x - 57.5| \le 6.5$$

51   64

     [3] inequality is written correctly, but graph is drawn with open circles

     [2] correct inequality, without graph drawn

     [1] correct inequality, without graph drawn, without work shown

31. **[4]** Let b = number of brownies and let c = number of cookies.

     a. $b + c \le 80$

$$0.1b + 0.05c \le 6$$

---

13. What is the sum of the solutions of the equation $1.5x^2 - 2.5x - 1.5 = 0$? Round to the nearest hundredth.

14. What is the value of y in the system of equations?

$$x + y = 10$$
$$y = 2x + 1$$

15. Zeroy and Darius shop at the mall during the special sale extravaganza. Zeroy spends $120 on 3 pairs of pants and 4 shirts. Darius buys 2 pairs of pants and 3 shirts and spends $85. What is the price of one shirt?

16. What is the sum of the solutions of $|5x - 4| = 8 - x$?

17. Suppose y varies directly with x, and $y = -4$ when $x = 5$. What is the constant of variation?

18. Molly is making a punch for the school picnic. The recipe calls for $\frac{3}{4}$ quart of lemonade, 3 cups of cranberry juice, 4 cans of orange juice concentrate, and 5 cups of water. If Molly uses $1\frac{2}{5}$ quarts of lemonade, how many cups of cranberry juice will she need?

19. What is the value of $3x^2 - 5x + 7$ when $x = \frac{2}{5}$? Express the answer as a decimal.

20. What is the real part of $(11 + 10i)(2 + 3i)$?

21. How many imaginary roots does $2x^2 + 3x - 5 = 0$ have?

22. What is the product of $(4 + 3i)(4 - 3i)$?

23. What is the greatest integer solution of $|2x + 3| - 4 \le 0$?

24. What is the coefficient of the x-term of the factorization of $25x^2 + 20x + 4$?

25. A piggy bank contains $2.40 in nickels and dimes. If there are 33 coins in all, how many nickels are there?

26. What are the solutions of the system? Solve by graphing.

$$y = x^2 - x - 2$$
$$y = -x + 2$$

27. A swimmer swam 1000 meters downstream in 15 minutes and swam back in 30 minutes against the current. What was the rate of the swimmer in still water? How fast was the current?

28. Claudia has a rectangular flowerbed. She decided that the original width w, in feet, was too small, so she increased the width by 3 feet. She also changed the length to be 1 foot less than twice the original width. What is an expression that represents the area of the new flower bed?

29. Explain how you would graph $y + 4 < 2|x - 3|$ on a coordinate grid.

Extended Response

30. A hat company is designing a one-size-fits-all hat with a strap in the back that makes the hat smaller or larger. Head sizes normally range from 51 to 64 centimeters. What absolute value inequality models the different sizes of the hat? Graph the solution.

31. Robby decided to earn extra money by making and selling brownies and cookies. He had space in his oven to make at most 80 brownies and cookies. Each brownie cost $.10 to make and each cookie cost $.05 to make. He had $6 to spend on ingredients.

     a. Write a system of inequalities to represent the situation.

     b. Graph the system, choose one point in the feasible region, and explain what the point means in terms of the problem.

     c. If Robby makes a profit of $.25 on each brownie and $.20 on each cookie, how many of each dessert should he make to maximize his profit?

---

b. The feasible region is any point that is below *both* lines. The point (c, b) represents the situation in which Robby makes c cookies and b brownies.

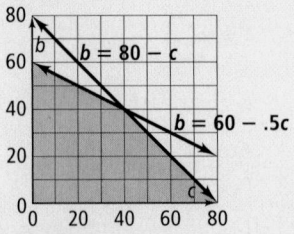

c. Let P = profit, then $P = .25b + .2c$. Test the vertices to find the maximum profit:

(0, 60): 0.25 (60) + 0.2(0) = 15
(40, 40): 0.25 (40) + 0.2(40) = 18
(80, 0): 0.25 (0) + 0.2(80) = 16
     Robby should make 40 cookies and 40 brownies.

[3] appropriate methods with one computational error OR feasible region is not shaded in graph

[2] correct answer for parts (a) – (b) only

[1] correct answer, without explanations or work shown

Get Ready!

Lesson 4-2 • **Graphing Quadratic Functions**

Graph each function.

1. $f(x) = x^2 - 8x + 7$ **2.** $f(x) = -\frac{1}{2}x^2 - 4x - 4$ **3.** $f(x) = x^2 + 4x + 4$

Lesson 4-3 • **Writing Equations of Parabolas**

Write in standard form the equation of the parabola passing through the given points.

4. $(-1, -6), (-3, -4), (2, 6)$ **5.** $(3, 4), (-2, 9), (2, 1)$ **6.** $(-5, -8), (4, -8), (-3, 6)$

Lesson 4-5 • **Solving Quadratic Equations by Graphing**

Solve each equation by graphing. Round to the nearest hundredth.

7. $1 = 4x^2 + 3x$ **8.** $\frac{1}{2}x^2 + x - 14 = 0$ **9.** $5x^2 + 30x = 12$

Lesson 4-5 • **Solving Quadratic Equations by Factoring**

Solve each equation by factoring.

10. $x^2 - x - 20 = 0$ **11.** $x^2 + 6x - 27 = 0$ **12.** $3x^2 - 9x + 6 = 0$

Lesson 4-7 • **Finding the Number and Type of Solutions**

Evaluate the discriminant of each equation. Tell how many solutions each equation has and whether the solutions are real or imaginary.

13. $x^2 - 12x + 30 = 0$ **14.** $-4x^2 + 20x - 25 = 0$ **15.** $2x^2 = 8x - 8$

Looking Ahead Vocabulary

16. A *turning point* is a place where a graph changes direction. Suppose you start hiking north on a winding trail, and the trail makes a turn and heads south, and then north again. If you make a total of 3 of these 180 degree turns, in which direction will you be hiking after the last turn?

17. A *relative maximum* is the greatest value in a region. The highest point in Maine is Mt. Katahdin at 5267 ft. How might that compare to the highest point in the United States? What might the relative maximum of a graph be?

18. A contraction is a shortened form of a word or phrase. The expanded form of the contraction "don't" is "do not." You can *expand* a math phrase by multiplying it out. For example, $(x - 2)^2 = (x - 2)(x - 2) = x^2 - 4x + 4$. Expand $(2x + 1)^2$.

Get Ready!

Assign this diagnostic assessment to determine if students have the prerequisite skills for Chapter 5.

Lesson	Skill
4-2	Graph Quadratic Functions
4-3	Write Equations of Parabolas
4-5	Solve Quadratic Equations by Graphing
4-5	Solve Quadratic Equations by Factoring
4-7	Find the Number and Type of Solutions

To remediate students, select from these resources (available for every lesson).
- Online Problems (PowerAlgebra.com)
- Reteaching (All-in-One Teaching Resources)
- Practice (All-in-One Teaching Resources)

Why Students Need These Skills

GRAPHING QUADRATIC FUNCTIONS
Students will apply the techniques for graphing quadratic functions to graph other polynomial functions.

WRITING EQUATIONS OF PARABOLAS
Students will apply the techniques for writing equations of parabolas to write equations for any polynomials.

SOLVING QUADRATIC EQUATIONS BY GRAPHING
Students will apply the techniques for solving quadratic equations by graphing to solve other polynomial equations by graphing.

SOLVING QUADRATIC EQUATIONS BY FACTORING
Students will apply the techniques for solving quadratic equations by factoring to solve other polynomial equations by factoring.

FINDING THE NUMBER AND TYPE OF SOLUTIONS
Finding the number and type of solutions to a polynomial equation allows students to check their work and graphs.

Looking Ahead Vocabulary

TURNING POINT Suggest students sketch a possible graph of the trail.

RELATIVE MAXIMUM Ask students how changing the size of a region affects the relative maximum.

EXPAND The opposite of expanding is factoring.

Answers

Get Ready!

1.

2.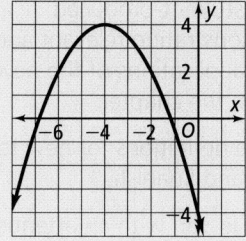

3.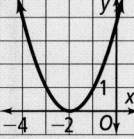

4. $y = x^2 + 3x - 4$

5. $y = x^2 - 2x + 1$

6. $y = -x^2 - x + 12$ **7.** $0.25, -1$

8. $-6.39, 4.39$ **9.** $-6.38, 0.38$

10. $-4, 5$ **11.** $-9, 3$ **12.** $1, 2$

13. 24; two real solutions

14. 0; one real solution

15. 0; one real solution   **16.** south

17. The highest pt. in Maine may be lower than the highest pt. in the United States. The relative maximum of a graph for a given region is the maximum for that region only, whereas the maximum of the graph may be greater than or equal to the relative maximum for the region.

18. $4x^2 + 4x + 1$

Chapter 5 Overview

Chapter 5 expands on students' understandings and skills related to functions, equations, and graphs. In this chapter, students will develop the answers to the Essential Questions as they learn the concepts and skills bulleted below.

BIG idea Function

ESSENTIAL QUESTION What does the degree of a polynomial tell you about its related polynomial function?
- Students will write a polynomial function given a polynomial equation.
- Students will identify the degree of a polynomial equation.
- Students will identify the highest power of a polynomial function.

BIG idea Equivalence

ESSENTIAL QUESTION For a polynomial function, how are factors, zeros, and x-intercepts related?
- Students will write a polynomial given its factors or zeros.
- Students will identify the zeros of a polynomial function by finding the x-intercepts of its graph.

BIG idea Solving Equations and Inequalities

ESSENTIAL QUESTION For a polynomial equation, how are factors and roots related?
- Students will factor a polynomial equation.
- Students will apply the Zero-Product Property.

Content Standards

Following are the standards covered in this chapter. Modeling standards are indicated by a star symbol (★).

CONCEPTUAL CATEGORY Numbers and Quantity

Domain The Complex Number System N-CN
  Cluster Use complex numbers in polynomial identities and equations.
  (Standards N-CN.C.7, N-CN.C.8, N-CN.C.9)
  LESSONS 5-5, 5-6

CONCEPTUAL CATEGORY Algebra

Domain Seeing Structure in Expressions A-SSE
  Cluster Interpret the structure of expressions.
  (Standards A-SSE.A.1a★, A-SSE.A.1b★, A-SSE.A.2)
  LESSONS 5-2, 5-3

Domain Arithmetic with Polynomials and Rational Expressions A-APR
  Cluster Understand the relationship between zeros and factors of polynomials.
  (Standards A-APR.B.2, A-APR.B.3)
  LESSONS 5-2, 5-4

  Cluster Use polynomial identities to solve problems.
  (Standards A-APR.C.4, A-APR.C.5, A-APR.C.6)
  LESSONS 5-4, 5-7, 5-8

CHAPTER 5 Polynomials and Polynomial Functions

Download videos connecting math to your world. VIDEO

Interactive! Vary numbers, graphs, and figures to explore math concepts.

The online **Solve It** will get you in gear for each lesson.

Math definitions in English and Spanish

Online access to stepped-out problems aligned to Common Core

Get and view your assignments online.

Extra practice and review online

Virtual Nerd™ tutorials with built-in support

Chapter Preview

5-1 **Polynomial Functions**
5-2 **Polynomials, Linear Factors, and Zeros**
5-3 **Solving Polynomial Equations**
5-4 **Dividing Polynomials**
5-5 **Theorems About Roots of Polynomial Equations**
5-6 **The Fundamental Theorem of Algebra**
5-7 **The Binomial Theorem**
5-8 **Polynomial Models in the Real World**
5-9 **Transforming Polynomial Functions**

Vocabulary

English/Spanish Vocabulary Audio Online:

English	Spanish
end behavior, *p. 282*	comportamiento extremo
monomial, *p. 280*	monomio
multiplicity, *p. 291*	multiplicidad
Pascal's Triangle, *p. 327*	Triángulo de Pascal
polynomial function, *p. 280*	función polinomial
relative maximum, *p. 291*	máximo relativo
relative minimum, *p. 291*	mínimo relativo
standard form of a polynomial function, *p. 281*	forma normal de una función polinomial
synthetic division, *p. 306*	división sintética
turning point, *p. 282*	punto de giro

BIG ideas

1 **Function**
  Essential Question What does the degree of a polynomial tell you about its related polynomial function?

2 **Equivalence**
  Essential Question For a polynomial function, how are factors, zeros, and x-intercepts related?

3 **Solving Equations and Inequalities**
  Essential Question For a polynomial equation, how are factors and roots related?

 DOMAINS
- Interpreting Functions
- Arithmetic with Polynomials and Rational Expressions
- The Complex Number System

 **PowerAlgebra.com**

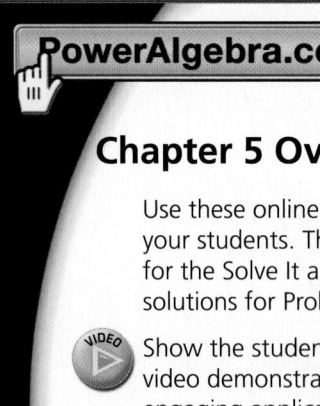

Chapter 5 Overview

Use these online assets to engage your students. These include support for the Solve It and step-by-step solutions for Problems.

Show the student-produced video demonstrating relevant and engaging applications of the new concepts in the chapter.

Find online definitions for new terms in English and Spanish.

Start each lesson with an attention-getting Problem. View the Problem online with helpful hints.

Common Core Performance Task

Determining the Dimensions of a Diorama

A diorama is a three-dimensional model of a scene in which small figures and objects are arranged against a background. Dioramas are often displayed in rectangular boxes with open fronts.

Eliana wants to make a diorama for an art contest. She starts with a rectangular sheet of cardboard that is 12 in. long and 8 in. wide. She plans to make the diorama box by cutting identical squares from the corners and folding the sides to create a box with an open front, as shown below.

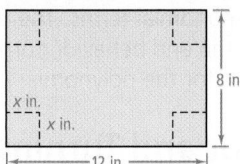
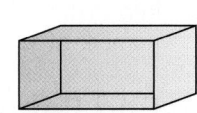

The art contest is accepting entries for miniature dioramas, requiring the volume to be no more than 36 in.³. Eliana wants her diorama box to have the maximum allowable volume.

Task Description

Determine all possible dimensions Eliana can use for a diorama box with volume 36 in.³. Round dimensions to the nearest hundredth of an inch.

Connecting the Task to the Math Practices

 **MATHEMATICAL PRACTICES**

As you complete the task, you'll apply several Standards for Mathematical Practice.

- You'll analyze the given information and write a function that models the volume of the diorama box. (MP 4)
- You'll graph the volume function and think about which points of the graph correspond to possible volumes of the diorama box. (MP 1)
- You'll look for and use structure in a polynomial to find the real roots of an equation. (MP 7)

 Increase students' depth of knowledge with interactive online activities.

 Show Problems from each lesson solved step by step. Instant replay allows students to go at their own pace when studying online.

 Assign homework to individual students or to an entire class.

 Prepare students for the Mid-Chapter Quiz and Chapter Test with online practice and review.

 Virtual Nerd™ Access Virtual Nerd student-centered math tutorials that directly relate to the content of the lesson.

 **Overview of the Performance Task**

Students will write and graph a polynomial function for the volume of a rectangular diorama box. They will use techniques for solving polynomial equations to find both the zeros of the function and the x-values that result in a specified volume.

Students will work on the Performance Task in the following places in the chapter.

- Lesson 5-1 (p. 287)
- Lesson 5-2 (p. 295)
- Lesson 5-5 (p. 317)
- Pull It All Together (p. 346)

Introducing the Performance Task

Tell students to read the problem on this page. Do not have them start work on the problem at this time, but ask them the following questions.

Q What is a strategy you could try in order to solve the problem? **[Sample: I could write a function that models the volume of the diorama box and then try to find values of x for which the value of the function is 36.]**

Q Based on the given figure, are there any constraints on the value of x? If so, what are they? **[Yes; since x is a length, it must be nonnegative; also, since the width of the rectangular sheet of cardboard is 8 in., x must be less than 4 in.]**

PARCC CLAIMS

Sub-Claim A: Major Content With Connections to Practices

Sub-Claim D: Highlighted Practice MP 4 With Connections to Content

SBAC CLAIMS

Claim 1: Concepts and Procedures

Claim 2: Problem Solving

Content Standards (cont')

Domain Reasoning with Equations and Inequalities A-REI

Cluster Represent and solve equations and inequalities graphically. (Standard A-REI.D.11★)
LESSON 5-3

CONCEPTUAL CATEGORY Functions

Domain Interpreting Functions F-IF

Cluster Interpret functions that arise in applications in terms of the context. (Standards F-IF.B.4, F-IF.B.5★, F-IF.B.6★)
LESSONS 5-1, 5-8

Cluster Analyze functions using different representations. (Standards F-IF.C.7c★, F-IF.C.8, F-IF.C.9)
LESSONS 5-1, 5-2, 5-9

Domain Building Functions F-BF

Cluster Build new functions from existing functions. (Standard F-BF.B.3★)
LESSONS 5-1, 5-9

Polynomials and Polynomial Functions 279

CHAPTER 5

POLYNOMIALS AND POLYNOMIAL FUNCTIONS
Math Background © PROFESSIONAL DEVELOPMENT

The Understanding by Design® methodology was central to the development of the Big Ideas and the Essential Understandings. These will help your students build a structure on which to make connections to prior learning.

PROGRAM ORGANIZATION · BIG IDEA · ESSENTIAL UNDERSTANDING · PROGRAM ORGANIZATION · BIG IDEA · ESSENTIAL UNDERSTANDING · PROGRAM ORGANIZATION

Function

BIG idea A function is a relationship between variables in which each value of the input variable is associated with a unique value of the output variable. Functions can be represented in a variety of ways, such as graphs, tables, equations, or words. Each representation is particularly useful in certain situations. Some important families of functions are developed through transformations of the simplest form of the function.

ESSENTIAL UNDERSTANDINGS

5-1 A polynomial function has distinguishing "behaviors." You can look at its algebraic form and know something about its graph. You can look at its graph and know something about its algebraic form.

5-2 Knowing the zeros of a polynomial function can help you understand the behavior of its graph.

5-3 If $(x - a)$ is a factor of a polynomial, then the polynomial has value 0 when $x = a$. If a is a real number, then the graph of the polynomial has $(a, 0)$ as an x–intercept.

5-9 The graph of the function $y = af(x - h) + k$ is a vertical stretch or compression by a factor $|a|$, a horizontal shift of h units, and a vertical shift of k units of the graph of $y = f(x)$.

Equivalence

BIG idea A single quantity may be represented by many different expressions. The facts about a quantity may be expressed by many different equations (or inequalities).

ESSENTIAL UNDERSTANDINGS

5-1 to 5-3 See above.

5-4 You can divide polynomials using steps that are similar to the long-division steps that you use to divide whole numbers.

5-5 The factors of the numbers a_n and a_0 in $P(x) = a_n x^n + a_{n-1} x^{n-1} + \ldots a_1 x + a_0$ can help you factor $P(x)$ and solve the equation $P(x) = 0$.

5-6 The degree of a polynomial equation tells you how many roots the equation has.

5-7 You can use a pattern of coefficients and the pattern $a^n, a^{n-1}b, a^{n-2}b^2, \ldots, a^1 b^{n-1}, b^n$, to write the expansion of $(a + b)^n$.

Solving Equations & Inequalities

BIG idea Solving an equation is the process of rewriting the equation to make what it says about its variable(s) as simple as possible. Properties of numbers and equality can be used to transform an equation (or inequality) into equivalent, simpler equations (or inequalities) in order to find solutions. Useful information about equations and inequalities (including solutions) can be found by analyzing graphs or tables. The numbers and types of solutions vary predictably, based on the type of equation.

ESSENTIAL UNDERSTANDINGS

5-5 to 5-6 See above.

Polynomial Functions

The degree of a polynomial equation is the greatest degree among its monomial terms. The degree provides information about the end behavior, turning points, and number of solutions for the polynomial function.

End Behavior and Turning Points

The end behavior describes the graph at the far left and at the far right. A turning point is where the graph changes direction. You can determine end behavior and turning points from the degree of the polynomial.

Degree is Odd
- even number of turning points
- $a > 0$, ends down then up
- $a < 0$, ends up then down

Degree is Even
- odd number of turning points
- $a > 0$, both ends up
- $a < 0$, both ends down

Examples:

$y = -x^3 + 4x^2 - 7$

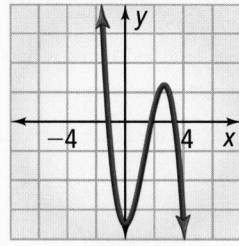

$y = x^4 - 4x^2$

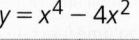
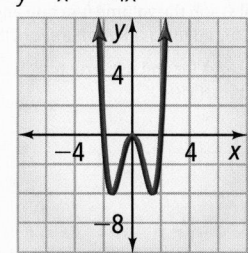

$y = -x^4 + 4x^2 + 2x - 3$

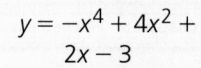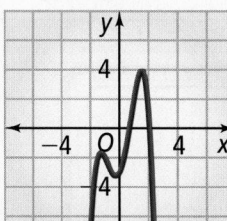

$y = x^5 - 4x^3 + 4x + 2$

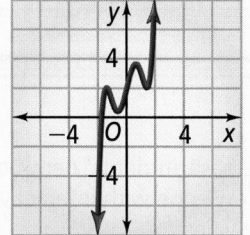

© Mathematical Practices

Look for and make use of structure. Reason abstractly and quantitatively. Polynomial functions are analyzed algebraically, graphically, and numerically, with continual emphasis on the connections among the various representations. Properties of polynomial functions are compared and contrasted to properties of quadratic and linear functions, including transformations.

UNDERSTANDING BY DESIGN® and UbD™ are trademarks of ASCD, and are used under license.

Zeros of Polynomial Equations

The **Fundamental Theorem of Algebra** and its corollary state that every polynomial has complex solutions and the degree of the polynomial equation gives the number of roots.

Students can use a combination of graphing, theorems, and factoring techniques to find all solutions of many polynomials. For example,

Find all solutions for $y = x^3 - x^2 - 3x - 9$.

The number of complex roots is 3.

Step 1) Use a graphing calculator to find the single real root (3).

Step 2) Use synthetic division to find the polynomial factor.

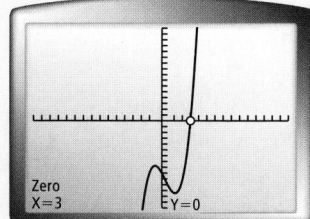

Zero
X=3   Y=0

$$\underline{3} \quad \begin{array}{rrrr} 1 & -1 & -3 & -9 \\ & 3 & 6 & 9 \\ \hline 1 & 2 & 3 & 0 \end{array}$$

So $(x - 3)(x^2 + 2x + 3)$

Step 3) Use the quadratic formula to determine the roots for the quadratic polynomial.

$$x = \frac{-b \pm \sqrt{b^2 - 4ac}}{2a} = \frac{-2 \pm \sqrt{2^2 - 4(1)(3)}}{2(1)}$$
$$= -1 \pm i\sqrt{2}$$

The roots are 3, $-1 + i\sqrt{2}$, $-1 - i\sqrt{2}$.

The following theorems can help identify all complex roots of polynomials with rational coefficients.

Conjugate Root Theorem

- If $a + \sqrt{b}$ is an irrational root with a and b rational, then $a - \sqrt{b}$ is also a root.
- If $a + bi$ is a complex root with a and b real, then $a - bi$ is also a root.

Rational Roots Theorem

Possible roots for a polynomial function with integer coefficients are determined by the reduced form of $\frac{p}{q}$ where p is a factor of the constant and q is a factor of the leading coefficient.

ⓒ Mathematical Practices

Use appropriate tools strategically. Graphing calculators are used as tools for problem solving, for additional explorations, and for reinforcing the connections among the graphical, analytic, and numerical representations of polynomial functions. In particular, calculators are used to solve polynomial equations that might be impossible to solve with classical factoring methods. Graphing calculators are used to analyze relative extrema of polynomial graphs, and additional polynomial regressions are introduced as statistical applications facilitated by the technology.

Writing Polynomial Functions

Real-world applications of polynomial functions include fitting a function to a given set of points. Note that most real-world data do not fit a function exactly. Statistical measures such as R^2 can help determine whether the function is a good fit. However, it is also possible that data are modeled by a certain function only over a certain domain. Both the behavior of the function and R^2 must be analyzed.

Care must always be taken when making predictions based on models. For example, estimating within the domain (**interpolation**) often yields reliable results. Estimating outside the domain (**extrapolation**) yields less reliable results.

Writing a Function from Zeros

If the zeros of a function are known, a polynomial can be written to satisfy the zeros. Because b is a root of $P(x)$ if $(x - b)$ is a factor, you can write factors of a polynomial function when given the zeros.

Example: Write a polynomial function in standard form with roots -2 and 2.

Write the roots as factors, and then multiply.
$(x + 2)(x - 2) = x^2 - 4$

Note that different functions can have the same zeros. Both functions below have roots -2 and 2.

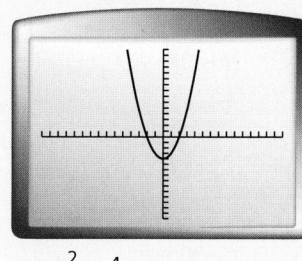 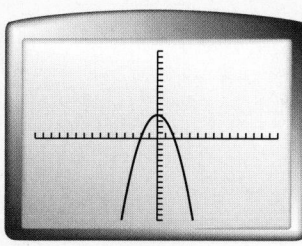

$y = x^2 - 4$ $y = -x^2 + 4$

Writing a Function from Other Points

The $n + 1$ principle states that for any $n + 1$ points in the coordinate plane that pass a vertical line test, there is a unique polynomial with degree at most n that fits the points.

ⓒ Mathematical Practices

Model with mathematics. Make sense of problems and persevere in solving them. Students use polynomial functions to model a variety of real-world contexts. Students develop methods for writing the equations of polynomial functions.

POLYNOMIALS AND POLYNOMIAL FUNCTIONS
Pacing and Assignment Guide

		TRADITIONAL			BLOCK
Lesson	**Teaching Day(s)**	**Basic**	**Average**	**Advanced**	**Block**
5-1	1	Problems 1–2 Exs. 8–31	Problems 1–2 Exs. 9–31 odd	Problems 1–4 Exs. 9–39 odd, 40–57	**Day 1** Problems 1–4 Exs. 9–39 odd, 40–54
	2	Problems 3–4 Exs. 32–39, 40–50 even, 51	Problems 3–4 Exs. 33–39 odd, 40–54		
5-2	1	Problems 1–4 Exs.7–34	Problems 1–4 Exs. 7–33 odd	Problems 1–4 Exs. 7–33 odd	**Day 2** Problems 1–6 Exs. 7–39 odd, 40–54
	2	Problems 5–6 Exs. 35–39, 41–43, 45–47, 50–52	Problems 5–6 Exs. 35–39 odd, 40–54	Problems 5–6 Exs. 35–39 odd, 40–56	
5-3	1	Problems 1–2 Exs. 10–24, 61–72	Problems 1–2 Exs. 11–23 odd, 61–72	Problems 1–2 Exs. 11–37 odd, 39–72	**Day 3** Problems 1–4 Exs. 11–37 odd, 39–57, 61–72
	2	Problems 3–4 Exs. 25–38, 40–50 even, 51–54	Problems 3–4 Exs. 25–37 odd, 39–57		
5-4	1	Problems 1–2 Exs. 9–20, 67–85	Problems 1–2 Exs. 9–19 odd, 67–85	Problems 1–2 Exs. 9–19 odd, 67–85	**Day 4** Problems 1–5 Exs. 9–39 odd, 40–62, 67–85
	2	Problems 3–5 Exs. 21–41, 43, 48, 50	Problems 3–5 Exs. 21–39 odd, 40–62	Problems 3–5 Exs. 21–39 odd, 40–66	
5-5	1	Problems 1–2 Exs. 9–17	Problems 1–2 Exs. 9–17 odd	Problems 1–2 Exs. 9–17 odd	**Day 5** Problems 1–5 Exs. 9–31 odd, 33–46
	2	Problems 3–5 Exs. 18–32, 34–40 even, 42–45	Problems 3–5 Exs. 19–31 odd, 33–46	Problem 3–5 Exs. 19–31 odd, 33–49	
5-6	1	Problem 1 Exs. 8–15, 50–65	Problems 1–2 Exs. 9–25 odd, 26–46, 50–65	Problems 1–2 Exs. 9–25 odd, 26–65	**Day 6** Problems 1–2 Exs. 9–25 odd, 26–46, 50–65
	2	Problem 2 Exs. 16–25, 26–30 even, 38–40, 44, 46			
5-7	1	Problems 1–2 Exs. 8–24, 30, 31, 44, 45, 54–68	Problems 1–2 Exs. 9–23 odd, 24–46, 54–68	Problems 1–2 Exs. 9–23 odd, 24–68	Problems 1–2 Exs. 9–23 odd, 24–46, 54–68
5-8	1	Problems 1–4 Exs. 8–25, 28, 31, 34, 38–58	Problems 1–4 Exs. 9–23 odd, 24–35, 38–58	Problems 1–4 Exs. 9–25 odd, 26–58	**Day 7** Problems 1–4 Exs. 9–23 odd, 24–35, 38–58
5-9	1	Problems 1–2 Exs. 7–18, 45–56	Problems 1–2 Exs. 7–25 odd, 27–41, 45–56	Problems 1–4 Exs. 7–25 odd, 27–56	Problems 1–4 Exs. 7–25 odd, 27–41, 45–56
	2	Problems 3–4 Exs. 19–26, 27, 30–34 even, 39, 40			
Review	1	Chapter 5 Review	Chapter 5 Review	Chapter 5 Review	**Day 8** Chapter 5 Review Chapter 5 Test
Assess	1	Chapter 5 Test	Chapter 5 Test	Chapter 5 Test	
Total		**18 Days**	**16 Days**	**14 Days**	**8 Days**

Resources

	For the Chapter	5-1	5-2	5-3	5-4	5-5	5-6	5-7	5-8	5-9
Planning										
Teacher Center Online Planner & Grade Book	I	I	I	I	I	I	I	I	I	I
Interactive Learning & Guided Instruction										
My Math Video	I									
Solve It!		I M	I M	I M	I M	I M	I M	I M	I M	I M
Student Companion		P M	P M	P M	P M	P M	P M	P M	P M	P M
Vocabulary Support		I P M	I P M	I P M	I P M	I P M	I P M	I P M	I P M	I P M
Got It? Support		I P	I P	I P	I P	I P	I P	I P	I P	I P
Dynamic Activity	I									
Online Problems		I	I	I	I	I	I	I	I	I
Additional Problems		M	M	M	M	M	M	M	M	M
English Language Learner Support (TR)		E P M	E P M	E P M	E P M	E P M	E P M	E P M	E P M	E P M
Activities, Games, and Puzzles		E M	E M	E M	E M	E M	E M	E M	E M	E M
Teaching With TI Technology With CD-ROM			✓ P							
TI-Nspire™ Support CD-ROM		✓	✓	✓	✓	✓	✓	✓	✓	✓
Lesson Check & Practice										
Student Companion		P M	P M	P M	P M	P M	P M	P M	P M	P M
Lesson Check Support		I P	I P	I P	I P	I P	I P	I P	I P	I P
Practice and Problem Solving Workbook		P	P	P	P	P	P	P	P	P
Think About a Plan (TR)		E P M	E P M	E P M	E P M	E P M	E P M	E P M	E P M	E P M
Practice Form G (TR)		E P M	E P M	E P M	E P M	E P M	E P M	E P M	E P M	E P M
Standardized Test Prep (TR)		P M	P M	P M	P M	P M	P M	P M	P M	P M
Practice *Form K* (TR)		E P M	E P M	E P M	E P M	E P M	E P M	E P M	E P M	E P M
Extra Practice	E M									
Find the Errors!	M									
Enrichment (TR)		E P M	E P M	E P M	E P M	E P M	E P M	E P M	E P M	E P M
Answers and Solutions CD-ROM	✓	✓	✓	✓	✓	✓	✓	✓	✓	✓
Assess & Remediate										
ExamView CD-ROM	✓	✓	✓	✓	✓	✓	✓	✓	✓	✓
Lesson Quiz		I M	I M	I M	I M	I M	I M	I M	I M	I M
Quizzes and Tests *Form G* (TR)	E P M				E P M					E P M
Quizzes and Tests *Form K* (TR)	E P M				E P M					E P M
Reteaching (TR)		E P M	E P M	E P M	E P M	E P M	E P M	E P M	E P M	E P M
Performance Tasks (TR)	P M									
Cumulative Review (TR)	P M									
Progress Monitoring Assessments	I P M									

(TR) Available in All-In-One Teaching Resources

1 Interactive Learning

Solve It!

PURPOSE To look for patterns in a sequence using common differences and then use those patterns to find unknown terms of the sequence

PROCESS Students may
- make a table and fill it in using addition and subtraction and then work backward beginning with the last column.
- look for a pattern rule and use the rule to find the eighth number.

FACILITATE

Q Copy the information in a table with four columns and eight rows. What number goes under the 46? How do you know? **[106; 156 − 50 = 106]**

Q Find the values represented by the question marks in the diagram. What do you notice about the third differences? **[They are all 24.]**

Q How can you use the third differences column to find the original sequence of numbers? **[Work backward, using addition.]**

ANSWER See Solve It in Answers on next page.

CONNECT THE MATH The Solve It uses the patterns of differences. In the lesson, students will examine difference patterns to determine the degree of a polynomial.

© **Common Core State Standards**
F-IF.C.7c Graph polynomial functions, identifying zeros when suitable factorizations are available and showing end behavior. Also A-SSE.A.1a
MP 1, MP 2, MP 3, MP 5

Objectives To classify polynomials
To graph polynomial functions and describe end behavior

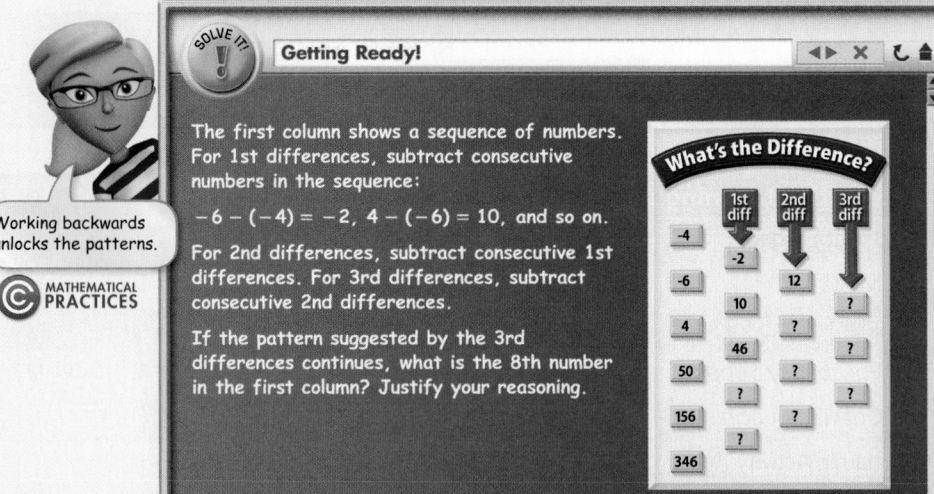

Working backwards unlocks the patterns.

© MATHEMATICAL PRACTICES

Getting Ready!

The first column shows a sequence of numbers. For 1st differences, subtract consecutive numbers in the sequence:

$-6 - (-4) = -2$, $4 - (-6) = 10$, and so on.

For 2nd differences, subtract consecutive 1st differences. For 3rd differences, subtract consecutive 2nd differences.

If the pattern suggested by the 3rd differences continues, what is the 8th number in the first column? Justify your reasoning.

What's the Difference?

	1st diff	2nd diff	3rd diff
-4			
	-2		
-6		12	
	10		?
4		46	
	50		?
50		?	
	156		?
156		?	
	?		
346			

Lesson Vocabulary
- monomial
- degree of a monomial
- polynomial
- degree of a polynomial
- polynomial function
- standard form of a polynomial function
- turning point
- end behavior

The sequence of numbers in the first column above are values of a particular *polynomial function*. For such a sequence, you can use patterns of 1st differences, 2nd differences, 3rd differences, and so on, to learn more about the polynomial function.

Essential Understanding A polynomial function has distinguishing "behaviors." You can look at its algebraic form and know something about its graph. You can look at its graph and know something about its algebraic form.

A **monomial** is a real number, a variable, or a product of a real number and one or more variables with whole-number exponents. The **degree of a monomial** in one variable is the exponent of the variable. A **polynomial** is a monomial or a sum of monomials. The **degree of a polynomial** in one variable is the greatest degree among its monomial terms.

A polynomial with the variable x defines a **polynomial function** of x. The degree of the polynomial function is the same as the degree of the polynomial.

5-1 Preparing to Teach

BIG ideas Equivalence
Function

ESSENTIAL UNDERSTANDINGS
- The algebraic form of a polynomial function gives information about its graph. Its graph gives information about its algebraic form.
- The shape and the end behavior of the graph of a polynomial is determined by the degree of the polynomial and by the sign of the leading coefficient.
- It's possible to determine the degree of a polynomial by analyzing the first, second, etc., differences of its y-values.

Math Background
The algebraic form of a polynomial function reveals certain information about the graph.

The degree of a polynomial function affects the shape of its graph.
- For a polynomial function of degree n, its graph has at most $n − 1$ turning points.

- The graph of a polynomial function of odd degree has an even number of turning points.
- The graph of a polynomial function of even degree has an odd number of turning points.

The degree of a polynomial function affects the end behavior, which can then be sketched using the leading coefficient of the polynomial function.

Similarly, the graph of a polynomial function reveals information about the algebraic form. The graph indicates whether the degree of the polynomial function is even or odd and whether the leading coefficient is positive or negative.

© Mathematical Practices
Use appropriate tools strategically. In Problem 2, students will use a graphing calculator to verify the end behavior of polynomial functions.

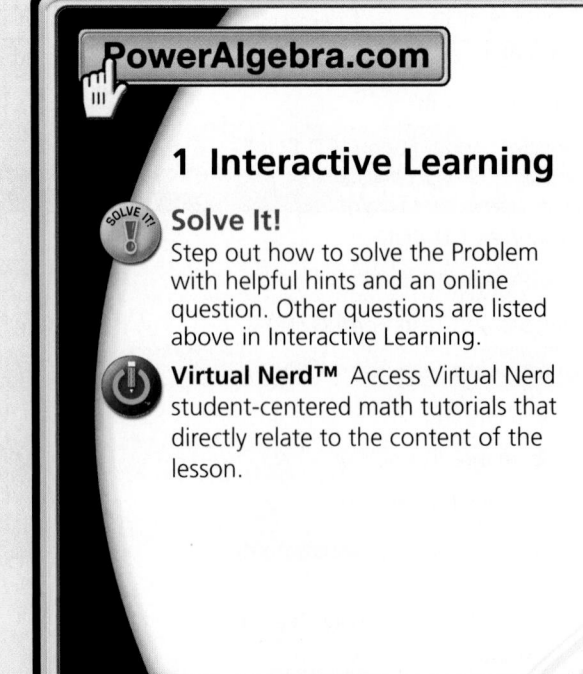

PowerAlgebra.com

1 Interactive Learning

Solve It!
Step out how to solve the Problem with helpful hints and an online question. Other questions are listed above in Interactive Learning.

Virtual Nerd™ Access Virtual Nerd student-centered math tutorials that directly relate to the content of the lesson.

Key Concept Standard Form of a Polynomial Function

The **standard form of a polynomial function** arranges the terms by degree in descending numerical order.

A polynomial function $P(x)$ in standard form is

$$P(x) = a_n x^n + a_{n-1} x^{n-1} + \cdots + a_1 x + a_0,$$

where n is a nonnegative integer and $a_n, \ldots, a_0$ are real numbers.

$$P(x) = 4x^3 + 3x^2 + 5x - 2$$

| Cubic term | Quadratic term | Linear term | Constant term |

You can classify a polynomial by its degree or by its number of terms. Polynomials of degrees zero through five have specific names, as shown in this table.

Degree	Name Using Degree	Polynomial Example	Number of Terms	Name Using Number of Terms
0	constant	5	1	monomial
1	linear	$x + 4$	2	binomial
2	quadratic	$4x^2$	1	monomial
3	cubic	$4x^3 - 2x^2 + x$	3	trinomial
4	quartic	$2x^4 + 5x^2$	2	binomial
5	quintic	$-x^5 + 4x^2 + 2x + 1$	4	polynomial of 4 terms

 Problem 1 Classifying Polynomials

Write each polynomial in standard form. What is the classification of each polynomial by degree? by number of terms?

Think

How do you write a polynomial in standard form?
Combine like terms if possible. Then, write the terms with their degrees in descending order.

A $3x + 9x^2 + 5$

$9x^2 + 3x + 5$

The polynomial has degree 2 and 3 terms. It is a quadratic trinomial.

B $4x - 6x^2 + x^4 + 10x^2 - 12$

$x^4 + 4x^2 + 4x - 12$

The polynomial has degree 4 and 4 terms. It is a quartic polynomial of 4 terms.

 Got It? 1. Write each polynomial in standard form. What is the classification of each by degree? by number of terms?

    a. $3x^3 - x + 5x^4$ **b.** $3 - 4x^5 + 2x^2 + 10$

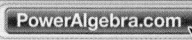
---

2 Guided Instruction

Take Note

Q In how many different orders could you write the terms of $3x^2 + 2x + 1$? **[6]**

Q In how many different orders could you write the terms of $4x^3 - 3x^2 + 3x + 2$? **[24]**

Q Why have a standard form for writing polynomial functions? **[Answers may vary. Samples: so everyone writes polynomial functions the same way; similar to having spelling rules for language]**

Q Why does a constant term have a degree of zero? **[Because $x^0 = 1$. For example, 5 could be written as $5x^0$.]**

Emphasize that the term with the greatest power in a polynomial function has the most influence over the behavior of the graph of the function.

Problem 1

Remind students to be careful of the signs as they reorder the terms of a polynomial to put it in standard form.

Q In 1B, where did the $4x^2$ come from? **[combining like terms]**

Got It?   ERROR PREVENTION

Q What do you have to do before classifying each polynomial? **[Answers may vary. Sample: Put them in standard form and combine like terms.]**

---

2 Guided Instruction

 Each Problem is worked out and supported online.

Problem 1
Classifying Polynomials

Problem 2
Describing End Behavior of Polynomial Functions

Problem 3
Graphing Cubic Functions
Animated

Alternative Problem 3
Graphing Cubic Functions
Animated

Problem 4
Using Differences to Determine Degree
Animated

Support in Algebra 2 Companion
• Vocabulary
• Key Concepts
• Got It?

Answers

Solve It!

1074; work backwards using the constant third difference, 24, to find the first and second differences and the seventh and eighth numbers in the first column.

Got It?

  1. a. $5x^4 + 3x^3 - x$; quartic trinomial
     b. $-4x^5 + 2x^2 + 13$; quintic trinomial

The degree of a polynomial function affects the shape of its graph and determines the maximum number of **turning points**, or places where the graph changes direction. It also affects the **end behavior**, or the directions of the graph to the far left and to the far right.

The table below shows you examples of polynomial functions and the four types of end behavior. The table also shows intervals where the functions are increasing and decreasing. A function is *increasing* when the *y*-values increase as *x*-values increase. A function is *decreasing* when the *y*-values decrease as *x*-values increase.

take note   Key Concept   Polynomial Functions

$y = 4x^4 + 6x^3 - x$

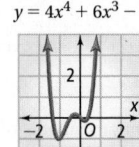

End Behavior: Up and Up

Turning Points: $(-1.07, -1.04), (-0.27, 0.17),$ and $(0.22, -0.15)$

The function is decreasing when $x < -1.07$ and $-0.27 < x < 0.22$. The function increases when $-1.07 < x < -0.27$ and $x > 0.22$.

$y = -x^2 + 2x$

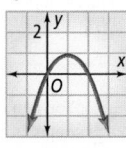

End Behavior: Down and Down

Turning Point: $(1, 1)$

The function is increasing when $x < 1$ and is decreasing when $x > 1$.

$y = x^3$

End Behavior: Down and Up

Zero turning points.

The function is increasing for all *x*.

$y = -x^3 + 2x$

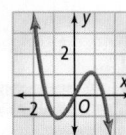

End Behavior: Up and Down

Turning Points: $(-0.82, -1.09)$ and $(0.82, 1.09)$

The function is decreasing when $x < -0.82$ and when $x > 0.82$. The function is increasing when $-0.82 < x < 0.82$.

You can determine the end behavior of a polynomial function of degree *n* from the leading term ax^n of the standard form.

End Behavior of a Polynomial Function With Leading Term ax^n

	n Even ($n \neq 0$)	*n* Odd
a Positive	Up and Up	Down and Up
a Negative	Down and Down	Up and Down

Additional Problems

1. Write $-3x + 4x^3 + 7x - 3$ in standard form. What is the classification of this polynomial by its degree? by its number of terms?

ANSWER $4x^3 + 4x - 3$; cubic trinomial

2. Consider the leading term of $y = 3x^4 - 2x^3 + x - 1$. What is the end behavior of the graph?

ANSWER up and up

3. a. What is the graph of $-x^3 + 12x$? Describe the graph.

ANSWER down and up; no turning points; increases from $-\infty$ to ∞

b. What is the graph of $-x^3 + 12x$? Describe the graph.

ANSWER up and down; turning points at $(-2, -16)$ and $(2, 16)$; decreases from $-\infty$ to -2, increases from -2 to 2, decreases from 2 to ∞

4. What is the degree of the polynomial function that generates the data shown in the table?

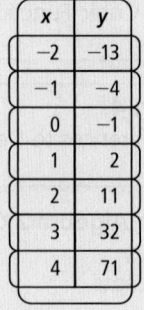

x	y
-2	-13
-1	-4
0	-1
1	2
2	11
3	32
4	71

ANSWER 3

In general, the graph of a polynomial function of degree n ($n \geq 1$) has at most $n - 1$ turning points. The graph of a polynomial function of odd degree has an even number of turning points. The graph of a polynomial function of even degree has an odd number of turning points.

ⓒ Problem 2 Describing End Behavior of Polynomial Functions

Consider the leading term of each polynomial function. What is the end behavior of the graph? Check your answer with a graphing calculator.

 $y = 4x^3 - 3x$

The leading term is $4x^3$. Since n is odd and a is positive, the end behavior is down and up.

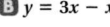 $y = -2x^4 + 8x^3 - 8x^2 + 2$

The leading term is $-2x^4$. Since n is even and a is negative, the end behavior is down and down.

Got It? 2. Consider the leading term of $y = -4x^3 + 2x^2 + 7$. What is the end behavior of the graph?

Think

What do a and n represent?
a is the coefficient of the leading term. n is the exponent of the leading term.

ⓒ Problem 3 Graphing Cubic Functions

What is the graph of each cubic function? Describe the graph, including end behavior, turning points, and increasing/decreasing intervals.

Ⓐ $y = \frac{1}{2}x^3$

Ⓑ $y = 3x - x^3$

Plan

How can you graph a polynomial function?
Make a table of values to help you sketch the middle part of the graph. Use what you know about end behavior to sketch the ends of the graph.

Step 1   **Step 2**

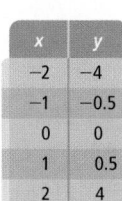 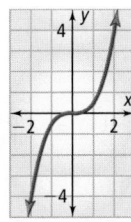

x	y
-2	-4
-1	-0.5
0	0
1	0.5
2	4

Step 1   **Step 2**

 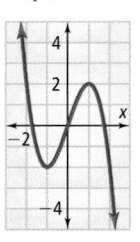

x	y
-2	2
-1	-2
0	0
1	2
2	-2

Step 3

The end behavior is down and up. There are no turning points. The function increases from $-\infty$ to ∞.

Step 3

The end behavior is up and down. There are turning points at $(-1, -2)$ and $(1, 2)$. The function decreases from $-\infty$ to -1, increases from -1 to 1, and decreases from 1 to ∞.

Got It? 3. What is the graph of each cubic function? Describe the graph.

a. $y = -x^3 + 2x^2 - x - 2$ **b.** $y = x^3 - 1$

Problem 2   EXTENSION

Q Why does the end behavior of a polynomial function not rely on any term other than the leading term? **[The leading term has the greatest degree, so as the value of x approaches positive infinity or negative infinity, the magnitude of the leading term is far greater than any other term.]**

Q If you forget the rules in the table regarding end behavior, how could you determine end behavior on your own? **[Answers may vary. Sample: Substitute extreme negative and positive integer values for x and determine only the sign of the leading term; if the leading term is positive, that end's behavior is up; if the leading term is negative, that end's behavior is down.]**

Got It?   ERROR PREVENTION

After graphing $y = -4x^3 + 2x^2 + 7$, to check, some students may say the end behavior is "down and down," since the graph first decreases from left to right. Use the graphs on page 282 to highlight that the end behavior correlates to the directions of the arrows on the ends of the curve.

Problem 3

Q For 3B, the first coefficient is positive 3, so why isn't the end behavior down and up? **[The polynomial is not written in standard form; the leading term is $-x^3$ with coefficient -1.]**

Got It?   ERROR PREVENTION

Prompt students to use the coefficient of the leading term to check that their graphs have proper end behavior.

Q What should be the end behavior of each graph? **[3a should be up and down; 3b should be down and up.]**

Answers

Got It? (continued)

2. up and down

3. a. end behavior: up and down; two turning points at $(0.33, -2.15)$ and $(1, -2)$; decreases from $-\infty$ to $\frac{1}{3}$, increases from $\frac{1}{3}$ to 1, and decreases from 1 to ∞

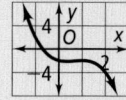

b. end behavior: down and up; no turning points; increases from $-\infty$ to ∞

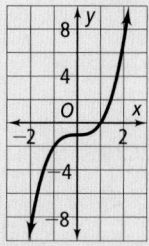

Q At least how many ordered pairs do you need to calculate second differences? Explain. **[Three; you need two first differences to calculate a second difference, and you need three *y*-values for two first differences.]**

Q Are four ordered pairs enough to determine whether a cubic function could have generated the data? Explain. **[No; with four ordered pairs you will be able to calculate only one third difference, which isn't enough to conclude that all of the third differences are constant.]**

Problem 4

Q What kind of polynomial function has constant second differences? **[quadratic]**

Q What kind of polynomial function has constant first differences? **[linear]**

Q The polynomial function that generates the data has two turning points, at $x = -2$ and $x \approx 1.33$. What happens to the first differences around these values? **[The signs of the first-difference values change from negative to positive or from positive to negative.]**

Got It?

Q How do you calculate the first value in the first differences? What is the difference? **[Subtract 23 from -16; $-16 - 23 = -39$.]**

Suppose you are given a set of polynomial function outputs. You know that their inputs are an ordered set of *x*-values in which consecutive *x*-values differ by a constant. By analyzing the differences of consecutive *y*-values, it is possible to determine the least-degree polynomial function that could generate the data.

If the first differences are constant, the function is linear. If the second differences (but not the first) are constant, the function is quadratic. If the third differences (but not the second) are constant, the function is cubic, and so on.

Problem 4 Using Differences to Determine Degree

What is the degree of the polynomial function that generates the data shown at the right?

x	y
−3	−1
−2	−7
−1	−3
0	5
1	11
2	9
3	−7

Know
A set of polynomial function values

Need
Degree of the polynomial function

Plan
Check first differences of *y*-values. Then check second differences, third differences, and so on until they are constant.

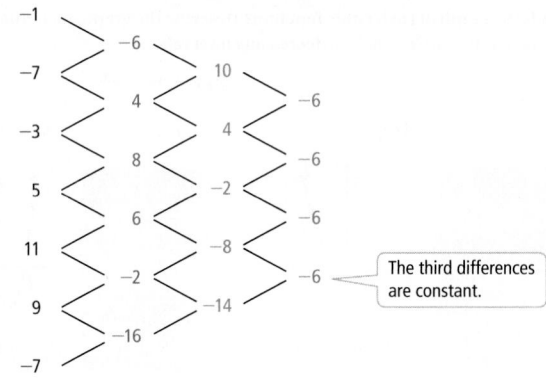

The third differences are constant.

Think
How do you find the second differences? Subtract the consecutive first differences.

The degree of the polynomial function is 3.

Got It? 4. a. What is the degree of the polynomial function that generates the data shown at the right?
b. Reasoning What is an example of a polynomial function whose fifth differences are constant but whose fourth differences are not constant?

x	y
−3	23
−2	−16
−1	−15
0	−10
1	−13
2	−12
3	29

Answers

Got It? (continued)
  4. a. degree: 4
    b. Answers may vary. Sample: $y = x^5$

Lesson Check

Do you know HOW?

Classify each polynomial by degree and by number of terms.

1. $5x^3$

2. $6x^2 + 4x - 2$

Write each polynomial in standard form.

3. $7x + 3 + 5x^2$

4. $-3 + 9x$

Do you UNDERSTAND?  MATHEMATICAL PRACTICES

5. Vocabulary Describe the end behavior of the graph of $y = -2x^7 - 8x$.

6. Reasoning Can the graph of a polynomial function be a straight line? If so, give an example.

7. Error Analysis Your friend claims the graph of the function $y = 4x^3 + 4$ has only one turning point. Describe the error your friend made and give the correct number of turning points.

Practice and Problem-Solving Exercises 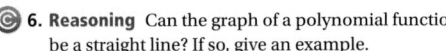 MATHEMATICAL PRACTICES

Ⓐ Practice Write each polynomial in standard form. Then classify it by degree and by number of terms.  See Problem 1.

8. $7x + 3x + 5$

9. $5 - 3x$

10. $2m^2 - 3 + 7m$

11. $-x^3 + x^4 + x$

12. $-4p + 3p + 2p^2$

13. $5a^2 + 3a^3 + 1$

14. $-x^5$

15. $3 + 12x^4$

16. $6x^3 - x^3$

17. $7x^3 - 10x^3 + x^3$

18. $4x + 5x^2 + 8$

19. $x^2 - x^4 + 2x^2$

Determine the end behavior of the graph of each polynomial function. 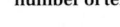 See Problem 2.

20. $y = -7x^3 + 8x^2 + x$

21. $y = -3x + 6x^2 - 1$

22. $y = 1 - 4x - 6x^3 - 15x^6$

23. $y = 8x^{11} - 2x^9 + 3x^6 + 4$

24. $y = -x^5 - 15x^7 - 4x^9$

25. $y = -3 - 6x^5 - 9x^8$

26. $y = x^4 - 7x^2 + 3$

27. $y = -8x^7 + 16x^6 + 9$

28. $y = -14x^6 + 11x^5 - 11$

29. $y = -x^3 - x^2 + 3$

30. $y = x^3 - 14x - 4$

31. $y = 5 - 17x^7 + 9x^{10}$

Describe the shape of the graph of each cubic function including end behavior, turning points, and increasing/decreasing intervals. See Problem 3.

32. $y = 3x^3 - x - 3$

33. $y = -9x^3 - 2x^2 + 5x + 3$

34. $y = 10x^3 + 9$

35. $y = 3x^3$

36. $y = -4x^3 - 5x^2$

37. $y = 8x^3$

Determine the degree of the polynomial function with the given data. See Problem 4.

38.

x	-2	-1	0	1	2
y	16	7	2	1	4

39.

x	-2	-1	0	1	2
y	-15	-9	-9	-9	-3

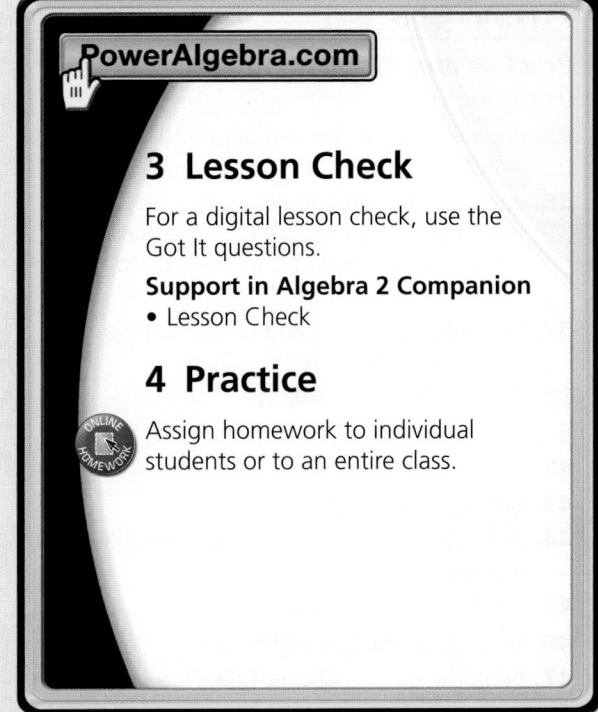

4 Practice

ASSIGNMENT GUIDE

Basic: 8–39 all, 40–50 even, 51

Average: 9–39 odd, 40–54

Advanced: 9–39 odd, 40–54

 Mathematical Practices are supported by exercises with red headings. Here are the Practices supported in this lesson:

MP 1: Make Sense of Problems Ex. 40
MP 2: Reason Abstractly Ex. 6, 50
MP 3: Communicate Ex. 57
MP 3: Compare Arguments Ex. 52
MP 3: Critique the Reasoning of Others Ex. 7

Applications exercises have blue headings.

EXERCISE 51: Use the Think About a Plan worksheet in the **Practice and Problem Solving Workbook** (also available in the Teaching Resources in print and online) to further support students' development in becoming independent learners.

HOMEWORK QUICK CHECK

To check students' understanding of key skills and concepts, go over Exercises 13, 33, 40, 48, and 51.

B Apply

C 40. Think About a Plan The data shows the power generated by a wind turbine. The *x* column gives the wind speed in meters per second. The *y* column gives the power generated in kilowatts. What is the degree of the polynomial function that models the data?
- What are the first differences of the *y*-values?
- What are the second differences of the *y*-values?
- When are the differences constant?

x	y
5	10
6	17.28
7	27.44
8	40.96
9	58.32

Classify each polynomial by degree and by number of terms. Simplify first if necessary.

41. $a^2 + a^3 - 4a^4$ **42.** 7   **43.** $2x(3x)$

44. $(2a - 5)(a^2 - 1)$ **45.** $(-8d^3 - 7) + (-d^3 - 6)$ **46.** $b(b - 3)^2$

Determine the sign of the leading coefficient and the least possible degree of the polynomial function for each graph.

47. 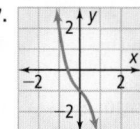   **48.** 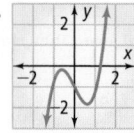   **49.**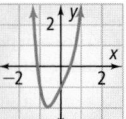

C 50. Open-Ended Write an equation for a polynomial function that has three turning points and end behavior up and up.

51. Show that the third differences of a polynomial function of degree 3 are nonzero and constant. First, use $f(x) = x^3 - 3x^2 - 2x - 6$. Then show third differences are nonzero and constant for $f(x) = ax^3 + bx^2 + cx + d, a \neq 0$.

C 52. Reasoning Suppose that a function pairs elements from set *A* with elements from set *B*. A function is called *onto* if it pairs every element in *B* with at least one element in *A*. For each type of polynomial function, and for each set *B*, determine whether the function is *always*, *sometimes*, or *never* onto.
- **a.** linear; *B* = all real numbers
- **b.** quadratic; *B* = all real numbers
- **c.** quadratic; *B* = all real numbers greater than or equal to 4
- **d.** cubic; *B* = all real numbers

53. Make a table of second differences for each polynomial function. Using your tables, make a conjecture about the second differences of quadratic functions.
- **a.** $y = 2x^2$ **b.** $y = 5x^2$ **c.** $y = 5x^2 - 2$
- **d.** $y = 7x^2$ **e.** $y = 7x^2 + 1$ **f.** $y = 7x^2 + 3x + 1$

54. a. Write the equation for the volume of a box with a length that is 5 in. less than its width and a height that is 3 in. less than its width.
- **b.** Graph the equation.
- **c.** For which interval(s) does the graph increase?
- **d.** For which interval(s) does the graph decrease?

Answers

Practice and Problem-Solving Exercises
(continued)

35. end behavior: down and up; no turning pts.; increases from $-\infty$ to ∞

36. end behavior: up and down; two turning pts. at $(-0.83, -1.2)$ and $(0, 0)$; decreases from $-\infty$ to -0.83, increases from -0.83 to 0, and decreases from 0 to ∞

37. end behavior: down and up; no turning pts.; increases from $-\infty$ to ∞

38. 2   **39.** 3   **40.** 3

41. $-4a^4 + a^3 + a^2$; quartic trinomial

42. 7; constant monomial

43. $6x^2$; quadratic monomial

44. $2a^3 - 5a^2 - 2a + 5$; cubic polynomial of 4 terms

45. $-9d^3 - 13$; cubic binomial

46. $b^3 - 6b^2 + 9b$; cubic trinomial

47. negative; 3   **48.** positive; 3

49. positive; 4

50. Answers may vary. Sample: $x^4 - 10x^2 + 9$

51. For $f(x) = x^3 - 3x^2 - 2x - 6$,

x	f(x)	1st diff	2nd diff	3rd diff
0	−6			
		−4		
1	−10		0	
		−4		6
2	−14		6	
		2		6
3	−12		12	
		14		6
4	2		18	
		32		
5	34			

For $f(x) = ax^3 + bx^2 + cx + d$,

x	f(x)	1st diff	2nd diff	3rd diff
0	d			
		a + b + c		
1	a + b + c + d		6a + 2b	
		7a + 3b + c		6a
2	8a + 4b + 2c + d		12a + 2b	
		19a + 5b + c		6a
3	27a + 9b + 3c + d		18a + 2b	
		37a + 7b + c		6a
4	64a + 16b + 4c + d		24a + 2b	
		61a + 9b + c		
5	125a + 25b + 5c + d			

52. a. sometimes   **b.** never
c. sometimes   **d.** always

53. a.

x	y	1st diff	2nd diff
−2	8		
		−6	
−1	2		4
		−2	
0	0		4
		2	
1	2		4
		6	
2	8		

 **Challenge**

55. Copy and complete the table, which shows the first and second differences in y-values for consecutive x-values for a polynomial function of degree 2.

56. The outputs for a certain function are 1, 2, 4, 8, 16, 32, and so on.
  a. Find the first differences of this function.
  b. Find the second differences of this function.
  c. Find the tenth differences of this function.
  d. Can you find a polynomial function that matches the original outputs? Explain your reasoning.

 57. Reasoning A cubic polynomial function f has leading coefficient 2 and constant term 7. If $f(1) = 7$ and $f(2) = 9$, what is $f(-2)$? Explain how you found your answer.

x	y	1st diff.	2nd diff.
−3	14	−8	2
−2	6		2
−1		−4	2
0	−4	−2	2
1		0	2
2	−6		
3			

Apply What You've Learned

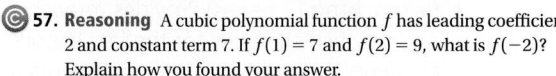 **MATHEMATICAL PRACTICES** MP 4

Look back at the information given on page 279 about the diorama Eliana plans to make for an art contest. The diagrams of the sheet of cardboard and the finished box are shown again below.

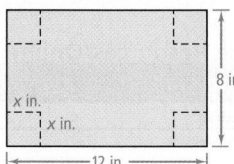 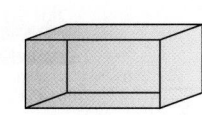

8 in.
x in.
x in.
12 in.

a. In the diagram, x represents the side length of the squares Eliana will cut from each corner. Which dimension of the diorama box does x represent: the length or the width of the back of the box, or the depth of the box from front to back?

b. Write expressions for the length and width of the back of the diorama box. Use your expressions to find a polynomial in standard form that represents the area of the back of the box. Classify the polynomial by degree and by number of terms.

c. Write a function $V(x)$ for the volume of the diorama box as a polynomial in standard form. Classify the polynomial function by degree and by number of terms.

d. Without graphing $y = V(x)$, describe the end behavior of the graph of the function $y = V(x)$. Explain.

e. Describe how you could identify which points on a graph of $y = V(x)$ correspond to a volume of 36 in.^{3}.

 **PowerAlgebra.com** | **Lesson 5-1** Polynomial Functions | **287**

 Apply What You've Learned

Here students write a function for the volume of the diorama box shown on page 279, and express the function as a polynomial in standard form. From the function's equation, students identify the end behavior of the graph. Later in the chapter, they will graph the function.

 Mathematical Practices

Students **model** the dimensions and volume of the diorama box by writing and analyzing polynomial expressions. (MP 4)

ANSWERS

a. the depth of the box from front to back

b. $12 − 2x$, $8 − 2x$; $4x^2 − 40x + 96$; quadratic trinomial

c. $V(x) = 4x^3 − 40x^2 + 96x$; cubic trinomial

d. The graph has down-and-up end behavior because it is an odd-degree polynomial with a leading term that has a positive coefficient.

e. Look for points with y-coordinate 36. You can identify these points by drawing the horizontal line $y = 36$ and looking for points where the line intersects the graph of $y = V(x)$.

---

53. b.

x	y	1st diff	2nd diff
−2	20		
		−15	
−1	5		10
		−5	
0	0		10
		5	
1	5		10
		15	
2	20		

c.

x	y	1st diff	2nd diff
−2	18		
		−15	
−1	3		10
		−5	
0	−2		10
		5	
1	3		10
		15	
2	18		

d.

x	y	1st diff	2nd diff
−2	28		
		−21	
−1	7		14
		−7	
0	0		14
		7	
1	7		14
		21	
2	28		

e.

x	y	1st diff	2nd diff
−2	29		
		−21	
−1	8		14
		−7	
0	1		14
		7	
1	8		14
		21	
2	29		

f.

x	y	1st diff	2nd diff
−2	23		
		−18	
−1	5		14
		−4	
0	1		14
		10	
1	11		14
		24	
2	35		

Second differences of quadratic functions are constant.

54. a. $x^3 − 8x^2 + 15x$

b.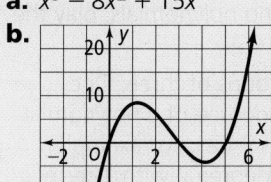

c. $−\infty$ to 1.21 and 4.12 to ∞

d. 1.21 to 4.12

55. missing values: y: 0, −6, −4; first differences: −6, 2

56. a. 1, 2, 4, 8, 16, 32 . . .
  b. 1, 2, 4, 8, 16, 32 . . .
  c. 1, 2, 4, 8, 16, 32 . . .
  d. No; the differences will never be constant, therefore there is no polynomial function that matches the outputs.

57. −35; Let $y = 2x^3 + bx^2 + cx + 7$. Evaluate $f(1) = 7$ and $f(2) = 9$ to find a system of equations for b and c. $b = −5$ and $c = 3$, so $f(−2) = −35$.

Lesson 5-1 **287**

5-1 Lesson Resources

Differentiated Remediation
Available in editable format online.

Additional Instructional Support

Algebra 2 Companion

Students can use the **Algebra 2 Companion** worktext (4 pages) as you teach the lesson. Use the Companion to support

- New Vocabulary
- Key Concepts
- Got It for each Problem
- Lesson Check

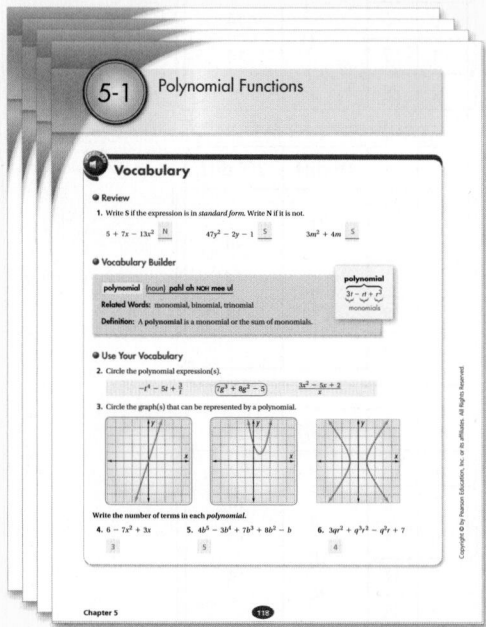

ELL Support

Use Role Playing To help students learn the vocabulary for classifying polynomials, play the following game:

Divide students into groups of three. One student says what the degree of a polynomial is and how many terms it has. For example, "I am a polynomial of degree 2 with 1 term. What am I?" One of the other two students responds, naming the polynomial. For example, "You are a quadratic monomial." The other student checks the answer.

You might want to start by allowing the students to look at the table in the book and then closing the book and continuing.

5 Assess & Remediate

Lesson Quiz

1. Write $2x^3 - 3x^2 + x^5$ in standard form. What is the classification of this polynomial by its degree? by its number of terms?

2. Consider the leading term of $y = -2x^2 - 3x + 3$. What is the end behavior of the graph?

3. Describe the end behavior and number of turning points in the graph of $y = x^3 + x + 3$.

4. Do you UNDERSTAND? What is the degree of the polynomial function that generates the data shown in the table?

x	y
1	−2
2	0
3	6
4	16
5	30
6	48
7	70
8	96

ANSWERS TO LESSON QUIZ

1. $x^5 + 2x^3 - 3x^2$; quintic trinomial

2. down and down

3. The end behavior is down and up. There are no turning points.

4. 2

PRESCRIPTION FOR REMEDIATION

Use the student work on the Lesson Quiz to prescribe a differentiated review assignment:

Points	Differentiated Remediation
0–2	Intervention
3	On-level
4	Extension

PowerAlgebra.com

5 Assess & Remediate

Assign the Lesson Quiz. Appropriate intervention, practice, or enrichment is automatically generated based on student performance.

Intervention

- **Reteaching** (2 pages) Provides reteaching and practice exercises for the key lesson concepts. Use with struggling students or absent students.

- **English Language Learner Support** Helps students develop and reinforce mathematical vocabulary and key concepts.

All-in-One Resources/Online
Reteaching

5-1 Reteaching
Polynomial Functions

Problem

What is the classification of the following polynomial by its degree? by its number of terms? What is its end behavior? $5x^4 - 3x + 4x^6 + 9x^3 - 12 - x^6 + 3x^4$

Step 1 Write the polynomial in standard form. First, combine any like terms. Then, place the terms of the polynomial in descending order from greatest exponent value to least exponent value.

$5x^4 - 3x + 4x^6 + 9x^3 - 12 - x^6 + 3x^4$

$8x^4 - 3x + 3x^6 + 9x^3 - 12$ Combine like terms.

$3x^6 + 8x^4 + 9x^3 - 3x - 12$ Place terms in descending order.

Step 2 The degree of the polynomial is equal to the value of the greatest exponent. This will be the exponent of the first term when the polynomial is written in standard form.

$3x^6 + 8x^4 + 9x^3 - 3x - 12$ The first term is $3x^6$.

The exponent of the first term is 6.

This is a sixth-degree polynomial.

Step 3 Count the number of terms in the simplified polynomial. It has 5 terms.

Step 4 To determine the end behavior of the polynomial (the directions of the graph to the far left and to the far right), look at the degree of the polynomial (n) and the coefficient of the leading term (a).

If a is positive and n is even, the end behavior is up and up.
If a is positive and n is odd, the end behavior is down and up.
If a is negative and n is even, the end behavior is down and down.
If a is negative and n is odd, the end behavior is up and down.
The leading term in this polynomial is $3x^6$.
a (+3) is positive and n (6) is even, so the end behavior is up and up.

Exercises

What is the classification of each polynomial by its degree? by its number of terms? What is its end behavior?

1. $8 - 6x^3 + 3x + x^3 - 2$
3rd degree; 3 terms; up and down

2. $15x^7 - 7$
7th degree; 2 terms; down and up

3. $2x - 6x^2 - 9$
2nd degree; 3 terms; down and down

All-in-One Resources/Online
English Language Learner Support

5-1 Additional Vocabulary Support
Polynomial Functions

Match each word in Column A with the matching polynomial in Column B.

Column A	Column B
1. cubic	A. 8
2. linear	B. $3x^4 + 5x^2 - 1$
3. quartic	C. $2x^2 - 2$
4. quintic	D. $7x^3 + 3x^2 + 4$
5. constant	E. $x + 10$
6. quadratic	F. $6x^5 + 3x^3 + 11x + 3$

Match each polynomial in Column A with the matching word in Column B.

Column A	Column B
7. $5x^3 + 7x$ C	A. trinomial
8. $4x^5 + 6x^2 + 3$ A	B. monomial
9. $8x^4$ B	C. binomial

Use the words from the lists below to name each polynomial by its degree and its number of terms.

Degree				
linear	quadratic	cubic	quartic	quintic

Number of Terms		
monomial	binomial	trinomial

10. $4x^2 - 2x + 3$ quadratic, trinomial

11. $6x^3$ cubic, monomial

12. $3x^5 + 7x^3 - 4$ quintic, trinomial

13. $8x + 3$ linear, binomial

14. $2x^4 + 5x^2$ quartic, binomial

Differentiated Remediation *continued*

Available in editable format online.

On-Level

- **Practice** (2 pages) Provides extra practice for each lesson. For simpler practice exercises, use the Form K Practice pages found in the All-in-One Teaching Resources and online.
- **Think About a Plan** Helps students develop specific problem-solving skills and strategies by providing scaffolded guiding questions.
- **Standardized Test Prep** Focuses on all major exercises, all major question types, and helps students prepare for the high-stakes assessments.

Extension

- **Enrichment** Provides students with interesting problems and activities that extend the concepts of the lesson.
- **Activities, Games, and Puzzles** Worksheets that can be used for concepts development, enrichment, and for fun!

Practice and Problem Solving Wkbk/ All-in-One Resources/Online

Practice page 1

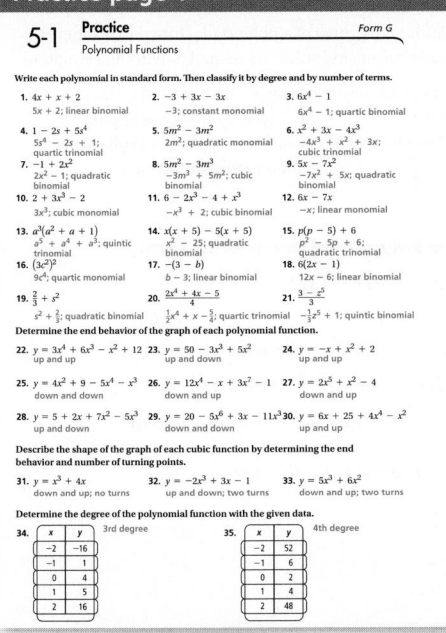

5-1 **Practice** Form G
Polynomial Functions

Write each polynomial in standard form. Then classify it by degree and by number of terms.

1. $4x + x + 2$ — $5x + 2$; linear binomial
2. $-3 + 3x - 3x$ — -3; constant monomial
3. $6x^4 - 1$ — $6x^4 - 1$; quartic binomial
4. $1 - 2s + 5s^4$ — $5s^4 - 2s + 1$; quartic trinomial
5. $5m^2 - 3m^2$ — $2m^2$; quadratic monomial
6. $x^2 + 3x - 4x^3$ — $-4x^3 + x^2 + 3x$; cubic trinomial
7. $-1 + 2x^2$ — $2x^2 - 1$; quadratic binomial
8. $5m^2 - 3m^3$ — $-3m^3 + 5m^2$; cubic binomial
9. $5x - 7x^2$ — $-7x^2 + 5x$; quadratic binomial
10. $2 + 3x^3 - 2$ — $3x^3$; cubic monomial
11. $6 - 2x^3 - 4 + x^3$ — $-x^3 + 2$; cubic binomial
12. $6x - 7x$ — $-x$; linear monomial
13. $a^3(a^2 + a + 1)$ — $a^5 + a^4 + a^3$; quintic trinomial
14. $x(x + 5) - 5(x + 5)$ — $x^2 - 25$; quadratic binomial
15. $p(p - 5) + 6$ — $p^2 - 5p + 6$; quadratic trinomial
16. $(3c^2)^2$ — $9c^4$; quartic monomial
17. $-(3 - b)$ — $b - 3$; linear binomial
18. $6(2x - 1)$ — $12x - 6$; linear binomial
19. $\frac{2}{3} + s^2$ — $s^2 + \frac{2}{3}$; quadratic binomial
20. $\frac{2x^4 + 4x - 5}{4}$ — $\frac{1}{2}x^4 + x - \frac{5}{4}$; quartic trinomial
21. $\frac{3 - z^5}{3}$ — $-\frac{1}{3}z^5 + 1$; quintic binomial

Determine the end behavior of the graph of each polynomial function.

22. $y = 3x^4 + 6x^3 - x^2 + 12$ — up and up
23. $y = 50 - 3x^3 + 5x^2$ — up and down
24. $y = -x + x^2 + 2$ — up and up
25. $y = 4x^2 + 9 - 5x^4 - x^3$ — down and down
26. $y = 12x^4 - x + 3x^7 - 1$ — down and up
27. $y = 2x^5 + x^2 - 4$ — down and up
28. $y = 5 + 2x + 7x^2 - 5x^3$ — up and down
29. $y = 20 - 5x^6 + 3x - 11x^3$ — down and down
30. $y = 6x + 25 + 4x^4 - x^2$ — up and up

Describe the shape of the graph of each cubic function by determining the end behavior and number of turning points.

31. $y = x^3 + 4x$ — down and up; no turns
32. $y = -2x^3 + 3x - 1$ — up and down; two turns
33. $y = 5x^3 + 6x^2$ — down and up; two turns

Determine the degree of the polynomial function with the given data.

34. 3rd degree

x	y
−2	−16
−1	1
0	4
1	5
2	16

35. 4th degree

x	y
−2	52
−1	6
0	2
1	4
2	48

Practice and Problem Solving Wkbk/ All-in-One Resources/Online

Practice page 2

5-1 **Practice** (continued) Form G
Polynomial Functions

Determine the sign of the leading coefficient and the degree of the polynomial function for each graph.

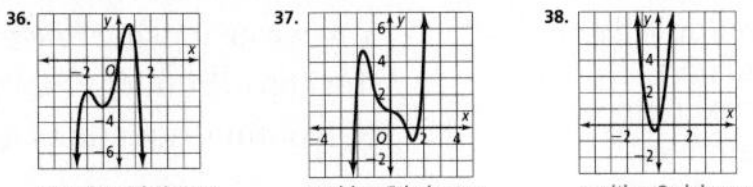

36. negative; 4th degree 37. positive; 5th degree 38. positive; 2nd degree

39. **Error Analysis** A student claims the function $y = 3x^4 - x^3 + 7$ is a fourth-degree polynomial with end behavior of down and down. Describe the error the student made. What is wrong with this statement? The degree is even and the leading coefficient is positive, so the end behavior should be up and up.

40. The table at the right shows data representing a polynomial function.
 a. What is the degree of the polynomial function? 5th degree
 b. What are the second differences of the y-values? −726, −126, −6, 6, 126
 c. What are the differences when they are constant? 114, 714 480

x	y
−3	−999
−2	−140
−1	−7
0	0
1	1
2	116
3	945

Classify each polynomial by degree and by number of terms. Simplify first if necessary.

41. $4x^5 - 5x^2 + 3 - 2x^2$ — 5th degree; 3 terms
42. $b(b - 3)^2$ — 3rd degree; 3 terms
43. $(7x^2 + 9x - 5) + (9x^2 - 9x)$ — 2nd degree; 2 terms
44. $(x + 2)^3$ — 3rd degree; 4 terms
45. $(4s^4 - s^2 - 3) - (3s - s^2 - 5)$ — 4th degree; 3 terms
46. 13 — 0 degree; 1 term

47. **Open-Ended** Write a third-degree polynomial function. Make a table of values and a graph. Check students' work.

48. **Writing** Explain why finding the degree of a polynomial is easier when the polynomial is written in standard form. When a polynomial is written in standard form, the term with the greatest exponent becomes the first term. This exponent is equal to the degree of the polynomial.

All-in-One Resources/Online

Enrichment

5-1 **Enrichment**
Polynomial Functions

Mathematicians use precise language to describe the relationships between sets. One important relationship is described as a function. You have graphed polynomial functions. Using this one word may not seem important, but it describes a very specific relationship between the domain and range of a polynomial. The word function tells you that every element of the domain corresponds with exactly one element of the range.

1. Another important relationship between two sets is described by the word *onto*. A function from set *A* to set *B* is onto if every element in set *B* is matched with an element in set *A*. Which of the following relations shows a function from set *A* to set *B* that is onto? Explain.

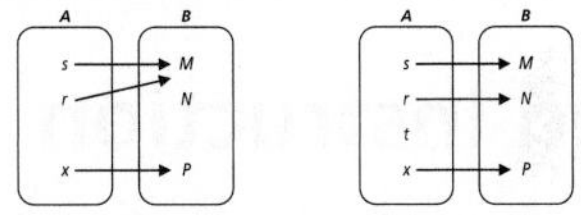

The second relation is a function that is onto because all of the elements in set *B* are matched with an element in set *A*.

2. Another relationship between two sets is described as *one-to-one*. A function from set *A* to set *B* is one-to-one if no element of set *B* is paired with more than one element of set *A*. Which of the following relations shows a function from set *A* to set *B* that is one-to-one? Explain.

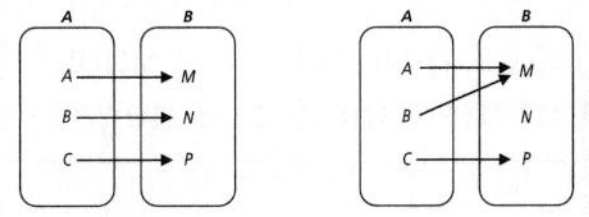

The first relation is a one-to-one function because all of the elements of set *B* are paired with exactly one element of set *A*.

Describe each polynomial function. If it is not possible, explain why.

3. Describe a polynomial function that is onto but not one-to-one. Answers may vary. Sample: A cubic with two turning points is onto because every y-value in the range is paired with an x-value, but not one-to-one because some y-values are paired with more than one x-value.
4. Is there a polynomial function that is one-to-one but not onto? no; Answers may vary. Sample: Odd degree polynomials are one-to-one, but they are also onto.
5. Describe a polynomial function that is both onto and one-to-one. Answers may vary. Sample: The cubic $y = x^3$ is onto because every y-value is paired with an x-value, and it is one-to-one because every y-value is paired with exactly one x-value.

Practice and Problem Solving Wkbk/ All-in-One Resources/Online

Think About a Plan

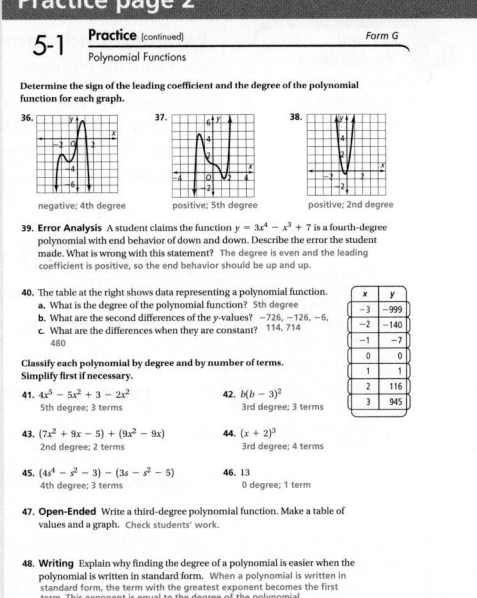

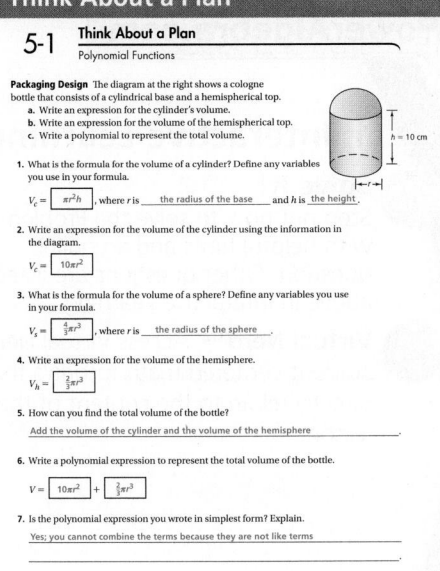

5-1 **Think About a Plan**
Polynomial Functions

Packaging Design The diagram at the right shows a cologne bottle that consists of a cylindrical base and a hemispherical top.
 a. Write an expression for the cylinder's volume.
 b. Write an expression for the volume of the hemispherical top.
 c. Write a polynomial to represent the total volume.

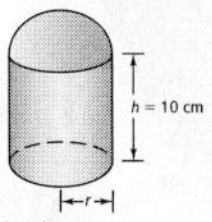

1. What is the formula for the volume of a cylinder? Define any variables you use in your formula. $V_c = \pi r^2 h$, where r is the radius of the base and h is the height.
2. Write an expression for the volume of the cylinder using the information in the diagram. $V_c = 10\pi r^2$
3. What is the formula for the volume of a sphere? Define any variables you use in your formula. $V_s = \frac{4}{3}\pi r^3$, where r is the radius of the sphere.
4. Write an expression for the volume of the hemisphere. $V_h = \frac{2}{3}\pi r^3$
5. How can you find the total volume of the bottle? Add the volume of the cylinder and the volume of the hemisphere.
6. Write a polynomial expression to represent the total volume of the bottle. $V = 10\pi r^2 + \frac{2}{3}\pi r^3$
7. Is the polynomial expression you wrote in simplest form? Explain. Yes; you cannot combine the terms because they are not like terms.

Practice and Problem Solving Wkbk/ All-in-One Resources/Online

Standardized Test Prep

5-1 **Standardized Test Prep**
Polynomial Functions

Multiple Choice

For Exercises 1–7, choose the correct letter.

1. Which expression is a binomial? D
 (A) $2x$ (B) $\frac{x}{2}$ (C) $3x^2 + 2x + 4$ (D) $x - 9$
2. Which polynomial function has an end behavior of up and down? F
 (F) $-6x^7 + 4x^2 - 3$ (H) $6x^7 - 4x^2 + 3$ (G) $-7x^6 + 3x - 2$ (I) $7x^6 - 3x + 2$
3. What is the degree of the polynomial $5x + 4x^2 + 3x^3 - 5x$? C
 (A) 1 (B) 2 (C) 3 (D) 4
4. What is the degree of the polynomial represented by the data in the table at the right? G
 (F) 2 (G) 3 (H) 4 (I) 5
5. For the table of values at the right, if the *n*th differences are constant, what is the constant value? B
 (A) −12 (B) 12 (C) 1 (D) 6

x	y
−3	77
−2	24
−1	1
0	−4
1	−3
2	−8
3	−31

6. What is the standard form of the polynomial $9x^2 + 5x + 27 + 2x^3$? I
 (F) $27 + 5x + 9x^2 + 2x^3$ (H) $9x^2 + 5x + 27 + 2x^3$ (G) $9x^2 + 5x + 2x^3 + 27$ (I) $2x^3 + 9x^2 + 5x + 27$
7. What is the number of terms in the polynomial $(2a - 5)(a^2 - 1)$? C
 (A) 2 (B) 3 (C) 4 (D) 5

Short Response

8. Simplify $(9x^3 - 4x + 2) - (x^3 + 3x^2 + 1)$. Then name the polynomial by degree and the number of terms.
 [2] $8x^3 - 3x^2 - 4x + 1$; 3rd degree; 4 terms
 [1] simplified polynomial is correct, but degree and/or number of terms is incorrect OR simplified polynomial is incorrect, but degree and terms are correct for the polynomial given.
 [0] no answers given

Online Teacher Resource Center

Activities, Games, and Puzzles

5-1 **Activity: Tables and Trends**
Polynomial Functions

Work in small groups and use tables to see how polynomial functions behave. These are cubic polynomial functions with leading coefficient 1. Each of these graphs crosses the x-axis three different times between −5 and 5.

Graph A: Complete the table for $P(x) = x^3 - 2x^2 - 11x + 12$.

x	−5	−4	−3	−2	−1	0	1	2	3	4	5
P(x)	−108	−40	0	18	20	12	0	−10	−12	0	32

Describe the trend of the graph including end behavior. up, down, up

Graph B: Complete the table for $P(x) = -x^3 + 4x^2 - x - 4$.

x	−5	−4	−3	−2	−1	0	1	2	3	4	5
P(x)	226	128	62	22	2	−4	−2	2	2	−8	−34

Describe the trend of the graph including end behavior. down, up, down

Graph C: Complete the table for $P(x) = 3x^3 - 6x^2 - 16x + 32$.

x	−5	−4	−3	−2	−1	0	1	2	3	4	5
P(x)	−413	−192	−55	16	39	32	13	0	11	64	177

Describe the trend of the graph including end behavior. up, down, up

Graph D: Complete the table for $P(x) = x^3 - 2x^2 - 5x + 6$.

x	−5	−4	−3	−2	−1	0	1	2	3	4	5
P(x)	−144	−70	−24	0	20	6	0	−4	0	18	56

Describe the trend of the graph including end behavior. up, down, up

As a group, explain how you know the graph does not turn again outside the range −5 to 5. Answers may vary. Sample: As absolute values of x increase, x^3 dominates the behavior of the function.

1 Interactive Learning

Solve It!

PURPOSE To explore the product of linear factors numerically, algebraically, and graphically

PROCESS Students may select several x-values, find corresponding y-values for each line, calculate the products, and plot product points. Alternatively, they may find the algebraic product $(x + 1)(x - 1)$ and use the quadratic polynomial to find product points and/or graph the parabola.

FACILITATE

Q How can $1.5 \cdot 3.5$ be expressed as the product of a sum and a difference? **[Samples: $(2.5 - 1)(2.5 + 1)$; $(x - 1)(x + 1)$ for $x = 2.5$]**

Q Which x-values result in a product of 0? What is special about those? **[-1 and 1; each of the lines has an x-intercept for those x-values.]**

ANSWER See Solve It in Answers on next page.

CONNECT THE MATH In the Solve It, students see numerical and graphical equivalence between the product of two linear factors and a quadratic function. The lesson solidifies connections between factors, roots, zeros, and x-intercepts of polynomials, related functions, and graphs.

2 Guided Instruction

Problem 1

Q Why do the constants of the factors of the quadratic trinomial have different signs? **[Sample: The constant of the trinomial is negative.]**

Got It?

Q What is the first step to factor this polynomial? **[Factor out the GCF, x.]**

Common Core State Standards

F-IF.C.7c Graph polynomial functions, identifying zeros when suitable factorizations are available and showing end behavior. **Also A-APR.B.3**

MP 1, MP 2, MP 3, MP 4, MP 5

Objectives To analyze the factored form of a polynomial
To write a polynomial function from its zeros

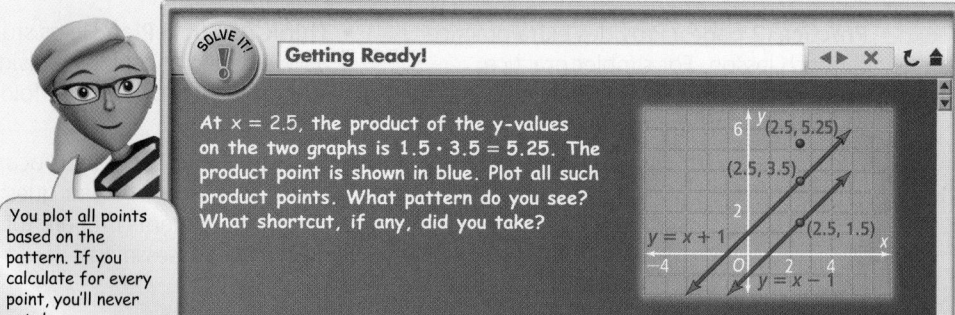

Getting Ready!

At $x = 2.5$, the product of the y-values on the two graphs is $1.5 \cdot 3.5 = 5.25$. The product point is shown in blue. Plot all such product points. What pattern do you see? What shortcut, if any, did you take?

> You plot _all_ points based on the pattern. If you calculate for every point, you'll never get done.

If $P(x)$ is a polynomial function, the solutions of the related polynomial equation $P(x) = 0$ are the zeros of the function.

Lesson Vocabulary
- Factor Theorem
- multiple zero
- multiplicity
- relative maximum
- relative minimum

Essential Understanding Finding the zeros of a polynomial function will help you factor the polynomial, graph the function, and solve the related polynomial equation.

In Chapter 4, you solved a quadratic equation of the form $x^2 + bx + c = 0$ by factoring. You wrote it using *linear factors* in the form $(x - r_1)(x - r_2) = 0$. Then you applied the Zero-Product Property to find the solutions $x = r_1$ and $x = r_2$. You can solve some polynomial equations $a_n x^n + a_{n-1} x^{n-1} + \cdots + a_0 = 0$ in much the same way.

Plan

How do you write the factored form of a polynomial? Write the polynomial as a product of factors. Make sure each factor cannot be factored any further.

Problem 1 Writing a Polynomial in Factored Form

What is the factored form of $x^3 - 2x^2 - 15x$?

$$x^3 - 2x^2 - 15x = x(x^2 - 2x - 15) \qquad \text{Factor out the GCF, } x.$$
$$= x(x - 5)(x + 3) \qquad \text{Factor } x^2 - 2x - 15.$$

Check $\quad x(x - 5)(x + 3) = x(x^2 - 2x - 15) \qquad$ Multiply $(x - 5)(x + 3)$.
$$= x^3 - 2x^2 - 15x \; ✔ \qquad \text{Distributive Property}$$

Got It? **1.** What is the factored form of $x^3 - x^2 - 12x$?

5-2 Preparing to Teach

BIG ideas Equivalence
Function

ESSENTIAL UNDERSTANDINGS
- Knowing the zeros of a polynomial function gives information about its graph.
- A polynomial of degree n has n linear factors. The graph of the related function crosses the x-axis an even or odd number of times depending on whether n is even or odd.
- $(x - a)$ is linear factor if and only if a is a zero.

Math Background

The linear factors of a polynomial are closely connected to the zeros of the related polynomial function. By applying the Zero Product Property, each linear factor is set equal to zero and solved

to obtain the zeros. The Factor Theorem makes the connection explicit, stating that $x - a$ is a linear factor when the value of a is a zero of the related polynomial function.

Thus the zeros of a polynomial function identify
- the linear factors of the polynomial.
- the x-intercepts of the function's graph.
- the solutions to $P(x) = 0$.

Mathematical Practices

Use appropriate tools strategically. In Problems 5 and 6, students will use a graphing calculator to determine the relative maximum and minimum of a polynomial function.

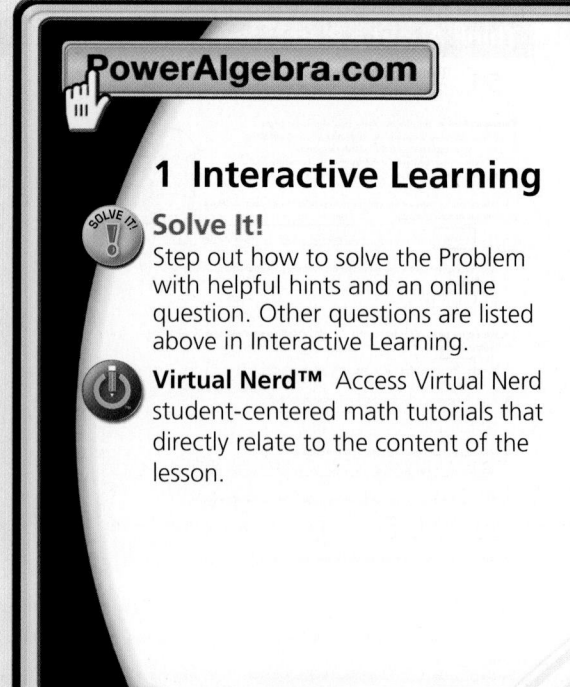

PowerAlgebra.com

1 Interactive Learning

Solve It!
Step out how to solve the Problem with helpful hints and an online question. Other questions are listed above in Interactive Learning.

Virtual Nerd™ Access Virtual Nerd student-centered math tutorials that directly relate to the content of the lesson.

Key Concepts Roots, Zeros, and *x*-intercepts

The following are equivalent statements about a real number b and a polynomial $P(x) = a_n x^n + a_{n-1} x^{n-1} + \cdots + a_1 x + a_0$.

- $x - b$ is a linear factor of the polynomial $P(x)$.
- b is a zero of the polynomial function $y = P(x)$.
- b is a root (or solution) of the polynomial equation $P(x) = 0$.
- b is an *x*-intercept of the graph of $y = P(x)$.

 Problem 2 Finding Zeros of a Polynomial Function

What are the zeros of $y = (x + 2)(x - 1)(x - 3)$? Graph the function.

Know	Need	Plan
Polynomial function	• Zeros • Additional points • End behavior	• Use the Zero-Product Property to find zeros. • Find points between the zeros. • Sketch the graph.

 Think

Does knowing the zeros of a function give you enough information to sketch it?
No; several different cubic functions could pass through $(-2, 0)$, $(1, 0)$, and $(3,0)$.

Step 1 Use the Zero-Product Property to find the zeros.

$$(x + 2)(x - 1)(x - 3) = 0$$

so $x + 2 = 0$ or $x - 1 = 0$ or $x - 3 = 0$.
The zeros of the function are $-2, 1,$ and 3.

Step 2 Find points for *x*-values between the zeros.
Evaluate $y = (x + 2)(x - 1)(x - 3)$ for $x = -1, 0,$ and 2.

$(-1 + 2)(-1 - 1)(-1 - 3) = 8 \quad (-1, 8)$

$(0 + 2)(0 - 1)(0 - 3) = 6 \quad (0, 6)$

$(2 + 2)(2 - 1)(2 - 3) = -4 \quad (2, -4)$

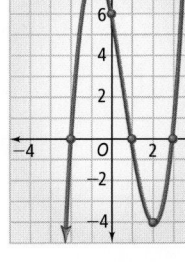

Step 3 Determine the end behavior.
The function $y = (x + 2)(x - 1)(x - 3)$ is cubic. The coefficient of x^3 is $+1$, so the end behavior is *down and up*.

Step 4 Use the zeros: $(-2, 0), (1, 0), (3, 0)$; the additional points: $(-1, 8), (0, 6), (2, -4)$; and end behavior to sketch the graph.

 Got It? **2.** What are the zeros of $y = x(x - 3)(x + 5)$? Graph the function.

The Factor Theorem describes the relationship between the linear factors of a polynomial and the zeros of a polynomial.

Take Note

An example might help students better understand the equivalent statements:

Let $P(x) = -x^3 + 2x + 4$, and let $x = 2$.

Then $P(2) = -(2)^3 + 2(2) + 4 = 0$.

Therefore,
- $x - 2$ is a factor of $-x^3 + 2x + 4$.
- 2 is a zero for the polynomial function $P(x)$.
- 2 is a solution to the equation $-x^3 + 2x + 4 = 0$.
- The point $(2, 0)$ is an *x*-intercept of the graph of $P(x) = -x^3 + 2x + 4$.

Problem 2

Q What is the value of *y* for any zero of a polynomial function? **[0]**

Q How does the graph of this function show that $-2, 1,$ and 3 are the zeros of the function? **[The graph of the function intersects the *x*-axis at $-2, 1,$ and 3.]**

Got It?

Use this polynomial to emphasize that 0 can be a zero of a polynomial function if one of the factors of the polynomial is *x*.

---

2 Guided Instruction

Each Problem is worked out and supported online.

Problem 1
Writing a Polynomial in Factored Form

Problem 2
Finding Zeros of a Polynomial Function

Problem 3
Writing a Polynomial Function From Its Zeros
Animated

Problem 4
Finding the Multiplicity of a Zero
Animated

Problem 5
Identifying Relative Maximums and Minimums

Problem 6
Using a Polynomial to Maximize Volume

Alternative Problem 6
Using a Polynomial to Maximize Volume
Animated

Support in Algebra 2 Companion
- Vocabulary
- Key Concepts
- Got It?

Answers

Solve It!
The product pts. form a parabola. The pts. can be found by plotting $y = (x + 1)(x - 1) = x^2 - 1$.

Got It?
1. $x(x - 4)(x + 3)$

2. $0, 3, -5$;

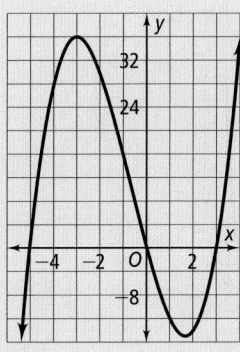

Take Note
EXTENSION

"If and only if" means that the reverse of the statement is also true: If $x - a$ is a factor, then $x = a$ is a zero; and if $x = a$ is a zero, then $x - a$ is a factor.

Problem 3

Q In 3A, could the factors $(x + 2)(x - 2)(x - 3)$ be rewritten as $(x^2 - 4)(x - 3)$? Explain. **[Yes; $(x + 2)(x - 2)$ are the factors of a difference of two squares: $(x^2 - 2^2)$.]**

EXTENSION

If a polynomial function is of degree n, then there are at most $n - 1$ turning points in the graph of that function. This means that in Problem 3, $f(x)$ has at most 2 turning points and $g(x)$ has at most 3 turning points. The graphs of both functions on this page show all the turning points of those functions.

Got It?
ERROR PREVENTION

Q What is the difference between a quartic polynomial and a quadratic polynomial? **[A quartic polynomial is of degree 4 and has the form $ax^4 + bx^3 + cx^2 + dx + e$, while a quadratic polynomial is of degree 2 and has the form $ax^2 + bx + c$.]**

---

take note
Theorem   Factor Theorem

The expression $x - a$ is a factor of a polynomial if and only if the value a is a zero of the related polynomial function.

 **Problem 3** Writing a Polynomial Function From Its Zeros

Ⓐ What is a cubic polynomial function in standard form with zeros -2, 2, and 3?

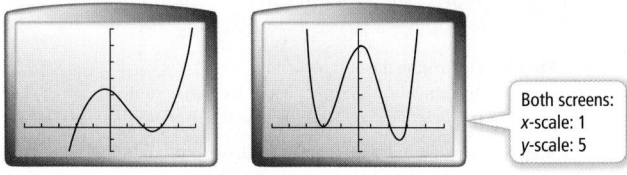
Plan

How can you use the zeros to find the function?
By the Factor Theorem, a is a zero means that $x - a$ is a factor of the related polynomial.

$$\begin{array}{ccc} -2 & 2 & 3 \\ \downarrow & \downarrow & \downarrow \end{array} \qquad -2, 2, \text{ and } 3 \text{ are zeros.}$$

$$\begin{aligned} f(x) &= (x + 2)(x - 2)(x - 3) & \text{Write a linear factor for each zero.} \\ &= (x + 2)(x^2 - 5x + 6) & \text{Multiply } (x-2) \text{ and } (x-3). \\ &= x(x^2 - 5x + 6) + 2(x^2 - 5x + 6) & \text{Distributive Property} \\ &= x^3 - 5x^2 + 6x + 2x^2 - 10x + 12 & \text{Distributive Property} \\ &= x^3 - 3x^2 - 4x + 12 & \text{Simplify.} \end{aligned}$$

The cubic polynomial $f(x) = x^3 - 3x^2 - 4x + 12$ has zeros -2, 2, and 3.

Ⓑ What is a quartic polynomial function in standard form with zeros -2, -2, 2, and 3?

$$\begin{array}{cccc} -2 & -2 & 2 & 3 \\ \downarrow & \downarrow & \downarrow & \downarrow \end{array} \qquad -2, -2, 2, \text{ and } 3 \text{ are zeros.}$$

$$\begin{aligned} g(x) &= (x + 2)(x + 2)(x - 2)(x - 3) & \text{Write a linear factor for each zero.} \\ &= x^4 - x^3 - 10x^2 + 4x + 24 & \text{Simplify.} \end{aligned}$$

The quartic polynomial $g(x) = x^4 - x^3 - 10x^2 + 4x + 24$ has zeros -2, -2, 2, and 3.

Ⓒ Graph both functions. How do the graphs differ? How are they similar?

Both screens:
x-scale: 1
y-scale: 5

Both graphs have x-intercepts at -2, 2, and 3. The cubic has down-and-up end behavior. The quartic has up-and-up end behavior.

The cubic function has two turning points, and it crosses the x-axis at -2. The quartic function touches the x-axis at -2 but does not cross it. The quartic function has three turning points.

Got It? 3. a. What is a quadratic polynomial function with zeros 3 and -3?
b. What is a cubic polynomial function with zeros 3, 3, and -3?
c. Reasoning Graph both functions. How do the graphs differ? How are they similar?

Additional Problems

1. What is the factored form of $x^3 + x^2 - 12x$?

ANSWER $x(x + 4)(x - 3)$

2. What are the zeros of $y = (x - 3)(x + 4)(x - 1)$? Graph the function.

ANSWER $3, -4, 1$

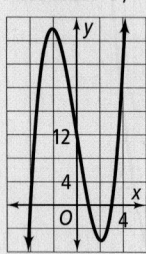

3. What is a cubic polynomial function in standard form with zeros 1, -1, and 4?

ANSWER $x^3 - 4x^2 - x + 4$

4. What are the zeros of $f(x) = x^3 - 5x^2 + 3x + 9$? What are the multiplicities? How does the graph behave at these zeros?

ANSWER 3 with a multiplicity of 2: the graph only touches the x-axis and turns around; -1 with a multiplicity of 1: the graph crosses the x-axis.

5. What are the relative maximum and minimum of $f(x) = x^3 - 9x$? Round to the nearest tenth.

ANSWER relative maximum: $(-1.7, 10.4)$; relative minimum: $(1.7, -10.4)$

6. A designer wants to make a rectangular prism box with maximum volume, while keeping the sum of its length, width, and height 12 in. The length must be 3 times the height. What should each dimension be?

ANSWER length: 6 in., width = 4 in., height = 2 in.

You can write the polynomial functions in Problem 3 in factored form as $f(x) = (x + 2)(x - 2)(x - 3)$ and $g(x) = (x + 2)^2(x - 2)(x - 3)$. In $g(x)$ the repeated linear factor $x + 2$ makes -2 a **multiple zero**.

In particular, since the linear factor $x + 2$ appears twice, you can say that -2 is a zero of **multiplicity** 2. In general, *a is a zero of multiplicity n* means that $x - a$ appears n times as a factor.

Key Concept How Multiple Zeros Affect a Graph

If a is a zero of multiplicity n in the polynomial function $y = P(x)$, then the behavior of the graph at the x-intercept a will be close to linear if $n = 1$, close to quadratic if $n = 2$, close to cubic if $n = 3$, and so on.

Ⓒ **Problem 4** Finding the Multiplicity of a Zero

What are the zeros of $f(x) = x^4 - 2x^3 - 8x^2$? What are their multiplicities? How does the graph behave at these zeros?

$$f(x) = x^4 - 2x^3 - 8x^2$$
$$= x^2(x^2 - 2x - 8) \quad \text{Factor out the GCF, } x^2.$$
$$= x^2(x + 2)(x - 4) \quad \text{Factor } (x^2 - 2x - 8).$$

Since $x^2 = (x - 0)^2$, the number 0 is a zero of multiplicity 2. The numbers -2 and 4 are zeros of multiplicity 1.

The graph looks close to linear at the x-intercepts -2 and 4. It resembles a parabola at the x-intercept 0.

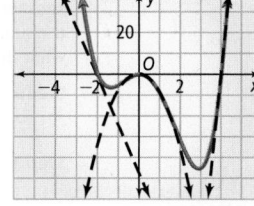

Think

How can you find the multiplicities?
Factor the polynomial. Find the number of times each linear factor appears.

✓ **Got It?** **4.** What are the zeros of $f(x) = x^3 - 4x^2 + 4x$? What are their multiplicities? How does the graph behave at these zeros?

If the graph of a polynomial function has several turning points, the function can have a **relative maximum** and a **relative minimum**. A relative maximum is the value of the function at an up-to-down turning point. A relative minimum is the value of the function at a down-to-up turning point.

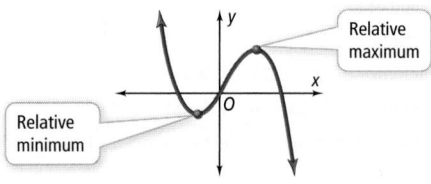

Relative maximum

Relative minimum

Take Note EXTENSION

This discussion of how multiple zeros affect a graph can be extended with the following facts:
- If a is a zero of **even** multiplicity, then the graph of its function touches the x-axis at a and turns around.
- If a is a zero of **odd** multiplicity, then the graph of its function crosses the x-axis at a.

Problem 4

Q How does this graph show that 0 is a multiple zero of the function? **[The graph has a turning point at (0, 0).]**

Q What is the end behavior of this function's graph? **[up and up]**

Got It? VISUAL LEARNERS

Since x is a common factor of this function, students can conclude that 0 is a zero with a multiplicity of 1. Note that this fact is displayed in the function's graph where it crosses the x-axis at (0, 0).

EXTENSION

Only polynomials of degree greater than 2 can have more than one maximum or minimum value. If n is the degree of a polynomial function, then $n - 1$ is the greatest possible total number of minimum and maximum values for that function.

Answers

Got It? (continued)

3. a. $f(x) = x^2 - 9$
  b. $P(x) = x^3 - 3x^2 - 9x + 27$
  c.

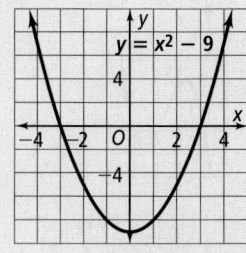

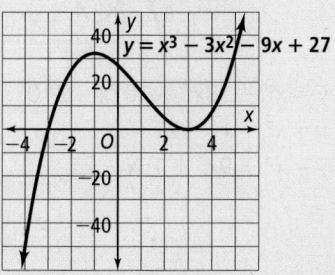

Both graphs have x-intercepts of 3 and -3.
The quadratic has up and up end behavior and one turning pt., and the cubic has down and up end behavior and two turning pts.

4. 0 is a zero of multiplicity 1, the graph looks close to linear at $x = 0$; 2 is a zero of multiplicity 2, the graph looks close to quadratic at $x = 2$.

Problem 5

To see the graph of the function as shown on this page, students should change the RANGE settings on their calculators to Ymax = 100 and Ymin = −100.

Q Why is (−4, 80) called a relative maximum of this function? **[It is a turning point of the function's graph, but it is not the greatest (absolute maximum) value of the function.]**

Got It?

Q How many x-intercepts does this graph have? **[3]**

Q What is the greatest number of relative maximums and relative minimums this graph can have? How do you know? **[2; it is a polynomial of degree 3.]**

Problem 6

Q What do the values of x represent? **[the height of the camera]**

Q What do the values of y represent? **[the volume of the camera]**

Q What does the point (1.6, 7.68) represent? **[A camera that is 1.6 in. tall will have the maximum volume of 7.68 in.^{3}.]**

Got It?   ERROR PREVENTION

Q What expression from the Problem do you have to change? **[Change the expression for the camera's width based on the new sum of its dimensions.]**

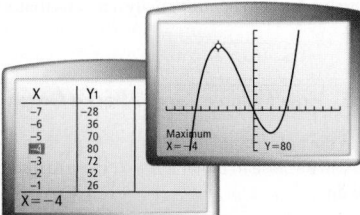 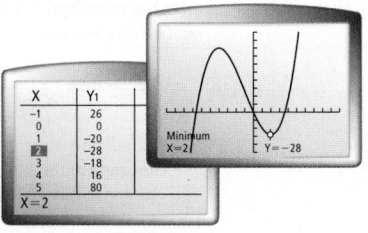

© **Problem 5** Identifying a Relative Maximum and Minimum

What are the relative maximum and minimum of $f(x) = x^3 + 3x^2 − 24x$?

Use a graphing calculator to find a relative maximum and a relative minimum.

Think

How is a relative maximum different from a maximum at the vertex of a parabola?
A relative maximum is the greatest y-value in the "neighborhood" of its x-value. The maximum at the vertex of a parabola is the greatest y-value for all x-values.

Relative maximum   Relative minimum

The relative maximum is 80 at $x = −4$ and the relative minimum is −28 at $x = 2$.

Got It? **5.** What are the relative maximum and minimum of $f(x) = 3x^3 + x^2 − 5x$?

© **Problem 6** Using a Polynomial Function to Maximize Volume

Technology The design of a digital box camera maximizes the volume while keeping the sum of the dimensions at 6 inches. If the length must be 1.5 times the height, what should each dimension be?

Step 1 Define a variable x.

> Let $x = $ the height of the camera.

Step 2 Determine length and width.

> length $= 1.5x$; width $= 6 − (x + 1.5x) = 6 − 2.5x$

Think

What is the formula for the volume of a "box"?
$V = \ell wh$

Step 3 Model the volume.

> $V = (\text{length})(\text{width})(\text{height}) = (1.5x)(6 − 2.5x)(x)$
> $= −3.75x^3 + 9x^2$

Step 4 Graph the polynomial function. Use the **MAXIMUM** feature to find that the maximum volume is 7.68 in.^{3} for a height of 1.6 in.

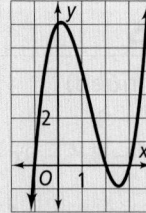

> height $= x = 1.6$
> length $= 1.5x = 1.5(1.6) = 2.4$
> width $= 6 − 2.5x = 6 − 2.5(1.6) = 2$

The dimensions of the camera should be 2.4 in. long by 2 in. wide by 1.6 in. high.

Got It? **6.** What is the maximum volume of the camera in Problem 6, if the sum of the dimensions is at most 4 inches?

Answers

Got It? (continued)

5. relative maximum: (−0.86, 3.13); relative minimum: (0.64, −2)

6. 2.28 in.^{3}

Lesson Check

1. 0, 6

2. −4, 5

3. −12, 7, 9

4. $f(x) = x^3 − x$

5. $h(x) = x^4 + 4x^3 − 26x^2 − 60x + 225$

6. Error in writing the factors: a function that has zeros at 3 and −1 has factors of $x − 3$ and $x + 1$ *not* $x + 3$ and $x − 1$, so $f(x) = x^2 − 2x − 3$ *not* $x^2 + 2x − 3$.

Practice and Problem-Solving Exercises

7. $x(x + 5)(x + 2)$

8. $x(x − 9)(x + 2)$

9. $x(x − 7)(x + 3)$

10. $x(x − 6)(x + 6)$

11. $x(x + 4)^2$

12. $3x(3x − 1)(x + 1)$

13. 1, −2;

14. 2, −9;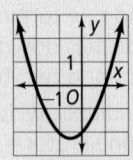

15. 0, −5, 8;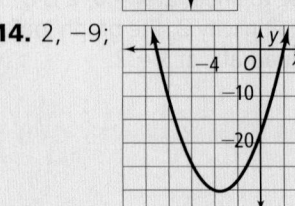

16. −1, 2, 3;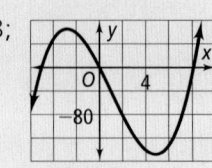

17. −1, 1, 2;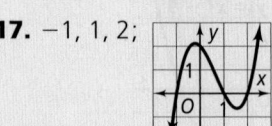

18. 0, −2, −3;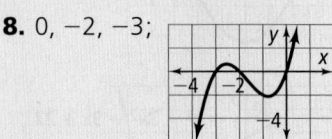

19. $y = x^3 − 18x^2 + 107x − 210$

20. $y = x^3 + x^2 − 2x$

21. $y = x^3 + 9x^2 + 15x − 25$

Lesson Check

Do you know HOW?

Find the zeros of each function.

1. $y = x(x - 6)$

2. $y = (x + 4)(x - 5)$

3. $y = (x + 12)(x - 9)(x - 7)$

4. Write a polynomial function in standard form with zeros -1, 1, and 0.

Do you UNDERSTAND? MATHEMATICAL PRACTICES

5. Vocabulary Write a polynomial function h in standard form that has 3 and -5 as zeros of multiplicity 2.

6. Error Analysis Your friend says that to write a function that has zeros 3 and -1, you should multiply the two factors $(x + 3)$ and $(x - 1)$ to get $f(x) = x^2 + 2x - 3$. Describe and correct your friend's error.

Practice and Problem-Solving Exercises MATHEMATICAL PRACTICES

A Practice

Write each polynomial in factored form. Check by multiplication.  See Problem 1.

7. $x^3 + 7x^2 + 10x$ **8.** $x^3 - 7x^2 - 18x$ **9.** $x^3 - 4x^2 - 21x$

10. $x^3 - 36x$ **11.** $x^3 + 8x^2 + 16x$ **12.** $9x^3 + 6x^2 - 3x$

Find the zeros of each function. Then graph the function. See Problem 2.

13. $y = (x - 1)(x + 2)$ **14.** $y = (x - 2)(x + 9)$ **15.** $y = x(x + 5)(x - 8)$

16. $y = (x + 1)(x - 2)(x - 3)$ **17.** $y = (x + 1)(x - 1)(x - 2)$ **18.** $y = x(x + 2)(x + 3)$

Write a polynomial function in standard form with the given zeros. See Problem 3.

19. $x = 5, 6, 7$ **20.** $x = -2, 0, 1$ **21.** $x = -5, -5, 1$ **22.** $x = 3, 3, 3$

23. $x = 1, -1, -2$ **24.** $x = 0, 4, -\frac{1}{2}$ **25.** $x = 0, 0, 2, 3$ **26.** $x = -1, -2, -3, -4$

Find the zeros of each function. State the multiplicity of multiple zeros. See Problem 4.

27. $y = (x + 3)^3$ **28.** $y = x(x - 1)^3$

29. $y = 2x^3 + x^2 - x$ **30.** $y = 3x^3 - 3x$

31. $y = (x - 4)^2$ **32.** $y = (x - 2)^2(x - 1)$

33. $y = (2x + 3)(x - 1)^2$ **34.** $y = (x + 1)^2(x - 1)(x - 2)$

Find the relative maximum and relative minimum of the graph of each function. See Problem 5.

35. $f(x) = x^3 + 4x^2 - 5x$ **36.** $f(x) = -x^3 + 16x^2 - 76x + 96$

37. $f(x) = -4x^3 + 12x^2 + 4x - 12$ **38.** $f(x) = x^3 - 7x^2 + 7x + 15$

---

22. $y = x^3 - 9x^2 + 27x - 27$

23. $y = x^3 + 2x^2 - x - 2$

24. $y = x^3 - \frac{7}{2}x^2 - 2x$

25. $y = x^4 - 5x^3 + 6x^2$

26. $y = x^4 + 10x^3 + 35x^2 + 50x + 24$

27. -3 (multiplicity 3)

28. $0, 1$ (multiplicity 3)

29. $-1, 0, \frac{1}{2}$

30. $-1, 0, 1$

31. 4 (multiplicity 2)

32. $1, 2$ (multiplicity 2)

33. $-\frac{3}{2}, 1$ (multiplicity 2)

34. -1 (multiplicity 2), $1, 2$

35. relative maximum: $(-3.19, 24.2)$; relative minimum: $(0.52, -1.38)$

36. relative maximum: $(7.10, 5.05)$; relative minimum: $(3.57, -16.9)$

37. relative maximum: $(2.15, 12.32)$; relative minimum: $(-0.15, -12.32)$

38. relative maximum: $(0.57, 16.9)$; relative minimum: $(4.10, -5.05)$

---

3 Lesson Check

Do you know HOW?   ERROR INTERVENTION

- If students confuse the signs of their zeros, then have them write each factor in a separate equation equal to 0 and solve each for x.
- For Exercise 4, remind students that here standard form means that all the factors are multiplied out and the polynomial's terms are written in order, starting with the greatest degree.

Do you UNDERSTAND?

- For Exercise 5, point out that the problem does not state that 3 and -5 are the *only* zeros of the polynomial. Challenge students to write three different polynomial functions that match the description.
- If students have difficulty identifying or explaining the error for Exercise 6, suggest that they start by solving the problem correctly and then use their own process to identify and describe the error.

Close

> **Q** What do the zeros of a polynomial function tell you about the function's graph? **[The zeros tell the x-intercepts.]**

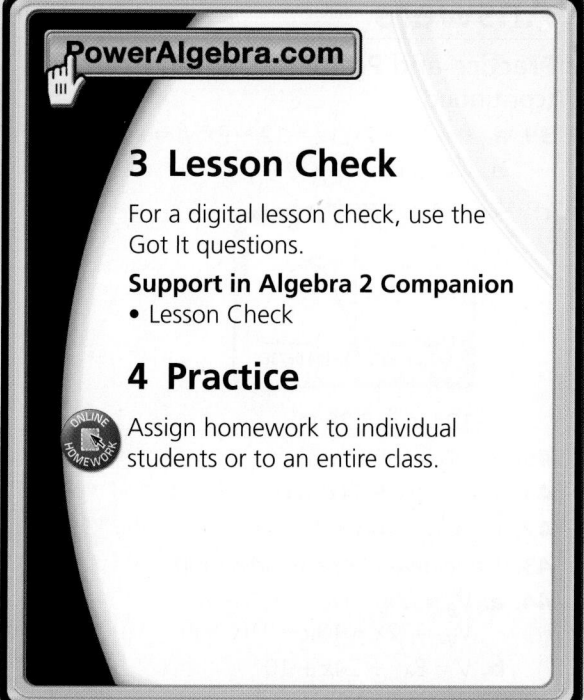

PowerAlgebra.com

3 Lesson Check

For a digital lesson check, use the Got It questions.

Support in Algebra 2 Companion
- Lesson Check

4 Practice

Assign homework to individual students or to an entire class.

4 Practice

ASSIGNMENT GUIDE

Basic: 7–39 all, 41–43, 45–47, 50–52

Average: 7–39 odd, 40–54

Advanced: 7–39 odd, 40–56

Ⓒ **Mathematical Practices** are supported by exercises with red headings. Here are the Practices supported in this lesson:

MP 1: Make Sense of Problems Ex. 43

MP 2: Reason Abstractly Ex. 50

MP 3: Communicate Ex. 51

MP 3: Construct Arguments Ex. 56c

MP 3: Critique the Reasoning of Others Ex. 6

Applications exercises have blue headings. Exercises 45 and 46 support MP 4: Model.

STEM exercises focus on science or engineering applications.

EXERCISE 46: Use the Think About a Plan worksheet in the **Practice and Problem Solving Workbook** (also available in the Teaching Resources in print and online) to further support students' development in becoming independent learners.

HOMEWORK QUICK CHECK

To check students' understanding of key skills and concepts, go over Exercises 19, 27, 43, 45, and 46.

STEM **39. Metalwork** A metalworker wants to make an open box from a sheet of metal, by cutting equal squares from each corner as shown. ◆ See Problem 6.
  a. Write expressions for the length, width, and height of the open box.
  b. Use your expressions from part (a) to write a function for the volume of the box. (*Hint:* Write the function in factored form.)
  c. Graph the function. Then find the maximum volume of the box and the side length of the cut-out squares that generates this volume.

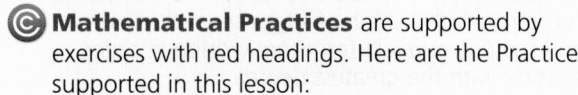

Ⓑ **Apply**   Write each function in factored form. Check by multiplication.

40. $y = 3x^3 - 27x^2 + 24x$ **41.** $y = -2x^3 - 2x^2 + 40x$ **42.** $y = x^4 + 3x^3 - 4x^2$

Ⓒ **43. Think About a Plan** A storage company needs to design a new storage box that has twice the volume of its largest box. Its largest box is 5 ft long, 4 ft wide, and 3 ft high. The new box must be formed by increasing each dimension by the same amount. Find the increase in each dimension.
  • How can you write the dimensions of the new storage box as polynomial expressions?
  • How can you use the volume of the current largest box to find the volume of the new box?

STEM **44. Carpentry** A carpenter hollowed out the interior of a block of wood as shown at the right.
  a. Express the volume of the original block and the volume of the wood removed as polynomials in factored form.
  b. What polynomial represents the volume of the wood remaining?

45. Geometry A rectangular box is $2x + 3$ units long, $2x - 3$ units wide, and $3x$ units high. What is its volume, expressed as a polynomial?

46. Measurement The volume in cubic feet of a CD holder can be expressed as $V(x) = -x^3 - x^2 + 6x$, or, when factored, as the product of its three dimensions. The depth is expressed as $2 - x$. Assume that the height is greater than the width.
  a. Factor the polynomial to find linear expressions for the height and the width.
  b. Graph the function. Find the x-intercepts. What do they represent?
  c. What is a realistic domain for the function?
  d. What is the maximum volume of the CD holder?

Find the relative maximum, relative minimum, and zeros of each function.

47. $y = 2x^3 - 23x^2 + 78x - 72$ **48.** $y = 8x^3 - 10x^2 - x - 3$ **49.** $y = (x + 1)^4 - 1$

Ⓒ **50. Open-Ended** Write a polynomial function with the following features: it has three distinct zeros; one of the zeros is 1; another zero has a multiplicity of 2.

Ⓒ **51. Writing** Explain how the graph of a polynomial function can help you factor the polynomial.

For each function, determine the zeros. State the multiplicity of any multiple zeros.

52. $f(x) = x^3 - 36x$ **53.** $y = (x + 1)(x - 4)(3 - 2x)$ **54.** $y = (x + 7)(5x + 2)(x - 6)^2$

Answers

Practice and Problem-Solving Exercises (continued)

39. a. $\ell = 16 - 2x$; $w = 12 - 2x$; $h = x$
  b. $V = x(16 - 2x)(12 - 2x)$
  c.

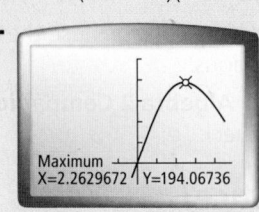

  194 in.³, 2.26 in.

40. $y = 3x(x - 8)(x - 1)$

41. $y = -2x(x + 5)(x - 4)$

42. $y = x^2(x + 4)(x - 1)$

43. 1 ft increase in each dimension

44. a. $V_B = (2x + 1)(x + 3)(x + 4)$
  $V_W = (2x + 1)(x + 1)(x + 2)$
  b. $V = 8x^2 + 24x + 10$

---

45. $V = 12x^3 - 27x$

46. a. $x(x + 3)(2 - x)$; $h = x + 3$; $w = x$
  b.

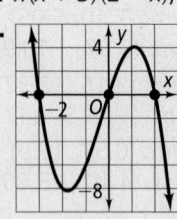

  0, −3, 2; where the volume is zero
  c. $0 < x < 2$
  d. about 4.06 ft³

47. relative maximum: (2.53, 10.51);
  relative minimum:
  $(5.14, -7.14)$; $\frac{3}{2}$, 4, 6

48. relative maximum: (−0.05, −2.98);
  relative minimum: (0.88, −6.17); 1.5

49. no relative maximum; relative
  minimum: (−1, −1); −2, 0

50. Answers may vary. Sample:
  $y = x^4 - x^2$

---

51. Answers may vary. Sample: The linear factors can be determined by examining the x-intercepts of the graph.

52. 0, 6, −6

53. $-1, 4, \frac{3}{2}$

54. $-7, -\frac{2}{5}, 6$ (multiplicity 2)

 **Challenge** 55. Find a fourth-degree polynomial function with zeros 1, −1, i, and −i. Write the function in factored form.

 56. **a.** Compare the graphs of $y = (x + 1)(x + 2)(x + 3)$ and $y = (x − 1)(x − 2)(x − 3)$. What transformation could you use to describe the change from one graph to the other?

b. Compare the graphs of $y = (x + 1)(x + 3)(x + 7)$ and $y = (x − 1)(x − 3)(x − 7)$. Does the transformation that you chose in part (a) still hold true? Explain.

c. Make a Conjecture What transformation could you use to describe the effect of changing the signs of the zeros of a polynomial function?

Apply What You've Learned

 **MATHEMATICAL PRACTICES**
MP 1

Look back at the information about the diorama box Eliana plans to make using the rectangular sheet of cardboard shown on page 279. In the Apply What You've Learned in Lesson 5-1, you wrote a polynomial function $V(x)$ in standard form for the volume of the diorama box.

Write the function $V(x)$ in factored form and then graph $y = V(x)$. Select all of the following that are true. Explain your reasoning.

A. $V(x) = (12 − 2x)(8 − 2x)x$

B. $V(x) = 4x(6 − x)(4 − x)$

C. $V(x) = −4x(x − 6)(x − 4)$

D. The zeros of $y = V(x)$ correspond to values of x that result in a diorama box with volume 36 in.^{3}.

E. The graph of $y = V(x)$ crosses the x-axis at $(0, 0)$, $(4, 0)$, and $(6, 0)$.

F. The graph of $y = V(x)$ shows that there is only one value of x for which the volume of the diorama box will be 36 in.^{3}.

G. The graph of $y = V(x)$ has a turning point between $x = 0$ and $x = 4$.

H. The only portion of the graph that represents the possible volumes of Eliana's diorama box is the portion for which $0 < x < 4$.

 Apply What You've Learned
In the Apply What You've Learned for Lesson 5-1, students wrote a polynomial function in standard form to model the volume of the diorama box shown on page 279. Here, students find the function's zeros from its factored form and interpret aspects of the graph of the function in terms of the real-world situation it models.

© Mathematical Practices
Students use a graph to **make sense of the problem** and understand the number of possible solutions. (MP 1)

ANSWERS
Choices A, B, E, G, and H are all true.

55. $y = x^4 − 1$
56. **a.** Answers may vary. Sample: translation 4 units to the right

b. No; the second graph is not the result of a horizontal translation.

c. Answers may vary. Sample: rotation of 180° about the origin

Lesson Resources

Differentiated Remediation
Available in editable format online.

Additional Instructional Support

Algebra 2 Companion
Students can use the **Algebra 2 Companion** worktext (4 pages) as you teach the lesson. Use the Companion to support

- New Vocabulary
- Key Concepts
- Got It for each Problem
- Lesson Check

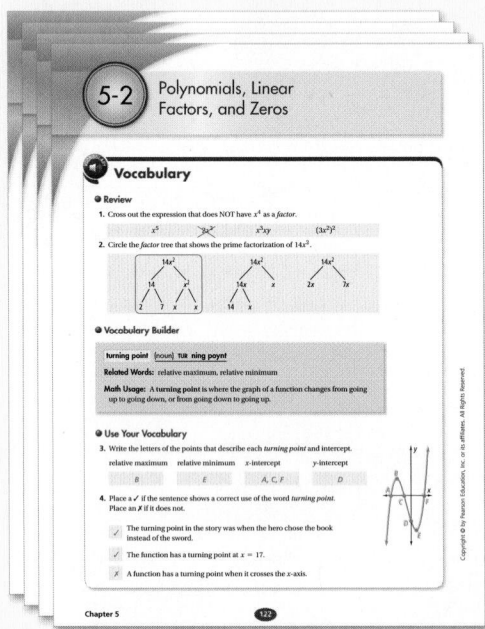

ELL Support
Focus on Language Ask the students, "What does *relative* mean?" [Samples: dependent upon other conditions for its specific nature, size, etc.; treated in relation to something else; comparative] Ask, "What are some synonyms?" [Samples: conditional; subject; dependent] Ask, "What are the relative maximums and minimum relative to? Why?" [Sample: The points directly around them: among these points, the relative maximum is the greatest *y*-value, and the relative minimum is the least *y*-value.]

5 Assess & Remediate

Lesson Quiz
1. Factor $x^3 + 4x^2 - 5x$.
2. What are the zeros of $y = (x + 1)(x - 3)(x + 2)$?
3. What is a cubic polynomial function in standard form with zeros 4, −1, and 2?
4. What are the zeros of $f(x) = x^3 - 3x^2 + 2x$? What are the multiplicities? How does the graph behave at these zeros?
5. What are the relative maximum and minimum of $f(x) = x^3 - 4x$? Round to the nearest tenth.
6. **Do you UNDERSTAND?** A designer is making a rectangular prism box with maximum volume, with the sum of its length, width, and height 8 in. The length must be 2 times the width. What should each dimension be? Round to the nearest tenth of an inch.

ANSWERS TO LESSON QUIZ
1. $x(x - 1)(x + 5)$
2. −1, 3, −2
3. $x^3 - 5x^2 + 2x + 8$
4. 0, 1, and 2; each has a multiplicity of 1; the graph crosses the *x*-axis and appears linear at each zero.
5. relative min: $(1.2, -3.1)$; relative max: $(-1.2, 3.1)$
6. width: 1.8 in.
   length: 3.6 in.
   height: 2.6 in.

PRESCRIPTION FOR REMEDIATION
Use the student work on the Lesson Quiz to prescribe a differentiated review assignment:

Points	Differentiated Remediation
0–3	Intervention
4–5	On-level
6	Extension

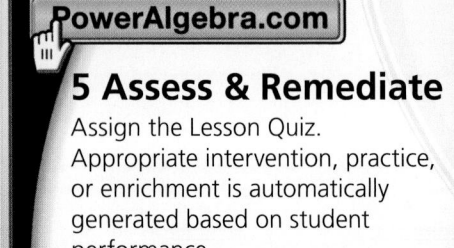

5 Assess & Remediate
Assign the Lesson Quiz. Appropriate intervention, practice, or enrichment is automatically generated based on student performance.

Intervention
- **Reteaching** (2 pages) Provides reteaching and practice exercises for the key lesson concepts. Use with struggling students or absent students.
- **English Language Learner Support** Helps students develop and reinforce mathematical vocabulary and key concepts.

All-in-One Resources/Online
Reteaching

5-2 Reteaching
Polynomials, Linear Factors, and Zeros

The Factor Theorem tells you that if you know the zeros of a polynomial function, you can write the polynomial.

Factor Theorem
The expression $x - a$ is a factor of a polynomial if and only if the value a is a zero of the related polynomial function.

Problem
What is a cubic polynomial function in standard form with zeros 0, 4, and −2?
Each zero (a) is part of a linear factor of the polynomial, so you can write each factor as $(x - a)$.

$$(x - a_1)(x - a_2)(x - a_3)$$ Set up the cubic polynomial factors.
$$a_1 = 0, a_2 = 4, a_3 = -2$$ Assign the zeros.
$$(x - 0)(x - 4)(x - (-2))$$ Substitute the zeros into the factors.
$$f(x) = x(x - 4)(x + 2)$$ Write the polynomial function in factored form.
$$f(x) = x(x^2 - 2x - 8)$$ Multiply $(x - 4)(x + 2)$.
$$f(x) = x^3 - 2x^2 - 8x$$ Multiply by x using the Distributive Property.

The polynomial function written in standard form is $f(x) = x^3 - 2x^2 - 8x$.

Exercises
Write a polynomial function in standard form with the given zeros.

1. 5, −1, 3 $f(x) = x^3 - 7x^2 + 7x + 15$ 2. 1, 7, −5 $f(x) = x^3 - 3x^2 - 33x + 35$
3. −1, 1, −6 $f(x) = x^3 + 6x^2 - x - 6$ 4. 2, −2, −3 $f(x) = x^3 + 3x^2 - 4x - 12$
5. 2, 1, 3 $f(x) = x^3 - 6x^2 + 11x - 6$ 6. 2, 3, −3, −1 $f(x) = x^4 - x^3 - 11x^2 + 9x + 18$
7. 0, −8, 2 $f(x) = x^3 + 6x^2 - 16x$ 8. −10, 0, 2 $f(x) = x^3 + 8x^2 - 20x$
9. −2, 2, −$\frac{3}{2}$ $f(x) = x^3 + \frac{3}{2}x^2 - 4x - 6$ 10. −1, $\frac{2}{3}$ $f(x) = x^2 + \frac{1}{3}x - \frac{2}{3}$

All-in-One Resources/Online
English Language Learner Support

5-2 Additional Vocabulary Support
Polynomials, Linear Factors, and Zeros

There are two sets of note cards below that show how to write a cubic polynomial function with zeros −3, 1, and 4 in standard form. The set on the left explains the thinking. The set on the right shows the steps. Write the thinking and the steps in the correct order.

Think Cards
- Multiply $(x - 1)$ and $(x - 4)$.
- Use the Distributive Property to multiply $(x + 3)$ and $(x^2 - 5x + 4)$.
- Simplify.
- Write a linear factor for each zero.

Write Cards
- $x(x^2 - 5x + 4) + 3(x^2 - 5x + 4)$ = $x^3 - 5x^2 + 4x + 3x^2 - 15x + 12$
- $(x + 3)(x^2 - 5x + 4)$
- $x^3 - 2x^2 - 11x + 12$
- $f(x) = (x + 3)(x - 1)(x - 4)$

Think	Write
First, you should write a linear factor for each zero.	**Step 1** $f(x) = (x + 3)(x - 1)(x - 4)$
Second, you should multiply $(x - 1)$ and $(x - 4)$.	**Step 2** $(x + 3)(x^2 - 5x + 4)$
Then, you should use the Distributive Property to multiply $(x + 3)$ and $(x^2 - 5x + 4)$.	**Step 3** $x(x^2 - 5x + 4) + 3(x^2 - 5x + 4) = x^3 - 5x^2 + 4x + 3x^2 - 15x + 12$
Finally, you should simplify.	**Step 4** $x^3 - 2x^2 - 11x + 12$

Differentiated Remediation *continued*

Available in editable format online.

On-Level

- **Practice** (2 pages) Provides extra practice for each lesson. For simpler practice exercises, use the Form K Practice pages found in the All-in-One Teaching Resources and online.

- **Think About a Plan** Helps students develop specific problem-solving skills and strategies by providing scaffolded guiding questions.

- **Standardized Test Prep** Focuses on all major exercises, all major question types, and helps students prepare for the high-stakes assessments.

Extension

- **Enrichment** Provides students with interesting problems and activities that extend the concepts of the lesson.

- **Activities, Games, and Puzzles** Worksheets that can be used for concepts development, enrichment, and for fun!

Practice and Problem Solving Wkbk/All-in-One Resources/Online
Practice page 1

5-2 Practice — Form G
Polynomials, Linear Factors, and Zeros

Write each polynomial in factored form. Check by multiplication.

1. $2x^2 + 10x^2 + 12x$ $2x(x + 2)(x + 3)$
2. $x^4 - x^3 - 6x^2$ $x^2(x + 2)(x - 3)$
3. $-3x^3 + 18x^2 - 27x$ $-3x(x - 3)^2$
4. $x^3 - 2x^2 + x$ $x(x - 1)^2$
5. $x^3 + 7x^2 + 15x + 9$ $(x + 3)^2(x + 1)$
6. $2x^4 + 23x^3 + 60x^2 - 125x - 500$ $(x + 4)(2x - 5)(x + 5)^2$

Find the zeros of each function. Then graph the function.

7. $y = (x + 1)(x - 1)(x - 3)$ −1, 1, 3
8. $y = (x + 2)(x - 3)$ −2, 3
9. $y = x(x - 2)(x + 5)$ −5, 0, 2

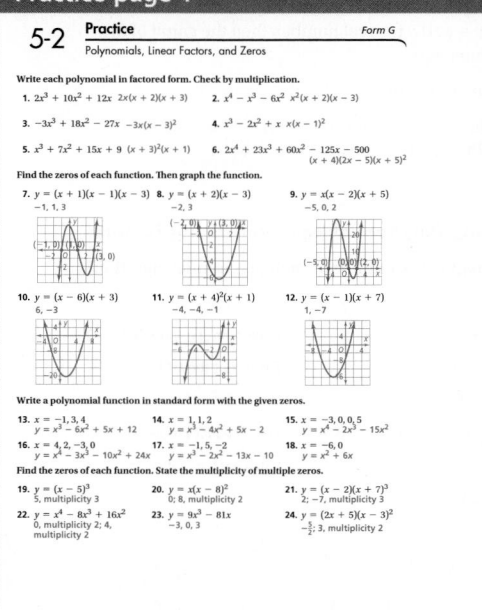

10. $y = (x - 6)(x + 3)$ 6, −3
11. $y = (x + 4)^2(x + 1)$ −4, −4, −1
12. $y = (x - 1)(x + 7)$ 1, −7

Write a polynomial function in standard form with the given zeros.

13. $x = -1, 3, 4$ $y = x^3 - 6x^2 + 5x + 12$
14. $x = 1, 1, 2$ $y = x^3 - 4x^2 + 5x - 2$
15. $x = -3, 0, 0, 5$ $y = x^4 - 2x^3 - 15x^2$
16. $x = 4, 2, -3, 0$ $y = x^4 - 3x^3 - 10x^2 + 24x$
17. $x = -1, 5, -2$ $y = x^3 - 2x^2 - 13x - 10$
18. $x = -6, 0$ $y = x^2 + 6x$

Find the zeros of each function. State the multiplicity of multiple zeros.

19. $y = (x - 5)^3$ 5, multiplicity 3
20. $y = x(x - 8)^2$ 0; 8, multiplicity 2
21. $y = (x - 2)(x + 7)^3$ 2; −7, multiplicity 3
22. $y = x^4 - 8x^3 + 16x^2$ 0, multiplicity 2; 4, multiplicity 2
23. $y = 9x^3 - 81x$ −3, 0, 3
24. $y = (2x + 5)(x - 3)^2$ $-\frac{5}{2}$; 3, multiplicity 2

Practice and Problem Solving Wkbk/All-in-One Resources/Online
Practice page 2

5-2 Practice *(continued)* — Form G
Polynomials, Linear Factors, and Zeros

Find the relative maximum and relative minimum of the graph of each function.

25. $f(x) = x^3 - 7x^2 + 10x$ rel. max.: 4.06; rel. min.: −8.21
26. $f(x) = x^3 - x^2 - 9x + 9$ rel. max.: 16.9; rel. min.: −5.05
27. $f(x) = x^4 + x^3 - 3x^2 - 5x - 2$ rel. min.: about −8.54
28. $f(x) = x^2 - 6x + 9$ rel. min.: 0

29. A rectangular box has a square base. The combined length of a side of the square base, and the height is 20 in. Let x be the length of a side of the base of the box.
   a. Write a polynomial function in factored form modeling the volume V of the box. $V = x^2(20 - x)$
   b. What is the maximum possible volume of the box? about 1185 in.^{3}

30. **Reasoning** A polynomial function has a zero at $x = -2a$. Find one of its factors. $(x + 2a)$

31. The side of a cube measures $3x + 2$ units long. Express the volume of the cube as a polynomial. $27x^3 + 54x^2 + 36x + 8$

32. **Writing** The volume of a box is $x^3 - 3x^2 + 3x - 1$ cubic units. Explain how to find the length of a side if the box is a cube. The factors of this polynomial are $(x - 1)(x - 1)(x - 1)$. Because all three factors are equal, and the sides of the box are equal, the side length would be $x - 1$.

33. You have a block of wood that you want to use to make a sculpture. The block is currently $3x$ units wide, $4x$ units high, and $5x$ units deep. You need to remove 1 unit from each dimension before you can make your sculpture.
   a. What is the original volume of the block? $60x^3$ cubic units
   b. What is the new volume of the block? $60x^3 - 47x^2 + 12x - 1$ cubic units
   c. What is the volume of the wood that you remove? $47x^2 - 12x + 1$ cubic units

34. What are the zeros and the multiplicity of each zero for the polynomial function $x^4 - 2x^2 + 1$? 1 of multiplicity 2, −1 of multiplicity 2

35. **Error Analysis** On your homework, you wrote that the polynomial function from the given zeros $x = 3, 0, -9, 1$ is $y = x^4 + 5x^3 - 33x^2 + 27x$. Your friend wrote that the polynomial function is $y = x^3 + 5x^2 - 33x + 27$. Who is correct? What mistake was made?
   You are correct. Your friend did not include the factor with the zero $x = 0$ from the polynomial. It should include the factor $(x - 0)$.

Practice and Problem Solving Wkbk/All-in-One Resources/Online
Think About a Plan

5-2 Think About a Plan
Polynomials, Linear Factors, and Zeros

Measurement The volume in cubic feet of a CD holder can be expressed as $V(x) = -x^3 - x^2 + 6x$, or when factored, as the product of its three dimensions. The depth is expressed as $2 - x$. Assume that the height is greater than the width.
   a. Factor the polynomial to find linear expressions for the height and the width.
   b. Graph the function. Find the x-intercepts. What do they represent?
   c. What is a realistic domain for the function?
   d. What is the maximum volume of the CD holder?

1. What do you know about the factors of the polynomial?
   One of the factors is $(2-x)$.

2. Factor the polynomial.
   $V(x) = -x^3 - x^2 + 6x = \boxed{(2 - x)}\ \boxed{(x)}\ \boxed{(x + 3)}$

3. What are the height and width of the CD holder? How do you know which factor is the height and which factor is the width?
   height: $x + 3$; width: x; the height is greater than the width, and $x + 3$ is greater than x

4. Graph the function on a graphing calculator. How can you find the x-intercepts?
   Set the factors equal to zero and solve or use the zero feature.

5. What are the x-intercepts? What do they represent?
   −3, 0, 2; values of x that result in a volume of 0

6. What are the limits of each of the factors? What is a realistic domain for the function? Explain.
   Each dimension of the CD holder must be greater than 0, so each factor should be greater than 0. So $2 - x > 0$, $x > 0$, and $x + 3 > 0$. The solution of all three inequalities is $0 < x < 2$.

7. How can you find the maximum volume of the CD holder?
   Find the maximum value of the function in the domain $0 < x < 2$. Use the maximum feature of the CALC menu with LeftBound = 0 and RightBound = 2.

8. What is the maximum volume of the CD holder? about 4.06 ft^3

Practice and Problem Solving Wkbk/All-in-One Resources/Online
Standardized Test Prep

5-2 Standardized Test Prep
Polynomials, Linear Factors, and Zeros

Multiple Choice

For Exercises 1–6, choose the correct letter.

1. What are the zeros of the polynomial function $y = (x - 3)(2x + 1)(x - 1)$? C
   Ⓐ $\frac{1}{2}, 1, 3$ Ⓑ −1, 1, 3   Ⓒ $-\frac{1}{2}, 1, 3$ Ⓓ $-3, \frac{1}{2}, -1$

2. What is the factored form of $2x^3 + 5x^2 - 12x$? H
   Ⓕ $(x + 4)(2x - 3)$ Ⓗ $x(x + 4)(2x - 3)$
   Ⓖ $(x - 4)(2x + 3)$ Ⓘ $x(x - 4)(2x + 3)$

3. Which is the cubic polynomial in standard form with roots 3, −6, and 0? D
   Ⓐ $x^2 - 3x - 18$ Ⓒ $x^3 - 3x^2 - 18x$
   Ⓑ $x^2 + 3x - 18$ Ⓓ $x^3 + 3x^2 - 18x$

4. What is the relative minimum and relative maximum of $f(x) = 6x^3 - 5x + 12$? I
   Ⓕ min = 0, max = 0   Ⓗ min = −1.5, max = 12
   Ⓖ min = −5, max = 6   Ⓘ min = 10.2, max = 13.8

5. What is the multiplicity of the zero of the polynomial function $f(x) = (x + 5)^4$? A
   Ⓐ 4   Ⓑ 5   Ⓒ 20   Ⓓ 625

6. For the polynomial function $y = (x - 2)^3$, how does the graph behave at the x-intercept? H
   Ⓕ linear   Ⓖ quadratic   Ⓗ cubic   Ⓘ quartic

Short Response

7. A rectangular box is 24 in. long, 12 in. wide, and 18 in. high. If each dimension is increased by x in., what is the polynomial function in standard form that models the volume V of the box? Show your work.
   [2] $V = x^3 + 54x^2 + 936x + 5184$ in.^{3}
   [1] correct process with one computational error OR correct polynomial without work shown
   [0] incorrect answer and no work shown OR no answer given

All-in-One Resources/Online
Enrichment

5-2 Enrichment
Polynomials, Linear Factors, and Zeros

Fast Factorization of Monic Trinomials

Thus far, you have factored trinomials primarily by trial and error. This method can be quite slow, especially if the constant term of a quadratic trinomial is, for example, 72, since there are many different ways to factor this number: 1 and 72, 2 and 36, 3 and 24, 4 and 18, 6 and 12, 8 and 9. With larger numbers, the trial-and-error method becomes time-consuming.

A polynomial is called monic if the coefficient of the term of highest degree is 1. Monic quadratic trinomials can be factored quite rapidly using a combination of difference of squares and equation solving.

Suppose that we wish to factor the monic quadratic trinomial $x^2 + bx + c$. Assume there are numbers r and s such that

$$x^2 + bx + c = [(x + r) + s][(x + r) - s]$$
$$= (x + r)^2 - s^2$$
$$= x^2 + 2rx + r^2 - s^2$$

Subtracting x^2 from both sides results in

$$bx + c = 2rx + r^2 - s^2$$

Therefore, $b = 2r$ and $c = r^2 - s^2$.

Solve for r and s in terms of b and c.

$$r = \frac{b}{2} \qquad s = \sqrt{\left(\frac{b}{2}\right)^2 - c}$$

The following example shows how this technique works.

Factor: $x^2 - 6x - 72$ $b = -6, c = -72$
   $r = \frac{b}{2} = -3$ $s = \frac{b}{2} - (-72)$
   $= \sqrt{81} = 9$
So $x^2 - 6x - 72$ $= [(x - 3) + 9][(x - 3) - 9]$
   $= (x + 6)(x - 12)$

Verify that this is the correct factorization.

$(x + 6)(x - 12) = x^2 - 12x + 6x - 72 = x^2 - 6x - 72$

Use this technique to factor each of the following.

1. $x^2 - 60x + 864$ $(x - 24)(x - 36)$
2. $x^2 - 25x + 144$ $(x - 9)(x - 16)$
3. $x^2 - 28x - 128$ $(x - 32)(x + 4)$
4. $x^2 - 44x - 540$ $(x - 54)(x + 10)$
5. $x^2 + 81x + 990$ $(x + 15)(x + 66)$
6. $x^2 - 50x + 576$ $(x - 32)(x - 18)$
7. $x^2 + 17x - 168$ $(x - 7)(x + 24)$
8. $x^2 - 17x - 630$ $(x - 35)(x + 18)$

Online Teacher Resource Center
Activities, Games, and Puzzles

5-2 Puzzle: Made in the Shade
Polynomials, Linear Factors, and Zeros

Find the zeros of each polynomial below. For each corresponding row, shade in each number that is a zero. The illustration made from shading the squares suggests the answer to the riddle below.

A. $P(x) = x(x^2 - 1)$ −1, 0, 1
B. $P(x) = x(x + 2)(x + 1)(x^2 + 2x - 3)$ −3, −2, −1, 0, 1
C. $P(x) = x(x - 4)(x + 1)(x - 1)$ −4, −3, −1, 0, 1
D. $P(x) = x(x^2 - 25)(x^2 + 4x + 3)$ −5, −3, −1, 0, 5
E. $P(x) = (x^2 + x - 20)(x + 2)(x^2 + 4x + 3)$ −5, −3, −2, −1, 4
F. $P(x) = (x^2 - 9)(x^2 - 25)$ −5, −3, 3, 5
G. $P(x) = (x^2 + 9x + 20)(x^2 - 5x + 6)(x - 1)$ −5, −4, 2, 3, 5
H. $P(x) = (x^2 - 5x + 6)(x^2 - 9x + 20)$ 2, 3, 4, 5
I. $P(x) = x^2 - 6x + 9$ 3
J. $P(x) = (x^2 - 4x + 4)(x^2 - 4x + 4)$ 2
K. $P(x) = x(x^2 - 2x + 1)(x - 2)$ 0, 1, 2

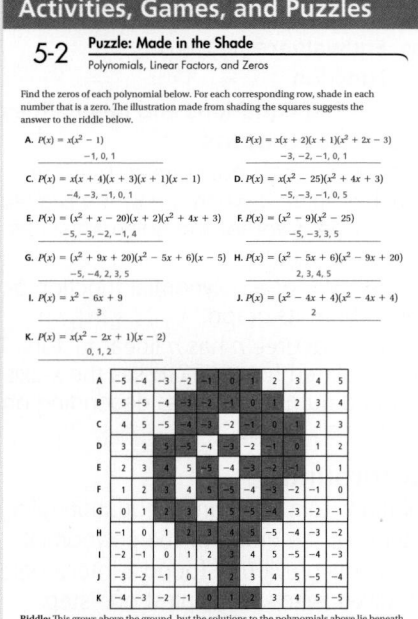

Riddle: This grows above the ground, but the solutions to the polynomials above lie beneath. And as it grows, it provides shade to those underneath. What is it? a tree

1 Interactive Learning

Solve It!

PURPOSE To model a polynomial with tiles
PROCESS Students may arrange the pieces so that the x-by-x squares are arranged vertically or horizontally.

FACILITATE

Q Where do the x-by-1 pieces have to be arranged in relationship to the x-by-x pieces? **[The sides with length x have to touch.]**

Q Where do the 1-by-1 pieces have to be arranged? **[They must be arranged so that they complete the rectangle.]**

Q Why can the 1-by-1 squares not be arranged in a 12-by-1 row? **[You do not have a 12 unit piece to line up with the side of the 12-by-1 row to form a rectangle.]**

Q What polynomial do the pieces represent? Factor it. **[$2x^2 + 11x + 12$; $(2x + 3)(x + 4)$]**

ANSWER See Solve It in Answers on next page.
CONNECT THE MATH The Solve It is a visual model of factoring, where students use tiles representing each part of the polynomial to create a rectangle. Students will use factoring in the lesson to solve polynomial equations.

2 Guided Instruction

Problem 1

Q When should you use the quadratic formula to solve a quadratic polynomial equation? **[when the discriminant is less than zero or when the polynomial does not factor]**

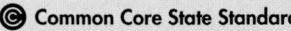

© **Common Core State Standards**
A-REI.D.11 Explain why the x-coordinates of the points where the graphs of the equations $y = f(x)$ and $y = g(x)$ intersect are the solutions of the equation $f(x) = g(x)$ . . . Also A-SSE.A.2
MP 1, MP 2, MP 3, MP 5, MP 6

Objectives To solve polynomial equations by factoring
To solve polynomial equations by graphing

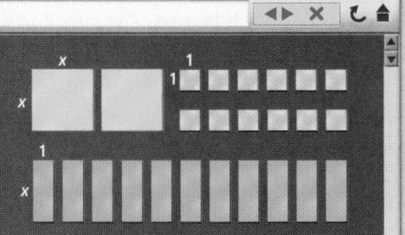

Getting Ready!

Can you arrange all of these pieces to make a rectangle with no pieces overlapping and no gaps? If you can, make a sketch. If you cannot, explain why.

I count 2 pieces with area x^2, 11 with area x, and 12 with area 1. The rectangle would have the same total area.

© **MATHEMATICAL PRACTICES**

Factoring a polynomial like $ax^2 + bx + c$ can help you solve a polynomial equation like $ax^2 + bx + c = 0$.

Essential Understanding If $(x - a)$ is a factor of a polynomial, then the polynomial has value 0 when $x = a$. If a is a real number, then the graph of the polynomial has $(a, 0)$ as an x-intercept.

Lesson Vocabulary
• sum of cubes
• difference of cubes

To solve a polynomial equation by factoring:

1. Write the equation in the form $P(x) = 0$ for some polynomial function P.
2. Factor $P(x)$. Use the Zero Product Property to find the roots.

© **Problem 1** Solving Polynomial Equations Using Factors

What are the real or imaginary solutions of each polynomial equation?

Plan
What does it mean if x is a common factor of every term in $P(x)$?
You can write $P(x)$ as $xQ(x)$, so 0 will be a solution of $P(x) = 0$.

Ⓐ $2x^3 - 5x^2 = 3x$

$2x^3 - 5x^2 - 3x = 0$	Rewrite in the form $P(x) = 0$.
$x(2x^2 - 5x - 3) = 0$	Factor out the GCF, x.
$x(2x + 1)(x - 3) = 0$	Factor $2x^2 - 5x - 3$.
$x = 0$ or $2x + 1 = 0$ or $x - 3 = 0$	Zero Product Property
$x = 0$ $x = -\frac{1}{2}$ $x = 3$	Solve each equation for x.

The solutions are 0, $-\frac{1}{2}$, and 3.

BIG ideas **Equivalence**
Function
Solving Equations and Inequalities

ESSENTIAL UNDERSTANDINGS
• If $(x - a)$ is a factor of a polynomial, then the polynomial has value 0 when $x = a$. If a is a real number, then the graph of the polynomial has $(a, 0)$ as an x-intercept.
• Knowing the zeros of a polynomial function gives information about its graph.
• A polynomial of degree n has n linear factors. The graph of the related function crosses the x-axis an even or odd number of times depending on whether n is even or odd.

Math Background

The real solutions to a polynomial equation give the x-intercepts of the graph of the polynomial function. Students previously found x-intercepts when they solved even the simplest one-step equation. You can demonstrate this with the following steps:

• start with a simple equation, such as $y = x + 4$;
• set the equation equal to 0: $x + 4 = 0$;
• solve for x: $x = -4$;
• find the x-intercept of the graph of the related function, $f(x) = x + 4$: $(-4, 0)$.
• Note that this is the same as $(a, 0)$. If you substitute a into $f(x)$ and evaluate the expression, the result would be 0.

This activity connects the advanced solving of polynomial equations of a greater degree to solving equations of degree one. It also connects the techniques that students use to solve various kinds of equations.

© **Mathematical Practices**
Attend to precision. Students will knowingly and flexibly use the Zero Product Property to determine the zeros of polynomial equations.

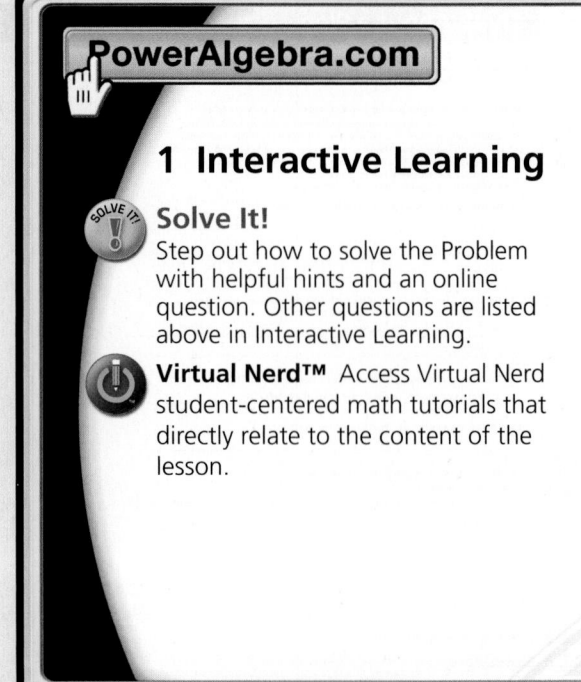

PowerAlgebra.com

1 Interactive Learning

Solve It!
Step out how to solve the Problem with helpful hints and an online question. Other questions are listed above in Interactive Learning.

Virtual Nerd™ Access Virtual Nerd student-centered math tutorials that directly relate to the content of the lesson.

B $3x^4 + 12x^2 = 6x^3$

$3x^4 - 6x^3 + 12x^2 = 0$ Rewrite in the form $P(x) = 0$.

$x^4 - 2x^3 + 4x^2 = 0$ Multiply by $\frac{1}{3}$ to simplify.

$x^2(x^2 - 2x + 4) = 0$ Factor out the GCF, x^2.

$x^2 = 0$ or $x^2 - 2x + 4 = 0$ Zero Product Property

Think

How will the solution be similar to the solution of the equation in part (a)? Both equations have 0 as a solution, but here it will have a multiplicity of 2.

$$x = 0 \quad \left| \quad \begin{array}{l} x = \dfrac{-(-2) \pm \sqrt{(-2)^2 - 4(1)(4)}}{2(1)} \\[2mm] x = \dfrac{2 \pm \sqrt{-12}}{2} = \dfrac{2 \pm 2i\sqrt{3}}{2} = 1 \pm i\sqrt{3} \end{array} \right.$$

> Use the Quadratic Formula to solve $x^2 - 2x + 4 = 0$. Substitute $a = 1$, $b = -2$, and $c = 4$.

The solutions are 0, $1 + i\sqrt{3}$, and $1 - i\sqrt{3}$.

 Got It? **1.** What are the real or imaginary solutions of each equation?

     a. $(x^2 - 1)(x^2 + 4) = 0$ **b.** $x^5 + 4x^3 = 5x^4 - 2x^3$

 take note

Concept Summary	**Polynomial Factoring Techniques**
Techniques	**Examples**
Factoring out the GCF Factor out the greatest common factor of all the terms.	$15x^4 - 20x^3 + 35x^2$ $= 5x^2(3x^2 - 4x + 7)$
Quadratic Trinomials For $ax^2 + bx + c$, find factors with product ac and sum b.	$6x^2 + 11x - 10$ $= (3x - 2)(2x + 5)$
Perfect Square Trinomials $a^2 + 2ab + b^2 = (a + b)^2$ $a^2 - 2ab + b^2 = (a - b)^2$	$x^2 + 10x + 25 = (x + 5)^2$ $x^2 - 10x + 25 = (x - 5)^2$
Difference of Squares $a^2 - b^2 = (a + b)(a - b)$	$4x^2 - 15 = (2x + \sqrt{15})(2x - \sqrt{15})$
Factoring by Grouping $ax + ay + bx + by$ $= a(x + y) + b(x + y)$ $= (a + b)(x + y)$	$x^3 + 2x^2 - 3x - 6$ $= x^2(x + 2) + (-3)(x + 2)$ $= (x^2 - 3)(x + 2)$
Sum or Difference of Cubes $a^3 + b^3 = (a + b)(a^2 - ab + b^2)$ $a^3 - b^3 = (a - b)(a^2 + ab + b^2)$	$8x^3 + 1 = (2x + 1)(4x^2 - 2x + 1)$ $8x^3 - 1 = (2x - 1)(4x^2 + 2x + 1)$

PowerAlgebra.com   **Lesson 5-3** Solving Polynomial Equations   **297**

Got It? **ERROR PREVENTION**

In 1a, watch for students who attempt to factor $x^2 + 4$ as if it were $x^2 - 4$.

Q In 1b, in what order do you need to arrange the terms of the polynomial equation? **[Put the polynomial equation in terms of descending powers of x.]**

Take Note

It may be helpful to review each type of factoring listed in the Take Note.

Have students make their own examples of each technique, such as the following examples:

Factoring out the GCF
$6x^3 + 15x^2 + 9x = 3x(2x^2 + 5x + 3)$

Quadratic Trinomials
$8x^2 + 10x - 3 = (4x - 1)(2x + 3)$

Perfect Square Trinomials
$4x^2 + 12x + 9 = (2x + 3)^2$

Difference of Squares
$x^2 - 36 = (x + 6)(x - 6)$

Factoring by Grouping
$2x^3 - 2x^2 + 3x - 3 = 2x^2(x - 1) + 3(x - 1)$
$\qquad\qquad\qquad\quad = (2x^2 + 3)(x - 1)$

Sum or Difference of Cubes
$x^3 - 27 = (x - 3)(x^2 + 3x + 9)$

---

2 Guided Instruction

© Each Problem is worked out and supported online.

Problem 1
Solving Polynomial Equations Using Factors
     Animated

Problem 2
Solving Polynomial Equations by Factoring
     Animated

Problem 3
Finding Real Roots by Graphing

Problem 4
Modeling a Problem Situation
     Animated

Support in Algebra 2 Companion
• Vocabulary
• Key Concepts
• Got It?

Answers

Solve It!
yes;

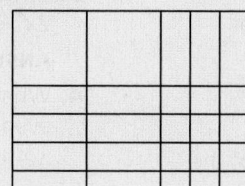

Got It?
   1. a. ± 1, $\pm 2i$
     b. 0, 2, 3

Here's Why It Works

Review the most common perfect cubes with students:

$2^3 = 8$
$3^3 = 27$
$4^3 = 64$
$5^3 = 125$
$6^3 = 216$

For $a^3 - b^3$, the steps are as follows.
$$a^3 - b^3 = a^3 - a^2b + a^2b - ab^2 + ab^2 - b^3$$
$$= a^2(a - b) + ab(a - b) + b^2(a - b)$$
$$= (a - b)(a^2 + ab + b^2)$$

> **Q** How is the first step equivalent to adding zero?
> [The expressions $-a^2b$ and a^2b cancel each other out, as do the expressions $-ab^2$ and ab^2.]

Problem 2

> **Q** Will a graph help you check all the solutions of a polynomial equation? Explain. **[Answers may vary. Sample: Only if all the solutions are real, since the imaginary solutions will not show on a graph.]**
>
> **Q** How can you check the imaginary solutions? **[Substitute each solution for x in the expression and see if it simplifies to zero.]**

Got It?   ERROR PREVENTION

> **Q** In 2a, if you simply take the fourth root of 16, will you get all of the solutions? Explain. **[No; answers may vary. Sample: You will miss the solution -2 and the imaginary solutions $2i$ and $-2i$.]**

The sum and difference of cubes is a new factoring technique.

Here's Why It Works Factoring $a^3 + b^3 = (a + b)(a^2 - ab + b^2)$:
$$a^3 + b^3 = a^3 + a^2b - a^2b - ab^2 + ab^2 + b^3 \quad \text{Add 0.}$$
$$= a^2(a + b) - ab(a + b) + b^2(a + b) \quad \text{Factor out } a^2, -ab, \text{ and } b^2.$$
$$= (a + b)(a^2 - ab + b^2) \quad \text{Factor out } (a + b).$$

For $a^3 - b^3 = (a - b)(a^2 + ab + b^2)$, you can follow steps similar to those above, or you can factor $a^3 - b^3$ as the sum of cubes $a^3 + (-b)^3$.

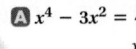 **Problem 2** Solving Polynomial Equations by Factoring

What are the real or imaginary solutions of each polynomial equation?

A $x^4 - 3x^2 = 4$

$$x^4 - 3x^2 - 4 = 0 \quad \text{Rewrite in the form } P(x) = 0.$$
$$a^2 - 3a - 4 = 0 \quad \text{Let } a = x^2.$$
$$(a - 4)(a + 1) = 0 \quad \text{Factor.}$$
$$(x^2 - 4)(x^2 + 1) = 0 \quad \text{Replace } a \text{ with } x^2.$$
$$(x + 2)(x - 2)(x^2 + 1) = 0 \quad \text{Factor } x^2 - 4 \text{ as a difference of squares.}$$

It follows from the Zero Product Property that $x = 2$, $x = -2$, or $x^2 = -1$. Solving $x^2 = -1$ yields two imaginary roots: $x = i$ or $x = -i$.

Check Graph the related function $y = x^4 - 3x^2 - 4$.

The graph shows zeros at $x = 2$ and $x = -2$. It also shows three turning points. This means that there are imaginary roots, which do not appear on the graph.

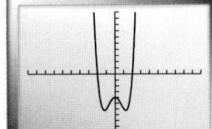

B $x^3 = 1$

$$x^3 - 1 = 0 \quad \text{Rewrite in the form } P(x) = 0.$$
$$(x - 1)(x^2 + x + 1) = 0 \quad \text{Factor the difference of cubes.}$$

It follows from the Zero Product Property that $x = 1$ or $x^2 + x + 1 = 0$. Use the Quadratic Formula to solve $x^2 + x + 1 = 0$.

$$x = \frac{-(1) \pm \sqrt{(1)^2 - 4(1)(1)}}{2(1)} = \frac{-1 \pm \sqrt{-3}}{2} = \frac{-1 \pm i\sqrt{3}}{2}$$

The three solutions of $x^3 = 1$ are 1, $-\frac{1}{2} + i\frac{\sqrt{3}}{2}$, and $-\frac{1}{2} - i\frac{\sqrt{3}}{2}$.

> **Think**
> **How can you write the polynomial in quadratic form?**
> Write in terms of x^2:
> $(x^2)^2 - 3(x^2) - 4 = 0$, which shows the factorable quadratic form $a^2 - 3a - 4 = 0$.

 Got It? **2.** What are the real or imaginary solutions of each polynomial equation?

    a. $x^4 = 16$ **b.** $x^3 = 8x - 2x^2$ **c.** $x(x^2 + 8) = 8(x + 1)$

Additional Problems

1. What are the real or imaginary solutions of $4x^3 - 6x^2 = 4x$?

    ANSWERS $-\frac{1}{2}$, 0, 2

2. What are the real or imaginary solutions of the equation $2x^3 = -54$?

    ANSWER -3, $\frac{3 \pm 3i\sqrt{3}}{2}$

3. What are the real solutions of $2x^3 + 5 = 3x^2 - 2x$?

    ANSWER -0.84

4. What are three consecutive even integers whose product is 4 times their sum?

    ANSWERS 2, 4, 6 or -6, -4, -2

While factoring is an effective way to solve a polynomial equation, you can also find the real roots quickly by using a graphing calculator.

Plan

Why is it helpful to graph Y_1 and Y_2?
The values of x for which $Y_1 = Y_2$ are the solutions of the original equation.

© **Problem 3** Finding Real Roots by Graphing

What are the real solutions of the equation $x^3 + 5 = 4x^2 + x$?

Method 1 Graph $Y_1 = x^3 + 5$ and $Y_2 = 4x^2 + x$. Use the **INTERSECT** feature to find the x-values of the points of intersection.

These two intersection points are visible in the standard viewing window.

You must adjust the window to obtain this point of intersection.

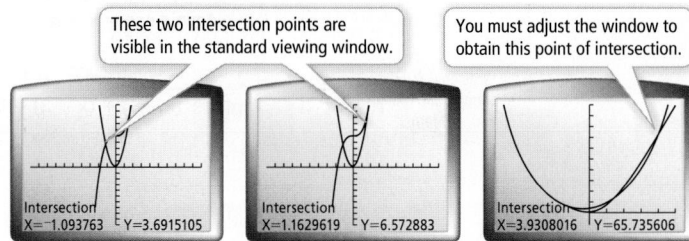

Intersection X=-1.093763 Y=3.6915105

Intersection X=1.1629619 Y=6.572883

Intersection X=3.9308016 Y=65.735606

Approximate solutions are $x = -1.09$, $x = 1.16$, and $x = 3.93$.

Method 2 Rewrite the equation as $x^3 - 4x^2 - x + 5 = 0$. Graph the related function $y = x^3 - 4x^2 - x + 5$. Use the **ZERO** feature.

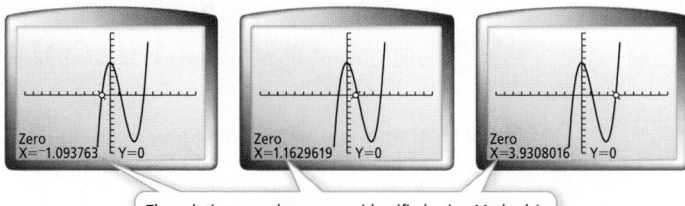

Zero X=-1.093763 Y=0

Zero X=1.1629619 Y=0

Zero X=3.9308016 Y=0

The solutions are the same as identified using Method 1.

Approximate solutions are $x = -1.09$, $x = 1.16$, and $x = 3.93$.

Check Verify the solutions by showing that they satisfy the original equation. Show values of $y_1 = x^3 + 5$ and $y_2 = 4x^2 + x$ in a table.

The solution checks.

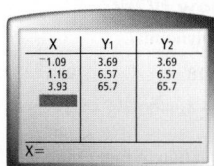

X	Y_1	Y_2
1.09	3.69	3.69
1.16	6.57	6.57
3.93	65.7	65.7

X=

© ✓ **Got It?** **3. a.** What are the real solutions of the equation $x^3 + x^2 = x - 1$?

b. Reasoning In Problem 3, which method seems to be an easier and more reliable way to find the solutions of an equation? Explain.

Problem 3

Q Why might you miss some real solutions when you use a calculator? **[Some solutions may not be visible in the standard viewing window.]**

Q Which value is the solution, the x or the y? **[The x-value is always the solution.]**

Q How does Method 1 work? **[It works like solving a system of equations.]**

Got It?

Q Compare and contrast the two methods. Which do you prefer? **[Answers may vary. Sample: For the first method, you do not need to write the equation in standard form, just graph each side of the equation as a separate function and find the intersections. For the second method, you do have to rewrite the equation, but then you can find the zeros as you normally would, and the solutions all lie along the x-axis, which simplifies the choice of Ymin and Ymax. Both methods use calculator features.]**

Answers

Got It? (continued)

2. a. $\pm 2, \pm 2i$

 b. $0, -4, 2$

 c. $2, -1 \pm i\sqrt{3}$

3. a. -1.84

 b. The second method seems to be a more reliable way to find the solutions because you do not risk missing a pt. of intersection.

Problem 4

Q Could you let another child's age be x? Explain. **[Yes, if you changed the expressions that represented the other ages.]**

Q When you know the value of x, how do you find the other ages? **[Go back to the expressions for the other children's ages and substitute for x in the expressions.]**

Got It? ERROR PREVENTION

Q What are consecutive integers? **[integers whose difference is one]**

3 Lesson Check

Do you know HOW?
- For Exercises 1–6, if students forget how to factor the polynomials, have them look up and list the different methods they have used and identify which method works best for each polynomial.

Do you UNDERSTAND?
- Before trying Exercise 7, have students write the definitions of the sum of cubes, the difference of cubes, and the difference of squares in their own words.

Close

Q What is the advantage of solving polynomial equations algebraically rather than by using a graph? **[Solving algebraically finds all the solutions, while solving with a graph finds only the real solutions. Solving algebraically provides exact answers, while solving with a graph may only give a decimal approximation.]**

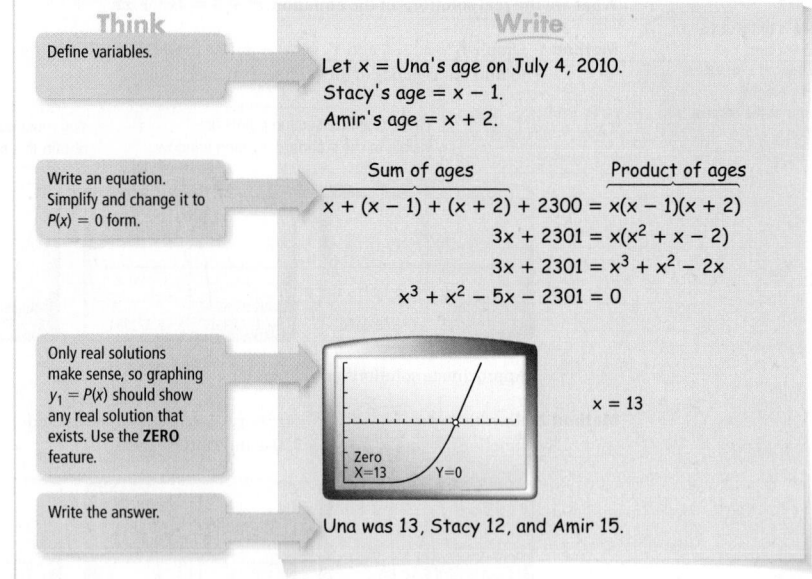

Problem 4 Modeling a Problem Situation

Close friends Stacy, Una, and Amir were all born on July 4. Stacy is one year younger than Una. Una is two years younger than Amir. On July 4, 2010, the product of their ages was 2300 more than the sum of their ages. How old was each friend on that day?

Think

Define variables.

Write an equation. Simplify and change it to $P(x) = 0$ form.

Only real solutions make sense, so graphing $y_1 = P(x)$ should show any real solution that exists. Use the **ZERO** feature.

Write the answer.

Write

Let x = Una's age on July 4, 2010.
Stacy's age = $x - 1$.
Amir's age = $x + 2$.

Sum of ages | Product of ages
$x + (x - 1) + (x + 2) + 2300 = x(x - 1)(x + 2)$
$3x + 2301 = x(x^2 + x - 2)$
$3x + 2301 = x^3 + x^2 - 2x$
$x^3 + x^2 - 5x - 2301 = 0$

$x = 13$
Zero
X=13 Y=0

Una was 13, Stacy 12, and Amir 15.

Got It? 4. What are three consecutive integers whose product is 480 more than their sum?

Lesson Check

Do you know HOW?

Factor each polynomial.

1. $x^2 - 3x - 18$ **2.** $x^3 - 27$

3. $x^3 + 3x^2 + 4x + 12$ **4.** $x^4 - 2^4$

Solve each equation by factoring.

5. $2x^2 + 7x - 4 = 0$

6. $2x^3 + 2x^2 - 4x = 0$

Do you UNDERSTAND? MATHEMATICAL PRACTICES

7. Vocabulary Identify each expression as a sum of cubes, difference of cubes, or difference of squares.
  a. $x^2 - 64$ **b.** $x^3 + 8$
  c. $x^3 - 125$ **d.** $x^2 - 81$

8. Reasoning Which method of solving polynomial equations will not identify the imaginary roots? Explain.

9. Reasoning Show two different ways to find the real roots of the polynomial equation $0 = x^6 - x^2$. Show your steps.

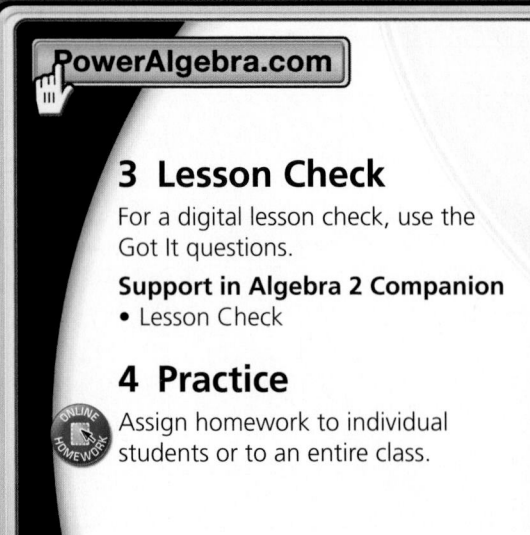

PowerAlgebra.com

3 Lesson Check
For a digital lesson check, use the Got It questions.

Support in Algebra 2 Companion
- Lesson Check

4 Practice
Assign homework to individual students or to an entire class.

Answers

Got It? (continued)
4. 7, 8, 9

Lesson Check
1. $(x - 6)(x + 3)$
2. $(x - 3)(x^2 + 3x + 9)$
3. $(x^2 + 4)(x + 3)$
4. $(x - 2)(x + 2)(x^2 + 2)$
5. $-4, \frac{1}{2}$ **6.** $-2, 0, 1$
7. a. difference of squares
   b. sum of cubes
   c. difference of cubes
   d. difference of squares
8. Graphing; imaginary numbers don't exist on the x-axis.

9. Method 1: Graph $y = x^6 - x^2$. Find the zeros for the real solutions.

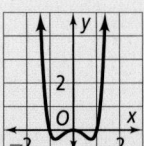

Method 2: Factor and solve x for $x^6 - x^2 = 0$.
$x^2(x^4 - 1) = x^2(x^2 - 1)(x^2 + 1)$
$\qquad = x^2(x - 1)(x + 1)(x^2 + 1)$
$\qquad x = 0, \pm 1$

Practice and Problem-Solving Exercises  MATHEMATICAL PRACTICES

Ⓐ Practice

Find the real or imaginary solutions of each equation by factoring. ◀ **See Problems 1 and 2.**

10. $x^3 + 64 = 0$ **11.** $x^3 - 1000 = 0$ **12.** $125x^3 - 27 = 0$

13. $64x^3 - 1 = 0$ **14.** $x^3 + 2x^2 + 5x + 10 = 0$ **15.** $6x^2 + 13x - 5 = 0$

16. $0 = x^3 - 27$ **17.** $0 = x^3 - 64$ **18.** $8x^3 = 1$

19. $64x^3 = -8$ **20.** $x^4 - 10x^2 = -9$ **21.** $x^4 - 8x^2 = -16$

22. $x^4 - 12x^2 = 64$ **23.** $x^4 + 7x^2 = 18$ **24.** $x^4 + 4x^2 = 12$

Find the real solutions of each equation by graphing. ◀ **See Problem 3.**

25. $x^3 - 4x^2 - 7x = -10$ **26.** $3x^3 - 6x^2 - 9x = 0$ **27.** $4x^3 - 8x^2 + 4x = 0$

28. $6x^2 = 48x$ **29.** $x^3 + 3x^2 + 2x = 0$ **30.** $2x^3 + 5x^2 = 7x$

31. $4x^3 = 4x^2 + 3x$ **32.** $2x^4 - 5x^3 - 3x^2 = 0$ **33.** $x^2 - 8x + 7 = 0$

34. $x^4 - 4x^3 - x^2 + 16x = 12$ **35.** $x^3 - x^2 - 16x = 20$ **36.** $3x^3 + 12x^2 - 3x = 12$

📟 **Graphing Calculator** Write an equation to model each situation. Then solve ◀ **See Problem 4.** each equation by graphing.

37. The Johnson twins were born two years after their older sister. This year, the product of the three siblings' ages is exactly 4558 more than the sum of their ages. How old are the twins?

38. The product of three consecutive integers is 210. What are the numbers?

Ⓑ Apply

Solve each equation.

39. $x^3 + 13x = 10x^2$ **40.** $x^3 - 6x^2 + 6x = 0$ **41.** $12x^3 = 60x^2 + 75x$

42. $125x^3 + 216 = 0$ **43.** $81x^3 - 192 = 0$ **44.** $x^4 - 64 = 0$

45. $-2x^4 + 100 = 0$ **46.** $27 = -x^4 - 12x^2$ **47.** $x^5 - 5x^3 + 4x = 0$

48. $5x^3 = 5x^2 + 12x$ **49.** $x^3 + x^2 + x + 1 = 0$ **50.** $x^3 + 1 = x^2 + x$

Ⓒ **51. Think About a Plan** The width of a plastic storage box is 1 ft longer than the height. The length is 4 ft longer than the height. The volume is 36 ft³. What are the dimensions of the box?
- What is the formula for the volume of a rectangular prism?
- What variable expressions represent the length, height, and width?
- What equation represents the volume of the plastic storage box?

Ⓒ **52. Error Analysis** A student claims that 1, 2, 3, and 4 are the zeros of a cubic polynomial function. Explain why the student is mistaken.

53. Geometry The width of a box is 2 m less than the length. The height is 1 m less than the length. The volume is 60 m³. What is the length of the box?

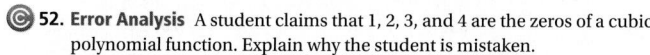

ASSIGNMENT GUIDE

Basic: 10–38 all, 50–54

Average: 11–37 odd, 39–57

Advanced: 1–37 odd, 39–60

Standardized Test Prep: 61–64

Mixed Review: 65–72

Ⓒ **Mathematical Practices** are supported by exercises with red headings. Here are the Practices supported in this lesson:

MP 1: Make Sense of Problems Ex. 51
MP 2: Reason Abstractly Ex. 59
MP 3: Communicate Ex. 8
MP 3: Construct Arguments Ex. 8, 9
MP 3: Compare Arguments Ex. 57
MP 3: Critique the Reasoning of Others Ex. 52
MP 5: Use Appropriate Tools Ex. 37, 38

Applications exercises have blue headings.

EXERCISE 53: Use the Think About a Plan worksheet in the **Practice and Problem Solving Workbook** (also available in the Teaching Resources in print and online) to further support students' development in becoming independent learners.

HOMEWORK QUICK CHECK

To check students' understanding of key skills and concepts, go over Exercises 21, 25, 51, 52, and 53.

Practice and Problem-Solving Exercises

10. $-4, 2 \pm 2i\sqrt{3}$

11. $10, -5 \pm 5i\sqrt{3}$

12. $\frac{3}{5}, \frac{-3 \pm 3i\sqrt{3}}{10}$

13. $\frac{1}{4}, \frac{-1 \pm i\sqrt{3}}{8}$

14. $-2, \pm i\sqrt{5}$

15. $\frac{1}{3}, -\frac{5}{2}$

16. $3, \frac{-3 \pm 3i\sqrt{3}}{2}$

17. $4, -2 \pm 2i\sqrt{3}$

18. $\frac{1}{2}, \frac{-1 \pm i\sqrt{3}}{4}$

19. $-\frac{1}{2}, \frac{1 \pm i\sqrt{3}}{4}$

20. $\pm 1, \pm 3$

21. ± 2

22. $\pm 4, \pm 2i$

23. $\pm \sqrt{2}, \pm 3i$

24. $\pm \sqrt{2}, \pm i\sqrt{6}$

25. $-2, 1, 5$

26. $-1, 0, 3$

27. $0, 1$

28. $0, 8$

29. $0, -1, -2$

30. $0, -3.5, 1$

31. $0, -0.5, 1.5$

32. $-0.5, 0, 3$

33. $1, 7$

34. $-2, 1, 2, 3$

35. $-2, 5$

36. $-4, -1, 1$

37. 16 yrs old; $x^2(x + 2) = 3x + 4560$;

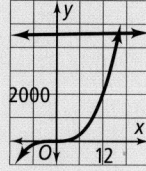

38. 5, 6, 7; $x(x + 1)(x + 2) = 210$;

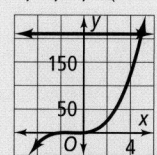

39. $0, 5 \pm 2\sqrt{3}$

40. $0, 3 \pm \sqrt{3}$

41. $0, \frac{5 \pm 5\sqrt{2}}{2}$

42. $-\frac{6}{5}, \frac{3 \pm 3i\sqrt{3}}{5}$

43. $\frac{4}{3}, \frac{-2 \pm 2i\sqrt{3}}{3}$

44. $\pm 2\sqrt{2}, \pm 2i\sqrt{2}$

45. $\pm \sqrt{5\sqrt{2}}, \pm i\sqrt{5\sqrt{2}}$

46. $\pm 3i, \pm i\sqrt{3}$

47. $0, \pm 1, \pm 2$

48. $0, \frac{1}{2} \pm \frac{\sqrt{265}}{10}$

49. $-1, \pm i$

50. $-1, 1$

51. 2 ft × 3 ft × 6 ft

52. A cubic function can have at most 3 zeros.

53. 5 m

Answers

Practice and Problem-Solving Exercises
(continued)

54. $-\frac{5}{2}$, 1; $y = (2x + 5)(x - 1)$;

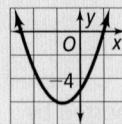

55. ± 3, ± 1; $y = (x - 1)(x + 1)(x - 3)(x + 3)$;

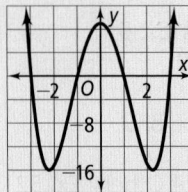

56. -1, 2; $y = (x + 1)(x - 2)^2$;

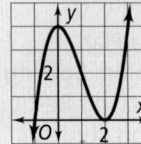

57. Check students' work.

58. The geometric figure consists of either 2 cubes or 3 rectangular blocks, each with total volume equal.

$V_{\text{large cube}} = a(a)[(a - b) + b] = a^3$

$V_{\text{small cube}} = b(b)[(a + b) - a] = b^3$

$V_{\text{total 2 cubes}} = V_{\text{large cube}} + V_{\text{small cube}} = a^3 + b^3$

$V_{\text{top rectangular block}} = a(a)(a - b) = a^2(a - b)$

$V_{\text{small bottom rectangular block}} = a(b)(a - b)$
$= ab(a - b)$

$V_{\text{long bottom rectangular block}} = b(b)(a + b)$
$= b^2(a + b)$

$V_{\text{total 3 rectangular blocks}} = a^2(a - b) + ab(a - b)$
$\qquad + b^2(a + b)$
$= a(a - b)(a + b) + b^2(a + b)$
$= (a + b)[a(a - b) + b^2]$
$= (a + b)(a^2 - ab + b^2)$

So, $V_{\text{total 2 cubes}} = V_{\text{total 3 rectangular blocks}}$
$\qquad a^3 + b^3 = (a + b)(a^2 - ab + b^2)$.

59. Answers may vary. Sample:

$f(x) = 4x(x + 12)\left(x - \frac{1}{4}\right)\left(x - \frac{1}{6}\right)$
$p(x) = x(x + 12)(4x - 1)(6x - 1)$

60. $\dfrac{-1 \pm i\sqrt{3}}{2}$

Standardized Test Prep

61. C **62.** I **63.** B

64. **[2]** Let q = number of quarters and let d = number of dimes:

$q + d = 12$
$q = 12 - d$

Graph each function to find the zeros. Rewrite the function with the polynomial in factored form.

54. $y = 2x^2 + 3x - 5$ **55.** $y = x^4 - 10x^2 + 9$ **56.** $y = x^3 - 3x^2 + 4$

G 57. Open-Ended To solve a polynomial equation, you can use any combination of graphing, factoring, and the Quadratic Formula. Write and solve an equation to illustrate each method.

C Challenge **58.** The geometric figure at the right has volume $a^3 + b^3$. You can split it into three rectangular blocks (including the long one with side $a + b$). Explain how to use this figure to prove the factoring formula for the sum of cubes, $a^3 + b^3 = (a + b)(a^2 - ab + b^2)$.

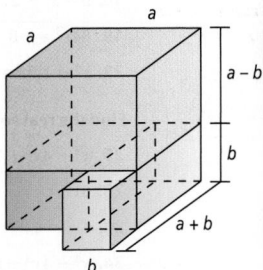

G 59. Open-Ended Find equations for two different polynomial functions whose zeros include -12, 0, $\frac{1}{4}$, and $\frac{1}{6}$.

60. What are the complex solutions of $x^5 + x^3 + 2x = 2x^4 + x^2 + 1$?

Standardized Test Prep

SAT/ACT

61. Which value is NOT a solution to the equation $x^4 - 3x^2 - 54 = 0$?
Ⓐ -3 Ⓑ 3 Ⓒ $-3i$ Ⓓ $-i\sqrt{6}$

62. Ava drove 3 hours at 45 miles per hour. How many miles did she drive?
Ⓕ 45 miles Ⓖ 48 miles Ⓗ 90 miles Ⓘ 135 miles

63. Which polynomial has the complex roots $1 + i\sqrt{2}$ and $1 - i\sqrt{2}$?
Ⓐ $x^2 + 2x + 3$ Ⓑ $x^2 - 2x + 3$ Ⓒ $x^2 + 2x - 3$ Ⓓ $x^2 - 2x - 3$

Short Response

64. Sam has only quarters and dimes in his pocket. He has a total of 12 coins, totaling $1.95. How many of each coin does Sam have?

Mixed Review

Write each polynomial in factored form. Check by multiplication. ◀ **See Lesson 5-2.**

65. $3x^2 - 18x + 24$ **66.** $2x^4 + 6x^3 - 18x^2 - 54x$ **67.** $x^4 - 4x^3 - 5x^2$

Solve each equation by factoring. Check your answers. ◀ **See Lesson 4-5.**

68. $x^2 - 4x = 12$ **69.** $x^2 + 1 = 37$ **70.** $2x^2 - 5x - 3 = 0$

Get Ready! **To prepare for Lesson 5-4, do Exercises 71 and 72.**

Evaluate each expression for the given values of the variables. ◀ **See Lesson 1-3.**

71. $\dfrac{16(x - 4)(y - 2)}{4(x - 3)y}$; $x = 1$ and $y = -2$ **72.** $\dfrac{2(x + 5)y}{10(x - 4)(y - 2)}$; $x = 1$ and $y = -2$

$.25q + 0.1d = 1.95$
$.25(12 - d) + 0.1d = 1.95$ Substitue for q.
$3 - 0.15d = 1.95$
$-0.15d = -1.05$
$d = 7$

$q = 12 - (7)$ Substitute for d.
$q = 5$

Sam has five quarters and seven dimes. (OR another appropriate method)

[1] correct answers, without work shown

Mixed Review

65. $3(x - 4)(x - 2)$
66. $2x(x + 3)^2(x - 3)$

67. $x^2(x - 5)(x + 1)$
68. -2, 6
69. ± 6
70. $-\frac{1}{2}$, 3
71. 12
72. $-\frac{1}{5}$

5-3 Lesson Resources

Additional Instructional Support

Algebra 2 Companion

Students can use the **Algebra 2 Companion** worktext (4 pages) as you teach the lesson. Use the Companion to support

- New Vocabulary
- Key Concepts
- Got It for each Problem
- Lesson Check

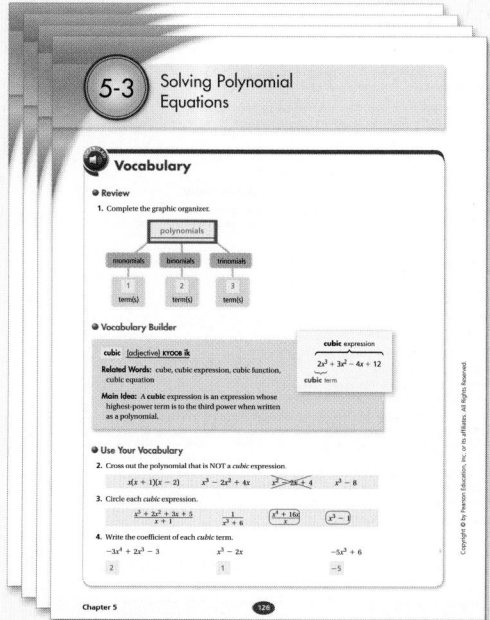

ELL Support

Use Graphic Organizers Help students make a flow chart for finding the roots of a polynomial function. It should include both algebraic and graphing methods.

For example, write the polynomial function P in the form $P(x) = 0$.

Then factor $P(x)$ (list and describe the methods) and use the Factor Theorem to list the roots.

Or graph the polynomial function with a graphing calculator. Then identify the real zeros.

5 Assess & Remediate

Lesson Quiz

1. What are the real or imaginary solutions of $2x^3 + 7x^2 = 15x$?
2. What are the real or imaginary solutions of $2x^4 - 7x^2 = 4$?
3. What are the real solutions of $x^3 - 2x = 3x^2 - 1$?
4. **Do you UNDERSTAND?** Yun Sil added twice as many new songs on her MP3 player as Matt, who added 5 more new songs on his MP3 player than Sierra. The sum of the songs added on all three players is 15 more than the cube of the number of songs added on Sierra's player. How many songs did each person add?

ANSWERS TO LESSON QUIZ

1. $0, \frac{3}{2}, -5$
2. $-2, 2, \frac{i\sqrt{2}}{2}, \frac{-i\sqrt{2}}{2}$
3. $-0.834, 0.343, 3.491$
4. Yun Sil added 14; Matt added 7; Sierra added 2.

PRESCRIPTION FOR REMEDIATION

Use the student work on the Lesson Quiz to prescribe a differentiated review assignment:

Points	Differentiated Remediation
0–2	Intervention
3	On-level
4	Extension

PowerAlgebra.com

5 Assess & Remediate

Assign the Lesson Quiz. Appropriate intervention, practice, or enrichment is automatically generated based on student performance.

Differentiated Remediation

Available in editable format online.

Intervention

- **Reteaching** (2 pages) Provides reteaching and practice exercises for the key lesson concepts. Use with struggling students or absent students.
- **English Language Learner Support** Helps students develop and reinforce mathematical vocabulary and key concepts.

All-in-One Resources/Online
Reteaching

All-in-One Resources/Online
English Language Learner Support

Differentiated Remediation *continued*

Available in editable format online.

On-Level

- **Practice** (2 pages) Provides extra practice for each lesson. For simpler practice exercises, use the Form K Practice pages found in the All-in-One Teaching Resources and online.

- **Think About a Plan** Helps students develop specific problem-solving skills and strategies by providing scaffolded guiding questions.

- **Standardized Test Prep** Focuses on all major exercises, all major question types, and helps students prepare for the high-stakes assessments.

Extension

- **Enrichment** Provides students with interesting problems and activities that extend the concepts of the lesson.

- **Activities, Games, and Puzzles** Worksheets that can be used for concepts development, enrichment, and for fun!

Practice and Problem Solving Wkbk/All-in-One Workbook/Resources/Online
Practice page 1

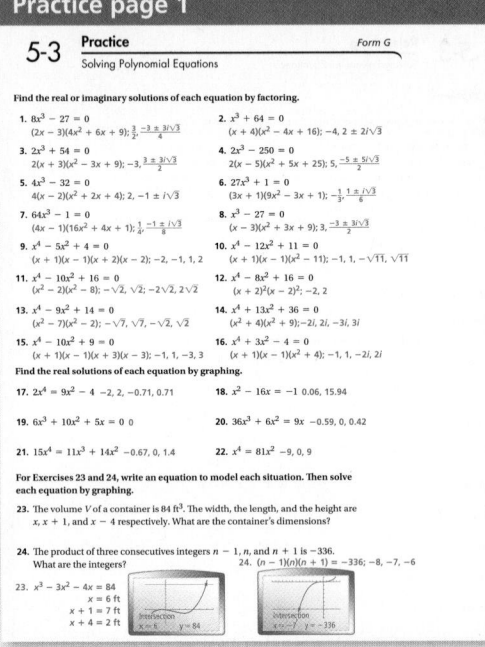

Practice and Problem Solving Wkbk/All-in-One Workbook/Resources/Online
Practice page 2

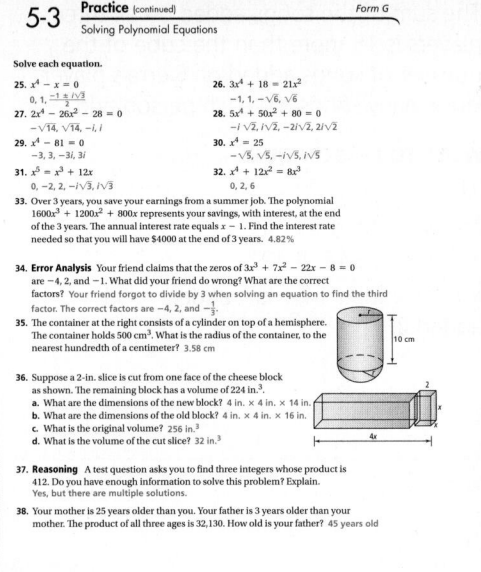

All-in-One Resources/Online
Enrichment

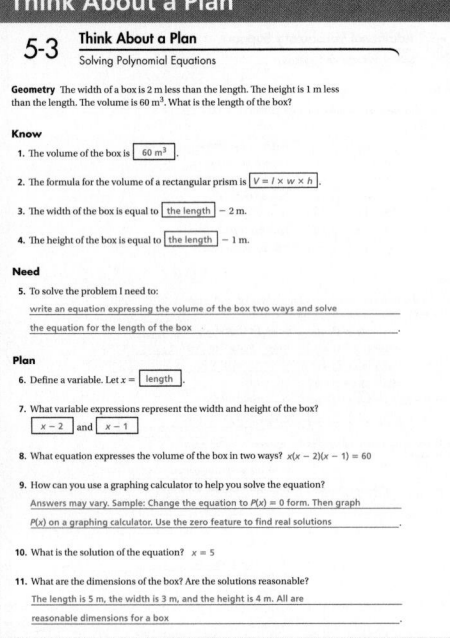

Practice and Problem Solving Wkbk/All-in-One Workbook Resources/Online
Think About a Plan

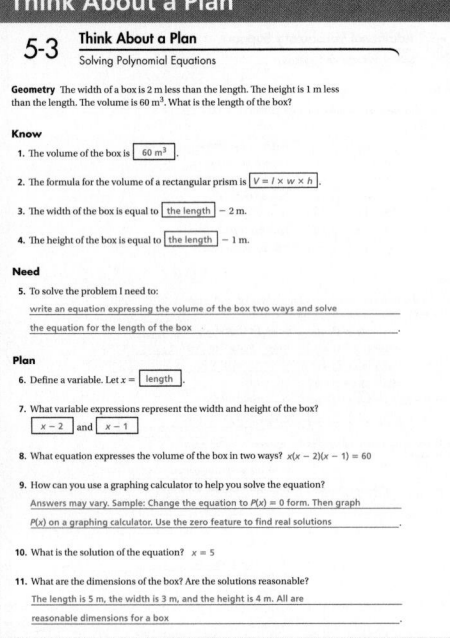

Practice and Problem Solving Wkbk/All-in-One Workbook/Resources/Online
Standardized Test Prep

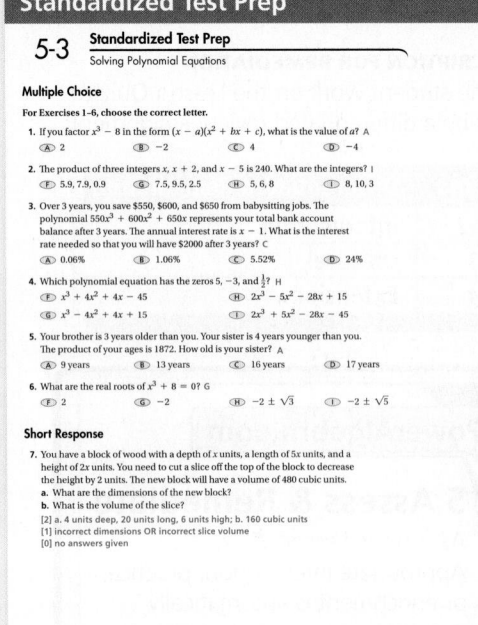

Online Teacher Resource Center
Activities, Games, and Puzzles

Dividing Polynomials

© **Common Core State Standards**

A-APR.B.2 Know and apply the Remainder Theorem: For a polynomial $p(x)$ and a number a, the remainder on division by $x - a$ is $p(a)$, so $p(a) = 0$ if and only if $(x - a)$ is a factor of $p(x)$. **Also A-APR.A.1, A-APR.D.6**

MP 1, MP 2, MP 3, MP 6, MP 7

Objectives To divide polynomials using long division
To divide polynomials using synthetic division

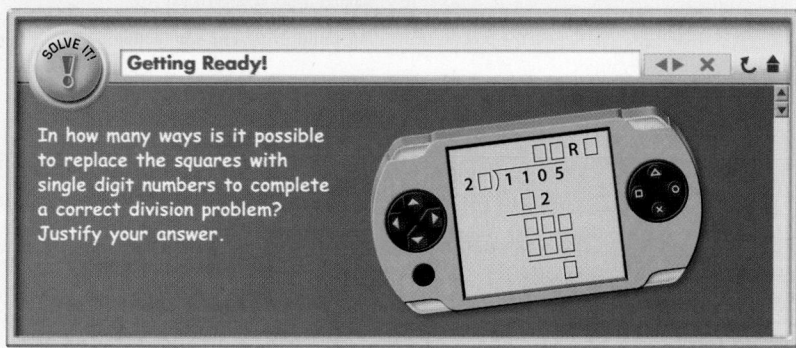

Getting Ready!

In how many ways is it possible to replace the squares with single digit numbers to complete a correct division problem? Justify your answer.

1 Interactive Learning

Solve It!

PURPOSE To review long division
PROCESS Students may

• estimate the dividend to determine the value of the missing digits.
• guess and check to determine the value of the missing digits.

FACILITATE

Q Using rules for divisibility, are there any digits that you can eliminate for the divisor? **[0, 5]**

Q Can you use 24 as your divisor? Explain. **[No; in this case, the first number below the divisor would be 96, which does not end in 2.]**

Q Is it possible for 7 to be the digit before the 2 in the first row under the dividend? Explain. **[No; when you subtract $110 - 72 = 38$ and 38 is greater than the divisor.]**

ANSWER See Solve It in Answers on next page.
CONNECT THE MATH The Solve It uses a puzzle to review long division. The students will use these skills when they divide polynomials.

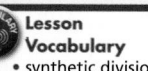

Lesson Vocabulary
• synthetic division
• Remainder Theorem

Long division is one of many methods you can use to divide whole numbers.

Essential Understanding You can divide polynomials using steps that are similar to the long-division steps that you use to divide whole numbers.

When you try to factor a polynomial, you are trying to find a divisor of the polynomial that gives a quotient (the other factor) and remainder 0. This suggests that being able to divide one polynomial by another could help you factor polynomials.

Numerical long division and polynomial long division are similar.

Numerical Long Division		Polynomial Long Division	
32		$3x + 2$	
$21\overline{)672}$	21 divides into	$2x + 1\overline{)6x^2 + 7x + 2}$	$(2x + 1)$ divides into
63	67 3 times	$6x^2 + 3x$	$(6x^2 + 7x)$ $3x$ times
42	21 divides into	$4x + 2$	$(2x + 1)$ divides into
42	42 2 times	$4x + 2$	$(4x + 2)$ 2 times
0		0	

The remainder from each division above is 0, so 21 is a factor of 672 and $2x + 1$ is a factor of $6x^2 + 7x + 2$.

Preparing to Teach

BIG idea **Solving Equations and Inequalities**

ESSENTIAL UNDERSTANDING

• Polynomials can be divided using steps that are similar to the long-division steps that are used to divide whole numbers.

Math Background

An algorithm is a specific set of instructions used to solve a problem. The Division Algorithm for Polynomials is a generalized version of the technique of long division in arithmetic. For polynomials $P(x)$ and $D(x)$, with $D(x)$ not equal to zero, there exist polynomials $Q(x)$ and $R(x)$ such that $P(x) = D(x) \, Q(x) + R(x)$. If $R(x) = 0$, then $D(x)$ is a factor of $P(x)$. Students divide polynomials using the process of long division and then move to dividing polynomials using synthetic division, which can be completed only if the factor is linear. Both methods are shown in order to illustrate the relationship between long division and synthetic division.

The Euclidean Algorithm works in a method similar to the Division Algorithm for polynomials and is used to find the greatest common divisor for two polynomials. For polynomials $P(x)$ and $D(x)$, with $D(x)$ not equal to zero and the degree of $D(x) <$ the degree of $P(x)$, use the following iteration:

• Use long division to find $P(x) = D(x) \, Q(x) + R(x)$. If $R(x) = 0$, then $D(x)$ is the greatest common divisor.

• If $R(x)$ is not equal to zero, divide $D(x)$ by $R(x)$. Use long division to find $D(x) = R(x) \, Q_2(x) + R_2(x)$. If $R_2(x) = 0$, then $R(x)$ is the greatest common factor.

• If $R_2(x)$ is not equal to zero, repeat the process dividing $R(x)$ by $R_2(x)$.

© **Mathematical Practices**

Attend to precision. Students will flexibly use the properties of long division and synthetic division in checking the factors of polynomial expressions.

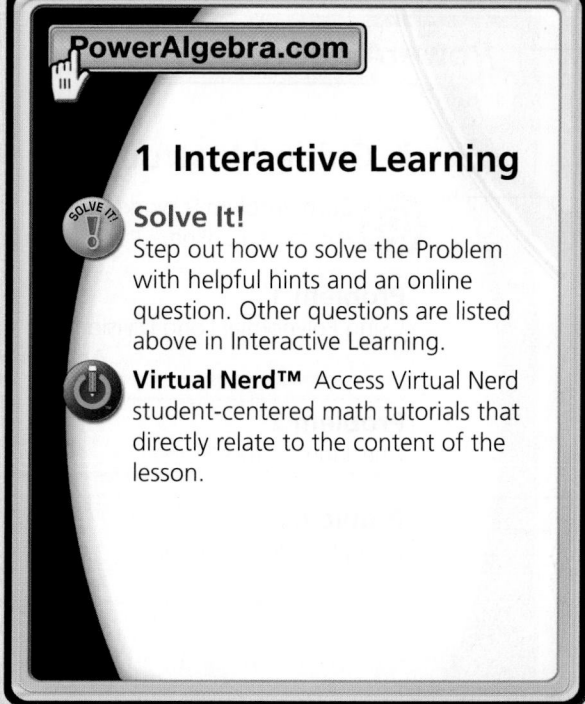

PowerAlgebra.com

1 Interactive Learning

Solve It!
Step out how to solve the Problem with helpful hints and an online question. Other questions are listed above in Interactive Learning.

Virtual Nerd™ Access Virtual Nerd student-centered math tutorials that directly relate to the content of the lesson.

2 Guided Instruction

Problem 1

Q In what order should you arrange the terms when you divide polynomials? **[descending]**

Q How do you determine where to place the first term in the quotient? **[The term of the quotient is placed over the term in the dividend of the same degree.]**

Q How do you know when you are finished dividing the polynomial? **[The degree of the remainder is less than the divisor.]**

Got It?

VISUAL LEARNERS

When performing long division, have students use a colored pencil to change the sign of each term being subtracted.

$$x - 7)\overline{\begin{array}{c} 3x \\ 3x^2 - 29x + 56 \\ \underline{3x^2 - 21x} \end{array}} \qquad x - 7)\overline{\begin{array}{c} 3x \\ 3x^2 - 29x + 56 \\ \underline{-3x^2 + 21x} \end{array}}$$

Take Note

Q When you divide a polynomial by a binomial and there is no remainder, what does that tell you about the quotient? **[The quotient is a factor of the dividend.]**

 Problem 1 Using Polynomial Long Division

Use polynomial long division to divide $4x^2 + 23x - 16$ by $x + 5$. What is the quotient and remainder?

$$x + 5)\overline{\begin{array}{c} 4x \\ 4x^2 + 23x - 16 \\ \underline{4x^2 + 20x} \\ 3x - 16 \end{array}}$$

Divide: $\frac{4x^2}{x} = 4x$.
Multiply: $4x(x + 5) = 4x^2 + 20x$.
Subtract to get $3x$. Bring down -16.

Repeat the process of dividing, multiplying, and subtracting.

$$x + 5)\overline{\begin{array}{c} 4x\ +3 \\ 4x^2 + 23x - 16 \\ \underline{4x^2 + 20x} \\ 3x - 16 \\ \underline{3x + 15} \\ -31 \end{array}}$$

Divide: $\frac{3x}{x} = 3$.
Multiply: $3(x + 5) = 3x + 15$.
Subtract to get -31.

The quotient is $4x + 3$ with remainder -31. ◁ You can say: $4x + 3$, R -31.

Think

How can you check your result?
Show that
(divisor)(quotient) + remainder = dividend.

Check

$(x + 5)(4x + 3) - 31 = (4x^2 + 3x + 20x + 15) - 31$ Multiply $(x + 5)(4x + 3)$.
$= 4x^2 + 23x - 16$ ✔   Simplify.

✅ **Got It?** **1.** Use polynomial long division to divide $3x^2 - 29x + 56$ by $x - 7$. What is the quotient and remainder?

📝 take note   **Key Concept**   The Division Algorithm for Polynomials

You can divide polynomial $P(x)$ by polynomial $D(x)$ to get polynomial quotient $Q(x)$ and polynomial remainder $R(x)$. The result is $P(x) = D(x)Q(x) + R(x)$.

$$D(x)\overline{\begin{array}{c} Q(x) \\ P(x) \end{array}}$$
$$\vdots$$
$$\overline{R(x)}$$

If $R(x) = 0$, then $P(x) = D(x)Q(x)$ and $D(x)$ and $Q(x)$ are factors of $P(x)$.

To use long division, $P(x)$ and $D(x)$ should be in standard form with zero coefficients where appropriate. The process stops when the degree of the remainder, $R(x)$, is less than the degree of the divisor, $D(x)$.

 PowerAlgebra.com

2 Guided Instruction

© Each Problem is worked out and supported online.

Problem 1
Using Polynomial Long Division
Animated

Problem 2
Checking Factors

Problem 3
Using Synthetic Division
Animated

Problem 4
Using Synthetic Division to Solve a Problem

Problem 5
Evaluating a Polynomial

Alternative Problem 5
Evaluating a Polynomial
Animated

Support in Algebra 2 Companion
• Vocabulary
• Key Concepts
• Got It?

Answers

Solve It!
One way: $1105 \div 23 = 48$, R 1; begin with $11 \div 2 \approx 5$, but 5 times any number results in a multiple of 5, not 2. So, the first number in the dividend must be 4. Next, think $4 \times 2■ = ■2.4 \times 3 = 12$, so the divisor must be 23. Once you know the divisor, you can fill in the rest of the blanks by doing long division. ($4 \times 23 = 92$; $110 - 92 = 18$; bring down the 5; $185 \div 23 \approx 8$; $8 \times 23 = 184$; the remainder is 1)

Got It?
1. $3x - 8$, R 0
2. a. yes; $P(x) = (x + 5)(x^4 - 1)$
    b. $(x + 2)(3x + 1)$

 **Problem 2** Checking Factors

A Is $x^2 + 1$ a factor of $3x^4 - 4x^3 + 12x^2 + 5$?

$$
\begin{array}{r}
3x^2 - 4x + 9 \\
x^2 + 0x + 1\overline{)3x^4 - 4x^3 + 12x^2 + 0x + 5} \quad \text{Include } 0x \text{ terms.} \\
\underline{3x^4 + 0x^3 + 3x^2} \\
-4x^3 + 9x^2 + 0x \\
\underline{-4x^3 + 0x^2 - 4x} \\
9x^2 + 4x + 5 \\
\underline{9x^2 + 0x + 9} \\
4x - 4
\end{array}
$$

> The degree of the remainder is less than the degree of the divisor. Stop!

The remainder is not zero. $x^2 + 1$ is not a factor of $3x^4 - 4x^3 + 12x^2 + 5$.

Plan

Can you use the Factor Theorem to help answer this question?
Yes; recall that if $P(a) = 0$, then $x - a$ is a factor of $P(x)$.

B Is $x - 2$ a factor of $P(x) = x^5 - 32$? If it is, write $P(x)$ as a product of two factors.

Step 1 Use the Factor Theorem to determine if $x - 2$ is a factor of $x^5 - 32$.

$$P(2) = 2^5 - 32$$
$$= 32 - 32$$
$$= 0$$

Since $P(2) = 0$, $x - 2$ is a factor of $P(x)$.

Step 2 Use polynomial long division to find the other factor.

$$
\begin{array}{r}
x^4 + 2x^3 + 4x^2 + 8x + 16 \\
x - 2\overline{)x^5 + 0x^4 + 0x^3 + 0x^2 + 0x - 32} \\
\underline{x^5 - 2x^4} \\
2x^4 + 0x^3 \\
\underline{2x^4 - 4x^3} \\
4x^3 + 0x^2 \\
\underline{4x^3 - 8x^2} \\
8x^2 + 0x \\
\underline{8x^2 - 16x} \\
16x - 32 \\
\underline{16x - 32} \\
0
\end{array}
$$

$$P(x) = (x - 2)(x^4 + 2x^3 + 4x^2 + 8x + 16)$$

 **Got It?** 2. **a.** Is $x^4 - 1$ a factor of $P(x) = x^5 + 5x^4 - x - 5$? If it is, write $P(x)$ as a product of two factors.

  b. Reasoning Use the fact that $12 \cdot 31 = 372$ to write $3x^2 + 7x + 2$ as the product of two factors.

Problem 2

When solving a long division problem, students may not recognize that a term is missing from either the dividend or the divisor. Remind students to write the terms in descending order and write a zero for any missing terms.

Q What terms are missing in 2A? **[The x term is missing in the dividend and divisor.]**

Q What is the purpose of the $0x$ term? **[It serves as a placeholder for the missing term.]**

Q Why must you stop dividing when the degree of the remainder is less than the degree of the divisor? **[There is no polynomial term that you can multiply the divisor by to get rid of the first term of the remainder.]**

EXTENSION

Q $x^2 - 1$ is a factor of $x^3 - 2x^2 - x + 2$. How do the factors of $x^2 - 1$ ($x + 1$ and $x - 1$) relate to $x^3 - 2x^2 - x + 2$? **[$x + 1$ and $x - 1$ are also factors of $x^3 - 2x^2 - x + 2$]**

Got It?   **ERROR PREVENTION**

Q Can you use the Factor Theorem to answer 2a? Explain why or why not. **[No; samples: $x^4 - 1$ is not a linear factor; $x^4 - 1$ is not in the form $x - a$; $x^4 - 1$ cannot be factored into real linear factors.]**

Additional Problems

1. Use polynomial long division to divide $5x^2 + 2x + 3$ by $x + 1$. What are the quotient and remainder?

ANSWER $5x - 3$, R6

2. Is $x^2 - 2$ a factor of $P(x) = x^4 - x^2 - 2$? If it is, write $P(x)$ as a product of two factors.

ANSWER Yes; $(x^2 - 2)(x^2 + 1)$

3. Use synthetic division to divide $4x^3 - 3x^2 + 2x - 3$ by $x - 1$. What are the quotient and the remainder?

ANSWER $4x^2 + x + 3$; remainder 0

4. The polynomial $x^3 + 9x^2 + 23x + 15$ expresses the volume, in cubic inches, of a box, and the length is $(x + 5)$ inches. What are the other two dimensions of the box?

ANSWER $(x + 1)$ and $(x + 3)$

5. Given that $P(x) = x^4 + 6x^3 + 9x^2 + 3x - 3$, what is $P(4)$?

ANSWER 793

Problem 3

Make sure students include the sign when writing the coefficients of the terms for synthetic division.

Q Why is the sign of the $x + 2$ term reversed when completing the synthetic division? **[The term has to be in the form $x - a$, so you must rewrite $x + 2$ as $x - (-2)$.]**

Q How would you describe the arithmetic process of synthetic division? **[A number above the line is added and a number below the line is multiplied by the divisor, moving over one space to the right.]**

Q What does the final number in the bottom row represent? **[The number 0 means the divisor is a factor of the dividend. If the final number is other than 0, then it is a remainder.]**

Got It?

Q What do you need to do first? **[Answers may vary. Sample: Identify the divisor, 7.]**

Problem 4

Q After you complete the synthetic division, what is the next step? **[Factor the trinomial.]**

Q How could you check your work? **[Use a graphing calculator to graph the given function and then calculate the zeros, or multiply the factors together and see if the result matches the original dividend.]**

Synthetic division simplifies the long-division process for dividing by a linear expression $x - a$. To use synthetic division, write the coefficients (including zeros) of the polynomial in standard form. Omit all variables and exponents. For the divisor, reverse the sign (use a). This allows you to add instead of subtract throughout the process.

© Problem 3 Using Synthetic Division

Use synthetic division to divide $x^3 - 14x^2 + 51x - 54$ by $x + 2$. What is the quotient and remainder?

Think

To divide by $x + 2$ what number do you use for the synthetic divisor?
$x + 2 = x - (-2)$ so use -2.

Step 1 Reverse the sign of $+2$. Write the coefficients of the polynomial.

$$-2 \, | \, 1 \; -14 \; 51 \; -54$$

Step 2 Bring down the first coefficient.

$$\underline{-2 \, | \, 1 \; -14 \; 51 \; -54}$$
$$1$$

Step 3 Multiply the coefficient by the divisor. Add to the next coefficient.

$$-2 \, | \; 1 \quad -14 \quad 51 \quad -54$$
$$\underline{\qquad \quad -2 \qquad}$$
$$1 \; -16$$

Step 4 Continue multiplying and adding through the last coefficient.

$$-2 \, | \; 1 \quad -14 \quad 51 \quad -54$$
$$\underline{\qquad -2 \quad 32 \; -166}$$
$$1 \; -16 \quad 83 \; -220$$

The quotient is $x^2 - 16x + 83$, R -220.

✓ Got It?

3. Use synthetic division to divide $x^3 - 57x + 56$ by $x - 7$. What is the quotient and remainder?

© Problem 4 Using Synthetic Division to Solve a Problem

Crafts The polynomial $x^3 + 7x^2 - 38x - 240$ expresses the volume, in cubic inches, of the shadow box shown.

Ⓐ What are the dimensions of the box? (*Hint:* The length is greater than the height (or depth).)

Plan

How can you use the picture to help solve the problem?
The picture gives the width of the box. Remember for a rectangular prism, $V = \ell \times w \times h$.

$$-5 \, | \; 1 \quad 7 \quad -38 \quad -240$$
$$\underline{\qquad -5 \; -10 \quad 240}$$
$$1 \quad 2 \quad -48 \qquad 0$$

$$x^2 + 2x - 48 = (x - 6)(x + 8)$$

So, $x^3 + 7x^2 - 38x - 240 = (x + 5)(x^2 + 2x - 48)$
$$= (x + 5)(x - 6)(x + 8)$$

The length, width, and height (or depth) of the box are $(x + 8)$ in., $(x + 5)$ in., and $(x - 6)$ in., respectively.

$x + 5$

306   Chapter 5   Polynomials and Polynomial Functions

Answers

Got It? (continued)

3. $x^2 + 7x - 8$, R 0

B If the width of the box is 15 in., what are the other two dimensions?

The width of the box is $x + 5$. So if $x + 5 = 15$, then $x = 10$.

Substitute for x to find the length and height (or depth).

    Length: $x + 8 = 10 + 8 = 18$ in.
    Height: $x - 6 = 10 - 6 = 4$ in.

 Got It? 4. If the polynomial $x^3 + 6x^2 + 11x + 6$ expresses the volume, in cubic inches, of the box, and the width is $(x + 1)$ in., what are the dimensions of the box?

The **Remainder Theorem** provides a quick way to find the remainder of a polynomial long-division problem.

Theorem The Remainder Theorem

If you divide a polynomial $P(x)$ of degree $n \geq 1$ by $x - a$, then the remainder is $P(a)$.

Here's Why It Works When you divide polynomial $P(x)$ by $D(x)$, you find $P(x) = D(x)Q(x) + R(x)$.

$P(x) = (x - a)Q(x) + R(x)$ Substitute $(x - a)$ for $D(x)$.
$P(a) = (a - a)Q(a) + R(a)$ Evaluate $P(a)$. Substitute a for x.
$\quad\quad = R(a)$ Simplify.

Think
Is there a way to find $P(3)$ without substituting?
Use synthetic division. $P(3)$ is the remainder.

© **Problem 5** Evaluating a Polynomial   **GRIDDED RESPONSE**

Given that $P(x) = x^5 - 2x^3 - x^2 + 2$, what is $P(3)$?

By the Remainder Theorem, $P(3)$ is the remainder when you divide $P(x)$ by $x - 3$.

$$
\begin{array}{r|rrrrrr}
3 & 1 & 0 & -2 & -1 & 0 & 2 \\
  &   & 3 & 9 & 21 & 60 & 180 \\
\hline
  & 1 & 3 & 7 & 20 & 60 & 182
\end{array}
$$

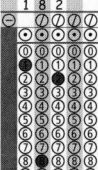

$P(3) = 182$.

 Got It? 5. Given that $P(x) = x^5 - 3x^4 - 28x^3 + 5x + 20$, what is $P(-4)$?

Got It?   EXTENSION

Q What are the length, width, height, and volume of the box when $x = 5$? **$[(x + 1)(x + 2)(x + 3)$; the width is 6 in., the other two dimensions are 7 in. and 8 in., and the volume is 336 in.^{3}.]**

Take Note

Q Divide $4x^2 - 5x - 20$ by $x - 4$ using synthetic division. What is the remainder? **[24]**

Here's Why It Works

Q What is $P(4)$ for $P(x) = 4x^2 - 5x - 20$? **[24]**

Q What is the connection between dividing the polynomial by $x - 4$ and evaluating the polynomial when $x = 4$? **[When the polynomial was evaluated at $x = 4$, the result, $P(4)$, is the same as the remainder when the polynomial was divided by $x - 4$.]**

Problem 5

Q When you use synthetic division, how do you determine the degree of the first term in the quotient? **[The degree of the quotient is one less than the degree of the dividend polynomial.]**

Q What is an advantage of using synthetic division and the Remainder Theorem to evaluate a polynomial? **[You minimize the calculations required of substituting the value for x and evaluating.]**

Got It?

Q When determining $P(-4)$, what factor are you dividing by? **[$x + 4$]**

4. width: $(x + 1)$ in.; height: $(x + 2)$ in.; length: $(x + 3)$ in.

5. 0

3 Lesson Check

Do you know HOW?

• For Exercises 1–5, remind students that the binomial needs to be in the form $x - a$. If the form is $x + a$, students will need to rewrite the term as $x - (-a)$.

Do you UNDERSTAND?

• For Exercise 7, suggest students discuss what could happen if the terms of both polynomials are not written in descending order. **[You may not be able to subtract the terms as you divide.]**

Close

> **Q** How are long division and synthetic division similar? **[They can both be used to divide a polynomial by a binomial.]**
>
> **Q** How are long division and synthetic division different? **[Synthetic division can only be performed on a linear binomial factor, whereas long division can be used to divide any two polynomials.]**
>
> **Q** What is an example of polynomial division that can be performed using synthetic division? that cannot be performed using synthetic division? **[Answers may vary. Samples: $3x^2 + 2x + 1$ divided by $x + 2$; $6x^2 + 2x - 1$ divided by $x^2 - 1$]**

 Lesson Check

Do you know HOW?

Divide using any method.

1. $(2x^2 + 7x + 11) \div (x + 2)$

2. $(x^3 + 5x^2 + 11x + 15) \div (x + 3)$

3. $(x^3 - x^2 - 4x + 4) \div (x - 2)$

4. $(4x^3 + 21x^2 - x - 24) \div (x + 5)$

5. $(9x^3 - 15x^2 + 4x) \div (x - 3)$

Do you UNDERSTAND?  MATHEMATICAL PRACTICES

6. **Reasoning** A polynomial $P(x)$ is divided by a binomial $x - a$. The remainder is 0. What conclusion can you draw? Explain.

7. **Writing** Explain why it is important to have the terms of both polynomials written in descending order of degree before dividing.

8. **Open-Ended** Write a polynomial division that has a quotient of $x + 3$ and a remainder of 2.

 Practice and Problem-Solving Exercises MATHEMATICAL PRACTICES

A Practice

Divide using long division. Check your answers. ◀ **See Problem 1.**

9. $(x^2 - 3x - 40) \div (x + 5)$

10. $(3x^2 + 7x - 20) \div (x + 4)$

11. $(x^3 + 3x^2 - x + 2) \div (x - 1)$

12. $(2x^3 - 3x^2 - 18x - 8) \div (x - 4)$

13. $(3x^3 + 9x^2 + 8x + 4) \div (x + 2)$

14. $(9x^2 - 21x - 20) \div (x - 1)$

15. $(x^2 - 7x + 10) \div (x + 3)$

16. $(x^3 - 13x - 12) \div (x - 4)$

Determine whether each binomial is a factor of $x^3 + 4x^2 + x - 6$. ◀ **See Problem 2.**

17. $x + 1$ 18. $x + 2$ 19. $x + 3$ 20. $x - 3$

Divide using synthetic division. ◀ **See Problem 3.**

21. $(x^3 + 3x^2 - x - 3) \div (x - 1)$

22. $(x^3 - 4x^2 + 6x - 4) \div (x - 2)$

23. $(x^3 - 7x^2 - 7x + 20) \div (x + 4)$

24. $(x^3 - 3x^2 - 5x - 25) \div (x - 5)$

25. $(x^2 + 3) \div (x - 1)$

26. $(3x^3 + 17x^2 + 21x - 9) \div (x + 3)$

27. $(x^3 + 27) \div (x + 3)$

28. $(6x^2 - 8x - 2) \div (x - 1)$

Use synthetic division and the given factor to completely factor each polynomial function. ◀ **See Problem 4.**

29. $y = x^3 + 2x^2 - 5x - 6; (x + 1)$

30. $y = x^3 - 4x^2 - 9x + 36; (x + 3)$

31. **Geometry** The volume, in cubic inches, of the decorative box shown can be expressed as the product of the lengths of its sides as $V(x) = x^3 + x^2 - 6x$. What linear expressions with integer coefficients represent the length and height of the box?

x

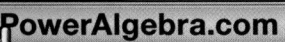 PowerAlgebra.com

3 Lesson Check

For a digital lesson check, use the Got It questions.

Support in Algebra 2 Companion
• Lesson Check

4 Practice

Assign homework to individual students or to an entire class.

Answers

Lesson Check

1. $2x + 3$, R 5
2. $x^2 + 2x + 5$
3. $x^2 + x - 2$
4. $4x^2 + x - 6$, R 26
5. $9x^2 + 12x + 40$, R 120
6. $x - a$ is a factor of $P(x)$.
7. The polynomials need to be written in standard form since the leading coefficient of both polynomials determines the leading term of the quotient.
8. Check students' work.

Practice and Problem-Solving Exercises

9. $x - 8$
10. $3x - 5$
11. $x^2 + 4x + 3$, R 5
12. $2x^2 + 5x + 2$
13. $3x^2 + 3x + 2$
14. $9x - 12$, R -32
15. $x - 10$, R 40
16. $x^2 + 4x + 3$
17. no
18. yes
19. yes
20. no
21. $x^2 + 4x + 3$
22. $x^2 - 2x + 2$
23. $x^2 - 11x + 37$, R -128
24. $x^2 + 2x + 5$
25. $x + 1$, R 4
26. $3x^2 + 8x - 3$
27. $x^2 - 3x + 9$
28. $6x - 2$, R -4
29. $y = (x + 1)(x + 3)(x - 2)$
30. $y = (x + 3)(x - 4)(x - 3)$
31. width = x; length = $x + 3$; height = $x - 2$

Use synthetic division and the Remainder Theorem to find $P(a)$. ◀ See Problem 5.

32. $P(x) = x^3 + 4x^2 - 8x - 6; a = -2$

33. $P(x) = x^3 + 4x^2 + 4x; a = -2$

34. $P(x) = x^3 - 7x^2 + 15x - 9; a = 3$

35. $P(x) = x^3 + 7x^2 + 4x; a = -2$

36. $P(x) = 6x^3 - x^2 + 4x + 3; a = 3$

37. $P(x) = 2x^3 - x^2 + 10x + 5; a = \frac{1}{2}$

38. $P(x) = 2x^3 + 4x^2 - 10x - 9; a = 3$

39. $P(x) = 2x^4 + 6x^3 + 5x^2 - 45; a = -3$

B Apply

© 40. Think About a Plan Your friend multiplies $x + 4$ by a quadratic polynomial and gets the result $x^3 - 3x^2 - 24x + 30$. The teacher says that everything is correct except for the constant term. Find the quadratic polynomial that your friend used. What is the correct result of multiplication?
- What does the fact that all the terms except for the constant are correct tell you?
- How can polynomial division help you solve this problem?
- What is the connection between the remainder of the division and your friend's error?

© 41. Error Analysis A student used synthetic division to divide $x^3 - x^2 - 2x$ by $x + 1$. Describe and correct the error shown.

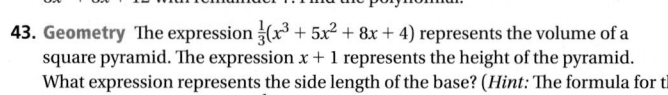

© 42. Reasoning When a polynomial is divided by $(x - 5)$, the quotient is $5x^2 + 3x + 12$ with remainder 7. Find the polynomial.

43. Geometry The expression $\frac{1}{3}(x^3 + 5x^2 + 8x + 4)$ represents the volume of a square pyramid. The expression $x + 1$ represents the height of the pyramid. What expression represents the side length of the base? (*Hint:* The formula for the volume of a pyramid is $V = \frac{1}{3}Bh$.)

Divide.

44. $(2x^3 + 9x^2 + 14x + 5) \div (2x + 1)$

45. $(x^4 + 3x^2 + x + 4) \div (x + 3)$

46. $(x^5 + 1) \div (x + 1)$

47. $(x^4 + 4x^3 - x - 4) \div (x^3 - 1)$

48. $(3x^4 - 5x^3 + 2x^2 + 3x - 2) \div (3x - 2)$

Determine whether each binomial is a factor of $x^3 + x^2 - 16x - 16$.

49. $x + 2$ **50.** $x - 4$ **51.** $x + 1$ **52.** $x - 1$

Use synthetic division to determine whether each binomial is a factor of $3x^3 + 10x^2 - x - 12$.

53. $x + 3$ **54.** $x - 1$ **55.** $x + 2$ **56.** $x - 4$

Divide using synthetic division.

57. $(x^4 - 2x^3 + x^2 + x - 1) \div (x - 1)$

58. $(x^4 + 3x^3 + 3x^2 + 4x + 3) \div (x + 1)$

59. $(x^4 + 3x^3 + 7x^2 + 26x + 15) \div (x + 3)$

60. $(x^4 - 6x^2 - 27) \div (x + 2)$

61. $(x^4 - 5x^2 + 4x + 12) \div (x + 2)$

62. $\left(x^4 - \frac{9}{2}x^3 + 3x^2 - \frac{1}{2}x\right) \div \left(x - \frac{1}{2}\right)$

4 Practice

ASSIGNMENT GUIDE

Basic: 9–39 all, 40, 41, 43, 48, 50

Average: 9–39 odd, 40–62

Advanced: 9–39 odd, 40–66

Standardized Test Prep: 67–70

Mixed Review: 71–85

© Mathematical Practices are supported by exercises with red headings. Here are the Practices supported in this lesson:

MP 1: Make Sense of Problems Ex. 40
MP 2: Reason Abstractly Ex. 42, 64
MP 3: Communicate Ex. 7, 8, 66
MP 3: Construct Arguments Ex. 6
MP 3: Critique the Reasoning of Others Ex. 41
MP 7: Look for Patterns Ex. 63

Applications exercises have blue headings.

EXERCISE 43: Use the Think About a Plan worksheet in the **Practice and Problem Solving Workbook** (also available in the Teaching Resources in print and online) to further support students' development in becoming independent learners.

HOMEWORK QUICK CHECK

To check students' understanding of key skills and concepts, go over Exercises 13, 29, 40, 41, and 43.

---

32. 18

33. 0

34. 0

35. 12

36. 168

37. 10

38. 51

39. 0

40. $x^2 - 7x + 4; x^3 - 3x^2 - 24x + 16$

41. There are 2 errors. The constant term of the dividend is missing and the divisor is -1 *not* 1:
$x^3 - x^2 - 2x = (x + 1)(x^2 - 2x)$
$= x(x + 1)(x - 2)$

42. $5x^3 - 22x^2 - 3x - 53$

43. $x + 2$

44. $x^2 + 4x + 5$

45. $x^3 - 3x^2 + 12x - 35$, R 109

46. $x^4 - x^3 + x^2 - x + 1$

47. $x + 4$

48. $x^3 - x^2 + 1$

49. no

50. yes

51. yes

52. no

53. yes

54. yes

55. no

56. no

57. $x^3 - x^2 + 1$

58. $x^3 + 2x^2 + x + 3$

59. $x^3 + 7x + 5$

60. $x^3 - 2x^2 - 2x + 4$, R -35

61. $x^3 - 2x^2 - x + 6$

62. $x^3 - 4x^2 + x$

Answers

Practice and Problem-Solving Exercises
(continued)

63. a. $x + 1$

  b. $x^2 + x + 1$

  c. $x^3 + x^2 + x + 1$

  d. $(x - 1)(x^4 + x^3 + x^2 + x + 1)$

64. 1

65. $x + 2i$

66. negative

Standardized Test Prep

67. D

68. I

69. A

70. [4] $\pi r^2 = A$

$$r^2 = \frac{A}{\pi}$$

$$r = \sqrt{\frac{A}{\pi}}$$

$$r = \sqrt{\frac{(78.5)}{3.14}} = \sqrt{25}$$

$$r = 5 \text{ cm}$$

  [3] appropriate methods, but with one computational error

  [2] solved for r incorrectly, radius found appropriately, given previous results

  [1] correct equation and radius, without work shown

Mixed Review

71. $0, -1$

72. $0, 1$

73. $-5, 0, 5$

74. $\dfrac{-3 \pm \sqrt{17}}{2}$

75. $-1 \pm \sqrt{3}$

76. $1, -\dfrac{5}{7}$

77. $\dfrac{5 \pm \sqrt{5}}{2}$

78. $3 \pm \sqrt{2}$

79. $\dfrac{-7 \pm \sqrt{5}}{2}$

80.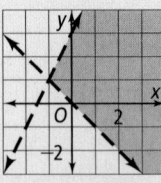

81.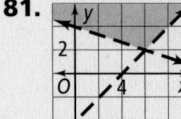

Challenge

63. Reasoning Divide. Look for patterns in your answers.

  a. $(x^2 - 1) \div (x - 1)$ **b.** $(x^3 - 1) \div (x - 1)$ **c.** $(x^4 - 1) \div (x - 1)$

  d. Using the patterns, factor $x^5 - 1$.

64. Reasoning The remainder from the division of the polynomial $x^3 + ax^2 + 2ax + 5$ by $x + 1$ is 3. Find a.

65. Use synthetic division to find $(x^2 + 4) \div (x - 2i)$.

66. Writing Suppose 3, -1, and 5 are zeros of a cubic polynomial function $f(x)$. What is the sign of $f(1) \cdot f(4)$? (*Hint:* Sketch the graph; consider all possibilities.)

Standardized Test Prep

SAT/ACT

67. What is the remainder when $x^2 - 5x + 7$ is divided by $x + 1$?

  Ⓐ 1   Ⓑ 3   Ⓒ 11   Ⓓ 13

68. What is the least degree of a polynomial that has a zero of multiplicity 3 at 1, a zero of multiplicity 1 at 0, and a zero of multiplicity 2 at 2?

  Ⓕ 3   Ⓖ 4   Ⓗ 5   Ⓘ 6

69. The equation $y = 0.17x$ represents your weight, in pounds, on the Moon y in relation to your weight on Earth x. If Al weighs 130 lb on Earth, what would he weigh on the Moon?

  Ⓐ 22.1 lb   Ⓑ 92.3 lb   Ⓒ 130 lb   Ⓓ 764.7 lb

Extended Response

70. The formula for the area of a circle is $A = \pi r^2$. Solve the equation for r. If the area of a circle is 78.5 cm², what is the radius? Use 3.14 for π.

Mixed Review

Find the real solutions of each equation by factoring.   ◀ See Lesson 5-3.

71. $x^3 + 2x^2 + x = 0$ **72.** $2x^4 - 2x^3 + 2x^2 = 2x$ **73.** $5x^5 = 125x^3$

Solve each equation using the Quadratic Formula.   ◀ See Lesson 4-7.

74. $x^2 + 3x - 2 = 0$ **75.** $2x^2 + 4x - 4 = 0$ **76.** $7x^2 - 2x - 5 = 0$

77. $x^2 - 5x = -5$ **78.** $x^2 - 6x = -7$ **79.** $x^2 + 7x + 11 = 0$

Find the solution of each system by graphing.   ◀ See Lesson 3-3.

80. $\begin{cases} y < 2x + 3 \\ y > -x \end{cases}$ **81.** $\begin{cases} y > x - 4 \\ y > 4 - \frac{1}{3}x \end{cases}$ **82.** $\begin{cases} y < -|x| + 3 \\ y > x + 1 \end{cases}$

Get Ready!   **To prepare for Lesson 5-5, do Exercises 83–85.**

Simplify each expression.   ◀ See Lesson 4-8.

83. $(-4i)(6i)$ **84.** $(2 + i)(2 - i)$ **85.** $(4 - 3i)(5 + i)$

82.

83. 24

84. 5

85. $23 - 11i$

Additional Instructional Support

Algebra 2 Companion

Students can use the **Algebra 2 Companion** worktext (4 pages) as you teach the lesson. Use the Companion to support

- New Vocabulary
- Key Concepts
- Got It for each Problem
- Lesson Check

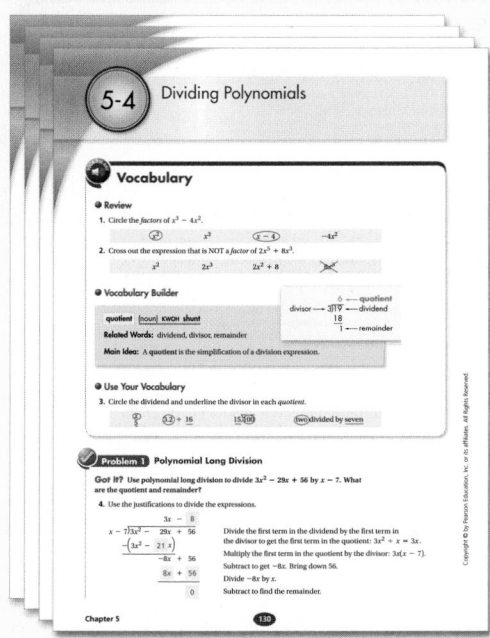

ELL Support

Focus on Communication Divide the class into pairs. Give each pair of students a synthetic division problem. Have the students work them out together in the following manner: One student explicitly states the steps to be taken and why, and the other student does the writing. When they finish, they reverse roles with another problem.

5 Assess & Remediate

Lesson Quiz

1. Use polynomial long division to divide $2x^2 + 3x - 1$ by $x + 4$. What are the quotient and remainder?

2. Is $x^2 - 1$ a factor of $P(x) = 2x^4 + 7$? If it is, write $P(x)$ as a product of two factors.

3. Use synthetic division to divide $x^3 - 3x^2 + x - 8$ by $x - 1$. What are the quotient and the remainder?

4. **Do you UNDERSTAND?** The polynomial $x^3 + 12x^2 + 39x + 28$ expresses the volume, in cubic inches, of a box, and the length is $(x + 7)$ inches. What are the other dimensions of the box?

5. Given that $P(x) = x^5 - 3x^3 - x^2 + 1$, what is $P(2)$?

ANSWERS TO LESSON QUIZ

1. $2x - 5$, R19

2. $x^2 - 1$ is not a factor.

3. The quotient is $x^2 - 2x - 1$, R -9.

4. $(x + 1)$ and $(x + 4)$

5. 5

PRESCRIPTION FOR REMEDIATION

Use the student work on the Lesson Quiz to prescribe a differentiated review assignment:

Points	Differentiated Remediation
0–2	Intervention
3–4	On-level
5	Extension

PowerAlgebra.com

5 Assess & Remediate

Assign the Lesson Quiz. Appropriate intervention, practice, or enrichment is automatically generated based on student performance.

Differentiated Remediation

Available in editable format online.

Intervention

- **Reteaching** (2 pages) Provides reteaching and practice exercises for the key lesson concepts. Use with struggling students or absent students.

- **English Language Learner Support** Helps students develop and reinforce mathematical vocabulary and key concepts.

All-in-One Resources/Online
Reteaching

5-4 Reteaching
Dividing Polynomials

All-in-One Resources/Online
English Language Learner Support

5-4 Additional Vocabulary Support
Dividing Polynomials

Differentiated Remediation *continued*

Available in editable format online.

On-Level

- **Practice** (2 pages) Provides extra practice for each lesson. For simpler practice exercises, use the Form K Practice pages found in the All-in-One Teaching Resources and online.

- **Think About a Plan** Helps students develop specific problem-solving skills and strategies by providing scaffolded guiding questions.
- **Standardized Test Prep** Focuses on all major exercises, all major question types, and helps students prepare for the high-stakes assessments.

Extension

- **Enrichment** Provides students with interesting problems and activities that extend the concepts of the lesson.
- **Activities, Games, and Puzzles** Worksheets that can be used for concepts development, enrichment, and for fun!

Practice and Problem Solving Wkbk/ All-in-One Resources/Online
Practice page 1

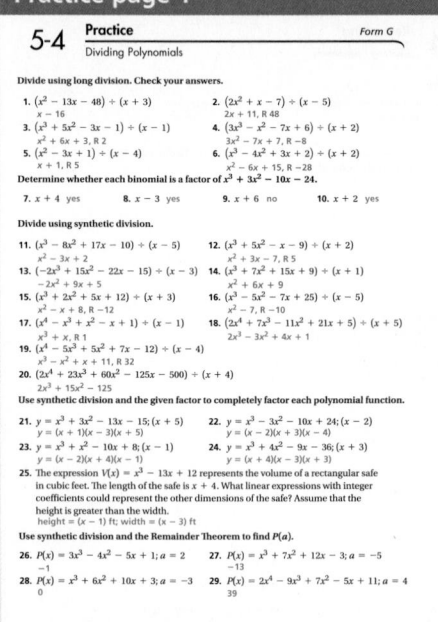

Practice and Problem Solving Wkbk/ All-in-One Resources/Online
Practice page 2

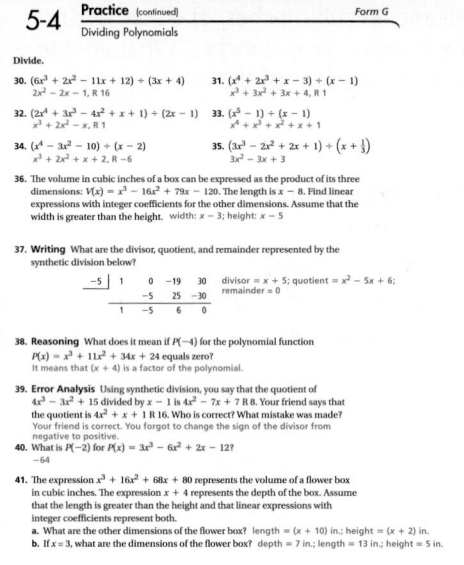

All-in-One Resources/Online
Enrichment

5-4 Enrichment — Dividing Polynomials

Practice and Problem Solving Wkbk/ All-in-One Resources/Online
Think About a Plan

5-4 Think About a Plan — Dividing Polynomials

Geometry The expression $\frac{1}{3}(x^3 + 5x^2 + 8x + 4)$ represents the volume of a square pyramid. The exercise $x + 1$ represents the height of the pyramid. What expression represents the side length of the base? (*Hint:* The formula for the volume of a pyramid is $V = \frac{1}{3}Bh$.)

Understanding the Problem

1. What expression represents the height of the pyramid? $x + 1$

2. What does B represent in the formula for the volume of a pyramid?
   the area of the base of the pyramid

3. What is the problem asking you to determine?
   the side length of the base of the pyramid

Planning the Solution

4. How can you find an expression that represents B?
   Factor $\frac{1}{3}$ and $(x + 1)$ out of the expression for the volume. The remaining expression represents B

5. How can polynomial division help you solve this problem?
   Divide the expression for the volume by $(x + 1)$ to find another factor of the expression

6. How can you find the side length of the base once you find an expression for B?
   The base is square because the pyramid is a square pyramid. The side length is $\sqrt{B}$

Getting an Answer

7. What expression represents B, the area of the base? $x^2 + 4x + 4$

8. What expression represents the side length of the base? $x + 2$

Practice and Problem Solving Wkbk/ All-in-One Resources/Online
Standardized Test Prep

5-4 Standardized Test Prep — Dividing Polynomials

Gridded Response

Solve each exercise and enter your answer in the grid provided.

1. What is $P(-2)$ given that $P(x) = x^4 - 3x^2 + 5x + 10$?

2. What is the missing value in the following synthetic division?

$$\begin{array}{c|cccc} -4 & 1 & 0 & -5 & 4 & 12 \\ & & -4 & & -44 & 160 \\ \hline & 1 & -4 & 11 & -40 & 172 \end{array}$$

3. What is the remainder when $x^6 - 4x^4 + 4x^2 - 10$ is divided by $x + 3$?

4. How many unique factors does $x^4 + 4x^3 - 3x^2 - 14x - 8$ have, including $(x + 4)$?

5. How many terms are there in the simplified form of $\frac{x^4 - 2x^3 - 23x^2 - 12x + 36}{x - 6}$?

Answers

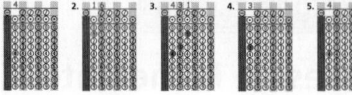

Online Teacher Resource Center
Activities, Games, and Puzzles

5-4 Activity: Researching the Factors — Dividing Polynomials

Work in small groups for this activity.

The polynomial $P(x) = x^4 + 3x^3 - 28x^2 + 20x + 48$ can be factored into exactly four distinct linear factors involving real numbers only. Write the polynomial in factored form $P(x) = (x - a)(x - b)(x - c)(x - d)$.

Notice that when the value of a polynomial changes from negative to positive (or from positive to negative) there is a root in between, as shown in the example at the right.

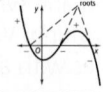

- Complete the following table to help find possible values for the roots of the polynomial.

x	-7	-5	-3	0	3	5	7
$P(x) = x^4 + x^3 - 28x^2 + 20x + 48$	594	-252	-210	48	-36	198	1560

- $P(x) = (x - a)(x - b)(x - c)(x - d)$. Devise a plan to find a, b, c, and d. Describe your plan in writing. Some possible strategies are shown at the right. Consider the advantages and disadvantages of each approach. Explore the use of repeated synthetic division on successive quotients.
  - Guess and Check
  - Synthetic Division
  - Graph and Check
  - Factoring

  Answers may vary. Sample: From the table, there is a root between -7 and -5. Try -6. There is a root between -3 and 0. Try -2 and -1. There is a root between 0 and 3. Try 1 and 2. There is a root between 3 and 5. Try 4. Use substitution to test different possibilities. $P(-6) = 0$ and $P(4) = 0$. Two of the four roots are -6 and 4.

- Write the polynomial in factored form. Show your group's work with your plan. You may use a combination of methods.
  Answers may vary. Sample:
  $P(x) = (x + 6)(x - 4)(x - 2)(x + 1)$

Wrap Up

Summarize your results in a complete logical and informative solution.
Answers may vary. Sample: A good solution should show how each of the four roots are found and should give a reason for each step along the way.

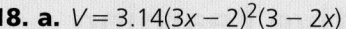 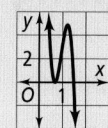
Do you know HOW?

For each polynomial function, describe the end behavior of its graph.

1. $f(x) = x^8 - 8x^4 + 6x^2$

2. $f(x) = -x^4 - x^3 + 1$

3. $f(x) = x^7 - 3x^5 - 5x^3$

4. What is the degree of the function that generates the data shown?

x	y
−3	159
−2	29
−1	−1
0	−3
1	−1
2	29
3	159

Find all the solutions of each equation by factoring.

5. $x^3 - 5x^2 = 36x$

6. $27x^3 = 8$

7. $x^4 - 20x^2 + 64 = 0$

8. $x^3 + 125 = 0$

9. Use the Remainder Theorem and synthetic division to find $P(4)$ for $P(x) = 2x^4 - 3x^2 + 4x - 1$.

You have several boxes with the same dimensions. They have a combined volume of $2x^4 + 4x^3 - 18x^2 - 4x + 16$. Determine whether each binomial below could represent the number of boxes you have.

10. $x - 1$

11. $x + 2$

12. $2x + 8$

Write each polynomial in standard form. Then classify it by degree and number of terms.

13. $-2x^3 + 6 - x^3 + 5x$

14. $3(x - 1)(x + 4)$

Describe the shape of the graph of each cubic function by determining the end behavior and number of turning points.

15. $y = -5x^3$

16. $y = 3x^3 + 4x^2 + 2x - 1$

Do you UNDERSTAND?

17. You buy one container each of strawberries, blueberries, and cherries. Cherries are $1 more per container than blueberries, which are $1 more per container than strawberries. The product of the 3 individual prices is 5 times the total cost of one container of each fruit.
  a. Write a polynomial function to model the cost of your purchase.
  b. Graph to find the price of each container.
  c. **Writing** Explain how you used the graph to find the prices.

18. A cylinder has a radius of $3x - 2$ and a height of $3 - 2x$.
  a. Use 3.14 as π and graph the equation for the volume.
  b. Find the relative maximum.
  c. **Reasoning** What kind of limitation on the radius would make your answer in part (b) the maximum possible volume?

19. **Open-Ended** Write a polynomial function in factored form with at least three zeros that are negative, one of which has multiplicity 2.

18. a. $V = 3.14(3x - 2)^2(3 - 2x)$

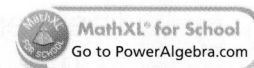

b. $(1.22, 4.85)$

c. $x \geq \dfrac{2}{3}$

19. Answers may vary. Sample:
$f(x) = (x + 1)(x + 2)(x + 3)^2$

Answers

1. up and up

2. down and down

3. down and up

4. 4

5. −4, 0, 9

6. $\dfrac{2}{3}, \dfrac{-1 \pm i\sqrt{3}}{3}$

7. ±4, ±2

8. −5, $\dfrac{5 \pm 5i\sqrt{3}}{2}$

9. 479

10. yes

11. no

12. yes

13. $-3x^3 + 5x + 6$; cubic trinomial

14. $3x^2 + 9x - 12$; quadratic trinomial

15. up and down; no turning pts.

16. down and up; no turning pts.

17. a. $P(x) = x^3 + 3x^2 - 13x - 15$

  b. strawberries: $3; blueberries: $4; cherries: $5

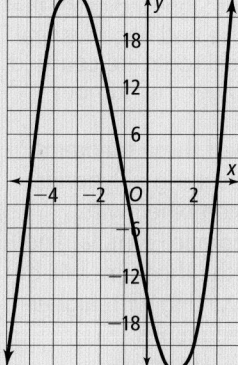

  c. The positive zero ($x = 3$) of the function in part (a) is the solution.

1 Interactive Learning

Solve It!

PURPOSE To use factors to solve a puzzle
PROCESS Students may
- list the factors of 6 and 4.
- find fractions whose sum of the numerator and denominator is 5.
- test each fraction to see if it is greater than its square.

FACILITATE

Q What are the factors of 6? [± 1, ± 2, ± 3, ± 6]

Q What are the factors of 4? [± 1, ± 2, ± 4]

Q Following the clues, what fractions can you write whose numerator and denominator add to 5? [$\frac{1}{4}$, $\frac{3}{2}$, $\frac{6}{-1}$]

Q Which fraction is greater than its square? [$\frac{1}{4}$]

ANSWER See Solve It in Answers on next page.
CONNECT THE MATH Students use factors to solve the Solve It. In this lesson students will apply the Rational Root Theorem using factors to generate possible rational roots of a polynomial equation.

2 Guided Instruction

Take Note
ERROR PREVENTION

The Rational Root Theorem does not necessarily give the zeros of the equation. It provides a list of first guesses to test as roots.

 **5-5**

Theorems About Roots of Polynomial Equations

Common Core State Standards
N-CN.C.7 Solve quadratic equations with real coefficients that have complex solutions. **Also N-CN.C.8**
MP 1, MP 2, MP 3, MP 4, MP 8

Objectives To solve equations using the Rational Root Theorem
To use the Conjugate Root Theorem

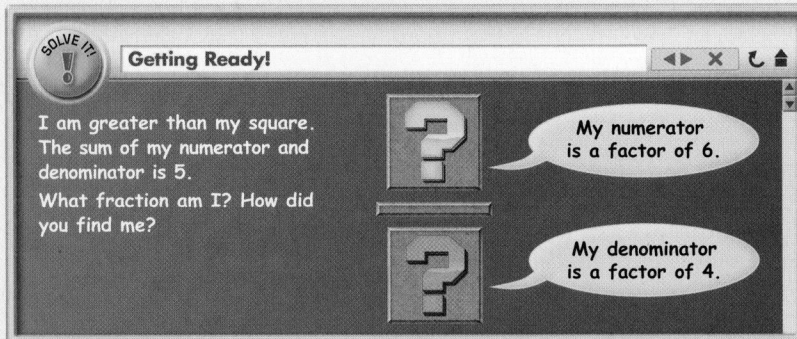

Lesson Vocabulary
- Rational Root Theorem
- Conjugate Root Theorem
- Descartes' Rule of Signs

Factoring the polynomial $P(x) = a_n x^n + a_{n-1}x^{n-1} + \cdots + a_1 x + a_0$ can be challenging, especially when both a_n and a_0 have many factors.

Essential Understanding The factors of the numbers a_n and a_0 in $P(x) = a_n x^n + a_{n-1}x^{n-1} + \cdots + a_1 x + a_0$ can help you factor $P(x)$ and solve the equation $P(x) = 0$.

One way to find a root of the polynomial equation $P(x) = 0$ is to guess and check. This is inefficient unless there is a way to minimize the number of guesses, or possible roots. The **Rational Root Theorem** does just that.

---

take note

Theorem   Rational Root Theorem

Let $P(x) = a_n x^n + a_{n-1}x^{n-1} + \cdots + a_1 x + a_0$ be a polynomial with integer coefficients. There are a limited number of possible roots of $P(x) = 0$:
- Integer roots must be factors of a_0.
- Rational roots must have reduced form $\frac{p}{q}$ where p is an integer factor of a_0 and q is an integer factor of a_n.

Factors of the leading coefficient:
± 1, ± 3, ± 7, and ± 21.

$21x^2 + 29x + 10 = 0$

$x^2 + \frac{29}{21}x + \frac{10}{21} = 0$

$\left(x + \frac{2}{3}\right)\left(x + \frac{5}{7}\right) = 0$

Factors of the constant term: ± 1, ± 2, ± 5, and ± 10.

The roots are $-\frac{2}{3}$ and $-\frac{5}{7}$.

BIG ideas **Solving Equations and Inequalities**
Equivalence

ESSENTIAL UNDERSTANDINGS
- The factors of the numbers a_n and a_0 in $P(x) = a_n x^n + a_{n-1}x^{n-1} + \ldots a_1 x + a_0$ can be used to factor $P(x)$ and solve the equation $P(x) = 0$.
- $(x - a)$ is linear factor if and only if a is a root of the related polynomial equation.

Math Background

When used together, the Rational Root Theorem, the Conjugate Root Theorem, and Descartes' Rule of Signs are powerful tools to solve polynomial equations.
- The Rational Root Theorem creates a finite list of possible rational roots of a polynomial equation with rational coefficients.
- The Conjugate Root Theorem is helpful when the polynomial equation has irrational or imaginary roots. Once an irrational or imaginary root is

found, remaining members of the conjugate pairs can be stated. This theorem gives a way to generate remaining roots for many polynomials with rational or real coefficents.
- Descartes' Rule of Signs indicates the number of positive and negative real roots. Multiple real roots are counted multiple times to get the number of roots.

Therefore, the use of these theorems is important when solving polynomial equations. When combined with factoring, the Quadratic Formula, and synthetic division, the theorems will be invaluable when working with higher-order polynomial equations.

Mathematical Practices
Look for and express regularity in repeated reasoning. Students will utilize the Rational Root Theorem and Conjugate Root Theorem to find general methods to determine roots that are not integers.

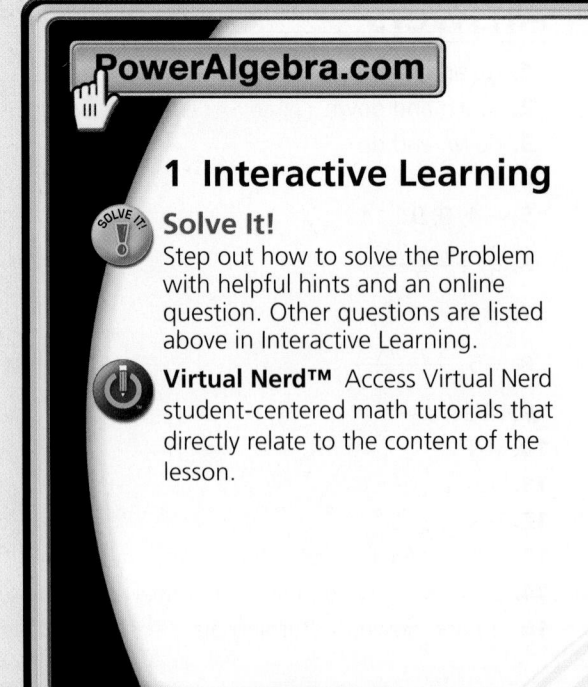

PowerAlgebra.com

1 Interactive Learning

Solve It!
Step out how to solve the Problem with helpful hints and an online question. Other questions are listed above in Interactive Learning.

Virtual Nerd™ Access Virtual Nerd student-centered math tutorials that directly relate to the content of the lesson.

Plan

What information can you get from the equation?
The equation gives you the leading coefficient and the constant term.

 Problem 1 Finding a Rational Root

What are the rational roots of $2x^3 - x^2 + 2x + 5 = 0$?

The only possible rational roots have the form $\dfrac{\text{factor of constant term}}{\text{factor of leading coefficient}}$.

The constant factors are ± 1, ± 5. The leading coefficient factors are ± 1, ± 2.
The only possible rational roots are ± 1, ± 5, $\pm\frac{1}{2}$, $\pm\frac{5}{2}$.

The table shows the values of the function $y = P(x)$ for the possible roots.

x	1	-1	5	-5	$\frac{1}{2}$	$-\frac{1}{2}$	$\frac{5}{2}$	$-\frac{5}{2}$
$P(x)$	8	0	240	-280	6	$\frac{7}{2}$	35	$-\frac{75}{2}$

The only rational root of $2x^3 - x^2 + 2x + 5 = 0$ is -1.

 Got It? 1. What are the rational roots of $3x^3 + 7x^2 + 6x - 8 = 0$?

Once you find one root, use synthetic division to factor the polynomial. Continue finding roots and dividing until you have a second-degree polynomial. Use the Quadratic Formula to find the remaining roots.

 Problem 2 Using the Rational Root Theorem

What are the rational roots of $15x^3 - 32x^2 + 3x + 2 = 0$?

Know	Need	Plan
Coefficients and the constant term of the polynomial	The roots of the polynomial equation	• Find one root. • Factor until you get a quadratic. • Use the Quadratic Formula to find the other roots.

Step 1 The constant term factors are ± 1 and ± 2. The leading coefficient factors are ± 1, ± 3, ± 5, and ± 15.

Step 2 The possible rational roots are: ± 1, ± 2, $\pm\frac{1}{3}$, $\pm\frac{2}{3}$, $\pm\frac{1}{5}$, $\pm\frac{2}{5}$, $\pm\frac{1}{15}$, and $\pm\frac{2}{15}$.

Step 3 Test each possible rational root in $15x^3 - 32x^2 + 3x + 2$ until you find a root.
Test 1: $15(1)^3 - 32(1)^2 + 3(1) + 2 = -12 \neq 0$
Test 2: $15(2)^3 - 32(2)^2 + 3(2) + 2 = 0$ So 2 is a root.

Step 4 Factor the polynomial by using synthetic division:
$P(x) = (x - 2)(15x^2 - 2x - 1)$.

$$\begin{array}{r|rrrr} 2 & 15 & -32 & 3 & 2 \\ & & 30 & -4 & -2 \\ \hline & 15 & -2 & -1 & 0 \end{array}$$

Step 5 Since $15x^2 - 2x - 1 = (5x + 1)(3x - 1)$, the other roots are $-\frac{1}{5}$ and $\frac{1}{3}$.

The rational roots of $15x^3 - 32x^2 + 3x + 2 = 0$ are 2, $-\frac{1}{5}$, and $\frac{1}{3}$.

 Got It? 2. What are the rational roots of $2x^3 + x^2 - 7x - 6 = 0$?

Problem 1   SYNTHESIZING

Q What can you conclude about the roots of the polynomial function if $P(x) \neq 0$ for all possible rational roots? **[The polynomial function has no rational roots, but it may have imaginary, complex, or irrational roots.]**

Got It?   SYNTHESIZING

Q How many possible rational roots are there? **[16]**

Problem 2   SYNTHESIZING

Q What is an advantage of combining the theorem with synthetic division? **[Answers may vary. Sample: It may save time, especially if the remaining quadratic polynomial is factorable.]**

Q If the remaining polynomial is not factorable, what techniques could be used to find the remaining roots? **[The Quadratic Formula could be used on a quadratic, or you could use a calculator.]**

Got It?   ERROR PREVENTION

Q What possible roots would you substitute in first? Explain. **[Answers may vary. Sample: 1 and -1, since they are the easiest to calculate.]**

Q How could you use your calculator to make the substitution accurate? **[On the TI-84 or TI-85, store the polynomial in Y_1 using the Y = menu. Store the root to be tested in x. Use VARS→Y−VARS→ 1: Function Y_1 to evaluate.]**

---

2 Guided Instruction

Each Problem is worked out and supported online.

Problem 1
Finding a Rational Root
Animated

Problem 2
Using the Rational Root Theorem

Problem 3
Using the Conjugate Root Theorem to Identify Roots

Problem 4
Using Conjugates to Construct a Polynomial

Alternative Problem 4
Using Conjugates to Construct a Polynomial
Animated

Problem 5
Using Descartes' Rule of Signs
Animated

Support in Algebra 2 Companion
• Vocabulary
• Key Concepts
• Got It?

Answers

Solve It!

$\frac{1}{4}$ There are two pairs of numbers that have a sum of 5: 1 and 4; 2 and 3. Try each pair to see if the numbers satisfy the constraints. Only $\frac{1}{4}$ satisfies all the constraints.

Got It?

1. $\frac{2}{3}$

2. 2, -1, $-\frac{3}{2}$

Take Note

In the book, $a + bi$ is referred to as complex and bi as pure imaginary. The Conjugate Root Theorem as it applies to complex numbers is sometimes called the Imaginary Root Theorem.

Problem 3
SYNTHESIZING

Q How do you know that this polynomial function has at most 4 roots? **[It is a quartic polynomial function.]**

Q Could a third-degree polynomial function with rational coefficients have the roots $2 - i$ and $\sqrt{3}$? Why or why not? **[No; by the Conjugate Root Theorem $2 + i$ and $-\sqrt{3}$ would also have to be roots of the function. A third-degree polynomial function cannot have 4 roots.]**

Got It?
ERROR PREVENTION

Q Is $\frac{5}{2}$ part of a conjugate pair? Why or why not? **[No; $\frac{5}{2}$ is a rational root. The Conjugate Root Theorem applies to irrational and imaginary roots.]**

Problem 4
ERROR PREVENTION

Q After applying the Conjugate Root Theorem, how do you know that you have all of the roots? **[Check the degree of the polynomial function. Since the problem refers to a third-degree polynomial function and 2 roots are given, one more root is needed.]**

Got It?
ERROR PREVENTION

Q How would you write the factors of the polynomial? **[$(x - (2 - 3i))(x - (2 + 3i))(x - 8)(x - 2)$]**

Recall from Lesson 4-8 that the complex numbers $a + bi$ and $a - bi$ are conjugates. Similarly, the irrational numbers $a + \sqrt{b}$ and $a - \sqrt{b}$ are conjugates. If a complex number or an irrational number is a root of a polynomial equation with rational coefficients, so is its conjugate.

take note

Theorem Conjugate Root Theorem

If $P(x)$ is a polynomial with *rational* coefficients, then irrational roots of $P(x) = 0$ that have the form $a + \sqrt{b}$ occur in conjugate pairs. That is, if $a + \sqrt{b}$ is an irrational root with a and b rational, then $a - \sqrt{b}$ is also a root.

If $P(x)$ is a polynomial with *real* coefficients, then the complex roots of $P(x) = 0$ occur in conjugate pairs. That is, if $a + bi$ is a complex root with a and b real, then $a - bi$ is also a root.

 Problem 3 Using the Conjugate Root Theorem to Identify Roots

A quartic polynomial $P(x)$ has rational coefficients. If $\sqrt{2}$ and $1 + i$ are roots of $P(x) = 0$, what are the two other roots?

Since $P(x)$ has rational coefficients and $0 + \sqrt{2}$ is a root of $P(x) = 0$, it follows from the Conjugate Root Theorem that $0 - \sqrt{2}$ is also a root.

Since $P(x)$ has real coefficients and $1 + i$ is a root of $P(x) = 0$, it follows that $1 - i$ is also a root.

The two other roots are $-\sqrt{2}$ and $1 - i$.

Think
Do you have real coefficients?
All rational numbers are real numbers. Therefore the rational coefficients are real coefficients.

Got It? 3. A cubic polynomial $P(x)$ has real coefficients. If $3 - 2i$ and $\frac{5}{2}$ are two roots of $P(x) = 0$, what is one additional root?

 Problem 4 Using Conjugates to Construct a Polynomial

Multiple Choice What is a third-degree polynomial function $y = P(x)$ with rational coefficients so that $P(x) = 0$ has roots -4 and $2i$?

Ⓐ $P(x) = x^3 - 2x^2 - 16x + 32$ 　　Ⓒ $P(x) = x^3 + 4x^2 + 4x + 16$

Ⓑ $P(x) = x^3 - 4x^2 + 4x - 16$ 　　Ⓓ $P(x) = x^3 + 4x^2 - 4x - 16$

Think
Does the Conjugate Root Theorem apply to -4?
No; the theorem does not apply because -4 is neither irrational nor imaginary.

Since $2i$ is a root, then $-2i$ is also a root.

$P(x) = (x + 2i)(x - 2i)(x + 4)$ 　Write the polynomial function.

$\quad = (x^2 + 4)(x + 4)$ 　　　　　Multiply the complex conjugates.

$\quad = x^3 + 4x^2 + 4x + 16$ 　　　Write the polynomial function in standard form.

The equation $x^3 + 4x^2 + 4x + 16 = 0$ has rational coefficients and has roots -4 and $2i$. The correct answer is C.

Got It? 4. What quartic polynomial equation has roots $2 - 3i$, 8, 2?

Additional Problems

1. What are the rational roots of $x^3 - 5x^2 - 2x + 10 = 0$?

　ANSWER 5

2. What are the rational roots of $x^3 - 2x^2 - 5x + 6 = 0$?

　ANSWER 1, -2, 3

3. A cubic polynomial $P(x)$ has rational coefficients. If $2 + 3i$ and $\frac{2}{3}$ are two roots of $P(x) = 0$, what is one additional root?

　ANSWER $2 - 3i$

4. What is a quartic polynomial function $P(x)$ with rational coefficients so that $P(x) = 0$ has roots 1, 3, and $1 + 2i$?

　ANSWER
　$x^4 - 6x^3 + 16x^2 - 26x + 15$

5. What does Descartes' Rule of Signs tell you about the real roots of $P(x) = -x^4 + x^3 - 2x^2 + x + 1 = 0$?

　ANSWER 1 or 3 positive, 1 negative

The French mathematician René Descartes (1596–1650) recognized a connection between the roots of a polynomial equation and the + and − signs of the standard form.

 take note

Theorem   Descartes' Rule of Signs

Let $P(x)$ be a polynomial with real coefficients written in standard form.

- The number of positive real roots of $P(x) = 0$ is either equal to the number of sign changes between consecutive coefficients of $P(x)$ or is less than that by an even number.
- The number of negative real roots of $P(x) = 0$ is either equal to the number of sign changes between consecutive coefficients of $P(-x)$ or is less than that by an even number.

In both cases, count multiple roots according to their multiplicity.

Problem 5   Using Descartes' Rule of Signs

What does Descartes' Rule of Signs tell you about the real roots of $x^3 - x^2 + 1 = 0$?

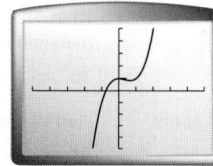

There are two sign changes, + to − and − to +.
Therefore, there are either 0 or 2 positive real roots.

$P(-x) = (-x)^3 - (-x)^2 + 1 = -x^3 - x^2 + 1 = 0$ has only one sign change − to +. There is one negative real root.

Recall that graphs of cubic functions have zero or two turning points. Because the graph already shows two turning points, it will not change direction again. So there are no positive real roots.

 Think

Why can't there be zero negative real roots?
The number of negative roots is equal to 1 or is less than 1 by an even number. Zero is less than 1 by an odd number.

✓ **Got It?**   **5. a.** What does Descartes' Rule of Signs tell you about the real roots of
$2x^4 - x^3 + 3x^2 - 1 = 0$?
b. Reasoning Can you confirm real and complex roots graphically? Explain.

✓ **Lesson Check**

Do you know HOW?

Use the Rational Root Theorem to list all possible rational roots for each equation.

1. $x^2 + x - 2 = 0$

2. $2x^3 - x^2 - 6 = 0$

3. $3x^4 + 2x^2 - 12 = 0$

Write a polynomial function with rational coefficients so that $P(x) = 0$ has the given roots.

4. 5 and 9   **5.** −4 and $2i$

Do you UNDERSTAND?   MATHEMATICAL PRACTICES

6. Vocabulary Give an example of a conjugate pair.

7. Reasoning In the statements below, r and s represent integers. Is each statement *always*, *sometimes*, or *never* true? Explain.
   a. A root of the equation
   $3x^3 + rx^2 + sx + 8 = 0$ could be 5.
   b. A root of the equation
   $3x^3 + rx^2 + sx + 8 = 0$ could be −2.

8. Error Analysis A student claims that $-4i$ is the only imaginary root of a polynomial equation that has real coefficients. What is the student's mistake?

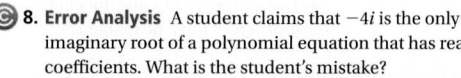 PowerAlgebra.com   Lesson 5-5   Theorems About Roots of Polynomial Equations   **315**

Take Note   SYNTHESIZING

This theorem implies that two tests must be done on a polynomial function to determine both positive and negative real roots.

Problem 5   SYNTHESIZING

Q Suppose $P(x) = x^4 - x^2 = 0$. Why does Descartes' Rule of Signs say $P(x)$ has one positive and one negative root? **[0 is neither positive nor negative.]**

Got It?   EXTENSION

Q What part of the polynomial indicates that $P(x) \neq P(-x)$? **[The odd exponent of the second term guarantees that the sign of this term will change in $P(-x)$.]**

3 Lesson Check

Do you know HOW?   ERROR INTERVENTION

- For Exercises 1–3, if students mistakenly list multiples of the same root, encourage them to simplify all roots and check that each is different.

Do you UNDERSTAND? ERROR INTERVENTION

- For Exercise 7, students must focus on the constant term and the leading coefficient. Refer to the Rational Root Theorem and Problem 1.

Close

Q What is the difference between the Rational Root Theorem and the Conjugate Root Theorem? **[The Rational Root Theorem generates a list of possible rational roots of a given polynomial function. The Conjugate Root Theorem generates additional irrational, imaginary, or complex roots when some roots are given.]**

Answers

Got It? (continued)

3. $3 + 2i$

4. $P(x) = x^4 - 14x^3 + 69x^2 - 194x + 208$

5. a. There are three or one positive real roots and one negative real root. The graph confirms one negative and one positive real root.

   b. Real roots can be confirmed graphically because they are *x*-intercepts. Complex roots cannot be confirmed graphically because they have an imaginary component.

Lesson Check

1. $\pm 1, \pm 2$

2. $\pm 1, \pm 2, \pm 3, \pm 6, \pm\frac{1}{2}, \pm\frac{3}{2}$

3. $\pm 1, \pm 2, \pm 3, \pm 4, \pm 6, \pm 12, \pm\frac{1}{3}, \pm\frac{2}{3}, \pm\frac{4}{3}$

4. $P(x) = x^2 - 14x + 45$

5. $P(x) = x^3 + 4x^2 + 4x + 16$

6. Answers may vary. Samples: $1 + 2i$ and $1 - 2i$; $1 + \sqrt{2}$ and $1 - \sqrt{2}$

7. a. never; 5 does not divide 8 evenly.
   b. always; −2 divides 8 evenly.

8. Complex number roots come in pairs; if $-4i$ is a root, so is $4i$.

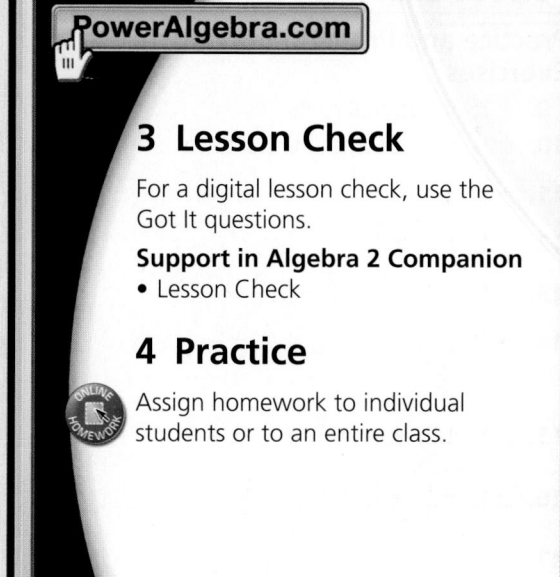

PowerAlgebra.com

3 Lesson Check

For a digital lesson check, use the Got It questions.

Support in Algebra 2 Companion
- Lesson Check

4 Practice

Assign homework to individual students or to an entire class.

4 Practice

ASSIGNMENT GUIDE

Basic: 9–32 all, 34–40 even, 42–45

Average: 9–31 odd, 33–46

Advanced: 9–31 odd, 33–49

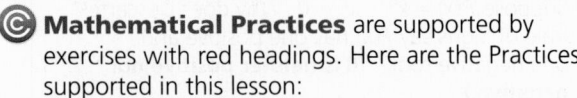 **Mathematical Practices** are supported by exercises with red headings. Here are the Practices supported in this lesson:

MP 1: Make Sense of Problems Ex. 42
MP 2: Reason Abstractly Ex. 46
MP 3: Communicate Ex. 44, 49
MP 3: Construct Arguments Ex. 44, 48c
MP 3: Compare Arguments Ex. 7
MP 3: Critique the Reasoning of Others Ex. 8, 43

Applications exercises have blue headings. Exercise 45 supports MP 4: Model.

EXERCISE 45: Use the Think About a Plan worksheet in the **Practice and Problem Solving Workbook** (also available in the Teaching Resources in print and online) to further support students' development in becoming independent learners.

HOMEWORK QUICK CHECK

To check students' understanding of key skills and concepts, go over Exercises 9, 19, 42, 44, and 45.

 Practice and Problem-Solving Exercises  MATHEMATICAL PRACTICES

 **Practice** Use the Rational Root Theorem to list all possible rational roots for each equation. Then find any actual rational roots. ◀ See Problems 1 and 2.

9. $x^3 - 4x + 1 = 0$ **10.** $x^3 + 2x - 9 = 0$ **11.** $x^3 - x^2 - 2x + 2 = 0$

12. $2x^3 + 5x^2 - 2x - 2 = 0$ **13.** $5x^3 - 6x^2 - 9x + 2 = 0$ **14.** $3x^4 - 5x^3 - 20x^2 + 6x + 4 = 0$

15. $7x^3 - 2x^2 - 14x + 4 = 0$ **16.** $8x^3 + 2x^2 - 5x + 1 = 0$ **17.** $6x^4 + 5x^3 - 20x^2 - 25x - 6 = 0$

A polynomial function $P(x)$ with rational coefficients has the given roots. Find two additional roots of $P(x) = 0$. ◀ See Problem 3.

18. $-2i$ and $\sqrt{10}$ **19.** $14 - \sqrt{2}$ and $-6i$ **20.** i and $7 + 8i$ **21.** $-\sqrt{3}$ and $5 - \sqrt{11}$

Write a polynomial function with rational coefficients so that $P(x) = 0$ has the given roots. ◀ See Problem 4.

22. 7 and 12   **23.** -9 and -15 **24.** $-10i$ **25.** $3i + 9$

26. 4, 16, and $1 + 19i$ **27.** $13i$ and $5 + 10i$ **28.** $11 - 2i$ and $8 + 13i$ **29.** $17 - 4i$ and $12 + 5i$

What does Descartes' Rule of Signs say about the number of positive real roots and negative real roots for each polynomial function? ◀ See Problem 5.

30. $P(x) = x^2 + 5x + 6$ **31.** $P(x) = 9x^3 - 4x^2 + 10$ **32.** $P(x) = 8x^3 + 2x^2 - 14x + 5$

Apply Find all rational roots for $P(x) = 0$.

33. $P(x) = 2x^3 - 5x^2 + x - 1$ **34.** $P(x) = 6x^4 - 13x^3 + 13x^2 - 39x - 15$

35. $P(x) = 7x^3 + 13x^2 - 16x + 2$ **36.** $P(x) = 3x^4 - 7x^3 + 10x^2 - x + 12$

37. $P(x) = 6x^3 + 5x^2 - 2x - 1$ **38.** $P(x) = x^3 - 10x^2 + 26x - 12$

Write a polynomial function $P(x)$ with rational coefficients so that $P(x) = 0$ has the given roots.

39. $-6, 3,$ and $-15i$ **40.** $4 + \sqrt{5}$ and $8i$ **41.** $-5 - 7i$ and $2 - \sqrt{11}$

42. Think About a Plan You are building a square pyramid out of clay and want the height to be 0.5 cm shorter than twice the length of each side of the base. If you have 18 cm³ of clay, what is the greatest height you could use for your pyramid?
- How can drawing a diagram help you solve this problem?
- What is the formula for the volume of a pyramid?
- What equation can you solve to find the height of the pyramid?

43. Error Analysis Your friend is using Descartes' Rule of Signs to find the number of negative real roots of $x^3 + x^2 + x + 1 = 0$. Describe and correct the error.

$P(-x) = (-x)^3 + (-x)^2 + (-x) + 1$
$= -x^3 - x^2 - x + 1$
Because there is only one sign change in $P(-x)$, there must be one negative real root.

44. Reasoning A quartic equation with integer coefficients has two real roots and one imaginary root. Explain why the fourth root must be imaginary.

Answers

Practice and Problem-Solving Exercises

9. ± 1; no rational roots

10. $\pm 1, \pm 3, \pm 9$; no rational roots

11. $\pm 1, \pm 2$; 1

12. $\pm 1, \pm 2, \pm \frac{1}{2}; -\frac{1}{2}$

13. $\pm 1, \pm 2, \pm \frac{1}{5}, \pm \frac{2}{5}; -1, \frac{1}{5}, 2$

14. $\pm 1, \pm 2, \pm 4, \pm \frac{1}{3}, \pm \frac{2}{3}, \pm \frac{4}{3}; -2, -\frac{1}{3}$

15. $\pm 1, \pm 2, \pm 4, \pm \frac{1}{7}, \pm \frac{2}{7}, \pm \frac{4}{7}; \frac{2}{7}$

16. $\pm 1, \pm \frac{1}{8}, \pm \frac{1}{4}, \pm \frac{1}{2}; -1, \frac{1}{4}, \frac{1}{2}$

17. $\pm 1, \pm 2, \pm 3, \pm 6, \pm \frac{1}{2}, \pm \frac{1}{3}, \pm \frac{1}{6}, \pm \frac{2}{3}, \pm \frac{3}{2}; -\frac{3}{2}, -1, -\frac{1}{3}, 2$

18. $2i, -\sqrt{10}$

19. $14 + \sqrt{2}, 6i$

20. $-i, 7 - 8i$

21. $\sqrt{3}, 5 + \sqrt{11}$

22. $P(x) = x^2 - 19x + 84$

23. $P(x) = x^2 + 24x + 135$

24. $P(x) = x^2 + 100$

25. $P(x) = x^2 - 18x + 90$

26. $P(x) = x^4 - 22x^3 + 466x^2 - 7368x + 23{,}168$

27. $P(x) = x^4 - 10x^3 + 294x^2 - 1690x + 21{,}125$

28. $P(x) = x^4 - 38x^3 + 710x^2 - 7126x + 29{,}125$

29. $P(x) = x^4 - 588x^3 + 1290x^2 - 13{,}066x + 51{,}545$

30. no positive real roots; two or no negative real roots

31. two or no positive real roots; one negative real root

32. two or no positive real roots; one negative real root

33. no rational roots

34. $\frac{5}{2}, -\frac{1}{3}$

35. $\frac{1}{7}$

36. no rational roots

37. $-1, -\frac{1}{3}, \frac{1}{2}$

38. 6

39. $P(x) = x^4 + 3x^3 + 207x^2 + 675x - 4050$

40. $P(x) = x^4 - 8x^3 + 75x^2 - 512x + 704$

41. $P(x) = x^4 + 6x^3 + 27x^2 - 366x - 518$

42. ≈ 5.67 cm

43. Error in second line, sign of second term; the line should be: $P(-1) = -x^3 + x^2 - x + 1$. Since there are three sign changes in $P(-x)$, there are three or one negative real roots.

44. Imaginary roots come in pairs; the imaginary root's conjugate is also a root.

45. Gardening A gardener is designing a new garden in the shape of a trapezoid. She wants the shorter base to be twice the height and the longer base to be 4 feet longer than the shorter base. If she has enough topsoil to create a 60 ft² garden, what dimensions should she use for the garden?

 **46. Open-Ended** Write a fourth-degree polynomial equation with integer coefficients that has two irrational roots and two imaginary roots.

 **Challenge**

47. a. Find a polynomial equation in which $1 + \sqrt{2}$ is the only root.
  b. Find a polynomial equation with root $1 + \sqrt{2}$ of multiplicity 2.
  c. Find c such that $1 + \sqrt{2}$ is a root of $x^2 - 2x + c = 0$.

48. a. Using *real* and *imaginary* as types of roots, list all possible combinations of root type for a fourth-degree polynomial equation.
  b. Repeat the process for a fifth-degree polynomial equation.
  c. Make a Conjecture Make a conjecture about the number of real roots of an odd-degree polynomial equation.

49. Writing A student states that $2 + \sqrt{3}$ is a root of $x^2 - 2x - (3 + 2\sqrt{3}) = 0$. The student claims that $2 - \sqrt{3}$ is another root of the equation by the Conjugate Root Theorem. Explain how you would respond to the student.

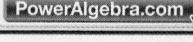

Apply What You've Learned

 MATHEMATICAL PRACTICES
MP 7

Look back at the information about the diorama box Eliana plans to make using the rectangular sheet of cardboard shown on page 279. In the Apply What You've Learned in Lesson 5-1, you wrote a polynomial function $V(x)$ in standard form for the volume of Eliana's diorama box. You graphed this function in the Apply What You've Learned in Lesson 5-2.

  a. Use your volume function to write an equation that you can solve to find the possible side lengths of the squares Eliana will cut from each corner.

  b. Rewrite your equation from part (a) as an equation in the form $P(x) = 0$, where $P(x)$ is a polynomial in standard form.

  c. Find all the real roots of $P(x) = 0$.

45. height: 5 ft; bases: 10 ft, 14 ft

46. Answers may vary. Sample: $x^4 - x^2 - 2 = 0$; roots: $\pm\sqrt{2}$, $\pm i$

47. Answers may vary. Samples:
  a. $x - 1 - \sqrt{2} = 0$
  b. $x^2 - 2(1 + \sqrt{2})x + (1 + \sqrt{2})^2 = 0$
  c. -1

48. a. two real, two imaginary; four imaginary; four real
  b. five real; three real, two imaginary; four imaginary, one real
  c. Answers may vary. Sample: It must have at least one real solution.

49. Answers may vary. Sample: You cannot use the Conjugate Root Theorem for irrational roots unless the equation has rational coefficients.

Apply What You've Learned

In the Apply What You've Learned for Lesson 5-1, students wrote a polynomial function in standard form to model the volume of Eliana's diorama box, as shown on page 279. Here students use the volume function to write an equation they can solve for possible side lengths of the squares Eliana will cut from each corner of the sheet of cardboard.

© Mathematical Practices
Students **look for structure** in a polynomial function in order to find its real roots. (MP 7)

ANSWERS

  a. $4x^3 - 40x^2 + 96x = 36$

  b. $4x^3 - 40x^2 + 96x - 36 = 0$

  c. $3, \dfrac{7 \pm \sqrt{37}}{2}$

5-5 Lesson Resources

Additional Instructional Support

Algebra 2 Companion

Students can use the **Algebra 2 Companion** worktext (4 pages) as you teach the lesson. Use the Companion to support

- New Vocabulary
- Key Concepts
- Got It for each Problem
- Lesson Check

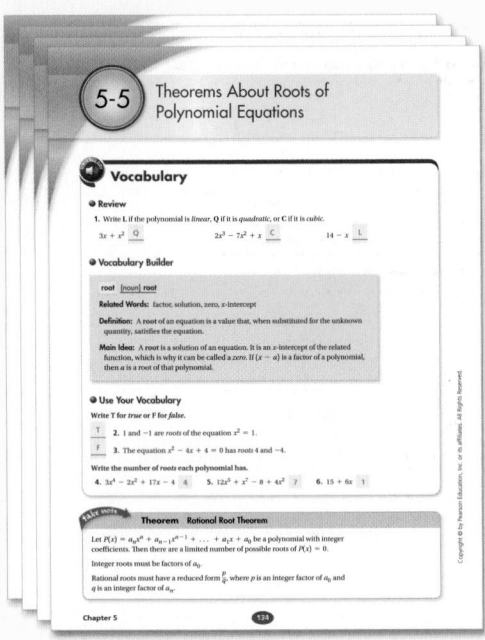

ELL Support

Use Role Playing Assign #11, 18, 26, 30, 33, and 39 from the Practice Exercises. Divide the class into groups of four. In each group, two students assume the role of the teacher. Using their notes, they ask the other two students to solve the problems and to state their steps as they work through each problem. "For Ex. 11, first we list the factors of 1 and 9. Then we use the Rational Root Theorem by ... " After completing problems #11, 18, and 26, the roles are switched and the second set of problems is completed.

5 Assess & Remediate

Lesson Quiz

1. What are the rational roots of $3x^3 - 6x^2 - x + 2 = 0$?

2. What are the rational roots of $3x^3 - 2x^2 - 19x - 6 = 0$?

3. **Do you UNDERSTAND?** A quartic polynomial $P(x)$ has rational coefficients. If $2 - i$ and $-\sqrt{5}$ are roots of $P(x) = 0$, what are the other two roots?

4. What is a third-degree polynomial function $P(x)$ with rational coefficients so that $P(x) = 0$ has roots -3 and i?
   - **A.** $P(x) = x^3 - 3x^2 + x - 3$
   - **B.** $P(x) = x^3 + 3x^2 + x + 3$
   - **C.** $P(x) = x^3 - 5x^2 - x + 3$
   - **D.** $P(x) = x^3 + 5x^2 + x + 3$

5. What does Descartes' Rule of Signs tell you about the real roots of $x^3 - x^2 + x + 1 = 0$?

ANSWERS TO LESSON QUIZ

1. 2
2. $-2, 3, -\dfrac{1}{3}$
3. $2 + i, \sqrt{5}$
4. B
5. 0 or 2 positive, 1 negative

PRESCRIPTION FOR REMEDIATION

Use the student work on the Lesson Quiz to prescribe a differentiated review assignment:

Points	Differentiated Remediation
0–2	Intervention
3–4	On-level
5	Extension

PowerAlgebra.com

5 Assess & Remediate

Assign the Lesson Quiz. Appropriate intervention, practice, or enrichment is automatically generated based on student performance.

Differentiated Remediation
Available in editable format online.

Intervention

- **Reteaching** (2 pages) Provides reteaching and practice exercises for the key lesson concepts. Use with struggling students or absent students.

- **English Language Learner Support** Helps students develop and reinforce mathematical vocabulary and key concepts.

All-in-One Resources/Online
Reteaching

All-in-One Resources/Online
English Language Learner Support

Differentiated Remediation *continued*

Available in editable format online.

On-Level

- **Practice** (2 pages) Provides extra practice for each lesson. For simpler practice exercises, use the Form K Practice pages found in the All-in-One Teaching Resources and online.
- **Think About a Plan** Helps students develop specific problem-solving skills and strategies by providing scaffolded guiding questions.
- **Standardized Test Prep** Focuses on all major exercises, all major question types, and helps students prepare for the high-stakes assessments.

Extension

- **Enrichment** Provides students with interesting problems and activities that extend the concepts of the lesson.
- **Activities, Games, and Puzzles** Worksheets that can be used for concepts development, enrichment, and for fun!

Practice and Problem Solving Wkbk/ All-in-One Resources/Online

Practice page 1

5-5 **Practice** *Form G*

Theorems About Roots of Polynomial Equations

Use the Rational Root Theorem to list all possible rational roots for each equation. Then find any actual rational roots.

1. $x^3 + 5x^2 - 2x - 15 = 0$ ±1, ±3, ±5, ±15; none
2. $36x^3 + 144x^2 - x - 4 = 0$ ±1, ±2, ±4, $\pm\frac{1}{2}$, $\pm\frac{1}{3}$, $\pm\frac{2}{3}$, $\pm\frac{4}{3}$, $\pm\frac{1}{4}$, $\pm\frac{1}{6}$, $\pm\frac{1}{9}$, $\pm\frac{2}{9}$, $\pm\frac{4}{9}$, $\pm\frac{1}{12}$, $\pm\frac{1}{18}$, $\pm\frac{1}{36}$; -4, $-\frac{1}{6}$, $\frac{1}{6}$
3. $2x^3 + 5x^2 + 4x + 1 = 0$ ±1, $\pm\frac{1}{2}$; -1, $-\frac{1}{2}$
4. $12x^4 + 14x^3 - 5x^2 - 14x - 4 = 0$ ±1, ±2, ±4, $\pm\frac{1}{2}$, $\pm\frac{1}{3}$, $\pm\frac{2}{3}$, $\pm\frac{4}{3}$, $\pm\frac{1}{4}$, $\pm\frac{1}{6}$, $\pm\frac{1}{12}$; none
5. $5x^3 - 11x^2 + 7x - 1 = 0$ ±1, $\pm\frac{1}{5}$; $\frac{1}{5}$, 1
6. $x^3 + 81x^2 - 49x - 49 = 0$ ±1, ±7, ±49; none

A polynomial function $P(x)$ with rational coefficients has the given roots. Find two additional roots of $P(x) = 0$.

7. $2 + 3i$ and $\sqrt{7}$ $2 - 3i$, $-\sqrt{7}$
8. $3 - \sqrt{2}$ and $1 + \sqrt{3}$ $3 + \sqrt{2}$, $1 - \sqrt{3}$
9. $-4i$ and $6 - i$ $4i$, $6 + i$
10. $5 - \sqrt{6}$ and $-2 + \sqrt{10}$ $5 + \sqrt{6}$, $-2 - \sqrt{10}$
11. $\sqrt{5}$ and $-\sqrt{13}$ $-\sqrt{5}$ and $\sqrt{13}$
12. $1 - \sqrt{10}$ and $2 + \sqrt{2}$ $1 + \sqrt{10}$ and $2 - \sqrt{2}$

Write a polynomial function with rational coefficients so that $P(x) = 0$ has the given roots.

13. 4 and 6 $P(x) = x^2 - 10x + 24$
14. -5 and -1 $P(x) = x^2 + 6x + 5$
15. $3i$ and $\sqrt{6}$ $P(x) = x^4 + 3x^2 - 54$
16. $2 + i$ and $1 - \sqrt{5}$ $P(x) = x^4 - 6x^3 + 9x^2 + 6x - 20$
17. -5 and $3i$ $P(x) = x^3 + 5x^2 + 9x + 45$
18. i and $5i$ $P(x) = x^4 + 26x^2 + 25$

What does Descartes' Rule of Signs say about the number of positive real roots and negative real roots for each polynomial function?

19. $P(x) = 3x^3 + x^2 - 8x - 12$ 1 positive real root; 2 or 0 negative real roots
20. $P(x) = 2x^4 - x^3 - 3x + 7$ 2 or 0 positive real roots; 0 negative real roots
21. $P(x) = 4x^5 - x^4 - x^3 + 6x^2 - 5$ 3 or 1 positive real roots; 2 or 0 negative real roots
22. $P(x) = x^3 + 4x^2 + x - 6$ 1 positive real root; 2 or 0 negative real roots

Practice and Problem Solving Wkbk/ All-in-One Resources/Online

Practice page 2

5-5 **Practice** (continued) *Form G*

Theorems About Roots of Polynomial Equations

Find all rational roots for $P(x) = 0$.

23. $P(x) = x^3 - 5x^2 + 2x + 8$ 4, 2, -1
24. $P(x) = x^3 + x^2 - 17x + 15$ 3, 1, -5
25. $P(x) = 2x^3 + 13x^2 + 17x - 12$ -4, -3, $\frac{1}{2}$
26. $P(x) = x^3 - x^2 - 34x - 56$ 7, -2, -4
27. $P(x) = x^3 - 18x + 27$ 3
28. $P(x) = x^4 - 5x^2 + 4$ -2, -1, 1, 2
29. $P(x) = x^3 - 6x^2 + 13x - 10$ 2
30. $P(x) = x^3 - 5x^2 + 4x + 10$ -1
31. $P(x) = x^3 - 5x^2 + 17x - 13$ 1
32. $P(x) = x^3 + x + 10$ -2
33. $P(x) = x^3 - 5x^2 - x + 5$ 1, -1, 5
34. $P(x) = x^3 - 12x + 16$ -4, 2
35. $P(x) = x^3 - 2x^2 - 5x + 6$ -2, 1, 3
36. $P(x) = x^3 - 8x^2 - 200$ 10
37. $P(x) = x^3 + x^2 - 5x + 3$ 1, -3
38. $P(x) = 4x^3 - 12x^2 - x + 3$ 3, $\frac{1}{2}$, $-\frac{1}{2}$
39. $P(x) = x^3 + x^2 - 7x + 2$ 2
40. $P(x) = 12x^3 + 31x^2 - 17x - 6$ -3, $\frac{2}{3}$, $-\frac{1}{4}$

Write a polynomial function $P(x)$ with rational coefficients so that $P(x) = 0$ has the given roots.

41. $\sqrt{3}$, 2, $-i$ $P(x) = x^5 - 2x^4 - 2x^3 + 4x^2 - 3x + 6$
42. 5, $2i$ $P(x) = x^3 - 5x^2 + 4x - 20$
43. -1, 3 + i $P(x) = x^3 - 5x^2 + 4x + 10$
44. $-\sqrt{7}$, i $P(x) = x^4 - 6x^2 - 7$
45. -4, $4i$ $P(x) = x^3 + 4x^2 + 16x + 64$
46. 6, $3 - 2i$ $P(x) = x^3 - 12x^2 + 49x - 78$
47. **Error Analysis** A student claims that $2i$ is the only imaginary root of a polynomial equation that has real coefficients. Explain the student's mistake. The student forgot the conjugate imaginary root $-2i$.
48. You are building a rectangular sandbox for a children's playground. The width of the sandbox is 4 times its height. The length of the sandbox is 8 ft more than 2 times its height. You have 40 ft³ of sand available to fill this sandbox. What are the dimensions of the sandbox? height = 1 ft, width = 4 ft, length = 10 ft
49. **Writing** According to the Rational Root Theorem, what is the relationship between the polynomial equation $2x^4 - x^3 - 7x^2 + 5x + 3 = 0$ and rational roots of the form $\frac{p}{q}$, where $\frac{p}{q}$ is in simplest form? p must be a factor of 3 and q must be a factor of 2.

All-in-One Resources/Online

Enrichment

5-5 **Enrichment**

Theorems About Roots of Polynomial Equations

Lower and Upper Bounds for Real Roots of Polynomial Equations

At times, the list of possible rational roots for a polynomial equation is rather lengthy. However, you can use patterns to shorten the list. One pattern involves finding lower and upper bounds for real roots. If a number is an upper bound, then there are no real roots for the equation greater than that number. If a number is a lower bound, then there are no real roots for the equation lower than that number.

Consider the polynomial equation $x^3 + 3x^2 - 34x - 42 = 0$

1. List all the possible rational zeros for the equation. ±1, ±2, ±3, ±6, ±7, ±14, ±21, ±42

When testing the possible rational roots, if the last row of numbers in the synthetic division table are all positive, then the number is an upper bound.

2. Use synthetic division to see whether 6 is a root of the given polynomial.

6	1	3	−34	−42
		6	54	120
	1	9	20	78

Notice the last row contains all positive numbers. Therefore, 6 is an upper bound. We can rule out any other numbers in our possible rational zeros list that are greater than 6.

3. Which numbers can be eliminated from our list of possible rational roots? 7, 14, 21, 42

When testing the possible negative rational roots, if the last row of numbers in the synthetic division table are of alternating signs, then the number is a lower bound.

4. Use synthetic division to see whether -14 is a root of the given polynomial.

−14	1	3	−34	−42
		−14	154	−1680
	1	−11	120	−1722

Notice the last row contains numbers with alternating signs. Therefore, -14 is a lower bound. We can rule out any other numbers in our possible rational roots list that are less than -14.

5. Which numbers can be eliminated from our list of possible rational roots? -21, -42
6. What numbers in our original list from Exercise 1 are still remaining? ±1, ±2, ±3, −6, −7
7. Find all roots of the given polynomial. -7, $2 \pm \sqrt{10}$
8. List all possible rational roots for the polynomial equation $x^4 + x^3 + 30x^2 + 36x - 216 = 0$. Then use synthetic division to find all zeros. Note any upper or lower bounds. ±1, ±2, ±3, ±4, ±6, ±8, ±9, ±12, ±18, ±24, ±27, ±36, ±54, ±72, ±108, ±216; −3, 2, −6i, 6i; upper: 3, lower: −4
9. List all possible rational roots for the polynomial equation $x^4 - 3x^3 + 8x^2 - 36x - 48 = 0$. Then use synthetic division to find all zeros. Note any upper or lower bounds. ±1, ±2, ±3, ±4, ±6, ±8, ±12, ±16, ±24, ±48; −1, 4, $-2i\sqrt{3}$, $2i\sqrt{3}$; upper: 6, lower: −2
10. List all possible rational roots for the polynomial equation $x^4 + 4x^3 - 29x^2 + 64x - 720 = 0$. Then use synthetic division to find all zeros. Note any upper or lower bounds. ±1, ±2, ±3, ±4, ±5, ±6, ±8, ±9, ±10, ±12, ±15, ±16, ±18, ±20, ±24, ±30, ±36, ±40, ±45, ±48, ±60, ±72, ±80, ±90, ±120, ±144, ±180, ±240, ±360, ±720; −9, 5, −4i, 4i; upper: 6, lower: −10

Practice and Problem Solving Wkbk/ All-in-One Resources/Online

Think About a Plan

5-5 **Think About a Plan**

Theorems About Roots of Polynomial Equations

Gardening A gardener is designing a new garden in the shape of a trapezoid. She wants the shorter base to be twice the height and the longer base to be 4 feet longer than the shorter base. If she has enough topsoil to create a 60 ft² garden, what dimensions should she use for the garden?

Understanding the Problem

1. What is the formula for the area of a trapezoid? $A = \frac{1}{2}h(b_1 + b_2)$
2. How can drawing a diagram help you solve the problem? Answers may vary. Sample: A diagram will help me write variable expressions for each part of the formula for the area of a trapezoid
3. What is the problem asking you to determine? all of the dimensions of a trapezoid with area 60 ft²

Planning the Solution

4. Define a variable. Let x = height
5. What variable expression represents the shorter base? The longer base? 2x 2x + 4
6. What expression represents the area of the trapezoid? What number is this equal to? Write the equation you obtain in standard form. $\frac{1}{2}x(4x + 4)$; 60; $2x^2 + 2x - 60 = 0$

Getting an Answer

7. Solve your equation. Are the solutions reasonable? −6, 5; Only the positive solution is reasonable for the height
8. What are the dimensions of the garden? height = 5 ft, shorter base = 10 ft, longer base = 14 ft

Practice and Problem Solving Wkbk/ All-in-One Resources/Online

Standardized Test Prep

5-5 **Standardized Test Prep**

Theorems About Roots of Polynomial Equations

Multiple Choice

For Exercises 1–5, choose the correct letter.

1. A fourth-degree polynomial with integer coefficients has roots at 1 and $3 + \sqrt{5}$. Which number *cannot* also be a root of this polynomial? D
   (A) −1 (B) −3 (C) $3 - \sqrt{5}$ (D) $3 + \sqrt{2}$
2. A quartic polynomial $P(x)$ has rational coefficients. If $\sqrt{7}$ and $6 + i$ are roots of $P(x) = 0$, what is one additional root? G
   (F) 7 (G) $-\sqrt{7}$ (H) $i - 6$ (I) $6i$
3. What is a quartic polynomial function with rational coefficients that has roots i and $2i$? C
   (A) $x^4 - 5x^2 - 4$ (B) $x^4 - 5x^2 + 4$ (C) $x^4 + 5x^2 + 4$ (D) $x^4 + 5x^2 - 4$
4. What does Descartes' Rule of Signs tell you about the real roots of $6x^4 + 29x^3 + 40x^2 + 7x - 12$? F
   (F) 1 positive real root and 1 or 3 negative real roots
   (G) 0 positive real roots and 1 negative real root
   (H) 1 or 3 positive real roots and 1 negative real root
   (I) 0 or 1 positive real roots and 3 negative real roots
5. What is a rational root of $x^3 + 3x^2 - 6x - 8 = 0$? B
   (A) 1 (B) −1 (C) 8 (D) −8

Extended Response

6. A third-degree polynomial with rational coefficients has roots −4 and −4i. If the leading coefficient of the polynomial is $\frac{3}{2}$, what is the polynomial? Show your work.
   [4] 3rd root = 4i; $P(x) = \frac{3}{2}(x + 4)(x + 4i)(x - 4i) = \frac{3}{2}(x + 4)(x^2 + 16) = \frac{3}{2}x^3 + 6x^2 + 24x + 96$
   [3] correct process, but with one computational error
   [2] correct process, with multiple computational errors
   [1] correct answer without work shown
   [0] incorrect answers and no work shown OR no answers given

Online Teacher Resource Center

Activities, Games, and Puzzles

5-5 **Game: Theory at Play**

Theorems About Roots of Polynomial Equations

This game is for two to four students. To play the game, make 20 game cards by cutting along the solid lines on the following sheet. Then fold each card along the dashed lines so the printed sides are shown. You can tape the cards closed. Lay the cards on a table so the category side is face up.

Decide who goes first. Players take turns selecting a card from the table. Do not return a card to the table once it has been selected. Each card is labeled by a category. The category determines what you must find.

- **Category A:** List the possible rational roots.
- **Category B:** A polynomial with rational coefficients has the given roots. Find two additional roots.
- **Category C:** Determine the maximum number of positive real roots.
- **Category D:** Determine the maximum number of negative real roots.

The answers are on the other side of the card. Players check each other's answers. Score each category as follows.

- **Category A:** Each correct possible rational root is worth 1 point. An incorrect root is worth −1 point. There is no penalty for not giving a possible rational root.
- **Category B:** Each correct root is worth 2 points. An incorrect root is worth 0 points.
- **Category C:** A correct answer is worth 4 points. An incorrect answer is worth 0 points.
- **Category D:** A correct answer is worth 4 points. An incorrect answer is worth 0 points.

The game continues until there are no more cards on the table. The player who earns the most points wins the game.

Check students' work.

Guided Instruction

PURPOSE To use polynomial identities to prove numerical relationships.

PROCESS Students will
- use polynomial identities to write expressions in different forms.
- use number theory to determine if an expression is odd or even.

DISCUSS Students first use polynomial identities and expressions for consecutive numbers to transform an expression into another form. Then they use number theory to show the expression is either even or odd. Discuss what consecutive numbers are and give some concrete examples.

Example 1

This example shows that the sum of two cubes $a^3 + b^3$ is always an odd number if a and b are consecutive positive integers.

> **Q** Is the product of two even numbers even or odd? **[even]**
>
> **Q** Is the product of two odd numbers even or odd? **[odd]**
>
> **Q** Is the product of an even number and an odd number even or odd? **[even]**
>
> **Q** Is the sum of two even numbers even or odd? **[even]**
>
> **Q** Is the sum of two odd numbers even or odd? **[even]**
>
> **Q** Is the sum of an even number and an odd number even or odd? **[odd]**

SYNTHESIZING

In Exercise 5, discuss with students why one of three consecutive integers must always have a factor of 3.

Ⓒ **Mathematical Practices** This Concept Byte supports students in looking for patterns, Mathematical Practice 7.

318 Chapter 5

Using Polynomial Identities

Ⓒ **Common Core State Standards**

A-APR.C.4 Prove polynomial identities and use them to describe numerical relationships.

MP 7

You can use what you know about polynomial identities to discover relationships among numbers.

Example

Use polynomial identities to prove that the sum of the cubes of any two consecutive positive integers is odd.

You can represent any two consecutive positive integers as n and $n + 1$, where n is a positive integer. Use the formula for factoring the sum of two cubes.

$$a^3 + b^3 = (a + b)(a^2 - ab + b^2)$$
$$= (n + (n + 1))(n^2 - n(n + 1) + (n + 1)^2) \quad \text{Substitute } n \text{ for } a \text{ and } n + 1 \text{ for } b.$$
$$= (2n + 1)(n^2 - n^2 - n + n^2 + 2n + 1) \quad \text{Simplify.}$$
$$= (2n + 1)(n^2 + n + 1)$$
$$= 2n^3 + 2n^2 + 2n + n^2 + n + 1$$
$$= 2n^3 + 3n^2 + 3n + 1$$

You know that $2n^3$ is always even because it has a factor of 2.

If n is even, then $3n^2$ is even and $3n$ is even. So $2n^3 + 3n^2 + 3n$ is even, and $2n^3 + 3n^2 + 3n + 1$ is odd, because it is 1 more than an even number.

If n is odd, then $3n^2$ is odd and $3n$ is odd. The sum of two odd integers is always even. So $2n^3 + 3n^2 + 3n$ is even, and $2n^3 + 3n^2 + 3n + 1$ is odd, because it is 1 more than an even number.

Therefore, $n^3 + (n + 1)^3$ is always odd for consecutive positive integers.

Exercises

1. Use polynomial identities to prove that the difference of the squares of any two consecutive integers is odd.

2. **a.** Prove that for any two positive consecutive integers a and b, where $a > b$, $a^3 - b^3 = a^2 + ab + b^2$.
   b. Prove that the difference of the cubes of two consecutive positive integers is always odd.

3. Prove that the square of the sum of two consecutive positive integers is odd.

4. Prove that the reciprocals of any two consecutive integers have a product that is equal to the reciprocal of the smaller integer minus the reciprocal of the larger integer.

5. Use the identity $n^3 - n = n(n - 1)(n + 1)$ to prove that 6 is a factor of $n^3 - n$ for all integers n. (*Hint:* n, $n - 1$, and $n + 1$ are consecutive integers.)

Answers

Exercises

1. $a^2 - b^2 = (a + b)(a - b)$
$= (n + (n + 1)) \cdot$
$(n - (n + 1))$
$= (2n + 1)(-1)$
$= -2n - 1$
Since $-2n$ is even, $-2n - 1$ is odd.

2. a. Let $a = b + 1$. From polynomial identities, you know
$a^3 - b^3 = (a - b)(a^2 + ab + b^2)$. If $a = b + 1$, then
$(a - b)(a^2 + ab + b^2) =$
$(b + 1 - b)(a^2 + ab + b^2) =$
$1(a^2 + ab + b^2) = a^2 + ab + b^2$.

b. By part (a), $(n + 1)^3 - n^3 =$
$(n + 1)^2 + n(n + 1) + n^2 =$
$3n^2 + 3n + 1$.
If n is even, $3n^2 + 3n$ is the sum of two even numbers and is therefore even, so $3n^2 + 3n + 1$ is odd. If n is odd, $3n^2 + 3n$ is the sum of two odd numbers and is therefore even, so $3n^2 + 3n + 1$ is odd.

3. $(a + b)^2 = a^2 + 2ab + b^2$
$= (n)^2 + 2(n)(n + 1) + (n + 1)^2$
$= n^2 + 2n^2 + 2n + n^2 + 2n + 1$
$= 4n^2 + 4n + 1$
Since $4n^2 + 4n$ is even, $4n^2 + 4n + 1$ is odd.

4. $\left(\frac{1}{n}\right)\left(\frac{1}{n + 1}\right) \overset{?}{=} \frac{1}{n} - \frac{1}{n + 1}$
$\frac{1}{n(n + 1)} \overset{?}{=} \frac{n + 1}{n(n + 1)} - \frac{n}{n(n + 1)}$
$\frac{1}{n(n + 1)} = \frac{1}{n(n + 1)}$

5. $n^3 - n = n(n - 1)(n + 1)$ is a product of three consecutive integers, $n - 1$, n, and $n + 1$. Exactly one of every three consecutive integers is divisible by 3, and at least one of every three consecutive integers is divisible by 2. Since the product $n(n - 1)(n + 1)$ is divisible by 2 and 3, it is divisible by 6.

5-6 The Fundamental Theorem of Algebra

Objective To use the Fundamental Theorem of Algebra to solve polynomial equations with complex solutions

Common Core State Standards
N-CN.C.7 Solve quadratic equations with real coefficients that have complex solutions. **Also** N-CN.C.8, N-CN.C.9, A-APR.B.3
MP 1, MP 2, MP 3, MP 4

How can the patterns you see help you find the solution?

MATHEMATICAL PRACTICES

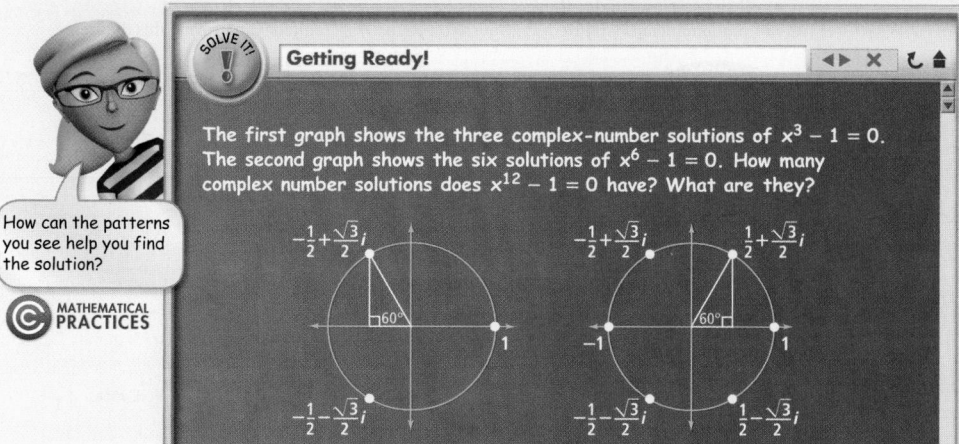

Getting Ready!

The first graph shows the three complex-number solutions of $x^3 - 1 = 0$. The second graph shows the six solutions of $x^6 - 1 = 0$. How many complex number solutions does $x^{12} - 1 = 0$ have? What are they?

Lesson Vocabulary
• Fundamental Theorem of Algebra

You can factor any polynomial of degree n into n linear factors, but sometimes the factors will involve imaginary numbers.

Essential Understanding The degree of a polynomial equation tells you how many roots the equation has.

It is easy to see graphically that every polynomial function of degree 1 has a single zero, the x-intercept. However, there appear to be three possibilities for polynomials of degree 2. They correspond to these three graphs:

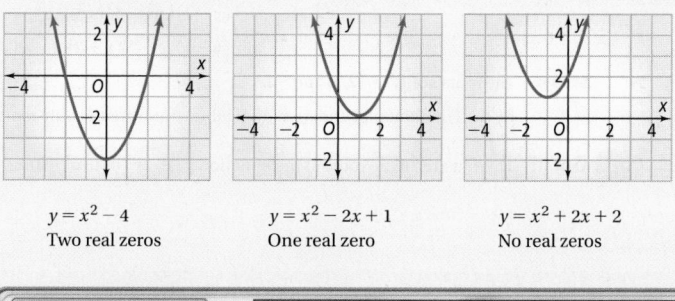

$y = x^2 - 4$
Two real zeros

$y = x^2 - 2x + 1$
One real zero

$y = x^2 + 2x + 2$
No real zeros

---

1 Interactive Learning

Solve It!

PURPOSE To realize that the number of roots of a polynomial equation is the same as the degree
PROCESS Students may
• notice the relationship between the exponent and the number of complex solutions.
• notice the pattern of the complex solutions on the unit circle.

FACILITATE

Q How are the three equations different? **[The powers of the x-term are different.]**

Q How does the exponent seem to affect the number of solutions? **[As the exponent doubles, the number of solutions doubles.]**

Q The solutions are all located on the unit circle. How are they spaced? **[evenly]**

Q Where are the solutions of $x^{12} - 1 = 0$ located? **[Answers may vary. Sample: in the same place as the solutions for $x^6 - 1$ plus midway between each of these solutions]**

ANSWER See Solve It in Answers on next page.
CONNECT THE MATH In the Solve It, students use patterns to identify the number and type of complex solutions of a polynomial equation. In this lesson, they will use the fact that the number of complex solutions of a polynomial equation is equal to its degree.

5-6 Preparing to Teach

BIG ideas Solving Equations and Inequalities
Equivalence

ESSENTIAL UNDERSTANDING
• The degree of a polynomial equation tells how many roots the equation has.

Math Background

This lesson is students' first introduction to the Fundamental Theorem of Algebra. It is important to note that this theorem does not *find* the roots of a function but instead identifies how many roots a function has.

This lesson applies and combines the theorems and techniques in the chapter to find roots of a polynomial function of degree $n \geq 1$.

A polynomial function with no constant term has 0 as one of its rational roots. Also, a polynomial function with odd degree and real coefficients must have a root in the set of real numbers. Show this by graphing. Based on the rules for end behavior, it is possible that the graph of a polynomial function of an even degree will never cross the x-axis, but a polynomial function of an odd degree must.

Mathematical Practices
Construct viable arguments and critique the reasoning of others.
Using their knowledge of factoring polynomials, students will ascertain the validity of the Fundamental Theorem of Algebra.

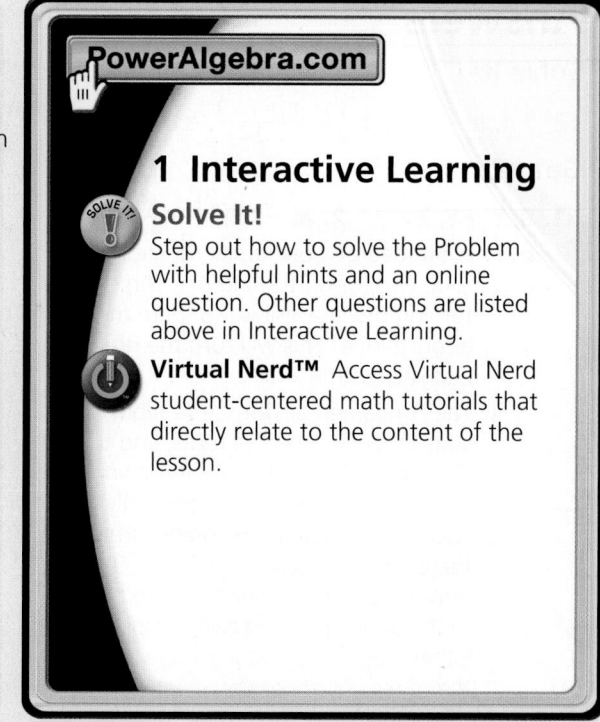

PowerAlgebra.com

1 Interactive Learning

Solve It!
Step out how to solve the Problem with helpful hints and an online question. Other questions are listed above in Interactive Learning.

Virtual Nerd™ Access Virtual Nerd student-centered math tutorials that directly relate to the content of the lesson.

Take Note
SYNTHESIZING

The polynomial equation must be set equal to 0. Review that complex roots include real roots and imaginary roots.

Problem 1
SYNTHESIZING

Students apply the Fundamental Theorem of Algebra to find all complex roots of the polynomial equation. They must have previous knowledge of the Rational Root Theorem, the Factor Theorem, and synthetic division.

Q How are the rational roots found? **[According to the Rational Root Theorem, the possible rational roots are $x = \pm\frac{p}{q}$, where p represents the integer factors of the constant term and q represents the integer factors of the leading coefficient.]**

Q What could you do instead of factoring $x^4 - 3x^2 - 4$? **[Answers may vary. Sample: Substitute the possible rational roots. If the value of the polynomial equals 0, use synthetic division.]**

Q How would you check your result? **[Multiply the binomials to make sure that you get the original polynomial.]**

Got It?
ERROR PREVENTION

Q Since there is no constant term, what will be your first step after the equation is in standard form? **[Factor x from the polynomial.]**

However, by factoring, you can see that each related equation has two roots.

$x^2 - 4 = (x - 2)(x + 2) = 0$ *two real roots, 2 and −2*

$x^2 - 2x + 1 = (x - 1)(x - 1) = 0$ *a root of multiplicity two at 1*

$x^2 + 2x + 2 = (x - (-1 + i))(x - (-1 - i)) = 0$ *two complex roots, −1 + i and −1 − i*

Every quadratic polynomial equation has two roots, every cubic polynomial equation has three roots, and so on.

This result is related to the *Fundamental Theorem of Algebra.* The German mathematician Carl Friedrich Gauss (1777–1855) is credited with proving this theorem.

take note

> **Theorem   The Fundamental Theorem of Algebra**
>
> If $P(x)$ is a polynomial of degree $n \geq 1$, then $P(x) = 0$ has exactly n roots, including multiple and complex roots.

Problem 1 Using the Fundamental Theorem of Algebra

What are all the roots of $x^5 - x^4 - 3x^3 + 3x^2 - 4x + 4 = 0$?

Know
The polynomial equation has degree 5. There are 5 roots.

Need
The zeros of the function

Plan
Use the Rational Root and Factor Theorems, synthetic division, and factoring.

Step 1 The polynomial is in standard form. The possible rational roots are ± 1, ± 2, ± 4.

Step 2 Evaluate the related polynomial function for $x = 1$. Since $P(1) = 0$, 1 is a root and $x - 1$ is a factor. Use synthetic division to factor out $x - 1$:

$$
\begin{array}{r|rrrrrr}
1 & 1 & -1 & -3 & 3 & -4 & 4 \\
  &   & 1 & 0 & -3 & 0 & -4 \\
\hline
  & 1 & 0 & -3 & 0 & -4 & 0
\end{array}
$$

Think

How many linear factors will there be? If there are five roots, there must be five linear factors.

Step 3 Continue factoring until you have five linear factors.

$$x^5 - x^4 - 3x^3 + 3x^2 - 4x + 4 = (x - 1)(x^4 - 3x^2 - 4)$$
$$= (x - 1)(x^2 - 4)(x^2 + 1)$$
$$= (x - 1)(x - 2)(x + 2)(x - i)(x + i)$$

Step 4 The roots are 1, 2, −2, i, and $-i$.

By the Fundamental Theorem of Algebra, these are the only roots.

 Got It? **1.** What are all the roots of the equation $x^4 + 2x^3 = 13x^2 - 10x$?

Answers

Solve It!

12; ± 1, $\pm\dfrac{\sqrt{3} \pm i}{2}$, $\pm\dfrac{1}{2}i$, $\dfrac{1 \pm i\sqrt{3}}{2}$, $\pm i$, $\dfrac{-1 \pm i\sqrt{3}}{2}$

Got It?

1. 0, 1, −5, 2   **2. a.** -1, 2, $\dfrac{1 \pm i\sqrt{23}}{4}$

b. i. A 5th degree polynomial function has four, two, or no turning pts. Three turning pts. are visible, so there must be a fourth one. This will turn the graph back across the x-axis.

ii. The Fundamental Thm. of Algebra states there will be five roots, and the Conjugate Root Thm. requires pairs of irrational or complex roots. Only two zeros appear in the graph, so there are three zeros remaining. Of the remaining roots, either there are three real roots, or one real and two complex roots. Either way, there is at least one real root that does not appear as a real zero in the graph.

PowerAlgebra.com

2 Guided Instruction

Each Problem is worked out and supported online.

Problem 1
Using the Fundamental Theorem of Algebra
Animated

Problem 2
Finding All the Zeros of a Polynomial Function
Animated

Support in Algebra 2 Companion
- Vocabulary
- Key Concepts
- Got It?

Problem 2 Finding All the Zeros of a Polynomial Function

What are the zeros of $f(x) = x^4 + x^3 - 7x^2 - 9x - 18$?

Step 1 Use a graphing calculator to find any real roots. The graph of
$y = x^4 + x^3 - 7x^2 - 9x - 18$ shows real zeros at $x = -3$ and $x = 3$.

Think

Does the graph show all of the real roots?
Yes; the graphs of quartic functions have one or three turning points. Since the graph shows three turning points, it will not turn again to cross the x-axis a third time.

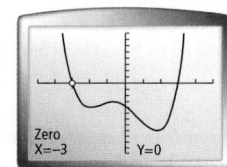
Zero
X=-3   Y=0

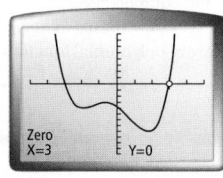
Zero
X=3   Y=0

Step 2 Factor out the linear factors $x + 3$ and $x - 3$. Use synthetic division twice.

$$\begin{array}{r|rrrrr} -3 & 1 & 1 & -7 & -9 & -18 \\ & & -3 & 6 & 3 & 18 \\ \hline & 1 & -2 & -1 & -6 & 0 \end{array} \qquad \begin{array}{r|rrrr} 3 & 1 & -2 & -1 & -6 \\ & & 3 & 3 & 6 \\ \hline & 1 & 1 & 2 & 0 \end{array}$$

$x^4 + x^3 - 7x^2 - 9x - 18 = (x + 3)(x^3 - 2x^2 - x - 6)$
$ = (x + 3)(x - 3)(x^2 + x + 2)$

Step 3 Use the Quadratic Formula. Find the complex roots of $x^2 + x + 2 = 0$.

$a = 1, b = 1, c = 2$ Identify the values of a, b, and c.

$\dfrac{-1 \pm \sqrt{1^2 - 4(1)(2)}}{2(1)}$ Substitute.

$\dfrac{-1 \pm \sqrt{-7}}{2}$ Simplify.

The complex roots are $\dfrac{-1 + i\sqrt{7}}{2}$ and $\dfrac{-1 - i\sqrt{7}}{2}$.

Step 4 The four zeros of the function are $-3, 3, \dfrac{-1 + i\sqrt{7}}{2}$, and $\dfrac{-1 - i\sqrt{7}}{2}$.

By the Fundamental Theorem of Algebra, there can be no other zeros.

 Got It? **2. a.** What are all the zeros of the function $g(x) = 2x^4 - 3x^3 - x - 6$?
b. Reasoning The graph of
$f(x) = x^5 + 4x^4 - 3x^2 - 12x^2 - 4x - 4$ is shown
at the right.
  i. Use the turning points to explain why the graph does
  NOT show all of the real zeros of the function.
  ii. The graph of $g(x) = f(x) + 4$ is a translation of the graph
  of f up 4 units. How many real zeros of g will the graph
  of g show? Explain.

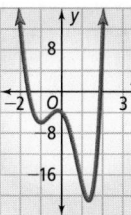

Problem 2 — SYNTHESIZING

Students use a graphing calculator to determine the real roots of the polynomial function and determine the remaining complex roots using the Quadratic Formula.

Q What are some advantages and disadvantages of using a calculator to find the real roots? **[Answers may vary. Sample: Adjusting the window to generate a complete graph may be difficult, but once the complete graph is visible, the real roots are easy to find.]**

Q Why is synthetic division used twice? **[The graph shows 2 real roots.]**

Q Why is the Quadratic Formula used? **[The trinomial of degree 2 cannot be factored, and there are no more possible real roots.]**

Got It? — ERROR PREVENTION

Q How many times will you use synthetic division in 2a? Why? **[The graph indicates that there are 2 real roots, so synthetic division will be used twice.]**

Q How many turning points does a fifth-degree polynomial function have? **[A fifth-degree polynomial function can have 0, 2, or 4 turning points.]**

Additional Problems

1. What are all the complex roots of
$x^5 - x^4 - 7x^3 + 7x^2 - 18x + 18 = 0$?
ANSWER $1, \pm 3, \pm i\sqrt{2}$

2. What are the zeros of
$f(x) = x^4 + 2x^3 - 4x^2 - 7x - 2$?
ANSWER $-1, 2, \dfrac{-3 \pm \sqrt{5}}{2}$

Take Note

If students have trouble seeing how the third statement implies the first two, present the following. Choose any polynomial function of degree $n \geq 1$. By the third statement, the function has at least one complex zero. Factor it out. The remaining polynomial is of degree $n - 1$. If $n - 1 \geq 1$, the new polynomial must also have at least one complex zero. Factor it out. Continue until the degree of the remaining polynomial is $n - n$, or zero.

> **Q** The original polynomial can be represented as the product of how many linear factors? **[n]**

3 Lesson Check

Do you know HOW?

• Exercises 1 and 2 only require students to find the *number* of roots. This is a direct application of the Fundamental Theorem of Algebra.

Do you UNDERSTAND?

• For Exercise 6, review that a root of multiplicity 2 means that there are 2 identical roots. If students have difficulty, then they should use the roots to work backward to find the polynomial function.
• For Exercise 7, suggest that students examine Problems 1 and 2. Hint: Look at the degrees of the polynomial functions.

Close

> **Q** How can the Fundamental Theorem of Algebra help you to solve polynomial equations? **[Answers may vary. Sample: The Fundamental Theorem of Algebra indicates the *number* of complex roots. When you identify the actual roots, you can use this number as a check.]**

 **Concept Summary** **The Fundamental Theorem of Algebra**

Here are equivalent ways to state the Fundamental Theorem of Algebra. You can use any one of these statements to prove the others.
• Every polynomial equation of degree $n \geq 1$ has exactly n roots, including multiple and complex roots.
• Every polynomial of degree $n \geq 1$ has n linear factors.
• Every polynomial function of degree $n \geq 1$ has at least one complex zero.

 Lesson Check

Do you know HOW?

Find the number of roots for each equation.

1. $5x^4 + 12x^3 - x^2 + 3x + 5 = 0$

2. $-x^{14} - x^8 - x + 7 = 0$

Find all the zeros for each function.

3. $y = x^3 - 5x^2 + 16x - 80$

4. $y = x^4 - 2x^3 + x^2 - 2x$

Do you UNDERSTAND?  **PRACTICES**

5. Vocabulary Given a polynomial equation of degree n, explain how you determine the number of roots of the equation.

6. Open-Ended Write a polynomial function of degree 4 with rational coefficients and two complex zeros of multiplicity 2.

7. Writing Describe when to use synthetic division and when to use the Quadratic Formula to determine the linear factors of a polynomial.

 Practice and Problem-Solving Exercises  **PRACTICES**

 Practice **Without using a calculator, find all the roots of each equation.** ◀ See Problem 1.

8. $x^3 - 3x^2 + x - 3 = 0$

9. $x^3 + x^2 + 4x + 4 = 0$

10. $x^3 + 4x^2 + x - 6 = 0$

11. $x^3 - 5x^2 + 2x + 8 = 0$

12. $x^4 + 4x^3 + 7x^2 + 16x + 12 = 0$

13. $x^4 - 4x^3 + x^2 + 12x - 12 = 0$

14. $x^5 + 3x^3 - 4x = 0$

15. $x^5 - 8x^3 - 9x = 0$

Find all the zeros of each function. ◀ See Problem 2.

16. $y = 2x^3 + x^2 + 1$

17. $f(x) = x^3 - 3x^2 + x - 3$

18. $g(x) = x^3 - 5x^2 + 5x - 4$

19. $y = x^3 - 2x^2 - 3x + 6$

20. $y = x^4 - 6x^2 + 8$

21. $f(x) = x^4 - 3x^2 - 4$

22. $y = x^3 - 3x^2 - 9x$

23. $y = x^3 + 6x^2 + x + 6$

24. $y = x^4 + 3x^3 + x^2 - 12x - 20$

25. $y = x^4 + x^3 - 15x^2 - 16x - 16$

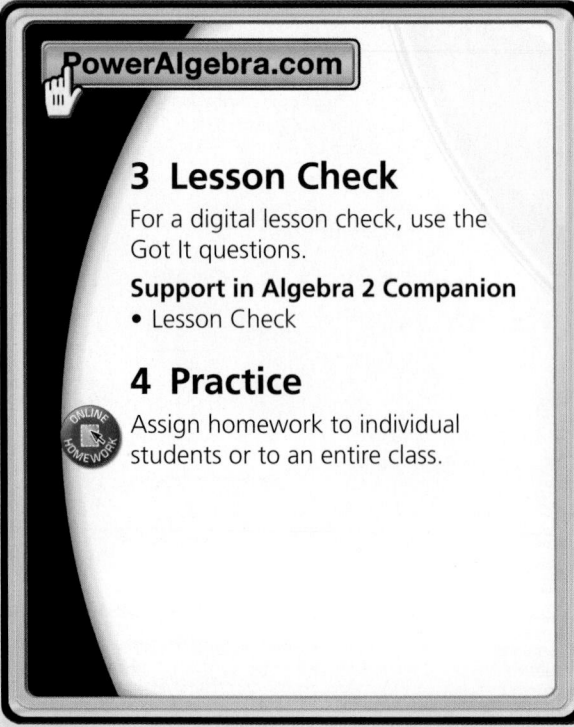

3 Lesson Check

For a digital lesson check, use the Got It questions.

Support in Algebra 2 Companion
• Lesson Check

4 Practice

Assign homework to individual students or to an entire class.

Answers

Lesson Check

1. four roots

2. fourteen roots

3. $5, \pm 4i$

4. $0, 2, \pm i$

5. By the Fundamental Thm. of Algebra, a polynomial equation of degree n has exactly n roots.

6. Answers may vary. Sample: $y = x^4 + 8x^2 + 16$

7. Use synthetic division to test for and factor out linear factors until a quadratic factor is obtained. Then use the Quadratic Formula if the quadratic factor cannot be factored further.

Practice and Problem-Solving Exercises

8. $3, \pm i$

9. $-1, \pm 2i$

10. $-3, -2, 1$

11. $-1, 2, 4$

12. $-3, -1, \pm 2i$

13. $2, \pm \sqrt{3}$

14. $0, \pm 1, \pm 2i$

15. $0, \pm 3, \pm i$

16. $-1; \dfrac{1 \pm i\sqrt{7}}{4}$

17. $3, \pm i$

18. $4; \dfrac{1 \pm i\sqrt{3}}{2}$

19. $2, \pm \sqrt{3}$

20. $\pm 2, \pm \sqrt{2}$

21. $\pm 2, \pm i$

22. $0; \dfrac{3 \pm 3\sqrt{5}}{2}$

23. $-6, \pm i$

24. $\pm 2, \dfrac{-3 \pm i\sqrt{11}}{2}$

25. $\pm 4, \dfrac{-1 \pm i\sqrt{3}}{2}$

For each equation, state the number of complex roots, the possible number of real roots, and the possible rational roots.

26. $2x^4 - x^3 + 2x^2 + 5x - 26 = 0$

27. $x^5 - x^3 - 11x^2 + 9x + 18 = 0$

28. $-12 + x + 10x^2 + 3x^3 = 0$

29. $4x^6 - x^5 - 24 = 0$

Find all the zeros of each function.

30. $y = x^3 - 4x^2 + 9x - 36$

31. $f(x) = x^3 + 2x^2 - 5x - 10$

32. $y = 2x^3 - 3x^2 - 18x - 8$

33. $y = 3x^3 - 7x^2 - 14x + 24$

34. $g(x) = x^3 - 4x^2 - x + 22$

35. $y = x^3 - x^2 - 3x - 9$

36. $y = x^4 - x^3 - 5x^2 - x - 6$

37. $y = 2x^4 + 3x^3 - 17x^2 - 27x - 9$

© 38. Think About a Plan A polynomial function, $f(x) = x^4 - 5x^3 - 28x^2 + 188x - 240$, is used to model a new roller coaster section. The loading zone will be placed at one of the zeros. The function has a zero at 5. What are the possible locations for the loading zone?
- Can you determine how many zeros you need to find?
- How can you use polynomial division?
- What other methods can be helpful?

STEM 39. Bridges A twist in a river can be modeled by the function $f(x) = \frac{1}{3}x^3 + \frac{1}{2}x^2 - x$, $-3 \le x \le 2$. A city wants to build a road that goes directly along the x-axis. How many bridges would it have to build?

© 40. Error Analysis Maurice says: "Every linear function has exactly one zero. It follows from the Fundamental Theorem of Algebra." Cheryl disagrees. "What about the linear function $y = 2$?" she asks. "Its graph is a line, but it has no x-intercept." Whose reasoning is incorrect? Where is the flaw?

Determine whether each of the following statements is *always*, *sometimes*, or *never* true.

41. A polynomial function with real coefficient has real zeros.

42. Polynomial functions with complex coefficients have one complex zero.

43. A polynomial function that does not intercept the x-axis has complex roots only.

© 44. Reasoning A 4th-degree polynomial function has zeros at 3 and $5 - i$. Can $4 + i$ also be a zero of the function? Explain your reasoning.

© 45. Open-Ended Write a polynomial function that has four possible rational zeros but no actual rational zeros.

© 46. Reasoning Show that the Fundamental Theorem of Algebra must be true for all quadratic polynomial functions.

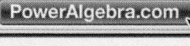
4 Practice

ASSIGNMENT GUIDE

Basic: 8–25 all, 26–30 even, 38–40, 44, 46

Average: 9–25 odd, 26–46

Advanced: 9–25 odd, 26–49

Standardized Test Prep: 50–53

Mixed Review: 54–65

Mathematical Practices are supported by exercises with red headings. Here are the Practices supported in this lesson:

MP 1: Make Sense of Problems Ex. 38

MP 2: Reason Abstractly Ex. 6, 45

MP 3: Communicate Ex. 7, 44

MP 3: Construct Arguments Ex. 46

MP 3: Critique the Reasoning of Others Ex. 40

Applications exercises have blue headings. Exercise 39 supports MP 4: Model.

STEM exercises focus on science or engineering applications.

EXERCISE 39: Use the Think About a Plan worksheet in the **Practice and Problem Solving Workbook** (also available in the Teaching Resources in print and online) to further support students' development in becoming independent learners.

HOMEWORK QUICK CHECK

To check students' understanding of key skills and concepts, go over Exercises 9, 17, 38, 39, and 44.

26. four complex roots; four, two, or no real roots; possible rational roots: $\pm\frac{1}{2}$, ±1, ±2, $\pm\frac{13}{2}$, ±13, ±26

27. five complex roots; one, three, or five real roots; possible rational roots: ±1, ±2, ±3, ±6, ±9, ±18

28. three complex roots; one or three real roots; possible rational roots: $\pm\frac{1}{3}$, $\pm\frac{2}{3}$, ±1, $\pm\frac{4}{3}$, ±2, ±3, ±4, ±6, ±12

29. six complex roots; zero, two, four, or six real roots; possible rational roots: $\pm\frac{1}{4}$, $\pm\frac{1}{2}$, $\pm\frac{3}{4}$, ±1, $\pm\frac{3}{2}$, ±2, ±3, ±4, ±6, ±8, ±12, ±24

30. 4, $\pm3i$

31. -2, $\pm\sqrt{5}$

32. -2, $-\frac{1}{2}$, 4

33. -2, $\frac{4}{3}$, 3

34. -2, $3 \pm i\sqrt{2}$

35. 3, $-1 \pm i\sqrt{2}$

36. -2, 3, $\pm i$

37. $-\frac{1}{2}$, -1, ±3

38. -6, 2, 4, or 5

39. 3 bridges

40. Maurice is incorrect. Although every function of degree 1 has exactly one zero, $y = 2$ is a function of degree 0 but it is still a linear function. So linear functions with degree zero may have no zero or x-intercept.

41. sometimes

42. never

43. always

44. No; a 4th degree polynomial has four roots. If $5 - i$ is a root, then by the Conjugate Root Theorem $5 + i$ must also be a root. Likewise, if $4 + i$ is a root, then $4 - i$ must also be a root. This would result in five roots, which is impossible.

45. Answers may vary. Sample: $y = x^4 + 3x^2 + 2$

46. Any quadratic polynomial $ax^2 + bx + c = 0$ has roots that can be found with $x = \frac{-b \pm \sqrt{b^2 - 4ac}}{2a}$. When the discriminant is positive, the function has 2 real roots. When the discriminant is negative, the function has 2 complex roots. When the discriminant is zero, the function has 1 real root of multiplicity two.

Answers

Practice and Problem-Solving Exercises
(continued)

47. Given any polynomial eq. of odd degree $n \geq 1$, the eq. has exactly n roots. Since imaginary roots occur in pairs, a polynomial of odd degree n will have an even number of imaginary roots and thus an odd number of real roots. So, any odd degree polynomial eq. with real coefficients has at least one real root.

48. 5

49. 5th degree; rational zero:

$$-\frac{5}{6}(x - \sqrt{2})(x + \sqrt{2})(x - \sqrt{3})(x + \sqrt{3})(x + \frac{5}{6})$$

$$= x^5 + \frac{5}{6}x^4 - 5x^3 - \frac{25}{6}x^2 + 6x + 5.$$

Standardized Test Prep

50. B

51. G

52. D

53. [2] Substitute $(2, -2)$ into both inequalities to see if the pt. satisfies both inequalities. If it does, then $(2, -2)$ is a solution of the system. If one or both inequalities are not satisfied by the pt. $(2, -2)$, then $(2, -2)$ is not a solution of the system.

[1] incomplete explanation

Mixed Review

54. $x^4 + 6x^3 + 14x^2 + 24x + 40 = 0$

55. $3 \pm 2\sqrt{2}$

56. $\dfrac{-5 \pm i\sqrt{47}}{4}$

57. $\dfrac{3 \pm i\sqrt{23}}{4}$

58. $f(x) = -x^2 + 2x + 3$

59. $f(x) = 2x^2 + 24x + 75$

60. $x^3 + 3x^2 + 3x + 1$

61. $x^3 - 9x^2 + 27x - 27$

62. $x^4 - 8x^3 + 24x^2 - 32x + 16$

63. $x^2 - 2x + 1$

64. $x^3 + 15x^2 + 75x + 125$

65. $-x^3 + 12x^2 + 48x + 64$

 **Challenge**

47. Use the Fundamental Theorem of Algebra and the Conjugate Root Theorem to show that any odd degree polynomial equation with real coefficients has at least one real root.

48. Reasoning What is the maximum number of points of intersection between the graphs of a quartic and a quintic polynomial function?

49. Reasoning What is the least possible degree of a polynomial with rational coefficients, leading coefficient 1, constant term 5, and zeros at $\sqrt{2}$ and $\sqrt{3}$? Show that such a polynomial has a rational zero and indicate this zero.

Standardized Test Prep

SAT/ACT

50. How many roots does $f(x) = x^4 + 5x^3 + 3x^2 + 2x + 6$ have?

Ⓐ 5   Ⓑ 4   Ⓒ 3   Ⓓ 2

51. Which translation takes $y = |x + 2| - 1$ to $y = |x| + 2$?

Ⓕ 2 units right, 3 units down   Ⓗ 2 units left, 3 units up

Ⓖ 2 units right, 3 units up   Ⓘ 2 units left, 3 units down

52. What is the factored form of the expression $x^4 - 3x^3 + 2x^2$?

Ⓐ $x^2(x - 1)(x + 2)$ Ⓒ $x^2(x + 1)(x - 2)$

Ⓑ $x^2(x + 1)(x + 2)$ Ⓓ $x^2(x - 1)(x - 2)$

Short Response

53. How would you test whether $(2, -2)$ is a solution of the system? $\begin{cases} y < -2x + 3 \\ y \geq x - 4 \end{cases}$

Mixed Review

54. Find a fourth-degree polynomial equation with real coefficients that has $2i$ and $-3 + i$ as roots.

◀ See Lesson 5-5.

Solve each equation using the Quadratic Formula.

◀ See Lesson 4-7.

55. $x^2 - 6x + 1 = 0$ **56.** $2x^2 + 5x = -9$ **57.** $2(x^2 + 2) = 3x$

Determine whether a quadratic model exists for each set of values. If so, write the model.

◀ See Lesson 4-3.

58. $f(-1) = 0, f(2) = 3, f(1) = 4$ **59.** $f(-4) = 11, f(-5) = 5, f(-6) = 3$

Get Ready! To prepare for Lesson 5-7, do Exercises 60–65.

◀ See Lesson 4-2.

Write each polynomial in standard form.

60. $(x + 1)^3$ **61.** $(x - 3)^3$ **62.** $(x - 2)^4$

63. $(x - 1)^2$ **64.** $(x + 5)^3$ **65.** $(4 - x)^3$

Lesson Resources

Additional Instructional Support

Algebra 2 Companion

Students can use the **Algebra 2 Companion** worktext (4 pages) as you teach the lesson. Use the Companion to support

- New Vocabulary
- Key Concepts
- Got It for each Problem
- Lesson Check

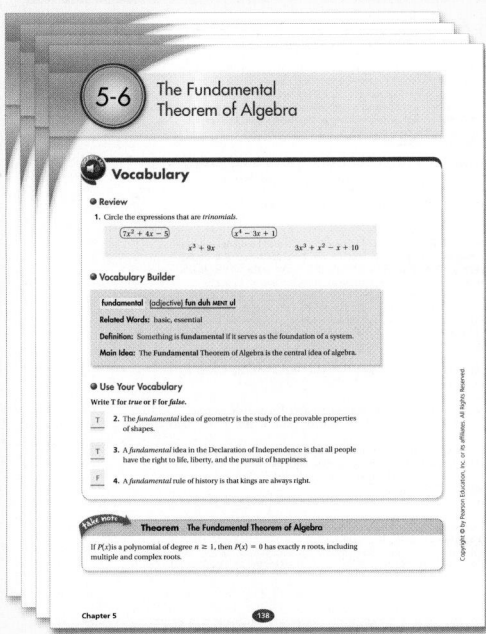

ELL Support

Use Graphic Organizers Have students label six index cards as shown. Add notes to the bottom three cards such as, "Use synthetic division when a real root is known," and "Use factoring when the polynomial is factorable." When solving a problem, students line up the first three cards as indicated. The last three cards depend on the problem.

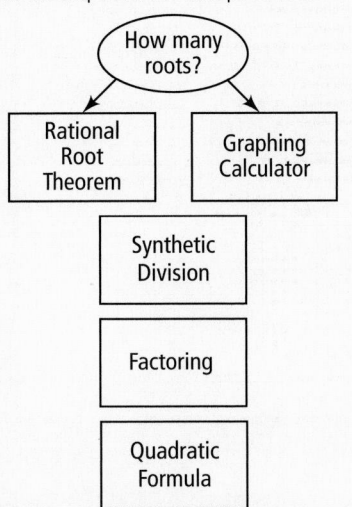

5 Assess & Remediate

Lesson Quiz

1. What are all the complex roots of $x^4 - 8x^2 = x^3 - 8x$?

2. **Do you UNDERSTAND?** What are the zeros of $f(x) = x^4 + x^3 - 3x^2 - 4x - 4$?

ANSWERS TO LESSON QUIZ

1. $0, 1, \pm 2\sqrt{2}$
2. $\pm 2, \dfrac{-1 \pm i\sqrt{3}}{2}$

PRESCRIPTION FOR REMEDIATION

Use the student work on the Lesson Quiz to prescribe a differentiated review assignment:

Points	Differentiated Remediation
0	Intervention
1	On-level
2	Extension

PowerAlgebra.com

5 Assess & Remediate

Assign the Lesson Quiz. Appropriate intervention, practice, or enrichment is automatically generated based on student performance.

Differentiated Remediation

Available in editable format online.

Intervention

- **Reteaching** (2 pages) Provides reteaching and practice exercises for the key lesson concepts. Use with struggling students or absent students.

- **English Language Learner Support** Helps students develop and reinforce mathematical vocabulary and key concepts.

All-in-One Resources/Online
Reteaching

5-6 Reteaching
The Fundamental Theorem of Algebra

Problem

What are all the complex roots of $x^4 + x^3 - 2x^2 + 4x - 24 = 0$?
Because this is a fourth-degree polynomial, you know it will have four roots.

Step 1 Because the polynomial is already in standard form, you can use the Rational Root Theorem to determine possible rational roots. The possible rational roots are: $\pm 1, \pm 2, \pm 3, \pm 4, \pm 6, \pm 8, \pm 12, \pm 24$.

Step 2 Evaluate the polynomial for each possible root until you find one that causes the polynomial to equal zero. This is a rational root. In this case, one rational root is 2.

Step 3 Use synthetic division with a divisor of 2 to begin factoring the polynomial.

$$\begin{array}{r|rrrr} 2 & 1 & 1 & -2 & 4 & -24 \\ & & 2 & 6 & 8 & 24 \\ \hline & 1 & 3 & 4 & 12 & 0 \end{array}$$

$x^3 + 3x^2 + 4x + 12 = 0$

Step 4 Repeat Steps 1–3 until you have a polynomial of degree 2 or less.

$$\begin{array}{r|rrrr} -3 & 1 & 3 & 4 & 12 \\ & & -3 & 0 & -12 \\ \hline & 1 & 0 & 4 & 0 \end{array}$$

$x^2 + 4 = 0$

Step 5 If the dividend is a second-degree polynomial, factor to find any additional roots. If the dividend does not factor easily, use the Quadratic Formula to find the additional roots.

$$\dfrac{-0 \pm \sqrt{0^2 - 4(1)(4)}}{2(1)} = \dfrac{\pm\sqrt{-16}}{2} = \dfrac{\pm 4i}{2} = \pm 2i$$

The four roots of $x^4 + x^3 - 4x^2 + 2x - 24 = 0$ are 2, −3, 2i, and −2i.

Exercises

Find all the complex roots of each polynomial.

1. $x^4 - 8x^3 + 11x^2 + 40x - 80$
   $4, \sqrt{5}, -\sqrt{5}$
2. $4x^4 - x^3 - 12x^2 + 4x - 16$
   $2, -2, \frac{1 + 3i\sqrt{7}}{8}, \frac{1 - 3i\sqrt{7}}{8}$
3. $x^6 + 2x^5 + 7x^4 + 20x^3 - 21x^2 + 18x - 27$
   $-3, 1, 3i, -3i, i, -i$
4. $x^3 - 4x^2 + 4x - 16$
   $4, 2i, -2i$

All-in-One Resources/Online
English Language Learner Support

5-6 Additional Vocabulary Support
The Fundamental Theorem of Algebra

Choose the word from the list that best completes each sentence.

complex roots	degree	Fundamental Theorem of Algebra
Quadratic Formula	synthetic division	

1. The _____degree_____ of a polynomial is the greatest degree among its monomial terms.

2. _____Synthetic division_____ can be used to factor a polynomial.

3. The degree of a polynomial tells you how many _____complex roots_____ the equation has.

4. The _____Fundamental Theorem of Algebra_____ states that the number of complex roots of a polynomial equation is equal to the degree of the polynomial.

5. The _____Quadratic Formula_____ can be used to find the complex roots of a quadratic equation.

Use your knowledge of the Fundamental Theorem of Algebra to answer the following question.

6. Which of the following statements does not correctly state the Fundamental Theorem of Algebra? B
   A. Every polynomial equation of degree $n \geq 1$ with complex coefficients has exactly n complex roots, including multiple roots.
   B. Every polynomial of degree $n \geq 1$ with complex coefficients has exactly $n + 1$ complex roots.
   C. Every polynomial function of degree $n \geq 1$ with complex coefficients has at least one complex zero.
   D. Every polynomial equation of degree $n \geq 1$ with complex coefficients has no less than one complex root.

Use your knowledge of the Fundamental Theorem of Algebra to identify the number of complex roots for each polynomial equation.

7. $x^4 + 2x^3 - x^2 + 2 = 0$ _____4 complex roots_____

8. $x^5 - 3x^4 + 2x^2 + 5x - 1 = 0$ _____5 complex roots_____

9. $x + 5 = 0$ _____1 complex root_____

10. $x^2 - 4x - 2 = 0$ _____2 complex roots_____

Differentiated Remediation *continued*

Available in editable format online.

On-Level

- **Practice** (2 pages) Provides extra practice for each lesson. For simpler practice exercises, use the Form K Practice pages found in the All-in-One Teaching Resources and online.
- **Think About a Plan** Helps students develop specific problem-solving skills and strategies by providing scaffolded guiding questions.
- **Standardized Test Prep** Focuses on all major exercises, all major question types, and helps students prepare for the high-stakes assessments.

Extension

- **Enrichment** Provides students with interesting problems and activities that extend the concepts of the lesson.
- **Activities, Games, and Puzzles** Worksheets that can be used for concepts development, enrichment, and for fun!

Practice and Problem Solving Wkbk/ All-in-One Resources/Online

Practice page 1

5-6 Practice — Form G
The Fundamental Theorem of Algebra

Without using a calculator, find all the complex roots of each equation.

1. $x^5 - 3x^4 - 8x^3 - 8x^2 - 9x - 5 = 0$ — $5, -1, -1, i, -i$
2. $x^3 - 2x^2 + 4x - 8 = 0$ — $-2, 2i, -2i$
3. $x^3 + x^2 - x + 2 = 0$ — $-2, \frac{1 + i\sqrt{3}}{2}, \frac{1 - i\sqrt{3}}{2}$
4. $x^4 - 2x^3 - x^2 - 4x - 6 = 0$ — $3, -1, i\sqrt{2}, -i\sqrt{2}$
5. $x^4 + 3x^3 - 21x^2 - 48x + 80 = 0$ — $4, -4, \frac{-3 + \sqrt{29}}{2}, \frac{-3 - \sqrt{29}}{2}$
6. $x^5 - 3x^4 + x^3 + x^2 + 4 = 0$ — $2, 2, -1, i, -i$

Find all the zeros of each function.

7. $y = 5x^3 - 5x$ — $-1, 0, 1$
8. $f(x) = x^3 - 16x$ — $-4, 0, 4$
9. $g(x) = 12x^3 - 2x^2 - 2x$ — $-\frac{1}{3}, 0, \frac{1}{2}$
10. $y = 6x^3 + x^2 - x$ — $-\frac{1}{2}, 0, \frac{1}{3}$
11. $f(x) = 5x^3 + 6x^2 + x$ — $-1, -\frac{1}{5}, 0$
12. $y = -4x^3 + 100x$ — $-5, 0, 5$

For each equation, state the number of complex roots, the possible number of real roots, and the possible rational roots.

13. $2x^2 + 5x + 3 = 0$ — 2; 2 or 0; $\pm1, \pm3, \pm\frac{1}{2}, \pm\frac{3}{2}$
14. $3x^2 + 11x - 10 = 0$ — 2; 2 or 0; $\pm1, \pm2, \pm5, \pm10, \pm\frac{1}{3}, \pm\frac{2}{3}, \pm\frac{5}{3}, \pm\frac{10}{3}$
15. $2x^4 - 18x^2 + 5 = 0$ — 4; 4, 2 or 0; $\pm1, \pm5, \pm\frac{1}{2}, \pm\frac{5}{2}$
16. $4x^3 - 12x + 9 = 0$ — 3; 3 or 1; $\pm1, \pm3, \pm9, \pm\frac{1}{2}, \pm\frac{3}{2}, \pm\frac{9}{2}, \pm\frac{1}{4}, \pm\frac{3}{4}, \pm\frac{9}{4}$
17. $6x^5 - 28x + 15 = 0$ — 5; 5, 3, or 1; $\pm1, \pm3, \pm5, \pm15, \pm\frac{1}{2}, \pm\frac{3}{2}, \pm\frac{5}{2}, \pm\frac{15}{2}, \pm\frac{1}{3}, \pm\frac{5}{3}, \pm\frac{1}{6}, \pm\frac{5}{6}$
18. $x^3 - x^2 - 2x + 7 = 0$ — 3; 3, or 1; $\pm1, \pm7$
19. $x^3 - 6x^2 - 7x - 12 = 0$ — 3; 3 or 1; $\pm1, \pm2, \pm3, \pm4, \pm6, \pm12$
20. $2x^4 + x^2 - x + 6 = 0$ — 4; 4, 2, or 0; $\pm1, \pm2, \pm3, \pm6, \pm\frac{1}{2}, \pm\frac{3}{2}$
21. $4x^5 - 5x^4 + x^3 - 2x^2 + 2x - 6 = 0$ — 5; 5, 3, or 1; $\pm1, \pm2, \pm3, \pm6, \pm\frac{1}{2}, \pm\frac{3}{2}, \pm\frac{1}{4}, \pm\frac{3}{4}$
22. $7x^6 + 3x^4 - 9x^2 + 18 = 0$ — 6; 6, 4, 2 or 0; $\pm1, \pm2, \pm3, \pm6, \pm9, \pm18, \pm\frac{1}{7}, \pm\frac{2}{7}, \pm\frac{3}{7}, \pm\frac{6}{7}, \pm\frac{9}{7}, \pm\frac{18}{7}$
23. $5 + x + x^2 + x^3 + x^4 + x^5 = 0$ — 5; 5, 3, or 1; $\pm1, \pm5$
24. $6 - x + 2x^3 - x^3 + x^4 - 8x^5 = 0$ — 5; 5, 3, or 1; $\pm1, \pm2, \pm3, \pm6, \pm\frac{1}{2}, \pm\frac{3}{2}, \pm\frac{1}{4}, \pm\frac{3}{4}, \pm\frac{1}{8}, \pm\frac{3}{8}$

Find the number of complex roots for each equation.

25. $x^8 - 5x^6 + x^4 + 2x - 16 = 0$ — 8
26. $x^{10} - 100 = 0$ — 10
27. $2x^4 + x^3 - 3x^2 + 4x - 2 = 0$ — 4
28. $-4x^3 + x^2 - 3x + 10 = 0$ — 3
29. $x^6 + 2x^5 + 3x^4 + 4x^3 + 5x^2 + 6x + 10 = 0$ — 6
30. $-3x^5 + 4x^4 + 5x^2 - 15 = 0$ — 5

Practice and Problem Solving Wkbk/ All-in-One Resources/Online

Practice page 2

5-6 Practice (continued) — Form G
The Fundamental Theorem of Algebra

Find all the zeros of each function.

31. $f(x) = x^3 - 9x^2 + 27x - 27$ — 3
32. $y = 2x^3 - 8x^2 + 18x - 72$ — $4, -3i, 3i$
33. $y = x^3 - 10x - 12$ — $-2, 1 \pm \sqrt{7}$
34. $y = x^3 - 4x^2 + 8$ — $2, 1 \pm \sqrt{5}$
35. $f(x) = 2x^3 + x - 3$ — $1, \frac{-1 \pm i\sqrt{5}}{2}$
36. $y = x^3 - 2x^2 - 11x + 12$ — $-3, 1, 4$
37. $g(x) = x^3 + 4x^2 + 7x + 28$ — $-4, -i\sqrt{7}, i\sqrt{7}$
38. $f(x) = x^3 + 3x^2 + 6x + 4$ — $-1, -1 \pm i\sqrt{3}$
39. $g(x) = x^4 - 5x^2 - 36$ — $-3, 3, -2i, 2i$
40. $y = x^4 - 7x^2 + 12$ — $-2, 2, -\sqrt{3}, \sqrt{3}$
41. $y = 9x^4 + 5x^2 - 4$ — $-\frac{2}{3}, \frac{2}{3}, -i, i$
42. $y = 4x^4 - 11x^2 - 3$ — $-\sqrt{3}, \sqrt{3}, -\frac{1}{2}i, \frac{1}{2}i$
43. **Error Analysis** Your friend says that the equation $4x^7 - 3x^3 + 4x^2 - x + 2 = 0$ has 5 complex roots. You say that the equation has 7 complex roots. Who is correct? What mistake was made?
You are correct. Your friend may have counted the number of terms in the equation instead of using the Fundamental Theorem of Algebra.
44. A section of roller coaster can be modeled by the function $f(x) = x^5 - 5x^4 - 31x^3 + 113x^2 + 282x - 360$. A walkway bridge will be placed at one of the zeros. What are the possible locations for the walkway bridge? $-4, -3, 1, 5, 6$
45. **Writing** Using the Fundamental Theorem of Algebra, explain how $x^3 = 0$ has 3 roots and 3 linear factors. The Fundamental Theorem of Algebra says that the degree of the function is equal to the number of zeros. The degree of $x^3 = 0$ is 3. x^3 can be written as $x \cdot x \cdot x = 0$ or $(x - 0)(x - 0)(x - 0) = 0$. This shows that there are 3 linear factors and 3 zeros, all equal to 0.
46. How many complex roots does the equation $x^4 = 256$ have? What are they?
4 complex roots; $4, -4, 4i, -4i$
47. **Reasoning** Can a fifth-degree polynomial with rational coefficients have 4 real roots and 1 irrational root? Explain why or why not?
No; a polynomial with rational coefficients cannot have only 1 irrational root, it must have both conjugates. So, a fifth-degree polynomial can have 0, 2 or 4 irrational roots and 5, 3 or 1 real roots.

All-in-One Resources/Online

Enrichment

5-6 Enrichment
The Fundamental Theorem of Algebra

The Fundamental Theorem of Algebra tells us that a polynomial, $P(x)$, of degree $n \geq 1$ has exactly n complex roots. An equivalent statement is that a polynomial, $P(x)$, of degree $n \geq 1$ can be factored into n linear factors. Linear factors are the building blocks for every polynomial. Let's consider a similar theorem that applies to the building blocks of all positive integers. The Fundamental Theorem of Arithmetic states that every integer $N > 1$ can be uniquely written as a product of finitely many prime numbers.

1. Explain why $N > 1$ is a condition of the Fundamental Theorem of Arithmetic.
Answers may vary. Sample: The number 1 is not considered prime because it cannot be written as a product of 1 and another number.
2. Write the number 36 as a product of primes. $36 = 2 \times 2 \times 3 \times 3$
3. The Fundamental Theorem of Arithmetic tells us that there is only one way to write 36 as a product of prime numbers. The prime factors of 36 can be rearranged but will always be a form of $2^2 \times 3^2$. Write the number 48 as a product of primes. Express your answer using exponents. $48 = 2^4 \times 3^1$

Knowing the prime factorization of a number gives us complete knowledge of all of the factors of that number. For example, once we know that the prime factorization of 100 is $2^2 \times 5^2$ we know that other factors of 100 will be $2 \times 5^2 = 50$, $2^2 \times 5 = 20$, $2^0 \times 5 = 5$ or $2 \times 5^0 = 2$.

4. Write the number 600 as a product of primes expressed using exponents.
$600 = 2^3 \times 3^1 \times 5^2$
5. Use your prime factorization to determine all of the other factors of 600.
1, 2, 3, 4, 5, 6, 8, 10, 12, 15, 20, 24, 25, 30, 40, 50, 60, 75, 100, 120, 150, 200, 300, 600
6. If the prime factorization can help you determine the factors of an integer, can the factored form of a polynomial help you determine nonlinear factors of a polynomial? For example, if $P(x) = (x - 1)(x + 2)(x - 5)$, then what are 3 quadratic factors of $P(x)$?
$(x - 1)(x + 2) = x^2 + x - 2$, $(x - 1)(x - 5) = x^2 - 6x + 5$, $(x + 2)(x - 5) = x^2 - 3x - 10$
7. Describe the similarities between the Fundamental Theorem of Algebra and the Fundamental Theorem of Arithmetic.
Answers may vary. Sample: Both theorems describe the number and types of factors. One addresses factors of a number and the other address factors of a polynomial.

Practice and Problem Solving Wkbk/ All-in-One Resources/Online

Think About a Plan

5-6 Think About a Plan
The Fundamental Theorem of Algebra

Bridges A twist in a river can be modeled by the function $f(x) = \frac{1}{3}x^3 + \frac{1}{2}x^2 - x$, $-3 \leq x \leq 2$. A city wants to build a road that goes directly along the x-axis. How many bridges would it have to build?

Know

1. The function has exactly 3 complex roots.
2. Check students' work.
3. Check students' work.

Need

4. To solve the problem I need to:
find the number of real roots of the function on the interval $-3 \leq x \leq 2$.

Plan

5. Graph the function on a graphing calculator. What viewing window should you use?
Answers may vary. Sample: Xmin = −5, Xmax = 5, Ymin = −5, Ymax = 5
6. What does the graph tell you?
The function has 3 real roots on the interval $-3 \leq x \leq 2$.
7. How many bridges would the city have to build? 3
Explain.
Answers may vary. Sample: Because the function has 3 real roots, it crosses the x-axis 3 times. So, the road will cross the river 3 times.

Practice and Problem Solving Wkbk/ All-in-One Resources/Online

Standardized Test Prep

5-6 Standardized Test Prep
The Fundamental Theorem of Algebra

Multiple Choice

For Exercises 1–6, choose the correct letter.

1. Which number is a zero of $f(x) = x^3 + 6x^2 + 9x$ with multiplicity 1? B
A. -3 B. 0 C. 1 D. 3
2. One root of the equation $x^3 + x^2 - 2 = 0$ is 1. What are the other two roots? F
F. $-1 \pm i$ G. $1 \pm 2i$ H. $\pm1 + 2i$ I. $\pm1 - i$
3. A polynomial with real coefficients has 3, $2i$, and $-i$ as three of its zeros. What is the least possible degree of the polynomial? C
A. 3 B. 4 C. 5 D. 6
4. How many times does the graph of $x^3 + 27$ cross the x-axis? G
F. 0 G. 1 H. 2 I. 4
5. Which of the following is the polynomial with zeros at 1, $-\frac{3}{2}$, $2i$, and $-2i$? A
A. $2x^4 + x^3 + 5x^2 + 4x - 12$
B. $2x^4 - x^3 + 5x^2 - 4x - 12$
C. $2x^4 + x^3 - 11x^2 - 4x + 12$
D. $2x^4 - x^3 - 11x^2 + 4x + 12$
6. A polynomial with real coefficients has roots of 6, -2, $-4i$, and $\sqrt{5}$. Which of the following *must* be another root of this polynomial? I
F. -6 G. $-\sqrt{5}$ H. 2 I. $4i$

Short Response

7. One root of the equation $x^4 - 4x^3 - 6x^2 + 4x + 5 = 0$ is -1. How many complex roots does this equation have? What are all the roots? Show your work. There are 4 complex roots.

[2] Use known zero as divisor and synthetic division to begin factoring. Then use Rational Root Theorem to determine that ±1 and ±5 are possible rational roots. Try each possible rational root until you find a root. Factor the remaining quadratic function to find the remaining roots. The roots are 1, −1, −1, 5.
[1] correct answer without work shown
[0] incorrect answers and no work shown OR no answers given

−1	1	−4	−6	4	5
		−1	5	1	−5
	1	−5	−1	5	0

1	1	−5	−1	5
		1	−4	−5
	1	−4	−5	0

Online Teacher Resource Center

Activities, Games, and Puzzles

5-6 Puzzle: An Unlikely Find
The Fundamental Theorem of Algebra

A complex number plane with several points marked with dots is shown below. Most of these points represent solutions to the questions below.

- Write the missing zero(s) for each polynomial function.
- On the complex number plane, cross out the points representing the missing zeros you find, as well as the given zeros.
- When you finish crossing out the points representing the zeros, connect the remaining points to find the solution to the puzzle.
- Write the answer to the puzzle.

Find the missing zeros.

1. degree 4 polynomial function with zeros $2 + 3i, 4 - 2i$ — $2 - 3i, 4 + 2i$
2. degree 4 polynomial function with zeros $-5 + 3i, 3 - 2i$ — $-5 - 3i, 3 + 2i$
3. degree 6 polynomial function with zeros $4 + i, 5 - 2i, -5 + i$ — $4 - i, 5 + 2i, -5 - i$
4. degree 6 polynomial function with zeros $-2 - 4i, -5 - 5i, -4 - i$ — $-2 + 4i, -5 + 5i, -4 + i$
5. degree 5 polynomial function with zeros $4, -3i, 4i$ — $3i, -4i$
6. degree 5 polynomial function with zeros $5, 3, -2, -5 + 6i$ — $-5 - 6i$
7. degree 2 polynomial function with zero $-2 - 5i$ — $-2 + 5i$
8. degree 2 polynomial function with zero $5 - 6i$ — $5 + 6i$
9. degree 3 polynomial function with zeros $-1, 2 - 6i$ — $2 + 6i$
10. degree 2 polynomial function with zeros $-6, -3$ — no more solutions

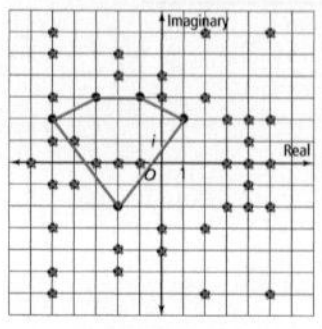

Puzzle: You might find one of these in the rough: a diamond

Graphing Polynomials Using Zeros

Common Core State Standards

A-APR.B.3 Identify zeros of polynomials when suitable factorizations are available, and use the zeros to construct a rough graph of the function defined by the polynomial.

MP 7

In this activity you will learn how to sketch the graph of a polynomial function by using the zeros, turning points, and end behavior.

Example

Sketch the graph of the function $f(x) = (x - 3)(x + 1)(x - 2)$.

Step 1 Identify the zeros and plot them on a coordinate grid.

$$f(x) = (x - 3)(x + 1)(x - 2)$$
$$0 = (x - 3)(x + 1)(x - 2)$$

$0 = x - 3$	or $0 = x + 1$	or $0 = x - 2$
$3 = x$	$-1 = x$	$2 = x$

The function has zeros at $(3, 0)$, $(-1, 0)$, and $(2, 0)$.

Step 2 Determine whether the polynomial is positive or negative over each interval.

To determine whether $f(x)$ is positive or negative over the interval $x < -1$, choose an x-value within the interval. Let $x = -2$. Then evaluate $f(-2)$.

$$f(-2) = (-2 - 3)(-2 + 1)(-2 - 2) = (-5)(-1)(-4) = -20$$

$f(x)$ is negative over the interval $x < -1$.

Repeat the process for the intervals $-1 < x < 2$, $2 < x < 3$, and $x > 3$.

Interval	x	$f(x)$
$x < -1$	-2	-20
$-1 < x < 2$	0	6
$2 < x < 3$	2.5	-0.875
$x > 3$	4	10

Step 3 Sketch the graph.

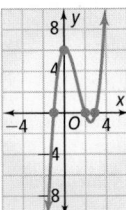

Exercises

Sketch a graph of each function. Check your answer using a graphing calculator.

1. $h(x) = (x + 6)(x - 7)$

2. $g(x) = (x + 1)(x - 3)(x - 5)$

3. $p(x) = x(x + 4)(x - 4)$

4. $h(x) = (x + 2)(x - 3)(x + 1)(x - 1)$

5. $f(x) = x^4 - 8x^2 + 16$

6. $k(x) = x^4 - 10x^2 + 9$

PowerAlgebra.com | Concept Byte Graphing Polynomials Using Zeros | **325**

Answers

Exercises

1.

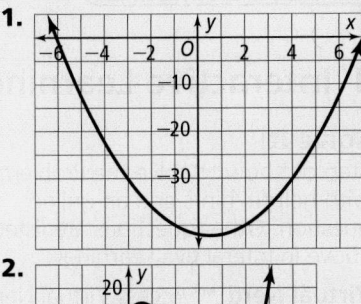

2.

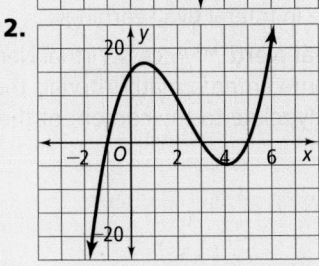

3.

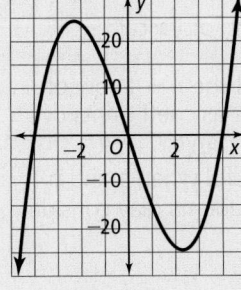

4.

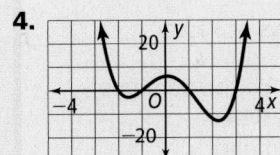

5–6. See back of book.

Guided Instruction

PURPOSE To use information about polynomial functions such as zeros, turning points, and end behavior to sketch the graph of the function.

PROCESS Students will

- use the factored form of a polynomial function to determine its zeros.
- determine whether the values of the function are positive or negative for each interval defined by the zeros.
- sketch the graph of the function.

DISCUSS The zeros of a function represent the values where the graph of the function crosses or touches the x-axis. Once these values are known, students can determine whether the graph of the function is above or below the x-axis for intervals defined by the zeros. Then students can use this information to sketch the graph of the function. The sketches do not have to be exact graphs of the functions. For this activity, students just need to determine the general look of the graph.

Example

This Example shows how to make a rough sketch of the function $f(x) = (x - 3)(x + 1)(x - 2)$ using information about its zeros.

Q What are the zeros of the function $f(x) = (x - 3)(x + 1)(x - 2)$ listed from least to greatest? **[–1, 2, 3]**

Q Can the function have both positive and negative values for values of x between –1 and 2? Explain. **[No; if the function had both positive and negative values for values of x between –1 and 2, then the function would have to cross the x-axis between –1 and 2. But there are no zeros between –1 and 2.]**

Q Can you graph a function using just the zeros of the function? **[No; you need to find additional points to determine whether the graph lies above or below the x-axis and you may need to approximate turning points.]**

Q How could you check to see if your sketch of the graph is approximately correct? **[Graph the function on a graphing calculator and compare the resulting graph with the sketch.]**

VISUAL LEARNERS

Have students locate the zeros on a coordinate plane. Explain to them that these are the only places where the graph can cross the x-axis. Between these points, the graph of the function must be either above or below the x-axis.

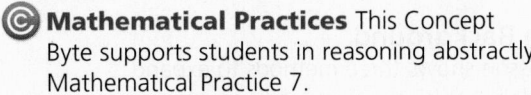 **Mathematical Practices** This Concept Byte supports students in reasoning abstractly, Mathematical Practice 7.

1 Interactive Learning

Solve It!

PURPOSE To find patterns within the numbers of ways to choose items from a group

PROCESS Students may

- make systematic lists of all arrangements and count the number of unique subgroups.
- solve simpler problems with fewer letters and recognize geometric or numeric patterns.
- use prior knowledge of counting techniques to calculate the number of combinations.

FACILITATE

Q In the diagram shown, why is BA not listed? **[Order is not important; BA is equivalent to AB.]**

Q How does the diagram represent a "systematic" method? **[The first row shows A paired with all other letters; the second row shows B paired with all other letters except A; the third row shows C paired with all other letters except A or B; the last row shows D paired with all other letters except A, B, or C.]**

ANSWER See Solve It in Answers on next page.

CONNECT THE MATH In the Solve It, students use patterns to calculate numbers of combinations. Numbers of combinations may also be calculated from the coefficients of a binomial expansion or Pascal's Triangle.

© **Common Core State Standards**
A-APR.C.5 Know and apply the Binomial Theorem for the expansion of $(x + y)^n$ in powers of x and y for a positive integer n, where x and y are any numbers, with coefficients determined for example by Pascal's Triangle.
MP 1, MP 3, MP 8

Objectives To expand a binomial using Pascal's Triangle
To use the Binomial Theorem

When counting seems complicated, it helps to be systematic.

© **MATHEMATICAL PRACTICES**

Getting Ready!

How many unique letter combinations are possible using each of the following?
a. 2 of 5 letters   b. 3 of 5 letters
c. 2 of 6 letters   d. 4 of 6 letters
e. 3 of 6 letters
Justify your reasoning.
Hint: Use the diagram, a previous response, or both. The same letters in different orders are one combination.

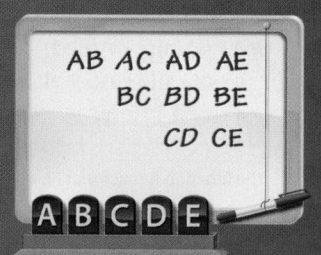

AB AC AD AE
BC BD BE
CD CE

A B C D E

Lesson Vocabulary
- expand
- Pascal's Triangle
- Binomial Theorem

There is a connection between the triangular pattern of numbers in the Solve It and the expansion of $(a + b)^n$.

Essential Understanding You can use a pattern of coefficients and the pattern $a^n, a^{n-1}b, a^{n-2}b^2, \ldots, a^2b^{n-2}, ab^{n-1}, b^n$ to write the expansion of $(a + b)^n$.

You can *expand* $(a + b)^3$ using the Distributive Property.

$$(a + b)^3 = (a + b)(a + b)(a + b) = a^3 + 3a^2b + 3ab^2 + b^3$$

To **expand** the power of a binomial in general, first multiply as needed. Then write the polynomial in standard form.

Consider the expansions of $(a + b)^n$ for the first few values of n:

Row	Power	Expanded Form	Coefficients Only
0	$(a + b)^0$	1	1
1	$(a + b)^1$	$1a^1 + 1b^1$	1 1
2	$(a + b)^2$	$1a^2 + 2a^1b^1 + 1b^2$	1 2 1
3	$(a + b)^3$	$1a^3 + 3a^2b^1 + 3a^1b^2 + 1b^3$	1 3 3 1
4	$(a + b)^4$	$1a^4 + 4a^3b^1 + 6a^2b^2 + 4a^1b^3 + 1b^4$	1 4 6 4 1

5-7 Preparing to Teach

BIG idea Equivalence

ESSENTIAL UNDERSTANDINGS

- A pattern of coefficients and the pattern $a^n, a^{n-1}b, a^{n-2}b^2, \ldots, a^1b^{n-1}, b^n$, can be used to write the expansion of $(a + b)^n$.
- To expand the power of a binomial in general, first multiply as needed. Then write the polynomial in standard form.

Math Background

This lesson shows three methods to expand binomials. For binomial $(a + b)^n$:

DISTRIBUTIVE PROPERTY

- Remove the power by rewriting the binomial as a product of n binomials.
- Multiply out, one binomial at a time.
- Simplify by combining like terms.

The Distributive Property works well if n is small. If n is large, calculations are time-consuming and lead to errors.

PASCAL'S TRIANGLE

- Generate $n + 1$ rows of Pascal's Triangle.
- Use the numbers of the $n + 1$ row of the triangle in order as coefficients of $a^n + a^{n-1}b + \ldots + ab^{n-1} + b^n$.

Pascal's Triangle is useful when a and b are both variables. Students may consider it a trick or shortcut.

BINOMIAL THEOREM

- Generate $n + 1$ rows of Pascal's Triangle.
- Let $P_0, P_1, \ldots, P_n$ be the numbers of the $n + 1$ row in order.
- Use the general formula $(a + b)^n = P_0a^n + P_1a^{n-1}b + \ldots + P_{n-1}ab^{n-1} + P_nb^n$.
- If a or b is not a variable, simplify.

© **Mathematical Practices**

Look for and express regularity in repeated reasoning. Students will use Pascal's Triangle as a shortcut in finding the coefficients of a binomial raised to a power.

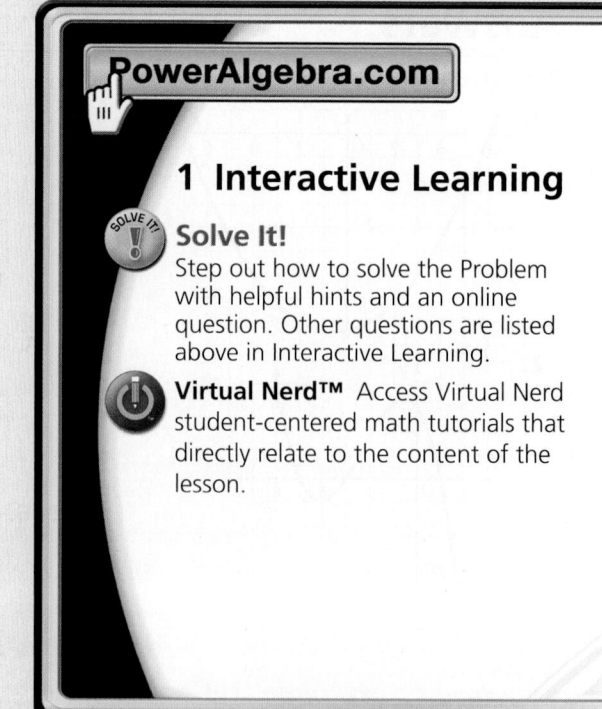

PowerAlgebra.com

1 Interactive Learning

Solve It!
Step out how to solve the Problem with helpful hints and an online question. Other questions are listed above in Interactive Learning.

Virtual Nerd™ Access Virtual Nerd student-centered math tutorials that directly relate to the content of the lesson.

The "coefficients only" column matches the numbers in *Pascal's Triangle*. **Pascal's Triangle**, named for the French mathematician Blaise Pascal (1623–1662), is a triangular array of numbers in which the first and last number of each row is 1. Each of the other numbers in the row is the sum of the two numbers above it.

For example, to generate row 5, use the sums of the adjacent elements in the row above it.

| Row | | | | | | Pascal's Triangle | | | | | | |

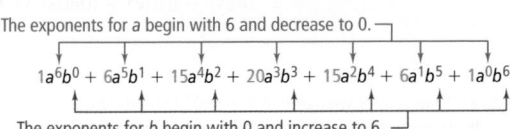

0							1						
1						1		1					
2					1		2		1				
3				1		3		3		1			
4			1		4		6		4		1		
5		1		5		10		10		5		1	
6	1		6		15		20		15		6		1
7	1	7		21		35		35		21		7	1
8	1	8	28		56		70		56		28	8	1

Plan

What row of Pascal's Triangle should you use for this expansion?
The expression is raised to the 6th power so use the 6th row.

Ⓒ **Problem 1** Using Pascal's Triangle

What is the expansion of $(a + b)^6$? Use Pascal's Triangle.

The exponents for a begin with 6 and decrease to 0.

$1a^6b^0 + 6a^5b^1 + 15a^4b^2 + 20a^3b^3 + 15a^2b^4 + 6a^1b^5 + 1a^0b^6$

The exponents for b begin with 0 and increase to 6.

$(a + b)^6 = a^6 + 6a^5b + 15a^4b^2 + 20a^3b^3 + 15a^2b^4 + 6ab^5 + b^6$.

✓ **Got It?** 1. What is the expansion of $(a + b)^8$? Use Pascal's Triangle.

The **Binomial Theorem** gives a general formula for expanding a binomial.

take note

Theorem Binomial Theorem

For every positive integer n,

$(a + b)^n = P_0a^n + P_1a^{n-1}b + P_2a^{n-2}b^2 + \cdots + P_{n-1}ab^{n-1} + P_nb^n$

where $P_0, P_1, \ldots, P_n$ are the numbers in the nth row of Pascal's Triangle.

---

2 Guided Instruction

To help students better understand Pascal's Triangle, use the following activity:
- Close the book.
- Place the 1 on the top of your page.
- Write two more 1's below it.
- Generate each row. For each new term, add the adjacent terms above it.
- Make your triangle as large as you can, and compare it with a partner's triangle.

Problem 1

It is possible to expand the power by repeatedly applying the Distributive Property, but the method of using Pascal's Triangle is much simpler.

> **Q** How many terms are in the expansion? **[7]**
> **Q** Do you see any pattern in the coefficients? **[They increase from the left to the middle, and decrease from the middle to the right in symmetrical fashion.]**

Got It?

It can be helpful to include the powers a^0 and b^0 in the expansion to see how the power of each variable is incremented in each term.

> **Q** What would be the coefficient of a^{20} in $(a + b)^{20}$? **[1]**

Take Note

The rules for expanding the square or cube of a binomial are the same as in the Binomial Theorem for $n = 2$ and $n = 3$.

> **Q** Which coefficients are the same as the power of the binomial? **[The second and the second to last.]**

---

2 Guided Instruction

 Each Problem is worked out and supported online.

Problem 1
Using Pascal's Triangle
Animated

Problem 2
Expanding a Binomial
Animated

Support in Algebra 2 Companion
- Vocabulary
- Key Concepts
- Got It?

Answers

Solve It!

a. 10; AB, AC, AD, AE, BC, BD, BE, CD, CE, DE

b. 10; ABC, ABD, ABE, ACD, ACE, ADE, BCD, BCE, BDE, CDE

c. 15; the combinations from part (a) and AF, BF, CF, DF, EF

d. 15; add an F to all combinations in part (b), and ABCD, ABCE, BCDE, ABDE, ACDE

e. 20; the combinations from part (b) and ABF, ACF, ADF, AEF, BCF, BDF, BEF, CDF, CEF, DEF

Got It?

1. $a^8 + 8a^7b + 28a^6b^2 + 56a^5b^3 + 70a^4b^4 + 56a^3b^5 + 28a^2b^6 + 8ab^7 + b^8$

Problem 2

When a binomial has a term with a coefficient other than 1, the coefficients of the expansion are not the same as the numbers in Pascal's Triangle.

> **Q** Which terms in the expansion have a negative coefficient? **[the terms with even powers of x]**

Got It?

> **Q** In 2a, how can you write the binomial in the form $(a + b)^n$? **[$(2x - 3)^4 = (2x + (-3))^4$]**
>
> **Q** Which terms in the expansion have a negative coefficient? **[the terms with odd powers of x]**

3 Lesson Check

Do you know HOW?

- In Exercises 3–4, the students may be confused by the coefficients of x or a. Suggest that they expand the binomial, replacing "x" with "$2x$" or "a" with "$3a$" in parentheses, and then simplify.

Do you UNDERSTAND?

- For Exercise 6, if students have difficulty understanding the relationship, suggest that they solve a problem with each method. Then have them compare the processes.

Close

> **Q** For what powers do the rows of Pascal's Triangle repeat the same number in the middle? **[odd powers]**
>
> **Q** Why is it easier to use the Binomial Theorem than expanding the power using the Distributive Property? **[Answers may vary. Sample: For greater powers, there are too many terms to write out to use the Distributive Property easily.]**

When you use the Binomial Theorem to expand $(x - 2)^4$, $a = x$ and $b = -2$. To expand a binomial such as $(3x - 2)^5$, $a = 3x$ so remember that $a^4 = (3x)^4$ not $3x^4$.

 **Problem 2** Expanding a Binomial

What is the expansion of $(3x - 2)^5$? Use the Binomial Theorem.

Think	Write
For $(3x - 2)^5$, use the 5th row of Pascal's Triangle.	**Pascal's Triangle** 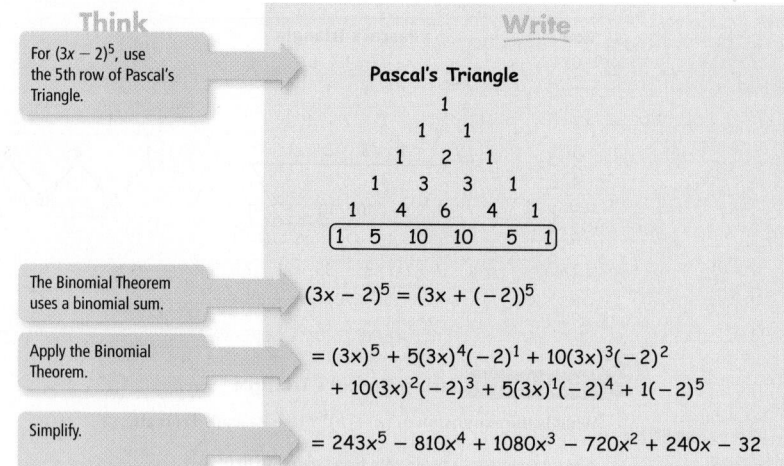
The Binomial Theorem uses a binomial sum.	$(3x - 2)^5 = (3x + (-2))^5$
Apply the Binomial Theorem.	$= (3x)^5 + 5(3x)^4(-2)^1 + 10(3x)^3(-2)^2 + 10(3x)^2(-2)^3 + 5(3x)^1(-2)^4 + 1(-2)^5$
Simplify.	$= 243x^5 - 810x^4 + 1080x^3 - 720x^2 + 240x - 32$

 Got It? 2. a. What is the expansion of $(2x - 3)^4$? Use the Binomial Theorem.

b. Reasoning Consider the following:

$$11^0 = 1 \qquad 11^1 = 11 \qquad 11^2 = 121 \qquad 11^3 = 1331 \qquad 11^4 = 14{,}641$$

Why do these powers of 11 have digits that mirror Pascal's Triangle?

Lesson Check

Do you know HOW?

Use Pascal's Triangle to expand each binomial.

1. $(x + a)^3$

2. $(x - 2)^5$

3. $(2x + 4)^2$

4. $(3a - 2)^3$

Do you UNDERSTAND?  MATHEMATICAL PRACTICES

5. **Vocabulary** Tell whether each expression can be expanded using the Binomial Theorem.
   a. $(2a - 6)^4$ b. $(5x^2 + 1)^5$ c. $(x^2 - 3x - 4)^3$

6. **Writing** Describe the relationship between Pascal's Triangle and the Binomial Theorem.

7. **Reasoning** Using Pascal's Triangle, determine the number of terms in the expansion of $(x + a)^{12}$. How many terms are there in the expansion of $(x + a)^n$?

Additional Problems

1. What is the expansion of $(x + 3)^4$?

   ANSWER $x^4 + 12x^3 + 54x^2 + 108x + 81$

2. What is the expansion of $(3 - z)^3$?

   ANSWER $27 - 27z + 9z^2 - z^3$

Answers

Got It? (continued)

2. **a.** $16x^4 - 96x^3 + 216x^2 - 216x + 81$

   b. If you express 11 as $(10 + 1)$ and calculate the powers using Pascal's triangle, it will be the coefficients.

Lesson Check

1. $x^3 + 3x^2a + 3xa^2 + a^3$

2. $x^5 - 10x^4 + 40x^3 - 80x^2 + 80x - 32$

3. $4x^2 + 16x + 16$

4. $27a^3 - 54a^2 + 36a - 8$

5. **a.** yes   **b.** yes   **c.** no

6. The coefficients for the expansion of $(a + b)^n$ are equal to the numbers in the nth row of Pascal's Triangle, respectively.

7. 13; $n + 1$

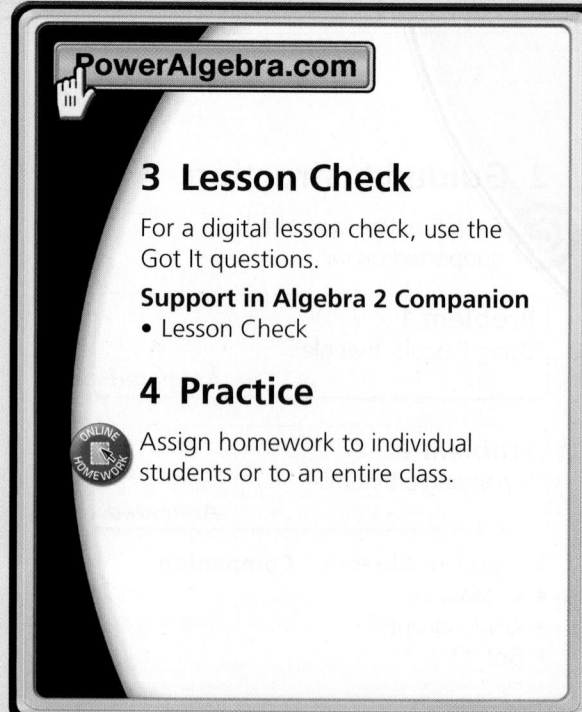

PowerAlgebra.com

3 Lesson Check

For a digital lesson check, use the Got It questions.

Support in Algebra 2 Companion
- Lesson Check

4 Practice

Assign homework to individual students or to an entire class.

Practice and Problem-Solving Exercises

 **MATHEMATICAL PRACTICES**

A Practice

Expand each binomial. ◀ **See Problems 1 and 2.**

8. $(x - y)^3$ **9.** $(a + 2)^4$ **10.** $(6 + a)^6$ **11.** $(x - 5)^3$

12. $(y + 1)^8$ **13.** $(x + 2)^{10}$ **14.** $(b - 4)^7$ **15.** $(b + 3)^9$

16. $(2x - y)^7$ **17.** $(a + 3b)^4$ **18.** $(4x + 2)^6$ **19.** $(4 - x)^8$

20. $(4x + 5)^2$ **21.** $(3a - 7)^3$ **22.** $(2a + 16)^6$ **23.** $(3y - 11)^4$

B Apply

24. Think About a Plan The side length of a cube is $\left(x^2 - \frac{1}{2}\right)$. Determine the volume of the cube.
- Rewrite the binomial as a sum.
- Consider $(a + b)^n$. Identify a and b in the given binomial.
- Which row of Pascal's Triangle can be used to expand the binomial?

25. In the expansion of $(2m - 3n)^9$, one of the terms contains m^3.
   a. What is the exponent of n in this term?
   b. What is the coefficient of this term?

Find the specified term of each binomial expansion.

26. Fourth term of $(x + 2)^5$ **27.** Third term of $(x - 3)^6$

28. Third term of $(3x - 1)^5$ **29.** Fifth term of $(a + 5b^2)^4$

30. Reasoning Explain why the coefficients in the expansion of $(x + 2y)^3$ do not match the numbers in the 3rd row of Pascal's Triangle.

31. Compare and Contrast What are the benefits and challenges of using the Binomial Theorem when expanding $(2x + 3)^2$? Using FOIL? Which method would you choose when expanding $(2x + 3)^6$? Why?

Expand each binomial.

32. $(2x - 2y)^6$ **33.** $(x^2 + 4)^{10}$ **34.** $(x^2 - y^2)^3$ **35.** $(a - b^2)^5$

36. $(3x + 8y)^3$ **37.** $(4x - 7y)^4$ **38.** $(7a + 2y)^{10}$ **39.** $(4x^3 + 2y^2)^6$

40. $(3b - 36)^7$ **41.** $(5a + 2b)^3$ **42.** $(b^2 - 2)^8$ **43.** $(-2y^2 + x)^5$

44. Geometry The side length of a cube is given by the expression $(2x + 8)$. Write a binomial power for the area of a face of the cube and for the volume of the cube. Then use the Binomial Theorem to expand and rewrite the powers in standard form.

45. Writing Explain why the terms of $(x - y)^n$ have alternating positive and negative signs.

46. Error Analysis A student expands $(3x - 8)^4$ as shown below. Describe and correct the student's error.

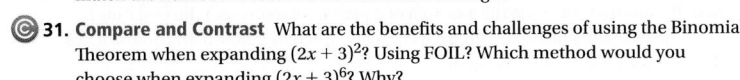

$(3x - 8)^4 = (3x)^4 + 4(3x)^3(-8) + 6(3x)^2(-8)^2 + 4(3x)(-8)^3 + (-8)^4$
$= 3x^4 - 96x^3 + 1152x^2 - 6144x + 4096$

---

4 Practice

ASSIGNMENT GUIDE
Basic: 8–23, 24, 30, 31, 44, 45
Average: 9–23 odd, 24–46
Advanced: 9–23 odd, 24–53
Standardized Test Prep: 54–57
Mixed Review: 58–68

Mathematical Practices are supported by exercises with red headings. Here are the Practices supported in this lesson:

MP 1: Make Sense of Problems Ex. 24
MP 3: Communicate Ex. 6, 45
MP 3: Construct Arguments Ex. 7, 30
MP 3: Compare Arguments Ex. 7, 31
MP 3: Critique the Reasoning of Others Ex. 46

Applications exercises have blue headings.

EXERCISE 44: Use the Think About a Plan worksheet in the **Practice and Problem Solving Workbook** (also available in the Teaching Resources in print and online) to further support students' development in becoming independent learners.

HOMEWORK QUICK CHECK
To check students' understanding of key skills and concepts, go over Exercises 9, 11, 24, 44, and 45.

Practice and Problem-Solving Exercises

8. $x^3 - 3x^2y + 3xy^2 - y^3$

9. $a^4 + 8a^3 + 24a^2 + 32a + 16$

10. $46{,}656 + 46{,}656a + 19{,}440a^2 + 4320a^3 + 540a^4 + 36a^5 + a^6$

11. $x^3 - 15x^2 + 75x - 125$

12. $y^8 + 8y^7 + 28y^6 + 56y^5 + 70y^4 + 56y^3 + 28y^2 + 8y + 1$

13. $x^{10} + 20x^9 + 180x^8 + 960x^7 + 3360x^6 + 8064x^5 + 13{,}440x^4 + 15{,}360x^3 + 11{,}520x^2 + 5120x + 1024$

14. $b^7 - 28b^6 + 336b^5 - 2240b^4 + 8960b^3 - 21{,}504b^2 + 28{,}672b - 16{,}384$

15. $b^9 + 27b^8 + 324b^7 + 2268b^6 + 10{,}206b^5 + 30{,}618b^4 + 61{,}236b^3 + 78{,}732b^2 + 59{,}049b + 19{,}683$

16. $128x^7 - 448x^6y + 672x^5y^2 - 560x^4y^3 + 280x^3y^4 - 84x^2y^5 + 14xy^6 - y^7$

17. $a^4 + 12a^3b + 54a^2b^2 + 108ab^3 + 81b^4$

18. $4096x^6 + 12{,}288x^5 + 15{,}360x^4 + 10{,}240x^3 + 3840x^2 + 768x + 64$

19. $65{,}536 - 131{,}072x + 114{,}688x^2 - 57{,}344x^3 + 17{,}920x^4 - 3584x^5 + 448x^6 - 32x^7 + x^8$

20. $16x^2 + 40x + 25$

21. $27a^3 - 189a^2 + 441a - 343$

22. $64a^6 + 3072a^5 + 61{,}440a^4 + 655{,}360a^3 + 3{,}932{,}160a^2 + 12{,}582{,}912a + 16{,}777{,}216$

23. $81y^4 - 1188y^3 + 6534y^2 - 15{,}972y + 14{,}641$

24. $V = x^6 - \frac{3}{2}x^4 + \frac{3}{4}x^2 - \frac{1}{8}$

25. a. 6   **b.** 489,888

26. $80x^2$ **27.** $135x^4$

28. $270x^3$ **29.** $625b^8$

30. Because the coefficient of 2 in $2y^2$ will affect the terms.

31. The challenge of the Binomial Theorem occurs when there is a coefficient with the x. However, it is much more efficient to use the Binomial Theorem than FOIL when expanding a binomial that is raised to a high power.

32. $64x^6 - 384x^5y + 960x^4y^2 - 1280x^3y^3 + 960x^2y^4 - 384xy^5 + 64y^6$

33. $x^{20} + 40x^{18} + 720x^{16} + 7680x^{14} + 53{,}760x^{12} + 258{,}048x^{10} + 860{,}160x^8 + 1{,}966{,}080x^6 + 2{,}949{,}120x^4 + 2{,}621{,}440x^2 + 1{,}048{,}576$

34. $x^6 - 3x^4y^2 + 3x^2y^4 - y^6$

35. $a^5 - 5a^4b^2 + 10a^3b^4 - 10a^2b^6 + 5ab^8 - b^{10}$

36. $27x^3 + 216x^2y + 576xy^2 + 512y^3$

37–46. See next page.

Answers

Practice and Problem-Solving Exercises
(continued)

37. $256x^4 - 1792x^3y$
$+ 4704x^2y^2 - 5488xy^3 + 2401y^4$

38. $282,475,249a^{10} + 807,072,140a^9y +$
$1,037,664,180a^8y^2 + 790,601,280a^7y^3 +$
$395,300,640a^6y^4 + 135,531,648a^5y^5 +$
$32,269,440a^4y^6 + 5,268,480a^3y^7 +$
$564,480a^2y^8 + 35,840ay^9 + 1024y^{10}$

39. $4096x^{18} + 12,288x^{15}y^2 + 15,360x^{12}y^4 +$
$10,240x^9y^6 + 3840x^6y^8 + 768x^3y^{10} + 64y^{12}$

40. $2187b^7 - 183,708b^6 + 6,613,488b^5 -$
$132,269,760b^4 + 1,587,237,120b^3 -$
$11,428,107,264b^2 + 45,712,429,056b -$
$78,364,164,096$

41. $125a^3 + 150a^2b + 60ab^2 + 8b^3$

42. $b^{16} - 16b^{14} + 112b^{12} - 448b^{10} + 1120b^8 -$
$1792b^6 + 1792b^4 - 1024b^2 + 256$

43. $-32y^{10} + 80y^8x - 80y^6x^2 + 40y^4x^3 -$
$10y^2x^4 + x^5$

44. Area $= (2x + 8)^2 = 4x^2 + 32x + 64$;
Volume $= (2x + 8)^3 = 8x^3 + 96x^2 + 384x + 512$

45. Answers may vary. Sample: Since one of the terms is negative $(-y)$ and it is alternately raised to odd and even powers; the term is negative when raised to an odd power and positive when raised to an even power.

46. In the expression on the right, the student did not simplify each power of $3x$ before multiplying.
$81x^4 - 864x^3 + 3456x^2 - 6144x + 4096$.

47. $-29,113 + 17,684i$

48. $702 - 486i$

49. $\left(x^{14} - 21x^{10} + 35x^6 - 7x^2\right) + i\left(-7x^{12} + 35x^8 - 21x^4 + 1\right)$

50. $n = 10$; $a = 2$

51. $\frac{1}{64}$

52. a. -4
b. $(1 - i)^4 = 1 - 4i - 6 + 4i + 1 = -4$

53. $(-1 + i\sqrt{3})^3 = -1 + 3i\sqrt{3}$
$+ 9 - 3i\sqrt{3} = 8$

Standardized Test Prep

54. C   **55.** G   **56.** B

57. **[4]** Let c_a = the first company's cost per month and let c_b = the second company's cost per month: $c_a = 2.25t + 7.95$ and $c_b = 2.75t$

$$c_a = c_b$$
$$2.25t + 7.95 = 2.75t$$
$$7.95 = 0.5t$$
$$15.9 = t$$

The cost will be equal after 15.9 hours of use.

[3] appropriate method, but with one computational error

Challenge Use the Binomial Theorem to expand each complex expression.

47. $(7 + \sqrt{-16})^5$ **48.** $(\sqrt{-81} - 3)^3$ **49.** $(x^2 - i)^7$

50. The first term in the expansion of a binomial $(ax + by)^n$ is $1024x^{10}$. Find a and n.

51. Determine the coefficient of x^7y in the expansion of $\left(\frac{1}{2}x + \frac{1}{4}y\right)^8$.

52. a. Expand $(1 + i)^4$.
b. Verify that $1 - i$ is a fourth root of -4 by repeating the process in part (a) for $(1 - i)^4$.

53. Verify that $-1 + \sqrt{3}i$ is a cube root of 8 by expanding $(-1 + \sqrt{3}i)^3$.

Standardized Test Prep

SAT/ACT

54. What is the fourth term in the expansion of $(2a + 4b)^5$?
Ⓐ $256a^4b$ Ⓑ $768a^3b^2$ Ⓒ $2560a^2b^3$ Ⓓ $2048ab^4$

55. Suppose y varies directly with x. If x is 30 when y is 10, what is x when y is 9?
Ⓕ 3 Ⓖ 27 Ⓗ 29 Ⓘ $\frac{300}{9}$

56. Which of following is a root of $9x^2 - 30x + 25 = 0$?
Ⓐ $x = \frac{3}{5}$ Ⓑ $x = \frac{5}{3}$ Ⓒ $x = -\frac{5}{3}$ Ⓓ $x = -\frac{3}{5}$

Extended Response

57. One company charges a monthly fee of $7.95 and $2.25 per hour for Internet access. Another company does not charge a monthly fee, but charges $2.75 per hour for Internet access. Write a system of equations to represent the cost c for t hours of access in one month for each company. Then find how many hours of use it will take for the costs to be equal.

Mixed Review

Find all the roots of each equation.   ◆ **See Lesson 5-6.**

58. $x^4 + 7x^3 + 20x^2 + 29x + 15 = 0$ **59.** $x^5 - x^4 + 10x^3 - 10x^2 + 9x - 9 = 0$

60. $2x^3 + 11x^2 + 14x + 8 = 0$ **61.** $x^4 - x^3 + 6x^2 - 13x + 7 = 0$

Simplify each expression.   ◆ **See Lesson 4-8.**

62. $(5i - 4)(-2i + 7)$ **63.** $(-3i)(20i)(10i)$

64. $\frac{-6 - 2i}{3 + i}$ **65.** $\frac{11i + 9}{2 - i}$

Get Ready! **To prepare for Lesson 5-8, do Exercises 66–68.**

Write each polynomial in standard form. Then classify it by degree and by number of terms.   ◆ **See Lesson 5-1.**

66. $5x^2 - x + 2x^3 + 9$ **67.** $1 + 4x - 7x^2$ **68.** $-9x^2 + x - 3x^3 - 8 + 12x^4$

[2] incorrect system solved correctly OR correct system solved incorrectly

[1] correct answers, without work shown

Mixed Review

58. $-3, -1, \dfrac{-3 \pm i\sqrt{11}}{2}$

59. $1, \pm i, \pm 3i$

60. $-4, \dfrac{-3 \pm i\sqrt{7}}{4}$

61. $1, \dfrac{-1 \pm 3i\sqrt{3}}{2}$

62. $-18 + 43i$ **63.** $600i$

64. -2

65. $\dfrac{7}{5} + \dfrac{31}{5}i$

66. $2x^3 + 5x^2 - x + 9$; cubic polynomial of 4 terms

67. $-7x^2 + 4x + 1$; quadratic trinomial

68. $12x^4 - 3x^3 - 9x^2 + x - 8$; quartic polynomial of 5 terms

Lesson Resources

Additional Instructional Support

Algebra 2 Companion

Students can use the **Algebra 2 Companion** worktext (4 pages) as you teach the lesson. Use the Companion to support

- New Vocabulary
- Key Concepts
- Got It for each Problem
- Lesson Check

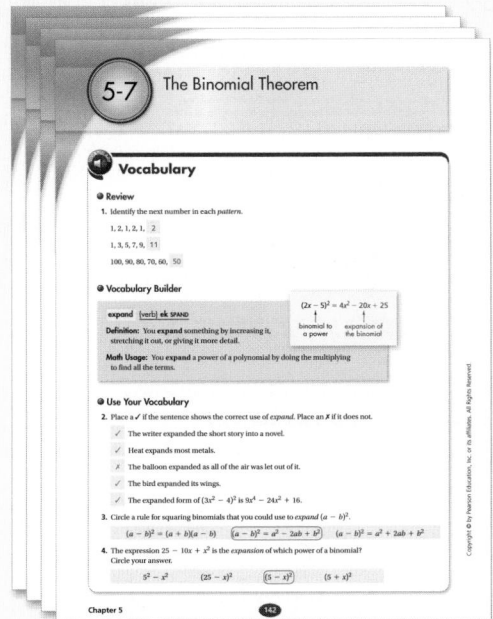

ELL Support

Assess Understanding Write the binomial power $(3x - 7)^3$ on the board. Ask a volunteer what the first step in expanding the power must be before they can use Pascal's Triangle or the Binomial Theorem. [It must be rewritten in the form $(a + b)^n$.] Have another volunteer explain how to handle the negative term and how the exponent helps them identify the row of Pascal's Triangle they must use.

5 Assess & Remediate

Lesson Quiz

1. What is the expansion of $(a + b)^4$?
2. **Do you UNDERSTAND?** What is the expansion of $(y - 4)^3$?

ANSWERS TO LESSON QUIZ

1. $a^4 + 4a^3b + 6a^2b^2 + 4ab^3 + b^4$
2. $y^3 - 12y^2 + 48y - 64$

PRESCRIPTION FOR REMEDIATION
Use the student work on the Lesson Quiz to prescribe a differentiated review assignment:

Points	Differentiated Remediation
0	Intervention
1	On-level
2	Extension

PowerAlgebra.com

5 Assess & Remediate

Assign the Lesson Quiz. Appropriate intervention, practice, or enrichment is automatically generated based on student performance.

Differentiated Remediation

Available in editable format online.

Intervention

- **Reteaching** (2 pages) Provides reteaching and practice exercises for the key lesson concepts. Use with struggling students or absent students.

- **English Language Learner Support** Helps students develop and reinforce mathematical vocabulary and key concepts.

All-in-One Resources/Online
Reteaching

5-7 Reteaching
The Binomial Theorem

You can find the coefficients of a binomial expansion in Pascal's Triangle.

To create Pascal's Triangle, start by writing a triangle of 1's. This triangle forms the first two rows. Each row has one more element than the one above it. Each row begins with a 1, and then each element is the sum of the two closest elements in the row above. The last element in each row is a 1.

Problem
What is the expansion of $(x + y)^5$? Use Pascal's Triangle.

Step 1 The power of the binomial corresponds to the second number in each row of Pascal's Triangle. Because the power of this binomial is 5, use the row of Pascal's Triangle with 5 as the second number. The numbers of this row are the coefficients of the expansion.

Step 2 The exponents of the x-terms of the expansion begin with the power of the binomial and decrease to 0. The exponents of the y-terms of the expansion begin with 0 and increase to the power of the binomial.

Step 3 Simplify all terms to write the expansion in standard form.

$(x + y)^5 = x^5 + 5x^4y + 10x^3y^2 + 10x^2y^3 + 5xy^4 + y^5$

Exercises
Write the expansion of each binomial.
1. $(a + b)^3$ $a^3 + 3a^2b + 3ab^2 + b^3$ 2. $(x - y)^4$ $x^4 - 4x^3y + 6x^2y^2 - 4xy^3 + y^4$

3. $(r + 1)^5$ $r^5 + 5r^4 + 10r^3 + 10r^2 + 5r + 1$ 4. $(a - b)^6$ $a^6 - 6a^5b + 15a^4b^2 - 20a^3b^3 + 15a^2b^4 - 6ab^5 + b^6$

All-in-One Resources/Online
English Language Learner Support

5-7 Additional Vocabulary Support
The Binomial Theorem

There are two sets of note cards that show how to expand the expression $(4x - 2)^4$. The set on the left explains the thinking. The set on the right shows the steps. Write the thinking and the steps in the correct order.

Think Cards
- Rewrite the expression as a binomial sum.
- Simplify the expansion.
- Use the fourth row of Pascal's Triangle.
- Apply the Binomial Theorem.

Write Cards
- $(4x - 2)^4 = (4x + (-2))^4$
- $(4x)^4 + 4(4x)^3(-2)^1 + 6(4x)^2(-2)^2 + 4(4x)^1(-2)^3 + (-2)^4$
- $256x^4 - 512x^3 + 384x^2 - 128x + 16$

Think
First, rewrite the expression as a binomial sum.
Second, use the fourth row of Pascal's Triangle.
Next, apply the Binomial Theorem.
Finally, simplify the expansion.

Write
Step 1
$(4x - 2)^4 = (4x + (-2))^4$

Step 2

Step 3
$(4x)^4 + 4(4x)^3(-2)^1 + 6(4x)^2(-2)^2 + 4(4x)^1(-2)^3 + (-2)^4$

Step 4
$256x^4 - 512x^3 + 384x^2 - 128x + 16$

Differentiated Remediation *continued*

Available in editable format online.

On-Level

- **Practice** (2 pages) Provides extra practice for each lesson. For simpler practice exercises, use the Form K Practice pages found in the All-in-One Teaching Resources and online.
- **Think About a Plan** Helps students develop specific problem-solving skills and strategies by providing scaffolded guiding questions.
- **Standardized Test Prep** Focuses on all major exercises, all major question types, and helps students prepare for the high-stakes assessments.

Extension

- **Enrichment** Provides students with interesting problems and activities that extend the concepts of the lesson.
- **Activities, Games, and Puzzles** Worksheets that can be used for concepts development, enrichment, and for fun!

Practice and Problem Solving Wkbk/ All-in-One Resources/Online

Practice page 1

5-7 Practice *Form G*

The Binomial Theorem

Expand each binomial. See answers below.

1. $(x + 2)^4$
2. $(a + 2)^7$
3. $(x + y)^7$
4. $(d - 2)^9$
5. $(2x - 3)^8$
6. $(x - 1)^9$
7. $(2x^2 - 2y^2)^6$
8. $(x^5 + 2y)^7$
9. $(n - 3)^3$
10. $(2n + 2)^4$
11. $(n - 6)^5$
12. $(n - 1)^6$
13. $(2a + 2)^3$
14. $(x^2 - y^2)^4$
15. $(2x + 3y)^5$
16. $(2x^2 + y^2)^6$
17. $(x^2 - y^2)^3$
18. $(2b + c)^4$
19. $(3m - 2n)^5$
20. $(x^3 - y^4)^6$

Find the specified term of each binomial expansion.

21. third term of $(x + 3)^{12}$ $594x^{10}$
22. second term of $(x + 3)^9$ $27x^8$
23. twelfth term of $(2 + x)^{11}$ x^{11}
24. third term of $(x - 2)^{12}$ $264x^{10}$
25. eighth term of $(x - 2y)^{15}$ $-823{,}680x^8y^7$
26. seventh term of $(x - 2y)^6$ $64y^6$
27. fifth term of $(x^2 + y^2)^{13}$ $715x^{18}y^8$
28. fourth term of $(x^2 - 2y)^{11}$ $-1320x^{16}y^3$
29. The term $126c^4d^5$ appears in the expansion of $(c + d)^n$. What is n? 9
30. The coefficient of the second term in the expansion of $(r + s)^n$ is 7. Find the value of n, and write the complete term. $n = 7$; $7r^6s$

State the number of terms in each expansion and give the first two terms.

31. $(d + e)^{12}$ 13; $d^{12} + 12d^{11}e$
32. $(x - y)^{15}$ 16; $x^{15} - 15x^{14}y$
33. $(2a + b)^5$ 6; $32a^5 + 80a^4b$
34. $(x - 3y)^7$ 8; $x^7 - 21x^6y$
35. $(4 - 2x)^8$ 9; $65{,}536 - 262{,}144x$
36. $(x^2 + y)^6$ 7; $x^{12} + 6x^{10}y$
37. The side of a number cube is $x + 4$ units long. Write a binomial for the volume of the number cube. Use the Binomial Theorem to expand and rewrite the expression in standard form. $(x + 4)^3 = x^3 + 12x^2 + 48x + 64$

1. $x^4 + 8x^3 + 24x^2 + 32x + 16$ 2. $a^7 + 14a^6 + 84a^5 + 280a^4 + 560a^3 + 672a^2 + 448a + 128$
3. $x^7 + 7x^6y + 21x^5y^2 + 35x^4y^3 + 35x^3y^4 + 21x^2y^5 + 7xy^6 + y^7$
4. $d^9 - 18d^8 + 144d^7 - 672d^6 + 2016d^5 - 4032d^4 + 5376d^3 - 4608d^2 + 2304d - 512$
5. $256x^8 - 3072x^7 + 16{,}128x^6 - 48{,}384x^5 + 90{,}720x^4 - 108{,}864x^3 + 81{,}648x^2 - 34{,}992x + 6561$
6. $x^9 - 9x^8 + 36x^7 - 84x^6 + 126x^5 - 126x^4 + 84x^3 - 36x^2 + 9x - 1$
7. $64x^{12} - 384x^{10}y^2 + 960x^8y^4 - 1280x^6y^6 + 960x^4y^8 - 384x^2y^{10} + 64y^{12}$
8. $x^{35} + 14x^{30}y + 84x^{25}y^2 + 280x^{20}y^3 + 560x^{15}y^4 + 672x^{10}y^5 + 448x^5y^6 + 128y^7$
9. $n^3 - 9n^2 + 27n - 27$ 10. $16n^4 + 64n^3 + 96n^2 + 64n + 16$
11. $n^5 - 30n^4 + 360n^3 - 2160n^2 + 6480n - 7776$ 12. $n^6 - 6n^5 + 15n^4 - 20n^3 + 15n^2 - 6n + 1$
13. $8a^3 + 24a^2 + 24a + 8$ 14. $x^8 - 4x^6y^2 + 6x^4y^4 - 4x^2y^6 + y^8$
15. $32x^5 + 240x^4y + 720x^3y^2 + 1080x^2y^3 + 810xy^4 + 243y^5$
16. $64x^{12} + 192x^{10}y^2 + 240x^8y^4 + 160x^6y^6 + 60x^4y^8 + 12x^2y^{10} + y^{12}$ 17. $x^6 - 3x^4y^2 + 3x^2y^4 - y^6$
18. $16b^4 + 32b^3c + 24b^2c^2 + 8bc^3 + c^4$ 19. $243m^5 - 810m^4n + 1080m^3n^2 - 720m^2n^3 + 240mn^4 - 32n^5$
20. $x^{18} - 6x^{15}y^4 + 15x^{12}y^8 - 20x^9y^{12} + 15x^6y^{16} - 6x^3y^{20} + y^{24}$

Practice and Problem Solving Wkbk/ All-in-One Resources/Online

Practice page 2

5-7 Practice (continued) *Form G*

The Binomial Theorem

Expand each binomial.

38. $(x + 1)^7$
$x^7 + 7x^6 + 21x^5 + 35x^4 + 35x^3 + 21x^2 + 7x + 1$
39. $(x + 4)^8$
$x^8 + 32x^7 + 448x^6 + 3584x^5 + 17{,}920x^4 + 57{,}344x^3 + 114{,}688x^2 + 131{,}072x + 65{,}536$
40. $(x - 3y)^6$
$x^6 - 18x^5y + 135x^4y^2 - 540x^3y^3 + 1215x^2y^4 - 1458xy^5 + 729y^6$
41. $(x + 2)^5$
$x^5 + 10x^4 + 40x^3 + 80x^2 + 80x + 32$
42. $(x^2 - y^2)^5$
$x^{10} - 5x^8y^2 + 10x^6y^4 - 10x^4y^6 + 5x^2y^8 - y^{10}$
43. $(3 + y)^5$
$y^5 + 15y^4 + 90y^3 + 270y^2 + 405y + 243$
44. $(x^2 + 3)^6$
$x^{12} + 18x^{10} + 135x^8 + 540x^6 + 1215x^4 + 1458x^2 + 729$
45. $(x - 5)^7$
$x^7 - 35x^6 + 525x^5 - 4375x^4 + 21{,}875x^3 - 65{,}625x^2 + 109{,}375x - 78{,}125$
46. $(x - 4y)^4$
$x^4 - 16x^3y + 96x^2y^2 - 256xy^3 + 256y^4$
47. **Open-Ended** Write a binomial in the form $(a + b)^n$ that has 3 as the coefficient of the first term. Answers may vary. Any binomial that has an a-term coefficient of $\sqrt[n]{3}$.
48. Use Pascal's Triangle to determine the binomial of the expanded expression $x^6 + 6x^5 + 15x^4 + 20x^3 + 15x^2 + 6x + 1$. $(x + 1)^6$
49. **Error Analysis** Your friend expands the binomial $(x - 2)^6$ as $x^6 + 12x^5 + 30x^4 + 160x^3 + 240x^2 + 192x + 64$. What mistake did your friend make? What is the correct expansion? Your friend used $b = 2$ instead of $b = -2$, and forgot to square the 2; $x^6 - 12x^5 + 60x^4 - 160x^3 + 240x^2 - 192x + 64$
50. **Reasoning** Without writing any of the previous terms, how do you know that 2187 is the eighth term of the expansion of the binomial $(x + 3)^7$? According to Pascal's Triangle, the eighth term of a binomial with $n = 7$ is equal to $1a^0b^7$. In this binomial $a = x$ and $b = 3$. $1x^03^7 = 2187$.
51. In the expansion of $(3x - y)^6$, one of the terms contains the factor y^4.
   a. What is the exponent of $3x$ in this term? 2
   b. What is the coefficient of this term? 135
52. You are shipping a cubic glass sculpture. Each side of the sculpture is x in. long. To adequately protect the sculpture, the shipping box must leave room for 5 in. of padding on either side in every dimension. Write and expand a binomial for the volume of the shipping box. $V = (x + 5)^3 = x^3 + 15x^2 + 75x + 125$ in.^{3}

All-in-One Resources/Online

Enrichment

5-7 Enrichment

The Binomial Theorem

Pascal's Triangle is helpful for expanding powers of a binomial sum, but what if you wanted to expand $(a + b)^{20}$? You may not want to write out all of the rows of Pascal's Triangle. In cases like this, you can use another form of the Binomial Theorem.

1. This form of the Binomial Theorem uses the operation called factorial. The expression 4! is read "four factorial" and is computed by multiplying all of the counting numbers from 4 down to 1. So, $4! = 4 \times 3 \times 2 \times 1 = 24$. What is 5!?
$5! = 5 \times 4 \times 3 \times 2 \times 1 = 120$
2. An unexpected fact arises for 0!. 0! is defined as 1. Fractions involving factorials can be simplified first. Rewrite each factorial in the fraction $\frac{6!}{3!}$ as multiplication and then reduce. What is the simplified form?
$\frac{6 \times 5 \times 4 \times 3 \times 2 \times 1}{3 \times 2 \times 1}$; $6 \times 5 \times 4$

Expressions involving factorials can be used to write a different form of the Binomial Theorem. This form states that the kth term in the expansion of $(a + b)^n$ is $\frac{n!}{(k - 1)!(n - k + 1)!}a^{n-k+1}b^{k-1}$.

3. Find the third term in the expansion of $(a + b)^8$ using the Binomial Theorem. What value will you substitute in for n? What value will you substitute in for k?
$n = 8$; $k = 3$; $28a^6b^2$
4. Use Pascal's Triangle to verify that you have the found the correct third term.
Answers may vary. Sample: The correct row is 1, 8, 28, 56, 70, 56, 28, 8, 1, and the third number, 28, is the correct coefficient.

Use the Binomial Theorem to find the indicated term of each expansion.

5. fifth term of $(x + y)^{15}$ $1365x^{11}y^4$
6. ninth term of $(x + 3)^{10}$ $295{,}245x^2$
7. twelfth term of $(2x + y)^{22}$ $1{,}444{,}724{,}736x^{11}y^{11}$

Practice and Problem Solving Wkbk/ All-in-One Resources/Online

Think About a Plan

5-7 Think About a Plan

The Binomial Theorem

Geometry The side length of a cube is given by the expression $(2x + 8)$. Write a binomial expression for the area of a face of the cube and the volume of the cube. Then use the Binomial Theorem to expand and rewrite the expressions in standard form.

Understanding the Problem

1. What is the formula for the area of a face of a cube? $A = s^2$
2. What is the formula for the volume of a cube? $V = s^3$
3. What is the problem asking you to determine?
expressions in standard form for the face area and volume of a cube with side length $(2x + 8)$

Planning the Solution

4. What is a binomial expression for the area of a face of this cube? $(2x + 8)^2$
5. What is a binomial expression for the volume of this cube? $(2x + 8)^3$
6. How can you use the Binomial Theorem to expand these expressions?
Answers may vary. Sample: Use $n = 2$ for the expression for area and use $n = 3$ for the expression for volume. For both expressions, $a = 2x$ and $b = 8$

Getting an Answer

7. What is an expression for the area of a face of the cube written in standard form?
$4x^2 + 32x + 64$
8. What is an expression for the volume of the cube written in standard form?
$8x^3 + 96x^2 + 384x + 512$

Practice and Problem Solving Wkbk/ All-in-One Resources/Online

Standardized Test Prep

5-7 Standardized Test Prep

The Binomial Theorem

Multiple Choice

For Exercises 1–7, choose the correct letter.

1. What is the expanded form of $(a - b)^3$? D
   A. $a^3 + a^2b + ab^2 + b^3$
   B. $a^3 - a^2b + ab^2 - b^3$
   C. $a^3 + 3a^2b + 3ab^2 + b^3$
   D. $a^3 - 3a^2b + 3ab^2 - b^3$
2. What is the third term in the expansion of $(x - y)^7$? F
   F. $21x^5y^2$ G. $-7x^6y$ H. $7x^6y$ I. $-21x^5y^2$
3. What is the coefficient of the third term in the expansion of $(2x - y)^5$? D
   A. -80 B. 32 C. 40 D. 80
4. Which term in the expansion of $(2a - 3b)^6$ has coefficient 2160? G
   F. second term G. third term H. fourth term I. fifth term
5. What is n if $-448x^5y^3$ appears in the expansion of $(x - 2y)^n$? C
   A. 6 B. 7 C. 8 D. 9
6. What is the 6th term in the 12th line of Pascal's Triangle? H
   F. 252 G. 462 H. 792 I. 1287
7. What is the expanded form of $(2x - y)^5$? B
   A. $32x^5 + 80x^4y + 80x^3y^2 + 40x^2y^3 + 10xy^4 + y^5$
   B. $32x^5 - 80x^4y + 80x^3y^2 - 40x^2y^3 + 10xy^4 - y^5$
   C. $2x^5 + 5x^4y + 20x^3y^2 + 20x^2y^3 + 10xy^4 + y^5$
   D. $2x^5 - 5x^4y + 20x^3y^2 - 20x^2y^3 + 10xy^4 - y^5$

Short Response

8. The coefficient of the fourth term in the expansion of $(x + y)^n$ is 84.
   a. What is the value of n?
   b. What is the complete term?
   [2] $n = 9$; the complete term is $84(x)^6(y)^3 = 84x^6y^3$.
   [1] incorrect number for n OR incorrect complete term
   [0] no answers given

Online Teacher Resource Center

Activities, Games, and Puzzles

5-7 Puzzle: Pyramid Power

The Binomial Theorem

Find each of the specified coefficients of $(a + b)^n$ and circle them in the diagram.

1. the coefficient in $(a + b)^2$ not equal to the others 2
2. the coefficient of ab^2 in $(a + b)^3$ 3
3. the coefficient of a^4 in $(a + b)^4$ 1
4. the coefficient of ab^4 in $(a + b)^5$ 5
5. the coefficients of a^4b^2 and a^3b^3 in $(a + b)^6$ 15, 20
6. the coefficient of a^3b^4 in $(a + b)^7$ 35
7. the coefficients of a^6b^2 and of a^2b^6 in $(a + b)^8$ 28, 28
8. the coefficient of a^9 in $(a + b)^9$ 1
9. the coefficient of a^5b^5 in $(a + b)^{10}$ 252
10. the coefficients of a^7b^4 and of a^4b^7 in $(a + b)^{11}$ 330, 330
11. the coefficient of a^7b^5 in $(a + b)^{12}$ 792
12. the coefficient of a^5b^8 in $(a + b)^{13}$ 1287
13. the coefficients of a^7b^7 and a^4b^{10} in $(a + b)^{14}$ 3432, 1001

What is the sum of the circled numbers? 7562

$n = 0$ → 1
$n = 1$ → 1 1
$n = 2$ → 1 (2) 1
$n = 3$ → 1 3 (3) 1
$n = 4$ → (1) 4 6 4 1
$n = 5$ → 1 5 10 10 (5) 1
$n = 6$ → 1 6 (15) (20) 15 6 1
$n = 7$ → 1 7 21 35 (35) 21 7 1
$n = 8$ → 1 8 (28) 56 70 56 (28) 8 1
$n = 9$ → (1) 9 36 84 126 126 84 36 9 1
$n = 10$ → 1 10 45 120 210 (252) 210 120 45 10 1
$n = 11$ → 1 11 55 165 (330) 462 462 (330) 165 55 11 1
$n = 12$ → 1 12 66 220 495 (792) 924 792 495 220 66 12 1
$n = 13$ → 1 13 78 286 715 1287 1716 1716 (1287) 715 286 78 13 1
$n = 14$ → 1 14 91 364 1001 2002 3003 (3432) 3003 2002 (1001) 364 91 14 1

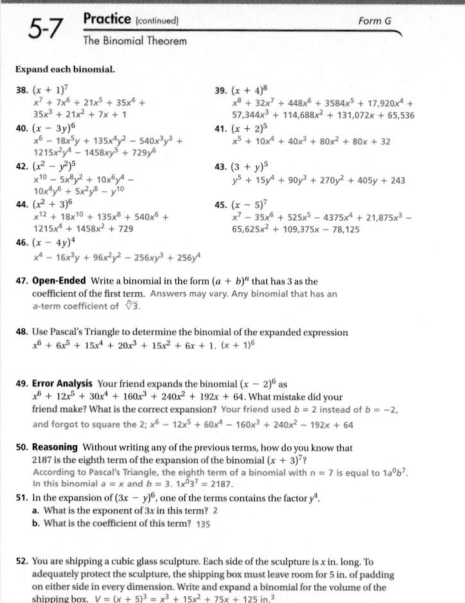

5-8 Polynomial Models in the Real World

Common Core State Standards
F-IF.B.5 Relate the domain of a function to its graph and, where applicable, to the quantitative relationship it describes. **Also F-IF.B.4, F-IF.B.6**
MP 1, MP 3, MP 4, MP 5

Objective To fit data to linear, quadratic, cubic, or quartic models

How do you analyze the data to determine the type of polynomial function?

MATHEMATICAL PRACTICES

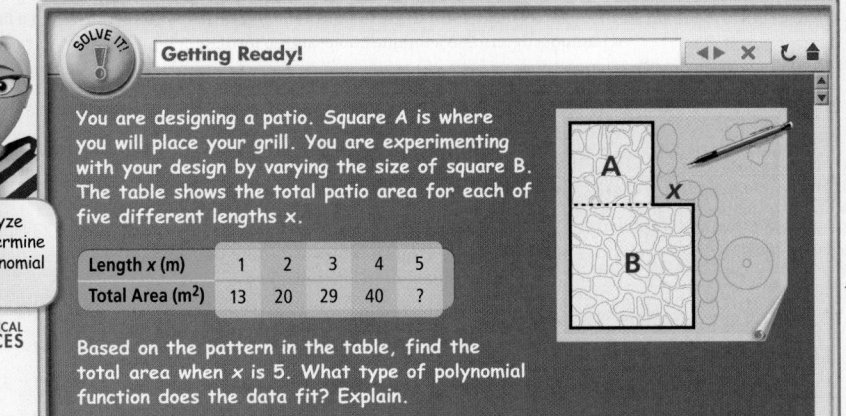

Getting Ready!

You are designing a patio. Square A is where you will place your grill. You are experimenting with your design by varying the size of square B. The table shows the total patio area for each of five different lengths x.

Length x (m)	1	2	3	4	5
Total Area (m²)	13	20	29	40	?

Based on the pattern in the table, find the total area when x is 5. What type of polynomial function does the data fit? Explain.

Polynomial functions can be degree 0 (constant), degree 1 (linear), degree 2 (quadratic), degree 3 (cubic), and so on.

Essential Understanding You can use polynomial functions to model many real-world situations. The behavior of the graphs of polynomial functions of different degrees can suggest what type of polynomial will best fit a particular data set.

You can use a graphing calculator to help you find functions that model the data in the table shown here.

Enter the data into calculator lists **L1** and **L2**. Use three different regressions: **LINREG**, **QUADREG**, and **CUBICREG**.

Graph each regression function and the scatter plot of the data in the same window. For this data, the cubic function appears to be a perfect fit.

x	y
0	10.1
5	2.8
10	8.1
15	16.0
20	17.8

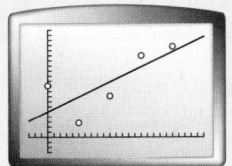 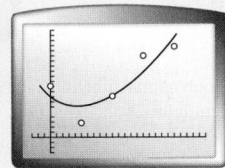 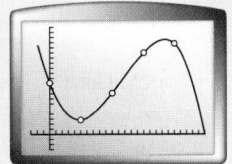

1 Interactive Learning

Solve It!

PURPOSE To use first and second differences to identify a pattern and to determine the degree of a polynomial function

PROCESS Students may determine the degree of the polynomial function by
- finding differences.
- plotting the data and evaluating the shape of the graph.

FACILITATE
Q What are the first differences of the areas? **[7, 9, 11]**
Q What is the pattern? **[Differences increase by 2.]**
Q What is the missing value? **[53]**
Q What are the second differences? **[all 2]**
Q What degree polynomial function is indicated? **[degree 2]**

ANSWER See Solve It in Answers on next page.
CONNECT THE MATH In the Solve It, differences may be used to determine the degree of a polynomial function that fits a set of data. In the lesson, students use polynomial models to solve real-world problems.

2 Guided Instruction

Note that if you use QuarticReg to model the data, the coefficient of the x^4 term will be very close to zero and the QuarticReg curve will be very similar to the CubicReg curve.

5-8 Preparing to Teach

BIG idea Function
ESSENTIAL UNDERSTANDING
- The behavior of the graphs of polynomial functions of different degrees can suggest which will best fit a particular real-world data set.

Math Background
Just as two points can be used to determine a unique line and three points not on the same line determine a unique quadratic function, polynomial functions of various degrees can be found that perfectly match a given data set that passes the vertical-line test. Regression analysis (LinReg, QuadReg, etc.) can also be used to determine best-fitting polynomial models for a given data set. The polynomial model can then be used

to make predictions. Such models may not always be the best even though they match the data perfectly. The best model often depends on the nature of the situation. If the situation being modeled is essentially a quadratic relationship based on principles of physics, then a quadratic model will most likely best fit the data and result in the most reliable predictions. One must be cautious when using any model not to be too confident of predictions outside of the domain of the data.

Mathematical Practices
Use appropriate tools strategically. Using graphing calculators, students will find the equation that best fits a particular set of data. They will also learn the limitations of three of these types of calculator functions.

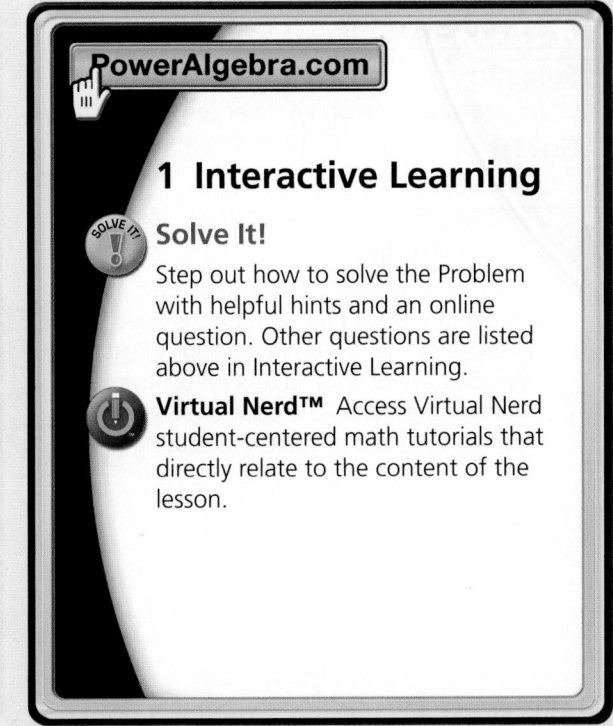

1 Interactive Learning

Solve It!

Step out how to solve the Problem with helpful hints and an online question. Other questions are listed above in Interactive Learning.

Virtual Nerd™ Access Virtual Nerd student-centered math tutorials that directly relate to the content of the lesson.

Take Note

This result follows from the fact that an *n*th-degree polynomial function
$P(x) = a_nx^n + a_{n-1}x^{n-1} + \ldots\ a_1x^1 + a_0x^0$ is uniquely determined by the values of its $n + 1$ numerical coefficients $a_0, \ldots, a_n$. Given a set of $n + 1$ points, a system of $n + 1$ linear equations can be written and solved to determine the values of a_0 to a_n.

Problem 1

> **Q** How can you verify that the points *do not* lie on a line or a parabola? **[Find the differences, starting with the fourth point. Since neither the first nor the second differences are constant, the four points do not lie on either a line or a parabola.]**

Got It?

> **Q** How do you know that the four points do not lie on a line? **[You cannot use differences since the changes in *x* are not constant. But if you calculate slopes between each pair of points you see that the slopes are not all the same, so the points cannot all lie on one line.]**
>
> **Q** The degree of the polynomial function whose graph passes through these four points is at most what? [$n + 1 = 4$, so $n = 3$, and the polynomial function is at most a cubic.]**

 Key Concept The ($n + 1$) Point Principle

For any set of $n + 1$ points in the coordinate plane that pass the vertical line test, there is a unique polynomial of degree at most n that fits the points perfectly.

This principle confirms that any two points determine a unique line. Three points that are not on a line determine a unique parabola. Four points that are not on a line or a parabola determine a unique cubic, and so forth.

 Problem 1 Using A Polynomial Function to Model Data

What polynomial function has a graph that passes through the four points $(0, -3)$, $(1, -1)$, $(2, 5)$, and $(-1, -7)$?

Step 1 By the ($n + 1$) Point Principle, there is a cubic polynomial $y = ax^3 + bx^2 + cx + d$ that fits the points perfectly.

Substitute the *x*- and *y*-values of the four points to get four linear equations in four unknowns.

$$-3 = a(0)^3 + b(0)^2 + c(0) + d \qquad 0a + 0b + 0c + 1d = -3$$
$$-1 = a(1)^3 + b(1)^2 + c(1) + d \qquad 1a + 1b + 1c + 1d = -1$$
$$5 = a(2)^3 + b(2)^2 + c(2) + d \qquad 8a + 4b + 2c + 1d = 5$$
$$-7 = a(-1)^3 + b(-1)^2 + c(-1) + d \qquad -1a + 1b - 1c + 1d = -7$$

Step 2 Write the system in augmented matrix form. Use the **RREF()** function to find the coefficient values *a*, *b*, *c*, and *d*.

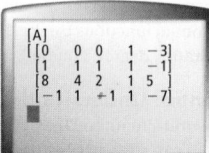 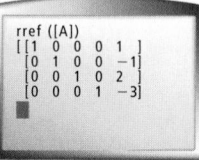

Step 3 $a = 1$, $b = -1$, $c = 2$, and $d = -3$. The polynomial function is $y = x^3 - x^2 + 2x - 3$.

Check Use **CUBICREG** with the four given points.

The solution checks.

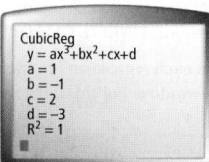 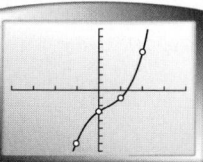

 Got It? 1. What polynomial function has a graph that passes through the four points $(-2, 1)$, $(0, 5)$, $(2, 9)$, and $(3, 36)$?

Plan

How can you use the four points to find a system of equations? Substitute each point into a polynomial function.

Answers

Solve It!

$53\ m^2$; quadratic; second differences are constant

Got It?

1. $y = 1.667x^3 + 1.3 \times 10^{-12}\ x^2 - 4.667x + 5$
2. 22.52 billion lb
3. Answers may vary. Sample: The cubic model would fit the data better than the linear model because of the ($n + 1$) Pt. Principle. Both models have down and up end behavior and increasing growth. The cubic shows slowing growth followed by rapidly increasing growth.

PowerAlgebra.com

2 Guided Instruction

Each Problem is worked out and supported online.

Problem 1
Using A Polynomial Function to Model Data
Animated

Problem 2
Modeling Data

Problem 3
Comparing Models
Animated

Problem 4
Using Interpolation and Extrapolation
Animated

Support in Algebra 2 Companion
• Vocabulary
• Key Concepts
• Got It?

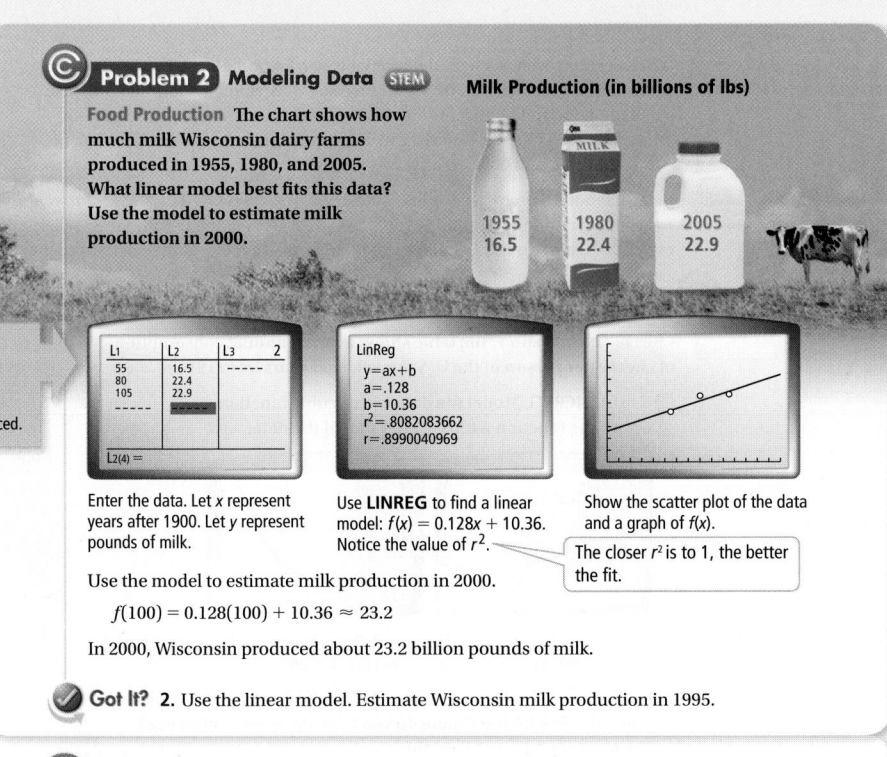

Problem 2 Modeling Data STEM

Food Production The chart shows how much milk Wisconsin dairy farms produced in 1955, 1980, and 2005. What linear model best fits this data? Use the model to estimate milk production in 2000.

Milk Production (in billions of lbs)

1955	1980	2005
16.5	22.4	22.9

Think
What data should you enter?
Enter the years, after 1900, and billions of pounds of milk produced.

Enter the data. Let x represent years after 1900. Let y represent pounds of milk.

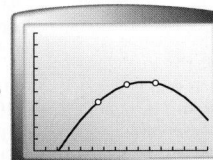

Use **LINREG** to find a linear model: $f(x) = 0.128x + 10.36$. Notice the value of r^2.

The closer r^2 is to 1, the better the fit.

Show the scatter plot of the data and a graph of $f(x)$.

Use the model to estimate milk production in 2000.

$f(100) = 0.128(100) + 10.36 \approx 23.2$

In 2000, Wisconsin produced about 23.2 billion pounds of milk.

Got It? **2.** Use the linear model. Estimate Wisconsin milk production in 1995.

Problem 3 Comparing Models STEM

Food Production The graph shows the quadratic model for the milk production data in Problem 2. The quadratic model fits the data points exactly because of the $(n + 1)$ Point Principle. Given that both models are good fits, which seems more likely to represent milk production over time?

Linear Model: This model continually rises.

Think
Is the quadratic model reasonable?
No; the quadratic model will show milk production eventually decreasing to below zero.

Quadratic Model: This model has down-and-down end behavior. It shows slowing growth, a turning point, and then a decline, eventually to 0 and negative values.

Despite the R^2 value of 1 for the quadratic model, the linear model is more likely to represent milk production over time since it shows a continuing increase.

Got It? **3.** If four data points were given, would a cubic function be the best model for the data? Explain your answer.

Problem 2

Q There are three points. Why choose a linear function model and not a quadratic function model? **[You *could* use a quadratic model, but the scatter plot shows that a line is a good fit.]**

Got It?

Q What value of x should you use to predict milk production in 1995? **[Let $x = 95$, since x represents years after 1900.]**

Problem 3

Either model can be used for estimating production within the domain of the data. The quadratic model only appears to result in questionable results when you make a prediction well outside of the domain of the data.

Got It?

A cubic function would match four data points exactly but will not necessarily result in a better model. The result would depend on what the fourth data point is.

Q What is the end behavior of a cubic polynomial function? **[down and up, or up and down]**

Q Are either of these end behaviors reasonable? **[Down and up end behavior might be reasonable, but up and down behavior is not.]**

Additional Problems

1. What polynomial function has a graph that passes through the points $(-2, 13)$, $(0, 9)$, $(1, 4)$, and $(2, 5)$?

ANSWER $y = x^3 - 6x + 9$

2. What is the linear model that best fits the data? Use the model to estimate egg consumption in 1995.

Year	US Per Capita Egg Consumption
1970	302
1980	266
1990	231
2000	247

ANSWER $y = -2x + 431.5$ ($x =$ years after 1900); 241.5 eggs in 1995

3. What is the quadratic model that best fits the above data? Use the model to estimate egg consumption in 1995.

ANSWER
$0.13x^2 - 24.1x + 1354.5$; 238.25 eggs in 1995

4. Which is the better model for estimating egg consumption between 1970 and 2000? Which is better for extrapolating egg consumption beyond 2000?

ANSWER The quadratic model is better for interpolation. The quadratic model is also better for extrapolation beyond year 2000, but neither model is reliable.

Remember: **in**terpolate refers to **in**side the domain of the data while **ex**trapolate refers to **out**side the domain of the data.

Problem 4

Q When the x value is low, what is the magnitude of the x^3 term? Explain. **[The x^3 coefficient is low, so the x^3 term is low when the x value is low.]**

Q For larger values of x, $(x > 100)$, what happens to the x^3 term? **[It gets very large very quickly and dominates the behavior of the model.]**

Got It?

Q What does the scatter plot indicate about the rate of increase of the data? **[The scatter plot shows a behavior of increasing at an increasing rate.]**

Q How will a linear model that fits this data when x is small fit the data for large values of x? **[It will tend to underestimate the data for large values of x.]**

When deciding whether a model is reliable, it is important to consider the source of the data. Data generated by a law of physics or a geometric formula will have a mathematical model that fits the data and yields accurate predictions. With other data, such as sales records, you can approximate the data only within, or close to, the domain over which it was generated.

Using a model to predict a y-value "outside" the domain of a data set is *extrapolation*. Estimating within the domain is *interpolation*. Interpolation usually yields reliable estimates. Extrapolation becomes less reliable as you move farther away from the data.

© Problem 4 Using Interpolation and Extrapolation

Cheese Consumption The table shows average annual consumption of cheese per person in the U. S. for selected years from 1910 to 2001.

A Use **CUBICREG**. Model the data with a cubic function. Graph the function with a scatter plot of the data.

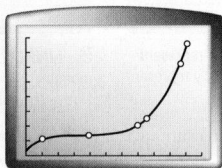

Since R^2 is close to 1, the fit is good. The cubic model is approximately $y = 0.0000924x^3 - 0.00958x^2 + 0.311x + 1.802$.

B Use the model to estimate cheese consumption for 1980, 2000, and 2012. In which estimate do you have the most confidence? The least confidence? Explain.

Use the cubic model from part A to estimate the cheese consumption for each year:

1980: 12.6 lb of cheese per person
2000: 29.4 lb of cheese per person
2012: 46.2 lb of cheese per person

You can be confident in interpolating the estimates for 1980 (**Y1(80)**) and 2000 (**Y1(100)**) because the cheese consumption fits the pattern of increase shown in the table. You should have the least confidence in the extrapolated 2012 (**Y1(112)**) estimate because the cubic model increases so quickly beyond 2001.

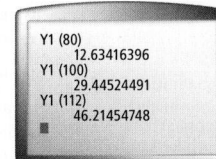

Cheese Consumption

Year	Pounds Consumed
1910	4
1940	5
1970	8
1975	10
1995	25
2001	30

Source: U.S. Department of Agriculture

Think

What affects your confidence in drawing conclusions from the model?
Your confidence can waver where model behavior is extreme or where there are large gaps in the data.

✓ **Got It? 4. a.** Use **LINREG** to find a linear model for cheese consumption. Graph it with a scatter plot.
   © **b. Reasoning** Use the model to estimate consumption for 1980, 2000, and 2012. In which of these estimates do you have the most confidence? The least confidence? Explain.

Answers

Got It? (continued)

4. a. $y = 0.269867411x - 3.919692952$

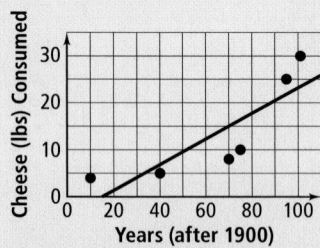

b. 1980: 17.7 lb; 2000: 23.07 lb; 2012: 26.31 lb; most confident for the yrs 1980 and 2000, since they are within the domain of the data set; least confident for the yr 2012, since it is outside of the domain of the data set

Lesson Check

Do you know HOW?

Determine which type of model best fits each set of points.

1. $(-2, -1)$, $(0, 3)$, and $(2, 7)$
2. $(0, 3)$, $(3, 4)$, and $(5, 6)$
3. $(2, 3)$, $(4, 2)$, $(6, 4)$, and $(8, 5)$
4. $(-5, 6)$, $(-4, 3)$, $(0, 2)$, $(2, 4)$, and $(5, 10)$

Do you UNDERSTAND?

5. **Vocabulary** Explain which form of estimation, interpolation or extrapolation, is more reliable.

6. **Reasoning** Is it possible to create a cubic function that passes through $(0, 0)$, $(-1, 1)$, $(-2, 2)$, and $(-3, 9)$? Explain.

7. **Writing** The R^2 value for a quartic model is 0.94561. The R^2 value for a cubic model of the same data is 0.99817. Which model seems to show a better fit? Explain.

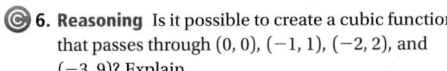

Practice and Problem-Solving Exercises

 **Practice**   Find a polynomial function whose graph passes through each set of points.   ◆ **See Problem 1.**

8. $(0, 5)$ and $(2, -13)$
9. $(-2, -4)$ and $(8, 1)$
10. $(-5, 14)$ and $(1, -16)$
11. $(7, 13)$, $(10, -11)$, and $(0, 4)$
12. $(-2, -16)$, $(3, 11)$, and $(0, 2)$
13. $(-1, 8)$, $(5, -4)$, and $(7, 8)$
14. $(-1, -15)$, $(1, -7)$, and $(6, -22)$
15. $(-1, 9)$, $(0, 6)$, $(1, 5)$, and $(2, 18)$

For each set of data, compare two models and determine which one better fits the data. Which model seems more likely to represent each set of data over time?   ◆ **See Problems 2 and 3.**

16. **U.S. Federal Spending**

Year	Total (billions $)
1965	630
1980	1300
1995	1950
2005	2650

17. **World Population**

Year	Average Growth Rate (%)
1972	1.96
1982	1.73
1992	1.5
2002	1.22

18. **U.S. Homes**

Year	Average Sale Price (thousands $)
1990	149
1995	158
2000	207

19. **U.S. Crude Oil and Petroleum**

Month (2008)	Products Supplied (millions of barrels/day)
2	19.782
4	19.768
6	19.553

Lesson Check

1. linear
2. quadratic
3. cubic
4. quartic
5. interpolation since the data point is within the domain of the data set
6. yes, since the four pts. pass the vertical line test a cubic function will fit the pts; $y = -x^3 - 3x^2 - 3x$
7. cubic model; the closer R^2 is to 1, the better the fit

Practice and Problem-Solving Exercises

8. $y = -9x + 5$
9. $y = \frac{1}{2}x - 3$
10. $y = -5x - 11$
11. $y = -0.929x^2 + 7.786x + 4$
12. $y = -1.2x^2 + 6.6x + 2$
13. $y = x^2 - 6x + 1$
14. $y = -x^2 + 4x - 10$
15. $y = 2x^3 + x^2 - 4x + 6$
16. (where x = yrs after 1900) linear: $y = 49.238x - 2614.286$, cubic: $y = 0.028x^3 - 6.711x^2 + 578.194x - 16226.667$; cubic; linear
17. (where x = yrs after 1900) quadratic: $y = -1.25 \times 10^{-4}x^2 - 0.003x + 2.804$, cubic: $y = -8.33 \times 10^{-6}x^3 + 0.002x^2 - 0.190x + 8.142$; cubic; cubic
18. (where x = yrs after 1900) linear: $y = 5.8x - 379.667$, quadratic: $y = 0.8x^2 - 146.2x + 6827$; linear; linear
19. linear: $y = -0.057x + 19.93$, quadratic: $y = -0.025x^2 + 0.14x + 19.595$; quadratic; quadratic

---

3 Lesson Check

Do you know HOW?

- Not every set of $n + 1$ points determines an nth-degree polynomial function. For example, 3 or more points might all lie on a line. Students may be able to use differences to determine the degree of the polynomial function that fits a given set of points.
- For Exercises 1–4, if students have trouble identifying the type of model that best fits the given data, have them review the $(n + 1)$ Point Principle and look at Problem 1.

Do you UNDERSTAND?

- For Exercise 5, remind students that interpolation refers to inside the domain of the data and that extrapolation refers to outside of the domain of the data.
- For Exercise 6, if students do not remember the meanings of "cubic" or "quartic," review Lesson 5-1 on classification of polynomial functions by degree.

Close

Q Why is it useful to represent data with a mathematical model? **[Answers may vary. Sample: A model allows one to make estimations and predictions.]**

Q What determines whether a model is a good model? **[Answers may vary. Sample: A good model closely matches the data in the region of interest.]**

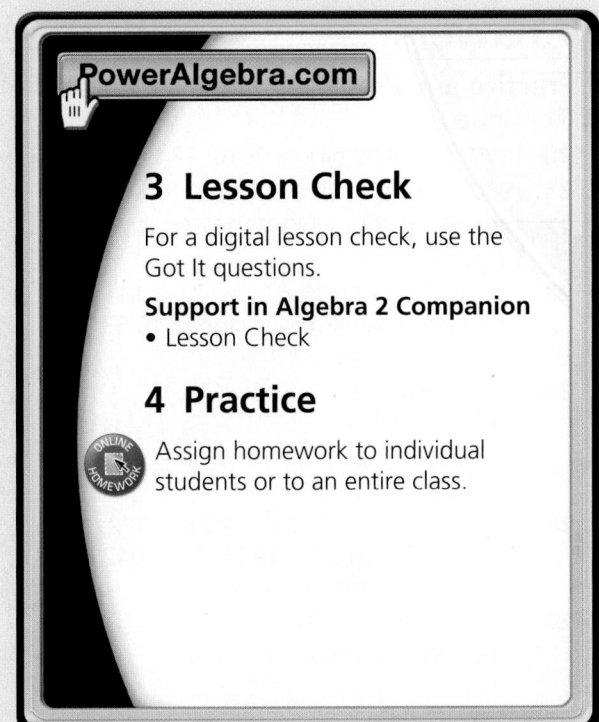

PowerAlgebra.com

3 Lesson Check

For a digital lesson check, use the Got It questions.

Support in Algebra 2 Companion
- Lesson Check

4 Practice

Assign homework to individual students or to an entire class.

4 Practice

ASSIGNMENT GUIDE

Basic: 8–25, 28, 31, 34

Average: 9–23 odd, 24–35

Advanced: 9–23 odd, 24–37

Standardized Test Prep: 38–42

Mixed Review: 43–58

Ⓒ **Mathematical Practices** are supported by exercises with red headings. Here are the Practices supported in this lesson:

MP 1: Make Sense of Problems Ex. 28

MP 3: Communicate Ex. 7, 32

MP 3: Construct Arguments Ex. 6, 35e

MP 3: Compare Arguments Ex. 34

MP 3: Critique the Reasoning of Others Ex. 33

Applications exercises have blue headings. Exercise 31 supports MP 4: Model.

EXERCISE 31: Use the Think About a Plan worksheet in the **Practice and Problem Solving Workbook** (also available in the Teaching Resources in print and online) to further support students' development in becoming independent learners.

HOMEWORK QUICK CHECK

To check students' understanding of key skills and concepts, go over Exercises 17, 21, 28, 31, and 34.

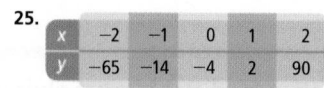 See Problem 4.

Use your models from Exercises 16-19 to make predictions.

20. Estimate total U.S. federal spending for 1990 and 2010.

21. Estimate the average annual growth rate of the world population for 1950, 1988, and 2010.

22. Estimate the average sale price of homes sold in the United States for 1985, 1999, and 2020.

23. Estimate the number of barrels of crude oil and petroleum supplied per day for January, March, and October of 2008.

Ⓑ **Apply** **Find a cubic and a quartic model for each set of values. Explain why one models the data better.**

24.

x	−2	−1	0	2	3
y	−25	−4	3	23	40

25.

x	−2	−1	0	1	2
y	−65	−14	−4	2	90

Find a polynomial function whose graph passes through the points.

26. $(−14, 14)$, $(−10, 0)$, $(0, −1)$, $(8, 0)$, and $(12, 4)$

27. $(−3, −50)$, $(−2, −4)$, $(−1, 10)$, $(0, 7)$, and $(2, −23)$

Ⓒ **28. Think About a Plan** The table at the right shows the amount of carbon dioxide in Earth's atmosphere for selected years. Predict the amount of carbon dioxide in Earth's atmosphere in 2022. How confident are you in your prediction?
  • How can you plot the data? (*Hint:* Let x equal the years after 1900.)
  • What polynomial model should you use?

Year	CO_2 in atmosphere (ppm)
1968	324.14
1983	343.91
1998	367.68
2003	376.68
2008	385.60

Source: The Weather Channel

Find a cubic model for each set of values. Then use the regression coefficient of each model to determine whether the model is a good fit.

29. $(−5, −60)$, $(−1, −5)$, $(0, 0.5)$, $(1, 8)$, $(5, 17)$, $(10, 32)$

30. $(8, −101)$, $(−1, 10)$, $(−8, 47)$, $(−10, 59)$

31. Air Travel The table shows the percent of on-time flights for selected years. Find a polynomial function to model the data. Use 1998 as Year 0.

Year	1998	2000	2002	2004	2006
On-time Flights (%)	77.20	72.59	82.14	78.08	75.45

Source: U.S. Bureau of Transportation Statistics

Ⓒ **32. Writing** Explain two ways to find a polynomial function to model a given set of data.

Answers

Practice and Problem-Solving Exercises
(continued)

20. 1990: $1863.69 billion; 2010: $3439.57 billion

21. 1950: 2.60%; 1988: 1.23%; 2010: 0.35%

22. 1985: $113,300; 1999: $194,500; 2020: $316,300

23. January: 19.714 million barrels/day; March: 19.8 million barrels/day; October: 18.535 million barrels/day

24. cubic: $y = 0.922x^3 − 1.462x^2 + 7.978x + 4.681$;
quartic: $y = −\frac{1}{3}x^4 + \frac{5}{3}x^3 + \frac{1}{3}x^2 + \frac{16}{3}x + 3$; quartic, $(R^2 = 1)$

25. cubic: $y = 10.25x^3 + 5x^2 − 2.25x − 8.2$;
quartic: $y = 2.042x^4 + 10.25x^3 − 4.042x^2 − 2.25x − 4$; quartic, $(R^2 = 1)$

26. $y = 0.001x^4 − 0.002x^3 − 0.035x^2 + 0.293x − 1$

27. $y = −0.275x^4 + 0.85x^3 − 4.025x^2 − 8.15x + 7$

28. 407.37 ppm; quite confident because both the linear and the quartic functions yield close to the same prediction. Also, for the linear function, $r^2 = .9965291461$ and for the quartic function, $R^2 = 1$. Although 2022 is outside the domain, the data goes far enough back to make this a reasonable prediction.

29. $y = 0.0611511911x^3 − 0.9276466231x^2 + 6.184642324x + 1.750778723$; $R^2 = 0.9994739765$; good fit

30. $y = −0.0288800705x^3 − 0.469356261x^2 − 7.401675485x + 3.038800705$; $R^2 = 1$; good fit

31. Answers may vary. Sample: $f(x) = 0.111x^4 − 1.916x^3 + 10.147x^2 − 15.825x + 77.2$

32. Method 1: Graph the scatter plot and determine which regression model best fits the data. Method 2: Enter the data into your calculator, and use the regression function with the correlation function closest to 1 as the model.

33. Error Analysis The table at the right shows the number of students enrolled in a high school personal finance course. A student says that a cubic model would best fit the data based on the $(n + 1)$ Point Principle. Explain why a quadratic model might be more appropriate.

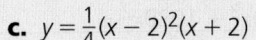

Year	Number of Students Enrolled
2000	50
2004	65
2008	94
2010	110

34. Compare and Contrast The table shows the United States gross domestic product for selected years. Construct curves using cubic regression and quartic regression to model the data. Which curve seems most likely to model gross domestic product over the years?

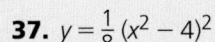

Year	1960	1970	1980	1990	2000
GDP (billions $)	526.4	1038.5	2789.5	5803.1	9817.0

35. The table below shows the percentage of the U.S. labor force in unions for selected years between 1955 and 2005.

Year	1955	1960	1965	1970	1975	1980	1985	1990	1995	2000	2005
%	33.2	31.4	28.4	27.3	25.5	21.9	18.0	16.1	14.9	13.5	12.5

    a. What is the average rate of change between 1955 and 1965? Between 1975 and 1985?

    b. Make a scatter plot of the data. Which kind of polynomial model seems to be most appropriate?

    c. Use a graphing calculator to find the type of model from part (b).

    d. Use the model you found in part (c) to predict the percent of the labor force in unions in the year 2020.

    e. Reasoning Do you have much confidence in this prediction? Explain.

Challenge

36. Your friend's teacher showed the class a graph of a cubic polynomial in the ZDecimal window, which is $[-4.7, 4.7]$ by $[-3.1, 3.1]$. She then challenged the class to find the polynomial *without using cubic regression on their calculators*, and your friend succeeded. Follow your friend's steps and see if you can find the polynomial.

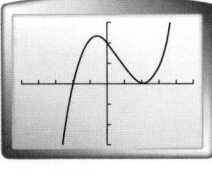

    a. The graph resembles a parabola with vertex $(2, 0)$ near $x = 2$. Find the equation in standard form for that parabola.

    b. Find the equation of a line in slope-intercept form through $(-2, 0)$ with slope 1. Multiply the linear expression by the quadratic expression from part (a) to get a cubic. (Leave it in factored form.) Graph the cubic function. What do you notice about the zeros and the y-intercept of the cubic function?

    c. Multiply the cubic by a constant to change the y-intercept to 2. Graph the function to see if you've found the right polynomial. What is the function?

37. The graph at the right is that of a certain quartic polynomial in the ZDecimal window, which is $[-4.7, 4.7]$ by $[-3.1, 3.1]$. Find the equation of the quartic *without using quartic regression on your calculator*. You may leave it in factored form.

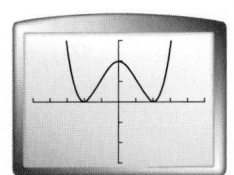

c. Answers may vary. Sample: $y = -0.4464x + 57.77$

d. 4.2%

e. No; although R^2 is close to 1, the model is not realistic since it predicts that the percentage will eventually become 0, and then negative.

36. a. $y = x^2 - 4x + 4$

    b. $y = (x - 2)^2(x + 2)$; the zeros are perfect, but the y-intercept (8) is too large.

    c. $y = \frac{1}{4}(x - 2)^2(x + 2)$

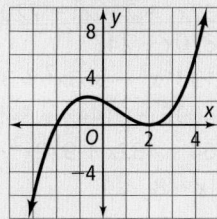

37. $y = \frac{1}{8}(x^2 - 4)^2$

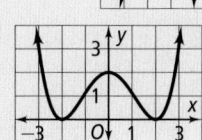

33. A quadratic model would be more appropriate, given the real world context. According to the cubic model, there would be a negative number of students enrolled in the course in the year 2024.

34. cubic:
$y = -0.01988x^3 + 10.676431x^2 - 1086.25x + 31,565.157$,
$R^2 = 0.9999803248$;

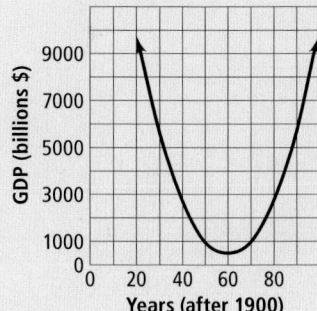

quartic:
$y = -0.00192x^4 + 0.36145x^3 - 34.558x^2 + 1269.845 - 13,892.5$,
$R^2 = 1$;

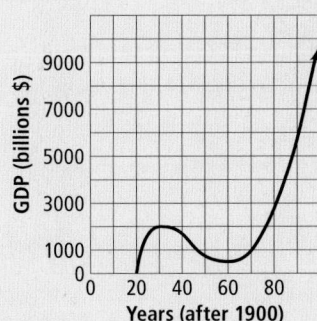

The quartic is the best model since $R^2 = 1$.

35. a. -0.48; -0.75

    b.

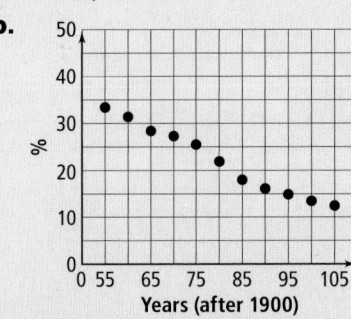

A linear model seems to be most appropriate.

Answers

Standardized Test Prep

38. 71.409 s
39. 1
40. 2
41. $-\dfrac{7}{8}$
42. 5

Mixed Review

43. $32x^5 + 240x^4 + 720x^3 + 1080x^2 + 810x + 243$
44. $1331x^3 - 363x^2 + 33x - 1$
45. $4096 - 6144x + 3456x^2 - 864x^3 + 81x^4$
46. $64 + 432x + 972x^2 + 729x^3$
47. $|x - 8| < 1$
48. $\left|x - \dfrac{3}{8}\right| \le \dfrac{1}{8}$
49. $|y - 2.8| < 1.1$
50. $|t - 750| < 250$
51. $s = \sqrt{A}$
52. $\ell = \dfrac{P}{2} - w$
53. $r = \dfrac{C}{2\pi}$
54. $b = \dfrac{A}{h}$

55.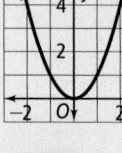

56.

57.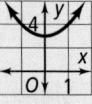

58.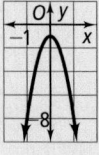

SAT/ACT

38. The table shows the time it takes a computer program to run, given the number of files used as input. Using a cubic model, what do you predict the run time will be if the input consists of 1000 files?

Files	Time(s)
100	0.5
200	0.9
300	3.5
400	8.2
500	14.8

39. Suppose you hit a ball and its flight follows the graph of $f(x) = -16x^2 + 20x + 3$. How many seconds will it take for the ball to hit the ground? Round your answer to the nearest second.

40. What is the multiplicity of the zeros of $y = 16x^2 - 8x + 1$?

41. What is the slope of the line shown?

42. What is the degree of the polynomial function $y = -9x^3 - 5x^2 - 2x^5 + 4x + x^4 + 1$?

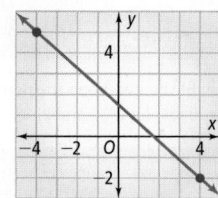

Mixed Review

Expand each binomial.   ◀ See Lesson 5-7.

43. $(2x + 3)^5$ **44.** $(11x - 1)^3$

45. $(8 - 3x)^4$ **46.** $(4 + 9x)^3$

Write each compound inequality as an absolute value inequality.   ◀ See Lesson 1-6.

47. $7 < x < 9$ **48.** $\dfrac{1}{4} \le x \le \dfrac{1}{2}$

49. $1.7 < y < 3.9$ **50.** $500 < t < 1000$

Solve each formula for the indicated variable.   ◀ See Lesson 1-4.

51. $A = s^2$, for s **52.** $P = 2(l + w)$, for l

53. $C = 2\pi r$, for r **54.** $A = bh$, for b

Get Ready!   To prepare for Lesson 5-9, do Exercises 55–58.

Graph each function.   ◀ See Lesson 4-1.

55. $y = x^2$ **56.** $y = -4x^2$

57. $y = x^2 + 3$ **58.** $y = -7x^2 - 1$

Differentiated Remediation
Available in editable format online.

Additional Instructional Support

Algebra 2 Companion
Students can use the **Algebra 2 Companion** worktext (4 pages) as you teach the lesson. Use the Companion to support

- New Vocabulary
- Key Concepts
- Got It for each Problem
- Lesson Check

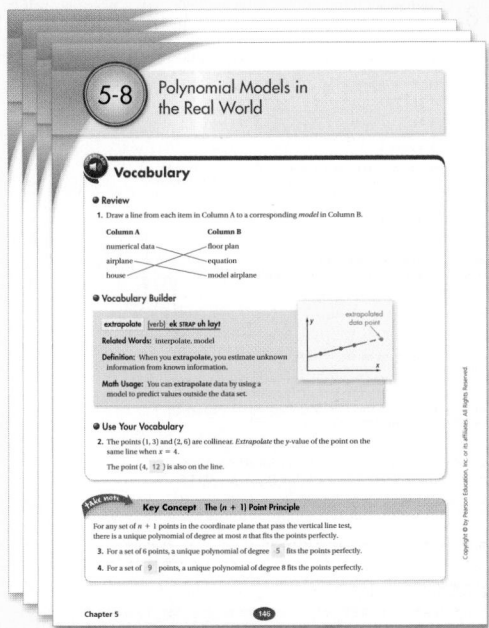

5 Assess & Remediate

Lesson Quiz

1. What polynomial function has a graph that passes through the three points $(-1, -4)$, $(0, -5)$, and $(1, -2)$?

2. **Do you UNDERSTAND?** Determine and compare quadratic and cubic models that fit the data in the table. Which model is best?

Speed (mi/h)	Total Stopping Distance (feet)
20	43
30	80
40	126
50	183
60	251

3. Using the models developed above, what is the predicted total stopping distance from 80 mi/h? Round to the nearest foot.

ANSWERS TO LESSON QUIZ

1. $y = 2x^2 + x - 5$

2. $y = 0.05214x^2 + 1.018571x + 2.0$ or $y = 0.00017x^3 + 0.03214x^2 + 1.76190x - 6.400$
   Both models match the data well. It is not obvious which is better.

3. 417 ft (Quadratic model) or 426 ft (Cubic model)

Intervention

- **Reteaching** (2 pages) Provides reteaching and practice exercises for the key lesson concepts. Use with struggling students or absent students.

- **English Language Learner Support** Helps students develop and reinforce mathematical vocabulary and key concepts.

All-in-One Resources/Online
Reteaching

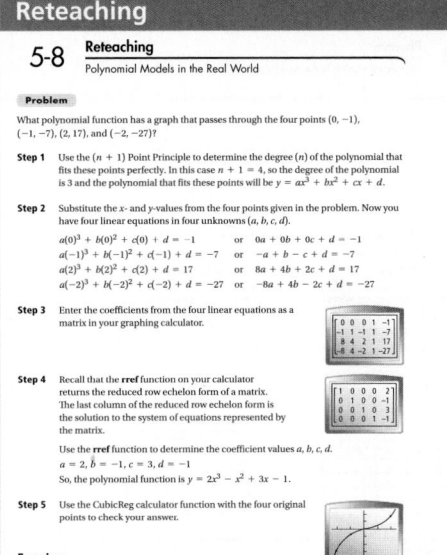

ELL Support
Focus on Communication Discuss the idea of confidence in general and with regard to estimations. Ask the following questions to help increase students' understanding of the concept of confidence:

- What would you feel more confident walking over: a bridge made of steel or one made of balsa wood?
- What song would you feel more confident singing: one you have heard only once or one you have heard 150 times?
- [Bring in a jar of pennies or other objects] What number of pennies would you feel confident estimating that the jar contains? If I say it holds 3, should I be confident about my answer? What if I say 10,000? 500? Why or why not?
- Suppose we hold a competition to guess how many siblings total this class has. Should I be confident about guessing that there are 4 siblings total? 1000? Explain.

PRESCRIPTION FOR REMEDIATION
Use the student work on the Lesson Quiz to prescribe a differentiated review assignment:

Points	Differentiated Remediation
0–1	Intervention
2	On-level
3	Extension

PowerAlgebra.com

5 Assess & Remediate
Assign the Lesson Quiz. Appropriate intervention, practice, or enrichment is automatically generated based on student performance.

All-in-One Resources/Online
English Language Learner Support

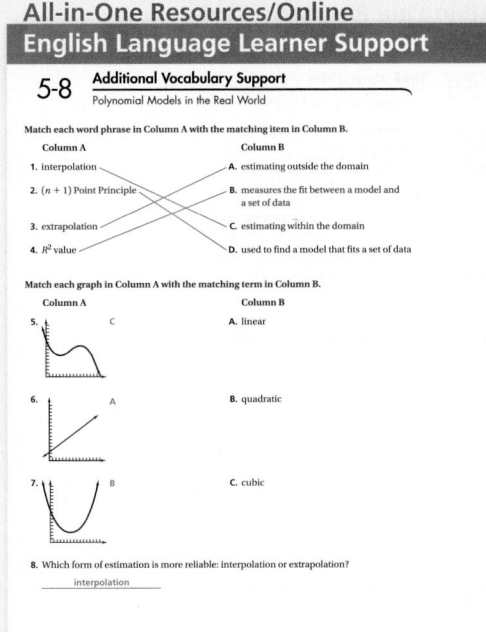

Differentiated Remediation *continued*

Available in editable format online.

On-Level

- **Practice** (2 pages) Provides extra practice for each lesson. For simpler practice exercises, use the Form K Practice pages found in the All-in-One Teaching Resources and online.

- **Think About a Plan** Helps students develop specific problem-solving skills and strategies by providing scaffolded guiding questions.

- **Standardized Test Prep** Focuses on all major exercises, all major question types, and helps students prepare for the high-stakes assessments.

Extension

- **Enrichment** Provides students with interesting problems and activities that extend the concepts of the lesson.

- **Activities, Games, and Puzzles** Worksheets that can be used for concepts development, enrichment, and for fun!

Practice and Problem Solving Wkbk/All-in-One Resources/Online
Practice page 1

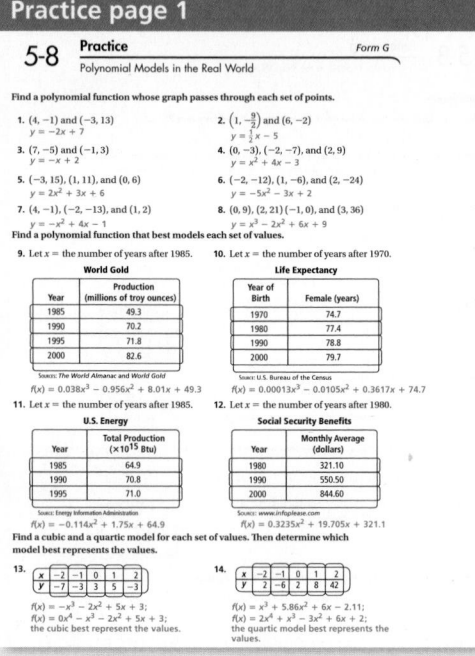

Practice and Problem Solving Wkbk/All-in-One Resources/Online
Practice page 2

5-8 Practice (continued) — Form G
Polynomial Models in the Real World

Use your models from Exercises 9–12 to make predictions.

15. Estimate world gold production for 2010, 2020, and 2025.
245.8 troy oz., 787.8 troy oz., 1272.1 troy oz.

16. Estimate the life expectancy for women born in 1986, 1992, and 2005.
78.3 years, 79.0 years, 80.1 years

17. Estimate the U.S. energy production for 2002, 2005, and 2010.
61.7×10^{15} Btu, 54.3×10^{15} Btu, 37.4×10^{15} Btu

18. Estimate the average monthly Social Security benefits for 1970, 1996, and 1999.
$156.40, $719.20, $812.28

19. Find a cubic function to model the data below. (*Hint:* Use x to represent the gestation period.) Then use the function to estimate the longevity of an animal with a gestation period of 151 days. $0.0000006x^3 - 0.0005101x^2 + 0.1270416x + 2.0612682$; about 12 yr

Gestation and Longevity of Certain Animals

Animal	Rat	Squirrel	Pig	Cow	Elephant
Gestation (in days)	21	44	115	280	624
Longevity (in years)	3	9	10	12	40

Source: www.infoplease.com

20. **Error Analysis** Your teacher gives the class the table at the right and asks you to find a polynomial model for the data set. Then he asks the class to estimate the percent of U.S. foreign-born population in 1920. Your friend uses $x = -10$ and estimates the percent as 16.1. What did your friend do wrong? What is the correct estimate?
Your friend should have used $x = 10$ because 1920 is 10 years after the data set began not 10 years before. The correct estimate is 13.1%.

U.S. Population

Year	Foreign-Born (percent)
1910	14.7
1930	11.6
1950	6.9
1970	4.7
1990	8.0
2000	10.4
2004	11.7

Source: Bureau of the Census

21. **Reasoning** Using the data set from Exercise 12 and the model you determined, find the average monthly Social Security benefits for the year 2050. Do you have much confidence in this prediction? Explain.
$3285.60; no, because the data point is so far from the data set used to create the model. There is no way to predict what changes may occur between 2000 and 2050.

22. Find a cubic model for the following set of values: $(0, -1), (-1, -6), (5, -264)$, and $(2, -18)$. Using the regression coefficient, determine whether the model is a good fit.
$y = -2x^3 - x^2 + 3x - 4$; this is a good fit because $R^2 = 1$.

Practice and Problem Solving Wkbk/All-in-One Resources/Online
Think About a Plan

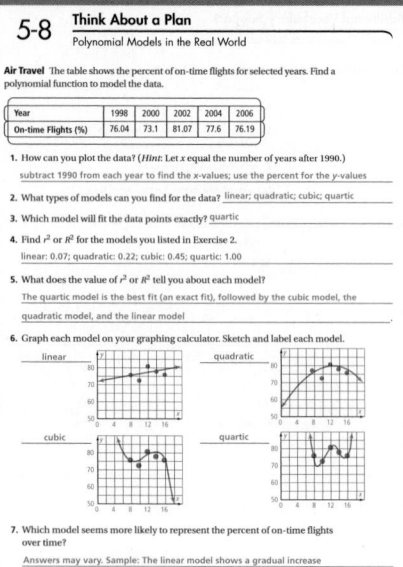

Practice and Problem Solving Wkbk/All-in-One Resources/Online
Standardized Test Prep

5-8 Standardized Test Prep
Polynomial Models in the Real World

Multiple Choice

For Exercises 1–4, choose the correct letter.

1. Which of the following is the polynomial function whose graph passes through (0, 4), (−2, 30), and (1, 6)? B
   A) $y = -9x + 10$
   B) $y = 9x - 10$
   C) $y = -5x^2 - 3x + 4$
   D) $y = -5x^2 + 3x - 4$

2. Which model type best represents the set of values at the right? I

x	−2	−1	0	1	2
y	−17	4	1	−4	−5

   F) linear
   G) cubic
   H) quadratic
   I) quartic

3. Which polynomial function best models the data set at the right? D

   A) $y = 0.0000006x^4 + 0.000119x^3 - 0.025x^2 + 2.13x + 71.6$
   B) $y = 0.00002163x^4 + 0.0012677x^3 - 0.155x^2 + 8.24x + 81.2$
   C) $y = 0.00003112x^4 + 0.000197x^3 - 0.219x^2 + 5.22x + 86.3$
   D) $y = 0.00000606x^4 + 0.000217x^3 - 0.079x^2 + 3.90x + 83.5$

   Paying Taxes for 1 Day

Year	Time Spent (minutes)
1940	83
1950	117
1960	130
1970	141
1980	145
1990	145
2000	160

   Source: Tax Foundation

4. Using a cubic model for the data set at the right, what is the estimated Consumer Price Index for 1965? H
   F) 102.5
   G) 130.034
   H) 116.564
   I) 147.384

   Consumer Prices

Year	Index
1920	60.0
1930	50.0
1940	42.0
1950	72.1
1960	88.7
1970	116.3
1980	248.8
1990	391.4
2000	515.8

   Source: Bureau of Labor Statistics

Short Response

5. Find both a cubic and quartic model for the set of values at the right. Which model is a better fit? How do you know?

x	1.2	1.4	1.6	1.8	2.0	2.2
y	3.1	−4.2	4.1	7.5	−8.9	10

   [2] cubic model $y = 62.27x^3 - 303.19x^2 + 481.81x - 248.52$ $R^2 = 0.142$; quartic model $y = 984.38x^4 - 6631.48x^3 + 16,498.68x^2 - 17,954.69x + 7208.88$ $R^2 = 0.936$; The quartic model is a better fit because R^2 is closer to 1.
   [1] incorrect models OR incorrect analysis
   [0] no answers given

All-in-One Resources/Online
Enrichment

5-8 Enrichment
Polynomial Models in the Real World

You can represent volume with a cubic function. If you start with a rectangular piece of cardboard, cut out a square from each corner, and then fold up the sides, you will have an open-top rectangular solid.

1. If you start with an 8.5-in.-by-11 in. piece of cardboard, what is the length, width, and height of the rectangular solid if you cut out a 1-in.-by-1 in. square from each corner?
length: 9 in.; width: 6.5 in.; height: 1 in.

2. What is the volume of the box?
58.5 in.^{3}

3. If you cut an x in.-square from each corner, what is a general equation for the volume of the rectangular solid?
$V = x(11 - 2x)(8.5 - 2x)$

4. Sketch a graph of your volume equation.

5. Explain which part of your graph does not make sense for this real-world application.
Answers may vary. Sample: Any part of the graph that has negative values for y does not make sense, because the volume can never be less than zero.

6. What is the domain of this function? That is, what are the possible values for x, the size of square that can be cut out?
$0 < x < 4.25$

7. Explain why you cannot cut out squares that are larger than 4.25 in. on each side.
Answers may vary. Sample: The width of the cardboard is 8.5 in., so two squares measuring more than 4.25 in. would need more cardboard than is available.

8. What are the coordinates of the x-intercepts?
(0, 0), (4.25, 0), (5.5, 0)

9. What do the x-intercepts tell you about the rectangular box? Answers may vary. Sample: The x-intercepts represent when the volume will be zero. This occurs when the box is flat, when no square has been cut out, or when the squares cut out equal the length or width (which is not possible).

10. Use your graph to estimate the maximum possible volume.
approximately 66.1 in.^{3}

Online Teacher Resource Center
Activities, Games, and Puzzles

5-8 Activity: Savings Plans
Polynomial Models in the Real World

Polynomials can play a role in determining the amount of money you accumulate in a savings account. Suppose you make an annual deposit of $1 into an account that pays simple interest compounded annually. The interest rate is represented by a decimal; for example, 4% = 0.04. At the end of the first year, you will have $(1 + 0.04), at the end of the second year you will have $(1 + 0.04)^2$, and so on. If the interest rate is represented by x, at the end of the first year you will have $(1 + x)$, at the end of the second year you will have $(1 + x)^2$, and so on.

Complete the table below by using x to represent the interest rate. The amount you finish with for one year is the amount you start with the next year. Each year you deposit $1, so the sum of the three polynomials in the far right column of each row is the total amount in the account after three years.

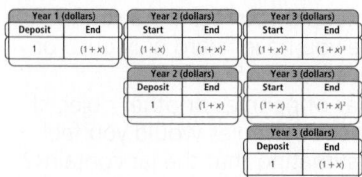

Year 1 (dollars)		Year 2 (dollars)		Year 3 (dollars)	
Deposit	End	Start	End	Start	End
1	(1 + x)	(1 + x)	(1 + x)^2	(1 + x)^2	(1 + x)^3

Year 2 (dollars)		Year 3 (dollars)	
Deposit	End	Start	End
1	(1 + x)	(1 + x)	(1 + x)^2

Year 3 (dollars)	
Deposit	End
1	(1 + x)

1. Expand the sum of the three polynomials in the far right column of each row. Show your work. Label the sum $S_3(x)$. Then compare your results to your classmates' to make sure all the calculations are correct.
$S_3(x) = x^3 + 4x^2 + 6x + 3$

2. Explain how to change $S_3(x)$ so it gives the total amount in the account over three years for an annual payment of $1000.
Multiply each power of $1 + x$ by 1000. Then add to get $1000(x^3 + 4x^2 + 6x + 3)$.

3. Explain how to find polynomials that give the total amounts in the account over four and five years for an annual payment of $1.
Simplify $(1 + x)^4 + (1 + x)^3 + (1 + x)^2 + (1 + x)$ to get $S_4(x) = x^4 + 5x^3 + 10x^2 + 10x + 4$.
Simplify $(1 + x)^5 + (1 + x)^4 + (1 + x)^3 + (1 + x)^2 + (1 + x)$ to get $S_5(x) = x^5 + 6x^4 + 15x^3 + 20x^2 + 15x + 5$.

5-9 Transforming Polynomial Functions

Common Core State Standards
F-BF.B.3 Identify the effect on the graph of replacing $f(x)$ by $f(x) + k$, $k\,f(x)$, $f(kx)$, and $f(x + k)$ for specific values of k (both positive and negative) find the value of k given the graphs. **Also F-IF.C.7c, F-IF.C.8, F-IF.C.9**
MP 1, MP 2, MP 3, MP 4, MP 7

Objective To apply transformations to graphs of polynomials

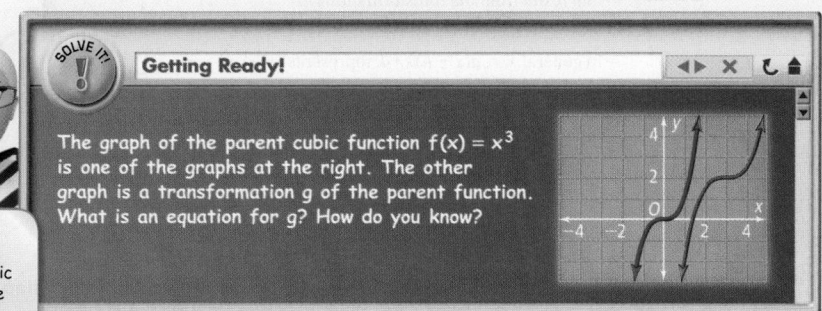

Getting Ready!

The graph of the parent cubic function $f(x) = x^3$ is one of the graphs at the right. The other graph is a transformation g of the parent function. What is an equation for g? How do you know?

> Remember you transformed the graphs of quadratic and absolute value functions.

MATHEMATICAL PRACTICES

Recall that you can obtain the graph of any quadratic function from the graph of the parent quadratic function, $y = x^2$, using one or more basic transformations. You will find that this is not true of cubic functions.

Lesson Vocabulary
• power function
• constant of proportionality

Essential Understanding The graph of the function $y = af(x - h) + k$ is a vertical stretch or compression by the factor $|a|$, a horizontal shift of h units, and a vertical shift of k units of the graph of $y = f(x)$.

Problem 1 Transforming $y = x^3$

What is an equation of the graph of $y = x^3$ under a vertical compression by the factor $\frac{1}{2}$ followed by a reflection across the x-axis, a horizontal translation 3 units to the right, and then a vertical translation 2 units up?

Step 1 Multiply by $\frac{1}{2}$ to compress.
$$y = x^3 \longrightarrow y = \tfrac{1}{2}x^3$$

Think
How is translating this cubic function like translating a quadratic function?
In each case you replace x with $x - h$ to translate h units to the right.

Step 2 Multiply by -1 to reflect.
$$y = \tfrac{1}{2}x^3 \longrightarrow y = -\tfrac{1}{2}x^3$$

Step 3 Replace x with $x - 3$ to translate horizontally.
$$y = -\tfrac{1}{2}x^3 \longrightarrow y = -\tfrac{1}{2}(x - 3)^3$$

Step 4 Add 2 to translate vertically.
$$y = -\tfrac{1}{2}(x - 3)^3 \longrightarrow y = -\tfrac{1}{2}(x - 3)^3 + 2$$

---

1 Interactive Learning

Solve It!

PURPOSE To identify the translations used to transform one cubic function into another
PROCESS Students may
• use the coordinates of the inflection point of the transformed function to identify the horizontal and vertical translations.
• compare the shapes of the graphs to see that the offspring function is simply a translation.

FACILITATE

Q What is the equation for the parent cubic function? $[y = x^3]$

Q Which equation on the grid shows the parent function $y = x^3$? Explain. **[The blue one; it goes through (0, 0); the red one does not.]**

Q How do you know the offspring function is simply a translation of $y = x^3$? **[The graphs have the same shape.]**

ANSWER See Solve It in Answers on next page.
CONNECT THE MATH In the Solve It, students apply what they know about transforming functions to solve the problem. In the lesson, students will transform polynomial functions of degrees 3 and 4.

2 Guided Instruction

Problem 1

Q How do you translate a cubic function two units to the right? **[Use 2 for h; subtract 2 from the x inside the parentheses.]**

Q How do you translate a cubic function three units down? **[Use -3 for k; subtract 3 from the constant term.]**

5-9 Preparing to Teach

BIG idea Function
ESSENTIAL UNDERSTANDING
• The graph of the function $y = af(x - h) + k$ is a vertical stretch or compression by the factor $|a|$, a horizontal shift of h units, and a vertical shift of k units of the graph of $y = f(x)$.

Math Background

Recall that this text defines a *parent function* as "the simplest form of a set of functions that form a family." The functions (or offspring) in the family are created by applying transformations to the parent function.

The most common of these transformations are translation, reflection across the x-axis, and stretch or compression. Students have explored transforming parent functions for linear, quadratic, and absolute value functions. This lesson focuses on polynomial functions of degrees 3 and 4.

The transformations used in this lesson change the values and sometimes the number of the real zeros.

At this level, working with parent functions and their offspring helps reinforce the idea that classes of functions can be recognized by the shapes of their graphs.

In subsequent courses, students will learn that transformations can be used to simplify polynomial functions; for example, the general quintic equation can be reduced to the form $x^5 + px + q = 0$ by applying the appropriate series of transformations.

Mathematical Practices
Look for and make use of structure.
Students will find polynomial functions to be transformations other polynomial functions of the same degree.

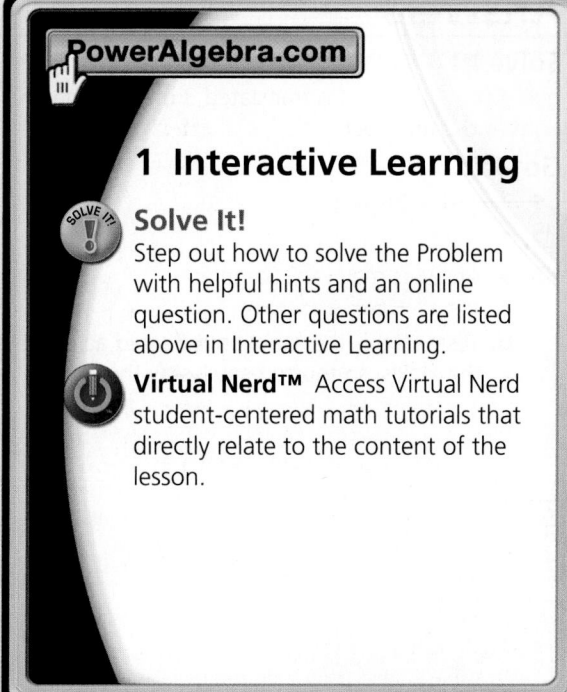

PowerAlgebra.com

1 Interactive Learning

Solve It!
Step out how to solve the Problem with helpful hints and an online question. Other questions are listed above in Interactive Learning.

Virtual Nerd™ Access Virtual Nerd student-centered math tutorials that directly relate to the content of the lesson.

Got It?

Q How can you check your answer by graphing? **[Compare the graph of the cubic function to the description of the transformations to make sure they match.]**

Problem 2

Q How can you find the real zeros of $y = -3(x - 1)^3 + 8$? **[Set *y* equal to 0 and solve for *x*.]**

Q How can you find the real zeros of the general form $y = -a(x - h)^3 + k$? What form will your answer have? **[Use the same procedure. Set *y* equal to 0 and solve for *x*. It will be a literal expression in the three variables *a*, *h*, and *k*.]**

Got It?

Q How do you know before you start that the function will have only one real zero? **[It is a transformation of the parent cubic function, and that function has only one real zero.]**

Students who have difficulty using the formula may want to solve the problem algebraically or by graphing.

 Got It? 1. What is an equation of the graph of $y = x^3$ under a vertical stretch by the factor 2 followed by a horizontal translation 3 units to the left and then a vertical translation 4 units down?

The graph shows $y = x^3$ and the graphs that result from the transformations in Problem 1.

In general, $y = a(x - h)^3 + k$ represents all of the cubic functions you can obtain by stretching, compressing, reflecting, or translating the cubic parent function $y = x^3$.

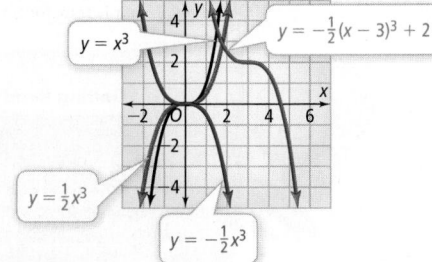

 Problem 2 Finding Zeros of a Transformed Cubic Function

Multiple Choice If *a*, *h*, and *k* are real numbers and $a \neq 0$, how many distinct real zeros does $y = -a(x - h)^3 + k$ have?

Ⓐ 0   Ⓑ 1   Ⓒ 2   Ⓓ 3

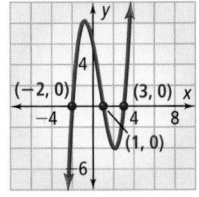

$-a(x - h)^3 + k = 0$ *x* is a zero means it is an *x*-intercept, so $y = 0$.

$-a(x - h)^3 = -k$ Subtract *k* from each side.

$(x - h)^3 = \dfrac{k}{a}$ Divide each side by $-a$.

$x - h = \sqrt[3]{\dfrac{k}{a}}$ Take the cube root of each side.

$x = \sqrt[3]{\dfrac{k}{a}} + h$ Solve for *x*.

Disregarding multiplicities, the function has a single real zero. The correct answer is B.

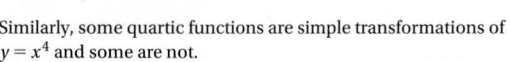 **Got It? 2.** What are all the real zeros of the function $y = 3(x - 1)^3 + 6$?

Problems 1 and 2 together illustrate that the graph of an "offspring" function of the parent cubic function $y = x^3$ has only one *x*-intercept.

The graph of the cubic function $y = x^3 - 2x^2 - 5x + 6$ has three *x*-intercepts. You cannot obtain this function or others like it by transforming the parent cubic function $y = x^3$ using stretches, reflections, and translations.

Similarly, some quartic functions are simple transformations of $y = x^4$ and some are not.

Answers

Solve It!
$g(x) = (x - 3)^3 + 2$; it is translated 3 units to the right and 2 units up.

Got It?
1. $y = 2(x + 3)^3 - 4$

2. $1 - \sqrt[3]{2}$

3. a. Answers may vary. Sample:
     $y = x^4 - 6x^3 + x^2 - 6x$

b. Yes; $-f(x)$ is the function reflected across the *x*-axis, so the zeros will stay the same.

PowerAlgebra.com

2 Guided Instruction

© Each Problem is worked out and supported online.

Problem 1
Transforming $y = x^3$
Animated

Alternative Problem 1
Transforming $y = x^3$

Problem 2
Finding Zeros of a Transformed Cubic Function
Animated

Problem 3
Constructing a Quartic Function with Two Real Zeros
Animated

Problem 4
Modeling with a Power Function

Support in Algebra 2 Companion
- Vocabulary
- Key Concepts
- Got It?

Problem 3 Constructing a Quartic Function with Two Real Zeros

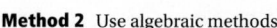

What is a quartic function with only two real zeros, $x = 5$ and $x = 9$?

Method 1 Use transformations.

First, find a quartic with zeros at ± 2.
Translate the basic quartic 16 units down:
$y = x^4 \rightarrow y = x^4 - 16$

9 is 7 units to the right of 2.
Translate 7 units to the right.
$y = x^4 - 16 \rightarrow y = (x - 7)^4 - 16$

A quartic function with its only real zeros at 5 and 9 is
$y = (x - 7)^4 - 16$.

> $y = x^4$
> $y = x^4 - 16$ $y = (x - 7)^4 - 16$

Method 2 Use algebraic methods.

$$y = (x - 5)(x - 9) \cdot Q(x)$$
$$= (x - 5)(x - 9)(x^2 + 1)$$
$$= (x^2 - 14x + 45)(x^2 + 1)$$
$$= x^4 - 14x^3 + 46x^2 - 14x + 45$$

> Make $Q(x)$ a quadratic with no real zeros.

Another quartic function with its only real zeros at
5 and 9 is $y = x^4 - 14x^3 + 46x^2 - 14x + 45$.

Think

What should you use for $Q(x)$?
Choose $Q(x)$ to be a quadratic with no real zeros. Keep it simple, such as $x^2 + 1$.

Got It? **3. a.** What is a quartic function $f(x)$ with only two real zeros, $x = 0$ and $x = 6$?
b. Reasoning Does the quartic function $-f(x)$ have the same zeros? Explain.

The "offspring" of the parent function $y = x^4$ is a subfamily of all quartic polynomials. This subfamily consists of quartics of the form $y = a(x - h)^4 + k$. These functions also belong to another category of polynomials, and in this category you can generate families as usual.

Key Concept Power Functions

Definition	Examples
A **power function** is a function of the form $y = a \cdot x^b$, where a and b are nonzero real numbers.	$y = 0.5x^6$ $y = \frac{1}{2}x^2$ $y = -4x^{\frac{2}{3}}$ $y = x^{0.25}$

If the exponent b in $y = ax^b$ is a positive integer, the function is also a *monomial function*.

If $y = ax^b$ describes y as a power function of x, then y *varies directly with*, or *is proportional to*, the bth power of x. The constant a is the **constant of proportionality**. Power functions arise in many real-world contexts related to the concept of direct variation, which you studied in Chapter 2.

PowerAlgebra.com | **Lesson 5-9** Transforming Polynomial Functions | **341**

Problem 3
In Method 1, it may be difficult for students to understand why they start by translating the function 16 units down. Have them graph the parent function $y = x^4$.

Q What points on the graph of $y = x^4$ have $+2$ and -2 as the x-coordinates? **(2, 16) and (-2, 16)]**
Q How far apart are these points? **[4 units]**
Q If you translate $y = x^4$ 16 units down, how far apart will the zeros be? **[4 units]**

Got It?

Q Why are there many different answers to this problem? Hint: Look at the solution steps in Method 2. **[The function $Q(x)$ could be any quadratic function, so there is an infinite number of solutions.]**

Take Note

Q How does setting h and k equal to 0 in $y = a(x - h)^4 + k$ change the transformed quartic function to the fourth-degree power function? **[Substituting 0 for h and k in $y = a(x - h)^4 - k$ gives $y = a(x - 0)^4 + 0$, which simplifies to $y = ax^4$, which is the fourth-degree power function.]**

Additional Problems

1. What cubic function do you obtain by applying the following transformations to $y = x^3$: vertical stretch by the factor 3; reflection in the x-axis; vertical translation 5 units up?

ANSWER $y = -3x^3 + 5$

2. What are all the real zeros of $y = \frac{1}{2}(x - 2)^3 - 3$?

ANSWER 3.82

3. What is a quartic function with only two real zeros: $x = -4$ and $x = -6$?

ANSWER Answers may vary. Samples: $y = (x + 5)^4 - 1$; $y = x^4 + 10x^3 + 25x^2 + 10x + 24$

4. A wind turbine generates 1200 kW of power in a 20 mi/h wind. How much power does this turbine generate in a 12 mi/h wind? Use the formula for P as a power function of velocity, $P = av^3$.

ANSWER 259.2 kW, or about 259 kW

Problem 4

> **Q** What is a method for using the direct variation equation $y = kx$ to solve a problem when you are given one set of values for x and y? **[Write the equation $y = kx$. Use the given values to find k. Substitute any value for x to find y.]**
>
> **Q** The point $(2, 2)$ is on the graph of the power function $y = ax^2$. What is a? What is the point with 5 as its x-coordinate? **[$a = 0.5$; $(5, 12.5)$]**

Got It?

> **Q** Why is the constant of proportionality different from the variation equation in the Problem? **[The values of P and v do not vary directly with the values of P and v in the Problem because the units have been changed.]**

3 Lesson Check

Do you know HOW?   ERROR INTERVENTION

- If students have trouble with Exercises 1–3, remind them that they can find the zeros either algebraically or by graphing, and then use the other method to check.

Do you UNDERSTAND?

- If students are confused by Exercise 5 because they know some cubic functions have 3 real roots, remind them that these functions cannot be obtained by transformations. Have them experiment with a graphing calculator to see for themselves.

Close

> **Q** What are the relationships among these sets?
> Set A = {all cubic polynomial functions}
> Set B = {transformed cubic polynomial functions}
> Set C = {third-degree power functions}
> **[B is a subset of A, and C is a subset of B.]**

 **Problem 4** Modeling With a Power Function **STEM**

Wind-Generated Power Wind farms are a source of renewable energy found around the world. The power P (in kilowatts) generated by a wind turbine varies directly as the cube of the wind speed v (in meters per second). The picture shows the power output of one turbine at one wind speed. To the nearest kilowatt, how much power does this turbine generate in a 10 m/s wind?

Wind 8 m/s

Electric Power 600 kW

Think
How is this problem like the direct variation you studied in Chapter 2?
With the direct variation, $y = kx$, you use a first power. Here you use a third power.

The formula for P as a power function of v is $P = a \cdot v^3$. From the picture, $P = 600$ when $v = 8$, or $600 = a \cdot 8^3$. Solve for a.

$$600 = a \cdot 8^3 \qquad \text{Use values of } P \text{ and } v \text{ to find } a.$$
$$600 = 512a$$
$$a \approx 1.1719$$
$$P \approx 1.1719v^3 \qquad \text{Use the value of } a \text{ in the original formula.}$$
$$P \approx 1.1719 \cdot 10^3 = 1171.9 \qquad \text{Substitute 10 for } v \text{ and simplify.}$$

This turbine generates about 1172 kW of power in a 10 m/s wind.

 Got It? **4.** Another turbine generates 210 kW of power in a 12 mi/h wind. How much power does this turbine generate in a 20 mi/h wind?

 Lesson Check

Do you know HOW?

Find all the real zeros of each function.

1. $y = -(x + 3)^3 + 1$

2. $y = -8(x - 5)^3 - 64$

3. $y = \frac{9}{2}(x - 1)^3 + \frac{4}{3}$

Do you UNDERSTAND? **MATHEMATICAL PRACTICES**

4. Vocabulary Is the function $y = 4x^3 + 5$ an example of a power function? Explain.

5. Error Analysis Your friend says that he has found a way to transform the graph of $y = x^3$ to obtain three real roots. Using the graph of the function, explain why this is impossible.

6. Compare and Contrast How are the graphs of $y = x^3$ and $y = 4x^3$ alike? How are they different? What transformation was used to get the second equation?

Answers

Got It? (continued)

4. 972 kW

Lesson Check

1. -2

2. 3

3. $\frac{1}{3}$

4. No; a power function is of the form $y = ax^b$, where y varies directly with the bth power of x.

5. $y = x^3$ has end behavior of down and up with no turning pt. Thus, at most, there is one real root.

6. Both $y = x^3$ and $y = 4x^3$ pass through the origin, have the same end behavior of down and up, and no turning pts. $y = 4x^3$ is $y = x^3$ stretched vertically by a factor of 4.

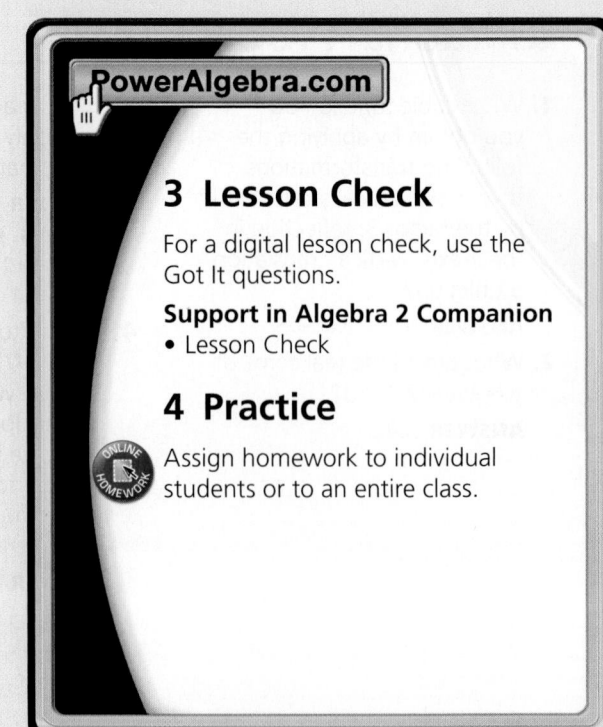

PowerAlgebra.com

3 Lesson Check

For a digital lesson check, use the Got It questions.

Support in Algebra 2 Companion
- Lesson Check

4 Practice

Assign homework to individual students or to an entire class.

Practice and Problem-Solving Exercises  MATHEMATICAL PRACTICES

 **Practice** Determine the cubic function that is obtained from the parent function $y = x^3$ after each sequence of transformations. ◆ **See Problem 1.**

7. a vertical stretch by a factor of 3;
a reflection across the x-axis;
a vertical translation 2 units up;
and a horizontal translation 1 unit right

8. a vertical stretch by a factor of 2;
a vertical translation 4 units up;
and a horizontal translation 3 units left

9. a reflection across the y-axis;
a vertical translation 1 unit down;
and a horizontal translation 5 units left

10. a vertical translation 3 units down;
and a horizontal translation 2 units right

11. a vertical stretch by a factor of 3;
a reflection across the y-axis;
a vertical translation $\frac{3}{4}$ unit up;
and a horizontal translation $\frac{1}{2}$ unit left

12. a vertical stretch by a factor of $\frac{5}{3}$;
a reflection across the x-axis;
a vertical translation 4 units down;
and a horizontal translation 3 units right

Find all the real zeros of each function. ◆ **See Problem 2.**

13. $y = -27(x - 2)^3 + 8$

14. $y = -\frac{1}{8}(x - 7)^3 - 8$

15. $y = -3\left(x + \frac{4}{5}\right)^3 + \frac{8}{9}$

16. $y = -16(x + 3)^3 + 9$

17. $y = 4(x - 1)^3 + 10$

18. $y = 2(x + 5)^3 + 10$

Find a quartic function with the given x-values as its only real zeros. ◆ **See Problem 3.**

19. $x = 2$ and $x = -1$

20. $x = -3$ and $x = -4$

21. $x = -1$ and $x = 3$

22. $x = 4$ and $x = 2$

23. $x = -4$ and $x = -1$

24. $x = -3$ and $x = 2$

25. Cooking The number of pepperoni slices that Kim puts on a pizza varies directly as the square of the diameter of the pizza. If she puts 15 slices on a 10" diameter pizza, how many slices should she put on a 16" diameter pizza? ◆ **See Problem 4.**

26. Volume The amount of water that a spherical tank can hold varies directly as the cube of its radius. If a tank with radius 7.5 ft holds 1767 ft^3 of water, how much water can a tank with radius 16 ft hold?

 Apply © **27. Think About a Plan** The kinetic energy generated by a 5 lb ball is represented by the formula $K = \frac{1}{2}(5)v^2$. If the ball is thrown with a velocity of 6 ft/sec, how much kinetic energy is generated?
• What does 5 represent in the function?
• What number should you substitute for v?

ASSIGNMENT GUIDE
Basic: 7–26 all, 27, 28–34 even, 39, 40
Average: 7–25 odd, 27–41
Advanced: 7–25 odd, 27–44
Standardized Test Prep: 45–47
Mixed Review: 48–56

© **Mathematical Practices** are supported by exercises with red headings. Here are the Practices supported in this lesson:

MP 1: Make Sense of Problems Ex. 27
MP 2: Reason Abstractly Ex. 40
MP 3: Communicate Ex. 42
MP 3: Construct Arguments Ex. 41
MP 3: Compare Arguments Ex. 6
MP 3: Critique the Reasoning of Others Ex. 5

Applications exercises have blue headings. Exercises 25 and 26 support MP 4: Model.

STEM exercises focus on science or engineering applications.

EXERCISE 39: Use the Think About a Plan worksheet in the **Practice and Problem Solving Workbook** (also available in the Teaching Resources in print and online) to further support students' development in becoming independent learners.

HOMEWORK QUICK CHECK
To check students' understanding of key skills and concepts, go over Exercises 7, 13, 27, 32, and 39.

Practice and Problem-Solving Exercises

7. $y = -3(x - 1)^3 + 2$

8. $y = 2(x + 3)^3 + 4$

9. $y = -(x + 5)^3 - 1$

10. $y = (x - 2)^3 - 3$

11. $y = -3\left(x + \frac{1}{2}\right)^3 + \frac{3}{4}$

12. $y = -\frac{5}{3}(x - 3)^3 - 4$

13. $\frac{8}{3}$

14. 3

15. $-\frac{2}{15}$

16. $-3 + \frac{1}{4}\sqrt[3]{36}$

17. $1 - \frac{1}{2}\sqrt[3]{20}$

18. $-5 - \sqrt[3]{5}$

For Exercises 19–24, answers may vary. Samples:

19. $x^4 - x^3 - x^2 - x - 2$

20. $x^4 + 7x^3 + 13x^2 + 7x + 12$

21. $x^4 - 2x^3 - 2x^2 - 2x - 3$

22. $x^4 - 6x^3 + 9x^2 - 6x + 8$

23. $x^4 + 5x^3 + 5x^2 + 5x + 4$

24. $x^4 + x^3 - 5x^2 + x - 6$

25. $38.4 \approx 38$ slices

26. 17,155.9 ft^3

27. 90 lb • ft^2/s^2

Answers

Practice and Problem-Solving Exercises
(continued)

28. Yes; using parent function $y = x^3$, stretch vertically by a factor of 4 and reflect across the x-axis.

29. Yes; using parent function $y = x^2$, stretch vertically by a factor of 2, then translate 5 units up and 3 units to the right.

30. no

31. Yes; using parent function $y = x^2$, translate 9 units down and 4 units to the right.

32. translation 4 units up and 1 unit to the left

33. reflection across the x-axis, vert. stretch by a factor of 2, translation 1 unit up and 1 unit to the right

34. reflection across the x-axis, translation 2 units down and 3 units to the right

35. vert. stretch by a factor of 3, translation 2 units down and 1 unit to the right

36. vert. stretch by a factor of 5, translation 1 unit up and 1 unit to the right

37. reflection across the x-axis, translation 2 units up and 4 units to the right

38. The function $y = 3x^3$ because it has a vertical stretch factor of 3 and the function graphed only has a vertical stretch factor of $\frac{1}{2}$.

39. 40 lb · ft² / s²

40. The parent function, $y = x^5$, has only one x-intercept.

41. Some quartic polynomials have four x-intercepts and cannot be written in that form; $y = x^4 - 20x^2 + 64$; $y = x^4 - 5x^2 + 4$.

Determine whether each function can be obtained from the parent function, $y = x^n$, using basic transformations. If so, describe the sequence of transformations.

28. $y = -4x^3$

29. $y = 2(x - 3)^2 + 5$

30. $y = x^3 - x$

31. $y = x^2 - 8x + 7$

Determine the transformations that were used to change the graph of the parent function $y = x^3$ to each of the following graphs.

32.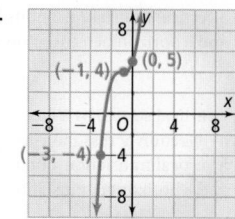

33.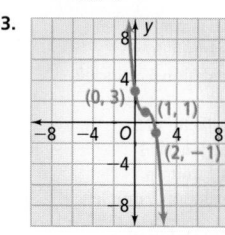

34.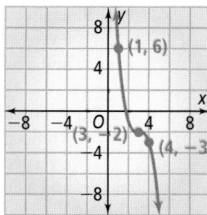

35.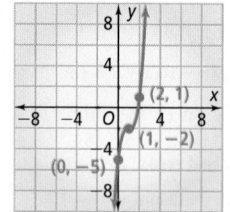

36.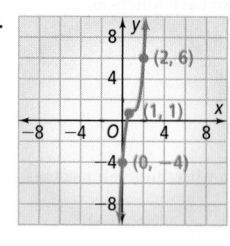

37.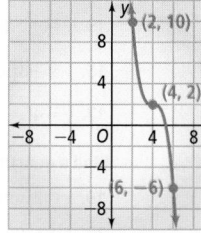

38. Compare the function $y = 3x^3$ to the function shown in the graph at the right. Which function has a greater vertical stretch factor? Explain.

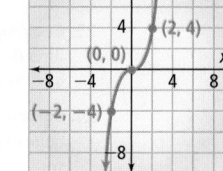

STEM 39. Physics The formula $K = \frac{1}{2}mv^2$ represents the kinetic energy of an object. If the kinetic energy of a ball is 10 lb-ft²/s² when it is thrown with a velocity of 4 ft/s, how much kinetic energy is generated if the ball is thrown with a velocity of 8 ft/s?

40. Reasoning Explain why the basic transformations of the parent function $y = x^5$ will only generate functions that can be written in the form $y = a(x - h)^5 + k$.

41. Reasoning Explain why some quartic polynomials cannot be written in the form $y = a(x - h)^4 + k$. Give two examples.

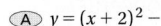 **Challenge**

42. Reasoning Find a sequence of basic transformations by which the polynomial function $y = 2x^3 - 6x^2 + 6x + 5$ can be derived from the cubic function $y = x^3$.

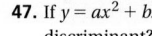 **43. Physics** For a constant resistance R (in ohms), the power P (in watts) dissipated across two terminals of a battery varies directly as the square of the current I (in amps). If a battery connected in a circuit dissipates 24 watts of power for 2 amps of current flow, how much power would be dissipated when the current flow is 5 amps?

44. Writing Give an argument that shows that *every* polynomial family of degree $n > 2$ contains polynomials that cannot be generated from the basic function $y = x^n$ by using stretches, compressions, reflections, and translations.

Standardized Test Prep

Use the graph to answer questions 45–47.

SAT/ACT

45. Which equation does the graph represent?

Ⓐ $y = (x + 2)^2 - 1$ Ⓒ $y = (x - 2)^2 + 1$

Ⓑ $y = (x - 2)^2 - 1$ Ⓓ $y = (x - 2)^4 - 1$

46. If $y = f(x)$ is an equation for the graph, what are factors of $f(x)$?

Ⓕ $(x - 1)$ and $(x + 3)$ Ⓗ $(x + 1)$ and $(x - 3)$

Ⓖ $(x - 1)$ and $(x - 3)$ Ⓘ $(x + 1)$ and $(x + 3)$

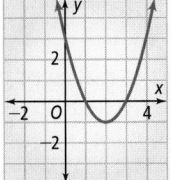

Short Response

47. If $y = ax^2 + bx + c$ is an equation for the graph, what type of number is its discriminant?

Mixed Review

Find a polynomial function whose graph passes through the given points.   ◀ **See Lesson 5-8.**

48. $(-1, 4), (0, -2), (1, -2), (2, -8)$ **49.** $(-2, -17), (0, -3), (1, -5), (3, 63)$

Write an equation of each line.   ◀ **See Lesson 2-4.**

50. slope $= -\frac{4}{5}$; through $(-1, 4)$ **51.** slope $= -3$; through $(2, -1)$

Determine whether each relation is a function.   ◀ **See Lesson 2-1.**

52. $\{(0, -1), (-1, 3), (2, 3), (-3, 3)\}$ **53.** $\{(-4, 0), (-7, 0), (-4, 1), (-7, 1)\}$

Get Ready!   To prepare for Lesson 6-1, do Exercises 54–56.

Factor each expression.   ◀ **See Lesson 5-2.**

54. $x^{10} + x^2$ **55.** $x^4 - y^4$ **56.** $169x^6y^{12} - 13x^3y^6$

---

42. vert. stretch by a factor of 2, translation 7 units up and 1 unit to the right

43. 150 watts

44. Even-degree parent functions and their offspring have two x-intercepts, odd-degree parent functions and their offspring have one x-intercept. Polynomial functions of degree n have as many as n x-intercepts; for example: $y = x^3 - 2x^2 - 5x + 6$ (with three x-intercepts) cannot be generated from the parent function $y = x^3$ (with one x-intercept).

Standardized Test Prep

45. B

46. G

47. [2] $y = (x - 2)^2 - 1$
$= x^2 - 4x + 4 - 1$
$= x^2 - 4x + 3$

The discriminant is:
$b^2 - 4ac = (-4)^2 - 4(1)(3) = 4$
which is positive.

[1] appropriate methods, with one computational error

Mixed Review

48. $y = -2x^3 + 3x^2 - x - 2$

49. $y = 3x^3 - 5x - 3$

50. $y = -\frac{4}{5}x + \frac{16}{5}$

51. $y = -3x + 5$

52. yes

53. no

54. $x^2(x^8 + 1)$

55. $(x - y)(x + y)(x^2 + y^2)$

56. $13x^3y^6(13x^3y^6 - 1)$

5-9 Lesson Resources

Differentiated Remediation
Available in editable format online.

Additional Instructional Support

Algebra 2 Companion
Students can use the **Algebra 2 Companion** worktext (4 pages) as you teach the lesson. Use the Companion to support
- New Vocabulary
- Key Concepts
- Got It for each Problem
- Lesson Check

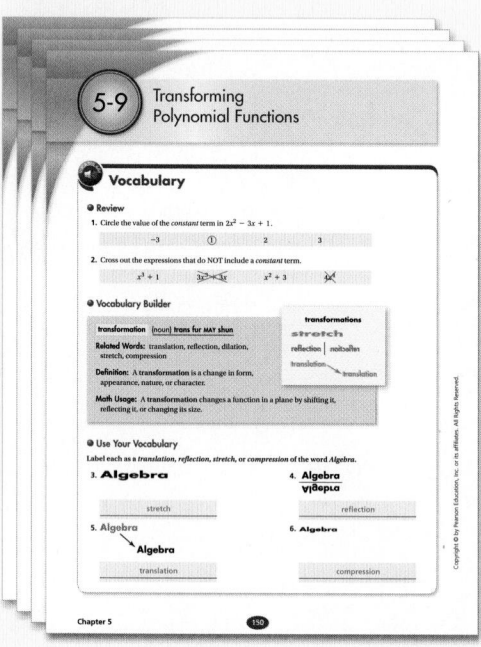

ELL Support
Focus on Language Ask students to consider each of the following and determine whether they are *always*, *sometimes*, or *never* true and explain why:
- A parent function has the same number of zeros as its offspring. [Sometimes true; a horizontal translation does not change the number of zeros but a vertical translation sometimes does]
- A parent function has the same degree as its offspring. [Always true, by definition. No transformation can change the degree of a function.]
- A parent function has the same leading coefficient as its offspring. [Sometimes true; vertical and horizontal translations do not change the leading coefficient; however, a vertical stretch or compression or reflection does.]

5 Assess & Remediate

Lesson Quiz

1. What function do you obtain by applying the following transformations to $y = x^3$: reflection in the *x*-axis; horizontal translation 2 units right; vertical translation 1 unit down?

2. What are the real zeros of $y = -2(x + 3)^3 + 8$?

3. What is a quartic function with only two real zeros, $x = 7$ and $x = 13$?

4. Do you UNDERSTAND? A wind turbine generates 100 kW of power in a 10 mi/h wind. How much power does this turbine generate in a 25 mi/h wind? Use the formula for P as a power function of velocity, $P = av^3$.

ANSWERS TO LESSON QUIZ

1. $y = -(x - 2)^3 - 1$

2. one: -1.41

3. Answers may vary. Samples:
$y = (x - 10)^4 - 81$;
$y = x^4 - 20x^3 + 92x^2 - 20x + 91$

4. 1562.5 kW

PRESCRIPTION FOR REMEDIATION
Use the student work on the Lesson Quiz to prescribe a differentiated review assignment:

Points	Differentiated Remediation
0–2	Intervention
3	On-level
4	Extension

PowerAlgebra.com

5 Assess & Remediate
Assign the Lesson Quiz. Appropriate intervention, practice, or enrichment is automatically generated based on student performance.

Intervention

- **Reteaching** (2 pages) Provides reteaching and practice exercises for the key lesson concepts. Use with struggling students or absent students.
- **English Language Learner Support** Helps students develop and reinforce mathematical vocabulary and key concepts.

All-in-One Resources/Online
Reteaching

5-9 Reteaching
Transforming Polynomial Functions

Problem

What is the equation of the graph of $y = x^3$ under the following transformations?
- vertical stretch by a factor of 4
- reflection across the *x*-axis
- horizontal translation 2 units left
- vertical translation 3 units up

Step 1 Begin by writing the general equation for stretching, reflecting, and/or translating the cubic parent function $y = a(x - h)^3 + k$.
$a = $ vertical stretch $h = $ horizontal translation $k = $ vertical translation
If a function is reflected in the *x*-axis, *a* is negative.

Step 2 The vertical stretch is 4 and the transformed function is reflected across the *x*-axis.
$a = -4$

Step 3 The horizontal translation is 2 units left. This is the negative *x* direction, so *h* is negative.
$h = -2$

Step 4 The vertical translation is 3 units up. This is the positive *y* direction, so *k* is positive.
$k = 3$

Step 5 Substitute *a*, *h*, and *k* into the general equation.
$y = a(x - h)^3 + k = -4[x - (-2)]^3 + 3 = -4(x + 2)^3 + 3$

Exercises

Determine the equation of the graph of $y = x^3$ under each set of transformations.

1. a reflection across the x-axis, a vertical translation 5 units up, and a horizontal translation 8 units right $y = -(x - 8)^3 + 5$

2. a vertical stretch by a factor of $\frac{1}{4}$, a reflection across the *y*-axis, and a vertical translation 2 units down $y = \frac{1}{4}(-x)^3 - 2$

3. a vertical stretch by a factor of 6, a horizontal translation 3 units left, and a vertical translation 1 unit up $y = 6(x + 3)^3 + 1$

All-in-One Resources/Online
English Language Learner Support

5-9 Additional Vocabulary Support
Transforming Polynomial Functions

Choose a word from the list below to complete each sentence.

constant of proportionality	power function

1. A function written in the form $y = a \cdot x^b$ is called a _power function_.

2. The constant *a* in the function $y = ax^b$ is called the _constant of proportionality_.

Determine whether each of the following functions is a power function.

3. $y = 3x^2 - 4$ _not a power function_

4. $y = 4x^3$ _power function_

5. $y = 0.25x^6$ _power function_

6. $y = 7x^5 + 5x$ _not a power function_

7. $y = \frac{1}{3}x^5$ _power function_

Identify the constant of proportionality in each of the following functions.

8. $y = 5x^7$ _5_

9. $y = 0.7x^3$ _0.7_

10. $y = \frac{1}{3}x^2$ _$\frac{1}{3}$_

11. $y = 0.35x^8$ _0.35_

Multiple Choice

12. Given the function $P = a \cdot w^2$, what is the value of *a* if $P = 225$ when $w = 5$? B
Ⓐ 5 Ⓑ 9 Ⓒ 25 Ⓓ 45

13. Given the function $P = a \cdot r^4$, what is the value of *a* if $P = 9$ when $r = 3$? F
Ⓕ $\frac{1}{9}$ Ⓖ $\frac{1}{3}$ Ⓗ 9 Ⓘ 81

Differentiated Remediation *continued*

Available in editable format online.

On-Level

- **Practice** (2 pages) Provides extra practice for each lesson. For simpler practice exercises, use the Form K Practice pages found in the All-in-One Teaching Resources and online.

- **Think About a Plan** Helps students develop specific problem-solving skills and strategies by providing scaffolded guiding questions.

- **Standardized Test Prep** Focuses on all major exercises, all major question types, and helps students prepare for the high-stakes assessments.

Extension

- **Enrichment** Provides students with interesting problems and activities that extend the concepts of the lesson.

- **Activities, Games, and Puzzles** Worksheets that can be used for concepts development, enrichment, and for fun!

Practice and Problem Solving Wkbk/All-in-One Resources/Online
Practice page 1

5-9 Practice *Form G*
Transforming Polynomial Functions

Determine the cubic function that is obtained from the parent function $y = x^3$ after each sequence of transformations.

1. a reflection in the x-axis; a vertical translation 3 units down; and a horizontal translation 2 units right
   $y = -(x - 2)^3 - 3$

2. a vertical stretch by a factor of 4; a reflection in the x-axis; and a horizontal translation $\frac{1}{2}$ unit left
   $y = -4\left(x + \frac{1}{2}\right)^3$

3. a vertical stretch by a factor of $\frac{1}{3}$; a reflection in the y-axis; and a vertical translation 6 units up
   $y = \frac{1}{3}(-x)^3 + 6$

4. a vertical stretch by a factor of 3; a reflection in the x-axis; a vertical translation 2 units down; and a horizontal translation 2 units left
   $y = -3(x + 2)^3 - 2$

Find all the real zeros of each function.

5. $y = 2(x + 1)^3 - 3$ $x = \sqrt[3]{\frac{3}{2}} - 1$

6. $y = -3(x - 2)^3 + 24$ $x = 4$

7. $y = -\frac{1}{2}(x + 4)^3 - 1$ $x = \sqrt[3]{-2} - 4$

8. $y = 8(-x - 2)^3 + 5$ $x = \frac{\sqrt[3]{5}}{2} - 2$

9. $y = -(x + 5)^3 + 1$ $x = -4$

10. $y = 4(x - 6)^3 - 2$ $x = \frac{1}{\sqrt[3]{2}} + 6$

Find a quartic function with the given x-values as its only real zeros.

11. $x = 2$ and $x = 8$
    Answers may vary. Sample:
    $y = (x - 5)^4 - 81$

12. $x = 3$ and $x = -1$
    Answers may vary. Sample:
    $y = (x - 1)^4 - 16$

13. $x = 1$ and $x = 3$
    Answers may vary. Sample:
    $y = (x - 2)^4 - 1$

14. $x = -2$ and $x = 6$
    Answers may vary. Sample:
    $y = (x - 2)^4 - 256$

15. $x = 5$ and $x = -2$
    Answers may vary. Sample:
    $y = x^4 - 3x^3 - 9x^2 - 3x - 10$

16. $x = -1$ and $x = 2$
    Answers may vary. Sample:
    $y = x^4 - x^3 - x^2 - x - 2$

17. $x = -3$ and $x = -5$
    Answers may vary. Sample:
    $y = x^4 + 8x^3 + 16x^2 + 8x + 15$

18. $x = -4$ and $x = 1$
    Answers may vary. Sample:
    $y = x^4 - 15x^2 - 16$

19. **Physics** If you stretch a spring to 5 ft, it has 310 ft-lb of potential energy (*PE*). Potential energy varies directly as the square of the stretched length (*l*). The potential energy can be represented by the formula $PE = \frac{1}{2}kl^2$, where *k* is the spring constant.
   a. What is the value of the spring constant for this spring?   24.8
   b. How many ft-lbs of *PE* would an 8 ft length of spring have?   793.6 ft-lb

---

Practice and Problem Solving Wkbk/All-in-One Resources/Online
Practice page 2

5-9 Practice (continued) *Form G*
Transforming Polynomial Functions

Determine whether each function can be obtained from the parent function $y = x^n$, using basic transformations. If so, describe the sequence of transformations.

20. $y = 2(x - 3)^3 + 4$ yes; vertical stretch by a factor of 2, horizontal translation 3 units right, vertical translation 4 units up

21. $y = x^4 + x - 3$ no

22. $y = -\frac{1}{3}x^5$ yes; vertical stretch by a factor of $\frac{1}{3}$, reflection across x-axis

23. $y = (-x + 5)^3$ yes; reflection across y-axis, horizontal translation 5 units right

24. $y = \frac{2}{x^3}$ yes; vertical stretch by a factor of 2

25. $y = 4(x)^4 - 12$ yes; vertical stretch by a factor of 4, vertical translation 12 units down

26. Graph the parent function $y = x^3$ after it has been transformed by the following changes.
    - vertical stretch by a factor of $2\frac{1}{4}$
    - reflection across the x-axis
    - vertical translation 4 units up

27. **Error Analysis** Your friend set up a problem to find a quartic function with the only real zeros of $x = -4$ and $x = 1$. She wrote down $y = (x + 4)(x - 1)(x^2 - 1)$. Will she get a correct quartic function? Why or why not?
    No; she used a quadratic that has additional real zeros; she should have used $x^2 + 1$ as her quadratic.

28. **Open-Ended** Transform the parent function $y = x^3$ by vertical stretch, reflection across the x-axis, horizontal translation, and vertical translation.
    Any cubic polynomial in the form of $y = a(x - h)^3 + k$ where $a < 0$ and h and $k \neq 0$.

29. You are swinging a bucket in a circle at a velocity of 7.8 ft/s. The radius of the circle you are making is 1.25 ft. The acceleration is equal to one over the radius multiplied by the velocity squared.
    a. What is the acceleration of the bucket?   about 48.7 ft/s²
    b. What is the velocity if the acceleration is 25 ft/sec²?   about 5.6 ft/s

---

All-in-One Resources/Online
Enrichment

5-9 Enrichment
Transforming Polynomial Functions

The discriminant of a quadratic equation is used to determine the number and type of solutions to a quadratic equation. A cubic equation also has a discriminant that determines the number and type of solutions to a cubic equation.

The general equation of a monic cubic equation that has a leading coefficient of 1 is

$$y = x^3 + bx^2 + cx + d$$

The discriminant of a monic cubic equation is $b^2c^2 - 4c^3 - 4b^3d - 27d^2 + 18bcd$. If
$b^2c^2 - 4c^3 - 4b^3d - 27d^2 + 18bcd > 0$, there are 3 real, distinct roots.
$b^2c^2 - 4c^3 - 4b^3d - 27d^2 + 18bcd = 0$, there are real roots and one has multiplicity 2.
$b^2c^2 - 4c^3 - 4b^3d - 27d^2 + 18bcd < 0$, there are 1 real and 2 complex, conjugate roots.

For each cubic, determine the value of the discriminant and state the number and type of roots.

1. $y = x^3 - 2x^2 + x + 7$ -1351; 1 real and 2 complex, conjugate roots

2. $y = x^3 + 4x^2 + 2x + 5$ -1203; 1 real and 2 complex, conjugate roots

3. $y = x^3 - 7x^2 - x - 2$ -3051; 1 real and 2 complex, conjugate roots

4. $y = x^3 - 9x^2 - 1$ -2943; 1 real and 2 complex, conjugate roots

5. $y = x^3 + 10x^2 + 2x - 3$ $11,045$; 3 real, distinct roots

6. $y = x^3 + 5x^2 + 3x - 9$ 0; real roots with 1 of multiplicity 2

7. $y = x^3 - 5x + 11$ -2767; 1 real and 2 complex, conjugate roots

8. $y = x^3 + 7x$ -1372; 1 real and 2 complex, conjugate roots

9. $y = x^3 + 5x^2$ 0; real roots with 1 of multiplicity 2

10. $y = x^3 + 4x^2 - x - 4$ 900; 3 real, distinct roots

Practice and Problem Solving Wkbk/All-in-One Resources/Online
Think About a Plan

5-9 Think About a Plan
Transforming Polynomial Functions

Physics The formula $K = \frac{1}{2}mv^2$ represents the kinetic energy of an object. If the kinetic energy of a ball is 10 lb-ft²/s² when it is thrown with a velocity of 4 ft/s, how much kinetic energy is generated if the ball is thrown with a velocity of 8 ft/s?

Know

1. The kinetic energy is [10 lb·ft²/s²] when the velocity of the ball is [4 ft/s]

2. Check students' work.

Need

3. To solve the problem I need to:
   solve the kinetic energy equation for *m*

Plan

4. What equation can you use to find the value of *m* for the ball? $10 = \frac{1}{2}m(4)^2$

5. Solve the equation. $m = 1.25$

6. What equation can you use to find the kinetic energy generated if the ball is thrown with a velocity of 8 ft/s? $K = \frac{1}{2}(1.25)(8)^2$

7. Simplify. $K = 40$ lb-ft²/s²

8. Is the solution reasonable? Explain.
   Yes; the kinetic energy increases by a factor of 4 when the velocity doubles. The change in the kinetic energy is the square of the change in the velocity

---

Practice and Problem Solving Wkbk/All-in-One Resources/Online
Standardized Test Prep

5-9 Standardized Test Prep
Transforming Polynomial Functions

Multiple Choice

For Exercises 1–5, choose the correct letter.

1. Which of the following describes the transformation of the parent function $y = x^3$ shown in the graph at the right?   A
   A. reflection across x-axis, vertical stretch by a factor of 2, and horizontal translation 1 unit left
   B. reflection across y-axis, vertical translation 1 unit up
   C. horizontal translation 2 units left, vertical translation 1 unit down
   D. vertical stretch by a factor of $\frac{1}{2}$, horizontal translation 1 unit right, and vertical translation 2 units down

2. What are all the real zeros for $y = 5(x - 4)^3 + 6$?   H
   F. $\sqrt[3]{\frac{-6}{5}} - 4$ G. $\sqrt[3]{\frac{6}{5}} - 4$ H. $\sqrt[3]{\frac{-6}{5}} + 4$ I. $\sqrt[3]{\frac{6}{5}} + 4$

3. Which of the following polynomial functions *cannot* be obtained from the parent function $y = x^4$ using basic transformations?   D
   A. $y = 6(x + 2)^3 - 3$ B. $y = (-x - 1)^4$ C. $y = \frac{x^4}{2}$ D. $y = x^2 + x$

4. Which quartic function has $x = 3$ and $x = 9$ as its only real zeros?   G
   F. $y = (x + 6)^4 - 81$ H. $y = (x + 3)^4 - 81$
   G. $y = (x - 6)^4 - 81$ I. $y = (x - 3)^4 - 81$

5. Which graph represents the polynomial $y = 2(-x + 6)^3 - 1$?   B

Short Response

6. The formula $s = \frac{1}{2}at^2$ represents the distance an object will travel in a specific amount of time if it travels at a constant acceleration. You roll a ball 20 ft in 6 s. How long will it take to roll the ball 45 ft? Show your work.
   [2] substitute $s = 20$ and $t = 6$ into formula and solve for a; $20 = \frac{1}{2}a(6)^2$; $a \approx 1.11$ ft/s²; substitute $s = 45$ and $a = 1.11$ into formula and solve for t; $t \approx 9$ s.
   [1] incorrect time OR incorrect work shown
   [0] no answers given

Online Teacher Resource Center
Activities, Games, and Puzzles

5-9 Game: Parent Functions
Transforming Polynomial Functions

In this game you will work in teams, using the parent functions graphed at the right.
Answer each question below. When your team is done, your teacher will check your answers and tally the scores to see who wins.

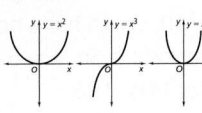

$y = x^2$ $y = x^3$ $y = x^4$

Write the function. (1 point each)

1. The graph of the quadratic parent function is moved 3 units right and 2 units down. $y = (x - 3)^2 - 2$

2. The graph of the cubic parent function is vertically stretched by a factor of 3. $y = 3x^3$

3. The graph of the fourth degree parent function is moved 3 units to the left. $y = (x + 3)^4$

4. The graph of the quadratic parent function is moved 3 units to the left and 2.5 units up. $y = (x + 3)^2 + 2.5$

Sketch the graph. (3 points each)

5. The graph of the fourth degree parent moved 2 units to the right.

6. The graph of the cubic parent function is moved 2 units up.

7. The graph of the quadratic parent function is moved 1 unit to the left.

Write the function. (5 points each)

8. $y = (x + 3)^4 - 3$

9. $y = (x - 2)^3 + 2$

10. $y = (x + 2)^2 - 3$

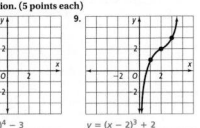

Completing the Performance Task

In the Apply What You've Learned sections in Lessons 5-1, 5-2, and 5-5, students wrote and analyzed a polynomial function that models the volume of the diorama box shown on page 279. Here, students use their findings to complete the Performance Task. Ask students the following questions as they work toward solving the problem.

Q How can you use the work you have done in the chapter to solve the problem? **[Sample: I can identify which solutions of the equation $4x^3 - 40x^2 + 96x = 36$ that I found in Lesson 5-5 are between $x = 0$ and $x = 4$, and then substitute those values in the expressions I wrote in Lesson 5-1 for the length and width of the back of the box.]**

Q How can you check that your answers are correct? **[Sample: I can check that the product of the dimensions is approximately equal to the desired volume, 36 in.^{3}.]**

FOSTERING MATHEMATICAL DISCOURSE

Have students discuss which set of possible diorama box dimensions seems more practical for Eliana's contest entry.

ANSWERS

1. 6 in. by 2 in. by 3 in., 11.08 in. by 7.08 in. by 0.46 in.

2. Check students' work.

On Your Own

This problem is similar to the problem posed on page 279, but now students write expressions for the dimensions of the box based on the thickness of its sides and back. Students should strive to solve this problem independently.

ANSWERS

a. 10 in. by 5 in. by 5 in.

b. Explanations may vary. Sample: Solve the equation $2x^3 - 8x^2 + 10x - 4 = 96$, which is equivalent to the equation $x^3 - 4x^2 + 5x - 50 = 0$. By synthetic division, $x = 5$ is a root. When $x - 5$ is factored out of $x^3 - 4x^2 + 5x - 50$, the quadratic factor is $x^2 + x + 10$, which has a negative discriminant and no real zeros. So, $x = 5$ is the only real solution of $V(x) = 96$.

---

 5 *Pull It* **All Together**

Completing the Performance Task

Look back at your results from the Apply What You've Learned sections in Lessons 5-1, 5-2, and 5-5. Use the work you did to complete the following.

To solve these problems, you will pull together concepts and skills related to working with polynomials and their related functions and equations.

1. Solve the problem in the Task Description on page 279 by determining all possible dimensions Eliana can use for a diorama box with volume 36 in.^{3}. Round dimensions to the nearest hundredth of an inch. Show all your work and explain each step of your solution.

2. **Reflect** Choose one of the Mathematical Practices below and explain how you applied it in your work on the Performance Task.

   MP 1: Make sense of problems and persevere in solving them.

   MP 4: Model with mathematics.

   MP 7: Look for and make use of structure.

On Your Own

After finishing her miniature diorama for the art contest, Eliana decides to make another diorama. Her new diorama will be inside a wooden box, as shown in the figure below. Eliana orders a wooden box online with sides and back panel that are 1 in. thick. The outside length is twice as long as the outside width and outside depth. According to the information Eliana finds online, the interior of the box has a volume of 96 in.^{3}.

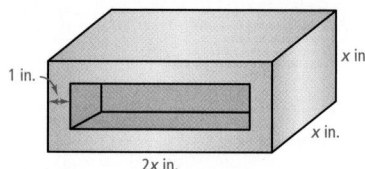

a. Determine all possible outside dimensions of the box.

b. Explain how you know that you found all possible answers in part (a).

5 Chapter Review

Connecting **BIG** ideas and Answering the Essential Questions

1 Function
A polynomial of degree n has n linear factors. The graph of the related function crosses the x-axis an even or odd number of times depending on whether n is even or odd.

2 Equivalence
$(x - a)$ is a linear factor if and only if a is a zero, and if and only if $(a, 0)$ is an x-intercept when a is a real number.

3 Solving Equations and Inequalities
$(x - a)$ is a linear factor if and only if a is a root of the related polynomial equation.

Polynomial Functions, Zeros, and Linear Factors (Lessons 5-1 and 5-2)
$y = 2x^3 + 7x^2 - 9$ has 3 linear factors $(x + 3)$, $(2x + 3)$, $(x - 1)$; it crosses the x-axis 3 times—at $(-3, 0)$, $(-\frac{3}{2}, 0)$, and $(1, 0)$. Its end behavior is down and up.

Theorems About Roots of Polynomial Equations (Lesson 5-5)
$P(x) = 2x^3 + 7x^2 - 9$ and $Q(x) = 2x^3 + 5x^2 + 9$ each have degree 3 so $P(x) = 0$ and $Q(x) = 0$ each have 3 complex roots.
Each has ± 1, ± 3, ± 9, $\pm \frac{1}{2}$, $\pm \frac{3}{2}$, $\pm \frac{9}{2}$ as its possible rational roots.
$P(-3) = 0$, so $x + 3$ is a factor of $2x^3 + 7x^2 - 9$.
$Q(-3) = 0$, so $x + 3$ is a factor of $2x^3 + 5x^2 + 9$.

Solving Polynomial Equations (Lesson 5-3)
$2x^3 + 7x^2 - 9 = 0$ has factored form $(x + 3)(2x + 3)(x - 1) = 0$. It has 3 roots or solutions, $x = -3$, $x = -\frac{3}{2}$, and $x = 1$.

The Fundamental Theorem of Algebra (Lesson 5-6)
$2x^3 + 5x^2 + 9 = 0$ has factored form $(x + 3)(2x^2 - x + 3) = 0$. It has 3 roots or solutions, $x = -3$, $x = \frac{1}{4} - \frac{\sqrt{23}}{4} i$, and $x = \frac{1}{4} + \frac{\sqrt{23}}{4} i$.

Chapter Vocabulary

- Binomial Theorem (p. 327)
- Conjugate Root Theorem (p. 314)
- constant of proportionality (p. 341)
- degree of a monomial (p. 280)
- degree of a polynomial (p. 280)
- Descartes' Rule of Signs (p. 315)
- difference of cubes (p. 297)
- end behavior (p. 282)
- expand a binomial (p. 326)
- Factor Theorem (p. 290)

- Fundamental Theorem of Algebra (p. 320)
- monomial (p. 280)
- multiple zero (p. 291)
- multiplicity (p. 291)
- Pascal's Triangle (p. 327)
- polynomial (p. 280)
- polynomial function (p. 280)
- power function (p. 341)
- Rational Root Theorem (p. 312)

- relative maximum (p. 291)
- relative minimum (p. 291)
- Remainder Theorem (p. 307)
- standard form of a polynomial function (p. 281)
- sum of cubes (p. 297)
- synthetic division (p. 306)
- turning point (p. 282)

Match each vocabulary term with the description that best fits it.

1. Conjugate Root Theorem
2. Fundamental Theorem of Algebra
3. Rational Root Theorem
4. Remainder Theorem

A. determines $P(a)$ by dividing the polynomial by $x - a$
B. the degree equals the number of roots
C. minimizes guessing fraction and integer solutions
D. complex numbers as roots come in pairs

Essential Questions

BIG idea **Function**
ESSENTIAL QUESTION What does the degree of a polynomial tell you about its related polynomial function?
ANSWER A polynomial of degree n has n linear factors. The graph of the related function crosses the x-axis an even or odd number of times depending on whether n is even or odd.

BIG idea **Equivalence**
ESSENTIAL QUESTION For a polynomial function, how are factors, zeros, and x-intercepts related?
ANSWER $(x - a)$ is a linear factor if and only if a is a zero and if and only if $(a, 0)$ is an x-intercept when a is a real number.

BIG idea **Solving Equations and Inequalities**
ESSENTIAL QUESTION For a polynomial equation, how are factors and roots related?
ANSWER $(x - a)$ is a linear factor if and only if a is a root of the related polynomial equation.

Answers

1. D
2. B
3. C
4. A

Summative Questions

Use the following prompts as you review this chapter with your students. The prompts are designed to help you assess your students' understanding of the Big Ideas they have studied.

- What must be true about the divisor when you use synthetic division?
- If you know the degree of a polynomial, what can you tell about its zeros?
- The vertex of a parabola is either the maximum or minimum value of the function. How are these different from the relative maximums and minimums of polynomial functions? How are they similar?
- When is Pascal's Triangle a better tool than the Distributive Property to expand the power of a binomial?
- What is a multiple zero? Graphically, when do they occur?

Answers

Chapter Review (continued)

5. $y = -x^4 + 12$; quartic binomial; down and down

6. $y = x^2 - x + 7$; quadratic trinomial; up and up

7. $y = -x^4 + 2x^3 + 3x^2 - 6x + 12$; quartic polynomial of five terms; down and down

8. $y = x^3 + 2x^2 - 4x + 8$; cubic polynomial of four terms; down and up

9. $y = x^4 - 3x^3 + 3x^2 + 10$; quartic polynomial of four terms; up and up

10. 3

11. If n is even there are an odd number of turning points; if n is odd there are an even number of turning points.

12. $f(x) = x^3 - 4x^2 - 11x - 6$

13. $f(x) = x^3 - x^2 - 2x$

14. $f(x) = x^3 - 6x^2 + 11x - 6$

15. $f(x) = x^3 - 3x^2 - 6x + 8$

16. $0, -2$ (multiplicity 3)

17. 2 (multiplicity 2), -2 (multiplicity 2)

18. $0, -\frac{1}{2}, 1$

19. $5, -2$ (multiplicity 2)

20. relative maximum: $(0.8672, -1.9351)$; relative minimums: $(0, -3)$, $(2.8828, -12.1704)$; zeros: $x = -0.5992$, $x = 3.7115$

21. relative maximum: $(-0.8441, 9.3023)$; relative minimum: $(0.7108, -0.0964)$; zeros: $x = -1.6180$, $x = 0.6180$, $x = 0.8$

22. relative minimum: $(1, -4)$; zeros: $x = -0.2490$, $x = 1.6633$

23. relative maximum: $(-0.4142, -3.3432)$; relative minimum: $(2.4142, -14.6569)$; zero: $x = 4$

5-1 Polynomial Functions

Quick Review

The **standard form of a polynomial function** is $P(x) = a_n x^n + a_{n-1} x^{n-1} + \cdots + a_1 x + a_0$, where n is a nonnegative integer and the coefficients are real numbers. A **polynomial function** is classified by degree. Its degree is the highest degree among its monomial term(s). The degree determines the possible number of **turning points** in the graph and the **end behavior** of the graph.

Example

Write the polynomial function in standard form and classify it by degree. How many terms does it have? What are the possible numbers of turning points of the graph of $P(x)$ given the degree of the polynomial?

$$P(x) = -4x^2 + x^4$$

Standard form arranges the terms by decreasing exponents, or $P(x) = x^4 - 4x^2$. Its degree is 4, so $x^4 - 4x^2$ is a quartic binomial. It has two terms. The graph of a quartic polynomial function can have either one or three turning points.

Exercises

Write each polynomial function in standard form, classify it by degree, and determine the end behavior of its graph.

5. $y = 12 - x^4$

6. $y = x^2 + 7 - x$

7. $y = 2x^3 - 6x + 3x^2 - x^4 + 12$

8. $y = 2x^2 + 8 - 4x + x^3$

9. $y = 10 - 3x^3 + 3x^2 + x^4$

10. If the volume of a cube can be represented by a polynomial of degree 9, what is the degree of the polynomial that represents each side length?

11. A polynomial function $P(x)$ has degree n. If n is even, is the number of turning points of the graph of $P(x)$ even or odd? What can you say about the number of turning points if n is odd?

5-2 Polynomials, Linear Factors, and Zeros

Quick Review

For any real number a and polynomial $P(x)$, if $x - a$ is a **factor** of $P(x)$, then a is:

- a **zero** of $y = P(x)$,
- a **root** (or **solution**) of $P(x) = 0$, and
- an **x-intercept** of the graph of $y = P(x)$.

If a is a **multiple zero**, its **multiplicity** is the same as the number of times $x - a$ appears as a factor.

A turning point is a **relative maximum** or **relative minimum** of a polynomial function.

Example

Find the zeros for $y = 3x^3 - 6x^2 + 3x$ and state the multiplicity of any multiple zeros.

$y = 3x(x^2 - 2x + 1)$ Factor out the GCF, $3x$.

$y = 3x(x - 1)(x - 1)$ Factor the quadratic.

The zeros are 0, and 1 with multiplicity 2.

Exercises

Write a polynomial function with the given zeros.

12. $x = -1, -1, 6$ **13.** $x = -1, 0, 2$

14. $x = 1, 2, 3$ **15.** $x = -2, 1, 4$

Find the zeros of each function. State the multiplicity of any multiple zeros.

16. $y = 3x(x + 2)^3$ **17.** $y = x^4 - 8x^2 + 16$

18. $y = 4x^3 - 2x^2 - 2x$ **19.** $y = (x - 5)(x + 2)^2$

Use a graphing calculator to find the relative maximum, relative minimum, and zeros of each function.

20. $y = x^4 - 5x^3 + 5x^2 - 3$

21. $y = 5x^3 + x^2 - 9x + 4$

22. $y = x^4 - 4x - 1$

23. $y = x^3 - 3x^2 - 3x - 4$

5-3 Solving Polynomial Equations

Quick Review

One way to solve a polynomial equation is by factoring. First write the equation in the form $P(x) = 0$, where $P(x)$ is the polynomial. Then factor the polynomial. Last, use the Zero-Product Property to find the solutions, or roots. The solutions may be real or imaginary. Real solutions and approximations of irrational solutions can also be found by using a graphing calculator.

Example

Solve $x^3 + 4x^2 = 12x$ by factoring.

$x^3 + 4x^2 - 12x = 0$	Subtract $12x$ from each side.
$x(x - 2)(x + 6) = 0$	Factor the left side.
$x = 0, x - 2 = 0, x + 6 = 0$	Zero Product Property
$x = 0, x = 2, x = -6$	Solve each equation.

The solutions are 0, 2, and -6.

Exercises

Find the real or imaginary solutions of each equation by factoring.

24. $x^2 - 11x = -24$ **25.** $4x^2 = -4x - 1$

26. $3x^3 + 3x^2 = 27x$ **27.** $2x^2 + 3 = 4x$

Find the real roots of each equation by graphing.

28. $x^4 + 3x^2 - 2x + 5 = 0$

29. $x^2 + 3 = x^3 - 5$

30. The height and width of a rectangular prism are each 2 inches shorter than the length of the prism. The volume of the prism is 40 cubic inches. Approximate the dimensions of the prism to the nearest hundredth.

5-4 Dividing Polynomials

Quick Review

You can divide a polynomial by one of its factors to find another factor. When you divide by a linear factor, you can simplify this division by writing only the coefficients of each term. This is called **synthetic division**. The **Remainder Theorem** says that $P(a)$ is the remainder when you divide $P(x)$ by $x - a$.

Example

Let $P(x) = 3x^2 - 13x + 15$. What is $P(3)$?

According to the Remainder Theorem, $P(3)$ is the remainder when you divide $P(x)$ by $x - 3$.

```
3 |  3   -13    15      Put the opposite of the
                        constant in the divisor
           9   -12      at the top left.
   ─────────────────
      3    -4     3
```

The quotient is $3x - 4$ with remainder 3, so $P(3) = 3$.

Exercises

Divide using long division. Check your answers.

31. $(x^3 + 7x^2 + 15x + 9) \div (x + 1)$

32. $(2x^3 - 7x^2 - 7x + 13) \div (x - 4)$

Determine whether each binomial is a factor of $x^3 + x^2 - 10x + 8$.

33. $x - 2$ **34.** $x - 4$

Divide using synthetic division.

35. $(x^3 + 5x^2 - x - 5) \div (x + 5)$

36. $(2x^3 + 14x^2 - 58x) \div (x + 10)$

37. $(5x^3 + 8x^2 - 60) \div (x - 2)$

Use the Remainder Theorem to determine the value of $P(a)$.

38. $P(x) = 2x^3 + 5x^2 + 7x - 4, a = -2$

39. $P(x) = x^3 - 4x^2 + 2x + 3, a = 1$

24. 3, 8

25. $-\dfrac{1}{2}$

26. $0, \dfrac{-1 \pm \sqrt{37}}{2}$

27. $\dfrac{2 \pm i\sqrt{2}}{2}$

28. no real roots;

29. 2.3949;

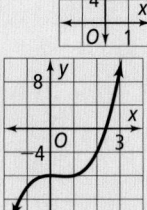

30. 4.87 in. $\times$ 2.87 in. $\times$ 2.87 in.

31. $x^2 + 6x + 9$

32. $2x^2 + x - 3$, R 1

33. yes

34. no

35. $x^2 - 1$

36. $2x^2 - 6x + 2$, R -20

37. $5x^2 + 18x + 36$, R 12

38. -14

39. 2

Answers

Chapter Review (continued)

40. $\pm 1,\ \pm 2,\ \pm 3,\ \pm 6$

41. $\pm 1,\ \pm 2,\ \pm \frac{1}{3},\ \pm \frac{2}{3}$

42. $\pm 1,\ \pm 2,\ \pm 3,\ \pm 4,\ \pm 6,\ \pm 12,\ \pm \frac{1}{4},\ \pm \frac{1}{2},$ $\pm \frac{3}{4},\ \pm \frac{3}{2}$

43. $\pm 1,\ \pm 7,\ \pm \frac{1}{3},\ \pm \frac{7}{3}$

44. -3

45. -5

46. $1,\ -4,\ -\frac{1}{2}$

47. $1,\ -2,\ -\frac{2}{3}$

48. $1 + i$

49. $5 - \sqrt{3},\ \sqrt{2}$

50. $3i,\ -7i$

51. $-2 - \sqrt{11},\ -4 + 6i$

52. $y = x^2 - 17x + 70$

53. $y = x^3 + 3x^2 + 25x + 75$

54. $y = x^2 - 12x + 37$

55. $y = x^4 - 4x^3 - 10x^2 + 68x - 80$

56. one positive real zero; two or no negative real zeros

57. two or no positive real zeros; one negative real zero

58. four, two, or no positive real zeros; no negative real zeros

59. two or no positive real zeros; two or no negative real zeros

---

5-5 Theorems About Roots of Polynomial Equations

Quick Review

The **Rational Root Theorem** gives a way to determine the possible roots of a polynomial equation $P(x) = 0$. If the coefficients of $P(x)$ are all integers, then every root of the equation can be written in the form $\frac{p}{q}$, where p is a factor of the constant term and q is a factor of the leading coefficient.

The **Conjugate Root Theorem** states that if $P(x)$ is a polynomial with rational coefficients, then irrational roots that have the form $a + \sqrt{b}$ and imaginary roots of $P(x) = 0$ come in conjugate pairs. Therefore, if $a + \sqrt{b}$ is an irrational root, where a and b are rational, then $a - \sqrt{b}$ is also a root. Likewise, if $a + bi$ is a root, where a and b are real and i is the imaginary unit, then $a - bi$ is also a root.

Descartes' Rule of Signs gives a way to determine the possible number of positive and negative real roots by analyzing the signs of the coefficients. The number of positive real roots is equal to the number of sign changes in consecutive coefficients of $P(x)$, or is less than that by an even number. The number of negative real roots is equal to the number of sign changes in consecutive coefficients of $P(-x)$, or is less than that by an even number.

Example

Find the rational roots of $P(x) = 0$ if $P(x) = 2x^3 - 4x^2 - 10x + 12$.

List the possible roots: $\pm \frac{1}{2}, \pm 1, \pm \frac{3}{2}, \pm 2, \pm 3, \pm 4, \pm 6, \pm 12$. Use synthetic division to test roots.

$$\begin{array}{r|rrrr} 3 & 2 & -4 & -10 & 12 \\ & & 6 & 6 & -12 \\ \hline & 2 & 2 & -4 & 0 \end{array}$$

So $x - 3$ and $(2x^2 + 2x - 4)$ are factors of $P(x)$.

$P(x) = (x - 3)(2x^2 + 2x - 4)$

Factor the quadratic.

$P(x) = 2(x - 3)(x + 2)(x - 1)$

Solve $2(x - 3)(x + 2)(x - 1) = 0$.

$x = 3,\ x = -2,\ \text{or}\ x = 1$

The rational roots are 3, -2, and 1.

Exercises

List the possible rational roots of $P(x)$ given by the Rational Root Theorem.

40. $P(x) = x^3 + 4x^2 - 10x + 6$

41. $P(x) = 3x^3 - x^2 - 7x + 2$

42. $P(x) = 4x^4 - 2x^3 + x^2 - 12$

43. $P(x) = 3x^4 - 4x^3 - x^2 - 7$

Find any rational roots of $P(x)$.

44. $P(x) = x^3 + 2x^2 + 4x + 21$

45. $P(x) = x^3 + 5x^2 + x + 5$

46. $P(x) = 2x^3 + 7x^2 - 5x - 4$

47. $P(x) = 3x^4 + 2x^3 - 9x^2 + 4$

A polynomial $P(x)$ has rational coefficients. Name additional roots of $P(x)$ given the following roots.

48. $1 - i$ and 5

49. $5 + \sqrt{3}$ and $-\sqrt{2}$

50. $-3i$ and $7i$

51. $-2 + \sqrt{11}$ and $-4 - 6i$

Write a polynomial function with the given roots.

52. 7 and 10

53. -3 and $5i$

54. $6 - i$

55. $3 + i$, 2, and -4

Determine the possible number of positive real zeros and negative real zeros for each polynomial function given by Descartes' Rule of Signs.

56. $P(x) = 5x^3 + 7x^2 - 2x - 1$

57. $P(x) = -3x^3 + 11x^2 + 12x - 8$

58. $P(x) = 6x^4 - x^3 + 5x^2 - x + 9$

59. $P(x) = -x^4 - 3x^3 + 8x^2 + 2x - 14$

5-6 The Fundamental Theorem of Algebra

Quick Review

The **Fundamental Theorem of Algebra** states that if $P(x)$ is a polynomial of degree n, where $n \geq 1$, then $P(x) = 0$ has exactly n roots. This includes multiple and complex roots.

Example

Use the Fundamental Theorem of Algebra to determine the number of roots for $x^4 + 2x^2 - 3 = 0$.

Because the polynomial is of degree 4, it has 4 roots.

Exercises

Find the number of roots for each equation.

60. $x^3 - 2x + 5 = 0$

61. $2 - x^4 + x^2 = 0$

62. $-x^5 - 6 = 0$

63. $5x^4 - 7x^6 + 2x^3 + 8x^2 + 4x - 11 = 0$

Find all the zeros for each function.

64. $P(x) = x^3 + 5x^2 - 4x - 2$

65. $P(x) = x^4 - 4x^3 - x^2 + 20x - 20$

66. $P(x) = 2x^3 - 3x^2 + 3x - 2$

67. $P(x) = x^4 - 4x^3 - 16x^2 + 21x + 18$

5-7 The Binomial Theorem

Quick Review

Rows 0–5 of Pascal's Triangle are shown below.

$$1$$
$$1 \quad 1$$
$$1 \quad 2 \quad 1$$
$$1 \quad 3 \quad 3 \quad 1$$
$$1 \quad 4 \quad 6 \quad 4 \quad 1$$
$$1 \quad 5 \quad 10 \quad 10 \quad 5 \quad 1$$

The **Binomial Theorem** uses Pascal's Triangle to expand binomial powers. For a positive integer n,
$(a + b)^n = P_0 a^n + P_1 a^{n-1}b + P_2 a^{n-2}b^2 + \cdots + P_{n-1}ab^{n-1} + P_n b^n$, where $P_0, P_1, \ldots, P_n$ are the coefficients of the nth row of Pascal's Triangle.

Example

Use the Binomial Theorem to expand $(2x + 3)^3$.

$(2x + 3)^3$

$= 1(2x)^3 + 3(2x)^2(3) + 3(2x)(3)^2 + 1(3)^3$

$= 8x^3 + 36x^2 + 54x + 27$

Exercises

68. How many numbers are in the eighth row of Pascal's Triangle?

69. List the numbers in the eighth row of Pascal's Triangle.

70. How many numbers are in the fifteenth row of Pascal's Triangle?

71. What is the third number in the fifteenth row of Pascal's Triangle?

Use the Binomial Theorem to expand each binomial.

72. $(x + 9)^3$ **73.** $(b + 2)^4$

74. $(3a + 1)^3$ **75.** $(x - 5)^3$

76. $(x - 2y)^3$ **77.** $(3a + 4b)^5$

78. $(x + 1)^6$ **79.** $(2x - 1)^6$

Find the coefficient of the x^2 term in each binomial expansion.

80. $(3x + 4)^3$ **81.** $(ax - c)^4$

Chapter 5 Chapter Review   **351**

60. 3

61. 4

62. 5

63. 6

64. $1, -3 \pm \sqrt{7}$

65. $2, \pm \sqrt{5}$

66. $1, \dfrac{1 \pm i\sqrt{15}}{4}$

67. $-3, 6, \dfrac{1 \pm \sqrt{5}}{2}$

68. 9

69. 1, 8, 28, 56, 70, 56, 28, 8, 1

70. 16

71. 105

72. $x^3 + 27x^2 + 243x + 729$

73. $b^4 + 8b^3 + 24b^2 + 32b + 16$

74. $27a^3 + 27a^2 + 9a + 1$

75. $x^3 - 15x^2 + 75x - 125$

76. $x^3 - 6x^2y + 12xy^2 - 8y^3$

77. $243a^5 + 1620a^4b + 4320a^3b^2 + 5760a^2b^3 + 3840ab^4 + 1024b^5$

78. $x^6 + 6x^5 + 15x^4 + 20x^3 + 15x^2 + 6x + 1$

79. $64x^6 - 192x^5 + 240x^4 - 160x^3 + 60x^2 - 12x + 1$

80. 108

81. $6a^2c^2$

Answers

Chapter Review (continued)

82. $y = 3.5x^2 - 4.5x + 5$

83. $y = 2.082999x - 2.475234$;
$y = 0.086232x^2 + 0.008929x + 5.963724$;
$y = -0.002554x^3 + 0.178307x^2 - 0.913645x + 8.205128$; cubic is best fit since $R^2 = 1$.

84. $y = -5.8667x^3 + 120.5333x^2 - 629.2667x + 1421$; $1097.2 \approx 1097$

85. $y = -(x - 2)^3 + 1$

86. $y = 6(x + 3)^3$

87. Answers may vary. Sample:
$y = x^4 - 10x^3 + 25x^2 - 10x + 24$

88. $y = 0.3x^5 + 3$

5-8 Polynomial Models in the Real World

Quick Review

A data set can be modeled by a polynomial function. Methods of finding a model that fits the data include the $(n + 1)$ Point Principle and **regression**. Linear, quadratic, cubic, and quartic regressions can be performed on a graphing calculator. A higher R^2 value means a better fit. Once the equation that models the data is known, it can be used to make predictions.

Example

For the data set $(8, 30)$, $(10, 45)$, and $(11, 65)$, predict y when $x = 15$.

Enter 8, 10, and 11 in **L1** and 30, 45, and 65 in **L2**. Choose **LINREG** to find the regression model $y \approx 11.071x - 60.357$. The r^2 value is about 0.928.

Now try **QUADREG**. The model is
$y \approx 4.17x^2 - 67.5x + 303.3$ with an R^2 value of 1. Assuming the model makes sense in context, it fits the data better.

Using the quadratic model, when $x = 15$, $y \approx 228.3$.

Exercises

82. Write a polynomial function whose graph passes through $(0, 5)$, $(2, 10)$, and $(1, 4)$. Use a regression to check your answer.

83. Find a linear, a quadratic, and a cubic model for the data. Which model best fits the data?

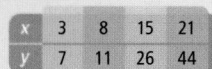

x	3	8	15	21
y	7	11	26	44

84. Use **CUBICREG** to model the data below. Then use the model to estimate the population in 2008. Let x be the number of years after 2000.

Year	2004	2007	2009	2010
Population	457	910	1244	1315

5-9 Transforming Polynomial Functions

Quick Review

A polynomial function can be transformed into other polynomial functions using stretches, reflections, and translations. The monomial function $y = ax^b$ is called a **power function**.

Example

This is the graph of a cubic function. Determine which sequence of transformations you can apply to the graph of the parent function $y = x^3$ to get this graph. Write an equation for the graph.

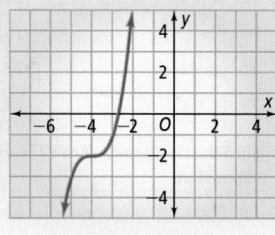

Translate the parent function 4 units left and 2 units down:
$y = (x + 4)^3 - 2$.

Exercises

Determine the cubic function obtained from the parent function $y = x^3$ after each sequence of transformations.

85. a reflection across the x-axis;
a translation 1 unit up;
and a translation 2 units right

86. a vertical stretch by a factor of 6;
and a translation 3 units left

87. Find a quartic function whose only real zeros are 4 and 6.

88. The parent power function $y = x^5$ is translated 3 units up and is compressed by the factor 0.3. Write the function.

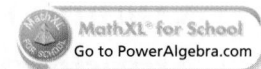
MathXL® for School
Go to PowerAlgebra.com

Do you know HOW?

Write each polynomial function in standard form. Then classify it by degree and by number of terms and describe its end behavior.

1. $y = 3x^2 - 7x^4 + 9 - x^4$

2. $y = 2x(x^2 - 3)(x^2 + 2)$

3. $y = (t - 2)(t + 1)(t + 1)$

Write a polynomial function for each set of zeros.

4. $x = 1, 2, \frac{3}{5}$

5. $x = \sqrt{2}, -i$

6. $x = 3 + i, -1 - \sqrt{5}$

Find the quotient and remainder.

7. $(x^2 + 3x - 4) \div (x - 1)$

8. $(x^3 + 7x^2 - 5x - 6) \div (x + 2)$

9. $(2x^3 + 9x^2 + 11x + 3) \div (2x + 3)$

For each equation, state the number of complex roots, the possible number of real roots, and the possible rational roots.

10. $3x^4 + 5x^3 - 2x^2 + x - 9 = 0$

11. $x^7 - 2x^5 - 4x^3 - 2x - 1 = 0$

For each equation, find all the roots.

12. $3x^4 - 11x^3 + 15x^2 - 9x + 2 = 0$

13. $x^3 - x^2 - x - 2 = 0$

14. One x-intercept of the graph of the cubic function $f(x) = x^3 - 2x^2 - 111x - 108$ is -9. What are the other zeros?

Use synthetic division and the Remainder Theorem to find $P(a)$.

15. $P(x) = 6x^4 + 19x^3 - 2x^2 - 44x - 24; a = -\frac{2}{3}$

16. $P(x) = x^4 + 3x^3 - 7x^2 - 9x + 12; a = 3$

17. $P(x) = x^3 + 3x^2 - 5x - 4; a = -1$

Expand each binomial.

18. $(x + z)^5$

19. $(1 - 2t)^2$

20. Graph and write the equation of the cubic function that is obtained from the parent function $y = x^3$ after this sequence of transformations: vertical stretch by a factor of 2, reflection across the x-axis, translation 3 units down and 4 units right.

Do you UNDERSTAND?

STEM 21. Physics You take measurements of the distance traveled by an object that is increasing its speed at a constant rate. The distance traveled as a function of time can be modeled by a quadratic function.
 a. Write a quadratic function that models distances of 10 ft at 1 sec, 30 ft at 2 sec, and 100 ft at 4 sec.
 b. Find the zeros of the function.
 c. Reasoning Describe what each zero represents for this real-world situation.

© 22. Writing For the polynomial $x^6 - 64$, could you apply the Difference of Cubes? Difference of Squares? Explain your answers.

23. The number of pairs of shoes Emily buys varies directly as the square of the area of the floor of her closet. If she could fit 12 pairs of shoes when her closet was 10 square feet, how many pairs of shoes will she fit when the area of her closet floor is 18 square feet?

22. both; difference of squares:
$x^6 - 64 = (x^2 - 4)(x^4 + 4x^2 + 16) =$
$(x - 2)(x + 2)(x^2 + 2x + 4)(x^2 - 2x + 4)$;
difference of cubes:
$x^6 - 64 = (x^3 - 8)(x^3 + 8) =$
$(x - 2)(x + 2)(x^2 + 2x + 4)(x^2 - 2x + 4)$

23. 38 pairs of shoes

Answers

1. $y = -8x^4 + 3x^2 + 9$; quartic trinomial; down and down

2. $y = 2x^5 - 2x^3 - 12x$; quintic trinomial; down and up

3. $y = t^3 - 3t - 2$; cubic trinomial; down and up

4. $p(x) = 5x^3 - 18x^2 + 19x - 6$

5. $p(x) = x^4 - x^2 - 2$

6. $p(x) = x^4 - 4x^3 - 6x^2 + 44x - 40$

7. $x + 4$, R 0

8. $x^2 + 5x - 15$, R 24

9. $x^2 + 3x + 1$, R 0

10. four complex roots; three or one positive real root, 1 negative real root; possible rational roots: $\pm 1, \pm 3, \pm 9, \pm \frac{1}{3}$

11. seven complex roots; one positive real root, two or no negative real roots; possible rational roots: ± 1

12. $\frac{2}{3}, 1$

13. $2, \dfrac{-1 \pm i\sqrt{3}}{2}$

14. $-1, 12$

15. 0

16. 84

17. 3

18. $x^5 + 5x^4z + 10x^3z^2 + 10x^2z^3 + 5xz^4 + z^5$

19. $1 - 4t + 4t^2$

20. $y = -2(x - 4)^3 - 3$
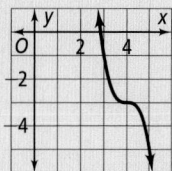

21. a. $d = 5t^2 + 5t$
 b. $0, -1$
 c. -1 is outside the real-world problem's domain, and 0 is "time zero," or takeoff.

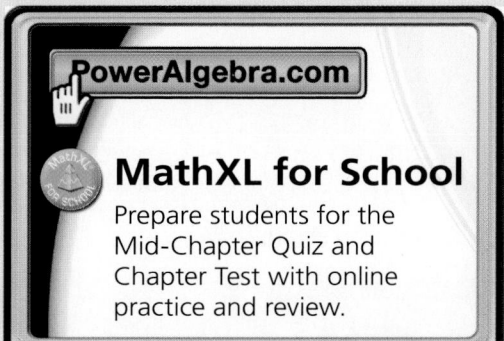
PowerAlgebra.com

MathXL for School

Prepare students for the Mid-Chapter Quiz and Chapter Test with online practice and review.

Item Number	Lesson	Content Standard
1	3-2	A-REI.C.6
2	5-1	F-IF.C.7c
3	3-2	A-REI.C.6
4	5-4	A-APR.D.6
5	4-5	A-APR.B.3
6	1-4	A-CED.A.4
7	4-2	A-CED.A.2
8	3-3	A-REI.D.12
9	2-2	A-CED.A.2
10	5-5	N-CN.C.7
11	4-8	N-CN.A.2
12	5-2	A-APR.B.3
13	2-2	A-CED.A.2
14	5-2	F-IF.C.7c
15	5-2	A-APR.B.2
16	4-8	N-CN.C.7
17	4-8	N-CN.A.2
18	2-7	F-BF.B.3
19	1-6	A-CED.A.1
20	2-4	A-CED.A.2
21	4-2	F-IF.B.4
22	4-5	A-CED.A.1
23	4-1	F-BF.B.3

Common Core Cumulative Standards Review

TIPS FOR SUCCESS

Some problems require you to simplify expressions that contain imaginary numbers.

TIP 1

When multiplying binomials, you should use the Distributive Property.

Which expression is equivalent to $(3 - 4i)(2 + i)$?

Ⓐ $2 - 5i$

Ⓑ $2 + 5i$

Ⓒ $10 - 5i$

Ⓓ $10 + 5i$

TIP 2

Recall that $i^2 = -1$.

Think It Through
$(3 - 4i)(2 + i)$
$= 6 + 3i - 8i - 4i^2$
$= 6 - 5i - 4(-1)$
$= 10 - 5i$

The correct answer is C.

🔊 Vocabulary Review

As you solve test items, you must understand the meanings of mathematical terms. Match each term with its mathematical meaning.

A. multiplicity

B. synthetic division

C. Conjugate Root Theorem

D. relative maximum

E. polynomial

I. the process of dividing a polynomial by a linear factor, omitting all variables and exponents

II. if $a + bi$ is an irrational root where a and b are real numbers, then $a - bi$ is also a root

III. a monomial or the sum of monomials

IV. the greatest y-value in a region of a graph

V. the number of times a zero is repeated in a polynomial function

Selected Response

Read each question. Then write the letter of the correct answer on your paper.

1. Which statement is true about this system of linear equations?

$$\begin{cases} 3x - 4y = 12 \\ 6x - 8y = 12 \end{cases}$$

Ⓐ The solution is $(0, -1)$.

Ⓑ The solution is $(8, 4)$.

Ⓒ There is no solution because the lines are parallel.

Ⓓ There are infinitely many solutions because the lines are coinciding.

2. Which of the following statements is *never* true about a quartic function?

Ⓕ The end behavior of the function is up and up.

Ⓖ The function has 4 zeros.

Ⓗ The function has 4 turning points.

Ⓘ The function has complex roots.

Answers

Common Core Cumulative Standards Review

A. V

B. I

C. II

D. IV

E. III

1. C

2. H

3. Tia deposited x dollars in a bank account that paid 4% interest. She also deposited y dollars in a bank account that paid 8% interest. The system below represents one year's interest on Tia's deposits.

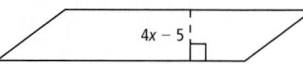

$$\begin{cases} 0.04x + 0.08y = 240 \\ \qquad\quad 0.04x = 0.08y \end{cases}$$

Based on the solution of the system of equations, which of the following can you conclude?

Ⓐ Tia deposited $3000 in each account, and the amounts of interest earned were $240 and $120.

Ⓑ Tia deposited $3000 in each account, and the amount of interest earned in each account was $120.

Ⓒ The deposit amounts were $3000 and $1500, and the amounts of interest earned in each account were $240 and $120.

Ⓓ The deposit amounts were $3000 and $1500, and the amount of interest earned in each account was $120.

4. The total area of the parallelogram below is $4x^4 + 3x^3 - 14x^2 + 33x - 35$. Which of the following expressions best represents the length of the base of the parallelogram? (*Hint:* $A = bh$)

$4x - 5$

Ⓕ $x^3 + 2x^2 - x + 7$

Ⓖ $x^3 - 2x^2 + x - 7$

Ⓗ $4x^4 + 3x^3 - 14x^2 + 33x - 7$

Ⓘ $x^3 + 5x^2 - x + 5$

5. Which point corresponds to a zero of the function $f(x) = x^2 + 2x - 15$?

Ⓐ $(0, -15)$ Ⓒ $(-5, 0)$

Ⓑ $(5, 0)$ Ⓓ $(-3, 0)$

6. Solve the equation $x^2 + 3w = P$ for x.

Ⓕ $x = P - 3w$ Ⓗ $x = \pm\sqrt{P - 3w}$

Ⓖ $x = \pm\sqrt{\dfrac{P}{3w}}$ Ⓘ $x = \pm\sqrt{P + 3w}$

7. A bridge supported by a parabolic arch spans a stream of water 180 feet wide. There must be a clearance of at least 40 feet over a 100-foot channel in the middle of the stream. The origin is placed at water level directly below the center of the arch. Which equation best represents the situation?

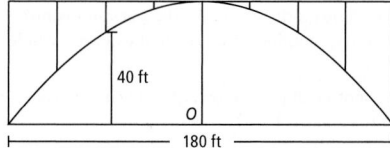

Ⓐ $y = 140(x + 180)(x - 180)$

Ⓑ $y = -\dfrac{1}{140}(x + 90)(x - 90)$

Ⓒ $y = -\dfrac{1}{140}(x + 40)(x - 40)$

Ⓓ $y = 140(x + 40)(x - 40)$

8. Sofia has $25 in her savings account. She plans to deposit between $5 and $10 each week into her account. On the graph, line m represents a deposit of exactly $5 per week and line n represents a deposit of exactly $10 per week.

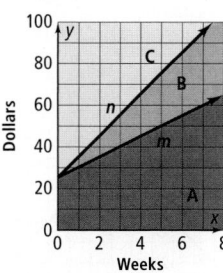

If Sofia deposits between $5 and $10 per week, which region on the graph represents all possible balances in her account?

Ⓕ A   Ⓗ C

Ⓖ B   Ⓘ A and C combined

3. D

4. F

5. C

6. H

7. B

8. G

Answers

Common Core Cumulative Standards Review (continued)

9. 1250

10. 1

11. 11

12. 6

13. 6

14. 2

15. 1

16. 2

17. 5

18. $-|x - 2| + 3$

19. $x \leq -5$ or $x \geq 11$

20. **[2]** The slope of line m is $\frac{3}{4}$, so the slope of

line $n = \dfrac{-1}{\left(\frac{3}{4}\right)} = \dfrac{-4}{3}$. Point P is $(1, 3)$.

$$y - (3) = \left(-\frac{4}{3}\right)(x - 1)$$

$$y - 3 = -\frac{4}{3}x + \frac{4}{3}$$

$$y = -\frac{4}{3}x + \frac{13}{3}$$

[1] appropriate methods, with one computational error

21. **[2]**

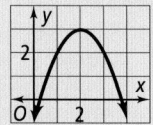

when the cat is at (2,3)

[1] graph is correct, but furthest location from pole is incorrect

22. **[2]** $x = -1, x = 8$

[1] one minor computational error

23. **[4]** **a.** Reflect across the x-axis; translate 4 units to the right and 4 units up.

b. Zeros at $x = 2, 6$; the function crosses the axis and $y = 0$ at $x = 2$ and $x = 6$.

c. $y = -(x - 4)^2 + 4$

d. Check points such as $(2, 0)$, $(4, 4)$, and $(6, 0)$ to test the accuracy of the function.

[3] three parts answered correctly

[2] two parts answered correctly OR three parts answered correctly, without explanations given

[1] one part answered correctly

Constructed Response

9. The power created by a wind turbine varies directly as the cube of the wind speed in miles per hour. A turbine with 30% efficiency spinning in a 50 mile per hour wind can be expected to produce approximately 10,000 watts of electricity. How many watts would the same turbine produce in a 25-mile-per-hour wind? If necessary, round your answer to the nearest whole number.

10. One root of a cubic equation is $2i$. How many real roots does the equation have?

11. What is the value of the real part of the sum of $(6 + 4i)$ and $(5 - i)$?

12. If the solutions of an equation are -1, 2, and 5, what is the sum of the zeros of the related function?

13. Assume y varies directly with x. If $y = -3$ when $x = -\frac{2}{5}$, what is x when y is 45?

14. What is the x-coordinate of the point where a relative maximum of $g(x) = -2x^3 + 6x^2 - 10$ occurs?

15. Using a graph, find the real zero of the function $y = 2x^3 - 2x^2 + x - 1$.

16. How many imaginary roots does $x^2 - 5x + 10 = 0$ have?

17. What is the product of $(2 + i)(2 - i)$?

18. Write the equation represented by the graph. Show your work.

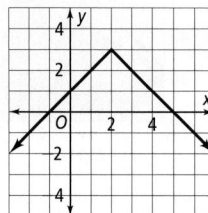

19. Solve the absolute value inequality $-2|x - 3| \leq -16$. Show your work.

20. The graph shows line m and point P. Write the equation of a line n that goes through point P and is perpendicular to line m. Show your work.

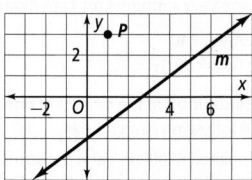

21. A cat ran around part of a telephone pole on a path modeled by the equation $y = -x^2 + 4x - 1$. Graph the cat's path in the first quadrant. If the pole is at $(2, 0)$, at what point is the cat furthest from the pole?

22. Solve the equation $x^2 - 7x = 8$.

Extended Response

23. Use the graph to answer the questions below.

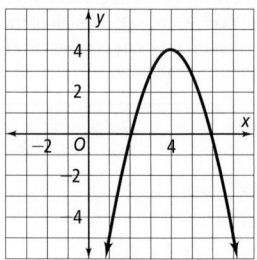

a. Describe the sequence of transformations that would take the graph of the parent function $y = x^2$ to the graph shown.

b. Identify the zeros of the function represented in the graph and explain your reasoning.

c. Write the equation of the function in the graph.

d. Explain how you could check to see that the equation is correct.

Get Ready!

Finding the Domain and Range of Functions

Find the domain and range of each function.

1. $\{(1, 2), (2, 3), (3, 4), (4, 5)\}$

2. $\{(1, 2), (2, 2), (3, 2), (4, 2)\}$

3. $f(x) = (x - 4)^2 - 8$

4. $f(x) = 2x^2 + 3$

Graphing Quadratic Functions

Graph each function.

5. $y = 2x^2 - 4$

6. $y = -3(x^2 + 1)$

7. $y = \frac{1}{2}(x - 3)^2 + 1$

Multiplying Binomials

Multiply.

8. $(3y - 2)(y - 4)$

9. $(7a + 10)(7a - 10)$

10. $(x - 3)(x + 6)(x + 1)$

Solving by Factoring

Solve each equation by factoring.

11. $x^2 - 5x - 14 = 0$

12. $2x^2 - 11x + 15 = 0$

13. $3x^2 + 10x - 8 = 0$

14. $12x^2 - 12x + 3 = 0$

15. $8x^2 - 98 = 0$

16. $x^4 - 14x^2 + 49 = 0$

Looking Ahead Vocabulary

17. Combining two or more elements forms composite chemical mixtures. In some cases, if you change the order in which you mix two chemicals, it can produce very different results. A *composite function* is made by combining two functions. If you are buying a $60 shirt and there is a 50% off sale and you have a $10 coupon, does it make a difference which discount is applied first?

18. One-to-one relationships describe situations where people are matched with unique identifiers, such as their social security numbers. A function is a relation that matches *x*-values to *y*-values. What do you suppose a *one-to-one function* is?

19. In an orchestra, the principal player is chosen among all the other musicians that play a certain instrument to sit in the first chair and lead his section. In math, what do you suppose a *principal root* is?

Answers

Get Ready!

1. domain: $\{1, 2, 3, 4\}$, range: $\{2, 3, 4, 5\}$

2. domain: $\{1, 2, 3, 4\}$, range: $\{2\}$

3. domain: all real numbers, range: $y \geq -8$

4. domain: all real numbers, range: $y \geq 3$

5.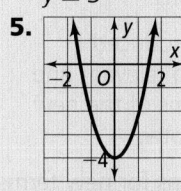

6.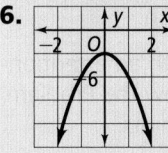

7.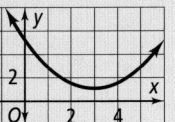

8. $3y^2 - 14y + 8$

9. $49a^2 - 100$

10. $x^3 + 4x^2 - 15x - 18$

11. $-2, 7$

12. $\frac{5}{2}, 3$

13. $-4, \frac{2}{3}$

14. $\frac{1}{2}$

15. $\pm\frac{7}{2}$

16. $\pm\sqrt{7}$

17. Yes; it is a better deal to first take 50% off the shirt and then use the $10 coupon.

18. A "one-to-one function" is a function where there is exact correspondence of every element of the domain with exactly one element of the range.

19. the nonnegative root

Get Ready!

Assign this diagnostic assessment to determine if students have the prerequisite skills for Chapter 6.

Lesson	Skill
2-1 and 4-1	Find the Domain and Range of Functions
4-1	Graph Quadratic Functions
4-4	Multiply Binomials
4-5 and 5-3	Solve by Factoring

To remediate students, select from these resources (available for every lesson).
- Online Problems (PowerAlgebra.com)
- Reteaching (All-in-One Teaching Resources)
- Practice (All-in-One Teaching Resources)

Why Students Need These Skills

FINDING THE DOMAIN AND RANGE OF FUNCTIONS
Finding the domain and range of functions is essential to understanding and describing inverse functions.

GRAPHING QUADRATIC FUNCTIONS
Graphing quadratic functions is essential to graphing square root functions, which are the inverse of quadratic functions with a restricted domain.

MULTIPLYING BINOMIALS
Multiplying binomials is an essential skill when multiplying binomial radical expressions.

SOLVING BY FACTORING
Solving by factoring is an important component of solving square root and other radical equations.

Looking Ahead Vocabulary

COMPOSITE FUNCTION Two different discounts are being applied. Have students determine both prices depending on the order in which they are applied.

ONE-TO-ONE FUNCTION Ask students what must be true about the domain and range of a one-to-one function.

PRINCIPAL ROOT Ask students to consider what a root is, for example, the square root of 4. Ask them if there is more than one possible root and why.

Chapter 6 Overview

Chapter 6 expands on student understandings and skills related to radical functions and rational exponents. In this chapter, students will develop the answers to the Essential Questions as they learn the concepts and skills bulleted below.

BIG idea **Equivalence**
ESSENTIAL QUESTION To simplify the nth root of an expression, what must be true about the expression?
• Students will simplify radical expressions.

BIG idea **Solving Equations and Inequalities**
ESSENTIAL QUESTION When you square each side of an equation, is the resulting equation equivalent to the original?
• Students will solve radical equations.
• Students will determine the domain of radical functions.
• Students will check for extraneous solutions.

BIG idea **Function**
ESSENTIAL QUESTION How are a function and its inverse function related?
• Students will find inverse functions.
• Students will graph functions and their inverses.

Content Standards

Following are the standards covered in this chapter. Modeling standards are indicated by a star symbol (★).

CONCEPTUAL CATEGORY Algebra

Domain Seeing Structure in Expressions A-SSE
Cluster Interpret the structure of expressions. (Standard A-SSE.A.2)
LESSONS 6-1, 6-2, 6-3

Domain Creating Equations A-CED
Cluster Create equations that describe numbers or relationships. (Standard A-CED.A.4★)
LESSON 6-5

Domain Reasoning with Equations and Inequalities A-REI
Cluster Understand solving equations as a process of reasoning and explain the reasoning. (Standard A-REI.A.2)
LESSON 6-5

CONCEPTUAL CATEGORY Functions

Domain Interpreting Functions F-IF
Cluster Analyze functions using different representations. (Standards F-IF.C.7b★, F-IF.C.8)
LESSON 6-8

Domain Building Functions F-BF
Cluster Build a function that models a relationship between two quantities. (Standard F-BF.A.1b★)
LESSON 6-6

Cluster Build new functions from existing functions. (Standard F-BF.B.4a)
LESSON 6-7

CHAPTER 6
Radical Functions and Rational Exponents

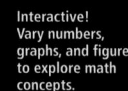
Download videos connecting math to your world.

Interactive! Vary numbers, graphs, and figures to explore math concepts.

The online Solve It will get you in gear for each lesson.

Math definitions in English and Spanish

Online access to stepped-out problems aligned to Common Core

Get and view your assignments online.

Extra practice and review online

Virtual Nerd™ tutorials with built-in support

Chapter Preview

6-1 Roots and Radical Expressions
6-2 Multiplying and Dividing Radical Expressions
6-3 Binomial Radical Expressions
6-4 Rational Exponents
6-5 Solving Square Root and Other Radical Equations
6-6 Function Operations
6-7 Inverse Relations and Functions
6-8 Graphing Radical Functions

Vocabulary

English/Spanish Vocabulary Audio Online:

English	Spanish
composite function, p. 399	función compuesta
inverse function, p. 405	función inversa
nth root, p. 361	raíz n-ésima
principal root, p. 361	raíz principal
radical equation, p. 390	ecuación radical
radicand, p. 362	radicando
rational exponent, p. 382	exponente racional
rationalize the denominator, p. 369	racionalizar el denominador
square root equation, p. 390	ecuación de raíz cuadrada
square root function, p. 415	función de raíz cuadrada

BIG ideas

1 **Equivalence**
Essential Question To simplify the nth root of an expression, what must be true about the expression?

2 **Solving Equations and Inequalities**
Essential Question When you square each side of an equation, is the resulting equation equivalent to the original?

3 **Function**
Essential Question How are a function and its inverse function related?

DOMAINS
• Seeing Structure in Expressions
• Interpreting Functions
• Reasoning with Equations and Inequalities

PowerAlgebra.com

Chapter 6 Overview

Use these online assets to engage your students. These include support for the Solve It and step-by-step solutions for Problems.

 Show the student-produced video demonstrating relevant and engaging applications of the new concepts in the chapter.

 Find online definitions for new terms in English and Spanish.

 Start each lesson with an attention-getting Problem. View the Problem online with helpful hints.

Common Core Performance Task

Analyzing the Dimensions of a Yacht

America's Cup is the name of both an international yacht race and the trophy that is awarded to the winner. To compete in America's Cup, a yacht must meet certain standards of design and construction. The inequality below describes one of the rules for the yachts.

$$\frac{L + 1.25S^{\frac{1}{2}} - 9.8D^{\frac{1}{3}}}{0.686} \leq 24$$

In the inequality, L is the boat's length (in meters), S is the sail area (in square meters), and D is the displacement (in cubic meters). Displacement is the volume of the boat that is underwater. Yacht designers try to make the value of the left side of the inequality as close to 24 as possible.

The table below lists data on the AC45 Wingsail Catamaran, a yacht that was built to compete in the 2013 America's Cup. You are going to design a new yacht that will satisfy the America's Cup rule and have twice the length and twice the sail area of the AC45.

AC45 Wingsail Catamaran	
Length	13.45 meters
Sail Area	93.7 square meters
Displacement	1.3 cubic meters

Task Description

Verify that the AC45 Wingsail Catamaran satisfies the America's Cup rule, and find all possible displacements for your new yacht.

Connecting the Task to the Math Practices

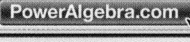 **MATHEMATICAL PRACTICES**

As you complete the task, you'll apply several Standards for Mathematical Practice.

- You'll write the America's Cup rule using a radical expression and then estimate the value of the expression for the AC45. (MP 2)
- You'll write a function and describe how to use it to analyze the displacement of the new yacht. (MP 6)
- You'll use a calculator to graph a function that models the rule for the new yacht. (MP 4, MP 5)

PowerAlgebra.com | Chapter 6 Radical Functions and Rational Exponents | 359

 Overview of the Performance Task

Students will rewrite the America's Cup rule using radicals and evaluate the rule with the given values. Then students will solve an inequality as they design a yacht with different dimensions.

Students will work on the Performance Task in the following places in the chapter.

- Lesson 6-4 (p. 388)
- Lesson 6-5 (p. 397)
- Lesson 6-8 (p. 420)
- Pull It All Together (p. 421)

Introducing the Performance Task

Tell students to read the problem on this page. Do not have them start work on the problem at this time, but ask them the following questions.

> **Q** What is a strategy you could try in order to solve the problem? **[Sample: I could substitute the given values in the given inequality and evaluate or solve to find the required information.]**
>
> **Q** In general, what happens to the value of the expression on the left side of the rule as the length of the yacht increases while the other dimensions remain constant? Explain. **[The value of the expression increases; as the length increases, the value of the numerator increases while the denominator remains constant.]**

PARCC CLAIMS

Sub-Claim A: Major Content With Connections to Practices
Sub-Claim D: Highlighted Practice MP 4 With Connections to Content

SBAC CLAIMS

Claim 2: Problem Solving
Claim 4: Modeling and Data Analysis

 Increase students' depth of knowledge with interactive online activities.

 Show Problems from each lesson solved step by step. Instant replay allows students to go at their own pace when studying online.

 Assign homework to individual students or to an entire class.

 Prepare students for the Mid-Chapter Quiz and Chapter Test with online practice and review.

 Virtual Nerd™ Access Virtual Nerd student-centered math tutorials that directly relate to the content of the lesson.

RADICAL FUNCTIONS AND RATIONAL EXPONENTS
Math Background © PROFESSIONAL DEVELOPMENT

The Understanding by Design® methodology was central to the development of the Big Ideas and the Essential Understandings. These will help your students build a structure on which to make connections to prior learning.

Equivalence

BIG idvea A single quantity may be represented by many different expressions. The facts about a quantity may be expressed by many different equations (or inequalities).

ESSENTIAL UNDERSTANDINGS

6-1 Corresponding to every power, there is a root. For example, just as there are squares (second powers), there are square roots. Just as there are cubes (third powers), there are cube roots, and so on.

6-2 If $\sqrt[n]{a}$ and $\sqrt[n]{b}$ are real numbers, then $\sqrt[n]{a} \cdot \sqrt[n]{b} = \sqrt[n]{ab}$.

6-3 You can combine like radicals using properties of real numbers.

6-4 You can write a radical expression in an equivalent form using a fractional (rational) exponent instead of a radical sign.

6-5 Solving a square root equation may require that you square each side of the equation. This can introduce extraneous solutions.

6-6 You can add, subtract, multiply, and divide functions based on how you perform these operations for real numbers. One difference, however, is that you must consider the domain of each function.

Solving Equations & Inequalities

BIG idea Solving an equation is the process of rewriting the equation to make what it says about its variable(s) as simple as possible. Properties of numbers and equality can be used to transform an equation (or inequality) into equivalent, simpler equations (or inequalities) in order to find solutions. Useful information about equations and inequalities (including solutions) can be found by analyzing graphs or tables. The numbers and types of solutions vary predictably, based on the type of equation.

ESSENTIAL UNDERSTANDINGS

6-7 The inverse of a function may or may not be a function.

6-8 A square root function is the inverse of a quadratic function that has a restricted domain.

Function

BIG idea A function is a relationship between variables in which each value of the input variable is associated with a unique value of the output variable. Functions can be represented in a variety of ways, such as graphs, tables, equations, or words. Each representation is particularly useful in certain situations. Some important families of functions are developed through transformations of the simplest form of the function.

ESSENTIAL UNDERSTANDINGS

6-6 to 6-8 See above.

Radical Expressions

Simplifying Radical Expressions

The practical value of simplifying numerical radicals has diminished with the widespread use of calculators. There is even reason to question whether, for example, $\frac{\sqrt{21}}{42}$ is still a "simpler form" of $\frac{1}{\sqrt{84}}$. Nonetheless, the simplification techniques used in this chapter provide practice making transformations between equivalent expressions.

Like radical terms can be *combined*. Simplify radical terms to determine whether they can be combined.

Example: $\sqrt{75} + 2\sqrt{3}$

$5\sqrt{3} + 2\sqrt{3} = 7\sqrt{3}$

Property For Products And Quotients

If $\sqrt[n]{a}$ and $\sqrt[n]{b}$ are real numbers, then

- $\sqrt[n]{a}\ \sqrt[n]{b} = \sqrt[n]{ab}$

- $\dfrac{\sqrt[n]{a}}{\sqrt[n]{b}} = \sqrt[n]{\dfrac{a}{b}}$ when $b \neq 0$.

Example: $\sqrt{5}\,(\sqrt{10} + 4)$

$\sqrt{50} + 4\sqrt{5} = 5\sqrt{2} + 4\sqrt{5}$

The product of **conjugates** results in no radical terms. Therefore, conjugates are used for rationalizing denominators.

Example: $\dfrac{4}{x + \sqrt{3}}$

$= \dfrac{4}{x + \sqrt{3}} \cdot \dfrac{x - \sqrt{3}}{x - \sqrt{3}}$

$= \dfrac{4x - 4\sqrt{3}}{(x)^2 - \left(\sqrt{3}\right)^2}$

$= \dfrac{4x - 4\sqrt{3}}{x^2 - 3}$

Function Operations

When adding, subtracting, multiplying or dividing functions, the domain will consist of the *x*-values of both functions.

© Mathematical Practices

Look for and make use of structure. Reason abstractly and quantitatively. Roots and radical expressions are connected to rational exponents, the properties of which are derived by connecting them to positive integer exponents. The connection between roots and powers is generalized to the connection between relations and their inverses and between functions and their inverses.

UNDERSTANDING BY DESIGN® and UbD™ are trademarks of ASCD, and are used under license.

Rational Exponents and Radical Equations

Rational Exponents

Radical terms can be written using rational exponents. The denominator of the exponent is the index of the root. The numerator is the power. The term can be simplified by finding the root and then raising it to the power or vice versa.

$$16^{\frac{3}{2}} = \sqrt[2]{16^3} \qquad \text{or} \qquad 16^{\frac{3}{2}} = \left(\sqrt{16}\right)^3$$
$$= \sqrt{4096} \qquad\qquad\qquad = 4^3$$
$$= 64 \qquad\qquad\qquad\qquad = 64$$

Radical Equations

A radical equation has a variable in the radicand or a variable with a rational exponent. Solve radical equations by raising each side to the power suggested by the index. Emphasize that raising each side to a power can create **extraneous solutions.**

Example: $\sqrt{30 - 2x} = x - 3$
$$30 - 2x = (x - 3)^2$$
$$30 - 2x = x^2 - 6x + 9$$
$$x^2 - 4x - 21 = 0$$
$$(x - 7)(x + 3) = 0$$
$$x = 7; \ x = -3$$

Check: $\sqrt{30 - 14} = 7 - 3$
$$\sqrt{16} = 4 \ \checkmark$$
$$\sqrt{30 - (-6)} = -3 - 3$$
$$\sqrt{36} \neq -6, \text{ thus } -3 \text{ is extraneous}$$

Solve equations with rational exponents by using the reciprocal of the power.

Example: $n^{\frac{3}{4}} = 27$
$$\left(n^{\frac{3}{4}}\right)^{\frac{4}{3}} = 27^{\frac{4}{3}}$$
$$n = \left(\sqrt[3]{27}\right)^4$$
$$= 81$$

ⓒ Mathematical Practices

Construct viable arguments and critique the reasoning of others. Attend to precision. The appearance of extraneous roots in solving equations is analyzed, and students learn the importance of verifying answers.

Graphing Radical Functions

Inverses

The inverse of a function is found by switching the x- and y-values in a function. The inverse may or may not be a function.

Example: Find the graphs of $y = x^2 + 4$ and its inverse.

Inverse: $\quad x = y^2 + 4$
$$x - 4 = y^2$$
$$\pm\sqrt{x - 4} = y$$

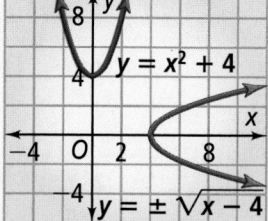

The **composition of functions** is used to determine whether functions are inverses of each other.

Functions f^{-1} and f are inverses if $(f^{-1} \circ f)(x) = x$ and $(f \circ f^{-1})(x) = x$.

Example: Are $f(x) = 3x - 6$ and $g(x) = \frac{1}{3}x + 2$ inverses?

$$(f \circ g)(x) = 3\left(\frac{1}{3}x + 2\right) - 6 \qquad (g \circ f)(x) = \frac{1}{3}(3x - 6) + 2$$
$$= x \qquad\qquad\qquad\qquad\qquad = x$$

The functions are inverses.

Transformations

Transformations of radical functions can be found by graphing the parent function, then reflecting, stretching, or translating.

- $y = -\sqrt{x}$ indicates reflection in the x-axis.
- For $y = a\sqrt{x}$, the graph stretches for $a > 1$ and shrinks for $0 < a < 1$ by the factor a.
- The transformed function $y = \sqrt{x - h} + k$ is shifted horizontally by h and vertically by k.

Example: Graph $y = \sqrt{x - 2} + 4$

Shift the parent function 2 units to the right then 4 units up.

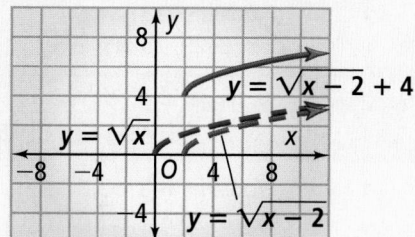

ⓒ Mathematical Practices

Use appropriate tools strategically. Graphing calculators are used to connect the algebraic and geometric representations of relations and their inverses. Calculators are deliberately *not* used in several lessons intended to reinforce manipulative skills and the understanding of how exponential laws work.

RADICAL FUNCTIONS AND RATIONAL EXPONENTS
Pacing and Assignment Guide

		TRADITIONAL			BLOCK
Lesson	Teaching Day(s)	Basic	Average	Advanced	Block
6-1	1	Problems 1–4 Exs. 10–30, 33–37, 56–67	Problems 1–4 Exs. 11–29 odd, 31–48, 56–67	Problems 1–4 Exs. 11–29 odd, 31–67	**Day 1** Problems 1–4 Exs. 11–29 odd, 31–48, 56–67
6-2	1	Problems 1–3 Exs. 10–36, 80–98	Problems 1–5 Exs. 11–51 odd, 52–75, 80–98	Problems 1–5 Exs. 11–51 odd, 52–98	Problems 1–5 Exs. 11–51 odd, 52–75, 80–98
	2	Problems 4–5 Exs. 37–55, 58–64 even, 71			
6-3	1	Problems 1–3 Exs. 10–22, 69–91	Problems 1–3 Exs. 11–21 odd, 69–91	Problems 1–3 Exs. 11–21 odd, 69–91	**Day 2** Problems 1–6 Exs. 11–35 odd, 37–64, 69–91
	2	Problems 4–6 Exs. 23–40, 53, 54–58 even	Problems 4–6 Exs. 23–35 odd, 37–64	Problems 4–6 Exs. 23–35 odd, 37–68	
6-4	1	Problems 1–3 Exs. 10–38	Problems 1–3 Exs. 11–37 odd	Problems 1–6 Exs. 11–65 odd, 67–97	**Day 3** Problems 1–6 Exs. 11–65 odd, 67–90
	2	Problems 4–6 Exs. 39–67, 72–82 even	Problems 4–6 Exs. 39–65 odd, 67–90		
6-5	1	Problems 1–3 Exs. 9–25, 73–76	Problems 1–3 Exs. 9–25 odd, 73–76	Problems 1–3 Exs. 9–25 odd, 73–76	**Day 4** Problems 1–5 Exs. 9–43 odd, 45–67, 73–76
	2	Problems 4–5 Exs. 26–47, 57–60, 63–65	Problems 4–5 Exs. 27–43 odd, 45–67	Problems 4–5 Exs. 27–43 odd, 45–72	
6-6	1	Problems 1–2 Exs. 9–26, 86–106	Problems 1–2 Exs. 9–25 odd, 86–106	Problems 1–4 Exs. 9–57 odd, 59–106	**Day 5** Problems 1–4 Exs. 9–57 odd, 59–78, 86–106
	2	Problems 3–4 Exs. 27–59, 61, 69–73 odd	Problems 3–4 Exs. 27–57 odd, 59–78		
6-7	1	Problems 1–3 Exs. 8–29, 75–95	Problems 1–3 Exs. 9–29 odd, 75–95	Problems 1–3 Exs. 9–29 odd, 75–95	**Day 6** Problems 1–6 Exs. 9–41 odd, 42–67, 75–95
	2	Problems 4–6 Exs. 30–43, 48–54 even, 65	Problems 4–6 Exs. 31–41 odd, 42–67	Problems 4–6 Exs. 31–41 odd, 42–74	
6-8	1	Problems 1–3 Exs. 7–20	Problems 1–3 Exs. 7–19 odd	Problems 1–3 Exs. 7–19 odd	**Day 7** Problems 1–6 Exs. 7–35 odd, 37–54
	2	Problems 4–6 Exs. 21–36, 37–39, 43, 53	Problems 4–6 Exs. 21–35 odd, 37–54	Problems 4–6 Exs. 21–35 odd, 37–59	
Review	1	Chapter 6 Review	Chapter 6 Review	Chapter 6 Review	**Day 8** Chapter 6 Review Chapter 6 Test
Assess	1	Chapter 6 Test	Chapter 6 Test	Chapter 6 Test	
Total		**17 Days**	**16 Days**	**14 Days**	**8 Days**

Note: Pacing does not include Concept Bytes and other feature pages.

Resources

	For the Chapter	6-1	6-2	6-3	6-4	6-5	6-6	6-7	6-8
Planning									
Teacher Center Online Planner & Grade Book	I	I	I	I	I	I	I	I	I
Interactive Learning & Guided Instruction									
My Math Video	I								
Solve It!		I　M	I　M	I　M	I　M	I　M	I　M	I　M	I　M
Student Companion		P M	P M	P M	P M	P M	P M	P M	P M
Vocabulary Support		I P M	I P M	I P M	I P M	I P M	I P M	I P M	I P M
Got It? Support		I P	I P	I P	I P	I P	I P	I P	I P
Dynamic Activity	I								
Online Problems		I	I	I	I	I	I	I	I
Additional Problems		M	M	M	M	M	M	M	M
English Language Learner Support (TR)		E P M	E P M	E P M	E P M	E P M	E P M	E P M	E P M
Activities, Games, and Puzzles		E　M	E　M	E　M	E　M	E　M	E　M	E　M	E　M
Teaching With TI Technology With CD-ROM									✓ P
TI-Nspire™ Support CD-ROM		✓	✓	✓	✓	✓	✓	✓	✓
Lesson Check & Practice									
Student Companion		P M	P M	P M	P M	P M	P M	P M	P M
Lesson Check Support		I P	I P	I P	I P	I P	I P	I P	I P
Practice and Problem Solving Workbook		P	P	P	P	P	P	P	P
Think About a Plan (TR)		E P M	E P M	E P M	E P M	E P M	E P M	E P M	E P M
Practice Form G (TR)		E P M	E P M	E P M	E P M	E P M	E P M	E P M	E P M
Standardized Test Prep (TR)		P M	P M	P M	P M	P M	P M	P M	P M
Practice *Form K* (TR)		E P M	E P M	E P M	E P M	E P M	E P M	E P M	E P M
Extra Practice	E　M								
Find the Errors!	M								
Enrichment (TR)		E P M	E P M	E P M	E P M	E P M	E P M	E P M	E P M
Answers and Solutions CD-ROM	✓	✓	✓	✓	✓	✓	✓	✓	✓
Assess & Remediate									
ExamView CD-ROM	✓	✓	✓	✓	✓	✓	✓	✓	✓
Lesson Quiz		I　M	I　M	I　M	I　M	I　M	I　M	I　M	I　M
Quizzes and Tests *Form G* (TR)	E P M				E P M				E P M
Quizzes and Tests *Form K* (TR)	E P M				E P M				E P M
Reteaching (TR)		E P M	E P M	E P M	E P M	E P M	E P M	E P M	E P M
Performance Tasks (TR)	P M								
Cumulative Review (TR)	P M								
Progress Monitoring Assessments	I P M								

(TR) Available in All-In-One Teaching Resources

Guided Instruction

PURPOSE To review and practice using the properties of exponents in preparation to simplify expressions containing exponents

PROCESS Students will
- review properties of exponents.
- apply exponent properties to simplify expressions containing exponents so that only positive exponents are used.

DISCUSS

Q Does a negative exponent change the sign of an answer? Explain. **[No, a negative exponent changes the base to its reciprocal, which does not affect the sign of either the base or the answer. For example, $4^{-3} = \left(\frac{1}{4}\right)^3$.]**

To explain the multiplication and division properties, you may use concrete examples:

$$x^5 \cdot x^3 = (x \cdot x \cdot x \cdot x \cdot x)(x \cdot x \cdot x) = x^8$$

$$\frac{x^7}{x^3} = \frac{x \cdot x \cdot x \cdot x \cdot x \cdot x \cdot x}{x \cdot x \cdot x} = x^4$$

Students may question in what order to use the properties when more than one applies. Have them rework parts (a) and (b) applying the properties in a different order. If the expressions are rewritten with positive exponents, everyone will get the same simplified expression.

EXTENSION

Q What are the restrictions on a variable when it is in the denominator of an expression? **[The denominator cannot be 0, so the variable cannot be a number that would make it 0.]**

Q Can an expression such as x^0 be in the denominator of an expression? Explain. **[Yes, since the value of x^0 is always 1.]**

Mathematical Practices This Concept Byte supports students in using repeated reasoning, Mathematical Practice 8.

Concept Byte

For Use With Lesson 6-1

REVIEW

Properties of Exponents

Common Core State Standards

Prepares for N-RN.A.1 Explain how the definition of the meaning of rational exponents follows from extending the properties of integer exponents to those values, allowing for a notation for radicals in terms of rational exponents.

MP 8

Exponents indicate powers. The table below lists the properties of exponents. Assume that no denominator is equal to zero and that m and n are integers.

take note

Properties   Properties of Exponents

- $a^0 = 1, a \neq 0$
- $\frac{a^m}{a^n} = a^{m-n}$

- $a^{-n} = \frac{1}{a^n}$
- $(ab)^n = a^n b^n$
- $(a^m)^n = a^{mn}$

- $a^m \cdot a^n = a^{m+n}$
- $\left(\frac{a}{b}\right)^n = \frac{a^n}{b^n}$

Example

Simplify and rewrite each expression using only positive exponents.

a. $(5a^3)(-3a^{-4})$

$(5a^3)(-3a^{-4}) = 5(-3)a^{(3+(-4))}$

$= -15a^{-1}$

$= \frac{-15}{a}$, or $-\frac{15}{a}$

b. $(-4x^{-3}y^5)^2$

$(-4x^{-3}y^5)^2 = (-4)^2(x^{-3})^2(y^5)^2$

$= 16x^{-6}y^{10}$

$= \frac{16y^{10}}{x^6}$

c. $\frac{4ab^6c^3}{a^5bc^3}$

$\frac{4ab^6c^3}{a^5bc^3} = 4a^{(1-5)}b^{(6-1)}c^{(3-3)}$

$= 4a^{-4}b^5c^0$

$= \frac{4b^5}{a^4}$

Exercises

Simplify each expression. Use only positive exponents.

1. $(2a^3)(5a^4)$

2. $(-3x^2)(-4x^{-2})$

3. $(3x^2y^3)^2$

4. $(3x^{-4}y^3)^2$

5. $\frac{4a^8}{2a^4}$

6. $\frac{12x^5y^3}{4x^{-1}}$

7. $\frac{(6x^3)^0}{3xy^2}$

8. $\left(\frac{2x^4}{3}\right)^3$

9. $(-4m^2n^3)(2mn)$

10. $(2x^3y^7)^{-2}$

11. $\frac{(3r^{-2}s^3t^0)^{-3}}{3rs}$

12. $(h^7k^3)^0$

13. $\frac{r^2s^4t^6}{r^3s^4t^{-6}}$

14. $\frac{x^2y}{4} \cdot \frac{16x}{y}$

15. $(s^4t)^2(st)$

16. $\left(\frac{1}{h^{-2}}\right)^{-1} \cdot h^3$

17. $\frac{1}{a^2b^{-3}}(a^2b^{-3})^{-1}$

18. $\left(\frac{r^{-1}s^2t^{-3}}{r^{-2}s^0t^1}\right)^{-1}$

19. Reasoning Your friend tells you that $(k^2)^{-5} = -k^{10}$. Did she apply the properties of exponents correctly? Explain why or why not.

Answers

Concept Byte
1. $10a^7$

2. 12

3. $9x^4y^6$

4. $\frac{9y^6}{x^8}$

5. $2a^4$

6. $3x^6y^3$

7. $\frac{1}{3xy^2}$

8. $\frac{8x^{12}}{27}$

9. $-8m^3n^4$

10. $\frac{1}{4x^6y^{14}}$

11. $\frac{r^5}{81s^{10}}$

12. 1

13. $\frac{t^{12}}{r}$

14. $4x^3$

15. s^9t^3

16. h

17. $\frac{b^6}{a^4}$

18. $\frac{t^4}{s^2r}$

19. No; $(k^2)^{-5} \neq -k^{10}$; by the prop. of exponents, $(k^2)^{-5} = k^{2(-5)} = k^{-10} = \frac{1}{k^{10}}$.

Roots and Radical Expressions

© **Common Core State Standards**
A-SSE.A.2 Use the structure of an expression to identify ways to rewrite it.
MP 1, MP 2, MP 3, MP 4

1 Interactive Learning

Solve It!

PURPOSE To take roots and apply substitution to solve a quadratic equation
PROCESS Students may
- square both sides of the equation, substitute x for the infinite radical, and solve.
- use a calculator to evaluate the infinite radical until an approximate value is reached.

Objective To find nth roots

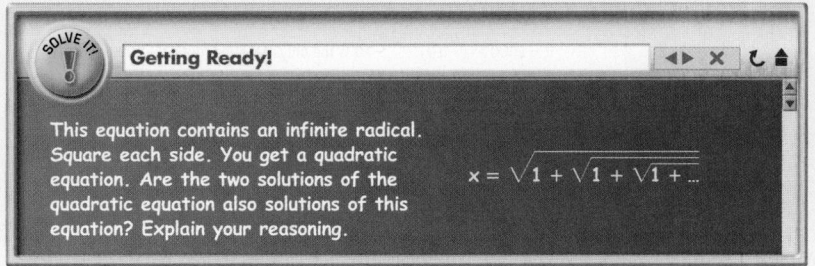

Getting Ready!

This equation contains an infinite radical. Square each side. You get a quadratic equation. Are the two solutions of the quadratic equation also solutions of this equation? Explain your reasoning.

$$x = \sqrt{1 + \sqrt{1 + \sqrt{1 + \ldots}}}$$

FACILITATE

Q What is $\left(\sqrt{1 + \sqrt{1 + \sqrt{1 + }}}\right)^2$?
$[1 + \sqrt{1 + \sqrt{1 + \ldots}}\,]$

Q How can you rewrite $x^2 = 1 + \sqrt{1 + \sqrt{1 + \ldots}}$ without radicals? **[Substitute x for the equivalent radical: $x^2 = 1 + x$.]**

Q Can you get an exact solution for $\sqrt{1 + \sqrt{1 + \sqrt{1 \ldots}}}$ on a calculator? Explain. **[No; you can only get an approximation.]**

Q Why is the original equation called an infinite radical? **[because the right side of the equation is never-ending]**

ANSWER See Solve It in Answers on next page.
CONNECT THE MATH The Solve It uses roots, radical expressions, substitution, and the Quadratic Formula to find solutions to the equation algebraically. In the lesson, students find real and principal roots and discover their properties.

In Chapter 5, you used *root* to represent a solution of an equation. For example, 2 is a root of the equation $x^3 = 8$. For such a simple power equation, you can simply refer to 2 as a cube root of 8.

Essential Understanding Corresponding to every power, there is a root. For example, just as there are squares (second powers), there are square roots. Just as there are cubes (third powers), there are cube roots, and so on.

$5^2 = 25$ 5 is a square root of 25.
$5^3 = 125$ 5 is a cube root of 125.
$5^4 = 625$ 5 is a fourth root of 625.
$5^5 = 3125$ 5 is a fifth root of 3125.

This pattern suggests a definition of an nth root.

---

take note

Key Concept   The nth Root

If $a^n = b$, with a and b real numbers and n a positive integer, then a is an **nth root** of b.

If n is odd...
there is one real nth root of b, denoted in radical form as $\sqrt[n]{b}$.

If n is even...
- and b is positive, there are two real nth roots of b. The positive root is the **principal root** (or principal nth root) and its symbol is $\sqrt[n]{b}$. The negative root is its opposite, or $-\sqrt[n]{b}$.
- and b is negative, there are no real nth roots of b.

The only nth root of 0 is 0.

---

2 Guided Instruction

Take Note

Q Why do negative radicands have no real roots when the index is even? **[There is no real number whose square or other even power is negative.]**

BIG idea Equivalence
ESSENTIAL UNDERSTANDINGS
- Corresponding to every power, there is a root. For example, just as there are squares (second powers), there are square roots. Just as there are cubes (third powers), there are cube roots, and so on.
- The nth root of an expression that contains an nth power as a factor can be simplified.
$$\sqrt[n]{x^n} = x^{\frac{n}{n}} = \begin{cases} x, & \text{if } n \text{ is odd} \\ |x|, & \text{if } n \text{ is even} \end{cases}$$

Math Background

Depending on the sign of the radicand, the root corresponding to every real power is not necessarily a real number.

Specifically, if the index is even, the root of a negative number is not a real number. For example, the square root of -9 cannot be 3 or -3 since $3^2 = 9$ and $(-3)^2 = 9$. The

two complex square roots of -9 are $3i$ and $-3i$.

When finding the roots of variables, students may be confused by the placement of the absolute value signs. They are needed if and only if all of the following are true:
- the index is even,
- the power of the variable in the radicand is even, and
- the power of the variable in the root is odd.

The absolute value will ensure that an even root is always nonnegative.

Note that although there are two real nth roots of b when n is even and b is positive, only the positive root is the principal root, $\sqrt[n]{b}$. The negative root is represented as $-\sqrt[n]{b}$. So, in Problems 2–4 where students are asked to find various roots $\sqrt[n]{b}$, they should give only the one positive root.

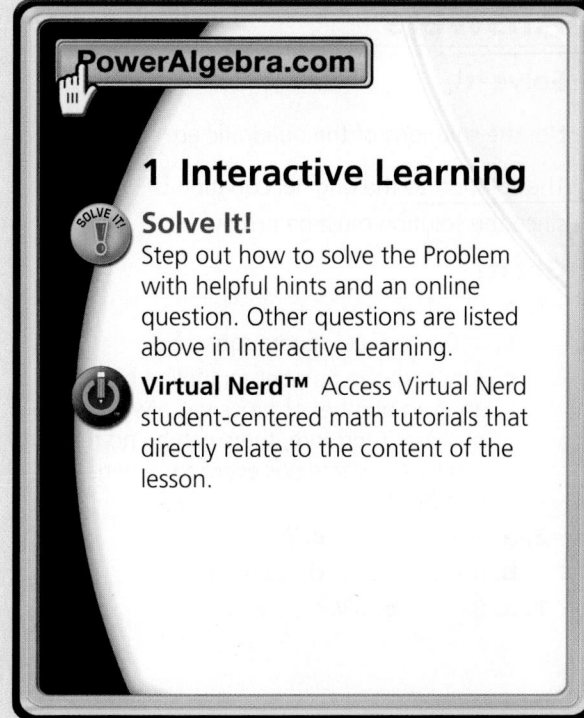

PowerAlgebra.com

1 Interactive Learning

Solve It!
Step out how to solve the Problem with helpful hints and an online question. Other questions are listed above in Interactive Learning.

Virtual Nerd™ Access Virtual Nerd student-centered math tutorials that directly relate to the content of the lesson.

Q How do you find the fourth root of a fraction, like $\frac{16}{81}$? [Consider the numerator and denominator separately, and find the root of each. The fourth root of 16 is 2 and the fourth root of 81 is 3, hence the fourth root of $\frac{16}{81}$ is $\frac{2}{3}$.]

Q You can find the cube root of -1000 by solving $x^3 + 1000 = 0$. According to the Fundamental Theorem of Algebra, how many roots does $x^3 + 1000 = 0$ have? How many are real? [Since the degree of this polynomial equation is 3, it has 3 complex solutions. Only one of them, -10, is real.]

Got It?

Q Can the square root of a negative number ever be real? Explain. [No, because the square of a real number can never be negative.]

Problem 2

Q Instead of guess-and-check, what is another efficient way to find a root? [Answers may vary. Sample: Use prime factorization. For example, $-8 = (-1)(2)(2)(2) = (-2)(-2)(-2) = (-2)^3$]

Q For 2D, $(-2)^2$ also equals 4. Why is -2 not listed as a root? [-2 is not listed as a root because $\sqrt{4}$ represents the positive square root.]

You use a radical sign to indicate a root. The number under the radical sign is the **radicand**. The **index** gives the degree of the root.

$$\sqrt[n]{a}$$

index · radical sign · radicand

Plan

How many real cube roots are there?
A cube root is the same as a third root, and 3 is odd. So there is only one real cube root of a number.

© Problem 1 Finding All Real Roots

Ⓐ What are the real cube roots of 0.008, -1000, and $\frac{1}{27}$?

$0.008 = (0.2)^3$ 0.2 is the only real cube root of 0.008.

$-1000 = (-10)^3$ -10 is the only real cube root of -1000.

$\frac{1}{27} = \left(\frac{1}{3}\right)^3$ $\frac{1}{3}$ is the only real cube root of $\frac{1}{27}$.

Ⓑ What are the real fourth roots of 1, -0.0001, and $\frac{16}{81}$?

Since 1 is positive, there are two real fourth roots.

$1 = 1^4$ 1 is a real fourth root of 1.

$1 = (-1)^4$ -1 is the other real fourth root of 1.

Since -0.0001 is negative, there are no real fourth roots of -0.0001.

Since $\frac{16}{81}$ is positive, there are two real fourth roots.

$\frac{16}{81} = \left(\frac{2}{3}\right)^4$ $\frac{2}{3}$ is a real fourth root of $\frac{16}{81}$.

$\frac{16}{81} = \left(-\frac{2}{3}\right)^4$ $-\frac{2}{3}$ is the other real fourth root of $\frac{16}{81}$.

© ✓ **Got It?** 1. **a.** What are the real fifth roots of 0, -1, and 32?
     b. What are the real square roots of 0.01, -1, and $\frac{36}{121}$?
     c. Reasoning Explain why a negative real number b has no real nth roots if n is even.

According to the Fundamental Theorem of Algebra, $x^4 - 1 = 0$ has four roots, only two of which are real. In this chapter, the focus is on real roots only.

Plan

How can you find a cube root?
Work backwards. Find a number whose cube is the radicand.

© Problem 2 Finding Roots

What is each real-number root?

Ⓐ $\sqrt[3]{-8}$
$(-2)^3 = -8$
So, $\sqrt[3]{-8} = -2$.

Ⓑ $\sqrt{0.04}$
$(0.2)^2 = 0.04$
So, $\sqrt{0.04} = 0.2$.
$(-0.2)^2 = 0.04$ also, but $\sqrt{0.04}$ represents the positive square root.

Ⓒ $\sqrt[4]{-1}$
There is no real root because there is no real number whose fourth power is -1.

Ⓓ $\sqrt{(-2)^2}$
$\sqrt{(-2)^2} = \sqrt{4} = 2$.

Answers

Solve It!

No; the solutions of the quadratic eq. are $\frac{1 \pm \sqrt{5}}{2}$.

The solution to the original equation is $\frac{1 + \sqrt{5}}{2}$, since the solution must be positive.

Got It?

1. **a.** 0; -1; 2
   b. ± 0.1; no real square root; $\pm\frac{6}{11}$
   c. Any negative number multiplied by itself an even number of times will always be positive. Therefore, there can be no real nth roots (where n is even) for a negative number b.

2. **a.** -3 **c.** 7
   b. no real root   **d.** no real root

3. **a.** $9x^2$ **b.** $a^4 b^5$ **c.** $|x^3| y^4$

PowerAlgebra.com

2 Guided Instruction

© Each Problem is worked out and supported online.

Problem 1
Finding All Real Roots
Animated

Problem 2
Finding Roots

Problem 3
Simplifying Radical Expressions
Animated

Problem 4
Using a Radical Expression
Animated

Support in Algebra 2 Companion
• Vocabulary
• Key Concepts
• Got It?

 **Got lt?** **2.** What is each real-number root?

    a. $\sqrt[3]{-27}$ **b.** $\sqrt[4]{-81}$ **c.** $\sqrt{(-7)^2}$ **d.** $\sqrt{-49}$

It is tempting to conclude that $\sqrt[n]{a^n} = a$ for all real numbers a, but part (d) of Problem 2 shows that this is not the case. If n is even, then $\sqrt[n]{a^n}$ is positive even if a itself is negative.

 take note

> ### Property   *n*th Roots of *n*th Powers
>
> For any real number a, $\sqrt[n]{a^n} = \begin{cases} a \text{ if } n \text{ is odd} \\ |a| \text{ if } n \text{ is even} \end{cases}$

It is easy to overlook this rule for simplifying radicals. It is particularly important that you remember it when the radicand contains a variable expression. You must *include* the absolute value when n is even, and you must *omit* it when n is odd.

© **Problem 3** Simplifying Radical Expressions

What is a simpler form of each radical expression?

A $\sqrt{16x^8}$

$\sqrt{16x^8} = \sqrt{4^2(x^4)^2} = \sqrt{(4x^4)^2} = |4x^4| = 4x^4$

You need to include absolute value symbols because the index of a square root is 2, which is even. However, $|4x^4| = 4x^4$ because x^4 is always nonnegative.

B $\sqrt[3]{a^6b^9}$

$\sqrt[3]{a^6b^9} = \sqrt[3]{(a^2)^3(b^3)^3} = \sqrt[3]{(a^2b^3)^3} = a^2b^3$

The index is odd, so you cannot include absolute value symbols here.

C $\sqrt[4]{x^8y^{12}}$

$\sqrt[4]{x^8y^{12}} = \sqrt[4]{(x^2)^4(y^3)^4} = \sqrt[4]{(x^2y^3)^4} = x^2|y^3|$

The index is even. The absolute value symbols ensure that the root is positive when y^3 is negative. Absolute value symbols are not needed for x^2 since x^2 is always nonnegative.

 **Got lt?** **3.** What is the simplified form of each radical expression?

    a. $\sqrt{81x^4}$ **b.** $\sqrt[3]{a^{12}b^{15}}$ **c.** $\sqrt[4]{x^{12}y^{16}}$

Plan

How can you get started?
You're simplifying a square root, so use properties of exponents to write the *entire* radicand as a perfect square.

Got lt?   ERROR PREVENTION

Q In 2c, is −7 a root? Why or why not? **[−7 is a real square root of 49 but not a principal root. The form $\sqrt{a}$ calls for the principal square root of a, and the principal square root cannot be negative.]**

Note that this statement is true since $\sqrt[n]{a^n}$ is a principal root when n is even, so it must be nonnegative.

Take Note

Q Why is it necessary to include absolute value bars when n is even? **[Answers may vary. Sample: The absolute value bars ensure that the root is nonnegative. For example, $\sqrt{x^2} = x$ is false when x is negative, while $\sqrt{x^2} = |x|$ is true.]**

Problem 3

Q Why is $\sqrt{x^2} = |x|$, but $\sqrt{x^4} = x^2$? **[The absolute value bars are unnecessary for x^2 because x^2 is always nonnegative.]**

Q Why does 3B not have absolute value bars around the answer? **[Absolute value is not needed because the index is odd.]**

Got lt?   ERROR PREVENTION

You may want to quickly review operations with exponents to help with factoring:
$a^{12} = a^{4(3)} = (a^4)^3$.

Q What should you do first? **[Answers may vary. Sample: Factor the radicand, and identify the multiples of the given power.]**

Additional Problems

1. What are all the real square roots of -0.81, $\frac{25}{49}$, and 121?

ANSWER none; $\frac{5}{7}$ and $-\frac{5}{7}$; 11 and -11

2. What is each real-number root of $\sqrt{0.36}$, $\sqrt[3]{-1}$ and $\sqrt{(-17)^2}$?

ANSWER 0.6, -1; 17

3. What is the simplified form of each radical?

  a. $\sqrt{25a^4}$

  b. $\sqrt[4]{p^{12}q^4}$

ANSWERS a. $5a^2$ **b.** $|p^3q|$

4. The speed s in meters per second of a car leaving a skid mark d meters long after the brakes are applied is given by the formula $s = \sqrt{15d}$. If you measure a skid mark and it is 180 m long, how fast was the car going before it braked?

ANSWER about 52 m/s

Problem 4

Q Why does the formula contain the number 10? **[Ten is the square root of the highest possible score achievable on the test.]**

A good point for discussion here is the fairness of adjusting test scores. Students may have an initial negative reaction to a student gaining 24 points versus a student gaining only 5 points. Point out that the person at the bottom of the scoring is still at the bottom.

Got It?

Q The raw scores of 0 and 100 are not altered by the formula. Do you think this is a good idea? Explain. **[Sample: Yes; no one can score more than 100 with this formula, and it does not make sense to give points to someone who scored zero.]**

3 Lesson Check

Do you know HOW?
• For Exercises 1–3, remind students to use the Take Note table (p. 361) to determine how many real roots they should find.

Do you UNDERSTAND? ERROR INTERVENTION
• If students have trouble finding the error in Exercise 7, remind them that the four is an index, not a divisor.

Close

Q Why does a positive integer have two real square roots but only one real cube root? **[Either a negative number squared or a positive number squared will produce a positive number, but only a positive number cubed will produce a positive number.]**

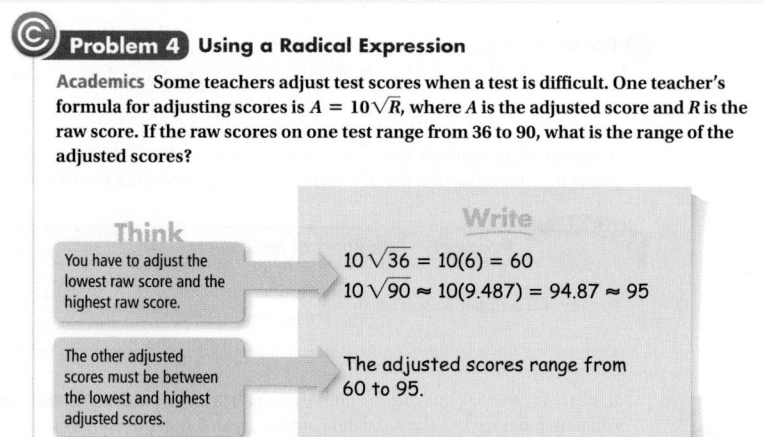

Problem 4 Using a Radical Expression

Academics Some teachers adjust test scores when a test is difficult. One teacher's formula for adjusting scores is $A = 10\sqrt{R}$, where A is the adjusted score and R is the raw score. If the raw scores on one test range from 36 to 90, what is the range of the adjusted scores?

Think

You have to adjust the lowest raw score and the highest raw score.

The other adjusted scores must be between the lowest and highest adjusted scores.

Write

$10\sqrt{36} = 10(6) = 60$
$10\sqrt{90} \approx 10(9.487) = 94.87 \approx 95$

The adjusted scores range from 60 to 95.

 Got It? 4. In Problem 4, what are the adjusted scores for raw scores of 0 and 100?

Lesson Check

Do you know HOW?

Find all the real square roots of each number.

1. 25   **2.** 0.16   **3.** −64

Simplify each radical expression.

4. $\sqrt{9b^2}$ **5.** $\sqrt{a^8b^{18}}$ **6.** $\sqrt[3]{-125a^3}$

Do you UNDERSTAND? MATHEMATICAL PRACTICES

7. Error Analysis A student said the only fourth root of 16 is 2. Describe and correct his error.

8. Vocabulary Explain the difference between a real root and the principal root.

9. Reasoning A number has only one real nth root. What can you conclude about the index n?

Practice and Problem-Solving Exercises
MATHEMATICAL PRACTICES

A Practice   Find all the real square roots of each number.   ◀ See Problem 1.

10. 225   **11.** 0.0049   **12.** $-\frac{1}{121}$ **13.** $\frac{64}{169}$

Find all the real cube roots of each number.

14. −64   **15.** 0.125   **16.** $-\frac{27}{216}$ **17.** 0.000343

Find all the real fourth roots of each number.

18. 16   **19.** −16   **20.** 0.0081   **21.** $\frac{10,000}{81}$

3 Lesson Check

For a digital lesson check, use the Got It questions.

Support in Algebra 2 Companion
• Lesson Check

4 Practice

Assign homework to individual students or to an entire class.

Answers

Got It? (continued)

4. 0; 100

Lesson Check

1. ±5
2. ±0.4
3. no real roots
4. $3|b|$
5. $a^4|b^9|$
6. −5a
7. 16 has two real fourth roots, 2 and −2.
8. The real roots of a number are the positive and negative (but not imaginary) roots of the number; the principal root of a number is the nonnegative root of the number.
9. n is odd.

Practice and Problem-Solving Exercises

10. ±15
11. ±0.07
12. none
13. $\pm\frac{8}{13}$
14. −4
15. 0.5
16. $-\frac{1}{2}$
17. 0.07
18. ±2
19. none
20. ±0.3
21. $\pm\frac{10}{3}$

Find each real root. See Problem 2.

22. $\sqrt{36}$ **23.** $\sqrt{0.25}$ **24.** $-\sqrt[3]{64}$ **25.** $\sqrt[3]{-27}$

Simplify each radical expression. Use absolute value symbols when needed. See Problem 3.

26. $\sqrt{16x^2}$ **27.** $\sqrt[3]{27y^6}$ **28.** $\sqrt[4]{x^{20}y^{28}}$ **29.** $\sqrt[5]{32y^{10}}$

30. Grades In many classes, a passing test grade is 70. Using the formula $A = 10\sqrt{R}$, what raw score would a student need to get a passing grade after her score is adjusted? See Problem 4.

 Apply

Find the two real solutions of each equation.

31. $x^2 = 100$ **32.** $x^4 = 1$ **33.** $x^2 = 0.25$ **34.** $x^4 = \frac{16}{81}$

35. Think About a Plan The radius of a spherical balloon can be expressed as $r = \sqrt[3]{\frac{3V}{4\pi}}$ inches, where r is the radius and V is the volume of the balloon in cubic inches. If air is pumped to inflate the balloon from 500 cubic inches to 800 cubic inches, by how many inches has the radius of the balloon increased?
• What was the radius of the balloon originally?
• What was the radius after inflating the balloon to 800 cubic inches?
• How can you use the two radii to find the amount of increase?

STEM **36. Electricity** The voltage V of an audio system's speaker can be represented by $V = 4\sqrt{P}$, where P is the power of the speaker. An engineer wants to design a speaker with 400 watts of power. What will the voltage be?

STEM **37. Boat Building** Boat builders share an old rule of thumb for sailboats. The maximum speed K in knots is 1.35 times the square root of the length L in feet of the boat's waterline.
a. A customer is planning to order a sailboat with a maximum speed of 12 knots. How long should the waterline be?
b. How much longer would the waterline have to be to achieve a maximum speed of 15 knots?

Simplify each radical expression. Use absolute value symbols when needed.

38. $\sqrt[3]{0.125}$ **39.** $\sqrt[3]{\frac{8}{216}}$ **40.** $\sqrt[4]{0.0016}$ **41.** $\sqrt[4]{\frac{1}{256}}$ **42.** $\sqrt[4]{16c^4}$

43. Open-Ended Write three radical expressions that simplify to $-2x^2$.

44. Reasoning For what positive integers n is each of the statements true?
a. If $x^n = b$, then x is an nth root of b.
b. If $x^n = b$, then $x = \sqrt[n]{b}$.

Is each equation *always, sometimes,* or *never* true? Explain your answer.

45. $\sqrt{x^4} = x^2$ **46.** $\sqrt{x^6} = x^3$ **47.** $\sqrt[3]{x^8} = x^2$ **48.** $\sqrt[3]{x^3} = |x|$

4 Practice

ASSIGNMENT GUIDE

Basic: 10–30 all, 33–37
Average: 11–29 odd, 31–48
Advanced: 11–29 odd, 31–55
Standardized Test Prep: 56–59
Mixed Review: 60–67

Mathematical Practices are supported by exercises with red headings. Here are the Practices supported in this lesson:

MP 1: Make Sense of Problems Ex. 35
MP 2: Reason Abstractly Ex. 43
MP 3: Communicate Ex. 54
MP 3: Construct Arguments Ex. 9, 44, 53
MP 3: Critique the Reasoning of Others Ex. 7

Applications exercises have blue headings. Exercises 37 and 55 support MP 4: Model.

EXERCISE 37: Use the Think About a Plan worksheet in the **Practice and Problem Solving Workbook** (also available in the Teaching Resources in print and online) to further support students' development in becoming independent learners.

HOMEWORK QUICK CHECK

To check students' understanding of key skills and concepts, go over Exercises 21, 29, 34, 35, and 37.

---

22. 6

23. 0.5

24. −4

25. −3

26. $4|x|$

27. $3y^2$

28. $|x^5 y^7|$

29. $2y^2$

30. 49

31. ± 10

32. ± 1

33. ± 0.5

34. $\pm \frac{2}{3}$

35. about 0.8 in.

36. 80 volts

37. a. about 79.01 ft
     b. about 44.44 ft

38. 0.5

39. $\frac{1}{3}$

40. 0.2

41. $\frac{1}{4}$

42. $2|c|$

43. Answers may vary. Sample:
$\sqrt[3]{-8x^6}$, $-\sqrt[4]{16x^8}$, $\sqrt[5]{-32x^{10}}$

44. a. for all positive integers
     b. for all odd positive integers

45. always; x^2 is always nonnegative

46. sometimes; they are equal for $x \geq 0$

47. sometimes; they are equal for $x = -1, 0, 1$

48. sometimes; they are equal for $x \geq 0$

Answers

Practice and Problem-Solving Exercises
(continued)

49. even: $|m|$; odd: m

50. even: m^2; odd: m^2

51. even: $|m^3|$; odd: m^3

52. even: m^4; odd: m^4

53. 48

54. No; the square root of 4 is ± 2.

55. a diagonal of a square with side 5

Standardized Test Prep

56. B

57. G

58. C

59. [4] System:
$-35 = (-3)^3a + (-3)^2b + (-3)c + d,$
$1 = (0)^3a + (0)^2b + (0)c + d, 3 = (2)^3a +$
$(2)^2b + (2)c + d, 7 = (4)^3a + (4)^2b +$
$(4)c + d$ (OR equivalent system); solution:
$a = 0.35, b = -1.85, c = 3.3, d = 1,$
cubic polynomial: $y = 0.35x^3 -$
$1.85x^2 + 3.3x + 1.$

  [3] appropriate methods, but with one
  computational error

  [2] incorrect system solved correctly OR
  correct system solved incorrectly; function
  written appropriately, given previous
  results

  [1] correct function, without work shown

Mixed Review

60. $y = (x + 2)^3 + 3$

61. $y = \frac{1}{2}x^3 - 2$

62. $1, \frac{3}{4}$

63. $\dfrac{5 \pm i\sqrt{11}}{6}$

64. $\dfrac{11}{6}$

65. $2x^3y^3$

66. $\dfrac{ac}{3}$

67. $\dfrac{4}{x^2}$

Challenge Simplify each radical expression if n is even, and then if n is odd.

49. $\sqrt[n]{m^n}$ **50.** $\sqrt[n]{m^{2n}}$ **51.** $\sqrt[n]{m^{3n}}$ **52.** $\sqrt[n]{m^{4n}}$

53. Reasoning How many square roots of integers are in the interval between 24 and 25?

54. Reasoning The square root of a positive integer is either a positive integer or an irrational number. Is this a true statement or not? Explain your reasoning.

55. Geometry Without using a calculator, determine which is greater: the altitude of an equilateral triangle with side 8 or the diagonal of a square with side 5. Show your work.

Standardized Test Prep

SAT/ACT

56. Which equation has more than one real-number solution?

  Ⓐ $x^2 = 0$ Ⓑ $x^2 = 1$ Ⓒ $x^2 = -1$ Ⓓ $x^3 = -1$

57. According to the Rational Root Theorem, which of the following is NOT a possible root of the polynomial equation $7x^5 + 3x^2 - 4x + 21 = 0$?

  Ⓕ $\frac{1}{7}$ Ⓖ $\frac{1}{3}$ Ⓗ 3   Ⓘ 7

58. The fuse of a three-break firework rocket is programmed to ignite three times with 2-second intervals between the ignitions. When the rocket is shot vertically in the air, its height h in feet after t seconds is given by the formula $h(t) = -5t^2 + 70t$. At how many seconds after the shot should the firework technician set the timer of the first ignition to make the second ignition occur when the rocket is at its highest point?

  Ⓐ 3   Ⓑ 9   Ⓒ 5   Ⓓ 7

Extended Response

59. Write a system of equations to find a cubic polynomial that goes through $(-3, -35), (0, 1), (2, 3),$ and $(4, 7)$.

Mixed Review

Determine the cubic function that is obtained from the parent function $y = x^3$ after each sequence of transformations. ◆ See Lesson 5-9.

60. translation up 3 units and to the left 2 units

61. vertical compression by a factor of $\frac{1}{2}$, translation down 2 units

Solve each equation by using the Quadratic Formula. ◆ See Lesson 4-7.

62. $-4x^2 + 7x - 3 = 0$ **63.** $3x^2 - 5x + 3 = 0$ **64.** $36x^2 - 132x + 121 = 0$

Get Ready!   To prepare for Lesson 6-2, do Exercises 65–67.

Simplify each algebraic expression. ◆ See Lesson 1-3.

65. $\frac{14x^7y^9}{7x^4y^6}$ **66.** $\frac{3abc}{9b}$ **67.** $\frac{20x}{5x^3}$

Differentiated Remediation

Additional Instructional Support

Algebra 2 Companion

Students can use the **Algebra 2 Companion** worktext (4 pages) as you teach the lesson. Use the Companion to support

- New Vocabulary
- Key Concepts
- Got It for each Problem
- Lesson Check

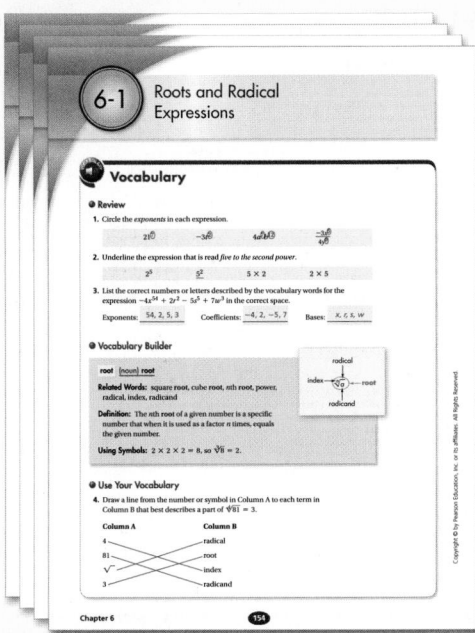

ELL Support

Use Manipulatives Divide students into small groups. Give each group 25 tiles and 125 small cubes (or less, 16 tiles and 64 cubes, or 9 tiles and 27 cubes, or 4 tiles and 8 cubes, as materials allow). Have them model 5^2 and $\sqrt{25}$ with tiles, and 5^3 and $\sqrt[3]{125}$ with cubes. Repeat using 4, 3, and 2 instead of 5. Have students identify and name the index and radicand of each.

Discuss the shape of each figure. What does 5^2 look like? [a 5 × 5 square] What represents $\sqrt{25}$? [5 tiles, or one side of the square] What does 5^3 look like? [a 5 × 5 × 5 cube] What represents $\sqrt[3]{125}$? [5 tiles, or one edge of the cube]

You may also want to make the following poster for the classroom or vocabulary board:
$$\overset{\text{Index}}{\sqrt{\overline{\text{Radicand}}}}$$

5 Assess & Remediate

Lesson Quiz

1. What are the real cube roots of -64, 0.001, and $\frac{27}{125}$?
2. What is each real-number root of $\sqrt{0.16}$, $\sqrt[3]{-343}$ and $\sqrt{(-5)^2}$?
3. What is the simplified form of $\sqrt{9x^2}$ and of $\sqrt[3]{x^6 y^{15}}$?
4. **Do you UNDERSTAND?** The formula $d = 1.35\sqrt{h}$ models the distance d in miles from the horizon where h is the distance in feet from a person's eyes to the water. If you are standing in a boat and the distance from the water to your eyes is 8 ft, what is your distance from the horizon to the nearest hundredth of a mile?

ANSWERS TO LESSON QUIZ

1. -4; 0.1; $\frac{3}{5}$
2. 0.4; -7; 5
3. $3|x|$; $x^2 y^5$
4. 3.82 mi

PRESCRIPTION FOR REMEDIATION
Use the student work on the Lesson Quiz to prescribe a differentiated review assignment:

Points	Differentiated Remediation
0–2	Intervention
3	On-level
4	Extension

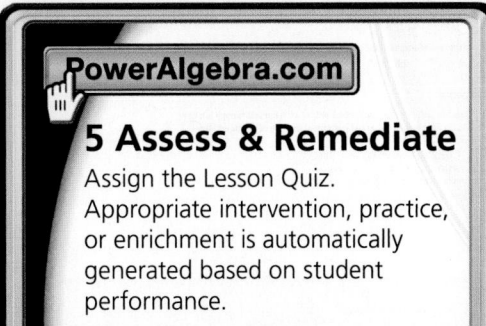

PowerAlgebra.com

5 Assess & Remediate

Assign the Lesson Quiz. Appropriate intervention, practice, or enrichment is automatically generated based on student performance.

Intervention

- **Reteaching** (2 pages) Provides reteaching and practice exercises for the key lesson concepts. Use with struggling students or absent students.
- **English Language Learner Support** Helps students develop and reinforce mathematical vocabulary and key concepts.

All-in-One Resources/Online
Reteaching

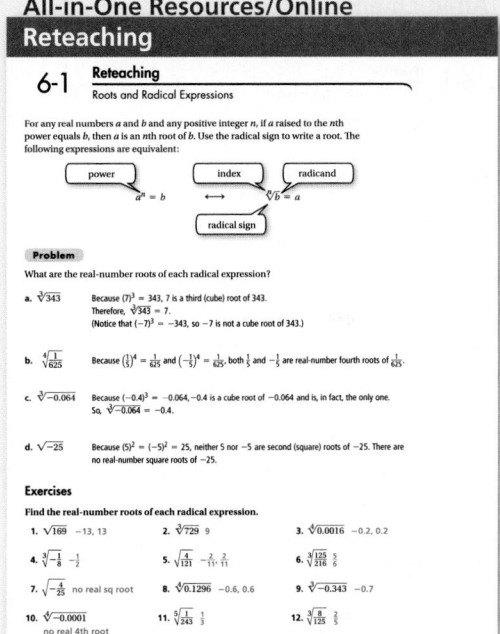

All-in-One Resources/Online
English Language Learner Support

Differentiated Remediation *continued*

Lesson Resources

On-Level

- **Practice** (2 pages) Provides extra practice for each lesson. For simpler practice exercises, use the Form K Practice pages found in the All-in-One Teaching Resources and online.

- **Think About a Plan** Helps students develop specific problem-solving skills and strategies by providing scaffolded guiding questions.

- **Standardized Test Prep** Focuses on all major exercises, all major question types, and helps students prepare for the high-stakes assessments.

Extension

- **Enrichment** Provides students with interesting problems and activities that extend the concepts of the lesson.

- **Activities, Games, and Puzzles** Worksheets that can be used for concepts development, enrichment, and for fun!

Practice and Problem Solving Wkbk/ All-in-One Resources/Online
Practice page 1

Practice and Problem Solving Wkbk/ All-in-One Resources/Online
Practice page 2

All-in-One Resources/Online
Enrichment

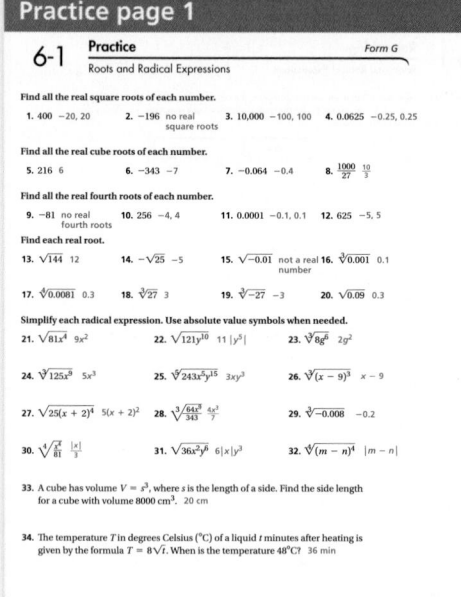

Practice and Problem Solving Wkbk/ All-in-One Resources/Online
Think About a Plan

Practice and Problem Solving Wkbk/ All-in-One Resources/Online
Standardized Test Prep

Online Teacher Resource Center
Activities, Games, and Puzzles

6-2 Multiplying and Dividing Radical Expressions

Common Core State Standards
A-SSE.A.2 Use the structure of an expression to identify ways to rewrite it.
MP 1, MP 2, MP 3, MP 4

Objective To multiply and divide radical expressions

Cutting *n*-squares into 1-squares doesn't count.

MATHEMATICAL PRACTICES

SOLVE IT!

Getting Ready!

You can cut the 36-square into four 9-squares or nine 4-squares. What other n-square can you cut into sets of smaller squares in two ways? Is there a square you can cut into smaller squares in three ways? Explain your reasoning.

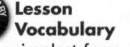
Lesson Vocabulary
• simplest form of a radical
• rationalize the denominator

Knowing the perfect squares greater than 1 (namely, 4, 9, 16, and so on) will help you simplify some radical expressions.

Essential Understanding You can simplify a radical expression when the exponent of one factor of the radicand is a multiple of the radical's index.

You can simplify the product of powers that have the same exponent. Similarly, you can simplify the product of radicals that have the same index.

Same Exponent	Same Index
$2^2 \cdot 3^2 = (2 \cdot 3)^2$	$\sqrt{2} \cdot \sqrt{3} = \sqrt{2 \cdot 3}$
$4^3 \cdot 5^3 = (4 \cdot 5)^3$	$\sqrt[3]{4} \cdot \sqrt[3]{5} = \sqrt[3]{4 \cdot 5}$

Property Combining Radical Expressions: Products

If $\sqrt[n]{a}$ and $\sqrt[n]{b}$ are real numbers, then $\sqrt[n]{a} \cdot \sqrt[n]{b} = \sqrt[n]{ab}$.

Problem 1 Multiplying Radical Expressions

Can you simplify the product of the radical expressions? Explain.

Ⓐ $\sqrt[3]{6} \cdot \sqrt{2}$

No. The indexes are different. The property above does not apply.

Ⓑ $\sqrt[3]{-4} \cdot \sqrt[3]{2}$

Yes. $\sqrt[3]{-4} \cdot \sqrt[3]{2} = \sqrt[3]{-4(2)} = \sqrt[3]{-8} = -2$.

Plan
What allows you to use the property for multiplying radicals?
The radicals must be real numbers. The indexes must be the same.

PowerAlgebra.com | **Lesson 6-2** Multiplying and Dividing Radical Expressions | **367**

---

1 Interactive Learning

Solve It!

PURPOSE To use sums of perfect squares to solve a problem

PROCESS Students may
• find the perfect squares that sum to 48.
• use trial and error by drawing and counting.

Q What is the factored form of 36? How does this relate to the two ways that you can divide a 36-square into smaller squares as shown? **[36 = 2 · 2 · 3 · 3 = 4 · 3^2 = 2^2 · 9; the factored form illustrates why a 36-square can be divided into four 3-by-3 squares or nine 2-by-2 squares. A 36-square can be divided in the two ways shown because 36 is the product of 2 squares.]**

ANSWER See Solve It in Answers on next page.

CONNECT THE MATH The Solve It is solved by finding factors and recognizing perfect squares. In the lesson, students find factors and use perfect squares to simplify radical expressions.

2 Guided Instruction

Take Note

Q How can this property be used to simplify $\sqrt[3]{a} \cdot \sqrt{b}$ when the radicals alone cannot be simplified? **[Answers may vary. Sample: You may be able to factor *ab* into factors of powers of a multiple of *n*. For example, $\sqrt[3]{4} \cdot \sqrt[3]{2} = \sqrt[3]{8} = \sqrt[3]{2^3} = 2$.]**

Problem 1

Q Do the radicands also need to be the same to use the property for multiplying radicals? Explain. **[No; only the indexes need to be the same.]**

6-2 Preparing to Teach

BIG idea Equivalence

ESSENTIAL UNDERSTANDINGS

• If $\sqrt[n]{a}$ and $\sqrt[n]{b}$ are real numbers, then $\sqrt[n]{a} \cdot \sqrt[n]{b} = \sqrt[n]{ab}$.

• A radical expression can be simplified when the exponent of one factor of the radicand is a multiple of the radical's index.

• The product of powers that have the same exponent can be simplified.

• The product of radicals that have the same index can be simplified.

Math Background

The fact that you can simplify a radical expression when the exponent of one factor of the radicand is a multiple of the radical's index is general and may be difficult to understand. Restate it in terms of the square root: You can simplify a square root expression if the exponent of a factor in the radicand is a multiple of 2.

For example, the expression $\sqrt{5^4 \cdot 7}$ has the factor 5^4 in the radicand. Four is a multiple of 2, so the radicand can be simplified:

$$\sqrt{5^4 \cdot 7} = 5^2\sqrt{7} = 25\sqrt{7}.$$

In general, a radical expression is considered simplified if the radicand cannot be reduced.

This lesson focuses on the properties for multiplying and dividing radicals. These properties apply only to real numbers, as shown in the following proof by contradiction:

• Assume the product property holds true for complex numbers.
• Thus $i \cdot i = \sqrt{-1} \cdot \sqrt{-1} = \sqrt{-1 \cdot -1} = \sqrt{1} = 1$.
• However, $i \cdot i = -1$, which is a contradiction.
• The property does not hold true for complex numbers.

Note that absolute value symbols are generally needed when simplifying roots with even-numbered indexes, as shown in Lesson 6-1.

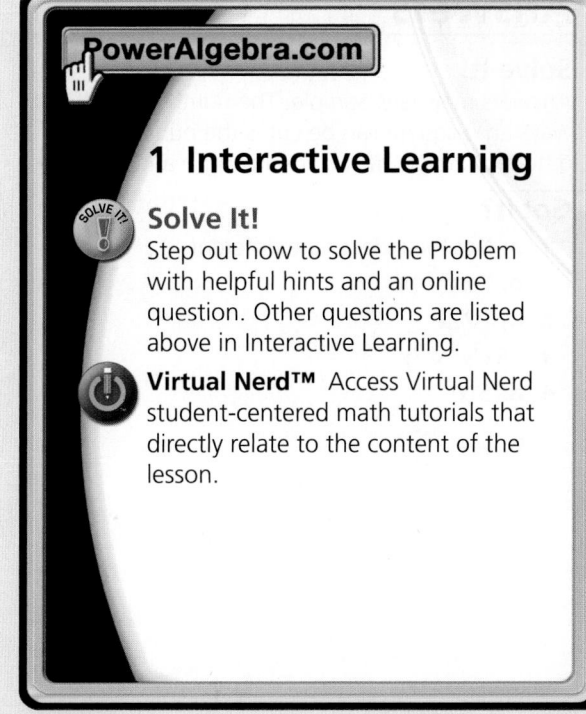

PowerAlgebra.com

1 Interactive Learning

Solve It!
Step out how to solve the Problem with helpful hints and an online question. Other questions are listed above in Interactive Learning.

Virtual Nerd™ Access Virtual Nerd student-centered math tutorials that directly relate to the content of the lesson.

Got It?

Q If the radicands are the same, is that enough to simplify a product using the Combining Radicals: Products property? Explain. **[You can only simplify a product when the indexes are also the same and both radicands are real. Otherwise you cannot use the property for multiplying radicals.]**

Problem 2

Q When can you simplify a cubic radical? **[when the radicand contains perfect cube factors]**

Got It?

Q What will you do first? **[Answers may vary. Sample: Factor the radicand and write it in terms of all the perfect cubes.]**

Problem 3

Q Solve $\sqrt{2x^{12}} \cdot \sqrt{9x^3}$ in the following two ways:
a. Simplify, then multiply.
b. Multiply, then simplify.
What is the solution in each case?
[$3x^7\sqrt{2x}$; both methods give the same answer.]

Got It?   EXTENSION

Q What is the simplest form of $\sqrt[3]{45x^5y^3} \cdot \sqrt[3]{35xy^4}$?
[$x^2y^2\sqrt[3]{1575y}$]

 Got It? **1.** Can you simplify the product of the radical expressions? Explain.
　　　　a. $\sqrt[4]{7} \cdot \sqrt[5]{7}$　　　　　　　　**b.** $\sqrt[5]{-5} \cdot \sqrt[5]{-2}$

If the radicand of $\sqrt[n]{a}$ has a perfect nth power among its factors, you can *reduce* the radical. If you reduce a radical as much as possible, the radical is in **simplest form**. For example, consider $\sqrt{24}$ and $\sqrt[3]{24}$.

$$\sqrt{24} = \sqrt{4 \cdot 6} = \sqrt{2^2 \cdot 6} = \sqrt{2^2} \cdot \sqrt{6} = 2\sqrt{6} \quad 2\sqrt{6} \text{ is in simplest form.}$$

$$\sqrt[3]{24} = \sqrt[3]{8 \cdot 3} = \sqrt[3]{2^3 \cdot 3} = \sqrt[3]{2^3} \cdot \sqrt[3]{3} = 2\sqrt[3]{3} \quad 2\sqrt[3]{3} \text{ is in simplest form.}$$

Ⓒ Problem 2 Simplifying a Radical Expression

What is the simplest form of $\sqrt[3]{54x^5}$?

Think
How do you know when you are done simplifying?
You are done when the radicand contains no perfect cube factors.

$\sqrt[3]{54x^5} = \sqrt[3]{3^3 \cdot 2 \cdot x^2 \cdot x^3}$　　Find all perfect cube factors.

$\quad\quad\quad = \sqrt[3]{3^3 x^3} \cdot \sqrt[3]{2x^2}$　　$\sqrt[n]{ab} = \sqrt[n]{a} \cdot \sqrt[n]{b}$

$\quad\quad\quad = 3x\sqrt[3]{2x^2}$　　Simplify.

 Got It? **2.** What is the simplest form of $\sqrt[3]{128x^7}$?

Problem 2 involves simplifying a cube root, so absolute value symbols are not needed. Remember that to combine $\sqrt[n]{a}$ and $\sqrt[n]{b}$ by multiplication, both radical expressions must be real numbers.

Ⓒ Problem 3 Simplifying a Product

What is the simplest form of $\sqrt{72x^3y^2} \cdot \sqrt{10xy^3}$?

Think
You need to multiply the radicands and find the perfect square factors.

Now find square roots. Since $\sqrt{72x^3y^2}$ and $\sqrt{10xy^3}$ must be real numbers, x and y are nonnegative, so no absolute value symbols are needed.

Write

$\sqrt{72x^3y^2} \cdot \sqrt{10xy^3} = \sqrt{(72x^3y^2)(10xy^3)}$

$\quad\quad\quad\quad = \sqrt{720x^4y^5}$

$\quad\quad\quad\quad = \sqrt{12^2(5)(x^2)^2(y^2)^2y}$

$\quad\quad\quad\quad = \sqrt{12^2(x^2)^2(y^2)^2} \cdot \sqrt{5y}$

$\quad\quad\quad\quad = 12|x^2y^2| \cdot \sqrt{5y}$

$\quad\quad\quad\quad = 12x^2y^2\sqrt{5y}$

The simplest form is $12x^2y^2\sqrt{5y}$.

 Got It? **3.** What is the simplest form of $\sqrt{45x^5y^3} \cdot \sqrt{35xy^4}$?

Answers

Solve It!
Answers may vary. Sample: The number of different ways an n-square can be cut is the number of different divisors of $\sqrt{n}$, excluding 1 and $\sqrt{n}$.

Got It?
1. a. No; the indexes are different.
b. Yes; $\sqrt[5]{10}$
2. $4x^2\sqrt[3]{2x}$
3. $15x^3y^3\sqrt{7y}$
4. a. $5|x|$
b. yes; $\dfrac{3x^2\sqrt{2x}}{x\sqrt{2x}} = 3x$

 PowerAlgebra.com

2 Guided Instruction

Ⓒ Each Problem is worked out and supported online.

Problem 1
Multiplying Radical Expressions

Alternative Problem 1
Multiplying Radical Expressions
Animated

Problem 2
Simplifying a Radical Expression

Problem 3
Simplifying a Product
Animated

Problem 4
Dividing Radical Expressions

Problem 5
Rationalizing the Denominator
Animated

Support in Algebra 2 Companion
• Vocabulary
• Key Concepts
• Got It?

Since you define division in terms of multiplication, you can extend the property for multiplying radical expressions. If the indexes are the same, you can write a quotient of roots as a root of a quotient.

Multiplying	Dividing
$\sqrt{2} \cdot \sqrt{3} = \sqrt{2 \cdot 3}$	$\frac{\sqrt{2}}{\sqrt{3}} = \sqrt{\frac{2}{3}}$
$\sqrt[3]{4} \cdot \sqrt[3]{5} = \sqrt[3]{4 \cdot 5}$	$\frac{\sqrt[3]{4}}{\sqrt[3]{5}} = \sqrt[3]{\frac{4}{5}}$

 take note

Property Combining Radical Expressions: Quotients

If $\sqrt[n]{a}$ and $\sqrt[n]{b}$ are real numbers and $b \neq 0$, then $\frac{\sqrt[n]{a}}{\sqrt[n]{b}} = \sqrt[n]{\frac{a}{b}}$.

 Problem 4 Dividing Radical Expressions

What is the simplest form of the quotient?

Think
Do you need to include absolute value symbols?
No. Both the divisor and dividend already require that x be nonnegative.

 $\dfrac{\sqrt{18x^5}}{\sqrt{2x^3}}$

$\dfrac{\sqrt{18x^5}}{\sqrt{2x^3}} = \sqrt{\dfrac{18x^5}{2x^3}}$

$= \sqrt{9x^2}$

$= 3x$

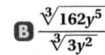 $\dfrac{\sqrt[3]{162y^5}}{\sqrt[3]{3y^2}}$

$\dfrac{\sqrt[3]{162y^5}}{\sqrt[3]{3y^2}} = \sqrt[3]{\dfrac{162y^5}{3y^2}}$

$= \sqrt[3]{54y^3}$

$= \sqrt[3]{27y^3} \cdot \sqrt[3]{2}$

$= \sqrt[3]{3^3 y^3} \cdot \sqrt[3]{2}$

$= 3y\sqrt[3]{2}$

Got It? 4. a. What is the simplest form of $\dfrac{\sqrt{50x^6}}{\sqrt{2x^4}}$?

b. **Reasoning** Can you simplify the expression in Problem 4(a) by first simplifying $\sqrt{18x^5}$ and $\sqrt{2x^3}$? Explain.

Another way to simplify a radical expression is to **rationalize the denominator**. You rewrite the expression so that there are no radicals in any denominator and no denominator in any radical.

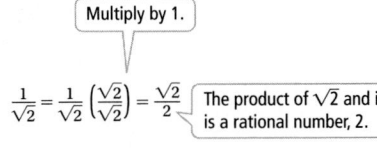

Multiply by 1.

$\dfrac{1}{\sqrt{2}} = \dfrac{1}{\sqrt{2}} \left(\dfrac{\sqrt{2}}{\sqrt{2}} \right) = \dfrac{\sqrt{2}}{2}$ — The product of $\sqrt{2}$ and itself is a rational number, 2.

Additional Problems

1. Can you simplify the product $\sqrt[4]{125} \cdot \sqrt[4]{405}$? Explain.

ANSWER Yes; the indexes are the same. 15

2. What is the simplest form of $\sqrt[3]{135x^5}$?

ANSWER $3x\sqrt[3]{5x^2}$

3. What is the simplest form of $\sqrt{48x^5y^2} \cdot \sqrt{50x^2y^4}$?

ANSWER $20x^3|y^3|\sqrt{6x}$

4. What is the simplest form of $\dfrac{\sqrt[3]{189x^7}}{\sqrt[3]{7x^2}}$?

ANSWER $3x\sqrt[3]{x^2}$

5. What is the simplest form of $\sqrt[3]{\dfrac{4x^4}{32yz^3}}$?

ANSWER $\dfrac{x\sqrt[3]{xy^2}}{2yz}$

Problem 5

> **Q** What is an advantage to writing the numerator and denominator using prime factors? **[You can determine what is needed to get a perfect cube.]**
>
> **Q** In the problem, why can you multiply the numerator and denominator by $\sqrt[3]{2 \cdot 3^2 yz^2}$ without changing the value of the fraction? **[You are multiplying by a factor of 1.]**

Got It?

> **Q** What factor do you multiply the numerator and denominator by to rationalize the denominator? Explain. **[$\sqrt[3]{5^2 y}$; this will make the denominator a perfect cube.]**

3 Lesson Check

Do you know HOW?
- For Exercise 3, have students circle the index on each term as a reminder that indexes must be the same.

Do you UNDERSTAND?
- For Exercise 7, have students factor the radicand using factors that are perfect cubes.
- For Exercise 8, review with students what constitutes a real number.

Close

> **Q** How do you know if your radical expression is simplified? **[The radical expression contains no radicand with a perfect nth power other than 1, there is no radical in the denominator, and there is no denominator in any radical.]**

 **Problem 5** Rationalizing the Denominator

Multiple Choice What is the simplest form of $\sqrt[3]{\dfrac{5x^2}{12y^2z}}$?

Ⓐ $\dfrac{\sqrt[3]{90x^2yz^2}}{6yz}$　　Ⓑ $\dfrac{\sqrt[3]{5x^2}}{\sqrt[3]{12y^2z}}$　　Ⓒ $\dfrac{5\sqrt[3]{x^2yz^2}}{yz}$　　Ⓓ $5\sqrt[3]{x^2z}$

 Think

How do you choose what to multiply by?
Choose a cube root with a radicand that will make each factor of the radicand in the denominator a perfect cube.

$\sqrt[3]{\dfrac{5x^2}{12y^2z}} = \dfrac{\sqrt[3]{5x^2}}{\sqrt[3]{2^2 \cdot 3y^2z}}$ 　　The radicand in the denominator needs 2, 3^2, y, and z^2 to make the factors perfect cubes.

$= \dfrac{\sqrt[3]{5x^2}}{\sqrt[3]{2^2 \cdot 3y^2z}} \cdot \dfrac{\sqrt[3]{2 \cdot 3^2yz^2}}{\sqrt[3]{2 \cdot 3^2yz^2}}$ 　　Multiply the numerator and denominator by $\sqrt[3]{2 \cdot 3^2 yz^2}$.

$= \dfrac{\sqrt[3]{90x^2yz^2}}{\sqrt[3]{2^3 \cdot 3^3y^3z^3}}$

$= \dfrac{\sqrt[3]{90x^2yz^2}}{2 \cdot 3yz}$ 　　Simplify.

$= \dfrac{\sqrt[3]{90x^2yz^2}}{6yz}$

The correct answer is A.

Got It? 5. a. What is the simplest form of $\dfrac{\sqrt[3]{7x}}{\sqrt[3]{5y^2}}$?

b. Reasoning Which choice in Problem 5 could be eliminated immediately? Explain your reasoning.

Lesson Check

Do you know HOW?

Multiply, if possible. Then simplify.

1. $\sqrt{2} \cdot \sqrt{5}$

2. $\sqrt[3]{-27} \cdot \sqrt[3]{4}$

3. $\sqrt[3]{2} \cdot \sqrt[2]{7}$

4. $\sqrt{3} \cdot \sqrt{-4}$

Divide and simplify.

5. $\dfrac{\sqrt[3]{15x^2}}{\sqrt[3]{5x}}$

6. $\dfrac{\sqrt{21x^{10}}}{\sqrt{7x^5}}$

Do you UNDERSTAND?  MATHEMATICAL PRACTICES

7. **Vocabulary** Write the simplest form of $\sqrt[3]{32x^4}$.

8. **Reasoning** For what values of x is $\sqrt{-4x^3}$ real? Justify your reasoning.

9. **Error Analysis** Explain the error in this simplification of radical expressions.

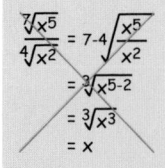

$\dfrac{\sqrt[7]{x^5}}{\sqrt[4]{x^2}} = {}^{7-4}\sqrt{\dfrac{x^5}{x^2}}$

$= \sqrt[3]{x^{5-2}}$

$= \sqrt[3]{x^3}$

$= x$

---

3 Lesson Check

For a digital lesson check, use the Got It questions.

Support in Algebra 2 Companion
- Lesson Check

4 Practice

Assign homework to individual students or to an entire class.

Answers

Got It? (continued)

5. a. $\dfrac{\sqrt[3]{175xy}}{5y}$

b. D; there is no y in the expression.

Lesson Check

1. $\sqrt{10}$

2. $-3\sqrt[3]{4}$

3. Cannot be simplified; the indexes are different.

4. No real solutions; $\sqrt{-4}$ is not a real number.

5. $\sqrt[3]{3x}$

6. $x^2\sqrt{3x}$

7. $2x\sqrt[3]{4x}$

8. $x \leq 0$; for $x \leq 0$, $-4x^3 \geq 0$ and $\sqrt{-4x^3}$ is real.

9. error in line 1: $\dfrac{\sqrt[7]{x^5}}{\sqrt[4]{x^2}} \neq {}^{7-4}\sqrt{\dfrac{x^5}{x^2}}$

Practice and Problem-Solving Exercises  MATHEMATICAL PRACTICES

A Practice

Multiply, if possible. Then simplify. ◀ See Problem 1.

10. $\sqrt{8} \cdot \sqrt{32}$

11. $\sqrt[3]{4} \cdot \sqrt[3]{16}$

12. $\sqrt[3]{9} \cdot \sqrt[3]{-81}$

13. $\sqrt[4]{8} \cdot \sqrt[3]{32}$

14. $\sqrt{-5} \cdot \sqrt{5}$

15. $\sqrt[3]{-5} \cdot \sqrt[3]{-25}$

16. $\sqrt[3]{9} \cdot \sqrt[3]{-24}$

17. $\sqrt[3]{-12} \cdot \sqrt[3]{-18}$

18. $\sqrt{50} \cdot \sqrt{75}$

Simplify. ◀ See Problem 2.

19. $\sqrt{20x^3}$

20. $\sqrt[3]{81x^3}$

21. $\sqrt{50x^5}$

22. $\sqrt[3]{32a^5}$

23. $\sqrt[3]{54y^{10}}$

24. $\sqrt{200a^6b^7}$

25. $\sqrt[3]{-250x^6y^5}$

26. $\sqrt[4]{64x^3y^6}$

27. $\sqrt[5]{-32x^6y^7}$

Multiply and simplify. ◀ See Problem 3.

28. $\sqrt[3]{6} \cdot \sqrt[3]{16}$

29. $\sqrt{8y^5} \cdot \sqrt{40y^2}$

30. $\sqrt{8x^5} \cdot \sqrt{3x}$

31. $4\sqrt{2x} \cdot 5\sqrt{6xy^2}$

32. $3\sqrt[3]{5y^3} \cdot 2\sqrt[3]{50y^4}$

33. $-\sqrt[3]{2x^2y^2} \cdot 2\sqrt[3]{15x^5y}$

34. $\sqrt[4]{81x^5y^4} \cdot \sqrt[4]{32x^3y}$

35. $2\sqrt[3]{2xy^2} \cdot \sqrt[3]{4x^2y^5}$

36. $3\sqrt[4]{18a^9} \cdot \sqrt[4]{6ab^2}$

Divide and simplify. ◀ See Problem 4.

37. $\dfrac{\sqrt{500}}{\sqrt{5}}$

38. $\dfrac{\sqrt{48x^3}}{\sqrt{3xy^2}}$

39. $\dfrac{\sqrt{56x^5y^5}}{\sqrt{7xy}}$

40. $\dfrac{\sqrt[3]{250x^7y^3}}{\sqrt[3]{2x^2y}}$

41. $\dfrac{\sqrt[3]{48x^3y^2}}{\sqrt[3]{6x^4y}}$

42. $\dfrac{\sqrt{20ab}}{\sqrt{45a^2b^3}}$

Rationalize the denominator of each expression. ◀ See Problem 5.

43. $\dfrac{\sqrt{x}}{\sqrt{2}}$

44. $\dfrac{\sqrt{5}}{\sqrt{8x}}$

45. $\dfrac{\sqrt[3]{x}}{\sqrt[3]{2}}$

46. $\sqrt[3]{\dfrac{5}{3x}}$

47. $\dfrac{\sqrt[4]{2}}{\sqrt[4]{5}}$

48. $\dfrac{15\sqrt{60x^5}}{3\sqrt{12x}}$

49. $\dfrac{\sqrt{3xy^2}}{\sqrt{5xy^3}}$

50. $\dfrac{\sqrt{5x^4y}}{\sqrt{2x^2y^3}}$

51. $\dfrac{\sqrt[3]{12ab^3c^2}}{\sqrt[3]{10a^3bc}}$

B Apply

52. **Think About a Plan** The formula $t = \sqrt{\dfrac{2s}{a}}$ shows the time t that any vehicle takes to travel a distance s at a constant acceleration a, starting from rest. What is the difference in time between a car accelerating at 16 m/s^2 and one accelerating at 25 m/s^2 for a distance of 200 m?
   • What is the time that a car accelerating at 16 m/s^2 takes to travel 200 m?
   • What is the time that a car accelerating at 25 m/s^2 takes to travel 200 m?

53. **Geometry** The base of a triangle is $\sqrt{18}$ cm and its height is $\sqrt{8}$ cm. Find its area.

---

4 Practice

ASSIGNMENT GUIDE

Basic: 10–51 all, 52–55, 58–64 even, 71

Average: 11–51 odd, 52–75

Advanced: 11–51 odd, 52–79

Standardized Test Prep: 80–84

Mixed Review: 85–98

© **Mathematical Practices** are supported by exercises with red headings. Here are the Practices supported in this lesson:

MP 1: Make Sense of Problems Ex. 52
MP 2: Reason Abstractly Ex. 79
MP 3: Communicate Ex. 70
MP 3: Construct Arguments Ex. 8
MP 3: Compare Arguments Ex. 71
MP 3: Critique the Reasoning of Others Ex. 9, 72

Applications exercises have blue headings. Exercise 55 supports MP 4: Model.

STEM exercises focus on science or engineering applications.

EXERCISE 55: Use the Think About a Plan worksheet in the **Practice and Problem Solving Workbook** (also available in the Teaching Resources in print and online) to further support students' development in becoming independent learners.

HOMEWORK QUICK CHECK

To check students' understanding of key skills and concepts, go over Exercises 31, 49, 52, 55, and 71.

Practice and Problem-Solving Exercises

10. 16

11. 4

12. -9

13. not possible

14. $5i$

15. 5

16. -6

17. 6

18. $25\sqrt{6}$

19. $2x\sqrt{5x}$

20. $3x\sqrt[3]{3}$

21. $5x^2\sqrt{2x}$

22. $2a\sqrt[3]{4a^2}$

23. $3y^3\sqrt[3]{2y}$

24. $10|a^3|b^3\sqrt{2b}$

25. $-5x^2y\sqrt[3]{2y^2}$

26. $2|y|\sqrt[4]{4x^3y^2}$

27. $-2xy\sqrt[5]{xy^2}$

28. $2\sqrt[3]{12}$

29. $8y^3\sqrt{5y}$

30. $2x^3\sqrt{6}$

31. $40x|y|\sqrt{3}$

32. $30y^2\sqrt[3]{2y}$

33. $-2x^2y\sqrt[3]{30x}$

34. $6x^2y\sqrt[4]{2y}$

35. $4xy^2\sqrt[3]{y}$

36. $3a^2\sqrt[4]{108a^2b^2}$

37. 10

38. $\dfrac{4\sqrt{x^3}}{|y|\sqrt{x}}$

39. $2x^2y^2\sqrt{2}$

40. $5x\sqrt[3]{x^2y^2}$

41. $\dfrac{2\sqrt[3]{x^2y}}{x}$

42. $\dfrac{2\sqrt{a}}{3ab}$

43. $\dfrac{\sqrt{2x}}{2}$

44. $\dfrac{\sqrt{10x}}{4x}$

45. $\dfrac{\sqrt[3]{4x}}{2}$

46. $\dfrac{\sqrt[3]{45x^2}}{3x}$

47. $\dfrac{\sqrt[4]{250}}{5}$

48. $5x^2\sqrt{5}$

49. $\dfrac{\sqrt{15y}}{5y}$

50. $\dfrac{|x|\sqrt{10}}{2|y|}$

51. $\dfrac{\sqrt[3]{150ab^2c}}{5a}$

52. 1 s

53. 6 cm^2

Answers

Practice and Problem-Solving Exercises
(continued)

54. $v = \dfrac{\sqrt{Fmr}}{m}$

55. about 212 mi/h

56. a. $\dfrac{\sqrt{6}+3}{15}$

b. $\dfrac{\sqrt{6}+3}{15}$

c. Answers may vary. Sample: first simplify the denominator. Since $\sqrt{98} = \sqrt{2(49)} = 7\sqrt{2}$, to rationalize the denominator, multiply the fraction by $\dfrac{\sqrt{2}}{\sqrt{2}}$. This yields $\dfrac{\sqrt{2(2)}+\sqrt{3(2)}}{7\sqrt{2(2)}} = \dfrac{2+\sqrt{6}}{14}$.

57. $5\sqrt{10}$

58. $4\sqrt[3]{5}$

59. $3x^6y^5\sqrt{2y}$

60. $20x^2y^3\sqrt{y}$

61. $10 + 7\sqrt{2}$

62. $5 + 5\sqrt{3}$

63. $\dfrac{|x|\sqrt{10y}}{2y^2}$

64. $\dfrac{5\sqrt{14x}}{21x}$

65. $\dfrac{\sqrt[3]{3x^2}}{3x}$

66. $\dfrac{2\sqrt[3]{25x}}{x}$

67. $\dfrac{\sqrt[3]{2xy^2}}{xy}$

68. $\dfrac{\sqrt{33x}}{-4x}$

69. 4 g/cm^3

70. For some values; it is easy to see that the equation is true if $x = 0$ or $x = 1$, but when $x < 0$, $\sqrt{x^3}$ is not a real number and $\sqrt[3]{x^2}$ is.

71. Check students' work.

72. A product of two square roots can be simplified in this way only if the square roots are real numbers. $\sqrt{-2}$ and $\sqrt{-8}$ are not real numbers.

73. always

74. sometimes

75. sometimes

76. $2xy$

77. $2\sqrt{5}$

78. $\dfrac{\sqrt[6]{x^4y^3}}{y}$

79. $a = -2c$, $b = -6d$

STEM 54. Physics The formula $F = \dfrac{mv^2}{r}$ gives the centripetal force F of an object of mass m moving along a circle of radius r, where v is the tangential velocity of the object. Solve the formula for v. Rationalize the denominator.

STEM 55. Satellites The circular velocity v in miles per hour of a satellite orbiting Earth is given by the formula $v = \sqrt{\dfrac{1.24 \times 10^{12}}{r}}$, where r is the distance in miles from the satellite to the center of Earth. How much greater is the velocity of a satellite orbiting at an altitude of 100 mi than the velocity of a satellite orbiting at an altitude of 200 mi? (The radius of Earth is 3950 mi.)

56. a. Simplify $\dfrac{\sqrt{2}+\sqrt{3}}{\sqrt{45}}$ by multiplying the numerator and denominator by $\sqrt{75}$.

b. Simplify the expression in (a) by multiplying by $\sqrt{3}$ instead of $\sqrt{75}$.

c. Explain how you would simplify $\dfrac{\sqrt{2}+\sqrt{3}}{\sqrt{98}}$.

Simplify each expression. Rationalize all denominators.

57. $\sqrt{5} \cdot \sqrt{50}$

58. $\sqrt[3]{4} \cdot \sqrt[3]{80}$

59. $\sqrt{x^5y^5} \cdot 3\sqrt{2x^7y^6}$

60. $5\sqrt{2xy^6} \cdot 2\sqrt{2x^3y}$

61. $\sqrt{2}(\sqrt{50} + 7)$

62. $\sqrt{5}(\sqrt{5} + \sqrt{15})$

63. $\dfrac{\sqrt{5x^4}}{\sqrt{2x^2y^3}}$

64. $\dfrac{5\sqrt{2}}{3\sqrt{7x}}$

65. $\dfrac{1}{\sqrt[3]{9x}}$

66. $\dfrac{10}{\sqrt[3]{5x^2}}$

67. $\dfrac{\sqrt[3]{14}}{\sqrt[3]{7x^2y}}$

68. $\dfrac{3\sqrt{11x^3y}}{-2\sqrt{12x^4y}}$

STEM 69. Physics The mass m of an object is $\sqrt{80}$ g and its volume V is $\sqrt{5}$ cm^3. Use the formula $D = \dfrac{m}{V}$ to find the density D of the object.

70. Writing Does $\sqrt{x^3} = \sqrt[3]{x^2}$ for *all*, *some*, or *no* values of x? Explain.

71. Open-Ended Of the equivalent expressions $\sqrt{\dfrac{2}{3}}$, $\dfrac{\sqrt{2}}{\sqrt{3}}$, and $\dfrac{\sqrt{6}}{3}$, which do you prefer to use for finding a decimal approximation with a calculator? Justify your reasoning.

72. Error Analysis Explain the error in this simplification of radical expressions.

$$\sqrt{-2} \cdot \sqrt{-8} = \sqrt{-2(-8)} = \sqrt{16} = 4$$

Determine whether each expression is *always*, *sometimes*, or *never* a real number. Assume that x can be any real number.

73. $\sqrt[3]{-x^2}$

74. $\sqrt{-x^2}$

75. $\sqrt{-x}$

Challenge

Simplify each expression. Rationalize all denominators.

76. $\sqrt{\sqrt{16x^4y^4}}$

77. $\sqrt{\sqrt[3]{8000}}$

78. $\sqrt[6]{\dfrac{y^{-3}}{x^{-4}}}$

79. Reasoning When $\sqrt{x^ay^b}$ is simplified, the result is $\dfrac{1}{x^cy^{3d}}$, where c and d are positive integers. Express a in terms of c, and b in terms of d.

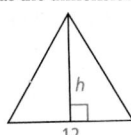

Standardized Test Prep

SAT/ACT

80. What is the simplified form of the expression $\frac{3}{\sqrt{18xy^2}}$ if x and y are positive?

Ⓐ $\frac{\sqrt{2x}}{2xy}$　　　Ⓑ $\frac{\sqrt{2y}}{2xy}$　　　Ⓒ $\frac{\sqrt{54xy^2}}{2xy}$　　　Ⓓ $\frac{\sqrt{27xy^2}}{2xy}$

81. What are the solutions, in simplest form, of the quadratic equation $3x^2 + 6x - 5 = 0$?

Ⓕ $\frac{-6 \pm \sqrt{96}}{6}$　　Ⓖ $\frac{-6 \pm i\sqrt{24}}{6}$　　Ⓗ $\frac{-3 \pm 2\sqrt{6}}{3}$　　Ⓘ $\frac{-3 \pm i\sqrt{6}}{3}$

82. Which inequality is shown by the graph at the right?

Ⓐ $y \geq \frac{2}{3}|x - 1| - 2$

Ⓒ $y \geq \frac{3}{2}|x - 1| - 2$

Ⓑ $y \geq \frac{2}{3}|x - 2| - 1$

Ⓓ $y \geq \left|\frac{2}{3}x - 1\right| - 2$

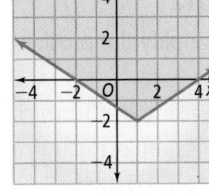

83. A triangle has the dimensions shown below.

What is the height of a triangle with equal area but a base of 36?

Ⓕ $\frac{h}{3}$　　　　Ⓖ $\frac{2h}{3}$　　　　Ⓗ $2h$　　　　Ⓘ $3h$

Short Response

84. Find the axis of symmetry of the graph of the function $y = -2x^2 - 5x + 4$. Show your work.

Mixed Review

Simplify each radical expression. Use absolute value symbols when needed.　　◆ **See Lesson 6-1.**

85. $\sqrt{121a^{90}}$　　　**86.** $\sqrt{81c^{48}d^{64}}$　　　**87.** $\sqrt[3]{64a^{81}}$　　　**88.** $\sqrt[5]{32y^{25}}$

Divide using synthetic division.　　◆ **See Lesson 5-4.**

89. $(y^3 - 64) \div (y + 4)$　　　　　**90.** $(6a^3 + a^2 - a + 4) \div (a + 1)$

Complete each square.　　◆ **See Lesson 4-6.**

91. $x^2 + 10x + \blacksquare$　　**92.** $x^2 - 10x + \blacksquare$　　**93.** $x^2 + 11x + \blacksquare$　　**94.** $x^2 - 11x + \blacksquare$

Get Ready! To prepare for Lesson 6-3, do Exercises 95–98.

Write each quotient as a complex number in the form $a \pm bi$.　　◆ **See Lesson 4-8.**

95. $\frac{2}{3 - i}$　　　**96.** $\frac{5}{2 + 3i}$　　　**97.** $\frac{4}{4 + i}$　　　**98.** $\frac{-1}{7 - 5i}$

Standardized Test Prep

80. A

81. H

82. A

83. F

84. [2] $x = \frac{-b}{2a} = \frac{-5}{4}$

[1] correct answer, but without work shown

Mixed Review

85. $11|a^{45}|$

86. $9c^{24}d^{32}$

87. $4a^{27}$

88. $2y^5$

89. $y^2 - 4y + 16$, R -128

90. $6a^2 - 5a + 4$

91. 25

92. 25

93. $\frac{121}{4}$

94. $\frac{121}{4}$

95. $\frac{3}{5} + \frac{1}{5}i$

96. $\frac{10}{13} - \frac{15}{13}i$

97. $\frac{16}{17} - \frac{4}{17}i$

98. $\frac{-7}{74} - \frac{5}{74}i$

Lesson Resources

Differentiated Remediation

Additional Instructional Support

Algebra 2 Companion

Students can use the **Algebra 2 Companion** worktext (4 pages) as you teach the lesson. Use the Companion to support
- New Vocabulary
- Key Concepts
- Got It for each Problem
- Lesson Check

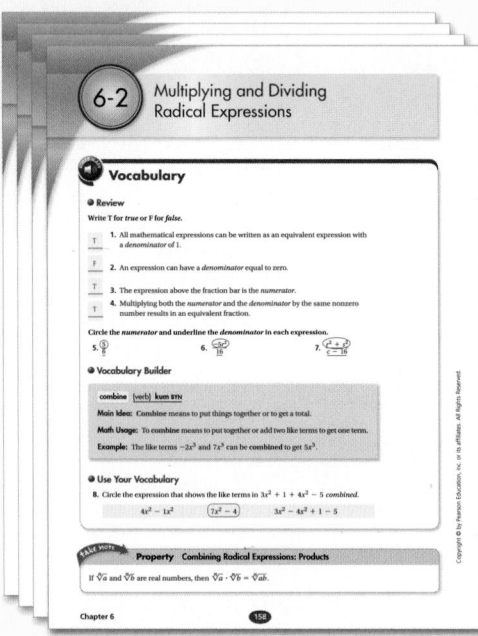

ELL Support

Focus on Language Write the following radical expression on the board: $\frac{\sqrt[3]{12x}}{\sqrt[3]{4y}}$.

Have volunteers come up and label each of the following as you call them out:
- radicals
- radicands
- indexes
- numerator
- denominator
- variables

Practice using the vocabulary. Ask, "When can you use the properties for multiplying and dividing *radicals*?" [When the *indexes* are the same and the *radicals* are real.]

5 Assess & Remediate

Lesson Quiz

1. Can you simplify the product $\sqrt[4]{64} \cdot \sqrt[4]{32}$? Explain.

2. What is the simplest form of $\sqrt[4]{162x^6}$?

3. What is the simplest form of $\sqrt{54x^4y^3} \cdot \sqrt{72xy^6}$?

4. What is the simplest form of $\frac{\sqrt{64x^7}}{\sqrt{4x^3}}$?

5. Do you UNDERSTAND? What is the simplest form of $\sqrt[3]{\frac{7x^2}{15yz^2}}$?

ANSWERS TO LESSON QUIZ

1. Yes, the indexes are the same. $4\sqrt[4]{8}$

2. $3|x| \sqrt[4]{2x^2}$

3. $36x^2y^4 \sqrt{3xy}$

4. $4x^2$

5. $\frac{\sqrt[3]{1575x^2y^2z}}{15yz}$

PRESCRIPTION FOR REMEDIATION

Use the student work on the Lesson Quiz to prescribe a differentiated review assignment:

Points	Differentiated Remediation
0–2	Intervention
3–4	On-level
5	Extension

PowerAlgebra.com

5 Assess & Remediate

Assign the Lesson Quiz. Appropriate intervention, practice, or enrichment is automatically generated based on student performance.

Intervention

- **Reteaching** (2 pages) Provides reteaching and practice exercises for the key lesson concepts. Use with struggling students or absent students.

- **English Language Learner Support** Helps students develop and reinforce mathematical vocabulary and key concepts.

All-in-One Resources/Online
Reteaching

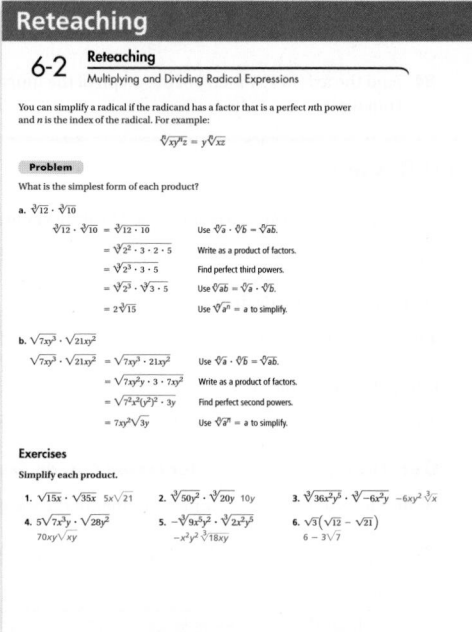

All-in-One Resources/Online
English Language Learner Support

Differentiated Remediation *continued*

On-Level

- **Practice** (2 pages) Provides extra practice for each lesson. For simpler practice exercises, use the Form K Practice pages found in the All-in-One Teaching Resources and online.
- **Think About a Plan** Helps students develop specific problem-solving skills and strategies by providing scaffolded guiding questions.
- **Standardized Test Prep** Focuses on all major exercises, all major question types, and helps students prepare for the high-stakes assessments.

Extension

- **Enrichment** Provides students with interesting problems and activities that extend the concepts of the lesson.
- **Activities, Games, and Puzzles** Worksheets that can be used for concepts development, enrichment, and for fun!

Practice and Problem Solving Wkbk/ All-in-One Resources/Online

Practice page 1

6-2 **Practice** *Form G*

Multiplying and Dividing Radical Expressions

Multiply, if possible. Then simplify.

1. $\sqrt{4}\cdot\sqrt{25}$ 10
2. $\sqrt{81}\cdot\sqrt{36}$ 54
3. $\sqrt{3}\cdot\sqrt[3]{27}$ 9
4. $\sqrt[3]{45}\cdot\sqrt[3]{75}$ 15
5. $\sqrt{18}\cdot\sqrt{50}$ 30
6. $\sqrt[3]{-16}\cdot\sqrt[3]{4}$ −4

Simplify. Assume that all variables are positive.

7. $\sqrt{36x^3}$ $6x\sqrt{x}$
8. $\sqrt[3]{125y^2z^4}$ $5z\sqrt[3]{y^2z}$
9. $\sqrt{18k^6}$ $3k^3\sqrt{2}$
10. $\sqrt[3]{-16a^{12}}$ $-2a^4\sqrt[3]{2}$
11. $\sqrt{x^2y^{10}z}$ $xy^5\sqrt{z}$
12. $\sqrt[4]{256s^7t^{12}}$ $4st^3\sqrt[4]{s^3}$
13. $\sqrt[3]{216x^4y^3}$ $6xy\sqrt[3]{x}$
14. $\sqrt{75r^3}$ $5r\sqrt{3r}$
15. $\sqrt[4]{625u^5v^8}$ $5uv^2\sqrt[4]{u}$

Multiply and simplify. Assume that all variables are positive.

16. $\sqrt{4}\cdot\sqrt{6}$ $2\sqrt{6}$
17. $\sqrt{9x^2}\cdot\sqrt{9y^5}$ $9xy^2\sqrt{y}$
18. $\sqrt[3]{50x^2z^5}\cdot\sqrt[3]{15y^3z}$ $5yz^2\sqrt[3]{6x^2}$
19. $4\sqrt{2x}\cdot 3\sqrt{8x}$ $48x$
20. $\sqrt{xy}\cdot\sqrt{4xy}$ $2xy$
21. $9\sqrt{2}\cdot 3\sqrt{y}$ $27\sqrt{2y}$
22. $\sqrt{12x^2y}\cdot\sqrt{3xy^4}$ $6xy^2\sqrt{xy}$
23. $\sqrt[3]{-9x^2y^4}\cdot\sqrt[3]{12xy}$ $-3xy\sqrt[3]{4y^2}$
24. $7\sqrt{3y^2}\cdot 2\sqrt{6x^3y}$ $42xy\sqrt{2xy}$

Divide and simplify. Assume that all variables are positive.

25. $\frac{\sqrt{75}}{\sqrt{3}}$ 5
26. $\frac{\sqrt{63xy^3}}{\sqrt{7y}}$ $3y\sqrt{x}$
27. $\frac{\sqrt{54x^5y^3}}{\sqrt{2x^2y}}$ $3xy\sqrt{3x}$
28. $\frac{\sqrt{6x}}{\sqrt{3x}}$ $\sqrt{2}$
29. $\frac{\sqrt[3]{4x^2}}{\sqrt[3]{x}}$ $\sqrt[3]{4x}$
30. $\sqrt[4]{\frac{243k^3}{3k^7}}$ $\frac{3}{k}$
31. $\frac{\sqrt{(2x)^2}}{\sqrt{(5y)^4}}$ $\frac{2x}{25y^2}$
32. $\frac{\sqrt[3]{18y^2}}{\sqrt[3]{12y}}$ $\frac{\sqrt[3]{12y}}{2}$
33. $\sqrt{\frac{162a}{6a^3}}$ $\frac{3\sqrt{3}}{a}$

Practice and Problem Solving Wkbk/ All-in-One Resources/Online

Practice page 2

6-2 **Practice** (continued) *Form G*

Multiplying and Dividing Radical Expressions

Rationalize the denominator of each expression. Assume that all variables are positive.

34. $\frac{\sqrt{y}}{\sqrt{5}}$ $\frac{\sqrt{5y}}{5}$
35. $\frac{\sqrt{18x^2y}}{\sqrt{2y^3}}$ $\frac{3x}{y}$
36. $\frac{\sqrt[3]{7xy^2}}{\sqrt[3]{4x^2}}$ $\frac{\sqrt[3]{14x^2y^2}}{2x}$
37. $\sqrt{\frac{9x}{2}}$ $\frac{3\sqrt{2x}}{2}$
38. $\frac{\sqrt{xy}}{\sqrt{3x}}$ $\frac{\sqrt{3y}}{3}$
39. $\sqrt[3]{\frac{x^2}{3y}}$ $\frac{\sqrt[3]{9x^2y^2}}{3y}$
40. $\frac{\sqrt[4]{2x}}{\sqrt[4]{3x^2}}$ $\frac{\sqrt[4]{54x^3}}{3x}$
41. $\sqrt{\frac{x}{8y}}$ $\frac{\sqrt{2xy}}{4y}$
42. $\sqrt[3]{\frac{3a}{4b^2c}}$ $\frac{\sqrt[3]{6abc^2}}{2bc}$
43. What is the area of a rectangle with length $\sqrt{175}$ in. and width $\sqrt{63}$ in.? 105 in.^{2}
44. The area of a rectangle is 30 m^2. If the length is $\sqrt{75}$ m, what is the width? $2\sqrt{3}$ m
45. The volume of a right circular cone is $V=\frac{1}{3}\pi r^2h$, where r is the radius of the base and h is the height of the cone. Solve the formula for r. Rationalize the denominator. $r=\frac{\sqrt{3\pi hV}}{\pi h}$
46. The volume of a sphere of radius r is $V=\frac{4}{3}\pi r^3$.
    a. Use the formula to find r in terms of V. Rationalize the denominator. $r=\sqrt[3]{\frac{3V}{4\pi}}$; $r=\frac{\sqrt[3]{6\pi^2V}}{2\pi}$
    b. Use your answer to part (a) to find the radius of a sphere with volume 100 cubic inches. Round to the nearest hundredth. 2.88 in.

Simplify each expression. Rationalize all denominators. Assume that all variables are positive.

47. $\sqrt{14}\cdot\sqrt{21}$ $7\sqrt{6}$
48. $\sqrt[3]{150}\cdot\sqrt[3]{20}$ $10\sqrt[3]{3}$
49. $\sqrt{3}(\sqrt{12}-\sqrt{6})$ $6-3\sqrt{2}$
50. $\frac{6\sqrt{2x}}{5\sqrt{3}}$ $\frac{2\sqrt{6x}}{5}$
51. $\frac{8}{\sqrt[3]{2x^2}}$ $\frac{4\sqrt[3]{4x}}{x}$
52. $\frac{5\sqrt[3]{xy^4}}{\sqrt[3]{25xy^2}}$ $\sqrt[3]{5y^2}$

All-in-One Resources/Online

Enrichment

6-2 **Enrichment**

Multiplying and Dividing Radical Expressions

To simplify the radical $\sqrt[n]{a}$, you look for a perfect nth power among the factors of the radicand a. When this factor is not obvious, it is helpful to factor the number into primes. Prime numbers are important in many aspects of mathematics. Several mathematicians throughout history have unsuccessfully tried to find a pattern that would generate the nth prime number. Other mathematicians have offered conjectures about primes that remain unresolved.

1. Goldbach's Conjecture states that every even number $n>2$ can be written as the sum of two primes. For example, $4=2+2$ and $10=3+7$. Choose three even numbers larger than 50 and write them as a sum of two primes.
   Answers may vary. Sample: $52=47+5$.
2. The Odd Goldbach's Conjecture states that every odd number $n>5$ can be written as the sum of three primes. For example, $7=2+2+3$. Choose three odd numbers larger than 50 and write them as the sum of three primes.
   Answers may vary. Sample: $51=37+11+3$.
3. Another interesting pattern emerges when you examine a subset of the prime numbers. Make a list of the primes less than 50.
   2, 3, 5, 7, 11, 13, 17, 19, 23, 29, 31, 37, 41, 43, 47
4. Make this list smaller by eliminating 2 and all primes that are 1 less than a multiple of 4.
   5, 13, 17, 29, 37, 41
5. The remaining primes in the list above are related in an interesting way. You can write each prime as the sum of two squares. Express each of these primes as a sum of two squares.
   $5=1+4$, $13=4+9$, $17=1+16$, $29=4+25$, $37=1+36$, $41=16+25$
6. A Cullen number, named after an Irish mathematician James Cullen, is a natural number of the form $n\times 2^n+1$. Determine the first four Cullen numbers. That is, let $n=1, 2, 3, 4$.
   3, 9, 25, 65
7. What is the smallest Cullen number that is a prime number? (The next Cullen number that is a prime occurs when $n=141$!)
   3 when $n=1$
8. A palindrome is a number that reads the same forward and backward. For example, 121 is a palindromic number. List the seven palindromic primes that are less than 140.
   2, 3, 5, 7, 11, 101, 131

Practice and Problem Solving Wkbk/ All-in-One Resources/Online

Think About a Plan

6-2 **Think About a Plan**

Multiplying and Dividing Radical Expressions

Satellites The circular velocity v, in miles per hour of a satellite orbiting Earth is given by the formula $v=\sqrt{\frac{1.24\times 10^{12}}{r}}$, where r is the distance in miles from the satellite to the center of the Earth. How much greater is the velocity of a satellite orbiting at an altitude of 100 mi than the velocity of a satellite orbiting at an altitude of 200 mi? (The radius of the Earth is 3950 mi.)

Know

1. The first satellite orbits at an altitude of 100 mi.
2. The second satellite orbits at an altitude of 200 mi.
3. The distance from the surface of the Earth to its center is 3950 mi.

Need

4. To solve the problem I need to find:
   the difference in the velocities of a satellite orbiting at an altitude of 100 mi and one orbiting at an altitude of 200 mi.

Plan

5. Rewrite the formula for the circular velocity of a satellite using a for the altitude of the satellite. $v=\sqrt{\frac{1.24\times 10^{12}}{a+3950}}$
6. Use your formula to find the velocity of a satellite orbiting at an altitude of 100 mi.
   about 17,498 mi/h
7. Use your formula to find the velocity of a satellite orbiting at an altitude of 200 mi.
   about 17,286 mi/h
8. How much greater is the velocity of a satellite orbiting at an altitude of 100 mi than one orbiting at an altitude of 200 mi? about 212 mi/h

Practice and Problem Solving Wkbk/ All-in-One Resources/Online

Standardized Test Prep

6-2 **Standardized Test Prep**

Multiplying and Dividing Radical Expressions

Multiple Choice

For Exercises 1–5, choose the correct letter. Assume that all variables are positive.

1. What is the simplest form of $\sqrt[3]{-49x}\cdot\sqrt[3]{7x^2}$? B
   (A) $7x\sqrt{7x}$ (B) $-7x$ (C) $7x$ (D) $-7\sqrt[3]{x^2}$
2. What is the simplest form of $\sqrt{80x^7y^6}$? I
   (F) $2x^3y^3\sqrt{20x}$ (G) $4x^6y^6\sqrt{5x^3}$ (H) $4\sqrt{5x^7y^6}$ (I) $4x^3y^3\sqrt{5x}$
3. What is the simplest form of $\sqrt[3]{25xy^2}\cdot\sqrt[3]{15x^2}$? A
   (A) $5x\sqrt[3]{3y^2}$ (B) $5x\sqrt[3]{3y}$ (C) $15xy\sqrt[3]{y}$ (D) $5xy\sqrt{15x}$
4. What is the simplest form of $\frac{\sqrt{75x^5}}{\sqrt{12xy^2}}$? G
   (F) $\frac{5\sqrt{3x^4}}{2\sqrt{3y^2}}$ (G) $\frac{5x^2}{2y}$ (H) $\frac{5x\sqrt{x}}{2y}$ (I) $\frac{5x^2y}{2}$
5. What is the simplest form of $\frac{2\sqrt[3]{x^2y}}{\sqrt[3]{4xy^2}}$? C
   (A) $\frac{\sqrt[3]{x^2y}}{2y}$ (B) $\frac{x\sqrt[3]{2y}}{y}$ (C) $\frac{\sqrt[3]{2xy^2}}{y}$ (D) $\frac{\sqrt[3]{2y}}{xy}$

Short Response

6. The volume V of a wooden beam is $V=ls^2$, where l is the length of the beam and s is the length of one side of its square cross section. If the volume of the beam is 1200 in.^{3} and its length is 96 in., what is the side length? Show your work.
   [2] $V=ls^2$; $s=\sqrt{\frac{V}{l}}=\sqrt{\frac{1200}{96}}=\sqrt{12.5}\approx 3.5$ in.
   [1] appropriate methods but with computational errors OR correct answer without work shown
   [0] incorrect answer and no work shown OR no answer given

Online Teacher Resource Center

Activities, Games, and Puzzles

6-2 **Puzzle: What's Underneath?**

Multiplying and Dividing Radical Expressions

Simplify each expression. The simplified expression directs you to a cell in the decoding grid. The exponent for the y-variable gives the row and the exponent for the z-variable gives the column. For example, the answer to Exercise 1 directs you to the intersection of the fifth row and fifth column where the letter I is located.

In the space below each expression, record its simplified form and its corresponding letter.

Enter the letters in the appropriate spaces at the bottom of the page. Some of the letters are already given.

A	B	C	D	E	F	G
H	I	J	K	L	M	N
O	P	Q	R	S	T	U
V	W	X	A	B	C	D
E	F	G	H	I	J	K
L	M	N	O	P	Q	R
S	T	U	V	W	X	A

1. $\sqrt[4]{z^4y^{20}}\sqrt{z^8}$ y^5z^5; I
2. $\sqrt[4]{z^4y^{28}}\sqrt{z^0}$ y^7z; S
3. $\sqrt[4]{y^{24}}\sqrt{z^2}$ y^6z; L
4. $\sqrt[7]{y^7}\sqrt[4]{y^{12}z^{16}}$ y^4z^4; A
5. $\sqrt[3]{y^9z^9}\sqrt[4]{y^{12}z^{16}}$ y^6z^7; R
6. $\sqrt[4]{z^4y^4}\sqrt{z^8}$ yz^5; E
7. $\sqrt[9]{y^9}\sqrt[3]{z^{15}}$ yz^5; E
8. $\sqrt[3]{y^{21}z^3}\sqrt[5]{z^5}$ y^7z^2; T
9. $\sqrt{y^8}\sqrt{z^6}\sqrt{y^6}$ y^7z^3; U
10. $\sqrt{z^2}\sqrt[3]{y^3}$ yz; A
11. $\sqrt[8]{z^{16}y^8}\sqrt{z^6}$ yz^5; E
12. $\sqrt[5]{y^{35}}\sqrt[4]{z^4}$ y^7z; S
13. $\sqrt[5]{y^5}\sqrt[3]{z^3y^{12}}\sqrt{y^4}$ y^7z; S
14. $\sqrt[7]{z^{21}y^{49}}$ y^7z^3; U
15. $\sqrt[5]{y^5}\sqrt[7]{z^7}$ yz; A
16. $\sqrt[4]{y^{20}}\sqrt{z^2}$ y^5z; E
17. $\sqrt[3]{z^{12}y^6}\sqrt{y^2}$ y^3z^4; R
18. $\sqrt[5]{z^{10}y^{20}}\sqrt{y^4z^4}$ y^6z^4; O

Question: WHAT I S BE L OW A T R E E WI T H SQ U A RE LEAV E S ? (1 2, 3, 4, 5 6 7, 8, 9 10, 11 12)

Answer: S Q U A R E R O O T S (13, 14 15, 16 17 18)

1 Interactive Learning

Solve It!

PURPOSE To find areas and perimeters of triangles to introduce a common use of radical expressions

PROCESS Students may
- sketch the triangles to scale and continue the pattern, calculating area and perimeter.
- know that an isosceles right triangle has a base angle of 45 degrees, so 8 triangles encircle *O*.
- find a pattern of hypotenuse lengths and areas of each triangle and use it to find the area of the entire figure.

FACILITATE

Q Is there a pattern for the hypotenuse of an isosceles right triangle with side *s*? **[Yes; the length of the hypotenuse is $s\sqrt{2}$.]**

Q How can you calculate the perimeter of the figure? **[Sketch the figure and add the lengths of the segments on the figure's exterior.]**

ANSWER See Solve It in Answers on next page.
CONNECT THE MATH The Solve It is solved using formulas for area and perimeter. In the lesson students add and subtract radical expressions, simplifying before adding or subtracting.

2 Guided Instruction

Take Note

Combining like terms is similar to combining like radicals. For example, $2x^3 + 3x^3 = 5x^3$ is analogous to $2\sqrt[3]{x} + 3\sqrt[3]{x} = 5\sqrt[3]{x}$.

6-3 Binomial Radical Expressions

Common Core State Standards
A-SSE.A.2 Use the structure of an expression to identify ways to rewrite it.
MP 1, MP 2, MP 3, MP 4

Objective To add and subtract radical expressions

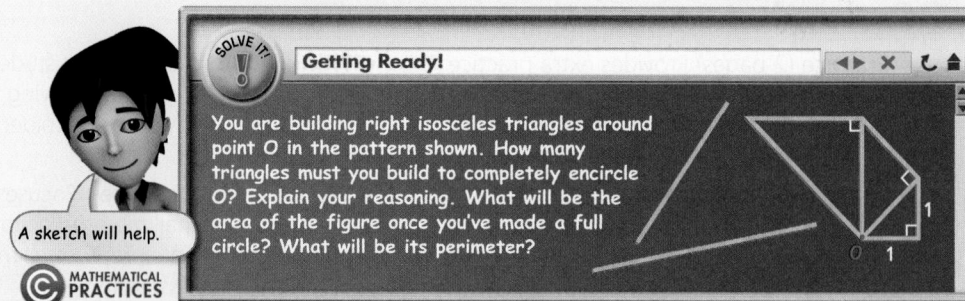

A sketch will help.

MATHEMATICAL PRACTICES

Lesson Vocabulary
- like radicals

Like radicals are radical expressions that have the same index and radicand.

Essential Understanding You can combine like radicals using properties of real numbers.

Here is how you can combine like radicals using the Distributive Property.

Like Radicals With Numbers	Like Radicals With Variables
$\sqrt{2} + 3\sqrt{2} = 4\sqrt{2}$	$\sqrt{5xy} + 8\sqrt{5xy} = 9\sqrt{5xy}$
$\sqrt[3]{7} - 5\sqrt[3]{7} = -4\sqrt[3]{7}$	$\sqrt[3]{9x^2y} - 8\sqrt[3]{9x^2y} = -7\sqrt[3]{9x^2y}$

take note

Property   Combining Radical Expressions: Sums and Differences

Use the Distributive Property to add or subtract like radicals.

$$a\sqrt[n]{x} + b\sqrt[n]{x} = (a + b)\sqrt[n]{x} \qquad a\sqrt[n]{x} - b\sqrt[n]{x} = (a - b)\sqrt[n]{x}$$

Combining radical expressions is different from *adding* them. The sum of any two real numbers is a real number, so you can add $\sqrt{2}$ and $\sqrt{3}$ to get the real number $\sqrt{2} + \sqrt{3}$. However, you cannot *combine* the result into a single radical, so $\sqrt{2} + \sqrt{3} \neq \sqrt{5}$.

$$\begin{array}{ll} \sqrt{2} \approx 1.414 & \sqrt{5} \approx 2.236 \\ + \sqrt{3} \approx 1.732 & \\ \hline \sqrt{2} + \sqrt{3} \approx 3.146 & \neq 2.236 \end{array}$$

6-3 Preparing to Teach

BIG idea   Equivalence

ESSENTIAL UNDERSTANDING
- Like radicals can be combined using properties of real numbers.

Math Background

Identifying and combining like radicals is similar to the Algebra 1 skill of identifying and combining like terms in polynomials. The lesson then uses combining like radicals as a springboard for several advanced skills with multiple-term radical expressions. All have connections to prior math content:
- Simplifying before combining like radicals connects to reducing radicals from Lesson 6-2.
- Multiplying binomial radical expressions relates to multiplying polynomials with the FOIL method from Algebra 1, multiplying radical expressions from Lesson 6-2, and multiplying complex numbers from Lesson 4-8.
- Writing and multiplying conjugates connects to differences of two squares from Algebra 1 and complex numbers from Lesson 4-8.

- Rationalizing two-term denominators is an extension of rationalizing single-term denominators from Lesson 6-2 and connects to rationalizing complex denominators in Lesson 4-8.

You can improve student success with Lesson 6-3 by pointing out any or all of these connections. Doing so helps students view the lesson as new applications of previously mastered skills, rather than a new set of disconnected rules.

Mathematical Practices

Reason abstractly and quantitatively.
Students will flexibly use properties of addition and subtraction to combine like radical terms and to multiply sums involving radical expressions using the FOIL method.

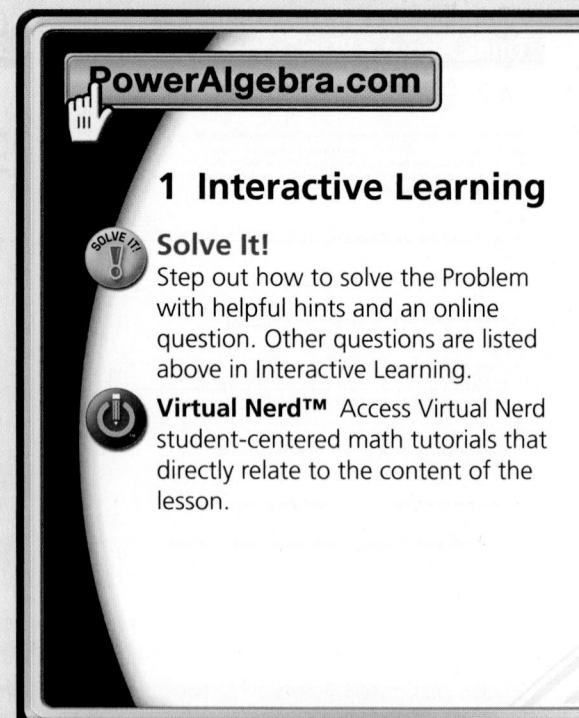

PowerAlgebra.com

1 Interactive Learning

Solve It!
Step out how to solve the Problem with helpful hints and an online question. Other questions are listed above in Interactive Learning.

Virtual Nerd™ Access Virtual Nerd student-centered math tutorials that directly relate to the content of the lesson.

 **Problem 1** Adding and Subtracting Radical Expressions

What is the simplified form of each expression?

A $3\sqrt{5x} - 2\sqrt{5x}$

$\quad 3\sqrt{5x} - 2\sqrt{5x} = (3-2)\sqrt{5x}$ Distributive Property

$\qquad\qquad\qquad\quad = \sqrt{5x}$ Simplify.

B $6x^2\sqrt{7} + 4x\sqrt{5}$

The radicands are different. You cannot combine the expressions.

C $12\sqrt[3]{7xy} - 8\sqrt[5]{7xy}$

The indexes are different. You cannot combine the expressions.

Got It? **1.** What is the simplified form of each expression?

a. $7\sqrt[3]{5} - 4\sqrt{5}$ b. $3x\sqrt{xy} + 4x\sqrt{xy}$ c. $17\sqrt[5]{3x^2} - 15\sqrt[5]{3x^2}$

 Problem 2 Using Radical Expressions **STEM**

Architecture In the stained-glass window design, the side of each small square is 5 in. Find the perimeter of the window to the nearest tenth of an inch.

Length of the diagonal of a square with side s: $s\sqrt{2}$.
Length of the diagonal of each 5-inch square: $5\sqrt{2}$.

Length of the window: $l = 3(5\sqrt{2}) = 15\sqrt{2}$
Width of the window: $w = 2(5\sqrt{2}) = 10\sqrt{2}$

Perimeter $= 2l + 2w$

$\quad = 2(15\sqrt{2}) + 2(10\sqrt{2})$ Substitute for length and width.

$\quad = 30\sqrt{2} + 20\sqrt{2}$ Simplify.

$\quad = 50\sqrt{2}$ Distributive Property

$\quad \approx 70.7$ Use a calculator to approximate.

The perimeter of the window is about 70.7 inches.

Got It? **2. a.** Find the perimeter of the window if the side of each small square is 6 in.

b. Reasoning Describe a different sequence of steps which you could use to compute the perimeter of the window.

Think

Can you always simplify a radical sum?
No. The radicands and the indexes must be the same.

Think

Does it make sense that you have a radical expression as the answer?
Yes, because perimeter is a linear measure, and there is no squaring in the calculations.

Problem 1 **VISUAL LEARNERS**

For 1A, you can model the problem with congruent physical or sketched tiles each labeled $\sqrt{5x}$. Model $3\sqrt{5x}$ as three tiles, $\boxed{\sqrt{5x}}\,\boxed{\sqrt{5x}}\,\boxed{\sqrt{5x}}$. Then model the subtraction by removing two tiles.

Q What property allows you to write $\sqrt{5x}$ instead of $1\sqrt{5x}$? **[Identity Property of Multiplication]**

Got It? **ERROR PREVENTION**

Be aware of students who attempt to operate with the radicands. For example, in 1b watch for $7x\sqrt{2xy}$ (incorrect because the like radical $\sqrt{xy}$ should remain unchanged by the Distributive Property).

Problem 2

Q By the Pythagorean Theorem, why does a square of side s have diagonal $s\sqrt{2}$? **[The diagonal creates two isosceles right triangles with legs s and hypotenuse d:**
$d^2 = s^2 + s^2$ **and** $d = \sqrt{2s^2} = s\sqrt{2}.$**]**

Got It?

Challenge students to find a pattern for the perimeter when the side of each square is 5 in. and 6 in., and then extend the pattern for any size square.

Q If each small square is x in. on a side, what radical expression represents the perimeter? **[$10x\sqrt{2}$]**

---

2 Guided Instruction

 Each Problem is worked out and supported online.

Problem 1
Adding and Subtracting Radical Expressions

Problem 2
Using Radical Expressions
Animated

Problem 3
Simplifying Before Adding or Subtracting
Animated

Problem 4
Multiplying Binomial Radical Expressions

Problem 5
Multiplying Conjugates

Problem 6
Rationalizing the Denominator
Animated

Support in Algebra 2 Companion
• Vocabulary
• Key Concepts
• Got It?

Answers

Solve It!

8; an isosceles triangle has base angle of 45° and $\frac{360}{45} = 8$. area: 127.5, perimeter: $30 + 15\sqrt{2}$

Got It?

1. a. The indexes are different. You cannot combine the expressions.

b. $7x\sqrt{xy}$

c. $2\sqrt[5]{3x^2}$

2. a. about 84.9 in.

b. The length of the diagonal of a square of side 6 can be found using the Pythagorean Thm. to be $\sqrt{6^2 + 6^2} = \sqrt{72}$. Using this information you can calculate the perimeter of the window and simplify the expression at the end.

Problem 3

Although you cannot combine radicals with different radicands, it may be possible to simplify the radicals so that the radicands are the same.

Q Why did the solution not factor $\sqrt{12}$ as $\sqrt{6 \cdot 2}$? **[To reduce a square root, you need perfect squares among the factors of the radicand; neither 6 nor 2 are perfect squares.]**

Q How can you check that $\sqrt{12} + \sqrt{75} - \sqrt{3}$ is equivalent to $6\sqrt{3}$? **[Sample: Use a calculator to find that the decimal approximations are equivalent.]**

Got It?

If students have trouble remembering or recognizing perfect cubes, suggest using any recognizable factors, leading toward prime factors; then look for cubed factors. For example, $\sqrt[3]{250} = \sqrt[3]{25 \cdot 10} = \sqrt[3]{5 \cdot 5 \cdot 2 \cdot 5} = \sqrt[3]{5^3} \cdot 2$.

Problem 4

Q How does $2\sqrt{2} \cdot 4\sqrt{2}$ simplify to 16? Support your answer with the properties of real numbers. **[Sample: $2\sqrt{2} \cdot 4\sqrt{2} = 2 \cdot 4 \cdot \sqrt{2} \cdot \sqrt{2}$ by the Commutative Property of Multiplication, then $2 \cdot 4 \cdot \sqrt{2} \cdot \sqrt{2} = 8 \cdot \sqrt{4}$ by the Associative Property of Multiplication, and $8 \cdot \sqrt{4} = 8 \cdot 2 = 16$.]**

Got It?   ERROR PREVENTION

Be aware of students who correctly use the FOIL method but then incorrectly simplify each product. For example, the "outer" product $3 \cdot 4\sqrt{5}$ could become $12\sqrt{15}$ (incorrectly multiplied 3 by both 4 and 5), or the "inner" product $2\sqrt{5} \cdot 2$ could become $2\sqrt{10}$ (incorrectly multiplied 5 by 2 because they are adjacent).

When you have a sum or difference of radical expressions, you should simplify each expression so that you can find all the like radicals.

**Problem 3** **Simplifying Before Adding or Subtracting**

What is the simplest form of the expression? $\sqrt{12} + \sqrt{75} - \sqrt{3}$

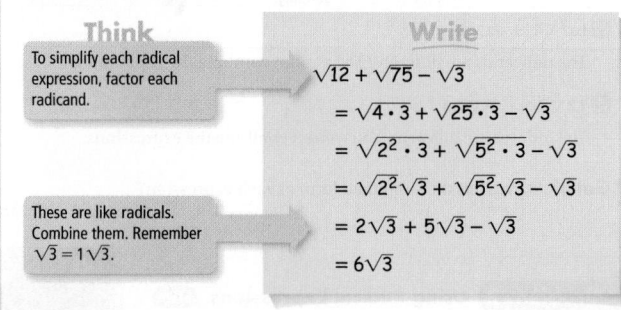

Think

To simplify each radical expression, factor each radicand.

These are like radicals. Combine them. Remember $\sqrt{3} = 1\sqrt{3}$.

Write

$$\sqrt{12} + \sqrt{75} - \sqrt{3}$$
$$= \sqrt{4 \cdot 3} + \sqrt{25 \cdot 3} - \sqrt{3}$$
$$= \sqrt{2^2 \cdot 3} + \sqrt{5^2 \cdot 3} - \sqrt{3}$$
$$= \sqrt{2^2}\sqrt{3} + \sqrt{5^2}\sqrt{3} - \sqrt{3}$$
$$= 2\sqrt{3} + 5\sqrt{3} - \sqrt{3}$$
$$= 6\sqrt{3}$$

Got It? **3.** What is the simplest form of the expression? $\sqrt[3]{250} + \sqrt[3]{54} - \sqrt[3]{16}$

You can use the FOIL method to multiply binomials that have radical expressions. Remember that the FOIL method ensures that you multiply each term of one binomial by each term of the other.

Problem 4 **Multiplying Binomial Radical Expressions**

What is the product of each radical expression?

A $(4 + 2\sqrt{2})(5 + 4\sqrt{2})$

$(4 + 2\sqrt{2})(5 + 4\sqrt{2})$

$= 4 \cdot 5 + 4 \cdot 4\sqrt{2} + 2\sqrt{2} \cdot 5 + 2\sqrt{2} \cdot 4\sqrt{2}$ Distribute.

$= 20 + 16\sqrt{2} + 10\sqrt{2} + 16$ Multiply.

$= 36 + 26\sqrt{2}$ Combine like radicals.

B $(3 - \sqrt{7})(5 + \sqrt{7})$

$(3 - \sqrt{7})(5 + \sqrt{7})$

$= 3 \cdot 5 + 3\sqrt{7} - \sqrt{7} \cdot 5 - \sqrt{7} \cdot \sqrt{7}$ Distribute.

$= 15 - 2\sqrt{7} - 7$ Multiply and combine like radicals.

$= 8 - 2\sqrt{7}$ Simplify.

Got It? **4.** What is the product $(3 + 2\sqrt{5})(2 + 4\sqrt{5})$?

Plan

How do you multiply two binomials?
Use the FOIL method:
First, **O**uter, **I**nner, **L**ast.
Then simplify.

Additional Problems

1. What is the simplified form of each expression?

   a. $14a\sqrt{7bc} + 5a\sqrt{7bc}$

   b. $3\sqrt[5]{x} - \sqrt[5]{3x}$

   ANSWERS

   a. $19a\sqrt{7bc}$

   b. cannot be simplified

2. This tile design is made of congruent right triangles with base 1 ft and height 2 ft. Find the perimeter of the tile to the nearest tenth of a foot.

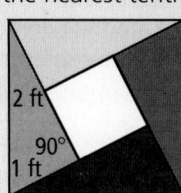

   ANSWER $4\sqrt{5}$ ft ≈ 8.9 ft

3. What is the simplest form of the expression?

   $\sqrt{28} - \sqrt{175} + \sqrt{63}$

   ANSWER 0

4. What is the product?

   $(1 + 2\sqrt{7})(4 - 3\sqrt{7})$

   ANSWER $-38 + 5\sqrt{7}$

5. What is the product?

   $(5 + 3\sqrt{2})(5 - 3\sqrt{2})$

   ANSWER 7

6. How can you write the expression $\frac{11}{6 + \sqrt{3}}$ with a rationalized denominator?

   ANSWER $\frac{6 - \sqrt{3}}{3}$

Conjugates are expressions, like $\sqrt{a} + \sqrt{b}$ and $\sqrt{a} - \sqrt{b}$, that differ only in the signs of the second terms. When a and b are rational numbers, the product of two radical conjugates is a rational number.

Think

Where have you seen conjugates before?
The complex number $a + bi$ has a conjugate, $a - bi$. Multiplying them results in a number with no imaginary part.

Ⓒ **Problem 5** **Multiplying Conjugates**

What is the product $(5 - \sqrt{7})(5 + \sqrt{7})$?

$$(5 - \sqrt{7})(5 + \sqrt{7}) = 5 \cdot 5 + 5\sqrt{7} - 5\sqrt{7} - (\sqrt{7})^2 \quad \text{Distribute.}$$
$$= 25 - 7 \quad \text{Simplify.}$$
$$= 18$$

✓ **Got It?** **5.** What is each product?
    a. $(6 - \sqrt{12})(6 + \sqrt{12})$ **b.** $(3 + \sqrt{8})(3 - \sqrt{8})$

Sometimes a denominator is a sum or difference involving radicals. If the radical expressions are square roots, you can rationalize the denominator by multiplying the numerator and the denominator by the conjugate of the denominator.

Think

What is a rationalized denominator?
A rationalized denominator contains no radicals.

Ⓒ **Problem 6** **Rationalizing the Denominator**

How can you write the expression with a rationalized denominator?

$$\frac{3\sqrt{2}}{\sqrt{5} - \sqrt{2}}$$

$$\frac{3\sqrt{2}}{\sqrt{5} - \sqrt{2}} = \frac{3\sqrt{2}}{\sqrt{5} - \sqrt{2}} \cdot \frac{\sqrt{5} + \sqrt{2}}{\sqrt{5} + \sqrt{2}} \quad \text{Multiply. Use the conjugate of the denominator.}$$

$$= \frac{3\sqrt{2}(\sqrt{5} + \sqrt{2})}{(\sqrt{5})^2 - (\sqrt{2})^2} \quad \text{The radicals in the denominator cancel out.}$$

$$= \frac{3(\sqrt{2} \cdot \sqrt{5} + \sqrt{2} \cdot \sqrt{2})}{5 - 2} \quad \text{Distribute } \sqrt{2} \text{ in the numerator.}$$

$$= \frac{3(\sqrt{10} + 2)}{3} \quad \text{Simplify.}$$

$$= \sqrt{10} + 2$$

Ⓒ ✓ **Got It?** **6.** How can you write the expression with a rationalized denominator?
    a. $\dfrac{2\sqrt{7}}{\sqrt{3} - \sqrt{5}}$ **b.** $\dfrac{4x}{3 - \sqrt{6}}$

    c. Reasoning Suppose you were going to rationalize the denominator of $\dfrac{1 - \sqrt{8}}{2 - \sqrt{8}}$. Would you simplify $\sqrt{8}$ before or after rationalizing? Explain your answer.

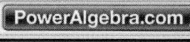

Answers

Got It? (continued)

3. $6\sqrt[3]{2}$

4. $46 + 16\sqrt{5}$

5. a. 24
   b. 1

6. a. $-\sqrt{21} - \sqrt{35}$
   b. $\frac{1}{3}(12x + 4x\sqrt{6})$
   c. after rationalizing; When the numerator is multiplied by the conjugate of the denominator it is more convenient if $\sqrt{8}$ is not yet simplified.

3 Lesson Check

Do you know HOW? ERROR INTERVENTION

- If students operate with the radicands when combining like radicals in Exercises 1 and 3, have them underline the like radicals. By the Distributive Property, the like radical remains unchanged during the process.

- If students multiply only the first non-radical terms and the last radical terms in Exercises 6 and 7, then have them look at the proper use of the FOIL method in Problem 4.

Do you UNDERSTAND?

- Extend Exercise 8 by asking students to justify why the expressions in (a) and (c) are not pairs of like radicals. **[The pairs in (a) and (c) do not have the same radicands.]**

Close

> **Q** What process do you use to identify like radicals?
> **[Answers may vary. Sample: First check that the indexes are the same; then simplify each radical to simplest form and check that the remaining radicands are the same.]**

 **Lesson Check**

Do you know HOW?

Simplify if possible.

1. $10\sqrt{6} + 2\sqrt{6}$ 2. $3\sqrt{2} + 4\sqrt[3]{2}$

3. $8\sqrt{3x} - 5\sqrt{3x}$ 4. $5\sqrt{3} + \sqrt{12}$

Multiply.

5. $(4 + \sqrt{3})(4 - \sqrt{3})$

6. $(5 + 2\sqrt{5})(7 + 4\sqrt{5})$

7. $(2 + 3\sqrt{2})(1 - 3\sqrt{2})$

Do you UNDERSTAND? MATHEMATICAL PRACTICES

8. **Vocabulary** Determine whether each of the following is a pair of like radicals. If so, add them.
   - a. $3x\sqrt{11}$ and $3x\sqrt{10}$
   - b. $2\sqrt{3xy}$ and $7\sqrt{3xy}$
   - c. $12\sqrt{13y}$ and $12\sqrt{6y}$

9. **Compare and Contrast** How are the processes of multiplying radical expressions and multiplying polynomial expressions alike? How are the processes different?

Practice and Problem-Solving Exercises

A Practice Simplify if possible. ◀ See Problem 1.

10. $5\sqrt{6} + \sqrt{6}$ 11. $6\sqrt[3]{3} - 2\sqrt[3]{3}$ 12. $4\sqrt{3} + 4\sqrt[3]{3}$

13. $3\sqrt{x} - 5\sqrt{x}$ 14. $14\sqrt{x} + 3\sqrt{y}$ 15. $7\sqrt[3]{x^2} - 2\sqrt[3]{x^2}$

16. The design of a garden path uses stone pieces shaped as squares with a side length of 15 in. Find the length of the path. ◀ See Problem 2.

Simplify. ◀ See Problem 3.

17. $6\sqrt{18} + 3\sqrt{50}$ 18. $14\sqrt{20} - 3\sqrt{125}$ 19. $\sqrt{18} + \sqrt{32}$

20. $\sqrt[3]{54} + \sqrt[3]{16}$ 21. $3\sqrt[3]{81} - 2\sqrt[3]{54}$ 22. $\sqrt[4]{32} + \sqrt[4]{48}$

Multiply. ◀ See Problem 4.

23. $(3 + \sqrt{5})(1 + \sqrt{5})$ 24. $(2 + \sqrt{7})(1 + 3\sqrt{7})$ 25. $(3 - 4\sqrt{2})(5 - 6\sqrt{2})$

26. $(\sqrt{3} + \sqrt{5})^2$ 27. $(\sqrt{13} + 6)^2$ 28. $(2\sqrt{5} + 3\sqrt{2})^2$

Multiply each pair of conjugates. ◀ See Problem 5.

29. $(5 - \sqrt{11})(5 + \sqrt{11})$ 30. $(4 - 2\sqrt{3})(4 + 2\sqrt{3})$

31. $(2\sqrt{6} + 8)(2\sqrt{6} - 8)$ 32. $(\sqrt{3} + \sqrt{5})(\sqrt{3} - \sqrt{5})$

Rationalize each denominator. Simplify your answer. ◀ See Problem 6.

33. $\dfrac{4}{1 + \sqrt{3}}$ 34. $\dfrac{4}{3\sqrt{3} - 2}$ 35. $\dfrac{5 + \sqrt{3}}{2 - \sqrt{3}}$ 36. $\dfrac{3 + \sqrt{8}}{2 - 2\sqrt{8}}$

 PowerAlgebra.com

3 Lesson Check

For a digital lesson check, use the Got It questions.

Support in Algebra 2 Companion
- Lesson Check

4 Practice

Assign homework to individual students or to an entire class.

Answers

Lesson Check

1. $12\sqrt{6}$
2. cannot combine
3. $3\sqrt{3x}$
4. $7\sqrt{3}$
5. 13
6. $75 + 34\sqrt{5}$
7. $-16 - 3\sqrt{2}$
8. a. not like radicals
   b. $9\sqrt{3xy}$
   c. not like radicals
9. They are alike in that you can also use the FOIL method and Distr. Prop. to multiply binomial radical expressions; they are different in that you cannot multiply like radicands together if they do not have the same index.

Practice and Problem-Solving Exercises

10. $6\sqrt{6}$ 11. $4\sqrt[3]{3}$
12. cannot combine
13. $-2\sqrt{x}$
14. cannot combine
15. $5\sqrt[3]{x^2}$
16. about 127.3 in.
17. $33\sqrt{2}$ 18. $13\sqrt{5}$
19. $7\sqrt{2}$ 20. $5\sqrt[3]{2}$
21. $9\sqrt[3]{3} - 6\sqrt[3]{2}$
22. $2\sqrt[4]{2} + 2\sqrt[4]{3}$
23. $8 + 4\sqrt{5}$
24. $23 + 7\sqrt{7}$
25. $63 - 38\sqrt{2}$
26. $8 + 2\sqrt{15}$
27. $49 + 12\sqrt{13}$
28. $38 + 12\sqrt{10}$
29. 14   30. 4   31. -40

© **37. Think About a Plan** The design on a parquet floor, shown at the right, is made of equilateral triangles. The side of a large triangle is 6 in., and the side of a small triangle is 3 in. Find the total area of the design to the nearest tenth of a square inch.

- How many large and how many small triangles form the design?
- Can you express the area of an equilateral triangle through its side?

Simplify.

38. $\sqrt{72} + \sqrt{32} + \sqrt{18}$

39. $\sqrt{75} + 2\sqrt{48} - 5\sqrt{3}$

40. $5\sqrt{32x} + 4\sqrt{98x}$

41. $\sqrt{75} - 4\sqrt{18} + 2\sqrt{32}$

42. $4\sqrt{216y^2} + 3\sqrt{54y^2}$

43. $3\sqrt[3]{16} - 4\sqrt[3]{54} + \sqrt[3]{128}$

44. $(1 + \sqrt{72})(5 + \sqrt{2})$

45. $(\sqrt{3} - \sqrt{7})(\sqrt{3} + 2\sqrt{7})$

46. $(\sqrt{y} + \sqrt{2})(\sqrt{y} - 7\sqrt{2})$

47. $(\sqrt{12} + \sqrt{72})^2$

48. $(\sqrt{1.25} - \sqrt{1.8})(\sqrt{5} + \sqrt{0.2})$

49. $(\sqrt{a+1} + \sqrt{a-1})(\sqrt{a+1} - \sqrt{a-1})$

© **50. Error Analysis** Describe and correct the error made while simplifying the expression $\frac{3+\sqrt{2}}{3-\sqrt{2}}$.

$$\frac{3+\sqrt{2}}{3-\sqrt{2}} = \frac{3+\sqrt{2}}{3-\sqrt{2}} \cdot \frac{3+\sqrt{2}}{3+\sqrt{2}}$$

$$\frac{3^2 + (\sqrt{2})^2}{3^2 - (\sqrt{2})^2} = \frac{9+2}{9-2} = \frac{11}{7}$$

STEM 51. Chemistry A scientist found that x grams of Metal A is completely oxidized in $2x\sqrt{3}$ seconds and x grams of Metal B is completely oxidized in $6x\sqrt{3}$ seconds. How much faster is Metal A oxidized than Metal B?

© **52. Reasoning** Describe the possible values of a such that $\sqrt{72} + \sqrt{a}$ simplifies to a single term.

© **53. Writing** Discuss the advantages and disadvantages of first simplifying $\sqrt{72} + \sqrt{32} + \sqrt{18}$ in order to estimate its decimal value.

54. Geometry Show that a right triangle with legs of lengths $\sqrt{2} - 1$ and $\sqrt{2} + 1$ is similar to a right triangle with legs of lengths $6 - \sqrt{32}$ and 2.

© **55. Open-Ended** Find two pairs of conjugates with a product of 3.

Rationalize the denominators and simplify.

56. $\frac{4 + \sqrt{27}}{2 - 3\sqrt{27}}$

57. $\frac{4 + \sqrt{6}}{\sqrt{2} + \sqrt{3}}$

58. $\frac{5 - \sqrt{21}}{\sqrt{3} - \sqrt{7}}$

59. $\frac{\sqrt{44x^2}}{\sqrt{11} + 3}$

60. $\frac{\sqrt{2} + \sqrt{6}}{\sqrt{1.5} + \sqrt{0.5}}$

61. $\frac{\sqrt{27} - \sqrt{5}}{\sqrt{15} - 3}$

62. $\frac{4 + \sqrt[3]{2}}{\sqrt[3]{2}}$

63. $\frac{5 + \sqrt[4]{x}}{\sqrt[4]{x}}$

64. $\frac{4 - 2\sqrt[3]{6}}{\sqrt[3]{4}}$

4 Practice

ASSIGNMENT GUIDE

Basic: 10–36 all, 37–40, 53, 54–58 even

Average: 11–35 odd, 37–64

Advanced: 11–35 odd, 37–68

Standardized Test Prep: 69–73

Mixed Review: 74–91

© **Mathematical Practices** are supported by exercises with red headings. Here are the Practices supported in this lesson:

MP 1: Make Sense of Problems Ex. 37

MP 2: Reason Abstractly Ex. 52

MP 3: Communicate Ex. 53

MP 3: Construct Arguments Ex. 55

MP 3: Compare Arguments Ex. 9

MP 3: Critique the Reasoning of Others Ex. 50

Applications exercises have blue headings. Exercises 51, 54 support MP 4: Model.

STEM exercises focus on science or engineering applications.

EXERCISE 54: Use the Think About a Plan worksheet in the **Practice and Problem Solving Workbook** (also available in the Teaching Resources in print and online) to further support students' development in becoming independent learners.

HOMEWORK QUICK CHECK

To check students' understanding of key skills and concepts, go over Exercises 29, 33, 37, 40, and 54.

Answers

32. -2

33. $-2 + 2\sqrt{3}$

34. $\frac{12\sqrt{3} + 8}{23}$

35. $13 + 7\sqrt{3}$

36. $\frac{11 + 8\sqrt{2}}{-14}$

37. 140.3 in.^{2}

38. $13\sqrt{2}$

39. $8\sqrt{3}$

40. $48\sqrt{2x}$

41. $5\sqrt{3} - 4\sqrt{2}$

42. $33|y|\sqrt{6}$

43. $-2\sqrt[3]{2}$

44. $17 + 31\sqrt{2}$

45. $-11 + \sqrt{21}$

46. $y - 6\sqrt{2y} - 14$

47. $84 + 24\sqrt{6}$

48. -0.6

49. 2

50. In the second step, the student did not use the FOIL method correctly. The steps should be:

$$\cdots = \frac{3^2 + 6\sqrt{2} + (\sqrt{2})^2}{3^2 - (\sqrt{2})^2}$$

$$= \frac{9 + 6\sqrt{2} + 2}{9 - 2}$$

$$= \frac{11 + 6\sqrt{2}}{7}$$

51. $4x\sqrt{3}$ s

52. a must be twice a perfect square.

53. Answers may vary. Sample: Without simplifying first, you must estimate three square roots and then add the estimates. If they are first simplified, then they can be combined as $13\sqrt{2}$. Then only one square root need be estimated.

54. $\frac{\sqrt{2} - 1}{\sqrt{2} + 1} = \frac{6 - \sqrt{32}}{2} = 3 - 2\sqrt{2}$

55. Answers may vary. Sample: $(\sqrt{7} + 2)(\sqrt{7} - 2), (2\sqrt{2} + \sqrt{5})(2\sqrt{2} - \sqrt{5})$

56. $\frac{89 + 42\sqrt{3}}{-239}$

57. $2\sqrt{3} - \sqrt{2}$

58. $\frac{1}{2}(\sqrt{3} - \sqrt{7})$

59. $11|x| - 3|x|\sqrt{11}$

60. 2

61. $\frac{3\sqrt{5} + 2\sqrt{3}}{3}$

62. $1 + 2\sqrt[3]{4}$

63. $\frac{x + 5\sqrt[4]{x^3}}{x}$

64. $2\sqrt[3]{2} - \sqrt[3]{12}$

Answers

Practice and Problem-Solving Exercises
(continued)

65. $-\frac{1}{2}$

66. $4\sqrt{3}$

67. $a = 0$ and $b \geq 0$, or $b = 0$ and $a \geq 0$

68. a. $m > n$

   b. m must be even or n must be odd, where $m > n$

   c. m must be even, where $m > n$

Standardized Test Prep

69. 13

70. 2

71. $\frac{15}{7}$

72. $\frac{5}{2}$

73. 9

Mixed Review

74. $3\sqrt[3]{2}$

75. $\frac{2\sqrt[3]{x^2}}{x}$

76. 4

77. 6

78. $2x$

79. $7x^2\sqrt{2}$

80. $x\sqrt{15}$

81. $15x^2$

82. $2, -1 \pm i\sqrt{3}$

83. $-10, 5 \pm 5i\sqrt{3}$

84. $\frac{1}{5}, \frac{-1 \pm i\sqrt{3}}{10}$

85. $\sqrt{7}$ (multiplicity 2), $-\sqrt{7}$ (multiplicity 2)

86. $\frac{2\sqrt{5}}{5}$ (multiplicity 2), $-\frac{2\sqrt{5}}{5}$ (multiplicity 2)

87. $\pm\frac{1}{3}, \pm\frac{1}{3}i$

88. x^6

89. p^5q^5

90. 2^9, or 512

91. 3^3, or 27

Challenge   Add or subtract.

65. $\frac{1}{1 - \sqrt{5}} + \frac{1}{1 + \sqrt{5}}$

66. $\frac{4}{\sqrt{5} - \sqrt{3}} - \frac{4}{\sqrt{5} + \sqrt{3}}$

67. For what values of a and b does $\sqrt{a} + \sqrt{b} = \sqrt{a + b}$?

68. In the expression $\sqrt[n]{x^m}$, m and n are positive integers and x is a real number. The expression can be simplified.

   a. If $x > 0$, what are the possible values for m and n?

   b. If $x < 0$, what are the possible values for m and n?

   c. If $x < 0$, and an absolute value symbol is needed in the simplified expression, what are the possible values of m and n?

Standardized Test Prep

GRIDDED RESPONSE

SAT/ACT

69. What is the value of the expression $(5 - 2\sqrt{3})(5 + 2\sqrt{3})$?

70. What is the value of z in the solution of the system of equations below?

$$\begin{cases} 2x - 3y + z = 6 \\ -x + y - 2z = -5 \\ 3x - y - 3z = -7 \end{cases}$$

71. What is the y-value of the y-intercept of the line $5x - 7y = -15$?

72. What is the slope of a line perpendicular to the line $2x + 5y = 10$?

73. What is the value of p for which the equation $x^2 - 12x + 4p = 0$ has exactly one real root?

Mixed Review

Simplify each expression. Rationalize all denominators.   ◀ See Lesson 6-2.

74. $\sqrt[3]{3} \cdot \sqrt[3]{18}$

75. $\sqrt[3]{\frac{4}{0.5x}}$

76. $\frac{\sqrt{32}}{\sqrt{2}}$

77. $\frac{\sqrt{216}}{\sqrt{6}}$

78. $\sqrt[3]{2x^2} \cdot \sqrt[3]{4x}$

79. $\sqrt{7x} \cdot \sqrt{14x^3}$

80. $\sqrt{3x} \cdot \sqrt{5x}$

81. $\sqrt{9x^2} \cdot \sqrt{25x^2}$

Find the real and imaginary solutions of each equation.   ◀ See Lesson 5-3.

82. $2x^3 - 16 = 0$

83. $x^3 + 1000 = 0$

84. $125x^3 - 1 = 0$

85. $x^4 - 14x^2 + 49 = 0$

86. $25x^4 - 40x^2 + 16 = 0$

87. $81x^4 - 1 = 0$

Get Ready!   To prepare for Lesson 6-4, do Exercises 88–91.

Simplify.   ◀ See p. 978.

88. $(x^2)^3$

89. $(pq)^5$

90. $(2^4)(2^5)$

91. $(3^{-2})(3^5)$

Additional Instructional Support

Algebra 2 Companion

Students can use the **Algebra 2 Companion** worktext (4 pages) as you teach the lesson. Use the Companion to support

- New Vocabulary
- Key Concepts
- Got It for each Problem
- Lesson Check

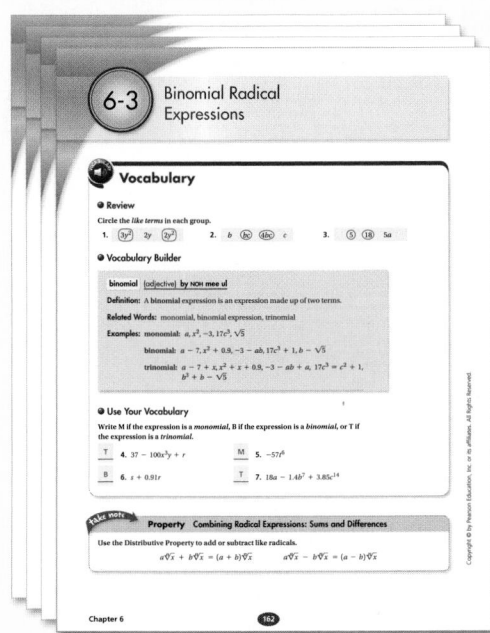

ELL Support

Use Graphic Organizers Have students fold a sheet of paper in half to make two columns. Label one column Like Radicals and the other Unlike Radicals. Have students work in groups of two or three to write at least five pairs of radical expressions that fit in each column.

Circulate and challenge students to write pairs that either appear to be like terms but are not (e.g., $\sqrt{2}$ and $\sqrt[3]{2}$) or do not appear to be like terms but are (e.g., $\sqrt{2}$ and $\sqrt{50}$). Come back together as a class and have each group share at least one pair from each column.

Encourage students to use the correct vocabulary. For example, "$\sqrt{2}$ and $\sqrt[3]{2}$ have the same *radicand* but are not *like radicals* because their *indexes* are different." Students may add illustrative examples to their own graphic organizers.

5 Assess & Remediate

Lesson Quiz

1. What is the simplified form of $15\sqrt[4]{8y^3} - 6\sqrt[4]{8y^3} + \sqrt[4]{y^3}$?

2. **Do you UNDERSTAND?** This wall-hanging is made of congruent 30°-60°-90° triangles with height 6 cm and hypotenuse 12 cm. What is the perimeter of the wall hanging to the nearest tenth of a centimeter?

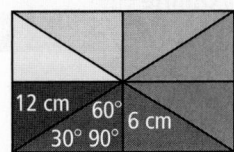

3. What is the simplest form of the expression? $\sqrt{180} - \sqrt{80} + \sqrt{45}$

4. What is the product? $(4 - \sqrt{3})(5 - 6\sqrt{3})$

5. What is the product? $(8 + \sqrt{20})(8 - \sqrt{20})$

6. How can you write the expression with a rationalized denominator? $\dfrac{3\sqrt{7}}{\sqrt{7} + \sqrt{3}}$

ANSWERS TO LESSON QUIZ

1. $9\sqrt[4]{8y^3} + \sqrt[4]{y^3}$
2. $(24 + 24\sqrt{3})$ cm ≈ 65.6 cm
3. $5\sqrt{5}$
4. $38 - 29\sqrt{3}$
5. 44
6. $\dfrac{21 - 3\sqrt{21}}{4}$

PRESCRIPTION FOR REMEDIATION
Use the student work on the Lesson Quiz to prescribe a differentiated review assignment:

Points	Differentiated Remediation
0–3	Intervention
4–5	On-level
6	Extension

PowerAlgebra.com

5 Assess & Remediate

Assign the Lesson Quiz. Appropriate intervention, practice, or enrichment is automatically generated based on student performance.

Intervention

- **Reteaching** (2 pages) Provides reteaching and practice exercises for the key lesson concepts. Use with struggling students or absent students.

- **English Language Learner Support** Helps students develop and reinforce mathematical vocabulary and key concepts.

All-in-One Resources/Online
Reteaching

6-3 Reteaching
Binomial Radical Expressions

Two radical expressions are *like radicals* if they have the same index and the same radicand.

Compare radical expressions to the terms in a polynomial expression.

Like terms:	$4x^3$ $11x^3$	The power and the variable are the same.
Unlike terms:	$4y^3$ $11x^3$ $4y^2$	Either the power or the variable are not the same.
Like radicals:	$4\sqrt[3]{6}$ $11\sqrt[3]{6}$	The index and the radicand are the same.
Unlike radicals:	$4\sqrt[3]{5}$ $11\sqrt[3]{6}$ $4\sqrt[4]{6}$	Either the index or the radicand are not the same.

When adding or subtracting radical expressions, simplify each radical so that you can find like radicals.

Problem

What is the sum? $\sqrt{63} + \sqrt{28}$

$\sqrt{63} + \sqrt{28} = \sqrt{9 \cdot 7} + \sqrt{4 \cdot 7}$ Factor each radicand.
$= \sqrt{3^2 \cdot 7} + \sqrt{2^2 \cdot 7}$ Find perfect squares.
$= \sqrt{3^2}\sqrt{7} + \sqrt{2^2}\sqrt{7}$ Use $\sqrt{ab} = \sqrt{a} \cdot \sqrt{b}$.
$= 3\sqrt{7} + 2\sqrt{7}$ Use $\sqrt[n]{a^n} = a$ to simplify.
$= 5\sqrt{7}$ Add like radicals.

The sum is $5\sqrt{7}$.

Exercises

Simplify.

1. $\sqrt{150} - \sqrt{24}$ $3\sqrt{6}$ 2. $\sqrt[3]{135} + \sqrt[3]{40}$ $5\sqrt[3]{5}$ 3. $6\sqrt{3} - \sqrt{75}$ $\sqrt{3}$

4. $5\sqrt[3]{2} - \sqrt[3]{54}$ $2\sqrt[3]{2}$ 5. $-\sqrt{48} + \sqrt{147} - \sqrt{27}$ 0   6. $8\sqrt[3]{3x} - \sqrt[3]{24x} + \sqrt[3]{192x}$ $10\sqrt[3]{3x}$

All-in-One Resources/Online
English Language Learner Support

6-3 Additional Vocabulary Support
Binomial Radical Expressions

The column on the left shows the steps used to rationalize a denominator. Use the column on the left to answer each question in the column on the right.

Problem **Rationalizing the Denominator**	1. What does it mean to rationalize a denominator?
Write the expression $\dfrac{4\sqrt{3}}{\sqrt{7} + \sqrt{3}}$ with a rationalized denominator.	Sample answer: It means to write an expression so that there are no radicals in any denominators and no denominators in any radicals.
Multiply the numerator and the denominator by the conjugate of the denominator. $\dfrac{4\sqrt{3}}{\sqrt{7} + \sqrt{3}} \cdot \dfrac{\sqrt{7} - \sqrt{3}}{\sqrt{7} - \sqrt{3}}$	2. What are conjugates? Conjugates are expressions that differ only in the signs of the first or second terms.
The radicals in the denominator cancel out. $\dfrac{4\sqrt{3}(\sqrt{7} - \sqrt{3})}{7 - 3}$	3. Write and solve an equation to show why the radicals in the denominator cancel out. $(\sqrt{7} + \sqrt{3})(\sqrt{7} - \sqrt{3}) = (\sqrt{7} \cdot \sqrt{7}) - (\sqrt{7} \cdot \sqrt{3}) + (\sqrt{7} \cdot \sqrt{3}) - (\sqrt{3} \cdot \sqrt{3}) = 7 - 3$
Distribute $\sqrt{3}$ in the numerator. $\dfrac{4(\sqrt{3} \cdot \sqrt{7} - \sqrt{3} \cdot \sqrt{3})}{7 - 3}$	4. What property allows you to distribute the $\sqrt{3}$? The Distributive Property
Simplify. $\dfrac{4(\sqrt{21} - 3)}{4}$	5. Why do the fours in the numerator and the denominator cancel out? Sample answer: Because 4 divided by 4 equals 1.
Simplify. $\sqrt{21} - 3$	6. What number multiplied by $\sqrt{21}$ would produce a product of 21? $\sqrt{21}$

Differentiated Remediation *continued*

On-Level

- **Practice** (2 pages) Provides extra practice for each lesson. For simpler practice exercises, use the Form K Practice pages found in the All-in-One Teaching Resources and online.

- **Think About a Plan** Helps students develop specific problem-solving skills and strategies by providing scaffolded guiding questions.

- **Standardized Test Prep** Focuses on all major exercises, all major question types, and helps students prepare for the high-stakes assessments.

Extension

- **Enrichment** Provides students with interesting problems and activities that extend the concepts of the lesson.

- **Activities, Games, and Puzzles** Worksheets that can be used for concepts development, enrichment, and for fun!

Practice and Problem Solving Wkbk/ All-in-One Resources/Online
Practice page 1

6-3 Practice Form G
Binomial Radical Expressions

Add or subtract if possible.

1. $9\sqrt{3} + 2\sqrt{3}$ $11\sqrt{3}$
2. $5\sqrt{2} + 2\sqrt{3}$ $5\sqrt{2} + 2\sqrt{3}$
3. $3\sqrt{7} - 7\sqrt[3]{x}$ $3\sqrt{7} - 7\sqrt[3]{x}$
4. $14\sqrt[3]{xy} - 3\sqrt[3]{xy}$ $11\sqrt[3]{xy}$
5. $8\sqrt[3]{x} + 2\sqrt[3]{y}$ $8\sqrt[3]{x} + 2\sqrt[3]{y}$
6. $5\sqrt[3]{xy} + \sqrt[3]{xy}$ $6\sqrt[3]{xy}$
7. $\sqrt{3x} - 2\sqrt{3x}$ $-\sqrt{3x}$
8. $6\sqrt{2} - 5\sqrt{2}$ $6\sqrt{2} - 5\sqrt{2}$
9. $7\sqrt{x} + x\sqrt{7}$ $7\sqrt{x} + x\sqrt{7}$

Simplify.

10. $3\sqrt{32} + 2\sqrt{50}$ $22\sqrt{2}$
11. $\sqrt{200} - \sqrt{72}$ $4\sqrt{2}$
12. $\sqrt[3]{81} - 3\sqrt[3]{3}$ 0
13. $2\sqrt[3]{48} + 3\sqrt[3]{243}$ $13\sqrt[3]{3}$
14. $3\sqrt{75} + 2\sqrt{12}$ $19\sqrt{3}$
15. $\sqrt[3]{250} - \sqrt[3]{54}$ $2\sqrt[3]{2}$
16. $\sqrt{28} - \sqrt{63}$ $-\sqrt{7}$
17. $3\sqrt[3]{32} - 2\sqrt[3]{162}$
18. $\sqrt{125} - 2\sqrt{20}$ $\sqrt{5}$

Multiply.

19. $(1 - \sqrt{5})(2 - \sqrt{5})$ $7 - 3\sqrt{5}$
20. $(1 + 4\sqrt{10})(2 - \sqrt{10})$ $-38 + 7\sqrt{10}$
21. $(1 - 3\sqrt{7})(4 - 3\sqrt{7})$ $67 - 15\sqrt{7}$
22. $(4 - 2\sqrt{3})^2$ $28 - 16\sqrt{3}$
23. $(\sqrt{2} + \sqrt{7})^2$ $9 + 2\sqrt{14}$
24. $(\sqrt{30} - \sqrt{2})^2$ $30 - 12\sqrt{6}$
25. $(4 - \sqrt{3})(2 + \sqrt{3})$ $5 + 2\sqrt{3}$
26. $(3 + \sqrt{11})(4 - \sqrt{11})$ $1 + \sqrt{11}$
27. $(3\sqrt{2} - 2\sqrt{3})^2$ $30 - 12\sqrt{6}$

Multiply each pair of conjugates.

28. $(3\sqrt{2} - 9)(3\sqrt{2} + 9)$ -63
29. $(1 - \sqrt{7})(1 + \sqrt{7})$ -6
30. $(5\sqrt{3} + \sqrt{2})(5\sqrt{3} - \sqrt{2})$ 73
31. $(3\sqrt{2} - 2\sqrt{3})(3\sqrt{2} + 2\sqrt{3})$ 6
32. $(\sqrt{11} + 5)(\sqrt{11} - 5)$ -14
33. $(2\sqrt{7} + 3\sqrt{3})(2\sqrt{7} - 3\sqrt{3})$ 1

Practice and Problem Solving Wkbk/ All-in-One Resources/Online
Practice page 2

6-3 Practice (continued) Form G
Binomial Radical Expressions

Rationalize each denominator. Simplify the answer.

34. $\frac{3 - \sqrt{10}}{\sqrt{5} - \sqrt{2}}$ $\sqrt{5} - 2\sqrt{2}$
35. $\frac{2 + \sqrt{14}}{\sqrt{7} + \sqrt{2}}$ $\sqrt{2}$
36. $\frac{2 + \sqrt[3]{x}}{\sqrt[3]{x}}$ $\frac{x + 2\sqrt[3]{x^2}}{x}$

Simplify. Assume that all the variables are positive.

37. $\sqrt{28} + 4\sqrt{63} - 2\sqrt{7}$ $12\sqrt{7}$
38. $6\sqrt{40} - 2\sqrt{90} - 3\sqrt{160}$ $-6\sqrt{10}$
39. $3\sqrt{12} + 7\sqrt{75} - 3\sqrt{27}$ $41\sqrt{3} - 3\sqrt{6}$
40. $4\sqrt[3]{81} + 2\sqrt[3]{72} - \sqrt[3]{24}$ $5\sqrt[3]{3} + 4\sqrt[3]{9}$
41. $(3\sqrt{225x} + 5\sqrt{144x})$ $105\sqrt{x}$
42. $6\sqrt{45p^2} + 4\sqrt{20p^2}$ $26y\sqrt{5}$
43. $(3\sqrt{y} - \sqrt{5})(2\sqrt{y} + 5\sqrt{5})$ $6y + 13\sqrt{5y} - 25$
44. $(\sqrt{x} - \sqrt{3})(\sqrt{x} + \sqrt{3})$ $x - 3$
45. A park in the shape of a triangle has a sidewalk dividing it into two parts.

a. If a man walks around the perimeter of the park, how far will he walk? $(900 + 300\sqrt{3} + 300\sqrt{6})$ ft or about 2154 ft
b. What is the area of the park? $\frac{270,000 + 90,000\sqrt{3}}{2}$ ft² or about 212,942 ft²
46. The area of a rectangle is 10 in.². The length is $(2 + \sqrt{2})$ in. What is the width? $5(2 - \sqrt{2})$ in.
47. One solution to the equation $x^2 + 2x - 2 = 0$ is $-1 + \sqrt{3}$. To show this, let $x = -1 + \sqrt{3}$ and answer each of the following questions.
a. What is x^2? $4 - 2\sqrt{3}$
b. What is $2x$? $-2 + 2\sqrt{3}$
c. Using your answers to parts (a) and (b), what is the sum $x^2 + 2x - 2$? 0

Practice and Problem Solving Wkbk/ All-in-One Resources/Online
Think About a Plan

6-3 Think About a Plan
Binomial Radical Expressions

Geometry Show that the right triangle with legs of length $\sqrt{2} - 1$ and $\sqrt{2} + 1$ is similar to the right triangle with legs of length $6 - \sqrt{32}$ and 2.

Understanding the Problem

1. What is the length of the shortest leg of the first triangle? Explain.
$\sqrt{2} - 1$; because $\sqrt{2} < \sqrt{2}$, $\sqrt{2} - 1$ must be less than $\sqrt{2} + 1$

2. What is the length of the shortest leg of the second triangle? Explain.
$6 - \sqrt{32}$; because $\sqrt{32}$ is between 5 and 6, $6 - \sqrt{32}$ must be between 0 and 1, which is less than 2.

3. Which legs in the two triangles are corresponding legs?
The smaller leg in the first triangle corresponds to the smaller leg in the second triangle. The larger leg in the first triangle corresponds to the larger leg in the second triangle.

Planning the Solution

4. Write a proportion that can be used to show that the two triangles are similar. $\frac{\sqrt{2} - 1}{\sqrt{2} + 1} \stackrel{?}{=} \frac{6 - \sqrt{32}}{2}$

Getting an Answer

5. Simplify your proportion to show that the two triangles are similar.
$\frac{\sqrt{2} - 1}{\sqrt{2} + 1} \stackrel{?}{=} \frac{6 - \sqrt{32}}{2}$
$2(\sqrt{2} - 1) \stackrel{?}{=} (\sqrt{2} + 1)(6 - \sqrt{32})$
$2\sqrt{2} - 2 \stackrel{?}{=} 6\sqrt{2} - \sqrt{64} + 6 - \sqrt{32}$
$2\sqrt{2} - 2 \stackrel{?}{=} 6\sqrt{2} - 8 + 6 - 4\sqrt{2}$
$2\sqrt{2} - 2 = 2\sqrt{2} - 2\checkmark$

Practice and Problem Solving Wkbk/ All-in-One Resources/Online
Standardized Test Prep

6-3 Standardized Test Prep
Binomial Radical Expressions

Multiple Choice

For Exercises 1–5, choose the correct letter.

1. What is the simplest form of $2\sqrt{72} - 3\sqrt{2}$? D
   Ⓐ $2\sqrt{72} - 3\sqrt{2}$ Ⓑ $24\sqrt{2}$ Ⓒ $-2\sqrt{2}$ Ⓓ $9\sqrt{2}$

2. What is the simplest form of $(2 - \sqrt{7})(1 + 2\sqrt{7})$? F
   Ⓕ $-12 + 3\sqrt{7}$ Ⓖ $16 + 5\sqrt{7}$
   Ⓗ $-12 - 3\sqrt{7}$ Ⓘ $3 + \sqrt{7}$

3. What is the simplest form of $(\sqrt{2} + \sqrt{7})(\sqrt{2} - \sqrt{7})$? C
   Ⓐ $9 + 2\sqrt{14}$ Ⓑ $9 - 2\sqrt{14}$ Ⓒ -5 Ⓓ 9

4. What is the simplest form of $\frac{7}{2 + \sqrt{5}}$? F
   Ⓕ $-14 + 7\sqrt{5}$ Ⓖ $-14 - 7\sqrt{5}$
   Ⓗ $14 + 7\sqrt{5}$ Ⓘ $14 - 7\sqrt{5}$

5. What is the simplest form of $8\sqrt[3]{5} - \sqrt[3]{40} - 2\sqrt[3]{135}$? D
   Ⓐ $16\sqrt[3]{5}$ Ⓑ $12\sqrt[3]{5}$ Ⓒ $4\sqrt[3]{5}$ Ⓓ 0

Short Response

6. A hiker drops a rock from the rim of the Grand Canyon. The distance it falls d in feet after t seconds is given by the function $d = 16t^2$. How far has the rock fallen after $(3 + \sqrt{2})$ seconds? Show your work.
[2] $d = 16t^2 = 16(3 + \sqrt{2})^2 = 16(11 + 6\sqrt{2}) = 176 + 96\sqrt{2}$ ft
[1] appropriate method but with computational errors
[0] incorrect answer and no work shown OR no answer given

All-in-One Resources/Online
Enrichment

6-3 Enrichment
Binomial Radical Expressions

Consider how you might use a calculator to find the square of negative three. If you enter the expression -3^2, your calculator produces an answer of -9. However, the square of negative three is $(-3)^2 = (-3)(-3) = 9$. Calculators follow the order of operations. Therefore, a calculator will compute -3^2 as the opposite of 3^2. The correct input is $(-3)^2$, which is correctly evaluated as 9. Be sure to follow the order of operations when expanding binomial radical expressions.

1. Consider the algebraic expression $(a + b)^2$. Is $(a + b)^2$ equivalent to $a^2 + b^2$? If yes, explain. If not, explain why it is not mathematically logical and give a counterexample.
Answer may vary. Sample: $(a + b)^2$ means $(a + b)(a + b)$ which, when expanded, is $a^2 + 2ab + b^2$, which is not equivalent to $a^2 + b^2$.

2. Are there values of a and b for which $(a + b)^2 = a^2 + b^2$?
Answers may vary. Sample: $a = 1$, $b = 0$

Consider each pair of expressions below for nonnegative values of the variables. State whether they are equivalent expressions. If yes, explain. If not, give a counterexample.

3. $\sqrt{x^2 + y^2}$, $\sqrt{x^2} + \sqrt{y^2}$
Answers may vary. Sample: These expressions are not equivalent. Let $x = 2$ and $y = 3$ then $\sqrt{2^2 + 3^2} = \sqrt{13} \neq \sqrt{4} + \sqrt{9}$

4. $\frac{\sqrt{a}}{\sqrt{b}}$, $\sqrt{\frac{a}{b}}$
Answers may vary. Sample: These expressions are not equivalent. Let $a = 6$ and $b = 2$ then $\frac{\sqrt{6}}{\sqrt{2}} = 1.22$ and $\sqrt{\frac{6}{2}} = \sqrt{3} = 1.73$

5. $(\sqrt{a})^2$, a
Answers may vary. Sample: These expressions are equivalent. $(\sqrt{a})^2 = (\sqrt{a})(\sqrt{a}) = \sqrt{a^2} = a$ for all $a \geq 0$.

6. $(\sqrt{x^2 + y^2})^2$, $x + y$
Answers may vary. Sample: These expressions are not equivalent. $(\sqrt{x^2 + y^2})(\sqrt{x^2 + y^2}) = \sqrt{(x^2 + y^2)^2} = x^2 + y^2$

Online Teacher Resource Center
Activities, Games, and Puzzles

6-3 Activity: Bringing Closure
Binomial Radical Expressions

Form five teams for this activity.

Each team will investigate one of the expressions shown below. Notice that each of the expressions has the general form $a + b\sqrt{p}$ where a and b are real numbers and p is a prime number. Are numbers of this form closed under multiplication? Let's find out.

Team A	Team B	Team C	Team D	Team E
$2 + \sqrt{2}$	$3 - \sqrt{3}$	$1 + 2\sqrt{5}$	$-1 + 2\sqrt{7}$	$2 + \sqrt{11}$

Complete the table below by raising your radical expression to the 1st, 2nd, and 3rd power.

	Team A	Team B	Team C	Team D	Team E
1st power	$2 + \sqrt{2}$	$3 - \sqrt{3}$	$1 + 2\sqrt{5}$	$-1 + 2\sqrt{7}$	$2 + \sqrt{11}$
2nd power	$6 + 4\sqrt{2}$	$12 - 6\sqrt{3}$	$21 + 4\sqrt{5}$	$29 - 4\sqrt{7}$	$15 + 4\sqrt{11}$
3rd power	$20 + 14\sqrt{2}$	$54 - 30\sqrt{3}$	$61 + 46\sqrt{5}$	$-85 + 62\sqrt{7}$	$74 + 23\sqrt{11}$

1. Look at the answers in your column. What do you notice about the general form of each of them?
Each answer is a binomial radical expression of the form $a + b\sqrt{p}$.

2. Raise your radical expression to the fourth and fifth powers using the space below. What do you notice about the general form of your answers?
Each answer is a binomial radical expression of the form $a + b\sqrt{p}$.

3. If you were to raise your radical expression to the fifth power, what can you predict about the general form of the answer?
Answers will have the general form $a + b\sqrt{p}$.

4. Which property is illustrated by your answers to Exercises 1–3? Explain.
The Closure Property of Multiplication; each time I raised a binomial radical expression to a power (repeated multiplication), the product was also a binomial radical expression. So, the set of numbers $a + b\sqrt{p}$ (where a and b are real numbers and p is a prime number) is closed under multiplication.

Discuss your findings as a class to see if each of the five teams came to the same conclusion. Check students' work.

6-4 Rational Exponents

© **Common Core State Standards**

N-RN.A.2 Rewrite expressions involving radicals and rational exponents using the properties of exponents.
Also reviews N-RN.A.1

MP 1, MP 3, MP 4

Objective To simplify expressions with rational exponents

It is easy to cut one 1-square into congruent pieces each with size $\frac{1}{2}$. How about size $\frac{1}{5}$?

MATHEMATICAL PRACTICES

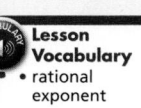
Lesson Vocabulary
• rational exponent

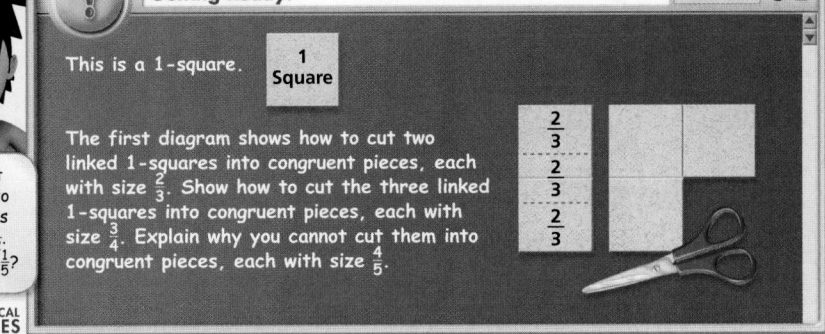

Getting Ready!

This is a 1-square.

| 1 Square |

The first diagram shows how to cut two linked 1-squares into congruent pieces, each with size $\frac{2}{3}$. Show how to cut the three linked 1-squares into congruent pieces, each with size $\frac{3}{4}$. Explain why you cannot cut them into congruent pieces, each with size $\frac{4}{5}$.

If $a^x = \sqrt[4]{a^3}$, then by definition, $a^x \cdot a^x \cdot a^x \cdot a^x = a^3$. By adding exponents, $a^{4x} = a^3$, then $4x = 3$. So x is $\frac{3}{4}$. This suggests an alternative notation for radical expressions in which, for example, $\sqrt[4]{a^3} = a^{\frac{3}{4}}$.

Essential Understanding You can write a radical expression in an equivalent form using a fractional (rational) exponent instead of a radical sign.

In general, $\sqrt[n]{x} = x^{\frac{1}{n}}$ for any positive integer n. Like the radical form, the exponent form indicates the principal root.

$$\sqrt{36} = 36^{\frac{1}{2}} \qquad \sqrt[3]{64} = 64^{\frac{1}{3}} \qquad \sqrt[4]{16} = 16^{\frac{1}{4}}$$

Think

What does the denominator of the fractional exponent represent?
The denominator of the fraction is the index of the radical.

© **Problem 1** Simplifying Expressions with Rational Exponents

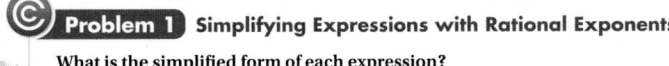

What is the simplified form of each expression?

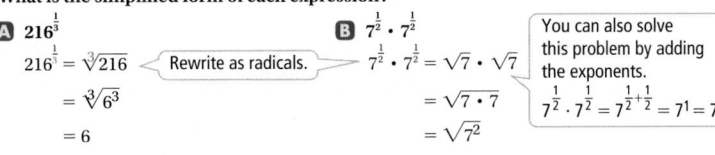

A $216^{\frac{1}{3}}$

$216^{\frac{1}{3}} = \sqrt[3]{216}$ ◁ Rewrite as radicals. ▷

$= \sqrt[3]{6^3}$

$= 6$

B $7^{\frac{1}{2}} \cdot 7^{\frac{1}{2}}$

$7^{\frac{1}{2}} \cdot 7^{\frac{1}{2}} = \sqrt{7} \cdot \sqrt{7}$

$= \sqrt{7 \cdot 7}$

$= \sqrt{7^2}$

$= 7$

You can also solve this problem by adding the exponents.

$7^{\frac{1}{2}} \cdot 7^{\frac{1}{2}} = 7^{\frac{1}{2}+\frac{1}{2}} = 7^1 = 7$

1 Interactive Learning

Solve It!

PURPOSE To use multiplication and division of fractions to prove a task is impossible

PROCESS Students may

• sketch the squares and use trial and error to cut the 1-squares into 4 congruent pieces.

• determine the number of congruent pieces of size $\frac{3}{4}$ that can be cut by dividing 3 by $\frac{3}{4}$.

FACILITATE

Q How can you find the number of congruent pieces of size $\frac{3}{4}$ that can be cut from the three 1-squares? **[by dividing: $3 \div \frac{3}{4} = 4$]**

Q Suppose you attempt to cut the 1-squares into congruent pieces of size $\frac{4}{5}$. How many pieces would you cut? **[$3 \div \frac{4}{5} = \frac{15}{4} = 3.75$]**

Q Is 3 evenly divisible by $\frac{3}{4}$? $\frac{4}{5}$? **[yes; no]**

ANSWER See Solve It in Answers on next page.

CONNECT THE MATH The students use multiplication and division of fractions to find the solutions for the Solve It. These skills are reinforced in the lesson as they use properties of rational exponents to simplify expressions with rational exponents as well as convert between exponential and radical form.

2 Guided Instruction

Problem 1

Q The exponent $\frac{1}{2}$ indicates a square root. What does the exponent $\frac{1}{3}$ indicate? **[a cube root]**

6-4 Preparing to Teach

BIG idea Equivalence

ESSENTIAL UNDERSTANDINGS

• A radical expression can be written in an equivalent form using a fractional (rational) exponent instead of a radical sign.

• $\sqrt[n]{x} = x^{\frac{1}{n}}$ for any positive integer n. Like the radical form, the exponent form indicates the principal root.

• The nth root of an expression that contains an nth power as a factor can be simplified.

$$\sqrt[n]{x^n} = x^{\frac{n}{n}} = \begin{cases} x, & \text{if } n \text{ is odd} \\ |x|, & \text{if } n \text{ is even} \end{cases}$$

Math Background

Extending exponents to include those that are not integers not only gives an alternative way to write radical expressions, but also allows students to apply all the previously learned properties of exponents to expressions containing radicals. When powers are extended to include all rational exponents, it is customary to restrict bases to the set of positive real numbers, so that all the familiar laws of exponents *do* hold.

Students may question why radicals can be expressed as fractional exponents. Explain that $(x^{\frac{1}{n}})^n = x^{\frac{n}{n}} = x$ by the laws of exponents, and $(\sqrt[n]{x})^n = x$ or $|x|$, so it makes sense to define $x^{\frac{1}{n}}$ as $\sqrt[n]{x}$.

© **Mathematical Practices**

Make sense of problems and persevere in solving them. Students will make conjectures about and gain insight into the relationship between rational exponents and integer roots and powers.

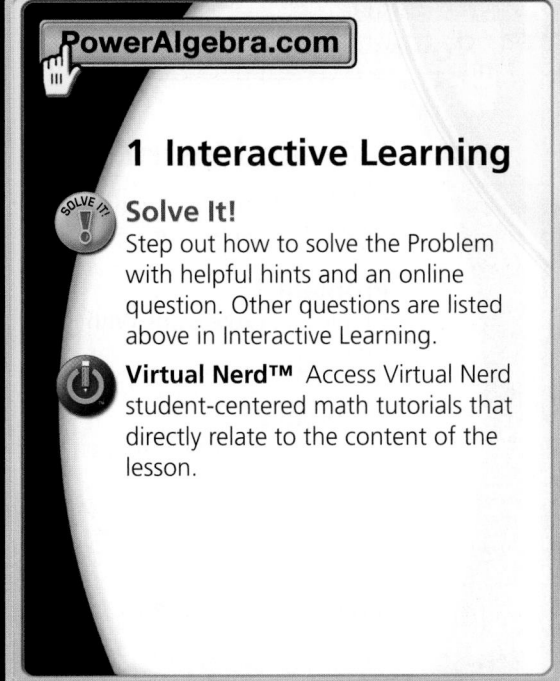

PowerAlgebra.com

1 Interactive Learning

Solve It!
Step out how to solve the Problem with helpful hints and an online question. Other questions are listed above in Interactive Learning.

Virtual Nerd™ Access Virtual Nerd student-centered math tutorials that directly relate to the content of the lesson.

Got It?

Students may use calculators with an x^y key to check these answers.

Take Note

- Use the example $\sqrt[3]{x} \cdot \sqrt[6]{x}$ to show students the advantages of changing radicals to exponential expressions.
- Once the expression has been converted to $x^{\frac{1}{3}} \cdot x^{\frac{1}{6}}$, students can use the laws of exponents to show $x^{\frac{1}{3}} \cdot x^{\frac{1}{6}} = x^{\frac{1}{2}} = \sqrt{x}$.
- Have a volunteer use 64 for x to confirm this result.

Problem 2

Q What is 2 to the 7th power? What is the value of $x^{\frac{3}{7}}$ for $x = 128$? Which form allows you to evaluate the expression for $x = 128$ without using a calculator? **[128; 8; radical form]**

Got It?

ERROR PREVENTION

Model this sequence of steps for converting a fractional exponent to a radical expression:
$$x^{\frac{2}{3}} = (x^2)^{\frac{1}{3}} = \sqrt[3]{x^2}$$

Q What part of a fractional exponent is the index of the radical? **[the denominator]**

C $5^{\frac{1}{4}} \cdot 125^{\frac{1}{4}}$

$5^{\frac{1}{4}} \cdot 125^{\frac{1}{4}} = \sqrt[4]{5} \cdot \sqrt[4]{125}$	Rewrite as radicals.
$= \sqrt[4]{5 \cdot 125}$	Property for multiplying radical expressions
$= \sqrt[4]{625}$	Multiply.
$= \sqrt[4]{5^4}$	Rewrite the radicand.
$= 5$	Simplify.

Got It? 1. What is the simplified form of each expression?

a. $64^{\frac{1}{2}}$ **b.** $11^{\frac{1}{2}} \cdot 11^{\frac{1}{2}}$ **c.** $3^{\frac{1}{2}} \cdot 12^{\frac{1}{2}}$

If $\sqrt[n]{x} = x^{\frac{1}{n}}$, it follows from the Laws of Exponents that for all real numbers $\sqrt[n]{x^m} = (x^m)^{\frac{1}{n}} = (x^{\frac{1}{n}})^m = (\sqrt[n]{x})^m$. This leads to the definition of a rational exponent.

Key Concept   Rational Exponent

If the nth root of a is a real number, m is an integer, and $\frac{m}{n}$ is in lowest terms, then
$$a^{\frac{1}{n}} = \sqrt[n]{a} \quad \text{and} \quad a^{\frac{m}{n}} = \sqrt[n]{a^m} = (\sqrt[n]{a})^m. \qquad \text{If } m \text{ is negative, } a \neq 0.$$

Problem 2   Converting Between Exponential and Radical Forms

A What are $x^{\frac{3}{7}}$ and $y^{-3.5}$ in radical form?

Think

Does the fraction $\frac{3}{7}$ first need to be simplified?
No. The fraction is already in lowest terms.

$$x^{\frac{3}{7}} = \sqrt[7]{x^3} \text{ or } (\sqrt[7]{x})^3$$
$$y^{-3.5} = y^{-\frac{7}{2}}$$
$$= \frac{1}{y^{\frac{7}{2}}}$$
$$= \frac{1}{\sqrt{y^7}} = \frac{1}{\sqrt{y^6 y}} = \frac{1}{y^3 \sqrt{y}} \text{ or } \frac{\sqrt{y}}{y^4}$$

B What are $\sqrt{a^5}$ and $(\sqrt[5]{b})^3$ in exponential form?
$$\sqrt{a^5} = (a^5)^{\frac{1}{2}} = a^{\frac{5}{2}}$$
$$(\sqrt[5]{b})^3 = (b^{\frac{1}{5}})^3 = b^{\frac{3}{5}}$$

Got It? 2. a. What are the expressions $w^{-\frac{5}{8}}$ and $w^{0.2}$ in radical form?

b. What are the expressions $\sqrt[4]{x^3}$ and $(\sqrt[5]{y})^4$ in exponential form?

c. Reasoning Refer to the definition of rational exponent. Explain the need for the restriction that $a \neq 0$ if m is negative.

PowerAlgebra.com

2 Guided Instruction

Each Problem is worked out and supported online.

Problem 1
Simplifying Expressions With Rational Exponents

Problem 2
Converting Between Exponential and Radical Form
Animated

Problem 3
Using Rational Exponents

Problem 4
Combining Radical Expressions
Animated

Problem 5
Simplifying Numbers With Rational Exponents

Problem 6
Writing Expressions in Simplest Form

Support in Algebra 2 Companion
- Vocabulary
- Key Concepts
- Got It?

Answers

Solve It!

You can determine how many congruent pieces to make by finding $3 \div \frac{3}{4} = 4$. Since $\frac{4}{5}$ does not divide 3 evenly, you cannot cut three 1-squares into congruent pieces of size $\frac{4}{5}$.

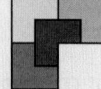

Got It?

1. a. 8   **b.** 11   **c.** 6

2. a. $\frac{\sqrt[8]{w^3}}{w}, \sqrt[5]{w}$ **b.** $x^{\frac{3}{4}}, y^{\frac{4}{5}}$

c. If m is negative, a is in the denominator and $\frac{1}{a}$ is undefined when $a = 0$.

3. a. The length of a Venusian year is about 0.61 Earth years.

b. The length of a Jovian year is about 12.76 Earth years.

Planetary Motion Kepler's Third Law of Orbital Motion shows how you can approximate the period P (in Earth years) it takes a planet to complete one orbit of the sun. Use the function $P = d^{\frac{3}{2}}$, where d is the distance from the planet to the sun in astronomical units (AU—about 93,000,000 miles or the distance from Earth to the sun). How many Earth years does it take Mars to orbit the sun?

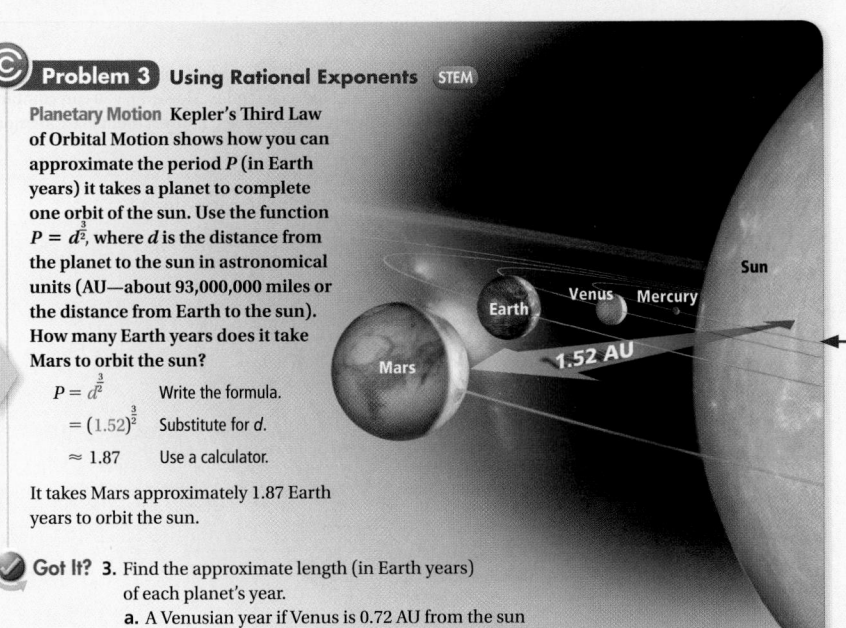

Sun

Venus   Mercury

Earth

Mars

1.52 AU

$P = d^{\frac{3}{2}}$ Write the formula.

$= (1.52)^{\frac{3}{2}}$ Substitute for d.

≈ 1.87 Use a calculator.

It takes Mars approximately 1.87 Earth years to orbit the sun.

Plan

How can you find a $\frac{3}{2}$ power on a calculator?
You can use ⌃.
You can also cube the number and then take the square root, or take the square root then cube.

✓ **Got It?** **3.** Find the approximate length (in Earth years) of each planet's year.
  a. A Venusian year if Venus is 0.72 AU from the sun
  b. A Jovian year if Jupiter is 5.46 AU from the sun

All the properties of integer exponents apply to rational exponents.

take note

Properties	**Properties of Rational Exponents**

Let m and n represent rational numbers. Assume that no denominator equals 0.

Property	**Example**	**Property**	**Example**
$a^m \cdot a^n = a^{m+n}$	$8^{\frac{1}{3}} \cdot 8^{\frac{2}{3}} = 8^{\frac{1}{3}+\frac{2}{3}} = 8^1 = 8$	$a^{-m} = \frac{1}{a^m}$	$9^{-\frac{1}{2}} = \frac{1}{9^{\frac{1}{2}}} = \frac{1}{3}$
$(a^m)^n = a^{mn}$	$\left(5^{\frac{1}{2}}\right)^4 = 5^{\frac{1}{2}\cdot 4} = 5^2 = 25$	$\dfrac{a^m}{a^n} = a^{m-n}$	$\dfrac{7^{\frac{3}{2}}}{7^{\frac{1}{2}}} = 7^{\frac{3}{2}-\frac{1}{2}} = 7^1 = 7$
$(ab)^m = a^m b^m$	$(4 \cdot 5)^{\frac{1}{2}} = 4^{\frac{1}{2}} \cdot 5^{\frac{1}{2}} = 2 \cdot 5^{\frac{1}{2}}$	$\left(\dfrac{a}{b}\right)^m = \dfrac{a^m}{b^m}$	$\left(\dfrac{5}{27}\right)^{\frac{1}{3}} = \dfrac{5^{\frac{1}{3}}}{27^{\frac{1}{3}}} = \dfrac{5^{\frac{1}{3}}}{3}$

Problem 3

An astronomical unit is approximately the mean distance between the Earth and the sun. It is a derived constant and used to indicate distances within the solar system.

Q Which planet will take longer to orbit the sun: Mars or Neptune? Why? **[Neptune; it is farther from the sun. As d increases, so does P.]**

Q How is $P^2 = d^3$ another way of writing the relationship in the problem? **[$P^2 = d^3$, so $\sqrt{P^2} = \sqrt{d^3}$: $P = d^{\frac{3}{2}}$.]**

Got It?   **ERROR PREVENTION**

Students may get a more accurate solution with this type of problem if they first convert the fraction $\frac{3}{2}$ to a decimal. Entering 1.5 may be easier than entering $\frac{3}{2}$.

Take Note   **AUDITORY LEARNERS**

List on the board these names of the properties shown in the chart. Have students match each name to its algebraic statement.

        Power of a Product
        Negative Exponent
        Product of Powers
        Power of a Quotient
        Quotient of Powers
        Power of a Power

If students seem at all uncertain of these properties, have them work in pairs or small groups to write several more numerical examples of each property.

Additional Problems

1. What is the simplified form of each expression?

  a. $625^{\frac{1}{4}}$

  b. $12^{\frac{1}{2}} \cdot 12^{\frac{1}{2}}$

  c. $12^{\frac{1}{3}} \cdot 18^{\frac{1}{3}}$

ANSWERS

  a. 5

  b. 12

  c. 6

2. a. What are $-2y^{\frac{4}{5}}$ and $d^{-\frac{3}{2}}$ in radical form?

  b. What are $\sqrt{ab^3}$ and $\sqrt[3]{w^2}$ in exponential form?

ANSWERS

  a. $-2\sqrt[5]{y^4}$, $\dfrac{\sqrt{d}}{d^2}$

  b. $a^{\frac{1}{2}}b^{\frac{3}{2}}$, $w^{\frac{2}{3}}$

3. For a $\frac{1}{4}$-in.-thick cookie, the diameter d of the cookie is related to the diameter c of the ball of dough by $d = 1.6c^{\frac{3}{2}}$. What is the diameter to the nearest tenth of an inch of a cookie made from a 2 in. ball of dough?

ANSWER 4.5 in.

4. What is $\sqrt[6]{10}(\sqrt[3]{10})$ in simplest form?

ANSWER $\sqrt{10}$

5. What is each number in simplest form?

  a. $(-64)^{\frac{5}{3}}$

  b. $32^{-1.2}$

ANSWERS

  a. -1024

  b. $\dfrac{1}{64}$

6. What is each expression in simplest form?

  a. $(9y\sqrt{x})^{\frac{3}{2}}$

  b. $(27x^6y^9)^{-\frac{1}{3}}$

ANSWERS

  a. $27y^{\frac{3}{2}}x^{\frac{3}{4}}$

  b. $\dfrac{1}{3x^2y^3}$

Problem 4

Q Is the statement $x^2y^2 = (xy)^4$ true? Why or why not? Give a specific example. **[No; you cannot add the exponents unless the bases are the same. For $x = 8$ and $y = 3$, $8^2 \cdot 3^2 = 576$ and $(8 \cdot 3)^4 = 331,776$.]**

Q How is radical multiplication like multiplying exponential expressions? **[Answers may vary. Sample: You may not be able to simplify the product unless the same expression is under both radical signs.]**

Got It?

Q How can you check your result for 4b? **[Substitute a numerical value, such as $x = 64$.]**

Problem 5

Q How are the two methods for 5A different? **[Method 1 changes the base to a power of 2; method 2 converts the expression to a fraction with a positive exponent and then to radical form.]**

Q How are the two methods for 5B different? **[Method 1 changes the base to a power of -2; method 2 converts the expression to radical form.]**

Recall from Lesson 6-2 that you simplified products or quotients involving radical expressions only when they had the same index. However, you can combine radical expressions with different indexes if you convert them to expressions with rational exponents.

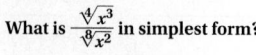

Problem 4 Combining Radical Expressions

What is $\dfrac{\sqrt[4]{x^3}}{\sqrt[8]{x^2}}$ in simplest form?

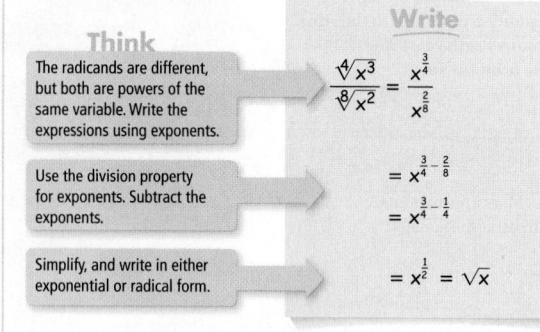

Think

The radicands are different, but both are powers of the same variable. Write the expressions using exponents.

Use the division property for exponents. Subtract the exponents.

Simplify, and write in either exponential or radical form.

Write

$$\dfrac{\sqrt[4]{x^3}}{\sqrt[8]{x^2}} = \dfrac{x^{\frac{3}{4}}}{x^{\frac{2}{8}}}$$

$$= x^{\frac{3}{4} - \frac{2}{8}}$$

$$= x^{\frac{3}{4} - \frac{1}{4}}$$

$$= x^{\frac{1}{2}} = \sqrt{x}$$

Got It? 4. What is each product or quotient in simplest form?

a. $\sqrt{3}\left(\sqrt[4]{3}\right)$ **b.** $\dfrac{\sqrt{x^3}}{\sqrt[3]{x^2}}$ **c.** $\sqrt{7}\left(\sqrt[3]{7}\right)$

You can simplify a number with a rational exponent by using the properties of exponents or by converting the expression to a radical expression.

Problem 5 Simplifying Numbers With Rational Exponents

What is each number in simplest form?

A $16^{-2.5}$

Plan

What is the first step?
Rewrite the decimal exponent as a fraction in lowest terms.

Method 1

$$16^{-2.5} = 16^{-\frac{5}{2}}$$

$$= (2^4)^{-\frac{5}{2}}$$

$$= 2^{4 \cdot -\frac{5}{2}}$$

$$= 2^{-10}$$

$$= \dfrac{1}{2^{10}} = \dfrac{1}{1024}$$

Method 2

$$16^{-2.5} = 16^{-\frac{5}{2}}$$

$$= \dfrac{1}{16^{\frac{5}{2}}}$$

$$= \dfrac{1}{\left(\sqrt{16}\right)^5}$$

$$= \dfrac{1}{4^5}$$

$$= \dfrac{1}{1024}$$

Answers

Got It? (continued)

4. a. $\sqrt[4]{27}$

   b. $\sqrt[6]{x^5}$

   c. $\sqrt[6]{16,807}$

B $(-32)^{\frac{4}{5}}$

Method 1

$$(-32)^{\frac{4}{5}} = ((-2)^5)^{\frac{4}{5}}$$
$$= (-2)^{5 \cdot \frac{4}{5}}$$
$$= (-2)^4$$
$$= 16$$

Method 2

$$(-32)^{\frac{4}{5}} = \left(\sqrt[5]{-32}\right)^4$$
$$= \left(\sqrt[5]{(-2)^5}\right)^4$$
$$= (-2)^4$$
$$= 16$$

✔ **Got It? 5.** What is each number in simplest form?

a. $32^{-\frac{3}{5}}$ **b.** $16^{\frac{3}{4}}$ **c.** $9^{-3.5}$

To write an expression with rational exponents in simplest form, write every exponent as a positive number.

© **Problem 6** Writing Expressions in Simplest Form

What is each expression in simplest form?

Plan

What is the first step in simplifying a radical expression using the properties of exponents?
Rewrite the radicals using rational exponents.

A $\left(-8x\sqrt{xy}\right)^{\frac{2}{3}}$

$$\left(-8x\sqrt{xy}\right)^{\frac{2}{3}} = (-8)^{\frac{2}{3}} \cdot x^{\frac{2}{3}} \cdot ((xy)^{\frac{1}{2}})^{\frac{2}{3}}$$
$$= ((-2)^3)^{\frac{2}{3}} \cdot x^{\frac{2}{3}} \cdot (xy)^{\frac{1}{3}}$$
$$= (-2)^2 \cdot x^{\frac{2}{3}} \cdot x^{\frac{1}{3}} \cdot y^{\frac{1}{3}}$$
$$= 4xy^{\frac{1}{3}}, \text{ or } 4x\sqrt[3]{y}$$

B $\left(16y^{-8}\right)^{-\frac{3}{4}}$

$$\left(16y^{-8}\right)^{-\frac{3}{4}} = 16^{-\frac{3}{4}} \cdot y^{-8 \cdot -\frac{3}{4}}$$
$$= (2^4)^{-\frac{3}{4}} \cdot y^6$$
$$= 2^{-3}y^6$$
$$= \frac{y^6}{8}$$

✔ **Got It? 6.** What is each expression in simplest form?

a. $(8x^{15})^{-\frac{1}{3}}$ **b.** $\left(9x\sqrt[4]{y}\right)^{\frac{3}{2}}$

✔ **Lesson Check**

Do you know HOW?

Simplify each expression.

1. $125^{\frac{1}{3}}$ **2.** $5^{\frac{1}{2}} \cdot 5^{\frac{1}{2}}$

3. $25^{-\frac{3}{2}}$ **4.** $4^{-3.5}$

5. $\sqrt{11}\left(\sqrt[4]{11}\right)$ **6.** $\dfrac{\sqrt[3]{x}}{\sqrt[6]{x^5}}$

Do you UNDERSTAND? © MATHEMATICAL PRACTICES

© **7. Open-Ended** Find a nonzero number q such that $q(1 - 2^{\frac{1}{2}})$ is a rational number. Explain.

© **8. Error Analysis** Explain why this simplification is incorrect.

$$5(4 - 5^{\frac{1}{2}})$$
$$5(4) - 5(5^{\frac{1}{2}})$$
$$20 - 25^{\frac{1}{2}}$$
$$15$$

© **9. Reasoning** Explain why $(-64)^{\frac{1}{3}} = -64^{\frac{1}{3}}$ but $(-64)^{\frac{1}{2}} \neq -64^{\frac{1}{2}}$.

PowerAlgebra.com Lesson 6-4 Rational Exponents 385

---

5. a. $\frac{1}{8}$

b. 8

c. $\frac{1}{2187}$

6. a. $\frac{1}{2x^5}$

b. $27x\sqrt[8]{x^4y^3}$

Lesson Check

1. 5

2. 5

3. $\frac{1}{125}$

4. $\frac{1}{128}$

5. $\sqrt[4]{11^3}$

6. $\frac{\sqrt{x}}{x}$

7. $(1 + \sqrt{2})$ or any nonzero rational number times $(1 + \sqrt{2})$

8. error in third line, second term; $5\left(5^{\frac{1}{2}}\right) = 5^{\frac{3}{2}}$. The third and fourth lines should be:
$$20 - 5^{\frac{3}{2}}$$
$$20 - 5\sqrt{5}$$

9. $(-64)^{\frac{1}{3}} = \sqrt[3]{-64} = -4$ and $-64^{\frac{1}{3}} = -\sqrt[3]{64} = -4$; $(-64)^{\frac{1}{2}} = \sqrt{-64}$, which is not a real number, but $-64^{\frac{1}{2}} = -\sqrt{64} = -8$, which is a real number.

4 Practice

ASSIGNMENT GUIDE

Basic: 10–66 all, 67, 72–82 even

Average: 11–65 odd, 67–90

Advanced: 11–65 odd, 67–97

Standardized Test Prep: 98–101

 Mathematical Practices are supported by exercises with red headings. Here are the Practices supported in this lesson:

MP 3: Communicate Ex. 7, 88

MP 3: Construct Arguments Ex. 7, 89a, 89b

MP 3: Compare Arguments Ex. 9

MP 3: Critique the Reasoning of Others Ex. 8

Applications exercises have blue headings. Exercises 35–38 and 78 support MP 4: Model.

STEM exercises focus on science or engineering applications.

EXERCISE 78: Use the Think About a Plan worksheet in the **Practice and Problem Solving Workbook** (also available in the Teaching Resources in print and online) to further support students' development in becoming independent learners.

HOMEWORK QUICK CHECK

To check students' understanding of key skills and concepts, go over Exercises 37, 51, 67, 78, and 82.

 **Practice and Problem-Solving Exercises**  **MATHEMATICAL PRACTICES**

A Practice

Simplify each expression. ◀ See Problem 1.

10. $36^{\frac{1}{2}}$ 11. $27^{\frac{1}{3}}$ 12. $49^{\frac{1}{2}}$

13. $10^{\frac{1}{2}} \cdot 10^{\frac{1}{2}}$ 14. $(-3)^{\frac{1}{3}} \cdot (-3)^{\frac{1}{3}} \cdot (-3)^{\frac{1}{3}}$ 15. $7^{\frac{1}{2}} \cdot 21^{\frac{1}{2}}$

16. $2^{\frac{1}{2}} \cdot 32^{\frac{1}{2}}$ 17. $3^{\frac{1}{3}} \cdot 9^{\frac{1}{3}}$ 18. $3^{\frac{1}{4}} \cdot 27^{\frac{1}{4}}$

Write each expression in radical form. ◀ See Problem 2.

19. $x^{\frac{1}{6}}$ 20. $x^{\frac{1}{5}}$ 21. $x^{\frac{2}{7}}$ 22. $y^{\frac{2}{5}}$

23. $y^{\frac{9}{8}}$ 24. $t^{-\frac{3}{4}}$ 25. $x^{1.5}$ 26. $y^{1.2}$

Write each expression in exponential form. ◀ See Problem 2.

27. $\sqrt{-10}$ 28. $\sqrt{7x^3}$ 29. $\sqrt{(7x)^3}$ 30. $\left(\sqrt{7x}\right)^3$

31. $\sqrt[3]{a^2}$ 32. $\left(\sqrt[3]{a}\right)^2$ 33. $\sqrt[4]{c^2}$ 34. $\sqrt[3]{(5xy)^6}$

Optimal Height The optimal height h of the letters of a message printed on pavement is given by the formula $h = \frac{0.00252d^{2.27}}{e}$. Here d is the distance of the driver from the letters and e is the height of the driver's eye above the pavement. All of the distances are in meters. Find h for the given values of d and e. ◀ See Problem 3.

35. $d = 100$ m, $e = 1.2$ m   36. $d = 50$ m, $e = 1.2$ m

37. $d = 50$ m, $e = 2.3$ m   38. $d = 25$ m, $e = 2.3$ m

Find each product or quotient. ◀ See Problem 4.

39. $\left(\sqrt[4]{6}\right)\left(\sqrt[4]{6}\right)$ 40. $\frac{\sqrt[9]{y^3}}{\sqrt[3]{y^9}}$ 41. $\sqrt{5} \cdot \sqrt[5]{5}$ 42. $\sqrt[3]{7} \cdot \sqrt[7]{7}$

43. $\frac{\sqrt[6]{4}}{\sqrt[3]{4}}$ 44. $\sqrt[4]{18} \cdot \sqrt{12}$ 45. $\frac{\sqrt{6}}{\sqrt[3]{36}}$ 46. $\frac{\sqrt{x^4y}}{\sqrt[4]{x^2y^8}}$

Simplify each number. ◀ See Problem 5.

47. $8^{\frac{2}{3}}$ 48. $64^{\frac{2}{3}} 64^{\frac{2}{3}}$ 49. $(-8)^{\frac{2}{3}}$ 50. $(-32)^{\frac{6}{5}}$

51. $(32)^{-\frac{4}{5}}$ 52. $4^{1.5}$ 53. $16^{1.5}$ 54. $10{,}000^{0.75}$

Write each expression in simplest form. ◀ See Problem 6.

55. $\left(x^{\frac{2}{3}}\right)^{-3}$ 56. $\left(x^{-\frac{4}{7}}\right)^7$ 57. $\left(3x^{\frac{2}{3}}\right)^{-1}$ 58. $5\left(x^{\frac{2}{3}}\right)^{-1}$

59. $\left(-27x^{-9}\right)^{\frac{1}{3}}$ 60. $\left(-32y^{15}\right)^{\frac{1}{5}}$ 61. $\left(x^{\frac{1}{3}}y^{-\frac{2}{3}}\right)^{-6}$ 62. $\left(x^{\frac{2}{3}}y^{-\frac{1}{6}}\right)^{-12}$

63. $\left(\frac{x^3}{x^{-1}}\right)^{-\frac{1}{4}}$ 64. $\left(\frac{x^2}{x^{-11}}\right)^{\frac{1}{3}}$ 65. $\left(\frac{x^{\frac{1}{4}}}{y^{-\frac{3}{4}}}\right)^{12}$ 66. $\left(\frac{x^{-\frac{2}{3}}}{y^{-\frac{1}{3}}}\right)^{15}$

PowerAlgebra.com

3 Lesson Check

For a digital lesson check, use the Got It questions.

Support in Algebra 2 Companion
• Lesson Check

4 Practice

Assign homework to individual students or to an entire class.

Answers

Practice and Problem-Solving Exercises

10. 6
11. 3
12. 7
13. 10
14. -3
15. $7\sqrt{3}$
16. 8
17. 3
18. 3
19. $\sqrt[6]{x}$
20. $\sqrt[5]{x}$
21. $\sqrt[7]{x^2}$ or $(\sqrt[7]{x})^2$
22. $\sqrt[5]{y^2}$ or $(\sqrt[5]{y})^2$
23. $\sqrt[8]{y^9}$ or $(\sqrt[8]{y})^9$
24. $\frac{1}{\sqrt[4]{t^3}}$ or $\frac{1}{(\sqrt[4]{t})^3}$
25. $\sqrt{x^3}$ or $(\sqrt{x})^3$
26. $\sqrt[5]{y^6}$ or $(\sqrt[5]{y})^6$
27. $(-10)^{\frac{1}{2}}$
28. $7^{\frac{1}{2}}x^{\frac{3}{2}}$
29. $(7x)^{\frac{3}{2}}$
30. $(7x)^{\frac{3}{2}}$
31. $a^{\frac{2}{3}}$
32. $a^{\frac{2}{3}}$
33. $c^{\frac{1}{2}}$
34. $25x^2y^2$
35. ≈ 72.8 m
36. ≈ 15.1 m
37. ≈ 7.9 m
38. ≈ 1.6 m
39. $\sqrt[12]{6^7}$
40. $\frac{\sqrt[3]{y}}{y^3}$
41. $\sqrt[10]{5^7}$
42. $\sqrt[21]{7^{10}}$
43. $\frac{\sqrt[3]{4}}{2}$
44. $6\sqrt[4]{2}$
45. $\frac{\sqrt[6]{7776}}{6}$
46. $\frac{x\sqrt{xy}}{y^2}$
47. 4
48. 256
49. 4
50. 64
51. $\frac{1}{16}$
52. 8
53. 64
54. 1000
55. $\frac{1}{x^2}$
56. $\frac{1}{x^4}$
57. $\frac{\sqrt[3]{x}}{3x}$
58. $\frac{5\sqrt[3]{x}}{x}$
59. $-\frac{3}{x^3}$
60. $-2y^3$
61. $\frac{y^4}{x^3}$
62. $\frac{y^2}{x^8}$
63. $\frac{1}{x}$
64. $x^{\frac{13}{3}}$
65. x^3y^9
66. $\frac{y^5}{x^{10}}$

Apply

 67. Think About a Plan The ratio R of radioactive carbon to nonradioactive carbon left in a sample of an organism that died T years ago can be approximated by the formula $R = A(2.7)^{-\frac{T}{8033}}$. Here A is the ratio of radioactive carbon to nonradioactive carbon in the living organism. What percent of A is left after 2000 years? After 4000 years? After 8000 years?
- What are the known and unknown values?
- How can you use the properties of exponents to solve this problem?

68. The expression $0.036m^{\frac{3}{4}}$ is used in the study of fluids. Which best represents the value of the expression for $m = 46 \times 10^4$?

    Ⓐ 636   Ⓑ 1460   Ⓒ 1660   Ⓓ 16,600

Simplify each number.

69. $(-343)^{\frac{1}{3}}$ **70.** $(-243)^{\frac{1}{5}}$ **71.** $32^{1.2}$

72. $243^{1.2}$ **73.** $64^{3.5}$ **74.** $100^{4.5}$

75. $-(-27)^{-\frac{4}{3}}$ **76.** $\dfrac{1000^{\frac{4}{3}}}{100^{\frac{3}{2}}}$ **77.** $25^{\frac{3}{2}}$

STEM 78. Science A desktop world globe has a volume of about 1386 cubic inches. The radius of Earth is approximately equal to the radius of the globe raised to the 10th power. Find the radius of Earth. (*Hint:* Use the formula $V = \frac{4}{3}\pi r^3$ for the volume of a sphere.)

Simplify each expression.

79. $x^{\frac{2}{7}} \cdot x^{\frac{3}{14}}$ **80.** $y^{\frac{1}{2}} \cdot y^{\frac{3}{10}}$ **81.** $x^{\frac{3}{5}} \div x^{\frac{3}{10}}$

82. $y^{\frac{5}{7}} \div y^{\frac{3}{14}}$ **83.** $\dfrac{x^{\frac{2}{3}} y^{-\frac{1}{4}}}{x^{\frac{1}{2}} y^{-\frac{1}{2}}}$ **84.** $\dfrac{x^{\frac{1}{2}} y^{-\frac{1}{3}}}{x^{\frac{3}{4}} y^{\frac{1}{2}}}$

85. $\left(\dfrac{16x^{14}}{81y^{18}}\right)^{\frac{1}{2}}$ **86.** $\left(\dfrac{81y^{16}}{16x^{12}}\right)^{\frac{1}{2}}$ **87.** $\left(\dfrac{8x^6}{27y^9}\right)^{\frac{1}{3}}$

88. Open-Ended Find three nonzero numbers a such that $a\left(4 + 5^{\frac{1}{2}}\right)$ is a rational number. Can a itself be a rational number? Explain.

89. a. Reasoning Show that $\sqrt[4]{x^2} = \sqrt{x}$ by using the definition of fourth root.
    b. Reasoning Show that $\sqrt[4]{x^2} = \sqrt{x}$ by rewriting $\sqrt[4]{x^2}$ in exponential form.

90. Simplify $4^{\frac{1}{2}} \cdot 4^{\frac{1}{2}}$ using the following methods. Show all your work.
    a. Use the properties of exponents.
    b. Simplify each term in the product, then multiply.
    c. Convert to radical form, then simplify.

67. about 78%; 61%; 37%

68. A

69. −7

70. −3

71. 64

72. 729

73. 2,097,152

74. 1,000,000,000 or 10^9

75. $-\dfrac{1}{81}$

76. 10

77. 125

78. about 251,000,000 in., or 3961 mi

79. $x^{\frac{1}{2}}$

80. $y^{\frac{4}{5}}$

81. $x^{\frac{3}{10}}$

82. $y^{\frac{1}{2}}$

83. $x^{\frac{1}{6}} y^{\frac{1}{4}}$

84. $\dfrac{x^{\frac{3}{4}} y^{\frac{1}{6}}}{xy}$

85. $\dfrac{4x^7}{9y^9}$

86. $\dfrac{9y^8}{4x^6}$

87. $\dfrac{2x^2}{3y^3}$

88. Answers may vary. Sample: $4 - 5^{\frac{1}{2}}$, $2\left(4 - 5^{\frac{1}{2}}\right)$, $\dfrac{4 - 5^{\frac{1}{2}}}{2}$; No, if a is rational and the product is rational, then $4 + 5^{\frac{1}{2}}$ would have to be rational.

89. a. $\sqrt{x} \cdot \sqrt{x} \cdot \sqrt{x} \cdot \sqrt{x} = x \cdot x = x^2$ so $\sqrt[4]{x^2} = \sqrt{x}$

    b. $\sqrt[4]{x^2} = (x^2)^{\frac{1}{4}} = x^{\frac{2}{4}} = x^{\frac{1}{2}} = \sqrt{x}$

90. a. $4^{\frac{1}{2}} \times 4^{\frac{1}{2}} = 4^1 = 4$

    b. $4^{\frac{1}{2}} \times 4^{\frac{1}{2}} = 2 \times 2 = 4$

    c. $\sqrt{4} \times \sqrt{4} = \sqrt{16} = 4$

Answers

91. 49

92. 9

93. $x^{2\pi}$

94. 1

95. $3^{\sqrt{2}}$

96. 9

97. 33.13 mi/h

Standardized Test Prep

98. 2

99. 12

100. 3

101. 3

 Challenge You can define the rules for irrational exponents so that they have the same properties as rational exponents. Use those properties to simplify each expression.

91. $\left(7^{\sqrt{2}}\right)^{\sqrt{2}}$

92. $\dfrac{3^{3+\sqrt{5}}}{3^{1+\sqrt{5}}}$

93. $\dfrac{x^{4\pi}}{x^{2\pi}}$

94. $5^{2\sqrt{3}} \cdot 25^{-\sqrt{3}}$

95. $9^{\frac{1}{\sqrt{2}}}$

96. $\left(3^{2+\sqrt{2}}\right)^{2-\sqrt{2}}$

STEM **97. Weather** Using data for the effect of temperature and wind on an exposed face, the National Weather Service uses the following formula to determine wind chill.

$$\text{Wind Chill Index} = 35.74 + 0.6215T - 35.75V^{0.16} + 0.4275TV^{0.16}$$

T is the temperature in degrees Fahrenheit and V is the velocity of the wind in miles per hour. Frostbite occurs in about 15 minutes when the wind chill index is -20. Find the wind velocity that produces a wind chill index of -20 when the temperature is 5°F.

Standardized Test Prep

GRIDDED RESPONSE

SAT/ACT

98. What is the simplified value of $\left(\frac{1}{64}\right)^{-\frac{1}{6}}$?

99. What positive value of b makes $9x^2 - bx + 4$ a perfect square trinomial?

100. How many real roots does the cubic polynomial equation $x^3 - 7x^2 + 13x - 4 = 0$ have?

101. What is the y-value of the y-intercept of the graph of $f(x) = 4|x - 2| - 5$?

 ## Apply What You've Learned

MATHEMATICAL PRACTICES
MP 2

Look back at the rule for America's Cup yachts given on page 359.

a. Write the expression on the left side of the rule in radical form.

b. What is the unit of measure associated with each variable in the expression? What is the unit associated with the expression as a whole? Explain.

c. Estimate the value of the expression for the AC45 Wingsail Catamaran detailed on page 359. Show your work and explain how you chose values for the length, sail area, and displacement to make the calculation easier.

Apply What You've Learned

Here students write the expression in the America's Cup rule in radical form and then estimate its value for the AC45 Wingsail Catamaran. Later in the chapter they will analyze the dimensions of the new yacht.

Mathematical Practices

Students **reason quantitatively** to understand the units involved in the expression and to estimate the value of the expression for the AC45. (MP 2)

ANSWERS

a. $\dfrac{L + 1.25\sqrt{S} - 9.8\sqrt[3]{D}}{0.686}$

b. L: meters, S: square meters, D: cubic meters; meters; S is in square meters, so $\sqrt{S}$ is in meters. D is in cubic meters, so $\sqrt[3]{D}$ is in meters. So, the unit for the sum in the numerator, and for the whole expression, is meters.

c. Sample: about 24; using 13.5 m for the length, 100 m² for the sail area, and 1 m³ for the displacement, and using 10 for 9.8 and $\frac{2}{3}$ for 0.686, results in the estimate $\dfrac{13.5 + 1.25(10) - 10}{\left(\frac{2}{3}\right)} = 24$.

6-4 Lesson Resources

Additional Instructional Support

Algebra 2 Companion

Students can use the **Algebra 2 Companion** worktext (4 pages) as you teach the lesson. Use the Companion to support

- New Vocabulary
- Key Concepts
- Got It for each Problem
- Lesson Check

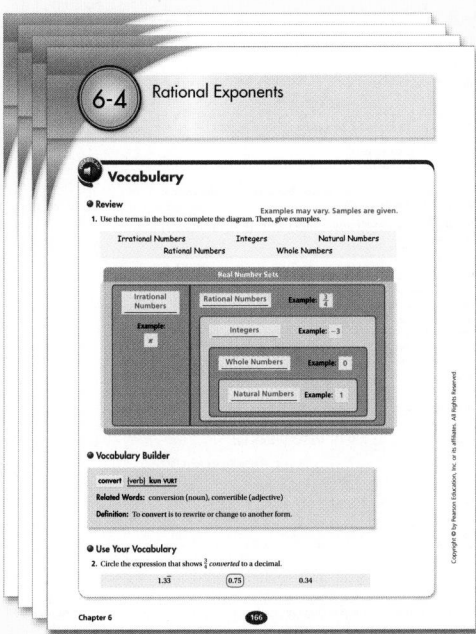

ELL Support

Connect to Prior Knowledge Write the terms *integer* and *rational number* on the board. Ask, "What is an integer? Give some examples." [a positive or negative whole number or zero; 4, −28, 0] "What is a rational number? Give some examples." [A number that can be expressed as a fraction; $\frac{1}{2}$, 3.8, 22] Change the terms to *integer exponent* and *rational exponent*. Ask, "What is an integer exponent? What are some examples?" [an exponent that is an integer, 81^{-3}, 4^2] "What is a rational exponent? What are some examples?" [an exponent that is a rational number, $81^{\frac{2}{3}}$, $16^{1.5}$]

5 Assess & Remediate

Lesson Quiz

1. What is the simplified form of $2^{\frac{1}{2}} \cdot 32^{\frac{1}{2}}$?
2. What is $x^{\frac{1}{2}}y^{\frac{2}{3}}$ in radical form?
3. **Do you UNDERSTAND?** The surface area A of a cube is related to its volume V by $A = 6 \cdot V^{\frac{2}{3}}$. If the volume of a cube is 35 cubic centimeters, what is its surface area to the nearest square centimeter?
4. What is $\frac{\sqrt[6]{w^5}}{\sqrt[3]{w^2}}$ in simplest form?
5. What is the simplest form of $64^{\frac{5}{6}}$?
6. What is the simplest form of $\sqrt[3]{8x^2y^7}$?

ANSWERS TO LESSON QUIZ

1. 8
2. $\sqrt{x} \cdot \sqrt[3]{y^2}$
3. 64 square centimeters
4. $\sqrt[6]{w}$
5. 32
6. $2x^{\frac{2}{3}}y^{\frac{7}{3}}$

PRESCRIPTION FOR REMEDIATION
Use the student work on the Lesson Quiz to prescribe a differentiated review assignment:

Points	Differentiated Remediation
0–3	Intervention
4–5	On-level
6	Extension

PowerAlgebra.com

5 Assess & Remediate

Assign the Lesson Quiz. Appropriate intervention, practice, or enrichment is automatically generated based on student performance.

Intervention

- **Reteaching** (2 pages) Provides reteaching and practice exercises for the key lesson concepts. Use with struggling students or absent students.
- **English Language Learner Support** Helps students develop and reinforce mathematical vocabulary and key concepts.

All-in-One Resources/Online
Reteaching

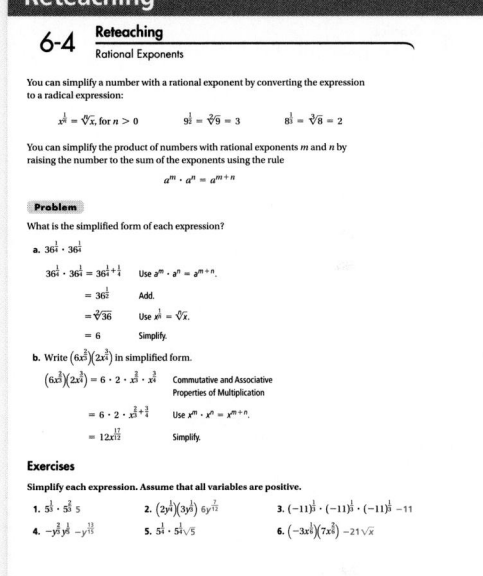

All-in-One Resources/Online
English Language Learner Support

Differentiated Remediation *continued*

On-Level

- **Practice** (2 pages) Provides extra practice for each lesson. For simpler practice exercises, use the Form K Practice pages found in the All-in-One Teaching Resources and online.

- **Think About a Plan** Helps students develop specific problem-solving skills and strategies by providing scaffolded guiding questions.
- **Standardized Test Prep** Focuses on all major exercises, all major question types, and helps students prepare for the high-stakes assessments.

Extension

- **Enrichment** Provides students with interesting problems and activities that extend the concepts of the lesson.
- **Activities, Games, and Puzzles** Worksheets that can be used for concepts development, enrichment, and for fun!

Practice and Problem Solving Wkbk/ All-in-One Workbook/Resources/Online
Practice page 1

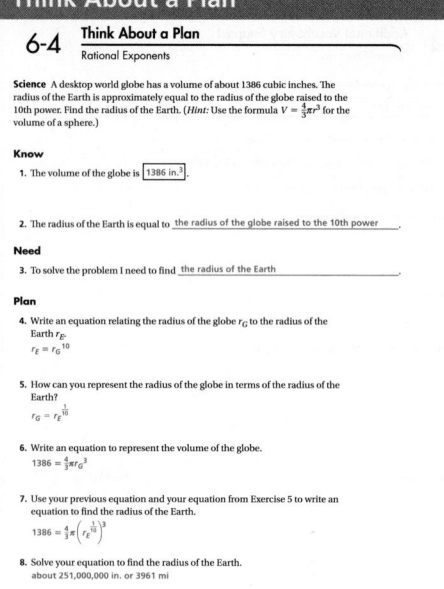

Practice and Problem Solving Wkbk/ All-in-One Workbook/Resources/Online
Practice page 2

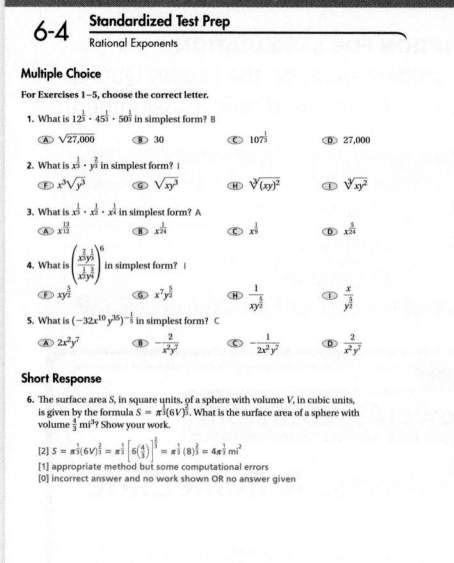

All-in-One Resources/Online
Enrichment

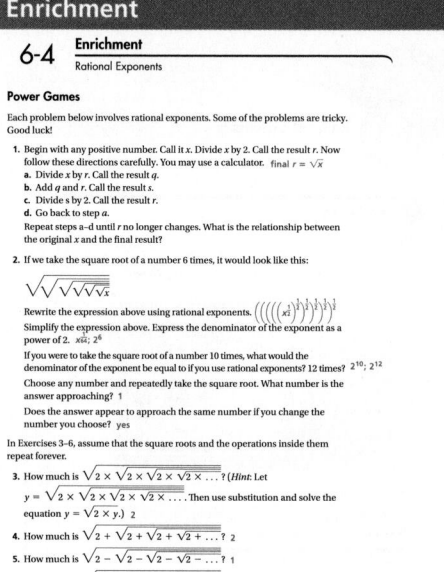

Practice and Problem Solving Wkbk/ All-in-One Workbook Resources/Online
Think About a Plan

Practice and Problem Solving Wkbk/ All-in-One Workbook/Resources/Online
Standardized Test Prep

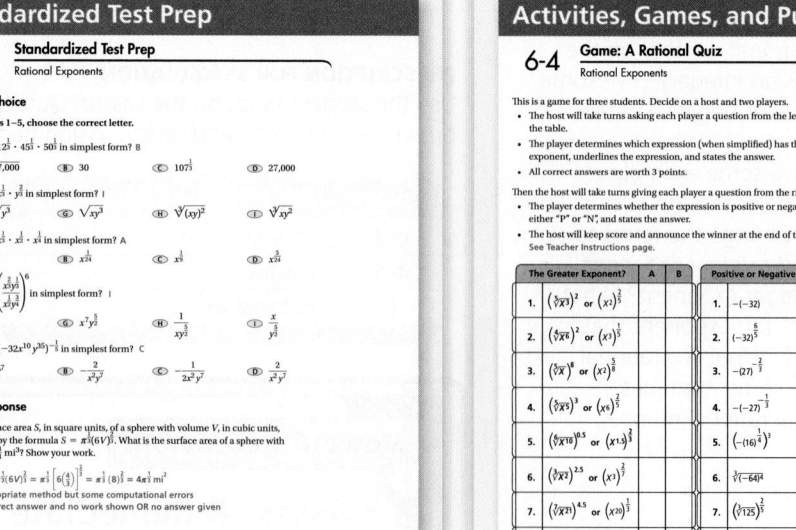

Online Teacher Resource Center
Activities, Games, and Puzzles

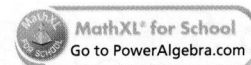
MathXL® for School
Go to PowerAlgebra.com

Do you know HOW?

Find all the real square roots of each number.

1. 100

2. 0.49

Simplify each radical expression. Use absolute value symbols when needed.

3. $\sqrt{36x^2}$

4. $\sqrt[3]{0.008y^3x^6}$

Simplify.

5. $\sqrt{50x^4y^8}$

6. $\sqrt[4]{32m^7n^9}$

Multiply and simplify.

7. $6\sqrt{4x^2} \cdot 2\sqrt{9x^2y^2}$

8. $\sqrt[3]{9} \cdot \sqrt[3]{9}$

9. $\sqrt[5]{16x^8} \cdot \sqrt[5]{x^{14}}$

Divide and simplify.

10. $\dfrac{\sqrt{36x^4}}{\sqrt{9x^6}}$

11. $\dfrac{\sqrt[3]{64x^9y^3}}{\sqrt[3]{8x^3}}$

Simplify. Rationalize all denominators.

12. $10\sqrt[3]{81} - 8\sqrt[3]{24}$

13. $\dfrac{4 + \sqrt{12}}{4 - \sqrt{12}}$

14. $\sqrt{48} - 3\sqrt{27} + 2\sqrt{75}$

15. $(3 + \sqrt{63})(1 + \sqrt{7})$

16. $\dfrac{\sqrt{x}}{\sqrt{6y^3}}$

Write each expression in exponential form.

17. $-\sqrt{17}$

18. $\sqrt[3]{y^8}$

Write each expression in radical form.

19. $m^{\frac{3}{7}}$

20. $y^{-\frac{4}{3}}$

Simplify each expression.

21. $(-27)^{\frac{2}{3}}$

22. $(16)^{\frac{3}{4}}$

Write each expression in simplest form.

23. $7\sqrt[3]{2x} - 3\sqrt[3]{2x}$

24. $2\sqrt{32x^2} + 3\sqrt{72x^2}$

25. $\sqrt[3]{125x^6} - \sqrt[3]{27x^6}$

26. $\sqrt[4]{7} - \sqrt[3]{7}$

27. $(\sqrt{y} - \sqrt{3})(\sqrt{y} + 2\sqrt{3})$

28. $\left(16x^{\frac{1}{4}}y^{\frac{3}{4}}\right)^{-4}$

29. $\left(\dfrac{x^{\frac{1}{3}}}{y^{\frac{2}{3}}}\right)^9$

30. $\left(\dfrac{x^{-10}}{x^5}\right)^{\frac{2}{5}}$

31. The radius of a circle can be expressed as $r = \sqrt{\frac{A}{\pi}}$ inches where r is the radius and A is the area of the circle. If the area of a circle is 169π in.^{2}, what is its radius?

Do you UNDERSTAND?

32. What are the real roots of $\sqrt{-16}$? Explain.

33. **Error Analysis** Identify the error in this statement.
$$\frac{\sqrt[3]{x}}{\sqrt[3]{y}} \cdot \frac{\sqrt[3]{y}}{\sqrt[3]{y}} = \frac{\sqrt[3]{xy}}{y}$$

34. **Reasoning** If $0^{\frac{2}{3}} = 0$, why is $0^{-\frac{2}{3}}$ undefined?

35. Given that x and y are integers, explain why the product of $x + \sqrt{y}$ and its conjugate will always be an integer.

36. **Reasoning** Explain why $(-8)^{\frac{1}{2}} \neq -(8)^{\frac{1}{2}}$, but $(-27)^{\frac{1}{3}} = -(27)^{\frac{1}{3}}$.

32. There are no real roots of $\sqrt{-16}$; there is no real number a such that $a^2 = -16$.

33. error in multiplication of the denominators:
$$\frac{\sqrt[3]{x}}{\sqrt[3]{y}} \cdot \frac{\sqrt[3]{y}}{\sqrt[3]{y}} = \frac{\sqrt[3]{xy}}{\sqrt[3]{y^2}} = \sqrt[3]{\frac{x}{y}}$$

34. $0^{-\frac{2}{3}} = \frac{1}{0}$, which is undefined.

35. The product of two integers will always be an integer, and the product $\sqrt{y} \cdot \sqrt{y} = y$, an integer. The other terms will cancel out and the difference of two integers is an integer.

36. $(-8)^{\frac{1}{2}} = \sqrt{-8}$, which is not a real number, but $-(8)^{\frac{1}{2}} = -\sqrt{8}$, which is a real number; $(-27)^{\frac{1}{3}} = \sqrt[3]{-27} = -3$, and $-\sqrt[3]{27} = -(3) = -3$

Answers

1. ± 10

2. ± 0.7

3. $6|x|$

4. $0.2x^2y$

5. $5x^2y^4\sqrt{2}$

6. $2mn^2\sqrt[4]{2m^3n}$

7. $72x^2|y|$

8. $3\sqrt[3]{3}$

9. $2x^5\sqrt{x}$

10. $\dfrac{2}{|x|}$

11. $2x^2y$

12. $14\sqrt[3]{3}$

13. $7 + 4\sqrt{3}$

14. $5\sqrt{3}$

15. $24 + 6\sqrt{7}$

16. $\dfrac{\sqrt{6xy}}{6y^2}$

17. $-17^{\frac{1}{2}}$

18. $y^{\frac{8}{3}}$

19. $\sqrt[7]{m^3}$

20. $\dfrac{\sqrt[3]{y^2}}{y^2}$

21. 9

22. 8

23. $4\sqrt[3]{2x}$

24. $26|x|\sqrt{2}$

25. $2x^2$

26. cannot be simplified

27. $y + \sqrt{3}y - 6$

28. $\dfrac{1}{65,536\,xy^3}$

29. $\dfrac{x^3}{y^6}$

30. $\dfrac{1}{x^6}$

31. 13 in.

PowerAlgebra.com

MathXL for School
Prepare students for the Mid-Chapter Quiz and Chapter Test with online practice and review.

1 Interactive Learning

Solve It!

PURPOSE To use the Pythagorean Theorem to solve a real-world problem with a solution that can be written in either decimal or radical form

PROCESS Students may use the Pythagorean Theorem to solve for the distance due east that the car will travel to reach the range of 6 mi.

FACILITATE

Q How can you draw a diagram that represents the location of the car when it is 6 mi away from the cell phone tower? **[Sketch a segment from the tower to the road, east of the car, and label the segment 6 mi. Mark the intersection of the segment and road.]**

Q What formula can you use to find the distance the car must travel to reach the 6-mi range? Explain. **[The Pythagorean Theorem; the diagram is a right triangle.]**

ANSWER See Solve It in Answers on next page.
CONNECT THE MATH The Pythagorean Theorem determines the distance the car can travel before the end of the effective range. The Solve It is a real-world application of square root equations, which students solve in the lesson.

2 Guided Instruction

Problem 1

Q What does it mean to "isolate the radical expression"? **[manipulate the equation so that the radical is alone on one side of the equals sign]**

Common Core State Standards
A-REI.A.2 Solve simple rational and radical equations in one variable, and . . . show how extraneous solutions may arise. **Also A-CED.A.4**
MP 1, MP 2, MP 3, MP 4

Objective To solve square root and other radical equations

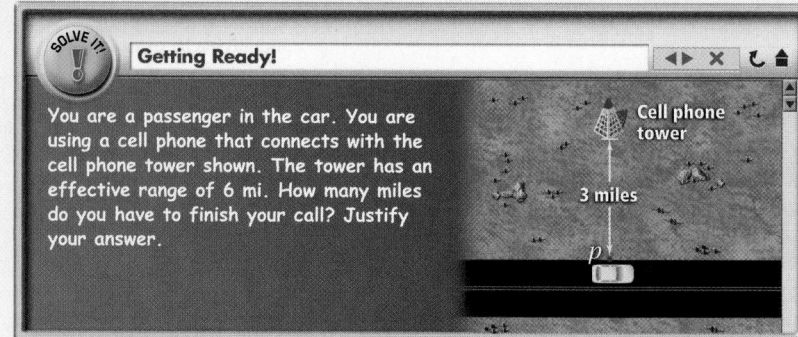

SOLVE IT
Getting Ready!

You are a passenger in the car. You are using a cell phone that connects with the cell phone tower shown. The tower has an effective range of 6 mi. How many miles do you have to finish your call? Justify your answer.

Cell phone tower
3 miles
p

Lesson Vocabulary
• radical equation
• square root equation

A **radical equation** is an equation that has a variable in a radicand or a variable with a rational exponent. If the radical has index 2, the equation is a **square root equation**. In this lesson, assume that all radicals and expressions with rational exponents represent real numbers.

Essential Understanding Solving a square root equation may require that you square each side of the equation. This can introduce extraneous solutions.

To solve a radical equation, isolate the radical on one side of the equation. Then raise each side to the power suggested by the index.

© Problem 1 Solving a Square Root Equation

Think
Do you need to introduce a ± sign here?
No, when you take the square root of each side of an equation you do, but here you are squaring both sides of the equation.

What is the solution of $3 + \sqrt{2x - 3} = 8$?

$$3 + \sqrt{2x - 3} = 8$$
$$\sqrt{2x - 3} = 5 \quad \text{Isolate the radical expression.}$$
$$(\sqrt{2x - 3})^2 = 5^2 \quad \text{Square each side.}$$
$$2x - 3 = 25$$
$$2x = 28 \quad \text{Add 3 to each side.}$$
$$x = 14 \quad \text{Divide each side by 2.}$$

BIG ideas **Equivalence**
Solving Equations and Inequalities

ESSENTIAL UNDERSTANDINGS
• Solving a square root equation may require squaring each side of the equation. This can introduce extraneous solutions.
• A radical equation can be solved by isolating the radical on one side of the equation, then raising each side to the power suggested by the index.
• The *n*th root of an expression that contains an *n*th power as a factor can be simplified.
$$\sqrt[n]{x^n} = x^{\frac{n}{n}} = \begin{cases} x, & \text{if } n \text{ is odd} \\ |x|, & \text{if } n \text{ is even} \end{cases}$$

Math Background

Squaring both sides of an equation does not always produce an equivalent equation. The extraneous solutions that may be introduced are solutions to the transformed equation but are not solutions to the original equation. Because of this, it is critical that students always check their answers in the

original equation. Alternatively, students can graph both sides of the original equation as separate functions and find all intersection points. If a solution is not an intersection, it is extraneous.

Solving a square root equation is both similar to and different from solving other kinds of equations in the following ways:

• Similar: The goal is to isolate the variable on one side of the equation by using inverse operations.
• Different: Extraneous (incorrect) solutions can occur.

© Mathematical Practices
Make sense of problems and persevere in solving them. In solving square root equations, students will check for extraneous solutions using substitution.

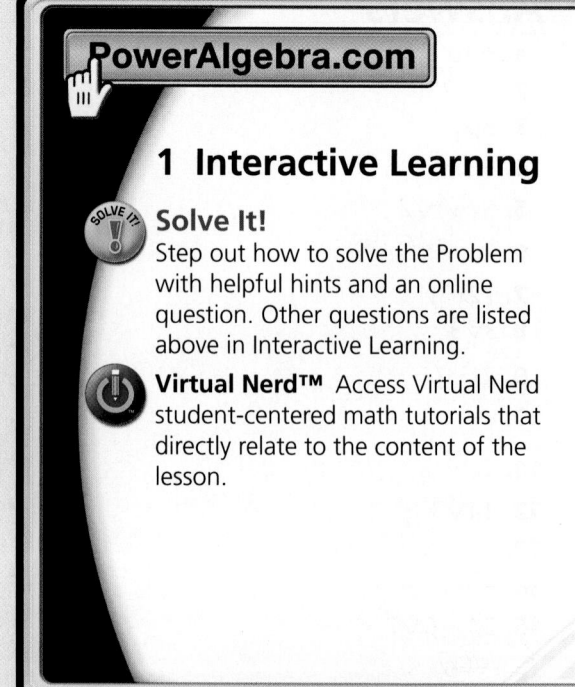

PowerAlgebra.com

1 Interactive Learning

SOLVE IT
Solve It!
Step out how to solve the Problem with helpful hints and an online question. Other questions are listed above in Interactive Learning.

Virtual Nerd™ Access Virtual Nerd student-centered math tutorials that directly relate to the content of the lesson.

Check

$$3 + \sqrt{2x - 3} = 8 \qquad \text{Write the original equation.}$$

$$3 + \sqrt{2(14) - 3} \stackrel{?}{=} 8 \qquad \text{Substitute 14 for } x.$$

$$3 + \sqrt{25} \stackrel{?}{=} 8 \qquad \text{Simplify.}$$

$$3 + 5 \stackrel{?}{=} 8$$

$$8 = 8 ✔$$

✅ **Got It? 1.** What is the solution of $\sqrt{4x + 1} - 5 = 0$?

To solve equations of the form $x^{\frac{m}{n}} = k$, raise each side of the equation to the power $\frac{n}{m}$, the reciprocal of $\frac{m}{n}$. If either m or n is even, then $\left(x^{\frac{m}{n}}\right)^{\frac{n}{m}} = |x|$.

© **Problem 2** Solving Other Radical Equations

Ⓐ What is the solution of $3(x + 1)^{\frac{2}{3}} = 12$?

Know	Need	Plan
• The equation • The power of the exponential expression	Solution of the equation	• Isolate the exponential expression. • Use the inverse of the power to simplify and solve the equation.

Think

How can you get rid of the rational exponent?
Raise each side to the reciprocal power.

$$3(x + 1)^{\frac{2}{3}} = 12$$

$$(x + 1)^{\frac{2}{3}} = 4 \qquad \text{Divide each side by 3.}$$

$$\left((x + 1)^{\frac{2}{3}}\right)^{\frac{3}{2}} = 4^{\frac{3}{2}} \qquad \text{Raise each side to the } \frac{3}{2} \text{ power.}$$

$$(x + 1)^{\frac{6}{6}} = 4^{\frac{3}{2}}$$

$$|x + 1| = 8 \quad \text{Since the numerator of } \frac{2}{3} \text{ is even, } (x^{\frac{2}{3}})^{\frac{3}{2}} = |x|$$

$$x + 1 = \pm 8$$

$$x = 7 \text{ or } x = -9$$

The solutions are 7 and −9.

Check

$$3(x + 1)^{\frac{2}{3}} = 12 \qquad\qquad 3(x + 1)^{\frac{2}{3}} = 12$$

$$3(7 + 1)^{\frac{2}{3}} \stackrel{?}{=} 12 \qquad\qquad 3(-9 + 1)^{\frac{2}{3}} \stackrel{?}{=} 12$$

$$3(2^3)^{\frac{2}{3}} \stackrel{?}{=} 12 \qquad\qquad 3((-2)^3)^{\frac{2}{3}} \stackrel{?}{=} 12$$

$$3(2)^2 \stackrel{?}{=} 12 \qquad\qquad 3(-2)^2 \stackrel{?}{=} 12$$

$$12 = 12 ✔ \qquad\qquad 12 = 12 ✔$$

 PowerAlgebra.com | **Lesson 6-5** Solving Square Root and Other Radical Equations | **391**

---

2 Guided Instruction

© Each Problem is worked out and supported online.

Problem 1
Solving a Square Root Equation

Problem 1 Alternative
Solving a Square Root Equation
Animated

Problem 2
Solving Other Radical Equations

Problem 3
Using Radical Equations

Problem 4
Checking for Extraneous Solutions
Animated

Problem 5
Solving an Equation with Two Radicals
Animated

Support in Algebra 2 Companion
• Vocabulary
• Key Concepts
• Got It?

Answers

Solve It!

about 5.2 mi; $6^2 - 3^2 \approx 5.2^2$

Got It?
1. 6

Got It?

If students have difficulty understanding why it is a good idea to use reciprocals to solve radical equations, show them how to solve an equation without using a rational exponent for the radical:

$2(x + 3)^{\frac{2}{3}} = 8$

$2\sqrt[3]{(x + 3)^2} = 8$

$\sqrt[3]{(x + 3)^2} = 4$

$\left(\sqrt[3]{(x + 3)^2}\right)^3 = 4^3$

$(x + 3)^2 = 64$

$\sqrt{(x + 3)^2} = \sqrt{64}$

$x + 3 = \pm 8$

$x = 5$ or $x = -11$

Problem 3

Q Why should you use 1,200 m for the diameter in this equation instead of 1.2 km? **[Answers may vary. Sample: The formula uses meters and cubic meters.]**

Q Why should you use the word *about* in the answer? **[The problem states that all values are approximate.]**

Got It?

Q What should you do first before substituting values into the equation? **[Convert 1 km to meters.]**

B What is the solution of $3\sqrt[5]{(x + 1)^3} + 1 = 25$?

$3\sqrt[5]{(x + 1)^3} + 1 = 25$

$3(x + 1)^{\frac{3}{5}} + 1 = 25$ Rewrite the radical using a rational exponent.

$3(x + 1)^{\frac{3}{5}} = 24$ Subtract 1 from each side.

$(x + 1)^{\frac{3}{5}} = 8$ Divide each side by 3.

$\left((x + 1)^{\frac{3}{5}}\right)^{\frac{5}{3}} = 8^{\frac{5}{3}}$ Raise each side to the $\frac{5}{3}$ power.

$x + 1 = 32$ Simplify.

$x = 31$ Subtract 1 from each side.

The solution is 31.

Think

Why is isolating the variable important?
If you raise each side of $3\sqrt[5]{(x + 1)^3} + 1 = 25$ to the $\frac{5}{3}$ power you will end up with a more complicated equation, not a simpler one.

Got It? **2.** What are the solution(s) of $2(x + 3)^{\frac{2}{3}} = 8$?

Problem 3 Using Radical Equations **STEM**

Earth Science For Meteor Crater in Arizona, the formula $d = 2\sqrt[3]{\dfrac{V}{0.3}}$ relates the diameter d of the rim (in meters) to the volume V (in cubic meters). What is the volume of Meteor Crater? (All values are approximate.)

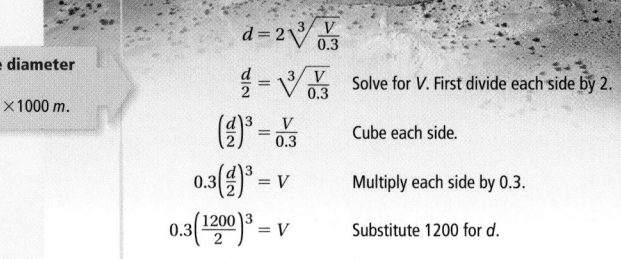

1.2 km

Think

What is the diameter in meters?
$1.2\ km = 1.2 \times 1000\ m.$

$d = 2\sqrt[3]{\dfrac{V}{0.3}}$

$\dfrac{d}{2} = \sqrt[3]{\dfrac{V}{0.3}}$ Solve for V. First divide each side by 2.

$\left(\dfrac{d}{2}\right)^3 = \dfrac{V}{0.3}$ Cube each side.

$0.3\left(\dfrac{d}{2}\right)^3 = V$ Multiply each side by 0.3.

$0.3\left(\dfrac{1200}{2}\right)^3 = V$ Substitute 1200 for d.

$64{,}800{,}000 = V$ Simplify.

The volume of Meteor Crater is about 64,800,000 m³.

Got It? **3.** Suppose the diameter of a similarly shaped crater is 1 km. What is the volume of the crater? Use the formula given in Problem 3.

Additional Problems

1. What is the solution of $\sqrt{x + 4} + 6 = 7$?

ANSWER -3

2. What is the solution of $(6x + 9)^{\frac{1}{3}} - 5 = -2$?

ANSWER 3

3. A parabolic goblet with a cup that is as wide as it is tall holds $1.74r^3$ oz of water when it is full, where r is the radius in inches of the circular rim. What is the radius, to the nearest hundredth of an inch, of a goblet that holds 9 oz?

ANSWER about 1.73 in.

4. What is the solution of $\sqrt{5x + 14} = x$? Check your results.

ANSWER 7

5. What is the solution of $2 + \sqrt{x - 6} = \sqrt{x + 10}$?

ANSWER 15

When you raise each side of an equation to a power, it is possible to introduce extraneous solutions. Therefore, it becomes very important that you check all solutions in the original equation. A correct solution will give a true statement. An extraneous solution will give a false statement.

© Problem 4 Checking for Extraneous Solutions

What is the solution of $\sqrt{x+7} - 5 = x$? Check your results.

$$\sqrt{x+7} - 5 = x$$
$$\sqrt{x+7} = x + 5 \qquad \text{Isolate the radical.}$$
$$(\sqrt{x+7})^2 = (x+5)^2 \qquad \text{Square each side.}$$
$$x + 7 = x^2 + 10x + 25 \qquad \text{Simplify.}$$
$$0 = x^2 + 9x + 18 \qquad \text{Combine like terms.}$$
$$0 = (x+3)(x+6) \qquad \text{Factor.}$$
$$x = -3 \text{ or } x = -6 \qquad \text{Zero-Product Property}$$

Check

$$\sqrt{x+7} - 5 = x$$
$$\sqrt{-3+7} - 5 \overset{?}{=} -3$$
$$\sqrt{4} - 5 \overset{?}{=} -3$$
$$2 - 5 \overset{?}{=} -3$$
$$-3 = -3 \checkmark$$

$$\sqrt{x+7} - 5 = x$$
$$\sqrt{-6+7} - 5 \overset{?}{=} -6$$
$$\sqrt{1} - 5 \overset{?}{=} -6$$
$$1 - 5 \overset{?}{=} -6$$
$$-4 \neq -6$$

The only solution is -3.

false

© ✔ Got It? **4. a.** What is the solution of $\sqrt{5x-1} + 3 = x$? Check your results.
b. Reasoning When should you check for extraneous solutions? Explain.

In this lesson you studied algebraic methods of solving square root and radical equations. In Lesson 6-8 you will study the graphs of square root functions. These graphs can help you find solutions and identify extraneous solutions.

The calculator screen shows the graphs **Y1** $= \sqrt{(x+7)} - 5$ and **Y2** $= x$. From the graph, it is clear that -3 is a solution of $\sqrt{x+7} - 5 = x$, and -6 is not a solution.

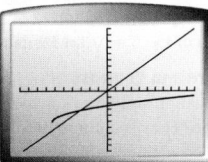

Problem 4   SYNTHESIZING

Sometimes students assume that all negative numbers are extraneous solutions for square root equations. Use this problem to emphasize that some negative numbers do satisfy the original radical equation.

Q How do you check an equation for extraneous solutions? **[Substitute each possible solution for x in the original equation and check to see if the equation is true.]**

Q Why is -6 called an extraneous solution for this equation? **[When it is substituted for x in the original equation, it gives a false statement.]**

Got It?

Q Will you have to check for extraneous solutions for this problem? Explain your answer. **[Yes; to solve the problem, you will have to square both sides of the equation, which may introduce extraneous solutions.]**

Q If you solve a square root equation by graphing, will you have to check for extraneous solutions? Explain. **[No; if a solution is extraneous, it will not be on the graph.]**

Answers

Got It? (continued)

2. 5, −11

3. 37,500,000 m^3

4. a. 10

b. when you raise each side of an equation to a power

Problem 5

Q Why do you square both sides of this equation *twice* to solve it? **[because squaring the first time did not eliminate both radicals]**

In this problem, students may do the following:

$(\sqrt{2x+1})^2 - (\sqrt{x})^2 = 1^2$

or $(\sqrt{2x+1})^2 = 1^2 + (\sqrt{x})^2$. Emphasize that they must raise each *side* to the *n*th power, not each *term*.

Got It?

Q Which radical should you isolate first? Explain. **[$\sqrt{5x+4}$; it is more complicated.]**

3 Lesson Check

Do you know HOW?

• For Exercises 1–6, emphasize that the first step for solving any radical equation is to isolate the radical on one side of the equation.

Do you UNDERSTAND?

• In Exercise 7, make sure students realize that the number they are looking for is *not* a solution to the equation.

Close

Q What are the steps to solving a radical equation? **[Sample: Isolate the radical on one side of the equation. Raise both sides to the power that is the reciprocal of the radical. Simplify. Repeat if there are more radicals. Solve the resulting polynomial equation; check for extraneous solutions.]**

If an equation contains two radical expressions (or two terms with rational exponents), isolate one of the radicals (or one of the terms), then eliminate it (or its rational exponent). Isolate the more complicated radical expression first. In the resulting equation, simplify the expressions before you eliminate the second radical.

 **Problem 5** Solving an Equation With Two Radicals

What is the solution of $\sqrt{2x+1} - \sqrt{x} = 1$?

Plan

Which radical expression should you isolate first? Isolate the more complicated radical first, $\sqrt{2x+1}$.

$$\sqrt{2x+1} - \sqrt{x} = 1$$

$\sqrt{2x+1} = \sqrt{x} + 1$	Isolate the more complicated radical.
$(\sqrt{2x+1})^2 = (\sqrt{x}+1)^2$	Square each side.
$2x+1 = x + 2\sqrt{x} + 1$	
$x = 2\sqrt{x}$	Isolate $2\sqrt{x}$.
$x^2 = (2\sqrt{x})^2$	Square each side.
$x^2 = 4x$	
$x^2 - 4x = 0$	Subtract $4x$ from each side.
$x(x-4) = 0$	Factor.
$x = 0$ or $x = 4$	Zero-Product Property

Check

$\sqrt{2x+1} - \sqrt{x} = 1$	$\sqrt{2x+1} - \sqrt{x} = 1$
$\sqrt{2(0)+1} - \sqrt{0} \stackrel{?}{=} 1$	$\sqrt{2(4)+1} - \sqrt{4} \stackrel{?}{=} 1$
$\sqrt{1} - 0 \stackrel{?}{=} 1$	$\sqrt{9} - \sqrt{4} \stackrel{?}{=} 1$
$1 - 0 \stackrel{?}{=} 1$	$3 - 2 \stackrel{?}{=} 1$
$1 = 1$ ✔	$1 = 1$ ✔

The solutions are 0 and 4.

Got It? 5. What is the solution of $\sqrt{5x+4} - \sqrt{x} = 4$?

Lesson Check

Do you know HOW?

Solve. Check for extraneous solutions.

1. $\sqrt{4x-23} - 3 = 2$
2. $-\sqrt[3]{x} + 3 = 0$
3. $5\sqrt{x} + 7 = 8$
4. $3\sqrt{x} = 6$
5. $5 - 2\sqrt{x} = 3$
6. $\sqrt[3]{x} = 8$

Do you UNDERSTAND?  MATHEMATICAL PRACTICES

7. **Vocabulary** Which value, 12 or 3, is an extraneous solution of $x - 6 = \sqrt{3x}$? Explain your reasoning.

8. **Compare and Contrast** How is solving a square root equation similar to solving an absolute value equation? How is it different?

---

3 Lesson Check

For a digital lesson check, use the Got It questions.

Support in Algebra 2 Companion
• Lesson Check

4 Practice

Assign homework to individual students or to an entire class.

Answers

Got It? (continued)

5. 9

Lesson Check

1. 12
2. 27
3. $\frac{1}{25}$
4. 4
5. 1
6. 512
7. 3; The solution of 3 yields a negative value for $x - 6$, but the right side of the equation ($\sqrt{3(3)}$) cannot be negative.
8. Solving square root equations is different from solving absolute value equations in that you use a different technique to isolate the variable. In square root equations, you square each side. In absolute value equations, you write two new equations and solve both. Solving square root equations is similar to solving absolute value equations in that both can introduce extraneous solutions.

Practice and Problem-Solving Exercises

 MATHEMATICAL PRACTICES

Solve.

See Problem 1.

9. $3\sqrt{x} + 3 = 15$

10. $4\sqrt{x} - 1 = 3$

11. $\sqrt{x+3} = 5$

12. $\sqrt{x+1} = 4$

13. $\sqrt{2x-1} = 3$

14. $\sqrt{x+2} - 2 = 0$

15. $\sqrt{3x+4} = 4$

16. $\sqrt{2x+3} - 7 = 0$

17. $\sqrt{6-3x} - 2 = 0$

Solve.

See Problem 2.

18. $(x+5)^{\frac{2}{3}} = 4$

19. $(x+2)^{\frac{2}{3}} = 9$

20. $3(x-2)^{\frac{3}{4}} = 24$

21. $3(x+3)^{\frac{3}{4}} = 81$

22. $(x+1)^{\frac{3}{2}} - 2 = 25$

23. $3 + (4-x)^{\frac{3}{2}} = 11$

24. **Volume** A spherical water tank holds 9000 ft³ of water. What is the diameter of the tank? $\left(Hint: \frac{1}{6}d^3\pi = V\right)$

See Problem 3.

STEM 25. **Hydraulics** The formula $\frac{\pi d^2 v}{4} = Q$ models the diameter of a pipe where Q is the maximum flow of water in a pipe, and v is the velocity of the water. What is the diameter of a pipe that allows a maximum flow of 30 ft³/min of water flowing at a velocity of 400 ft/min? Round your answer to the nearest inch.

Solve. Check for extraneous solutions.

See Problem 4.

26. $\sqrt{3x+7} = x - 1$

27. $(5-x)^{\frac{1}{2}} = x + 1$

28. $\sqrt{-3x-5} = x + 3$

29. $\sqrt{11x+3} - 2x = 0$

30. $(5x-4)^{\frac{1}{2}} - x = 0$

31. $\sqrt{3x+13} - 5 = x$

32. $\sqrt{x+7} + 5 = x$

33. $(x+3)^{\frac{1}{2}} - 1 = x$

34. $\sqrt{x+7} - x = 1$

Solve. Check for extraneous solutions.

See Problem 5.

35. $\sqrt{3x} = \sqrt{x+6}$

36. $(2x)^{\frac{1}{2}} = (x+5)^{\frac{1}{2}}$

37. $(7x+6)^{\frac{1}{2}} - (9+4x)^{\frac{1}{2}} = 0$

38. $\sqrt{3x+2} - \sqrt{2x+7} = 0$

39. $(x+5)^{\frac{1}{2}} - (5-2x)^{\frac{1}{4}} = 0$

40. $(x-2)^{\frac{1}{2}} - (28-2x)^{\frac{1}{4}} = 0$

41. $\sqrt{5-x} - \sqrt{x} = 1$

42. $\sqrt{3x+1} - \sqrt{x+1} = 2$

43. $\sqrt{2x+6} - \sqrt{x-1} = 2$

44. $\sqrt{3-x} + \sqrt{x+2} = 3$

45. **Think About a Plan** A hexagonal tray of vegetables has an area of 450 cm². What is the length of each side of the hexagon?
- What is the area of the triangle at the bottom in terms of the side length?
- How can you use the diagram at the right to find the formula for the area of the hexagon? (*Hint:* Six triangles make one hexagon.)

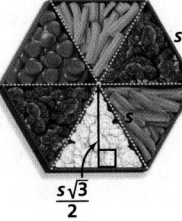

46. **Traffic Signs** A stop sign is a regular octagon, formed by cutting triangles off the corners of a square. If a stop sign measures 36 in. from top to bottom, what is the length of each side?

---

4 Practice

ASSIGNMENT GUIDE

Basic: 9–44, 45–47, 57–60, 63–65

Average: 9–43 odd, 45–67

Advanced: 9–43 odd, 45–72

Standardized Test Prep: 73–76

Mathematical Practices are supported by exercises with red headings. Here are the Practices supported in this lesson:

MP 1: Make Sense of Problems Ex. 45, 68

MP 2: Reason Abstractly Ex. 47

MP 2: Reason Quantitatively Ex. 61

MP 3: Construct Arguments Ex. 62

MP 3: Compare Arguments Ex. 8

MP 3: Critique the Reasoning of Others Ex. 59

Applications exercises have blue headings. Exercises 24, 25, and 46 support MP 4: Model.

STEM exercises focus on science or engineering applications.

EXERCISE 46: Use the Think About a Plan worksheet in the **Practice and Problem Solving Workbook** (also available in the Teaching Resources in print and online) to further support students' development in becoming independent learners.

HOMEWORK QUICK CHECK

To check students' understanding of key skills and concepts, go over Exercises 25, 37, 45, 46, and 60.

Answers

Practice and Problem-Solving Exercises

9. 16

10. 1

11. 22

12. 15

13. 5

14. 2

15. 4

16. 23

17. $\frac{2}{3}$

18. 3, −13

19. −29, 25

20. 18

21. 78

22. 8

23. 0

24. about 25.8 ft

25. about 4 in.

26. 6

27. 1

28. −2

29. 3

30. 1, 4

31. −3, −4

32. 9

33. 1

34. 2

35. 3

36. 5

37. 1

38. 5

39. −2

40. 6

41. 1

42. 8

43. 5

44. −1, 2

45. $10\sqrt[4]{3}$ cm, or about 13.16 cm

46. $36\sqrt{2} - 36$

Answers

Practice and Problem-Solving Exercises (continued)

47. 5

48. B

49. 8

50. 4

51. 5

52. 23

53. 1

54. 6.5

55. 9, −7

56. $\frac{81}{16}$

57. 9

58. 11

59. $x = 4$ is a solution, but $x = 1$ is an extraneous solution.

60. $d = \frac{v^2}{64}$

61. Answers may vary. Sample: $\sqrt{x - 3} = \sqrt{3x + 5}$

62. a. A counterexample is $a = 3$, $b = -3$.
   b. A counterexample is $a = -5$, $b = 3$.

63. C

64. 1

65. 0, 2

66. 2

67. 0

---

47. Mental Math What is the solution? $\sqrt{x + 11} = 4$

48. You can find the area A of a square whose side is s units with the formula $A = s^2$. What is the best estimate for the side of a square with an area of 32 m²?

   Ⓐ 4.2 m   Ⓒ 8.0 m
   Ⓑ 5.7 m   Ⓓ 16 m

Solve. Check for extraneous solutions.

49. $3\sqrt{2x} - 3 = 9$ **50.** $2(2x)^{\frac{1}{3}} + 1 = 5$

51. $\sqrt{2x - 1} - 3 = 0$ **52.** $(2x + 3)^{\frac{1}{2}} - 7 = 0$

53. $\sqrt{x^2 + 3} = x + 1$ **54.** $(2x + 3)^{\frac{3}{4}} - 3 = 5$

55. $2(x - 1)^{\frac{4}{3}} + 4 = 36$ **56.** $x^{\frac{1}{2}} - (x - 5)^{\frac{1}{2}} = 2$

57. $\sqrt{x} = \sqrt{x - 8} + 2$ **58.** $(x - 3)^{\frac{2}{3}} = x - 7$

59. Error Analysis A student said that 4 and 1 are the solutions of the problem shown. Describe and correct the student's error.

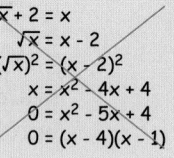

$\sqrt{x} + 2 = x$
$\sqrt{x} = x - 2$
$(\sqrt{x})^2 = (x - 2)^2$
$x = x^2 - 4x + 4$
$0 = x^2 - 5x + 4$
$0 = (x - 4)(x - 1)$

STEM 60. Physics The velocity v of an object dropped from a tall building is given by the formula $v = \sqrt{64d}$, where d is the distance the object has dropped. Solve the formula for d.

61. Open-Ended Write an equation that has two radical expressions and no real roots.

62. Reasoning You have solved equations containing square roots by squaring each side. You were using the property that if $a = b$ then $a^2 = b^2$. Show that the following statements are *not* true for all real numbers.
   a. If $a^2 = b^2$ then $a = b$.
   b. If $a \leq b$ then $a^2 \leq b^2$.

63. A teacher asked students why it is necessary to check for extraneous roots when squaring both sides of the equation. Which of the following answers is the best? Is this answer complete? Explain.
   Ⓐ Because the squared equation can have negative roots.
   Ⓑ Because squaring is multiplication, and any multiplication is a potential source of extraneous roots.
   Ⓒ Because when you square both sides of the equation $a = b$, you add to the solution set the roots of the equation $a = -b$.
   Ⓓ Because any operation with an equation may result in extraneous roots.

Solve. Check for extraneous solutions.

64. $\sqrt{x + 1} + \sqrt{2x} = \sqrt{5x + 3}$ **65.** $\sqrt{x + \sqrt{2x}} = \sqrt{2x}$

66. $\sqrt{x + \sqrt{2x}} = 2$ **67.** $\sqrt{\sqrt{x + 25}} = \sqrt{x + 5}$

Challenge

68. Reasoning Devise a plan to find the value of x.

$$x = \sqrt{2 + \sqrt{2 + \sqrt{2 + \cdots}}}$$

For each set of values, determine which is greater without using a calculator.

69. $\sqrt{6}$ or $\sqrt{2} + 1$

70. $\sqrt{3} + \sqrt{11}$ or 5

71. $\sqrt{10}$ or $\sqrt{2} + \sqrt{3}$

72. $\sqrt{19} + \sqrt{3}$ or $\sqrt{5} + \sqrt{13}$

Standardized Test Prep

SAT/ACT

73. What is the solution of $(x + 2)^{\frac{3}{4}} = 27$?

Ⓐ $x = 27$ Ⓑ $x = 79$ Ⓒ $x = 81$ Ⓓ $x = 83$

74. A problem on a test asked students to solve a fifth-degree polynomial equation with rational coefficients. Adam found the following roots: -11.5, $\sqrt{2}$, $\frac{2i + 6}{2}$, $-\sqrt{2}$ and $3 - i$. His teacher wrote that four of these roots are correct, and one is incorrect. Which root is incorrect?

Ⓕ -11.5 Ⓖ $\sqrt{2}$ Ⓗ $\frac{2i + 6}{2}$ Ⓘ $3 - i$

75. Which expression represents the solution of the equation $\frac{x}{y} = \frac{c}{a + b}$ solved for a?

Ⓐ $\frac{c}{b} - \frac{x}{y}$ Ⓑ $\frac{yc}{a + b}$ Ⓒ $\frac{yc}{x} + b$ Ⓓ $\frac{yc - xb}{x}$

Short Response

76. To rationalize the denominator of $\sqrt[4]{\frac{4}{25}}$, by what number would you multiply the numerator and denominator of the fraction?

Apply What You've Learned

MATHEMATICAL PRACTICES
MP 6

Look back at the information on page 359 about the America's Cup rule and the dimensions for the new yacht you are designing. In the Apply What You've Learned in Lesson 6-4, you wrote the expression on the left side of the America's Cup rule in radical form. Now, you will use this form of the expression to write a function $f(D)$ that gives the value of the expression for the new yacht in terms of the displacement D.

a. To write the function, what variables will you replace with specific values? What are those values?

b. Write and simplify the function.

c. Describe how you could use the function to write and solve an equation to find the displacement that makes the value of the left side of the America's Cup rule exactly 24.

---

68. Plan 1: Use a calculator to evaluate $\sqrt{2}$ and record it. Add 2, take the square root, and record it. Repeat this procedure about seven times until it becomes clear that the values are approaching 2.
Plan 2: The given eq. is equivalent to $x = \sqrt{2 + x}$. Solve this eq. to find that $x = 2$.

69. $\sqrt{6}$

70. $\sqrt{3} + \sqrt{11}$

71. $\sqrt{10}$

72. $\sqrt{19} + \sqrt{3}$

Standardized Test Prep

73. B

74. F

75. D

76. [2] $\sqrt[4]{25^3}$; $\dfrac{\sqrt[4]{4}}{\sqrt[4]{25}} \cdot \dfrac{\sqrt[4]{25^3}}{\sqrt[4]{25^3}} = \dfrac{\sqrt[4]{62,500}}{25}$

$= \dfrac{\sqrt[4]{625} \cdot \sqrt[4]{100}}{25} = \dfrac{5\sqrt[4]{100}}{25} = \dfrac{\sqrt[4]{100}}{5}$

[1] correct answer, but without any work shown

Apply What You've Learned

In the Apply What You've Learned for Lesson 6-4, students analyzed the expression on the left side of the America's Cup rule for the AC45 Wingsail Catamaran. Now students turn their attention to the dimensions of the proposed new yacht, described on page 359.

Mathematical Practices

Students **attend to precision** to write a function based on the America's Cup rule and describe how to use it to solve for a displacement. (MP 6)

ANSWERS

a. Replace L with 26.9 and replace S with 187.4.

b. $f(D) = \dfrac{44.012 - 9.8\sqrt[3]{D}}{0.686}$

c. Sample: First, I would set the function equal to 24. Second, I would multiply both sides by 0.686. Third, I would subtract 44.012 from both sides. Fourth, I would divide both sides by -9.8. Last, I would cube both sides of the equation.

Additional Instructional Support

Algebra 2 Companion

Students can use the **Algebra 2 Companion** worktext (4 pages) as you teach the lesson. Use the Companion to support

- New Vocabulary
- Key Concepts
- Got It for each Problem
- Lesson Check

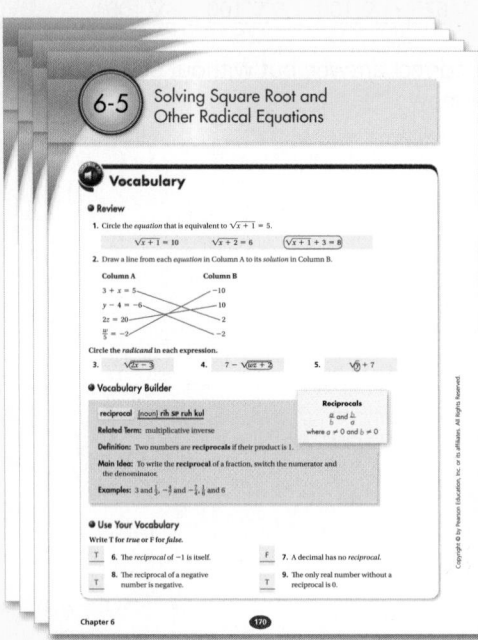

ELL Support

Focus on Language Use examples and nonexamples to help students understand the definition of *radical equation* given in this lesson.

Write these equations on the board:

$4 = 2x$ $4 = \sqrt{2x}$

$4 = \sqrt{2} + x$ $4 = \sqrt{2 + x}$

Point to each equation and ask, "What are these?" [equations]

Point to x in each equation and ask, "What are these?" [variables]

Point to the radicand in the last three equations and ask, "What are these?" [radicands]

Point to x in the last two equations and ask, "Where is the variable?" [in a radicand]

Say, "A radical equation has a variable in a radicand." Then, point to each equation and ask, "Does this equation have a variable in a radicand?"

5 Assess & Remediate

Lesson Quiz

1. What is the solution of $\sqrt{x-2} + 1 = 5$?

2. What is the solution of $(4x + 1)^{\frac{1}{4}} - 4 = -1$?

3. Do you UNDERSTAND? The radius r of a sphere is related to its volume V by $r = \sqrt[3]{\dfrac{3V}{4\pi}}$. If the radius of a sphere is 3 centimeters, what is its volume?

4. What is the solution of $\sqrt{x-1} = x - 7$? Check your results.

5. What is the solution of $\sqrt{2x - 2} + \sqrt{x} = 7$?

ANSWERS TO LESSON QUIZ

1. 18

2. 20

3. about 113 cubic centimeters

4. 10

5. 9

PRESCRIPTION FOR REMEDIATION

Use the student work on the Lesson Quiz to prescribe a differentiated review assignment:

Points	Differentiated Remediation
0–2	Intervention
3–4	On-level
5	Extension

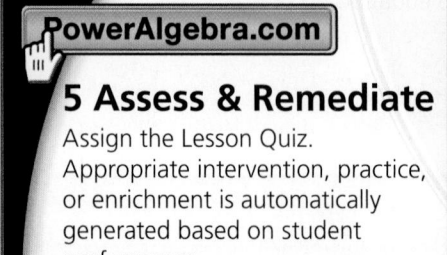

PowerAlgebra.com

5 Assess & Remediate

Assign the Lesson Quiz. Appropriate intervention, practice, or enrichment is automatically generated based on student performance.

Differentiated Remediation

Intervention

- **Reteaching** (2 pages) Provides reteaching and practice exercises for the key lesson concepts. Use with struggling students or absent students.

- **English Language Learner Support** Helps students develop and reinforce mathematical vocabulary and key concepts.

All-in-One Resources/Online
Reteaching

All-in-One Resources/Online
English Language Learner Support

Differentiated Remediation *continued*

On-Level

- **Practice** (2 pages) Provides extra practice for each lesson. For simpler practice exercises, use the Form K Practice pages found in the All-in-One Teaching Resources and online.

- **Think About a Plan** Helps students develop specific problem-solving skills and strategies by providing scaffolded guiding questions.

- **Standardized Test Prep** Focuses on all major exercises, all major question types, and helps students prepare for the high-stakes assessments.

Extension

- **Enrichment** Provides students with interesting problems and activities that extend the concepts of the lesson.

- **Activities, Games, and Puzzles** Worksheets that can be used for concepts development, enrichment, and for fun!

Practice and Problem Solving Wkbk/ All-in-One Resources/Online
Practice page 1

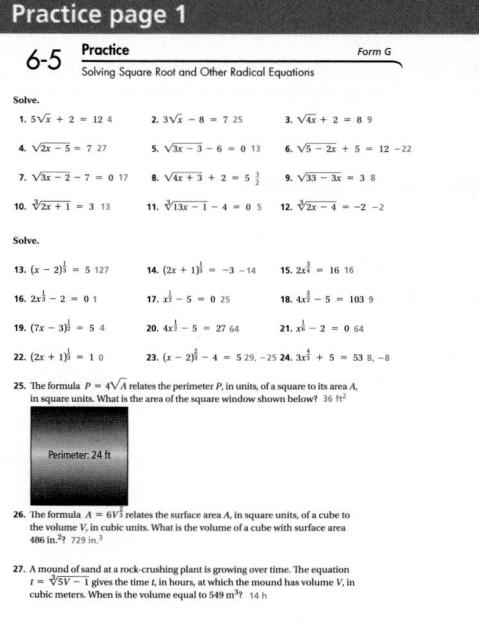

Practice and Problem Solving Wkbk/ All-in-One Resources/Online
Practice page 2

All-in-One Resources/Online
Enrichment

Practice and Problem Solving Wkbk/ All-in-One Resources/Online
Think About a Plan

Practice and Problem Solving Wkbk/ All-in-One Resources/Online
Standardized Test Prep

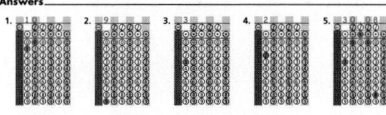

Online Teacher Resource Center
Activities, Games, and Puzzles

1 Interactive Learning

Solve It!

PURPOSE To write and subtract equations to solve a percentage problem

PROCESS Students may
- find the final cost using each option, and find the difference.
- write general equations to represent both options, identify which equation gives a lower price, and find the difference between the equations to find how much money is saved.

FACILITATE

Q How can you represent a payment including a 5% sales tax before the discount? **[(1.05)x, where x is the cost before the sales tax]**

Q Can you write mathematical expressions to represent both options? Explain. **[yes; (1.05)x − 50 and (x − 50)1.05, where x is the original cost]**

ANSWER See Solve It in Answers on next page.
CONNECT THE MATH The students write and subtract equations in the Solve It. In the lesson, students add and subtract functions and prove that function composition is not commutative.

2 Guided Instruction

Take Note   AUDITORY LEARNERS
The symbols may confuse some students, and they may think that the parentheses imply multiplication. Read each operation out loud, using the correct terminology. For example, "The sum of f and g of x equals the sum of f of x and g of x."

Common Core State Standards
F-BF.A.1b Combine standard function types using arithmetic operations.
F-BF.A.1c Compose functions.
MP 1, MP 2, MP 3, MP 4

Objectives To add, subtract, multiply, and divide functions
To find the composite of two functions

Getting Ready!

You want to buy a sofa that has already been marked down by $100. The furniture store may add the 5% sales tax before applying the additional discount, or it may add the sales tax after applying the additional discount. Which way is better for you, the customer? How much better?

Clearance sale Take $50 off

Solve a simpler problem first. Use a value for the cost of the sofa.

 **MATHEMATICAL PRACTICES**

Lesson Vocabulary
- composite function

The final cost of the sofa in the Solve It involves two functions: one that gives an additional discount and one that multiplies to find the sales tax.

Essential Understanding You can add, subtract, multiply, and divide functions based on how you perform these operations for real numbers. One difference, however, is that you must consider the domain of each function.

take note

Key Concepts	Function Operations
Addition	$(f + g)(x) = f(x) + g(x)$
Subtraction	$(f - g)(x) = f(x) - g(x)$
Multiplication	$(f \cdot g)(x) = f(x) \cdot g(x)$
Division	$\left(\dfrac{f}{g}\right)(x) = \dfrac{f(x)}{g(x)}, g(x) \neq 0$

The domains of the sum, difference, product, and quotient functions consist of the x-values that are in the domains of *both* f and g. Also, the domain of the quotient function does not contain any x-value for which $g(x) = 0$.

 **6-6** **Preparing to Teach**

BIG idea Function

ESSENTIAL UNDERSTANDINGS
- Functions can be added, subtracted, multiplied, and divided based on how these operations are performed for real numbers. One difference, however, is that the domain of each function must be considered.

Math Background
The notation for the composition of two functions is easily confused with the notation for the product of two functions.
Highlight the differences:
- While multiplication of functions is commutative, composition of functions generally is not. Problem 4 in the text highlights this; the price is different when the coupon is applied first than when the discount is applied first.
- The product of two functions involves multiplying each term of one function by each term of the other. The composition of two functions involves replacing the variable of one function with the expression equal to the other function.

- By definition, the composition of the function f with the function g can also be written as $f(g(x))$. This is in contrast to the product of f and g which can be written as $f(x) \cdot g(x)$.

© Mathematical Practices
Reason abstractly and quantitatively.
In performing operations with two functions, students will decontextualize the functions, representing them with symbols, and manipulate the symbols according to the operation performed.

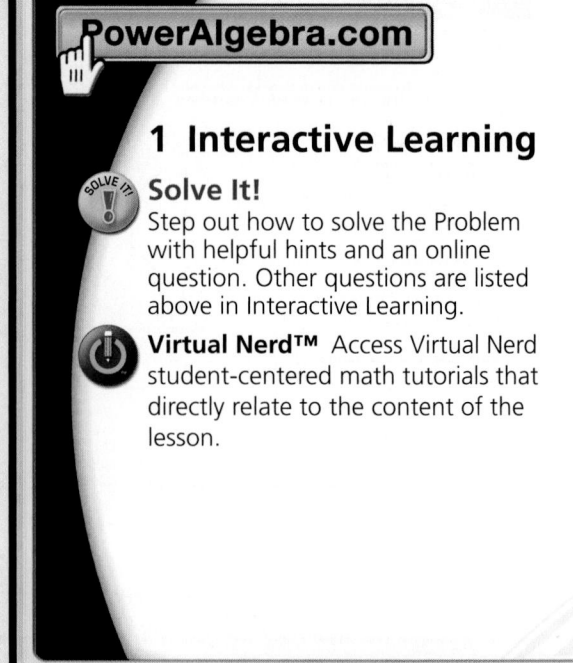

PowerAlgebra.com

1 Interactive Learning

Solve It!
Step out how to solve the Problem with helpful hints and an online question. Other questions are listed above in Interactive Learning.

Virtual Nerd™ Access Virtual Nerd student-centered math tutorials that directly relate to the content of the lesson.

Problem 1 Adding and Subtracting Functions

Let $f(x) = 4x + 7$ and $g(x) = \sqrt{x} + x$. What are $f + g$ and $f - g$? What are their domains?

$$(f + g)(x) = f(x) + g(x) = (4x + 7) + (\sqrt{x} + x) = 5x + \sqrt{x} + 7$$
$$(f - g)(x) = f(x) - g(x) = (4x + 7) - (\sqrt{x} + x) = 3x - \sqrt{x} + 7$$

Think

What determines the domain of g?
Because there is a square root of x, x must be ≥ 0.

The domain of f is the set of all real numbers. The domain of g is all $x \geq 0$. The domain of both $f + g$ and $f - g$ is the set of numbers common to the domains of both f and g, which is all $x \geq 0$.

 Got It? **1.** Let $f(x) = 2x^2 + 8$ and $g(x) = x - 3$. What are $f + g$ and $f - g$? What are their domains?

 Problem 2 Multiplying and Dividing Functions

Let $f(x) = x^2 - 9$ and $g(x) = x + 3$. What are $f \cdot g$ and $\frac{f}{g}$ and their domains?

$$(f \cdot g)(x) = f(x) \cdot g(x) = (x^2 - 9)(x + 3)$$
$$= x^3 + 3x^2 - 9x - 27$$

$$\left(\frac{f}{g}\right)(x) = \frac{f(x)}{g(x)} = \frac{x^2 - 9}{x + 3} = \frac{(x - 3)(x + 3)}{x + 3} = x - 3, x \neq -3$$

Think

Is the domain of $\frac{f}{g}$ the domain of $x - 3$?
No; the fraction can only be simplified and the function is only defined when $g(x) \neq -3$.

The domain of both f and g is the set of real numbers, so the domain of $f \cdot g$ is also the set of real numbers.

The domain of $\frac{f}{g}$ is the set of all real numbers except $x \neq -3$, because $g(-3) = 0$. The definition of $\frac{f}{g}$ requires that you consider the zero denominator in the *original* expression for $\frac{f(x)}{g(x)}$ despite the fact that the simplified form has the domain all real numbers.

 Got It? **2.** Let $f(x) = 3x^2 - 11x - 4$ and $g(x) = 3x + 1$. What are $f \cdot g$ and $\frac{f}{g}$ and their domains?

The diagram shows what happens when you apply one function $g(x)$ after another function $f(x)$.

The output from the first function becomes the input for the second function. When you combine two functions as in the diagram, you form a **composite function**.

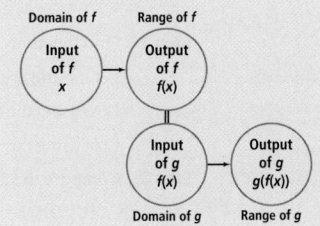

Problem 1

Q How do you add or subtract functions? **[By definition, you add or subtract the functions' expressions resulting in one expression that is equal to the new function.]**

Got It?

Q When simplified, why does $(f - g)(x) = 2x^2 - x + 11$ instead of $2x^2 - x + 5$? **[Since $g(x)$ is in parentheses when the subtraction is done, the subtraction sign gets distributed, yielding $2x^2 + 8 - x + 3$ before the answer is simplified.]**

Problem 2

Q How does the domain of $\left(\frac{f}{g}\right)(x)$ compare to the domain of $\left(\frac{g}{f}\right)(x)$? **[The domain of $\left(\frac{f}{g}\right)(x)$ excludes only -3 while the domain of $\left(\frac{g}{f}\right)(x)$ excludes both -3 and 3.]**

Got It?

Q Why do you factor $3x^2 - 11x - 4$ when dividing but not when multiplying? **[Answers may vary. Sample: When you divide, you end up with a fraction, and factoring the numerator makes it possible to simplify the denominator. When you multiply, you will have no denominator so you do not need to simplify it.]**

---

2 Guided Instruction

 Each Problem is worked out and supported online.

Problem 1
Adding and Subtracting Functions
Animated

Problem 2
Multiplying and Dividing Functions
Animated

Problem 3
Composing Functions
Animated

Problem 4
Using Composite Functions

Support in Algebra 2 Companion
- Vocabulary
- Key Concepts
- Got It?

Answers

Solve It!
It is better for the customer to take the additional discount before adding the sales tax; $2.50

Got It?
1. $(f + g)(x) = 2x^2 + x + 5$, domain: all real numbers; $(f - g)(x) = 2x^2 - x + 11$, domain: all real numbers

2. $(f \cdot g)(x) = 9x^3 - 30x^2 - 23x - 4$, domain: all real numbers; $\left(\frac{f}{g}\right)(x) = x - 4$, domain: all real numbers except $x = -\frac{1}{3}$

Take Note ERROR PREVENTION

Stress that the symbol ∘ is not related to multiplication, though it looks like the symbol · for multiplication. You can read "g ∘ f" as "g composed with f."

Problem 3

Q What is the range of g(f(x))? **[all real numbers greater than or equal to 0]**

Got It?

Q What is the difference between the two methods? Which do you prefer? **[Answers may vary. Sample: In Method 1, you first find the function rule for (g ∘ f)(x), and in Method 2 you directly find the value of (g ∘ f)(−3). I prefer Method 1 because you can look at the function rule.]**

Problem 4

Q Which discount would you want to be applied first? **[the 10% student discount]**

Q Is the composition of functions commutative? Explain. **[No; if it were, it would not matter which discount you applied first, and you would get the same answer both ways. Since you pay less when you apply the 10% discount first, the composition of these functions is not commutative.]**

 **Key Concept** Composition of Functions

The composition of function g with function f is written as $g \circ f$ and is defined as $(g \circ f)(x) = g(f(x))$. The domain of $g \circ f$ consists of the x-values in the domain of f for which $f(x)$ is in the domain of g.

$(g \circ f)(x) = g(\underbrace{f(x)}_{2})$ 1. Evaluate $f(x)$ first.
2. Then use $f(x)$ as the input for g.

Function composition is not commutative since $f(g(x))$ does not always equal $g(f(x))$.

Problem 3 Composing Functions   GRIDDED RESPONSE

Let $f(x) = x - 5$ and $g(x) = x^2$. What is $(g \circ f)(-3)$?

Think
Which function is substituted into the other?
Use $f(x)$ as the input for g.

Method 1

$(g \circ f)(x) = g(f(x))$

$= g(x - 5) = (x - 5)^2$

$(g \circ f)(-3) = (-3 - 5)^2$

$= (-8)^2$

$= 64$

Method 2

$(g \circ f)(-3) = g(f(-3))$

$= g(-3 - 5)$

$= g(-8)$

$= (-8)^2$

$= 64$

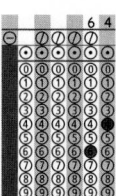

✓ **Got It? 3.** What is $(f \circ g)(-3)$ for the functions f and g defined in Problem 3?

Problem 4 Using Composite Functions

You have a coupon good for $5 off the price of any large pizza. You also get a 10% discount on any pizza if you show your student ID. How much more would you pay for a large pizza if the cashier applies the coupon first?

Know
The coupon value and the discount rate

Need
The difference between the results of applying the discount or coupon first

Plan
• Compose two functions in two ways.
• Then find the difference in their results.

Step 1 Find functions C and D that model the cost of a large pizza.

Let $x =$ the price of a large pizza.

Cost using the coupon: $C(x) = x - 5$

Cost using the 10% discount: $D(x) = x - 0.1x = 0.9x$

Step 2 Compose the functions to apply the discount and then the coupon.

$(C \circ D)(x) = C(D(x))$ Apply the discount, $D(x)$, first.

$= C(0.9x) = 0.9x - 5$

Additional Problems

1. Let $f(x) = 5x^3 + 1$ and $g(x) = x^2 - 4$. What are $f + g$ and $f - g$? What are their domains?

ANSWER
$(f + g)(x) = 5x^3 + x^2 - 3$;
$(f - g)(x) = 5x^3 - x^2 + 5$;
the domain of each is all real numbers.

2. Let $f(x) = x^2 + x - 6$ and $g(x) = x - 2$. What are $f \cdot g$ and $\frac{f}{g}$ and their domains?

ANSWER
$(f \cdot g)(x) = x^3 - x^2 - 8x + 12$
$(\frac{f}{g})(x) = x + 3$; the domain of $(f \cdot g)(x)$ is all real numbers; the domain of $(\frac{f}{g})(x)$ is all real numbers except $x = 2$.

3. Let $f(x) = x^2 + 1$ and $g(x) = x - 2$. What is $(g \circ f)(-2)$?

ANSWER 3

4. A car manufacturer offers a $2000 rebate, but the buyer must pay the 7% sales tax on the full price of the car. Write a composite function to represent the cost to purchase a car listed for x dollars.

ANSWER
$f(x) = 1.07x$;
$g(x) = x - 2000$;
$(g \circ f)(x) = 1.07x - 2000$

Answers

Got It? (continued)

3. 4

4. Let $D(x) =$ cost after applying the 15% store discount, $E(x) =$ cost after applying the 20% employee discount, and $x =$ cost of items, then $D(x) = 0.85x$ and $E(x) = 0.80x$.

a. $(E \circ D)(x) = 0.68x$

b. $(D \circ E)(x) = 0.68x$

c. The total discounts are the same.

Step 3 Compose the functions to apply the coupon and then the discount.

$(D \circ C)(x) = D(C(x))$ Apply the coupon, $C(x)$, first.

$= D(x - 5) = 0.9(x - 5) = 0.9x - 4.5$

Step 4 Subtract the functions to find how much more you would pay if the cashier applies the coupon first.

$(D \circ C)(x) - (C \circ D)(x) = (0.9x - 4.5) - (0.9x - 5)$

$= -4.5 + 5$

$= 0.5$

You pay \$.50 more if the cashier applies the coupon first.

 Got It? **4.** A store is offering a 15% discount on all items. Also, employees get a 20% employee discount. Write composite functions
  a. to model taking the 15% discount and then the 20% discount.
  b. to model taking the 20% discount and then the 15% discount.
  c. **Reasoning** If you were an employee, which discount would you take first? Why?

Lesson Check

Do you know HOW?

Let $f(x) = 3x - 2$ and $g(x) = x^2 + 1$. Perform each function operation.

1. $(f \cdot g)(x)$ **2.** $(f - g)(x)$

3. $(f \circ g)(x)$ **4.** $f(x) + g(x)$

5. $g(x) - f(x)$ **6.** $f(x) - g(x)$

Do you UNDERSTAND?  **MATHEMATICAL PRACTICES**

 7. Error Analysis Your friend used some simple functions and found that $(f \circ g)(x) = (g \circ f)(x)$, and concluded that function composition is commutative. Give an example to show that your friend is mistaken.

8. Open-Ended Find two functions f and g such that $f(g(x)) = x$ for all real numbers x.

Practice and Problem-Solving Exercises  **MATHEMATICAL PRACTICES**

 **Practice**   Let $f(x) = 7x + 5$ and $g(x) = x^2$. Perform each function operation and then find the domain of the result.   ◀ **See Problems 1 and 2.**

9. $(f + g)(x)$ **10.** $(f - g)(x)$ **11.** $(g - f)(x)$

12. $(f \cdot g)(x)$ **13.** $\frac{f}{g}(x)$ **14.** $\frac{g}{f}(x)$

Let $f(x) = 2 - x$ and $g(x) = \frac{1}{x}$. Perform each function operation and then find the domain of the result.

15. $(f + g)(x)$ **16.** $(f - g)(x)$ **17.** $(g - f)(x)$

18. $(f \cdot g)(x)$ **19.** $\frac{f}{g}(x)$ **20.** $\frac{g}{f}(x)$

Got It?
In contrast to Problem 4, the composition of D and E does happen to be commutative.

Q How is it that $(D \circ E)(x) = (E \circ D)(x)$ when functions in previous problems did not commute? **[Answers may vary. Sample: These two functions only involve multiplication, and multiplication is associative and commutative.]**

3 Lesson Check

Do you know HOW?
• If students have difficulty combining functions algebraically, have them use the Take Notes "Function Operations" and "Composition of Functions" to write out the five definitions on an index card to refer to until they are comfortable with them.

Do you UNDERSTAND?
• For Exercise 7, if students have trouble understanding that composition of functions is not commutative, review how the operation is different from multiplication. Explain that finding one counterexample is enough to prove that composition of functions is not commutative.

Close

Q How are multiplying two functions and composing two functions the same? How are they different? **[Answers may vary. Sample: In both cases, you form a new function. The product of two functions is found by multiplying the expressions for the functions. When composing functions, the output of one function becomes the input of the other function.]**

Lesson Check
1. $3x^3 - 2x^2 + 3x - 2$
2. $-x^2 + 3x - 3$
3. $3x^2 + 1$
4. $x^2 + 3x - 1$
5. $x^2 - 3x + 3$
6. $-x^2 + 3x - 3$
7. Answers may vary. Sample:
$f(x) = 3x^2 + 1$, $g(x) = 2x + 1$; $(f \circ g)(x) = 12x^2 + 12x + 4$; $(g \circ f)(x) = 6x^2 + 3$
8. Answers may vary. Sample:
$f(x) = 2x$, $g(x) = 0.5x$; $f(g(x)) = x$

Practice and Problem-Solving Exercises
9. $x^2 + 7x + 5$; domain: all real numbers
10. $-x^2 + 7x + 5$; domain: all real numbers
11. $x^2 - 7x - 5$; domain: all real numbers
12. $7x^3 + 5x^2$; domain: all real numbers

13. $\frac{7x + 5}{x^2}$;
domain: all real numbers except $x = 0$
14. $\frac{x^2}{7x + 5}$;
domain: all real numbers except $x = -\frac{5}{7}$
15. $2 - x + \frac{1}{x}$;
domain: all real numbers except $x = 0$
16. $2 - x - \frac{1}{x}$;
domain: all real numbers except $x = 0$
17. $\frac{1}{x} + x - 2$;
domain: all real numbers except $x = 0$
18. $\frac{2 - x}{x}$;
domain: all real numbers except $x = 0$
19. $2x - x^2$;
domain: all real numbers except $x = 0$
20. $\frac{1}{2x - x^2}$;
domain: all real numbers except $x = 0, 2$

 **PowerAlgebra.com**

3 Lesson Check
For a digital lesson check, use the Got It questions.

Support in Algebra 2 Companion
• Lesson Check

4 Practice
 Assign homework to individual students or to an entire class.

4 Practice

ASSIGNMENT GUIDE

Basic: 9–58 all, 59, 61, 69–73 odd

Average: 9–57 odd, 59–78

Advanced: 9–57 odd, 59–85

Standardized Test Prep: 86–89

Mixed Review: 90–106

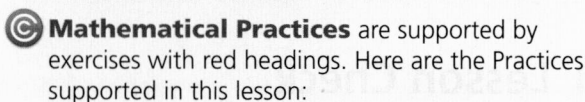 **Mathematical Practices** are supported by exercises with red headings. Here are the Practices supported in this lesson:

MP 1: Make Sense of Problems Ex. 59
MP 2: Reason Abstractly Ex. 8
MP 2: Reason Quantitatively Ex. 78
MP 3: Construct Arguments Ex. 60b
MP 3: Critique the Reasoning of Others Ex. 7

Applications exercises have blue headings. Exercises 45 and 46 support MP 4: Model.

EXERCISE 61: Use the Think About a Plan worksheet in the **Practice and Problem Solving Workbook** (also available in the Teaching Resources in print and online) to further support students' development in becoming independent learners.

HOMEWORK QUICK CHECK

To check students' understanding of key skills and concepts, go over Exercises 17, 51, 59, 61, and 71.

Let $f(x) = 2x^2 + x - 3$ and $g(x) = x - 1$. Perform each function operation and then find the domain.

21. $(f + g)(x)$ **22.** $(f - g)(x)$ **23.** $(g - f)(x)$

24. $(f \cdot g)(x)$ **25.** $\frac{f}{g}(x)$ **26.** $\frac{g}{f}(x)$

Let $g(x) = 2x$ and $h(x) = x^2 + 4$. Find each value or expression.   ◆ See Problem 3.

27. $(h \circ g)(1)$ **28.** $(h \circ g)(-5)$ **29.** $(h \circ g)(-2)$

30. $(g \circ h)(-2)$ **31.** $(g \circ h)(0)$ **32.** $(g \circ h)(a)$

33. $(g \circ g)(a)$ **34.** $(h \circ h)(a)$ **35.** $(h \circ g)(a)$

Let $f(x) = x^2$ and $g(x) = x - 3$. Find each value or expression.

36. $(g \circ f)(-2)$ **37.** $(f \circ g)(-2)$ **38.** $(g \circ f)(0)$

39. $(f \circ g)(0)$ **40.** $(g \circ f)(3.5)$ **41.** $(f \circ g)(3.5)$

42. $(f \circ g)(a)$ **43.** $(g \circ f)(-a)$ **44.** $(f \circ g)(-a)$

45. Sales A computer store offers a 5% discount off the list price x for any computer   ◆ See Problem 4.
bought with cash, rather than put on credit. At the same time, the manufacturer offers a $200 rebate for each purchase of a computer.
  a. Write a function $f(x)$ to represent the price after the cash discount.
  b. Write a function $g(x)$ to represent the price after the $200 rebate.
  c. Suppose the list price of a computer is $1500. Use a composite function to find the price of the computer if the discount is applied before the rebate.
  d. Suppose the list price of a computer is $1500. Use a composite function to find the price of the computer if the rebate is applied before the discount.

46. Economics Suppose the function $f(x) = 0.15x$ represents the number of U.S. dollars equivalent to x Chinese yuan and the function $g(y) = 14.07y$ represents the number of Mexican pesos equivalent to y U.S. dollars.
  a. Write a composite function that represents the number of Mexican pesos equivalent to x Chinese yuan.
  b. Find the value in Mexican pesos of an item that costs 15 Chinese yuan.

Let $f(x) = 2x + 5$ and $g(x) = x^2 - 3x + 2$. Perform each function operation and then find the domain.

47. $f(x) + g(x)$ **48.** $3f(x) - 2$ **49.** $g(x) - f(x)$

50. $-2g(x) + f(x)$ **51.** $f(x) - g(x) + 10$ **52.** $4f(x) + 2g(x)$

53. $-f(x) + 4g(x)$ **54.** $f(x) - 2g(x)$ **55.** $f(x) \cdot g(x)$

56. $-3f(x) \cdot g(x)$ **57.** $\frac{f(x)}{g(x)}$ **58.** $\frac{5f(x)}{g(x)}$

Answers

Practice and Problem-Solving Exercises (continued)

21. $2x^2 + 2x - 4$; domain: all real numbers

22. $2x^2 - 2$; domain: all real numbers

23. $-2x^2 + 2$; domain: all real numbers

24. $2x^3 - x^2 - 4x + 3$; domain: all real numbers

25. $2x + 3$; domain: all real numbers except $x = 1$

26. $\frac{1}{2x + 3}$; domain: all real numbers except $x = -\frac{3}{2}, 1$

27. 8
28. 104
29. 20
30. 16
31. 8
32. $2a^2 + 8$

33. $4a$
34. $a^4 + 8a^2 + 20$
35. $4a^2 + 4$
36. 1
37. 25
38. -3
39. 9
40. 9.25
41. 0.25
42. $a^2 - 6a + 9$
43. $a^2 - 3$
44. $a^2 + 6a + 9$
45. a. $f(x) = 0.95x$
  b. $g(x) = x - 200$
  c. $1225
  d. $1235
46. a. $(g \circ f)(x) = 2.1105x$
  b. 31.6575 pesos
47. $x^2 - x + 7$; domain: all real numbers
48. $6x + 13$; domain: all real numbers

49. $x^2 - 5x - 3$; domain: all real numbers

50. $-2x^2 + 8x + 1$; domain: all real numbers

51. $-x^2 + 5x + 13$; domain: all real numbers

52. $2x^2 + 2x + 24$; domain: all real numbers

53. $4x^2 - 14x + 3$; domain: all real numbers

54. $-2x^2 + 8x + 1$; domain: all real numbers

55. $2x^3 - x^2 - 11x + 10$; domain: all real numbers

56. $-6x^3 + 3x^2 + 33x - 30$; domain: all real numbers

57. $\frac{2x + 5}{x^2 - 3x + 2}$; domain: all real numbers except $x = 1$ and 2

58. $\frac{10x + 25}{x^2 - 3x + 2}$; domain: all real numbers except $x = 1$ and 2

Apply

59. **Think About a Plan** A craftsman makes and sells violins. The function $I(x) = 5995x$ represents the income in dollars from selling x violins. The function $P(y) = y - 100,000$ represents his profit in dollars if he makes an income of y dollars. What is the profit from selling 30 violins?
- How can you write a composite function to represent the craftsman's profit?
- How can you use the composite function to find the profit earned when he sells 30 violins?

60. Suppose your teacher offers to give the whole class a bonus if everyone passes the next math test. The teacher says she will give everyone a 10-point bonus and increase everyone's grade by 9% of their score.
  a. You earned a 75 on the test. Would you rather have the 10-point bonus first and then the 9% increase, or the 9% increase first and then the 10-point bonus?
  b. **Reasoning** Is this the best plan for all students? Explain.

61. **Sales** A salesperson earns a 3% bonus on weekly sales over $5000. Consider the following functions.

$$g(x) = 0.03x \qquad\qquad h(x) = x - 5000$$

  a. Explain what each function above represents.
  b. Which composition, $(h \circ g)(x)$ or $(g \circ h)(x)$, represents the weekly bonus? Explain.

62. If $(f \circ g)(x) = x^2 - 6x + 8$ and $g(x) = x - 3$, what is $f(x)$?

Let $g(x) = 3x + 2$ and $f(x) = \dfrac{x-2}{3}$. Find each value.

63. $f(g(1))$ **64.** $g(f(-4))$ **65.** $f(g(0))$ **66.** $g(f(2))$

67. $g(g(0))$ **68.** $(g \circ g)(1)$ **69.** $(f \circ g)(-2)$ **70.** $(f \circ f)(0)$

71. **Geometry** You toss a pebble into a pool of water and watch the circular ripples radiate outward. You find that the function $r(x) = 12.5x$ describes the radius r, in inches, of a circle x seconds after it was formed. The function $A(x) = \pi x^2$ describes the area A of a circle with radius x.
  a. Find $(A \circ r)(x)$ when $x = 2$. Interpret your answer.
  b. Find the area of a circle 4 seconds after it was formed.

For each pair of functions, find $f(g(x))$ and $g(f(x))$.

72. $f(x) = 3x, g(x) = x^2$ **73.** $f(x) = x + 3, g(x) = x - 5$

74. $f(x) = 3x^2 + 2, g(x) = 2x$ **75.** $f(x) = \dfrac{x-3}{2}, g(x) = 2x - 3$

76. $f(x) = -x - 7, g(x) = 4x$ **77.** $f(x) = \dfrac{x+5}{2}, g(x) = x^2$

78. **Open-Ended** Write a function rule that approximates each value.
  a. The amount you save is a percent of what you earn. (You choose the percent.)
  b. The amount you earn depends on how many hours you work. (You choose the hourly wage.)
  c. Write and simplify a composite function that expresses your savings as a function of the number of hours you work. Interpret your results.

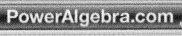   **Lesson 6-6** Function Operations   **403**

---

59. $79,850

60. a. 10-point bonus first then the 9% increase
  b. Yes; the "10-point bonus first then the 9% increase" is $1.09x + 10.9$ and the "9% increase first then the 10-point bonus" is $1.09x + 10$. The first option is 0.9 points greater than the second option.

61. a. $g(x)$ is the bonus earned when x is the amount of sales over $5000. $h(x)$ is the excess sales over $5000.
  b. $(g \circ h)(x)$; you first need to find the excess sales over $5000 to calculate the bonus.

62. $f(x) = x^2 - 1$

63. 1

64. -4

65. 0

66. 2

67. 8

68. 17

69. -2

70. $-\dfrac{8}{9}$

71. a. ≈ 1963; The area after 2 seconds is about 1963 in.^{2}
  b. ≈ 7854 in.^{2}

72. $3x^2$; $9x^2$

73. $x - 2$; $x - 2$

74. $12x^2 + 2$; $6x^2 + 4$

75. $x - 3$; $x - 6$

76. $-4x - 7$; $-4x - 28$

77. $\dfrac{x^2 + 5}{2}$; $\dfrac{x^2 + 10x + 25}{4}$

78. Answers may vary. Samples:
  a. $g(x) = 0.12x$
  b. $f(x) = 9.50x$
  c. $(g \circ f)(x) = 1.14x$; Your savings will be $1.14 for each hour you work.

Answers

Practice and Problem-Solving Exercises
(continued)

79. $x^7 - x^6 - 16x^5 + 10x^4 + 85x^3 - 25x^2$
$- 150x$; domain: all real numbers

80. $\dfrac{x^2 + 2x}{x - 3}$, domain: all real numbers except $x = 3$,
$\sqrt{5}$ and $-\sqrt{5}$

81. $\dfrac{x - 3}{x^2 + 2x}$; domain: all real numbers except $x = 0$
-2, $\sqrt{5}$ and $-\sqrt{5}$

82. $\dfrac{1}{x}$

83. 2

84. 4

85. $8a + 4h$

Standardized Test Prep

86. D

87. H

88. C

89. **[2]** Look at the 5th number in Row 7 of
Pascal's triangle to find the coefficient of
the x^3y^4 term in the expansion of $(x + y)^7$.
$35(3x)^3 (-y)^4 = 945x^3y^4$, so 945 is the
coefficient.

[1] correct coefficient, but without work
shown

Mixed Review

90. 1

91. -3

92. 4

93. 3

94. 2

95. 3

96. $x^8 + 32x^7 + 448x^6 + 3584x^5 + 17{,}920x^4 +$
$57{,}344x^3 + 114{,}688x^2 + 131{,}072x + 65{,}536$

97. $x^6 + 6x^5y + 15x^4y^2 + 20x^3y^3 + 15x^2y^4$
$+ 6xy^5 + y^6$

98. $16x^4 - 32x^3y + 24x^2y^2 - 8xy^3 + y^4$

99. $128x^7 - 1344x^6y + 6048x^5y^2 - 15{,}120x^4y^3$
$+ 22{,}680x^3y^4 - 20{,}412x^2y^5 + 10{,}206xy^6$
$- 2187y^7$

100. $59{,}049 - 65{,}610x + 29{,}160x^2 - 6480x^3 +$
$720x^4 - 32x^5$

101. $1024x^5 - 1280x^4y + 640x^3y^2 - 160x^2y^3 +$
$20xy^4 - y^5$

102. $x^8 + 4x^7 + 6x^6 + 4x^5 + x^4$

103. $x^{12} + 12x^{10}y^3 + 60x^8y^6 + 160x^6y^9 +$
$240x^4y^{12} + 192x^2y^{15} + 64y^{18}$

104. no solution
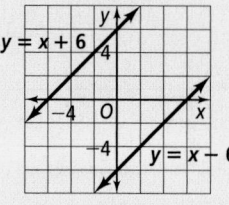

404 Chapter 6

**Challenge**   Let $f(x) = x^4 + 2x^3 - 5x^2 - 10x$ and $g(x) = x^3 - 3x^2 - 5x + 15$. Perform
each function operation and simplify, and then find the domain.

79. $f(x) \cdot g(x)$ **80.** $\dfrac{f(x)}{g(x)}$ **81.** $\dfrac{g(x)}{f(x)}$

Find each composition of functions. Simplify your answer.

82. Let $f(x) = \frac{1}{x}$. Find $f(f(f(x)))$.

83. Let $f(x) = 2x - 3$. Find $\dfrac{f(1 + h) - f(1)}{h}$, $h \neq 0$.

84. Let $f(x) = 4x - 1$. Find $\dfrac{f(a + h) - f(a)}{h}$, $h \neq 0$.

85. Let $f(x) = 4x^2 - 1$. Find $\dfrac{f(a + h) - f(a)}{h}$, $h \neq 0$.

Standardized Test Prep

SAT/ACT

86. Let $f(x) = x + 5$ and $g(x) = x^2 - 25$. What is the domain of $\dfrac{f}{g}(x)$?

 Ⓐ All real numbers   Ⓒ All real numbers except -5

 Ⓑ All real numbers except 5   Ⓓ All real numbers except -5 and 5

87. Let $g(x) = x - 3$ and $h(x) = x^2 + 6$. What is $(h \circ g)(1)$?

 Ⓕ -14 Ⓖ 4   Ⓗ 10   Ⓘ 15

88. Which number is a solution of $|3 - 2x| < 5$?

 Ⓐ -6 Ⓑ -1 Ⓒ 2   Ⓓ 4

Short Response

89. What is the coefficient of the x^3y^4 term in the expansion of $(3x - y)^7$? Show your
work.

Mixed Review

Solve. Check for extraneous solutions.   ◆ **See Lesson 6-5.**

90. $\sqrt{x^2 + 3} = x + 1$ **91.** $x + 8 = (x^2 + 16)^{\frac{1}{2}}$ **92.** $\sqrt{x^2 + 9} = x + 1$

93. $(x^2 - 9)^{\frac{1}{2}} - x = -3$ **94.** $\sqrt{x^2 + 12} - 2 = x$ **95.** $(3x)^{\frac{1}{2}} = (x + 6)^{\frac{1}{2}}$

Expand each binomial.   ◆ **See Lesson 5-7.**

96. $(x + 4)^8$ **97.** $(x + y)^6$ **98.** $(2x - y)^4$ **99.** $(2x - 3y)^7$

100. $(9 - 2x)^5$ **101.** $(4x - y)^5$ **102.** $(x^2 + x)^4$ **103.** $(x^2 + 2y^3)^6$

Get Ready!   To prepare for Lesson 6-7, do Exercises 104–106.

Graph and solve each system.   ◆ **See Lesson 3-1.**

104. $\begin{cases} y = x - 6 \\ y = x + 6 \end{cases}$ **105.** $\begin{cases} y = 0.5x + 1 \\ y = 2x - 2 \end{cases}$ **106.** $\begin{cases} y = \frac{x + 4}{5} \\ y = 5x - 4 \end{cases}$

105. $(2, 2)$
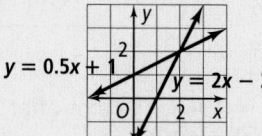

106. $(1, 1)$
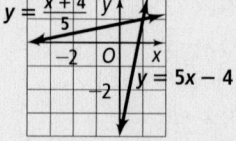

Additional Instructional Support

Algebra 2 Companion

Students can use the **Algebra 2 Companion** worktext (4 pages) as you teach the lesson. Use the Companion to support

- New Vocabulary
- Key Concepts
- Got It for each Problem
- Lesson Check

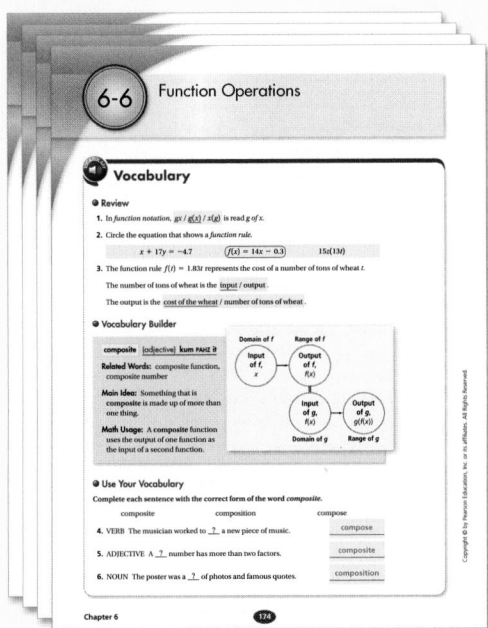

ELL Support

Connect to Prior Knowledge You may want to discuss the background behind Problem 4 before teaching it.

Ask students the following questions:
"What is a discount?" [a reduction in price]
"What is a coupon? How does it work?" [a discount from the original price. It may be a certain dollar amount, or a percentage of the total price.]

"Suppose you have a coupon for $5 off of a purchase. Does the amount you spend affect your savings? Explain." [No; the coupon will save you just $5 regardless of how much you spend.]

"Suppose you have a coupon for 20% off. Does the amount you spend affect your savings? Explain." [Yes; the more you spend, the more total money you will save.]

5 Assess & Remediate

Lesson Quiz

1. Let $f(x) = \sqrt{x} - 4$ and $g(x) = x + 6$. What are $f + g$ and $f - g$? What are their domains?

2. Let $f(x) = x^2 - 16$ and $g(x) = x - 4$. What are $f \cdot g$ and $\frac{f}{g}$? What are their domains?

3. Let $f(x) = x - 2$ and $g(x) = x^3$. What is $(f \circ g)(2)$?

4. **Do you UNDERSTAND?** The function $f(x) = 12x$ gives the number of inches in x feet and $g(x) = 3.28x$ gives the approximate number of feet in x meters. Write a composite function that could be used to convert meters to inches.

ANSWERS TO LESSON QUIZ

1. $(f + g)(x) = \sqrt{x} + x + 2$; $(f - g)(x) = \sqrt{x} - x - 10$; the domain of each is $x \geq 0$.

2. $(f \cdot g)(x) = x^3 - 4x^2 - 16x + 64$; $(\frac{f}{g})(x) = x + 4$; the domain of $(f \cdot g)(x)$ is all real numbers; the domain of $(\frac{f}{g})(x)$ is all real numbers except $x = 4$.

3. 6

4. $(f \circ g)(x) = 39.36x$

PRESCRIPTION FOR REMEDIATION

Use the student work on the Lesson Quiz to prescribe a differentiated review assignment:

Points	Differentiated Remediation
0–2	Intervention
3	On-level
4	Extension

PowerAlgebra.com

5 Assess & Remediate

Assign the Lesson Quiz. Appropriate intervention, practice, or enrichment is automatically generated based on student performance.

Intervention

- **Reteaching** (2 pages) Provides reteaching and practice exercises for the key lesson concepts. Use with struggling students or absent students.

- **English Language Learner Support** Helps students develop and reinforce mathematical vocabulary and key concepts.

All-in-One Resources/Online
Reteaching

6-6 Reteaching
Function Operations

When you combine functions using addition, subtraction, multiplication, or division, the domain of the resulting function has to include the domains of both of the original functions.

Problem

Let $f(x) = x^2 - 4$ and $g(x) = \sqrt{x}$. What is the solution of each function operation? What is the domain of the result?

a. $(f + g)(x) = f(x) + g(x) = (x^2 - 4) + (\sqrt{x}) = x^2 + \sqrt{x} - 4$
b. $(f - g)(x) = f(x) - g(x) = (x^2 - 4) - (\sqrt{x}) = x^2 - \sqrt{x} - 4$
c. $(g - f)(x) = g(x) - f(x) = (\sqrt{x}) - (x^2 - 4) = -x^2 + \sqrt{x} + 4$
d. $(f \cdot g)(x) = f(x) \cdot g(x) = (x^2 - 4)(\sqrt{x}) = x^2\sqrt{x} - 4\sqrt{x}$

The domain of f is all real numbers. The domain of g is all $x \geq 0$. For parts a–d, there are no additional restrictions on the values for x, so the domain for each of these is $x \geq 0$.

e. $\frac{f}{g}(x) = \frac{f(x)}{g(x)} = \frac{x^2 - 4}{\sqrt{x}} = \frac{(x^2 - 4)\sqrt{x}}{x}$

As before, the domain is $x \geq 0$. But, because the denominator cannot be zero, eliminate any values of x for which $g(x) = 0$. The only value for which $\sqrt{x} = 0$ is $x = 0$. Therefore, the domain of $\frac{f}{g}$ is $x > 0$.

f. $\frac{g}{f}(x) = \frac{g(x)}{f(x)} = \frac{\sqrt{x}}{x^2 - 4}$

Similarly, begin with $x \geq 0$ and eliminate any values of x that make the denominator $f(x)$ zero: $x^2 - 4 = 0$ when $x = -2$ and $x = 2$. Therefore, the domain of $\frac{g}{f}$ is $x \geq 0$ combined with $x \neq -2$ and $x \neq 2$. In other words, the domain is $x \geq 0$ and $x \neq 2$, or all nonnegative numbers except 2.

Exercises

Let $f(x) = 4x - 3$ and $g(x) = x^2 + 2$. Perform each function operation and then find the domain of the result.

1. $(f + g)(x)$
   $x^2 + 4x - 1$; all real numbers

2. $(f - g)(x)$
   $-x^2 + 4x - 5$; all real numbers

3. $(g - f)(x)$
   $x^2 - 4x + 5$; all real numbers

4. $(f \cdot g)(x)$
   $4x^3 - 3x^2 + 8x - 6$; all real numbers

5. $\frac{f}{g}(x)$
   $\frac{4x - 3}{x^2 + 2}$; all real numbers

6. $\frac{g}{f}(x)$
   $\frac{x^2 + 2}{4x - 3}$; $x \neq \frac{3}{4}$

All-in-One Resources/Online
English Language Learner Support

6-6 Additional Vocabulary Support
Function Operations

Darnell wrote the steps to compose the following functions on index cards, but the cards got mixed up.

Let $f(x) = x + 7$ and $g(x) = x^3$. What is $(g \circ f)(-4)$?

Subtract 4 from 7.	Substitute −4 for x in f(x).

Raise 3 to the 3rd power.	Substitute 3 into g(x).

Use the note cards to write the steps in order.

1. **First,** substitute −4 for x in f(x)

2. **Second,** subtract 4 from 7

3. **Then,** substitute 3 into g(x)

4. **Finally,** raise 3 to the 3rd power

Differentiated Remediation continued

On-Level

- **Practice** (2 pages) Provides extra practice for each lesson. For simpler practice exercises, use the Form K Practice pages found in the All-in-One Teaching Resources and online.

- **Think About a Plan** Helps students develop specific problem-solving skills and strategies by providing scaffolded guiding questions.

- **Standardized Test Prep** Focuses on all major exercises, all major question types, and helps students prepare for the high-stakes assessments.

Extension

- **Enrichment** Provides students with interesting problems and activities that extend the concepts of the lesson.

- **Activities, Games, and Puzzles** Worksheets that can be used for concepts development, enrichment, and for fun!

Practice and Problem Solving Wkbk/ All-in-One Resources/Online
Practice page 1

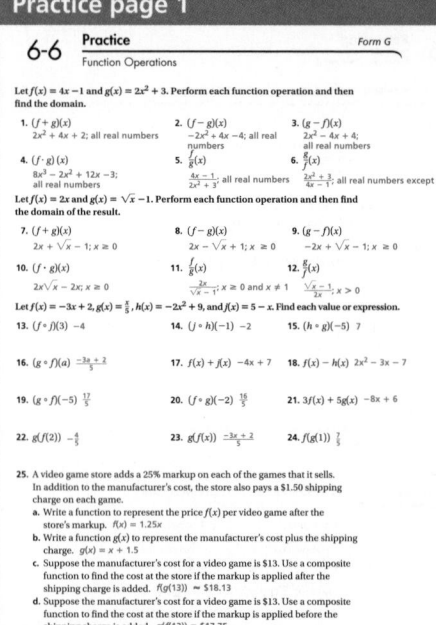

Practice and Problem Solving Wkbk/ All-in-One Resources/Online
Practice page 2

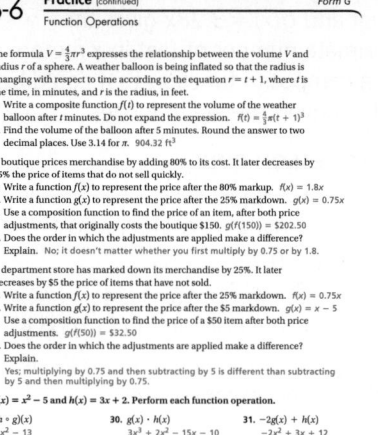

All-in-One Resources/Online
Enrichment

Practice and Problem Solving Wkbk/ All-in-One Resources/Online
Think About a Plan

Practice and Problem Solving Wkbk/ All-in-One Resources/Online
Standardized Test Prep

Online Teacher Resource Center
Activities, Games, and Puzzles

6-7 Inverse Relations and Functions

Objective To find the inverse of a relation or function

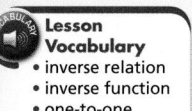
Lesson Vocabulary
- inverse relation
- inverse function
- one-to-one function

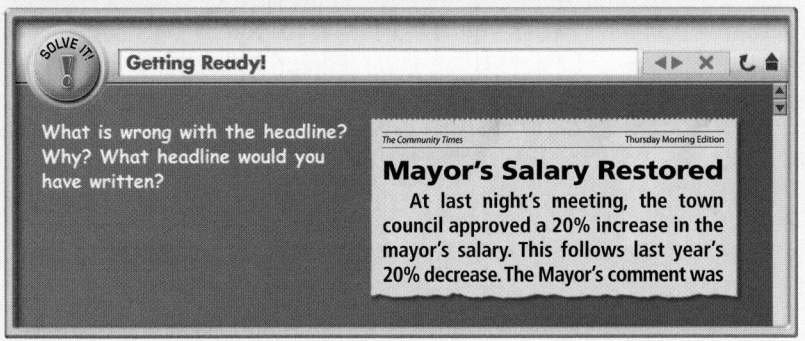

If a relation pairs element *a* of its domain to element *b* of its range, the **inverse relation** pairs *b* with *a*. So, if (*a*, *b*) is an ordered pair of a relation, then (*b*, *a*) is an ordered pair of its inverse. If both a relation and its inverse happen to be functions, they are **inverse functions**.

Essential Understanding The inverse of a function may or may not be a function.

This diagram shows a relation *r* (a function) and its inverse (not a function). The range of the relation is the domain of the inverse. The domain of the relation is the range of the inverse.

Relation *r*		Inverse of *r*	
Domain	Range	Domain	Range
1.2 → 1		1 → 1.2	
1.4 → 1		→ 1.4	
1.6 → 2		2 → 1.6	
1.9 → 2		→ 1.9	

Think
(0, −1) is in *s*. How do you find the corresponding pair in the inverse of *s*?
Switch the coordinates. (−1, 0) is in the inverse of *s*.

Problem 1 Finding the Inverse of a Relation

A What is the inverse of relation *s*?

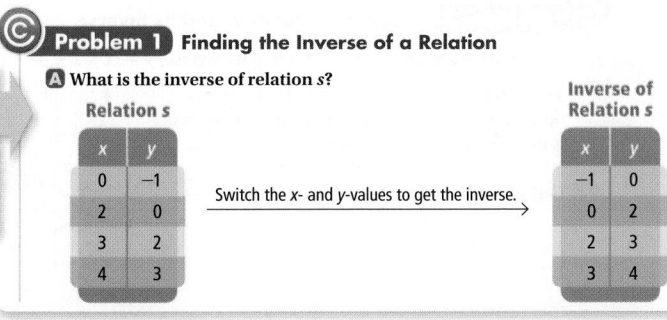

Switch the *x*- and *y*-values to get the inverse.

Relation *s*

x	y
0	−1
2	0
3	2
4	3

Inverse of Relation *s*

x	y
−1	0
0	2
2	3
3	4

PowerAlgebra.com

Lesson 6-7   Inverse Relations and Functions   **405**

6-7 Preparing to Teach

BIG ideas Function
Solving Equations and Inequalities

ESSENTIAL UNDERSTANDINGS
- The inverse of a function may or may not be a function.
- When you square each side of an equation, the resulting equation may have more solutions than the original equation.
- If *f* and f^{-1} are functions and if either maps *a* to *b*, then the other maps *b* to *a*, i.e., $(f \circ f^{-1})(a) = (f^{-1} \circ f)(a) = a$.
- The range of the relation is the domain of the inverse. The domain of the relation is the range of the inverse.

Math Background

Be careful to differentiate between inverse functions and the inverse of a function. The inverse of a function may not be a function.

The inverse of a function will only be a function if the function is one-to-one.

A common mistake students make is confusing *f* inverse with *f* to the negative one. Make sure to clarify that the notation for *f* inverse is $f^{-1}(x)$ and for *f* to the negative one is $f(x)^{-1}$.

Mathematical Practices

Reason abstractly and quantitatively. Students will find the inverse function by swapping *x* and *y* and solving for *y*. In finding the inverse of a function, students will manipulate *x* and *y* independent of their referents.

Common Core State Standards
F-BF.B.4a Solve an equation of the form *f(x) = c* for a simple function *f* that has an inverse and write an expression for the inverse. **Also F-BF.B.4c**
MP 1, MP 2, MP 3

1 Interactive Learning

Solve It!

PURPOSE To explore the outcome of increasing and decreasing a value by the same percentage
PROCESS Students may
- choose a starting salary for the mayor and find the salary for each year based on it.
- generalize the salaries for each year based on a starting salary *x*.

FACILITATE
Q How can you represent a 20% cut in pay of a salary *x*? **[(.80)x]**
Q How can you represent a 20% increase in a salary *x*? **[(1.2)x]**
Q How can you represent the mayor's salary this year? **[(1.2)(.8)x]**
Q If the council restored the mayor's salary to its first-year level, what should that value equal? Does it? **[x; no]**
Q Which is greater: *x*% of a greater number or lesser number? **[x% of a greater number, unless *x* is negative]**

ANSWER See Solve It in Answers on next page.
CONNECT THE MATH In the Solve It students use percentages to determine why the headline is incorrect, that is, increasing a salary by 20% does not "undo" the 20% decrease from the previous year. In the lesson, students find inverse functions, which "undo" what another function does.

2 Guided Instruction

Problem 1

Q How are the columns of the table of *s* and its inverse related? **[They are reversed.]**

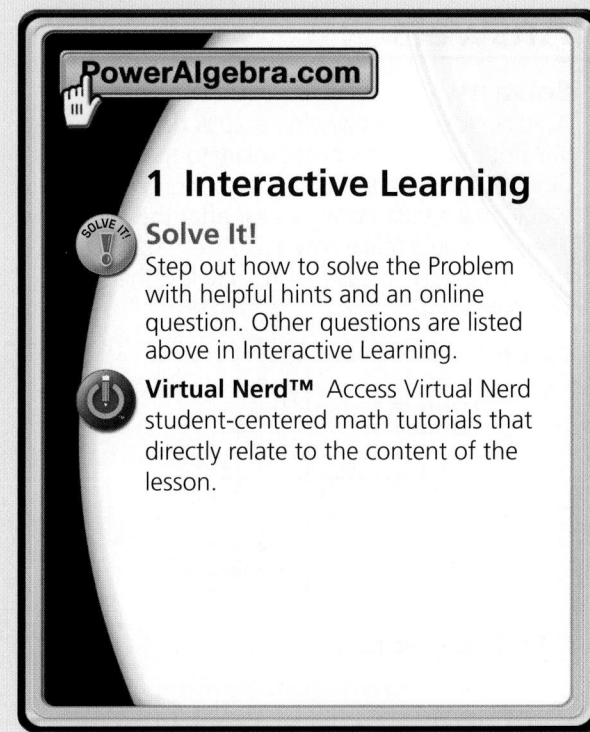

PowerAlgebra.com

1 Interactive Learning

Solve It!
Step out how to solve the Problem with helpful hints and an online question. Other questions are listed above in Interactive Learning.

Virtual Nerd™ Access Virtual Nerd student-centered math tutorials that directly relate to the content of the lesson.

Got It?

Q What points are on the graph of the inverse of t?
[(−5, 0), (−4, 1), (−3, 2), (−3, 3)]

Problem 2

Q What is the output of the inverse of the function? [the input of the original function]

Q Is the inverse of y a function? Explain. [No, because for every x-value except −1 there are two y-values.]

Got It?

Q How does the slope of the function relate to the slope of its inverse? [It is the reciprocal.]

Problem 3

To reflect a graph over the line $y = x$, plot the points (y, x) for points (x, y) that are on the original graph.

Q What is the shape of the graph of the inverse relation? [It is a parabola that opens rightward.]

Q Is the inverse of y a function? Explain. [No, it does not pass the vertical-line test.]

Got It?

Q How are the intercepts of the graph of the function and the graph of the inverse relation related? [They are switched. For example, (0, 8) is the y-intercept of the function and (8, 0) is the x-intercept of the graph of the inverse relation.]

B What are the graphs of s and its inverse?

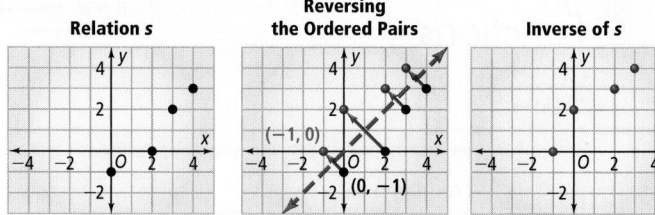

Relation s   Reversing the Ordered Pairs   Inverse of s

Got It? 1. a. What are the graphs of t and its inverse?
   b. Reasoning Is t a function? Is the inverse of t a function? Explain.

Relation t

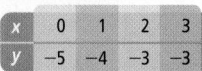

x	0	1	2	3
y	−5	−4	−3	−3

As shown in Problem 1, the graphs of a relation and its inverse are the reflections of each other in the line $y = x$. If you describe a relation or function by an equation in x and y, you can switch x and y to get an equation for the inverse.

Problem 2 Finding an Equation for the Inverse

Think

Why do you solve for y?
If you solve the equation for y, you can use it to easily generate ordered pairs that are part of the inverse relation.

What is the inverse of the relation described by $y = x^2 − 1$?

$y = x^2 − 1$
$x = y^2 − 1$ Switch x and y.
$x + 1 = y^2$ Add 1 to each side.
$\pm\sqrt{x + 1} = y$ Find the square root of each side to solve for y.

Got It? 2. What is the inverse of $y = 2x + 8$?

Problem 3 Graphing a Relation and Its Inverse

Think

What does the graph of $y = x^2 − 1$ look like?
The graph of $y = x^2 − 1$ is a translation of $y = x^2$ down one unit.

What are the graphs of $y = x^2 − 1$ and its inverse, $y = \pm\sqrt{x + 1}$?

The graph of $y = x^2 − 1$ is a parabola that opens upward with vertex $(0, −1)$. The graph of the inverse is the reflection of the parabola in the line $y = x$.

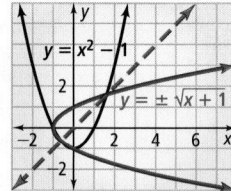

$y = x^2 − 1$
$y = \pm\sqrt{x + 1}$

Got It? 3. What are the graphs of $y = 2x + 8$ and its inverse?

Answers

Solve It!

A 20% increase in pay after a 20% decrease in pay will not restore the mayor's salary to the same amount. If he made x dollars a year originally, he would make $0.8x$ dollars a year after the cut in pay. Then he would make only $1.2(0.8x) = 0.96x$ after the increase. He is still making 4% less than his original salary.

Got It?

1. a.

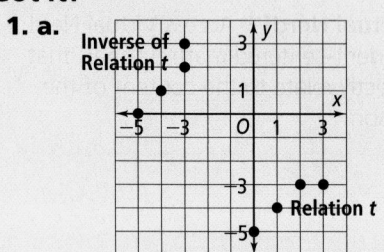

Inverse of Relation t

Relation t

1b, 2–4. See page 408.

PowerAlgebra.com

2 Guided Instruction

Each Problem is worked out and supported online.

Problem 1
Finding the Inverse of a Relation

Problem 2
Finding an Equation for the Inverse

Problem 2 Alternative
Finding an Equation for the Inverse
Animated

Problem 3
Graphing a Relation and Its Inverse

Problem 4
Finding an Inverse Function
Animated

Problem 5
Finding the Inverse of a Formula

Problem 6
Composing Inverse Functions
Animated

Problem 6 Alternative
Composing Inverse Functions

The inverse of a function f is denoted by f^{-1}. You read f^{-1} as "the inverse of f" or as "f inverse." The notation $f(x)$ is used for functions, but the relation f^{-1} may not even be a function.

© **Problem 4** Finding an Inverse Function

Consider the function $f(x) = \sqrt{x - 2}$.

Ⓐ **What are the domain and range of f?**

The radicand cannot be negative, so the numbers $x \geq 2$ make up the domain. The principal square root is nonnegative, so the numbers $y \geq 0$ make up the range.

Ⓑ **What is f^{-1}, the inverse of f?**

$$f(x) = \sqrt{x - 2}$$
$$y = \sqrt{x - 2} \quad \text{Rewrite the equation using } y.$$
$$x = \sqrt{y - 2} \quad \text{Switch } x \text{ and } y. \text{ Since } x \text{ equals a principal square root, } x \geq 0.$$
$$x^2 = y - 2 \quad \text{Square both sides.}$$
$$y = x^2 + 2 \quad \text{Solve for } y.$$

So, $f^{-1}(x) = x^2 + 2$, for $x \geq 0$.

Ⓒ **What are the domain and range of f^{-1}?**

Part (b) shows that the domain of f^{-1} is the range of f—the numbers $x \geq 0$. Since $x^2 \geq 0$, $x^2 + 2 \geq 2$. Therefore, the numbers $y \geq 2$ make up the range of f^{-1}. Note that the range of f^{-1} is the same as the domain of f.

Ⓓ **Is f^{-1} a function? Explain.**

For each x in the domain ($x \geq 0$) of f^{-1}, there is only one value of y in the range. So $f^{-1}(x) = x^2 + 2$, $x \geq 0$, is a function.

Think

How could a graph help you check your answer?
You could graph f^{-1} and see whether the graph passes the vertical line test. If it does, f^{-1} is a function.

✓ **Got It?** 4. Let $g(x) = 6 - 4x$.
    a. What are the domain and range of g?
    b. What is the inverse of g?
    c. What are the domain and range of g^{-1}?
    d. Is g^{-1} a function? Explain.

Functions that model real-world behavior are often expressed as formulas with meaningful variables, like $A = \pi r^2$ for the area of a circle. Strictly speaking, the inverse formula would be $r^2 = \pi A$, but this expresses a false relationship between A and r. It is better to leave the variables in place and solve for r as a function of A.

$$A = \pi r^2 \quad \text{Original formula.}$$
$$r = \sqrt{\frac{A}{\pi}} \quad \text{Same formula, but inversely expressed.}$$

Problem 4
In this problem, the domain of the inverse function is restricted, as not all valid inputs of the function are in the range of the original function.

Q How does knowing the domain and range of $y = \sqrt{x}$ help you find the domain and range of $f(x)$? **[Answers may vary. Sample: By knowing the translation of two units to the right, you can see that the range is the same and the domain is translated two units to the right.]**

Q How can you determine whether an inverse of a function is itself a function? **[You can use the same methods you use to determine whether any other relation is a function: use the vertical-line test, or determine whether for each x in the domain there is only one value of y in the range.]**

Got It?

Q What is the graph of $g(x)$? **[It is a line.]**
Q How could you determine where this line and the graph of the inverse of its function intersect? **[Answers may vary. Sample: This is the point where $y = x$.]**

Additional Problems

1. Relation v

x	-2	-1	0	1
y	2	0	3	0

a. What is the inverse of relation v?
b. What are the graphs of v and its inverse?

ANSWERS

a. Inverse

x	2	0	3	0
y	-2	-1	0	1

b.
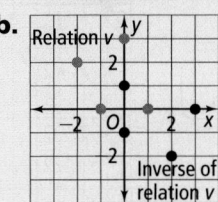

2. What is the inverse of the relation described by $y = 5x^2 + 2$?

ANSWER $y = \pm\sqrt{\frac{x - 2}{5}}$

3. What is the graph of $y = 5x^2 + 2$ and its inverse?

ANSWER
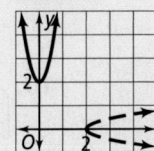

4. Consider the function $g(x) = -\frac{2}{3}x + 7$.
    a. What are the domain and range of g?
    b. What is g^{-1}, the inverse of g?
    c. What are the domain and range of g^{-1}?
    d. Is g^{-1} a function? Explain.

ANSWERS

a. domain is all real numbers; range is all real numbers
b. $g^{-1}(x) = -\frac{3}{2}x + 10.5$
c. domain is all real numbers; range is all real numbers
d. Yes; for each x in the domain, there is only one value of y in the range.

5. The formula for finding the area of a circle is $A = \pi r^2$. What is the inverse of this function? What is the radius of a circle with area 30 ft²?

ANSWER $r = \sqrt{\frac{A}{\pi}} \approx 3.09$ ft

6. For $h(x) = \frac{3}{2 - x}$, what is each of the following?
    a. $h^{-1}(x)$
    b. $(h \circ h^{-1})(2)$
    c. $(h^{-1} \circ h)(2)$

ANSWERS

a. $h^{-1}(x) = -\frac{3}{x} + 2$
b. 2
c. undefined

Problem 5 — ERROR PREVENTION

Previously, students switched the variables when finding an inverse. This is to find the resulting inverse relation with y as the traditional dependent variable. However, in real-world applications, the dependence of variables is fixed and their order should not be switched.

> **Q** What is the input and output of d? Its inverse? **[The input of d is time and the output is distance. The input of its inverse is distance and its output is time.]**

Got It?

The formula in this question assumes that the initial velocity of the object is 0 when it begins to fall due to gravity.

> **Q** What value of d do you use to find the velocity? **[24 m]**
>
> **Q** What would be the velocity if the height of the cliff were 12 m? 36 m? **[approximately 15.3 m/s; 26.6 m/s]**

Take Note

> **Q** Why does it make sense that the composition of inverse functions leaves x unchanged when x is in both respective domains? **[Answers may vary. Sample: The inverse functions "undo" each other, leaving x unchanged.]**

 **Problem 5** Finding the Inverse of a Formula

The function $d = 4.9t^2$ represents the distance d, in meters, that an object falls in t seconds due to Earth's gravity. Find the inverse of this function. How long, in seconds, does it take for the cliff diver shown to reach the water below?

$$d = 4.9t^2$$

$t^2 = \dfrac{d}{4.9}$ — Solve for t. Do not switch the variables.

$t = \sqrt{\dfrac{d}{4.9}}$ — Time must be nonnegative.

$= \sqrt{\dfrac{24}{4.9}}$ — Substitute 24 for d.

≈ 2.2 — Use a calculator.

It will take about 2.2 seconds for the diver to reach the water.

24 meters

Think

Why shouldn't you interchange the variables? Interchanging the variables leads to a false relationship between distance and time.

Got It? 5. The function $d = \dfrac{v^2}{19.6}$ relates the distance d, in meters, that an object has fallen to its velocity v, in meters per second. Find the inverse of this function. What is the velocity of the cliff diver in meters per second as he enters the water?

You know that for any function f, each x-value in the domain corresponds to exactly one y-value in the range. For a **one-to-one function**, it is also true that each y-value in the range corresponds to exactly one x-value in the domain. A one-to-one function f has an inverse f^{-1} that is also a function. If f maps a to b, then f^{-1} must map b to a.

Domain of f Range of f
Range of f^{-1} Domain of f^{-1}

take note   Key Concept   Composition of Inverse Functions

If f and f^{-1} are inverse functions, then

$(f^{-1} \circ f)(x) = x$ and $(f \circ f^{-1})(x) = x$ for x in the domains of f and f^{-1}, respectively.

This says that the composition of a function and its inverse is essentially the identity function, $id(x) = x$, or $y = x$.

Answers

Got It? (continued)

1b. t is a function; the inverse of t is not a function; there are 2 y-values for one x-value.

2. $y = \dfrac{x}{2} - 4$

3.

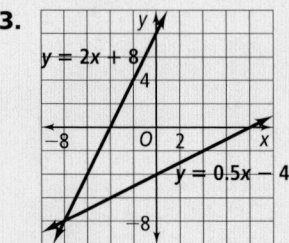

$y = 2x + 8$
$y = 0.5x - 4$

4. a. domain: all real numbers; range: all real numbers

b. $g^{-1}(x) = -\dfrac{1}{4}x + \dfrac{3}{2}$

c. domain: all real numbers; range: all real numbers

d. Yes; for each x in the domain of g^{-1}, there is only one value of y in the range.

5. $v = \sqrt{19.6d}$; about 21.7 m/s

6. a. $g^{-1}(x) = \dfrac{4 - 2x}{x}$

b. 0 is not in the domain of g^{-1} so $(g \circ g^{-1})(0)$ does not exist.

c. 0

Lesson Check

1. $f^{-1}(x) = \dfrac{x - 3}{4}$; yes

2. $f^{-1}(x) = \pm\sqrt{x + 1}$; no

3. $f^{-1}(x) = -1 \pm \sqrt{x}$; no

4. a. $h^{-1}(x) = -\dfrac{1}{x} - 2$

b. -2.25 **c.** 0

5. no; yes

6. 2, 5

7. Answers may vary. Samples: $f(x) = 2x + 1$ and $g(x) = x - 2$; $f(x) = x^2$ and $g(x) = x + 1$

Practice and Problem-Solving Exercises

8.

x	0	1	0	2
y	1	2	3	4

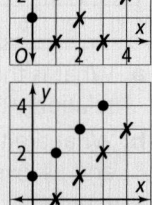

9.

x	0	1	2	3
y	1	2	3	4

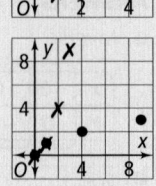

10.

x	0	1	4	9
y	0	1	2	3

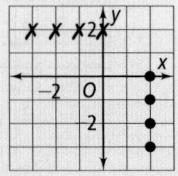

11.

x	2	2	2	2
y	-3	-2	-1	0

Problem 6 Composing Inverse Functions

For $f(x) = \frac{1}{x-1}$, what is each of the following?

A $f^{-1}(x)$

$f(x) = \frac{1}{x-1}$

$y = \frac{1}{x-1}$ Rewrite the equation using y.

$x = \frac{1}{y-1}$ Switch x and y.

$x(y-1) = 1$ Solve for y.

$y - 1 = \frac{1}{x}$

$y = \frac{1}{x} + 1$

So $f^{-1}(x) = \frac{1}{x} + 1$.

 Think

Is this a function?
Yes. For each value of x, there is only one value for y.

B $(f \circ f^{-1})(1)$

$(f \circ f^{-1})(1) = f(f^{-1}(1))$

$= f\left(\frac{1}{1} + 1\right)$

$= f(2)$

$= \frac{1}{2-1} = 1$

C $(f^{-1} \circ f)(1)$

$(f^{-1} \circ f)(1) = f^{-1}(f(1))$

$= f^{-1}\left(\frac{1}{1-1}\right)$

$= f^{-1}\left(\frac{1}{0}\right)$ ⟵ undefined

1 is not in the domain of f. Therefore $(f^{-1} \circ f)(1)$ does not exist.

 **Got It?** **6.** Let $g(x) = \frac{4}{x+2}$. What is each of the following?
     a. $g^{-1}(x)$ **b.** $(g \circ g^{-1})(0)$ **c.** $(g^{-1} \circ g)(0)$

Lesson Check

Do you know HOW?

Find the inverse of each function. Is the inverse a function?

1. $f(x) = 4x + 3$

2. $f(x) = x^2 - 1$

3. $f(x) = (x+1)^2$

4. For $h(x) = -\frac{1}{x+2}$, find:
   a. $h^{-1}(x)$
   b. $h^{-1}(4)$
   c. Value of x for which the equality $(h \circ h^{-1})(x) = x$
      does not hold.

Do you UNDERSTAND? MATHEMATICAL PRACTICES

5. Vocabulary Does every function have an inverse which is a function? Does every relation have an inverse which is a relation?

6. Reasoning A function consists of the pairs (2, 3), $(x, 4)$, and (5, 6). What values, if any, may x not assume?

7. Error Analysis A classmate says that $(f \circ g)^{-1}(x) = (f^{-1} \circ g^{-1})(x)$. Show that this is incorrect by finding examples of $f(x)$ and $g(x)$ for which the equation does not hold.

Answers

12. $y = \frac{1}{3}x - \frac{1}{3}$; yes

13. $y = \frac{1}{2}x + \frac{1}{2}$; yes

14. $y = -\frac{1}{3}x + \frac{4}{3}$; yes

15. $y = \pm\sqrt{\frac{5-x}{2}}$; no

16. $y = \pm\sqrt{x-4}$; no

17. $y = \pm\sqrt{\frac{x+5}{3}}$; no

18. $y = \pm\sqrt{x} + 8$; no

19. $y = \frac{4 \pm \sqrt{x}}{3}$; no

20. $y = \frac{1 \pm \sqrt{x-5}}{2}$; no

21.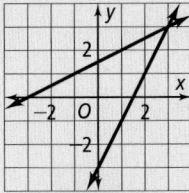

22.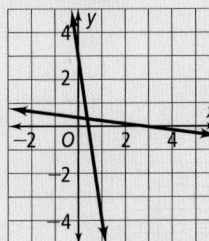

23.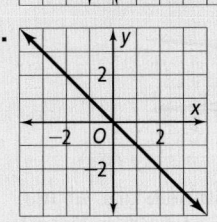

Problem 6

Q Why is the function defined at $x = 1$ in 6B but not in 6C? **[The composition $f^{-1} \circ f$ creates a zero denominator at $x = 1$, while $f \circ f^{-1}$ does not.]**

Got It?

Q At what value of x would $(g^{-1} \circ g)(x)$ be undefined? **[$x = -2$]**

3 Lesson Check

Do you know HOW?

- For Exercises 1–3, if students have difficulty finding an inverse function algebraically, have them list the steps: 1) switch the variables and 2) solve for y.

Do you UNDERSTAND?

- For Exercise 7, remind students that an example cannot show that something is true, but one counterexample is enough to prove that something is not true.

Close

Q How can you tell from the graph of a function whether its inverse is a function? **[Answers may vary. Sample: If no horizontal line intersects the graph of f in more than one point, then f^{-1} will be a function.]**

4 Practice

ASSIGNMENT GUIDE

Basic: 8–41 all, 42, 43, 48–54 even, 65

Average: 9–41 odd, 42–67

Advanced: 9–41 odd, 42–74

Standardized Test Prep: 75–78

Mixed Review: 79–95

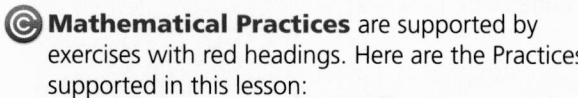 **Mathematical Practices** are supported by exercises with red headings. Here are the Practices supported in this lesson:

MP 1: Make Sense of Problems Ex. 48
MP 2: Reason Abstractly Ex. 67
MP 3: Communicate Ex. 50, 64, 67
MP 3: Construct Arguments Ex. 6, 63a, 64
MP 3: Critique the Reasoning of Others Ex. 7

Applications exercises have blue headings.

STEM exercises focus on science or engineering applications.

EXERCISE 65: Use the Think About a Plan worksheet in the **Practice and Problem Solving Workbook** (also available in the Teaching Resources in print and online) to further support students' development in becoming independent learners.

HOMEWORK QUICK CHECK

To check students' understanding of key skills and concepts, go over Exercises 33, 37, 48, 54, and 65.

 Practice and Problem-Solving Exercises  MATHEMATICAL PRACTICES

Ⓐ Practice   Find the inverse of each relation. Graph the given relation and its inverse.   ◀ See Problem 1.

8.

x	y
1	0
2	1
3	0
4	2

9.

x	y
1	0
2	1
3	2
4	3

10.

x	y
0	0
1	1
2	4
3	9

11.

x	y
−3	2
−2	2
−1	2
0	2

Find the inverse of each function. Is the inverse a function?   ◀ See Problem 2.

12. $y = 3x + 1$

13. $y = 2x - 1$

14. $y = 4 - 3x$

15. $y = 5 - 2x^2$

16. $y = x^2 + 4$

17. $y = 3x^2 - 5$

18. $y = (x - 8)^2$

19. $y = (3x - 4)^2$

20. $y = (1 - 2x)^2 + 5$

Graph each relation and its inverse.   ◀ See Problem 3.

21. $y = 2x - 3$

22. $y = 3 - 7x$

23. $y = -x$

24. $y = 3x^2$

25. $y = -x^2$

26. $y = 4x^2 - 2$

27. $y = (x - 1)^2$

28. $y = (2 - x)^2$

29. $y = (3 - 2x)^2 - 1$

For each function, find the inverse and the domain and range of the function and its inverse. Determine whether the inverse is a function.   ◀ See Problem 4.

30. $f(x) = 3x + 4$

31. $f(x) = \sqrt{x - 5}$

32. $f(x) = \sqrt{x + 7}$

33. $f(x) = \sqrt{-2x + 3}$

34. $f(x) = 2x^2 + 2$

35. $f(x) = -x^2 + 1$

36. Temperature The formula for converting from Celsius to Fahrenheit temperatures is $F = \frac{9}{5}C + 32$.   ◀ See Problem 5.
   a. Find the inverse of the formula. Is the inverse a function?
   b. Use the inverse to find the Celsius temperature that corresponds to 25°F.

37. Geometry The formula for the volume of a sphere is $V = \frac{4}{3}\pi r^3$.
   a. Find the inverse of the formula. Is the inverse a function?
   b. Use the inverse to find the radius of a sphere that has a volume of 35,000 ft³.

For Exercises 38–41, $f(x) = 10x - 10$. Find each value.   ◀ See Problem 6.

38. $(f^{-1} \circ f)(10)$

39. $(f \circ f^{-1})(-10)$

40. $(f^{-1} \circ f)(0.2)$

41. $(f \circ f^{-1})(d)$

Answers

Practice and Problem-Solving Exercises (continued)

8–23.   See pages 408–409.

24.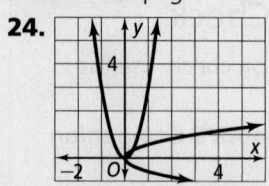

25.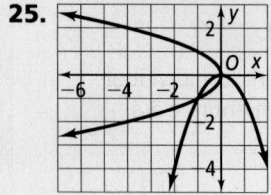

26.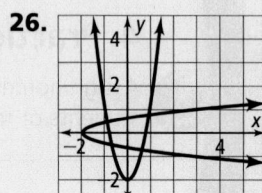

27.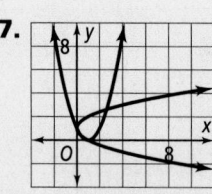

28.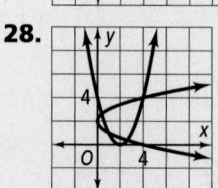

29.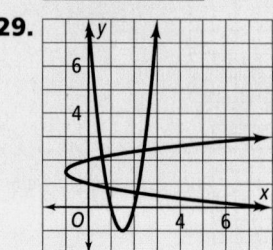

30. $f^{-1}(x) = \frac{x - 4}{3}$, domain of f: all real numbers, range of f: all real numbers, domain of f^{-1}: all real numbers, range of f^{-1}: all real numbers; f^{-1} is a function.

31. $f^{-1}(x) = x^2 + 5$, $x \geq 0$; domain of f: $x \geq 5$, range of f: $y \geq 0$, domain of f^{-1}: $x \geq 0$, range of f^{-1}: $y \geq 5$; f^{-1} is a function.

32. $f^{-1}(x) = x^2 - 7$, $x \geq 0$; domain of f: $x \geq -7$, range of f: $y \geq 0$, domain of f^{-1}: $x \geq 0$, range of f^{-1}: $y \geq -7$; f^{-1} is a function.

33. $f^{-1}(x) = \frac{3 - x^2}{2}$, $x \geq 0$; domain of f: $x \leq \frac{3}{2}$, range of f: $y \geq 0$, domain of f^{-1}: $x \geq 0$, range of f^{-1}: $y \leq \frac{3}{2}$; f^{-1} is a function.

34. $f^{-1}(x) = \pm\sqrt{\frac{x - 2}{2}}$, domain of f: all real numbers, range of f: $y \geq 2$, domain of f^{-1}: $x \geq 2$, range of f^{-1}: all real numbers; f^{-1} is not a function.

35. $f^{-1}(x) = \pm\sqrt{1 - x}$, domain of f: all real numbers, range of f: $y \leq 1$, domain of f^{-1}: $x \leq 1$, range of f^{-1}: all real numbers; f^{-1} is not a function.

Find the inverse of each function. Is the inverse a function?

42. $f(x) = x^3$

43. $f(x) = x^4$

44. $f(x) = \frac{2x^2}{5} + 1$

45. $f(x) = 1.5x^2 - 4$

46. $f(x) = \frac{3x^2}{4}$

47. $f(x) = \sqrt{2x - 1} + 3$

Ⓖ **48. Think About a Plan** The velocity of the water that flows from an opening at the base of a tank depends on the height of water above the opening. The function $v(x) = \sqrt{2gx}$ models the velocity v in feet per second where g, the acceleration due to gravity, is about 32 ft/s^2 and x is the height in feet of the water. What is the depth of water when the flow is 40 ft/s, and when the flow is 20 ft/s?
• How can you use inverse functions to help you find the answer?
• What restrictions are on the domain of $v(x)$? of $v^{-1}(x)$?

49. Let $f(x) = 3x^2 - 4$ and $g(x) = x - 2$. Calculate $(f \circ g^{-1})(x)$ for $x = -3$.

Ⓖ **50. Writing** Explain how you can find the range of the inverse of $f(x) = \sqrt{x-1}$ without finding the inverse itself.

For each function, find the inverse and the domain and range of the function and its inverse. Determine whether the inverse is a function.

51. $f(x) = -\sqrt{x}$

52. $f(x) = \sqrt{x} + 3$

53. $f(x) = \sqrt{-x+3}$

54. $f(x) = \sqrt{x+2}$

55. $f(x) = \frac{x^2}{2}$

56. $f(x) = \frac{1}{x^2}$

57. $f(x) = (x-4)^2$

58. $f(x) = (7-x)^2$

59. $f(x) = \frac{1}{(x+1)^2}$

60. $f(x) = 4 - 2\sqrt{x}$

61. $f(x) = \frac{3}{\sqrt{x}}$

62. $f(x) = \frac{1}{\sqrt{-2x}}$

Ⓖ **63. a. Open-Ended** Copy the mapping diagram at the right. Complete it by writing members of the domain and range and connecting them with arrows so that r is a function and r^{-1} is not a function.
b. Repeat part (a) so that r is not a function and r^{-1} is a function.

Relation r
Domain   Range

Ⓖ **64. Reasoning** Relation r has one element in its domain and two elements in its range. Is r a function? Is the inverse of r a function? Explain.

65. Geometry Write a function that gives the length of the hypotenuse of an isosceles right triangle with side length s. Evaluate the inverse of the function to find the side length of an isosceles right triangle with a hypotenuse of 6 in.

66. For the function $f(x) = \sqrt[3]{2x}$, find $f^{-1}(x)$. Then determine the value of x when $f(x) = 16$.

Ⓖ **67. Reasoning** To determine if the inverse of function f is also a function, you can use a *horizontal line test*. It says that if no horizontal line intersects the graph of the function f in more than one point, then the inverse of f is a function.
a. Explain why the horizontal line test works.
b. The graph of a polynomial function passes through the points $(-1, 1)$, $(0, 4)$ and $(2, 3)$. Can its inverse be a function?

---

36. a. $C = \frac{5}{9}(F - 32)$; yes   **b.** $-3.9°C$

37. a. $r = \sqrt[3]{\frac{3V}{4\pi}}$; yes   **b.** 20.29 ft

38. 10

39. -10

40. 0.2

41. d

42. $f^{-1}(x) = \sqrt[3]{x}$; yes

43. $f^{-1}(x) = \pm\sqrt[4]{x}$; no

44. $f^{-1}(x) = \pm\sqrt{\frac{5x-5}{2}}$; no

45. $f^{-1}(x) = \pm\sqrt{\frac{2x+8}{3}}$; no

46. $f^{-1}(x) = \pm2\sqrt{\frac{x}{3}}$; no

47. $f^{-1}(x) = \frac{x^2 - 6x + 10}{2}$, $x \geq 3$; yes

48. 25 ft; 6.25 ft

49. -1

50. The range of the inverse of f is the domain of f, which is $x \geq 1$.

51. $f^{-1}(x) = x^2$, $x \leq 0$; domain of f: $x \geq 0$, range of f: $y \leq 0$, domain of f^{-1}: $x \leq 0$, range of f^{-1}: $y \geq 0$; f^{-1} is a function.

52. $f^{-1}(x) = (x - 3)^2$, $x \geq 3$; domain of f: $x \geq 0$, range of f: $y \geq 3$, domain of f^{-1}: $x \geq 3$, range of f^{-1}: $y \geq 0$; f^{-1} is a function.

53. $f^{-1}(x) = 3 - x^2$, domain of f: $x \leq 3$, range of f: $y \geq 0$, domain of f^{-1}: $x \geq 0$, range of f^{-1}: $y \leq 3$; f^{-1} is a function.

54. $f^{-1}(x) = x^2 - 2$, domain of f: $x \geq -2$, range of f: $y \geq 0$, domain of f^{-1}: $x \geq 0$, range of f^{-1}: $y \geq -2$; f^{-1} is a function.

55. $f^{-1}(x) = \pm\sqrt{2x}$, domain of f: all real numbers, range of f: $y \geq 0$, domain of f^{-1}: $x \geq 0$, range of f^{-1}: all real numbers; f^{-1} is not a function.

56. $f^{-1}(x) = \pm\frac{1}{\sqrt{x}}$, domain of f: $x \neq 0$, range of f: $y > 0$, domain of f^{-1}: $x > 0$, range of f^{-1}: $y \neq 0$; f^{-1} is not a function.

57. $f^{-1}(x) = \pm\sqrt{x} + 4$, domain of f: all real numbers, range of f: $y \geq 0$, domain of f^{-1}: $x \geq 0$, range of f^{-1}: all real numbers; f^{-1} is not a function.

58. $f^{-1}(x) = 7 \pm \sqrt{x}$, domain of f: all real numbers, range of f: $y \geq 0$, domain of f^{-1}: $x \geq 0$, range of f^{-1}: all real numbers; f^{-1} is not a function.

59. $f^{-1}(x) = \pm\frac{1}{\sqrt{x}} - 1$, domain of f: $x \neq -1$, range of f: $y > 0$, domain of f^{-1}: $x > 0$, range of f^{-1}: $y \neq -1$; f^{-1} is not a function.

60. $f^{-1}(x) = \left(\frac{4-x}{2}\right)^2$, $x \leq 4$; domain of f: $x \geq 0$, range of f: $y \leq 4$, domain of f^{-1}: $x \leq 4$, range of f^{-1}: $y \geq 0$; f^{-1} is a function.

61. $f^{-1}(x) = \left(\frac{3}{x}\right)^2$, $x > 0$; domain of f: $x > 0$, range of f: $y > 0$, domain of f^{-1}: $x > 0$, range of f^{-1}: $y > 0$; f^{-1} is a function.

62. $f^{-1}(x) = -\frac{1}{2}\left(\frac{1}{x}\right)^2$, $x \geq 0$; domain of f: $x < 0$, range of f: $y > 0$, domain of f^{-1}: $x > 0$, range of f^{-1}: $y < 0$; f^{-1} is a function.

63. a.
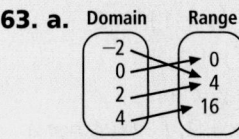
Domain   Range

b.
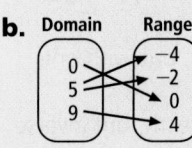
Domain   Range

64. r is not a function because there are two y-values for one x-value. r^{-1} is a function because each of its x-values has one y-value.

65. $h = s\sqrt{2}$; $s = \frac{h\sqrt{2}}{2} = 3\sqrt{2} \approx 4.2$ in.

66. $f^{-1}(x) = \frac{x^3}{2}$; $x = 2048$

67. a. The horizontal line test tells you if there is more than one x-value for every y-value. Since the graph of f^{-1} interchanges the x and y values of f, if f passes the horizontal line test, f^{-1} will pass the vertical line test and it will be a function.

b. no

Answers

Practice and Problem-Solving Exercises
(continued)

68. $f^{-1}(x) = \sqrt[3]{5x}$; yes

69. $f^{-1}(x) = x^3 + 5$; yes

70. $f^{-1}(x) = 27x^3$; yes

71. $f^{-1}(x) = 2 + \sqrt[3]{x}$; yes

72. $f^{-1}(x) = x^4$, $x \geq 0$; yes

73. $f^{-1}(x) = \pm\sqrt[4]{\frac{5x}{6}}$; no

74. Yes; $f(x)$ is a one-to-one function, and its graph will pass the horizontal line test.

Standardized Test Prep

75. D

76. F

77. B

78. **[4]** To find the x-intercepts of $f(x)$:
$$0 = (x+1)^2 - 2$$
$$2 = (x+1)^2$$
$$\pm\sqrt{2} = x + 1$$
$-1 \pm \sqrt{2} = x$, so x-intercepts are $(-1 \pm \sqrt{2}, 0)$. To find the y-intercept of $f(x)$: $f(x) = (0+1)^2 - 2 = -1$, so the y-intercept is $(0, -1)$. To find the inverse of $f(x)$:
$$x = (y+1)^2 - 2$$
$$\pm\sqrt{x+2} = y + 1$$
$$-1 \pm \sqrt{x+2} = y,$$
so $f^{-1}(x) = -1 \pm \sqrt{x+2}$; $f^{-1}(x)$ is not a function.

[3] appropriate methods, but with one computational error

[2] intercepts found correctly, but inverse function is incorrect

[1] correct answers, but without work shown

Mixed Review

79. $2x + 7$

80. $-x - 10$

81. $-\frac{3}{2}x + 11$

82. $2x^2 + 28x$

83. 32

84. $2x + 28$

85. -2

86. no real root

87. 3

88. -3

89. -3

90. 0.4

91. 30

92. 0.05

93.

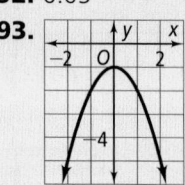

Challenge Find the inverse of each function. Is the inverse a function?

68. $f(x) = \frac{1}{5}x^3$
69. $f(x) = \sqrt[3]{x-5}$
70. $f(x) = \frac{\sqrt[3]{x}}{3}$
71. $f(x) = (x-2)^3$
72. $f(x) = \sqrt[4]{x}$
73. $f(x) = 1.2x^4$

74. Function $f(x)$ is defined the following way:
- if x is an integer, then $f(x) = x + 1$;
- for all other x, $f(x) = x + 2$.

Is the inverse of $f(x)$ a function? Explain.

Standardized Test Prep

SAT/ACT

75. Which pair of words makes this sentence FALSE?
The product of two ____(I)____ numbers is always a (n) ____(II)____ number.
Ⓐ (I) complex; (II) complex
Ⓒ (I) rational; (II) real
Ⓑ (I) real; (II) complex
Ⓓ (I) imaginary; (II) imaginary

76. If $f(x) = x + 1$ and $g(x) = x^2 - 3x - 4$, what is $(f \circ g)(x)$?
Ⓕ $x^2 - 3x - 3$
Ⓖ $x^2 - x - 6$
Ⓗ $x^2 - x$
Ⓘ $x^2 - x - 3$

77. What is the simplified form of $\left(a^{\frac{2}{3}}b^{\frac{3}{4}}\right)^2$?
Ⓐ $a^{\frac{4}{9}}b^{\frac{9}{16}}$
Ⓑ $a^{\frac{4}{3}}b^{\frac{3}{2}}$
Ⓒ ab
Ⓓ $(ab)^{\frac{17}{6}}$

Extended Response

78. Let $f(x) = (x+1)^2 - 2$. Find the x- and y-intercepts of $f(x)$ and the inverse of $f(x)$. Is the inverse a function?

Mixed Review

Let $f(x) = 4x$, $g(x) = \frac{1}{2}x + 7$, and $h(x) = -2x + 4$. Perform each function operation. ◆ **See Lesson 6-6.**

79. $(g \circ f)(x)$
80. $(h \circ g)(x)$
81. $h(x) + g(x)$
82. $f(x) \cdot g(x)$
83. $(f \circ g)(x) + h(x)$
84. $(f \circ g)(x)$

Find each real root. ◆ **See Lesson 6-1.**

85. $-\sqrt[4]{16}$
86. $\sqrt[5]{-16}$
87. $\sqrt[5]{243}$
88. $-\sqrt[5]{243}$
89. $\sqrt[5]{-243}$
90. $\sqrt[3]{0.064}$
91. $\sqrt[4]{810,000}$
92. $\sqrt[4]{\frac{1}{160,000}}$

Get Ready! **To prepare for Lesson 6-8, do Exercises 93–95.**

Graph each function. ◆ **See Lesson 4-1.**

93. $y = -x^2 - 1$
94. $y = -(x+1)^2 + 1$
95. $y = 3x^2 + 3$

94.

95.

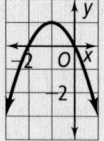

Additional Instructional Support

Algebra 2 Companion
Students can use the **Algebra 2 Companion** worktext (4 pages) as you teach the lesson. Use the Companion to support

- New Vocabulary
- Key Concepts
- Got It for each Problem
- Lesson Check

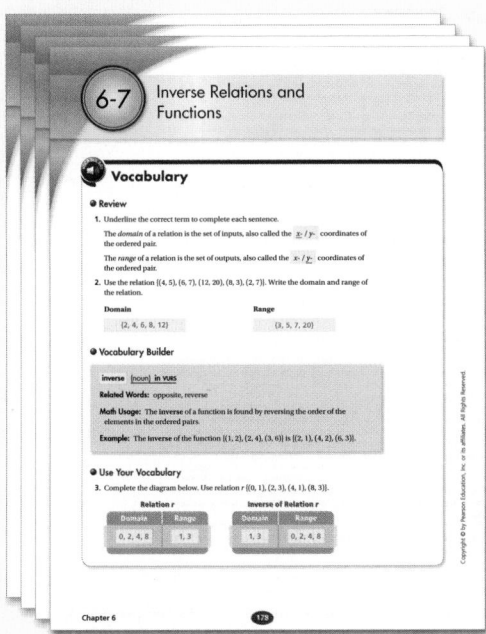

ELL Support
Assess Understanding Ask students the following questions:

- What are some other real-world examples of inverses? [converting currencies, converting from the metric system to the customary, system, unit conversion]
- Are these inverses functions? How do you know? [The ones listed above are, because you can convert both ways and always get the same answer.]
- Can you think of an example of a real-world relation that is not a function and its inverse? [Perhaps a dictionary that translates one language to another. Both languages will have several words with the same meaning.]

Explain to students that the word *inverse* applies in many mathematical contexts as well. Have students ask each other questions that use the word *inverse*:

- What number is the additive inverse of 3? Multiplicative inverse of 3? $[-3; \frac{1}{3}]$
- What is the inverse operation of subtraction? Multiplication? [addition; division]

5 Assess & Remediate

Lesson Quiz

1. What is the inverse of the relation described by $y = 2x^2 + 7$?

2. Consider the function $h(x) = 4\sqrt{x + 3}$.
   a. Find the domain and range of h.
   b. What is the inverse of h?
   c. Find the domain and range of h^{-1}.
   d. Is h^{-1} a function? Explain.

3. **Do you UNDERSTAND?** The formula for converting temperatures from degrees Fahrenheit F to degrees Celsius C is $C = \frac{5}{9}(F - 32)$. What is the inverse function? What is the temperature in Fahrenheit when it is 12 degrees Celsius?

4. Let $k(x) = \frac{2}{x - 1}$. What is each of the following?
   a. $k^{-1}(x)$
   b. $(k \circ k^{-1})(1)$
   c. $(k^{-1} \circ k)(1)$

ANSWERS TO LESSON QUIZ

1. $y = \pm\sqrt{\frac{x - 7}{2}}$

2. **a.** domain is $x \geq -3$; range is $y \geq 0$
   b. $h^{-1}(x) = \frac{x^2}{16} - 3$ for $x \geq 0$
   c. domain is $x \geq 0$; range is $y \geq -3$
   d. Yes; for each x in the domain, there is only one value of y in the range.

3. $F = \frac{9}{5}C + 32$; 53.6°F

4. **a.** $k^{-1}(x) = \frac{2}{x} + 1$
   b. 1
   c. undefined

PRESCRIPTION FOR REMEDIATION
Use the student work on the Lesson Quiz to prescribe a differentiated review assignment:

Points	Differentiated Remediation
0–2	Intervention
3	On-level
4	Extension

PowerAlgebra.com

5 Assess & Remediate
Assign the Lesson Quiz. Appropriate intervention, practice, or enrichment is automatically generated based on student performance.

Intervention
- **Reteaching** (2 pages) Provides reteaching and practice exercises for the key lesson concepts. Use with struggling students or absent students.

- **English Language Learner Support** Helps students develop and reinforce mathematical vocabulary and key concepts.

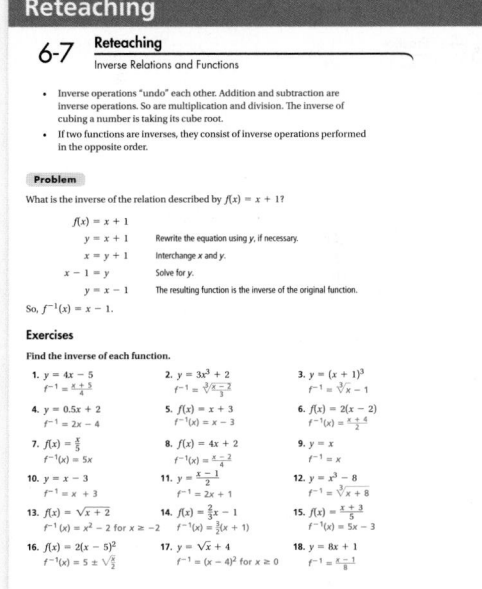

All-in-One Resources/Online
Reteaching

All-in-One Resources/Online
English Language Learner Support

Differentiated Remediation *continued*

On-Level

- **Practice** (2 pages) Provides extra practice for each lesson. For simpler practice exercises, use the Form K Practice pages found in the All-in-One Teaching Resources and online.

- **Think About a Plan** Helps students develop specific problem-solving skills and strategies by providing scaffolded guiding questions.

- **Standardized Test Prep** Focuses on all major exercises, all major question types, and helps students prepare for the high-stakes assessments.

Extension

- **Enrichment** Provides students with interesting problems and activities that extend the concepts of the lesson.

- **Activities, Games, and Puzzles** Worksheets that can be used for concepts development, enrichment, and for fun!

Practice and Problem Solving Wkbk/ All-in-One Resources/Online
Practice page 1

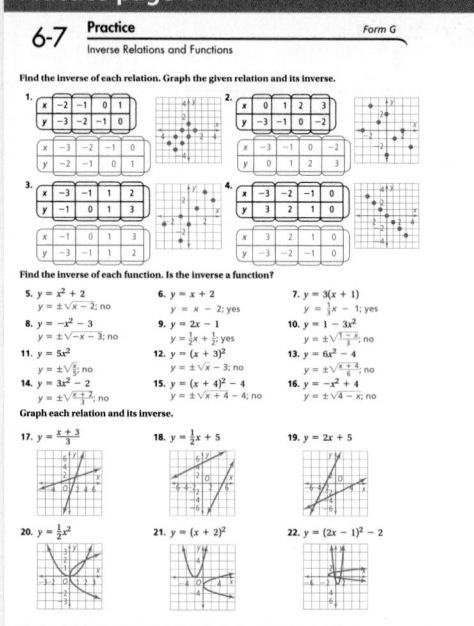

Practice and Problem Solving Wkbk/ All-in-One Resources/Online
Practice page 2

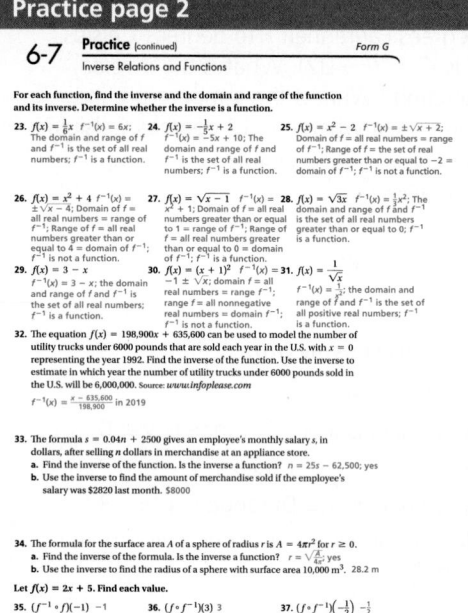

All-in-One Resources/Online
Enrichment

6-7 Enrichment
Inverse Relations and Functions

Composition, Inverses, and Linear Functions

Solving an equation for one variable in terms of another is an important step in finding inverses. This step is also used in conversion formulas.

Consider the following linear functions. Let F denote the temperature in degrees Fahrenheit, C the temperature in degrees Celsius, and K the temperature in degrees Kelvin. The formula for converting degrees Fahrenheit to degrees Celsius is $C = \frac{5}{9}(F - 32)$, and the formula for converting degrees Celsius to degrees Kelvin is $K = C + 273$.

1. Use composition to determine the formula for converting degrees Fahrenheit to degrees Kelvin. $K = \frac{5(F - 32)}{9} + 273$
2. Solve this function for F. $F = \frac{9}{5}(K - 273) + 32$
3. This new equation converts degrees ___Kelvin___ to degrees ___Fahrenheit___.
4. Derive a formula to convert degrees Celsius to degrees Fahrenheit. $F = \frac{9}{5}C + 32$
5. Derive a formula to convert degrees Kelvin to degrees Celsius. $C = K - 273$
6. Compose these two functions to find a formula for converting degrees Kelvin to degrees Fahrenheit. $F = \frac{9}{5}(K - 273) + 32$

Solve each of the following problems involving functions.

7. In 1940, the cost of a new house was $10,000. By 1980, this cost had risen to $90,000. Assuming that the increase is linear, find a function expressing the cost c of a new house in terms of the year y. Solve this function for y. What does this new function enable you to do? $c = 10,000 + 2000(y - 1940)$; $y = \frac{c - 10,000}{2000} + 1940$; find the year given the cost of a house
8. Between the ages of 5 and 15, a typical child grows at a fixed annual rate. If Mary was 42 in. in height when she was 5 yr old and grew at a rate of 2 in. a year, find a formula that expresses Mary's height h in inches when her age is a years. Solve this function for a. What does this new function enable you to do? $h = 2(a - 5) + 42$; $a = \frac{h - 42}{2} + 5$; compute Mary's age given her height
9. The air temperature, in degrees Fahrenheit, surrounding an airplane on a certain particular day was modeled by $T = -\frac{1}{280}a + 110$, where a is the altitude, in feet, of the airplane. Solve this function for a. What does this new function enable you to do? $a = 280(-T + 110)$; find the altitude of the airplane given the temperature
10. The formula $L = 0.25W + 0.5$ models the length of a certain spring, in inches, when a weight of W ounces is attached to it. Solve this function for W. What does this new function enable you to do? $W = \frac{L - 0.5}{0.25}$; find the weight attached to the spring given the length of the stretched spring

Practice and Problem Solving Wkbk/ All-in-One Resources/Online
Think About a Plan

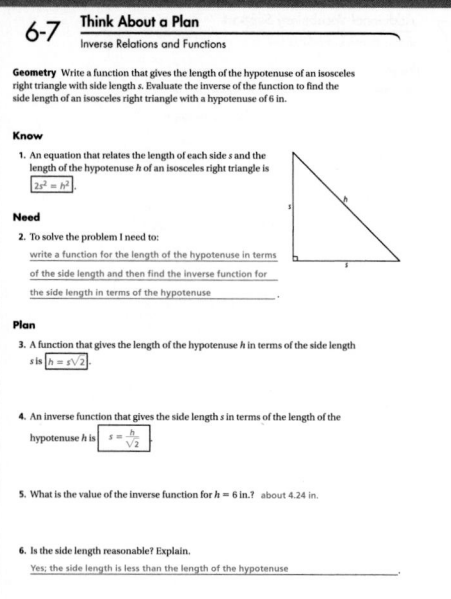

Practice and Problem Solving Wkbk/ All-in-One Resources/Online
Standardized Test Prep

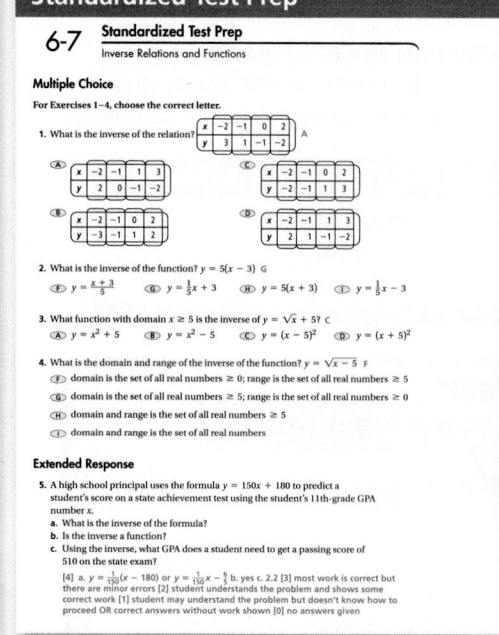

Online Teacher Resource Center
Activities, Games, and Puzzles

6-7 Game: Flip-Flop
Inverse Relations and Functions

This is a game for two players. Players take turns answering the questions below. One player answers the odd-numbered questions, and the other player answers the even-numbered questions. Players check each other's answers.

- Players circle the correct inverse relation for the given relation. A correct answer is worth 5 points.
- If a player answers a question incorrectly, he or she has one additional chance to answer it. If the answer is correct, the player earns 3 points.

Correct answer choices are shown in red.

1. $y = 2x - 3$
   Ⓐ $y = 3x - 2$ Ⓑ $y = 2 - 3x$ Ⓒ $y = \frac{1}{2}x - 3$ Ⓓ $y = \frac{1}{2}x + \frac{3}{2}$

2. $y = \frac{1}{2}x + 5$
   Ⓔ $y = 2x + 10$ Ⓖ $y = 2x - 10$ Ⓗ $y = 2x - 5$ Ⓘ $y = -\frac{1}{2}x - 5$

3. $y = x^2 + 3$
   Ⓐ $y = \pm\sqrt{x - 3}$ Ⓑ $y = \sqrt{-x + 3}$ Ⓒ $y = \pm\sqrt{x + 3}$ Ⓓ $y = \pm\sqrt{-x - 3}$

4. $y = -x^2 + 5$
   Ⓔ $y = \sqrt{x + 5}$ Ⓖ $y = \pm\sqrt{-x - 5}$ Ⓗ $y = \sqrt{-x + 5}$ Ⓘ $y = \sqrt{x - 5}$

5. $y = \frac{2}{3}x - \frac{1}{2}$
   Ⓐ $y = \frac{3}{2}x + \frac{1}{3}$ Ⓑ $y = \frac{2}{3}x + \frac{3}{4}$ Ⓒ $y = \frac{3}{2}x - \frac{3}{4}$ Ⓓ $y = -\frac{2}{3}x - \frac{3}{4}$

6. $y = 2(3x - 5)$
   Ⓔ $y = -x + \frac{5}{3}$ Ⓖ $y = \frac{1}{6}x - \frac{5}{3}$ Ⓗ $y = \frac{1}{6}x + \frac{5}{3}$ Ⓘ $y = -\frac{5}{3}x + 6$

7. $y = \frac{1}{2}x^2 + 1$
   Ⓐ $y = \sqrt{2x + 2}$ Ⓑ $y = \pm\sqrt{2x - 2}$ Ⓒ $y = \pm\sqrt{2x - 1}$ Ⓓ $y = \pm\sqrt{x - 2}$

8. $y = 2x^2 - 0.5$
   Ⓔ $y = \sqrt{\frac{1}{2}x - \frac{1}{4}}$ Ⓖ $y = \sqrt{-\frac{1}{2}x + \frac{1}{4}}$ Ⓗ $y = \pm\sqrt{x + 4}$ Ⓘ $y = \pm\sqrt{\frac{1}{2}x + \frac{1}{4}}$

Graphing Inverses

Common Core State Standards

Extends F-BF.B.4a Solve an equation of the form $f(x) = c$ for a simple function f that has an inverse and write an expression for the inverse.

MP 5

You can graph inverses of functions on a graphing calculator by using the **DrawInv** feature or by using parametric equations. It takes more keystrokes to set up parametric equations, but once you do you can easily change from one function to another and quickly see the graphs of the new function and its inverse.

MATHEMATICAL
PRACTICES

Activity

Graph $y = 0.3x^2 + 1$ and its inverse.

Method 1 Use the **DrawInv** feature.

  Step 1 Press (y=) and enter the equation. Press (zoom) 5 to see a graph of the function with equal x- and y-intervals.

  Step 2 Press (2nd) (draw) 8. You will see **DrawInv** followed by a flashing cursor. Select equation Y_1 by pressing (vars) ▷ 1 1. Press (enter) to see the graph of the function and its inverse.

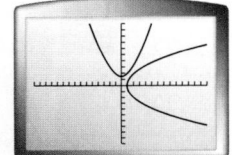

Method 2 Use parametric equations.

  Step 1 Set to parametric mode. Press (mode), select **Par**, and press (2nd) (quit).

  Step 2 Enter the given equation in parametric form. Press (y=) and enter the equations $X_{1T} = T$ and $Y_{1T} = .3T^2 + 1$.

  Step 3 Now use $X_{2T} = Y_{1T}$ and $Y_{2T} = X_{1T}$ to interchange the x- and y-values of the first parametric equation. Press (y=) and move the cursor to follow $X_{2T} =$. Select Y_{1T} by pressing (vars) ▷ 2 2. Enter the equation $Y_{2T} = X_{1T}$ in a similar fashion.

  Step 4 Press (zoom) 5. Adjust the **Window** so that **Tmin** and **Tmax** approximately agree with **Xmin** and **Xmax**. Press (graph) to see the graph of the function and its inverse.

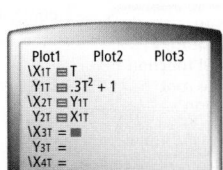

Plot1   Plot2   Plot3
\X₁ᴛ ▪ T
Y₁ᴛ ▪ .3T² + 1
\X₂ᴛ ▪ Y₁ᴛ
Y₂ᴛ ▪ X₁ᴛ
\X₃ᴛ = ■
Y₃ᴛ =
\X₄ᴛ =

Exercises

Graph each function and its inverse with a graphing calculator. Then sketch the graphs.

1. $y = x^2 - 5$ **2.** $y = (x - 3)^2$ **3.** $y = 0.01x^4$ **4.** $y = 0.5x^3 - 3$

5. Writing Change the parametric equation $X_{2T} = Y_{1T}$ in Method 2, Step 3 to $X_{2T} = -Y_{1T}$. Describe the graph that results.

6. Explain how once you set up parametric equations, you can change from one function to another and quickly see the graphs of the new function and its inverse.

Guided Instruction

PURPOSE To use a graphing calculator to graph inverse functions

PROCESS Students will

- use a graphing calculator to graph a function and its inverse.
- use parametric functions to graph a family of functions and their inverses.
- analyze the parametric family of functions and inverses.

DISCUSS

The **DrawInv** feature is used to find the graph of the inverse relation. This can be used to view the shape of the graph and find particular points on the graph. It will not, however, provide the equation that defines the inverse.

> **Q** What is the advantage of using parametric equations to graph the function? **[Answers may vary. Sample: You can easily change the function and its inverse slightly to observe the differences.]**

Activity

Parametric equations can be confusing, since they introduce an additional variable. Explain that T acts as the variable x throughout and that Step 3 acts like switching the variables when solving for an inverse relation by hand.

> **Q** Do you get the same graphs using Method 1 and Method 2? **[yes]**
>
> **Q** In Method 2, why does it make sense to define X_{2T} and Y_{2T} this way? **[You find the inverse function by switching x and y.]**

Mathematical Practices This Concept Byte supports students in becoming proficient in using appropriate tools, Mathematical Practice 5.

Answers

Exercises

1.
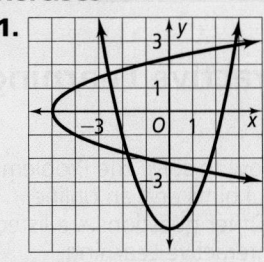

2.
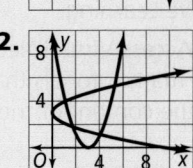

3.
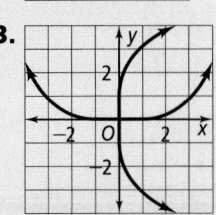

4.
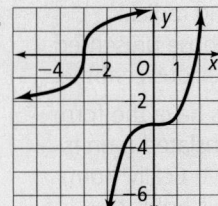

5. The graph is the reflection of the first graph across the x-axis.

6. Answers may vary. Sample: Using parametric equations, you only have to change Y_{1T} to see a new function and its inverse.

1 Interactive Learning

Solve It!

PURPOSE Combine area formulas to write an equation and solve for the radius of a circle

PROCESS Students may draw an equilateral triangle by connecting the centers of each cylinder, draw three rectangles by drawing two radii out of each cylinder that will make a right angle with the strip, and use area formulas to write an expression that represents the cross-sectional area of the strip.

FACILITATE

Q Why would it help to divide the cross-sectional area of the strip into geometric shapes that you recognize? **[You can write equations for the areas of the shapes that you recognize and set their sum equal to 115.]**

Q Into which shapes can you divide the cross-sectional area? **[1 equilateral triangle, 3 rectangles, and 3 thirds of a circle]**

Q What are the area formulas that you need to use?

[area of an equilateral triangle $= \frac{s^2\sqrt{3}}{4}$; area of a rectangle $= \ell w$; area of a circle $= 2\pi r$]

ANSWER See Solve It in Answers on next page.

CONNECT THE MATH In the Solve It, students use the formulas for the area of a circle, a rectangle, and an equilateral triangle to write a square root equation for the radius of each cylinder. In this lesson, students graph square root and radical functions.

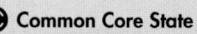

Common Core State Standards

F-IF.C.7b Graph square root *and* cube root functions . . .
F-IF.C.8 Write a function defined by an expression in different but equivalent forms . . .
MP 1, MP 2, MP 3, MP 4, MP 5

Objective To graph square root and other radical functions

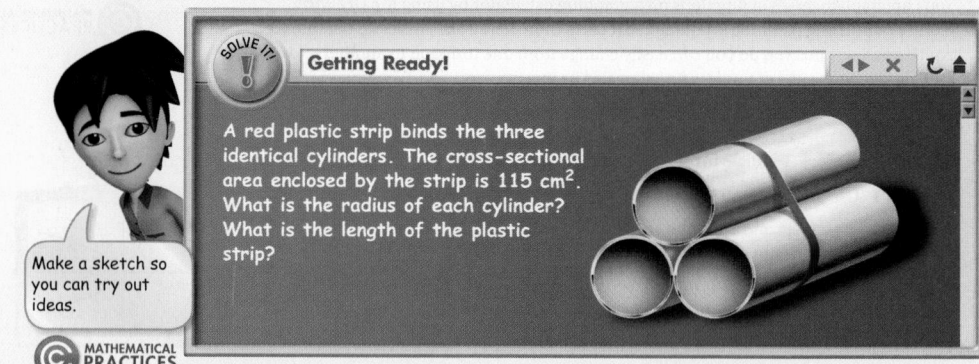

Getting Ready!

A red plastic strip binds the three identical cylinders. The cross-sectional area enclosed by the strip is 115 cm². What is the radius of each cylinder? What is the length of the plastic strip?

Make a sketch so you can try out ideas.

MATHEMATICAL PRACTICES

Lesson Vocabulary
- radical function
- square root function

The formula $A = \pi r^2$ shows that area is a quadratic function of a circle. The formula $r = \frac{1}{\sqrt{\pi}}\sqrt{A}$ shows that the radius of a circle is a square root function of the area.

Essential Understanding A square root function is the inverse of a quadratic function that has a restricted domain.

A horizontal line can intersect the graph of $f(x) = x^2$ in two points—where $f(-2) = f(2)$, for example. Thus, a vertical line can intersect the graph of f^{-1} in two points. f^{-1} is *not* a function because it fails the vertical line test.

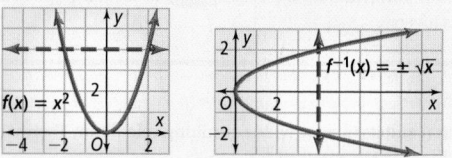

However, you can restrict the domain of f so that the inverse of the restricted function is a function.

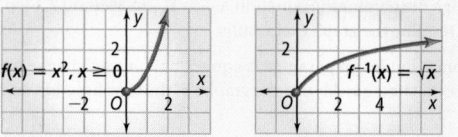

6-8 Preparing to Teach

BIG ideas   **Function**
                 Solving Equations
                 and Inequalities

ESSENTIAL UNDERSTANDINGS

- A square root function is the inverse of a quadratic function that has a restricted domain.
- When you square each side of an equation, the resulting equation may have more solutions than the original equation.
- If f and f^{-1} are functions and if either maps a to b, then the other maps b to a, i.e., $(f \circ f^{-1})(a) = (f^{-1} \circ f)(a) = a$.

Math Background

Square root functions are important because they are inverses of quadratic functions, so they model the same real-world behavior as quadratic polynomials, but in reverse.

The graphs of square root functions are halves of parabolic curves opening sideways.

The methods for graphing radical functions are similar to those presented for other functions in previous chapters.

Graphs whose equations have the form $y = a(x - h)^2 + k$ are translated h units horizontally and k units vertically from the graph of $y = ax^2$. This holds true for functions of the form $y = a\sqrt[n]{x - h} + k$; the graphs are transformations of the graph of the parent function $y = \sqrt[n]{x}$.

In this lesson, students will use graphing calculators to graph radical functions and determine the solutions to problems.

Mathematical Practices

Make sense of problems and persevere in solving them. Students will make correspondences between radical functions and their inverses, as well as between the graphs of each.

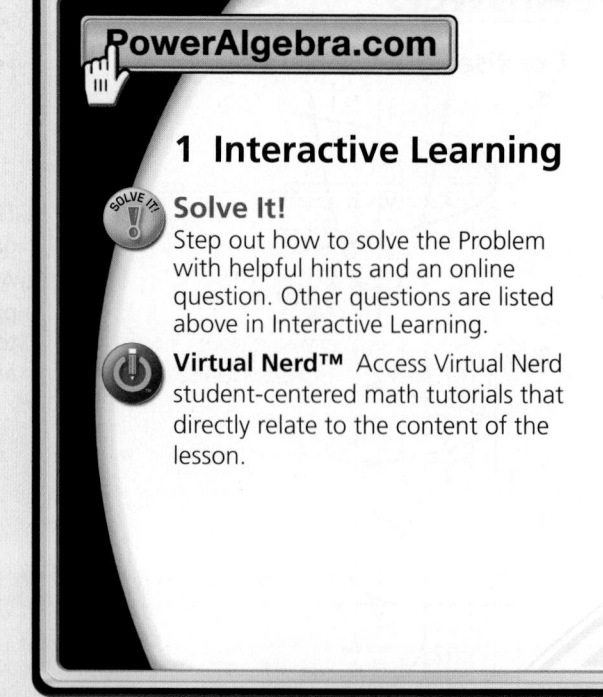

PowerAlgebra.com

1 Interactive Learning

Solve It!
Step out how to solve the Problem with helpful hints and an online question. Other questions are listed above in Interactive Learning.

Virtual Nerd™ Access Virtual Nerd student-centered math tutorials that directly relate to the content of the lesson.

Inverses of the power functions $y = x^n$ (with domains restricted as needed) form parent functions $y = \sqrt[n]{x}$ for families of **radical functions**. In particular, $f(x) = \sqrt{x}$ is the parent for the family of **square root functions**. Members of this family have the general form $f(x) = a\sqrt{x - h} + k$.

take note

Key Concepts   Families of Radical Functions

	Square Root	Radical
Parent function:	$y = \sqrt{x}$	$y = \sqrt[n]{x}$
Reflection in x-axis:	$y = -\sqrt{x}$	$y = -\sqrt[n]{x}$
Stretch ($a > 1$), shrink ($0 < a < 1$) by the factor a:	$y = a\sqrt{x}$	$y = a\sqrt[n]{x}$
Translation: Horizontal by h Vertical by k	$y = \sqrt{x - h} + k$	$y = \sqrt[n]{x - h} + k$

© **Problem 1** Translating a Square Root Function Vertically

What are the graphs of $y = \sqrt{x} - 2$ and $y = \sqrt{x} + 1$?

Think

How is $y = \sqrt{x} + k$ related to the parent function $y = \sqrt{x}$?
It is related to the parent function in the same way that $y = f(x) + k$ is related to $y = f(x)$. It is a vertical translation of k units.

The graph of $y = \sqrt{x} - 2$ is the graph of $y = \sqrt{x}$ shifted down 2 units.

The graph of $y = \sqrt{x} + 1$ is the graph of $y = \sqrt{x}$ shifted up 1 unit.

The domains of both functions are the set of nonnegative numbers, but their ranges differ.

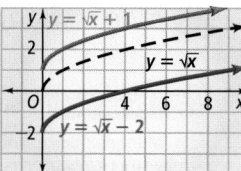

✓ **Got It?** **1.** What are the graphs of $y = \sqrt{x} + 2$ and $y = \sqrt{x} - 3$?

© **Problem 2** Translating a Square Root Function Horizontally

What are the graphs of $y = \sqrt{x + 4}$ and $y = \sqrt{x - 1}$?

Think

How is $y = \sqrt{x - h}$ related to the parent function $y = \sqrt{x}$?
It is a horizontal translation of h units.

The graph of $y = \sqrt{x + 4}$ is the graph of $y = \sqrt{x}$ shifted left 4 units.

The graph of $y = \sqrt{x - 1}$ is the graph of $y = \sqrt{x}$ shifted right 1 unit.

The ranges of both functions are the set of nonnegative numbers, but their domains differ.

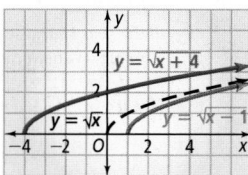

✓ **Got It?** **2.** What are the graphs of $y = \sqrt{x - 3}$ and $y = \sqrt{x + 2}$?

---

2 Guided Instruction

Take Note

Q What is the difference between a square root function and a radical function? **[A square root function has an index of 2. A radical function can have an index of any number.]**

Problem 1

Q What do you notice about the placement of the k-value for each given function? **[The k-value is outside the radical sign.]**

Q How does the sign of the k affect the graph? **[A positive k shifts the graph up and a negative k shifts the graph down.]**

Q Why do the graphs look similar? **[They have the same parent function.]**

Got It?

Q When graphing square root functions, why choose x-values that are perfect squares? **[They yield whole number range values, which are easier to graph.]**

Problem 2

Q What do you notice about the h-value for each function? **[It is under the radical sign.]**

Q How can you obtain the graph of $y = \sqrt{x + 2}$ from the graph of $y = \sqrt{x}$? **[Shift the graph two units to the left.]**

Got It?   ERROR PREVENTION

Students may translate the graph in the wrong direction. Have them circle the sign of the h-value and write an arrow in the direction of the translation.

---

2 Guided Instruction

© Each Problem is worked out and supported online.

Problem 1
Translating a Square Root Function Vertically

Problem 2
Translating a Square Root Function Horizontally
Animated

Problem 3
Graphing a Square Root Function
Animated

Problem 4
Solving a Radical Equation by Graphing

Problem 5
Graphing a Cube Root Function
Animated

Problem 6
Rewriting a Radical Function

Support in Algebra 2 Companion
• Vocabulary
• Key Concepts
• Got It?

Answers

Solve It!
$r \approx 3.3$ cm; length ≈ 39.9 cm

Got It?

1.

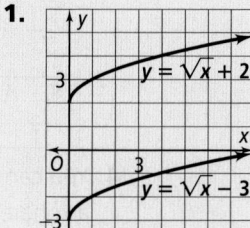

2.

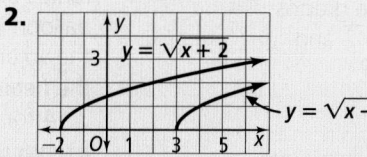

Problem 3

> **Q** What is the effect of a on the graph with a value between 0 and 1? **[The graph is shrunk.]**
>
> **Q** How would the graph of $y = \frac{1}{2}\sqrt{x-3} - 1$ compare to the graph of $y = -\frac{1}{2}\sqrt{x-3} + 1$? **[The graph would be reflected across the x-axis and shifted down two units.]**

Got It?

VISUAL LEARNERS

> **Q** In the equation $y = a\sqrt{x-h} + k$ what does each variable do to the parent function $y = \sqrt{x}$? **[a is a vertical stretch or shrink, h is a horizontal translation, k is a vertical translation]**

Problem 4

> **Q** Why is the equation $y = \sqrt[3]{x-1950}$ entered as $y = (x - 1950)^{(1/3)}$ on a graphing calculator? **[Rewriting a radical in exponential form is a general way to enter radicals with an index greater than 2.]**

Got It?

> **Q** What effect does the change in population have on the two equations? **[The first equation remains the same. The second equation changes to $y_2 = 275{,}000$.]**

Recall from Lesson 2-7 that for any transformation, $y = af(x - h) + k$ of the parent function $f(x)$, a indicates a vertical stretch or shrink.

Similarly, for the combined transformation $y = a\sqrt{x - h} + k$, a indicates a vertical stretch ($|a| > 1$) or shrink ($|a| < 1$). A negative value of a indicates a reflection in the x-axis.

Ⓒ Problem 3 Graphing a Square Root Function

What is the graph of $y = -\frac{1}{2}\sqrt{x-3} + 1$?

Think

What would be good points to choose?
Points that have integer x- and y-coordinates.

Step 1 Choose several points from the parent function $y = \sqrt{x}$.

Step 2 Multiply the y-coordinates by $a = -\frac{1}{2}$. This shrinks the parent graph vertically by the factor $\frac{1}{2}$ and reflects the result in the x-axis.

Step 3 The values of h and k give the horizontal and vertical translations. Translate the graph from Step 2 to the right 3 units and up 1 unit.

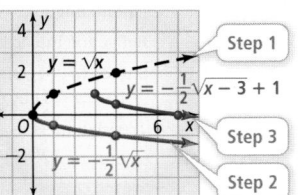

✓ **Got It?** **3.** What is the graph of $y = 3\sqrt{x+2} - 4$?

Ⓒ Problem 4 Solving a Radical Equation by Graphing

Multiple Choice You can model the population P of Corpus Christi, Texas, between the years 1970 and 2005 by the radical function $P(x) = 75{,}000 \sqrt[3]{x - 1950}$, where x is the year. Using this model, in what year was the population of Corpus Christi 250,000?

   Ⓐ 1980   Ⓑ 1983   Ⓒ 1987   Ⓓ 1990

For $P = 250{,}000$, solve the equation $250{,}000 = 75{,}000 \sqrt[3]{x - 1950}$.

Think

How can you rewrite a radical function using an exponent?
You can write a radical function $y = \sqrt[n]{x}$ as $y = x^{\frac{1}{n}}$.

Graph **Y1 = 75000(X − 1950)^(1/3)** and **Y2 = 250000**. Adjust the window to find where the graphs intersect.

Use the **INTERSECT** feature to find the x-coordinate of the intersection.

In the year 1987, the population of Corpus Christi was 250,000. The correct answer is C.

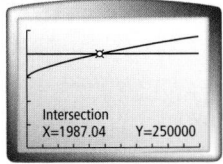
Intersection
X=1987.04   Y=250000

✓ **Got It?** **4.** In what year was the population of Corpus Christi 275,000?

Problem 4 uses a transformation of $y = \sqrt[3]{x}$. The function $f(x) = \sqrt[3]{x}$ is the inverse of $g(x) = x^3$. Unlike $y = \sqrt{x}$, the domain and range of $f(x) = \sqrt[3]{x}$ are all real numbers.

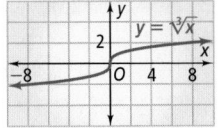

Additional Problems

1. What are the graphs of $y = \sqrt{x} + 4$ and $y = \sqrt{x} - 4$?

ANSWER

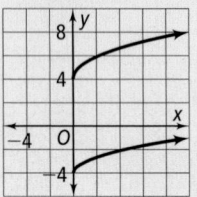

2. What are the graphs of $y = \sqrt{x} - 2$ and $y = \sqrt{x} + 7$?

ANSWER

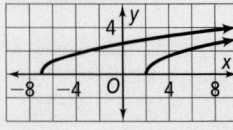

3. What is the graph of $y = 2\sqrt{x+1} - 2$?

ANSWER

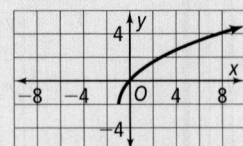

4. You can model the radius of a sphere by $r = \sqrt[3]{\frac{3V}{4\pi}}$. If the radius of a child's spherical balloon is 4.5 inches, what is the volume of the balloon to the nearest cubic inch? (Use 3.14 for π.)

ANSWER approximately 382 in³

5. What is the graph of $y = 2\sqrt[3]{x+2} - 3$?

ANSWER

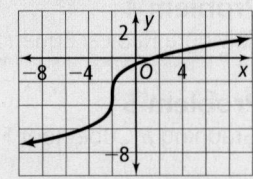

6. How can you rewrite $y = \sqrt{4x - 12}$ so you can graph it using transformations? Describe the graph.

ANSWER $y = 2\sqrt{x - 3}$; graph of $y = \sqrt{x}$ translated 3 units right, stretched by a factor of 2

Answers

Got It? (continued)

3.

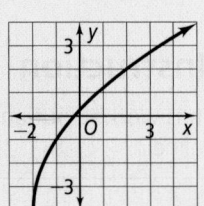

4. 1999   **5.**

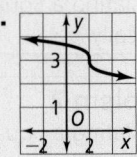

6. a. $y = \sqrt[3]{8x + 32} - 2$ is the graph of $y = 2\sqrt[3]{x}$ translated 4 units to the left and 2 units down.

  b. $y = 9|x + 2|$; the graph of $y = 9|x + 2|$ is the graph of $y = 9|x|$ translated 2 units to the left; You are rewriting the function so that x has a coefficient of 1.

The patterns for graphing square root functions apply to other radical functions.

ⓒ Problem 5 Graphing a Cube Root Function

What is the graph of $y = 2\sqrt[3]{x+1} - 4$?

Step 1 Graph the parent function, $y = \sqrt[3]{x}$.

Step 2 Multiply the y-coordinates by 2. This stretches the graph vertically.

Step 3 Translate the graph from step 2, 1 unit to the left and 4 units down.

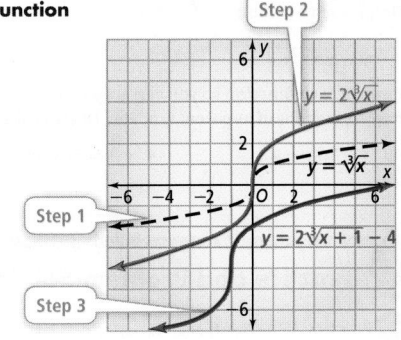

✓ Got It? 5. What is the graph of $y = 3 - \frac{1}{2}\sqrt[3]{x-2}$?

You can graph functions of the form $y = \sqrt[n]{bx+c}$ using transformations, if you can simplify the radicand so that x has a coefficient of 1. This is also true for functions in the form $y = a\sqrt[n]{bx+c} + k$.

ⓒ Problem 6 Rewriting a Radical Function

How can you rewrite $y = \sqrt{9x+18}$ so you can graph it using transformations? Describe the graph.

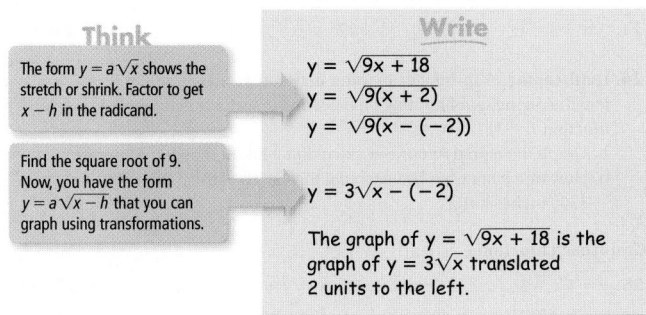

Think

The form $y = a\sqrt{x}$ shows the stretch or shrink. Factor to get $x - h$ in the radicand.

Find the square root of 9. Now, you have the form $y = a\sqrt{x-h}$ that you can graph using transformations.

Write

$y = \sqrt{9x+18}$
$y = \sqrt{9(x+2)}$
$y = \sqrt{9(x-(-2))}$

$y = 3\sqrt{x-(-2)}$

The graph of $y = \sqrt{9x+18}$ is the graph of $y = 3\sqrt{x}$ translated 2 units to the left.

ⓒ ✓ Got It? 6. **a.** How can you rewrite $y = \sqrt[3]{8x+32} - 2$ so you can graph it using transformations? Describe the graph.

b. Reasoning Describe the graph of $y = |9x+18|$ by rewriting it in the form $y = a|x-h|$. How is this similar to rewriting $y = \sqrt{9x+18}$ in Problem 6?

Problem 5   ERROR PREVENTION

When graphing a square root or cube root function, students sometimes try to simplify the numbers under the radical with the numbers outside the radical. Try circling each change from the parent function with a colored pencil.

Q When graphing cube root functions, why do you want to select x-values that are perfect cubes? **[You will get whole number values, which are easier to graph.]**

Got It?

Q What is the difference between the graph of $y = 3 - \frac{1}{2}\sqrt[3]{x-2}$ and the graph of $y = -\frac{1}{2}\sqrt[3]{x-2} + 3$? **[The two graphs are the same. The value of k was moved before the radical in the first function; this can be done since k is not contained under the radical sign.]**

Problem 6

Some radical equations are more easily graphed after they have been written in the form $y = a\sqrt[n]{x-h} + k$.

Q Why do you need to factor the 9 and take the square root? **[to find the stretch or shrink factor]**
Q How does the 3 change the graph? **[It stretches the graph.]**

Got It?

Have students graph the equation two ways:
a. by graphing the given equation
b. by using transformations

Q Which method do you prefer? **[Answers will vary. Results will be the same using both methods.]**

Answers

Lesson Check

1.
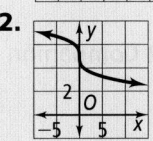

2.

3. $y = 2\sqrt{x-1}$; the graph of $y = 2\sqrt{x}$ translated 1 unit to the right

4. $y = 2\sqrt[3]{x+2}$; the graph of $y = 2\sqrt[3]{x}$ translated 2 units to the left

5. When $|a| < 1$, a will vertically compress $y = a\sqrt{x}$ and when $|a| > 1$, a will vertically stretch $y = a\sqrt{x}$; this is similar to its effect on other functions.

6. $g(x)$ is the reflection of $f(x)$ across the x-axis and again across $x = -1$.

Practice and Problem-Solving Exercises

7.

8.

9.

10.

11.

12.

13.

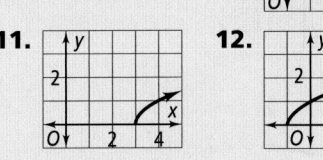
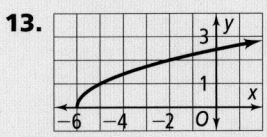

14.
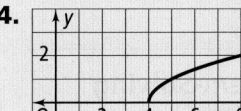

3 Lesson Check

Do you know HOW?

- For Exercises 1 and 2, if students are having difficulty graphing the function, have them first graph the parent function.

Do you UNDERSTAND?

- For Exercise 5, have students graph several functions with positive and negative values for *a*.
- For Exercise 6, have students graph each function using different colored pencils. Make sure students understand the meaning of a reflection.

Close

> **Q** How is the graph of $y = 3\sqrt[3]{x+3} - 2$ transformed from the graph of $y = 3\sqrt[3]{x}$? **[The graph is shifted 3 units left and 2 units down.]**

Lesson Check

Do you know HOW?

Graph each function.

1. $y = -\sqrt{x} + 3$ **2.** $y = -\sqrt[3]{x} + 5$

Rewrite each function so you can graph it using transformations of its parent function. Describe the graph.

3. $y = \sqrt{4x - 4}$ **4.** $y = \sqrt[3]{8x + 16}$

Do you UNDERSTAND?  MATHEMATICAL PRACTICES

5. Writing Explain the effect that *a* has on the graph of $y = a\sqrt{x}$. How does this compare to its effect on other functions you have studied?

6. Error Analysis Your friend states that the graph of the function $g(x) = \sqrt{-x-1}$ is a reflection of the graph of the function $f(x) = -\sqrt{x+1}$ across the *x*-axis. Describe your friend's error.

Practice and Problem-Solving Exercises MATHEMATICAL PRACTICES

A Practice

Graph each function.   ◀ See Problems 1 and 2.

7. $y = \sqrt{x} + 1$ **8.** $y = \sqrt{x} - 2$ **9.** $y = \sqrt{x} - 4$ **10.** $y = \sqrt{x} + 5$

11. $y = \sqrt{x-3}$ **12.** $y = \sqrt{x+1}$ **13.** $y = \sqrt{x+6}$ **14.** $y = \sqrt{x-4}$

Graph each function.   ◀ See Problem 3.

15. $y = 3\sqrt{x}$ **16.** $y = -\sqrt{x-1}$ **17.** $y = -5\sqrt{x+2}$

18. $y = -0.5\sqrt{x} + 3$ **19.** $y = \frac{1}{2}\sqrt{x+2} - 1$ **20.** $y = 3\sqrt{x+1} + 4$

Solve each square root equation by graphing. Round the answer to the nearest   ◀ See Problem 4.
hundredth, if necessary. If there is no solution, explain why.

21. $\sqrt{x-3} = 12$ **22.** $\sqrt{2x-3} = 4$ **23.** $\sqrt{2x+5} = \sqrt{2-x}$

24. Landscaping A sprinkler can water between 1 and 130 square yards of a lawn. The length *L* in inches of rotating pipe needed to water *A* square yards is given by the function $L = 117.75\sqrt{A}$.
   a. Graph the equation on your calculator. Make a sketch of the graph.
   b. How much area can be watered if the length of the pipe is 500, 800, or 1300 inches long?

Graph each function.   ◀ See Problem 5.

25. $y = \sqrt[3]{x+5}$ **26.** $y = \sqrt[3]{x} - 4$ **27.** $y = \sqrt[3]{x+2} - 7$

28. $y = -\sqrt[3]{x+3} - 1$ **29.** $y = 2\sqrt[3]{x-6} - 9$ **30.** $y = \frac{1}{2}\sqrt[3]{x-1} + 3$

Rewrite each function to make it easy to graph using transformations of its   ◀ See Problem 6.
parent function. Describe the graph.

31. $y = \sqrt{9x - 9}$ **32.** $y = -\sqrt{16x + 32}$ **33.** $y = -2\sqrt{4x + 16}$

34. $y = \sqrt[3]{64x + 128}$ **35.** $y = \sqrt{25x + 125} - 3$ **36.** $y = \sqrt[3]{8x - 24} + 1$

Answers

Practice and Problem-Solving Exercises (continued)

15. 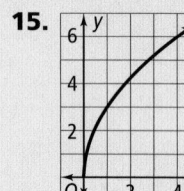   **16.**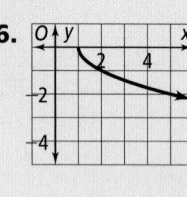

17. 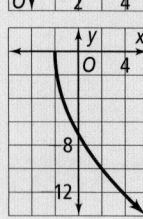   **18.**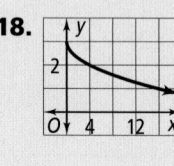

19. 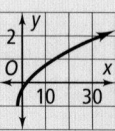   **20.**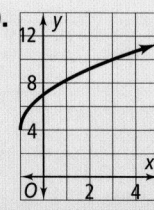

21. 147   **22.** 9.5   **23.** −1

24. a.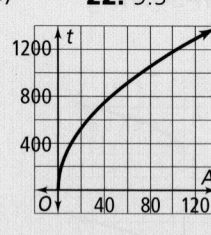

b. ≈ 18 sq yds, ≈ 46 sq yds, ≈ 122 sq yds

25.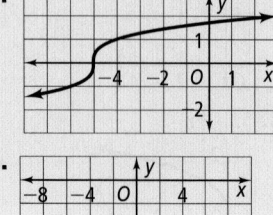

26.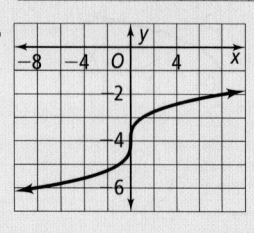

3 Lesson Check

For a digital lesson check, use the Got It questions.

Support in Algebra 2 Companion
- Lesson Check

4 Practice

Assign homework to individual students or to an entire class.

Apply

37. Think About a Plan The time t in seconds for a pendulum to complete one full cycle is given by the function $t = 1.11\sqrt{l}$, where l is the length of the pendulum in feet. How long is a pendulum that takes 4.5 seconds to complete one full cycle? 6 seconds to complete one full cycle? Round your answers to the nearest hundredth.
- How can you use a graph to approximate the length of a pendulum?
- How can you check your answers algebraically?

Graph each function. Find the domain and range.

38. $y = 4\sqrt[3]{x-2} + 1$ **39.** $y = \frac{1}{2}\sqrt{x-1} + 3$ **40.** $y = 3\sqrt[3]{x-6} + 2$

41. Suppose that a function pairs elements from set A with elements from set B. Recall that a function is called *onto* if every element in B is paired with at least one element in A.

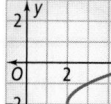

a. The graph shows a transformation of $y = \sqrt{x}$. Write the function.
b. What are the domain and range of the function?
c. For the domain, is the function onto the set of nonnegative real numbers? Explain.

42. Open-Ended Write a radical function such that for its domain, the function is onto the set of real numbers such that $y \le 3$.

Rewrite each function to make it easy to graph using transformations of its parent function. Describe the graph.

43. $y = \sqrt{25x - 100} - 1$ **44.** $y = \sqrt{36x + 108} + 4$ **45.** $y = -\sqrt[3]{8x - 2}$

46. $y = \sqrt{\frac{x-1}{4}} - 2$ **47.** $y = 10 - \sqrt[3]{\frac{x+3}{27}}$ **48.** $y = \sqrt{\frac{x}{9} + 1} + 5$

Graphing Calculator Solve the following radical equations.

49. $2\sqrt{x} = \sqrt{(x+1)}$ **50.** $\sqrt{(x+3)} = 4\sqrt{(x)} - 2$ **51.** $\sqrt[3]{x-1} = \sqrt{x} - 1$

52. a. Solve $3 - \sqrt{(x-3)} = x$ algebraically.
b. Solve the equation from part (a) graphically.
c. What do you notice about your answer to part (a) compared to your answer to part (b)?

STEM 53. Electronics The size of a computer monitor is given as the length of the screen's diagonal d in inches. The equation $d = \frac{5}{6}\sqrt{3A}$ models the length of a diagonal of a monitor screen with area A in square inches.
a. Graph the equation on your calculator.
b. Suppose you want to buy a new monitor with a screen that is twice the area of your old screen. Your old screen has a diagonal of 15 inches. What will be the diagonal of your new screen?

STEM 54. Physics You can model time t, in seconds, an object takes to reach the ground falling from height H, in meters, by $t(H) = \sqrt{\frac{2H}{g}}$. The value of g is 9.81 m/s². If an object takes 7 seconds to fall to the ground, what was its initial height?

ASSIGNMENT GUIDE
Basic: 7–36 all, 37–39, 43, 53
Average: 7–35 odd, 37–54
Advanced: 7–35 odd, 37–59

Mathematical Practices are supported by exercises with red headings. Here are the Practices supported in this lesson:

MP 1: Make Sense of Problems Ex. 37
MP 2: Reason Abstractly Ex. 42
MP 3: Communicate Ex. 5
MP 3: Compare Arguments Ex. 58b
MP 3: Critique the Reasoning of Others Ex. 6
MP 5: Use Appropriate Tools Ex. 49–52

Applications exercises have blue headings. Exercises 24, 53 and 54 support MP 4: Model.

STEM exercises focus on science or engineering applications.

EXERCISE 53: Use the Think About a Plan worksheet in the **Practice and Problem Solving Workbook** (also available in the Teaching Resources in print and online) to further support students' development in becoming independent learners.

HOMEWORK QUICK CHECK
To check students' understanding of key skills and concepts, go over Exercises 17, 33, 37, 43, and 53.

27.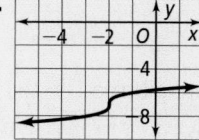

28.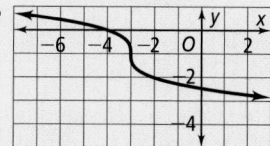

29.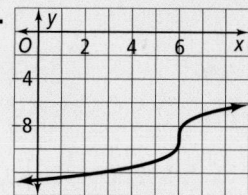

30.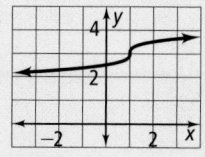

31. $y = 3\sqrt{x - 1}$; the graph of $y = 3\sqrt{x}$ translated 1 unit to the right

32. $y = -4\sqrt{x + 2}$; the graph of $y = -4\sqrt{x}$ translated 2 units to the left

33. $y = -4\sqrt{x + 4}$; the graph of $y = -4\sqrt{x}$ translated 4 units to the left

34. $y = 4\sqrt[3]{x + 2}$; the graph of $y = 4\sqrt[3]{x}$ translated 2 units to the left

35. $y = 5\sqrt{x + 5} - 3$; the graph of $y = 5\sqrt{x}$ translated 5 units to the left and 3 units down

36. $y = 2\sqrt[3]{x - 3} + 1$; the graph of $y = 2\sqrt[3]{x}$ translated 3 units to the right and 1 unit up

37. graph l vs. t and find the value of l for $t = 4.5$ and $t = 6$; use the equation $t = 1.11\sqrt{l}$ and substitute $t = 4.5$ and $t = 6$; ≈ 16.44 ft; ≈ 29.22 ft

38. 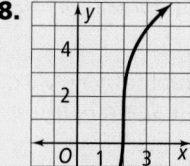 domain: all real numbers, range: all real numbers

39. 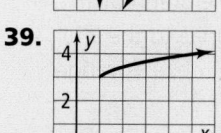 domain: $x \ge 1$, range: $y \ge 3$

40. 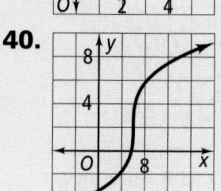 domain: all real numbers, range: all real numbers

41. a. $y = \sqrt{x - 2} - 2$
b. domain: $x \ge 2$, range: $y \ge -2$
c. No; the function pairs the number 3 with the number -1, which is not a non-negative real number.

42–54. See next page.

Lesson 6-8   **419**

Answer

Practice and Problem-Solving Exercises (continued)

42. Sample: $y = -\sqrt{x-2} + 3$

43. a. $y = 5\sqrt{x-4} - 1$; the graph of $y = 5\sqrt{x}$, translated 4 units to the right and 1 unit down

44. $y = 6\sqrt{x+3} + 4$; the graph of $y = 6\sqrt{x}$, translated 3 units to the left and 4 units up

45. $y = -2\sqrt[3]{x - \frac{1}{4}}$; the graph of $y = -2\sqrt[3]{x}$, translated $\frac{1}{4}$ unit to the right

46. $y = \frac{1}{2}\sqrt{x-1} - 2$; the graph of $y = \frac{1}{2}\sqrt{x}$, translated 1 unit to the right and 2 units down

47. $y = 10 - \frac{1}{3}\sqrt[3]{x+3}$; the graph of $y = -\frac{1}{3}\sqrt[3]{x}$, translated 3 units to the left and 10 units up

48. $y = \frac{1}{3}\sqrt{x+9} + 5$; the graph of $y = \frac{1}{3}\sqrt{x}$, translated 9 units to the left and 5 units up

49. $\frac{1}{3}$ **50.** 1   **51.** 0, 1, 9

52. a. $x = 3$ **b.**
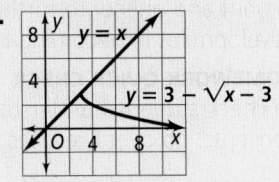

c. There is an extraneous solution that must be eliminated when solving algebraically.

53. a.
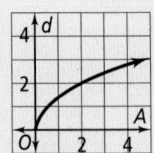
b. $15\sqrt{2}$ in. ≈ 21.2 in.

54. 240.345 m

55. $y = -\sqrt{8}\sqrt{x - \frac{3}{4}}$; the graph of $y = -\sqrt{8x}$, translated $\frac{3}{4}$ unit to the right; domain: $x \geq \frac{3}{4}$, range: $y \leq 0$

56. $y = \sqrt{3}\sqrt{x - \frac{5}{3}} + 6$; the graph of $y = \sqrt{3x}$, translated $\frac{5}{3}$ units to the right and 6 units up; domain: $x \geq \frac{5}{3}$, range: $y \geq 6$

57. $y = -\sqrt{12}\sqrt{x + \frac{3}{2}} - 3$; the graph of $y = -\sqrt{12x}$, translated $\frac{3}{2}$ units to the left and 3 units down; domain: $x \geq -\frac{3}{2}$, range: $y \leq -3$

58. a.
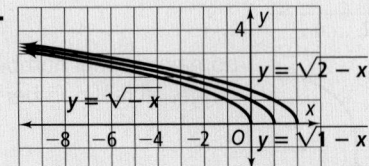

b. The graph of $y = \sqrt{h-x}$ is a reflection of the graph of $y = \sqrt{x-h}$ across the line $x = h$.

59. for all odd positive integers

 **Challenge** Rewrite each function to make it easy to graph using transformations of its parent function. Describe the graph. Find the domain and range of each function.

55. $y = -\sqrt{2(4x-3)}$ **56.** $y = \sqrt{3x-5} + 6$ **57.** $y = -3 - \sqrt{12x+18}$

 58. a. Graph $y = \sqrt{-x}$, $y = \sqrt{1-x}$, and $y = \sqrt{2-x}$.
  b. Make a Conjecture How does the graph of $y = \sqrt{h-x}$ differ from the graph of $y = \sqrt{x-h}$?

59. For what positive integers n are the domain and range of $y = \sqrt[n]{x}$ the set of real numbers? Assume that x is a real number.

 Apply What You've Learned    MATHEMATICAL PRACTICES MP 4, MP 5

In the Apply What You've Learned in Lesson 6-5, you wrote a function $f(D)$ for the new yacht, described on page 359. The function gives the value of the expression on the left side of the America's Cup rule for any displacement D. Use a graphing calculator to graph this function. Select all of the following that are true. Explain your reasoning.

A. For any viewing window, the graph of $f(D)$ lies entirely above the x-axis.

B. In the context of this real-world situation, the relevant domain of the function is all real numbers.

C. As the value of D increases, the value of $f(D)$ decreases.

D. The graph of the function intersects the horizontal line $y = 24$ at exactly one point.

E. The graph shows that when $D = 10$, $f(D)$ is less than 24.

F. The graph shows that a displacement of 30 cubic meters is one possible displacement for the new yacht.

Apply What You've Learned

In the Apply What You've Learned section in Lesson 6-5, students wrote a function $f(D)$ which gives the value of the left side of the rule on page 359 for the new yacht in terms of the displacement D. Here students use a graphing calculator to further analyze the function $f(D)$.

© Mathematical Practices

Students make a graph to **model** a real-world situation and they interpret their mathematical results in the context of the situation. (MP 4)

Students use a graphing calculator or other **appropriate tool** to graph and analyze a function. (MP 5)

ANSWERS

Choices C, D, and F are all true.

Differentiated Remediation

Additional Instructional Support

Algebra 2 Companion

Students can use the **Algebra 2 Companion** worktext (4 pages) as you teach the lesson. Use the Companion to support

- New Vocabulary
- Key Concepts
- Got It for each Problem
- Lesson Check

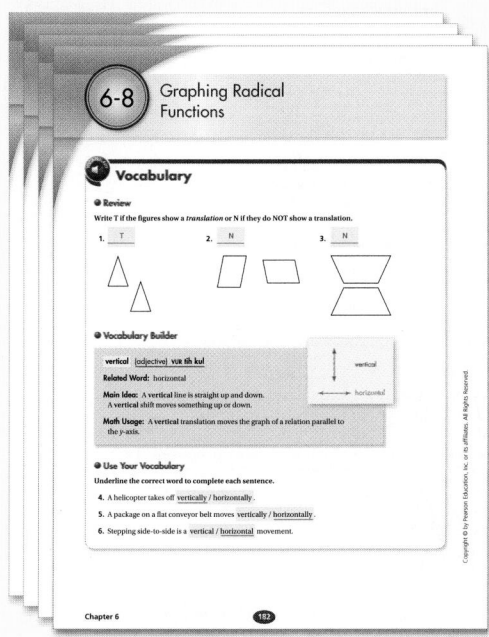

ELL Support

Focus on Language To help students remember that the domain is the set of x-values and the range is the set of y-values, state that d comes before r as x comes before y alphabetically.

Role Playing On a number of index cards equal to half the class, write either $f(x)$ or $g(x)$ and list 2–3 transformations to be performed on the function. Divide the class in pairs. Tell them that $f(x) = x^2$ and $g(x) = x^3$. Pass out an index card to one student in each pair. Without showing it to his or her partner, the student with the card graphs the given transformed function. Then, the partner tells the first student whether the function is a transformation of $f(x)$ or of $g(x)$ and identifies the transformations. Together, they write the equation of the function.

Then they shuffle the cards and switch roles to play again.

5 Assess & Remediate

Lesson Quiz

1. What is the graph of $y = 2\sqrt{x-2} - 1$?
2. **Do you UNDERSTAND?** The speed of a tsunami s (in meters/second) is approximated by $s = \sqrt{gd}$, where g is the acceleration due to gravity (9.8 m/s²) and d is the depth of the water (in meters). If the speed of a tsunami is 200 m/s, about how deep is the water?
3. How can you rewrite $y = \sqrt{4x + 16}$ so you can graph it using transformations? Describe the graph.

ANSWERS TO LESSON QUIZ

1.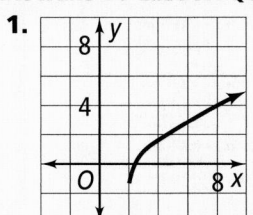

2. about 4082 meters
3. $y = 2\sqrt{x+4}$; the graph is shifted 4 units left and stretched by a factor of 2.

PRESCRIPTION FOR REMEDIATION

Use the student work on the Lesson Quiz to prescribe a differentiated review assignment:

Points	Differentiated Remediation
0–1	Intervention
2	On-level
3	Extension

PowerAlgebra.com

5 Assess & Remediate

Assign the Lesson Quiz. Appropriate intervention, practice, or enrichment is automatically generated based on student performance.

Intervention

- **Reteaching** (2 pages) Provides reteaching and practice exercises for the key lesson concepts. Use with struggling students or absent students.
- **English Language Learner Support** Helps students develop and reinforce mathematical vocabulary and key concepts.

All-in-One Resources/Online
Reteaching

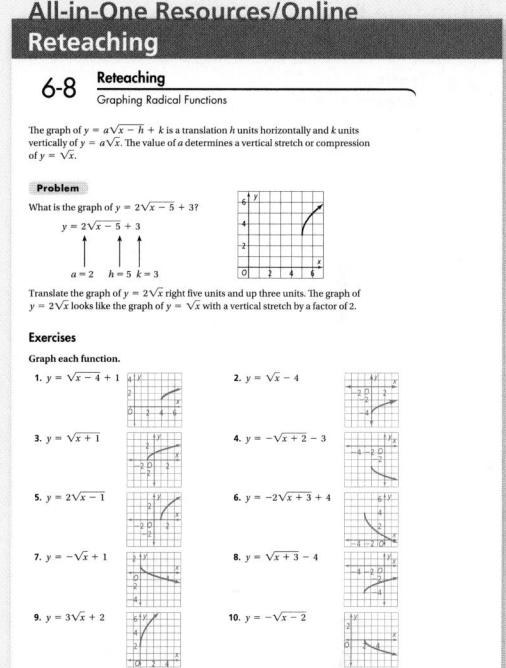

All-in-One Resources/Online
English Language Learner Support

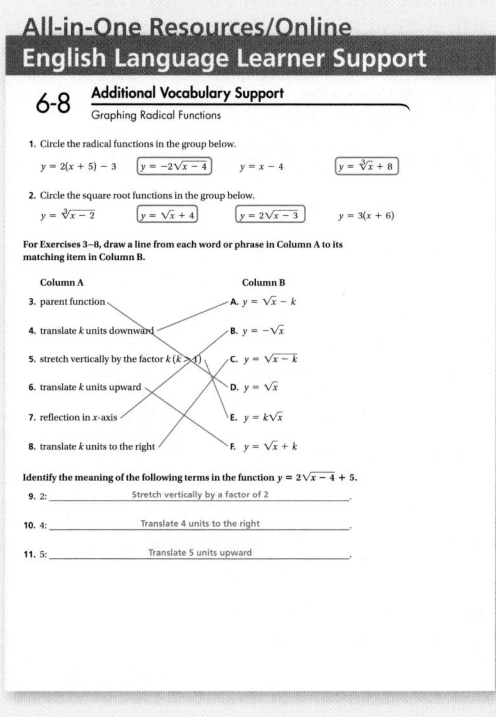

Differentiated Remediation *continued*

On-Level

- **Practice** (2 pages) Provides extra practice for each lesson. For simpler practice exercises, use the Form K Practice pages found in the All-in-One Teaching Resources and online.

- **Think About a Plan** Helps students develop specific problem-solving skills and strategies by providing scaffolded guiding questions.

- **Standardized Test Prep** Focuses on all major exercises, all major question types, and helps students prepare for the high-stakes assessments.

Extension

- **Enrichment** Provides students with interesting problems and activities that extend the concepts of the lesson.

- **Activities, Games, and Puzzles** Worksheets that can be used for concepts development, enrichment, and for fun!

Practice and Problem Solving Wkbk/ All-in-One Resources/Online
Practice page 1

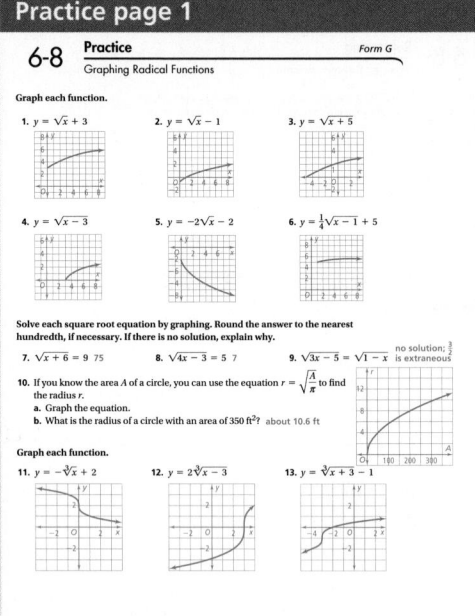

Practice and Problem Solving Wkbk/ All-in-One Resources/Online
Practice page 2

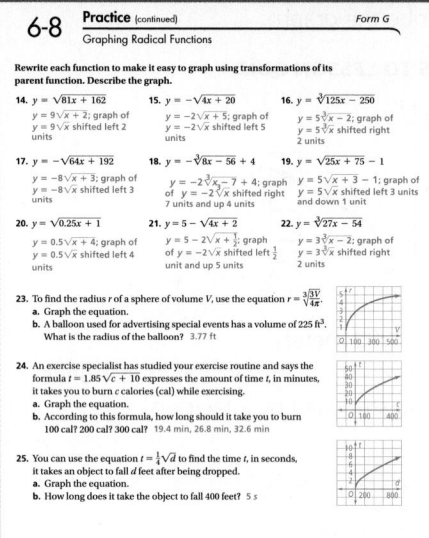

All-in-One Resources/Online
Enrichment

6-8 Enrichment — Graphing Radical Functions

Transformations of Other Functions

You can obtain the graph of any function of the form $y = a \cdot f(x - h) + k$ by using the shifting rules similar to those used to obtain the graph of $y = a\sqrt{x - h} + k$. Note that the second function is a special case of the first when $f(x) = \sqrt{x}$. To obtain the graph of $y = a \cdot f(x - h) + k$, given the graph of $y = f(x)$, use the following general rules:

- If $a < 0$, reflect the graph of $y = f(x)$ across the x-axis.
- If $|a| > 1$, the graph of $y = f(x)$ is stretched by a factor of a.
- If $0 < |a| < 1$, the graph of $y = f(x)$ is compressed by a factor of a.
- The graph of $y = f(x)$ is shifted right h units if $h > 0$ and left h units if $h < 0$.
- The graph of $y = f(x)$ is shifted up k units if $k > 0$ and down k units if $k < 0$.

1. Use the general rules to describe how the graph of $y = -3(x - 5)^2 + 7$ can be obtained from the graph of $f(x) = x^2$.
reflect across the x-axis, stretch by a factor of 3, shift 5 units and shift up 7 units

2. Write the equation for the graph that looks like $y = \sqrt[3]{x}$ but that is shifted right four units, reflected across the x-axis, and shifted down six units.
$y = -\sqrt[3]{x - 4} - 6$

3. Use the graph of $y = f(x)$ given below to sketch the graph of $y = f(x + 2) - 1$.

4. The graph of $y = f(x)$ and $y = g(x)$ is given below. The graph of g is a transformation of the graph of f. Write the equation for the graph of g in terms of f. $g(x) = f(x + 1) - 3$

Practice and Problem Solving Wkbk/ All-in-One Resources/Online
Think About a Plan

6-8 Think About a Plan — Graphing Radical Functions

Electronics The size of a computer monitor is given as the length of the screen's diagonal d in inches. The equation $d = \frac{3}{5}\sqrt{3A}$ models the length of a diagonal of a monitor screen with area A in square inches.

a. Graph the equation on your calculator.

b. Suppose you want to buy a new monitor that has twice the area of your old monitor. Your old monitor has a diagonal of 15 inches. What will be the diagonal of your new monitor?

1. How can you use a graph to approximate the area of the old monitor?
Graph the equation and graph $y = 15$. The x-coordinate of their intersection will be the area of the old monitor

2. Graph the equation on your calculator. Make a sketch of the graph.

3. What is the area of the old monitor? 108 in.²

4. How can you check your answer algebraically?
Substitute 15 for d and solve the equation for A

5. Show that your answer checks.
$15 = \frac{3}{5}\sqrt{3A}, 15(\frac{5}{3}) = \sqrt{3A}, 18 = \sqrt{3A}, 18^2 = 3A, 324 = 3A, A = 108$

6. How can you find the diagonal of a new monitor with twice the area of the old monitor?
Substitute 2 times the area of the old monitor for A in the equation

7. Use your method to find the diagonal of your new monitor.
$d = \frac{3}{5}\sqrt{3A} = \frac{3}{5}\sqrt{3 \cdot 2 \cdot 108} = \frac{3}{5}\sqrt{648} \approx 21.2$ in.

8. What will be the diagonal of your new monitor? about 21.2 in.

Practice and Problem Solving Wkbk/ All-in-One Resources/Online
Standardized Test Prep

6-8 Standardized Test Prep — Graphing Radical Functions

Multiple Choice

For Exercises 1–4, choose the correct letter.

1. What is the graph of $y = \sqrt{x} + 4$? C
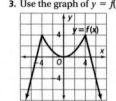 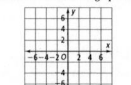 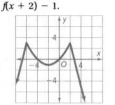

2. What is the graph of $y = \sqrt{x - 3} - 2$? F
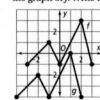

3. What is the graph of $y = 1 - \sqrt[3]{x + 3}$? D

4. What is the description of $y = \sqrt{9x} - 3$ to make it easy to graph using transformations of its parent function? G
F the graph of $y = 3\sqrt{x}$, shifted right 3 units
G the graph of $y = 3\sqrt{x}$, shifted right $\frac{1}{3}$ unit
H the graph of $y = \sqrt{x}$, shifted right 3 units and up 9 units
I the graph of $y = \sqrt{x}$, shifted right $\frac{1}{3}$ unit and up 9 units

Short Response

5. What is the graph of $y = 2\sqrt{x - 1} + 3$?
[2] The graph is correct.
[1] One of the transformations (horizontal, vertical, or stretch) is incorrect.
[0] no answer given

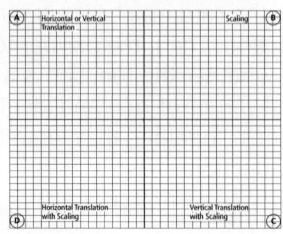

Online Teacher Resource Center
Activities, Games, and Puzzles

6-8 Activity: Lost in Translation — Graphing Radical Functions

Your teacher will divide the class into teams of three or four students. Each team will be assigned a number.

Use a sheet of graph paper and divide it into four regions of equal size similar to the one shown below. In each of the four regions, draw a set of coordinate axes in order to graph square root functions. Each region represents a transformation of the square root function $y = \sqrt{x}$ as described below.

- Choose a square root function that satisfies the description in Region A of the graph. Write the function on a separate sheet of paper, and then graph the function in Region A.
- Choose a square root function that satisfies the description in Region B of the graph, and follow the same steps as you did for Region A.
- Choose a square root function that satisfies the description in Region C of the graph, and follow the same steps as you did for Region A.
- Choose a square root function that satisfies the description in Region D of the graph, and follow the same steps as you did for Region A.

Once your team has drawn a graph for each of the four regions, write your team number and the team leader's below the grid.

Place your team's grid on a desk or on the board. Teams should examine the grids from the other teams, and write the functions for the four different graphs drawn by each team. As a class, compare and discuss the graphs. Check students' work.

6

Pull It **All Together**

To solve these problems, you will pull together concepts and skills related to roots and radical functions.

Completing the Performance Task

Look back at your results from the Apply What You've Learned sections in Lessons 6-4, 6-5, and 6-8. Use the work you did to complete the following.

1. Solve the problem in the Task Description on page 359 by verifying that the AC45 Wingsail Catamaran satisfies the America's Cup rule, and by finding the possible displacements for your yacht. Show all your work and explain each step of your solution.

 2. Reflect Choose one of the Mathematical Practices below and explain how you applied it in your work on the Performance Task.

   MP 2: Reason abstractly and quantitatively.

   MP 4: Model with mathematics.

   MP 5: Use appropriate tools strategically.

   MP 6: Attend to precision.

On Your Own

A yacht designer is considering the dimensions shown below for a new yacht called the SailSmart Catamaran.

SailSmart Catamaran	
Length	17.35 meters
Sail Area	97.5 square meters
Displacement	2.1 cubic meters

   a. Does the SailSmart Catamaran satisfy the rule on page 359? Explain.

   b. The designer would like to change only the sail area so that the value of the expression on the left side of the rule is at least 20 but no more than 24. Determine a range of sail areas the designer could use to meet this goal.

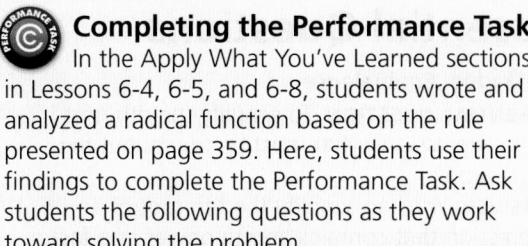

Completing the Performance Task

In the Apply What You've Learned sections in Lessons 6-4, 6-5, and 6-8, students wrote and analyzed a radical function based on the rule presented on page 359. Here, students use their findings to complete the Performance Task. Ask students the following questions as they work toward solving the problem.

Q How can you use the work you have done in the chapter to solve the problem? **[Sample: I can use the expression I wrote in Lesson 6-4 to determine whether the AC45 satisfies the America's Cup rule. Then I can use the function I wrote in Lesson 6-5 and its graph from Lesson 6-8 to find all possible values of *D* for the new yacht.]**

Q How can you check that your answer is reasonable? **[Sample: I can take the lower bound that I found for *D* and the given values of *L* and *S* for the new yacht and substitute these into the original expression on page 359. I can check that this results in a value of approximately 24.]**

FOSTERING MATHEMATICAL DISCOURSE

Have students exchange their solutions to the Performance Task and critique each other's work.

ANSWERS

1. The AC45 Wingsail Catamaran satisfies the America's Cup rule because the value of the expression on the left side of the rule is approximately 21.7, which is less than 24.

$$\frac{13.45 + 1.25\sqrt{93.7} - 9.8\sqrt[3]{1.3}}{0.686} \approx 21.7$$

For the new yacht, the possible displacements are any value of *D* greater than or equal to approximately 22.2 m³.

2. Check students' work.

On Your Own

This problem is similar to the problem posed on page 359, but now students must find a range of appropriate sail areas. Students should strive to solve this problem independently.

ANSWERS

a. The SmartSail Catamaran does not satisfy the America's Cup rule because the value of the expression on the left side of the rule is approximately 25.0, which is greater than 24.

$$\frac{17.35 + 1.25\sqrt{97.5} - 9.8\sqrt[3]{2.1}}{0.686} \approx 25.0$$

b. The designer can use sail areas between approximately 50.9 m² and 87.1 m².

Essential Questions

BIG idea Equivalence

ESSENTIAL QUESTION To simplify the *n*th root of an expression, what must be true about the expression?

ANSWER You can simplify the *n*th root of an expression that contains an *n*th power as a factor.

$$\sqrt[n]{x^n} = x^{\frac{n}{n}} = \begin{cases} x, & n \text{ odd} \\ |x|, & n \text{ even} \end{cases}$$

BIG idea Solving Equations and Inequalities

ESSENTIAL QUESTION When you square each side of an equation, is the resulting equation equivalent to the original?

ANSWER When you square each side of an equation, the resulting equation may have more solutions than the original equation.

BIG idea Function

ESSENTIAL QUESTION How are a function and its inverse function related?

ANSWER If f and f^{-1} are inverse functions and if one maps a to b, then the other maps b to a, i.e.,
$$\left(f \circ f^{-1}\right)(a) = \left(f^{-1} \circ f\right)(a) = a$$

---

6 Chapter Review

Connecting BIG ideas and Answering the Essential Questions

1 Equivalence
You can simplify the *n*th root of an expression that contains an *n*th power as a factor.
$$\sqrt[n]{x^n} = x^{\frac{n}{n}} = \begin{matrix} x, & n \text{ odd} \\ |x|, & n \text{ even} \end{matrix}$$

Radical Expressions and Rational Exponents (Lessons 6-1, 6-2 and 6-4)
$$\sqrt[3]{-8x^5} \ \sqrt[3]{x^2} = \sqrt[3]{-8x^7}$$
$$= \sqrt[3]{(-2)^3 x^6 \cdot x}$$
$$= -2x^2 \sqrt[3]{x}$$
$$(-8x^5)^{\frac{1}{3}} (x^2)^{\frac{1}{3}} = (-8x^7)^{\frac{1}{3}}$$
$$= ((-2)^3 \cdot x^6 \cdot x)^{\frac{1}{3}}$$
$$= -2x^2 x^{\frac{1}{3}}$$

Solving Square Root Equations (Lesson 6-5)
$$x - 2 = \sqrt{x}$$
$$x^2 - 4x + 4 = x$$
$$x^2 - 5x + 4 = 0$$
$$(x - 4)(x - 1) = 0$$
$$x = 4 \text{ or } x = 1$$
$$4 - 2 = \sqrt{4} \ \checkmark$$
$$1 - 2 \neq \sqrt{1} \ ✗$$

2 Solving Equations and Inequalities
When you square each side of an equation, the resulting equation may have more solutions than the original equation.

Inverse Relations and Functions (Lesson 6-7)
The inverse of $y = \sqrt{x} + 2, x \geq 0, y \geq 2$ is $x = \sqrt{y} + 2$, or $\sqrt{y} = x - 2$, or $y = (x - 2)^2, y \geq 0, x \geq 2$.

3 Function
If f and f^{-1} are inverse functions and if one maps a to b, then the other maps b to a, i.e.,
$$(f \circ f^{-1})(a) = (f^{-1} \circ f)(a)$$
$$= a.$$

Graphing Radical Functions (Lesson 6-8)

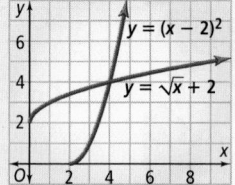

Chapter Vocabulary

- composite function (p. 399)
- index (p. 362)
- inverse function (p. 405)
- inverse relation (p. 405)
- like radicals (p. 374)
- *n*th root (p. 361)
- one-to-one function (p. 408)
- principal root (p. 361)
- radical equation (p. 390)
- radical function (p. 415)
- radicand (p. 362)
- rational exponent (p. 382)
- rationalize the denominator (p. 369)
- simplest form of a radical (p. 368)
- square root equation (p. 390)
- square root function (p. 415)

Choose the correct term to complete each sentence.

1. The number under a radical sign is called the (index/radicand).

2. (Radical functions/Inverse functions) are of the form $f(x) = \sqrt[n]{x}$.

3. A radical expression can always be rewritten using a(n) (rational exponent/inverse relation).

4. When two functions are combined so the range of one becomes the domain of the other, the resulting function is called a (square root function/composite function).

Summative Questions

Use the following prompts as you review this chapter with your students. The prompts are designed to help you assess your students' understanding of the Big Ideas they have studied.

- Under what conditions can you simplify a radical expression? How do the conditions change depending on the operation involved?

- What properties would you use to write $\left(9x^{-4}\right)^{-\frac{1}{2}}$ in simplest form?

- What would be your first step in the solution of $2(x + 1)^{\frac{2}{3}} = 8$?

- What operations can you perform on functions? For each, how do you determine the domain of the new function?

Answers

Chapter Review

1. radicand
2. radical functions
3. rational exponent
4. composite function

6-1 Roots and Radical Expressions

Quick Review

You can simplify a radical expression by finding the roots. The **principal root** of a number with two real roots is the positive root. The principal **nth root** of b is written as $\sqrt[n]{b}$, where b is the **radicand** and n is the **index** of the radical expression.

For any real number a, $\sqrt[n]{a^n} = \begin{cases} a \text{ if } n \text{ is odd} \\ |a| \text{ if } n \text{ is even} \end{cases}$.

Example

What is the simplified form of $\sqrt{36x^6}$?

$\sqrt{6^2 x^6}$ Find the root of the integer.

$= \sqrt{6^2(x^3)^2}$ Find the root of the variable.

$= 6|x^3|$ Take the square root of each term. Since the index is even, include the absolute value symbol to ensure that the root is positive even when x^3 is negative.

Exercises

Find each real root.

5. $\sqrt{25}$ **6.** $\sqrt{0.49}$

7. $\sqrt[3]{-8}$ **8.** $-\sqrt[3]{8}$

Simplify each radical expression. Use absolute value symbols when needed.

9. $\sqrt{81x^2}$ **10.** $\sqrt[3]{64x^6}$

11. $\sqrt[4]{16x^{12}}$ **12.** $\sqrt[5]{0.00032x^5}$

13. $\sqrt{\dfrac{9x^4}{36}}$ **14.** $\sqrt[3]{125x^6y^9}$

6-2 Multiplying and Dividing Radical Expressions

Quick Review

If $\sqrt[n]{a}$ and $\sqrt[n]{b}$ are real numbers, then

$\left(\sqrt[n]{a}\right)\left(\sqrt[n]{b}\right) = \sqrt[n]{ab}$, and, if $b \neq 0$, then $\dfrac{\sqrt[n]{a}}{\sqrt[n]{b}} = \sqrt[n]{\dfrac{a}{b}}$.

To **rationalize the denominator** of an expression, rewrite it so that the denominator contains no radical expressions.

Example

What is the simplest form of $\sqrt{32x^2y} \cdot \sqrt{18xy^3}$?

$\sqrt{(32x^2y)(18xy^3)}$ Combine terms.

$= \sqrt{(4^2 \cdot 2x^2y)(3^2 \cdot 2xy^3)}$ Factor.

$= \sqrt{4^2 \cdot 3^2 \cdot 2^2 x^3 y^4}$ Consolidate like terms.

$= \sqrt{4^2 \cdot 3^2 \cdot 2^2(x^2x)(y^2)^2}$ Identify perfect squares.

$= 4 \cdot 3 \cdot 2xy^2 \sqrt{x} = 24xy^2 \sqrt{x}$ Extract perfect squares.

Exercises

Multiply if possible. Then simplify.

15. $\sqrt[3]{9} \cdot \sqrt[3]{3}$ **16.** $\sqrt[3]{-7} \cdot \sqrt[3]{49}$ **17.** $\sqrt{2} \cdot \sqrt{8}$

Multiply and simplify.

18. $\sqrt{8x^2} \cdot \sqrt{2x^2}$ **19.** $5\sqrt[3]{9y^2} \cdot \sqrt[3]{24y}$

Divide and simplify.

20. $\sqrt{\dfrac{128}{8}}$ **21.** $\dfrac{\sqrt[3]{81x^5y^3}}{\sqrt[3]{3x^2}}$ **22.** $\dfrac{\sqrt[4]{162x^4}}{\sqrt[4]{2y^8}}$

Divide. Rationalize all denominators.

23. $\dfrac{\sqrt{8}}{\sqrt{6}}$ **24.** $\dfrac{\sqrt{3x^5}}{8x^2}$ **25.** $\dfrac{\sqrt[3]{6x^2y^4}}{2\sqrt[3]{5x^7y}}$

5. 5

6. 0.7

7. −2

8. −2

9. $9|x|$

10. $4x^2$

11. $2|x^3|$

12. $0.2x$

13. $\dfrac{x^2}{2}$

14. $5x^2y^3$

15. 3

16. −7

17. 4

18. $4x^2$

19. $30y$

20. 4

21. $3xy$

22. $\dfrac{3|x|}{y^2}$

23. $\dfrac{2\sqrt{3}}{3}$

24. $\dfrac{\sqrt{3x}}{8}$

25. $\dfrac{y\sqrt[3]{150x}}{10x^2}$

Answers

Chapter Review (continued)

26. $22\sqrt{3}$

27. $26\sqrt{5x}$

28. $x\sqrt[3]{2}$

29. $14 + 7\sqrt{2}$

30. -6

31. $100 + 10\sqrt{6} - 10\sqrt{3} - 3\sqrt{2}$

32. $\dfrac{5 + 2\sqrt{5}}{5}$

33. $\dfrac{9 + 3\sqrt{2}}{7}$

34. 5

35. 3

36. 4

37. 25

38. x

39. $-2y^3$

40. $81x^2y^4$

41. $\dfrac{1}{x^3y^6}$

42. $\dfrac{1}{x}$

43. x^3y^6

6-3 Binomial Radical Expressions

Quick Review

Like radicals have the same index and the same radicand. Use the distributive property to add and subtract them. Use the FOIL method to multiply binomial radical expressions. To rationalize a denominator that is a square root binomial, multiply the numerator and denominator by the conjugate of the denominator.

Example

What is the simplified form of $\sqrt{18} + \sqrt{50} - \sqrt{8}$?

$$\sqrt{18} + \sqrt{50} - \sqrt{8}$$
$$= \sqrt{3^2 \cdot 2} + \sqrt{5^2 \cdot 2} - \sqrt{2^2 \cdot 2} \quad \text{Factor.}$$
$$= 3\sqrt{2} + 5\sqrt{2} - 2\sqrt{2} \quad \text{Simplify each radical.}$$
$$= (3 + 5 - 2)\sqrt{2} \quad \text{Combine like terms.}$$
$$= 6\sqrt{2} \quad \text{Simplify.}$$

Exercises

Add or subtract if possible.

26. $10\sqrt{27} - 4\sqrt{12}$

27. $3\sqrt{20x} + 8\sqrt{45x} - 4\sqrt{5x}$

28. $\sqrt[3]{54x^3} - \sqrt[3]{16x^3}$

Multiply.

29. $(3 + \sqrt{2})(4 + \sqrt{2})$

30. $(\sqrt{5} + \sqrt{11})(\sqrt{5} - \sqrt{11})$

31. $(10 + \sqrt{6})(10 - \sqrt{3})$

Divide. Rationalize all denominators.

32. $\dfrac{2 + \sqrt{5}}{\sqrt{5}}$

33. $\dfrac{3 + \sqrt{18}}{1 + \sqrt{8}}$

6-4 Rational Exponents

Quick Review

You can rewrite a radical expression with a rational exponent. By definition, if the nth root of a is a real number and m is an integer, then $a^{\frac{m}{n}} = \sqrt[n]{a^m} = (\sqrt[n]{a})^m$; if m is negative then $a \neq 0$. Rational exponents can be used to simplify radical expressions.

Example

Multiply and simplify $\sqrt{x}(\sqrt[4]{x^3})$.

$$\sqrt{x}(\sqrt[4]{x^3}) = x^{\frac{1}{2}} \cdot x^{\frac{3}{4}} \quad \text{Rewrite with rational exponents.}$$
$$= x^{\frac{5}{4}} \quad \text{Combine exponents.}$$
$$= \sqrt[4]{x^5} \quad \text{Rewrite as a radical expression.}$$

Exercises

Simplify each expression.

34. $25^{\frac{1}{2}}$

35. $81^{\frac{1}{4}}$

36. $16^{\frac{1}{3}} \cdot 4^{\frac{1}{3}}$

37. $5^{\frac{3}{2}} \cdot 5^{\frac{1}{2}}$

Write each expression in simplest form.

38. $\left(x^{\frac{1}{4}}\right)^4$

39. $\left(-8y^9\right)^{\frac{1}{3}}$

40. $\left(\sqrt{9xy^2}\right)^4$

41. $\left(x^{\frac{1}{6}} y^{\frac{1}{3}}\right)^{-18}$

42. $\left(\dfrac{x^4}{x^{-1}}\right)^{-\frac{1}{5}}$

43. $\left(\dfrac{x^{\frac{1}{3}}}{y^{-\frac{2}{3}}}\right)^9$

6-5 Solving Square Root and Other Radical Equations

Quick Review

To solve a **radical equation**, you must isolate a radical expression on one side of the equation. You can then rewrite the radical expression using a rational exponent and use the reciprocal of the exponent to solve the equation.

For example, to solve a square root equation, you square each side of the equation. Check all possible solutions in the original equation to eliminate extraneous solutions.

Example

What is the solution of $4(x - 2)^{\frac{2}{3}} = 16$?

$(x - 2)^{\frac{2}{3}} = 4$ Isolate the radical.

$((x - 2)^{\frac{2}{3}})^{\frac{3}{2}} = 4^{\frac{3}{2}}$ Raise both sides to the $\frac{3}{2}$ power.

$(x - 2)^{\frac{6}{6}} = 4^{\frac{3}{2}}$ Law of exponents.

$|x - 2| = 8$ Simplify.

$x = 10 \text{ or } x = -6$ Solve for x.

Exercises

Solve each equation. Check for extraneous solutions.

44. $2 + \sqrt{x + 5} = 4$ **45.** $3\sqrt{2x + 6} = 18$

46. $5(3x + 1)^{\frac{1}{4}} = 10$ **47.** $4(3x - 3)^{\frac{2}{3}} = 36$

48. $\sqrt{3x + 3} - 1 = x$ **49.** $\sqrt{x + 6} + 2 = x + 6$

50. $\sqrt{5x + 1} - 2\sqrt{x} = 1$ **51.** $\sqrt{2x + 9} - \sqrt{x} = 3$

52. Electricity The power P, in watts, that a circular solar cell produces and the radius of the cell r in centimeters are related by the square root equation $r = \sqrt{\frac{P}{0.02\pi}}$. About how much power is produced by a cell with a radius of 12 cm?

6-6 Function Operations

Quick Review

When performing function operations, you can use the same rules you used for real numbers, but you must take into consideration the domain and range of each function. The composition of function g with function f is defined as $(g \circ f)(x) = g(f(x))$.

Example

Let $f(x) = x + 3$ and $g(x) = x^2 - 2$. What is $(g \circ f)(-2)$?

$g(f(-2)) = g((-2) + 3)$ Evaluate $f(-2)$.

$= g(1)$ Simplify.

$= (1)^2 - 2$ Evaluate $g(f(-2))$.

$= -1$ Simplify.

Therefore, $(g \circ f)(-2) = -1$.

Exercises

Let $f(x) = x - 4$ and $g(x) = x^2 - 16$. Perform each function operation and then find the domain.

53. $f(x) + g(x)$ **54.** $g(x) - f(x)$

55. $f(x) \cdot g(x)$ **56.** $\frac{g(x)}{f(x)}$

Let $g(x) = 5x - 2$ and $h(x) = x^2 + 1$. Find the value of each expression.

57. $(h \circ g)(-1)$ **58.** $(h \circ g)(0)$

59. $(g \circ h)(2)$ **60.** $(g \circ h)(a)$

61. Discounts A grocery store is offering a 50% discount off a $4.00 box of cereal. You also have a $1.00 off coupon for the same cereal. Use a composite function to show whether it is better to use the coupon before or after the store discount.

---

44. -1

45. 15

46. 5

47. 10, -8

48. 2, -1

49. -2

50. 0, 16

51. 0, 36

52. 9.05 W

53. $x^2 + x - 20$; domain: all real numbers

54. $x^2 - x - 12$; domain: all real numbers

55. $x^3 - 4x^2 - 16x + 64$; domain: all real numbers

56. $x + 4$; domain: all real numbers except $x = 4$

57. 50

58. 5

59. 23

60. $5a^2 + 3$

61. $D(C(x)) = 0.5x - 0.5$, $C(D(x)) = 0.5x - 1$; use the coupon after the store discount.

Answers

Chapter Review (continued)

62. $f^{-1}(x) = \pm\sqrt{\dfrac{x+8}{2}}$; no

63. $f^{-1}(x) = 5 - \dfrac{1}{3}x$; yes

64. $f^{-1}(x) = x^2 - 6$; yes

65. $f^{-1}(x) = \dfrac{3 \pm \sqrt{x}}{2}$; no

66. 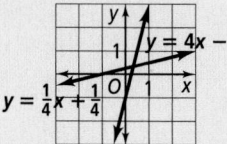 domain of f: all real numbers, range of f: all real numbers, domain of f^{-1}: all real numbers, range of f^{-1}: all real numbers.

67. domain of f: all real numbers, range of f: $y \geq 0$; domain of f^{-1}: $x \geq 0$, range of f^{-1}: all real numbers

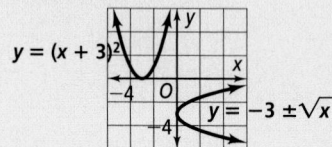

68. domain of f: $x \geq 3$, range of f: $y \geq 0$, domain of f^{-1}: $x \geq 0$, range of f^{-1}: $y \geq 3$

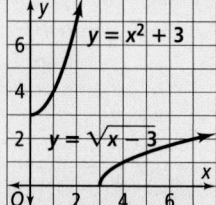

69. domain of f: all real numbers, range of f: $y \leq 6$, domain of f^{-1}: $x \leq 6$, range of f^{-1}: all real numbers

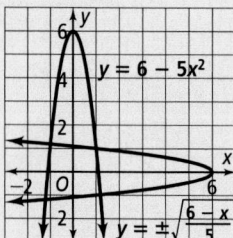

70. $s = \sqrt[3]{V}$; 4 ft

71. domain: $x \geq 0$, range: $y \geq -5$

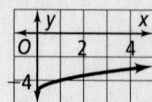

72. domain: $x \geq -8$, range: $y \geq 0$

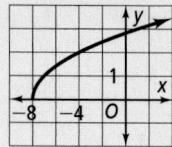

Quick Review

If a relation or a function is described by an equation in x and y, you can interchange x and y to get the inverse. The domain of a function becomes the range of its inverse, and the range of a function becomes the domain of its inverse.

Example

What is the inverse of $f(x) = \sqrt{x - 10}$?

$y = \sqrt{x - 10}$	Rewrite using y.
$x = \sqrt{y - 10}$	Interchange the x and y values.
$x^2 = y - 10$	Square each side.
$y = x^2 + 10$	Solve for y.
$f^{-1}(x) = x^2 + 10$	Write the inverse function.

The domain of $f(x)$ is $x \geq 10$, which means the range of $f^{-1}(x)$ is $y \geq 10$. Also, since the range of $f(x)$ is $y \geq 0$, the domain of $f^{-1}(x)$ is $x \geq 0$.

Exercises

Find the inverse of each function. Determine whether each inverse is a function.

62. $f(x) = 2x^2 - 8$ **63.** $f(x) = 15 - 3x$

64. $f(x) = \sqrt{x + 6}$ **65.** $f(x) = (2x - 3)^2$

Graph each function and its inverse. Describe the domain and range of each.

66. $f(x) = 4x - 1$ **67.** $f(x) = (x + 3)^2$

68. $f(x) = \sqrt{x - 3}$ **69.** $f(x) = 6 - 5x^2$

70. Geometry The volume of a cube is determined by the formula $V = s^3$, where s is the length of one side. Find the inverse formula. Use it to find the side length of a cube with a volume of 64 ft³.

6-8 Graphing Radical Functions

Quick Review

The function $f(x) = \sqrt{x}$ is the parent function of the **square root function** $f(x) = a\sqrt{x - h} + k$. The graph of $f(x) = a\sqrt{x}$ is a stretch $(a > 1)$ or a shrink $(0 < a < 1)$ of the parent function. The graph of $f(x) = a\sqrt{x - h} + k$ is a translation h units horizontally and k units vertically of $y = a\sqrt{x}$. The graph of $f(x) = \sqrt[n]{x}$ is transformed by a, h, and k in the same way as the graph of $f(x) = \sqrt{x}$.

Example

Describe the graph of $y = \sqrt{4x + 12}$.

$y = \sqrt{4x + 12}$	
$y = \sqrt{4(x + 3)}$	Factor the polynomial.
$y = 2\sqrt{x + 3}$	Simplify the radical.

The graph of $y = \sqrt{4x + 12}$ is the graph of $y = 2\sqrt{x}$ translated 3 units to the left.

Exercises

Graph each function. Find the domain and range.

71. $y = \sqrt{x} - 5$ **72.** $y = \sqrt{x + 8}$

73. $y = 5\sqrt{x} + 9$ **74.** $y = -\sqrt{x - 4}$

75. $y = \sqrt[3]{x + 10}$ **76.** $y = -\sqrt[3]{x - 2} + 5$

Rewrite each function to make it easy to graph using transformations. Describe each graph.

77. $y = \sqrt{9x - 27} + 4$ **78.** $y = -3\sqrt{4x - 16}$

79. $y = \sqrt[3]{8x + 24}$ **80.** $y = \sqrt{\dfrac{x - 4}{4}} + 6$

Solve each equation by graphing.

81. $5 = -\sqrt{x - 3}$

82. $\sqrt{8x - 16} = 2\sqrt{x + 2}$

73. domain: $x \geq 0$, range: $y \geq 9$

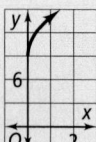

74. domain: $x \geq 4$, range: $y \leq 0$

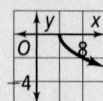

75. domain: all real numbers, range: all real numbers

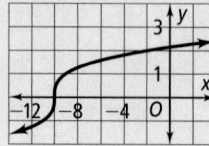

76. domain: all real numbers, range: all real numbers

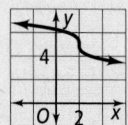

77. $y = 3\sqrt{x - 3} + 4$ the graph of $y = 3\sqrt{x}$ translated 3 units to the right and 4 units up

78. $y = -6\sqrt{x - 4}$; the graph of $y = -6\sqrt{x}$ translated 4 units to the right

79. $y = 2\sqrt[3]{x + 3}$; the graph of $y = 2\sqrt[3]{x}$ translated 3 units to the left

80. $y = \dfrac{1}{2}\sqrt{x - 4} + 6$; the graph of $y = \dfrac{1}{2}\sqrt{x}$ translated 4 units to the right and 6 units up

81. no solution

82. 6

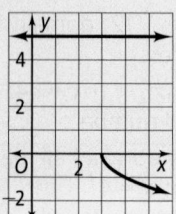

6 Chapter Test

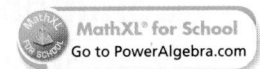 MathXL® for School
Go to PowerAlgebra.com

Do you know HOW?

Simplify each radical expression. Use absolute value symbols when needed.

1. $\sqrt{54x^3y^5}$

2. $\sqrt[3]{-0.027}$

3. $\sqrt[5]{-64x^{14}y^{20}}$

Simplify each expression. Rationalize all denominators.

4. $\sqrt{7x^3} \cdot \sqrt{14x}$

5. $\dfrac{1 - \sqrt{3x}}{\sqrt{6x}}$

6. $\sqrt{48} + 2\sqrt{27} + 5\sqrt{12}$

7. $\left(3 + 2\sqrt{5}\right)\left(1 - \sqrt{20}\right)$

8. $4\sqrt{7xz} + 2\sqrt{7xz}$

9. $\dfrac{5\sqrt{2}}{\sqrt{7} - \sqrt{2}}$

Simplify each expression.

10. $(125)^{-\frac{2}{3}}$

11. $x^{\frac{1}{6}} \cdot x^{\frac{1}{3}}$

12. $\left(\dfrac{8x^9y^3}{27x^2y^{12}}\right)^{\frac{2}{3}}$

13. $\sqrt{8x^5} - \sqrt{18x^5}$

Solve each equation. Check for extraneous solutions.

14. $\sqrt{x - 3} = x - 5$

15. $\sqrt{x + 4} = \sqrt{3x}$

16. $2(x - 1)^{\frac{3}{4}} = 16$

17. $\sqrt{x + 3} - 1 = x$

Let $f(x) = x - 2$ and $g(x) = x^2 - 3x + 2$. Perform each function operation and then find the domain.

18. $-2g(x) + f(x)$

19. $-f(x) \cdot g(x)$

20. $\dfrac{g(x)}{f(x)}$

Find each product or quotient.

21. $\sqrt{5}\left(\sqrt[4]{5}\right)$

22. $\dfrac{\sqrt{x^3}}{\sqrt[5]{x^2}}$

For each pair of functions, find $(g \circ f)(x)$ and $(f \circ g)(x)$.

23. $f(x) = x^2 - 2$, $g(x) = 4x + 1$

24. $f(x) = 2x^2 + x - 7$, $g(x) = -3x - 1$

Find the inverse of each function. Is the inverse a function?

25. $f(x) = (x + 3)^2 + 1$

26. $f(x) = \sqrt{2x + 1}$

27. $g(x) = 3x^3 - 4$

28. $f(x) = \frac{1}{4}x$

Rewrite each function to make it easy to graph using transformations. Describe the graph.

29. $y = \sqrt{16x + 80} - 1$ **30.** $y = \sqrt{9x + 3}$

Graph. Find the domain and range of each function.

31. $y = 2\sqrt{x} + 3$

32. $y = -\sqrt{2x + 3}$

33. $y = \sqrt{x + 3} - 4$

Do you UNDERSTAND?

34. Writing Explain why -108 has no real 6th roots.

35. Open-Ended Write a relation that is not a function, but whose inverse is a function.

36. Measurement The time t in seconds for a swinging pendulum to complete one full cycle is given by the function $t = 0.2\sqrt{l}$, where l is the length of the pendulum in centimeters. To the nearest tenth, how long is a full cycle if the pendulum is 10 cm long? 20 cm long? How long, in centimeters, is a pendulum that takes 2 seconds for one full cycle?

30. $y = 3\sqrt{x + \frac{1}{3}}$; the graph of $y = 3\sqrt{x}$ translated $\frac{1}{3}$ units to the left

31. domain: $x \geq 0$, range: $y \geq 3$

32. domain: $x \geq -\frac{3}{2}$, range: $y \leq 0$

33. domain: $x \geq -3$, range: $y \geq -4$

34. $\sqrt[6]{-108}$ has no real roots, since there is no real number x such that $x^6 = -108$.

35. Answers may vary. Sample: $f(x) = \pm\sqrt{x}$ is not a function, but $f^{-1}(x) = x^2$ is a function.

36. 0.6 s; 0.9 s; 100 cm

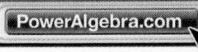 PowerAlgebra.com

Chapter 6   Chapter Test   427

Answers

1. $3|x|y^2\sqrt{6xy}$

2. -0.3

3. $-2x^2y^4\sqrt[5]{2x^4}$

4. $7x^2\sqrt{2}$

5. $\dfrac{\sqrt{6x} - 3x\sqrt{2}}{6x}$

6. $20\sqrt{3}$

7. $-17 - 4\sqrt{5}$

8. $6\sqrt{7xz}$

9. $2 + \sqrt{14}$

10. $\dfrac{1}{25}$

11. $x^{\frac{1}{2}}$

12. $\dfrac{4x^4\sqrt[3]{x^2}}{9y^6}$

13. $-x^2\sqrt{2x}$

14. 7

15. 2

16. 17

17. 1

18. $-2x^2 + 7x - 6$; domain: all real numbers

19. $-x^3 + 5x^2 - 8x + 4$; domain: all real numbers

20. $x - 1$; domain: all real numbers except $x = 2$

21. $\sqrt[4]{125}$

22. $x\sqrt[10]{x}$

23. $(g \circ f)(x) = 4x^2 - 7$; $(f \circ g)(x) = 16x^2 + 8x - 1$

24. $(g \circ f)(x) = -6x^2 - 3x + 20$; $(f \circ g)(x) = 18x^2 + 9x - 6$

25. $f^{-1}(x) = -3 \pm \sqrt{x - 1}$; no

26. $f^{-1}(x) = \dfrac{x^2 - 1}{2}$, $x \geq 0$; yes

27. $g^{-1}(x) = \sqrt[3]{\dfrac{x + 4}{3}}$; yes

28. $f^{-1}(x) = 4x$; yes

29. $y = 4\sqrt{x + 5} - 1$; the graph of $y = 4\sqrt{x}$ translated 5 units to the left and 1 unit down

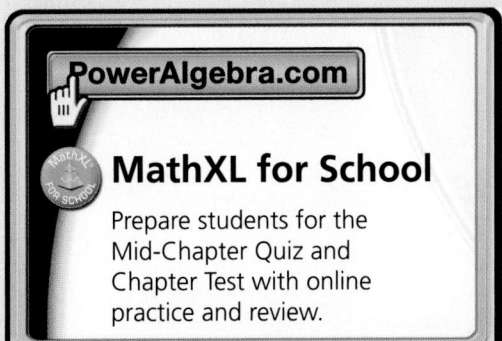

Item Number	Lesson	Content Standard
1	5-2	A-APR.B.3
2	1-4	A-CED.A.2
3	5-3	A-SSE.A.2
4	2-2	A-CED.A.2
5	2-7	F-IF.C.7b
6	4-1	F-IF.C.7a
7	6-2	A-SSE.A.2
8	4-8	N-CN.C.7
9	1-6	A-CED.A.1
10	3-2	A-REI.C.6
11	3-5	A-CED.A.2
12	4-8	N-CN.A.2
13	6-6	F-BF.A.1b
14	3-1	A-CED.A.2
15	3-2	A-CED.A.1
16	4-5	A-APR.B.3
17	4-8	N-CN.C.7
18	6-2	A-SSE.A.2
19	6-5	A-REI.A.2
20	3-2	A-CED.A.2
21	4-2	F-IF.C.8
22	4-1	F-BF.B.3
23	5-4	A-APR.D.7
24	6-6	F-BF.A.1b
25	3-2	A-CED.A.2
26	5-6	A-APR.B.3
27	5-1	F-IF.C.7c
28	6-1	A-SSE.A.2
29	6-3	A-APR.D.6
30	6-6	A-CED.A.2

Common Core Cumulative Standards Review

 ASSESSMENT

TIPS FOR SUCCESS

Some problems require you to find the inverse of a function.

TIP 1
To find the inverse of a function, interchange x and y.

What is the inverse of the function $y = x^2 + 3$?

- Ⓐ $y = x - 3$
- Ⓑ $y = \pm\sqrt{x-3}$
- Ⓒ $y = \pm\sqrt{x^2+3}$
- Ⓓ $y = (x-3)^2$

TIP 2
After you interchange x and y, solve for y.

Think It Through
$y = x^2 + 3$
$x = y^2 + 3$
$x - 3 = y^2$
$\pm\sqrt{x-3} = y$
$y = \pm\sqrt{x-3}$
The correct answer is B.

Vocabulary Review

As you solve test items, you must understand the meanings of mathematical terms. Match each term with its mathematical meaning.

A. radicand

B. index

C. composite function

D. inverse functions

E. radical function

I. the combination of two functions such that the output from the first becomes the input for the second

II. the degree of a root in a radical expression

III. the number under the radical sign in a radical expression

IV. a function that can be written in the form $f(x) = a\sqrt[n]{x-h} + k$

V. the range of one function is the domain of the other and vice versa

Selected Response

Read each question. Then write the letter of the correct answer on your paper.

1. Find all the roots of $2x^4 + x^3 - 8x^2 - 4x = 0$.
- Ⓐ $x = -2, x = -0.5, x = 0, x = 2$
- Ⓑ $x = -2, x = -0.5, x = 2$
- Ⓒ $x = -2, x = 0.5, x = 0, x = 2$
- Ⓓ $x = -2, x = 0.5, x = 2$

2. Solve the equation $ax^2 + bx + c = 0$ for b.
- Ⓕ $b = -cx - ax^2$
- Ⓖ $b = \frac{-c - ax^2}{x}$
- Ⓗ $b = -(cx - ax^2)$
- Ⓘ $b = \frac{-(c - ax^2)}{x}$

3. Use the sum of cubes formula to factor $x^3 + 64$.
- Ⓐ $(x + 4)(x^2 - 4x + 4)$
- Ⓑ $(x + 4)(x^2 + 4x + 4)$
- Ⓒ $(x + 4)(x^2 - 4x + 16)$
- Ⓓ $(x + 4)(x^2 + 4x + 16)$

428 Chapter 6 Common Core Cumulative Standards Review

Answers

Common Core Cumulative Standards Review

A. III
B. II
C. I
D. V
E. IV
1. A
2. G
3. C

428 Chapter 6

4. The time it takes to copy pages varies directly with the number of pages being copied. The copier at your office can copy 21 color pages per minute and 40 black and white pages per minute. Approximately how long will it take to copy 60 color pages and 35 black and white pages?

Ⓕ 0.9 minute   Ⓗ 2.9 minutes

Ⓖ 2.5 minutes   Ⓘ 3.7 minutes

5. Which equation is modeled by the graph?

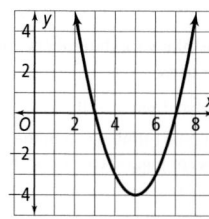

Ⓐ $y = |2x - 3|$ Ⓒ $y = |2x + 3|$

Ⓑ $y = 2|x - 3|$ Ⓓ $y = 2|x + 3|$

6. What are the vertex and axis of symmetry for the given parabola?

Ⓕ $(-4, 5), y = 5$

Ⓖ $(-4, 5), x = 5$

Ⓗ $(5, -4), y = -4$

Ⓘ $(5, -4), x = 5$

7. What is the product of $\sqrt[3]{3}$ and $\sqrt[5]{3}$?

Ⓐ $\sqrt[8]{3}$

Ⓑ $\sqrt[8]{9}$

Ⓒ $\sqrt[15]{3^8}$

Ⓓ $\sqrt[8]{3^{15}}$

8. Solve $7x^2 + 196 = 0$ for x.

Ⓕ $\pm 4i\sqrt{7}$

Ⓖ $\pm 4\sqrt{7}$

Ⓗ $\pm 2i\sqrt{7}$

Ⓘ $\pm 2\sqrt{7}$

9. Which inequality is modeled by the graph?

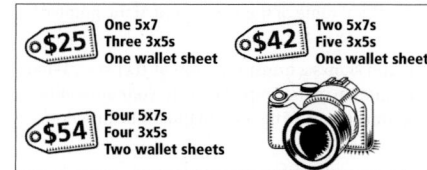

Ⓐ $k + 1 \leq 7$

Ⓑ $|k + 1| \leq 7$

Ⓒ $k - 4 \leq 3$

Ⓓ $|k - 4| \leq 3$

10. What is the solution of the system? $\begin{cases} 4x + 2y = 4 \\ 6x + 2y = 8 \end{cases}$

Ⓕ $(-2, 2)$

Ⓖ $(2, -2)$

Ⓗ $(1, 2)$

Ⓘ $(-1, 2)$

11. A photographer is promoting three photo specials. How much does it cost for each type of print?

ⓞ$25   One 5x7 / Three 3x5s / One wallet sheet

ⓞ$42   Two 5x7s / Five 3x5s / One wallet sheet

ⓞ$54   Four 5x7s / Four 3x5s / Two wallet sheets

Ⓐ 5×7 costs $7, 3×5 costs $5, Wallet costs $3

Ⓑ 5×7 costs $11, 3×5 costs $7, Wallet costs $3

Ⓒ 5×7 costs $12, 3×5 costs $11, Wallet costs $7

Ⓓ 5×7 costs $7, 3×5 costs $5, Wallet costs $5

12. What is an equivalent form of $\frac{5}{2 + 2i}$?

Ⓕ $\frac{5}{4i}$ Ⓗ $\frac{5 + 5i}{4}$

Ⓖ $\frac{10 - 10i}{4 - 4i}$ Ⓘ $\frac{5 - 5i}{4}$

4. I
5. C
6. I
7. C
8. H
9. D
10. G
11. A
12. I

Answers

13. -14

14. 9

15. 32

16. 12

17. 0

18. 1

19. $\frac{4}{3}$

20. 210

21. -2

22. $g(x) = (x+2)^2 - 3$; the graph is translated 2 units left and 3 units down from the parent graph.

23. a. $x^2 + 3x - 4$

b. 36 cents

24. [2] a. domain of f: all real numbers, range of f: $y \geq 4$; domain of g: all real numbers, range of g: all real numbers

b. $f(x) + g(x) = (x^2 + 4) + (3x - 1) = x^2 + 3x + 3$

c. all real numbers

[1] one incorrect statement of a domain or a range

25. [2] hat: $25, shirt: $20

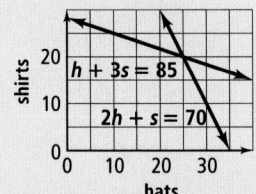

[1] graph is not labeled appropriately

26. [2] $y = 3(x - 16)(x - (1 - 2i))(x - (1 + 2i))$, multiply the constant terms only: $3(-16)(-1 + 2i)(-1 - 2i) = -240$

[1] constant term is correct, but no work is shown OR one computational error

27. [2] degree: 6, polynomial of 4 terms; down and down end behavior with one turning point

[1] end behavior is described correctly, but no other description is given

28. sometimes

29. always

30. [4] a. rebate: $R(x) = 5x$, where x is the number of CDs bought; discount: $M(y) = 0.15y$, where y is the amount of money paid

b. If the rebate is taken off first, the customer will pay $(13x - 5x)(1 - 0.15) = 6.8x$. If the discount is given first, the customer will pay $(1 - 0.15)(13x) - 5x = 6.05x$. The customer receives the greatest discount if the 15% off is taken before the $5 rebate is applied.

c. 5 CDs at regular price costs $13(5) = $60

Constructed Response

13. Let $g(x) = x - 3$ and $h(x) = x^2 + 6$. What is $h(1) \times g(1)$?

14. A laptop comes without any programs installed on it. Each program costs $20 and the laptop you want costs $319. What is the greatest number of programs you can buy if you want to spend at most $500 for the laptop?

15. You are building an entertainment center with shelves that are x in. deep by x in. long. The height of the unit will be twice the depth. If the volume of the unit will be 8,192 in.^{3}, what is the height, in inches, of the entertainment center?

16. What is the solution of the equation $x^2 - 24x + 144 = 0$?

17. What is the number of real roots of the equation $2x^2 + 3x = -4$?

18. What is the quotient $\dfrac{\sqrt[3]{8x^6 y^{12}}}{\sqrt{4x^4 y^8}}$?

19. What is the solution of $4 + \sqrt{3x + 5} = 7$?

20. All 385 tickets for a high-school play sold in 10 days. The ticket receipts totaled $1960. If the cost of a child's ticket was $4 and the cost of an adult's ticket was $6, how many adult tickets were sold?

21. What is the x-value of the x-intercept of the graph of $f(x) = x^2 + 4x + 4$?

22. The graph shows a transformation of $f(x) = x^2$. What is an equation of the graph? Explain your answer by using translations of the parent quadratic function.

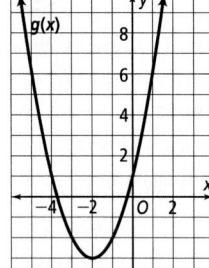

23. The total cost (in cents) of $x + 2$ markers is $x^3 + 5x^2 + 2x - 8$.

a. Write an expression that models the cost of each marker.

b. If you buy 7 markers, how much would each marker cost?

24. You are given that $f(x) = x^2 + 4$ and $g(x) = 3x - 1$.

a. What are the domain and range of $f(x)$ and $g(x)$?

b. Find $f(x) + g(x)$.

c. What is the domain of your answer to part (b)?

25. Two friends went shopping together. One friend bought 2 hats and 1 shirt and spent $70, while the other friend bought 1 hat and 3 shirts and spent $85. Use a graph to determine the costs of each shirt and hat.

26. A student found that a cubic function has zeros 16 and $1 - 2i$ with a leading coefficient of 3. What is the constant term of this polynomial function with real coefficients?

27. Describe the graph of the polynomial function $f(x) = -x^6 + 3x^5 + 4x - 10$. What is its end behavior?

Decide whether the following statements are *always,* **sometimes, or** *never* **true.**

28. If n is a real number, then $0^n = 0$.

29. If a and b are rational numbers, then the product of $(a + \sqrt{b})$ and its conjugate is a rational number.

Extended Response

30. An online music store is having a promotion. Customers receive a $5 rebate if they buy any regular priced CD at $13 each. They can also receive 15% off if they register as a store member.

a. What functions model the two discounts?

b. In which order should the discounts be applied for the customer to receive the greatest discount?

c. Use your answer from part (b) to determine the amount a customer will save if she buys 5 CDs.

---

5 CDs at a discount costs $6.05(5) = 30.25 The customer saves $29.75.

[3] appropriate methods, but with one computational error

[2] incorrect function(s), but work done appropriately given previous results

[1] correct answers, but without work shown

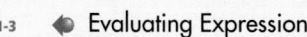

Get Ready!

Lesson 1-3 **Evaluating Expressions**

Evaluate each expression for $x = -2, 0,$ and 2.

1. 10^{x+1} **2.** $\left(\frac{3}{2}\right)^x$ **3.** -5^{x-2} **4.** $-(3)^{0.5x}$

Lesson 2-5 **Using Linear Models**

Draw a scatter plot and find the line of best fit for each set of data.

5. $(0, 2), (1, 4), (2, 6.5), (3, 8.5), (4, 10), (5, 12), (6, 14)$

6. $(3, 100), (5, 150), (7, 195), (9, 244), (11, 296), (13, 346), (15, 396)$

Lessons 4-1 and 5-9 **Graphing Transformations**

Identify the parent function of each equation. Graph each equation as a transformation of its parent function.

7. $y = (x + 5)^2 - 3$ **8.** $y = -2(x - 6)^3$

Lesson 6-4 **Simplifying Rational Exponents**

Simplify each expression.

9. $\left(x^{\frac{1}{5}}\right)^{10}$ **10.** $\left(-8x^3\right)^{\frac{4}{3}}$

Lesson 6-7 **Finding Inverses**

Find the inverse of each function. Is the inverse a function?

11. $y = 10 - 2x^2$ **12.** $y = (x + 4)^3 - 1$

 **Looking Ahead Vocabulary**

13. In advertising, the *decay factor* describes how an advertisement loses its effectiveness over time. In math, would you expect a decay factor to increase or decrease the value of y as x increases?

14. There are many different kinds of growth patterns. Patterns that increase by a constant rate are linear. Patterns that grow *exponentially* increase by an ever-increasing rate. If your allowance doubles each week, does that represent linear growth or exponential growth?

15. The word *asymptote* comes from a Greek word meaning "not falling together." When looking at the end behavior of a function, do you expect the graph to intersect its asymptote?

Get Ready!

Assign this diagnostic assessment to determine if students have the prerequisite skills for Chapter 7.

Lesson	Skill
1-3	Evaluate Expressions
2-5	Use Linear Models
4-1 and 5-9	Graph Transformations
6-4	Simplify Radicals
6-7	Find Inverses

To remediate students, select from these resources (available for every lesson).
• Online Problems (PowerAlgebra.com)
• Reteaching (All-in-One Teaching Resources)
• Practice (All-in-One Teaching Resources)

Why Students Need These Skills
EVALUATING EXPRESSIONS
Evaluating expressions is essential to determining the values of logarithms and exponents.
USING LINEAR MODELS
Students extend their skill of using linear models to finding exponential and logarithmic models.
GRAPHING TRANSFORMATIONS
Graphing transformations is an essential skill when graphing certain logarithmic and exponential functions.
SIMPLIFYING RADICALS
Simplifying radicals is essential to simplifying exponents when solving exponential equations.
FINDING INVERSES
Understanding how to find inverses is essential in understanding the relationship between exponential and logarithmic functions.

Looking Ahead Vocabulary
DECAY FACTOR Ask students for other examples of decay. How does decay change things?
EXPONENTIALLY Ask students to choose an allowance, doubling it at regular intervals. Ask them what a graph of the allowance over time would look like.
ASYMPTOTE Ask students to consider what it means to intersect something.

Answers

Get Ready!

1. $0.1; 10; 1000$

2. $\frac{4}{9}; 1; \frac{9}{4}$

3. $-\frac{1}{625}; -\frac{1}{25}; -1$

4. $-\frac{1}{3}; -1; -3$

5. 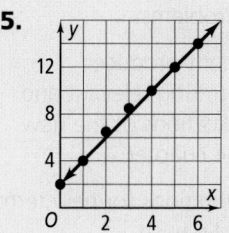 ; $y \approx 1.98x + 2.20$

6. ; $y \approx 24.66x + 24.77$

7. $y = x^2$

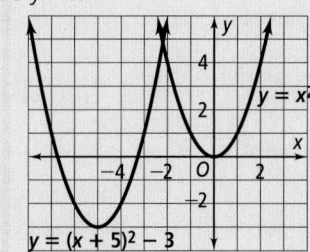

$y = (x + 5)^2 - 3$

8. $y = x^3$

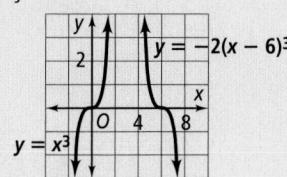

9. x^2

10. $16x^4$

11. $y = \pm\sqrt{\dfrac{10 - x}{2}}$; no

12. $y = -4 + \sqrt[3]{x + 1}$; yes

13. decrease

14. exponential

15. no

Chapter 7 Overview

Chapter 7 expands on student understandings and skills related to exponential and logarithmic functions. In this chapter, students will develop the answers to the Essential Questions as they learn the concepts and skills bulleted below.

BIG idea Modeling
ESSENTIAL QUESTION How do you model a quantity that changes regularly over time by the same percentage?
- Students will model situations with exponential functions.

BIG idea Equivalence
ESSENTIAL QUESTION How are exponents and logarithms related?
- Students will use exponents to solve logarithmic equations and logarithms to solve exponential equations.

BIG idea Function
ESSENTIAL QUESTION How are exponential functions and logarithmic functions related?
- Students will show that exponents and logarithms are inverse functions.
- Students will graph exponential and logarithmic functions.

Content Standards

Following are the standards covered in this chapter. Modeling standards are indicated by a star symbol (★).

CONCEPTUAL CATEGORY Algebra

Domain Seeing Structure in Expressions A-SSE
Cluster Interpret the structure of expressions. (Standards A-SSE.A.1a★, A-SSE.A.1b★)
LESSON 7-3

Cluster Write expressions in equivalent forms to solve problems. (Standards A-SSE.B.3c)
LESSON 7-1

Domain Creating Equations A-CED
Cluster Create equations that describe numbers. (Standards A-CED.A.1★, A-CED.A.2★, A-CED.A.3★)
LESSONS 7-1, 7-2

Domain Reasoning with Equations and Inequalities A-REI
Cluster Represent and solve equations and inequalities graphically. (Standard A-REI.D.11)
LESSON 7-5

CHAPTER 7 Exponential and Logarithmic Functions

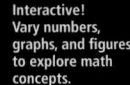
Download videos connecting math to your world.

Interactive! Vary numbers, graphs, and figures to explore math concepts.

The online Solve It will get you in gear for each lesson.

Math definitions in English and Spanish

Online access to stepped-out problems aligned to Common Core

Get and view your assignments online.

Extra practice and review online

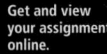
Virtual Nerd™ tutorials with built-in support

Chapter Preview
7-1 Exploring Exponential Models
7-2 Properties of Exponential Functions
7-3 Logarithmic Functions as Inverses
7-4 Properties of Logarithms
7-5 Exponential and Logarithmic Equations
7-6 Natural Logarithms

Vocabulary
English/Spanish Vocabulary Audio Online:

English	Spanish
asymptote, p. 435	asíntota
Change of Base Formula, p. 464	fórmula de cambio de base
common logarithm, p. 453	logaritmo común
exponential equation, p. 469	ecuación exponencial
exponential function, p. 434	función exponencial
exponential growth, p. 435	incremento exponencial
logarithm, p. 451	logaritmo
logarithmic equation, p. 471	ecuación logarítmica
logarithmic function, p. 454	función logarítmica
natural logarithmic function, p. 478	función logarítmica natural

BIG ideas
1 Modeling
Essential Question How do you model quantity that changes regularly over time by the same percentage?

2 Equivalence
Essential Question How are exponents and logarithms related?

3 Function
Essential Question How are exponential functions and logarithmic functions related?

 DOMAINS
- Linear and Exponential Models
- Creating Equations that Describe Numbers
- Interpreting Functions

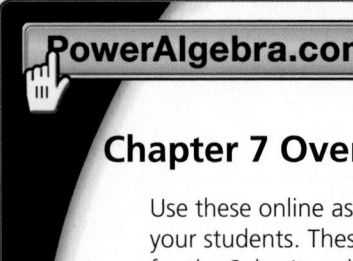
PowerAlgebra.com

Chapter 7 Overview

Use these online assets to engage your students. These include support for the Solve It and step-by-step solutions for Problems.

 Show the student-produced video demonstrating relevant and engaging applications of the new concepts in the chapter.

 Find online definitions for new terms in English and Spanish.

 Start each lesson with an attention-getting Problem. View the Problem online with helpful hints.

Common Core Performance Task

Apparent Magnitudes of Stars

Astronomers refer to the brightness of a star as its *apparent magnitude*. Apparent magnitude is measured on a decreasing scale, meaning that brighter stars have lower apparent magnitudes. For example, Polaris (the North Star) is one of the brighter stars in the night sky and has an apparent magnitude of 1.97, while stars that can barely be seen with the unaided eye have apparent magnitudes of about 6.5. The Sun has an apparent magnitude of -26.74.

Apparent magnitude does not indicate how brightly a star burns. Many stars burn brighter than our Sun, but they appear faint and dim because of their great distance from us.

In the apparent magnitude scale, a decrease of 1 unit corresponds to an increase in brightness by a factor of $\sqrt[5]{100}$. For example, a star of magnitude 3 and a star of magnitude 1 are separated by 2 units on the apparent magnitude scale, so the star of magnitude 1 is $(\sqrt[5]{100})^2$ times (or about 6.3 times) as bright as the star of magnitude 3.

Task Description

Sirius, the brightest star in the night sky, is about 24 times as bright as Polaris. What is the apparent magnitude of Sirius?

Connecting the Task to the Math Practices

As you complete the task, you'll apply several Standards for Mathematical Practice.

- You'll make sense of the information provided and write an exponential function that models the problem situation. (MP 1, MP 2)
- You'll solve an equation algebraically and by using a graph. (MP 5)

 Increase students' depth of knowledge with interactive online activities.

 Show Problems from each lesson solved step by step. Instant replay allows students to go at their own pace when studying online.

 Assign homework to individual students or to an entire class.

 Prepare students for the Mid-Chapter Quiz and Chapter Test with online practice and review.

 Virtual Nerd™ Access Virtual Nerd student-centered math tutorials that directly relate to the content of the lesson.

 Overview of the Performance Task

Students will write an exponential equation to model the problem. They will use logarithms to solve the equation. Students will also interpret their results.

Students will work on the Performance Task in the following places in the chapter.

- Lesson 7-1 (p. 441)
- Lesson 7-5 (p. 476)
- Pull It All Together (p. 486)

Introducing the Performance Task

Tell students to read the problem on this page. Do not have them start work on the problem at this time, but ask them the following questions.

Q What is a strategy you could try in order to solve this problem? **[Sample: I can write and solve an equation that relates the relative brightness of the two stars to the difference in their magnitudes.]**

Q From the given information, is the apparent magnitude of Sirius greater than or less than the apparent magnitude of Polaris? Explain. **[Sample: Less than; a brighter star has an apparent magnitude that is less than that of a dimmer star.]**

PARCC CLAIMS

Sub-Claim A: Major Content with Connections to Practices
Sub-Claim B: Additional and Supporting Content with Connections to Practices

SBAC CLAIMS

Claim 1: Concepts and Procedures
Claim 2: Problem Solving

Content Standards (cont')

CONCEPTUAL CATEGORY Functions

Domain Interpreting Functions F-IF
  Cluster Analyze functions using different representations. (Standards F-IF.C.7e★, F-IF.C.8, F-IF.C.9)
  LESSONS 7-1, 7-2, 7-3

Domain Build Functions F-BF
  Cluster Build a function that models a relationship between quantities. (Standard F-BF.A.1b★)
  LESSON 7-2

  Cluster Build new functions from existing functions. (Standard F-BF.B.4a)
  LESSON 7-3

Domain Linear and Exponential Models F-LE
  Cluster Construct and compare linear and exponential models and solve problems. (Standard F-LE.4★)
  LESSONS 7-5, 7-6

EXPONENTIAL AND LOGARITHMIC FUNCTIONS
Math Background © PROFESSIONAL DEVELOPMENT

The Understanding by Design® methodology was central to the development of the Big Ideas and the Essential Understandings. These will help your students build a structure on which to make connections to prior learning.

Modeling

BIG idea Many real-world mathematical problems can be represented algebraically. These representations can lead to algebraic solutions. A function that models a real-world situation can then be used to make estimates or predictions about future occurrences.

ESSENTIAL UNDERSTANDINGS

7-1 You can represent repeated multiplication with a function in the form of $y = ab^x$ where b is a positive number other than 1.

7-4 Logarithms and exponents have corresponding properties.

Equivalence

BIG idea A single quantity may be represented by many different expressions. The facts about a quantity may be expressed by many different equations (or inequalities).

ESSENTIAL UNDERSTANDINGS

7-1 See above.

7-3 The exponential function $y = b^x$ is one-to-one, so its inverse $x = b^y$ is a function. To express "y as a function of x" for the inverse, write $y = \log_b x$.

7-4 Logarithms and exponents have corresponding properties.

7-5 You can use logarithms to solve exponential equations. You can use exponents to solve logarithmic equations.

7-6 The functions $y = e^x$ and $y = \ln x$ are inverse functions. Just as before, this means that if $a = e^b$, then $b = \ln a$, and vice versa.

Function

BIG idea A function is a relationship between variables in which each value of the input variable is associated with a unique value of the output variable. Functions can be represented in a variety of ways, such as graphs, tables, equations, or words. Each representation is particularly useful in certain situations. Some important families of functions are developed through transformations of the simplest form of the function.

ESSENTIAL UNDERSTANDINGS

7-1 See above.

7-2 The factor a in $y = ab^x$ can stretch or compress, and possibly reflect the graph of the parent function $y = b^x$.

7-3 The exponential function $y = b^x$ is one-to-one, so its inverse $x = b^y$ is a function. To express "y as a function of x" for the inverse, write $y = \log_b x$.

7-5 to 7-6 See above.

Exponential and Logarithmic Models

Exponential Models

The function $y = ab^x$, represents
- exponential growth if $a > 0$ and $b > 1$
- exponential decay if $a > 0$ and $0 < b < 1$

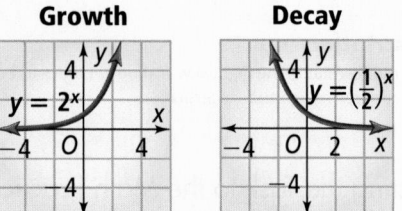

The factor a can stretch, compress, or reflect the graph of the parent function $y = b^x$.

Translations occur for nonzero values of h (horizontal) and k (vertical) in the function $y = ab^{(x-h)} + k$.

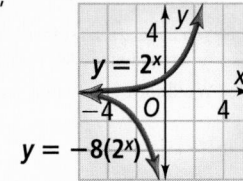

Logarithmic Models

The equation $y = \log_b x$ is the inverse of the exponential function $y = b^x$.

The fact that exponential and logarithmic functions are inverses can be used to find values of logarithms.

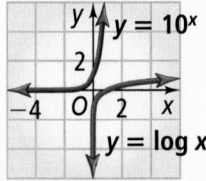

Common Errors When Using Exponential and Logarithmic Models

Exponential Models Students may make errors when converting the factors for growth and decay from percent to decimal. For example, a growth rate of 3% indicates that the value b should be 1.03. Remind students to check the first few terms to be sure their models are correct.

Logarithmic Models Students sometimes confuse the domain and range of logarithmic models. Point out that because the functions are inverses of each other, the domain and range of the exponential model are the range and domain of the logarithmic model.

© Mathematical Practices

Model with mathematics. Look for and make use of structure. Exponential and logarithmic functions are explored as models of real-world behavior before algebraic manipulations are introduced. Function transformations are revisited with families of exponential and logarithmic functions, which are analyzed algebraically, graphically, and numerically with tables.

Solving Logarithmic Equations

The properties of logarithms can be used to solve logarithmic equations.

For any positive numbers m, n, and b where $b \neq 1$:

Product Property $\quad \log_b mn = \log_b m + \log_b n$

Quotient Property $\quad \log_b \frac{m}{n} = \log_b m - \log_b n$

Power Property $\quad \log_b m^n = n \log_b m$

Example: What is the solution of $\log 3 + \log 2x = 2$?

$$\log 3 + \log 2x = 2$$
$$\log(6x) = 2 \qquad \text{Product Property}$$
$$10^{\log 6x} = 10^2 \qquad \text{Exponential Form}$$
$$6x = 100$$
$$x = \frac{50}{3}$$

Natural Logarithms

Natural logarithms (ln) are logarithms to the base e. They follow the same rules and properties as logarithms to other bases. The functions $y = e^x$ and $y = \ln x$ are inverse functions.

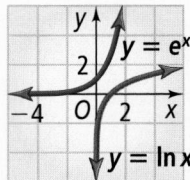

Example: What are the solutions of $\ln 3x^2 - 2 \ln 3 = 2$?

$$\ln 3x^2 - 2 \ln 3 = 2$$
$$\ln 3x^2 - \ln 3^2 = 2 \qquad \text{Power Property}$$
$$\ln \frac{x^2}{3} = 2 \qquad \text{Quotient Property}$$
$$\frac{x^2}{3} = e^2 \qquad \text{Exponential Form}$$
$$x^2 \approx 22.1672$$
$$x \approx \pm 4.708$$

Common Errors When Solving Logarithmic Equations

Exponential Form Errors occur when students write logarithmic equations in exponential form. Encourage them to write steps as needed. For example, in the natural logarithm example above, write $e^{\ln \frac{x^2}{3}} = e^2$ to get the equation in exponential form. Because natural log and e are inverses, the left side of the equation becomes $\frac{x^2}{3}$.

Ⓒ Mathematical Practices

Use appropriate tools strategically. Graphing calculators are used throughout the chapter to analyze the behavior of exponential and logarithmic functions. Technology enables students to solve real-world equations that would have been computationally tedious in the past. Exponential and logarithmic regressions are introduced as statistical applications facilitated by the graphing calculator.

Solving Exponential Equations

Solve Algebraically

Exponential equations can be solved by taking logarithms of each side. Although logarithms to any base can be used, common logs and natural logs are generally used.

Example: Solve $13^{n+10} = 80$.

$$13^{n+10} = 80$$
$$\log 13^{n+10} = \log 80$$
$$(n + 10)(\log 13) = \log 80 \qquad \text{Power Property}$$
$$n + 10 = \frac{\log 80}{\log 13}$$
$$n \approx -8.9216$$

An equation need not contain e to use the natural log.

Example: What is the solution of $5^x = 30$?

$$5^x = 30 \qquad\qquad 5^x = 30$$
$$x \ln 5 = \ln 30 \qquad x \log 5 = \log 30$$
$$x = \frac{\ln 30}{\ln 5} \qquad\quad x = \frac{\log 30}{\log 5}$$
$$x \approx 2.113 \qquad\qquad x \approx 2.113$$

Solve Graphically

Both exponential and logarithmic equations can be solved using a graph or table.

Example: Solve $3^{4x} = 500$.

Enter $3^{(4x)}$ in Y_1 and 500 in Y_2. Find the intersection.

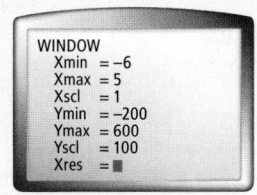
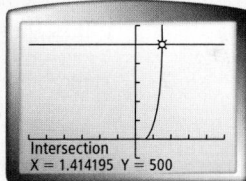

Solve using the table.

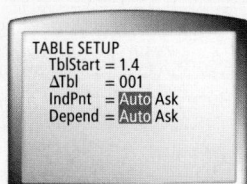
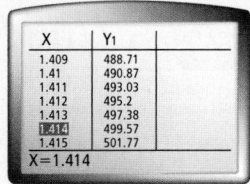

Ⓒ Mathematical Practices

Attend to precision. Look for and express regularity in repeated reasoning. Construct viable arguments and critique the reasoning of others. Do You Understand? exercises in every lesson ensure that students can justify true statements and analyze flawed statements. The uses of properties of exponents and logarithms in solving equations are analyzed and reinforced in comprehensive exercise sets.

EXPONENTIAL AND LOGARITHMIC FUNCTIONS
Pacing and Assignment Guide

		TRADITIONAL			BLOCK
Lesson	Teaching Day(s)	Basic	Average	Advanced	Block
7-1	1	Problems 1–2 Exs. 10–32, 34–40 even, 46–50	Problems 1–5 Exs. 11–29 odd, 30–41, 46–50	Problems 1–5 Exs. 11–29 odd, 30–50	**Day 1** Problems 1–5 Exs. 11–29 odd, 30–41, 46–50
7-2	1	Problems 1–5 Exs. 7–33, 35, 38–40 even, 44–62	Problems 1–5 Exs. 7–29 odd, 31–41, 44–62	Problems 1–5 Exs. 7–29 odd, 31–62	Problems 1–5 Exs. 7–29 odd, 31–41, 44–62
7-3	1	Problems 1–3 Exs. 12–35	Problems 1–3 Exs. 13–35 odd	Problems 1–3 Exs. 13–35 odd	**Day 2** Problems 1–5 Exs. 13–43 odd, 44–79
	2	Problems 4–5 Exs. 36–47, 58–61, 72–76 even	Problems 4–5 Exs. 37–43 odd, 44–79	Problems 4–5 Exs. 37–43 odd, 44–84	
7-4	1	Problems 1–2 Exs. 9–29, 80–95	Problems 1–2 Exs. 9–29 odd, 80–95	Problems 1–2 Exs. 9–29 odd, 80–95	**Day 3** Problems 1–4 Exs. 9–37 odd, 39–74, 80–95
	2	Problems 3–4 Exs. 30–38, 43–47, 50–60 even	Problems 3–4 Exs. 31–37 odd, 39–74	Problems 3–4 Exs. 31–37 odd, 39–79	
7-5	1	Problems 1–3 Exs. 7–30	Problems 1–3 Exs. 7–29 odd	Problems 1–3 Exs. 7–29 odd	**Day 4** Problems 1–6 Exs. 7–45 odd, 46–78
	2	Problems 4–6 Exs. 31–45, 46–54 even, 60, 61	Problems 4–6 Exs. 31–45 odd, 46–78	Problems 4–6 Exs. 31–45 odd, 46–83	
7-6	1	Problems 1–2 Exs. 11–28, 66–84	Problems 1–2 Exs. 11–27 odd, 66–84	Problems 1–2 Exs. 11–27 odd, 66–84	**Day 5** Problems 1–4 Exs. 11–39 odd, 40–59, 66–84
	2	Problems 3–4 Exs. 29–44, 52, 53	Problems 3–4 Exs. 29–39 odd, 40–59	Problems 3–4 Exs. 29–39 odd, 40–65	
Review	1	Chapter 7 Review	Chapter 7 Review	Chapter 7 Review	**Day 6** Chapter 7 Review Chapter 7 Test
Assess	1	Chapter 7 Test	Chapter 7 Test	Chapter 7 Test	
Total		**12 Days**	**12 Days**	**12 Days**	**6 Days**

Note: Pacing does not include Concept Bytes and other feature pages.

Resources

	For the Chapter	7–1	7–2	7–3	7–4	7–5	7–6
Planning							
Teacher Center Online Planner & Grade Book	I	I	I	I	I	I	I
Interactive Learning & Guided Instruction							
My Math Video	I						
Solve It!		I M	I M	I M	I M	I M	I M
Student Companion		P M	P M	P M	P M	P M	
Vocabulary Support		I P M	I P M	I P M	I P M	I P M	I P M
Got It? Support		I P	I P	I P	I P	I P	I P
Dynamic Activity	I						
Online Problems		I	I	I	I	I	I
Additional Problems		M	M	M	M	M	M
English Language Learner Support (TR)		E P M	E P M	E P M	E P M	E P M	E P M
Activities, Games, and Puzzles		E M	E M	E M	E M	E M	E M
Teaching With TI Technology With CD-ROM		✓ P	✓ P				
TI-Nspire™ Support CD-ROM		✓	✓	✓	✓	✓	✓
Lesson Check & Practice							
Student Companion		P M	P M	P M	P M	P M	P M
Lesson Check Support		I P	I P	I P	I P	I P	I P
Practice and Problem Solving Workbook		P	P	P	P	P	P
Think About a Plan (TR)		E P M	E P M	E P M	E P M	E P M	E P M
Practice Form G (TR)		E P M	E P M	E P M	E P M	E P M	E P M
Standardized Test Prep (TR)		P M	P M	P M	P M	P M	P M
Practice *Form K* (TR)		E P M	E P M	E P M	E P M	E P M	E P M
Extra Practice	E M						
Find the Errors!	M						
Enrichment (TR)		E P M	E P M	E P M	E P M	E P M	E P M
Answers and Solutions CD-ROM	✓	✓	✓	✓	✓	✓	✓
Assess & Remediate							
ExamView CD-ROM	✓	✓	✓	✓	✓	✓	✓
Lesson Quiz		I M	I M	I M	I M	I M	I M
Quizzes and Tests *Form G* (TR)	E P M			E P M			E P M
Quizzes and Tests *Form K* (TR)	E P M			E P M			E P M
Reteaching (TR)		E P M	E P M	E P M	E P M	E P M	E P M
Performance Tasks (TR)	P M						
Cumulative Review (TR)	P M						
Progress Monitoring Assessments	I P M						

(TR) Available in All-In-One Teaching Resources

1 Interactive Learning

Solve It!

PURPOSE To express an exponential pattern in algebraic terms

PROCESS Students may
- sketch simpler models and extrapolate results to apply to more complex models.
- write an equation for the model.

FACILITATE

Q How many times does the original bottom ring move? **[once]**

Q How many times does the smallest ring move from its original position to its final position if there are n rings? Explain. **[2^{n-1} times; the smallest ring gets every second move. In between moving it, there is only one legal move that is not moving it again.]**

Q Is there a post you have to move the smallest ring to as the first move if you want the final stack on a specific post? Explain. **[Yes; for n odd, move it to the post where you want the stack, and for n even, move it to the post where you do not want the stack.]**

ANSWER See Solve It in Answers on next page.

CONNECT THE MATH The Solve It introduces an exponential expression as part of a solution to a problem. In the lesson students will write and use exponential equations to solve problems.

2 Guided Instruction

Problem 1

Q What would happen to the graph of 2^x if the 2 was replaced by a 5? **[The graph would be steeper.]**

7-1 Exploring Exponential Models

Common Core State Standards
F-IF.C.7e Graph exponential . . . functions, showing intercepts and end behavior . . . Also A-SSE.A.1b, A-CED.A.2, F-IF.C.8
MP 1, MP 2, MP 3, MP 4, MP 5

Objective To model exponential growth and decay

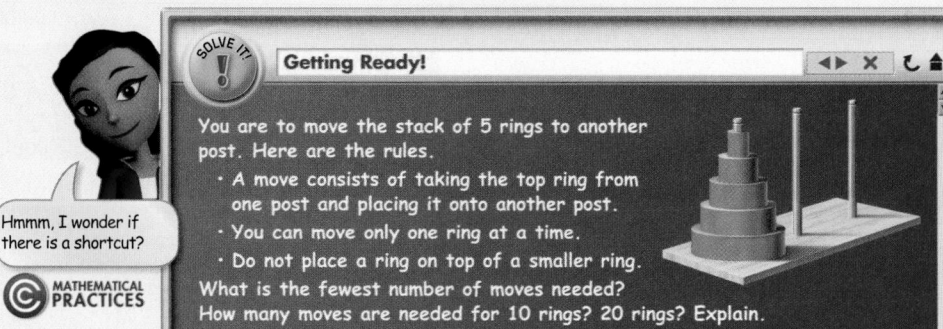

Hmmm, I wonder if there is a shortcut?

MATHEMATICAL PRACTICES

Getting Ready!

You are to move the stack of 5 rings to another post. Here are the rules.
- A move consists of taking the top ring from one post and placing it onto another post.
- You can move only one ring at a time.
- Do not place a ring on top of a smaller ring.

What is the fewest number of moves needed? How many moves are needed for 10 rings? 20 rings? Explain.

Lesson Vocabulary
- exponential function
- exponential growth
- exponential decay
- asymptote
- growth factor
- decay factor

The number of moves needed for additional rings in the Solve It suggests a pattern that approximates repeated multiplication.

Essential Understanding You can represent repeated multiplication with a function of the form $y = ab^x$ where b is a positive number other than 1.

An **exponential function** is a function with the general form $y = ab^x$, $a \neq 0$, with $b > 0$, and $b \neq 1$. In an exponential function, the base b is a constant. The exponent x is the independent variable with domain the set of real numbers.

Problem 1 Graphing an Exponential Function

What is the graph of $y = 2^x$?

Plan

How does making a table help you sketch the graph?
The table shows coordinates of several points on the graph.

Step 1 Make a table of values.

x	2^x	y
-4	2^{-4}	$\frac{1}{16} = 0.0625$
-3	2^{-3}	$\frac{1}{8} = 0.125$
-2	2^{-2}	$\frac{1}{4} = 0.25$
-1	2^{-1}	$\frac{1}{2} = 0.5$

x	2^x	y
0	2^0	1
1	2^1	2
2	2^2	4
3	2^3	8

Step 2 Plot and connect the points.

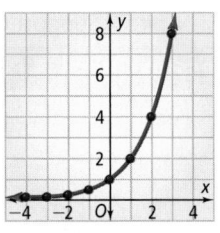

7-1 Preparing to Teach

BIG ideas Equivalence
Function
Modeling

ESSENTIAL UNDERSTANDINGS
- Repeated multiplication can be represented with a function in the form of $y = ab^x$ where b is a positive number other than 1.
- An exponential function is a function with the general form $y = ab^x$, $a \neq 0$, with $b > 0$, and $b \neq 1$. In an exponential function, the base b is a constant. The exponent x is the independent variable with domain the set of real numbers.

Math Background

Exponential notation is a simplified way to represent repeated multiplication. For example, $2 \cdot 2 \cdot 2 \cdot 2 \cdot 2 \cdot 2 \cdot 2 = 2^7$. Repeated multiplication by the same factor can be represented by an exponential function.

Such functions have the form $y = ab^x$ where b is greater than 0 and not equal to 1, and x is any real number.

For $a > 0$, the value of b determines whether the function grows or decays exponentially:
- When $b > 1$, the function *grows* exponentially.
- When $0 < b < 1$, the function *decays* exponentially.

Note that if $b = 1$, the function would simplify to $y = a$, which is a constant function.

Exponential functions can be used to model many real-world situations, including half-life, radiometric dating, interest-bearing savings accounts, population growth, and a bouncing ball.

Mathematical Practices

Model with mathematics. In Problem 3, students will use exponential functions to model compound interest.

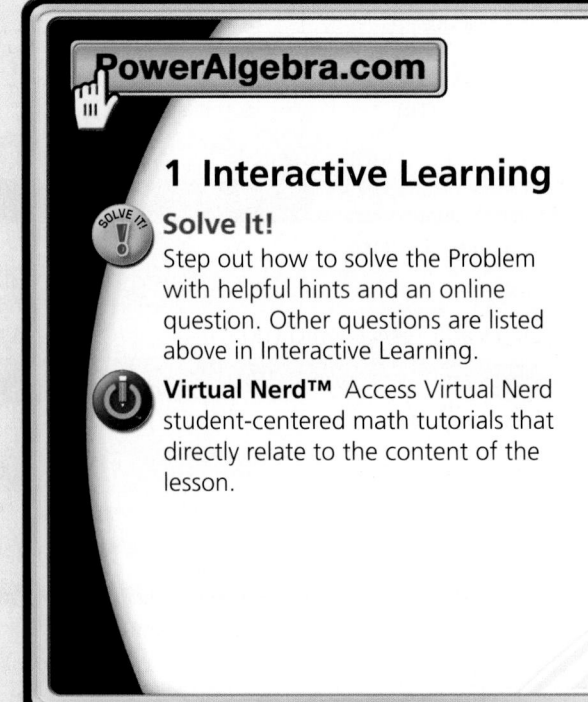

PowerAlgebra.com

1 Interactive Learning

Solve It!
Step out how to solve the Problem with helpful hints and an online question. Other questions are listed above in Interactive Learning.

Virtual Nerd™ Access Virtual Nerd student-centered math tutorials that directly relate to the content of the lesson.

Got It? 1. What is the graph of each function?

a. $y = 4^x$ b. $y = \left(\frac{1}{3}\right)^x$ c. $y = 2(3)^x$

d. Reasoning What generalizations can you make about the domain, range, and y-intercepts of these functions?

Two types of exponential behavior are *exponential growth* and *exponential decay*.

For **exponential growth**, as the value of x increases, the value of y increases. For **exponential decay**, as the value of x increases, the value of y decreases, approaching zero.

The exponential functions shown here are *asymptotic* to the x-axis. An **asymptote** is a line that a graph approaches as x or y increases in absolute value.

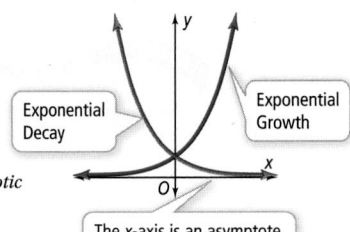

Exponential Decay

Exponential Growth

The x-axis is an asymptote.

 Concept Summary   Exponential Functions

For the function $y = ab^x$,

- if $a > 0$ and $b > 1$, the function represents exponential growth.
- if $a > 0$ and $0 < b < 1$, the function represents exponential decay.

In either case, the y-intercept is $(0, a)$, the domain is all real numbers, the asymptote is $y = 0$, and the range is $y > 0$.

© **Problem 2   Identifying Exponential Growth and Decay**

Identify each function or situation as an example of exponential growth or decay. What is the y-intercept?

A $y = 12(0.95)^x$

Since $0 < b < 1$, the function represents exponential decay. The y-intercept is $(0, a) = (0, 12)$.

B $y = 0.25(2)^x$

Since $b > 1$, the function represents exponential growth. The y-intercept is $(0, a) = (0, 0.25)$.

C You put $1000 into a college savings account for four years. The account pays 5% interest annually.

The amount of money in the bank grows by 5% annually. It represents exponential growth. The y-intercept is 1000, which is the dollar value of the initial investment.

Think
What quantity does the y-intercept represent?
The y-intercept is the amount of money at $t = 0$, which is the initial investment.

✓ **Got It? 2.** Identify each function or situation as an example of exponential growth or decay. What is the y-intercept?

a. $y = 3\left(4^x\right)$ b. $y = 11\left(0.75^x\right)$

c. You put $2000 into a college savings account for four years. The account pays 6% interest annually.

---

2 Guided Instruction

© Each Problem is worked out and supported online.

Problem 1
Graphing an Exponential Function

Problem 2
Identifying Exponential Growth and Decay
Animated

Problem 3
Modeling Exponential Growth
Animated

Problem 4
Using Exponential Growth

Problem 5
Writing an Exponential Function

Support in Algebra 2 Companion
- Vocabulary
- Key Concepts
- Got It?

Answers

Solve It!
31; 1023; 1048575; The number of moves follows the pattern $2^x - 1$.

Got It?

1. a. 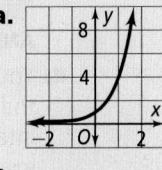 **b.**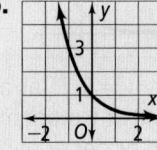

c.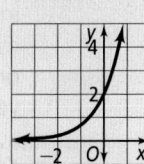

d. domain: all real numbers, range: $y > 0$; y-intercept: $(0, a)$ where $y = ab^x$

2. a. exponential growth; 3

b. exponential decay; 11

c. exponential growth; 2000

Take Note

Q Does *t* always represent time in years? Explain. **[No; time may need to be calculated in units other than years, for example, some bacteria grow exponentially in hours or minutes.]**

Problem 3

Q When is an exponential function an appropriate model? **[If finding the solution would require iterative multiplication, an exponential model is appropriate.]**

Q Why would you advise a friend who wants to make his savings account grow as much as possible not to withdraw the interest at the end of each year? **[If you leave the interest in the account, the savings account will pay interest on the interest, but if you withdraw the interest, the account will only pay interest on the original principal.]**

ERROR PREVENTION

Even advanced students may occasionally write a 5% growth rate as 1.5 or a growth rate of 4.5% as 1.45. Making students aware of the error may help prevent it.

EXTENSION

Q How much money would you have if you invested the money at the end of first grade? **[$1710.34]**

Got It?   EXTENSION

Q What model will you use? **[$A(t) = a(1 + r)^t$, where *t* is the number of years since the money was invested and $A(t)$ is the amount in the account after each year]**

For exponential growth $y = ab^x$, with $b > 1$, the value *b* is the **growth factor**. A quantity that exhibits exponential growth increases by a constant percentage each time period. The percentage increase *r*, written as a decimal, is the *rate of increase* or *growth rate*. For exponential growth, $b = 1 + r$.

For exponential decay, $0 < b < 1$ and *b* is the **decay factor**. The quantity decreases by a constant percentage each time period. The percentage decrease, *r*, is the *rate of decay*. Usually a rate of decay is expressed as a negative quantity, so $b = 1 + r$.

take note

Key Concept Exponential Growth and Decay

You can model exponential growth or decay with this function.

Amount after *t* time periods	Rate of growth ($r > 0$) or decay ($r < 0$)

$$A(t) = a(1 + r)^t$$

Initial amount	Number of time periods

For growth or decay to be exponential, a quantity changes by a fixed percentage each time period.

ⓒ Problem 3 Modeling Exponential Growth

You invested $1000 in a savings account at the end of 6th grade. The account pays 5% annual interest. How much money will be in the account after six years?

Step 1 Determine if an exponential function is a reasonable model.

The money grows at a fixed rate of 5% per year. An exponential model is appropriate.

Step 2 Define the variables and determine the model.

Let t = the number of years since the money was invested.
Let $A(t)$ = the amount in the account after each year.

A reasonable model is $A(t) = a(1 + r)^t$.

Think
What is the growth rate *r*?
It is the annual interest rate, written as a decimal: 5% = 0.05.

Step 3 Use the model to solve the problem.

$$A(6) = 1000(1 + 0.05)^6 \quad \text{Substitute } a = 1000, r = 0.05, \text{ and } t = 6.$$
$$= 1000(1.05)^6 \quad \text{Simplify.}$$
$$\approx \$1340.10$$

The account contains $1340.10 after six years.

✓ Got It? 3. Suppose you invest $500 in a savings account that pays 3.5% annual interest. How much will be in the account after five years?

Additional Problems

1. What is the graph of $y = 3.1^x$?

ANSWER

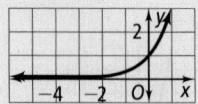

2. Identify $y = 0.7^x$ as an example of exponential growth or decay. What is the *y*-intercept?

ANSWER decay; (0, 1)

3. You buy a savings bond for $25 that pays a yearly interest rate of 4.2%. What will the savings bond be worth after fifteen years?

ANSWER $46.34

4. You open a savings account that pays 4.5% annual interest. If your initial investment is $300 and you make no additional deposits or withdrawals, how many years will it take for the account to grow to at least $500?

ANSWER 12 years

5. The initial value of a car is $30,000. After one year, the value of the car is $20,000. Estimate the value of the car after five years.

ANSWER $3950.62

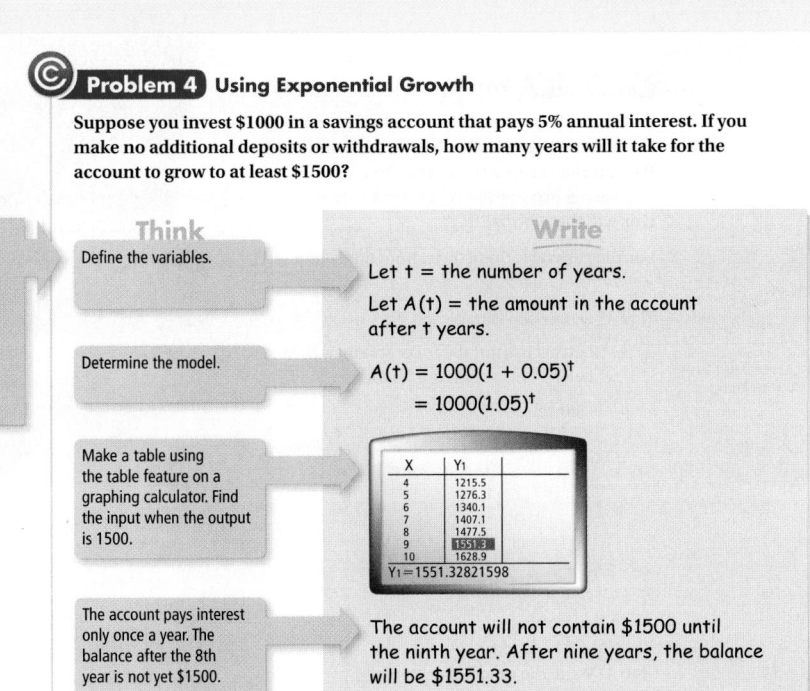

Problem 4 · Using Exponential Growth

Suppose you invest $1000 in a savings account that pays 5% annual interest. If you make no additional deposits or withdrawals, how many years will it take for the account to grow to at least $1500?

Plan

How can you make a table to solve this problem?
Define the variables, write an equation and enter it into a graphing calculator. Then you can inspect a table to find the solution.

Think

Write

Define the variables.

Let t = the number of years.

Let A(t) = the amount in the account after t years.

Determine the model.

$A(t) = 1000(1 + 0.05)^t$

$= 1000(1.05)^t$

Make a table using the table feature on a graphing calculator. Find the input when the output is 1500.

X	Y₁
4	1215.5
5	1276.3
6	1340.1
7	1407.1
8	1477.5
9	1551.3
10	1628.9

Y₁=1551.32821598

The account pays interest only once a year. The balance after the 8th year is not yet $1500.

The account will not contain $1500 until the ninth year. After nine years, the balance will be $1551.33.

Got It? 4. a. Suppose you invest $500 in a savings account that pays 3.5% annual interest. When will the account contain at least $650?

b. **Reasoning** Use the table in Problem 4 to determine when that account will contain at least $1650. Explain.

Exponential functions are often discrete. In Problem 4, interest is paid only once a year. So the graph consists of individual points corresponding to t = 1, 2, 3, and so on. It is not continuous. Both the table and the graph show that there is never *exactly* $1500 in the account and that the account will not contain more than $1500 until the ninth year.

To model a discrete situation using an exponential function of the form $y = ab^x$, you need to find the growth or decay factor b. If you know y-values for two consecutive x-values, you can find the rate of change r, and then find b using $r = \frac{(y_2 - y_1)}{y_1}$ and $b = 1 + r$.

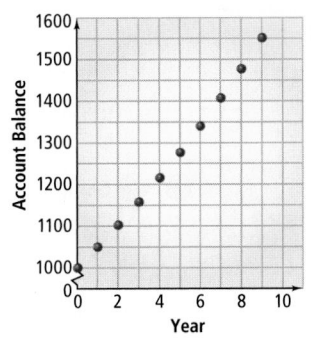

Problem 4   EXTENSION

Q If you withdrew the interest at the end of each year, how long would it take the savings account to pay you $500? Explain. **[The account would pay you $50 each year, so it would take ten years, which is a year longer than if you leave the interest in the account.]**

Q If you double the original investment, would the amount in the account at the end of the term also double? Explain. **[Yes; you are changing the constant of multiplication, so your end value will change by that same constant.]**

Q Use tables to answer the following questions. Would doubling the interest rate from the original rate or doubling the time double the final amount from the original final amount? Why? **[No; answers may vary. Samples: $(1 + 2r)^t$ does not equal $2(1 + r)^t$; $(1 + r)^{2t}$ does not equal $2(1 + r)^t$.]**

Got It?

Q Is an exponential function a reasonable model for this situation? Explain. **[Yes; answers may vary. Sample: Your savings account grows at a fixed, constant rate per year, so an exponential model is appropriate.]**

Answers

Got It? (continued)

3. $593.84

4. a. after 8 yrs

   b. after 11 yrs; then the account contains $1710.34.

Problem 5

Q What is the meaning of 0.8? **[Each year, the population is 80% of what it was the year before.]**

Q If the trend has been occurring since the Iberian Lynx was placed on the Endangered Species List in 1970, how many Iberian Lynx were there when it was placed on the list? Do you think this is reasonable? Explain. **[About 236,658; sample: yes; 236,658(.8)^{33} ≈ 150.]**

EXTENSION

Q Can you sketch a graph of what a population recovery would look like? **[Answers may vary. Sample: A population recovery graph would begin to turn upward.]**

Got It?

Q If the trend continues, in what year will there be no hope of a wild Iberian Lynx population recovery (excluding captive animals)? **[In 2023, there will be fewer than two wild Iberian lynx, so there will be no possibility of a wild Iberian lynx mating pair.]**

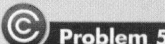 **Problem 5** Writing an Exponential Function **STEM**

Endangered Species The table shows the world population of the Iberian lynx in 2003 and 2004. If this trend continues and the population is decreasing exponentially, how many Iberian lynx will there be in 2014?

Use the general form of the exponential equation, $y = ab^x = a(1 + r)^x$.

Step 1 Define the variables.

Let x = the number of years since 2003.
Let y = the population of the Iberian lynx.

Think

How can you find the value of r?
You can use the populations for two consecutive years to find r.

Step 2 Determine r.

Use the populations for 2003 and 2004.

$r = \dfrac{y_2 - y_1}{y_1}$

$= \dfrac{120 - 150}{150}$

$= -0.2$

Step 3 Use r to determine b.

$b = 1 + r = 1 + (-0.2) = 0.8$

Step 4 Write the model.

$y = ab^x$

$150 = a(0.8)^0$ — Solve for a using the initial values $x = 0$ and $y = 150$.

$150 = a$

Think

How do you find the x-value corresponding to 2014?
The initial x-value corresponds to 2003, so find the difference.

The model is $y = 150(0.8)^x$.

Step 5 Use the model to find the population in 2014.
For the year 2014, $x = 2014 - 2003 = 11$.

$y = 150(0.8)^x$

$= 150(0.8)^{11}$

≈ 13

If the 2003–2004 trend continues, there will be approximately 13 Iberian lynx in the wild in 2014.

World Population of Iberian Lynx

Year	2003	2004
Population	150	120

© ✔ **Got It? 5. a.** For the model in Problem 5, what will be the world population of Iberian lynx in 2020?
b. Reasoning If you graphed the model in Problem 5, would it ever cross the x-axis? Explain.

Answers

Got It? (continued)

5. a. ≈ 3
b. No; the function is asymptotic to the x-axis.

Lesson Check

1. decay; 10 **2.** growth; 0.75
3. growth; 1 **4.** decay; 1
5.

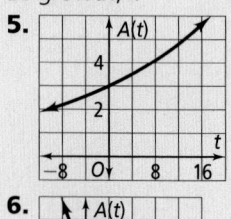

6.

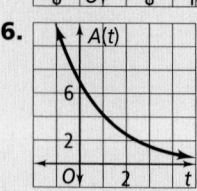

7. If $a > 0$ and $b > 1$, then the function represents exponential growth; if $a > 0$ and $0 < b < 1$, then the function represents exponential decay.

8. a. quadratic; degree 2 with $3x^2$ as the leading term
b. exponential; the equation is of the form $y = ab^x$
c. linear; degree 1 with x as the leading term
d. exponential; the equation is of the form $y = ab^x$

9. $0.3 < 1$, so 0.3 is the decay factor

Practice and Problem-Solving Exercises

10.

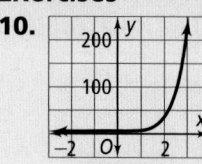

11.

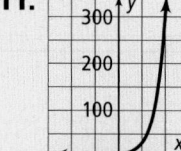

12.

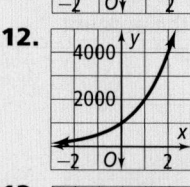

13.

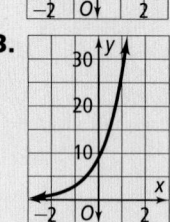

Lesson Check

Do you know HOW?

Without graphing, determine whether the function represents exponential growth or exponential decay. Then find the *y*-intercept.

1. $y = 10(0.45)^x$
2. $y = 0.75(4)^x$
3. $y = 3^x$
4. $y = 0.95^x$

Graph each function.

5. $A(t) = 3(1.04)^t$
6. $A(t) = 7(0.6)^t$

Do you UNDERSTAND?  MATHEMATICAL PRACTICES

7. **Vocabulary** Explain how you can tell if $y = ab^x$ represents exponential growth or exponential decay.

8. **Reasoning** Identify each function as *linear, quadratic,* or *exponential.* Explain your reasoning.
   a. $y = 3(x + 1)^2$
   b. $y = 4(3)^x$
   c. $y = 2x + 5$
   d. $y = 4(0.2)^x + 1$

9. **Error Analysis** A classmate says that the growth factor of the exponential function $y = 15(0.3)^x$ is 0.3. What is the student's mistake?

Practice and Problem-Solving Exercises  MATHEMATICAL PRACTICES

A Practice

Graph each function. **◆ See Problem 1.**

10. $y = 6^x$
11. $y = 3(10)^x$
12. $y = 1000(2)^x$
13. $y = 9(3)^x$
14. $f(x) = 2(3)^x$
15. $s(t) = 1.5^t$
16. $y = 8(5)^x$
17. $y = 2^{2x}$

Without graphing, determine whether the function represents exponential growth or exponential decay. Then find the *y*-intercept. **◆ See Problem 2.**

18. $y = 129(1.63)^x$
19. $f(x) = 2(0.65)^x$
20. $y = 12\left(\frac{17}{10}\right)^x$
21. $y = 0.8\left(\frac{1}{8}\right)^x$
22. $f(x) = 4\left(\frac{5}{6}\right)^x$
23. $y = 0.45(3)^x$
24. $y = \frac{1}{100}\left(\frac{4}{3}\right)^x$
25. $f(x) = 2^{-x}$

26. **Interest** Suppose you deposit $2000 in a savings account that pays interest at an annual rate of 4%. If no money is added or withdrawn from the account, answer the following questions. **◆ See Problems 3 and 4.**
   a. How much will be in the account after 3 years?
   b. How much will be in the account after 18 years?
   c. How many years will it take for the account to contain $2500?
   d. How many years will it take for the account to contain $3000?

Write an exponential function to model each situation. Find each amount after the specified time. **◆ See Problem 5.**

27. A population of 120,000 grows 1.2% per year for 15 years.

28. A population of 1,860,000 decreases 1.5% each year for 12 years.

29. a. **Sports** Before a basketball game, a referee noticed that the ball seemed underinflated. She dropped it from 6 feet and measured the first bounce as 36 inches and the second bounce as 18 inches. Write an exponential function to model the height of the ball.
   b. How high was the ball on its fifth bounce?

14.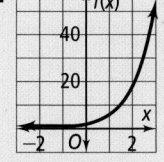
15.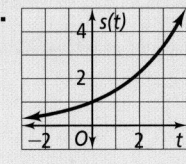
16.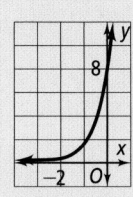
17.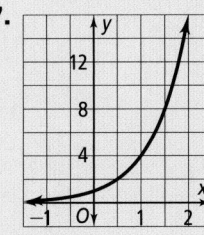

18. exponential growth; 129
19. exponential decay; 2
20. exponential growth; 12
21. exponential decay; 0.8
22. exponential decay; 4
23. exponential growth; 0.45
24. exponential growth; $\frac{1}{100}$
25. exponential decay; 1
26. a. $2249.73
   b. $4051.63
   c. 6 yrs
   d. 11 yrs
27. $y = 120,000(1.012)^x$; 143,512
28. $y = 1,860,000(0.985)^x$; 1,551,485
29. a. $y = 72\left(\frac{1}{2}\right)^x$
   b. 2.25 in.

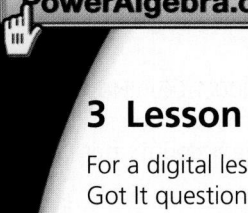

4 Practice

ASSIGNMENT GUIDE

Basic: 10–29 all, 30–32, 34–40 even

Average: 11–29 odd, 30–41

Advanced: 11–29 odd, 30–45

Standardized Test Prep: 46-50

Ⓒ Mathematical Practices are supported by exercises with red headings. Here are the Practices supported in this lesson:

MP 1: Make Sense of Problems Ex. 30
MP 2: Reason Abstractly Ex. 44
MP 3: Communicate Ex. 8
MP 3: Construct Arguments Ex. 45
MP 3: Critique the Reasoning of Others Ex. 9
MP 5: Use Appropriate Tools Ex. 32b

Applications exercises have blue headings. Exercises 26, 29 and 33 support MP 4: Model.

STEM exercises focus on science or engineering applications.

EXERCISE 32: Use the Think About a Plan worksheet in the **Practice and Problem Solving Workbook** (also available in the Teaching Resources in print and online) to further support students' development in becoming independent learners.

HOMEWORK QUICK CHECK

To check students' understanding of key skills and concepts, go over Exercises 11, 19, 30, 31, and 32.

Ⓑ Apply

Ⓒ 30. Think About a Plan Your friend invested $1000 in an account that pays 6% annual interest. How much interest will your friend have after her college graduation in 4 years?
- Is an exponential model reasonable for this situation?
- What equation should you use to model this situation?
- Is the solution of the equation the final answer to the problem?

STEM 31. Oceanography The function $y = 20(0.975)^x$ models the intensity of sunlight beneath the surface of the ocean. The output y represents the percent of surface sunlight intensity that reaches a depth of x feet. The model is accurate from about 20 feet to about 600 feet beneath the surface.
- **a.** Find the percent of sunlight 50 feet beneath the surface of the ocean.
- **b.** Find the percent of sunlight at a depth of 370 feet.

32. Population The population of a certain animal species decreases at a rate of 3.5% per year. You have counted 80 of the animals in the habitat you are studying.
- **a.** Write a function that models the change in the animal population.
- **Ⓒ b. Graphing Calculator** Graph the function. Estimate the number of years until the population first drops below 15 animals.

33. Sports While you are waiting for your tennis partner to show up, you drop your tennis ball from 5 feet. Its rebound was approximately 35 inches on the first bounce and 21.5 inches on the second. What exponential function would be a good model for the bouncing ball?

For each annual rate of change, find the corresponding growth or decay factor.

34. +70%	**35.** +500%	**36.** −75%	**37.** −55%
38. +12.5%	**39.** −0.1%	**40.** +0.1%	**41.** +100%

Ⓒ Challenge

42. Manufacturing The value of an industrial machine has a decay factor of 0.75 per year. After six years, the machine is worth $7500. What was the original value of the machine?

STEM 43. Zoology Determine which situation best matches the graph.
- Ⓐ A population of 120 cougars decreases 98.75% yearly.
- Ⓑ A population of 120 cougars increases 1.25% yearly.
- Ⓒ A population of 115 cougars decreases 1.25% yearly.
- Ⓓ A population of 115 cougars decreases 50% yearly.

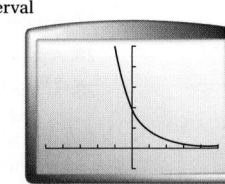

Ⓒ 44. Open-Ended Write a problem that could be modeled with $y = 20(1.1)^x$.

Ⓒ 45. Reasoning Which function does the graph represent? Explain. (Each interval represents one unit.)
- Ⓐ $y = \left(\frac{1}{3}\right)2^x$
- Ⓑ $y = 2\left(\frac{1}{3}\right)^x$
- Ⓒ $y = -2\left(\frac{1}{3}\right)^x$

Answers

Practice and Problem-Solving Exercises
(continued)

30. $262.48; yes; $A(t) = 1000(1.06)^t$; No, when $t = 4$, $A(t) = 1262.48 which represents the amount of money in the account after four yrs.

31. a. about 5.6%
  b. about 0.0017%

32. a. $y = 80(0.965)^x$
  b.

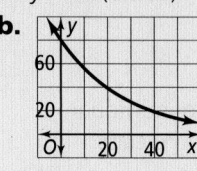

  about 47 yrs

33. Answers may vary. Sample: $y = 59.5(0.6)^x$

34. 1.70

35. 6

36. 0.25

37. 0.45

38. 1.125

39. 0.999

40. 1.001

41. 2

42. about $42,140

43. C

44. Check students' work.

45. B; The graph shows a decreasing function, which eliminates A. The y-values are all positive, which eliminates C.

SAT/ACT

46. Which function represents the value after x years of a new delivery van that costs $25,000 and depreciates 15% each year?

Ⓐ $y = -15(25,000)^x$ Ⓒ $y = 25,000(0.85)^x$

Ⓑ $y = 25,000(0.15)^x$ Ⓓ $y = 25,000(1.15)^x$

47. What is $f(x) = 3x^{\frac{1}{3}}$ for $x = \frac{1}{125}$?

Ⓕ 15   Ⓖ $\frac{3}{5}$ Ⓗ $\frac{\sqrt[3]{3}}{5}$ Ⓘ $5\sqrt[3]{3}$

48. What is the simplified form of $\frac{2+i}{2-i}$?

Ⓐ -1 Ⓑ $\frac{3+4i}{3}$ Ⓒ $\frac{5+4i}{5}$ Ⓓ $\frac{3+4i}{5}$

49. Which graph represents the equation $y = x^2 - x - 2$?

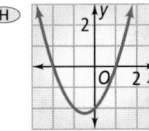

Extended Response

50. You are driving a car when a deer suddenly darts across the road in front of you. Your brain registers the emergency and sends a signal to your foot to hit the brake. The car travels a reaction distance D, in feet, during this time, where D is a function of the speed r, in miles per hour, that the car is traveling when you see the deer, given by $D(r) = \frac{11r + 5}{10}$. Find the inverse and explain what it represents. Is the inverse a function?

Apply What You've Learned

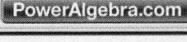

MATHEMATICAL PRACTICES
MP 1, MP 2

Look back at the information on page 433 about the apparent magnitudes of stars. Suppose Star 1 is separated from Star 2 on the apparent magnitude scale by x, and is y times as bright as Star 2.

a. Write an exponential function relating the variables x and y.

b. Graph the exponential function from part (a).

c. Using properties of exponents, rewrite the function in part (a) as an exponential function with a base of 10. Show your work.

d. Which properties of exponents did you use in part (c) to rewrite the function as an exponential function with a base of 10?

Standardized Test Prep

46. C

47. G

48. D

49. G

50. [4] $r = \frac{11D^{-1}(r) + 5}{10}$

$10r - 5 = 11D^{-1}(r)$

$\frac{10r - 5}{11} = D^{-1}(r)$; this function tells you the speed the car is traveling when you see the deer, given the number of ft the car travels during your reaction time. $D^{-1}(r)$ is a function.

[3] appropriate method and explanation, but with one computational error

[2] incomplete explanation OR inverse and explanation are correct, but inverse is not labeled a function

[1] correct inverse function, but without explanation of what the inverse represents

---

Apply What You've Learned

Here students write and graph an exponential function based on the information in the problem on page 433. They also apply properties of exponents to rewrite the function.

Mathematical Practices

Students **make sense** of the given information to create and graph an exponential function. (MP 1)

Students **reason quantitatively** as they use properties of exponents to rewrite an exponential function. (MP 2)

ANSWERS

a. $y = (\sqrt[5]{100})^x$

b.
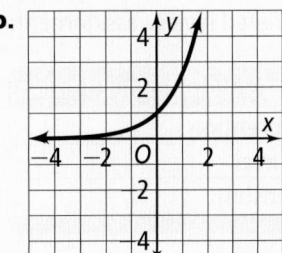

c. $y = (\sqrt[5]{100})^x$

$y = (100^{\frac{1}{5}})^x$

$y = (100)^{\frac{x}{5}}$

$y = (10^2)^{\frac{x}{5}}$

$y = (10)^{\frac{2x}{5}}$

$y = 10^{0.4x}$

d. I used the definition of a rational exponent and the power to a power property.

Differentiated Remediation
Available in editable format online.

Additional Instructional Support

Algebra 2 Companion
Students can use the **Algebra 2 Companion** worktext (4 pages) as you teach the lesson. Use the Companion to support
- New Vocabulary
- Key Concepts
- Got It for each Problem
- Lesson Check

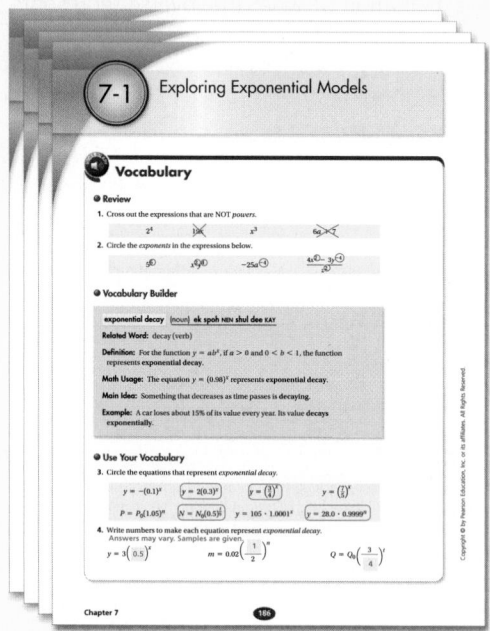

ELL Support
Use Graphic Organizers Have students make a two-column chart. Label the first column *growth* and the second column *decay*. In pairs, have students discuss and decide what words and symbols will help them decode the word problems. Have each pair exchange lists with another pair of students and review their classmates' work. If they disagree on a word in the list, ask them to explain why it should be changed or eliminated. Check the lists when they are finished, and make sure that they have at least the following terms and symbols for growth: *interest*, *appreciation*, *increase*, +, *returns*. For decay, they should have *depreciation*, *decrease*, −, *decline*. Then at the bottom of each column, have students sketch a basic shape of the corresponding graph with *a* labeled and a description of valid values for *b*.

5 Assess & Remediate

Lesson Quiz
1. What is the graph of $y = \left(\frac{1}{3}\right)^x$?
2. Identify $y = 3(1.2)^x$ as an example of exponential growth or decay. What is the *y*-intercept?
3. You deposit $3000 in an account that pays 5% annual interest. What is the balance after 2 years?
4. You invest $75 in a savings account that pays 2% annual interest. If you make no additional deposits or withdrawals, how many years will it take for the account to grow to at least $100?
5. **Do you UNDERSTAND?** There were 50,000 bacteria in a petri dish yesterday at noon, and 40,000 bacteria at noon today. If the trend continues, on what day at noon can you expect to find less than 5,000 bacteria?

ANSWERS TO LESSON QUIZ
1.

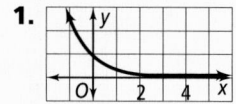

2. growth; (0, 3)
3. $3307.50
4. 15 years
5. on the eleventh day

PRESCRIPTION FOR REMEDIATION
Use the student work on the Lesson Quiz to prescribe a differentiated review assignment:

Points	Differentiated Remediation
0–2	Intervention
3–4	On-level
5	Extension

PowerAlgebra.com

5 Assess & Remediate
Assign the Lesson Quiz. Appropriate intervention, practice, or enrichment is automatically generated based on student performance.

Intervention
- **Reteaching** (2 pages) Provides reteaching and practice exercises for the key lesson concepts. Use with struggling students or absent students.
- **English Language Learner Support** Helps students develop and reinforce mathematical vocabulary and key concepts.

All-in-One Resources/Online
Reteaching

7-1 Reteaching
Exploring Exponential Models

- The general form of an exponential function is $y = ab^x$, where *a* is the initial amount and *b* is the growth or decay factor.
- To find *b*, use the formula $b = 1 + r$, where *r* is the constant rate of growth or decay. If *r* is a rate of growth, it will be positive. If *r* is a rate of decay, it will be negative. Therefore, if *b* is greater than 1, the function models growth. If *b* is between zero and 1, the function models decay. When you see words like *increase* or *appreciation*, think growth. When you see words like *decrease* or *depreciation*, think decay.
- For an exponential function, the *y*-intercept is always equal to the value of *a*.

Problem

Carl's weight at 12 yr is 82 lb. Assume that his weight increases at a rate of 16% each year. Write an exponential function to model the increase. What is his weight after 5 years?

Step 1 Find *a* and *b*.

$a = 82$ *a* is the original amount.

$b = 1 + 0.16$ *b* is the growth or decay factor. Since this problem models growth, *r* will be positive. Make sure to rewrite the rate, *r*, as a decimal.

$= 1.16$

Step 2 Write the exponential function.

$y = ab^x$ Use the formula.

$y = 82(1.16)^x$ Substitute.

Step 3 Calculate.

$y = 82(1.16)^5$ Substitute 5 for *x*.

$y \approx 172.228$ Use a calculator.

Carl will weigh about 172 lb in 5 years.

Exercises

Determine whether the function represents exponential growth or exponential decay. Then find the *y*-intercept.

1. $y = 8000(1.15)^x$ growth; 8000
2. $y = 20(0.75)^x$ decay; 20
3. $y = 15\left(\frac{1}{3}\right)^x$ decay; 15
4. $f(x) = 6\left(\frac{5}{3}\right)^x$ growth; 6

All-in-One Resources/Online
English Language Learner Support

7-1 Additional Vocabulary Support
Exploring Exponential Models

Choose the word or phrase from the list that best completes each sentence.

exponential function	exponential growth	exponential decay
asymptote	growth factor	decay factor

1. In the function $y = 12(2.3)^x$, the value 2.3 is the __growth factor__.
2. An __asymptote__ is a line that a graph approaches as *x* or *y* increases in absolute value.
3. For __exponential decay__, as the value of *x* increases, the value of *y* decreases.
4. A function in the general form $y = ab^x$ is called an __exponential function__.
5. For __exponential growth__, as the value of *x* increases, the value of *y* increases.
6. In the function $y = 4(0.3)^x$, the value 0.3 is the __decay factor__.

Identify whether each function represents exponential growth or exponential decay.

7. $y = 0.75(4)^x$ exponential growth
8. $y = 0.63(0.5)^x$ exponential decay
9. $y = 9(0.83)^x$ exponential decay
10. $y = 12(7)^x$ exponential growth

Identify the *y*-intercept for each function.

11. $y = 4.5(7)^x$ 4.5
12. $y = 5(3.2)^x$ 5

Differentiated Remediation *continued*

Available in editable format online.

On-Level

- **Practice** (2 pages) Provides extra practice for each lesson. For simpler practice exercises, use the Form K Practice pages found in the All-in-One Teaching Resources and online.

- **Think About a Plan** Helps students develop specific problem-solving skills and strategies by providing scaffolded guiding questions.

- **Standardized Test Prep** Focuses on all major exercises, all major question types, and helps students prepare for the high-stakes assessments.

Extension

- **Enrichment** Provides students with interesting problems and activities that extend the concepts of the lesson.

- **Activities, Games, and Puzzles** Worksheets that can be used for concepts development, enrichment, and for fun!

Practice and Problem Solving Wkbk/All-in-One Resources/Online
Practice page 1

7-1 Practice *Form G*

Exploring Exponential Models

Graph each function.

1. $y = (0.3)^x$
2. $y = 3^x$
3. $y = 2\left(\frac{1}{3}\right)^x$

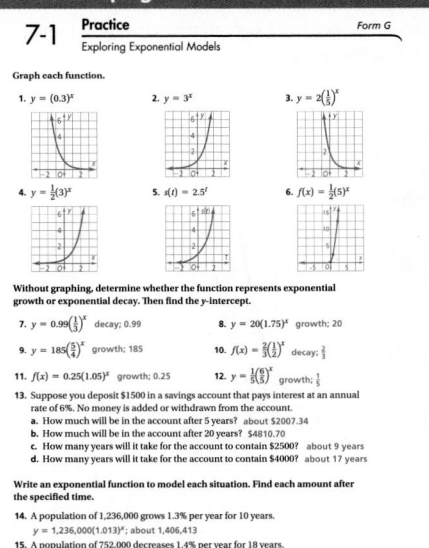

4. $y = \frac{1}{3}(3)^x$
5. $s(t) = 2.5^t$
6. $f(x) = \frac{1}{2}(5)^x$

Without graphing, determine whether the function represents exponential growth or exponential decay. Then find the y-intercept.

7. $y = 0.99\left(\frac{1}{3}\right)^x$ decay; 0.99
8. $y = 20(1.75)^x$ growth; 20
9. $y = 185\left(\frac{5}{4}\right)^x$ growth; 185
10. $f(x) = \frac{2}{3}\left(\frac{1}{4}\right)^x$ decay; $\frac{2}{3}$
11. $f(x) = 0.25(1.05)^x$ growth; 0.25
12. $y = \frac{1}{3}\left(\frac{6}{5}\right)^x$ growth; $\frac{1}{3}$

13. Suppose you deposit $1500 in a savings account that pays interest at an annual rate of 6%. No money is added or withdrawn from the account.
   a. How much will be in the account after 5 years? about $2007.34
   b. How much will be in the account after 20 years? $4810.70
   c. How many years will it take for the account to contain $2500? about 9 years
   d. How many years will it take for the account to contain $4000? about 17 years

Write an exponential function to model each situation. Find each amount after the specified time.

14. A population of 1,236,000 grows 1.3% per year for 10 years.
   $y = 1,236,000(1.013)^x$; about 1,406,413
15. A population of 752,000 decreases 1.4% per year for 18 years.
   $y = 752,000(0.986)^x$; about 583,448
16. A new car that sells for $18,000 depreciates 25% each year for 4 years.
   $y = 18,000(0.75)^x$; $5695.31

Practice and Problem Solving Wkbk/All-in-One Resources/Online
Practice page 2

7-1 Practice *(continued)* *Form G*

Exploring Exponential Models

For each annual rate of change, find the corresponding growth or decay factor.

17. +45% 1.45
18. −10% 0.9
19. −40% 0.6
20. +200% 3
21. +28% 1.28
22. +100% 2
23. −5% 0.95
24. +3% 1.03

25. In 2009, there were 1570 bears in a wildlife refuge. In 2010, the population had increased to approximately 1884 bears. If this trend continues and the bear population is increasing exponentially, how many bears will there be in 2018? 8100 bears

26. The value of a piece of equipment has a decay factor of 0.80 per year. After 5 years, the equipment is worth $98,304. What was the original value of the equipment? $300,000

27. Your friend drops a rubber ball from 4 ft. You notice that its rebound is 32.5 in. on the first bounce and 22 in. on the second bounce.
   a. What exponential function would be a good model for the height of the ball? $y = 48(0.677)^x$
   b. How high will the ball bounce on the fourth bounce? about 10.08 in.

28. An investment of $75,000 increases at a rate of 12.5% per year. What is the value of the investment after 30 years? $2,568,247.87

29. A new truck that sells for $29,000 depreciates 12% each year. What is the value of the truck after 7 years? $11,851.59

30. The price of a new home is $350,000. The value of the home appreciates 2% each year. How much will the home be worth in 10 years? $426,648.05

31. The population of an endangered bird is decreasing at a rate of 0.75% per year. There are currently about 200,000 of these birds.
   a. What exponential function would be a good model for the population of these endangered birds? $y = 200,000(0.9925)^x$
   b. How many birds will there be in 100 years? almost 94,207 birds

---

All-in-One Resources/Online
Enrichment

7-1 Enrichment

Exploring Exponential Models

Determining Relationships Between Variables

On the basis of data, scientists sometimes hypothesize that a quantity z depends on two quantities x and y such that

$$z = Cx^r y^s$$

where C is a constant and r and s are integers. By doing experiments in which the values of x and y are varied, they determine the values of integers r and s.

For instance, suppose the momentum M of a moving object seems to be related to the mass m and velocity v by the equation $M = Cm^r v^s$. Later, scientists find that doubling the mass and keeping the velocity constant doubles the momentum, so

$$2M = C(2m)^r v^s$$

Using substitution and simplifying: $2(Cm^r v^s) = C2^r m^r v^s$

Dividing each side by $Cm^r v^s$: $2 = 2^r$

$1 = r$

1. Suppose that doubling the velocity while holding the mass constant also doubles the momentum. Express this relationship in an equation. $2M = Cm^r(2v)^s$

2. Solve your equation for s. $s = 1$

3. Use the values of r and s to write an expression for momentum in terms of mass m, velocity v, and the constant C. $M = Cmv$

Use a similar method to solve the following problems.

4. The price P of a diamond is related to both the weight W of the diamond and its brilliance B. If both the weight and brilliance are simultaneously doubled, the price of the diamond increases by a factor of 32. If the weight is doubled and, at the same time, the brilliance is halved, the price increases by a factor of 2. Write a formula for P in terms of W, B, and the constant C. $P = CW^3 B^2$

5. The price of wheat depends upon the weight and the water content. A particular wheat trader pays according to this pattern: the price P increases by a factor of 2 when the weight is doubled and the water content is constant. If the weight is doubled and the water content is halved, the price is constant. Write a formula for P in terms of weight w, water content h, and the constant C. $P = Cwh$

Practice and Problem Solving Wkbk/All-in-One Resources/Online
Think About a Plan

7-1 Think About a Plan

Exploring Exponential Models

Population The population of a certain animal species decreases at a rate of 3.5% per year. You have counted 80 of the animals in the habitat you are studying.
   a. Write a function that models the change in the animal population.
   b. **Graphing Calculator** Graph the function. Estimate the number of years until the population first drops below 15 animals.

1. Is an exponential model reasonable for this situation? Explain.
   Yes; the population decreases at a fixed, constant rate of 3.5% per year.
   An exponential model is reasonable.

2. Write the function that models exponential growth or decay. $A(t) = a(1 + r)^t$

3. The initial population is [80 animals].

4. Is the rate of change positive or negative? Explain.
   The population is decreasing, so the rate of change is negative

5. The rate of change is [−0.035].

6. Write a function that models the change in the animal population. $P(t) = $ [$80(0.965)^t$]

7. Graph your function on a graphing calculator. Sketch your graph.

8. How can you find the x-value that produces a given y-value?
   Answers may vary. Sample: Use the TRACE function

9. Use your graph to estimate the number of years until the population first drops below 15 animals. 47 years

---

Practice and Problem Solving Wkbk/All-in-One Resources/Online
Standardized Test Prep

7-1 Standardized Test Prep

Exploring Exponential Models

Multiple Choice

For Exercises 1 and 2, choose the correct letter.

1. Which of the following functions represents exponential decay and has a y-intercept of 2? D
   Ⓐ $y = 2\left(\frac{4}{3}\right)^x$
   Ⓒ $y = \frac{1}{4}(2)^x$
   Ⓑ $y = \frac{1}{2}(0.95)^x$
   Ⓓ $y = 2\left(\frac{2}{3}\right)^x$

2. Suppose you deposit $3000 in a savings account that pays interest at an annual rate of 4%. If no other money is added or withdrawn from the account, how much will be in the account after 10 years? H
   Ⓕ $3122.18
   Ⓗ $4440.73
   Ⓖ $4994.50
   Ⓘ $86,776.40

Extended Response

3. In 2009 there was an endangered population of 270 cranes in a western state. Due to wildlife efforts, the population is increasing at a rate of 5% per year.
   a. What exponential function would be a good model for this population of cranes? Explain in words or show work for how you determined the exponential function.
   b. If this trend continues, how many cranes will there be in this population in 2020? Show your work.
   [4] a. The general form of an exponential function is $y = a(b)^x$. x represents time in years, y represents the population of cranes, and a is the initial value of 270 cranes. Because the crane population is increasing by 5%, $b = 1 + r = 1 + 0.05 = 1.05$. The exponential function that models the crane population is $y = 270(1.05)^x$ OR equivalent explanation.
   b. $y = 270(1.05)^{11} = 461.79$; almost 462 cranes
   [3] appropriate methods and correct function, but with one computational error in evaluating the function
   [2] incorrect function or multiple computational errors in evaluating the function
   [1] correct function and population, without work shown
   [0] incorrect answers and no work shown OR no answers given

---

Online Teacher Resource Center
Activities, Games, and Puzzles

7-1 Activity: Financial Considerations

Exploring Exponential Models

You can work on your own or with a partner.

Suppose you received a gift of $10,000 and want to invest it. You visit two banks to see what they have to offer. Bank A is near your home and pays 5% interest compounded annually. Bank B is farther from your home and pays 6% interest compounded annually. You don't think a 1% difference in rates is that significant, but you want to check.

Calculate the amount of interest each plan will earn after one year. Record your answers on the lines provided.

Bank A: $10,000(1.05) − $10,000 = $500   **Bank B:** $10,000(1.06) − $10,000 = $600

You decide to calculate how long it will take each bank to pay $5000 interest.

Complete the table below. Round your answers to the nearest dollar.
Then record the number of years below the table.

Years	1	2	3	4	5	6	7	8	9
Bank A($)	500	1025	1576	2155	2763	3401	4071	4775	5513
Bank B($)	600	1236	1910	2625	3382	4185	5036	5938	6895

Bank A: about __9__ years

Bank B: about __7__ years

Complete the bar graph to show the amount by which Bank B will outperform Bank A over nine years. Use estimation to determine the heights of the bars.

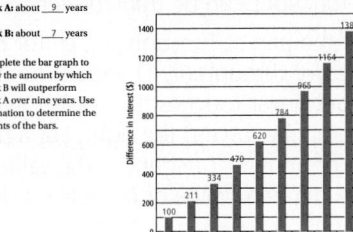

---

1 Interactive Learning

Solve It!

PURPOSE To identify transformations of exponential functions

PROCESS Students may

- trace one function by hand and place the tracing on top of the other function to determine how it was transformed.
- make a table of plotted points for each function and compare values.

FACILITATE

Q What are the definitions of a compression, reflection, and translation? **[Answers may vary. Sample: compression: shrink; reflection: flip; translation: slide]**

Q Which transformation(s) can be eliminated? Why? **[Reflection. The orientation of the functions has not changed.]**

Q Could the transformation be a compression? A translation? Explain. **[The transformation could be either a compression or a translation. You can divide the function f by 4 to get g, or translate f 2 units to the right to get g.]**

ANSWER See Solve It in Answers on next page.

CONNECT THE MATH To complete the Solve It, students must identify compressions, reflections, and translations given the graphs of two exponential functions. In the lesson they will identify transformations of the families of exponential functions.

Properties of Exponential Functions

Common Core State Standards
F-IF.C.8 Write a function defined by an expression in different but equivalent forms . . . **Also F-IF.C.7e, F-BF.A.1b, A-CED.A.2, A-SSE.A.1b**
MP 1, MP 2, MP 3, MP 4, MP 5, MP 7

Objectives To explore the properties of functions of the form $y = ab^x$
To graph exponential functions that have base e

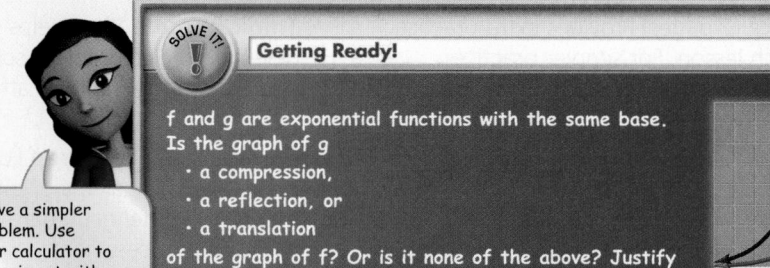

Solve a simpler problem. Use your calculator to experiment with transformations of $y = 2^x$.

Getting Ready!

f and g are exponential functions with the same base. Is the graph of g
- a compression,
- a reflection, or
- a translation

of the graph of f? Or is it none of the above? Justify your reasoning.

MATHEMATICAL PRACTICES

You can apply the four types of transformations—stretches, compressions, reflections, and translations—to exponential functions.

Essential Understanding The factor a in $y = ab^x$ can stretch or compress, and possibly reflect the graph of the parent function $y = b^x$.

The graphs of $y = 2^x$ (in red) and $y = 3 \cdot 2^x$ (in blue) are shown. Each y-value of $y = 3 \cdot 2^x$ is 3 times the corresponding y-value of the parent function $y = 2^x$.

Lesson Vocabulary
- natural base exponential function
- continuously compounded interest

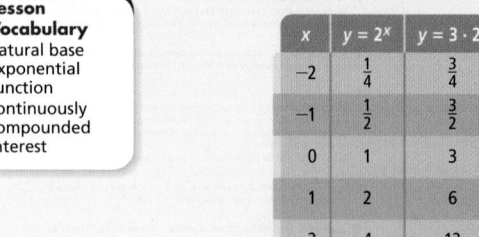

x	$y = 2^x$	$y = 3 \cdot 2^x$
-2	$\frac{1}{4}$	$\frac{3}{4}$
-1	$\frac{1}{2}$	$\frac{3}{2}$
0	1	3
1	2	6
2	4	12

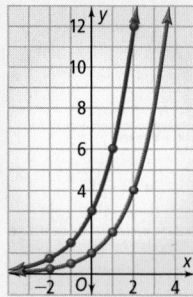

$y = 3 \cdot 2^x$ stretches the graph of the parent function $y = 2^x$ by the factor 3.

Preparing to Teach

BIG idea Function

ESSENTIAL UNDERSTANDINGS

- The factor a in $y = ab^x$ can stretch or compress, and possibly reflect the graph of the parent function $y = b^x$.
- The function $y = ab^x$, $a > 0$, $b > 1$, models exponential growth. $y = ab^x$ models exponential decay if $0 < b < 1$.

Math Background

Like the other functions seen so far, the graphs of exponential functions can be transformed.

The graph of the parent function $y = b^x$ for $b > 1$ is a smooth curve through $(0, 1)$ and $(1, b)$. It approaches but never touches the x-axis toward the left and rises rapidly toward the right. For a parent function $y = b^x$ and its "offspring", the value of b is constant. A different value of b implies a different parent function.

Whether the graph of the parent function is stretched, compressed, or reflected depends on the factor a.

- $a > 1$: stretch
- $a < -1$: stretch and reflection in x-axis
- $0 < a < 1$: compression
- $0 > a > -1$: compression and reflection in x-axis

The graph of the parent function $y = b^x$ can also be translated. The general form is $y = ab^{(x-h)} + k$, where h is a horizontal translation and k is a vertical translation. Using the laws of exponents, the general form can also be written as $y = (ab^{-h})b^x + k$.

If a factor of a is the constant b^{-h}, then a also translates the parent function horizontally and stretches or compresses it by $\frac{a}{b^b}$.

Mathematical Practices

Look for and make use of structure.
Students will see a complicated exponential function as a simple exponential function that has undergone several different types of transformations.

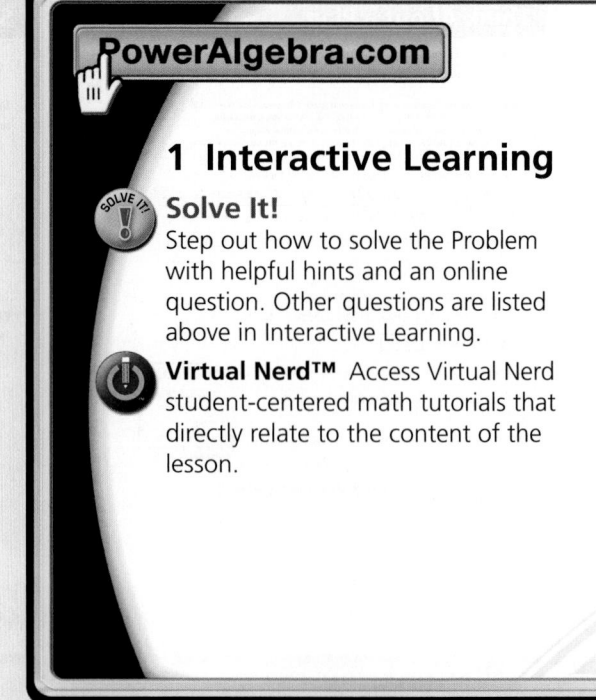

PowerAlgebra.com

1 Interactive Learning

Solve It!
Step out how to solve the Problem with helpful hints and an online question. Other questions are listed above in Interactive Learning.

Virtual Nerd™ Access Virtual Nerd student-centered math tutorials that directly relate to the content of the lesson.

© Problem 1 Graphing $y = ab^x$

Think

Which x-values should you use to make a table?
Use $x = 0$ and then choose both positive and negative values.

How does the graph of $y = -\frac{1}{3} \cdot 3^x$ compare to the graph of the parent function?

Step 1 Make a table of values.

x	$y = 3^x$	$y = -\frac{1}{3} \cdot 3^x$
-2	$\frac{1}{9}$	$-\frac{1}{27}$
-1	$\frac{1}{3}$	$-\frac{1}{9}$
0	1	$-\frac{1}{3}$
1	3	-1
2	9	-3

Each value is $-\frac{1}{3}$ times the corresponding value of the parent function.

Step 2 Graph the function.

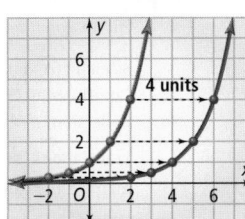

The $-\frac{1}{3}$ in $y = -\frac{1}{3} \cdot 3^x$ reflects the graph of the parent function $y = 3^x$ across the x-axis and compresses it by the factor $\frac{1}{3}$. The domain and asymptote remain unchanged. The y-intercept becomes $-\frac{1}{3}$ and the range becomes $y < 0$.

Got It? **1.** How does the graph of $y = -0.5 \cdot 5^x$ compare to the graph of the parent function?

A horizontal shift $y = ab^{(x-h)}$ is the same as the vertical stretch or compression $y = (ab^{-h})b^x$. A vertical shift $y = ab^x + k$ also shifts the horizontal asymptote from $y = 0$ to $y = k$.

© Problem 2 Translating the Parent Function $y = b^x$

Think

How is the graph of $y = 2^{(x-4)}$ different from the graph of $y = 2^x$?
The graph of $y = 2^{(x-4)}$ is a horizontal translation of $y = 2^x$ to the right 4 units.

How does the graph of each function compare to the graph of the parent function?

A $y = 2^{(x-4)}$

Step 1 Make a table of values of the parent function $y = 2^x$.

x	$y = 2^x$
-2	$\frac{1}{4}$
-1	$\frac{1}{2}$
0	1

x	$y = 2^x$
1	2
2	4
3	8

Step 2 Graph $y = 2^x$ then translate 4 units to the right.

4 units

The $(x - 4)$ in $y = 2^{(x-4)}$ translates the graph of $y = 2^x$ to the right 4 units. The asymptote remains $y = 0$. The y-intercept becomes $\frac{1}{16}$.

PowerAlgebra.com | **Lesson 7-2** Properties of Exponential Functions | **443**

---

2 Guided Instruction

Problem 1 — SYNTHESIZING

Students compare the transformation of an exponential function to its parent function. The transformation consists of a reflection and compression.

Q How does multiplying the parent function by -1 affect the graph of the parent function? **[The y-coordinates are opposites of those of the parent function, so the graph is reflected across the x-axis.]**

Q How does multiplying the parent function by $\frac{1}{3}$ affect its graph? **[Each y-coordinate is multiplied by $\frac{1}{3}$, so the graph is compressed.]**

Q Is it necessary to use the parent function when graphing this problem? Explain. **[Answers may vary. Sample: No, but constructing a table and graph of the parent function allows you to use transformations to graph the new function.]**

Got It? — ERROR PREVENTION

Q How is this function a transformation of the parent function $y = 5^x$? **[The graph of the parent function is reflected across the x-axis and compressed by a factor of 0.5.]**

Problem 2 — SYNTHESIZING

Q Will a horizontal shift ever change a horizontal asymptote? Explain. **[No; the x-coordinates are changed but the y-coordinates stay the same.]**

---

2 Guided Instruction

© Each Problem is worked out and supported online.

Problem 1
Graphing $y = ab^x$

Alternative Problem 1
Graphing $y = ab^x$
Animated

Problem 2
Translating the Parent Function $y = b^x$
Animated

Problem 3
Using an Exponential Model

Problem 4
Evaluating e^x

Problem 5
Continuously Compounded Interest
Animated

Support in Algebra 2 Companion
• Vocabulary
• Key Concepts
• Got It?

Answers

Solve It!
compression or translation; for each x, $g(x) = f(x - 2)$ and $g(x) = \frac{f(x)}{4}$

Got It?
1. reflects across the x-axis; compresses by a factor of 0.5

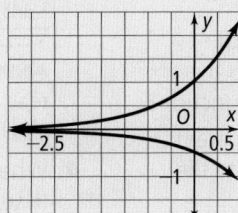

Lesson 7-2 **443**

Students graph a vertical shift of a given parent function.

Q What is the parent function? What are the transformations of the parent function. **[$y = (\frac{1}{2})^x$. To obtain the new function, stretch the parent by a factor of 20, and move it up 10 units.]**

Got It? ERROR PREVENTION

Q What indicates a horizontal shift in a given exponential equation? **[A value is added to or subtracted from the exponent.]**

Q What indicates a vertical shift in a given exponential equation? **[A value is added to or subtracted from the function.]**

Q What indicates a stretch or compression in a given exponential equation? **[A value is multiplied by the function.]**

Take Note VISUAL LEARNERS

Write the equations for Problems 1 and 2 under each equation form. Identify a, b, h, and k, and discuss each transformation. For example, $y = -\frac{1}{3} \cdot 3^x$ is in the form $y = ab^x$ where $a = -\frac{1}{3}$ and $b = 3$. Since $a < 0$, this is a reflection in the x-axis.

B $y = 20(\frac{1}{2})^x + 10$

Step 1 Make a table of values for $y = 20(\frac{1}{2})^x$.

x	$y = 20 \cdot (\frac{1}{2})^x$
−1	40
0	20
1	10
2	5
3	2.5

Step 2 Graph $y = 20(\frac{1}{2})^x$, then translate 10 units up.

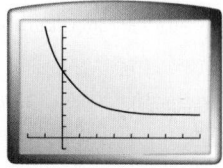

Where have you seen this situation before? The graph of a function like $y = 20(\frac{1}{2})^x + 10$ is both a stretch and a vertical translation of its parent function.

The "+ 10" in $y = 20(\frac{1}{2})^x + 10$ translates the graph of $y = 20(\frac{1}{2})^x$ up 10 units. It also translates the asymptote, the y-intercept, and the range 10 units up. The asymptote becomes $y = 10$, the y-intercept becomes 30, and the range becomes $y > 10$. The domain is unchanged.

Check Use a graphing calculator to graph $y = 20(\frac{1}{2})^x + 10$.

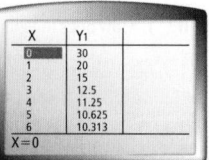

Got It? 2. How does the graph of each function compare to the graph of the parent function?

a. $y = 4^{(x+2)}$ b. $y = 5 \cdot 0.25^x + 5$

take note

Concept Summary Families of Exponential Functions

Parent function	$y = b^x$
Stretch ($|a| > 1$) Compression (Shrink) ($0 < |a| < 1$) Reflection ($a < 0$) in x-axis	$y = ab^x$
Translations (horizontal by h; vertical by k)	$y = b^{(x-h)} + k$
All transformations combined	$y = ab^{(x-h)} + k$

Additional Problems

1. How does the graph of $y = -\frac{1}{5} \cdot 4^x$ compare to the graph of the parent function?

ANSWER it compresses the parent graph $y = 4^x$ by a factor of $\frac{1}{5}$ and reflects the graph in the x-axis.

2. How does the graph of $y = 3^{(x+1)}$ compare to the graph of the parent function?

ANSWER It shifts the parent graph $y = 3^x$ one unit to the left.

3. Some insects reproduce exponentially. The chart shows the population of roaches in a colony at 36-day intervals. On what day will the colony reach 50,000,000 roaches?

Day	Number of Roaches
1	50
37	1125
73	25,290
109	569,025
145	12,803,040

ANSWER The colony will reach 50,000,000 during the 161ˢᵗ day.

4. What is the value of $2e^6$? (Use a graphing calculator.)

ANSWER about 806.86

5. You have $1500 in a bank account that pays 4.5% annual interest compounded continuously. How much will you have in the account after 15 years? Round the answer to the nearest dollar.

ANSWER $2946

Answers

Got It? (continued)

2. a. translate 2 units to the left; the y-intercept becomes 16

b. Stretch the graph of $y = (0.25)^x$ by a factor of 5 and translate the graph of $y = 5 \cdot 0.25^x$ up 5 units.

Problem 3 Using an Exponential Model STEM

Physics The best temperature to brew coffee is between 195°F and 205°F. Coffee is cool enough to drink at 185°F. The table shows temperature readings from a sample cup of coffee. How long does it take for a cup of coffee to be cool enough to drink? Use an exponential model.

Time (min)	Temp (°F)
0	203
5	177
10	153
15	137
20	121
25	111
30	104

Know
• Set of values
• Best serving temperature

Need
Time it takes for a cup of coffee to become cool enough to drink

Plan
Use an exponential model to find the time it takes for coffee to reach 185°F.

Think

Why does it make sense that a graph of this data would have an asymptote?
The temperature of the hot coffee will get closer and closer to room temperature as it cools, but it cannot cool below room temperature.

Step 1
Plot the data to determine if an exponential model is realistic.

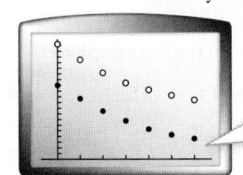

Step 2
The graphing calculator exponential model assumes the asymptote is $y = 0$. Since room temperature is about 68°F, subtract 68 from each temperature value. Calculate the third list by letting **L3 = L2 − 68**.

> The graphing calculator exponential model assumes the asymptote is $y = 0$.

Step 3
Use the **ExpReg L1, L3** function on the transformed data to find an exponential model.

```
ExpReg
y = a•b^x
a = 134.5169825
b = .956011669
r² = .9981659939
r = ⁻.9990825761
```

Step 4
Translate $y = 134.5(0.956)^x$ vertically by 68 units to model the original data. Use the model $y = 134.5 \cdot 0.956^x + 68$ to find how long it takes the coffee to cool to 185°F.

X	Y1
2.6	187.65
2.7	187.11
2.8	186.58
2.9	186.05
3	185.52
3.1	184.99
3.2	184.46

X=3.1

The coffee takes about 3.1 min to cool to 185°F.

© ✓ **Got It? 3. a.** Use the exponential model. How long does it take for the coffee to reach a temperature of 100 degrees?
   b. Reasoning In Problem 3, would the model of the exponential data be useful if you did not translate the data by 68 units? Explain.

Problem 3   SYNTHESIZING

Q What transformation does the calculator include in the exponential model? Explain. **[In $y = ab^x$, a suggests a compression. Other transformations will have to be adjusted by you.]**

Q What information that the calculator gives you indicates the exponential model is the best fit? Explain. **[$r = -.9990$ is close to -1, which indicates that the exponential model is the best fit.]**

Q What is the horizontal asymptote of your model? Why? **[$y = 68$; 68° represents room temperature. In this model, as the coffee cools, its temperature approaches 68° but never equals 68°.]**

Got It?   ERROR PREVENTION

Q What is an approximation for your answer? Explain. **[Since it takes coffee 3.1 min. to cool to 185°, the answer would be greater than 3.1 min.]**

Q If the function was not translated by 68, would the calculated time to cool the coffee be less than or greater than 3.1 min? Would the result make sense? **[The time would be less than 3.1 (2.7 min.) because room temperature would not be a factor. The answer would not make sense, since the original data are for a room-temperature environment, not one of 0°F.]**

---

3. a. about 31.9 min

   b. No; a hot coffee cannot cool below room temperature. So, to use exponential data, it is important to translate the data by 68 units.

Problem 4

Q What is the approximate value of *e*? **[2.7182]**

Q How can you use a function to evaluate a power of *e*? Explain. **[Evaluate the function $y = e^x$ at the given value of *x* by using the e^x key on a graphing calculator or by finding the value on a graph or table.]**

Q Consider the graph of $y = e^x$. Why does the graphing calculator give an error message when *x* is sufficiently large? **[The overflow error occurs because the calculator does not have enough memory to store sufficiently large values. $y = e^x$ does not have an upper bound.]**

Got It?

Q How would you calculate $3e^2 + 1$? **[Answers may vary. Sample: Calculate e^2, multiply it by 3, and add 1.]**

Q Consider the function $y = 3e^2 + 1$. How does its graph compare to the graph of its parent function? **[The graph of the parent function is stretched by a factor of 3 and moved up 1 unit.]**

Take Note

Q What does it mean to have interest compounding continuously? **[It means that the balance increases a small amount every instant, unlike compounding in other time frames such as annually, monthly, or quarterly.]**

Up to this point you have worked with rational bases. However, exponential functions can have irrational bases as well. One important irrational base is the number *e*. The graph of $y = \left(1 + \frac{1}{x}\right)^x$ has an asymptote at $y = e$ or $y \approx 2.71828$.

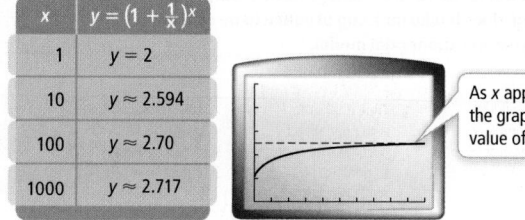

x	$y = \left(1 + \frac{1}{x}\right)^x$
1	$y = 2$
10	$y \approx 2.594$
100	$y \approx 2.70$
1000	$y \approx 2.717$

As *x* approaches infinity the graph approaches the value of *e*.

Natural base exponential functions are exponential functions with base *e*. These functions are useful for describing continuous growth or decay. Exponential functions with base *e* have the same properties as other exponential functions.

Ⓒ Problem 4 Evaluating e^x

How can you use a graphing calculator to evaluate e^3?

Think
After you press the e^x key, what keys should you press?
Press **3**, **)**, and **enter**.

Method 1
Use the e^x key.

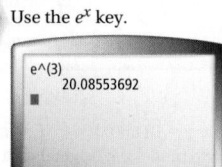
e^(3)
20.08553692

Method 2
Use the graph of $y = e^x$.

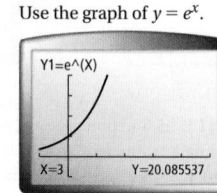
Y1=e^(X)
X=3   Y=20.085537

Method 3
Use a table of values for $y = e^x$.

X	Y1
0	1
1	2.7183
2	7.3891
3	20.086
4	54.598
5	148.41
6	403.43
Y1=20.086

$e^3 \approx 20.086$

Got It? 4. How can you use a graphing calculator to calculate e^8?

In Lesson 7-1 you studied interest that was compounded annually. The formula for continuously compounded interest uses the number *e*.

take note

Key Concept   Continuously Compounded Interest

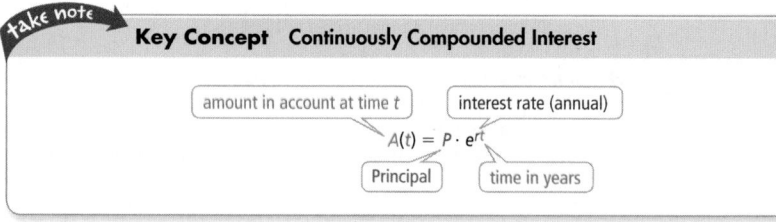

amount in account at time *t*   interest rate (annual)

$$A(t) = P \cdot e^{rt}$$

Principal   time in years

Answers

Got It? (continued)

4. $e^8 \approx 2980.957987$; three methods: use the e^x key, $x = 8$; graph $y = e^x$ and find *y* for $x = 8$; or use the table of values for $y = e^x$ and find *y* for $x = 8$

5. about $4475

Lesson Check

1. stretch by a factor of 2 and reflection across the *x*-axis

2. compress by a factor of $\frac{1}{2}$

3. translate 5 units to the right

4. translate 3 units up

5. yes

6. no; $2000e^{0.05t} \neq 1000\left(e^{0.04t} + e^{0.06t}\right)$

Practice and Problem-Solving Exercises

7.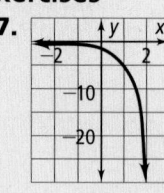

8.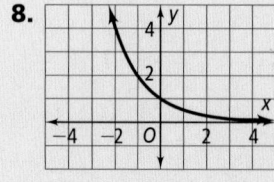

9.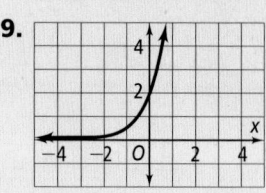

10.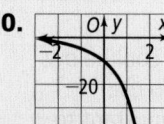

11.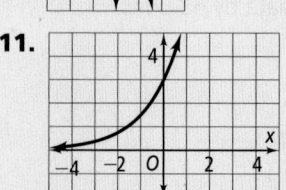

12.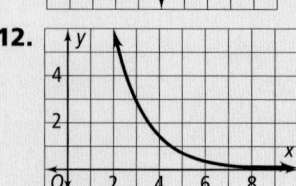

13.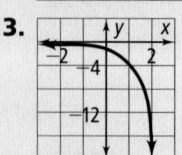

Problem 5 Continuously Compounded Interest   **GRIDDED RESPONSE**

Scholarships Suppose you won a contest at the start of 5th grade that deposited $3000 in an account that pays 5% annual interest compounded continuously. How much will you have in the account when you enter high school 4 years later? Express the answer to the nearest dollar.

Plan

What is the unknown?
The amount *A* in the account after 4 years.

$A = P \cdot e^{rt}$

$= 3000e^{(0.05)(4)}$ Substitute values for *P*, *r*, and *t*.

$= 3000e^{0.2}$ Simplify.

≈ 3664 Use a calculator. Round to the nearest dollar.

The amount in the account, to the nearest dollar, is $3664.
Write your answer, 3664 in the grid.

 Got It? 5. About how much will be in the account after 4 years of high school?

 Lesson Check

Do you know HOW?

For each function, identify the transformation from the parent function $y = b^x$.

1. $y = -2 \cdot 3^x$ **2.** $y = \frac{1}{2}(9)^x$

3. $y = 7^{(x-5)}$ **4.** $y = 5^x + 3$

Do you UNDERSTAND? **MATHEMATICAL PRACTICES**

5. Vocabulary Is $y = e^{(x+7)}$ a natural base exponential function?

6. Reasoning Is investing $2000 in an account that pays 5% annual interest compounded continuously the same as investing $1000 at 4% and $1000 at 6%, each compounded continuously? Explain.

 Practice and Problem-Solving Exercises  **MATHEMATICAL PRACTICES**

 **Practice** Graph each function.   **See Problem 1.**

7. $y = -5^x$ **8.** $y = \left(\frac{1}{2}\right)^x$ **9.** $y = 2(4)^x$

10. $y = -9(3)^x$ **11.** $y = 3(2)^x$ **12.** $y = 24\left(\frac{1}{2}\right)^x$

13. $y = -4^x$ **14.** $y = -\left(\frac{1}{3}\right)^x$ **15.** $y = 2\left(\frac{3}{2}\right)^x$

Graph each function as a transformation of its parent function.   **See Problem 2.**

16. $y = 2^x + 5$ **17.** $y = 5\left(\frac{1}{3}\right)^x - 8$ **18.** $y = -(0.3)^{x-2}$

19. $y = -2(5)^{x+3}$ **20.** $y = 3(2)^{x-1} + 4$ **21.** $y = -2(3)^{x+1} - 5$

Problem 5   SYNTHESIZING

Q Which method of compounding will yield more money: compounding continuously or compounding annually? Assume all other values remain the same. Explain. **[Compounding continuously yields the greatest return, because compounding is performed more often, so you get more interest on your interest.]**

Got It?   ERROR PREVENTION

Q What is the variable whose value you want to find? What variable are you given the value of? **[You want to find the amount *A* given the time *t*.]**

3 Lesson Check

Do you know HOW?

• For Exercises 1–4, students may get confused when identifying the transformations. Suggest they write the parent function and then identify which value represents the transformation.

Do you UNDERSTAND?

• For Exercise 5, make sure students understand the natural base exponential function definition.

Close

Q In the equation $y = ab^{(x-h)} + k$, what are the roles of *a*, *h*, and *k*? Consider both positive and negative values. **[If $|a| > 1$, the function is stretched by a factor of *a*. If $0 < |a| < 1$, the function is compressed by a factor of *a*. If $a < 0$, the function is reflected in the *x*-axis. Positive *h* moves the function to the right *h* units and negative *h* moves the function to the left *h* units. Positive *k* moves the function up *k* units and negative *k* moves the function down *k* units.]**

14.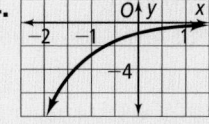

15.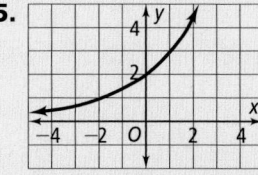

16.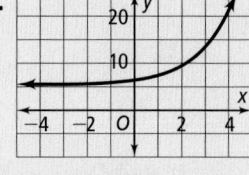

17.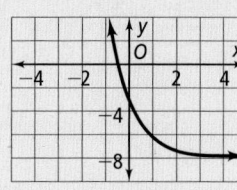

18.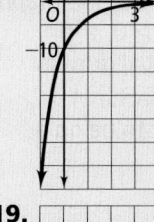

19.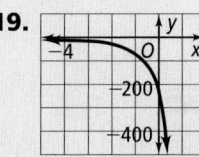

20.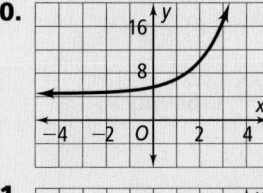

21.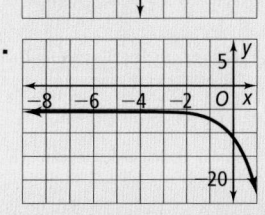

 PowerAlgebra.com

3 Lesson Check

For a digital lesson check, use the Got It questions.

Support in Algebra 2 Companion
• Lesson Check

4 Practice

Assign homework to individual students or to an entire class.

4 Practice

ASSIGNMENT GUIDE

Basic: 7–30 all, 31–33, 35, 38–40 even

Average: 7–29 odd, 31–41

Advanced: 7–29 odd, 31–43

Standardized Test Prep: 44–49

Mixed Review: 50–62

Ⓒ **Mathematical Practices** are supported by exercises with red headings. Here are the Practices supported in this lesson:

MP 1: Make Sense of Problems Ex. 31
MP 2: Reason Abstractly Ex. 5
MP 3: Communicate Ex. 6
MP 3: Compare Arguments Ex. 6
MP 3: Critique the Reasoning of Others Ex. 33
MP 4: Model With Mathematics Ex. 43c
MP 5: Use Appropriate Tools Ex. 23–27, 35

Applications exercises have blue headings. Exercises 22, 36 and 37 support MP 4: Model.

STEM exercises focus on science or engineering applications.

EXERCISE 32: Use the Think About a Plan worksheet in the **Practice and Problem Solving Workbook** (also available in the Teaching Resources in print and online) to further support students' development in becoming independent learners.

HOMEWORK QUICK CHECK
To check students' understanding of key skills and concepts, go over Exercises 7, 17, 31, 32, and 33.

---

22. Baking A cake recipe says to bake the cake until the center is 180°F, then let the cake cool to 120°F. The table shows temperature readings for the cake.

Time (min)	Temp (°F)
0	180
5	126
10	94
15	80
20	73

◀ See Problem 3.

  a. Given a room temperature of 70°F, what is an exponential model for this data set?
  b. How long does it take the cake to cool to the desired temperature?

Graphing Calculator Use the graph of $y = e^x$ to evaluate each expression to four decimal places. ◀ See Problem 4.

23. e^6 **24.** e^{-2} **25.** e^0 **26.** $e^{\frac{5}{2}}$ **27.** e^e

Find the amount in a continuously compounded account for the given conditions. ◀ See Problem 5.

28. principal: $2000
annual interest rate: 5.1%
time: 3 years

29. principal: $400
annual interest rate: 7.6%
time: 1.5 years

30. principal: $950
annual interest rate: 6.5%
time: 10 years

Ⓑ Apply

Ⓒ **31. Think About a Plan** A student wants to save $8000 for college in five years. How much should be put into an account that pays 5.2% annual interest compounded continuously?
  • What formula should you use?
  • What information do you know?
  • What do you need to find?

32. Investment How long would it take to double your principal in an account that pays 6.5% annual interest compounded continuously?

Ⓒ **33. Error Analysis** A student says that the graph of $f(x) = \left(\frac{1}{3}\right)^{x+2} + 1$ is a shift of the parent function 2 units up and 1 unit to the left. Describe and correct the student's error.

34. Assume that a is positive and $b \geq 1$. Describe the effects of $c > 0$, $c = 0$, and $c < 0$ on the graph of the function $y = ab^{cx}$.

35. Graphing Calculator Using a graphing calculator, graph each of the functions below on the same coordinate grid. What do you notice? Explain why the definition of exponential functions has the constraint that $b \neq 1$.

$y = \left(\frac{1}{2}\right)^x$ $y = \left(\frac{8}{10}\right)^x$ $y = \left(\frac{9}{10}\right)^x$ $y = \left(\frac{99}{100}\right)^x$

STEM **36. Botany** The half-life of a radioactive substance is the time it takes for half of the material to decay. Phosphorus-32 is used to study a plant's use of fertilizer. It has a half-life of 14.3 days. Write the exponential decay function for a 50-mg sample. Find the amount of phosphorus-32 remaining after 84 days.

STEM **37. Archaeology** Archaeologists use carbon-14, which has a half-life of 5730 years, to determine the age of artifacts in carbon dating. Write the exponential decay function for a 24-mg sample. How much carbon-14 remains after 30 millennia? (*Hint:* 1 millennium = 1000 years)

Answers

Practice and Problem-Solving Exercises
(continued)

22. a. $y = 127.27(0.837)^x + 70$
  b. about 5.25 min

23. 403.4288

24. 0.1353

25. 1

26. 12.1825

27. 15.1543

28. $2330.65

29. $448.30

30. $1819.76

31. $6168.41

32. about 10.7 yrs

33. graph is a shift of the parent function 2 units to the left and 1 unit up

34. If $c < 0$, the graph models exponential decay. If $c = 0$, the graph is a horizontal line. If $c > 0$, the graph models exponential growth.

35. As the value of b approaches 1, the graph comes closer to being a straight line.

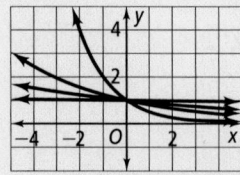

36. $y = 50\left(\frac{1}{2}\right)^{\frac{1}{14.3}x}$; 0.85 mg

37. $y = 24\left(\frac{1}{2}\right)^{\frac{1}{5730}x}$; 0.64 mg

The parent function for each graph below is of the form $y = ab^x$. Write the parent function. Then write a function for the translation indicated.

38.
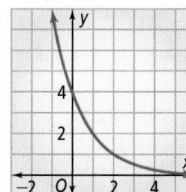

translation: left 4 units, up 3 units

39.
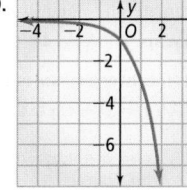

translation: right 8 units, up 2 units

40. Two financial institutions offer different deals to new customers. The first bank offers an interest rate of 3% for the first year and 2% for the next two years. The second bank offers an interest rate of 2.49% for three years. You decide to invest the same amount of principal in each bank. To answer the following, assume you make no withdrawals or deposits during the three-year period.

   a. Write a function that represents the total amount of money in the account in the first bank after three years.

   b. Write a function that represents the total amount of money in the account in the second bank after three years.

   c. Write a function that represents the total amount of money in both accounts at the end of three years.

STEM 41. Physics At a constant temperature, the atmospheric pressure p in pascals is given by the formula $p = 101.3e^{-0.001h}$, where h is the altitude in meters. What is p at an altitude of 500 m?

 Challenge **42. Landscaping** A homeowner is planting hedges and begins to dig a 3-ft-deep trench around the perimeter of his property. After the first weekend, the homeowner recruits a friend to help. After every succeeding weekend, each digger recruits another friend. One person can dig 405 ft³ of dirt per weekend. The figure at the right shows the dimensions of the property and the width of the trench.

   a. Geometry Determine the volume of dirt that must be removed for the trench.

   b. Write an exponential function to model the volume of dirt remaining to be shoveled after x weekends. Then, use the model to determine how many weekends it will take to complete the trench.

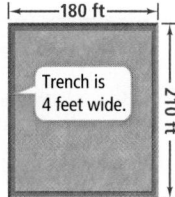

Trench is 4 feet wide.

180 ft

210 ft

STEM 43. Psychology Psychologists use an exponential model of the learning process, $f(t) = c(1 - e^{-kt})$, where c is the total number of tasks to be learned, k is the rate of learning, t is time, and $f(t)$ is the number of tasks learned.

   a. Suppose you move to a new school, and you want to learn the names of 25 classmates in your homeroom. If your learning rate for new tasks is 20% per day, how many complete names will you know after 2 days? After 8 days?

   b. Graphing Calculator Graph the function on your graphing calculator. How many days will it take to learn everyone's name? Explain.

   c. Open-Ended Does this function seem to describe your own learning rate? If not, how could you adapt it to reflect your learning rate?

38. $y = 4\left(\frac{1}{2}\right)^x$; $y = 4\left(\frac{1}{2}\right)^{x+4} + 3$

39. $y = -3^x$; $y = -3^{x-8} + 2$

40. a. $A = Pe^{(0.03)(1)} + (Pe^{(0.03)(1)})e^{(0.02)(2)}$

   b. $A = Pe^{(0.0249)(3)}$

   c. $A = Pe^{(0.03)(1)} + (Pe^{(0.03)(1)})e^{(0.02)(2)} + Pe^{(0.0249)(3)}$

41. ≈ 61.4 pascals

42. a. 9,168 ft³

   b. $V = 9168 - 405(2^x - 1)$; about 5 weekends

43. a. about 8 names; about 20 names

   b. Graphically, it will never happen; the graph has $y = 25$ as an asymptote. (In reality, you would be close to knowing all the names in about 21 days.)

   c. Answers may vary. Sample: My learning rate might be higher since I can learn names quickly.

Answers

Standardized Test Prep

44. C

45. G

46. A

47. H

48. C

49. [2] $A(t) = Pe^{rt}$

$8000 = Pe^{(0.06)(4)}$

$P = \dfrac{8000}{e^{(0.06)(4)}}$

$P = \$6293.02$

[1] correct amount, but without work shown

Mixed Review

50. exponential growth; 23

51. exponential growth; 3

52. exponential decay; 2

53. exponential growth; 5

54. $6\sqrt{5}$

55. $-\sqrt[3]{4}$

56. $5(\sqrt{3} + \sqrt{5})$

57. $2(\sqrt[4]{2} + \sqrt[4]{8})$

58. $\sqrt{3}$

59. $11\sqrt{7}$

60. $f^{-1}(x) = \dfrac{x+1}{4}$; yes

61. $f^{-1}(x) = x^{\frac{1}{7}}$; yes

62. $f^{-1}(x) = \left(\dfrac{x-1}{5}\right)^{\frac{1}{3}}$; yes

---

Standardized Test Prep

SAT/ACT

44. A savings account earns 4.62% annual interest, compounded continuously. After approximately how many years will a principal of $500 double?

Ⓐ 2 years　　　Ⓑ 10 years　　　Ⓒ 15 years　　　Ⓓ 44 years

45. What is the inverse of the function $f(x) = \sqrt{x-4}$?

Ⓕ $f^{-1}(x) = x^2 - 4, x \geq 0$　　　Ⓗ $f^{-1}(x) = \sqrt{x+4}$

Ⓖ $f^{-1}(x) = x^2 + 4, x \geq 0$　　　Ⓘ $f^{-1}(x) = \dfrac{\sqrt{x-4}}{x-4}$

In Exercises 46 and 47, let $f(x) = x^2 - 4$ and $g(x) = \dfrac{1}{x+4}$.

46. What is $(g \circ f)(x)$?

Ⓐ $\dfrac{1}{x^2}$　　Ⓑ $\dfrac{1}{x^2 - 8x + 16} - 4$　　Ⓒ $\dfrac{x^2 - 4}{x+4}$　　Ⓓ $x - 4$

47. What is $(f \circ f)(3)$?

Ⓕ 1　　　Ⓖ 5　　　Ⓗ 21　　　Ⓘ 77

48. What is the equation of the line shown at the right?

Ⓐ $y = -\dfrac{4}{5}x + 2$　　　Ⓒ $-4x + 5y = 7$

Ⓑ $y = \dfrac{5}{4}x - 2$　　　Ⓓ $4x - 5y = 15$

Short Response

49. How much should you invest in an account that pays 6% annual interest compounded continuously if you want exactly $8000 after four years? Show your work.

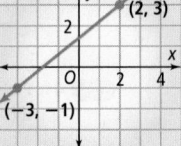

Mixed Review

Without graphing, determine whether the function represents exponential growth or exponential decay. Then find the y-intercept.

◀ See Lesson 7-1.

50. $y = 23(3.03)^x$　　　　　　**51.** $f(x) = 3(5)^x$

52. $y = 2\left(\dfrac{3}{4}\right)^x$　　　　　　**53.** $y = 5\left(\dfrac{8}{3}\right)^x$

Simplify.

◀ See Lesson 6-3.

54. $5\sqrt{5} + \sqrt{5}$　　　**55.** $\sqrt[3]{4} - 2\sqrt[3]{4}$　　　**56.** $\sqrt{75} + \sqrt{125}$

57. $\sqrt[4]{32} + \sqrt[4]{128}$　　　**58.** $5\sqrt{3} - 2\sqrt{12}$　　　**59.** $3\sqrt{63} + \sqrt{28}$

Get Ready!　To prepare for Lesson 7-3, do Exercises 60–62.

Find the inverse of each function. Is the inverse a function?

◀ See Lesson 6-7.

60. $f(x) = 4x - 1$　　　**61.** $f(x) = x^7$　　　**62.** $f(x) = 5x^3 + 1$

7-2 Lesson Resources

Additional Instructional Support

Algebra 2 Companion

Students can use the **Algebra 2 Companion** worktext (4 pages) as you teach the lesson. Use the Companion to support

- New Vocabulary
- Key Concepts
- Got It for each Problem
- Lesson Check

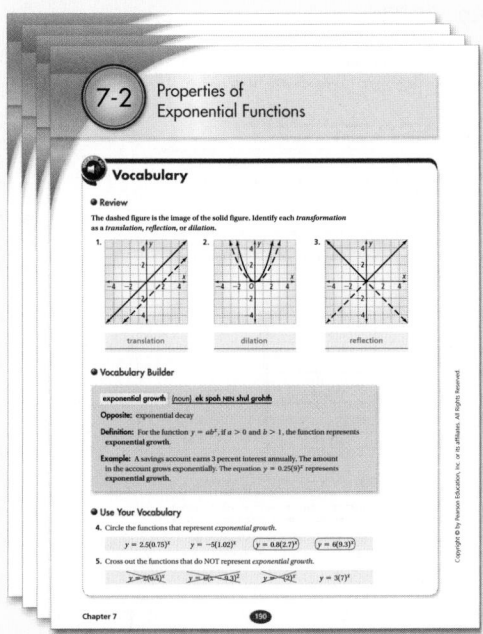

ELL Support

Use Graphic Organizers Instruct students to make a six-column organizer titled "Families of Exponential Functions" with the following column heads: Stretch, Compression, Reflection, Horizontal Translation, Vertical Translation, and All.

Divide students in pairs. Assign Exercises 1–21. Each pair is required to place each exercise in one of the five columns. For each exercise, the pair should discuss what the parent function is and what transformation or transformations the problem represents. The pair should be ready to justify each decision. At the end of the activity, the pair of students should write an example for each column.

Each pair should present one exercise to the class explaining their conclusion and justification. They should field questions from the class if necessary.

5 Assess & Remediate

Lesson Quiz

1. How does the graph of $y = 2 \cdot 2^x$ compare to the graph of the parent function?

2. How does the graph of $y = 4^{(x-6)}$ compare to the graph of the parent function?

3. **Do you UNDERSTAND?** A pot of water is heated to 200°F. The table shows typical temperature readings for the pot. The room temperature is 70°F. How long will it take the water to cool to 150°F?

Time (min)	Temp (°F)
0	200
5	164
10	140
15	124
20	108
25	98

4. You have $10,000. You place it in an account that pays 6.1% annual interest compounded continuously. How much will you have in 20 years? Round the answer to the nearest dollar.

ANSWERS TO LESSON QUIZ

1. $y = 2 \cdot 2^x$ stretches the parent graph $y = 2^x$ by a factor of 2.
2. $y = 4^{(x-6)}$ shifts the parent graph $y = 4^x$ six units to the right.
3. The water will reach 150°F in about 7.9 min.
4. $33,871

PRESCRIPTION FOR REMEDIATION

Use the student work on the Lesson Quiz to prescribe a differentiated review assignment:

Points	Differentiated Remediation
0–2	Intervention
3	On-level
4	Extension

PowerAlgebra.com

5 Assess & Remediate

Assign the Lesson Quiz. Appropriate intervention, practice, or enrichment is automatically generated based on student performance.

Differentiated Remediation

Available in editable format online.

Intervention

- **Reteaching** (2 pages) Provides reteaching and practice exercises for the key lesson concepts. Use with struggling students or absent students.

- **English Language Learner Support** Helps students develop and reinforce mathematical vocabulary and key concepts.

All-in-One Resources/Online
Reteaching

All-in-One Resources/Online
English Language Learner Support

Differentiated Remediation *continued*

Available in editable format online.

On-Level

- **Practice** (2 pages) Provides extra practice for each lesson. For simpler practice exercises, use the Form K Practice pages found in the All-in-One Teaching Resources and online.

- **Think About a Plan** Helps students develop specific problem-solving skills and strategies by providing scaffolded guiding questions.

- **Standardized Test Prep** Focuses on all major exercises, all major question types, and helps students prepare for the high-stakes assessments.

Extension

- **Enrichment** Provides students with interesting problems and activities that extend the concepts of the lesson.

- **Activities, Games, and Puzzles** Worksheets that can be used for concepts development, enrichment, and for fun!

Practice and Problem Solving Wkbk/All-in-One Resources/Online
Practice page 1

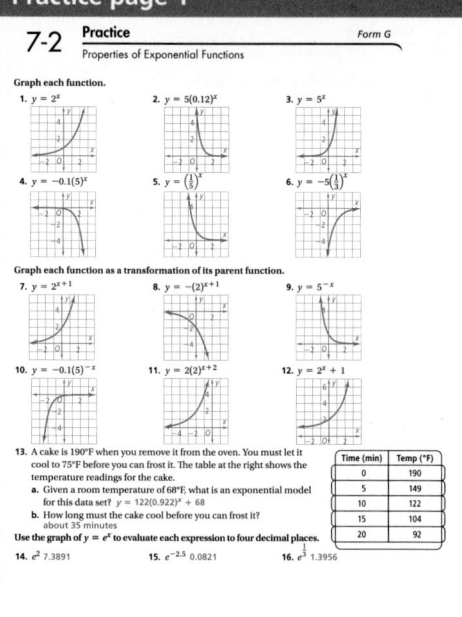

Practice and Problem Solving Wkbk/All-in-One Resources/Online
Practice page 2

7-2 Practice (continued) — Form G
Properties of Exponential Functions

Find the amount in a continuously compounded account for the given conditions.

17. principal: $5000 $39,624.11
annual interest rate: 6.9%
time: 30 yr

18. principal: $20,000 $21,557.68
annual interest rate: 3.75%
time: 2 yr

19. How long would it take to double your principal at an annual interest rate of 7% compounded continuously? about 9.9 yr

20. **Error Analysis** A student says that the graph of $f(x) = 2^{x+3} + 4$ is a shift of 3 units up and 4 units to the right of the parent function. Describe and correct the student's error.
The student reversed the horizontal and vertical translations of h and k. The graph shifts the parent function left 3 units and up 4 units.

21. The isotope Hg-197 is used in kidney scans. It has a half-life of 64.128 h. After that time, half the isotope will have decayed. Write the exponential decay function for a 12-mg sample. Find the amount remaining after 72 h.
$y = 12(0.5)^{0.0156x}$; about 5.5 mg

22. The isotope Sr-85 is used in bone scans. It has a half-life of 64.9 days. Write the exponential decay function for an 8-mg sample. Find the amount remaining after 100 days.
$y = 8(0.5)^{0.0154x}$; about 2.7 mg

23. Suppose you invest $2000 at an annual interest of 5.5% compounded continuously.
a. How much will you have in the account in 10 years? $3466.50
b. How long will it take for the account to reach $5000? about 17 years

The parent function for each graph below is of the form $y = ab^x$. Write the parent function. Then write a function for the translation indicated.

24. $y = 2^x$; $y = 2^{x+3} + 1$
translation: left 3 units, up 1 unit

25. $y = -4(\frac{1}{3})^x$; $y = -4(\frac{1}{3})^{x-2} + 3$
translation: right 2 units, up 3 units

All-in-One Resources/Online
Enrichment

7-2 Enrichment
Properties of Exponential Functions

A Closer Look at Compounding

The formula for finding the amount of money accumulated in an account is

$A = P\left(1 + \frac{r}{n}\right)^{nt}$

The variable **P** represents the **principal**, or amount initially invested.
The variable **r** represents the interest **rate** as a decimal.
The variable **n** represents the number of times per year the interest is **compounded**.
The variable **t** represents the **time**, or number of years for which the money is invested.

1. $750 is invested at 11% compounded quarterly. How much is in the account after 10 yr? $2219.91

2. Write the new formula for $P = 1, $r = 1.0$, and $t = 1$ yr. $A = \left(1 + \frac{1}{n}\right)^n$

3. Remember that *n* is the number of times the interest is compounded. What happens as *n* grows? In other words, what is the effect of compounding more often? Fill in the following table. Round answers to eight decimal places.

n	$\left(1 + \frac{1}{n}\right)^n$
1	2.00000000
10	2.59374246
100	2.70481383
1,000	2.71692393
10,000	2.71814593
100,000	2.71826824
1,000,000	2.71828047
10,000,000	2.71828169
100,000,000	2.71828181
1,000,000,000	2.71828183

4. The table suggests that as *n* increases, the value of $\left(1 + \frac{1}{n}\right)^n$ gets closer to [____]. If the value of *n* is increased further, the decimal approximation in the table will get very close to the value of a number known as *e*. This number is used in many growth and decay applications. 2.71828183

5. As *n* grows, you get closer to compounding continuously. This is why the formula used for compounding continuously is $A = Pe^{rt}$. Rework Exercise 1 assuming that compounding is continuous. $2253.12

Practice and Problem Solving Wkbk/All-in-One Resources/Online
Think About a Plan

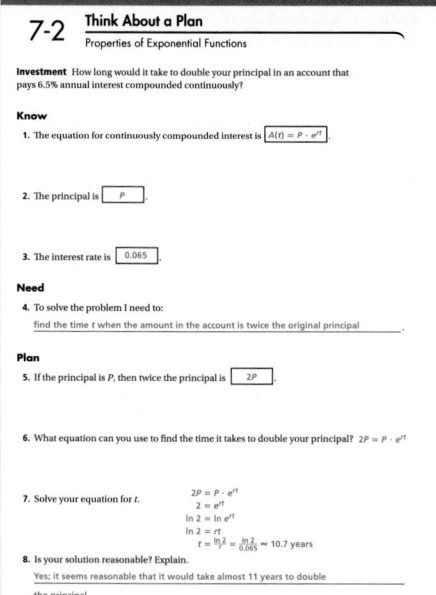

Practice and Problem Solving Wkbk/All-in-One Resources/Online
Standardized Test Prep

7-2 Standardized Test Prep
Properties of Exponential Functions

Gridded Response

Solve each exercise and enter your answer in the grid provided.

1. Suppose you deposit $6000 in a savings account that pays interest at an annual rate of 4% compounded continuously. How many years will it take for the balance in your savings account to reach $8000? Round your answer up to the nearest number of years.

2. Suppose you make $1500 at your summer job and you decide to invest this money in a savings account that pays interest at an annual rate of 5.5% compounded continuously. How many dollars will be in the account after 5 years? Express the answer to the nearest whole dollar.

3. The half-life of a radioactive substance is the time it takes for half of the material to decay. Phosphorus-32 is used to study a plant's use of fertilizer. It has a half-life of 14.3 days. How many milligrams of phosphorus-32 remain after 92 days from a 100-mg sample? Express the answer to the nearest whole milligram.

4. A scientist notes the bacteria count in a petri dish is 40. Three hours later, she notes the count has increased to 75. Using an exponential model, how many hours will it take for the bacteria count to grow from 75 to 120? Express the answer to the nearest tenth of an hour.

Answers

1.
2.
3.
4.

Online Teacher Resource Center
Activities, Games, and Puzzles

7-2 Game: Transforming Graphs
Properties of Exponential Functions

The graph of $y = 2^x$ crosses the y-axis at (0, 1) and contains (1, 2). If you know the images of these points under a transformation of the parent function, then you know an equation for the function you have.

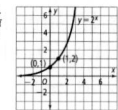

In this game, you are given the image of (0, 1) and (1, 2) under one or more transformations of the graph of $y = 2^x$. If you can write the correct equation, you earn 5 points.

Option 1

Your teacher can play host and all students can be contestants. Play until all the game items have been answered. The highest score wins.

Option 2

Challenge another student to play the game. Players must agree on the correct answers. Play until all the game items have been answered. The highest score wins.

For each item below, write an equation of the form $y = a(2^{x-h}) + k$.

1. $(0, 1) \rightarrow (0, 0.5)$ and $(1, 2) \rightarrow (1, 1)$
$y = 2^{x-1}$

2. $(0, 1) \rightarrow (0, 2)$ and $(1, 2) \rightarrow (1, 3)$
$y = 2^x + 1$

3. $(0, 1) \rightarrow (0, 2)$ and $(1, 2) \rightarrow (1, 4)$
$y = 2^{x+1}$

4. $(0, 1) \rightarrow (0, 0)$ and $(1, 2) \rightarrow (1, 1)$
$y = 2^x - 1$

5. $(0, 1) \rightarrow (0, 3)$ and $(1, 2) \rightarrow (1, 6)$
$y = 3(2^x)$

6. $(0, 1) \rightarrow (0, 0.4)$ and $(1, 2) \rightarrow (1, 0.8)$
$y = 0.4(2^x)$

7. $(0, 1) \rightarrow (1, 2)$ and $(1, 2) \rightarrow (2, 3)$
$y = 2^{x-1} + 1$

8. $(0, 1) \rightarrow (-1, 0)$ and $(1, 2) \rightarrow (0, 1)$
$y = 2^{x+1} - 1$

9. $(0, 1) \rightarrow (2, 3)$ and $(1, 2) \rightarrow (3, 4)$
$y = 2^{x-2} + 2$

10. $(0, 1) \rightarrow (-2, -2)$ and $(1, 2) \rightarrow (-1, -1)$
$y = 2^{x+2} - 3$

11. $(0, 1) \rightarrow (0, 0.75)$ and $(1, 2) \rightarrow (1, 1.5)$
$y = 3(2^{x-2})$

12. $(0, 1) \rightarrow (1, 5)$ and $(1, 2) \rightarrow (2, 11)$
$y = 3(2^{x-1})$

My Total Score: [____]

7-3 Logarithmic Functions as Inverses

Objectives To write and evaluate logarithmic expressions
To graph logarithmic functions

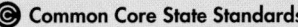

© Common Core State Standards
F-BF.B.4a Solve an equation of the form $f(x) = c$ for
a simple function f that has an inverse and write . . . the
inverse. Also A-SSE.A.1b, F-IF.C.7e, F-IF.C.8, F-IF.C.9
MP 1, MP 2, MP 3, MP 4, MP 5

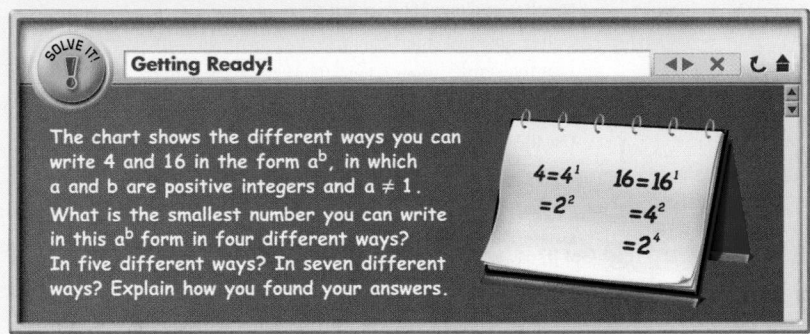

SOLVE IT!

Getting Ready!

The chart shows the different ways you can write 4 and 16 in the form a^b, in which a and b are positive integers and $a \neq 1$. What is the smallest number you can write in this a^b form in four different ways? In five different ways? In seven different ways? Explain how you found your answers.

$4 = 4^1$ $16 = 16^1$
  $= 2^2$ $= 4^2$
                     $= 2^4$

Lesson Vocabulary
• logarithm
• logarithmic function
• common logarithm
• logarithmic scale

Many even numbers can be written as power functions with base 2. In this lesson you will find ways to express all numbers as powers of a common base.

Essential Understanding The exponential function $y = b^x$ is one-to-one, so its inverse $x = b^y$ is a function. To express "y as a function of x" for the inverse, write $y = \log_b x$.

take note

Key Concept   Logarithm

A **logarithm** base b of a positive number x satisfies the following definition.

For $b > 0$, $b \neq 1$, $\log_b x = y$ if and only if $b^y = x$.

You can read $\log_b x$ as "log base b of x." In other words, the logarithm y is the exponent to which b must be raised to get x.

The exponent y in the expression b^y is the logarithm in the equation $\log_b x = y$. The base b in b^y and the base b in $\log_b x$ are the same. In both, $b \neq 1$ and $b > 0$.

Since $b \neq 1$ and $b > 0$, it follows that $b^y > 0$. Since $b^y = x$ then $x > 0$, so $\log_b x$ is defined only for $x > 0$.

Because $y = b^x$ and $y = \log_b x$ are inverse functions, their compositions map a number a to itself. In other words, $b^{\log_b a} = a$ for $a > 0$ and $\log_b b^a = a$ for all a.

PowerAlgebra.com   Lesson 7-3   Logarithmic Functions as Inverses   **451**

7-3 Preparing to Teach

BIG idea Function
ESSENTIAL UNDERSTANDINGS
• The exponential function $y = b^x$ is one-to-one, so its inverse $x = b^y$ is a function. To express "y as a function of x" for the inverse, write $y = \log_b x$.
• An exponential function is a function with the general form $y = ab^x$, $a \neq 0$, with $b > 0$, and $b \neq 1$. In an exponential function, the base b is a constant. The exponent x is the independent variable with domain the set of real numbers.
• Logarithms are exponents. In fact, $\log_b a = c$ if and only if $b^c = a$.

Math Background
The inverse of the exponential function is the logarithmic function. By definition, $y = b^x$ is equivalent to $\log_b y = x$.

As inverse functions, the domain of $y = \log_b x$ is the range of $y = b^x$, and the range of $y = \log_b x$ is the domain of $y = b^x$. Logarithms exist only for positive real numbers, which makes sense when you consider that the range of exponential functions is always positive.

Converting between exponential and logarithmic functions is useful for
• finding the value of a logarithm using properties of exponents,
• making a table of values when graphing a logarithmic function,
• solving exponential and logarithmic equations, as shown in Lesson 7-5.

© Mathematical Practices
Construct viable arguments and critique the reasoning of others. Students will build on their knowledge of graphing the inverse of a function in Lesson 6-7 and make conjectures about the nature of logarithmic functions.

---

1 Interactive Learning

Solve It!
PURPOSE To find multiple ways to represent numbers as powers of other numbers
PROCESS Students may
• try to write 2^5 as powers of other numbers and realize the power cannot be a prime such as 5.
• notice that $4^2 = 16$ and write $16^2 = 256$ as powers of numbers.

FACILITATE
Q What operation can you do to 4 to get 16? **[Answers may vary. Samples: You can multiply 4 by 4; you can square 4.]**
Q What is the pattern of smallest numbers? **[Each number must be a power of 2 whose exponent can be factored in the required number of ways For example, $2^6 = (2^6)^1 = (2^3)^2 = (2^2)^3 = (2^1)^6$.]**
Q What must be the smallest base of each of the smallest numbers? Explain. **[Sample: 2; if the smallest base was 3, the first smallest number would be $9 = 9^1 = 3^2$, and the second smallest would be $81 = 81^1 = 9^2 = 3^4$; 9 and 81 are larger than 4 and 16.]**

ANSWER See Solve It in Answers on next page.
CONNECT THE MATH Students find numbers that can be written as a power function of base 2 to solve this problem. In the lesson they will express numbers as powers of a common base.

2 Guided Instruction

Take Note
Each different base b defines a different logarithmic parent function $y = \log_b x$, just as each base b defines a different exponential parent function $y = b^x$.

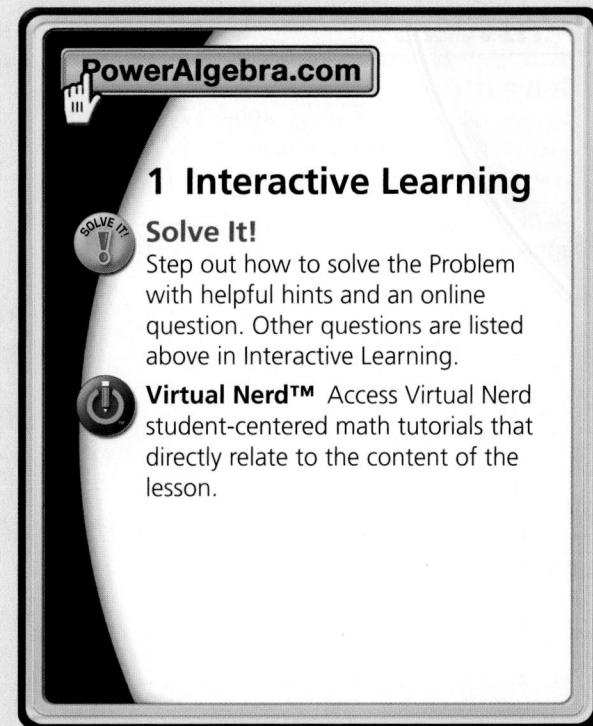

PowerAlgebra.com

1 Interactive Learning

SOLVE IT! Solve It!
Step out how to solve the Problem with helpful hints and an online question. Other questions are listed above in Interactive Learning.

Virtual Nerd™ Access Virtual Nerd student-centered math tutorials that directly relate to the content of the lesson.

Lesson 7-3 **451**

Problem 1

Q How does the logarithmic form of an exponential equation compare to the original equation? **[They are equivalent.]**

ERROR PREVENTION

Use these examples as a model for how students should solve this kind of problem. Make sure they write out the definition each time if: $x = b^y$ then $\log_b x = y$. This will help reduce errors when applying the definition.

Got It?

Q For any $b > 0$, what is $\log_b 1$? Explain.
[$\log_b 1 = 0$, because $b^0 = 1$ for any $b > 0$.]

Problem 2   ERROR PREVENTION

Students can check the reasonableness of their answer when evaluating a logarithm by checking integer powers of the base close to the answer.

Q Between which two integers is $\frac{5}{3}$? **[1 and 2]**
Q What are 8^1 and 8^2? **[8 and 64]**
Q Is your answer reasonable? Explain. **[Yes; the function $y = 8^x$ is increasing, so $8^{\frac{5}{3}}$ should be greater than 8^1 and less than 8^2, and $8 < 32 < 64$.]**

Got It?   ERROR INTERVENTION

To use the method shown in Problem 2 to evaluate logarithms both the value of the base, b, and the number, x, must be expressed as numbers of a common base.

You can use the definition of a logarithm to write exponential equations in logarithmic form.

ⓒ Problem 1 Writing Exponential Equations in Logarithmic Form

What is the logarithmic form of each equation?

Ⓐ $100 = 10^2$

Use the definition of logarithm.

| If $x = b^y$ | then | $\log_b x = y$ |
| If $100 = 10^2$ | then | $\log_{10} 100 = 2$ |

Ⓑ $81 = 3^4$

Use the definition of logarithm.

| If $x = b^y$ | then | $\log_b x = y$ |
| If $81 = 3^4$ | then | $\log_3 81 = 4$ |

Think
To what power do you raise 10 to get 100?
10 raised to the 2nd power equals 100.

✔ **Got It? 1.** What is the logarithmic form of each equation?

   a. $36 = 6^2$ **b.** $\frac{8}{27} = \left(\frac{2}{3}\right)^3$ **c.** $1 = 3^0$

You can use the exponential form to help you evaluate logarithms.

ⓒ Problem 2 Evaluating a Logarithm

Multiple Choice What is the value of $\log_8 32$?

  Ⓐ $\frac{3}{5}$ Ⓑ $\frac{5}{3}$ Ⓒ 3   Ⓓ 5

$\log_8 32 = x$	Write a logarithmic equation.
$32 = 8^x$	Use the definition of a logarithm to write an exponential equation.
$2^5 = (2^3)^x$	Write each side using base 2.
$2^5 = 2^{3x}$	Power Property of Exponents
$5 = 3x$	Since the bases are the same, the exponents must be equal.
$\frac{5}{3} = x$	Solve for x.

Since $8^{\frac{5}{3}} = 32$, then $\log_8 32 = \frac{5}{3}$.
The correct answer is B.

Plan
How can you use the definition of logarithm to help you find the value of $\log_8 32$?
If $\log_b x = y$ then $x = b^y$, so to what power must you raise 8 to get 32?

✔ **Got It? 2.** What is the value of each logarithm?

   a. $\log_5 125$ **b.** $\log_4 32$ **c.** $\log_{64} \frac{1}{32}$

Answers

Solve It!

4 ways: 64; at least 5 ways: 4096; exactly 5 ways: 65,536; at least 7 ways: 16,777,216; exactly 7 ways: 18,446,744,073,709,551,616
$64 = 2^6 = (2^2)^3 = (2^3)^2 = (2^6)^1$;
$4096 = (2^{12})^1 = (2^2)^6 = (2^3)^4 = (2^4)^3 = (2^6)^2 = (2^1)^{12}$;
$16,777,216 = (2^{24})^1 = (2^2)^{12} = (2^3)^8 = (2^4)^6 = (2^6)^4 = (2^8)^3 = (2^{12})^2 = (2^1)^{24}$

Got It?

  1. a. $\log_6 36 = 2$

    b. $\log_{\frac{2}{3}} \frac{8}{27} = 3$

    c. $\log_3 1 = 0$

  2. a. 3

    b. $\frac{5}{2}$

    c. $-\frac{5}{6}$

PowerAlgebra.com

2 Guided Instruction

ⓒ Each Problem is worked out and supported online.

Problem 1
Writing Exponential Equations in Logarithmic Form
       Animated

Problem 2
Evaluating a Logarithm
       Animated

Problem 3
Using a Logarithmic Scale

Problem 4
Graphing a Logarithmic Function

Problem 5
Translating $y = \log_b x$

Alternative Problem 5
Translating $y = \log_b x$
       Animated

Support in Algebra 2 Companion
• Vocabulary
• Key Concepts
• Got It?

A **common logarithm** is a logarithm with base 10. You can write a common logarithm $\log_{10} x$ simply as $\log x$, without showing the 10.

Many measurements of physical phenomena have such a wide range of values that the reported measurements are logarithms (exponents) of the values, not the values themselves. When you use the logarithm of a quantity instead of the quantity, you are using a **logarithmic scale**. The Richter scale is a logarithmic scale. It gives logarithmic measurements of earthquake magnitude.

The Richter Scale

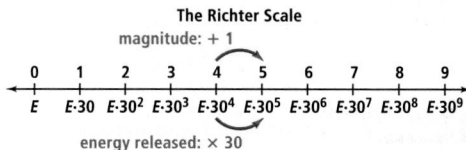

magnitude: + 1

0	1	2	3	4	5	6	7	8	9
E	$E \cdot 30$	$E \cdot 30^2$	$E \cdot 30^3$	$E \cdot 30^4$	$E \cdot 30^5$	$E \cdot 30^6$	$E \cdot 30^7$	$E \cdot 30^8$	$E \cdot 30^9$

energy released: × 30

© **Problem 3** Using a Logarithmic Scale

In December 2004, an earthquake with magnitude 9.3 on the Richter scale hit off the northwest coast of Sumatra. The diagram shows the magnitude of an earthquake that hit Sumatra in March 2005. The formula $\log \frac{I_1}{I_2} = M_1 - M_2$ compares the intensity levels of earthquakes where I is the intensity level determined by a seismograph, and M is the magnitude on a Richter scale. How many times more intense was the December earthquake than the March earthquake?

THAILAND

Magnitude 8.7

MALAYSIA

Epicenter, March 2005

Sumatra

INDONESIA

Think

What is the base of this logarithm?
This is the common logarithm. It has base 10.

$$\log \frac{I_1}{I_2} = M_1 - M_2 \qquad \text{Use the formula.}$$

$$\log \frac{I_1}{I_2} = 9.3 - 8.7 \qquad \text{Substitute } M_1 = 9.3 \text{ and } M_2 = 8.7.$$

$$\log \frac{I_1}{I_2} = 0.6 \qquad \text{Simplify.}$$

$$\frac{I_1}{I_2} = 10^{0.6} \qquad \text{Apply the definition of common logarithm.}$$

$$\approx 4 \qquad \text{Use a calculator.}$$

The December earthquake was about 4 times as strong as the one in March.

✓ **Got It?** **3.** In 1995, an earthquake in Mexico registered 8.0 on the Richter scale. In 2001, an earthquake of magnitude 6.8 shook Washington state. How many times more intense was the 1995 earthquake than the 2001 earthquake?

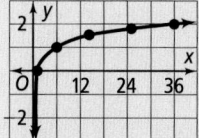

Q Why is the Richter scale more convenient to use than the explicit measurements of the released energy? **[Answers may vary. Sample: Small changes in the Richter scale correspond to large changes in intensity. The numbers are small and easy to work with.]**

Q What is the difference in magnitude on the Richter scale of two earthquakes if the amount of energy released from one is 900 times as great as the amount of energy released from the other? Explain. **[2; because $30^2 = 900$]**

Problem 3
For an increase of 1 on the Richter scale, the amplitude of the ground motion recorded by a seismograph increases by a factor of ten.

Q What does $\log \frac{I_1}{I_2}$ represent? **[The difference in intensity level determined by a seismograph of two earthquakes]**

Got It?

Q How does the difference in magnitude on the Richter scale of the earthquakes in Problem 3 compare to the difference in magnitude of the earthquakes in the Got It? **[The difference in magnitude is twice as great in the Got It.]**

Q How will the difference in intensities of the earthquakes in the Problem and Got It compare to the difference in the magnitudes on the Richter scale? **[Answers may vary. Sample: The difference in intensity will be much greater than the difference in magnitude on the Richter scale.]**

Additional Problems

1. What is the logarithmic form of each equation?
  a. $8^0 = 1$
  b. $4^3 = 64$
  ANSWERS
  a. $\log_8 1 = 0$ **b.** $\log_4 64 = 3$

2. What is the value of $\log_{16} 64$?
  ANSWER $\frac{3}{2}$

3. The loudness of a sound in decibels, dB, is defined as $10 \log \frac{I}{10^{-12}}$, where I is the intensity of the sound. How loud is a whisper with an intensity of 10^{-10}?
  ANSWER 20 dB

4. What is the graph of $y = \log_6 x$? Describe the domain and range and identify the y-intercept and the asymptote.
  ANSWER

domain: all nonnegative real numbers; range: all real numbers; y-intercept: does not exist; asymptote: $x = 0$

5. How does the graph of $y = \frac{3}{4} \log x - 2$ compare to the graph of the parent function?
  ANSWER The graph is compressed by a factor of $\frac{3}{4}$ and translated down 2 units.

Answers

Got It? (continued)
  3. ≈ 16 times

Q If $y = \log_b x$ and $y = a^x$ are inverse functions, what must be true about a and b? **[$a = b$; the bases must be the same.]**

Q How do the coordinates of the points on the graph of a function compare to the coordinates of the corresponding points on the graph of its inverse? **[The x-coordinates and y-coordinates are reversed.]**

Problem 4

Q Does the graph of $y = \log_3 x$ have a horizontal asymptote? Explain. **[No; the graph increases as x increases in the same way that the exponent decreases as x decreases.]**

Got It?

Q How does the graph of $y = \log_3 x$ compare to the graph of $y = \log_4 x$? **[The domain, range, y-intercept and asymptotes are the same. The graph of $y = \log_4 x$ is steeper and above the graph of $y = \log_3 x$ for $x > 1$, and $y = \log_3 x$ is steeper and above the graph of $y = \log_4 x$ for $x < 1$.]**

Q To make a table of values to graph $y = \log_4 x$, what are the best values of x to use to make calculations easy? **[powers of 4, for example, $\frac{1}{16}$, $\frac{1}{4}$, 1, 4, and 16.]**

A **logarithmic function** is the inverse of an exponential function. The graph shows $y = 10^x$ and its inverse $y = \log x$. Note that $(0, 1)$ and $(1, 10)$ are on the graph of $y = 10^x$, and that $(1, 0)$ and $(10, 1)$ are on the graph of $y = \log x$.

Recall that the graphs of inverse functions are reflections of each other across the line $y = x$. You can graph $y = \log_b x$ as the inverse of $y = b^x$.

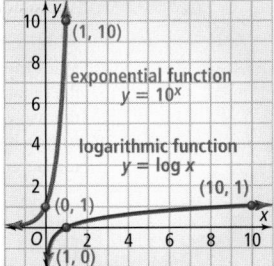

Problem 4 Graphing a Logarithmic Function

What is the graph of $y = \log_3 x$? Describe the domain and range and identify the y-intercept and the asymptote.

$y = \log_3 x$ is the inverse of $y = 3^x$.

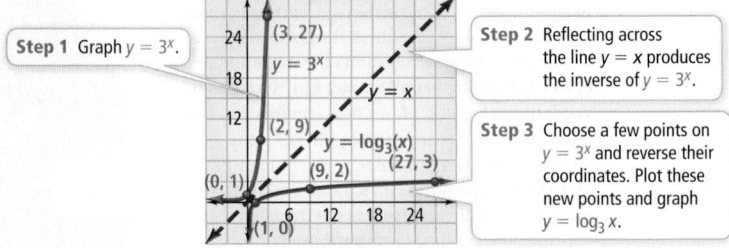

Step 1 Graph $y = 3^x$.

Step 2 Reflecting across the line $y = x$ produces the inverse of $y = 3^x$.

Step 3 Choose a few points on $y = 3^x$ and reverse their coordinates. Plot these new points and graph $y = \log_3 x$.

Think

How are the domain and range of $y = 3^x$ and $y = \log_3 x$ related?
Since they are inverse functions, the domain and range of $y = \log_3 x$ are the same as the range and domain of $y = 3^x$.

The domain is $x > 0$. The range is all real numbers. There is no y-intercept. The vertical asymptote is $x = 0$.

Got It? **4. a.** What is the graph of $y = \log_4 x$? Describe the domain, range, y-intercept and asymptotes.

b. Reasoning Suppose you use the following table to help you graph $y = \log_2 x$. (Recall that if $y = \log_2 x$, then $2^y = x$.) Copy and complete the table. Explain your answers.

x	$2^y = x$	y
−1	$2^y = -1$	
0	$2^y = 0$	
1	$2^y = 1$	
2	$2^y = 2$	

Answers

Got It? (continued)

4. a. domain: $x > 0$; range: all real numbers; no y-intercept; vertical asymptote: $x = 0$

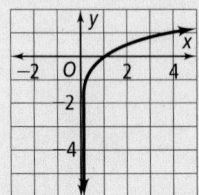

b.

x	$2^y = x$	y
−1	$2^y = -1$	undefined
0	$2^y = 0$	undefined
1	$2^y = 1$	0
2	$2^y = 2$	1

The function $y = \log_b x$ is the parent for a function family. You can graph $y = \log_b (x - h) + k$ by translating the graph of the parent function, $y = \log_b x$, horizontally by h units and vertically by k units. The a in $y = a \log_b x$ indicates a stretch, a compression, and possibly a reflection.

take note

Concept Summary   Families of Logarithmic Functions

Parent functions:	$y = \log_b x, b > 0, b \neq 1$
Stretch ($\|a\| > 1$) Compression (Shrink) ($0 < \|a\| < 1$) Reflection ($a < 0$) in x-axis	$y = a \log_b x$
Translations (horizontal by h; vertical by k)	$y = \log_b (x - h) + k$
All transformations together	$y = a \log_b (x - h) + k$

© **Problem 5** Translating $y = \log_b x$

How does the graph of $y = \log_4 (x - 3) + 4$ compare to the graph of the parent function?

Step 1

Make a table of values for the parent function. Use the definition of logarithm.

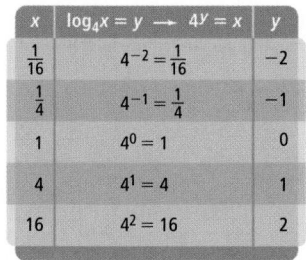

x	$\log_4 x = y \longrightarrow 4^y = x$	y
$\frac{1}{16}$	$4^{-2} = \frac{1}{16}$	-2
$\frac{1}{4}$	$4^{-1} = \frac{1}{4}$	-1
1	$4^0 = 1$	0
4	$4^1 = 4$	1
16	$4^2 = 16$	2

Step 2

Graph the parent function. Shift the graph to the right 3 units and up 4 units to graph $y = \log_4 (x - 3) + 4$.

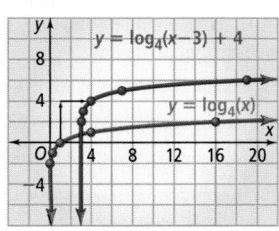

Because $y = \log_4 (x - 3) + 4$ translates the graph of the parent function 3 units to the right, the asymptote changes from $x = 0$ to $x = 3$. The domain changes from $x > 0$ to $x > 3$. The range remains all real numbers.

✔ **Got It?** **5.** How does the graph of each function compare to the graph of the parent function?

  a. $y = \log_2(x - 3) + 4$ **b.** $y = 5 \log_2 x$

Think

How is the function $y = \log_4(x - 3) + 4$ similar to other functions you have seen?
Recall that the graph of $y = f(x - h) + k$ is a vertical and horizontal translation of the parent function, $y = f(x)$.

Take Note   **ERROR PREVENTION**
Note that the base of the logarithm is one parameter that does not change within a family of logarithmic functions. Each base of a logarithm is formally a separate family of functions.

Problem 5

> **Q** How does the shape of the graph of the transformed function compare to the graph of the parent function? **[Answers may vary. Sample: There is no stretch or compression, so the shape is the same.]**
>
> **Q** How does a horizontal translation by h units affect the domain? **[It translates the domain by h units.]**
>
> **Q** Could you use the definition of logarithms to make a table of values for the given function and then graph it directly? Explain. **[No; the definition of logarithms only considers the base, x, and y and does not allow for the translations.]**

Got It?

> **Q** What is the parent function of the logarithmic functions in 5a and 5b? **[$y = \log_2 x$]**
>
> **Q** Does the stretch factor change the intercept or asymptote? Explain. **[No; multiplying the function by a stretch factor does not change the x-value for which $y = 0$ or change the domain of the function.]**

---

5. a. translates the graph of the parent function 3 units to the right and 4 units up; The asymptote changes from $x = 0$ to $x = 3$. The domain changes from $x > 0$ to $x > 3$. The range remains all real numbers.

  b. stretch the graph of the parent function by a factor of 5; The asymptote, domain, and the range remain the same.

3 Lesson Check

Do you know HOW?

- For Exercises 1–8, if students have trouble converting between logarithmic form and exponential form, remind them to write out the definition of logarithms before beginning.

- For Exercises 5–8, if students have trouble relating the logarithmic *expressions* to the definition for logarithms, which is in the form of an *equation*, then remind them to set the logarithm equal to x before proceeding to evaluate it.

Do you UNDERSTAND?

- If students have difficulty with Exercise 10, remind them that $y = \log_b x$ and $y = b^x$ are inverses. Then remind them that inverses are reflections across the line $y = x$.

Close

Q How can you use the properties of exponents to evaluate a logarithm? **[Answers may vary. Sample: Rewrite the logarithm as a logarithmic function equal to x, convert it to an exponential function, and use the properties of exponents to solve for x.]**

Q How can you use the graph of an exponential function to graph its inverse? **[Answers may vary. Samples: Reflect the graph over the line $y = x$; Choose several points on the graph, reverse the x- and y-coordinates, and plot them.]**

Lesson Check

Do you know HOW?

Write each equation in logarithmic form.

1. $25 = 5^2$ **2.** $64 = 4^3$

3. $243 = 3^5$ **4.** $16 = 2^4$

Evaluate each logarithm.

5. $\log_2 8$ **6.** $\log_9 9$

7. $\log_7 49$ **8.** $\log_2 \frac{1}{4}$

Do you UNDERSTAND? **MATHEMATICAL PRACTICES**

9. Vocabulary Determine whether each logarithm is a common logarithm.

   a. $\log_2 4$ **b.** $\log 64$ **c.** $\log_{10} 100$ **d.** $\log_5 5$

10. Reasoning Explain how you could use an inverse function to graph the logarithmic function $y = \log_6 x$.

11. Compare and Contrast Compare the graph of $y = \log_2 (x + 4)$ to the graph of $y = \log_2 x$. How are the graphs alike? How are they different?

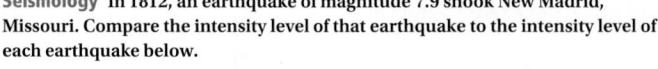

Practice and Problem-Solving Exercises   MATHEMATICAL PRACTICES

A Practice   Write each equation in logarithmic form.   **See Problem 1.**

12. $49 = 7^2$ **13.** $10^3 = 1000$ **14.** $625 = 5^4$ **15.** $\frac{1}{10} = 10^{-1}$

16. $8^2 = 64$ **17.** $4 = \left(\frac{1}{2}\right)^{-2}$ **18.** $\left(\frac{1}{3}\right)^3 = \frac{1}{27}$ **19.** $10^{-2} = 0.01$

Evaluate each logarithm.   **See Problem 2.**

20. $\log_2 16$ **21.** $\log_4 2$ **22.** $\log_8 8$ **23.** $\log_4 8$

24. $\log_2 8$ **25.** $\log_{49} 7$ **26.** $\log_5 (-25)$ **27.** $\log_3 9$

28. $\log_2 2^5$ **29.** $\log_{\frac{1}{2}} \frac{1}{2}$ **30.** $\log 10{,}000$ **31.** $\log_5 125$

STEM **Seismology** In 1812, an earthquake of magnitude 7.9 shook New Madrid, Missouri. Compare the intensity level of that earthquake to the intensity level of each earthquake below.   **See Problem 3.**

32. magnitude 7.7 in San Francisco, California, in 1906

33. magnitude 9.5 in Valdivia, Chile, in 1960

34. magnitude 3.2 in Charlottesville, Virginia, in 2001

35. magnitude 6.9 in Kobe, Japan, in 1995

Graph each function on the same set of axes.   **See Problem 4.**

36. $y = \log_2 x$ **37.** $y = 2^x$ **38.** $y = \log_{\frac{1}{2}} x$ **39.** $y = \left(\frac{1}{2}\right)^x$

Describe how the graph of each function compares with the graph of the parent function, $y = \log_b x$.   **See Problem 5.**

40. $y = \log_5 x + 1$ **41.** $y = \log_7 (x - 2)$

42. $y = \log_3 (x - 5) + 3$ **43.** $y = \log_4 (x + 2) - 1$

---

3 Lesson Check

For a digital lesson check, use the Got It questions.

Support in Algebra 2 Companion
- Lesson Check

4 Practice

Assign homework to individual students or to an entire class.

Answers

Lesson Check

1. $\log_5 25 = 2$ **2.** $\log_4 64 = 3$

3. $\log_3 243 = 5$ **4.** $\log_2 16 = 4$

5. 3   **6.** 1   **7.** 2   **8.** −2

9. a. no   **b.** yes   **c.** yes   **d.** no

10. Choose a few points on the graph of $y = 6^x$, reverse their coordinates, and plot them.

11. $y = \log_2 (x + 4)$ translates the graph of $y = \log_2 x$ 4 units to the left. Asymptote changes from $x = 0$ to $x = -4$. Domain changes from $x > 0$ to $x > -4$. Range remains the same.

Practice and Problem-Solving Exercises

12. $\log_7 49 = 2$ **13.** $\log 1000 = 3$

14. $\log_5 625 = 4$ **15.** $\log \frac{1}{10} = -1$

16. $\log_8 64 = 2$ **17.** $\log_{\frac{1}{2}} 4 = -2$

18. $\log_{\frac{1}{3}} \frac{1}{27} = 3$ **19.** $\log 0.01 = -2$

20. 4   **21.** $\frac{1}{2}$ **22.** 1

23. $\frac{3}{2}$ **24.** 3   **25.** $\frac{1}{2}$

26. undefined   **27.** 2

28. 5   **29.** 1   **30.** 4   **31.** 3

32. The earthquake in Missouri was about 1.58 times more intense.

33. The earthquake in Chile was about 39.81 times more intense.

34. The earthquake in Missouri was about 50,119 times more intense.

35. The earthquake in Missouri was about 10 times more intense.

36–39.

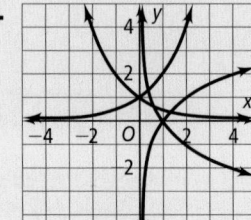

40. translate the graph 1 unit up

41. translate the graph 2 units to the right

44. Think About a Plan The pH of a substance equals $-\log[H^+]$, where $[H^+]$ is the concentration of hydrogen ions, and it ranges from 0 to 14. A pH level of 7 is neutral. A level greater than 7 is basic, and a level less than 7 is acidic. The table shows the hydrogen ion concentration $[H^+]$ for selected foods. Is each food basic or acidic?
- How can you find the pH value of each food?
- What rule can you use to determine if the food is basic or acidic?

Approximate $[H^+]$ of Foods

Food	$[H^+]$
Apple juice	3.2×10^{-4}
Buttermilk	2.5×10^{-5}
Cream	2.5×10^{-7}
Ketchup	1.3×10^{-4}
Shrimp sauce	7.9×10^{-8}
Strained peas	1.0×10^{-6}

STEM 45. Chemistry Find the concentration of hydrogen ions in seawater, if the pH level of seawater is 8.5.

Write each equation in exponential form.

46. $\log_2 128 = 7$ **47.** $\log 0.0001 = -4$ **48.** $\log_6 6 = 1$ **49.** $\log_4 1 = 0$

50. $\log_7 16{,}807 = 5$ **51.** $\log_2 \frac{1}{2} = -1$ **52.** $\log_3 \frac{1}{9} = -2$ **53.** $\log 10 = 1$

Find the greatest integer that is less than the value of the logarithm. Use your calculator to check your answers.

54. $\log 5$ **55.** $\log 0.08$ **56.** $\log 17.52$ **57.** $\log(1.3 \times 10^7)$

58. Compare the graph at the right to the function $y = \log_5 x$. Describe the domain and range and identify the y-intercept of $y = \log_5 x$.

59. Write $5 = \log_{2x+1}(a + b)$ in exponential form.

60. Open-Ended Write a logarithmic function of the form $y = \log_b x$. Find its inverse function. Graph both functions on one set of axes.

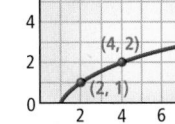

Find the inverse of each function.

61. $y = \log_4 x$ **62.** $y = \log_{0.5} x$ **63.** $y = \log_{10} x$ **64.** $y = \log_2 2x$

65. $y = \log(x + 1)$ **66.** $y = \log 10x$ **67.** $y = \log_2 4x$ **68.** $y = \log(x - 6)$

Graph each logarithmic function.

69. $y = \log 2x$ **70.** $y = 2\log_2 x$ **71.** $y = \log_4(2x + 3)$ **72.** $y = \log_3(x + 5)$

Find the domain and the range of each function.

73. $y = \log_5 x$ **74.** $y = 3\log x$ **75.** $y = \log_2(x - 3)$ **76.** $y = 2\log(x - 2)$

You can write $5^3 = 125$ in logarithmic form using the fact that $\log_b b^x = x$.

$\log_5(5^3) = \log_5(125)$ Apply the log base 5 to each side.

$3 = \log_5 125$ Use $\log_b b^x = x$ to simplify.

Use this method to write each equation in logarithmic form. Show your work.

77. $3^4 = 81$ **78.** $x^4 = y$ **79.** $6^8 = a + 1$

---

4 Practice

ASSIGNMENT GUIDE

Basic: 12–43 all, 44–47, 58–61, 72–76 even

Average: 13–43 odd, 44–79

Advanced: 13–43 odd, 44–84

Standardized Test Prep: 85–88

Mixed Review: 89–98

Mathematical Practices are supported by exercises with red headings. Here are the Practices supported in this lesson:

MP 1: Make Sense of Problems Ex. 44
MP 2: Reason Quantitatively Ex. 60
MP 3: Communicate Ex. 9, 30
MP 3: Compare Arguments Ex. 11
MP 3: Critique the Reasoning of Others Ex. 33
MP 5: Use Appropriate Tools Ex. 35

Applications exercises have blue headings. Exercise 45 support MP 4: Model.

STEM exercises focus on science or engineering applications.

EXERCISE 45: Use the Think About a Plan worksheet in the **Practice and Problem Solving Workbook** (also available in the Teaching Resources in print and online) to further support students' development in becoming independent learners.

HOMEWORK QUICK CHECK

To check students' understanding of key skills and concepts, go over Exercises 13, 21, 44, 45, and 59.

---

42. translate the graph 5 units to the right and 3 units up

43. translate the graph 2 units to the left and 1 unit down

44. apple juice: acidic; buttermilk: acidic; cream: acidic; ketchup: acidic; shrimp sauce: basic; strained peas: acidic

45. $\approx 3.16 \times 10^{-9}$

46. $2^7 = 128$

47. $10^{-4} = 0.0001$

48. $6^1 = 6$ **49.** $4^0 = 1$

50. $7^5 = 16{,}807$

51. $2^{-1} = \frac{1}{2}$ **52.** $3^{-2} = \frac{1}{9}$

53. $10^1 = 10$ **54.** 0

55. -2 **56.** 1 **57.** 7

58. The graph of $y = \log_5 x$ grows more quickly than the graph shown. The domain of $y = \log_5 x$ is $x > 0$, the range of $y = \log_5 x$ is all real numbers, and there is no y-intercept.

59. $(2x + 1)^5 = (a + b)$

60. Answers may vary. Sample: $y = \log_3 x$; $y = 3^x$

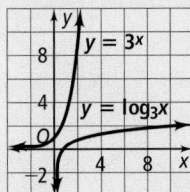

61. $y = 4^x$ **62.** $y = 0.5^x$
63. $y = 10^x$ **64.** $y = 2^{x-1}$
65. $y = 10^x - 1$ **66.** $y = 10^{x-1}$
67. $y = 2^{x-2}$ **68.** $y = 10^x + 6$

69.

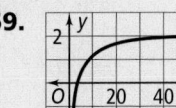

70.

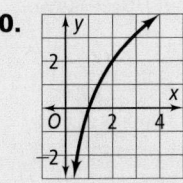

71.

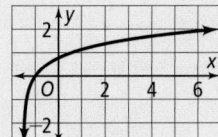

72.

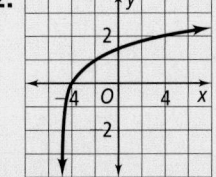

73. domain $x > 0$, range: all real numbers
74. domain $x > 0$, range: all real numbers
75. domain $x > 3$, range: all real numbers
76. domain $x > 2$, range: all real numbers
77. $4 = \log_3(81)$
78. $4 = \log_x(y)$
79. $8 = \log_6(a + 1)$

Answers

Practice and Problem-Solving Exercises
(continued)

80. 4

81. 3

82. 3

83. −2

84. a. II

   b. III

   c. I

Standardized Test Prep

85. D

86. I

87. C

88. [2] $\sqrt[3]{\left(\sqrt{a}\right)^7} = \left(\left(a^{\frac{1}{2}}\right)^7\right)^{\frac{1}{3}} = a^{\frac{7}{6}}$

   [1] correct answer, without work shown

Mixed Review

89.

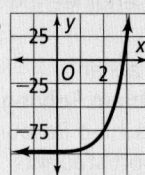

90.

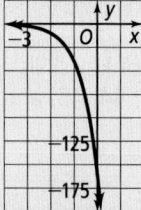

91.

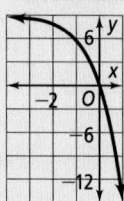

92. $(2x - 3)(2x - 1)$

93. $4(b - 5)(b + 5)$

94. $(5x - 2)(x + 3)$

95. 2

96. 256

97. $\frac{1}{4}$

98. 12

Find the least integer greater than each number. Do not use a calculator.

80. $\log_3 38$ **81.** $\log_{1.5} 2.5$ **82.** $\log_{\sqrt{7}} \sqrt{50}$ **83.** $\log_5 \frac{1}{47}$

84. Match each function with the graph of its inverse.

   a. $y = \log_3 x$ **b.** $y = \log_2 4x$ **c.** $y = \log_{\frac{1}{2}} x$

   I.   **II.**   **III.**

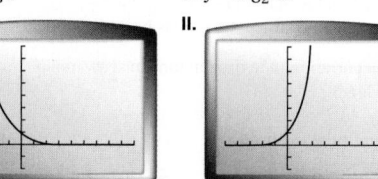
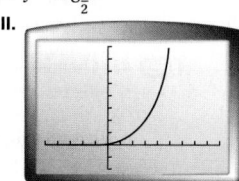

Standardized Test Prep

SAT/ACT

85. Which is the logarithmic form of the exponential equation $2^3 = 8$?

   (A) $\log_8 2 = 3$ (B) $\log_8 3 = 2$ (C) $\log_3 8 = 2$ (D) $\log_2 8 = 3$

86. Dan will begin advertising his video production business online using a pay-per-click method, which charges \$30 as an initial fee, plus a fixed amount each time the ad is clicked. Dan estimates that with the cost of 8 cents per click, his ad will be clicked about 150 times per day. Which expression represents Dan's total estimated cost of advertising, in dollars, after x days?

   (F) $(30 + 0.08x)150$ (G) $360x$ (H) $30 + 1200x$ (I) $30 + 12x$

87. Which translation takes $y = |x|$ to $y = |x + 3| - 1$?

   (A) 3 units right, 1 unit down   (C) 3 units left, 1 unit down

   (B) 3 units right, 1 unit up   (D) 3 units left, 1 unit up

Short Response

88. What is the expression $\sqrt[3]{(\sqrt{a})^7}$ written as a variable raised to a single rational exponent?

Mixed Review

Graph each function.   ◀ See Lesson 7-2.

89. $y = 5^x - 100$ **90.** $y = -10(4)^{x+2}$ **91.** $y = -27(3)^{x-1} + 9$

Factor each expression.   ◀ See Lesson 4-4.

92. $4x^2 - 8x + 3$ **93.** $4b^2 - 100$ **94.** $5x^2 + 13x - 6$

Get Ready!   To prepare for Lesson 7-4, do Exercises 95–98.   ◀ See Lesson 1-3.

Evaluate each expression for the given value of the variable.

95. $x^2 - x; x = 2$ **96.** $x^3 \cdot x^5; x = 2$ **97.** $\frac{x^8}{x^{10}}; x = 2$ **98.** $x^3 + x^2; x = 2$

Additional Instructional Support

Algebra 2 Companion

Students can use the **Algebra 2 Companion** worktext (4 pages) as you teach the lesson. Use the Companion to support

- New Vocabulary
- Key Concepts
- Got It for each Problem
- Lesson Check

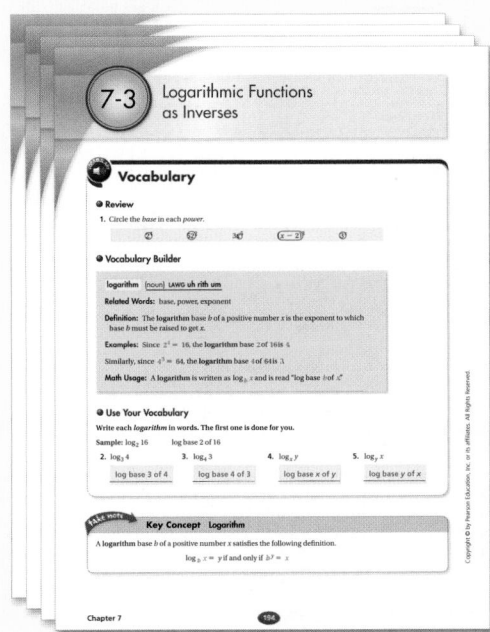

ELL Support

Connect to Prior Knowledge Have a volunteer graph the exponential function $y = 5^x$ on the board. Have students name points that appear on the exponential graph to help the volunteer graph $y = \log_5 x$. Have the class explain how each property of the graph of $y = \log_5 x$ is related to the graph of $y = 5^x$, including the domain, range, intercepts, and asymptotes.

Have another volunteer graph the exponential function $y = 4^x$ and this time reflect the graph over the line $y = x$ to find the graph of $y = \log_4 x$. Ask how the graph of $y = \log_4 x$ compares to the graph of $y = \log_5 x$. Ask students to specifically identify why the graphs have the same intercepts and asymptotes and why $\log_4 x < \log_5 x$ when $x < 1$.

5 Assess & Remediate

Lesson Quiz

1. What is the logarithmic form of $144 = 12^2$?

2. What is the value of $\log_9 27$?

3. **Do you UNDERSTAND?** The pH of a substance equals $-\log[H^+]$, where $[H^+]$ is the concentration of hydrogen ions. $[H^+]$ for tomato juice is 10^{-4}. What is the pH of tomato juice?

4. What is the graph of $y = \log_5 x$? Describe the domain and range, and identify the y-intercept and the asymptote.

5. How does the graph of $y = 2 \log (x + 5)$ compare to the graph of the parent function?

ANSWERS TO LESSON QUIZ

1. $\log_{12} 144 = 2$

2. $\frac{3}{2}$

3. 4

4. 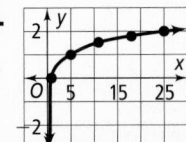 domain: all positive real numbers; range: all real numbers; y-intercept: does not exist; asymptote: $x = 0$

5. The graph is stretched by a factor of 2 and translated to the left 5 units.

PRESCRIPTION FOR REMEDIATION

Use the student work on the Lesson Quiz to prescribe a differentiated review assignment:

Points	Differentiated Remediation
0–2	Intervention
3–4	On-level
5	Extension

PowerAlgebra.com

5 Assess & Remediate

Assign the Lesson Quiz. Appropriate intervention, practice, or enrichment is automatically generated based on student performance.

Differentiated Remediation

Available in editable format online.

Intervention

- **Reteaching** (2 pages) Provides reteaching and practice exercises for the key lesson concepts. Use with struggling students or absent students.

- **English Language Learner Support** Helps students develop and reinforce mathematical vocabulary and key concepts.

All-in-One Resources/Online
Reteaching

7-3 Reteaching
Logarithmic Functions as Inverses

A logarithmic function is the inverse of an exponential function. To evaluate logarithmic expressions, use the fact that $x = \log_b y$ is the same as $y = b^x$. Keep in mind that $x = \log y$ is another way of writing $x = \log_{10} y$.

Problem
What is the logarithmic form of $6^3 = 216$?

Step 1 Determine which equation to use.
The equation is in the form $b^x = y$.
Step 2 Find x, y, and b.
$b = 6$, $x = 3$, and $y = 216$
Step 3 Because $y = b^x$ is the same as $x = \log_b y$, rewrite the equation in logarithmic form by substituting for x, y, and b.
$3 = \log_6 216$

Exercises
Write each equation in logarithmic form.

1. $4^{-3} = \frac{1}{64}$ 2. $5^{-2} = \frac{1}{25}$ 3. $8^{-1} = \frac{1}{8}$ 4. $11^0 = 1$
$\log_4 \frac{1}{64} = -3$ $\log_5 \frac{1}{25} = -2$ $\log_8 \frac{1}{8} = -1$ $\log_{11} 1 = 0$

5. $6^1 = 6$ 6. $6^{-3} = \frac{1}{216}$ 7. $17^0 = 1$ 8. $17^1 = 17$
$\log_6 6 = 1$ $\log_6 \frac{1}{216} = -3$ $\log_{17} 1 = 0$ $\log_{17} 17 = 1$

Problem
What is the exponential form of $4 = \log_5 625$?

Step 1 Determine which equation to use.
The equation is in the form $x = \log_b y$.
Step 2 Find x, y, and b.
$x = 4$, $b = 5$, and $y = 625$
Step 3 Because $x = \log_b y$ is the same as $y = b^x$, rewrite the equation in exponential form by substituting for x, y, and b.
$625 = 5^4$

All-in-One Resources/Online
English Language Learner Support

7-3 Additional Vocabulary Support
Logarithmic Functions as Inverses

For Exercises 1–3, draw a line from each word or phrase in Column A to the matching item in Column B.

Column A	Column B
1. logarithmic function	A. a logarithm with base 10
2. common logarithm	B. the inverse of an exponential function
3. logarithmic scale	C. uses the logarithm of a quantity instead of the quantity itself

For Exercises 4–9, draw a line from each word or phrase in Column A to the matching item in Column B.

Column A	Column B
4. parent function	A. $y = 0.75 \log_4 x$
5. stretch	B. $y = 5 \log_4 x$
6. compression	C. $y = \log_4 x - 3$
7. reflection in x-axis	D. $y = \log_4 x$
8. translation 3 units to the right	E. $y = -\log_4 x$
9. translation 3 units downward	F. $y = \log_4 (x - 3)$

Differentiated Remediation *continued*

Available in editable format online.

On-Level

- **Practice** (2 pages) Provides extra practice for each lesson. For simpler practice exercises, use the Form K Practice pages found in the All-in-One Teaching Resources and online.

- **Think About a Plan** Helps students develop specific problem-solving skills and strategies by providing scaffolded guiding questions.

- **Standardized Test Prep** Focuses on all major exercises, all major question types, and helps students prepare for the high-stakes assessments.

Extension

- **Enrichment** Provides students with interesting problems and activities that extend the concepts of the lesson.

- **Activities, Games, and Puzzles** Worksheets that can be used for concepts development, enrichment, and for fun!

Practice and Problem Solving Wkbk/All-in-One Resources/Online
Practice page 1

7-3 Practice   Form G
Logarithmic Functions as Inverses

Write each equation in logarithmic form.

1. $9^2 = 81$ $\log_9 81 = 2$
2. $\frac{1}{64} = \left(\frac{1}{4}\right)^3$ $\log_{\frac{1}{4}}\left(\frac{1}{64}\right) = 3$
3. $8^3 = 512$ $\log_8 512 = 3$
4. $\left(\frac{1}{3}\right)^{-2} = 9$ $\log_{\frac{1}{3}} 9 = -2$

5. $2^9 = 512$ $\log_2 512 = 9$
6. $4^5 = 1024$ $\log_4 1024 = 5$
7. $5^4 = 625$ $\log_5 625 = 4$
8. $10^{-3} = 0.001$ $\log_{10} 0.001 = -3$

Evaluate each logarithm.

9. $\log_2 128$ 7
10. $\log_4 32$ $\frac{5}{2}$
11. $\log_9 (27)$ $\frac{3}{2}$
12. $\log_2 (-32)$ undefined

13. $\log_1 \frac{1}{9}$
14. $\log 100{,}000$ 5
15. $\log_7 7^6$ 6
16. $\log_3 \frac{1}{81}$ -4

In 2004, an earthquake of magnitude 7.0 shook Papua, Indonesia. Compare the intensity level of that earthquake to the intensity level of each earthquake below.

17. magnitude 6.1 in Costa Rica, in 2009
The Papua earthquake was about 8 times as strong as the Costa Rica earthquake.

18. magnitude 5.1 in Greece, in 2008
The Papua earthquake was about 79 times as strong as the Greece earthquake.

19. magnitude 7.8 in the Fiji Islands, in 2007
The Fiji Islands earthquake was about 6 times as strong as the Papua earthquake.

20. magnitude 8.3 in the Kuril Islands, in 2006
The Kuril Islands earthquake was about 20 times as strong as the Papua earthquake.

Graph each logarithmic function.

21. $y = \log x$
22. $y = \log_3 x$
23. $y = \log_6 x$

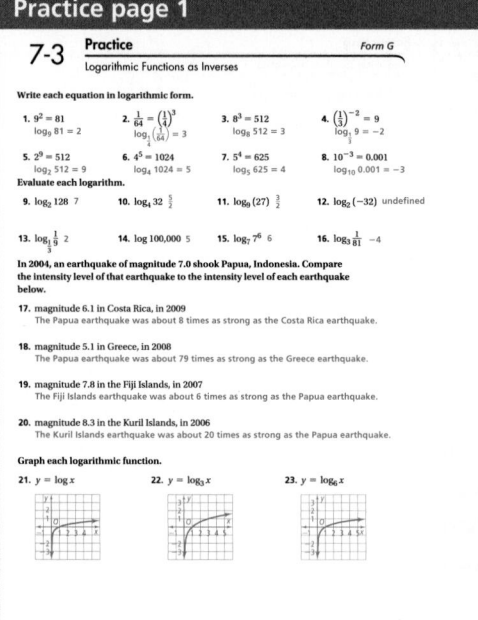

Practice and Problem Solving Wkbk/All-in-One Resources/Online
Think About a Plan

7-3 Think About a Plan
Logarithmic Functions as Inverses

Chemistry Find the concentration of hydrogen ions in seawater, if the pH level of seawater is 8.5.

Understanding the Problem

1. What is the pH of seawater?   8.5

2. How do you represent the concentration of hydrogen ions? H^+

3. What is the problem asking you to determine?
the concentration of hydrogen ions in seawater

Planning the Solution

4. Write the formula for the pH of a substance. $pH = -\log[H^+]$

5. Write an equation relating the pH of seawater to the concentration of hydrogen ions in seawater. $8.5 = -\log[H^+]$

Getting an Answer

6. Solve your equation to find the concentration of hydrogen ions in seawater.
$8.5 = -\log[H^+]$
$-8.5 = \log[H^+]$
$10^{-8.5} = 10^{\log[H^+]}$
$10^{-8.5} = [H^+]$
$[H^+] = 10^{-8.5}$ or 3.16×10^{-9}

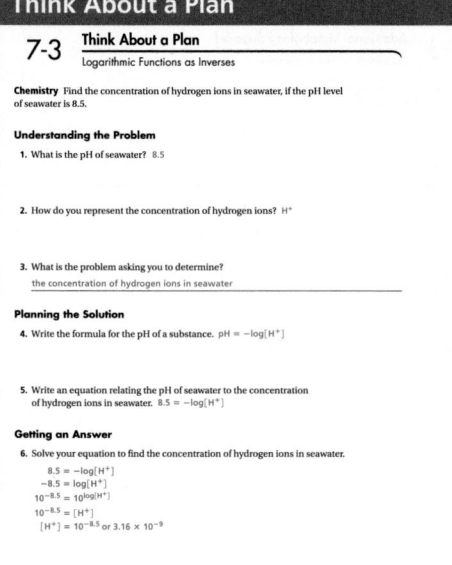

Practice and Problem Solving Wkbk/All-in-One Resources/Online
Practice page 2

7-3 Practice *(continued)*   Form G
Logarithmic Functions as Inverses

Describe how the graph of each function compares with the graph of the parent function, $y = \log_6 x$.

24. $y = \log_6 x - 2$ translates 2 units down

25. $y = \log_6 (x - 2)$ translates 2 units to the right

26. $y = \log_6 (x + 1) - 5$ translates 1 unit to the left and 5 units down

27. $y = \log_6 (x - 4) + 1$ translates 4 units to the right and 1 unit up

Write each equation in exponential form.

28. $\log_4 256 = 4$ $4^4 = 256$
29. $\log_7 1 = 0$ $7^0 = 1$
30. $\log_2 32 = 5$ $2^5 = 32$

31. $\log 10 = 1$ $10^1 = 10$
32. $\log_5 5 = 1$ $5^1 = 5$
33. $\log_8 \frac{1}{64} = -2$ $8^{-2} = \frac{1}{64}$

34. $\log_5 59{,}049 = 5$ $5^5 = 59{,}049$
35. $\log_{17} 289 = 2$ $17^2 = 289$
36. $\log_{56} 1 = 0$ $56^0 = 1$

37. $\log_{12} \frac{1}{144} = -2$ $12^{-2} = \frac{1}{144}$
38. $\log_2 \frac{1}{1024} = -10$ $2^{-10} = \frac{1}{1024}$
39. $\log_3 6561 = 8$ $3^8 = 6561$

40. A single-celled bacterium divides every hour. The number N of bacteria after t hours is given by the formula $\log_2 N = t$. After how many hours will there be 32 bacteria?   5 hours

For each pH given, find the concentration of hydrogen ions [H^+]. Use the formula $pH = -\log[H^+]$.

41. 7.2 6.3×10^{-8}
42. 7.3 5.0×10^{-8}
43. 8.2 6.3×10^{-9}
44. 6.2 6.3×10^{-7}

45. 5.6 2.5×10^{-6}
46. 4.6 2.5×10^{-5}
47. 7.0 1.0×10^{-7}
48. 2.9 1.3×10^{-3}

Find the inverse of each function.

49. $y = \log_2 x$ $y = 2^x$
50. $y = \log_{0.7} x$ $y = (0.7)^x$
51. $y = \log_{100} x$ $y = 10^{2x}$

52. $y = \log_4 x$ $y = 4^x$
53. $y = \log (4x)$ $y = 2^{x-2}$
54. $y = \log (x + 4)$ $y = 10^x - 4$

Find the domain and range of each function.

55. $y = \log_3 x - 2$
domain: $x > 0$; range: all real numbers
56. $y = 2\log_5 x$
domain: $x > 0$; range: all real numbers
57. $y = \log (x + 1)$
domain: $x > -1$; range: all real numbers

Practice and Problem Solving Wkbk/All-in-One Resources/Online
Standardized Test Prep

7-3 Standardized Test Prep
Logarithmic Functions as Inverses

Multiple Choice

For Exercises 1–4, choose the correct letter.

1. Which of the following is the logarithmic form of the equation $4^{-3} = \frac{1}{64}$?   C
   Ⓐ $\log_{-3}\left(\frac{1}{64}\right) = 4$
   Ⓒ $\log_4\left(\frac{1}{64}\right) = -3$
   Ⓑ $\log_{-3} 4 = \frac{1}{64}$
   Ⓓ $\log_{\frac{1}{64}} 4 = -3$

2. What is the value of $\log_2 8$?   I
   Ⓕ 64
   Ⓗ 16
   Ⓖ 8
   Ⓘ 3

3. How does the graph of $y = \log_5 (x - 3)$ compare with the graph of the parent function, $y = \log_5 x$?   C
   Ⓐ translated 3 units to the left
   Ⓒ translated 3 units to the right
   Ⓑ translated 3 units down
   Ⓓ translated 3 units up

4. In 2009, an earthquake of magnitude 6.7 shook the Kermadec Islands off the coast of New Zealand. Also in 2009, an earthquake of magnitude 5.1 occurred in the Alaska Peninsula. How many times stronger was the Kermadec earthquake than the Alaska earthquake?   F
   Ⓕ 39.811
   Ⓗ 5.77
   Ⓖ 20.593
   Ⓘ 0.025

Short Response

5. A single-celled bacterium divides every hour. The number N of bacteria after t hours is given by the formula $\log_2 N = t$.
   a. After how many hours will there be 64 bacteria?
   b. Explain in words or show work for how you determined the number of hours.
[2] a. 6 hours
   b. $\log_2 N = t$ can be written in the exponential form $2^t = N$. Substituting 64 for N, the equation becomes $2^t = 64$. Rewriting 64 with base 2, the equation is $2^t = 2^6$. Since the bases are equal, $t = 6$.
[1] incorrect exponential form OR incorrect explanation
[0] incorrect answers and no explanation OR no answers given

All-in-One Resources/Online
Enrichment

7-3 Enrichment
Logarithmic Functions as Inverses

Log Jams

The logarithm is a tool originally developed and used to aid in calculations, yet this viewpoint of logarithms is not the only one of interest. Logarithms are also useful when thought of as real-valued functions, or as inverse functions of the corresponding exponential functions. The idea of a logarithm as an inverse function of an exponential function means that $\log_2 x$ is a question to be answered. For example, you can read the expression $\log_2 8$ as "what exponent on base 2 gives 8?" The answer is 3, because $2^3 = 8$.

Thinking of a logarithm as an exponent helps to order some logarithms without evaluating them. For example, the logarithms $\log_7 8$, $\log_7 7$, and $\log_7 6$ are in descending order since the exponent needed on base 7 that gives 8 would be greater than 1 and 1 is in turn greater than the exponent needed on base 7 that gives 6.

You can also compose logarithms as you would compose other functions, where their domain and ranges agree. Thus, you evaluate $\log_4 (\log_5 25)$ by evaluating $\log_5 25 = 2$, then evaluating $\log_4 2 = \frac{1}{2}$.

Rewrite each equation in exponential form to solve the equation.

1. Solve for x: $\log_x 81 = 4$ 3
2. Solve for x: $\log_x 2 = 2$ $\sqrt{2}$
3. Which is greater, $\log_2 3$ or $\log_3 2$? $\log_2 3$ is greater
4. Solve for x: $\log_3 x = \log_9 \frac{1}{3}$ 3
5. Which is greater, $\frac{1}{3}$ of $\log_4 2$ or $\frac{1}{2}$ of $\log 10$? $\frac{1}{2}$ log 10 is greater
6. Solve for x: $\log_2 (\log_2 x) = 2$ 16
7. Which is greater, $\frac{1}{2}$ $\log_2 (\log_3 8.5)$ or $\frac{1}{3}$ $\log_3 (\log_2 8.5)$? $\frac{1}{3}$ $\log_3 (\log_2 8.5)$ is greater
8. Which of the following are equal? $\log \frac{1}{2}$ and $\log 1 - \log 2$ are equal
   $\log \frac{1}{2}$ $\frac{\log 1}{\log 2}$ $\log 1 - \log 2$

Rewrite in exponential form and solve for x.

9. $\log_5 1 = x$ 0
10. $\log_2 (2x^2 - 7) = 0$ $-2, 2$
11. $\log_x 7 = 1$ 7
12. $\log_3 x^2 = 2$ ± 2
13. $\log_3 1 = x$ 0
14. $\log_{17} 17 = x$ 1
15. $\log_x 3^4 = 1$ 81
16. $\log_x 0 = 1$ 0
17. $\log_3 3^2 = x$ 2
18. $\log_4 (x + 1) = 0$ 0
19. $1 + \log_6 (x - 1) = 1$ 2
20. $-1 + \log x = -1$ 1

Online Teacher Resource Center
Activities, Games, and Puzzles

7-3 Puzzle: Evaluating Logs
Logarithmic Functions as Inverses

The puzzle at the bottom of the page has been separated into twelve sections. Each section contains three squares. In each section, there is a number in a circle. This tells the sum of the two numbers in the section's empty squares. All missing numbers are natural numbers: 1, 2, 3, ... Additional instructions (A–L) are given for each section of missing numbers.

For example, look at the section marked by Ⓐ. The sum of the two missing numbers in the empty squares is 11. Complete each equation with numbers that meet the requirements for each given section, and then place them in the puzzle.

A. $\log_2$ __8__ = __3__
B. $\log_5$ 25 = __2__
C. $\log_3$ __27__ = __3__
D. $\log_5$ __125__ = __3__
E. $\log_{10}$ 10 = __1__
F. $\log_2$ 32 = __5__
G. $\log_7$ __49__ = __2__
H. $\log_2$ 16 = __4__
I. $\log_4$ __64__ = __3__
J. $\log_3$ __81__ = 4
K. $\log_2$ __32__ = 5
L. $\log_5$ 25 = 2

Final Question: Use four letters from the puzzle to find the value of $\log_2 \sqrt{2}$.
"ONE- __H__ __A__ __L__ __F__"

Fitting Curves to Data

Common Core State Standards

F-IF.B.4 For a function that models a relationship between two quantities, interpret key features of graphs . . . and sketch graphs showing key features . . .

MP 5

Example 1

Which type of function models the data best—linear, logarithmic, or exponential?

Connect the points with a smooth curve. Since the points do not fall along a line, the function is not linear. The graph appears to approach a horizontal asymptote, so an exponential function models the data best.

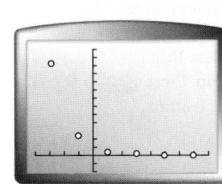 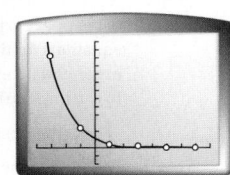

Example 2

Which type of function models the data best—quadratic, logarithmic, or cubic?

Step 1 Press (stat) (enter) to enter the data in lists.

Step 2 Use the (stat plot) feature to draw a scatter plot.

Step 3 If you connect the points with a smooth curve, the end behavior of the graph is up and up. The graph is not cubic or logarithmic, so a quadratic function best models the data.

x	y
0	14
1	7.5
2	4
3	1.8
4	1.8
5	3.9

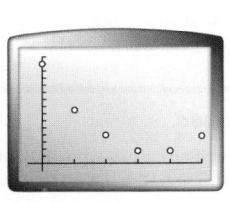

Exercises

1. Which type of function models the data shown in the graphing calculator screen best—*linear, quadratic, logarithmic, cubic,* or *exponential*?

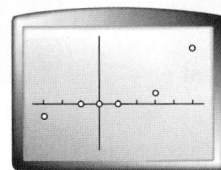

2. Which type of function models the data in the table best—*linear, quadratic, logarithmic, cubic,* or *exponential*?

x	y
−1	0
1	1.4
3	2.09
5	2.53
7	2.81
9	3.12

3. Reasoning Could you use a different model for the data in Exercises 1 and 2? Explain.

Guided Instruction

PURPOSE To fit data to a curve and extrapolate to find a new point that fits the data

PROCESS Students will

- connect data points to determine the type of function that models the data.
- use the **STAT PLOT** feature on a calculator to graph a table of data and regression features to find the best-fitting function.
- use the model to extrapolate a new point that fits the data.

DISCUSS The purpose of fitting a curve to data is to *approximate* a function that has the points on its graph. Sometimes not all of the points will lie exactly on the curve. Not all data will have a reasonable model of linear, quadratic, logarithmic, or exponential type.

Q If a set of data is always increasing, could the best-fitting curve be a parabola? **[Yes; the curve that fits the data could be the increasing portion of an upward-facing parabola.]**

Example 1

Q Why is a linear function not a reasonable model? **[Answers may vary. Sample: The slope of the model is not constant because the ratio of the change in *x*-values to the change in *y*-values is not constant.]**

Example 2   VISUAL LEARNERS

Q How can you tell by looking at the table that the function that models the graph is not logarithmic? **[The *y*-values decrease and then increase. A logarithmic function is always increasing or always decreasing.]**

Mathematical Practices This Concept Byte supports students in becoming proficient in using appropriate tools, Mathematical Practice 5.

Answers

Concept Byte

1. cubic

2. quadratic

3. Yes; problem 1 could also be linear with outliers; problem 2 could also be linear or cubic. They cannot be logarithmic due to negative values.

Example 3

When the ExpReg feature on the calculator is used, the function that models the data is not given in explicit form. The feature reads the data listed in the table and returns the constants a and b that define the function $y = ab^x$.

> **Q** Do you think you can make a reasonable prediction about the bacteria population 10 days from now? Explain. **[No; the data only covers the population growth over 10 hours. The model may not continue to be reasonable for the much larger time period of 10 days.]**

Exercises   SYNTHESIS

For Exercises 4–7, either a quadratic or an exponential function could be used to model the graph. The exponential model would consist of only half of the parabola. Choose which function to use based on which models the graph of the points most closely.

> **Q** Why is the scale of the axes in the graph important? How can you choose an appropriate scale? **[To see the shape of the curve, the scale must be adjusted so that the points are not clustered too closely on the *x*- or *y*-axis. The range of each axis should be slightly larger than the range of the *x*- and *y*-values of the data points.]**
>
> **Q** In Exercise 5, do you think that the quadratic or exponential function would predict a larger *y*-value for the model when $x = 9$? Why? **[The exponential model, because exponential functions increase more rapidly than quadratic functions.]**

Example 3

The table shows the number of bacteria in a culture after the given number of hours. Find a good model for the data. Based on the model, how many bacteria will be in the culture after an additional ten hours?

Hour	Bacteria
1	2205
2	2270
3	2350
4	2653
5	3052
6	3417
7	3890
8	4522
9	5107
10	5724

Step 1 Press `stat` `enter` to enter the data in lists. Use the `stat plot` feature to draw a scatter plot.

Step 2 Notice from the scatter plot that the data appear exponential. Find the equations for the best-fitting exponential function. Press `stat` ▷ **0** to use the **ExpReg** feature.

$$y = 1779.404(1.121)^x$$

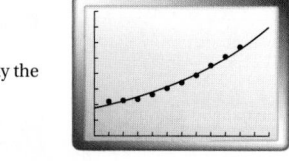

Step 3 Graph the function. Press `y=` `clear` `vars` **5** ▷ ▷ `enter` to enter the **ExpReg** results. Press `graph` to display the function and the scatter plot together. Press `zoom` **9** to automatically adjust the window.

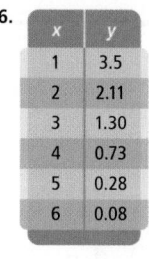 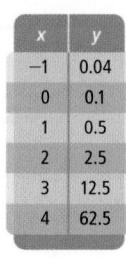

Step 4 In 10 more hours, there will be approximately $y = 1779.404(1.121)^{20} \approx 17{,}474$ bacteria in the culture.

Exercises

Use a graphing calculator to find the exponential or quadratic function that best fits each set of data. Graph each function.

4.
x	y
−1	4.9
0	3.8
1	5.0
2	8.1
3	13.3
4	70.2

5.
x	y
−3	0.1
−1	0.4
1	1.6
3	6.4
5	25.6
7	102.4

6.
x	y
1	3.5
2	2.11
3	1.30
4	0.73
5	0.28
6	0.08

7.
x	y
−1	0.04
0	0.1
1	0.5
2	2.5
3	12.5
4	62.5

ⓒ **8. Writing** In Exercise 6 the function appears to level off. Explain why.

9. A savings account begins with $14.00. After 1 year, the account has a balance of $16.24. After 2 years, the account has a balance of $18.84. Assuming no additional deposits or withdrawals are made, find the equation for the best-fitting exponential function to represent the balance of the account after x years. How much money will be in the account after 20 years?

Answers

Concept Byte (continued)

4. $y = 5.46x^2 - 6.16x - 1.44$

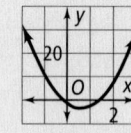

5. $y = 0.8(2)^x$

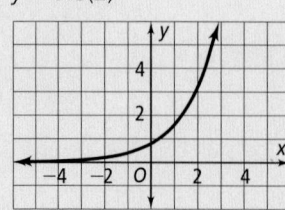

6. $y = 0.13x^2 - 1.59x + 4.88$

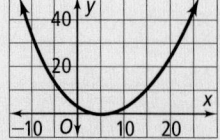

7. $y = 0.13(4.5)^x$

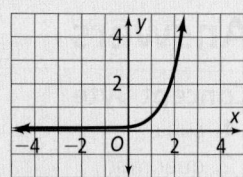

8. $x = 0$ is an asymptote.

9. $y = 14(1.16)^x$; $272.68

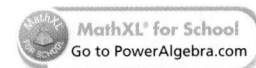
MathXL® for School
Go to PowerAlgebra.com

Do you know HOW?

Determine whether each function is an example of exponential growth or decay. Then find the *y*-intercept.

1. $y = 100(0.25)^x$ **2.** $y = 0.6\left(\frac{1}{10}\right)^x$ **3.** $y = \frac{7}{8}(18)^x$

Graph each function. Then find the domain, range, and *y*-intercept.

4. $y = -4(2)^x$ **5.** $y = \frac{1}{4}(10)^x$ **6.** $y = 8(0.25)^x$

7. Investment Suppose you deposit $600 into a savings account that pays 3.9% annual interest. How much will you have in the account after 3 years if no money is added or withdrawn?

8. Depreciation The initial value of a car is $25,000. After one year, the value of the car is $21,250. Write an exponential function to model the expected value of the car. Estimate the value of the car after 5 years.

Graph each function as a transformation of its parent function. Write the parent function.

9. $y = 3^x - 2$ **10.** $y = \frac{1}{2}(5)^{x-1} + 4$

11. $y = -(0.5)^{x+3}$ **12.** $y = -6\left(\frac{3}{4}\right)^x - 10$

Evaluate each expression to four decimal places.

13. e^5 **14.** $e^{\frac{3}{2}}$ **15.** e^{-4}

Find the amount in a continuously compounded account for the given conditions.

16. principal: $500; annual interest rate: 4.9%; time: 2.5 years

17. principal: $6000; annual interest rate: 6.8%; time: 10 years

Write each equation in logarithmic form.

18. $10^4 = 10,000$ **19.** $\frac{1}{4} = 4^{-1}$ **20.** $8 = \left(\frac{1}{2}\right)^{-3}$

Evaluate each logarithm.

21. $\log_8 64$ **22.** $\log_4(256)$ **23.** $\log_{\frac{1}{5}} 625$

Graph each logarithmic function. Find the domain and range.

24. $y = \log_5(x - 1)$ **25.** $y = 4\log x + 5$

26. Crafts For glass to be shaped, its temperature must stay above 1200°F. The temperature of a piece of glass is 2200°F when it comes out of the furnace. The table shows temperature readings for the glass. Write an exponential model for this data set and then find how long it takes for the piece of glass to cool to 1200°F.

Time (min)	Temp (°F)
0	2200
5	1700
10	1275
15	1000
20	850
25	650

Do you UNDERSTAND?

27. Error Analysis A student claims the *y*-intercept of the graph of the function $y = ab^x$ is the point $(0, b)$. What is the student's mistake? What is the actual *y*-intercept?

28. Writing Without graphing, how can you tell whether an exponential function represents exponential growth or exponential decay?

29. Compare and Contrast Compare the graph of $y = \log_3(x + 1)$ to the graph of its inverse $y = 3^x - 1$. How are the graphs alike? How are they different?

30. Vocabulary Explain how the continuously compounded interest formula differs from the annually compounded interest formula.

7. $672.97

8. $y = 25000(0.85)^x$; $11,093

9. $y = 3^x - 2$
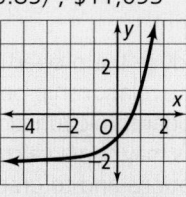

10. $y = 5^x$
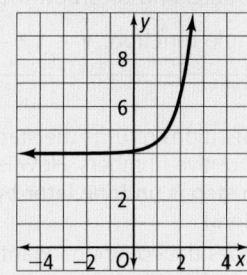

11. $y = -(0.5)^x$
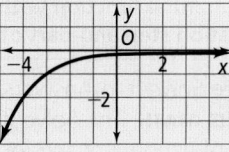

12. $y = \left(\frac{3}{4}\right)^x$
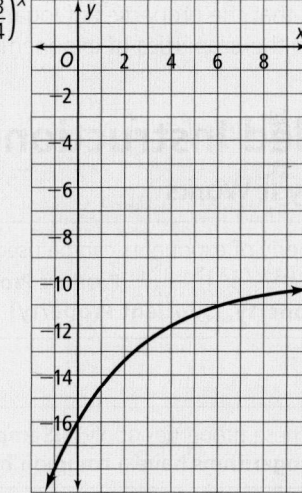

13. ≈ 148.4132 **14.** ≈ 4.4817

15. ≈ 0.0183 **16.** $565.16

17. $11,843.27   **18.** $\log 10000 = 4$

19. $\log_4 \frac{1}{4} = -1$ **20.** $\log_{\frac{1}{2}} 8 = -3$

21. 2   **22.** 4   **23.** -4

24–30. See back of book.

Answers

1. exponential decay; 100

2. exponential decay; 0.6

3. exponential growth; $\frac{7}{8}$

4. domain: all real numbers; range: $y < 0$; *y*-intercept: $(0, -4)$
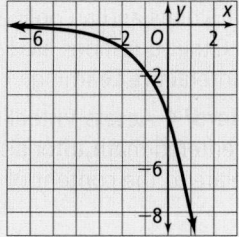

5. domain: all real numbers; range: $y > 0$; *y*-intercept: $\left(0, \frac{1}{4}\right)$
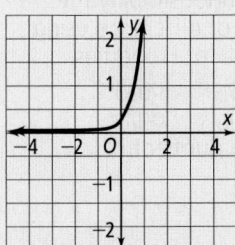

6. domain: all real numbers; range: $y > 0$; *y*-intercept: $(0, 8)$
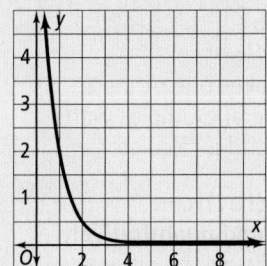

1 Interactive Learning

Solve It!

PURPOSE To introduce the properties of logarithms by using the inverse relationship between exponential and logarithmic functions

PROCESS Students may use a calculator to perform the series of operations and to graph the series of operations as a single function: $y = \sqrt{\dfrac{10^{4+2\log x}}{100}}$.

FACILITATE

Q The series of operations returns the starting number for all positive numbers. How is this possible? **[Each step is undone later by an inverse operation.]**

Q Which step undoes the common logarithm? Which step does taking the square root undo? **[the exponential function with base 10; the multiplication step and part of the addition step]**

ANSWER See Solve It in Answers on next page.
CONNECT THE MATH The Solve It uses the inverse relationship of exponents and logarithms. The lesson shows that the properties of logarithms correspond to the properties of exponents.

2 Guided Instruction

Here's Why It Works

Q What property of exponents can be used to simplify $a^5 b^4$? $\left(a^3\right)^2$? $\dfrac{a^6}{a^2}$? **[Product Property; Power Property; Quotient Property]**

Take Note

Q When do these properties apply? **[Sample: when all of the logarithms have a common base]**

© **Common Core State Standards**
Prepares for F-LE.A.4 For exponential models, express as a logarithm the solution to $ab^{ct} = d$ where a, c, and d are numbers and the base b is 2, 10, or e; evaluate the logarithm using technology.
MP 1, MP 2, MP 3

Objective To use the properties of logarithms

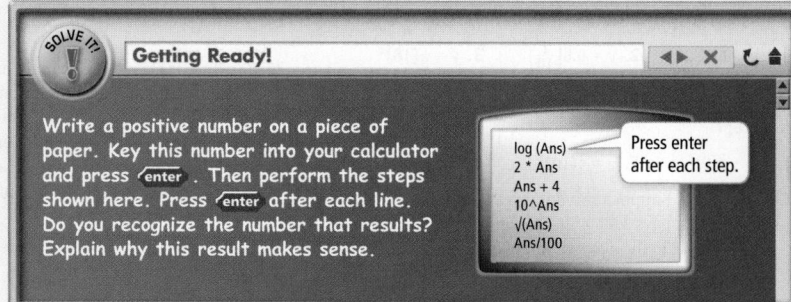

Getting Ready!

Write a positive number on a piece of paper. Key this number into your calculator and press ⏎ enter. Then perform the steps shown here. Press ⏎ enter after each line. Do you recognize the number that results? Explain why this result makes sense.

log (Ans)
2 * Ans
Ans + 4
10^Ans
√(Ans)
Ans/100

Press enter after each step.

Lesson Vocabulary
• Change of Base Formula

You can derive the properties of logarithms from the properties of exponents.

Essential Understanding Logarithms and exponents have corresponding properties.

Here's Why It Works You can use a product property of exponents to derive a product property of logarithms.

Let $x = \log_b m$ and $y = \log_b n$.

$m = b^x$ and $n = b^y$	Definition of logarithm
$mn = b^x \cdot b^y$	Write mn as a product of powers.
$mn = b^{x+y}$	Product Property of Exponents
$\log_b mn = x + y$	Definition of logarithm
$\log_b mn = \log_b m + \log_b n$	Substitute for x and y.

take note

Properties **Properties of Logarithms**

For any positive numbers m, n, and b where $b \neq 1$, the following properties apply.

Product Property	$\log_b mn = \log_b m + \log_b n$
Quotient Property	$\log_b \dfrac{m}{n} = \log_b m - \log_b n$
Power Property	$\log_b m^n = n \log_b m$

BIG ideas **Equivalence**
Function
Modeling

ESSENTIAL UNDERSTANDINGS
• Logarithms and exponents have corresponding properties.
• An exponential function is a function with the general form $y = ab^x$, $a \neq 0$, with $b > 0$, and $b \neq 1$. In an exponential function, the base b is a constant. The exponent x is the independent variable with domain the set of real numbers.

Math Background

The Product, Quotient, and Power Properties of Logarithms allow many expressions and equations to be simplified. For instance, the Power Property allows the equation $4 = 9^x$ to be solved for x:
$$\log 4 = x \log 9$$
$$x = \frac{\log 4}{\log 9}$$
Logarithmic expressions that you cannot simplify using the properties, however, are not always obvious to students.

• The logarithm function is not distributive over addition or subtraction. You cannot simplify the logarithm of a sum or difference using the Product or Quotient Properties.
$$\log_b (x + y) \neq \log_b x + \log_b y$$
$$\log_b (x - y) \neq \log_b x - \log_b y$$
• You cannot factor a quotient of logarithms.
$$\frac{\log_b x}{\log_b y} \neq \log_b \frac{x}{y}$$
• You cannot factor out a logarithm, except in the manner prescribed by the Product Property.
$$\log_b 6 \neq 3 \log_b 2$$
$$\neq (\log_b 3)(\log_b 2)$$

When a student makes one of these mistakes, show several examples with concrete numbers and a calculator.

© **Mathematical Practices**
Reason abstractly and quantitatively. Students will flexibly use the different properties of logarithms.

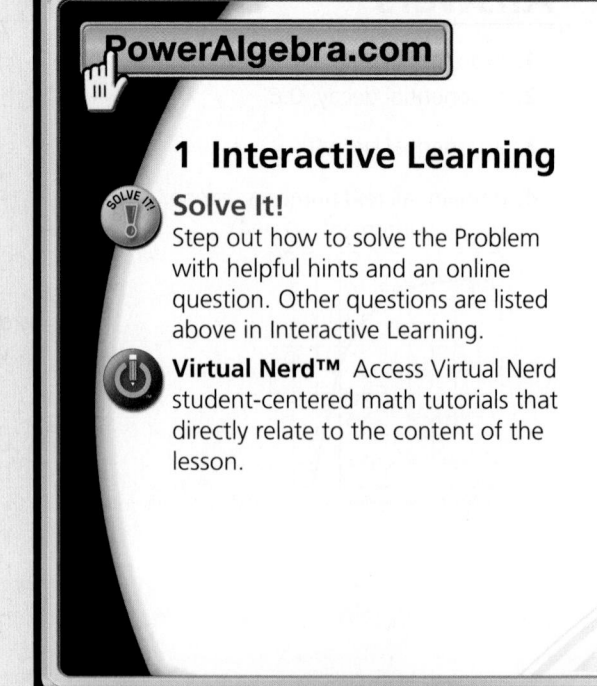

PowerAlgebra.com

1 Interactive Learning

Solve It!
Step out how to solve the Problem with helpful hints and an online question. Other questions are listed above in Interactive Learning.

Virtual Nerd™ Access Virtual Nerd student-centered math tutorials that directly relate to the content of the lesson.

Problem 1 Simplifying Logarithms

What is each expression written as a single logarithm?

Ⓐ $\log_4 32 - \log_4 2$

$\log_4 32 - \log_4 2 = \log_4 \frac{32}{2}$ Quotient Property of Logarithms

$= \log_4 16$ Divide.

$= \log_4 4^2$ Write 16 as a power of 4.

$= 2$ Simplify.

Ⓑ $6 \log_2 x + 5 \log_2 y$

$6 \log_2 x + 5 \log_2 y = \log_2 x^6 + \log_2 y^5$ Power Property of Logarithms

$= \log_2 x^6 y^5$ Product Property of Logarithms

Think

What must you do with the numbers that multiply the logarithms?
Apply the Power Property of Logarithms.

 Got It? 1. What is each expression written as a single logarithm?

   a. $\log_4 5x + \log_4 3x$ **b.** $2\log_4 6 - \log_4 9$

You can expand a single logarithm to involve the sum or difference of two or more logarithms.

 Problem 2 Expanding Logarithms

What is each logarithm expanded?

Ⓐ $\log \frac{4x}{y}$

$\log \frac{4x}{y} = \log 4x - \log y$ Quotient Property of Logarithms

$= \log 4 + \log x - \log y$ Product Property of Logarithms

Ⓑ $\log_9 \frac{x^4}{729}$

$\log_9 \frac{x^4}{729} = \log_9 x^4 - \log_9 729$ Quotient Property of Logarithms

$= 4 \log_9 x - \log_9 729$ Power Property of Logarithms

$= 4 \log_9 x - \log_9 9^3$ Write 729 as a power of 9.

$= 4 \log_9 x - 3$ Simplify.

Think

Can you apply the Power Property of Logarithms first?
No; the fourth power applies only to x.

 Got It? 2. What is each logarithm expanded?

   a. $\log_3 \frac{250}{37}$ **b.** $\log_3 9x^5$

Problem 1

Q How can you use the Power Property to solve 1A? **[Express 32 and 2 as powers of 4: $\log_4 4^{\frac{5}{2}} - \log_4 4^{\frac{1}{2}}$; use the Product Property: $\frac{5}{2}\log_4 4 - \frac{1}{2}\log_4 4$; Simplify: $\frac{5}{2} - \frac{1}{2} = 2$.]**

Got It?

Q What property of logarithms can be used to solve 1a? **[Product Property]**

Problem 2

Q Is there a way to simplify $\log \frac{4x}{y}$ without using the Quotient Property? Explain. **[Yes; answers may vary. Sample: Rewrite the expression with the y term in the numerator: $\log 4xy^{-1}$. Use the Product Property: $\log 4 + \log x + \log y^{-1}$. Finally, use the Power Property and simplify: $\log 4 + \log x + (-1)\log y$ $= \log 4 + \log x - \log y$.]**

Got It?   EXTENSION

Q How do you know that neither term in 2a will simplify to an integer? **[The number inside the logarithm must be a power of the base, so it must be divisible by the base. Neither 250 nor 37 is divisible by 3.]**

Q How many units and in what direction is the graph of $y = \log_3 9x$ translated compared with $y = \log_3 x$? **[two units up]**

---

2 Guided Instruction

 Each Problem is worked out and supported online.

Problem 1
Simplifying Logarithms
       Animated

Problem 2
Expanding Logarithms
       Animated

Problem 3
Using the Change of Base Formula
       Animated

Problem 4
Using a Logarithmic Scale

Support in Algebra 2 Companion
• Vocabulary
• Key Concepts
• Got It?

Answers

Solve It!

You get the number that you wrote on paper;

$$\frac{\sqrt{10^{4+2\log x}}}{100} = \frac{(10^{4+2\log x})^{\frac{1}{2}}}{100} = \frac{10^{\frac{4+2\log x}{2}}}{100} = \frac{10^{2+\log x}}{100}$$

$$= \frac{10^2 \cdot 10^{\log x}}{100} = 10^{\log x} = x$$

Got It?

 1. a. $\log_4 15x^2$

   b. 1

 2. a. $\log_3 2 + 3 \log_3 5 - \log_3 37$

    b. $2 + 5 \log_3 x$

Take Note

Here's Why It Works

The Change of Base Formula can also be derived by setting $\log_b m = x$.

$m = b^x$	Definition of Logarithm
$\log_c m = \log_c b^x$	Take logarithm base c of both sides.
$\log_c m = x\log_c b$	Power Property of Logarithms
$x = \dfrac{\log_c m}{\log_c b}$	Solve for x.
$\log_b m = \dfrac{\log_c m}{\log_c b}$	Substitute $\log_b m$ for x.

Problem 3

Got It?

You have seen logarithms with many bases. The **log** key on a calculator finds $\log_{10}$ of a number. To evaluate a logarithm with any base, use the **Change of Base Formula**.

take note

Property Change of Base Formula

For any positive numbers m, b, and c, with $b \neq 1$ and $c \neq 1$,

$$\log_b m = \frac{\log_c m}{\log_c b}.$$

Here's Why It Works

$$\log_b m = \frac{(\log_b m)(\log_c b)}{\log_c b} \qquad \text{Multiply } \log_b m \text{ by } \frac{\log_c b}{\log_c b} = 1.$$

$$= \frac{\log_c b^{\log_b m}}{\log_c b} \qquad \text{Power Property of Logarithms}$$

$$= \frac{\log_c m}{\log_c b} \qquad b^{\log_b m} = m$$

Problem 3 Using the Change of Base Formula

What is the value of each expression?

Ⓐ $\log_{81} 27$

Think
What common base has powers that equal 27 and 81?
3; $3^3 = 27$ and $3^4 = 81$.

Method 1 Use a common base.

$$\log_{81} 27 = \frac{\log_3 27}{\log_3 81} \qquad \text{Change of Base Formula}$$

$$= \frac{3}{4} \qquad \text{Simplify.}$$

Method 2 Use a calculator.

$$\log_{81} 27 = \frac{\log 27}{\log 81} \qquad \text{Change of Base Formula}$$

$$= 0.75 \qquad \text{Use a calculator.}$$

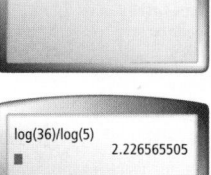
log(27)/log(81)
.75

Ⓑ $\log_5 36$

Think
What would be a reasonable result?
$5^2 = 25$ and $5^3 = 125$, so $\log_5 36$ should be between 2 and 3.

$$\log_5 36 = \frac{\log 36}{\log 5} \qquad \text{Change of Base Formula}$$

$$\approx 2.23 \qquad \text{Use a calculator to evaluate.}$$

log(36)/log(5)
2.226565505

Got It? 3. Use the Change of Base Formula. What is the value of each expression?

  a. $\log_8 32$ **b.** $\log_4 18$

Additional Problems

1. What is each expression written as a single logarithm? If possible, simplify the single logarithm.

  a. $\log_3 x - 2\log_3 7$

  b. $\log_8 48 + \log_8 \frac{4}{3}$

  ANSWERS

  a. $\log_3 \frac{x}{49}$ **b.** 2

2. What is each logarithm expanded? Simplify your answer, if possible.

  a. $\log_5 \frac{125}{xy}$

  b. $\log x^2 y^2 z^{-1}$

  ANSWERS

  a. $3 - \log_5 x - \log_5 y$

  b. $2\log x + 2\log y - \log z$

3. What is the value of each expression?

  a. $\log_9 111$ **b.** $\log_{216} 36$

  ANSWERS

  a. about 2.14 **b.** $\frac{2}{3}$

4. The speed s (in mi/h) of the wind near the center of a tornado is related to the distance d (in miles) the tornado travels by $s = 93\log d + 65$. What was the difference in speed between a tornado that traveled 16 mi and one that traveled 8 mi?

  ANSWER about 28 mi/h

Answers

Got It? (continued)

3. a. $\frac{5}{3}$

  b. ≈ 2.085

Problem 4 Using a Logarithmic Scale STEM

Chemistry The pH of a substance equals $-\log[H^+]$, where $[H^+]$ is the concentration of hydrogen ions. $[H^+_a]$ for household ammonia is 10^{-11}. $[H^+_v]$ for vinegar is 6.3×10^{-3}. What is the difference of the pH levels of ammonia and vinegar?

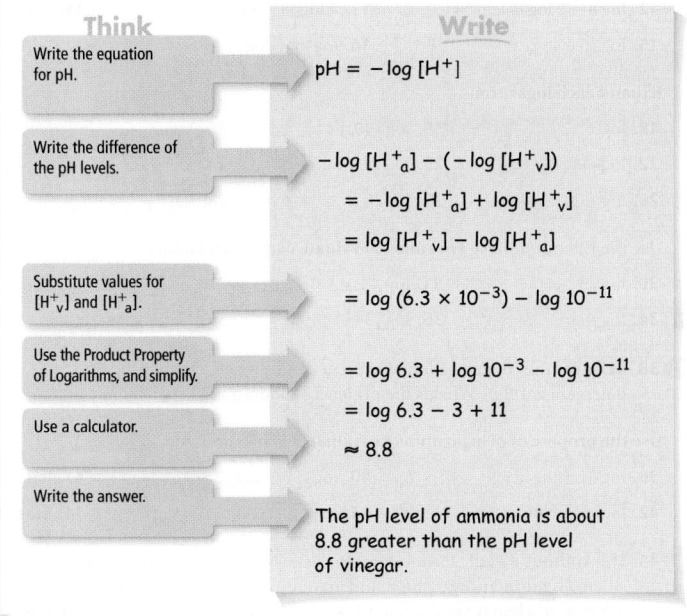

Think	Write
Write the equation for pH.	$pH = -\log[H^+]$
Write the difference of the pH levels.	$-\log[H^+_a] - (-\log[H^+_v])$ $= -\log[H^+_a] + \log[H^+_v]$ $= \log[H^+_v] - \log[H^+_a]$
Substitute values for $[H^+_v]$ and $[H^+_a]$.	$= \log(6.3 \times 10^{-3}) - \log 10^{-11}$
Use the Product Property of Logarithms, and simplify.	$= \log 6.3 + \log 10^{-3} - \log 10^{-11}$ $= \log 6.3 - 3 + 11$
Use a calculator.	≈ 8.8
Write the answer.	The pH level of ammonia is about 8.8 greater than the pH level of vinegar.

Got It? 4. Reasoning Suppose the hydrogen ion concentration for Substance A is twice that for Substance B. Which substance has the greater pH level? What is the greater pH level minus the lesser pH level? Explain.

Lesson Check

Do you know HOW?

Write each expression as a single logarithm.

1. $\log_4 2 + \log_4 8$

2. $\log_6 24 - \log_6 4$

Expand each logarithm.

3. $\log_3 \frac{x}{y}$ 4. $\log m^2 n^5$ 5. $\log_2 \sqrt{x}$

Do you UNDERSTAND? MATHEMATICAL PRACTICES

6. **Vocabulary** State which property or properties need to be used to write each expression as a single logarithm.

   a. $\log_4 5 + \log_4 5$ b. $\log_5 4 - \log_5 6$

7. **Reasoning** If $\log x = 5$, what is the value of $\log \frac{1}{x}$?

8. **Open-Ended** Write log 150 as a sum or difference of two logarithms. Simplify if possible.

4. Substance B; log 2; $-\log[H^+_B] + \log[H^+_B] = \log 2$

Lesson Check

1. $\log_4 16$
2. $\log_6 6$
3. $\log_3 x - \log_3 y$
4. $2 \log m + 5 \log n$
5. $\frac{1}{2}\log_2 x$
6. **a.** Product Prop. and Power Prop.
   b. Quotient Prop.
7. 0.00001
8. Answers may vary. Samples:
   log 150 = log 25 + log 6

Problem 4

Q What does the 8.8 difference mean in terms of $[H^+]$ concentration? Why? **[Answers may vary. Sample: The 8.8 pH difference is on a logarithmic scale with base 10, so the concentration of $[H^+]$ in vinegar is $10^{8.8}$ (or 630,000,000) times that of the concentration of $[H^+]$ in ammonia.]**

Q The pH level of pure water is 7. What is the concentration of $[H^+]$ in pure water? Explain your method. **[Answers may vary. Sample: Write the formula: pH = $-\log[H^+]$; Substitute: $7 = -\log[H^+]$; Solve for $[H^+]$: $10^{-7} = [H^+]$.]**

Got It?

Because the pH scale is a negative logarithmic scale, a smaller concentration of $[H^+]$ has a greater pH value than a larger concentration.

3 Lesson Check

Do you know HOW?

• If students do not know how to proceed with Exercise 5, then remind them that $\sqrt{x} = x^{\frac{1}{2}}$.

Do you UNDERSTAND?

• In Exercise 8, be sure that students separate out factors of 150 and not addends.

Close

Q How can you derive the Power Property of Logarithms from the Power Property of Exponents? **[Sample: Let $x = \log_b m$; $m = b^x$ (Definition of Logarithm); $m^n = (b^x)^n$ (Raise each side to the n power.); $m^n = b^{nx}$ (Power Property of Exponents); $\log_b m^n = nx$ (Definition of Logarithm); $\log_b m^n = n\log_b m$ (Substitute for x.)]**

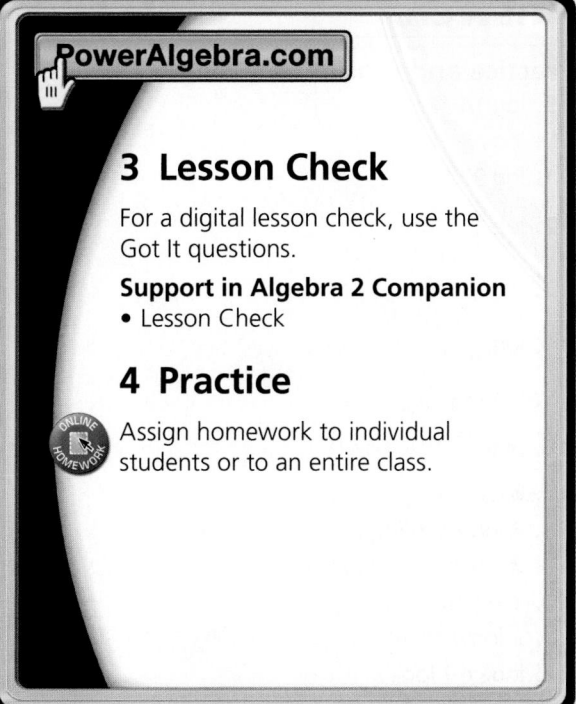

PowerAlgebra.com

3 Lesson Check

For a digital lesson check, use the Got It questions.

Support in Algebra 2 Companion
• Lesson Check

4 Practice

Assign homework to individual students or to an entire class.

4 Practice

ASSIGNMENT GUIDE

Basic: 9–38 all, 43–47, 50–60 even

Average: 9–37 odd, 39–74

Advanced: 9–37 odd, 39–79

Standardized Test Prep: 80–83

Mixed Review: 84–95

Mathematical Practices are supported by exercises with red headings. Here are the Practices supported in this lesson:

MP 1: Make Sense of Problems Ex. 45

MP 2: Reason Abstractly Ex. 7

MP 3: Communicate Ex. 49

MP 3: Construct Arguments Ex. 8, 48

MP 3: Critique the Reasoning of Others Ex. 47

Applications exercises have blue headings.

STEM exercises focus on science or engineering applications.

EXERCISE 46: Use the Think About a Plan worksheet in the **Practice and Problem Solving Workbook** (also available in the Teaching Resources in print and online) to further support students' development in becoming independent learners.

HOMEWORK QUICK CHECK

To check students' understanding of key skills and concepts, go over Exercises 9, 31, 45, 46, and 47.

Practice and Problem-Solving Exercises

A Practice   Write each expression as a single logarithm.   ◆ See Problem 1.

9. $\log 7 + \log 2$ **10.** $\log_2 9 - \log_2 3$ **11.** $5\log 3 + \log 4$

12. $\log 8 - 2\log 6 + \log 3$ **13.** $4\log m - \log n$ **14.** $\log 5 - k\log 2$

15. $\log_6 5 + \log_6 x$ **16.** $\log_7 x + \log_7 y - \log_7 z$ **17.** $\log_3 4 + \log_3 y + \log_3 8x$

Expand each logarithm.   ◆ See Problem 2.

18. $\log x^3 y^5$ **19.** $\log_7 49xyz$ **20.** $\log_b \frac{b}{x}$ **21.** $\log a^2$

22. $\log_5 \frac{r}{s}$ **23.** $\log_3 (2x)^2$ **24.** $\log_3 7(2x-3)^2$ **25.** $\log \frac{a^2 b^3}{c^4}$

26. $\log_4 5\sqrt{x}$ **27.** $\log_8 8\sqrt{3a^5}$ **28.** $\log_5 \frac{25}{x}$ **29.** $\log 10m^4 n^{-2}$

Use the Change of Base Formula to evaluate each expression.   ◆ See Problem 3.

30. $\log_2 9$ **31.** $\log_{12} 20$ **32.** $\log_7 30$ **33.** $\log_5 10$

34. $\log_4 7$ **35.** $\log_3 54$ **36.** $\log_5 62$ **37.** $\log_3 33$

STEM 38. Science The concentration of hydrogen ions in household dish detergent is 10^{-12}. What is the pH level of household dish detergent?   ◆ See Problem 4.

B Apply   Use the properties of logarithms to evaluate each expression.

39. $\log_2 4 - \log_2 16$ **40.** $\log_2 96 - \log_2 3$ **41.** $\log_3 27 - 2\log_3 3$

42. $\log_6 12 + \log_6 3$ **43.** $\log_4 48 - \frac{1}{2}\log_4 9$ **44.** $\frac{1}{2}\log_5 15 - \log_5 \sqrt{75}$

45. Think About a Plan The loudness in decibels (dB) of a sound is defined as $10\log \frac{I}{I_0}$, where I is the intensity of the sound in watts per square meter (W/m^2). I_0, the intensity of a barely audible sound, is equal to $10^{-12}\ \text{W/m}^2$. Town regulations require the loudness of construction work not to exceed 100 dB. Suppose a construction team is blasting rock for a roadway. One explosion has an intensity of $1.65 \times 10^{-2}\ \text{W/m}^2$. Is this explosion in violation of town regulations?
- Which physical value do you need to calculate to answer the question?
- What values should you use for I and I_0?

STEM 46. Construction The foreman of a construction team puts up a sound barrier that reduces the intensity of the noise by 50%. By how many decibels is the noise reduced? Use the formula $L = 10\log \frac{I}{I_0}$ to measure loudness. (*Hint:* Find the difference between the expression for loudness for intensity I and the expression for loudness for intensity $0.5I$.)

47. Error Analysis Explain why the expansion at the right of $\log_4 \sqrt{\frac{t}{s}}$ is incorrect. Then do the expansion correctly.

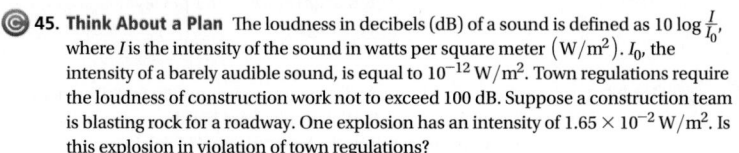

48. Reasoning Can you expand $\log_3 (2x + 1)$? Explain.

49. Writing Explain why $\log (5 \cdot 2) \neq \log 5 \cdot \log 2$.

Answers

Practice and Problem-Solving Exercises

9. $\log 14$

10. $\log_2 3$

11. $\log 972$

12. $\log \frac{2}{3}$

13. $\log \frac{m^4}{n}$

14. $\log \frac{5}{2^k}$

15. $\log_6 5x$

16. $\log_7 \frac{xy}{z}$

17. $\log_3 32xy$

18. $3\log x + 5\log y$

19. $2 + \log_7 x + \log_7 y + \log_7 z$

20. $1 - \log_b x$

21. $2\log a$

22. $\log_5 r - \log_5 s$

23. $2\log_3 2 + 2\log_3 x$

24. $\log_3 7 + 2\log_3 (2x - 3)$

25. $2\log a + 3\log b - 4\log c$

26. $\log_4 5 + \frac{1}{2}\log_4 x$

27. $1 + \frac{1}{2}\log_8 3 + \frac{5}{2}\log_8 a$

28. $2 - \log_5 x$

29. $1 + 4\log m - 2\log n$

30. ≈ 3.17

31. ≈ 1.2

32. ≈ 1.748

33. ≈ 1.43

34. ≈ 1.4

35. ≈ 3.631

36. ≈ 2.564

37. ≈ 3.183

38. 12

39. -2

40. 5

41. 1

42. 2

43. 2

44. $-\frac{1}{2}$

45. Yes, because the loudness of the sound is 102 dB.

46. about 3 dB

47. The coefficient $\frac{1}{2}$ is missing in $\log_4 s$;

$$\log_4 \sqrt{\frac{t}{s}} = \frac{1}{2}\log_4 \frac{t}{s}$$

$$= \frac{1}{2}(\log_4 t - \log_4 s)$$

$$= \frac{1}{2}\log_4 t - \frac{1}{2}\log_4 s$$

48. No; the expression $(2x + 1)$ is a sum, so it is not covered by the Product, Quotient, or Power Props.

49. The log of a product is equal to the sum of the logs. $\log(MN) = \log M + \log N$.

Determine if each statement is *true* or *false*. Justify your answer.

50. $\log_2 4 + \log_2 8 = 5$

51. $\log_3 \frac{3}{2} = \frac{1}{2}\log_3 3$

52. $\log(x-2) = \frac{\log x}{\log 2}$

53. $\frac{\log_b x}{\log_b y} = \log_b \frac{x}{y}$

54. $(\log x)^2 = \log x^2$

55. $\log_4 7 - \log_4 3 = \log_4 4$

Write each logarithmic expression as a single logarithm.

56. $\frac{1}{4}\log_3 2 + \frac{1}{4}\log_3 x$

57. $\frac{1}{2}(\log_x 4 + \log_x y) - 3\log_x z$

58. $x\log_4 m + \frac{1}{y}\log_4 n - \log_4 p$

59. $\left(\frac{2\log_b x}{3} + \frac{3\log_b y}{4}\right) - 5\log_b z$

Expand each logarithm.

60. $\log\sqrt{\frac{2x}{y}}$

61. $\log\frac{s\sqrt{7}}{t^2}$

62. $\log\left(\frac{2\sqrt{x}}{5}\right)^3$

63. $\log\frac{m^3}{n^4 p^{-2}}$

64. $\log 4\sqrt{\frac{4r}{s^2}}$

65. $\log_b \frac{\sqrt{x}\sqrt[3]{y^2}}{\sqrt[5]{z^2}}$

66. $\log_4 \frac{\sqrt{x^5 y^7}}{zw^4}$

67. $\log\frac{\sqrt{x^2-4}}{(x+3)^2}$

Write each logarithm as the quotient of two common logarithms. Do not simplify the quotient.

68. $\log_7 2$

69. $\log_3 8$

70. $\log_5 140$

71. $\log_9 3.3$

72. $\log_4 3x$

STEM **Astronomy** The apparent brightness of stars is measured on a logarithmic scale called magnitude, in which lower numbers mean brighter stars. The relationship between the ratio of apparent brightness of two objects and the difference in their magnitudes is given by the formula $m_2 - m_1 = -2.5\log\frac{b_2}{b_1}$, where m is the magnitude and b is the apparent brightness.

Capella ⊙
m = 0.1

73. How many times brighter is a magnitude 1.0 star than a magnitude 2.0 star?

74. The star Rigel has a magnitude of 0.12. How many times brighter is Capella than Rigel?

Challenge

Expand each logarithm.

75. $\log\sqrt{\frac{x\sqrt{2}}{y^2}}$

76. $\log_3 [(xy^{\frac{1}{3}}) + z^2]^3$

77. $\log_7 \frac{\sqrt{r+9}}{s^2 t^{\frac{1}{3}}}$

Simplify each expression.

78. $\log_3(x+1) - \log_3(3x^2 - 3x - 6) + \log_3(x-2)$

79. $\log(a^2 - 10a + 25) + \frac{1}{2}\log\frac{1}{(a-5)^3} - \log(\sqrt{a-5})$

---

71. $\frac{\log 3.3}{\log 9}$

72. $\frac{\log 3x}{\log 4}$

73. A 1.0 magnitude star is about 2.5 times brighter than a 2.0 magnitude star.

74. Capella is about 1.02 times brighter than Rigel.

75. $\frac{1}{2}\log x + \frac{1}{4}\log 2 - \log y$

76. $3\log_3\left[xy^{\frac{1}{3}} + z^2\right]$

77. $\frac{1}{2}\log_7(r+9) - 2\log_7 s - \frac{1}{3}\log_7 t$

78. -1

79. 0

---

50. true; $\log_2 4 = 2$ and $\log_2 8 = 3$; $2 + 3 = 5$

51. false; $\frac{1}{2}\log_3 3 = \log_3 3^{\frac{1}{2}}$, not $\log_3 \frac{3}{2}$

52. False; this is not an example of the Quotient Prop. $\log(x-2) \neq \log x - \log 2$

53. false; $\log_b \frac{x}{y} = \log_b x - \log_b y$

54. false; $(\log x)^2 = (\log x) \times (\log x) \neq \log x^2$

55. false; $\log_4 7 - \log_4 3 = \log_4 \frac{7}{3}$ not $\log_4 4$.

56. $\log_3 \sqrt[4]{2x}$

57. $\log_x \frac{2\sqrt{y}}{z^3}$

58. $\log_4 \frac{m^x n^{\frac{1}{y}}}{p}$

59. $\log_b \frac{\sqrt[3]{x^2}\sqrt[4]{y^3}}{z^5}$

60. $\frac{1}{2}\log 2 + \frac{1}{2}\log x - \frac{1}{2}\log y$

61. $\log s + \frac{1}{2}\log 7 - 2\log t$

62. $3\log 2 + \frac{3}{2}\log x - 3\log 5$

63. $3\log m - 4\log n + 2\log p$

64. $3\log 2 + \frac{1}{2}\log r - \log s$

65. $\frac{1}{2}\log_b x + \frac{2}{3}\log_b y - \frac{2}{5}\log_b z$

66. $\frac{5}{2}\log_4 x + \frac{7}{2}\log_4 y - \log_4 z - 4\log_4 w$

67. $\frac{1}{2}\log(x+2) + \frac{1}{2}\log(x-2) - 2\log(x+3)$

68. $\frac{\log 2}{\log 7}$

69. $\frac{\log 8}{\log 3}$

70. $\frac{\log 140}{\log 5}$

Answers

Standardized Test Prep

80. B

81. I

82. C

83. [2] $\log 18 = \log \frac{36}{2} = \log 36 - \log 2$;
Quotient Prop.

$\quad = \log 2 \cdot 9 = \log 2 + \log 9$;
Product Prop.

$\quad = \log 324^{\frac{1}{2}} = \frac{1}{2}\log 324$;
Power Prop.

$\quad = \log 2 \cdot 3^2 = \log 2 + 2 \log 3$;
Product and Power Prop.

[1] log 18 is written in only 2 ways with the properties named OR properties are not named

Mixed Review

84. $\log_7 49 = 2$

85. $\log_8 \frac{1}{4} = -\frac{2}{3}$

86. $-3 = \log_5 \frac{1}{125}$

87. ± 8

88. $\frac{64}{7}$

89. 2

90. $x^3 + 5x^2 - 3x - 15$

91. $x^4 + 17x^2 + 16$

92. $x^4 - 2x^3 - 2x^2 + 14x - 35$

93. 2

94. 3

95. $\frac{1}{3}$

Standardized Test Prep

SAT/ACT

80. Which expression is NOT equivalent to $\sqrt[6]{16r^2}$?

Ⓐ $\left(16r^2\right)^{\frac{1}{6}}$ Ⓑ $4r^{\frac{1}{3}}$ Ⓒ $(4r)^{\frac{1}{3}}$ Ⓓ $\sqrt[3]{4r}$

81. Assume that there are no more turning points beyond those shown. Which graph CANNOT be the graph of a fourth degree polynomial?

Ⓕ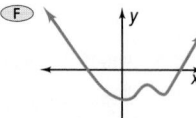

Ⓗ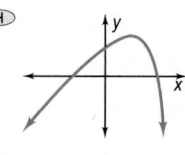

Ⓖ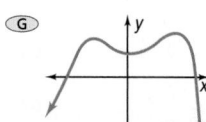

Ⓘ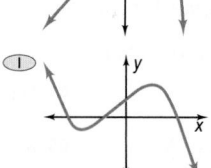

82. A florist is arranging a bouquet of daisies and tulips. He wants twice as many daisies as tulips in the bouquet. If the bouquet contains 24 flowers, how many daisies are in the bouquet?

Ⓐ 8 daisies   Ⓑ 12 daisies   Ⓒ 16 daisies   Ⓓ 24 daisies

Short Response

83. Use the properties of logarithms to write log 18 in four different ways. Name each property you use.

Mixed Review

Write each equation in logarithmic form.   ◆ See Lesson 7-3.

84. $49 = 7^2$ **85.** $\frac{1}{4} = 8^{-\frac{2}{3}}$ **86.** $5^{-3} = \frac{1}{125}$

Solve. Check for extraneous solutions.   ◆ See Lesson 6-5.

87. $\sqrt[3]{y^4} = 16$ **88.** $\sqrt[3]{7x} - 4 = 0$ **89.** $2\sqrt{w-1} = \sqrt{w+2}$

Write a polynomial function with rational coefficients and the given roots.   ◆ See Lesson 5-5.

90. $\sqrt{3}, -5$ **91.** $-i, 4i$ **92.** $-\sqrt{7}, 1 + 2i$

Get Ready!   To prepare for Lesson 7-5, do Exercises 93–95.

Evaluate each logarithm.   ◆ See Lesson 7-3.

93. $\log_{12} 144$ **94.** $\log_4 64$ **95.** $\log_{64} 4$

7-4 Lesson Resources

Additional Instructional Support

Algebra 2 Companion

Students can use the **Algebra 2 Companion** worktext (4 pages) as you teach the lesson. Use the Companion to support

- New Vocabulary
- Key Concepts
- Got It for each Problem
- Lesson Check

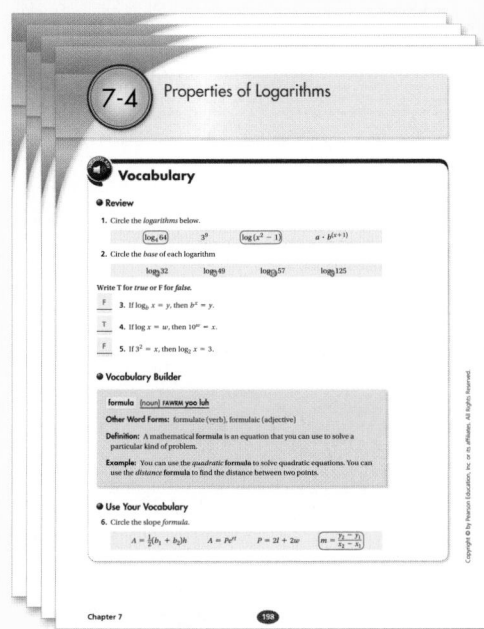

ELL Support

Connect to Prior Knowledge Write the expressions "$m \cdot n$," "$m \times n$," and "mn." Have students work in pairs to brainstorm any words associated with the expression. Expected responses include *times, multiply, factor, product, of, variable*, etc.

After brainstorming has slowed down, have the group list responses as a whole. If a response does not apply (e.g., *addend*), ask the pair to describe their reasoning. Write "product" above the expressions.

Ask for a volunteer to say the Product Property of Exponents. (Students may use their textbooks.) Have students write the property and circle the multiplication, *mn*. Now ask for a volunteer to say the Product Property of Logarithms. Have students write the property and circle the multiplication.

Repeat this exercise for the Quotient and Power Properties of Exponents and Logarithms.

5 Assess & Remediate

Lesson Quiz

1. What is $\log_5 4 + \log_5 3$ written as a single logarithm? If possible, simplify the single logarithm.
2. What is $\log \frac{10}{x^2}$ expanded? Simplify your answer, if possible.
3. What is the value of $\log_7 25$? Use the Change of Base Formula.
4. **Do you UNDERSTAND?** The magnitude of a city can be defined as the common logarithm of the population, *P*. In 2007, Tallahassee had a population of about 1.7×10^5 people. The town of Bascom, FL, had a population of about 1.1×10^2 people. What is the difference in magnitude between Tallahassee and Bascom?

ANSWERS TO LESSON QUIZ

1. $\log_5 12$
2. $1 - 2 \log x$
3. about 1.65
4. about 3.19

PRESCRIPTION FOR REMEDIATION

Use the student work on the Lesson Quiz to prescribe a differentiated review assignment:

Points	Differentiated Remediation
0–1	Intervention
2–3	On-level
4	Extension

PowerAlgebra.com

5 Assess & Remediate

Assign the Lesson Quiz. Appropriate intervention, practice, or enrichment is automatically generated based on student performance.

Differentiated Remediation

Available in editable format online.

Intervention

- **Reteaching** (2 pages) Provides reteaching and practice exercises for the key lesson concepts. Use with struggling students or absent students.
- **English Language Learner Support** Helps students develop and reinforce mathematical vocabulary and key concepts.

All-in-One Resources/Online
Reteaching

All-in-One Resources/Online
English Language Learner Support

Differentiated Remediation *continued*

Available in editable format online.

On-Level

- **Practice** (2 pages) Provides extra practice for each lesson. For simpler practice exercises, use the Form K Practice pages found in the All-in-One Teaching Resources and online.

- **Think About a Plan** Helps students develop specific problem-solving skills and strategies by providing scaffolded guiding questions.

- **Standardized Test Prep** Focuses on all major exercises, all major question types, and helps students prepare for the high-stakes assessments.

Extension

- **Enrichment** Provides students with interesting problems and activities that extend the concepts of the lesson.

- **Activities, Games, and Puzzles** Worksheets that can be used for concepts development, enrichment, and for fun!

Practice and Problem Solving Wkbk/ All-in-One Resources/Online
Practice page 1

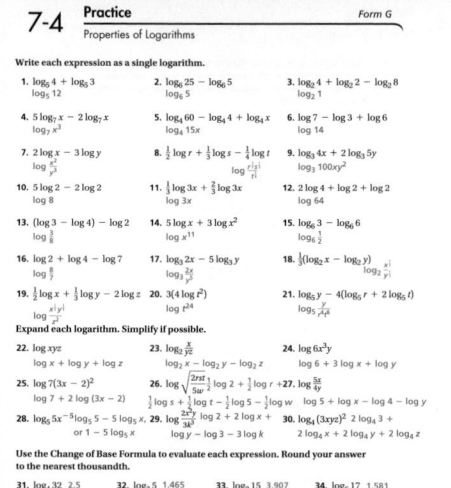

Practice and Problem Solving Wkbk/ All-in-One Resources/Online
Practice page 2

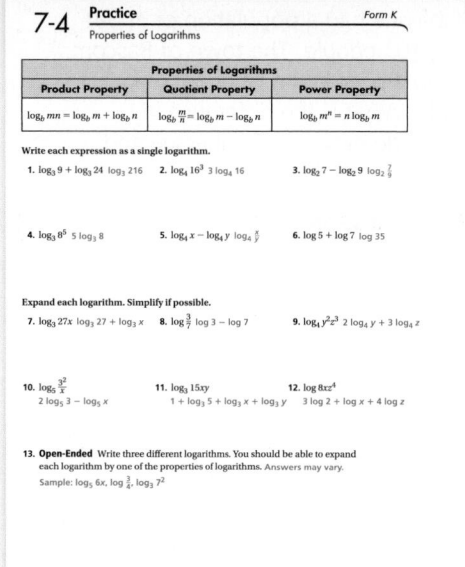

All-in-One Resources/Online
Enrichment

Practice and Problem Solving Wkbk/ All-in-One Resources/Online
Think About a Plan

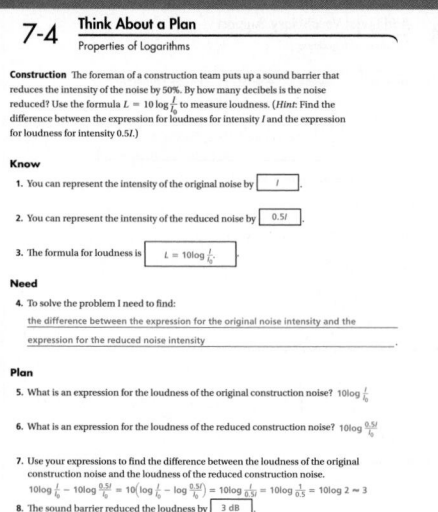

Practice and Problem Solving Wkbk/ All-in-One Resources/Online
Standardized Test Prep

Online Teacher Resource Center
Activities, Games, and Puzzles

Exponential and Logarithmic Equations

© **Common Core State Standards**

F-LE.A.4 For exponential models, express as a logarithm the solution to $ab^{ct} = d$ where a, c, and d are numbers and the base b is 2, 10, or e; evaluate the logarithm using technology. **Also A-REI.D.11**

MP 1, MP 3, MP 4, MP 5, MP 7

Objective To solve exponential and logarithmic equations

Getting Ready!

You are a winner on a TV game show. Which prize would you choose? Explain.

Make sure you win the most money.

© MATHEMATICAL PRACTICES

Prize A
$10,000
per week

Prize B
1¢ today,
2¢ tomorrow,
4¢ the next day,
and so on,
doubling each day

Lesson Vocabulary
• exponential equation
• logarithmic equation

Any equation that contains the form b^{cx}, such as $a = b^{cx}$ where the exponent includes a variable, is an **exponential equation**.

Essential Understanding You can use logarithms to solve exponential equations. You can use exponents to solve logarithmic equations.

Plan

What common base is appropriate?
2 because 16 and 8 are both powers of 2.

© **Problem 1** Solving an Exponential Equation—Common Base

Multiple Choice What is the solution of $16^{3x} = 8$?

Ⓐ $x = \frac{1}{4}$　　　Ⓑ $x = \frac{3}{7}$　　　Ⓒ $x = 1$　　　Ⓓ $x = 4$

$16^{3x} = 8$

$(2^4)^{3x} = 2^3$ Rewrite the terms with a common base.

$2^{12x} = 2^3$ Power Property of Exponents

$12x = 3$ If two numbers with the same base are equal, their exponents are equal.

$x = \frac{1}{4}$ Solve and simplify.

The correct answer is A.

✓ **Got It?** 1. What is the solution of $27^{3x} = 81$?

---

1 Interactive Learning

Solve It!

PURPOSE To use equations with variable exponents to make a decision

PROCESS Students may

• estimate the total amount of money for either prize and draw a conclusion when the amount of one prize exceeds the other.

• calculate the total amount of money received in prize B by adding exponential terms.

FACILITATE

Q How can you find an expression to represent each day for Prize B? **[List the amounts for each day to determine a pattern. 1, 2, 4, 8, 16…; the pattern is exponential because the numbers are doubled, so 2^{n-1} where n is the number of days.]**

Q How much additional money would you receive from prize B on day 10? 20? [$5.12; $5,242.88]**

ANSWER See Solve It in Answers on next page.

CONNECT THE MATH Students use their knowledge of exponential growth to make a decision in the Solve It. In this lesson, students will write and solve exponential equations.

2 Guided Instruction

Problem 1

Q How can you check your answer? **[If $x = \frac{1}{4}$, then $16^{\frac{3}{4}} = 8$. So $\sqrt[4]{16} = 2$ and $2^3 = 8$]**

Got It?

Q What common base do you recognize? **[Both 27 and 81 are powers of 3.]**

7-5 **Preparing to Teach**

BIG ideas Equivalence
　　　　　Function

ESSENTIAL UNDERSTANDINGS

• Logarithms can be used to solve exponential equations. Exponents can be used to solve logarithmic equations.

• An exponential function is a function with the general form $y = ab^x$, $a \neq 0$, with $b > 0$, and $b \neq 1$. In an exponential function, the base b is a constant. The exponent x is the independent variable with domain the set of real numbers.

• The exponential function $y = b^x$ and the logarithmic function $y = \log_b x$ are inverse functions.

Math Background

Exponential and logarithmic functions are inverse functions. This relationship allows you to use logarithms to simplify

exponential equations and exponents to simplify logarithmic equations.

• To solve an exponential equation that cannot be rewritten with a common base, take the logarithm of both sides, and use the properties of logs to simplify.

• To solve a logarithmic equation, rewrite both sides in exponential form to remove the log, and use the properties of exponents to simplify.

The common log or $\log_{10}$ is most often used due to the ease of calculations. Any other base could be used, but the Change of Base formula from Lesson 7-4 would need to be applied in order to find the log using a calculator.

PowerAlgebra.com

1 Interactive Learning

Solve It!
Step out how to solve the Problem with helpful hints and an online question. Other questions are listed above in Interactive Learning.

Virtual Nerd™ Access Virtual Nerd student-centered math tutorials that directly relate to the content of the lesson.

Problem 2

Q What logarithmic base is being used to solve this equation? Explain. **[When no base is shown, it is assumed that the logarithm is base 10. This is easier to calculate, because the log button on a calculator is $\log_{10}$.]**

Q Can the method used in this problem be used to solve exponential equations with common bases? Give an example. **[Yes; by taking the log of each side of the equation in Problem 1, you get $3x = \frac{\log 8}{\log 16}$. So $x = 0.25$]**

Got It? EXTENSION

Q How can you use the log of any base to solve an exponential equation with a calculator? **[Use the Change of Base Formula to convert to $\log_{10}$, and then solve the equation.]**

Problem 3

An estimate of the solution is helpful to determine window or table parameters when solving by graphing or using a table.

Q If no parentheses are used to enter $y = 4^{3x}$, how does the calculator interpret what is entered? **[If no parentheses are used, $y = 4^{3x}$ is interpreted as $y = 4^3 x$ which is a linear equation.]**

Got It?

Q How can you determine whether your solution is reasonable? **[For 3a, $7^3 = 343$ and $7^4 = 2401$. Because the exponent is $4x$, x will be between 0.75 and 1.]**

When bases are not the same, you can solve an exponential equation by taking the logarithm of each side of the equation. If m and n are positive and $m = n$, then $\log m = \log n$.

 Problem 2 Solving an Exponential Equation—Different Bases

What is the solution of $15^{3x} = 285$?

Think

Which property of logarithms will help isolate x?
The rule $\log a^x = x \log a$ moves x out of the exponent position.

$$15^{3x} = 285$$
$$\log 15^{3x} = \log 285 \qquad \text{Take the logarithm of each side.}$$
$$3x \log 15 = \log 285 \qquad \text{Power Property of Logarithms}$$
$$x = \frac{\log 285}{3 \log 15} \qquad \text{Divide each side by 3 log 15 to isolate } x.$$
$$x \approx 0.6958 \qquad \text{Use a calculator.}$$

Check $15^{3x} = 285$
$$15^{3(0.6958)} \approx 285.0840331 \approx 285 \checkmark$$

 Got It? 2. a. What is the solution of $5^{2x} = 130$?

b. Reasoning Why can't you use the same method you used in Problem 1 to solve Problem 2?

 Problem 3 Solving an Exponential Equation With a Graph or Table

What is the solution of $4^{3x} = 6000$?

Method 1 Solve using a graph.
Use a graphing calculator. Graph the equations.
$$Y_1 = 4^{3x}$$
$$Y_2 = 6000$$

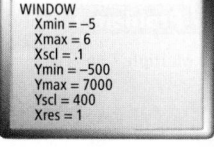
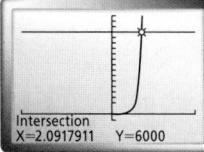

Adjust the window to find the point of intersection. The solution is $x \approx 2.09$.

Method 2 Solve using a table.
Use the table feature of a graphing calculator. Enter $Y_1 = 4^{3x}$.

Think

How do you choose TblStart and ΔTbl values?
Start with 0 and 1, respectively. Adjust both values as you close in on the solution.

Use the **TABLE SETUP** and Δ**Tbl** features to locate the x-value that gives the y-value closest to 6000. The solution is $x \approx 2.09$.

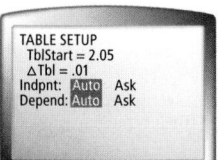
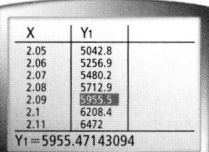

 Got It? 3. What is the solution of each exponential equation? Check your answer.

a. $7^{4x} = 800$ **b.** $5.2^{3x} = 400$

Answers

Solve It!
Prize B; compare the prizes over a year:
$$2^{365} > 520{,}000$$

Got It?

1. $\frac{4}{9}$

2. a. ≈ 1.5122

  b. because the terms cannot be written with a common base

3. a. ≈ 0.8588

  b. ≈ 1.2114

 **PowerAlgebra.com**

2 Guided Instruction

Each Problem is worked out and supported online.

Problem 1
Solving an Exponential Equation—Common Base

Problem 2
Solving an Exponential Equation—Different Bases
Animated

Problem 3
Solving an Exponential Equation With a Graph or Table

Problem 4
Modeling With an Exponential Equation
Animated

Problem 5
Solving a Logarithmic Equation

Problem 6
Using Logarithmic Properties to Solve an Equation
Animated

Support in Algebra 2 Companion
• Vocabulary
• Key Concepts
• Got It?

 **Problem 4** Modeling With an Exponential Equation **STEM**

Resource Management Wood is a sustainable, renewable, natural resource when you manage forests properly. Your lumber company has 1,200,000 trees. You plan to harvest 7% of the trees each year. How many years will it take to harvest half of the trees?

Know	Need	Plan
• Number of trees • Rate of decay	Number of years it takes to harvest 600,000 trees	• Write an exponential equation. • Use logarithms to solve the equation.

Think

What equation should you use to model this situation?
Since you are planning to harvest 7% of the trees each year, you should use $y = ab^x$, where b is the decay factor.

Step 1 Is an exponential model reasonable for this situation?

Yes, you are harvesting a fixed percentage each year.

Step 2 Define the variables and determine the model.

Let n = the number of years it takes to harvest half of the trees.

Let $T(n)$ = the number of trees remaining after n years.

A reasonable model is $T(n) = a(b)^n$.

Step 3 Use the model to write an exponential equation.

$T(n) = 600,000$

$a = 1,200,000$

$r = -7\% = -0.07$

$b = 1 + r = 1 + (-0.07) = 0.93$

So, $1,200,000(0.93)^n = 600,000$.

Step 4 Solve the equation. Use logarithms.

$1,200,000(0.93)^n = 600,000$

$0.93^n = \dfrac{600,000}{1,200,000}$ Isolate the term with n.

$\log 0.93^n = \log 0.5$ Take the logarithm of each side.

$n \log 0.93 = \log 0.5$ Power Property of Logarithms

$n = \dfrac{\log 0.5}{\log 0.93}$ Solve for n.

$n \approx 9.55$ Use a calculator.

It will take about 9.55 years to harvest half of the original trees.

 Got It? **4.** After how many years will you have harvested half of the trees if you harvest 5% instead of 7% yearly?

A **logarithmic equation** is an equation that includes one or more logarithms involving a variable.

PowerAlgebra.com   Lesson 7-5   Exponential and Logarithmic Equations   **471**

Problem 4
Suggest students look for key words in the situation to determine if the model represents an increase or decrease, and define the variable accordingly.

Q What does b represent in $y = ab^x$? What does r represent in $T(n) = a(1 + r)^n$? **[The variable b represents the growth factor if $b > 1$, and it represents the decay factor if $b < 1$. The variable r represents the rate of increase if $r > 0$, and it represents the rate of decrease if $r < 0$.]**

Q How can either model be used when writing this equation? Explain. **[The 7% harvest can be used to find the decay factor, or it can represent the rate of decrease. Because 93% of the harvest will remain after each year, a decay factor of $b = 0.93$ can be used. Using the 7% harvest as a rate of decrease, $r = -0.07$.]**

Got It?   **VISUAL LEARNERS**
Students can use a recursive routine with a graphing calculator to check the reasonableness of their answer. Input the following:

1,200,000   press Enter
Ans * 0.95   press Enter

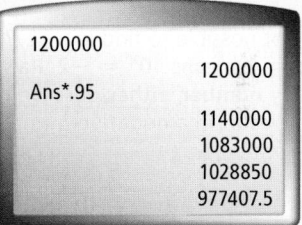

Count the number of times Enter is pressed to find the total number of years.

Additional Problems

1. What is the solution of $256^{2x} = 64$?

ANSWER $\frac{3}{8}$

2. What is the solution of $6^{4x} = 512$?

ANSWER 0.8704

3. What is the solution of $5^{2x} = 3500$?

ANSWER 2.54

4. Your MP3 player has about 126,000,000 bytes of memory. Each month you plan to use 5% of the memory remaining. How many months will it take you to use $\frac{1}{4}$ of the memory?

ANSWER 5.61 months

5. What is the solution of $\log (5x + 2) = 2$?

ANSWER 19.6

6. What is the solution of $\log 2x^2 - \log 5 = 1$?

ANSWER 5, −5

Answers

Got It? (continued)
4. ≈ 13.51 yrs

Lesson 7-5   **471**

Problem 5

Converting a logarithmic equation to exponential form can be thought of as raising both sides to the power of 10. Note that $\log(4x - 3) = 2$ is the same as $10^{\log(4x-3)} = 10^2$.

> **Q** What are the advantages and disadvantages of using a graph or table to solve a logarithmic equation? **[An advantage is that you can see how the exponential equation changes for values of x. A disadvantage is that you must either zoom in at the intersection or change the ΔTbl values to find more precise answers.]**

Got It?

> **Q** Which method would you choose to solve this problem? Explain. **[Sample: You would choose exponents, because it is simpler to rewrite the equation as $3 - 2x = 10^{-1}$ and solve for x. You need an estimate to set the window or the TblStart values in a calculator. Since you have to rewrite the equation in exponential form to estimate, it is easier to just solve for x.]**

Problem 6

> **Q** Why is it not possible to find $\log(-2)$? **[$\log(-2) = x$ means $10^x = -2$. Raising a positive base to any number, either positive or negative, will never result in a negative number.]**

Got It?

> **Q** How can you determine which property of logarithms to use when solving the equation? **[If logarithms are added, use the Product Property. If they are subtracted, use the Quotient Property. If a number is multiplied by a logarithm, use the Power Property.]**

Plan

How do you convert between log form and exponential form?
Use the rule: $\log a = b$ if and only if $a = 10^b$.

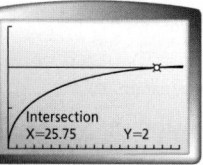 **Problem 5** Solving a Logarithmic Equation

What is the solution of $\log(4x - 3) = 2$?

Method 1 Solve using exponents.

$$\log(4x - 3) = 2$$
$$4x - 3 = 10^2 \qquad \text{Write in exponential form.}$$
$$4x = 103 \qquad \text{Simplify.}$$
$$x = \frac{103}{4} = 25.75 \qquad \text{Solve for } x.$$

Method 2 Solve using a graph.
Graph the equations $Y_1 = \text{LOG } (4x - 3)$ and $Y_2 = 2$.
Find the point of intersection.
The solution is $x = 25.75$.

Method 3 Solve using a table.
Enter $Y_1 = \text{LOG } (4x - 3)$.
Use the **TABLE SETUP** feature to find the x-value that corresponds to a y-value of 2 in the table.
The solution is $x = 25.75$.

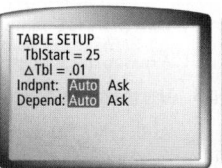

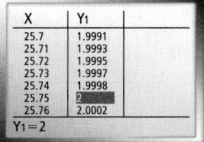

 Got It? 5. What is the solution of $\log(3 - 2x) = -1$?

 Problem 6 Using Logarithmic Properties to Solve an Equation

What is the solution of $\log(x - 3) + \log x = 1$?

$$\log(x - 3) + \log x = 1$$
$$\log((x - 3)x) = 1 \qquad \text{Product Property of Logarithms}$$
$$(x - 3)x = 10^1 \qquad \text{Write in exponential form.}$$
$$x^2 - 3x - 10 = 0 \qquad \text{Simplify to a quadratic equation in standard form.}$$
$$(x - 5)(x + 2) = 0 \qquad \text{Factor the trinomial.}$$
$$x = 5 \quad \text{or} \quad x = -2 \qquad \text{Solve for } x.$$

Check

$$\log(x - 3) + \log(x) = 1 \qquad\qquad \log(x - 3) + \log(x) = 1$$
$$\log(-2 - 3) + \log(-2) \stackrel{?}{=} 1 ✗ \qquad \log(5 - 3) + \log(5) \stackrel{?}{=} 1$$
$$\log 2 + \log 5 \stackrel{?}{=} 1$$
$$0.3010 + 0.6990 = 1 ✔$$

If $\log(x - 3) + \log(x) = 1$, $x = 5$.

Think

What is the domain of the logarithmic function?
Logs are defined only for positive numbers. The log of a negative number is undefined.

Got It? 6. What is the solution of $\log 6 - \log 3x = -2$?

Answers

Got It? (continued)
5. 1.45
6. 200

Lesson Check

Do you know HOW?

Solve each equation.

1. $3^x = 9$

2. $2^{y+1} = 25$

3. $\log 4x = 2$

4. $\log x - \log 2 = 3$

Do you UNDERSTAND?

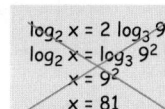

5. **Error Analysis** Describe and correct the error made in solving the equation.

$$\log_2 x = 2\log_3 9$$
$$\log_2 x = \log_3 9^2$$
$$x = 9^2$$
$$x = 81$$

6. **Reasoning** Is it possible for an exponential equation to have no solutions? If so, give an example. If not, explain why.

Practice and Problem-Solving Exercises  MATHEMATICAL PRACTICES

A Practice

Solve each equation. ◀ **See Problem 1.**

7. $2^x = 8$
8. $3^{2x} = 27$
9. $4^{3x} = 64$
10. $5^{3x} = \frac{1}{125}$

11. $2^{5x+1} = 32$
12. $3^{-2x+2} = 81$
13. $2^{3x} = 4^{x+1}$
14. $3^{x+2} = 27^{2x}$

Solve each equation. Round to the nearest ten-thousandth. Check your answers. ◀ **See Problem 2.**

15. $2^x = 3$
16. $4^x = 19$
17. $8 + 10^x = 1008$
18. $5 - 3^x = -40$

19. $9^{2y} = 66$
20. $12^{y-2} = 20$
21. $25^{2x+1} = 144$
22. $2^{3x-4} = 5$

Graphing Calculator Solve by graphing. Round to the nearest ten-thousandth. ◀ **See Problem 3.**

23. $4^{7x} = 250$
24. $5^{3x} = 500$
25. $6^x = 4565$
26. $1.5^x = 356$

Use a table to solve each equation. Round to the nearest hundredth.

27. $2^{x+3} = 512$
28. $3^{x-1} = 72$
29. $6^{2x} = 10$
30. $5^{2x} = 56$

31. The equation $y = 6.72(1.014)^x$ models the world population y, in billions of people, x years after the year 2000. Find the year in which the world population is about 8 billion. ◀ **See Problem 4.**

Solve each equation. Check your answers. ◀ **See Problem 5.**

32. $\log 2x = -1$
33. $2\log x = -1$
34. $\log(3x + 1) = 2$
35. $\log x + 4 = 8$

36. $\log 6x - 3 = -4$
37. $3\log x = 1.5$
38. $2\log(x + 1) = 5$
39. $\log(5 - 2x) = 0$

Solve each equation. ◀ **See Problem 6.**

40. $\log x - \log 3 = 8$
41. $\log 2x + \log x = 11$
42. $2\log x + \log 4 = 2$

43. $\log 5 - \log 2x = 1$
44. $3\log x - \log 6 + \log 2.4 = 9$
45. $\log(7x + 1) = \log(x - 2) + 1$

---

3 Lesson Check

Do you know HOW? ERROR INTERVENTION

- If students have difficulty with Exercises 1–2, remind them they can either search for a common base or take the logarithm of each side. Taking the logarithm of each side will work for both types of equations, while finding a common base may not be possible.

- For Exercise 2, students might mistakenly believe they can use a common base. Point out that the right side of the equation would have base 5.

Do you UNDERSTAND?

- For Exercise 6, if students cannot find an exponential equation that has no solutions, point out Problem 6. The logarithm of a negative number does not have a real solution.

Close

> **Q** How is the relationship between exponents and logarithms used to solve problems? Explain. **[Exponential and logarithmic functions are inverse functions. You can solve an exponential equation by taking logarithms of both sides. You can solve a logarithmic equation by rewriting it in exponential form.]**
>
> **Q** What methods can be used to solve an exponential equation? **[Rewrite the terms with a common base, or take a logarithm of each side. You can also use a graphing calculator to graph or find a solution using a table.]**
>
> **Q** What methods can be used to solve a logarithmic equation? **[Rewrite the problem using exponents, use a graph, use a table, or use logarithmic properties.]**

Lesson Check

1. 2
2. ≈ 3.6439
3. 25
4. 2000
5. The log bases are not equal.
$$\log_2 x = 2\log_3 9$$
$$\log_2 x = \log_3 9^2$$
$$\log_2 x = 4$$
$$x = 2^4$$
$$x = 16$$
6. Yes; $5^x = 0$ has no solution.

Practice and Problem-Solving Exercises

7. 3
8. $\frac{3}{2}$
9. 1
10. -1
11. $\frac{4}{5}$
12. -1
13. 2
14. $\frac{2}{5}$
15. 1.5850
16. 2.1240
17. 3
18. 3.4650
19. 0.9534
20. 3.2056
21. 0.2720
22. 2.1073
23. 0.5690
24. 1.2871
25. 4.7027
26. 14.4894
27. 6
28. 4.89
29. 0.64
30. 1.25
31. about the yr 2012
32. 0.05
33. $\frac{\sqrt{10}}{10}$ or about 0.3162
34. 33
35. 10,000
36. $\frac{1}{60}$ or ≈ 0.0167
37. $\sqrt{10}$ or ≈ 3.1623
38. $100\sqrt{10} - 1$ or ≈ 315.2
39. 2
40. 3×10^8
41. $100,000\sqrt{5}$ or $\approx 223,606.8$
42. 5
43. $\frac{1}{4}$
44. 1357.2
45. 7

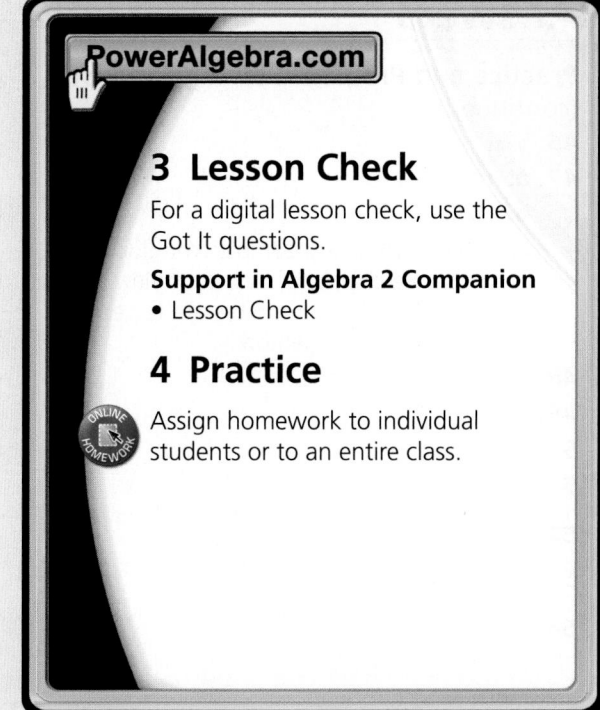

3 Lesson Check

For a digital lesson check, use the Got It questions.

Support in Algebra 2 Companion
- Lesson Check

4 Practice

Assign homework to individual students or to an entire class.

4 Practice

ASSIGNMENT GUIDE

Basic: 7–45 all, 46–54 even, 60, 61

Average: 7–45 odd, 46–78

Advanced: 7–45 odd, 46–83

Standardized Test Prep: 84–88

Ⓒ Mathematical Practices are supported by exercises with red headings. Here are the Practices supported in this lesson:

MP 1: Make Sense of Problems Ex. 46

MP 3: Communicate Ex. 47c

MP 3: Construct Arguments Ex. 6, 59, 60, 61

MP 3: Critique the Reasoning of Others Ex. 5

MP 5: Use Appropriate Tools Ex. 23–26

MP 7: Use Structure Ex. 50–57

Applications exercises have blue headings. Exercises 58, 62 & 63 support MP 4: Model.

STEM exercises focus on science or engineering applications.

EXERCISE 48: Use the Think About a Plan worksheet in the **Practice and Problem Solving Workbook** (also available in the Teaching Resources in print and online) to further support students' development in becoming independent learners.

HOMEWORK QUICK CHECK

To check students' understanding of key skills and concepts, go over Exercises 9, 33, 46, 48, and 61.

Ⓑ Apply

Ⓒ 46. Think About a Plan An earthquake of magnitude 9.1 occurred in 2004 in the Indian Ocean near Indonesia. It was about 74,900 times as strong as the greatest earthquake ever to hit Texas. Find the magnitude of the Texas earthquake. (Remember that an increase of 1.0 on the Richter scale means an earthquake is 30 times stronger.)
• Can you write an exponential or logarithmic equation?
• How does the solution of your equation help you find the magnitude?

Ⓒ 47. Consider the equation $2^{\frac{x}{3}} = 80$.
  a. Solve the equation by taking the logarithm base 10 of each side.
  b. Solve the equation by taking the logarithm base 2 of each side.
  c. Writing Compare your result in parts (a) and (b). What are the advantages of each method? Explain.

STEM 48. Seismology An earthquake of magnitude 7.7 occurred in 2001 in Gujarat, India. It was about 4900 times as strong as the greatest earthquake ever to hit Pennsylvania. What is the magnitude of the Pennsylvania earthquake? (*Hint:* Refer to the Richter scale on page 453.)

49. As a town gets smaller, the population of its high school decreases by 6% each year. The senior class has 160 students now. In how many years will it have about 100 students? Write an equation. Then solve the equation without graphing.

Ⓒ Mental Math Solve each equation.

50. $2^x = \frac{1}{2}$ **51.** $3^x = 27$ **52.** $\log_9 3 = x$ **53.** $\log_4 64 = x$

54. $\log_8 2 = x$ **55.** $10^x = \frac{1}{100}$ **56.** $\log_7 343 = x$ **57.** $25^x = \frac{1}{5}$

58. Demography The table below lists the states with the highest and with the lowest population growth rates. Determine in how many years each event can occur. Use the model $P = P_0(1 + r)^x$, where P_0 is population from the table, as of July, 2007; x is the number of years after July, 2007, P is the projected population, and r is the growth rate.
  a. Population of Idaho exceeds 2 million.
  b. Population of Michigan decreases by 1 million.
  c. Population of Nevada doubles.

State	Growth rate (%)	Population (in thousands)	State	Growth rate (%)	Population (in thousands)
1. Nevada	2.93	2,565	46. New York	0.08	19,298
2. Arizona	2.81	6,339	47. Vermont	0.08	621
3. Utah	2.55	2,645	48. Ohio	0.03	11,467
4. Idaho	2.43	1,499	49. Michigan	−0.30	10,072
5. Georgia	2.17	9,545	50. Rhode Island	−0.36	1,058

Source: U.S. Census Bureau

474   Chapter 7   Exponential and Logarithmic Functions

Answers

Practice and Problem-Solving Exercises
(continued)

46. 5.8

47. a. 18.9658
  b. 18.9658
  c. Answers may vary. Sample: You don't have to use the change of base formula with the base-10 method, but there are fewer steps with the base-2 method.

48. about 5.2

49. ≈ 7.6 yrs

50. −1

51. 3

52. $\frac{1}{2}$

53. 3

54. $\frac{1}{3}$

55. −2

56. 3

57. $-\frac{1}{2}$

58. a. 13 yrs after July 2007
  b. 35 yrs after July 2007
  c. 25 yrs after July 2007

474   Chapter 7

59. Open-Ended Write and solve a logarithmic equation.

60. Reasoning The graphs of $y = 2^{3x}$ and $y = 3^{x+1}$ intersect at approximately (1.1201, 10.2692). What is the solution of $2^{3x} = 3^{x+1}$?

61. Reasoning If $\log 12^{0.5x} = \log 143.6$, then $12^{0.5x} = $? .

STEM Acoustics In Exercises 62–63, the loudness measured in decibels (dB) is defined by loudness $= 10 \log \frac{I}{I_0}$, where I is the intensity and $I_0 = 10^{-12}$ W/m^2.

62. The human threshold for pain is 120 dB. Instant perforation of the eardrum occurs at 160 dB.
   a. Find the intensity of each sound.
   b. How many times as intense is the noise that will perforate an eardrum as the noise that causes pain?

63. The noise level inside a convertible driving along the freeway with its top up is 70 dB. With the top down, the noise level is 95 dB.
   a. Find the intensity of the sound with the top up and with the top down.
   b. By what percent does leaving the top up reduce the intensity of the sound?

Solve each equation. If necessary, round to the nearest ten-thousandth.

64. $8^x = 444$

65. $\frac{1}{2} \log x + \log 4 = 2$

66. $4 \log_3 2 - 2 \log_3 x = 1$

67. $\log x^2 = 2$

68. $9^{2x} = 42$

69. $\log_8 (2x - 1) = \frac{1}{3}$

70. $\log (5x - 4) = 3$

71. $12^{4-x} = 20$

72. $5^{3x} = 125$

73. $\log 4 + 2 \log x = 6$

74. $4^{3x} = 77.2$

75. $\log_7 3x = 3$

Use the properties of exponential and logarithmic functions to solve each system. Check your answers.

76. $\begin{cases} y = 2^{x+4} \\ y - 4^{x-1} = 0 \end{cases}$

77. $\begin{cases} 2^{x+y} = 16 \\ 4^{x-y} = 1 \end{cases}$

78. $\begin{cases} \log(2x - y) = 1 \\ \log(x + y) = 3 \log 2 \end{cases}$

 **Challenge** **Solve each equation.**

79. $\log_7 (2x - 3)^2 = 2$

80. $\log_2 (x^2 + 2x) = 3$

81. $\frac{3}{2} \log_2 4 - \frac{1}{2} \log_2 x = 3$

STEM 82. Meteorology In the formula $P = P_0 \left(\frac{1}{2} \right)^{\frac{h}{4795}}$, P is the atmospheric pressure in millimeters of mercury at elevation h meters above sea level. P_0 is the atmospheric pressure at sea level. If P_0 equals 760 mm, at what elevation is the pressure 42 mm?

---

59. Answers may vary. Sample:
   $\log x = 1.6$; $x \approx 39.81$

60. 1.1201

61. 143.6

62. a. 1 W/m^2; 10^4 W/m^2
   b. 10,000 times as intense

63. a. top up: 10^{-5} W/m^2 top down: $10^{-2.5}$ W/m^2
   b. 99.68%

64. 2.9315

65. 625

66. 2.3094

67. 10

68. 0.8505

69. 1.5

70. 200.8

71. 2.7944

72. 1

73. 500

74. 1.0451

75. $114.\overline{3}$

76. $x = 6, y = 1024$

77. $x = y = 2$

78. $x = 6, y = 2$

79. $-2, 5$

80. $-4, 2$

81. 1

82. $\approx 20,031$ m above sea level

Answers

Practice and Problem-Solving Exercises
(continued)

83 a. bassoon, guitar, harp, violin, viola, cello

b. bassoon, guitar, harp, cello, bass

c. harp, violin

d. harp

Standardized Test Prep

84. 4

85. 333

86. 25

87. 4

88. 18

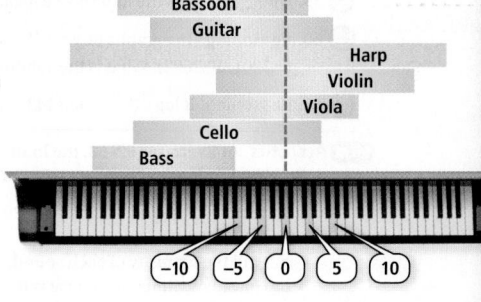

STEM **83. Music** The pitch, or frequency, of a piano note is related to its position on the keyboard by the function $F(n) = 440 \cdot 2^{\frac{n}{12}}$, where F is the frequency of the sound waves in cycles per second and n is the number of piano keys above or below Concert A, as shown. If $n = 0$ at Concert A, which of the instruments shown in the diagram can sound notes at the given frequency?

a. 590 **c.** 1440

b. 120 **d.** 2093

Standardized Test Prep

SAT/ACT

GRIDDED RESPONSE

84. The graph at the right shows the translation of the graph of the parent function $y = |x|$ down 2 units and 3 units to the right. What is the area of the shaded triangle in square units?

85. What does x equal if $\log(1 + 3x) = 3$?

86. Using the change of base formula, what is the value of x for which $\log_9 x = \log_3 5$?

87. The polynomial $x^4 + 3x^3 + 16x^2 - 19x + 8$ is divided by the binomial $x - 1$. What is the coefficient of x^2 in the quotient?

88. What positive value of b makes $x^2 + bx + 81$ a perfect square trinomial?

 **Apply What You've Learned**

MATHEMATICAL PRACTICES
MP 5

Look back at the information on page 433 about apparent magnitudes of stars. In the Apply What You've Learned section in Lesson 7-1, you wrote an exponential function to model the problem on page 433.

a. Use the exponential function you wrote in part (c) on page 441 to write an exponential equation that you can solve for the difference in apparent magnitude between Polaris and Sirius.

b. Explain how to use a graphing calculator to solve the equation you wrote in part (a).

c. Solve the equation algebraically, and use a graphing calculator to check your answer. Round your answer to the nearest hundredth.

 Apply What You've Learned

In the Apply What You've Learned section in Lesson 7-1, students wrote an exponential function to model the problem on page 433. Now, they will use this function to find the difference in magnitudes between Sirius and Polaris.

Mathematical Practices
Students will create an exponential equation and **use an appropriate tool** (a calculator) to solve the equation. (MP 5)

ANSWERS

a. $24 = 10^{0.4x}$

b. Graph $y = 10^{0.4x}$ and $y = 24$ on the same set of axes. Adjust the viewing window to see the point of intersection. The x-coordinate of the point of intersection is the solution of the equation.

c. 3.45

Additional Instructional Support

Algebra 2 Companion

Students can use the **Algebra 2 Companion** worktext (4 pages) as you teach the lesson. Use the Companion to support

- New Vocabulary
- Key Concepts
- Got It for each Problem
- Lesson Check

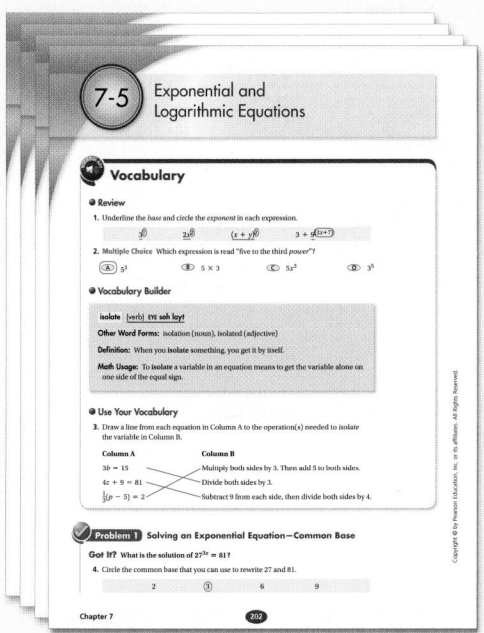

ELL Support

Focus on Communication Have students write exponential or logarithmic properties used to solve equations on index cards and an example of the property on the back. For example, students can write the Power Property of Exponents, Power Property of Logarithms, Product Property of Logarithms, and Quotient Property of Logarithms. Divide students into pairs, and have one person solve the problem while the other asks a question. Have students ask, "How did you complete that step?" A student might respond by stating, "I used the Power Property of Logarithms," or the student may show the index card with the correct property. If the student uses the index card, encourage the student to read the words of the property to practice using the academic language. Next, have the students switch roles so that each has practice solving the problem and answering questions.

5 Assess & Remediate

Lesson Quiz

1. What is the solution of $16^{-3n+2} = 64$?
2. What is the solution of $12^{4x} = 256$?
3. What is the solution of $36^{-3x} = 1500$?
4. **Do you UNDERSTAND?** A population of 12,000 fish has a growth rate of 4% each year. Write a model for the situation. How many years will it take for the population to reach 20,000?
5. What is the solution of $\log 5x - 3 = 2$?
6. Solve $\log 2x - \log 8 = 3$.

ANSWERS TO LESSON QUIZ

1. $\frac{1}{6}$
2. 0.5579
3. −0.68
4. $12,000(1.04)^n = 20,000$; 13.02 years
5. 20,000
6. 4000

PRESCRIPTION FOR REMEDIATION
Use the student work on the Lesson Quiz to prescribe a differentiated review assignment:

Points	Differentiated Remediation
0–2	Intervention
3–5	On-level
6	Extension

PowerAlgebra.com

5 Assess & Remediate

Assign the Lesson Quiz. Appropriate intervention, practice, or enrichment is automatically generated based on student performance.

Differentiated Remediation
Available in editable format online.

Intervention

- **Reteaching** (2 pages) Provides reteaching and practice exercises for the key lesson concepts. Use with struggling students or absent students.

- **English Language Learner Support** Helps students develop and reinforce mathematical vocabulary and key concepts.

All-in-One Resources/Online
Reteaching

All-in-One Resources/Online
English Language Learner Support

Differentiated Remediation continued

Available in editable format online.

On-Level

- **Practice** (2 pages) Provides extra practice for each lesson. For simpler practice exercises, use the Form K Practice pages found in the All-in-One Teaching Resources and online.

- **Think About a Plan** Helps students develop specific problem-solving skills and strategies by providing scaffolded guiding questions.

- **Standardized Test Prep** Focuses on all major exercises, all major question types, and helps students prepare for the high-stakes assessments.

Extension

- **Enrichment** Provides students with interesting problems and activities that extend the concepts of the lesson.

- **Activities, Games, and Puzzles** Worksheets that can be used for concepts development, enrichment, and for fun!

Practice and Problem Solving Wkbk/All-in-One Resources/Online
Practice page 1

7-5 Practice Form G
Exponential and Logarithmic Equations

Solve each equation.

1. $8^{2x} = 32$ $\frac{5}{4}$
2. $7^n = 343$ 3
3. $9^{2x} = 27$ $\frac{3}{4}$
4. $25^{2n+1} = 625$ $\frac{1}{2}$
5. $36^{-2x+1} = 216$ $-\frac{1}{4}$
6. $64^x = 4096$ 2

Solve each equation. Round answers to the nearest hundredth.

7. $5^{2x} = 20$ 0.93
8. $8^{n+1} = 3$ −0.47
9. $4^{n-2} = 3$ 2.79
10. $4^{3n} = 5$ 0.39
11. $15^{2n-3} = 245$ 2.52
12. $4^x - 5 = 12$ 2.04

Solve by graphing. Round to the nearest hundredth.

13. $2^{n+5} = 120$ 1.91
14. $8^{n+1} = 175$ 2.21
15. $8^x = 58$ 1.95
16. $10^n = 3$ 0.48
17. $10^{3y} = 5$ 0.23
18. $10^{k-2} = 20$ 3.30
19. $5^x = 4$ 0.86
20. $2^{4x} = 8$ 0.75
21. $3^{x+5} = 15$ −2.54

Use a table to solve each equation. Round to the nearest hundredth.

22. $8^{2n} = 3$ 0.26
23. $12^{2n-1} = 64$ 1.34
24. $12^{n-2} = 8$ 2.84
25. $10^x = 182$ 2.26
26. $8^n = 12$ 1.19
27. $10^{2x} = 9$ 0.48
28. $5^{n+1} = 3$ −0.32
29. $10^{n-2} = 0.3$ 1.48
30. $3^{3n} = 50$ 1.19

31. The equation $y = 281(1.01)^x$ is a model for the population of the United States y, in millions of people, x years after the year 2000. Estimate when the United States population will reach 400 million people. in the year 2035

Solve each equation. Check your answers.

32. $\log x = 2$ 100
33. $\log 4x = -1$ $\frac{1}{40}$
34. $\log 3x = 2$ $\frac{100}{3}$
35. $\log x = 2$ 25
36. $\log x = 4$ 10
37. $\log x = 16$ 100
38. $2 \log x = 2$ 10
39. $\log(2x + 5) = 3$ $\frac{995}{2}$
40. $\log(3x - 2) = 3$ 334
41. $\log(x - 25) = 2$ 125
42. $2 \log(2x + 5) = 4$ $\frac{95}{2}$
43. $3 \log(1 - 2x) = 6$ $-\frac{99}{2}$

Practice and Problem Solving Wkbk/All-in-One Resources/Online
Practice page 2

7-5 Practice (continued) Form G
Exponential and Logarithmic Equations

Solve each equation.

44. $\log x - \log 4 = 3$ 4000
45. $\log x - \log 4 = -2$ $\frac{1}{25}$
46. $2 \log x - \log 4 = 2$ 20
47. $\log 3x - \log 5 = 1$ $\frac{50}{3}$
48. $2 \log x - \log 3 = 1$ $\sqrt{30}$
49. $\log 8 - 2x = -1$ 40
50. $2 \log 3x - \log 9 = 1$ $\sqrt{10}$
51. $2 \log x - \log 5 = -2$ $\frac{\sqrt{20}}{20}$
52. $\log(x + 21) + \log x = 2$ 4

53. The function $y = 1000(1.005)^x$ models the value of $1000 deposited at an interest rate of 6% per year (0.005 per month) x months after the money is deposited.
   a. Use a graph (on your graphing calculator) to predict how many months it will be until the account is worth $1100. about 19 months
   b. Predict how many years it will be until the account is worth $5000. about 27 years

54. Suppose the population of a country is currently 8,100,000. Studies show this country's population is increasing 2% each year.
   a. What exponential function would be a good model for this country's population? $y = 8,100,000(1.02)^x$
   b. Using the equation you found in part (a), how many years will it take for the country's population to reach 9 million? Round your answer to the nearest hundredth. 5.32 years

55. Suppose you deposit $2500 in a savings account that pays you 5% interest per year.
   a. How many years will it take for you to double your money? about 14 years
   b. How many years will it take for your account to reach $8,000? about 24 years

Mental Math Solve each equation.

56. $5^x = \frac{1}{25}$ −2
57. $4^x = 64$ 3
58. $10^x = 0.0001$ −4
59. $\log_3 81 = x$ 4
60. $\log_2 \frac{1}{32} = x$ −5
61. $\log 1,000,000 = x$ 6

Use the properties of exponential and logarithmic functions to solve each system. Check your answers.

62. $\begin{cases} -2^{10-x} + y = 0 \\ y = 8^{x+2} \end{cases}$ (1, 512)
63. $\begin{cases} 3^{2x-y} = 1 \\ 4^{x+y} - 8 = 0 \end{cases}$ $(\frac{1}{2}, 1)$
64. $\begin{cases} \log_5(x - 2y) = 3 \\ \log_5(x + y) = \log_5 8 \end{cases}$ (8, 0)

All-in-One Resources/Online
Enrichment

7-5 Enrichment
Exponential and Logarithmic Equations

When solving logarithm equations, you primarily use the Product Property, Quotient Property, and Power Property to simplify the equation. Here is an interesting, lesser-known property of logarithms to explore.

1. Determine the value of each pair of expressions.

   $\log_2 4, \log_4 2$ 2, $\frac{1}{2}$
   $\log_3 81, \log_{81} 3$ 4, $\frac{1}{4}$
   $\log_{10} 1000, \log_{1000} 10$ 3, $\frac{1}{3}$

2. How are the values of each pair of expressions related?
   Answers may vary. Sample: When the base and argument are switched, the expressions are reciprocals.

3. This reciprocal property states that $\log_a b = \frac{1}{\log_b a}$. To prove this property, assume $r = \log_a b$ and $s = \log_b a$. Rewrite each of these equations in exponential form. $a^r = b, b^s = a$

4. Next, use one equation to substitute an equivalent expression in for a. What is your new equation? $(b^s)^r = b$

5. Use the laws of exponents to simplify. $b^{sr} = b$

6. Because the bases are the same, what equation can you write for the exponents? $sr = 1$

7. What must be true about s and r if the product equals 1? s and r must be reciprocals.

8. Use this new property to solve the equation $\log_5 x + \frac{1}{\log_x 5} = 4$. 25

Practice and Problem Solving Wkbk/All-in-One Resources/Online
Think About a Plan

7-5 Think About a Plan
Exponential and Logarithmic Equations

Seismology An earthquake of magnitude 7.6 occurred in 2001 in Gujarat, India. It was 251 times as strong as the greatest earthquake ever to hit Pennsylvania. What is the magnitude of the Pennsylvania earthquake? (*Hint:* Refer to the Richter scale on page 453.)

Know

1. The magnitude of the Gujarat earthquake is 7.6 .

2. The ratio of the intensity of the Gujarat earthquake to the intensity of Pennsylvania's greatest earthquake is 251 .

Need

3. To solve the problem I need to find:
   the magnitude of the greatest Pennsylvania earthquake

Plan

4. Let I_1 and M_1 be the intensity and magnitude of the Gujarat earthquake. Let I_2 and M_2 be the intensity and magnitude of Pennsylvania's greatest earthquake. What equation should you use to model this situation?
   $\log \frac{I_1}{I_2} = M_1 - M_2$

5. What does $\frac{I_1}{I_2}$ represent? the ratio of the intensity of the Gujarat earthquake to the intensity of Pennsylvania's greatest earthquake

6. What can you substitute for $\frac{I_1}{I_2}$ in your equation? 251

7. Solve your equation for the magnitude of Pennsylvania's greatest earthquake.
   $M_2 = M_1 - \log \frac{I_1}{I_2} = 7.6 - \log 251 \approx 5.2$

8. The magnitude of Pennsylvania's greatest earthquake was about 5.2 .

Practice and Problem Solving Wkbk/All-in-One Resources/Online
Standardized Test Prep

7-5 Standardized Test Prep
Exponential and Logarithmic Equations

Multiple Choice

For Exercises 1–5, choose the correct letter.

1. If $9^x = 243$, what is the value of x? C
   Ⓐ 2 Ⓑ 5 Ⓒ 2.5 Ⓓ 10

2. If $2^{3x+2} = 64$, what is the value of x? G
   Ⓕ $\frac{8}{3}$ Ⓖ $\frac{4}{3}$ Ⓗ 2 Ⓘ $\frac{3}{4}$

3. If $\log(3x + 25) = 2$, what is the value of x? A
   Ⓐ 25 Ⓑ 75 Ⓒ $41\frac{2}{3}$ Ⓓ 100

4. Which best approximates the solution of $16^{2x} = 124$? F
   Ⓕ 0.869 Ⓖ 1.150 Ⓗ 1.739 Ⓘ 3.477

5. Which equation represents the solution of $2^{3x+1} = 7$? D
   Ⓐ $x = 3\left(\frac{\log 7}{\log 2} - 1\right)$
   Ⓒ $x = \frac{1}{3}\left(\frac{\log 7}{\log 2} - 1\right)$
   Ⓑ $x = \frac{\log 7}{3 \log 2} - 1$
   Ⓓ $x = \frac{1}{3}\left(\frac{\log 7}{\log 2} - 1\right)$

Short Response

6. In 2007, the population of Tallahassee, Florida was 168,979. Some researchers believe that the population of Tallahassee will increase at a rate of 1% each year for the 10 years following this.
   a. If the researchers are correct, how many years will it take for the population of Tallahassee to reach 180,000?
   b. Explain in words or show your work for how you determined the number of years found in part (a).
   [2] a. about 7 years
   b. Because the population grows at a constant rate each year, an exponential model of the situation is $y = 168,979(1.01)^x$. $180,000 = 168,979(1.01)^x \rightarrow \frac{180,000}{168,979} = 1.01^x \rightarrow \log 1.0652 = x \log 1.01 \rightarrow x = \frac{\log 1.0652}{\log 1.01} = 6.348$.
   [1] incorrect number of years OR incorrect explanation
   [0] incorrect answers and no work shown OR no answers given

---

Online Teacher Resource Center
Activities, Games, and Puzzles

7-5 Game: Analyzing Equations
Exponential and Logarithmic Equations

This is a game for the entire class. You will work in teams of three students. Your teacher can serve as the host. Your teacher will decide the order in which the questions are chosen and he or she may also decide on a time limit for each question. No calculators allowed!

- Write your answer next to each question. A correct response is worth three points.
  - **Category 1:** Answer *none*, *one*, or *two*.
  - **Category 2:** Give two consecutive numbers such as *5 and 6.*
  - **Category 3:** Write *A* or *B.*

	Category 1: How Many Solutions?	Score
1.	$2^x = x + 3$ two	
2.	$\log_2 x = x + 2$ none	
3.	$2^x = 5$ one	
4.	$\log_2 x = 2$ one	
5.	$2^x = -5$ none	
6.	$\log_2 x = x - 2$ two	
7.	$2^x + 2 = 0$ none	
8.	$\log_2(x - 2) = 4x$ none	

	Category 2: Between Which Two Whole Numbers is x?	Score
1.	$3 \times 2^x = 75$ 4 and 5	
2.	$2 \times 2^x = 20$ 3 and 4	
3.	$\log_2 x = 3.1$ 8 and 9	
4.	$\log_2 x = 0.1$ 1 and 2	
5.	$5 \times 2^x = 60$ 3 and 4	
6.	$-3 \times 2^x = -9$ 1 and 2	

	Category 3: Which Equation Has the Greater Solution?			Score
1.	A. $2^x = 64$	or	B. $3^x = 81$ A	
2.	A. $10^x = 1000$	or	B. $5^x = 25$ A	
3.	A. $4^x = 81$	or	B. $5^x = 125$ B	
4.	A. $3^x = 27$	or	B. $2^x = 32$ B	

Using Logarithms for Exponential Models

Common Core State Standards

F-IF.C.8 Write a function defined by an expression in different but equivalent forms to reveal and explain different properties of the function. **Also F-IF.C.7c**

MP 5

You can transform an exponential function into a linear function by taking the logarithm of each side. Since linear models are easy to recognize, you can then determine whether an exponential function is a good model for a set of values.

MATHEMATICAL
PRACTICES

$y = ab^x$	Write the general form of an exponential function.
$\log y = \log ab^x$	Take the logarithm of each side.
$\log y = \log a + x(\log b)$	Use the Product Property and the Power Property.

If $\log b$ and $\log a$ are constants, then $\log y = (\log b)x + \log a$ is a linear equation in slope-intercept form when you plot the points as $(x, \log y)$.

Activity

Determine whether an exponential function is a good model for the values in the table.

x	0	2	4	6	8	10
y	0.5	2	7.8	32	127.9	511.7

Step 1 Enter the values into **stat** lists L_1 and L_2. To enter the values of $\log y$, place the cursor in the heading of L_3 and press **log** L_2 **enter**.

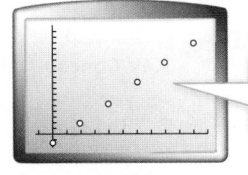

$L_3(7) =$

Step 2 To graph $\log y$, access the **stat plot** feature and press **1**. Then enter L_3 next to **YLIST:**. Then press **zoom** **9**.

The points $(x, \log y)$ lie on a line, so an exponential model is appropriate.

Step 3 Press **stat** ▷ **0** **enter** to find the exponential function $y = 0.5(2)^x$.

Exercises

For each set of values, determine whether an exponential function is a good model. If so, find the exponential function.

1.

x	1	3	5	7	9
y	6	22	54	102	145

2.

x	−1	0	1	2	3
y	40.2	19.8	9.9	5.1	2.5

3. Writing Explain how you could determine whether a logarithmic function is a good model for a set of data.

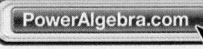

Guided Instruction

PURPOSE To use logarithms to determine the appropriateness of an exponential model

PROCESS Students will

- take the logarithms of the y-values in a table.
- graph the new points $(x, \log y)$ to see if the new data is linear.

DISCUSS The Product Property of Logarithms is used to write an exponential equation in linear form.

- A linear function in slope-intercept form is $y = mx + b$.
- Visual inspection or a line of best fit can be used to determine if data are linear.

Activity

An exponential model of the original data is appropriate if the points $(x, \log y)$ are linear.

Q What is the difference between using logarithms to solve an exponential equation and using logarithms to determine whether an exponential model is appropriate? **[When solving equations, logarithms of both sides must be taken. When determining appropriateness of an exponential model, use $(x, \log y)$ to see whether the data appears linear.]**

Q What happens if you try to find the logs of the values in a list that contains 0? Explain. **[The calculator gives the message ERR: DOMAIN because the domain contains 0 and log 0 is not defined.]**

Mathematical Practices This Concept Byte supports students in becoming proficient in using appropriate tools, Mathematical Practice 5.

Answers

Concept Byte

1. not a good model

2. $y = 20.0(0.50)^x$

3. Answers may vary. Sample: Use the Change of Base Formula to get $\log x = \frac{\log b}{a}y$. Let $L_1 = x$, $L_2 = y$, and $L_3 = \log x$. Graph L_2 and L_3. If it is linear, then the equation is logarithmic.

1 Interactive Learning

Solve It!

PURPOSE To determine whether a bounding number exists for $y = \ln x$

PROCESS Students may

- use the asymptotes of $y = e^x$ to draw conclusions about a bounding number for $y = \ln x$.
- use graphs and tables to determine whether a bounding number exists.

FACILITATE

Q How can you use $y = e^x$ to find the range of $y = \ln x$? [**The domain of $y = e^x$ is the range of $y = \ln x$, so the range of $y = \ln x$ is all real numbers.**]

ANSWER See Solve It in Answers on next page.
CONNECT THE MATH Students use asymptotes to draw conclusions about a bounding number for the natural logarithm function. In the lesson, students apply the same properties of regular logarithms to natural logarithms.

2 Guided Instruction

Take Note

Q How can you write ln 5x using $\log_b$ notation? Explain. [$\log_e 5x$; **the natural log uses the number e as its base.**]

Problem 1   EXTENSION

Q How are log 3 and ln 3 different? Explain. [**Log 3 means 10 raised to some number is 3. log 3 ≈ 0.477. ln 3 means e raised to some number is 3. ln 3 ≈ 1.099**]

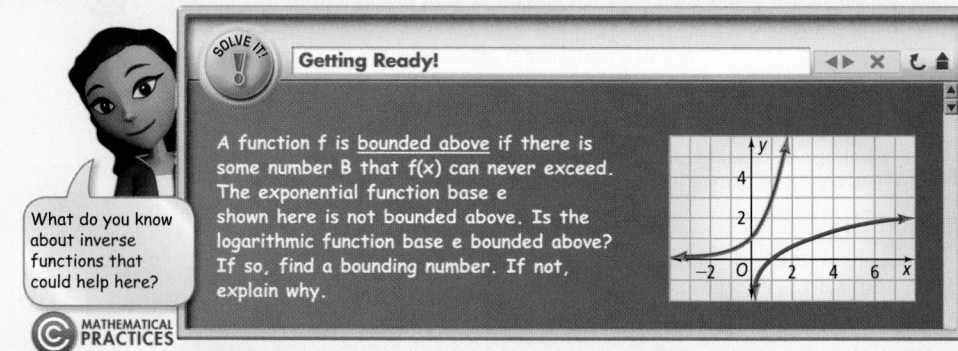
Objectives To evaluate and simplify natural logarithmic expressions
To solve equations using natural logarithms

What do you know about inverse functions that could help here?

© MATHEMATICAL PRACTICES

SOLVE IT!

Getting Ready!

A function f is <u>bounded above</u> if there is some number B that f(x) can never exceed. The exponential function base e shown here is not bounded above. Is the logarithmic function base e bounded above? If so, find a bounding number. If not, explain why.

The function $y = e^x$ has an inverse, the **natural logarithmic function**, $y = \log_e x$, or $y = \ln x$.

Lesson Vocabulary
- natural logarithmic function

Essential Understanding The functions $y = e^x$ and $y = \ln x$ are inverse functions. Just as before, this means that if $a = e^b$, then $b = \ln a$, and vice versa.

take note

Key Concept Natural Logarithmic Function

If $y = e^x$, then $x = \log_e y = \ln y$. The natural logarithmic function is the inverse of $x = \ln y$, so you can write it as $y = \ln x$.

① $y = e^x$
② $y = \ln x$

Plan

Can you use properties of logarithms?
Yes; the properties you studied in Lesson 7-4 apply to logarithms with any base.

© **Problem 1** **Simplifying a Natural Logarithmic Expression**

What is $2 \ln 15 - \ln 75$ written as a single natural logarithm?

$2 \ln 15 - \ln 75 = \ln 15^2 - \ln 75$ Power Property of Logarithms

$= \ln \dfrac{15^2}{75}$ Quotient Property of Logarithms

$= \ln 3$ Simplify.

BIG idea Function
ESSENTIAL UNDERSTANDINGS

- The function $y = e^x$ and $y = \ln x$ are inverse functions. Just as before, this means that if $a = e^b$, then $b = \ln a$, and vice versa.
- The exponential function $y = b^x$ and the logarithmic function $y = \log_b x$ are inverse functions.

Math Background

Just as 10 is the base of common logarithms, the number e is the base of natural logarithms. The natural logarithm function and the exponential functions with base e are inverse functions. The rules and properties used for solving regular logarithms can also be used for solving natural logarithms. This is evident because the only restriction for logarithms of the form $\log_b y = x$ is that y is positive and b is greater than 0 but not equal to 1. Because $e \approx 2.71828$, it falls within the restrictions for b, and the properties can be used. In fact, $\ln x$ is

equivalent to $\log_e x$. Convention dictates using ln for natural logarithms. Natural logarithms are introduced here because they arise in so many situations. Biology, banking, physics, and statistics are just a few of the areas that use natural logarithms.

© **Mathematical Practices**
Use appropriate tools strategically.
Students will use calculators to determine the value of natural logarithms and, while checking their answers, they will realize the limitation calculators have in rounding figures.

PowerAlgebra.com

1 Interactive Learning

SOLVE IT! **Solve It!**
Step out how to solve the Problem with helpful hints and an online question. Other questions are listed above in Interactive Learning.

Virtual Nerd™ Access Virtual Nerd student-centered math tutorials that directly relate to the content of the lesson.

Got It? 1. What is each expression written as a single natural logarithm?

a. $\ln 7 + 2 \ln 5$ b. $3 \ln x - 2 \ln 2x$ c. $3 \ln x + 2 \ln y + \ln 5$

You can use the inverse relationship between the functions $y = \ln x$ and $y = e^x$ to solve certain logarithmic and exponential equations.

 Problem 2 Solving a Natural Logarithmic Equation

Think

How do you go from logarithmic form to exponential form?
Use the definition of logarithm: $\ln x = y$ if and only if $x = e^y$.

What are the solutions of $\ln (x - 3)^2 = 4$?

$\ln (x - 3)^2 = 4$

$(x - 3)^2 = e^4$ Rewrite in exponential form.

$x - 3 = \pm e^2$ Find the square root of each side.

$x = 3 \pm e^2$ Solve for x.

$x \approx 10.39$ or -4.39 Use a calculator.

Check

$\ln (10.39 - 3)^2 \stackrel{?}{=} 4$ $\ln (-4.39 - 3)^2 \stackrel{?}{=} 4$

$4.0003 \approx 4$ ✔ $4.0003 \approx 4$ ✔

 Got It? 2. What are the solutions of each equation? Check your answers.

a. $\ln x = 2$ b. $\ln (3x + 5)^2 = 4$ c. $\ln 2x + \ln 3 = 2$

Problem 3 Solving an Exponential Equation

Plan

How can you solve this equation?
First get e^x by itself on one side of the equation. Then rewrite the equation in logarithmic form and solve for x.

What is the solution of $4e^{2x} + 2 = 16$?

$4e^{2x} + 2 = 16$

$4e^{2x} = 14$ Subtract 2 from each side.

$e^{2x} = 3.5$ Divide each side by 4.

$2x = \ln 3.5$ Rewrite in logarithmic form.

$x = \dfrac{\ln 3.5}{2}$ Divide each side by 2.

$x \approx 0.626$ Use a calculator.

Check

$4e^{2x} + 2 = 16$

$4e^{2(0.626)} + 2 \stackrel{?}{=} 16$

$15.99 \approx 16$ ✔

Got It? 3. What is the solution of each equation? Check your answers.

a. $e^{x-2} = 12$ b. $2e^{-x} = 20$ c. $e^{3x} + 5 = 15$

Got It?   ERROR PREVENTION

Q What do you need to do first before applying the Quotient or Product Property? [**Apply the Power Property.**]

Problem 2

Q What are all the steps when writing a natural logarithmic equation in exponential form? [**Rewrite in exponential form by raising each side to the power of e, simplify the equation algebraically, and then solve with a calculator.**]

Got It?

Q How can you use a graph or table to solve 2b? [**Answers may vary. Sample: Enter $Y_1 = 2 \ln (3x + 5)$ and $Y_2 = 4$ in your graphing calculator. Set your window, and find the intersection.**]

Problem 3   EXTENSION

Q Can e be raised to a negative power? Explain. [**Yes; answers may vary. Sample: Negative exponents indicate division by the base. Because e is the irrational number $2.718\ldots$, it is possible to write e^{-x} as a fraction. So e^{-x} is equal to $\frac{1}{e^x}$**]

Got It?   EXTENSION

Logarithms to any base can be used to solve exponential equations. Therefore, natural logarithms can be used to solve exponential equations that do not include the number e. For example, $2^x = 8$ can be solved by finding $\ln 2^x = \ln 8$. Thus, $x = \frac{\ln 8}{\ln 2} = 3$.

---

2 Guided Instruction

 Each Problem is worked out and supported online.

Problem 1
Simplifying a Natural Logarithmic Expression

Problem 2
Solving a Natural Logarithmic Equation
         Animated

Problem 3
Solving an Exponential Equation
         Animated

Problem 4
Using Natural Logarithms

Support in Algebra 2 Companion
• Vocabulary
• Key Concepts
• Got It?

Answers

Solve It!

No; $y = \ln x$ is the inverse of $y = e^x$. Since the domain of $y = e^x$ is all real numbers, the range of $y = \ln x$ is all real numbers.

Got It?

1. a. $\ln 175$

   b. $\ln \frac{x}{4}$

   c. $\ln 5x^3 y^2$

2. a. e^2, or about 7.39

   b. $\frac{-5 \pm e^2}{3}$, or about 0.8 or -4.13

   c. $\frac{e^2}{6}$, or about 1.23

3. a. $\ln 2 + 2$, or about 4.48

   b. $-\ln 10$, or about -2.3

   c. $\frac{\ln 10}{3}$, or about 0.77

Problem 4

Q What is $v = -0.0098t + c \ln R$ solved for R?
Describe your steps. [$R = e^{\frac{v + 0.0098t}{c}}$; answers may
vary. Sample: First add 0.0098t to both sides,
then divide both sides by c. Then rewrite in
exponential form.]

Got It?

Encourage students to experiment with the formula
on a calculator to see how the velocity will change
given changes in t, c, or R.

3 Lesson Check

Do you know HOW?   ERROR INTERVENTION

• If students have difficulty with Exercises 1–4,
remind them to use the same properties as
regular logarithms.

Do you UNDERSTAND?

• If students have trouble with Exercise 9, review
that $\ln 4x = 5$ means e raised to some number is
equal to $4x$.

Close

Q How can you use the relationship between $y = e^x$
and $y = \ln x$ to solve exponential and logarithmic
equations? [The functions are inverses, so
use exponents with base e to solve natural
logarithms and natural logarithms to solve
equations with e.]

Natural logarithms are useful because they help express
many relationships in the physical world.

 Problem 4 Using Natural Logarithms STEM

Space A spacecraft can attain a stable orbit 300 km above
Earth if it reaches a velocity of 7.7 km/s. The formula for
a rocket's maximum velocity v in kilometers per second
is $v = -0.0098t + c \ln R$. The booster rocket fires for t
seconds and the velocity of the exhaust is c km/s. The
ratio of the mass of the rocket filled with fuel to its mass
without fuel is R. Suppose the rocket shown in the photo
has a mass ratio of 25, a firing time of 100 s and an
exhaust velocity as shown. Can the spacecraft
attain a stable orbit 300 km above Earth?

2.8 km/s

Plan

**How can you solve
the problem?**
Use the given formula
to find the maximum
velocity v of the
spacecraft. If $v \geq 7.7$,
the spacecraft can attain
a stable orbit.

Let $R = 25$, $c = 2.8$, and $t = 100$. Find v.

$v = -0.0098t + c \ln R$	Use the formula.
$= -0.0098(100) + 2.8 \ln 25$	Substitute.
$\approx -0.98 + 2.8(3.219)$	Use a calculator.
≈ 8.0	Simplify.

The maximum velocity of 8.0 km/s is greater than the 7.7 km/s needed for a stable orbit.
Therefore, the spacecraft can attain a stable orbit 300 km above Earth.

 Got It? 4. a. A booster rocket for a spacecraft has a mass ratio of about 15, an exhaust
velocity of 2.1 km/s, and a firing time of 30 s. Can the spacecraft achieve
a stable orbit 300 km above Earth?
b. Reasoning Suppose a rocket, as designed, cannot provide enough
velocity to achieve a stable orbit. Could alterations to the rocket make
a stable orbit achievable? Explain.

 Lesson Check

Do you know HOW?

Write each expression as a single natural logarithm.

1. $4 \ln 3$
2. $\ln 18 - \ln 10$
3. $\ln 3 + \ln 4$
4. $-2 \ln 2$

Solve each equation.

5. $\ln 5x = 4$
6. $\ln (x - 7) = 2$
7. $2 \ln x = 4$
8. $\ln (2 - x) = 1$

Do you UNDERSTAND?  MATHEMATICAL PRACTICES

9. Error Analysis Describe the error
made in solving the equation.
Then find the correct solution.

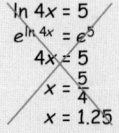
$\ln 4x = 5$
$e^{\ln 4x} = e^5$
$4x = 5$
$x = \frac{5}{4}$
$x = 1.25$

10. Reasoning Can $\ln 5 + \log_2 10$ be
written as a single logarithm?
Explain your reasoning.

Additional Problems

1. What is each expression
written as a single natural
logarithm?

a. $3 \ln 2 - 3 \ln x$
b. $2 \ln 3 + \ln 8$
c. $20 \ln x + 5 \ln y - 2 \ln z$

ANSWER

a. $\ln \frac{8}{x^3}$
b. $\ln 72$
c. $\ln \frac{x^{20} y^5}{z^2}$

2. What are the solutions of
each equation?

a. $\ln x = 5$
b. $\ln (6x + 1) = 3$
c. $\ln (2x + 1)^2 = 6$

ANSWER

a. about 148.41
b. about 3.18
c. about 9.54 or −10.54

3. What is the solution of each
equation?

a. $e^{x+3} = 24$
b. $5e^{-3x} = 45$
c. $2e^{5x} - 8 = 30$

ANSWER

a. about 0.18
b. about −0.73
c. about 0.59

4. Carbon dating is a method
used to determine the age
of organic material less than
50,000 years old. One of
the formulas for carbon-14
dating is $t = \dfrac{\ln \left(\frac{N_f}{N_o} \right)}{-0.693} \times 5700$

where $\frac{N_f}{N_o}$ is the percent of
carbon-14 remaining and
t is the time in years. A
fossil is found to have 30%
carbon-14 compared to a
living sample. Using this
formula, what is the age of
the fossil?

ANSWER about 9903 years

Answers

Got It? (continued)

4. a. No; the maximum velocity
of 5.4 km/s is less than the
7.7 km/s needed for a
stable orbit.

b. Yes; if R could be changed
so that $V > 7.7$.

Practice and Problem-Solving Exercises

 MATHEMATICAL PRACTICES

A Practice

Write each expression as a single natural logarithm. ◀ **See Problem 1.**

11. $3 \ln 5$ **12.** $\ln 9 + \ln 2$ **13.** $\ln 24 - \ln 6$

14. $5 \ln m - 3 \ln n$ **15.** $\frac{1}{3}(\ln x + \ln y) - 4 \ln z$ **16.** $\ln a - 2 \ln b + \frac{1}{3}\ln c$

17. $4 \ln 8 + \ln 10$ **18.** $\ln 3 - 5 \ln 3$ **19.** $2 \ln 8 - 3 \ln 4$

Solve each equation. Check your answers. ◀ **See Problem 2.**

20. $\ln 3x = 6$ **21.** $\ln x = -2$ **22.** $\ln(4x - 1) = 36$

23. $1.1 + \ln x^2 = 6$ **24.** $\ln \frac{x-1}{2} = 4$ **25.** $\ln 4r^2 = 3$

26. $2 \ln 2x^2 = 1$ **27.** $\ln(2m + 3) = 8$ **28.** $\ln(t - 1)^2 = 3$

Use natural logarithms to solve each equation. ◀ **See Problem 3.**

29. $e^x = 18$ **30.** $e^{\frac{x}{5}} + 4 = 7$ **31.** $e^{2x} = 12$

32. $e^{\frac{x}{2}} = 5$ **33.** $e^{x+1} = 30$ **34.** $e^{2x} = 10$

35. $e^{3x} + 5 = 6$ **36.** $e^{\frac{x}{9}} - 8 = 6$ **37.** $7 - 2e^{\frac{x}{2}} = 1$

STEM Space For Exercises 38 and 39, use $v = -0.0098t + c \ln R$, where v is the velocity of the rocket, t is the firing time, c is the velocity of the exhaust, and R is the ratio of the mass of the rocket filled with fuel to the mass of the rocket without fuel. ◀ **See Problem 4.**

38. Find the velocity of a spacecraft whose booster rocket has a mass ratio of 20, an exhaust velocity of 2.7 km/s, and a firing time of 30 s. Can the spacecraft achieve a stable orbit 300 km above Earth?

39. A rocket has a mass ratio of 24 and an exhaust velocity of 2.5 km/s. Determine the minimum firing time for a stable orbit 300 km above Earth.

B Apply

40. Think About a Plan By measuring the amount of carbon-14 in an object, a paleontologist can determine its approximate age. The amount of carbon-14 in an object is given by $y = ae^{-0.00012t}$, where a is the amount of carbon-14 originally in the object, and t is the age of the object in years. In 2003, a bone believed to be from a dire wolf was found at the La Brea Tar Pits. The bone contains 14% of its original carbon-14. How old is the bone?
- What numbers should you substitute for y and t?
- What properties of logarithms and exponents can you use to solve the equation?

STEM 41. Archaeology A fossil bone contains 25% of its original carbon-14. What is the approximate age of the bone?

Simplify each expression.

42. $\ln 1$ **43.** $\frac{\ln e}{4}$ **44.** $\frac{\ln e^2}{2}$ **45.** $\ln e^{83}$ **46.** $\ln e$

47. $\ln e^2$ **48.** $\ln e^{10}$ **49.** $10 \ln e$ **50.** $\ln e^3$ **51.** $\frac{\ln e^4}{8}$

Answers

Lesson Check

1. $\ln 81$ **2.** $\ln 1.8$ **3.** $\ln 12$

4. $-\ln 4$ **5.** ≈ 10.9 **6.** ≈ 14.4

7. ≈ 7.39 **8.** ≈ -0.718

9. error in 3rd line: $4x = 5$
     should be: $4x = e^5$
     $x = \frac{e^5}{4}$; $x \approx 37.1$

10. No; $\ln 5$ has base e and $\log_2 10$ has base 2.

Practice and Problem-Solving Exercises

11. $\ln 125$ **12.** $\ln 18$ **13.** $\ln 4$

14. $\ln \frac{m^5}{n^3}$ **15.** $\ln \frac{\sqrt[3]{xy}}{z^4}$ **16.** $\ln \frac{a\sqrt[3]{c}}{b^2}$

17. $\ln 40{,}960$ **18.** $\ln \frac{1}{81}$

19. $\ln 1$ **20.** 134.476

21. 0.135 **22.** 1.078×10^{15}

23. ± 11.588 **24.** 110.196

25. ± 2.241 **26.** ± 0.908

27. 1488.979 **28.** $5.482, -3.482$

29. ≈ 2.890 **30.** ≈ 5.493

31. ≈ 1.242 **32.** ≈ 3.219

33. ≈ 2.401 **34.** ≈ 1.151

35. 0 **36.** ≈ 23.752

37. ≈ 2.2 **38.** 7.79 km/s; yes

39. at least 25 s   **40.** $\approx 16{,}384$ yrs

41. $\approx 11{,}552$ yrs   **42.** 0

43. $\frac{1}{4}$ **44.** 1

45. 83 **46.** 1

47. 2 **48.** 10

49. 10 **50.** 3

51. $\frac{1}{2}$

---

4 Practice

ASSIGNMENT GUIDE

Basic: 11–39 all, 40–44 all, 52, 53

Average: 11–39 odd, 40–59

Advanced: 11–39 odd, 40–65

Standardized Test Prep: 66–71

Mixed Review: 72–84

© **Mathematical Practices** are supported by exercises with red headings. Here are the Practices supported in this lesson:

MP 1: Make Sense of Problems Ex. 40
MP 3: Communicate Ex. 64e
MP 3: Critique the Reasoning of Others Ex. 9, 52, 63

Applications exercises have blue headings. Exercises 38, 39, 58 and 59 support MP 4: Model.

STEM exercises focus on science or engineering applications.

EXERCISE 41: Use the Think About a Plan worksheet in the **Practice and Problem Solving Workbook** (also available in the Teaching Resources in print and online) to further support students' development in becoming independent learners.

HOMEWORK QUICK CHECK

To check students' understanding of key skills and concepts, go over Exercises 13, 21, 40, 41, and 53.

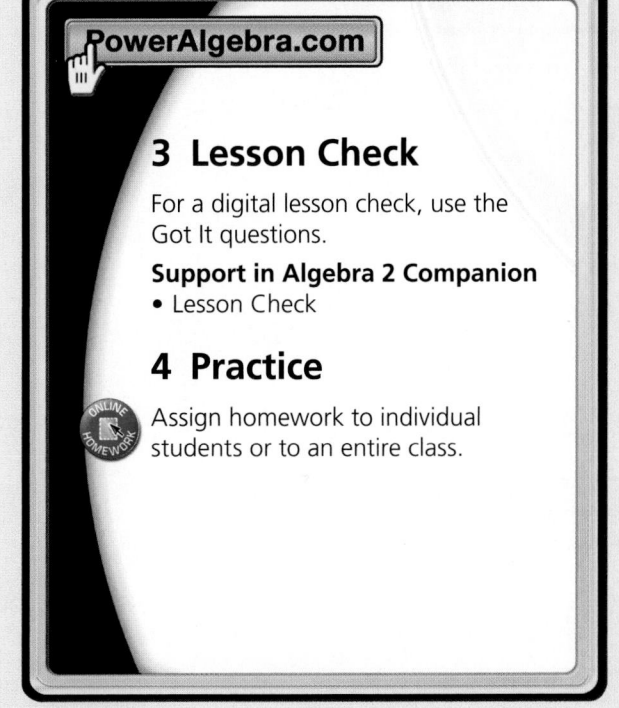

PowerAlgebra.com

3 Lesson Check

For a digital lesson check, use the Got It questions.

Support in Algebra 2 Companion
- Lesson Check

4 Practice

Assign homework to individual students or to an entire class.

Answers

52. $\log e \neq 1$;

$$\ln 100 = \frac{\log 100}{\log e} = \frac{\log 10^2}{\log e} = \frac{2}{\log e} \approx 4.61$$

53. ≈ 301 days

54. sometimes

55. never

56. always

57. 10.8

58. $\approx 5.8\%$ per h

59. ≈ 19.8 h

60. 27,347.9

61. 78.342

62. no solution

63. Because the function is simplified in the beginning and the sq. root of the exponential function is not calculated.

64. a. $y = 1.5e^{0.12104t}$

b. 2010

c. 2018

d. $t = \dfrac{\ln\left(\dfrac{y}{1.5}\right)}{0.12104}$

e. Substitute the number of users found in (b) and (c) into the equation in (d). Determine whether your answers in years are the same as t.

---

52. Error Analysis A student has broken the natural logarithm key on his calculator, so he decides to use the Change of Base Formula to find $\ln 100$. Explain his error and find the correct answer.

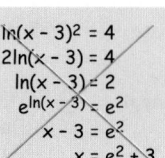

$$\ln 100 = \frac{\log 100}{\log e}$$
$$= \frac{\log 10^2}{\log e}$$
$$= \frac{2\log 10}{\log e}$$
$$= \frac{2(1)}{1}$$
$$= 2$$

53. Satellite The battery power available to run a satellite is given by the formula $P = 50\,e^{-\frac{t}{250}}$, where P is power in watts and t is time in days. For how many days can the satellite run if it requires 15 watts of power?

Determine whether each statement is *always*, *sometimes*, or *never* true.

54. $\ln e^x \geq 1$ **55.** $\ln e^x = \ln e^x + 1$ **56.** $\ln t = \log_e t$

STEM 57. Space Use the formula for maximum velocity $v = -0.0098t + c \ln R$. Find the mass ratio of a rocket with an exhaust velocity of 3.1 km/s, a firing time of 50 s, and a maximum shuttle velocity of 6.9 km/s.

STEM Biology The formula $H = \frac{1}{r}(\ln P - \ln A)$ models the number of hours it takes a bacteria culture to decline, where H is the number of hours, r is the rate of decline, P is the initial bacteria population, and A is the reduced bacteria population.

58. A scientist determines that an antibiotic reduces a population of 20,000 bacteria to 5000 in 24 hours. Find the rate of decline caused by the antibiotic.

59. A laboratory assistant tests an antibiotic that causes a rate of decline of 0.14. How long should it take for a population of 8000 bacteria to shrink to 500?

Challenge Solve each equation.

60. $\frac{1}{3}\ln x + \ln 2 - \ln 3 = 3$ **61.** $\ln(x + 2) - \ln 4 = 3$ **62.** $2e^{x-2} = e^x + 7$

63. Error Analysis Consider the solution to the equation $\ln(x-3)^2 = 4$ at the right. In Problem 2 you saw that there are two solutions to this equation, $3 + e^2$ and $3 - e^2$. Why do you get only one solution using this method?

$$\ln(x-3)^2 = 4$$
$$2\ln(x-3) = 4$$
$$\ln(x-3) = 2$$
$$e^{\ln(x-3)} = e^2$$
$$x - 3 = e^2$$
$$x = e^2 + 3$$

STEM 64. Technology In 2008, there were about 1.5 billion Internet users. That number is projected to grow to 3.5 billion in 2015.

a. Let t represent the time, in years, since 2008. Write a function of the form $y = ae^{ct}$ that models the expected growth in the population of Internet users.

b. In what year were there 2 billion Internet users?

c. In what year will there be 5 billion Internet users?

d. Solve your equation for t.

e. Writing Explain how you can use your equation from part (d) to verify your answers to parts (b) and (c).

STEM 65. Physics The function $T(t) = T_r + (T_i - T_r)e^{kt}$ models Newton's Law of Cooling. $T(t)$ is the temperature of a heated substance t minutes after it has been removed from a heat (or cooling) source. T_i is the substance's initial temperature, k is a constant for that substance, and T_r is room temperature.

a. The initial surface temperature of a beef roast is 236°F and room temperature is 72°F. If $k = -0.041$, how long will it take for this roast to cool to 100°F?

b. **Graphing Calculator** Write and graph an equation that you can use to check your answer to part (a). Use your graph to complete the table below.

Temperature (°F)	225	200	175	150	125	100	75
Minutes Later	■	■	■	■	■	■	■

Standardized Test Prep

GRIDDED RESPONSE

SAT/ACT

66. An investment of $750 will be worth $1500 after 12 years of continuous compounding at a fixed interest rate. What percent is the interest rate?

67. What is $\log 33{,}000 - \log 99 + \log 30$?

68. If $f(x) = 5 - x^2$ and $g(x) = x^2 - 3$, what is $(g \circ f)(6)$?

69. What is the positive root of $y = 2x^2 - 35x - 57$?

70. What is the real part of $3 + 2i$?

71. What is $\dfrac{\sqrt{36}}{\sqrt{4}}$?

Mixed Review

Solve each equation.

See Lesson 7-5.

72. $3^{2x} = 6561$

73. $7^x - 2 = 252$

74. $25^{2x+1} = 144$

75. $\log 3x = 4$

76. $\log 5x + 3 = 3.7$

77. $\log 9 - \log x + 1 = 6$

Find the inverse of each function. Is the inverse a function?

See Lesson 6-7.

78. $y = 5x + 7$

79. $y = 2x^3 + 10$

80. $y = -x^2 + 5$

81. $y = 3x + 2$

Get Ready! To prepare for Lesson 8-1, do Exercises 82–84.

For Exercises 82–84, y varies directly with x.

See Lesson 2-2.

82. If $x = 2$ when $y = 4$, find y when $x = 5$.

83. If $x = 1$ when $y = 5$, find y when $x = 3$.

84. If $x = 10$ when $y = 3$, find y when $x = 4$.

---

65. a. ≈ 43 min

b. $t = -\dfrac{1}{0.041} \ln\left(\dfrac{T - 72}{164}\right)$

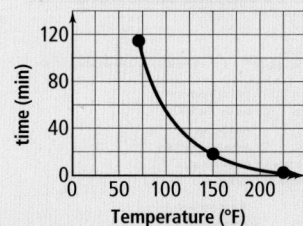

Temperature (°F)	225	200	175	150	125	100	75
Minutes Later	1.7	6.0	11.3	18.1	27.6	43.1	97.6

Standardized Test Prep

66. 5.78

67. 4

68. 958

69. 0.2975

70. 3

71. 3

Mixed Review

72. 4

73. 2.846

74. 0.272

75. $3333.\overline{3}$

76. 1.002

77. 9.0×10^{-5}

78. $y = \dfrac{x - 7}{5}$; yes

79. $y = \sqrt[3]{\dfrac{x - 10}{2}}$; yes

80. $y = \pm\sqrt{5 - x}$; no

81. $y = \dfrac{x - 2}{3}$; yes

82. 10

83. 15

84. $\dfrac{6}{5}$

Additional Instructional Support

Algebra 2 Companion

Students can use the **Algebra 2 Companion** worktext (4 pages) as you teach the lesson. Use the Companion to support

- New Vocabulary
- Key Concepts
- Got It for each Problem
- Lesson Check

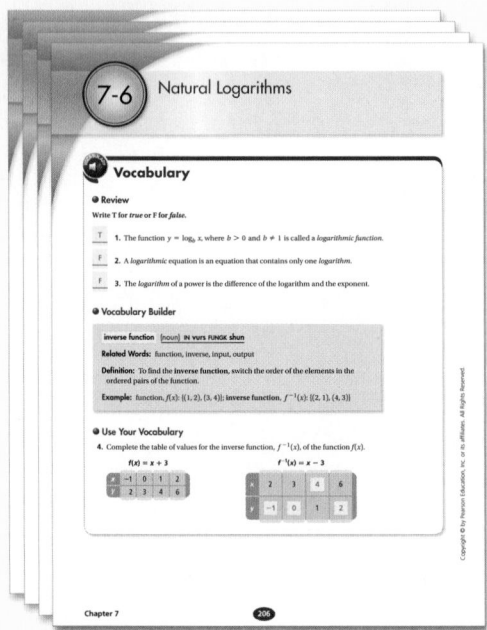

ELL Support

Connect to Prior Knowledge Discuss the conventions for naming mathematical terms. First, explain to students that many Latin-based languages place the modifier after the noun. If students speak Spanish, Italian, French, Portuguese, or Romanian, ask them to give an example of a phrase in their language in which this convention is shown. Thus the term natural logarithms can be thought of as "logarithms, natural" which can be abbreviated as ln.

Continue the discussion by having students think of different mathematical terms that have been abbreviated. Examples might include *r* for rate, *t* for time, and *P* for principal or probability. Examples of vocabulary terms that do not appear to be abbreviations include *m* for slope and *b* for *y*-intercept.

5 Assess & Remediate

Lesson Quiz

1. What is $3 \ln 5 + \ln x$ written as a single natural logarithm?

2. What is the solution of $\ln (x + 2)^2 = 10$?

3. What is the solution of $3e^{-2x} + 5 = 23$?

4. Do you UNDERSTAND? The formula $t = \dfrac{\ln 2}{\ln(1 + r)}$, where *r* is the interest rate and *t* is the time in years, can be used to calculate the number of years it takes an investment to double in value. If an amount of money is invested at 3% interest, how many years will it take the investment to double?

ANSWERS TO LESSON QUIZ

1. $\ln 125x$

2. about 146.41 or -150.41

3. about -0.896

4. about 23.4 years

PRESCRIPTION FOR REMEDIATION
Use the student work on the Lesson Quiz to prescribe a differentiated review assignment:

Points	Differentiated Remediation
0–1	Intervention
2–3	On-level
4	Extension

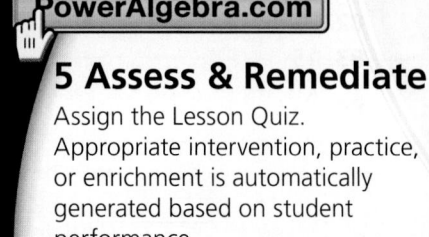

PowerAlgebra.com

5 Assess & Remediate

Assign the Lesson Quiz. Appropriate intervention, practice, or enrichment is automatically generated based on student performance.

Differentiated Remediation

Available in editable format online.

Intervention

- **Reteaching** (2 pages) Provides reteaching and practice exercises for the key lesson concepts. Use with struggling students or absent students.

- **English Language Learner Support** Helps students develop and reinforce mathematical vocabulary and key concepts.

All-in-One Resources/Online
Reteaching

7-6 Reteaching
Natural Logarithms

The **natural logarithmic function** is a logarithm with base *e*, an irrational number. You can write the natural logarithmic function as $y = \log_e x$, but you usually write it as $y = \ln x$.

$y = e^x$ and $y = \ln x$ are inverses, so if $y = e^x$, then $x = \ln y$.

To solve a natural logarithm equation:
- If the term containing the variable is an exponential expression, rewrite the equation in logarithmic form.
- If the term containing the variable is a logarithmic expression, rewrite the equation in exponential form.

Problem

What is the solution of $4e^{2x} - 2 = 3$?

Step 1 Isolate the term containing the variable on one side of the equation.

$4e^{2x} - 2 = 3$

$4e^{2x} = 5$ Add 2 to each side of the equation.

$e^{2x} = \frac{5}{4}$ Divide each side of the equation by 4.

Step 2 Take the natural logarithm of each side of the equation.

$\ln (e^{2x}) = \ln \left(\frac{5}{4}\right)$

$2x = \ln \left(\frac{5}{4}\right)$ Definition of natural logarithm

Step 3 Solve for the variable.

$x = \dfrac{\ln \left(\frac{5}{4}\right)}{2}$ Divide each side of the equation by 2.

$x \approx 0.112$ Use a calculator.

Step 4 Check the solution.

$4e^{2(0.112)} - 2 \stackrel{?}{=} 3$

$4e^{0.224} - 2 \stackrel{?}{=} 3$

$3.004 \approx 3$

The solution is $x \approx 0.112$.

All-in-One Resources/Online
English Language Learner Support

7-6 Additional Vocabulary Support
Natural Logarithms

Problem

What is the solution of the equation $3e^{4x} + 5 = 26$? Explain your work and check your solution.

$3e^{4x} + 5 = 26$	Write the original equation.
$3e^{4x} = 21$	Subtract 5 from each side.
$e^{4x} = 7$	Divide each side by 3.
$4x = \ln 7$	Rewrite in logarithmic form.
$x = 0.25 \ln 7$	Divide each side by 4.
$x \approx 0.486$	Use a calculator.

Check
$3e^{4x} + 5 = 26$	Write the original equation.
$3e^{4(0.486)} + 5 = 26$	Substitute 0.486 for *x*.
$25.96 \approx 26$	Use a calculator.

Exercise

What is the solution of the equation $5e^{2x} - 2 = 12$? Explain your work and check your solution.

$5e^{2x} - 2 = 12$	Write the original equation.
$5e^{2x} = 14$	Add 2 to each side.
$e^{2x} = 2.8$	Divide each side by 5.
$2x = \ln 2.8$	Write in logarithmic form.
$x = 0.5 \ln 2.8$	Divide each side by 2.
$x \approx 0.515$	Use a calculator.

Check
$5e^{2x} - 2 = 12$	Write the original equation.
$5e^{2(0.515)} - 2 = 12$	Substitute 0.515 for *x*.
$12.005 \approx 12$	Use a calculator.

Differentiated Remediation *continued*

Available in editable format online.

On-Level

- **Practice** (2 pages) Provides extra practice for each lesson. For simpler practice exercises, use the Form K Practice pages found in the All-in-One Teaching Resources and online.

- **Think About a Plan** Helps students develop specific problem-solving skills and strategies by providing scaffolded guiding questions.

- **Standardized Test Prep** Focuses on all major exercises, all major question types, and helps students prepare for the high-stakes assessments.

Extension

- **Enrichment** Provides students with interesting problems and activities that extend the concepts of the lesson.

- **Activities, Games, and Puzzles** Worksheets that can be used for concepts development, enrichment, and for fun!

Practice and Problem Solving Wkbk/ All-in-One Resources/Online
Practice page 1

7-6 Practice   Form G
Natural Logarithms

Write each expression as a single natural logarithm.

1. $\ln 16 - \ln 8$ $\ln 2$
2. $3 \ln 3 + \ln 9$ 243
3. $a \ln 4 - \ln b$ $\ln \frac{4^a}{b}$
4. $\ln z - 3 \ln x$ $\ln \frac{z}{x^3}$
5. $\frac{1}{2} \ln 9 + \ln 3x$ 9x
6. $4 \ln x + 3 \ln y$ $\ln x^4 y^3$
7. $\frac{1}{3} \ln 8 + \ln x$ $\ln 2x$
8. $3 \ln a - b \ln 2$ $\ln \frac{a^3}{2^b}$
9. $2 \ln 4 - \ln 8$ $\ln 2$

Solve each equation. Check your answers. Round your answer to the nearest hundredth.

10. $4 \ln x = -2$ 0.61
11. $2 \ln (3x - 4) = 7$ 12.37
12. $5 \ln (4x - 6) = 6$ 1.58
13. $-7 + \ln 2x = 4$ 29,937.07
14. $3 - 4 \ln (8x + 1) = 12$ -0.11
15. $\ln x + \ln 3x = 14$ 633.14
16. $2 \ln x + \ln x^2 = 3$ 2.12
17. $\ln x + \ln 4 = 2$ 1.85
18. $\ln x - \ln 5 = -1$ 1.84
19. $\ln e^x = 3$ 3
20. $3 \ln e^{2x} = 12$ 2
21. $\ln e^{x+5} = 17$ 12
22. $\ln 3x + \ln 2x = 3$ 1.83
23. $5 \ln (3x - 2) = 15$ 7.36
24. $7 \ln (2x + 5) = 8$ -0.93
25. $\ln (3x + 4) = 5$ 48.14
26. $\ln \frac{2x}{4} = 2$ 151.48
27. $\ln (2x - 1)^2 = 4$ 4.19

Use natural logarithms to solve each equation. Round your answer to the nearest hundredth.

28. $e^x = 15$ 2.71
29. $4e^x = 10$ 0.92
30. $e^{x+2} = 50$ 1.91
31. $4e^{3x-1} = 5$ 0.41
32. $e^{x-4} = 2$ 4.69
33. $5e^{6x+3} = 0.1$ -1.15
34. $e^x = 1$ 0
35. $e^{\frac{x}{3}} = 32$ 17.33
36. $3e^{3x-5} = 49$ 2.60
37. $7e^{5x+8} = 0.23$ -2.28
38. $6 - e^{12x} = 5.2$ -0.02
39. $e^{\frac{x}{5}} = 25$ 6.44
40. $e^{2x} = 25$ 1.61
41. $e^{\ln 5x} = 20$ 4
42. $e^{\ln x} = 21$ 21
43. $e^{x+6} + 5 = 1$ no solution

Practice and Problem Solving Wkbk/ All-in-One Resources/Online
Practice page 2

7-6 Practice *(continued)*   Form G
Natural Logarithms

The formula $P = 50e^{-\frac{t}{44}}$ gives the power output P, in watts, needed to run a certain satellite for t days. Find how long a satellite with the given power output will operate.

44. 10 W   about 40.2 days
45. 12 W   about 35.7 days
46. 14 W   about 31.8 days

The formula for the maximum velocity v of a rocket is $v = -0.0098t + c \ln R$, where c is the exhaust velocity in km/s, t is the firing time, and R is the mass ratio of the rocket. A rocket must reach 7.7 km/s to attain a stable orbit 300 km above Earth.

47. What is the maximum velocity of a rocket with a mass ratio of 18, an exhaust velocity of 2.2 km/s, and a firing time of 25 s?   about 6.11 km/s

48. Can the rocket in Exercise 47 achieve a stable orbit? Explain your answer.
No; the maximum velocity of 6.11 km/s is less than the 7.7 km/s needed to attain a stable orbit. Therefore, the spacecraft cannot attain a stable orbit 300 km above Earth.

49. What mass ratio would be needed to achieve a stable orbit for a rocket with an exhaust velocity of 2.5 km/s and a firing time of 29 s?   about 24.38

50. A rocket with an exhaust velocity of 2.4 km/s and a 28 second firing time can reach a maximum velocity of 7.8 km/s. What is the mass ratio of the rocket?   about 28.91

By measuring the amount of carbon-14 in an object, a paleontologist can determine its approximate age. The amount of carbon-14 in an object is given by $y = ae^{-0.00012t}$, where a is the amount of carbon-14 originally in the object, and t is the age of the object in years.

51. A fossil of a bone contains 32% of its original carbon-14. What is the approximate age of the bone?   about 9495 years old

52. A fossil of a bone contains 83% of its original carbon-14. What is the approximate age of the bone?   about 1553 years old

Simplify each expression.

53. $\ln e^4$ 4
54. $5 \ln e^5$ 25
55. $\frac{\ln e^2}{2}$ 1
56. $\ln e^{100}$ 100

All-in-One Resources/Online
Enrichment

7-6 Enrichment
Natural Logarithms

Calculating Natural Logarithms

You can compute natural logarithms with

$$\ln x = \frac{(x-1)^1}{1} - \frac{(x-1)^2}{2} + \frac{(x-1)^3}{3} - \frac{(x-1)^4}{4} + \frac{(x-1)^5}{5} - \cdots$$

where the pattern continues forever. Notice that there are actually three patterns involved as the terms progress.

1. What is the pattern of the signs?
The signs alternate as the terms progress beginning with a positive term.

2. What is the pattern of the exponents?
The exponents increase by 1 as the terms progress beginning with 1.

3. What is the pattern of the denominators?
The denominators increase by 1 as the terms progress beginning with 1.

4. For $x = 1$, what is the sum of the series?   0

5. Use a calculator to fill in the blanks in the following chart to four decimal places. Then compare your results with the value of $\ln x$ obtained directly.

	$x = 1.1$	$x = 1.5$
$(x-1)^1$	0.1000	0.5000
$-\frac{(x-1)^2}{2}$	-0.0050	-0.1250
Result	0.0950	0.3750
$+\frac{(x-1)^3}{3}$	0.0003	0.0417
Result	0.0953	0.4167
$-\frac{(x-1)^4}{4}$	0.0000	-0.0156
Result	0.0953	0.4011
$+\frac{(x-1)^5}{5}$	0.0000	0.0063
Result	0.0953	0.4074
$\ln x$	0.0953	0.4055

Practice and Problem Solving Wkbk/ All-in-One Resources/Online
Think About a Plan

7-6 Think About a Plan
Natural Logarithms

Archaeology A fossil bone contains 25% of its original carbon-14. What is the approximate age of the bone?

Understanding the Problem

1. What is the amount of carbon-14 remaining in the fossil bone?
25% of the original amount

2. If a is the amount of carbon-14 originally in an object and t is the object's age in years, what equation gives the amount of carbon-14 in the object? $y = ae^{-0.00012t}$

3. What is the problem asking you to determine?
the approximate age of the fossil bone

Planning the Solution

4. What number should you substitute for y in the equation above?   0.25a

5. Write an equation you can use to determine the approximate age of the bone. $0.25a = ae^{-0.00012t}$

Getting an Answer

6. How can logarithms help you solve your equation?
After dividing each side by a, take the natural log of both sides of the equation to eliminate e.

7. Solve your equation to find the approximate age of the bone.
$0.25a = ae^{-0.00012t}$
$0.25 = e^{-0.00012t}$
$\ln(0.25) = \ln(e^{-0.00012t})$
$\ln(0.25) = -0.00012t$
$t = \frac{\ln(0.25)}{-0.00012} \approx 11,552$ years

Practice and Problem Solving Wkbk/ All-in-One Resources/Online
Standardized Test Prep

7-6 Standardized Test Prep
Natural Logarithms

Multiple Choice

For Exercises 1–4, choose the correct letter. Do not use a calculator.

1. What is $3 \ln 5 - \ln 2$ written as a single natural logarithm?   D
Ⓐ ln 7.5   Ⓑ ln 27   Ⓒ $\ln \left(\frac{5}{2}\right)^3$ Ⓓ ln 62.5

2. What is the solution of $e^{x+1} = 137$?   G
Ⓕ $x = \ln 13 + 1$ Ⓖ $x = \ln 13 - 1$ Ⓗ $x = \ln 13$ Ⓘ $x = \ln 12$

3. What is the solution of $\ln(x - 2)^2 = 6$?   C
Ⓐ $2 + e^3$ Ⓑ $2 - e^3$ Ⓒ $2 \pm e^3$ Ⓓ $2 \pm e^6$

4. What is the solution of $e^{t+1} + 3 = 8$?   G
Ⓕ $x = 2 \ln 5 - 1$ Ⓖ $x = 2 \ln 5 - 2$ Ⓗ $x = 2 \ln 4$ Ⓘ $x = \frac{1}{2}(\ln 5 - 1)$

Short Response

5. The maximum velocity v of a rocket is $v = -0.0098t + c \ln R$. The rocket fires for t seconds and the velocity of the exhaust is c km/s. The ratio of the mass of the rocket filled with fuel to the mass of the rocket without fuel is R. A spacecraft can attain a stable orbit 300 km above Earth if it reaches a velocity of 7.7 km/s.
a. What is the velocity of a spacecraft whose booster rocket has a mass ratio of 16, an exhaust velocity of 3.2 km/s, and a firing time of 40 s?
b. Can this rocket attain a stable orbit 300 km above Earth? Explain in words or show work for how you determined your answer.
[2] a. 8.48 km/s
b. Yes; the maximum velocity of 8.48 km/s is greater than the 7.7 km/s needed for a stable orbit. Therefore, the spacecraft can attain a stable orbit 300 km above the Earth.
[1] incorrect velocity OR incorrect explanation
[0] incorrect answers and no work shown OR no answers given

Online Teacher Resource Center
Activities, Games, and Puzzles

7-6 Activity: An Irrational Pattern
Natural Logarithms

This is an activity for the entire class. It involves a fraction that never ends.

Your teacher or a student can lead the activity. Begin by writing the following fractional expressions on the board.

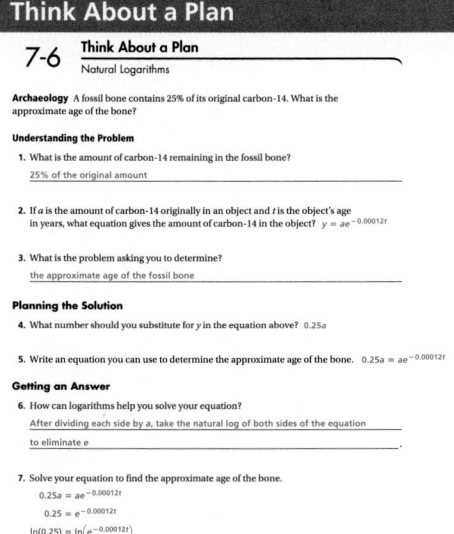

- Write the fourth expression in the fraction pattern on the board and in the space below.

$$2 + \cfrac{1}{1 + \cfrac{1}{2 + \cfrac{3}{4 + \frac{4}{5}}}}$$

- Write the fifth expression in the space below. Use parentheses to group numbers in denominators. *Hint:* Start from the bottommost part of $(4 + 4/5)$. Build the fraction from denominators to numerators.

$$2 + \cfrac{1}{1 + \cfrac{1}{2 + \cfrac{2}{3 + \cfrac{4}{4 + \cfrac{4}{5 + \frac{5}{6}}}}}}$$

- Evaluate the fifth expression on a calculator. Write your answer in the space below.
2.71845; e

- Which two familiar numbers do these expressions give? Write your answers in the space between the two expressions. $\sqrt{2}$ and π

$$1 + \cfrac{1}{2 + \cfrac{1}{2 + \cfrac{1}{2 + \frac{1}{2}}}} \qquad 3 + \cfrac{1}{6 + \cfrac{9}{6 + \cfrac{25}{6 + \cfrac{49}{6 + \frac{81}{121}}}}}$$

Guided Instruction

PURPOSE To show how to solve exponential and logarithmic inequalities using graphs or tables

PROCESS Students will
- find the point of intersection for two functions and use this information to solve the inequality.
- define the window and table start values to find all solutions of the inequalities.

DISCUSS Point out that you are using a system of equations to determine the solution to the inequality. Each side of the equation is written as a function, and then the intersection is found. Elicit that
- the intersection of two functions represents the solution to an equality. Use the trace function to find values that make the inequality true.
- it is not possible to find the logarithm of 0 or a negative number.

Example 1

Q Why are you not shading above and/or below the functions? **[Shading above and below functions indicates you are solving a system of inequalities. The inequality being solved contains 1 variable, so your solution is shown on a number line.]**

Exercises

It is important to visualize a graph before using a graphing calculator to minimize mistakes in input.

Q How would you describe the graph used to determine the solution for Exercise 2? **[The graph of $y = \log x + 3 \log(x - 1)$ resides only in Quadrants I and IV. The domain is all positive real numbers greater than 1 and the range is all real numbers.]**

Ⓒ **Mathematical Practices** This Concept Byte supports students in becoming proficient in using appropriate tools, Mathematical Practice 5.

Exponential and Logarithmic Inequalities

Ⓒ **Common Core State Standard**
A-REI.D.11 Explain why the x-coordinates of t points where the graphs of the equations $y = f$ and $y = g(x)$ intersect are the solutions of the equation $f(x) = g(x)$ . . .
MP 5

You can use the graphing and table capabilities of your calculator to solve problems involving exponential and logarithmic inequalities.

Example 1

Solve $2(3)^{x+4} > 10$ using a graph.

Step 1 Define **Y1** and **Y2**.

Step 2 Make a graph and find the point of intersection.

Step 3 Identify the x-values that make the inequality true.

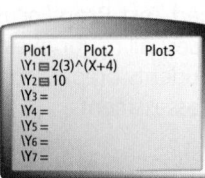

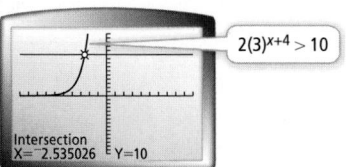

The solution is $x > -2.535$.

Exercises

Solve each inequality using a graph.

1. $4(3)^{x+1} > 6$

2. $\log x + 3 \log(x - 1) < 4$

3. $3(2)^{x+2} \geq 5$

4. $x + 1 < 12 \log x$

5. $2(3)^{x-4} > 7$

6. $\log x + 2 \log(x - 1) < 1$

7. $4(2)^{x-1} \leq 5$

8. $2 \log x + 4 \log(x + 3) > 3$

9. $5(4)^{x-1} < 2$

STEM 10. Bacteria Growth Scientists are growing bacteria in a laboratory. They start with a known population of bacteria and measure how long it takes the population to double.
  a. Write an exponential function that models the population in Sample A as a function of time in hours.
  b. Write an exponential function that models the population in Sample B as a function of time in hours.
  c. Write an inequality that models the population in Sample B overtaking the population in Sample A.
  d. Use a graphing calculator to solve the inequality in part (c).

Bacteria Population

Sample	Initial Population	Doubling Time (in hours)
Sample A	200,000	1
Sample B	50,000	0.5

Ⓒ **11. Writing** Describe the solution sets to the inequality $x + c < \log x$ as c varies over the real numbers.

Answers

Concept Byte

1. $x > -0.63093$

2. $1 < x < 10.7591$

3. $x \geq -1.26303$

4. $1.67 < x < 11.9$

5. $x > 5.14031$

6. $1 < x < 2.86746$

7. $x \leq 1.32193$

8. $x > 1.53655$

9. $x < 0.339036$

10. a. $A(t) = 200,000(2)^t$

  b. $B(t) = 50,000(2)^{2t}$

  c. $200,000(2)^t < 50,000(2)^{2t}$

  d. $t > 2$

11. $x > 0$ and $c < 0$

Example 2

Solve $\log x + 2\log(x+1) < 2$ using a table.

Step 1 Define **Y1** and **Y2**.

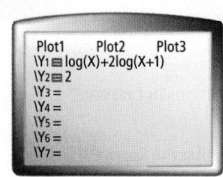

Step 2 Make a table and examine the values.

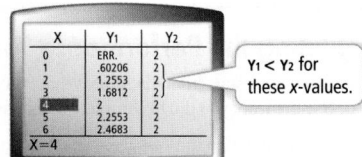

Y₁ < Y₂ for these x-values.

Step 3 Identify the x-values that make the inequality true.

The solution is $0 < x < 4$.

Exercises

Solve each inequality using a table.
(Hint: For more accurate results, set $\Delta\text{Tbl} = 0.001$.)

12. $\log x + \log(x+1) < 3$

13. $3(2)^{x+1} > 5$

14. $\log x + 5\log(x-1) \geq 3$

15. $5(3)^x \leq 2$

16. $3\log x + \log(x+2) > 1$

17. $2(4)^{x+3} \leq 8$

Barometric Pressure Average barometric pressure varies with the altitude of a location. The greater the altitude is, the lower the pressure. The altitude A is measured in feet above sea level. The barometric pressure P is measured in inches of mercury (in. Hg). The altitude can be modeled by the function $A(P) = 90{,}000 - 26{,}500 \ln P$.

18. What is a reasonable domain of the function? What is the range of the function?

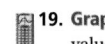 **19. Graphing Calculator** Use a graphing calculator to make a table of function values. Use **TblStart** = 30 and $\Delta\text{Tbl} = -1$.

20. Write an equation to find what average pressure the model predicts at sea level, or $A = 0$. Use your table to solve the equation.

21. Kilimanjaro is a mountain in Tanzania that formed from three extinct volcanoes. The base of the mountain is at 3000 ft above sea level. The peak is at 19,340 ft above sea level. On Kilimanjaro, $3000 \leq A(P) \leq 19{,}340$ is true for the altitude. Write an inequality from which you can find minimum and maximum values of normal barometric pressure on Kilimanjaro. Use a table and solve the inequality for P.

22. Denver, Colorado, is nicknamed the "Mile High City" because its elevation is about 1 mile, or 5280 ft, above sea level. The lowest point in Phoenix, Arizona, is 1117 ft above sea level. Write an inequality that describes the range of $A(P)$ as you drive from Phoenix to Denver. Then solve the inequality for P. (Assume that you never go lower than 1117 ft and you never go higher than 5280 ft.)

Example 2

Students solved exponential and logarithmic equations using tables in Example 3 of Lesson 7-5. Briefly review this example if needed.

Q Why is the TblStart value set at 0? **[Although it is not possible to find log 0, you still must look at all positive solutions. If you had started the table at 1, you might have missed the solutions between 0 and 1.]**

Q How do you use properties of logarithms to write the left side of the inequality in a different way? Enter this new expression into your calculator and explain what you find. **[Apply the Power Property to rewrite the expression as $\log x + \log(x+1)^2$. Apply the Product Property to rewrite the expression as $\log(x(x+1)^2)$. Starting the table at 0, you see the expressions are equivalent.]**

Caution students that when using the properties of logarithms to rewrite expressions, the calculator might give y-values for some negative values of x. Have students identify the domain and range in the original equation.

Exercises

Compare solving inequalities using graphs versus tables. Have students pick their preferred method and state the reasons for their choice.

Q How can you determine the table values for Exercise 13? Explain your method. **[Sample: Begin the TblStart value at zero and $\Delta\text{Tbl} = 1$, so you can narrow the possible solutions. The table shows that when $x = -1$, $y = 3$ and when $x = 0$, $y = 6$. You must find where $3(2)^{x+1}$ is greater than 5, so the solution begins between -1 and 0. Reset the TblStart value, and set $\Delta\text{Tbl} = 0.1$. Continue until the solution to the inequality is found.]**

12. $0 < x < 31.125$

13. $x > -0.263$

14. $x \geq 4.015$

15. $x \leq -0.835$

16. $x > 1.429$

17. $x \leq -2$

18. positive real numbers; real numbers

19.

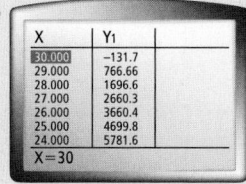

20. $0 = 90{,}000 - 26{,}500 \ln P$; ≈ 29.85 in.

21. $3000 \leq 90{,}000 - 26{,}500 \ln P \leq 19{,}340$; $14.4 \leq P \leq 26.7$

22. $1117 \leq 90{,}000 - 26{,}500 \ln P \leq 5280$; $24.5 \leq P \leq 28.6$

Completing the Performance Task

In the Apply What You've Learned sections in Lessons 7-1 and 7-5, students modeled the problem situation on page 433 with an exponential function and wrote and solved an exponential equation to find the difference in magnitude between Polaris and Sirius. Now, they can use their result to complete the task on page 433. Ask students the following questions as they work toward solving the problem.

Q How can you use the work you have done in the chapter to solve the problem? **[Sample: I can use the difference in magnitudes that I wrote in Lesson 7-5 to find the apparent magnitude of Sirius by subtracting it from the given value of the apparent magnitude of Polaris, 1.97.]**

Q How can you check that your answer to the problem is reasonable? **[Sample: Use a calculator to evaluate the exponential expression $10^{0.4x}$ when $x = 3.45$, and check that the result is approximately equal to 24.]**

FOSTERING MATHEMATICAL DISCOURSE

Have students show that the function they wrote on page 441 expresses the same relationship as the equation given on page 467 for Exercises 73 and 74.

ANSWERS

1. -1.48
2. Check students' work.

On Your Own

This problem is similar to the problem posed on page 433, but now students must determine which of several stars has the given brightness relationship with Polaris.

ANSWERS

a. $7.8 = \left(\sqrt[5]{100}\right)^x$, where x is the apparent magnitude separation between Polaris and the unknown star; 2.23

b. Alpha Centauri

Completing the Performance Task

Look back at your results from the Apply What You've Learned sections in Lessons 7-1 and 7-5. Use the work you did to complete the following.

To solve these problems, you will pull together concepts and skills related to exponential functions and logarithms.

1. Solve the problem in the Task Description on page 433 by finding the apparent magnitude of Sirius. Show all your work and explain each step of your solution.

2. **Reflect** Choose one of the Mathematical Practices below and explain how you applied it in your work on the Performance Task.

   MP 1: Make sense of problems and persevere in solving them.

   MP 2: Reason abstractly and quantitatively.

   MP 5: Use appropriate tools strategically.

On Your Own

Use the information on page 433 about apparent magnitude. The table below shows the apparent magnitudes of several stars in the night sky. One of these stars is 7.8 times as bright as Polaris.

Star	Apparent Magnitude
Betelgeuse	0.43
Vega	0.03
Alpha Centauri	−0.26

a. Write and solve an exponential equation to find the apparent magnitude difference between Polaris and the star that is 7.8 times as bright as Polaris.

b. Which star is 7.8 times as bright as Polaris?

 **Chapter Review**

Connecting **BIG** ideas to the Math You've Learned

1 Modeling
The function $y = ab^x$, $a > 0$, $b > 1$, models exponential growth. $y = ab^x$ models exponential decay if $0 < b < 1$.

2 Equivalence
Logarithms are exponents. In fact, $\log_b a = c$ if and only if $b^c = a$.

3 Function
The exponential function $y = b^x$ and the logarithmic function $y = \log_b x$ are inverse functions.

Exponential Models (Lesson 7-1)
The population P is 1000 at the start. In each time period,
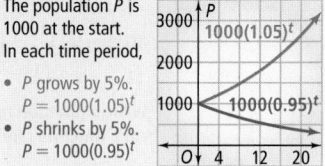
- P grows by 5%. $P = 1000(1.05)^t$
- P shrinks by 5%. $P = 1000(0.95)^t$

Logarithmic Functions as Inverses (Lesson 7-3)
- $y = 2^x$
- $y = \log_2 x$
- $y = 2^{x-1}$
- $y = (\log_2 x) + 1$
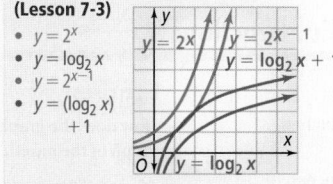

Properties of Logarithms (Lesson 7-4)
$$b^a b^c = b^{a+c}$$
$$\log_b mn = \log_b m + \log_b n$$
$$\frac{b^a}{b^c} = b^{a-c}$$
$$\log_b \frac{m}{n} = \log_b m - \log_b n$$
$$\log_b m^n = n \log_b m$$
$$\log_n m = \frac{\log_b m}{\log_b n}$$

Exponential and Natural Logarithm Equations (Lessons 7-5 and 7-6)
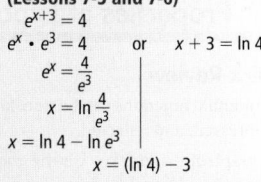
$$e^{x+3} = 4$$
$$e^x \cdot e^3 = 4 \quad \text{or} \quad x + 3 = \ln 4$$
$$e^x = \frac{4}{e^3}$$
$$x = \ln \frac{4}{e^3}$$
$$x = \ln 4 - \ln e^3$$
$$x = (\ln 4) - 3$$

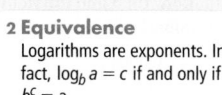 Chapter Vocabulary

- asymptote (p. 435)
- Change of Base Formula (p. 464)
- common logarithm (p. 453)
- continuously compounded interest (p. 446)
- decay factor (p. 436)
- exponential decay (p. 435)
- exponential equation (p. 469)
- exponential function (p. 434)
- exponential growth (p. 435)
- growth factor (p. 436)
- logarithm (p. 451)
- logarithmic equation (p. 471)
- logarithmic function (p. 454)
- logarithmic scale (p. 453)
- natural base exponential functions (p. 446)
- natural logarithmic function (p. 478)

Fill in the blanks.

1. There are two types of exponential functions. For ?, as the value of x increases, the value of y decreases, approaching zero. For ?, as the value of x increases, the value of y increases.

2. As x or y increases in absolute value, the graph may approach a(n) ?.

3. A(n) ? with a base e is a ?.

4. $A = Pe^{rt}$ is known as the ? formula.

5. The inverse of an exponential function with a base e is the ?.

Essential Questions

BIG idea Modeling
ESSENTIAL QUESTION How do you model a quantity that changes regularly over time by the same percentage?
ANSWER The function $y = ab^x$, $a > 0$, $b > 1$, models exponential growth. $y = ab^x$ models exponential decay if $0 < b < 1$.

BIG idea Equivalence
ESSENTIAL QUESTION How are exponents and logarithms related?
ANSWER Logarithms are exponents. In fact, $\log_b a = c$ if and only if $b^c = a$.

BIG idea Function
ESSENTIAL QUESTION How are exponential functions and logarithmic functions related?
ANSWER The exponential function $y = b^x$ and the logarithmic function $y = \log_b x$ are inverse functions.

Answers

Chapter Review
1. exponential decay; exponential growth
2. asymptote
3. logarithm; natural logarithm function
4. continuously compounded interest
5. natural logarithmic function

Summative Questions

Use the following prompts as you review this chapter with your students. The prompts are designed to help you assess your students' understanding of the BIG Ideas they have studied.

- How could you find the value of $\log_{16} 8$ without using a calculator?
- Compare continuously compounded interest to annual interest. Which method of compounding gives the most interest?
- How can you use exponents to solve a logarithmic equation? How can you use logarithms to solve an exponential equation?

Answers

Chapter Review (continued)

6. exponential growth; $(0, 1)$

7. exponential growth; $(0, 2)$

8. exponential growth; $(0, 0.2)$

9. exponential decay; $(0, 3)$

10. exponential growth; $\left(0, \frac{25}{7}\right)$

11. exponential growth; $(0, 0.0015)$

12. exponential decay; $(0, 2.25)$

13. exponential decay; $(0, 0.5)$

14. $y = 12,500(0.91)^x$; $7800

15. $y = 50(1.03)^x$; $58

16. The parent graph $y = 2^x$ is stretched by a factor of 5, translated 1 unit to the left, and 3 units up.

17. The parent graph $y = \left(\frac{1}{3}\right)^x$ is reflected across the x-axis, stretched by a factor of 2, and translated 2 units to the right.

18. $1100.76

19. $291.91

20. 0.0498

21. 0.3679

22. 148.4132

23. 0.6065

7-1 Exploring Exponential Models

Quick Review

The general form of an **exponential function** is $y = ab^x$, where x is a real number, $a \neq 0$, $b > 0$, and $b \neq 1$. When $b > 1$, the function models **exponential growth**, and b is the **growth factor**. When $0 < b < 1$, the function models **exponential decay**, and b is the **decay factor**. The y-intercept is $(0, a)$.

Example

Determine whether $y = 2(1.4)^x$ is an example of exponential growth or decay. Then, find the y-intercept.

Since $b = 1.4 > 1$, the function represents exponential growth.

Since $a = 2$, the y-intercept is $(0, 2)$.

Exercises

Determine whether each function is an example of exponential growth or decay. Then, find the y-intercept.

6. $y = 5^x$

7. $y = 2(4)^x$

8. $y = 0.2(3.8)^x$

9. $y = 3(0.25)^x$

10. $y = \frac{25}{7}\left(\frac{7}{5}\right)^x$

11. $y = 0.0015(10)^x$

12. $y = 2.25\left(\frac{1}{3}\right)^x$

13. $y = 0.5\left(\frac{1}{4}\right)^x$

Write a function for each situation. Then find the value of each function after five years. Round to the nearest dollar.

14. A $12,500 car depreciates 9% each year.

15. A baseball card bought for $50 increases 3% in value each year.

7-2 Properties of Exponential Functions

Quick Review

Exponential functions can be translated, stretched, compressed, and reflected.

The graph of $y = ab^{x-h} + k$ is the graph of the parent function $y = b^x$ stretched or compressed by a factor $|a|$, reflected across the x-axis if $a < 0$, and translated h units horizontally and k units vertically.

The **continuously compounded interest** formula is $A = Pe^{rt}$, where P is the principal, r is the annual interest rate, and t is time in years.

Example

How does the graph of $y = -3^x + 1$ compare to the graph of the parent function?

The parent function is $y = 3^x$.

Since $a = -1$, the graph is reflected across the x-axis.

Since $k = 1$, it is translated up 1 unit.

Exercises

How does the graph of each function compare to the graph of the parent function?

16. $y = 5(2)^{x+1} + 3$

17. $y = -2\left(\frac{1}{3}\right)^{x-2}$

Find the amount in a continuously compounded account for the given conditions.

18. principal: $1000
    annual interest rate: 4.8%
    time: 2 years

19. principal: $250
    annual interest rate: 6.2%
    time: 2.5 years

Evaluate each expression to four decimal places.

20. e^{-3}

21. e^{-1}

22. e^5

23. $e^{-\frac{1}{2}}$

7-3 Logarithmic Functions as Inverses

Quick Review

If $x = b^y$, then $\log_b x = y$. The **logarithmic function** is the inverse of the exponential function, so the graphs of the functions are reflections of one another across the line $y = x$. Logarithmic functions can be translated, stretched, compressed, and reflected, as represented by $y = a\log_b(x - h) + k$, similarly to exponential functions. When $b = 10$, the logarithm is called a **common logarithm**, which you can write as $\log x$.

Example

Write $5^{-2} = 0.04$ in logarithmic form.

If $y = b^x$, then $\log_b y = x$.

$y = 0.04$, $b = 5$ and $x = -2$.

So, $\log_5 0.04 = -2$.

Exercises

Write each equation in logarithmic form.

24. $6^2 = 36$ **25.** $2^{-3} = 0.125$

26. $3^3 = 27$ **27.** $10^{-3} = 0.001$

Evaluate each logarithm.

28. $\log_2 64$ **29.** $\log_3 \frac{1}{9}$

30. $\log 0.00001$ **31.** $\log_2 1$

Graph each logarithmic function.

32. $y = \log_3 x$ **33.** $y = \log x + 2$

34. $y = 3\log_2(x)$ **35.** $y = \log_5(x + 1)$

How does the graph of each function compare to the graph of the parent function?

36. $y = 3\log_4(x + 1)$ **37.** $y = -\ln x + 2$

7-4 Properties of Logarithms

Quick Review

For any positive numbers, m, n, and b where $b \neq 1$, each of the following statements is true. Each can be used to rewrite a logarithmic expression.

- $\log_b mn = \log_b m + \log_b n$, by the Product Property
- $\log_b \frac{m}{n} = \log_b m - \log_b n$, by the Quotient Property
- $\log_b m^n = n\log_b m$, by the Power Property

Example

Write $2\log_2 y + \log_2 x$ as a single logarithm. Identify any properties used.

$2\log_2 y + \log_2 x$

$= \log_2 y^2 + \log_2 x$ Power Property

$= \log_2 xy^2$ Product Property

Exercises

Write each expression as a single logarithm. Identify any properties used.

38. $\log 8 + \log 3$ **39.** $\log_2 5 - \log_2 3$

40. $4\log_3 x + \log_3 7$ **41.** $\log x - \log y$

42. $\log 5 - 2\log x$ **43.** $3\log_4 x + 2\log_4 x$

Expand each logarithm. State the properties of logarithms used.

44. $\log_4 x^2 y^3$ **45.** $\log 4s^4 t$

46. $\log_3 \frac{2}{x}$ **47.** $\log(x + 3)^2$

48. $\log_2(2y - 4)^3$ **49.** $\log \frac{z^2}{5}$

Use the Change of Base Formula to evaluate each expression.

50. $\log_2 7$ **51.** $\log_3 10$

45. $\log 4 + 4\log s + \log t$; Product and Power Prop.

46. $\log_3 2 - \log_3 x$; Quotient Prop.

47. $2\log(x + 3)$; Power Prop.

48. $3\log_2 2 + 3\log_2(y - 2)$; Power and Product Prop.

49. $2\log z - \log 5$; Power and Quotient Prop.

50. ≈ 2.8

51. ≈ 2.1

24. $2 = \log_6 36$

25. $-3 = \log_2 0.125$

26. $3 = \log_3 27$

27. $-3 = \log 0.001$

28. 6   **29.** -2 **30.** -5 **31.** 0

32.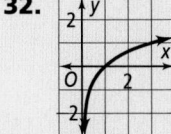

33.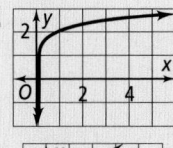

34.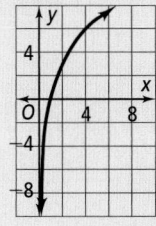

35.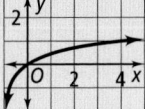

36. The parent graph $y = \log_4 x$ is stretched by a factor of 3 and translated 1 unit to the left.

37. The parent graph $y = \ln x$ is reflected across the x-axis and translated 2 units up.

38. $\log 24$; Product Prop.

39. $\log_2 \frac{5}{3}$; Quotient Prop.

40. $\log_3 7x^4$; Power and Product Prop.

41. $\log \frac{x}{y}$; Quotient Prop.

42. $\log \frac{5}{x^2}$; Power and Quotient Prop.

43. $\log_4 x^5$; Power and Product Prop.

44. $2\log_4 x + 3\log_4 y$; Product and Power Prop.

Answers

Chapter Review (continued)

52. 0.75

53. 3.2619

54. 4.6542

55. 1.3652

56. 3.3333

57. 8

58. 50

59. 7.6256×10^{12}

60. 0.9307

61. 0.6599

62. 0.6658

63. 3.0589

64. $\approx 18.2\ h$

65. ≈ 0.83

66. ≈ 2.26

67. ≈ 4.31

68. ≈ 0.54

69. ≈ 3.77

70. ≈ 6.03

71. $\approx 3.4\%$

7-5 Exponential and Logarithmic Equations

Quick Review

An equation in the form $b^{cx} = a$, where the exponent includes a variable, is called an **exponential equation**. You can solve exponential equations by taking the logarithm of each side of the equation. An equation that includes one or more logarithms involving a variable is called a **logarithmic equation**.

Example

Solve and round to the nearest ten-thousandth.

$$6^{2x} = 75$$

$\log 6^{2x} = \log 75$ Take the logarithm of both sides.

$2x \log 6 = \log 75$ Power Property of Logarithms

$x = \dfrac{\log 75}{2 \log 6}$ Divide both sides by 2 log 6.

$x \approx 1.2048$ Evaluate using a calculator.

Exercises

Solve each equation. Round to the nearest ten-thousandth.

52. $25^{2x} = 125$ **53.** $3^x = 36$

54. $7^{x-3} = 25$ **55.** $5^x + 3 = 12$

56. $\log 3x = 1$ **57.** $\log_2 4x = 5$

58. $\log x = \log 2x^2 - 2$ **59.** $2 \log_3 x = 54$

Solve by graphing. Round to the nearest ten-thousandth.

60. $5^{2x} = 20$ **61.** $3^{7x} = 160$

62. $6^{3x+1} = 215$ **63.** $0.5^x = 0.12$

64. A culture of 10 bacteria is started, and the number of bacteria will double every hour. In about how many hours will there be 3,000,000 bacteria?

7-6 Natural Logarithms

Quick Review

The inverse of $y = e^x$ is the **natural logarithmic function** $y = \log_e x = \ln x$. You solve natural logarithmic equations in the same way as common logarithmic equations.

Example

Use natural logarithms to solve $\ln x - \ln 2 = 3$.

$\ln x - \ln 2 = 3$

$\ln \dfrac{x}{2} = 3$ Quotient Property

$\dfrac{x}{2} = e^3$ Rewrite in exponential form.

$\dfrac{x}{2} \approx 20.0855$ Use a calculator to find e^3.

$x \approx 40.171$ Simplify.

Exercises

Solve each equation. Check your answers.

65. $e^{3x} = 12$

66. $\ln x + \ln (x + 1) = 2$

67. $2 \ln x + 3 \ln 2 = 5$

68. $\ln 4 - \ln x = 2$

69. $4e^{(x-1)} = 64$

70. $3 \ln x + \ln 5 = 7$

71. An initial investment of \$350 is worth \$429.20 after six years of continuous compounding. Find the annual interest rate.

7 Chapter Test

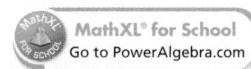
MathXL® for School
Go to PowerAlgebra.com

Do you know HOW?

Determine whether each function is an example of exponential growth or decay. Then find the y-intercept.

1. $y = 3(0.25)^x$ **2.** $y = 2(6)^{-x}$

3. $y = 0.1(10)^x$ **4.** $y = 3e^x$

Describe how the graph of each function is related to the graph of its parent function. Then find the domain, range, and asymptotes.

5. $y = 3^x + 2$

6. $y = \left(\frac{1}{2}\right)^{x+1}$

7. $y = -(2)^{x+2}$

Write each equation in logarithmic form.

8. $5^4 = 625$ **9.** $e^0 = 1$

Evaluate each logarithm.

10. $\log_2 8$ **11.** $\log_7 7$

12. $\log_5 \frac{1}{125}$ **13.** $\log_{11} 1$

Graph each logarithmic function. Compare each graph to the graph of its parent function. List each function's domain, range, y-intercept, and asymptotes.

14. $y = \log_3 (x - 1)$

15. $y = \frac{1}{2}\log_3 (x + 2)$

16. $y = 1 - \log_2 x$

Write each logarithmic expression as a single logarithm.

17. $\log_2 4 + 3 \log_2 9$

18. $3 \log a - 2 \log b$

Expand each logarithm.

19. $\log_7 \frac{a}{b}$ **20.** $\log 3x^3y^2$

Use the properties of logarithms to evaluate each expression.

21. $\log_9 27 - \log_9 9$

22. $2 \log 5 + \log 40$

Solve each equation.

23. $(27)^{3x} = 81$ **24.** $3^{x-1} = 24$

25. $2e^{3x} = 16$ **26.** $2 \log x = -4$

Use the Change of Base Formula to rewrite each expression using common logarithms.

27. $\log_3 16$ **28.** $\log_2 10$

29. $\log_7 8$ **30.** $\log_4 9$

Use the properties of logarithms to simplify and solve each equation. Round to the nearest thousandth.

31. $\ln 2 + \ln x = 1$

32. $\ln (x + 1) + \ln (x - 1) = 4$

33. $\ln (2x - 1)^2 = 7$

34. $3 \ln x - \ln 2 = 4$

Do you UNDERSTAND?

35. Writing Show that solving the equation $3^{2x} = 4$ by taking the common logarithm of each side is equivalent to solving it by taking the logarithm with base 3 of each side.

36. Open-Ended Give an example of an exponential function that models exponential growth and an example of an exponential function that models exponential decay.

37. Investment You put $1500 into an account that pays 7% annual interest compounded continuously. How long will it be before you have $2000 in your account?

16.
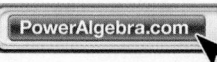

The parent graph $y = \log_2 x$ is reflected across the x-axis and translated 1 unit up; domain: $x > 0$, range: all real numbers; no y-intercept; asymptote: $x = 0$

17. $\log_2 2916$

18. $\log \frac{a^3}{b^2}$

19. $\log_7 a - \log_7 b$

20. $\log 3 + 3 \log x + 2 \log y$

21. $\frac{1}{2}$

22. 3

23. $0.\overline{44}$

24. ≈ 3.89

25. ≈ 0.69

26. 0.01

27. $\frac{\log 16}{\log 3}$

28. $\frac{1}{\log 2}$

29. $\frac{\log 8}{\log 7}$

30. $\frac{\log 9}{\log 4}$

31. 1.359

32. 7.456

33. $17.058, -16.058$

34. 4.780

35.
$$3^{2x} = 4$$
$$\log 3^{2x} = \log 4$$
$$2x \log 3 = \log 4$$
and
$$x = \frac{\log 4}{2 \log 3}$$
$$x \approx 0.6309$$

$$3^{2x} = 4$$
$$\log_3 3^{2x} = \log_3 4$$
$$2x = \log_3 4$$
$$x = \frac{1}{2}\log_3 4$$
$$x \approx 0.6309$$

36. Answers may vary. Sample: exponential growth: $y = \frac{1}{3}(2)^x$; exponential decay: $y = 7\left(\frac{1}{5}\right)^x$

37. 4.11 yrs

Answers

Chapter Test

1. exponential decay, (0, 3)

2. exponential decay, (0, 2)

3. exponential growth, (0, 0.1)

4. exponential growth, (0, 3)

5. The parent graph $y = 3^x$ is translated 2 units up; domain: all real numbers, range: $y > 2$; asymptote: $y = 2$

6. The parent graph $y = \left(\frac{1}{2}\right)^x$ is translated 1 unit to the left; domain: all real numbers, range $y > 0$; asymptote: $y = 0$

7. The parent graph $y = 2^x$ is translated 2 units to the left and reflected across the x-axis; domain: all real numbers, range: $y > 0$; asymptote: $y = 0$

8. $\log_5 625 = 4$

9. $\log_e 1 = 0$

10. 3 **11.** 1 **12.** -3 **13.** 0

14.
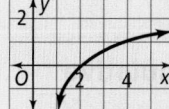

The parent graph $y = \log_3 x$ is translated 1 unit to the right; domain: $x > 1$, range: all real numbers; no y-intercept; asymptote: $x = 1$

15.
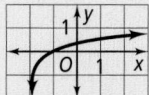

The parent graph $y = \log_3 x$ is compressed by the factor $\frac{1}{2}$, then translated 2 units to the left; domain: $x > -2$, range: all real numbers; y-intercept: $\left(0, \frac{1}{2}\log_3 2\right) \approx (0, 0.3155)$; asymptote: $x = -2$

PowerAlgebra.com
MathXL for School
Prepare students for the Mid-Chapter Quiz and Chapter Test with online practice and review.

Item Number	Lesson	Content Standard
1	7-1	A-CED.A.2
2	4-8	N-CN.A.2
3	7-4	F-LE.A.4
4	4-3	F-IF.B.4
5	7-5	F-IF.C.7e
6	7-6	F-BF.B.5
7	2-5	F-IF.B.6
8	1-4	A-CED.A.4
9	5-4	A-APR.D.7
10	3-2	A-REI.C.6
11	5-2	A-APR.A.2
12	5-3	A-SSE.B.3a
13	6-6	F-BF.A.1b
14	5-2	F-IF.B.4
15	7-5	F-BF.B.3
16	7-1	F-IF.C.7c
17	5-5	F-BF.B.5
18	7-4	A-SSE.B.4
19	7-5	F-IF.B.4
20	4-7	F-BF.B.5
21	5-6	F-LE.A.4
22	4-9	A-REI.C.7
23	6-5	A-CED.A.2
24	5-3	A-REI.A.2
25	4-1	F-IF.A.1
26	4-6	A-REI.B.4b
27	6-8	F-IF.A.1b
28	5-1	F-IF.C.7c
29	3-3	A-CED.A.3
30	5-5	A-REI.B.4b
31	7-2	F-BF.B.3
32	2-7	F-BF.B.3

7 Common Core Cumulative Standards Review

ASSESSMENT

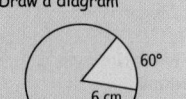
Vocabulary Builder

As you solve problems, you must understand the meanings of mathematical terms. Match each term with its mathematical meaning.

A. growth factor

B. asymptote

C. logarithmic function

D. exponential equation

I. the inverse of an exponential function

II. a line that a graph approaches as x or y increases in absolute value

III. the value of b in $y = ab^x$, when $b > 1$

IV. an equation of the form $b^{cx} = a$, where the exponent includes a variable

Selected Response

Read each question. Then write the letter of the correct answer on your page.

1. The population of a town is modeled by the equation $P = 16{,}581e^{0.02t}$ where P represents the population t years after 2000. According to the model, what will the population of the town be in 2020?

- A 16,916
- B 17,258
- C 20,252
- D 24,736

2. If $i = \sqrt{-1}$, then which expression is equal to $9i(13i)$?

- F −117
- G 117i
- H 117
- I −117i

3. Which expression is equivalent to $\log_5 32$?

- A $\log 5 + \log 32$
- B $\log 5 - \log 32$
- C $(\log 5)(\log 32)$
- D $\frac{\log 32}{\log 5}$

Answers

Common Core Cumulative Standards Review

A. III
B. II
C. I
D. IV
1. D
2. F
3. D

4. The table shows the height of a ball that was tossed into the air. Which equation best models the relationship between time t and the height of the ball h?

Time (seconds)	0	0.25	0.5	0.75
Height (feet)	4	10.5	15	17.5

- Ⓕ $h = 26t + 4$
- Ⓖ $h = -16t^2 + 30t + 4$
- Ⓗ $h = 4t^2$
- Ⓘ $h = -16t^2 + 4$

5. Which is the graph of $y = 3^x$?

Ⓐ 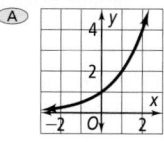   Ⓒ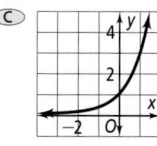

Ⓑ 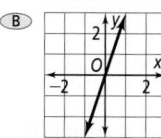   Ⓓ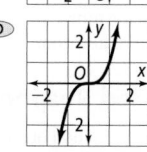

6. Which exponential function is equivalent to $y = \log_3 x$?

- Ⓕ $y = 3^x$
- Ⓖ $y = \frac{x}{3}$
- Ⓗ $y = x^3$
- Ⓘ $x = 3^y$

7. What is the simplest form of the quotient $\frac{\sqrt{72x^5y^3z^8}}{\sqrt{3xy^2z^2}}$?

- Ⓐ $\sqrt{24x^4yz^6}$
- Ⓒ $24x^4yz^6$
- Ⓑ $2x^2z^3\sqrt{6y}$
- Ⓓ $12x^2yz^6$

8. Solve the mass energy equivalence formula $e = mc^2$ for c.

- Ⓕ $c = e^2m$
- Ⓗ $c = \sqrt{\frac{e}{m}}$
- Ⓖ $c = \sqrt{\frac{m}{e}}$
- Ⓘ $c = \sqrt{(e - m)}$

9. What is the quotient of $(x^3 + 2x^2 - x + 6) \div (x + 3)$?

- Ⓐ $x^2 + 5x + 14$, R 42
- Ⓒ $x^3 + 5x^2 + 14x + 42$
- Ⓑ $x^2 - x + 2$
- Ⓓ $x^2 + x - 2$

10. On a certain night, a restaurant employs x servers at $25 per hour and y bus persons at $8 per hour. The total hourly cost for the restaurant's 12 employees that night is $249. The following system of equations can be used to find the number of servers and the number of bus persons at work.

$$\begin{cases} 25x + 8y = 249 \\ x + y = 12 \end{cases}$$

Based on the solution of the system of equations, which of the following can you conclude?

- Ⓕ Fewer than 2 bus persons were working.
- Ⓖ More than ten servers were working.
- Ⓗ 50% of the people working were bus persons.
- Ⓘ 75% of the people working were servers.

11. Which polynomial equation has the real roots of $-3, 1, 1,$ and $\frac{3}{2}$?

- Ⓐ $x^4 - \frac{1}{2}x^3 - \frac{13}{2}x^2 + \frac{21}{2}x - \frac{9}{2} = 0$
- Ⓑ $x^4 - \frac{1}{2}x^3 - \frac{17}{2}x^2 - 10x - \frac{9}{2} = 0$
- Ⓒ $x^4 + x^3 - 5x^2 + 3x - \frac{3}{2} = 0$
- Ⓓ $(x - 3)(x + 1)(x + 1)\left(x + \frac{3}{2}\right) = 0$

12. What is the factored form of $2x^3 + 5x^2 - 12x$?

- Ⓕ $x(2x - 3)(x + 4)$
- Ⓗ $x(2x + 4)(x - 3)$
- Ⓖ $(2x^2 - 3)(x + 4)$
- Ⓘ $(2x - 4)(x + 3)$

13. If $f(x) = 5\sqrt[3]{x^2}$ and $g(x) = 3\sqrt[3]{x^2}$, what is $f(x) + g(x)$?

- Ⓐ $8\sqrt[3]{x^2}$
- Ⓑ $8\sqrt[6]{x^2}$
- Ⓒ $8\sqrt[3]{x^4}$
- Ⓓ $8\sqrt[6]{x^4}$

14. What is the equation of the function graphed below?

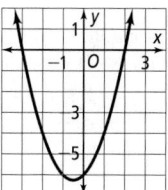

- Ⓕ $y = (x + 2)(x - 3)$
- Ⓗ $y = (x + 3)(x - 2)$
- Ⓖ $y = (x - 6)^2$
- Ⓘ $y = (x - 1)(x + 5)$

4. G
5. C
6. I
7. B
8. H
9. B
10. I
11. A
12. F
13. A
14. H

Answers

Gridded Response

15. 1

16. 15

17. 3

18. $\frac{3}{2}$

19. 1.25

20. 0

21. 7

22. 4

23. 2

24. −0.75

25. 5

26. −4

Short Response

27. [2] a. The graph is of the parent graph $y = \sqrt{x}$ reflected across the x-axis and translated 3 units to the left and 2 units up.

b. $y = -\sqrt{x + 3} + 2$

[1] partial correct answer

28. [2] The end behavior of $f(x)$ is down and up. The end behavior of $g(x)$ is up and up.

[1] partial correct answer

29. [2] let x = a child's weight, then $15 \le x \le 35$

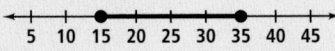

[1] graph drawn with open circles

30. [2] No, imaginary roots are always in pairs with one positive and one negative root.

[1] incomplete explanation

31. [2]

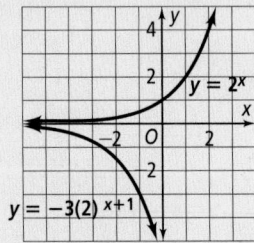

$y = -3(2)^{x+1}$

[1] graph is not labeled correctly

Extended Response

32. [4] a. The graph of $y = -|x - 3| + 2$ is the graph of $y = |x|$ reflected across the x-axis and translated 3 units to the right and 2 units up.

b. $y = -|x + 3| - 2$

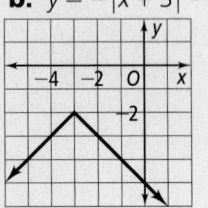

Constructed Response

15. What is the solution of the equation $\log_9 x = \log_6 x$?

16. A savings account pays 4.62% annual interest, compounded continuously. After approximately how many years will a principal of $500 double?

17. The graph of a polynomial has x-intercepts at $(-3, 0)$, $(-1, 0)$, and $(1, 0)$. What is the least possible degree of the polynomial?

18. Evaluate $\log_4 8$.

19. Solve $4^{2x} = 32$.

20. How many different real solutions are there for the equation $4x^2 = -4x - 4$?

21. Use the Fundamental Theorem of Algebra to determine the total number of complex zeros of $f(x) = x^2 - 3x^5 + 4x - x^7 - 44$.

22. Solve the following system of equations. What is the x-coordinate of the solution?

$$\begin{cases} y - 3 = x \\ \dfrac{y}{x^2 - 9} = 1 \end{cases}$$

23. What is the solution of $\sqrt{x + 2} = x$?

24. What is the x-intercept of $f(x) = x^3 - x^2 + 1$? Round the answer to the nearest hundredth.

25. What is the maximum y-value of the parabola?

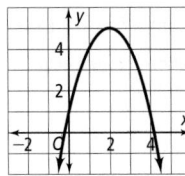

26. What is solution of the equation $-16 = x^2 + 8x$?

27. The graph below is transformation of the radical parent function $y = \sqrt{x}$.

a. Describe the transformations used to create the graph shown.

b. What is an equation of the graph shown?

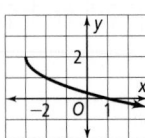

28. Compare the end behaviors of the functions below.

$$f(x) = x^3 + 1 \qquad g(x) = 5x^2 - 7$$

29. To use an outdoor toddler swing, a child must weigh at least 15 pounds, and can weigh no more than 35 pounds. Draw a graph to model this situation.

30. Can a quadratic equation with real coefficients have exactly one imaginary root? Explain your answer.

31. Graph the function $y = -3(2)^{x+1}$ as a translation of its parent function.

Extended Response

32. A transformation of the parent absolute value function is shown in the graph.

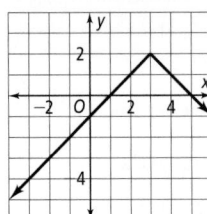

a. What is the transformation from the parent function $y = |x|$?

b. Draw the graph of the transformed function after reflecting it across the y-axis and translating it 4 units down.

[3] graph is not labeled correctly

[2] only part (a) is correct OR only part (b) is correct

[1] part (a) is incorrect and the graph is not labeled correctly

Skills Handbook Contents

Skills **Handbook**

Percents and Percent Applications

Percent means "per hundred." Find fraction, decimal, and percent equivalents by replacing one symbol for *hundredths* with another.

Example 1

Write each number as a percent.

a. $0.082 = 8.2\%$

Move the decimal point two places to the right and write a percent sign.

b. $\frac{3}{5} = \frac{60}{100} = 60\%$

Write the fraction as hundredths. Then replace the hundredths with a percent sign.

c. $1\frac{1}{6} = \frac{7}{6} = 1.166\overline{6} = 116.\overline{6}\%$

First, use $7 \div 6$ to write $1\frac{1}{6}$ as a decimal.

Example 2

Write each percent as a decimal.

a. $50\% = 0.50 = 0.5$

Move the decimal point two places to the left and drop the percent sign.

b. $\frac{1}{2}\% = 0.5\% = 00.5\% = 0.005$

Example 3

Use an equation to solve each percent problem.

a. What is 30% of 12?

$n = 0.3 \times 12$

$n = 3.6$

b. 18 is 0.3% of what?

$18 = 0.003 \times n$

$\frac{18}{0.003} = \frac{0.003n}{0.003}$

$6000 = n$

c. What percent of 60 is 9?

$n \times 60 = 9$

$60n = 9$

$n = \frac{9}{60} = 0.15 = 15\%$

Exercises

Write each decimal as a percent and each percent as a decimal.

1. 0.46
2. 1.506
3. 0.007
4. 8%
5. 103.5%
6. 3.3%

Write each fraction or mixed number as a percent.

7. $\frac{1}{4}$
8. $\frac{3}{8}$
9. $\frac{2}{3}$
10. $\frac{4}{9}$
11. $1\frac{3}{20}$
12. $\frac{1}{200}$

Use an equation to solve each percent problem. Round your answer to the nearest tenth, if necessary.

13. What is 25% of 50?
14. What percent of 58 is 37?
15. 120% of what is 90?
16. 8 is what percent of 40?
17. 15 is 75% of what?
18. 80% of 58 is what?

Answers

Percents and Percent Applications

1. 46%
2. 1150.6%
3. 0.7%
4. 0.08
5. 1.035
6. 0.033
7. 25%
8. 37.5%
9. $66.\overline{6}\%$
10. $44.\overline{4}\%$
11. 115%
12. 0.5%
13. 12.5
14. 63.8%
15. 75
16. 20%
17. 20%
18. 46.4

Operations With Fractions

To add or subtract fractions, use a common denominator. The common denominator is the least common multiple of the denominators.

Example 1

Simplify $\frac{2}{3} + \frac{3}{5}$.

$\frac{2}{3} + \frac{3}{5} = \frac{2}{3} \cdot \frac{5}{5} + \frac{3}{5} \cdot \frac{3}{3}$ For 3 and 5, the least common multiple is 15.

$= \frac{10}{15} + \frac{9}{15}$ Write $\frac{2}{3}$ and $\frac{3}{5}$ as equivalent fractions with denominators of 15.

$= \frac{19}{15}$ or $1\frac{4}{15}$ Add the numerators.

Example 2

Simplify $5\frac{1}{4} - 3\frac{2}{3}$.

$5\frac{1}{4} - 3\frac{2}{3} = 5\frac{3}{12} - 3\frac{8}{12}$ Write equivalent fractions.

$= 4\frac{15}{12} - 3\frac{8}{12}$ Write $5\frac{3}{12}$ as $4\frac{15}{12}$ so you can subtract the fractions.

$= 1\frac{7}{12}$ Subtract the fractions. Then subtract the whole numbers.

To multiply fractions, multiply the numerators and multiply the denominators. You can simplify by using a greatest common factor.

Example 3

Simplify $\frac{3}{4} \cdot \frac{8}{11}$

Method 1 $\frac{3}{4} \cdot \frac{8}{11} = \frac{24}{44} = \frac{24 \div 4}{44 \div 4} = \frac{6}{11}$

Divide 24 and 44 by 4, their greatest common factor.

Method 2 $\frac{3}{4} \cdot \frac{8^{\,2}}{11} = \frac{6}{11}$

Divide 4 and 8 by 4, their greatest common factor.

To divide fractions, use a reciprocal to change the problem to multiplication.

Example 4

Simplify $3\frac{1}{5} \div 1\frac{1}{2}$

$3\frac{1}{5} \div 1\frac{1}{2} = \frac{16}{5} \div \frac{3}{2}$ Write mixed numbers as improper fractions.

$= \frac{16}{5} \cdot \frac{2}{3}$ Multiply by the reciprocal of the divisor.

$= \frac{32}{15}$ or $2\frac{2}{15}$ Simplify.

Exercises

Perform the indicated operation.

1. $\frac{3}{5} + \frac{4}{5}$ 2. $\frac{1}{2} + \frac{2}{3}$ 3. $4\frac{1}{2} + 2\frac{1}{3}$ 4. $5\frac{3}{4} + 4\frac{2}{5}$ 5. $\frac{2}{3} - \frac{3}{7}$

6. $5\frac{1}{2} - 3\frac{2}{5}$ 7. $7\frac{3}{4} - 4\frac{4}{5}$ 8. $3\frac{4}{5} \cdot 10$ 9. $2\frac{1}{2} \cdot 3\frac{1}{5}$ 10. $6\frac{3}{4} \cdot 5\frac{2}{3}$

11. $\frac{1}{2} \div \frac{1}{3}$ 12. $\frac{6}{5} \div \frac{3}{5}$ 13. $8\frac{1}{2} \div 4\frac{1}{4}$ 14. $\frac{8}{9} - \frac{2}{3}$ 15. $5\frac{1}{4} \cdot 8$

Operations With Fractions

1. $1\frac{2}{5}$ 2. $1\frac{1}{6}$

3. $6\frac{5}{6}$ 4. $10\frac{3}{20}$

5. $\frac{5}{21}$ 6. $2\frac{1}{10}$

7. $2\frac{19}{20}$ 8. 38

9. 8   10. $38\frac{1}{4}$

11. $1\frac{1}{2}$ 12. 2

13. 2   14. $\frac{2}{9}$

15. 42

Ratios and Proportions

A *ratio* is a comparison of two quantities by division. You can write *equal ratios* by multiplying or dividing each quantity by the same nonzero number.

Ways to Write a Ratio
$a:b \quad a \text{ to } b \quad \frac{a}{b} \ (b \neq 0)$

Example 1

Write $3\frac{1}{3} : \frac{1}{2}$ as a ratio in simplest form.

$$3\frac{1}{3} : \frac{1}{2} \rightarrow \frac{3\frac{1}{3}}{\frac{1}{2}} = \frac{20}{3} \text{ or } 20:3$$

In simplest form, both terms should be integers.
Multiply by the common denominator, 6.

A rate is a ratio that compares different types of quantities. In simplest form for a rate, the second quantity is one unit.

Example 2

Write 247 mi in 5.2 h as a rate in simplest form.

$$\frac{247 \text{ mi}}{5.2 \text{ h}} = \frac{47.5 \text{ mi}}{1 \text{ h}} \text{ or } 47.5 \text{ mi/h}$$

Divide by 5.2 to make the second quantity one unit.

A proportion is a statement that two ratios are equal. You can find a missing term in a proportion by using the cross products.

Cross Products of a Proportion
$\frac{a}{b} = \frac{c}{d} \ \rightarrow \ ad = bc$

Example 3

The Copy Center charges $2.52 for 63 copies. At that rate, how much will the Copy Center charge for 140 copies?

$$\begin{aligned} \text{cost} &\rightarrow \\ \text{copies} &\rightarrow \end{aligned} \quad \frac{2.52}{63} = \frac{c}{140}$$ Set up a proportion.

$$2.52 \cdot 140 = 63c$$ Use cross products.

$$c = \frac{2.52 \cdot 140}{63}$$ Solve for c.

$$= 5.6 \text{ or } \$5.60$$

Exercises

Write each ratio or rate in simplest form.

1. 15 to 20
2. 85 : 34
3. 38 g in 4 oz
4. 375 mi in 4.3 h
5. $\frac{84}{30}$

Solve each proportion. Round your answer to the nearest tenth, if necessary.

6. $\frac{a}{5} = \frac{12}{15}$
7. $\frac{21}{12} = \frac{14}{x}$
8. $8:15 = n:25$
9. $2.4:c = 4:3$
10. $\frac{17}{8} = \frac{n}{20}$
11. $\frac{13}{n} = \frac{20}{3}$
12. $5:7 = y:5$
13. $\frac{0.4}{3.5} = \frac{5.2}{x}$
14. $\frac{4}{x} = \frac{7}{6}$
15. $4:n = n:9$

16. A canary's heart beats 130 times in 12 s. Use a proportion to find about how many times its heart beats in 50 s.

Answers

Ratios and Proportions

1. 3 to 4
2. 5 : 2
3. 19 g in 2 oz
4. approximately 87.2 mi in 1 h
5. $\frac{14}{5}$
6. 4
7. 8
8. $13.\overline{3}$
9. 1.8
10. 42.5
11. 1.95
12. 3.6
13. 45.5
14. 3.4
15. ± 6
16. about 542 times

Simplifying Expressions With Integers

To add two numbers with the same sign, *add* their absolute values. The sum has the same sign as the numbers. To add two numbers with different signs, find the *difference* between their absolute values. The sum has the same sign as the number with the greater absolute value.

Example 1

Add.

a. $-8 + (-5) = -13$ **b.** $-8 + 5 = -3$ **c.** $8 + (-5) = 3$

To subtract a number, add its opposite.

Example 2

Subtract.

a. $4 - 7 = 4 + (-7)$ **b.** $-4 - (-7) = -4 + 7$ **c.** $-4 - 7 = -4 + (-7)$

$\quad\quad = -3$ $\quad\quad = 3$ $\quad\quad = -11$

The product or quotient of two numbers with the same sign is positive. The product or quotient of two numbers with different signs is negative.

Example 3

Multiply or divide.

a. $(-3)(-5) = 15$ **b.** $-35 \div 7 = -5$ **c.** $24 \div (-6) = -4$

Example 4

Simplify $2^2 - 3(4 - 6) - 12$.

Order of Operations

$2^2 - 3(4 - 6) - 12 = 2^2 - 3(-2) - 12$

                $= 4 - 3(-2) - 12$

                $= 4 - (-6) - 12$

                $= 4 + 6 - 12 = -2$

1. Perform any operation(s) inside grouping symbols.

2. Simplify any terms with exponents.

3. Multiply and divide in order from left to right.

4. Add and subtract in order from left to right.

Exercises

Simplify each expression.

1. $-4 + 5$ **2.** $12 - 12$ **3.** $-15 + (-23)$ **4.** $4 - 17$ **5.** $-5 - 12$

6. $3 - (-5)$ **7.** $-8 - (-12)$ **8.** $-19 + 5$ **9.** $(-7)(-4)$ **10.** $-120 \div 30$

11. $(-3)(4)$ **12.** $75 \div (-3)$ **13.** $(-6)(15)$ **14.** $(18)(-4)$ **15.** $-84 \div (-7)$

16. $-2(1 + 5) + (-3)(2)$ **17.** $-4(-2 - 5) + 3(1 - 4)$ **18.** $20 - (3)(12) + 4^2$

19. $\frac{-15}{-5} - \frac{36}{-12} + \frac{-12}{-4}$ **20.** $5^2 - 6(5 - 9)$ **21.** $(-3 + 2^3)(4 + \frac{-42}{7})$

Simplifying Expressions With Integers

1. 1   **2.** 0

3. −38   **4.** −13

5. −17   **6.** 8

7. 4   **8.** −14

9. 28   **10.** −4

11. −12   **12.** −25

13. −90   **14.** −72

15. 12   **16.** −18

17. 19   **18.** 0

19. 9   **20.** 49

21. −10

Area and Volume

The *area* of a plane figure is the number of square units contained in the figure.
The *volume* of a space figure is the number of cubic units contained in the figure.
Formulas for area and volume are listed on page 693.

Example 1

Find the area of each figure.

a.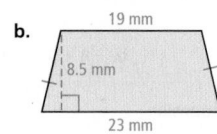

$A = \pi r^2$

$\approx \frac{22}{7} \cdot \left(\frac{21}{10}\right)^2$

$= \frac{693}{50} = 13\frac{43}{50}$ in.^{2}

b.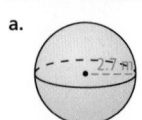

$A = \frac{1}{2}(b_1 + b_2)h$

$= \frac{1}{2}(19 + 23) \cdot 8.5$

$= 178.5$ mm^2

Example 2

Find the volume of each figure.

a.

$V = \frac{4}{3}\pi r^3$

$\approx \frac{4}{3} \cdot 3.14 \cdot 2.7^3$

$= 82.40616 \approx 82.4 m^3$

b.

$V = \frac{1}{3}Bh$

$= \frac{1}{3}(37^2) \cdot 24$

$= 10,952$ ft^3

Exercises

Find the exact area of each figure.

1.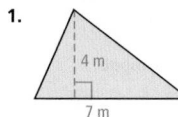
2.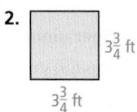
3.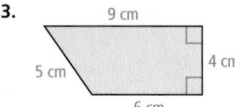
4.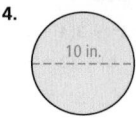

Find the exact volume of each figure.

5.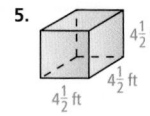
6.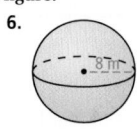
7.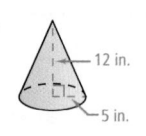
8.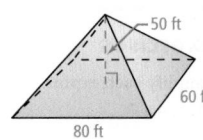

9. Find the area of a triangle with a base of 17 in. and a height of 13 in.

10. Find the volume of a rectangular box 64 cm long, 48 cm wide, and 58 cm high.

11. Find the surface area of the cube in Exercise 5.

Answers

Area and Volume

1. 14 m^2
2. $14\frac{1}{16}$ ft^2
3. 30 cm^2
4. 25π in.^{2}
5. $91\frac{1}{8}$ ft^3
6. $\frac{2048}{3}\pi$ m^3
7. 100π in.^{3}
8. 80,000 ft^3
9. 110.5 in.^{2}
10. 178,176 cm^3
11. $121\frac{1}{2}$ ft^2

The Coordinate Plane, Slope, and Midpoint

The *coordinate plane* is formed when two perpendicular number lines intersect at a point called the origin, forming four quadrants.

Example 1

In which quadrant would you find each point?

a. $(3, -4)$ Move 3 units right and 4 units down. The point is in Quadrant IV.

b. $(-2, -5)$ Move 2 units left and 5 units down. The point is in Quadrant III.

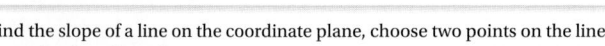

To find the slope of a line on the coordinate plane, choose two points on the line and use the slope formula.

Example 2

Find the slope of each line.

a.
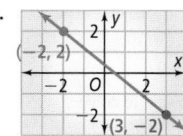

$m = \dfrac{y_2 - y_1}{x_2 - x_1}$

$= \dfrac{2 - (-2)}{-2 - 3}$

$= \dfrac{4}{-5}$ or $-\dfrac{4}{5}$

b.
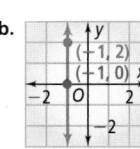

$m = \dfrac{y_2 - y_1}{x_2 - x_1}$

$= \dfrac{2 - 0}{-1 - (-1)} = \dfrac{2}{0}$

Since you cannot divide by zero, this line has an undefined slope.

If (x_m, y_m) is the midpoint of the segment joining (x_1, y_1) and (x_2, y_2), then $x_m = \dfrac{x_1 + x_2}{2}$ and $y_m = \dfrac{y_1 + y_2}{2}$.

Example 3

Find the coordinates of the midpoint of the segment with endpoints $(-2, 5)$ and $(6, -3)$.

$\dfrac{-2 + 6}{2} = 2$ and $\dfrac{5 + (-3)}{2} = 1$ so the midpoint is $(2, 1)$.

Exercises

In which quadrant would you find each point? Graph each point on a coordinate plane.

1. $(3, 2)$ **2.** $(-4, 3)$ **3.** $(2, -3)$ **4.** $(4, -2)$ **5.** $(-4, -5)$ **6.** $(-1, -3)$

Find the slope of each line.

7.
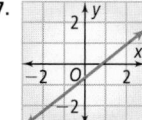

8.
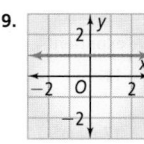

9.
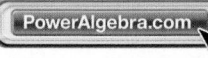

10. the line containing $(-3, 4)$ and $(2, -6)$

11. the line containing $(25, 40)$ and $(100, 55)$

Find the midpoint of the segment with the given endpoints.

12. $(-4, 4), (2, -5)$ **13.** $(3, 3), (7, -6)$ **14.** $(-1, -8), (0, -3)$ **15.** $(3, 4), (2, -6)$

The Coordinate Plane, Slope, and Midpoint

1. I   **2.** II

3. IV   **4.** IV

5. III   **6.** III

7. $\dfrac{4}{5}$ **8.** -1

9. 0 **10.** -2

11. $\dfrac{1}{5}$ **12.** $\left(-1, -\dfrac{1}{2}\right)$

13. $\left(5, -\dfrac{3}{2}\right)$ **14.** $\left(-\dfrac{1}{2}, -\dfrac{11}{2}\right)$

15. $\left(\dfrac{5}{2}, -1\right)$

Operations With Exponents

An exponent indicates how many times a number is used as a factor.

$2^n = \blacksquare$	$10^n = \blacksquare$
$2^2 = 4$	$10^2 = 100$
$2^1 = 2$	$10^1 = 10$
$2^0 = 1$	$10^0 = 1$
$2^{-1} = \frac{1}{2}$	$10^{-1} = \frac{1}{10}$
$2^{-2} = \frac{1}{4}$	$10^{-2} = \frac{1}{100}$

Example 1

Write using exponents.

a. $3 \cdot 3 \cdot 3 \cdot 3 \cdot 3 = 3^5$ **b.** $a \cdot a \cdot b \cdot b \cdot b \cdot b = a^2b^4$

The patterns shown at the right indicate that $a^0 = 1$ and that $a^{-n} = \frac{1}{a^n}$.

Example 2

Write each expression so that all exponents are positive.

a. $a^{-2}b^3 = \frac{1}{a^2} \cdot b^3 = \frac{b^3}{a^2}$ **b.** $x^3y^0z^{-1} = x^3 \cdot 1 \cdot \frac{1}{z} = \frac{x^3}{z}$

You can simplify expressions that contain powers with the same base.

Example 3

Simplify each expression.

a. $b^5 \cdot b^3 = b^{5+3}$ Add exponents to multiply
       $= b^8$ powers with the same base.

b. $\frac{x^5}{x^7} = x^{5-7}$ Subtract exponents to divide
       $= x^{-2} = \frac{1}{x^2}$ powers with the same base.

You can simplify expressions that contain parentheses and exponents.

Example 4

Simplify each expression.

a. $\left(\frac{ab}{n}\right)^3 = \frac{a^3b^3}{n^3}$ Raise each factor in the
       parentheses to the third power.

b. $(c^2)^4 = c^{2\cdot4} = c^8$ Multiply exponents to raise a
       power to a power.

Exercises

Write each expression using exponents.

1. $x \cdot x \cdot x$ **2.** $x \cdot x \cdot x \cdot y \cdot y$ **3.** $a \cdot a \cdot a \cdot a \cdot b$ **4.** $\frac{a \cdot a \cdot a \cdot a}{b \cdot b}$

Write each expression so that all exponents are positive.

5. c^{-4} **6.** $m^{-2}n^0$ **7.** $x^5y^{-7}z^{-3}$ **8.** $ab^{-1}c^2$

Simplify each expression. Use positive exponents.

9. d^2d^6 **10.** $\frac{a^5}{a^2}$ **11.** $\frac{c^7}{c}$ **12.** $\frac{n^3}{n^6}$ **13.** $\frac{a^5b^3}{ab^8}$ **14.** $(3x)^2$

15. $\left(\frac{a}{b}\right)^4$ **16.** $\left(\frac{xz}{y}\right)^6$ **17.** $(c^3)^4$ **18.** $\left(\frac{x^2}{y^5}\right)^3$ **19.** $(u^4v^2)^3$ **20.** $(p^5)^{-2}$

21. $\frac{(2a^4)(3a^2)}{6a^3}$ **22.** $(x^{-2})^3$ **23.** $(mg^3)^{-1}$ **24.** $g^{-3}g^{-1}$ **25.** $\frac{(3a^3)^2}{18a}$ **26.** $\frac{c^3d^7}{c^{-3}d^{-1}}$

Answers

Operations With Exponents

1. x^3 **2.** x^3y^2

3. a^4b **4.** $\frac{a^4}{b^2}$

5. $\frac{1}{c^4}$ **6.** $\frac{1}{m^2}$

7. $\frac{x^5}{y^7z^3}$ **8.** $\frac{ac^2}{b}$

9. d^8 **10.** a^3

11. c^6 **12.** $\frac{1}{n^3}$

13. $\frac{a^4}{b^5}$ **14.** $9x^2$

15. $\frac{a^4}{b^4}$ **16.** $\frac{x^6z^6}{y^6}$

17. c^{12} **18.** $\frac{x^6}{y^{15}}$

19. $u^{12}v^6$ **20.** $\frac{1}{p^{10}}$

21. a^3 **22.** $\frac{1}{x^6}$

23. $\frac{1}{mg^3}$ **24.** $\frac{1}{g^4}$

25. $\frac{a^5}{2}$ **26.** c^6d^8

Factoring and Operations With Polynomials

Example 1

Perform each operation.

a. $(3y^2 - 4y + 5) + (y^2 + 9y)$

$= (3y^2 + y^2) + (-4y + 9y) + 5$ To add, group like terms.

$= 4y^2 + 5y + 5$

b. $(n + 4)(n - 3)$

$= n(n) + n(-3) + 4(n) + 4(-3)$ Distribute n and 4.

$= n^2 - 3n + 4n - 12$ Combine like terms.

$= n^2 + n - 12$

To factor a polynomial, first find the greatest common factor (GCF) of the terms.
Then use the distributive property to factor out the GCF.

Example 2

Factor $6x^3 - 12x^2 + 18x$.

$6x^3 = 6 \cdot x \cdot x \cdot x; -12x^2 = 6 \cdot (-2) \cdot x \cdot x; 18x = 6 \cdot 3 \cdot x$ List the factors of each term. The GCF is $6x$.

$6x^3 - 12x^2 + 18x = 6x(x^2) + 6x(-2x) + 6x(3)$ Use the distributive property to factor out $6x$.

$\qquad = 6x(x^2 - 2x + 3)$

When a polynomial is the product
of two binomials, you can work
backward to find the factors.

$x^2 + bx + c = (x + \blacksquare)(x + \blacksquare)$

The *sum* of these numbers must equal b.
The *product* of these numbers must equal c.

Example 3

Factor $x^2 - 13x + 36$.

Choose numbers that are factors of 36. Look for a pair with the sum -13.

The numbers -4 and -9 have a product of 36 and a sum of -13. The
factors are $(x - 4)$ and $(x - 9)$. So, $x^2 - 13x + 36 = (x - 4)(x - 9)$.

Factors	Sum
$-6 \cdot (-6)$	-12
$-4 \cdot (-9)$	-13

Exercises

Perform the indicated operations.

1. $(x^2 + 3x - 1) + (7x - 4)$ **2.** $(5y^2 + 7y) - (3y^2 + 9y - 8)$ **3.** $4x^2(3x^2 - 5x + 9)$

4. $-5d(13d^2 + 7d + 8)$ **5.** $(x - 5)(x + 3)$ **6.** $(n - 7)(n - 2)$

Factor each polynomial.

7. $a^2 - 8a + 12$ **8.** $n^2 - 2n - 8$ **9.** $x^2 + 5x + 4$ **10.** $3m^2 - 9$

11. $y^2 + 5y - 24$ **12.** $s^3 + 6s^2 + 11s$ **13.** $2x^3 + 4x^2 - 8x$ **14.** $y^2 - 10y + 25$

Factoring and Operations With Polynomials

1. $x^2 + 10x - 5$

2. $2y^2 - 2y + 8$

3. $12x^4 - 20x^3 + 36x^2$

4. $-65d^3 - 35d^2 - 40d$

5. $x^2 - 2x - 15$

6. $n^2 - 9n + 14$

7. $(a - 6)(a - 2)$

8. $(n - 4)(n + 2)$

9. $(x + 4)(x + 1)$

10. $3(m^2 - 3)$

11. $(y + 8)(y - 3)$

12. $s(s^2 + 6s + 11)$

13. $2x(x^2 + 2x - 4)$

14. $(y - 5)^2$

Scientific Notation and Significant Digits

In *scientific notation*, a number has the form $a \times 10^n$, where n is an integer and $1 \le a < 10$.

Example 1

Write 5.59×10^6 in standard form.

$5.59 \times 10^6 = 5\ 590\ 000 = 5,\ 590,\ 000$ A positive exponent indicates a value greater than 1.
Move the decimal point six places to the right.

Example 2

Write 0.0000318 in scientific notation.

$0.0000318 = 3.18 \times 10^{-5}$ Move the decimal point to create a number between 1 and 10.
Since the original number is less than 1, use a negative exponent.

When a measurement is in scientific notation, all the digits of the number between 1 and 10 are *significant digits*. When you multiply or divide measurements, your answer should have as many significant digits as the least number of significant digits in any of the numbers involved.

Example 3

Multiply $(6.71 \times 10^8\,\text{mi/h})$ and $(3.8 \times 10^4\,\text{h})$.

$(6.71 \times 10^8\,\text{mi/h})(3.8 \times 10^4\,h) = (6.71 \cdot 3.8)(10^8 \cdot 10^4)$ Rearrange factors.

three significant digits   two significant digits

$= 25.498 \times 10^{12}$ Add exponents when multiplying powers of 10.
$= 2.5498 \times 10^{13}$ Write in scientific notation.
$\approx 2.5 \times 10^{13}\text{mi}$ Round to two significant digits.

Exercises

Change each number to scientific notation or to standard form.

1. 1,340,000   **2.** 6.88×10^{-2} **3.** 0.000775   **4.** 0.0072   **5.** 1.113×10^5

6. 8.0×10^{-4} **7.** 1895   **8.** 2.3×10^3 **9.** 123,400   **10.** 7.985×10^4

Write each product or quotient in scientific notation. Round to the appropriate number of significant digits.

11. $(1.6 \times 10^2)(4.0 \times 10^3)$ **12.** $(2.5 \times 10^{-3})(1.2 \times 10^4)$ **13.** $(4.237 \times 10^4)(2.01 \times 10^{-2})$

14. $\dfrac{7.0 \times 10^5}{2.89 \times 10^3}$ **15.** $\dfrac{1.4 \times 10^4}{8.0 \times 10^2}$ **16.** $\dfrac{6.48 \times 10^6}{3.2 \times 10^5}$

17. $(1.78 \times 10^{-7})(5.03 \times 10^{-5})$ **18.** $(7.2 \times 10^{11})(5 \times 10^6)$ **19.** $(8.90 \times 10^8) \div (2.36 \times 10^{-2})$

20. $(3.95 \times 10^4) \div (6.8 \times 10^8)$ **21.** $(4.9 \times 10^{-8}) \div (2.7 \times 10^{-2})$ **22.** $(3.972 \times 10^{-5})(4.7 \times 10^{-4})$

Answers

Scientific Notation and Significant Digits

1. 1.34×10^6 **2.** 0.0688

3. 7.75×10^{-4} **4.** 7.2×10^{-3}

5. 111,300   **6.** 0.0008

7. 1.895×10^3 **8.** 2300

9. 1.234×10^5 **10.** 79,850

11. 6.4×10^5 **12.** 30

13. 8.52×10^2 **14.** 2.4×10^2

15. 17.5   **16.** 20

17. 8.95×10^{-12} **18.** 3.6×10^{18}

19. 3.77×10^{10} **20.** 5.8×10^{-5}

21. 1.8×10^{-6} **22.** 1.9×10^{-8}

The Pythagorean Theorem and the Distance Formula

In a right triangle, the sum of the squares of the lengths of the legs is equal to the square of the length of the hypotenuse. Use this relationship, known as the Pythagorean Theorem, to find the length of a side of a right triangle.

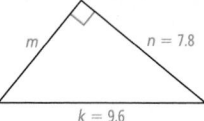
The Pythagorean Theorem

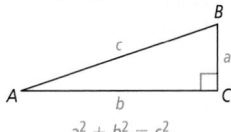

$$a^2 + b^2 = c^2$$

Example 1

Find m in the triangle below, to the nearest tenth.

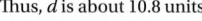

$$m^2 + n^2 = k^2$$
$$m^2 + 7.8^2 = 9.6^2$$
$$m^2 = 9.6^2 - 7.8^2 = 31.32$$
$$m = \sqrt{31.32} \approx 5.6$$

To find the distance between two points on the coordinate plane, use the distance formula.

The distance d between any two points (x_1, y_1) and (x_2, y_2) is

$$d = \sqrt{(x_2 - x_1)^2 + (y_2 - y_1)^2}$$

Example 2

Find the distance between $(-3, 2)$ and $(6, -4)$.

$$d = \sqrt{(6 - (-3))^2 + (-4 - 2)^2}$$
$$= \sqrt{9^2 + (-6)^2}$$
$$= \sqrt{81 + 36}$$
$$= \sqrt{117}$$
$$\approx 10.8$$

Thus, d is about 10.8 units.

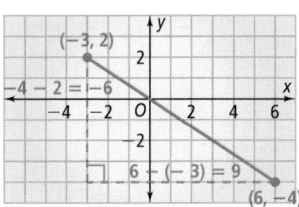

Exercises

In each problem, a and b are the lengths of the legs of a right triangle and c is the length of the hypotenuse. Find each missing length. Round your answer to the nearest tenth.

1. c if $a = 6$ and $b = 8$ **2.** a if $b = 12$ and $c = 13$ **3.** b if $a = 8$ and $c = 17$

4. c if $a = 10$ and $b = 3$ **5.** a if $b = 100$ and $c = 114$ **6.** b if $a = 12.0$ and $c = 30.1$

Find the distance between each pair of points, to the nearest tenth.

7. $(0, 0), (4, -3)$ **8.** $(-5, -5), (1, 3)$ **9.** $(-1, 0), (4, 12)$ **10.** $(-4, 2), (4, -2)$

11. $(0, 15), (17, 0)$ **12.** $(-8, 8), (8, 8)$ **13.** $(-1, 1), (1, -1)$ **14.** $(-2, 9), (0, 0)$

15. $(-5, 3), (4, 3)$ **16.** $(2, 1), (3, 4)$ **17.** $(3, -2), (3, 5)$ **18.** $(5, 4), (-3, 1)$

The Pythagorean Theorem and the Distance Formula

1. 10 **2.** 5

3. 15 **4.** 10.4

5. 54.7 **6.** 27.6

7. 5 **8.** 10

9. 13 **10.** 8.9

11. 22.7 **12.** 16

13. 2.8 **14.** 9.2

15. 9 **16.** 3.2

17. 7 **18.** 8.5

Bar and Circle Graphs

Sometimes you can draw different graphs to represent the same data, depending on the information you want to share. A *bar graph* is useful for comparing amounts; a *circle graph* is useful for comparing percents.

Example

Display the 2007 data on immigration to the United States in a bar graph and a circle graph.

To make a circle graph, first find the *percent* of the data in each category. Then express each percent as a decimal and multiply by 360° to find the size of each *central angle*.

$$\text{Africa} \rightarrow \frac{89.3}{1003.7} \approx 0.09 \text{ or } 9\%$$
$$\text{Total} \rightarrow$$

$$0.09 \times 360° \approx 32°$$

Draw a circle and use a protractor to draw each central angle.

Immigration to the United States, 2007

Place of Origin	Immigrants (1000's)
Africa	89.2
Asia	359.4
Europe	120.8
North America	331.7
South America	102.6

Source: Department of Homeland Security

To make a bar graph, place the categories along the bottom axis. Decide on a scale for the side axis. An appropriate scale would be 0–400, marked in intervals of 100. For each data item, draw a bar whose height is equal to the data value.

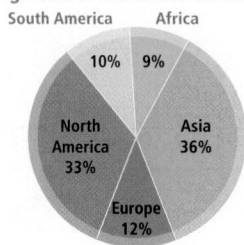

Immigration to the United States, 2007

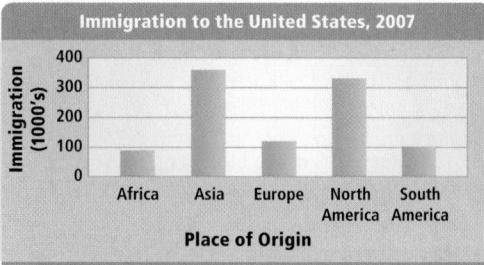

Immigration to the United States, 2007

Exercises

Display the data from each table in a bar graph and a circle graph.

1. NASA Space Shuttle Expenses, 2000

Operation	Millions of Dollars
Orbiter, integration	698.8
Propulsion	1,053.1
Mission, launch operations	738.8
Flight operations	244.6
Ground operations	510.3

Source: U.S. National Aeronautics and Space Administration

2. Cable TV Revenue, 2006

	Millions of Dollars
Airtime	4,566
Basic service	42,918
Pay-per-view, premium services	13,322
Installation	729
Other	27,188

Source: U.S. Census Bureau

982

Answers

Bar and Circle Graphs

1.

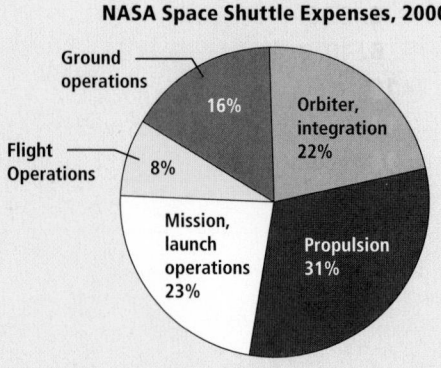

NASA Space Shuttle Expenses, 2000

NASA Space Shuttle Expenses, 2000

Descriptive Statistics and Histograms

For numerical data, you can find the *mean*, the *median*, and the *mode*.

Mean   The sum of the data values in a data set divided by the number of data values

Median   The middle value of a data set that has been arranged in increasing or decreasing order. If the data set has an even number of values, the median is the mean of the middle two values.

Mode   The most frequently occurring value in a data set

Example 1

Find the mean, median, and mode for the following data set.   5   7   6   3   1   7   9   5   10   7

Mean $\frac{5 + 7 + 6 + 3 + 1 + 7 + 9 + 5 + 10 + 7}{10} = 6$

Median   5, 7, 6, 3, 1, 7, 9, 5, 10, 7   Rearrange the numbers from least to greatest.

   1, 3, 5, 5, 6, 7, 7, 7, 9, 10   The median is the mean of the two middle numbers, 6 and 7.

   The median is $\frac{6 + 7}{2} = 6.5$.

Mode   The most frequently occurring data value is 7.

The frequency of a data value is the number of times it occurs in a data set.
A *histogram* is a bar graph that shows the frequency of each data value.

Example 2

Use the survey results to make a histogram for the cost of a movie ticket at various theaters.

Survey of Movie Ticket Prices
$7 $8 $7 $9 $8 $9 $8 $10 $8

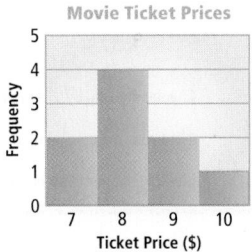
Movie Ticket Prices

Exercises

Find the mean, the median, and the mode of each data set.

1. −3 4 5 5 −2 7 1 8 9

2. 0 0 1 1 2 3 3 5 3 8 7

3. 2.4 2.4 2.3 2.3 2.4 12.0

4. 1 1 1 1 2 2 2 3 3 4

5. 1.2 1.3 1.4 1.5 1.6 1.7 1.8

6. −4 −3 −2 −1 0 1 2 3 4

Make a histogram for each data set.

7. 7 4 8 6 6 8 7 7 5 7

8. 73 75 76 75 74 75 76 74 76 75

2.

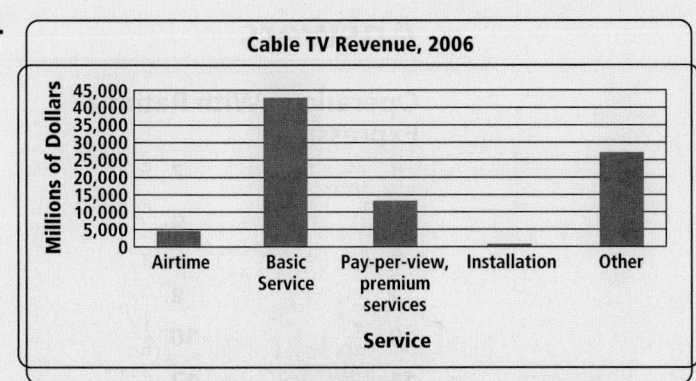
Cable TV Revenue, 2006

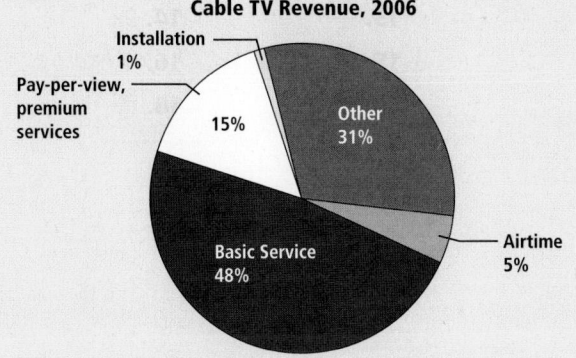
Cable TV Revenue, 2006

- Installation — 1%
- Pay-per-view, premium services 15%
- Other 31%
- Basic Service 48%
- Airtime 5%

Descriptive Statistics and Histograms

1. $3.\overline{7}$; 5; 5

2. 3; 3; 3

3. $3.9\overline{6}$; 2.4; 2.4

4. 2; 2; 1

5. 1.5; 1.5; no mode

6. 0; 0; no mode

7.

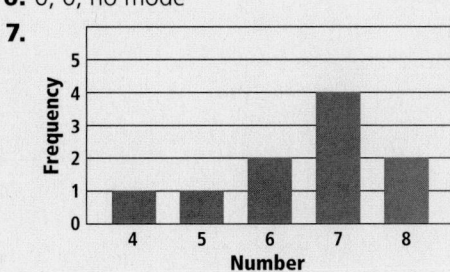

8.

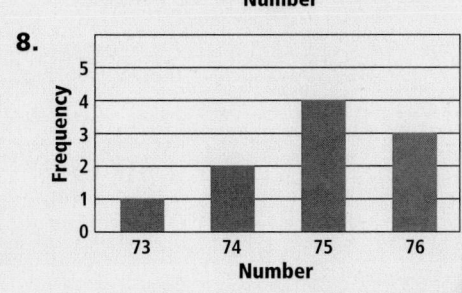

Operations With Rational Expressions

A *rational expression* is an expression that can be written in the form $\frac{\text{polynominal}}{\text{polynominal}}$, where the denominator is not zero. A rational expression is in simplest form if the numerator and denominator have no common factors except 1.

Example 1

Write the expression $\frac{4x + 8}{x + 2}$ in simplest form.

$\frac{4x + 8}{x + 2} = \frac{4(x + 2)}{x + 2}$ Factor the numerator.

$= 4$ Divide out the common factor $x + 2$.

To add or subtract two rational expressions, use a common denominator.

Example 2

Simplify $\frac{x}{2y} + \frac{x}{3y}$.

$\frac{x}{2y} + \frac{x}{3y} = \frac{x}{2y} \cdot \frac{3}{3} + \frac{x}{3y} \cdot \frac{2}{2}$ The common denominator of 3y and 2y is 6y.

$= \frac{3x}{6y} + \frac{2x}{6y}$

$= \frac{5x}{6y}$ Add the numerators.

To multiply rational expressions, first find and divide out any common factors in the numerators and the denominators. Then multiply the remaining numerators and denominators. To divide rational expressions, first use a reciprocal to change the problem to multiplication.

Example 3

Simplify $\frac{40x^2}{21} \div \frac{5x}{14}$.

$\frac{40x^2}{21} \div \frac{5x}{14} = \frac{40x^2}{21} \cdot \frac{14}{5x}$ Change dividing by $\frac{5x}{14}$ to multiplying by the reciprocal, $\frac{14}{5x}$.

$= \frac{8}{3} \frac{40x^2}{21} \times \frac{14}{5x} \frac{2}{1}$ Divide out the common factors 5, x, and 7.

$= \frac{16x}{3}$ Multiply the numerators ($8x \cdot 2$). Multiply the denominators ($3 \cdot 1$).

Exercises

Write each expression in simplest form.

1. $\frac{4a^2b}{12ab^3}$ **2.** $\frac{5n + 15}{n + 3}$ **3.** $\frac{x - 7}{2x - 14}$ **4.** $\frac{28c^2(d - 3)}{35c(d - 3)}$

Perform the indicated operation.

5. $\frac{3x}{2} + \frac{5x}{2}$ **6.** $\frac{3x}{8} + \frac{5x}{8}$ **7.** $\frac{5}{h} - \frac{3}{h}$ **8.** $\frac{6}{11p} - \frac{9}{11p}$ **9.** $\frac{3x}{5} - \frac{x}{2}$

10. $\frac{13}{2x} - \frac{13}{3x}$ **11.** $\frac{7x}{5} + \frac{5x}{7}$ **12.** $\frac{5a}{b} + \frac{3a}{5b}$ **13.** $\frac{7x}{8} \cdot \frac{32x}{35}$ **14.** $\frac{3x^2}{2} \cdot \frac{6}{x}$

15. $\frac{8x^2}{5} \cdot \frac{10}{x^3}$ **16.** $\frac{7x}{8} \cdot \frac{64}{14x}$ **17.** $\frac{16}{3x} \div \frac{5}{3x}$ **18.** $\frac{4x}{5} \div \frac{16}{15x}$ **19.** $\frac{x^3}{8} \div \frac{x^2}{16}$

Answers

Operations With Rational Expressions

1. $\frac{a}{3b^2}$ **2.** 5

3. $\frac{1}{2}$ **4.** $\frac{4c}{5}$

5. $4x$ **6.** x

7. $\frac{2}{h}$ **8.** $\frac{-3}{11p}$

9. $\frac{x}{10}$ **10.** $\frac{13}{6x}$

11. $\frac{74x}{35}$ **12.** $\frac{28a}{5b}$

13. $\frac{4x^2}{5}$ **14.** $9x$

15. $\frac{16}{x}$ **16.** 4

17. $\frac{16}{5}$ **18.** $\frac{3x^2}{4}$

19. $2x$

Reference

Table 1 Measures

	United States Customary	Metric
Length	12 inches (in.) = 1 foot (ft) 36 in. = 1 yard (yd) 3 ft = 1 yard 5280 ft = 1 mile (mi) 1760 yd = 1 mile	10 millimeters (mm) = 1 centimeter (cm) 100 cm = 1 meter (m) 1000 mm = 1 meter 1000 m = 1 kilometer (km)
Area	144 square inches (in.^{2}) = 1 square foot (ft^2) 9 ft^2 = 1 square yard (yd^2) 43,560 ft^2 = 1 acre (a) 4840 yd^2 = 1 acre	100 square millimeters (mm^2) = 1 square centimeter (cm^2) 10,000 cm^2 = 1 square meter (m^2) 10,000 m^2 = 1 hectare (ha)
Volume	1728 cubic inches (in.^{3}) = 1 cubic foot (ft^3) 27 ft^3 = 1 cubic yard (yd^3)	1000 cubic millimeters (mm^3) = 1 cubic centimeter (cm^3) 1,000,000 cm^3 = 1 cubic meter (m^3)
Liquid Capacity	8 fluid ounces (fl oz) = 1 cup (c) 2 c = 1 pint (pt) 2 pt = 1 quart (qt) 4 qt = 1 gallon (gal)	1000 milliliters (mL) = 1 liter (L) 1000 L = 1 kiloliter (kL)
Weight or Mass	16 ounces (oz) = 1 pound (lb) 2000 pounds = 1 ton (t)	1000 milligrams (mg) = 1 gram (g) 1000 g = 1 kilogram (kg) 1000 kg = 1 metric ton
Temperature	32°F = freezing point of water 98.6°F = normal human body temperature 212°F = boiling point of water	0°C = freezing point of water 37°C = normal human body temperature 100°C = boiling point of water

Customary Units and Metric Units		
Length	1 in. ≈ 2.54 cm 1 ft ≈ 0.305 m 1mi ≈ 1.61 km	1 cm ≈ 0.39 in. 1 m ≈ 3.28 ft 1 km ≈ 0.62 mi
Area	1 acre ≈ 0.40 ha	1 ha ≈ 2.47 acres
Capacity	1 qt ≈ 0.95 L	1 L ≈ 1.06 qt
Weight and Mass	1 oz ≈ 28.4 g 1 lb ≈ 0.45 kg	1 g ≈ 0.035 oz 1 kg ≈ 2.205 lb

Time		
60 seconds (s) = 1 minute (min) 60 minutes = 1 hour (h) 24 hours = 1 day (d) 7 days = 1 week (wk)	4 weeks (approx.) = 1 month (mo) 365 days = 1 year (yr) 52 weeks (approx.) = 1 year	12 months = 1 year 10 years = 1 decade 100 years = 1 century

---

Table 2 Reading Math Symbols

Symbols	Words
·, ×	multiplication sign, times
±	plus or minus positive or negative
=	equals
≟	equals?
≈	is approximately equal to
≠	is not equal to
<	is less than
>	is greater than
≤	is less than or equal to
≥	is greater than or equal to
≅	is congruent to
∼	is similar to
( )	parentheses for grouping
[ ]	brackets for grouping
{ }	braces for a set
%	percent
$|a|$	absolute value of a
$-a$	opposite of a
$a : b; \frac{a}{b}$	ratio of a to b
$\frac{1}{a}, a^{-1}, a \neq 0$	reciprocal of a
a^n	nth power of a
a^{-n}	$\frac{1}{a^n}, a \neq 0$
$\sqrt{a}$	nonnegative square root of a
$\sqrt[n]{a}$	nth root of a (nonnegative if n even)
° as in $a°$	degree(s)
∘ as in $f \circ g$	composition of functions
π	pi, an irrational number, approximately equal to 3.14
e	an irrational number approximately equal to 2.72
i	the imaginary number $\sqrt{-1}$
$a + bi, b \neq 0$	a complex number
∞	infinity
$\sum$	sigma, summation
σ	sigma, standard deviation
σ^2	variance
$\overleftrightarrow{AB}$	line through points A and B
$\overrightarrow{AB}$	vector AB

Symbols	Words
$\overline{AB}$	segment with endpoints A and B
AB	length of $\overline{AB}$; distance between points A and B
$\angle A$	angle A
$m\angle A$	measure of angle A
$\triangle ABC$	triangle ABC
(x, y)	ordered pair
$x_1, x_2, \ldots$	specific values of the variable x
$y_1, y_2, \ldots$	specific values of the variable y
$\bar{x}$	mean of data values x_i
$f(x)$	f of x; the function value at x
f^{-1}	function inverse
log	logarithm
ln	natural logarithm
$\begin{bmatrix} a & b \\ c & d \end{bmatrix}$	matrix
a_{mn}	element in mth row, nth column of matrix A
A^{-1}	inverse of matrix A
$\begin{vmatrix} a & b \\ c & d \end{vmatrix}$	determinant of a matrix
det A	determinant of matrix A
$n!$	n factorial
$_nC_r$	combinations of n things chosen r at a time
$_nP_r$	permutations of n things arranged r at a time
$P(event)$	probability of the event
$P(A|B)$	probability of event A, given event B
sin A	sine of $\angle A$
cos A	cosine of $\angle A$
tan A	tangent of $\angle A$
csc A	cosecant of $\angle A$
sec A	secant of $\angle A$
cot A	cotangent of $\angle A$
^	raised to a power (in a spreadsheet formula)
*	multiply (in a spreadsheet formula)
/	divide (in a spreadsheet formula)
...	and so on

Properties and Formulas

Order of Operations
1. Perform any operation(s) inside grouping symbols.
2. Simplify any terms with exponents.
3. Multiply and divide in order from left to right.
4. Add and subtract in order from left to right.

The Pythagorean Theorem
In a right triangle, the sum of the squares of the lengths of the legs is equal to the square of the length of the hypotenuse.
$$a^2 + b^2 = c^2$$

The Distance Formula
The distance d between any two points (x_1, y_1) and (x_2, y_2) is $d = \sqrt{(x_2 - x_1)^2 + (y_2 - y_1)^2}$.

The Midpoint Formula
The midpoint M of a line segment with endpoints $A(x_1, y_1)$ and $B(x_2, y_2)$ is $\left(\frac{x_1 + x_2}{2}, \frac{y_1 + y_2}{2} \right)$.

Chapter 1 Expressions, Equations, and Inequalities

Closure
For all real numbers a and b, $a + b$ and $a \cdot b$ are real numbers.

The Associative Properties
For all real numbers a, b, and c:
$(a + b) + c = a + (b + c)$
$(a \cdot b) \cdot c = a \cdot (b \cdot c)$

The Commutative Properties
For all real numbers a and b:
$a + b = b + a$ and $a \cdot b = b \cdot a$

The Identity Properties
For every real number a:
$a + 0 = a$ and $0 + a = a$ $a \cdot 1 = a$ and $1 \cdot a = a$
0 is the additive identity.   1 is the multiplicative identity.

The Inverse Properties
For every real number a:
$a + (-a) = 0$ and $a \cdot \frac{1}{a} = 1$ $(a \neq 0)$

The Distributive Properties
For all real numbers a, b, and c:
$a(b + c) = ab + ac$ $(b + c)a = ba + ca$
$a(b - c) = ab - ac$ $(b - c)a = ba - ca$

Multiplication
Let a represent a real number.
Multiplication by 0: $0 \cdot a = 0$.
Multiplication by -1: $-1 \cdot a = -a$

Opposites
Let a and b represent real numbers.
Opposite of a Sum: $-(a + b) = -a + (-b) = -a - b$
Opposite of a Difference: $-(a - b) = -a + b = b - a$
Opposite of a Product: $-(ab) = -a \cdot b = a \cdot (-b)$
Opposite of an Opposite: $-(-a) = a$

Properties of Equality
Assume a, b, and c represent real numbers.
Reflexive: $a = a$
Symmetric: If $a = b$, then $b = a$.
Transitive: If $a = b$ and $b = c$, then $a = c$.
Substitution: If $a = b$, then you can replace a with b and vice versa.
Addition: If $a = b$, then $a + c = b + c$.
Subtraction: If $a = b$, then $a - c = b - c$.
Multiplication: If $a = b$, then $ac = bc$.
Division: If $a = b$ and $c \neq 0$, then $\frac{a}{c} = \frac{b}{c}$.

Properties of Inequality
Let a, b, and c represent real numbers.
Transitive: If $a > b$ and $b > c$, then $a > c$.
Addition: If $a > b$, then $a + c > b + c$.
Subtraction: If $a > b$, then $a - c > b - c$.
Multiplication: If $a > b$ and $c > 0$, then $ac > bc$.
          If $a > b$ and $c < 0$, then $ac < bc$.
Division: If $a > b$ and $c > 0$, then $\frac{a}{c} > \frac{b}{c}$.
          If $a > b$ and $c < 0$, then $\frac{a}{c} < \frac{b}{c}$.

Chapter 2 Functions, Equations, and Graphs

Direct Variation
$y = kx$ or $\frac{y}{x} = k$, where $k \neq 0$.

Slope of a Line Containing (x_1, y_1) and (x_2, y_2)
slope $= \frac{\text{vertical change (rise)}}{\text{horizontal change (run)}} = \frac{y_2 - y_1}{x_2 - x_1}$,
where $x_2 - x_1 \neq 0$

Point-Slope Equation of a Line
The equation of the line through point (x_1, y_1) with slope m is $y - y_1 = m(x - x_1)$.

Reference

Reference

Function Families

Assume a, k, and h are positive numbers.

Parent	$y = f(x)$
Reflection across x-axis	$y = -f(x)$
Vertical stretch ($a > 1$) Vertical shrink ($0 < a < 1$)	$y = af(x)$
Translation	
horizontal to left by h	$y = f(x + h)$
horizontal to right by h	$y = f(x - h)$
vertical up by k	$y = f(x) + k$
vertical down by k	$y = f(x) - k$

Chapter 4 Quadratic Functions and Equations

Quadratic Functions

Parent	$y = x^2$
Reflection across x-axis	$y = -x^2$
Stretch ($a > 1$) Shrink ($0 < a < 1$)	$y = ax^2$
Translation	
horizontal by h vertical by k	$y = (x - h)^2 + k$
Vertex Form	$y = a(x - h)^2 + k$
Standard Form	$y = f(x) = ax^2 + bx + c$

The graph is a parabola that opens up if $a > 0$ and down if $a < 0$.
The vertex is (h, k) (Vertex Form) and $\left(-\frac{b}{2a}, f\left(-\frac{b}{2a}\right)\right)$ (Standard Form).
The axis of symmetry is $x = h$ (Vertex Form) and $x = -\frac{b}{2a}$ (Standard Form).

Factoring Perfect-Square Trinomials

$a^2 + 2ab + b^2 = (a + b)^2$
$a^2 - 2ab + b^2 = (a - b)^2$

Factoring a Difference of Two Squares

$a^2 - b^2 = (a + b)(a - b)$

Multiplication Property of Square Roots

For any numbers $a \geq 0$ and $b \geq 0$, $\sqrt{ab} = \sqrt{a} \cdot \sqrt{b}$.

Division Property of Square Roots

For any numbers $a \geq 0$ and $b > 0$, $\sqrt{\frac{a}{b}} = \frac{\sqrt{a}}{\sqrt{b}}$.

Zero-Product Property

If $ab = 0$, then $a = 0$ or $b = 0$.

The Quadratic Formula

If $ax^2 + bx + c = 0$, then $x = \frac{-b \pm \sqrt{b^2 - 4ac}}{2a}$

Discriminant

The discriminant of a quadratic equation in the form $ax^2 + bx + c = 0$ is $b^2 - 4ac$.
$b^2 - 4ac > 0 \Rightarrow$ two real solutions
$b^2 - 4ac = 0 \Rightarrow$ one real solution
$b^2 - 4ac < 0 \Rightarrow$ two complex solutions

Square Root of a Negative Real Number

For any positive number a,
$\sqrt{-a} = \sqrt{-1 \cdot a} = \sqrt{-1} \cdot \sqrt{a} = i\sqrt{a}$.
Example: $\sqrt{-5} = i\sqrt{5}$
Note that
$(\sqrt{-5})^2 = (i\sqrt{5})^2 = i^2(\sqrt{5})^2 = -1 \cdot 5 = -5$ (not 5).

Chapter 5 Polynomials and Polynomial Functions

End Behavior of a Polynomial Function

The end behavior of a polynomial function of degree n with leading term ax^n:

a	n	end behavior
positive	even	up and up
positive	odd	down and up
negative	even	down and down
negative	odd	up and down

Factor Theorem

The expression $x - a$ is a linear factor of a polynomial if and only if the value a is a zero of the related polynomial function.

Remainder Theorem

If you divide a polynomial $P(x)$ of degree $n \geq 1$ by $x - a$, then the remainder is $P(a)$.

Factoring a Sum or Difference of Cubes

$a^3 + b^3 = (a + b)(a^2 - ab + b^2)$
$a^3 - b^3 = (a - b)(a^2 + ab + b^2)$

Rational Root Theorem

Let $P(x) = a_nx^n + a_{n-1}x^{n-1} + \cdots + a_1x + a_0$ be a polynomial with integer coefficients.
Integer roots of $P(x) = 0$ must be factors of a_0.
Rational roots have reduced form $\frac{p}{q}$ where p is an integer factor of a_0 and q is an integer factor of a_n.

Conjugate Root Theorems

Suppose $P(x)$ is a polynomial with *rational* coefficients.
If $a + \sqrt{b}$ is an irrational root with a and b rational, then $a - \sqrt{b}$ is also a root.

Suppose $P(x)$ is a polynomial with *real* coefficients.
If $a + bi$ is a complex root with a and b real, then $a - bi$ is also a root.

Fundamental Theorem of Algebra

If $P(x)$ is a polynomial of degree $n \geq 1$, then $P(x) = 0$ has exactly n roots, including multiple and complex roots.

Binomial Theorem

For every positive integer n, $(a + b)^n =$
$P_0a^n + P_1a^{n-1}b + P_2a^{n-2}b^2 + \cdots + P_{n-1}ab^{n-1} + P_nb^n$
where $P_0, P_1, \ldots, P_n$ are the numbers in the nth row of Pascal's Triangle.

Chapter 6 Radical Functions and Rational Exponents

Properties of Exponents

For any nonzero number a and any integers m and n,

$a^0 = 1$ $\qquad (ab)^n = a^nb^n$
$\frac{a^m}{a^n} = a^{m-n}$ $\qquad a^m \cdot a^n = a^{m+n}$
$a^{-n} = \frac{1}{a^n}$ $\qquad (a^m)^n = a^{mn}$
$\left(\frac{a}{b}\right)^n = \frac{a^n}{b^n}$

nth Roots of nth Powers

For any real number a,

$$\sqrt[n]{a^n} = \begin{cases} a \text{ if } n \text{ is odd} \\ |a| \text{ if } n \text{ is even} \end{cases}$$

Combining Radical Expressions: Products

If $\sqrt[n]{a}$ and $\sqrt[n]{b}$ are real numbers, then $\sqrt[n]{a} \cdot \sqrt[n]{b} = \sqrt[n]{ab}$.

Combining Radical Expressions: Quotients

If $\sqrt[n]{a}$ and $\sqrt[n]{b}$ are real numbers and $b \neq 0$, then $\frac{\sqrt[n]{a}}{\sqrt[n]{b}} = \sqrt[n]{\frac{a}{b}}$

Properties of Rational Exponents

If the nth root of a is a real number and m is an integer, then $a^{\frac{1}{n}} = \sqrt[n]{a}$ and $a^{\frac{m}{n}} = \sqrt[n]{a^m} = \left(\sqrt[n]{a}\right)^m$. If m is negative, $a \neq 0$.

Composition of Inverse Functions

If f and f^{-1} are inverse functions, then $(f^{-1} \circ f)(x) = x$ and $(f \circ f^{-1})(x) = x$ for x in the domains of f and f^{-1}, respectively.

Radical Functions

	Square Root	nth Root
Parent	$y = \sqrt{x}$	$y = \sqrt[n]{x}$
Reflection across x-axis	$y = -\sqrt{x}$	$y = -\sqrt[n]{x}$
Stretch ($a > 1$) Shrink ($0 < a < 1$)	$y = a\sqrt{x}$	$y = a\sqrt[n]{x}$
Translation		
horizontal by h vertical by k	$y = \sqrt{x - h} + k$	$y = \sqrt[n]{x - h} + k$

Chapter 7 Exponential and Logarithmic Functions

Exponential Functions

Parent, $b > 0$, $b \neq 1$	$y = b^x$
Reflection across x-axis	$y = -b^x$
Stretch ($a > 1$) Shrink ($0 < a < 1$)	$y = ab^x$
Translation	
horizontal by h vertical by k	$y = b^{x-h} + k$

Continuously Compounded Interest

$A(t) = P \cdot e^{rt}$, where $A(t)$ represents the total, P represents the principal, r represents the interest rate, and t represents time in years.

Logarithmic Functions

	Base b	Base e
Parents, $b > 0$, $b \neq 1$	$y = \log_b x$	$y = \ln x$
Reflection across x-axis	$y = -\log_b x$	$y = -\ln x$
Stretch ($a > 1$) Shrink ($0 < a < 1$)	$y = a \log_b x$	$y = a \ln x$
Translation		
horizontal by h vertical by k	$y = \log_b (x - h) + k$	$y = \ln (x - h) + k$

Properties of Logarithms

For any positive numbers m, n, and b where $b \neq 1$

Product Property:	$\log_b mn = \log_b m + \log_b n$
Quotient Property:	$\log_b \frac{m}{n} = \log_b m - \log_b n$
Power Property:	$\log_b m^n = n \log_b m$

Change of Base Formula

For any positive numbers, m, b, and c, with $b \neq 1$ and $c \neq 1$, $\log_b m = \frac{\log_c m}{\log_c b}$.

Chapter 8 Rational Functions

Inverse Variation

$xy = k$, $y = \frac{k}{x}$, or $x = \frac{k}{y}$, where $k \neq 0$.

Combined Variation

z varies jointly with x and y: $z = kxy$
z varies jointly with x and y and inversely with w: $z = \frac{kxy}{w}$
z varies directly with x and inversely with the product wy: $z = \frac{kx}{wy}$

Reciprocal Functions

Parent	$y = \frac{1}{x}, x \neq 0$
Reflection across x-axis	$y = -\frac{1}{x}, x \neq 0$
Stretch ($a > 1$) Shrink ($0 < a < 1$)	$y = \frac{a}{x}, x \neq 0$
Translation	
horizontal by h vertical by k	$y = \frac{a}{x-h} + k, x \neq h$
Asymptotes	$y = k$ (horiz.), $x = h$ (vert.)

Reference

Chapter 9 Sequences and Series

Arithmetic Mean of Two Numbers

$\frac{x + y}{2}$

Arithmetic Sequence

A recursive definition for an arithmetic sequence with a starting value a and a common difference d has two parts:
$a_1 = a$: initial condition
$a_{n+1} = a_n + d$, for $n \geq 1$: recursive formula
An explicit definition for this sequence is the formula:
$a_n = a + (n - 1)d$ for $n \geq 1$.

Geometric Sequence

A recursive definition for a geometric sequence with a starting value a and a common ratio r has two parts:
$a_1 = a$: initial condition
$a_{n+1} = a_n \cdot r$, for $n \geq 1$: recursive formula
An explicit definition for this sequence is the formula:
$a_n = ar^{n-1}$, for $n \geq 1$.

Sum of a Finite Arithmetic Series

The sum S_n of a finite arithmetic series
$a_1 + a_2 + a_3 + \cdots + a_n$ is $S_n = \frac{n}{2}(a_1 + a_n)$
where a_1 is the first term, a_n is the nth term, and n is the number of terms.

Sum of a Finite Geometric Series

The sum S_n of a finite geometric series
$a_1 + a_1r + a_1r^2 + \cdots + a_1r^{n-1}$ is $S_n = \frac{a_1(1 - r^n)}{1 - r}$
where a_1 is the first term, r is the common ratio, and n is the number of terms.

Sum of an Infinite Geometric Series

An infinite geometric series with $|r| < 1$ converges to the sum S given by the following formula:
$S = \frac{a_1}{1 - r}$.

Chapter 10 Quadratic Relations and Conic Sections

Parabolas

Vertical	Vertex (0, 0)	Vertex (h, k)
Equation	$y = \frac{1}{4c}x^2$	$y = \frac{1}{4c}(x - h)^2 + k$
Focus	$(0, c)$	$(h, c + k)$
Directrix	$y = -c$	$y = -c + k$
Horizontal	**Vertex (0, 0)**	**Vertex (h, k)**
Equation	$x = \frac{1}{4c}y^2$	$x = \frac{1}{4c}(y - k)^2 + h$
Focus	$(c, 0)$	$(c + h, k)$
Directrix	$x = -c$	$x = -c + h$

Circles, radius = r

	Center (0, 0)	Center (h, k)
Equation	$x^2 + y^2 = r^2$	$(x - h)^2 + (y - k)^2 = r^2$

Ellipses

Horizontal, $a > b$	Center (0, 0)	Center (h, k)
Equation	$\frac{x^2}{a^2} + \frac{y^2}{b^2} = 1$	$\frac{(x-h)^2}{a^2} + \frac{(y-k)^2}{b^2} = 1$
Vertices	$(\pm a, 0)$	$(\pm a + h, k)$
Co-Vertices	$(0, \pm b)$	$(h, \pm b + k)$
Foci, $c^2 = a^2 - b^2$	$(\pm c, 0)$	$(\pm c + h, k)$
Major axis	$y = 0$	$y = k$
Minor axis	$x = 0$	$x = h$
Vertical, $a > b$	**Center (0, 0)**	**Center (h, k)**
Equation	$\frac{x^2}{b^2} + \frac{y^2}{a^2} = 1$	$\frac{(x-h)^2}{b^2} + \frac{(y-k)^2}{a^2} = 1$
Vertices	$(0, \pm a)$	$(h, \pm a + k)$
Co-Vertices	$(\pm b, 0)$	$(\pm b + h, k)$
Foci, $c^2 = a^2 - b^2$	$(0, \pm c)$	$(h, \pm c + k)$
Major axis	$x = 0$	$x = h$
Minor axis	$y = 0$	$y = k$

Hyperbolas

Horizontal, $a > b$	Center (0, 0)	Center (h, k)
Equation	$\frac{x^2}{a^2} - \frac{y^2}{b^2} = 1$	$\frac{(x-h)^2}{a^2} - \frac{(y-k)^2}{b^2} = 1$
Vertices	$(\pm a, 0)$	$(\pm a + h, k)$
Foci, $c^2 = a^2 + b^2$	$(\pm c, 0)$	$(\pm c + h, k)$
Transverse axis	$y = 0$	$y = k$
Asymptotes	$y = \pm\frac{b}{a}x$	$y = \pm\frac{b}{a}(x - h) + k$
Vertical, $a > b$	**Center (0, 0)**	**Center (h, k)**
Equation	$\frac{y^2}{a^2} - \frac{x^2}{b^2} = 1$	$\frac{(y-k)^2}{a^2} - \frac{(x-h)^2}{b^2} = 1$
Vertices	$(0, \pm a)$	$(h, \pm a + k)$
Foci, $c^2 = a^2 + b^2$	$(0, \pm c)$	$(h, \pm c + k)$
Transverse axis	$x = 0$	$x = h$
Asymptotes	$y = \pm\frac{a}{b}x$	$y = \pm\frac{a}{b}(x - h) + k$

Chapter 11 Probability and Statistics

Fundamental Counting Principle

If event M can occur in m ways and is followed by event N that can occur in n ways, then event M followed by event N can occur in $m \cdot n$ ways.

Number of Permutations

The number of permutations of n items of a set arranged r items at a time is
${}_nP_r = \frac{n!}{(n - r)!}$ for $0 \leq r \leq n$.

Number of Combinations

The number of combinations of n items of a set chosen r items at a time is
${}_nC_r = \frac{n!}{r!(n - r)!}$ for $0 \leq r \leq n$.

Probability of A and B

If A and B are independent events, then
$P(A \text{ and } B) = P(A) \cdot P(B)$.

Probability of A or B

$P(A \text{ or } B) = P(A) + P(B) - P(A \text{ and } B)$
If A and B are mutually exclusive events, then
$P(A \text{ or } B) = P(A) + P(B)$.

Conditional Probability

For any two events A and B with $P(A) \neq 0$, the probability of event B, given event A, is:
$P(B|A) = \frac{P(A \text{ and } B)}{P(A)}$

Mean, Variance, and Standard Deviation

Mean: $\bar{x} = \frac{x_1 + x_2 + x_3 + \cdots + x_n}{n}$
Variance: $\sigma^2 = \frac{\Sigma(x - \bar{x})^2}{n}$
Standard deviation: $\sigma = \sqrt{\frac{\Sigma(x - \bar{x})^2}{n}}$

Binomial Probability

For repeated independent trials, each with a probability of success p and a probability of failure q (with $p + q = 1$), the probability of x successes in n trials is $P(x) = {}_nC_xp^xq^{n-x}$.

Binomial Theorem Using Combinations

For every positive integer n, use the combinations formula ${}_nC_r$ to expand $(a + b)^n$:
$(a + b)^n = {}_nC_0a^n + {}_nC_1a^{n-1}b + {}_nC_2a^{n-2}b^2 + \cdots + {}_nC_{n-1}ab^{n-1} + {}_nC_nb^n$

Chapter 12 Matrices

Properties of Matrix Addition

If A, B, and C are $m \times n$ matrices, then

Closure Property:	$A + B$ is an $m \times n$ matrix
Commutative Property:	$A + B = B + A$
Associative Property:	$(A + B) + C = A + (B + C)$
Identity Property:	There is a unique $m \times n$ matrix O such that $O + A = A + O = A$
Inverse Property:	For each A, there is a unique opposite, $-A$, such that $A + (-A) = O$

Properties of Scalar Multiplication

If A and B are $m \times n$ matrices, c and d are scalars, and O is the $m \times n$ zero matrix, then

Closure Property:	cA is an $m \times n$ matrix
Associative Property:	$(cd)A = c(dA)$
Distributive Property:	$c(A + B) = cA + cB$ $(c + d)A = cA + dA$
Identity Property:	$1 \cdot A = A$
Property of Zero:	$0 \cdot A = O$ and $cO = O$

Properties of Matrix Multiplication

If A, B, and C are $n \times n$ matrices and O is the $n \times n$ zero matrix, then

Closure Property:	AB is an $n \times n$ matrix
Associative Property:	$(AB)C = A(BC)$
Distributive Property:	$A(B + C) = AB + AC$ $(B + C)A = BA + CA$
Property of Zero:	$OA = AO = O$

Determinants of 2 × 2 and 3 × 3 Matrices

The determinant of a 2×2 matrix $\begin{bmatrix} a & b \\ c & d \end{bmatrix}$ is $ad - bc$.

The determinant of a 3×3 matrix $\begin{bmatrix} a_1 & b_1 & c_1 \\ a_2 & b_2 & c_2 \\ a_3 & b_3 & c_3 \end{bmatrix}$ is
$a_1b_2c_3 + b_1c_2a_3 + c_1a_2b_3 - (a_3b_2c_1 + b_3c_2a_1 + c_3a_2b_1)$

Inverse of a 2 × 2 Matrix

If $A = \begin{bmatrix} a & b \\ c & d \end{bmatrix}$ and $\det A \neq 0$,
then the inverse of A is
$A^{-1} = \frac{1}{\det A}\begin{bmatrix} d & -b \\ -c & a \end{bmatrix} = \frac{1}{ad - bc}\begin{bmatrix} d & -b \\ -c & a \end{bmatrix}$.

Chapter 13 Periodic Functions and Trigonometry

Convert Between Radians and Degrees

Use the proportion $\frac{d^\circ}{180^\circ} = \frac{r \text{ radians}}{\pi \text{ radians}}$ to convert between radians and degrees.

To convert degrees to radians, multiply by $\frac{\pi \text{ radians}}{180^\circ}$.

To convert radians to degrees, multiply by $\frac{180^\circ}{\pi \text{ radians}}$.

Length of an Intercepted Arc

For a circle of radius r and a central angle of measure θ (in radians), the length s of the intercepted arc is $s = r\theta$.

Sine and Cosine Functions

	Sine	Cosine
Parents	$y = \sin x$	$y = \cos x$
Reflection across x-axis	$y = -\sin x$	$y = -\cos x$
Amplitude $\lvert a \rvert$	$y = a \sin x$	$y = a \cos x$
Period $\frac{2\pi}{b}, b > 0$	$y = \sin bx$	$y = \cos bx$
Translation horizontal by h vertical by k	$y = \sin(x - h) + k$	$y = \cos(x - h) + k$

Tangent Function

Parent	$y = \tan x$
Reflection across x-axis	$y = -\tan x$
Period $\frac{\pi}{b}$	$y = \tan bx$
Translation horizontal by h vertical by k	$y = \tan(x - h) + k$
Asymptotes ($\tan bx$)	$x = n\frac{\pi}{2b}, n$ odd

Chapter 14 Trigonometric Identities and Equations

Basic Identities

Reciprocal Identities:

$\csc\theta = \frac{1}{\sin\theta}$　$\sec\theta = \frac{1}{\cos\theta}$　$\tan\theta = \frac{1}{\cot\theta}$

$\sin\theta = \frac{1}{\csc\theta}$　$\cos\theta = \frac{1}{\sec\theta}$　$\cot\theta = \frac{1}{\tan\theta}$

Tangent Identity:　Cotangent Identity:

$\tan\theta = \frac{\sin\theta}{\cos\theta}$　$\cot\theta = \frac{\cos\theta}{\sin\theta}$

Pythagorean Identities

$\cos^2\theta + \sin^2\theta = 1$　$1 + \tan^2\theta = \sec^2\theta$　$\cot^2\theta + 1 = \csc^2\theta$

Area of a Triangle

In $\triangle ABC$ with a, b, and c the lengths of the sides opposite $\angle A$, $\angle B$, and $\angle C$, respectively,

Area $\triangle ABC = \frac{1}{2}bc \sin A = \frac{1}{2}ac \sin B = \frac{1}{2}ab \sin C$.

Law of Sines

In $\triangle ABC$ with a, b, and c the lengths of the sides opposite $\angle A$, $\angle B$, and $\angle C$, respectively,

$\frac{\sin A}{a} = \frac{\sin B}{b} = \frac{\sin C}{c}$.

Law of Cosines

In $\triangle ABC$ with a, b, and c the lengths of the sides opposite $\angle A$, $\angle B$, and $\angle C$, respectively,

$a^2 = b^2 + c^2 - 2bc \cdot \cos A$
$b^2 = a^2 + c^2 - 2ac \cdot \cos B$
$c^2 = a^2 + b^2 - 2ab \cdot \cos C$

Negative Angle Identities

$\sin(-\theta) = -\sin\theta$　$\cos(-\theta) = \cos\theta$　$\tan(-\theta) = -\tan\theta$

Cofunction Angle Identities

$\sin\left(\frac{\pi}{2} - \theta\right) = \cos\theta$　$\cos\left(\frac{\pi}{2} - \theta\right) = \sin\theta$　$\tan\left(\frac{\pi}{2} - \theta\right) = \cot\theta$

Angle Difference Identities

$\sin(A - B) = \sin A \cos B - \cos A \sin B$
$\cos(A - B) = \cos A \cos B + \sin A \sin B$
$\tan(A - B) = \frac{\tan A - \tan B}{1 - \tan A \tan B}$

Angle Sum Identities

$\sin(A + B) = \sin A \cos B + \cos A \sin B$
$\cos(A + B) = \cos A \cos B - \sin A \sin B$
$\tan(A + B) = \frac{\tan A + \tan B}{1 - \tan A \tan B}$

Double-Angle Identities

$\cos 2\theta = \cos^2\theta - \sin^2\theta$　$\sin 2\theta = 2 \sin\theta \cos\theta$
$\cos 2\theta = 2\cos^2\theta - 1$　$\tan 2\theta = \frac{2\tan\theta}{1 - \tan^2\theta}$
$\cos 2\theta = 1 - 2\sin^2\theta$

Half-Angle Identities

$\sin\frac{A}{2} = \pm\sqrt{\frac{1 - \cos A}{2}}$

$\cos\frac{A}{2} = \pm\sqrt{\frac{1 + \cos A}{2}}$

$\tan\frac{A}{2} = \pm\sqrt{\frac{1 - \cos A}{1 + \cos A}}$

Formulas of **Geometry**

You will use a number of geometric formulas as you work through your algebra book. Here are some perimeter, area, and volume formulas.

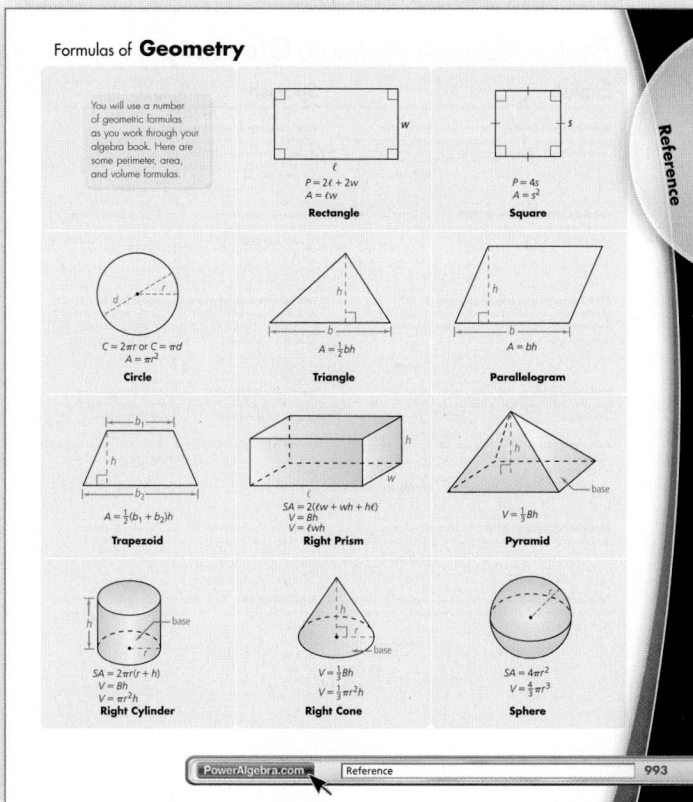

$P = 2\ell + 2w$
$A = \ell w$
Rectangle

$P = 4s$
$A = s^2$
Square

$C = 2\pi r$ or $C = \pi d$
$A = \pi r^2$
Circle

$A = \frac{1}{2}bh$
Triangle

$A = bh$
Parallelogram

$A = \frac{1}{2}(b_1 + b_2)h$
Trapezoid

$SA = 2(\ell w + wh + h\ell)$
$V = Bh$
$V = \ell wh$
Right Prism

$V = \frac{1}{3}Bh$
Pyramid

$SA = 2\pi r(r + h)$
$V = Bh$
$V = \pi r^2 h$
Right Cylinder

$V = \frac{1}{3}Bh$
$V = \frac{1}{3}\pi r^2 h$
Right Cone

$SA = 4\pi r^2$
$V = \frac{4}{3}\pi r^3$
Sphere

English/Spanish Illustrated **Glossary**

English   A   Spanish

Absolute value (p. 41) The absolute value of a real number, x, written $|x|$, is its distance from zero on the number line.

> Example $|3| = 3$
> $|-4| = 4$

Valor absoluto de un número real (p. 41) El valor absoluto de un número real, x, escrito como $|x|$, es su distancia desde cero en la recta numérica.

Absolute value function (p. 107) A function of the form $f(x) = |mx + b| + c$, where $m \neq 0$, is an absolute value function.

> Example $f(x) = |3x - 2| + 3$
> $f(x) = |2x|$

Función de valor absoluto (p. 107) Una función de la forma $f(x) = |mx + b| + c$, donde $m \neq 0$, es una función de valor absoluto.

Absolute value of a complex number (p. 249) The absolute value of a complex number is its distance from the origin on the complex number plane. In general, $|a + bi| = \sqrt{a^2 + b^2}$.

> Example $|3 - 4i| = \sqrt{3^2 + (-4)^2} = 5$

Valor absoluto de un número complejo (p. 249) El valor absoluto de un número complejo es la distancia a la que está del origen en el plano de números complejo. Generalmente, $|a + bi| = \sqrt{a^2 + b^2}$.

Additive identity (p. 14) The additive identity is 0. The sum of 0 and any number is that number. The sum of opposites is 0.

Identidad aditiva (p. 14) La identidad aditiva es 0. La suma de 0 y cualquier número es ese mismo número. La suma de opuestos es 0.

Additive inverse (p. 14) The opposite or additive inverse of any number a is $-a$. The sum of opposites is 0, the additive identity.

> Example $3 + (-3) = 0$
> $5.2 + (-5.2) = 0$

Inverso aditivo (p. 14) El opuesto o inverso aditivo de un número a es $-a$. La suma de opuestos es 0, la identidad aditiva.

Algebraic expression (p. 5) An algebraic expression is a mathematical phrase that contains one or more variables.

> Example $2x + 3$
> $z - y$

Expresión algebraica (p. 5) Una expresión algebraica es una frase matemática que contiene una o más variables.

Amplitude (p. 830) The amplitude of a periodic function is half the difference between the maximum and minimum values of the function.

> Example   The maximum and minimum values of $y = 4 \sin x$ are 4 and -4, respectively.
>   amplitude $= \dfrac{4 - (-4)}{2} = 4$

Amplitud (p. 830) La amplitud de una función periódica es la mitad de la diferencia entre los valores máximo y mínimo de la función.

English   Spanish

Arithmetic mean (p. 574) The arithmetic mean, or average, of two numbers is their sum divided by two.

> Example   The arithmetic mean of 12 and 15 is $\dfrac{12 + 15}{2} = 13.5$.

Media aritmética (p. 574) La media aritmética, o promedio, de dos números es su suma dividida por dos.

Arithmetic sequence (p. 572) An arithmetic sequence is a sequence with a constant difference between consecutive terms.

> Example   The arithmetic sequence 1, 5, 9, 13, . . . has a common difference of 4.

Secuencia aritmética (p. 572) Una secuencia aritmética es una secuencia de números en la que la diferencia entre dos números consecutivos es constante.

Arithmetic series (p. 587) An arithmetic series is a series whose terms form an arithmetic sequence.

> Example $1 + 5 + 9 + 13 + 17 + 21$ is an arithmetic series with six terms.

Serie aritmética (p. 587) Una serie aritmética es una serie cuyos términos forman una progresión aritmética.

Asymptote (p. 435) An asymptote is a line that a graph approaches as x or y increases in absolute value.

> Example   The function $y = \dfrac{x+2}{x-2}$ has $x = 2$ as a vertical asymptote and $y = 1$ as a horizontal asymptote.

Asíntota (p. 435) Una asíntota es una recta a la cual se acerca una gráfica a medida que x o y aumentan de valor absoluto.

Axis of symmetry (pp. 107, 194) The axis of symmetry is the line that divides a figure into two parts that are mirror images.

> Example

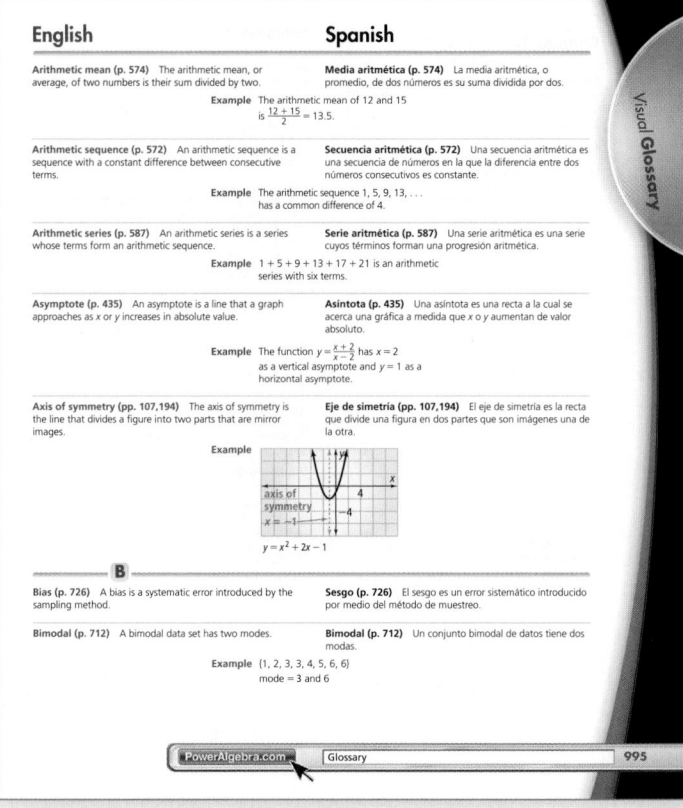

$y = x^2 + 2x - 1$

Eje de simetría (p. 107, 194) El eje de simetría es la recta que divide una figura en dos partes que son imágenes una de la otra.

    B

Bias (p. 726) A bias is a systematic error introduced by the sampling method.

Sesgo (p. 726) El sesgo es un error sistemático introducido por medio del método de muestreo.

Bimodal (p. 712) A bimodal data set has two modes.

> Example   {1, 2, 3, 3, 4, 5, 6, 6}
>   mode = 3 and 6

Bimodal (p. 712) Un conjunto bimodal de datos tiene dos modas.

English   Spanish

Binomial experiment (p. 731) A binomial experiment is one in which the situation involves repeated trials. Each trial has two possible outcomes (success or failure), and the probability of success is constant throughout the trials.

Experimento binomial (p. 731) Un experimento binomial es un experimento que requiere varios ensayos. Cada ensayo tiene dos resultados posibles (éxito o fracaso), y la probabilidad de éxito es constante durante todos los ensayos.

Binomial probability (p. 732) In a binomial experiment with probability of success p and probability of failure q, the probability of x successes in n trials is given by $_nC_x p^x q^{n-x}$.

> Example   Suppose you roll a standard number cube and that you call rolling a 1 a success. Then $p = \frac{1}{6}$ and $q = \frac{5}{6}$. The probability of rolling nine 1's in twenty rolls is $_{20}C_9 \left(\frac{1}{6}\right)^9 \left(\frac{5}{6}\right)^{11} \approx 0.0022$.

Probabilidad binomial (p. 732) En un experimento binomial con una probabilidad de éxito p y una probabilidad de fracaso q, la probabilidad de x éxitos en n ensayos se expresa con $_nC_x p^x q^{n-x}$.

Binomial Theorem (pp. 327, 733) For every positive integer n, $(a + b)^n = P_0 a^n + P_1 a^{n-1}b + P_2 a^{n-2}b^2 + \cdots + P_{n-1}ab^{n-1} + P_n b^n$ where $P_0, P_1, \ldots, P_n$ are the numbers in the row of Pascal's Triangle that has n as its second number.

> Example $(x + 1)^3 = {_3C_0}(x)^3 + {_3C_1}(x)^2(1)^1$
> $+ {_3C_2}(x)^1(1)^2 + {_3C_3}(1)^3$
> $= x^3 + 3x^2 + 3x + 1$

Teorema binomial (pp. 327, 733) Para cada número entero positivo n, $(a + b)^n = P_0 a^n + P_1 a^{n-1}b + P_2 a^{n-2}b^2 + \cdots + P_{n-1}ab^{n-1} + P_n b^n$, donde $P_0, P_1, \ldots, P_n$ son los números de la fila del Triángulo de Pascal cuyo segundo número es n.

Boundary (p. 114) A boundary of the graph of a linear inequality is a line in the coordinate plane. It separates the solutions of the inequality from the nonsolutions. Points of the line itself may or may not be solutions.

Límite (p. 114) Un límite de la gráfica de una desigualdad lineal es una línea en el plano de coordenadas. Ésta separa las soluciones de la desigualdad de las no soluciones. Las soluciones pueden ser o no puntos de la línea.

Box-and-whisker plot (p. 714) A box-and-whisker plot is a method of displaying data that uses quartiles to form the center box and the maximum and minimum values to form the whiskers.

> Example

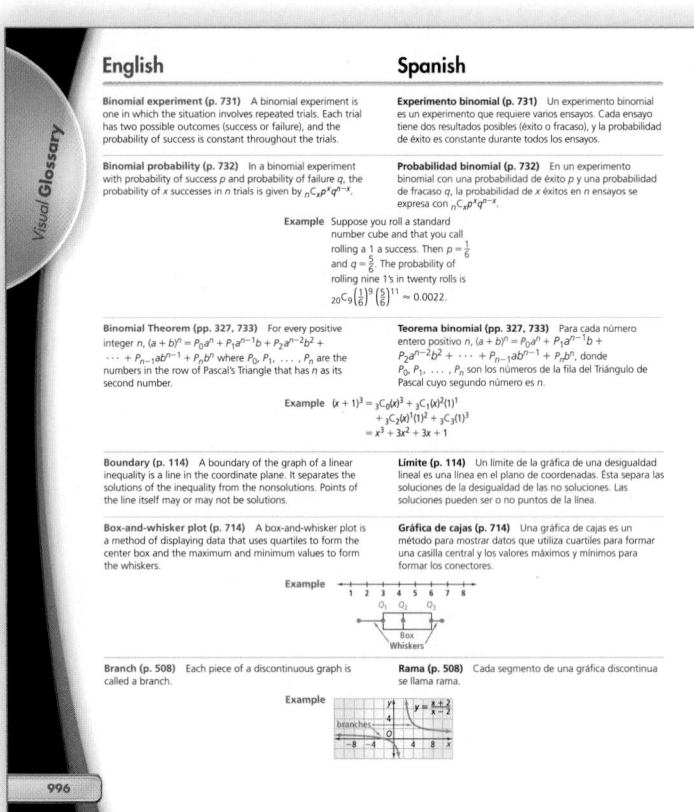

Gráfica de cajas (p. 714) Una gráfica de cajas es un método para mostrar datos que utiliza cuartiles para formar una casilla central y los valores máximos y mínimos para formar los conectores.

Branch (p. 508) Each piece of a discontinuous graph is called a branch.

> Example

Rama (p. 508) Cada segmento de una gráfica discontinua se llama rama.

English   C   Spanish

Center of a circle (p. 630) The center of a circle is the point that is the same distance from every point on the circle.

Centro de un círculo (p. 630) El centro de un círculo es el punto que está situado a la misma distancia de cada punto del círculo.

Center of an ellipse (p. 639) The center of an ellipse is the midpoint of the major axis.

Centro de una elipse (p. 639) El centro de una elipse es el punto medio del eje mayor.

Center of rotation (p. 804) A center of rotation is the fixed point of a rotation.

> Example

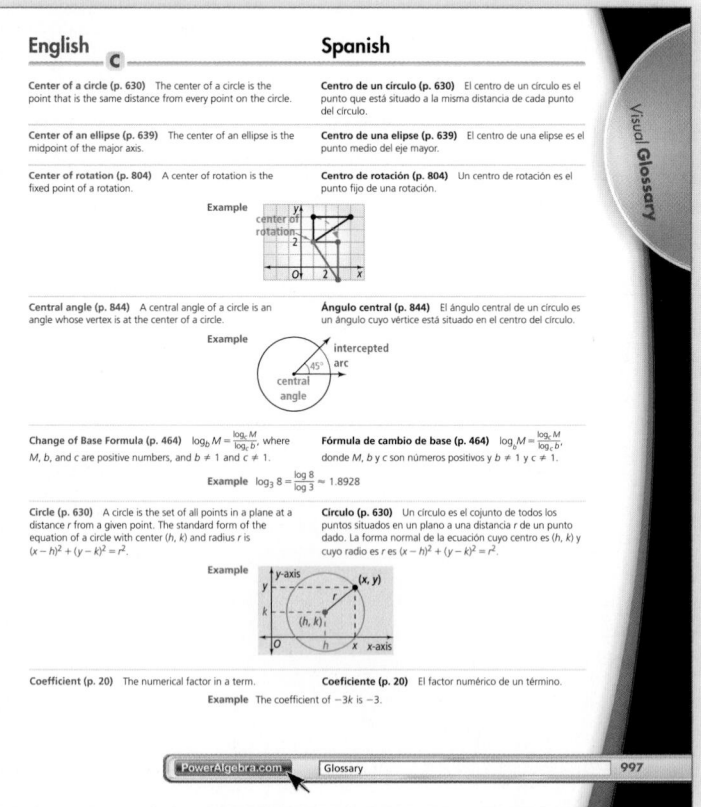

Centro de rotación (p. 804) Un centro de rotación es el punto fijo de una rotación.

Central angle (p. 844) A central angle of a circle is an angle whose vertex is at the center of a circle.

> Example

Ángulo central (p. 844) El ángulo central de un círculo es un ángulo cuyo vértice está situado en el centro del círculo.

Change of Base Formula (p. 464) $\log_b M = \dfrac{\log_c M}{\log_c b}$, where M, b, and c are positive numbers, and $b \neq 1$ and $c \neq 1$.

> Example $\log_3 8 = \dfrac{\log 8}{\log 3} \approx 1.8928$

Fórmula de cambio de base (p. 464) $\log_b M = \dfrac{\log_c M}{\log_c b}$, donde M, b y c son números positivos y $b \neq 1$ y $c \neq 1$.

Circle (p. 630) A circle is the set of all points in a plane at a distance r from a given point. The standard form of the equation of a circle with center (h, k) and radius r is $(x - h)^2 + (y - k)^2 = r^2$.

> Example

Círculo (p. 630) Un círculo es el conjunto de todos los puntos situados en un plano a una distancia r de un punto dado. La forma normal de la ecuación cuyo centro es (h, k) y cuyo radio de r es $(x - h)^2 + (y - k)^2 = r^2$.

Coefficient (p. 20) The numerical factor in a term.

> Example   The coefficient of $-3k$ is -3.

Coeficiente (p. 20) El factor numérico de un término.

English / Spanish

Coefficient matrix (p. 793) When representing a system of equations with a matrix equation, the matrix containing the coefficients of the system is the coefficient matrix.

Matriz de coeficientes (p. 793) Al representar un sistema de ecuaciones con una ecuación de matriz, la matriz que contiene los coeficientes del sistema es la matriz de coeficientes.

Example $\begin{cases} x + 2y = 5 \\ 3x + 5y = 14 \end{cases}$

coefficient matrix $\begin{bmatrix} 1 & 2 \\ 3 & 5 \end{bmatrix}$

Combination (p. 676) Any unordered selection of r objects from a set of n objects is a combination. The number of combinations of n objects taken r at a time is $_nC_r = \dfrac{n!}{r!(n-r)!}$ for $0 \le r \le n$.

Combinación (p. 676) Cualquier selección no ordenada de r objetos tomados de un conjunto de n objetos es una combinación. El número de combinaciones de n objetos, cuando se toman r objetos cada vez, es $_nC_r = \dfrac{n!}{r!(n-r)!}$ para $0 \le r \le n$.

Example The number of combinations of seven items taken four at a time is

$_7C_4 = \dfrac{7!}{4!(7-4)!} = 35.$

There are 35 ways to choose four items from seven items without regard to order.

Combined variation (p. 501) A combined variation is a relation in which one variable varies with respect to each of two or more variables.

Variación combinada (p. 501) Una variación combinada es una relación en la que una variable varía con respecto a cada una de dos o más variables.

Example $y = kx^2\sqrt{z}$

$z = \dfrac{kx}{y}$

Common difference (p. 572) A common difference is the difference between consecutive terms of an arithmetic sequence.

Diferencia común (p. 572) La diferencia común es la diferencia entre los términos consecutivos de una progresión aritmética.

Example The arithmetic sequence 1, 5, 9, 13, . . . has a common difference of 4.

Common logarithm (p. 453) A common logarithm is a logarithm that uses base 10. You can write the common logarithm $\log_{10} y$ as $\log y$.

Logaritmo común (p. 453) El logaritmo común es un logaritmo de base 10. El logaritmo común $\log_{10} y$ se expresa como $\log y$.

Example $\log 1 = 0$
$\log 10 = 1$
$\log 50 = 1.698970004 \ldots$

Common ratio (p. 580) A common ratio is the ratio of consecutive terms of a geometric sequence.

Razón común (p. 580) Una razón común es la razón de términos consecutivos en una secuencia geométrica.

Example The geometric sequence 2.5, 5, 10, 20, . . . has a common ratio of 2.

English / Spanish

Completing the square (p. 235) Completing the square is the process of finding a constant c to add to $x^2 + bx$ so that $x^2 + bx + c$ is the square of a binomial.

Completar el cuadrado (p. 235) Completar un cuadrado es el proceso mediante el cual se halla una constante c que se le pueda sumar a $x^2 + bx$, de manera que $x^2 + bx + c$ sea el cuadrado de un binomio.

Example $x^2 - 12x + \blacksquare$
$x^2 - 12x + \left(\dfrac{-12}{2}\right)^2$
$x^2 - 12x + 36$

Complex conjugates (p. 251) Number pairs of the form $a + bi$ and $a - bi$ are complex conjugates.

Conjugados complejos (p. 251) Los pares de números de la forma $a + bi$ y $a - bi$ son conjugados complejos.

Example The complex numbers $2 - 3i$ and $2 + 3i$ are complex conjugates.

Complex fraction (p. 536) A complex fraction is a rational expression that has a fraction in its numerator or denominator, or in both its numerator and denominator.

Fracción compleja (p. 536) Una fracción compleja es una expresión racional en la que el numerador, el denominador o ambos son una fracción.

Example $\dfrac{\frac{2}{3}}{5}$, $\dfrac{\frac{2}{3}}{\frac{4}{5}}$

Complex number (p. 249) Complex numbers are the real numbers and the imaginary numbers.

Número complejo (p. 249) Los números complejos son los números reales y los números imaginarios.

Example $6 + i$
$7, 2i$

Complex number plane (p. 249) The complex number plane is identical to the coordinate plane except each ordered pair (a, b) represents the complex number $a + bi$. The horizontal axis is the Real axis. The vertical axis is the Imaginary axis.

Plano de números complejos (p. 249) El plano de los números complejos es idéntico al plano de coordenadas, a excepción de que cada par ordenado (a, b) representa el número complejo $a + bi$. El eje horizontal es el eje real. El eje vertical es el eje imaginario.

Example

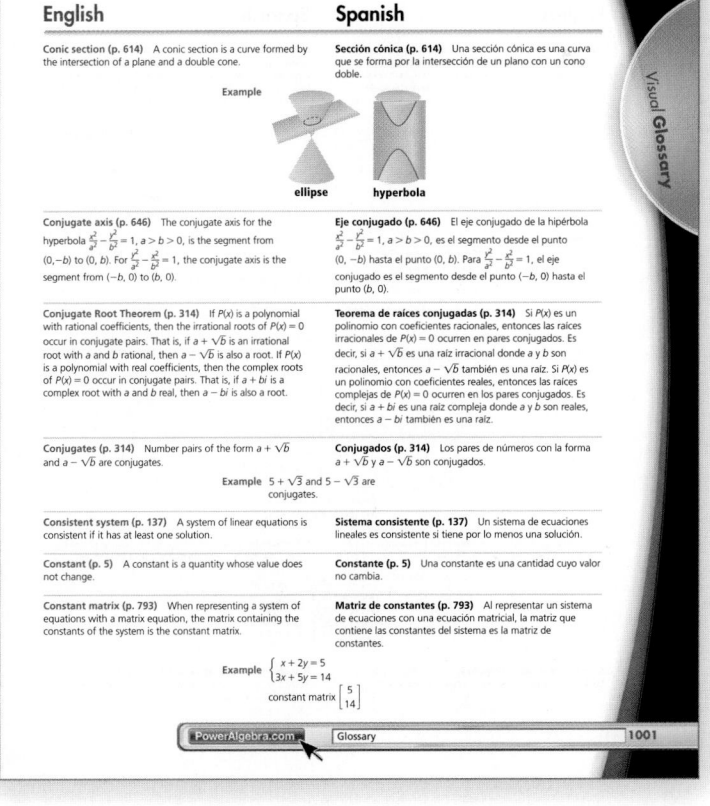

English / Spanish

Composite function (p. 399) A composite function is a combination of two functions such that the output from the first function becomes the input for the second function.

Función compuesta (p. 399) Una función compuesta es la combinación de dos funciones. La cantidad de salida de la primera función es la cantidad de entrada de la segunda función.

Example $f(x) = 2x + 1$, $g(x) = x^2 - 1$
$(g \circ f)(5) = g(f(5)) = g(2(5) + 1)$
$= g(11)$
$= 11^2 - 1 = 120$

Compound inequality (p. 36) You can join two inequalities with the word *and* or the word *or* to form a compound inequality.

Desigualdad compuesta (p. 36) Puedes unir dos desigualdades por medio de la palabra *y* o la palabra *o* para formar una desigualdad compuesta.

Example $-1 < x$ and $x \le 3$
$x < -1$ or $x \ge 3$

Conditional probability (p. 696) A conditional probability contains a condition that may limit the sample space for an event. The notation $P(B|A)$ is read "the probability of event B, given event A." For any two events A and B in the sample space, $P(B|A) = \dfrac{P(A \text{ and } B)}{P(A)}$.

Probabilidad condicional (p. 696) Una probabilidad condicional contiene una condición que puede limitar el espacio muestral de un suceso. La notación $P(B|A)$ se lee "la probabilidad del suceso B, dado el suceso A". Para dos sucesos cualesquiera A y B en el espacio muestral, $P(B|A) = \dfrac{P(A \text{ y } B)}{P(A)}$.

Example $= \dfrac{P(\text{departs and arrives on time})}{P(\text{departs on time})}$
$= \dfrac{0.75}{0.83}$
≈ 0.9

Confidence interval (p. 746) Based on the mean of a sample or a sample proportion, the confidence interval indicates the interval in which the population mean or population proportion is likely to lie for a given confidence level.

Intervalo de confianza (p. 746) El intervalo de confianza se basa en la media de una muestra o en la proporción de una muestra, e indica el intervalo en el que probablemente se encuentra dicha media o proporción de la población para un nivel de confianza dado.

Example For an elementary history book, a sample of 30 trials indicates that the mean number of words in a sentence is 12.7. The margin of error at a 95% confidence level is 1.5 words per sentence. The mean number of words μ in all of the sentences in the book at a 95% confidence level is $12.7 - 1.5 \le \mu \le 12.7 + 1.5$.

English / Spanish

Conic section (p. 614) A conic section is a curve formed by the intersection of a plane and a double cone.

Sección cónica (p. 614) Una sección cónica es una curva que se forma por la intersección de un plano con un cono doble.

Example

ellipse　　hyperbola

Conjugate axis (p. 646) The conjugate axis for the hyperbola $\dfrac{x^2}{a^2} - \dfrac{y^2}{b^2} = 1$, $a > b > 0$, is the segment from $(0, -b)$ to $(0, b)$. For $\dfrac{y^2}{a^2} - \dfrac{x^2}{b^2} = 1$, the conjugate axis is the segment from $(-b, 0)$ to $(b, 0)$.

Eje conjugado (p. 646) El eje conjugado de la hipérbola $\dfrac{x^2}{a^2} - \dfrac{y^2}{b^2} = 1$, $a > b > 0$, es el segmento desde el punto $(0, -b)$ hasta el punto $(0, b)$. Para $\dfrac{y^2}{a^2} - \dfrac{x^2}{b^2} = 1$, el eje conjugado es el segmento desde el punto $(-b, 0)$ hasta el punto $(b, 0)$.

Conjugate Root Theorem (p. 314) If $P(x)$ is a polynomial with rational coefficients, then the irrational roots of $P(x) = 0$ occur in conjugate pairs. That is, if $a + \sqrt{b}$ is an irrational root with a and b rational, then $a - \sqrt{b}$ is also a root. If $P(x)$ is a polynomial with real coefficients, then the complex roots of $P(x) = 0$ occur in conjugate pairs. That is, if $a + bi$ is a complex root with a and b real, then $a - bi$ is also a root.

Teorema de raíces conjugadas (p. 314) Si $P(x)$ es un polinomio con coeficientes racionales, entonces las raíces irracionales de $P(x) = 0$ ocurren en pares conjugados. Es decir, si $a + \sqrt{b}$ es una raíz irracional donde a y b son racionales, entonces $a - \sqrt{b}$ también es una raíz. Si $P(x)$ es un polinomio con coeficientes reales, entonces las raíces complejas de $P(x) = 0$ ocurren en los pares conjugados. Es decir, si $a + bi$ es una raíz compleja donde a y b son reales, entonces $a - bi$ también es una raíz.

Conjugates (p. 314) Number pairs of the form $a + \sqrt{b}$ and $a - \sqrt{b}$ are conjugates.

Conjugados (p. 314) Los pares de números con la forma $a + \sqrt{b}$ y $a - \sqrt{b}$ son conjugados.

Example $5 + \sqrt{3}$ and $5 - \sqrt{3}$ are conjugates.

Consistent system (p. 137) A system of linear equations is consistent if it has at least one solution.

Sistema consistente (p. 137) Un sistema de ecuaciones lineales es consistente si tiene por lo menos una solución.

Constant (p. 5) A constant is a quantity whose value does not change.

Constante (p. 5) Una constante es una cantidad cuyo valor no cambia.

Constant matrix (p. 793) When representing a system of equations with a matrix equation, the matrix containing the constants of the system is the constant matrix.

Matriz de constantes (p. 793) Al representar un sistema de ecuaciones con una ecuación matricial, la matriz que contiene las constantes del sistema es la matriz de constantes.

Example $\begin{cases} x + 2y = 5 \\ 3x + 5y = 14 \end{cases}$

constant matrix $\begin{bmatrix} 5 \\ 14 \end{bmatrix}$

English | Spanish

Constant of proportionality (p. 341) If $y = ax^b$ describes y as a power function of x, then y varies directly with, or is proportional to, the bth power of x. The constant a is the constant of proportionality.

Constante de proporcionalidad (p. 341) Si $y = ax^b$ describe a y como una potencia de la función de x, entonces y varía directamente con, o es proporcional a, la b^{ma} potencia de x. La constante a es la constante de proporcionalidad.

Constant of variation (p. 68) The constant of variation is the ratio of the two variables in a direct variation and the product of the two variables in an inverse variation.

Constante de variación (p. 68) La constante de variación es la razón de dos variables en una variación directa y el producto de las dos variables en una variación inversa.

> **Example** In $y = 3.5x$, the constant of variation k is 3.5. In $xy = 5$, the constant of variation k is 5.

Constant term (p. 20) A constant term is a term with no variables.

Término constante (p. 20) Un término constante es un término que no tiene variables.

Constraint (p. 157) Constraints are restrictions on the variables of the objective function in a linear programming problem. See **Linear programming.**

Restricción (p. 157) Las restricciones son limitaciones a las variables de una función objetiva en un problema de programación lineal. Ver **Linear programming.**

Continuous graph (p. 516) A graph is continuous if it has no jumps, breaks, or holes.

Gráfica continua (p. 516) Una gráfica es continua si no tiene saltos, interrupciones o huecos.

Continuous probability distribution (p. 739) A continuous probability distribution has as its events any of the infinitely many values in an interval of real numbers.

Distribución de probabilidad continua (p. 739) Una distribución de probabilidad continua tiene como sucesos a cualquiera del número infinito de valores en un intervalo de números reales.

Continuously compounded interest (p. 446) When interest is compounded continuously on principal P, the value A of an account is $A = Pe^{rt}$.

Interés compuesto continuo (p. 446) En un sistema donde el interés es compuesto continuamente sobre el capital P, el valor de A de una cuenta es $A = Pe^{rt}$.

> **Example** Suppose that $P = \$1200$, $r = 0.05$, and $t = 3$. Then
> $A = 1200e^{0.05 \cdot 3}$
> $= 1200(2.718 \ldots)^{0.15}$
> ≈ 1394.20

Controlled experiment (p. 726) In a controlled experiment, you divide the sample into two groups. You impose a treatment on one group but not the other "control" group. Then you compare the effect on the treated group to the control group.

Experimento controlado (p. 726) En un experimento controlado, se divide la muestra en dos grupos. Uno de los grupos se manipula y el otro grupo "controlado" se mantiene en su estado original. Luego se comparan el estado del grupo manipulado y el estado del grupo controlado.

Convenience sample (p. 725) In a convenience sample you select any members of the population who are conveniently and readily available.

Muestra de conveniencia (p. 725) En una muestra de conveniencia se selecciona a cualquier miembro de la población que está convenientemente disponible.

English | Spanish

Converge (p. 598) An infinite series $a_1 + a_2 + \cdots + a_n + \cdots$ converges if the sum $a_1 + a_2 + \cdots + a_n$ gets closer and closer to a real number as n increases.

Convergir (p. 598) Una serie infinita $a_1 + a_2 + \cdots + a_n + \cdots$ es convergente si la suma $a_1 + a_2 + \cdots + a_n$ se aproxima cada vez más a un número real a medida que el valor de n incrementa.

> **Example** $1 + \frac{1}{2} + \frac{1}{4} + \frac{1}{8} + \cdots$ converges.

Coordinate space (p. 164) Coordinate space is a three-dimensional space where each point is described uniquely using an ordered triple of numbers.

Espacio de coordenadas (p. 164) Un espacio de coordenadas es un espacio tridimensional en el cual cada punto es definido de manera única por una tripleta ordenada de números.

> **Example**

> $A (2, -1, 3)$

Correlation (p. 92) A correlation indicates the strength of a relationship between two data sets.

Correlación (p. 92) Una correlación indica la fuerza de una relación entre dos conjuntos de datos.

Correlation coefficient (p. 94) The correlation coefficient, r, indicates the strength of the correlation. The closer r is to 1 or -1, the more closely the data resembles a line and the more accurate your model is likely to be.

Coeficiente de correlación (p. 94) El coeficiente de correlación, r, indica la fuerza de la correlación. Mientras más cerca está r de 1 ó -1, más se parecen los datos a una línea y será más probable que tu modelo sea preciso.

Corresponding elements (p. 764) Corresponding elements are elements in the same position in each matrix.

Elementos correspondientes (p. 764) Los elementos correspondientes son elementos que se encuentran en la misma posición de cada matriz.

Cosecant function (p. 883) The cosecant (csc) function is the reciprocal of the sine function. For all real numbers θ except those that make $\sin \theta = 0$, $\csc \theta = \frac{1}{\sin \theta}$.

Función cosecante (p. 883) La función cosecante (csc) se define como el recíproco de la función seno. Para todos los números reales θ, excepto aquéllos para los que $\sin \theta = 0$, $\csc \theta = \frac{1}{\sin \theta}$.

> **Example** If $\sin \theta = \frac{5}{13}$, then $\csc \theta = \frac{13}{5}$.

English | Spanish

Cosine function, Cosine of θ (pp. 838, 861) The cosine function, $y = \cos \theta$, matches the measure θ of an angle in standard position with the x-coordinate of a point on the unit circle. This point is where the terminal side of the angle intersects the unit circle. The x-coordinate is the cosine of θ.

Función coseno, Coseno de θ (pp. 838, 861) La función coseno, $y = \cos \theta$, empareja la medida θ de un ángulo en posición estándar con la coordenada x de un punto en el círculo unitario. Este es el punto en el que el lado terminal del ángulo interseca al círculo unitario. La coordenada x es el coseno de θ.

> **Example**
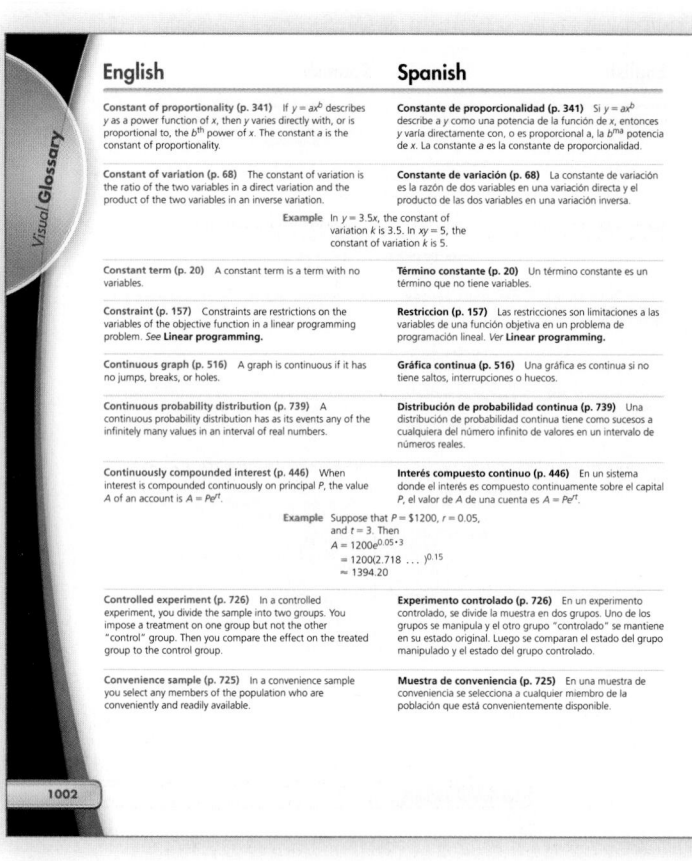
> $P(\cos \theta, \sin \theta)$

Cotangent function (p. 883) The cotangent (cot) function is the reciprocal of the tangent function. For all real numbers θ except those that make $\tan \theta = 0$, $\cot \theta = \frac{1}{\tan \theta}$.

Función cotangente (p. 883) La función cotangente (cot) es el recíproco de la función tangente. Para todos los números reales θ, excepto aquéllos para los que $\tan \theta = 0$, $\cot \theta = \frac{1}{\tan \theta}$.

> **Example** If $\tan \theta = \frac{5}{12}$, then $\cot \theta = \frac{12}{5}$.

Coterminal angle (p. 837) Two angles in standard position are coterminal if they have the same terminal side.

Ángulo coterminal (p. 827) Dos ángulos que están en posición normal son coterminales si tienen el mismo lado terminal.

> **Example**
> $135°$
> $-225°$
> coterminal angles
>
> Angles that have measures $135°$ and $-225°$ are coterminal.

Co-vertices (p. 639) The endpoints of the minor axis of an ellipse are the co-vertices of the ellipse.

Co-vértices (p. 639) Los puntos de intersección entre una elipse y los ejes menores son los co-vértices de la elipse.

> **Example**
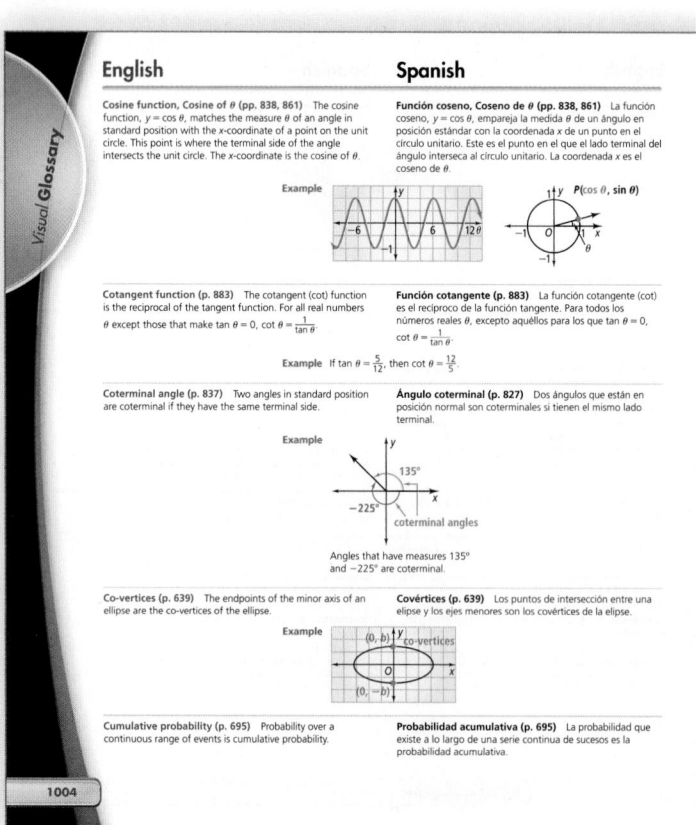
> $(0, b)$ co-vertices
> $(0, -b)$

Cumulative probability (p. 695) Probability over a continuous range of events is cumulative probability.

Probabilidad acumulativa (p. 695) La probabilidad que existe a lo largo de una serie continua de sucesos es la probabilidad acumulativa.

English | Spanish

Cycle (p. 828) A cycle of a periodic function is an interval of x-values over which the function provides one complete pattern of y-values.

Ciclo (p. 828) El ciclo de una función periódica es un intervalo de valores de x de los cuales la función produce un patrón completo de valores de y.

> **Example**
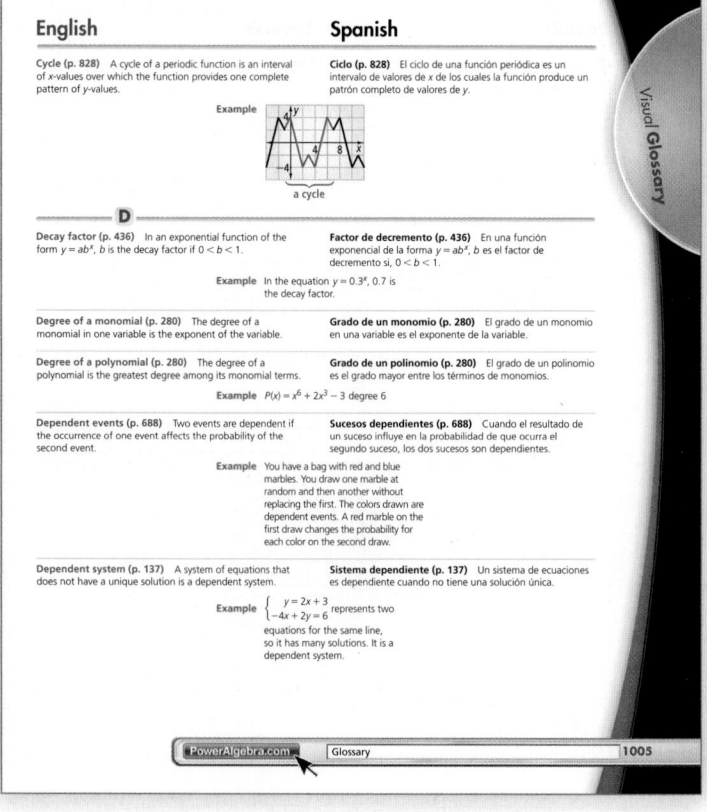
> a cycle

D

Decay factor (p. 436) In an exponential function of the form $y = ab^x$, b is the decay factor if $0 < b < 1$.

Factor de decremento (p. 436) En una función exponencial de la forma $y = ab^x$, b es el factor de decremento si, $0 < b < 1$.

> **Example** In the equation $y = 0.3^x$, 0.7 is the decay factor.

Degree of a monomial (p. 280) The degree of a monomial in one variable is the exponent of the variable.

Grado de un monomio (p. 280) El grado de un monomio en una variable es el exponente de la variable.

Degree of a polynomial (p. 280) The degree of a polynomial is the greatest degree among its monomial terms.

Grado de un polinomio (p. 280) El grado de un polinomio es el grado mayor entre los términos de monomios.

> **Example** $P(x) = x^6 + 2x^3 - 3$ degree 6

Dependent events (p. 688) Two events are dependent if the occurrence of one event affects the probability of the second event.

Sucesos dependientes (p. 688) Cuando el resultado de un suceso influye en la probabilidad de que ocurra el segundo suceso, los dos sucesos son dependientes.

> **Example** You have a bag with red and blue marbles. You draw one marble at random and then another without replacing the first. The colors drawn are dependent events. A red marble on the first draw changes the probability for each color on the second draw.

Dependent system (p. 137) A system of equations that does not have a unique solution is a dependent system.

Sistema dependiente (p. 137) Un sistema de ecuaciones es dependiente cuando no tiene una solución única.

> **Example** $\begin{cases} y = 2x + 3 \\ -4x + 2y = 6 \end{cases}$ represents two equations for the same line, so it has many solutions. It is a dependent system.

Page 1006

English	Spanish

Dependent variable (p. 63) If a function is defined by an equation using the variables x and y, where y represents output values, then y is the dependent variable.

Variable dependiente (p. 63) Si una función es definida por una ecuación que usa las variables x e y, donde y representa valores de salida, entonces y es la variable dependiente.

Example $y = 2x + 1$
y is the dependent variable.

Descartes' Rule of Signs (p. 315) Let $P(x)$ be a polynomial with real coefficients written in standard form.
– The number of positive real roots of $P(x) = 0$ is either equal to the number of sign changes between consecutive coefficients of $P(x)$ or is less than that by an even number;
– The number of negative real roots of $P(x) = 0$ is either equal to the number of sign changes between consecutive coefficients of $P(-x)$ or is less than that by an even number. (Count multiple roots according to their multiplicity.)

Regla de los signos de Descartes (p. 315) Sea $P(x)$ un polinomio con coeficientes reales escritos en forma normal.
– El número de raíces positivas reales de $P(x) = 0$ es igual al número de cambios de signos entre coeficientes consecutivos de $P(-x)$ o es menor que eso un un número par;
– El número de raíces negativas reales de $P(x) = 0$ es igual al número de cambios de signos entre coeficientes consecutivos de $P(-x)$ o es menor que eso en un número par. (Cuenta las raíces múltiples según su multiplicidad.)

Determinant (p. 784) The determinant of a square matrix is a real number that can be computed from its elements according to a specific formula.

Determinante (p. 784) El determinante de una matriz cuadrada es un número real que se puede calcular a partir de sus elementos por medio de una fórmula específica.

Example The determinant of $\begin{bmatrix} 3 & -2 \\ 5 & 6 \end{bmatrix}$ is
$3(6) - 5(-2) = 28.$

Difference of cubes (p. 297) A difference of cubes is an expression of the form $a^3 - b^3$. It can be factored as $(a - b)(a^2 + ab + b^2)$.

Diferencia de dos cubos (p. 297) La diferencia de dos cubos es una expresión de la forma $a^3 - b^3$. Se puede factorizar como $(a - b)(a^2 + ab + b^2)$.

Example $x^3 - 27 = (x - 3)(x^2 + 3x + 9)$

Difference of two squares (p. 220) A difference of two squares is an expression of the form $a^2 - b^2$. It can be factored as $(a + b)(a - b)$.

Diferencia de dos cuadrados (p. 220) La diferencia de dos cuadrados es una expresión de la forma $a^2 - b^2$. Se puede factorizar como $(a + b)(a - b)$.

Example $25a^2 - 4 = (5a + 2)(5a - 2)$
$m^6 - 1 = (m^3 + 1)(m^3 - 1)$

Dilation (p. 802) A dilation is a transformation that can change the size of a figure. When the center of the dilation is the origin, you can use scalar multiplication to find the coordinates of the vertices of an image.

Dilatación (p. 802) Una dilatación es una transformación que puede cambiar el tamaño de una figura. Cuando el centro de dilatación está en el origen, se hallan las coordenadas de los vértices de la imagen por medio de la multiplicación de escalar.

Example

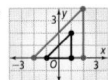

Page 1007

English	Spanish

Direct variation (p. 68) A linear function defined by an equation of the form $y = kx$, where $k \neq 0$, represents direct variation.

Variación directa (p. 68) Una función lineal definida por una ecuación de la forma $y = kx$, donde $k \neq 0$, representa una variación directa.

Example $y = 3.5x, y = 7x, y = -\frac{1}{2}x$

Directrix (p. 622) The directrix of a parabola is the fixed line used to define a parabola. Each point of the parabola is the same distance from the focus and the directrix.

Directriz (p. 622) La directriz de una parábola es la recta fija con que se define una parábola. Cada punto de la parábola está a la misma distancia del foco y de la directriz.

Example

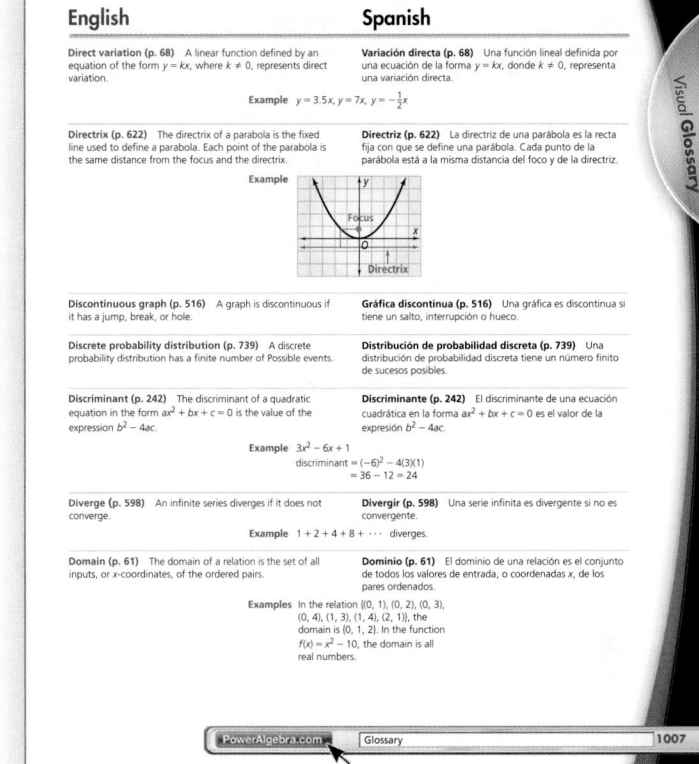

Discontinuous graph (p. 516) A graph is discontinuous if it has a jump, break, or hole.

Gráfica discontinua (p. 516) Una gráfica es discontinua si tiene un salto, interrupción o hueco.

Discrete probability distribution (p. 739) A discrete probability distribution has a finite number of Possible events.

Distribución de probabilidad discreta (p. 739) Una distribución de probabilidad discreta tiene un número finito de sucesos posibles.

Discriminant (p. 242) The discriminant of a quadratic equation in the form $ax^2 + bx + c = 0$ is the value of the expression $b^2 - 4ac$.

Discriminante (p. 242) El discriminante de una ecuación cuadrática en la forma $ax^2 + bx + c = 0$ es el valor de la expresión $b^2 - 4ac$.

Example $3x^2 - 6x + 1$
discriminant is $(-6)^2 - 4(3)(1)$
$= 36 - 12 = 24$

Diverge (p. 598) An infinite series diverges if it does not converge.

Divergir (p. 598) Una serie infinita es divergente si no es convergente.

Example $1 + 2 + 4 + 8 + \cdots$ diverges.

Domain (p. 61) The domain of a relation is the set of all inputs, or x-coordinates, of the ordered pairs.

Dominio (p. 61) El dominio de una relación es el conjunto de todos los valores de entrada, o coordenadas x, de los pares ordenados.

Examples In the relation $\{(0, 1), (0, 2), (0, 3), (0, 4), (1, 3), (1, 4), (2, 1)\}$, the domain is $\{0, 1, 2\}$. In the function $f(x) = x^2 - 10$, the domain is all real numbers.

Page 1008

English	Spanish

Dot product (p. 812) Given vectors $\mathbf{v} = \langle v_1, v_2 \rangle$ and $\mathbf{w} = \langle w_1, w_2 \rangle$, the dot product $\mathbf{v} \cdot \mathbf{w}$ is the quantity $v_1w_1 + v_2w_2$.

Producto escalar (p. 812) Dados los vectores $\mathbf{v} = \langle v_1, v_2 \rangle$ y $\mathbf{w} = \langle w_1, w_2 \rangle$, el producto escalar $\mathbf{v} \cdot \mathbf{w}$ es la suma $v_1w_1 + v_2w_2$.

E

Ellipse (p. 638) An ellipse is the set of points P in a plane such that the sum of the distances from P to two fixed points $F1$ and $F2$ is a given constant k. The standard form of the equation of an ellipse with its center at the origin is $\frac{x^2}{a^2} + \frac{y^2}{b^2} = 1$ if the major axis is horizontal and $\frac{x^2}{b^2} + \frac{y^2}{a^2} = 1$ if the major axis is vertical, where $a > b$.

Elipse (p. 638) Una elipse es el conjunto de puntos P situados en un plano tal que la suma de las distancias entre P y dos puntos fijos F_1 y F_2 sea una constante dada k. La forma normal de la ecuación de una elipse con su centro en el origen es $\frac{x^2}{a^2} + \frac{y^2}{b^2} = 1$ si el eje mayor es horizontal y $\frac{x^2}{b^2} + \frac{y^2}{a^2} = 1$ si el eje mayor es vertical, donde $a > b$.

Example

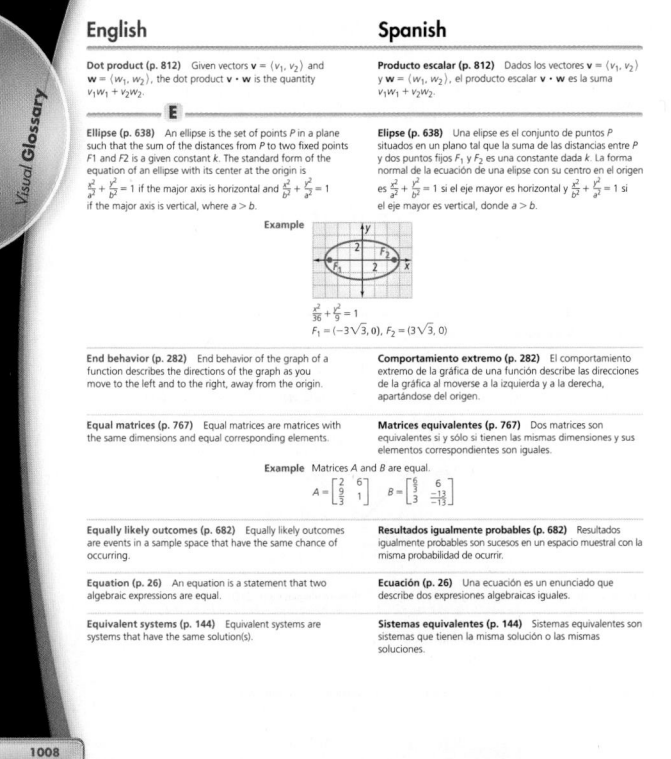

$\frac{x^2}{36} + \frac{y^2}{9} = 1$
$F_1 = (-3\sqrt{3}, 0), F_2 = (3\sqrt{3}, 0)$

End behavior (p. 282) End behavior of the graph of a function describes the directions of the graph as you move to the left and to the right, away from the origin.

Comportamiento extremo (p. 282) El comportamiento extremo de la gráfica de una función describe las direcciones de la gráfica al moverse a la izquierda y a la derecha, apartándose del origen.

Equal matrices (p. 767) Equal matrices have the same dimensions and equal corresponding elements.

Matrices equivalentes (p. 767) Dos matrices son equivalentes si y sólo si tienen las mismas dimensiones y sus elementos correspondientes son iguales.

Example Matrices A and B are equal.
$A = \begin{bmatrix} 2 & 6 \\ \frac{9}{3} & 1 \end{bmatrix}$ $B = \begin{bmatrix} \frac{4}{2} & 6 \\ 3 & \frac{-13}{-13} \end{bmatrix}$

Equally likely outcomes (p. 682) Equally likely outcomes are events in a sample space that have the same chance of occurring.

Resultados igualmente probables (p. 682) Resultados igualmente probables son sucesos en un espacio muestral con la misma probabilidad de ocurrir.

Equation (p. 26) An equation is a statement that two algebraic expressions are equal.

Ecuación (p. 26) Una ecuación es un enunciado que describe dos expresiones algebraicas iguales.

Equivalent systems (p. 144) Equivalent systems are systems that have the same solution(s).

Sistemas equivalentes (p. 144) Sistemas equivalentes son sistemas que tienen la misma solución o las mismas soluciones.

Page 1009

English	Spanish

Evaluate (p. 19) To evaluate an algebraic expression, substitute a number for each variable in the expression. Then simplify using the order of operations.

Evaluar (p. 19) Para evaluar una expresión algebraica, sustituye cada variable de la expresión con un número. Luego, simplifica usando el orden de operaciones.

Example When $x = 2$ and $y = -1$,
$2x + 3y$ evaluates to 1.

Expand (p. 326) To expand the power of a binomial, multiply as needed, then write the polynomial in standard form.

Expandir (p. 326) Para expandir la potencia de un binomio, multiplica como sea necesario. Luego, escribe el polinomio en forma normal.

Example $(x + 4)^3 = (x + 4)(x + 4)^2$
$= (x + 4)(x^2 + 8x + 16)$
$= x^3 + 8x^2 + 16x + 4x^2 + 32x + 64$
$= x^3 + 12x^2 + 48x + 64$

Experimental probability (p. 681) The experimental probability of an event is the ratio $\frac{number\ of\ times\ the\ event\ occurs}{number\ of\ trials}$

Probabilidad experimental (p. 681) La probabilidad experimental de un suceso es la razón $\frac{number\ of\ times\ the\ event\ occurs}{number\ of\ trials}$

Example Suppose a basketball player has scored 19 times in 28 attempts at a basket. The experimental probability of the player's scoring is $P(\text{score}) = \frac{19}{28} \approx 0.68$, or 68%.

Explicit formula (p. 565) An explicit formula expresses the nth term of a sequence in terms of n.

Fórmula explícita (p. 565) Una fórmula explícita expresa el n-ésimo término de una progresión en función de n.

Example Let $a_n = 2n + 5$ for positive integers n. If $n = 7$, then
$a_7 = 2(7) + 5 = 19.$

Exponential decay (p. 435) Exponential decay is modeled by a function of the form $y = ab^x$ with $0 < b < 1$.

Decaimiento exponencial (p. 435) El decaimiento exponencial se expresa con una función $y = ab^x$ donde $0 < b < 1$.

Exponential equation (p. 469) An exponential equation contains the form b^{cx}, with the exponent including a variable.

Ecuación exponencial (p. 469) Una ecuación exponencial tiene la forma b^{cx}, y su exponente incluye una variable.

Example $5^{2x} = 270$
$\log 5^{2x} = \log 270$
$2x \log 5 = \log 270$
$2x = \frac{\log 270}{\log 5}$
$2x \approx 3.4785$
$x \approx 1.7392$

Visual Glossary

English | Spanish

Exponential function (p. 434) The general form of an exponential function is $y = ab^x$, where x is a real number, $a \neq 0$, $b > 0$, and $b \neq 1$. When $b > 1$, the function models exponential growth with growth factor b. When $0 < b < 1$, the function models exponential decay with decay factor b.

Función exponencial (p. 434) La forma general de una función exponencial es $y = ab^x$, donde x es un número real, $a \neq 0$, $b > 0$ y $b \neq 1$. Cuando $b > 1$, la función representa un incremento exponencial con factor de incremento b. Cuando $0 < b < 1$, la función representa el decremento exponencial con factor de decremento b.

Example

Exponential growth (p. 435) Exponential growth is modeled by a function of the form $y = ab^x$ with $b > 1$.

Crecimiento exponencial (p. 435) El crecimiento exponencial se expresa con una función de la forma $y = ab^x$ donde $b > 1$.

Extraneous solution (p. 42) An extraneous solution is a solution of an equation derived from an original equation but it is not a solution of the original equation.

Solución extraña (p. 42) Una solución extraña es una solución de una ecuación derivada de una ecuación dada, pero que no satisface la ecuación dada.

Example $\sqrt{x-3} = x - 5$
$x - 3 = x^2 - 10x + 25$
$0 = x^2 - 11x + 28$
$0 = (x - 4)(x - 7)$
$x = 4$ or 7
The number 7 is a solution, but 4 is not, since $\sqrt{4 - 3} \neq 4 - 5$.

F

Factor Theorem (p. 289) The expression $x - a$ is a linear factor of a polynomial if and only if the value of a is a root of the related polynomial function.

Teorema de factores (p. 289) La expresión $x - a$ es un factor lineal de un polinomio si y sólo si el valor de a es una raíz de la función polinomial con la que se relaciona.

Example The value 2 makes the polynomial $x^2 + 2x - 8$ equal to zero. So, $x - 2$ is a factor of $x^2 + 2x - 8$.

Factoring (p. 216) Factoring is rewriting an expression as the product of its factors.

Descomposición factorial (p. 216) Descomponer en factores es el proceso de escribir de nuevo una expresión como el producto de sus factores.

Example expanded form $x^2 + x - 56$
factored form $(x + 8)(x - 7)$

Feasible region (p. 157) In a linear programming problem, the feasible region contains all the values that satisfy the constraints on the objective function.

Región factible (p. 157) En un problema de programación lineal, la región factible contiene todos los valores que satisfacen las restricciones de la función objetiva.

English | Spanish

Finite Series (p. 587) A finite series is a series with a finite number of terms.

Serie finita (p. 587) Una serie finita es una serie con un número finito de términos.

Focal length (p. 622) The focal length of a parabola is the distance between the vertex and the focus.

Distancia focal (p. 622) La distancia focal de una parábola es la distancia entre el vértice y el foco.

Focus (plural: foci) of a hyperbola (p. 645) A hyperbola is the set of all points P in a plane such that the difference of the distances from P to two fixed points is constant. Each of the fixed points is a focus of the hyperbola.

Foco de una hipérbola (p. 645) Una hipérbola es el conjunto de puntos P en un plano tal que la diferencia de las distancias desde P hasta dos puntos fijos es constante. Cada uno de los puntos fijos es el foco de la hipérbola.

Focus (plural: foci) of a parabola (p. 622) A parabola is the set of all points in a plane that are the same distance from a fixed line and a fixed point not on the line. The fixed point is the focus of the parabola.

Foco de una parábola (p. 622) Una parábola es el conjunto de todos los puntos en un plano con la misma distancia desde una línea fija y un punto fijo que no permanece en la línea. El punto fijo es el foco de la parábola.

Focus (plural: foci) of an ellipse (p. 638) An ellipse is the set of all points P in a plane such that the sum of the distances from P to two fixed points is constant. Each of the fixed points is a focus of the ellipse.

Foco de una elipse (p. 638) Una elipse es el conjunto de todos los puntos P en un plano en el cual la suma de las distancias desde P hasta dos puntos fijos es constante. Cada uno de estos puntos fijos es un foco de la elipsis.

Frequency table (p. 694) A frequency table is a list of the outcomes in a sample space and the number of times each outcome occurs.

Tabla de frecuencias (p. 694) Una tabla de frecuencias es una lista de los resultados de un espacio muestral y el número de veces que cada resultado ocurre.

Function (p. 62) A function is a relation in which each element of the domain corresponds with exactly one element in the range.

Función (p. 62) Una función es una relación en la que cada elemento del dominio corresponde exactamente con un elemento del rango.

Example The relation $y = 3x^3 - 2x + 3$ is a function. $f(x) = 3x^3 - 2x + 3$ is the same relation written in function notation.

Function notation (p. 63) If f is the name of a function, the function notation $f(x)$ shows the function name f and also represents the range value $f(x)$ for the domain value x. You read the function notation $f(x)$ as "f of x" or "a function of x." Note that $f(x)$ does not mean "f times x."

Notación de una función (p. 63) Si f es el nombre de una función, la notación de la función $f(x)$ indica el nombre de la función y también representa el valor del rango $f(x)$ para el valor del dominio x. La función de la notación $f(x)$ se lee "f de x" o "una función de x." Observa que $f(x)$ no significa "f por x."

Example When the value of x is 3, $f(3)$, read "f of 3," represents the value of the function at 3.

Function rule (p. 63) A function rule represents an output value in terms of an input value.

Regla de función (p. 63) Una regla de función representa un valor de salida en función de un valor de entrada.

Fundamental Counting Principle (p. 674) The Fundamental Counting Principle is a tool that you can use to quickly count the number of ways certain things can happen.

Principio básico de conteo (p. 674) El principio básico de conteo es una herramienta que se puede utilizar para hacer un conteo rápido del número de formas en que pueden ocurrir ciertas cosas.

English | Spanish

Fundamental Theorem of Algebra (p. 320) If $P(x)$ is a polynomial of degree $n \geq 1$ with complex coefficients, then $P(x) = 0$ has at least one complex root.

Teorema fundamental de álgebra (p. 320) Si $P(x)$ es un polinomio de grado $n \geq 1$ con coeficientes complejos, entonces $P(x) = 0$ tiene por lo menos una raíz compleja.

Example $P(x) = 3x^3 - 2x + 3$ is of degree 3, so $P(x) = 0$ has at least one complex root.

G

Geometric mean (p. 583) The geometric mean of any two positive numbers is the positive square root of the product of the two numbers.

Media geométrica (p. 583) La media geométrica de dos números positivos es la raíz cuadrada positiva del producto de los dos números.

Example The geometric mean of 12 and 18 is $\sqrt{12 \cdot 18} \approx 14.6969$.

Geometric sequence (p. 580) A geometric sequence is a sequence with a constant ratio between consecutive terms.

Secuencia geométrica (p. 580) Una secuencia geométrica es una secuencia con una razón constante entre términos consecutivos.

Example The geometric sequence 2.5, 5, 10, 20, 40 . . . , has a common ratio of 2.

Geometric series (p. 595) A geometric series is the sum of the terms in a geometric sequence.

Serie geométrica (p. 595) Una serie geométrica es la suma de términos en una progresión geométrica.

Example One geometric series with five terms is $2.5 + 5 + 10 + 20 + 40$.

Greatest common factor (p. 218) The greatest common factor (GCF) of an expression is the common factor of each term of the expression that has the greatest coefficient and the greatest exponent.

Máximo factor común (p. 218) El máximo factor común de una expresión es el factor común de cada término de la expresión que tiene el mayor coeficiente y el mayor exponente.

Example The GCF of $4x^2 + 20x - 12$ is 4.

Greatest integer function (p. 90) The greatest integer function corresponds each input x to the greatest integer less than or equal to x.

Función del entero mayor (p. 90) La función del entero mayor relaciona cada entrada x con el entero mayor que es menor o igual a x.

Growth factor (p. 436) In an exponential function of the form $y = ab^x$, b is the growth factor if $b > 1$.

Factor de incremento (p. 436) En una función exponencial de la forma $y = ab^x$, b es el factor de incremento si $b > 1$.

Example In the exponential equation $y = 2^x$, 2 is the growth factor.

H

Half-plane (p. 114) A half-plane is the set of points in a coordinate plane that are on one side of the boundary of the graph of a linear inequality.

Semiplano (p. 114) Un semiplano es el conjunto de puntos de un plano de coordenadas que están a un lado del límite de la gráfica de desigualdad lineal.

English | Spanish

Hyperbola (p. 645) A hyperbola is a set of points P in a plane such that the difference between the distances from P to the foci F_1 and F_2 is a given constant k. $|PF_1 - PF_2| = k$. The standard form of an equation of a hyperbola centered at $(0, 0)$ is $\frac{x^2}{a^2} - \frac{y^2}{b^2} = 1$ if the transverse axis is horizontal and $\frac{y^2}{a^2} - \frac{x^2}{b^2} = 1$ if the transverse axis is vertical.

Hipérbola (p. 645) Una hipérbola es un conjunto de puntos P en un plano tal que la diferencia entre las distancias de P a los focos F_1 y F_2 es una constante k dada. $|PF_1 - PF_2| = k$. La forma normal de la ecuación de una hipérbola centrada en $(0, 0)$ es $\frac{x^2}{a^2} - \frac{y^2}{b^2} = 1$, si el eje transversal es horizontal, y $\frac{y^2}{a^2} - \frac{x^2}{b^2} = 1$, si el eje transversal es vertical.

Example

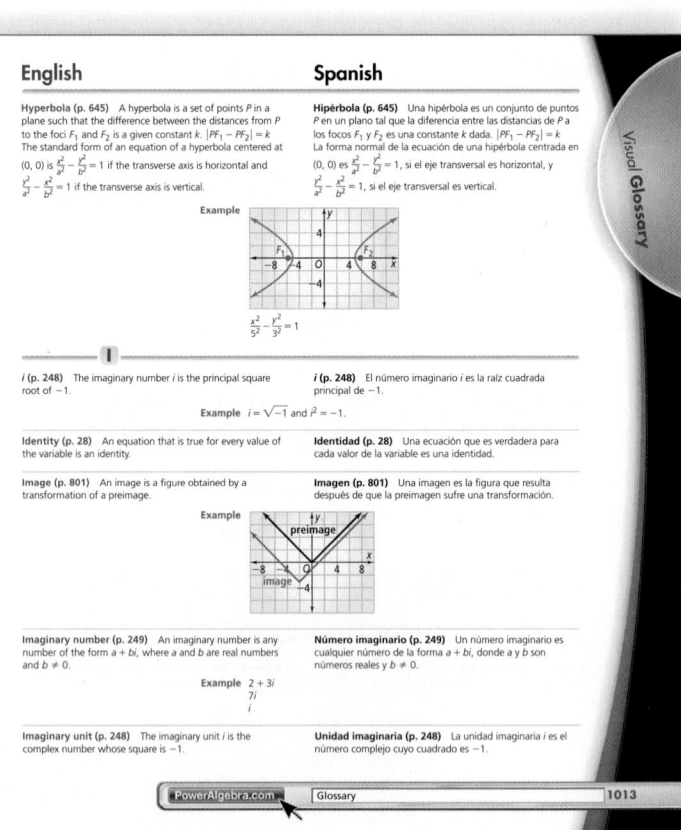

$$\frac{x^2}{5^2} - \frac{y^2}{3^2} = 1$$

I

i (p. 248) The imaginary number i is the principal square root of -1.

i (p. 248) El número imaginario i es la raíz cuadrada principal de -1.

Example $i = \sqrt{-1}$ and $i^2 = -1$.

Identity (p. 28) An equation that is true for every value of the variable is an identity.

Identidad (p. 28) Una ecuación que es verdadera para cada valor de la variable es una identidad.

Image (p. 801) An image is a figure obtained by a transformation of a preimage.

Imagen (p. 801) Una imagen es la figura que resulta después de que la preimagen sufre una transformación.

Example

Imaginary number (p. 249) An imaginary number is any number of the form $a + bi$, where a and b are real numbers and $b \neq 0$.

Número imaginario (p. 249) Un número imaginario es cualquier número de la forma $a + bi$, donde a y b son números reales y $b \neq 0$.

Example $2 + 3i$
$7i$
i

Imaginary unit (p. 248) The imaginary unit i is the complex number whose square is -1.

Unidad imaginaria (p. 248) La unidad imaginaria i es el número complejo cuyo cuadrado es -1.

English — Spanish

Inconsistent system (p. 137) A system of equations that has no solution is an inconsistent system.

Sistema incompatible (p. 137) Un sistema incompatible es un sistema de ecuaciones para el cual no hay solución.

Example $\begin{cases} y = 2x + 3 \\ -2x + y = 1 \end{cases}$ is a system of parallel lines, so it has no solution. It is an inconsistent system.

Independent events (p. 688) When the outcome of one event does not affect the probability of a second event, the two events are independent.

Sucesos independientes (p. 688) Cuando el resultado de un suceso no altera la probabilidad de otro, los dos sucesos son independientes.

Example The results of two rolls of a number cube are independent. Getting a 5 on the first roll does not change the probability of getting a 5 on the second roll.

Independent system (p. 137) A system of linear equations that has a unique solution is an independent system.

Sistema independiente (p. 137) Un sistema de ecuaciones lineales que tenga una sola solución es un sistema independiente.

Example $\begin{cases} x + 2y = -7 \\ 2x - 3y = 0 \end{cases}$ has the unique solution $(-3, -2)$. It is an independent system.

Independent variable (p. 63) If a function is defined by an equation using the variables x and y, where x represents input values, then x is the independent variable.

Variable independiente (p. 63) Si una función es definida por una ecuación con las variables x e y, donde x representa los valores de entrada, entonces x es la variable independiente.

Example $y = 2x + 1$
x is the independent variable.

Index (p. 362) With a radical sign, the index indicates the degree of the root.

Índice (p. 362) Con un signo de radical, el índice indica el grado de la raíz.

Example index 2 $\quad$ index 3 $\quad$ index 4
$\sqrt{16} \quad \sqrt[3]{16} \quad \sqrt[4]{16}$

Infinite series (p. 587) An infinite series is a series with infinitely many terms.

Serie infinita (p. 587) Una serie infinita es una serie con un número infinito de términos.

Initial point (p. 809) The initial point of a vector is the endpoint (not the tip) of a vector arrow.

Punto de inicio (p. 809) El punto de inicio de un vector es el extremo (no la punta) de una flecha vectorial.

English — Spanish

Initial side (p. 836) When an angle is in standard position, the initial side of the angle is given to be on the positive x-axis. The other ray is the terminal side of the angle.

Lado inicial (p. 836) Cuando un ángulo está en posición normal, el lado inicial del ángulo se ubica en el eje positivo de las x. El otro rayo, o semirrecta, forma el lado terminal del ángulo.

Example

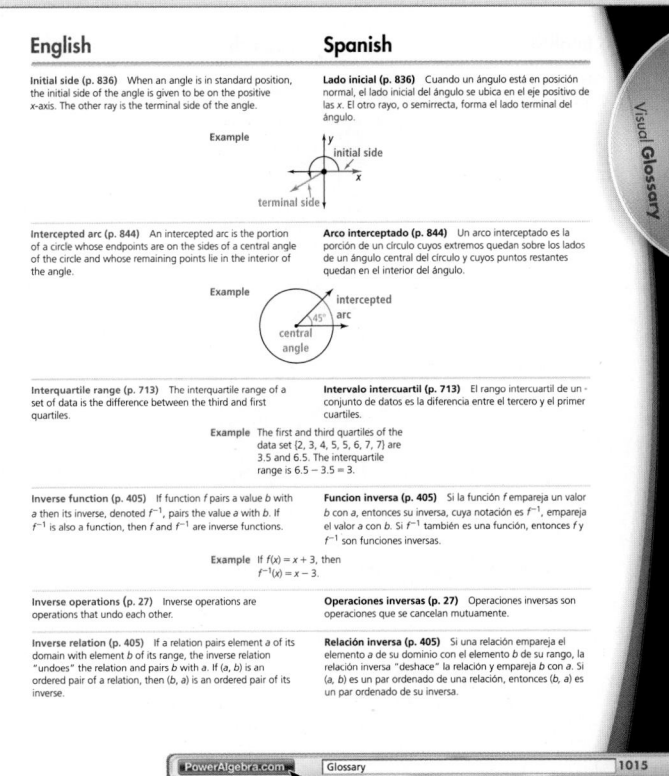

Intercepted arc (p. 844) An intercepted arc is the portion of a circle whose endpoints are on the sides of a central angle of the circle and whose remaining points lie in the interior of the angle.

Arco interceptado (p. 844) Un arco interceptado es la porción de un círculo cuyos extremos quedan sobre los lados de un ángulo central del círculo y cuyos puntos restantes quedan en el interior del ángulo.

Example

Interquartile range (p. 713) The interquartile range of a set of data is the difference between the third and first quartiles.

Intervalo intercuartil (p. 713) El rango intercuartil de un conjunto de datos es la diferencia entre el tercero y el primer cuartiles.

Example The first and third quartiles of the data set $\{2, 3, 4, 5, 5, 6, 7, 7\}$ are 3.5 and 6.5. The interquartile range is $6.5 - 3.5 = 3$.

Inverse function (p. 405) If function f pairs a value b with a then its inverse, denoted f^{-1}, pairs the value a with b. If f^{-1} is also a function, then f and f^{-1} are inverse functions.

Función inversa (p. 405) Si la función f empareja un valor b con a, entonces su inversa, cuya notación es f^{-1}, empareja el valor a con b. Si f^{-1} también es una función, entonces f y f^{-1} son funciones inversas.

Example If $f(x) = x + 3$, then $f^{-1}(x) = x - 3$.

Inverse operations (p. 27) Inverse operations are operations that undo each other.

Operaciones inversas (p. 27) Operaciones inversas son operaciones que se cancelan mutuamente.

Inverse relation (p. 405) If a relation pairs element a of its domain with element b of its range, the inverse relation "undoes" the relation and pairs b with a. If (a, b) is an ordered pair of a relation, then (b, a) is an ordered pair of its inverse.

Relación inversa (p. 405) Si una relación empareja el elemento a de su dominio con el elemento b de su rango, la relación inversa "deshace" la relación y empareja b con a. Si (a, b) es un par ordenado de una relación, entonces (b, a) es un par ordenado de su inversa.

English — Spanish

Inverse variation (p. 498) An inverse variation is a relation represented by an equation of the form $xy = k$, $y = \frac{k}{x}$, or $x = \frac{k}{y}$, where $k \neq 0$.

Variación inversa (p. 498) Una variación inversa es una relación representada por la ecuación $xy = k$, $y = \frac{k}{x}$, ó $x = \frac{k}{y}$, donde $k \neq 0$.

Example

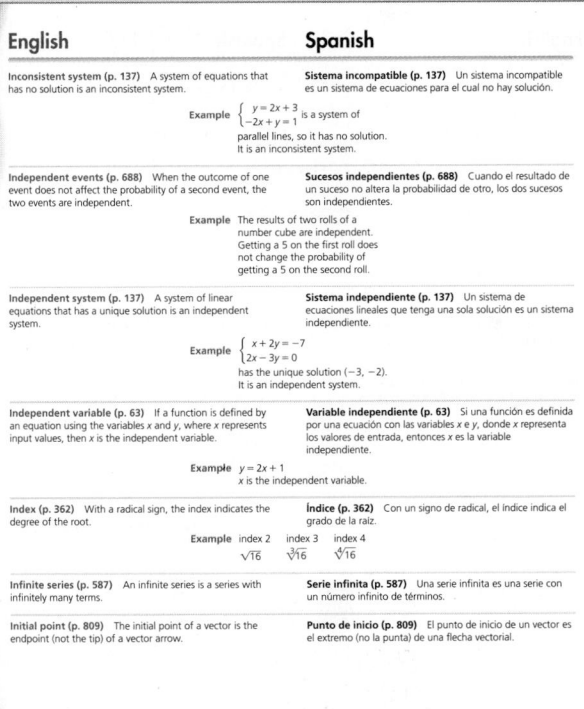

$xy = 5$, or $y = \frac{5}{x}$

J

Joint variation (p. 501) A joint variation is a relation in which one variable varies directly with respect to each of two or more variables.

Variación conjunta (p. 501) Una variación conjunta es una relación en la cual el valor de una variable varía directamente con respecto a cada una de dos o más variables.

Example $z = 8xy$
$T = kPV$

L

Law of Cosines (p. 936) In $\triangle ABC$, let a, b, and c represent the lengths of the sides opposite $\angle A$, $\angle B$, and $\angle C$, respectively. Then
$a^2 = b^2 + c^2 - 2bc \cos A$,
$b^2 = a^2 + c^2 - 2ac \cos B$, and
$c^2 = a^2 + b^2 - 2ab \cos C$

Ley de cosenos (p. 936) En $\triangle ABC$, sean a, b y las longitudes de los lados opuestos a $\angle A$, $\angle B$ y $\angle C$, respectivamente. Entonces
$a^2 = b^2 + c^2 - 2bc \cos A$,
$b^2 = a^2 + c^2 - 2ac \cos B$ y
$c^2 = a^2 + b^2 - 2ab \cos C$

Example

$LM^2 = 11.41^2 + 8.72^2 - 2(11.42)(8.72) \cos 18°$
$LM^2 = 16.9754$
$LM = 4.12$

Law of Sines (p. 929) In $\triangle ABC$, let a, b, and c represent the lengths of the sides opposite $\angle A$, $\angle B$, and $\angle C$, respectively. Then $\frac{\sin A}{a} = \frac{\sin B}{b} = \frac{\sin C}{c}$.

Ley de senos (p. 929) En $\triangle ABC$, sean a, b y c las longitudes de los lados opuestos a $\angle A$, $\angle B$ y $\angle C$, respectivamente. Entonces $\frac{\text{sen } A}{a} = \frac{\text{sen } B}{b} = \frac{\text{sen } C}{c}$.

Example

$m\angle L = 180 - (120 + 18) = 42°$
$\frac{KL}{\sin 120°} = \frac{872}{\sin 42°}$
$KL = \frac{872 \sin 120°}{\sin 42°}$
$KL = 11.26$

English — Spanish

Like radicals (p. 374) Like radicals are radical expressions that have the same index and the same radicand.

Radicales semejantes (p. 374) Los radicales semejantes son expresiones radicales que tienen el mismo índice y el mismo radicando.

Example $4\sqrt[7]{7}$ and $\sqrt[7]{7}$ are like radicals.

Like terms (p. 21) Like terms have the same variables raised to the same powers.

Términos semejantes (p. 21) Los términos semejantes tienen las mismas variables elevadas a las mismas potencias.

Limits (p. 589) Limits in summation notation are the least and greatest integer values of the index n.

Límites (p. 589) Los límites en notación de sumatoria son el menor y el mayor valor del índice n en números enteros.

Example $\text{limits } \displaystyle\sum_{n=1}^{3} (3n + 5)$

Line of best fit (p. 94) The trend line that gives the most accurate model of related data is the line of best fit.

Recta de mayor aproximación (p. 94) La línea de tendencia que representa con mayor precisión los datos relacionados es la recta de mayor aproximación.

Linear equation (p. 75) A linear equation in two variables is an equation that can be written in the form $ax + by = c$. See also **Standard form of a linear equation.**

Ecuación lineal (p. 75) Una ecuación lineal de dos variables es una ecuación que se puede escribir de la forma $ax + by = c$. Ver también **Standard form of a linear equation.**

Example $y = 2x + 1$ can be written as $-2x + y = 1$.

Linear function (p. 75) A function whose graph is a line is a linear function. You can represent a linear function with a linear equation.

Función lineal (p. 75) Una función cuya gráfica es una recta es una función lineal. La función lineal se representa con una ecuación lineal.

Example

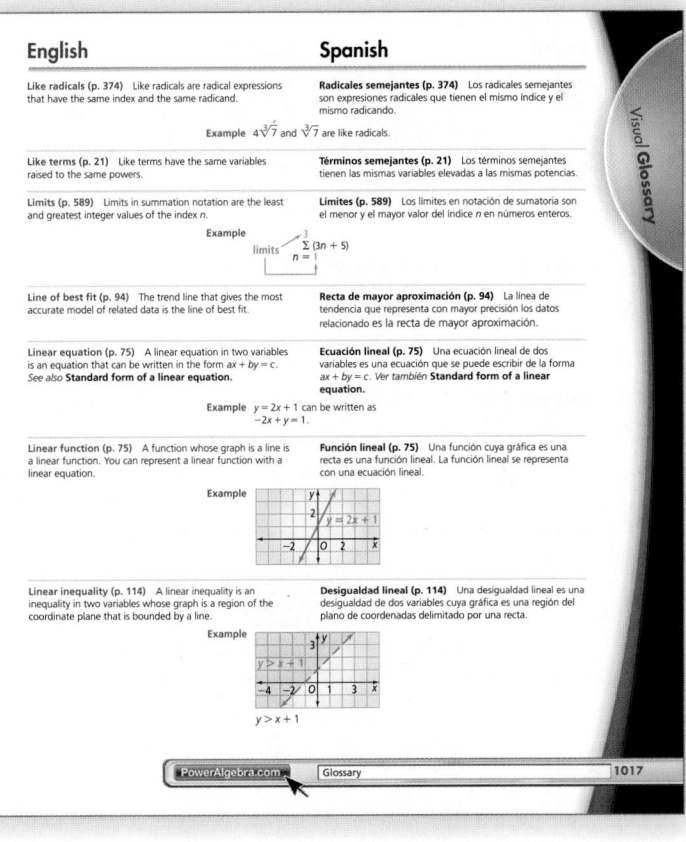

$y = 2x + 1$

Linear inequality (p. 114) A linear inequality is an inequality in two variables whose graph is a region of the coordinate plane that is bounded by a line.

Desigualdad lineal (p. 114) Una desigualdad lineal es una desigualdad de dos variables cuya gráfica es una región del plano de coordenadas delimitado por una recta.

Example

$y > x + 1$

English / Spanish

Linear programming (p. 157) Linear programming is a method for finding a minimum or maximum value of some quantity, given a set of constraints.

Programación lineal (p. 157) Programación lineal es un método para hallar el valor mínimo o máximo de una cantidad que se expresa como un conjunto de limitaciones.

Example   Restrictions $x \geq 0$, $y \geq 0$, $x + y \leq 7$, and $y \leq -2x + 8$
Objective function: $B = 2x + 4y$.
Evaluate $B = 2x + 4y$ at each vertex.
The minimum value of B occurs when $x = 0$ and $y = 0$. The maximum value of B occurs when $x = 0$ and $y = 7$.

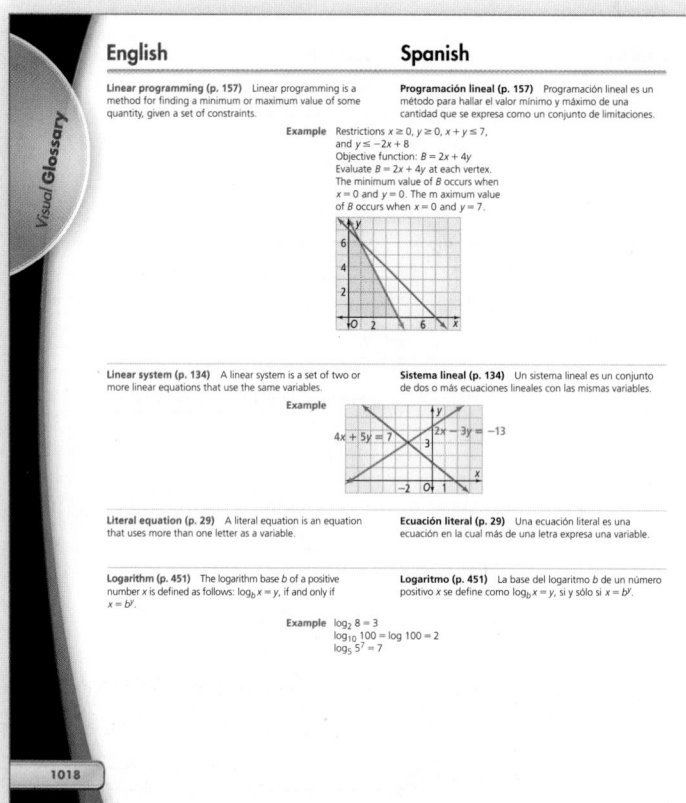

Linear system (p. 134) A linear system is a set of two or more linear equations that use the same variables.

Sistema lineal (p. 134) Un sistema lineal es un conjunto de dos o más ecuaciones lineales con las mismas variables.

Example

Literal equation (p. 29) A literal equation is an equation that uses more than one letter as a variable.

Ecuación literal (p. 29) Una ecuación literal es una ecuación en la cual más de una letra expresa una variable.

Logarithm (p. 451) The logarithm base b of a positive number x is defined as follows: $\log_b x = y$, if and only if $x = b^y$.

Logaritmo (p. 451) La base del logaritmo base b de un número positivo x se define como $\log_b x = y$, si y sólo si $x = b^y$.

Example $\log_2 8 = 3$
$\log_{10} 100 = \log 100 = 2$
$\log_5 5^7 = 7$

Logarithmic equation (p. 471) A logarithmic equation is an equation that includes a logarithm involving a variable.

Ecuación logarítmica (p. 471) Una ecuación logarítmica es una ecuación que incluye un logaritmo con una variable.

Example $\log_3 x = 4$

Logarithmic function (p. 454) A logarithmic function is the inverse of an exponential function.

Función logarítmica (p. 454) Una función logarítmica es la inversa de una función exponencial.

Example

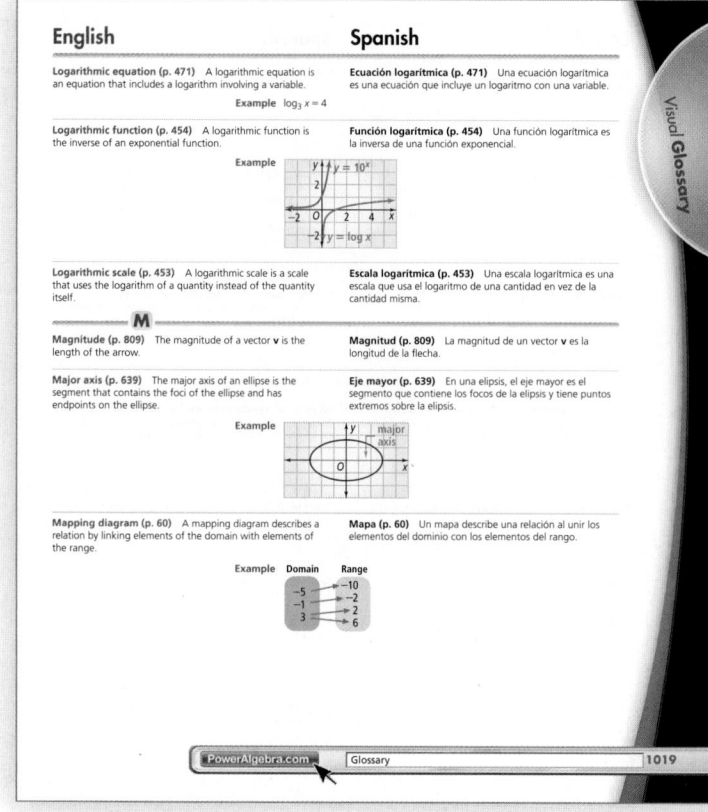

Logarithmic scale (p. 453) A logarithmic scale is a scale that uses the logarithm of a quantity instead of the quantity itself.

Escala logarítmica (p. 453) Una escala logarítmica es una escala que usa el logaritmo de una cantidad en vez de la cantidad misma.

M

Magnitude (p. 809) The magnitude of a vector **v** is the length of the arrow.

Magnitud (p. 809) La magnitud de un vector **v** es la longitud de la flecha.

Major axis (p. 639) The major axis of an ellipse is the segment that contains the foci of the ellipse and has endpoints on the ellipse.

Eje mayor (p. 639) En una elipsis, el eje mayor es el segmento que contiene los focos de la elipsis y tiene puntos extremos sobre la elipsis.

Example

Mapping diagram (p. 60) A mapping diagram describes a relation by linking elements of the domain with elements of the range.

Mapa (p. 60) Un mapa describe una relación al unir los elementos del dominio con los elementos del rango.

Example   Domain   Range

Margin of error (p. 746) The distance from the sample mean or sample proportion that is used to create a confidence interval for the population mean or the population proportion. For a 95% confidence level, $ME = 1.96 \cdot \frac{s}{\sqrt{n}}$, where ME is the margin of error, s is the standard deviation of the sample data, and n is the number of values in the sample.

Margen de error (p. 746) La distancia desde la media de una muestra o desde la proporción de una muestra que se usa para crear el intervalo de confianza para la media o proporción de una población. Para un nivel de confianza de 95%, $ME = 1.96 \cdot \frac{s}{\sqrt{n}}$, siendo ME el margen de error, s la desviación estándar de los datos de la muestra, y n el número de valores en la muestra.

Example   The standard deviation of a sample is 5.0 and the number of trials is 30. The margin of error at a 95% confidence level is $ME = 1.96 \cdot \frac{5.0}{\sqrt{30}} \approx 1.79$.

Matrix (p. 174) A matrix is a rectangular array of numbers written within brackets.

Matriz (p. 174) Una matriz es un conjunto de números encerrados en corchetes y dispuestos en forma de rectángulo.

Example $A = \begin{bmatrix} 1 & -2 & 0 & 10 \\ 9 & 7 & -3 & 8 \\ 2 & -10 & 1 & -6 \end{bmatrix}$

The number 2 is the element in the third row and first column. A is a 3×4 matrix.

Matrix element (p. 174) Every item listed in a matrix is an element of the matrix. An element is identified by its position in the matrix.

Elemento matricial (p. 174) Cada cifra de una matriz es un elemento de la matriz. El elemento se identifica según la posición que ocupa en la matriz.

Example $A = \begin{bmatrix} 1 & -2 & 0 & 10 \\ 9 & 7 & -3 & 8 \\ 2 & -10 & 1 & -6 \end{bmatrix}$

Element a_{21} is 9, the element in the second row and first column.

Matrix equation (p. 765) A matrix equation is an equation in which the variable is a matrix.

Ecuación matricial (p. 765) Una ecuación matricial es una ecuación en que la variable es una matriz.

Example   Solve $X + \begin{bmatrix} 3 & -2 \\ 5 & 1 \end{bmatrix} = \begin{bmatrix} 4 & 0 \\ 0 & 3 \end{bmatrix}$
$X = \begin{bmatrix} 4 & 0 \\ 0 & 3 \end{bmatrix} - \begin{bmatrix} 3 & -2 \\ 5 & 1 \end{bmatrix} = \begin{bmatrix} 1 & 2 \\ -5 & 2 \end{bmatrix}$

Maximum value (p. 195) The maximum value of a function $y = f(x)$ is the greatest y-value of the function. It is the y-coordinate of the highest point on the graph of f.

Valor máximo (p. 195) El valor máximo de una función $y = f(x)$ es el valor más alto de y de la función. Es la coordenada y del punto más alto de la gráfica de f.

Mean (p. 711) The sum of the data values divided by the number of data values is the mean. *See also* **Arithmetic mean.**

Media (p. 711) La suma de los valores de datos dividida por el número de valores de datos sumados es la media. *Ver también* **Arithmetic mean.**

Example $\{1, 2, 3, 3, 6, 6\}$
mean $= \dfrac{1 + 2 + 3 + 3 + 6 + 6}{6}$
$= \dfrac{21}{6} = 3.5$

Measures of central tendency (p. 711) The mean, the median, and the mode are each central values that help describe a set of data. They are called measures of central tendency.

Medidas de tendencia central (p. 711) La media, la mediana y la moda son los valores centrales que facilitan la descripción de un conjunto de datos. A estos valores se les llama medidas de tendencia central.

Example $\{1, 2, 3, 3, 4, 5, 6, 6\}$
mean $= 3.75$
median $= 3.5$
modes $= 3$ and 6

Measure of variation (p. 719) Measures of variation, such as the range, the interquartile range, and the standard deviation, describe how the data in a data set are spread out.

Medida de dispersión (p. 719) Las medidas de dispersión, tal como el rango, el intervalo intercuartil y la desviación típica, describen cómo se dispersan los datos en un conjunto de datos.

Median (p. 711) The median is the middle value in a data set. If the data set contains an even number of values, the median is the mean of the two middle values.

Mediana (p. 711) La mediana es el valor situado en el medio en un conjunto de datos. Si el conjunto de datos contiene un número par de valores, la mediana es la media de los dos valores del medio.

Example $\{1, 2, 3, 3, 4, 5, 6, 6\}$
median $= \dfrac{3 + 4}{2} = \dfrac{7}{2} = 3.5$

Midline (p. 830) The horizontal line through the average of the maximum and minimum values.

Línea media (p. 830) Recta horizontal que pasa a través de la media de los valores máximos y mínimos.

Example

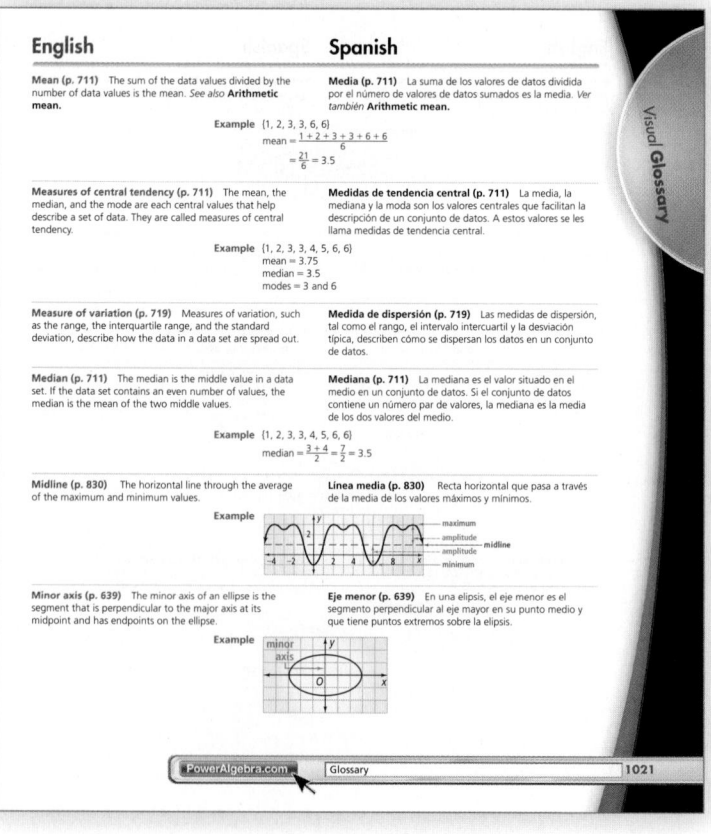

Minor axis (p. 639) The minor axis of an ellipse is the segment that is perpendicular to the major axis at its midpoint and has endpoints on the ellipse.

Eje menor (p. 639) En una elipsis, el eje menor es el segmento perpendicular al eje mayor en su punto medio y que tiene puntos extremos sobre la elipsis.

Example

English | Spanish

Minimum value (p. 195) The minimum value of a function $y = f(x)$ is the least y-value of the function. It is the y-coordinate of the lowest point on the graph of f.

Valor mínimo (p. 195) El valor mínimo de una función $y = f(x)$ es el valor más bajo de y de la función. Es la coordenada y del punto más bajo de la gráfica de f.

Mode (p. 711) The mode is the most frequently occurring value (or values) in a set of data.

Moda (p. 711) La moda es el valor o valores que ocurren con mayor frecuencia en un conjunto de datos.

Example {1, 2, 3, 3, 4, 5, 6, 6}
The modes are 3 and 6.

Monomial (p. 280) A monomial is either a real number, a variable, or a product of real numbers and variables with whole number exponents.

Monomio (p. 280) Un monomio es un número real, una variable o un producto de números reales y variables cuyos exponentes son números enteros.

Example 1, x, $2z$, $4ab^2$

Multiple zero (p. 291) If a linear factor is repeated in the complete factored form of a polynomial, the zero related to that factor is a multiple zero.

Cero múltiplo (p. 291) Si un factor lineal se repite en la forma factorizada completa de un polinomio, el cero relacionado con ese factor es un cero múltiplo.

Example The zeros of the function
$P(x) = 2x(x - 3)^2(x + 1)$ are 0, 3, and -1. Since $(x - 3)$ occurs twice as a factor, 3 is a multiple zero.

Multiplicative identity (p. 14) The multiplicative identity is 1. The product of 1 and any number is that number. The product of reciprocals is 1.

Identidad multiplicativa (p. 14) La identidad multiplicativa es 1. El producto de 1 y cualquier otro número es ese número. El producto del recíproco es 1.

Multiplicative identity matrix (p. 782) For an $n \times n$ square matrix, the multiplicative identity matrix is an $n \times n$ square matrix I, or $I_{n \times n}$, with 1's along the main diagonal and 0's elsewhere.

Matriz de identidad multiplicativa (p. 782) Para una matriz cuadrada $n \times n$, la matriz de identidad multiplicativa es la matriz cuadrada I de $n \times n$, o $I_{n \times n}$, con unos por la diagonal principal y ceros en los demás lugares.

Example $I_{2 \times 2} = \begin{bmatrix} 1 & 0 \\ 0 & 1 \end{bmatrix}$, $I_{3 \times 3} = \begin{bmatrix} 1 & 0 & 0 \\ 0 & 1 & 0 \\ 0 & 0 & 1 \end{bmatrix}$

Multiplicative inverse (p. 14) The reciprocal or multiplicative inverse of any nonzero number a is $\frac{1}{a}$. The product of reciprocals is 1, the multiplicative identity.

Inverso multiplicativo (p. 14) El recíproco o inverso multiplicativo de cualquier número a, que no sea cero, es $\frac{1}{a}$. El producto de recíprocos es 1, la identidad multiplicativa.

Example $5 \times \frac{1}{5} = 1$

Multiplicative inverse of a matrix (p. 782) If A and X are $n \times n$ matrices, and $AX = XA = I$, then X is the multiplicative inverse of A, written A^{-1}.

Inverso multiplicativo de una matriz (p. 782) Si A y X son matrices $n \times n$, y $AX = XA = I$, entonces X es el inverso multiplicativo de A, expresado como A^{-1}.

Example $A = \begin{bmatrix} 2 & 1 \\ 4 & 0 \end{bmatrix}$, $X = \begin{bmatrix} 0 & \frac{1}{4} \\ 1 & \frac{1}{2} \end{bmatrix}$

$AX = \begin{bmatrix} 1 & 0 \\ 0 & 1 \end{bmatrix} = I$, so $X = A^{-1}$

English | Spanish

Multiplicity (p. 291) The multiplicity of a zero of a polynomial function is the number of times the related linear factor is repeated in the factored form of the polynomial.

Multiplicidad (p. 291) La multiplicidad de un cero de una función polinomial es el número de veces que el factor lineal relacionado se repite en la forma factorizada del polinomio.

Example The zeros of the function
$P(x) = 2x(x - 3)^2(x + 1)$ are 0, 3, and -1. Since $(x - 3)$ occurs twice as a factor, the zero 3 has multiplicity 2.

Mutually exclusive events (p. 689) When two events cannot happen at the same time, the events are mutually exclusive. If A and B are mutually exclusive events, then $P(A \text{ or } B) = P(A) + P(B)$.

Sucesos mutuamente excluyentes (p. 689) Cuando dos sucesos no pueden ocurrir al mismo tiempo, son mutuamente excluyentes. Si A y B son sucesos mutuamente excluyentes, entonces $P(A \text{ or } B) = P(A) + P(B)$.

Example Rolling an even number E and rolling a multiple of five M on a standard number cube are mutually exclusive events.

$P(E \text{ or } M) = P(E) + P(M)$
$= \frac{3}{6} + \frac{1}{6}$
$= \frac{4}{6}$, or $\frac{2}{3}$

N

n factorial ($n!$) (p. 675) For any positive integer n, n factorial is $n(n - 1) \cdots \cdot 3 \cdot 2 \cdot 1$. Zero factorial (0!) = 1.

n factorial ($n!$) (p. 675) Para cualquier entero n, n factorial es $n(n - 1) \cdots \cdot 3 \cdot 2 \cdot 1$. El cero factorial (0!) = 1.

Example $4! = 4 \cdot 3 \cdot 2 \cdot 1 = 24$

nth root (p. 361) For any real numbers a and b, and any positive integer n, if $a^n = b$, then a is an nth root of b.

raíz n-ésima (p. 361) Para todos los números reales a y b, y todo número entero positivo n, si $a^n = b$, entonces a es la n-ésima raíz de b.

Example $\sqrt[5]{32} = 2$ because $2^5 = 32$.
$\sqrt[4]{81} = 3$ because $3^4 = 81$.

Natural base exponential function (p. 446) A natural base exponential function is an exponential function with base e.

Función exponencial con base natural (p. 446) Una función exponencial con base natural es una función exponencial con base e.

English | Spanish

Natural logarithmic function (p. 478) A natural logarithmic function is a logarithmic function with base e. The natural logarithmic function, $y = \ln x$, is $y = \log_e x$. It is the inverse of $y = e^x$.

Función logarítmica natural (p. 478) Una función logarítmica natural es una función logarítmica con base e. La función logarítmica natural, $y = \ln x$, es $y = \log_e x$. Ésta es la función inversa de $y = e^x$.

Example

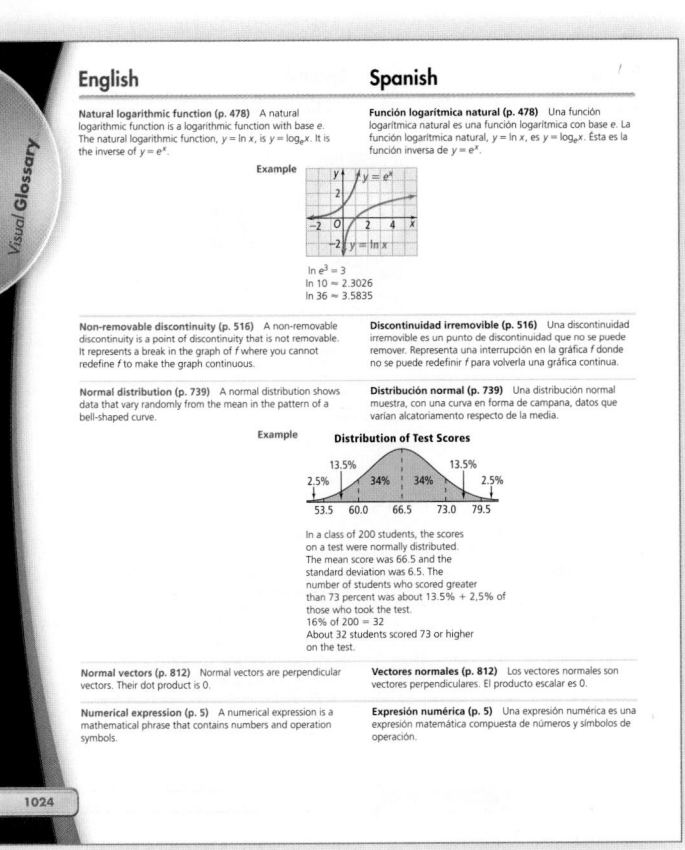

$\ln e^3 = 3$
$\ln 10 \approx 2.3026$
$\ln 36 \approx 3.5835$

Non-removable discontinuity (p. 516) A non-removable discontinuity is a point of discontinuity that is not removable. It represents a break in the graph of f where you cannot redefine f to make the graph continuous.

Discontinuidad irremovible (p. 516) Una discontinuidad irremovible es un punto de discontinuidad que no se puede remover. Representa una interrupción en la gráfica f donde no se puede redefinir f para volverla una gráfica continua.

Normal distribution (p. 739) A normal distribution shows data that vary randomly from the mean in the pattern of a bell-shaped curve.

Distribución normal (p. 739) Una distribución normal muestra, con una curva en forma de campana, datos que varían alcatoriamente respecto de la media.

Example

Distribution of Test Scores

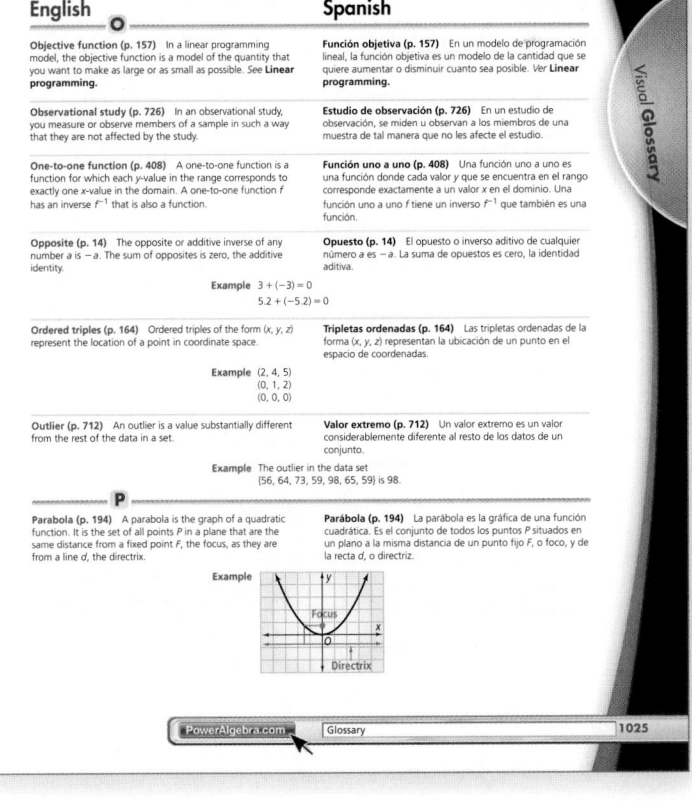

2.5% | 13.5% | 34% | 34% | 13.5% | 2.5%
53.5 | 60 | 66.5 | 73.0 | 79.5

In a class of 200 students, the scores on a test were normally distributed. The mean score was 66.5 and the standard deviation was 6.5. The number of students who scored greater than 73 percent was about 13.5% + 2.5% of those who took the test.
16% of 200 = 32
About 32 students scored 73 or higher on the test.

Normal vectors (p. 812) Normal vectors are perpendicular vectors. Their dot product is 0.

Vectores normales (p. 812) Los vectores normales son vectores perpendiculares. El producto escalar es 0.

Numerical expression (p. 5) A numerical expression is a mathematical phrase that contains numbers and operation symbols.

Expresión numérica (p. 5) Una expresión numérica es una expresión matemática compuesta de números y símbolos de operación.

English | Spanish

O

Objective function (p. 157) In a linear programming model, the objective function is a model of the quantity that you want to make as large or as small as possible. *See* **Linear programming.**

Función objetiva (p. 157) En un modelo de programación lineal, la función objetiva es un modelo de la cantidad que se quiere aumentar o disminuir cuanto sea posible. *Ver* **Linear programming.**

Observational study (p. 726) In an observational study, you measure or observe members of a sample in such a way that they are not affected by the study.

Estudio de observación (p. 726) En un estudio de observación, se miden u observan a los miembros de una muestra de tal manera que no les afecte el estudio.

One-to-one function (p. 408) A one-to-one function is a function for which each y-value in the range corresponds to exactly one x-value in the domain. A one-to-one function f has an inverse f^{-1} that is also a function.

Función uno a uno (p. 408) Una función uno a uno es una función donde cada valor y que se encuentra en el rango corresponde exactamente a un valor x en el dominio. Una función uno a uno f tiene un inverso f^{-1} que también es una función.

Opposite (p. 14) The opposite or additive inverse of any number a is $-a$. The sum of opposites is zero, the additive identity.

Opuesto (p. 14) El opuesto o inverso aditivo de cualquier número a es $-a$. La suma de opuestos es cero, la identidad aditiva.

Example $3 + (-3) = 0$
$5.2 + (-5.2) = 0$

Ordered triples (p. 164) Ordered triples of the form (x, y, z) represent the location of a point in coordinate space.

Tripletas ordenadas (p. 164) Las tripletas ordenadas de la forma (x, y, z) representan la ubicación de un punto en el espacio de coordenadas.

Example $(2, 4, 5)$
$(0, 1, 2)$
$(0, 0, 0)$

Outlier (p. 712) An outlier is a value substantially different from the rest of the data in a set.

Valor extremo (p. 712) Un valor extremo es un valor considerablemente diferente al resto de los datos de un conjunto.

Example The outlier in the data set {56, 64, 73, 59, 98, 65, 59} is 98.

P

Parabola (p. 194) A parabola is the graph of a quadratic function. It is the set of all points P in a plane that are the same distance from a fixed point F, the focus, as they are from a line d, the directrix.

Parábola (p. 194) La parábola es la gráfica de una función cuadrática. Es el conjunto de todos los puntos P situados en un plano a la misma distancia de un punto fijo F, o foco, y de la recta d, o directriz.

Example

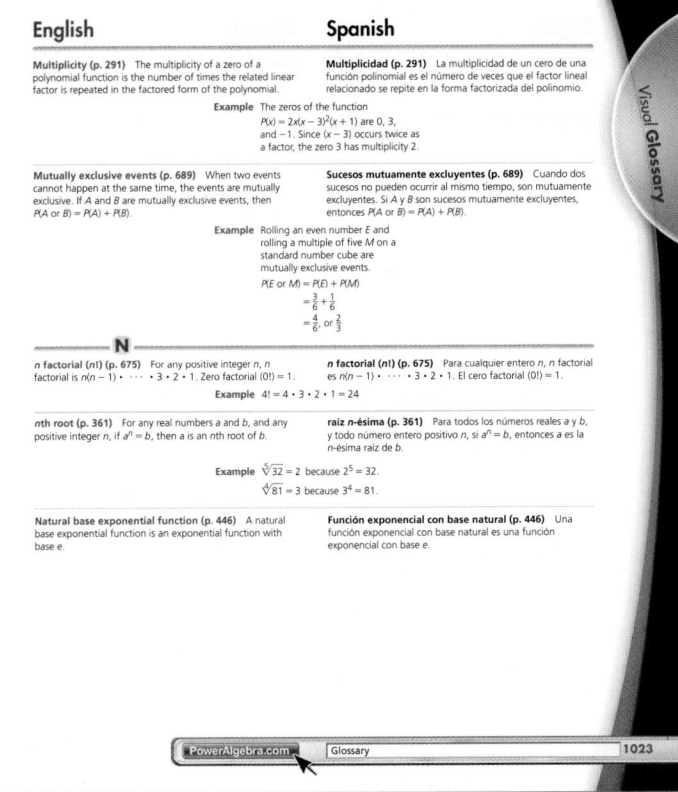

English | Spanish

Parallel lines (p. 85) Parallel lines are coplanar lines that do not intersect. In the coordinate plane, parallel lines have the same slope.

Rectas paralelas (p. 85) Rectas paralelas son líneas coplanares que no se intersecan. En un plano de coordenadas, las rectas paralelas tienen la misma pendiente.

Parent function (p. 99) A parent function is the simplest form of a set of functions that form a family.

Función elemental (p. 99) Una función madre es la mínima expresión de un conjunto de funciones que forma una familia.

Example $y = x$ is the parent function for the functions of the form $y = x + k$.

Pascal's Triangle (p. 327) Pascal's Triangle is a triangular array of numbers in which the first and last number is 1. Each of the other numbers in the row is the sum of the two numbers above it.

Triángulo de Pascal (p. 327) El Triángulo de Pascal es una distribución triangular de números en la cual el primer número y el último número son 1. Cada uno de los otros números en la fila es la suma de los dos números de encima.

Example Pascal's Triangle

```
        1
       1 1
      1 2 1
     1 3 3 1
    1 4 6 4 1
  1 5 10 10 5 1
```

Percentiles (p. 714) A percentile is a number from 0 to 100 that you can associate with a value x from a data set. It shows the percent of the data that are less than or equal to x.

Percentiles (p. 714) Un percentil es un número de 0 a 100 que se puede asociar con un valor x de un conjunto de datos. Éste muestra el porcentaje de los datos que son menores o iguales a x.

Perfect square trinomial (p. 219) A perfect square trinomial is a trinomial that is the square of a binomial.

Trinomio cuadrado perfecto (p. 219) Un trinomio cuadrado perfecto es un trinomio que es el cuadrado de un binomio.

Example
perfect square trinomial = binominal square
$16x^2 - 24x + 9 = (4x - 3)^2$

Period (p. 828) The period of a periodic function is the horizontal length of one cycle.

Período (p. 828) El período de una función periódica es el intervalo horizontal de un ciclo.

Example

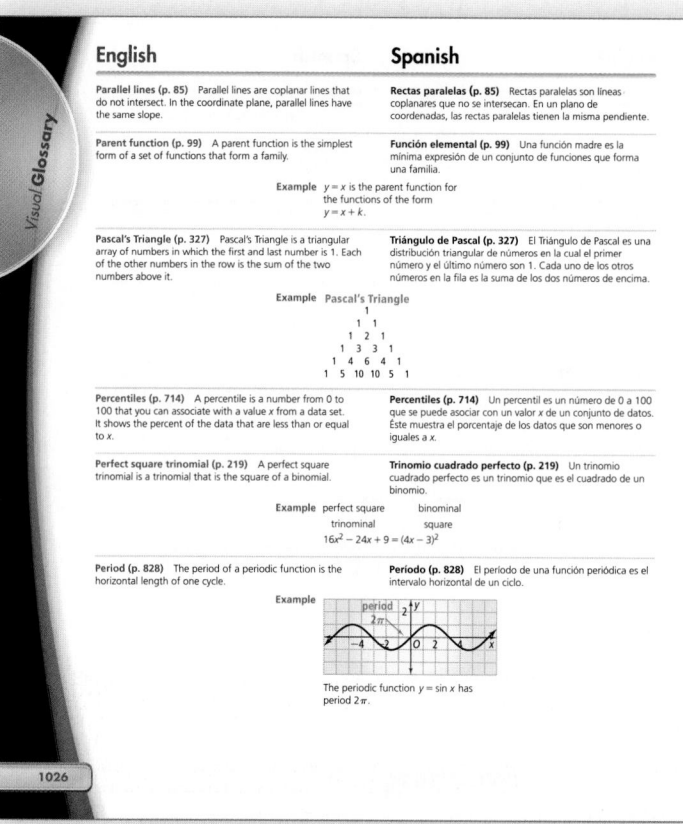

The periodic function $y = \sin x$ has period 2π.

English | Spanish

Periodic function (p. 828) A periodic function repeats a pattern of y-values at regular intervals.

Función periódica (p. 828) Una función periódica repite un patrón de valores y a intervalos regulares.

Example

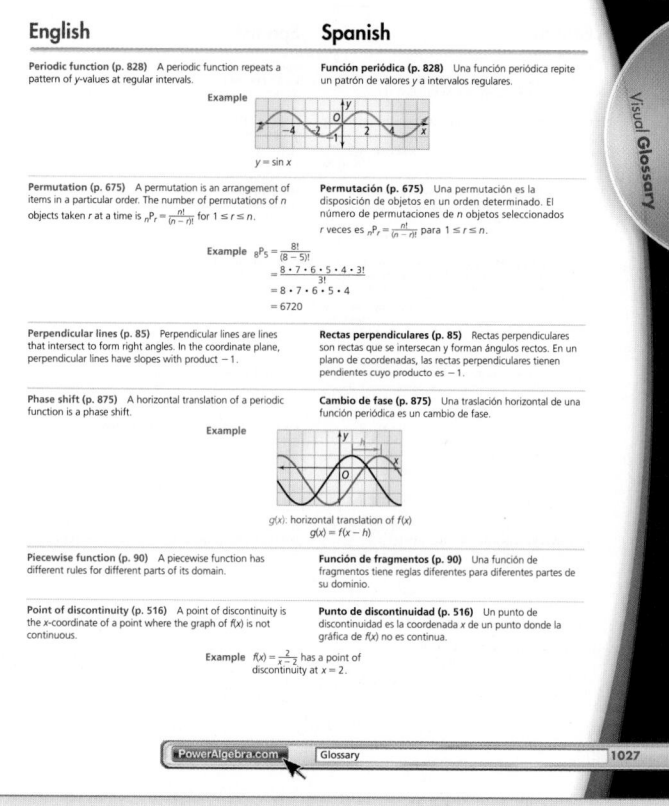

$y = \sin x$

Permutation (p. 675) A permutation is an arrangement of items in a particular order. The number of permutations of n objects taken r at a time is $_nP_r = \frac{n!}{(n-r)!}$ for $1 \le r \le n$.

Permutación (p. 675) Una permutación es la disposición de objetos en un orden determinado. El número de permutaciones de n objetos seleccionados r veces es $_nP_r = \frac{n!}{(n-r)!}$ para $1 \le r \le n$.

Example
$$_8P_5 = \frac{8!}{(8-5)!}$$
$$= \frac{8 \cdot 7 \cdot 6 \cdot 5 \cdot 4 \cdot 3!}{3!}$$
$$= 8 \cdot 7 \cdot 6 \cdot 5 \cdot 4$$
$$= 6720$$

Perpendicular lines (p. 85) Perpendicular lines are lines that intersect to form right angles. In the coordinate plane, perpendicular lines have slopes with product -1.

Rectas perpendiculares (p. 85) Rectas perpendiculares son rectas que se intersecan y forman ángulos rectos. En un plano de coordenadas, las rectas perpendiculares tienen pendientes cuyo producto es -1.

Phase shift (p. 875) A horizontal translation of a periodic function is a phase shift.

Cambio de fase (p. 875) Una traslación horizontal de una función periódica es un cambio de fase.

Example

$g(x)$: horizontal translation of $f(x)$
$g(x) = f(x - h)$

Piecewise function (p. 90) A piecewise function has different rules for different parts of its domain.

Función de fragmentos (p. 90) Una función de fragmentos tiene reglas diferentes para diferentes partes de su dominio.

Point of discontinuity (p. 516) A point of discontinuity is the x-coordinate of a point where the graph of $f(x)$ is not continuous.

Punto de discontinuidad (p. 516) Un punto de discontinuidad es la coordenada x de un punto donde la gráfica de $f(x)$ no es continua.

Example $f(x) = \frac{2}{x-2}$ has a point of discontinuity at $x = 2$.

English | Spanish

Point-slope form (p. 81) The point-slope form of an equation of a line is $y - y_1 = m(x - x_1)$, where m is the slope of the line and (x_1, y_1) is a point on the line.

Forma punto-pendiente (p. 81) La forma punto-pendiente de una ecuación lineal es $y - y_1 = m(x - x_1)$, donde m es la pendiente de la recta y (x_1, y_1) es un punto de la recta.

Example
$y - 3 = 2(x - 1)$
$y + 4 = 5(x - 2)$
$y - 2 = 3(x + 2)$

Polynomial (p. 280) A polynomial is a monomial or the sum of monomials.

Polinomio (p. 280) Un polinomio es un monomio o la suma de dos o más monomios.

Example $3x^3 + 4x^2 - 2x + 5$
$8x$
$x^2 + 4x + 2$

Polynomial function (p. 280) A polynomial in the variable x defines a polynomial function of x.

Función polinomial (p. 280) Un polinomio en la variable x define una función polinomial de x.

Example $P(x) = a_nx^n + a_{n-1}x^{n-1} + \cdots + a_1x + a_0$ is a polynomial function, where n is a nonnegative integer and the coefficients $a_n, \ldots, a_0$ are real numbers.

Population (p. 725) A population is the members of a set.

Población (p. 725) Una población está compuesta por los miembros de un conjunto.

Power function (p. 341) A power function is a function of the form $y = a \cdot x^b$, where a and b are nonzero real numbers.

Función de potencia (p. 341) Una función de potencia es una función de la forma $y = a \cdot x^b$, donde a y b son números reales diferentes de cero.

Preimage (p. 801) The preimage is the original figure before a transformation.

Preimagen (p. 801) La preimagen es la figura original antes de sufrir una transformación.

Example

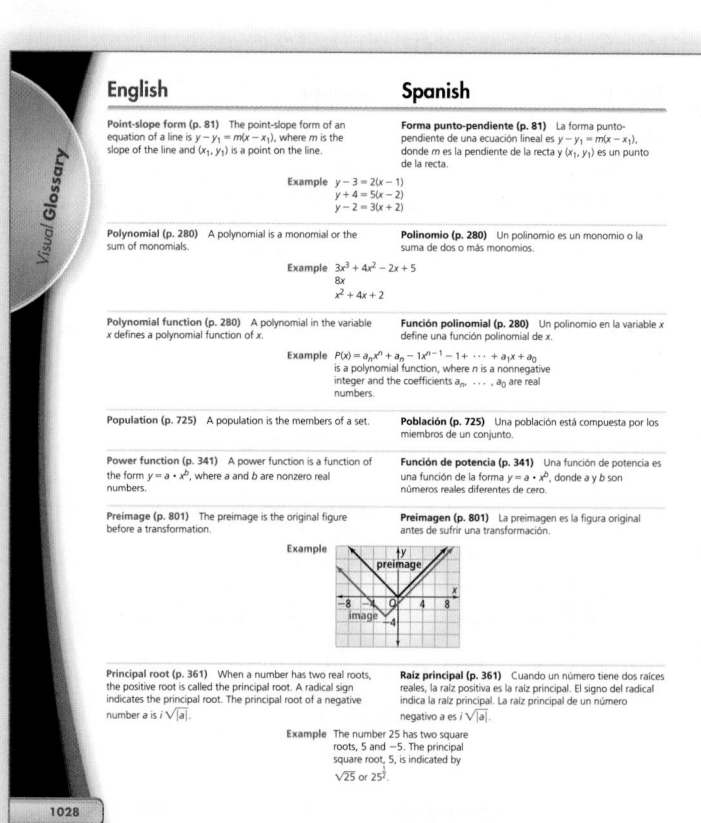

Principal root (p. 361) When a number has two real roots, the positive root is called the principal root. A radical sign indicates the principal root. The principal root of a negative number a is $i \sqrt{|a|}$.

Raíz principal (p. 361) Cuando un número tiene dos raíces reales, la raíz positiva es la raíz principal. El signo del radical indica la raíz principal. La raíz principal de un número negativo a es $i \sqrt{|a|}$.

Example The number 25 has two square roots, 5 and -5. The principal square root, 5, is indicated by $\sqrt{25}$ or $25^{\frac{1}{2}}$.

English | Spanish

Probability distribution (p. 694) A probability distribution is a function that tells the probability of each outcome in a sample space.

Distribución de probabilidades (p. 694) Una distribución de probabilidades es una función que señala la probabilidad de que cada resultado ocurra en un espacio muestral.

Example

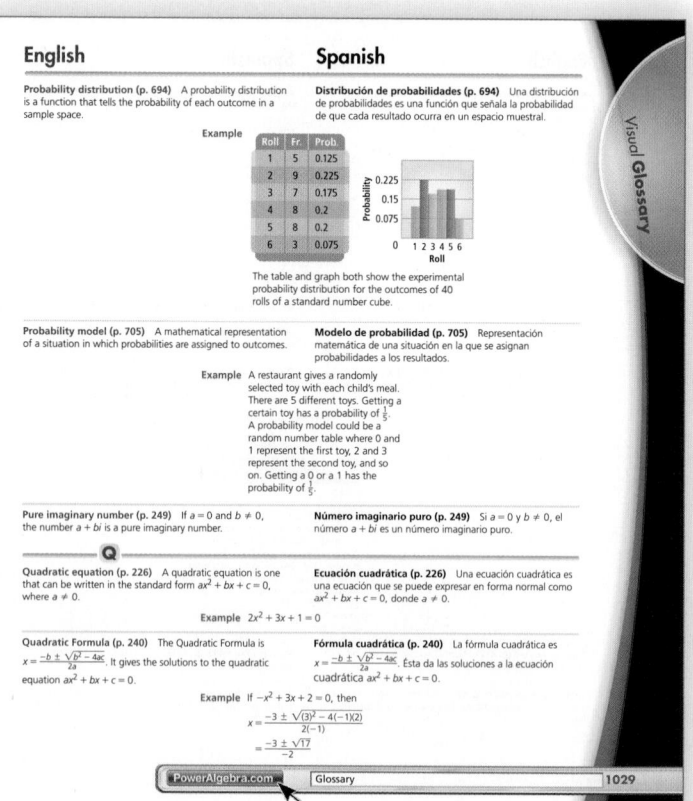

Roll	Fr.	Prob.
1	5	0.125
2	9	0.225
3	7	0.175
4	8	0.2
5	8	0.2
6	3	0.075

The table and graph both show the experimental probability distribution for the outcomes of 40 rolls of a standard number cube.

Probability model (p. 705) A mathematical representation of a situation in which probabilities are assigned to outcomes.

Modelo de probabilidad (p. 705) Representación matemática de una situación en la que se asignan probabilidades a los resultados.

Example A restaurant gives a randomly selected toy with each child's meal. There are 5 different toys. Getting a certain toy has a probability of $\frac{1}{5}$. A probability model could be a random number table where 0 and 1 represent the first toy, 2 and 3 represent the second toy, and so on. Getting a 0 or a 1 has the probability of $\frac{1}{5}$.

Pure imaginary number (p. 249) If $a = 0$ and $b \ne 0$, the number $a + bi$ is a pure imaginary number.

Número imaginario puro (p. 249) Si $a = 0$ y $b \ne 0$, el número $a + bi$ es un número imaginario puro.

Q

Quadratic equation (p. 226) A quadratic equation is one that can be written in the standard form $ax^2 + bx + c = 0$, where $a \ne 0$.

Ecuación cuadrática (p. 226) Una ecuación cuadrática es una ecuación que se puede expresar en forma normal como $ax^2 + bx + c = 0$, donde $a \ne 0$.

Example $2x^2 + 3x + 1 = 0$

Quadratic Formula (p. 240) The Quadratic Formula is $x = \frac{-b \pm \sqrt{b^2 - 4ac}}{2a}$. It gives the solutions to the quadratic equation $ax^2 + bx + c = 0$.

Fórmula cuadrática (p. 240) La fórmula cuadrática es $x = \frac{-b \pm \sqrt{b^2 - 4ac}}{2a}$. Ésta da las soluciones a la ecuación cuadrática $ax^2 + bx + c = 0$.

Example If $-x^2 + 3x + 2 = 0$, then
$$x = \frac{-3 \pm \sqrt{(3)^2 - 4(-1)(2)}}{2(-1)}$$
$$= \frac{-3 \pm \sqrt{17}}{-2}$$

Page 1030

English	Spanish

Quadratic function (p. 194) A quadratic function is a function that you can write in the form $f(x) = ax^2 + bx + c$ with $a \neq 0$.

Función cuadrática (p. 194) Una función cuadrática es una función que puedes escribir como $f(x) = ax^2 + bx + c$ con $a \neq 0$.

Example

$$y = x^2 + 2x - 2$$

Quantity (p. 5) A mathematical quantity is anything that can be measured or counted.

Cantidad (p. 5) Una cantidad matemática es cualquier cosa que se puede medir o contar.

Quartile (p. 713) Quartiles are values that separate a finite data set into four equal parts. The second quartile (Q_2) is the median of the data. The first and third quartiles (Q_1 and Q_3) are the medians of the lower half and upper half of the data, respectively.

Cuartil (p. 713) Los cuartiles son valores que separan un conjunto finito de datos en cuatro partes iguales. El segundo cuartil (Q_2) es la mediana de los datos. Los cuartiles primero y tercero (Q_1 y Q_3) son las medianas de la mitad superior e inferior de los datos, respectivamente.

Example $\{2, 3, 4, 5, 5, 6, 7, 7\}$
$Q_1 = 3.5$
$Q_2 \text{ (median)} = 5$
$Q_3 = 6.5$

R

Radian (p. 844) $\frac{d^\circ}{180^\circ} = \frac{r\text{ radians}}{\pi\text{ radians}}$

Radián (p. 844) $\frac{d^\circ}{180^\circ} = \frac{r\text{ radianes}}{\pi\text{ radianes}}$

Example $60^\circ \to \frac{60}{180} = \frac{x}{\pi}$
$x = \frac{60\pi}{180}$
$= \frac{\pi}{3}$
Thus, $60^\circ = \frac{\pi}{3}$ radians.

Radical equation (p. 390) A radical equation is an equation that has a variable in a radicand or has a variable with a rational exponent.

Ecuación radical (p. 390) La ecuación radical es una ecuación que contiene una variable en el radicando o una variable con un exponente racional.

Example $(\sqrt{x})^3 + 1 = 65$
$x^{\frac{3}{2}} + 1 = 65$

Radical function (p. 415) A radical function is a function that can be written in the form $f(x) = a\sqrt[n]{x - h} + k$, where $a \neq 0$. For even values of n, the domain of a radical function is the real numbers $x \geq h$. See also **Square root function.**

Función radical (p. 415) Una función radical es una función quepuede expresarse como $f(x) = a\sqrt[n]{x - h} + k$, donde $a \neq 0$. Para n par, el dominio de la función radical son los números reales tales que $x \geq h$. Ver también **Square root function.**

Example $f(x) = \sqrt{x - 2}$

Page 1031

English	Spanish

Radicand (p. 362) The number under a radical sign is the radicand.

Radicando (p. 362) La expresión que aparece debajo del signo radical es el radicando.

Example The radicand in $3\sqrt[4]{7}$ is 7.

Radius (p. 630) The radius r of a circle is the distance between the center of the circle and any point on the circumference.

Radio (p. 630) El radio r de un círculo es la distancia entre el centro del círculo y cualquier punto de la circunferencia.

Example

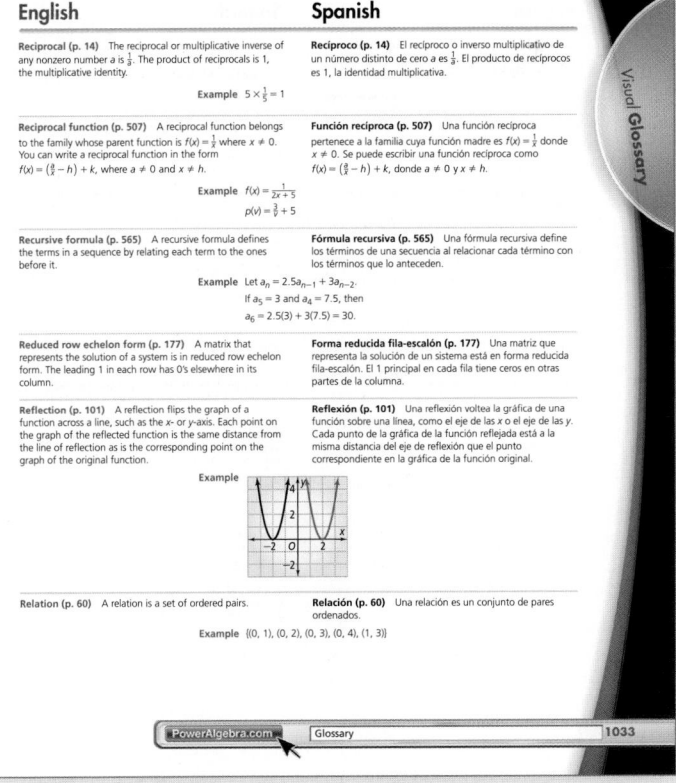

Random sample (p. 725) In a random sample, all members of the population are equally likely to be chosen as every other member.

Muestra aleatoria (p. 725) En una muestra aleatoria, la probabilidad de ser seleccionado es igual para todos los miembros.

Example Let the set of all females between the ages of 19 and 34 be the population. A random selection of 900 females between those ages would be a sample of the population

Range (p. 61) The range of a relation is the set of all outputs or y-coordinates of the ordered pairs.

Rango (p. 61) El rango de una relación es el conjunto de todas las salidas posibles, o coordenadas y, de los pares ordenados.

Example In the relation $\{(0, 1), (0, 2), (0, 3), (0, 4), (1, 3), (1, 4), (2, 1)\}$, the range is $\{1, 2, 3, 4\}$. In the function $f(x) = |x - 3|$, the range is the set of real numbers greater than or equal to 0.

Range of a set of data (p. 713) The range of a set of data is the difference between the greatest and least values.

Rango de un conjunto de datos (p. 713) El rango de un conjunto de datos es la diferencia entre el valor máximo y el valor mínimo de los datos.

Example The range of the set $\{3.2, 4.1, 2.2, 3.4, 3.8, 4.0, 4.2, 2.8\}$ is $4.2 - 2.2 = 2$.

Rational equation (p. 542) A rational equation is an equation that contains a rational expression.

Ecuación racional (p. 542) Una ecuación racional es una ecuación que contiene una expresión racional.

Rational exponent (p. 382) If the nth root of a is a real number and m is an integer, then $a^{\frac{1}{n}} = \sqrt[n]{a}$ and $a^{\frac{m}{n}} = \sqrt[n]{a^m} = (\sqrt[n]{a})^m$. If m is negative, $a \neq 0$.

Exponente racional (p. 382) Si la raíz n-ésima de a es un número real y m es un número entero, entonces $a^{\frac{1}{n}} = \sqrt[n]{a}$ y $a^{\frac{m}{n}} = \sqrt[n]{a^m} = (\sqrt[n]{a})^m$. Si m es negativo, $a \neq 0$.

Example $4^{\frac{1}{3}} = \sqrt[3]{4}$
$5^{\frac{3}{2}} = \sqrt{5^3} = (\sqrt{5})^3$

Page 1032

English	Spanish

Rational expression (p. 527) A rational expression is the quotient of two polynomials.

Expresión racional (p. 527) Una expresión racional es el cociente de dos polinomios.

Rational function (p. 515) A rational function $f(x)$ can be written as $f(x) = \frac{P(x)}{Q(x)}$, where $P(x)$ and $Q(x)$ are polynomial functions. The domain of a rational function is all real numbers except those for which $Q(x) = 0$.

Función racional (p. 515) Una función racional $f(x)$ se puede expresar como $f(x) = \frac{P(x)}{Q(x)}$, donde $P(x)$ y $Q(x)$ son funciones de polinomios. El dominio de una función racional son todos los números reales excepto aquéllos para los cuales $Q(x) = 0$.

Example

The function $y = \frac{x - 2}{x^2 - 9}$ is a rational function with three branches separated by asymptotes $x = -3$ and $x = 3$.

Rational Root Theorem (p. 312) Let $P(x) = a_nx^n + a_{n-1}x^{n-1} + \cdots + a_1x + a_0$ be a polynomial with integer coefficients. Then there are a limited number of possible roots of $P(x) = 0$:
–Integer roots must be factors of a_0.
–Rational roots must have reduced form p/q where p is an integer factor of a_0 and q is an integer factor of a_n.

Teorema de la Raíz Racional (p. 312) Sea $P(x) = a_nx^n + a_{n-1}x^{n-1} + \cdots + a_1x + a_0$ un polinomio con enteros como coeficientes. Entonces hay un número limitado de raíces posibles para $P(x) = 0$:
–Las raíces enteras deben ser factores de a_0.
–Las raíces racionales deben ser de forma simplificada p/q, donde p es un factor entero de a_0 y q es un factor entero de a_n.

Example The polynomial equation $10x^3 + 6x^2 - 11x - 2 = 0$ has leading coefficient 10 (with factors $\pm 1, \pm 2, \pm 5, \pm 10$) and constant term -2 (with factors ± 1 and ± 2). Its only possible rational roots are $\pm 1, \pm 2, \pm \frac{1}{2}, \pm \frac{1}{5}, \pm \frac{2}{5}, \pm \frac{1}{10}$.

Rationalize the denominator (p. 369) To rationalize the denominator of an expression, rewrite it so there are no radicals in any denominator and no denominators in any radical.

Racionalizar el denominador (p. 369) Para racionalizar el denominador de una expresión, ésta se escribe de modo que no haya radicales en ningún denominador y no haya denominadores en ningún radical.

Example $\frac{1}{\sqrt{2}} = \frac{1}{\sqrt{2}} \times \frac{\sqrt{2}}{\sqrt{2}} = \frac{\sqrt{2}}{2}$

Page 1033

English	Spanish

Reciprocal (p. 14) The reciprocal or multiplicative inverse of any nonzero number a is $\frac{1}{a}$. The product of reciprocals is 1, the multiplicative identity.

Recíproco (p. 14) El recíproco o inverso multiplicativo de un número distinto de cero a es $\frac{1}{a}$. El producto de recíprocos es 1, la identidad multiplicativa.

Example $5 \times \frac{1}{5} = 1$

Reciprocal function (p. 507) A reciprocal function belongs to the family whose parent function is $f(x) = \frac{1}{x}$ where $x \neq 0$. You can write a reciprocal function in the form $f(x) = (\frac{a}{x} - h) + k$, where $a \neq 0$ and $x \neq h$.

Función recíproca (p. 507) Una función recíproca pertenece a la familia cuya función madre es $f(x) = \frac{1}{x}$ donde $x \neq 0$. Se puede escribir una función recíproca como $f(x) = (\frac{a}{x} - h) + k$, donde $a \neq 0$ y $x \neq h$.

Example $f(x) = \frac{1}{2x + 5}$
$p(v) = \frac{3}{v} + 5$

Recursive formula (p. 565) A recursive formula defines the terms in a sequence by relating each term to the ones before it.

Fórmula recursiva (p. 565) Una fórmula recursiva define los términos de una secuencia al relacionar cada término con los términos que lo anteceden.

Example Let $a_n = 2.5a_{n-1} + 3a_{n-2}$.
If $a_5 = 3$ and $a_4 = 7.5$, then
$a_6 = 2.5(3) + 3(7.5) = 30$.

Reduced row echelon form (p. 177) A matrix that represents the solution of a system is in reduced row echelon form. The leading 1 in each row has 0's elsewhere in its column.

Forma reducida fila-escalón (p. 177) Una matriz que representa la solución de un sistema está en forma reducida fila-escalón. El 1 principal en cada fila tiene ceros en otras partes de la columna.

Reflection (p. 101) A reflection flips the graph of a function across a line, such as the x- or y-axis. Each point on the graph of the reflected function is the same distance from the line of reflection as the corresponding point on the graph of the original function.

Reflexión (p. 101) Una reflexión voltea la gráfica de una función sobre una línea, como el eje de las x o el eje de las y. Cada punto de la gráfica de la función reflejada está a la misma distancia del eje de reflexión que el punto correspondiente en la gráfica de la función original.

Example

Relation (p. 60) A relation is a set of ordered pairs.

Relación (p. 60) Una relación es un conjunto de pares ordenados.

Example $\{(0, 1), (0, 2), (0, 3), (0, 4), (1, 3)\}$

English

Spanish

Relative maximum (minimum) (p. 291)   A relative maximum (minimum) is the value of the function at an up-to-down (down-to-up) turning point.

Máximo (mínimo) relativo (p. 291)   El máximo (mínimo) relativo es el valor de la función en un punto de giro de arriba hacia abajo (de abajo hacia arriba).

Example

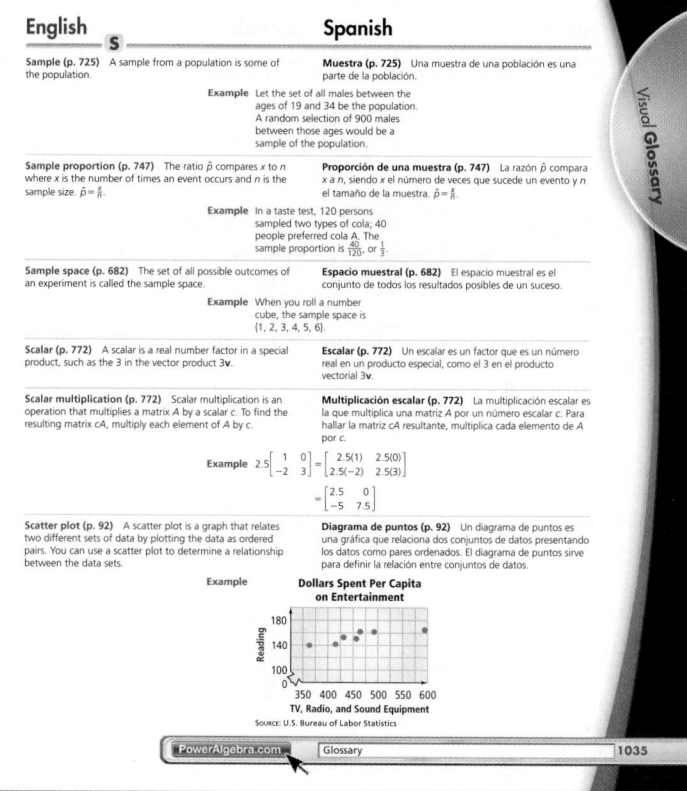

Remainder Theorem (p. 307)   If you divide a polynomial $P(x)$ of degree $n > 1$ by $x - a$, then the remainder is $P(a)$.

Teorema del residuo (p. 307)   Si divides un polinomio $P(x)$ con un grado $n > 1$ por $x - a$, el residuo es $P(a)$.

Example   If $P(x) = x^3 - 4x^2 + x + 6$ is divided by $x - 3$, then the remainder is $P(3) = 3^3 - 4(3)^2 + 3 + 6 = 0$ (which means that $x - 3$ is a factor of $P(x)$).

Removable discontinuity (p. 516)   A removable discontinuity is a point of discontinuity, a, of function f that you can remove by redefining f at $x = a$. Doing so fills in a hole in the graph of f with the point $(a, f(a))$.

Discontinuidad removible (p. 516)   Una discontinuidad removible es un punto de discontinuidad a en una función f que se puede remover al redefinir f en $x = a$. Al hacer esto, se llena su hueco en la gráfica f con el punto $(a, f(a))$.

Root (p. 232)   A root of a function is the input value for which the value of the function is zero. A root of an equation is a value that makes the equation true. *See also* **Zero of a function.**

Raíz (p. 232)   La raíz de una función es el valor de entrada para el cual el valor de la función es cero. La raíz de una ecuación es un valor que hace verdadera la ecuación. *Ver también* **Zero of a function.**

Example   −2 and 3 are roots of the function $f(x) = (x + 2)(x - 3)$ and the equation $(x + 2)(x - 3) = 0$.

Rotation (p. 804)   A rotation is a transformation that turns a figure about a fixed point called the center of rotation.

Rotación (p. 804)   Rotación es una transformación que hace girar una figura alrededor de un punto fijo llamado centro de rotación.

Example

Row operation (p. 176)   A row operation on an augmented matrix is any of the following: switch two rows, multiply a row by a constant, add one row to another.

Operación de fila (p. 176)   Una operación de fila en una matriz ampliada es cualquiera de las siguientes opciones: el intercambio de dos filas, la multiplicación de una fila por una constante o la suma de dos filas.

English

S

Spanish

Sample (p. 725)   A sample from a population is some of the population.

Muestra (p. 725)   Una muestra de una población es una parte de la población.

Example   Let the set of all males between the ages of 19 and 34 be the population. A random selection of 900 males between those ages would be a sample of the population.

Sample proportion (p. 747)   The ratio $\hat{p}$ compares x to n where x is the number of times an event occurs and n is the sample size. $\hat{p} = \frac{x}{n}$.

Proporción de una muestra (p. 747)   La razón $\hat{p}$ compara x a n, siendo x el número de veces que sucede un evento y n el tamaño de la muestra. $\hat{p} = \frac{x}{n}$.

Example   In a taste test, 120 persons sampled two types of cola; 40 people preferred cola A. The sample proportion is $\frac{40}{120}$, or $\frac{1}{3}$.

Sample space (p. 682)   The set of all possible outcomes of an experiment is called the sample space.

Espacio muestral (p. 682)   El espacio muestral es el conjunto de todos los resultados posibles de un suceso.

Example   When you roll a number cube, the sample space is {1, 2, 3, 4, 5, 6}.

Scalar (p. 772)   A scalar is a real number factor in a special product, such as the 3 in the vector product 3**v**.

Escalar (p. 772)   Un escalar es un factor que es un número real en un producto especial, como el 3 en el producto vectorial 3**v**.

Scalar multiplication (p. 772)   Scalar multiplication is an operation that multiplies a matrix A by a scalar c. To find the resulting matrix cA, multiply each element of A by c.

Multiplicación escalar (p. 772)   La multiplicación escalar es la que multiplica una matriz A por un número escalar c. Para hallar la matriz cA resultante, multiplica cada elemento de A por c.

Example
$$2.5 \begin{bmatrix} 1 & 0 \\ -2 & 3 \end{bmatrix} = \begin{bmatrix} 2.5(1) & 2.5(0) \\ 2.5(-2) & 2.5(3) \end{bmatrix}$$
$$= \begin{bmatrix} 2.5 & 0 \\ -5 & 7.5 \end{bmatrix}$$

Scatter plot (p. 92)   A scatter plot is a graph that relates two different sets of data by plotting the data as ordered pairs. You can use a scatter plot to determine a relationship between the data sets.

Diagrama de puntos (p. 92)   Un diagrama de puntos es una gráfica que relaciona dos conjuntos de datos presentando los datos como pares ordenados. El diagrama de puntos sirve para definir la relación entre conjuntos de datos.

Example

Dollars Spent Per Capita on Entertainment

TV, Radio, and Sound Equipment

Source: U.S. Bureau of Labor Statistics

English

Spanish

Secant function (p. 883)   The secant (sec) function is the reciprocal of the cosine function. For all real numbers θ except those that make $\cos \theta = 0$, $\sec \theta = \frac{1}{\cos \theta}$.

Función secante (p. 883)   La función secante (sec) es el recíproco de la función coseno. Para todos los números reales θ, excepto aquéllos para los que $\cos \theta = 0$, $\sec \theta = \frac{1}{\cos \theta}$.

Example   If $\cos \theta = \frac{5}{13}$, then $\sec \theta = \frac{13}{5}$.

Self-selected sample (p. 725)   In a self-selected sample you select only members of the population who volunteered for the sample.

Muestra de voluntarios (p. 725)   En una muestra de voluntarios se seleccionan sólo a los miembros de la población que se ofrecen voluntariamente para ser parte de la muestra.

Sequence (p. 564)   A sequence is an ordered list of numbers.

Progresión (p. 564)   Una progresión es una sucesión de números.

Example   1, 4, 7, 10, . . .

Series (p. 587)   A series is the sum of the terms of a sequence.

Serie (p. 587)   Una serie es la suma de los términos de una secuencia.

Example   The series 3 + 6 + 9 + 12 + 15 corresponds to the sequence 3, 6, 9, 12, 15. The sum of the series is 45.

Simplest form of a radical expression (p. 368)   A radical expression with index n is in simplest form if there are no radicals in any denominator, no denominators in any radical, and any radicand has no nth power factors.

Mínima expresión de una expresión radical (p. 368)   Una expresión radical con índice n está en su mínima expresión si no tiene radicales en ningún denominador ni denominadores en ningún radical y los radicandos no tienen factores de potencia.

Simplest form of a rational expression (p. 527)   A rational expression is in simplest form if its numerator and denominator are polynomials that have no common divisor other than 1.

Forma simplificada de una expresión racional (p. 527)   Una expresión racional se encuentra en su mínima expresión si su numerador y su denominador son polinomios que no tienen otro divisor aparte de 1.

Example $\frac{x^2 - 7x + 12}{x^2 - 9} = \frac{(x - 4)(x - 3)}{(x + 3)(x - 3)} = \frac{x - 4}{x + 3}$, where $x \neq -3$

Simulation (p. 682)   A simulation is a model that imitates one or more events.

Simulación (p. 682)   Una simulación es un modelo que imita uno o más sucesos.

Example   Suppose a weather forecaster predicts a 50% chance of rain for the next three days. You can use three coins landing heads up to simulate three days in a row of rain.

English

Spanish

Sine curve (p. 852)   A sine curve is the graph of a sine function.

Sinusoide (p. 852)   Sinusoide es la gráfica de la función seno.

Example

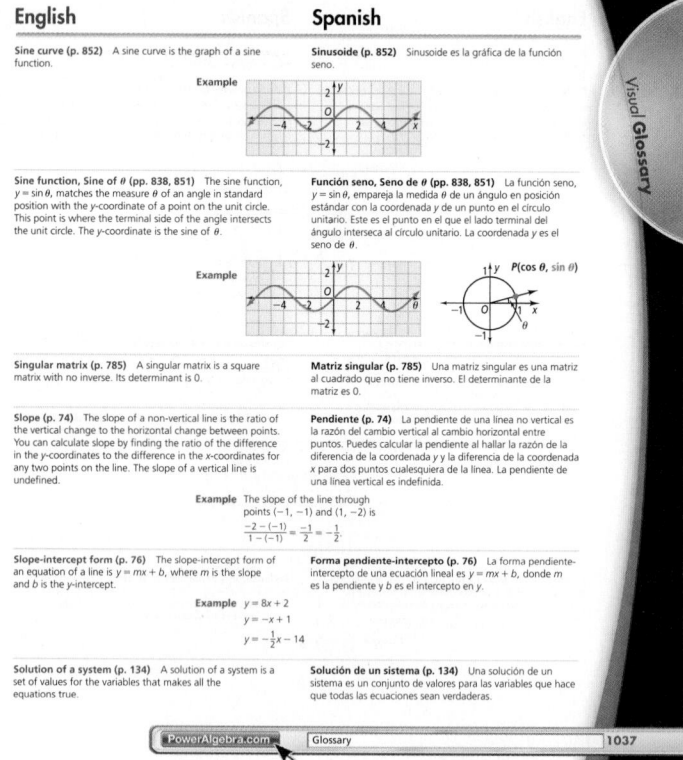

Sine function, Sine of θ (pp. 838, 851)   The sine function, $y = \sin \theta$, matches the measure θ of an angle in standard position to the y-coordinate of a point on the unit circle. This point is where the terminal side of the angle intersects the unit circle. The y-coordinate is the sine of θ.

Función seno, Seno de θ (pp. 838, 851)   La función seno, $y = \sin \theta$, empareja la medida θ de un ángulo en posición estándar con la coordenada y de un punto en el círculo unitario. Este es el punto en el que el lado terminal del ángulo interseca al círculo unitario. La coordenada y es el seno de θ.

Example

$P(\cos \theta, \sin \theta)$

Singular matrix (p. 785)   A singular matrix is a square matrix with no inverse. Its determinant is 0.

Matriz singular (p. 785)   Una matriz singular es una matriz al cuadrado que no tiene inverso. El determinante de la matriz es 0.

Slope (p. 74)   The slope of a non-vertical line is the ratio of the vertical change to the horizontal change between points. You can calculate slope by finding the ratio of the difference in the y-coordinates to the difference in the x-coordinates for any two points on the line. The slope of a vertical line is undefined.

Pendiente (p. 74)   La pendiente de una línea no vertical es la razón del cambio vertical al cambio horizontal entre puntos. Puedes calcular la pendiente al hallar la razón de la diferencia de la coordenada y y la diferencia de la coordenada x para dos puntos cualesquiera de la línea. La pendiente de una línea vertical es indefinida.

Example   The slope of the line through points $(-1, -1)$ and $(1, -2)$ is $\frac{-2 - (-1)}{1 - (-1)} = \frac{-1}{2} = -\frac{1}{2}$.

Slope-intercept form (p. 76)   The slope-intercept form of an equation of a line is $y = mx + b$, where m is the slope and b is the y-intercept.

Forma pendiente-intercepto (p. 76)   La forma pendiente-intercepto de una ecuación lineal es $y = mx + b$, donde m es la pendiente y b es el intercepto en y.

Example $y = 8x + 2$
$y = -x + 1$
$y = -\frac{1}{2}x - 14$

Solution of a system (p. 134)   A solution of a system is a set of values for the variables that makes all the equations true.

Solución de un sistema (p. 134)   Una solución de un sistema es un conjunto de valores para las variables que hace que todas las ecuaciones sean verdaderas.

English — Spanish

Solution of an equation (p. 27) A solution of an equation is a number that makes the equation true.

Solución de una ecuación (p. 27) Una solución de una ecuación es cualquier número que haga verdadera la ecuación.

Example The solution of $2x - 7 = -12$ is $x = -2.5$.

Square matrix (p. 782) A square matrix is a matrix with the same number of columns as rows.

Matriz cuadrada (p. 782) Una matriz cuadrada es la que tiene la misma cantidad de columnas y filas.

Example Matrix A is a square matrix.
$$A = \begin{bmatrix} 1 & 2 & 0 \\ -1 & 0 & -2 \\ 1 & 2 & 3 \end{bmatrix}$$

Square root equation (p. 390) A square root equation is a radical equation in which the radical has index 2.

Ecuación de raíz cuadrada (p. 390) Una ecuación de raíz cuadrada es una ecuación radical en la cual el radical tiene índice 2.

Example $\sqrt{x} = 4$

Square root function (p. 415) A square root function is a function that can be written in the form $f(x) = a\sqrt{x - h} + k$, where $a \neq 0$. The domain of a square root function is all real numbers $x \geq h$.

Función de raíz cuadrada (p. 415) Una función de raíz cuadrada es una función que puede ser expresada como $f(x) = a\sqrt{x - h} + k$, donde $a \neq 0$. El dominio de una función de raíz cuadrada son todos los números reales tales que $x \geq h$.

Example $f(x) = 2\sqrt{x - 3} + 4$

Standard deviation (p. 719) Standard deviation is a measure of how much the values in a data set vary, or deviate, from the mean, $\bar{x}$. To find the standard deviation, follow five steps:
· Find the mean of the data set.
· Find the difference between each data value and the mean.
· Square each difference.
· Find the mean of the squares.
· Take the square root of the mean of the squares. This is the standard deviation.

Desviación típica (p. 719) La desviación típica denota cuánto los valores de un conjunto de datos varían, o se desvían, de la media, $\bar{x}$. Para hallar la desviación típica, se siguen cinco pasos:
· Se halla la media del conjunto de datos.
· Se calcula la diferencia entre cada valor de datos y la media.
· Se eleva al cuadrado cada diferencia.
· Se halla la media de los cuadrados.
· Se calcula la raíz cuadrada de la media de los cuadrados. Ésa es la desviación típica.

Example $\{0, 2, 3, 4, 6, 7, 8, 9, 10, 11\}$
$\bar{x} = 6$
standard deviation $= \sqrt{12} \approx 3.46$

Standard form of a circle (p. 630) See **Circle**.

Forma normal de un círculo (p. 630) Ver **Circle**.

Example $(x - 3)^2 + (y - 4)^2 = 4$

English — Spanish

Standard form of a linear equation (p. 82) The standard form of a linear equation is $Ax + By = C$, where A, B, and C are real numbers, and A and B are not *both* zero.

Forma normal de una ecuación lineal (p. 82) La forma normal de una ecuación lineal es $Ax + By = C$, donde A, B y C son números reales, y A y B no son cero *ambos*.

Example In standard form, the equation
$$y = \frac{4}{3}x - 1 \text{ is}$$
$$4x + (-3)y = 3.$$

Standard form of a polynomial function (p. 281) The standard form of a polynomial function arranges the terms by degree in descending numerical order. A polynomial function, $P(x)$, in standard form is $P(x) = a_n x^n + a_{n-1}x^{n-1} + \cdots + a_1 x + a_0$, where n is a nonnegative integer and $a_n, \ldots, a_0$ are real numbers.

Forma normal de una función polinomial (p. 281) La forma normal de una función polinomial organiza los términos por grado en orden numérico descendente. Una función polinomial, $P(x)$, en forma normal es $P(x) = a_n x^n + a_{n-1}x^{n-1} + \cdots + a_1 x + a_0$, donde n es un número entero no negativo y $a_n, \ldots, a_0$ son números reales.

Example $2x^3 - 5x^2 - 2x + 5$

Standard form of a quadratic function (p. 202) The standard form of a quadratic function is $f(x) = ax^2 + bx + c$ with $a \neq 0$.

Forma normal de una función cuadrática (p. 202) La forma normal de una función cuadrática es $f(x) = ax^2 + bx + c$ CON $a \neq 0$.

Example $f(x) = 2x^2 + 5x + 2$

Standard position (p. 836) An angle in the coordinate plane is in **standard position** when the vertex is at the origin and one ray is on the positive x-axis.

Posición estándar (p. 836) Un ángulo en el plano de coordenadas se encuentra en **posición estándar** si el vértice se encuentra en el origen y una semirrecta se encuentra en el eje x positivo.

Example

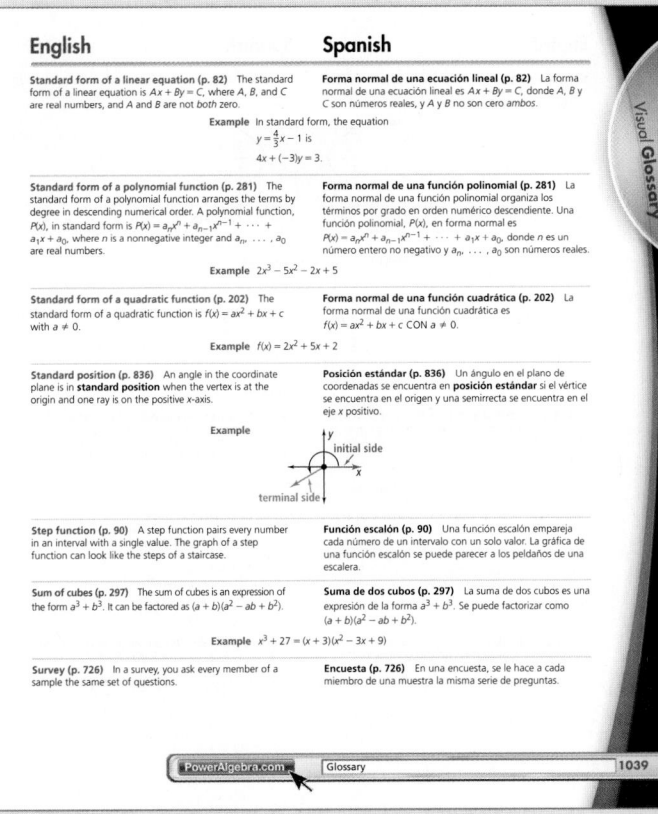

Step function (p. 90) A step function pairs every number in an interval with a single value. The graph of a step function can look like the steps of a staircase.

Función escalón (p. 90) Una función escalón empareja cada número de un intervalo con un solo valor. La gráfica de una función escalón se puede parecer a los peldaños de una escalera.

Sum of cubes (p. 297) The sum of cubes is an expression of the form $a^3 + b^3$. It can be factored as $(a + b)(a^2 - ab + b^2)$.

Suma de dos cubos (p. 297) La suma de dos cubos es una expresión de la forma $a^3 + b^3$. Se puede factorizar como $(a + b)(a^2 - ab + b^2)$.

Example $x^3 + 27 = (x + 3)(x^2 - 3x + 9)$

Survey (p. 726) In a survey, you ask every member of a sample the same set of questions.

Encuesta (p. 726) En una encuesta, se le hace a cada miembro de una muestra la misma serie de preguntas.

English — Spanish

Synthetic division (p. 306) Synthetic division is a process for dividing a polynomial by a linear expression $x - a$. You list the standard-form coefficients (including zeros) of the polynomial, omitting all variables and exponents. You use a for the "divisor" and add instead of subtract throughout the process.

División sintética (p. 306) La división sintética es un proceso para dividir un polinomio por una expresión lineal $x - a$. En este proceso, escribes los coeficientes de forma normal (incluyendo los ceros) del polinomio, omitiendo todas las variables y todos los exponentes. Usas a como "divisor" y sumas, en vez de restar, a lo largo del proceso.

Example
$$-3 \begin{array}{|rrrr} 2 & 5 & 0 & -2 & -8 \\ & -6 & 3 & -9 & 33 \\ \hline 2 & -1 & 3 & -11 & 25 \end{array}$$
Divide $2x^4 + 5x^3 - 2x - 8$ by
$x + 3$. $2x^4 + 5x^3 - 2x - 8$
divided by $x + 3$ gives
$2x^3 - x^2 + 3x - 11$ as quotient
and 25 as remainder.

System of equations (p. 134) A system of equations is a set of two or more equations using the same variables.

Sistema de ecuaciones (p. 134) Un sistema de ecuaciones es un conjunto de dos o más ecuaciones que contienen las mismas variables.

Example $\begin{cases} 2x - 3y = -13 \\ 4x + 5y = 7 \end{cases}$

Systematic sample (p. 725) In a systematic sample you order the population in some way, and then select from it at regular intervals.

Muestra sistemática (p. 725) En una muestra sistemática se ordena la población de cierta manera y luego se selecciona una muestra de esa población a intervalos regulares.

T

Tangent function, Tangent of θ (pp. 868, 869) The tangent function, $y = \tan\theta$, matches the measure θ, of an angle in standard position with the y/x ratio of the (x, y) coordinates of a point on the unit circle. This point is where the terminal side of the angle intersects the unit circle. y/x is the tangent of θ.

Función tangente, Tangente de θ (pp. 868, 869) La función tangente, $y = \tan\theta$, empareja la medida θ, de un ángulo en posición estándar con la razón y/x de las coordenadas (x, y) de un punto en el círculo unitario. Este es el punto en el que el lado terminal del ángulo interseca al círculo unitario. y/x es la tangente de θ.

Example

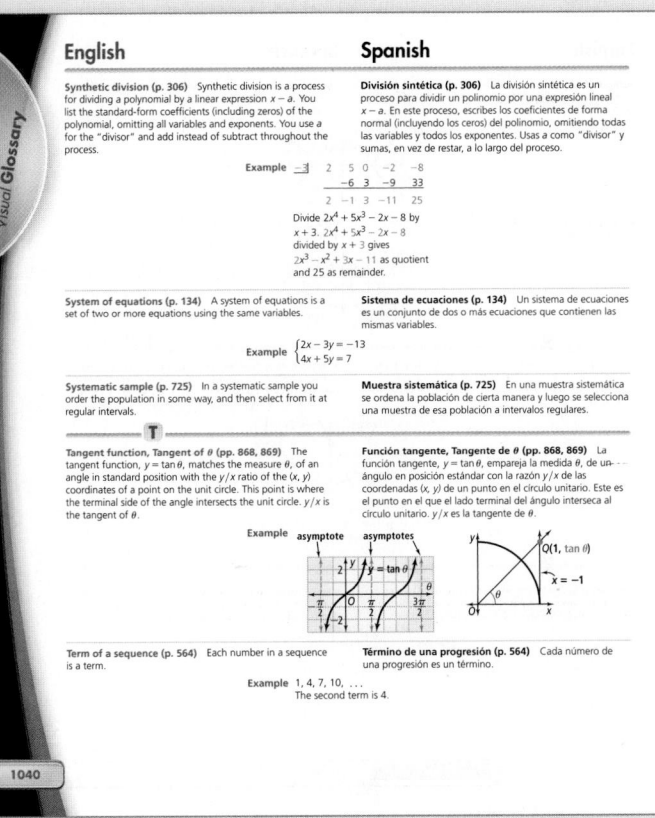

Term of a sequence (p. 564) Each number in a sequence is a term.

Término de una progresión (p. 564) Cada número de una progresión es un término.

Example $1, 4, 7, 10, \ldots$
The second term is 4.

English — Spanish

Term of an expression (p. 20) A term is a number, a variable, or the product of a number and one or more variables.

Término de una expresión (p. 20) Un término es un número, una variable o el producto de un número y una o más variables.

Example The expression $4x^2 - 3y + 7.3$ has 3 terms.

Terminal point (p. 809) The terminal point of a vector is the tip (not the endpoint) of a vector arrow.

Punto terminal (p. 809) El punto terminal de un vector es la punta (no el extremo) de una flecha vectorial.

Terminal side (p. 836) See **Initial side**.

Lado terminal (p. 836) Ver **Initial side**.

Test point (p. 115) A test point is a point that you pick on one side of the boundary of the graph of a linear inequality. If the test point makes the inequality true, then all points on that side of the boundary are solutions of the inequality. If the test point makes the inequality false, then all points on the other side are solutions.

Punto de prueba (p. 115) Un punto de prueba es un punto que escoges a un lado del límite de la gráfica de una desigualdad lineal. Si el punto de prueba hace que la desigualdad sea verdadera, entonces todos los puntos en ese límite son soluciones de la desigualdad. Si el punto de prueba hace que la desigualdad sea falsa, entonces todos los puntos al otro lado del límite son soluciones.

Theoretical probability (p. 683) If a sample space has n equally likely outcomes, and an event A occurs in m of these outcomes, then the theoretical probability of event A is $P(A) = \frac{m}{n}$.

Probabilidad teórica (p. 683) Si un espacio muestral tiene n resultados con la misma probabilidad de ocurrir, y ocurre un suceso A en m de estos resultados, entonces la probabilidad teórica del suceso A es $P(A) = \frac{m}{n}$.

Example Use the set $\{1, 4, 9, 16, 25, 36, 49, 64, 81, 100\}$. The probability that a number selected at random is greater than 50 is $P(A) = \frac{3}{10} = 0.3$.

Transformation (p. 99) A transformation of a function $y = af(x - h) + k$ is a change made to at least one of the values a, h, and k. The four types of transformations are dilations, reflections, rotations, and translations.

Transformación (p. 99) Una transformación de una función $y = af(x - h) + k$ es un cambio que se le hace a por lo menos uno de los valores a, h y k. Hay cuatro tipos de transformaciones: dilataciones, reflexiones, rotaciones y traslaciones.

Example $g(x) = 2(x - 3)$ is a transformation of $f(x) = x$.

Translation (p. 99) A translation shifts the graph of the parent function horizontally, vertically, or both without changing its shape or orientation.

Traslación (p. 99) Una traslación desplaza la gráfica de la función madre horizontalmente, verticalmente o en ambas direcciones, sin cambiar su forma u orientación.

Example

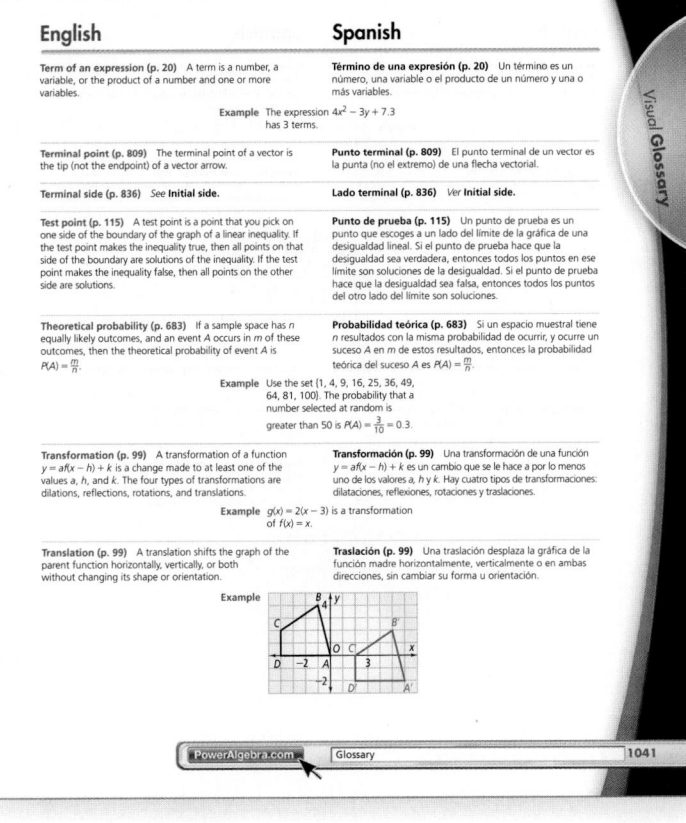

Transverse axis (p. 646) The transverse axis of a hyperbola is the segment that is on the line containing the foci and has endpoints on the hyperbola.

Eje transversal (p. 646) El eje transversal de una hipérbola es el segmento que se encuentra sobre la línea que contiene los focos y tiene sus puntos extremos sobre la hipérbola.

Example
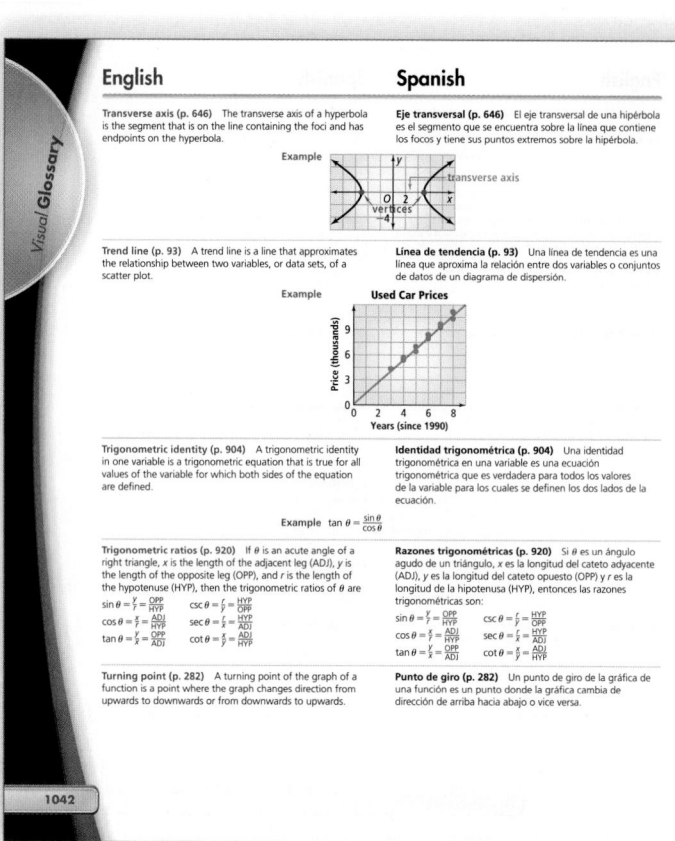
transverse axis / vertices

Trend line (p. 93) A trend line is a line that approximates the relationship between two variables, or data sets, of a scatter plot.

Línea de tendencia (p. 93) Una línea de tendencia es una línea que aproxima la relación entre dos variables o conjuntos de datos de un diagrama de dispersión.

Example

Used Car Prices

Trigonometric identity (p. 904) A trigonometric identity in one variable is a trigonometric equation that is true for all values of the variable for which both sides of the equation are defined.

Identidad trigonométrica (p. 904) Una identidad trigonométrica en una variable es una ecuación trigonométrica que es verdadera para todos los valores de la variable para las cuales se definen los dos lados de la ecuación.

Example $\tan\theta = \frac{\sin\theta}{\cos\theta}$

Trigonometric ratios (p. 920) If θ is an acute angle of a right triangle, x is the length of the adjacent leg (ADJ), y is the length of the opposite leg (OPP), and r is the length of the hypotenuse (HYP), then the trigonometric ratios of θ are
$\sin\theta = \frac{y}{r} = \frac{OPP}{HYP}$ $\csc\theta = \frac{r}{y} = \frac{HYP}{OPP}$
$\cos\theta = \frac{x}{r} = \frac{ADJ}{HYP}$ $\sec\theta = \frac{r}{x} = \frac{HYP}{ADJ}$
$\tan\theta = \frac{y}{x} = \frac{OPP}{ADJ}$ $\cot\theta = \frac{x}{y} = \frac{ADJ}{HYP}$

Razones trigonométricas (p. 920) Si θ es un ángulo agudo de un triángulo, x es la longitud del cateto adyacente (ADJ), y es la longitud del cateto opuesto (OPP) y r es la longitud de la hipotenusa (HYP), entonces las razones trigonométricas son:
$\sin\theta = \frac{y}{r} = \frac{OPP}{HYP}$ $\csc\theta = \frac{r}{y} = \frac{HYP}{OPP}$
$\cos\theta = \frac{x}{r} = \frac{ADJ}{HYP}$ $\sec\theta = \frac{r}{x} = \frac{HYP}{ADJ}$
$\tan\theta = \frac{y}{x} = \frac{OPP}{ADJ}$ $\cot\theta = \frac{x}{y} = \frac{ADJ}{HYP}$

Turning point (p. 282) A turning point of the graph of a function is a point where the graph changes direction from upwards to downwards or from downwards to upwards.

Punto de giro (p. 282) Un punto de giro de la gráfica de una función es un punto donde la gráfica cambia de dirección de arriba hacia abajo o vice versa.

Uniform Distribution (p. 694) A uniform distribution is a probability distribution that is equal for each event in the sample space.

Distribución uniforme (p. 694) Una distribución uniforme es una distribución de probabilidad que es igual para cada suceso en el espacio muestral.

Unit circle (p. 838) The unit circle has a radius of 1 unit and its center is at the origin of the coordinate plane.

Círculo unitario (p. 838) El círculo unitario tiene un radio de 1 unidad y el centro está en el origen del plano de coordenadas.

Example
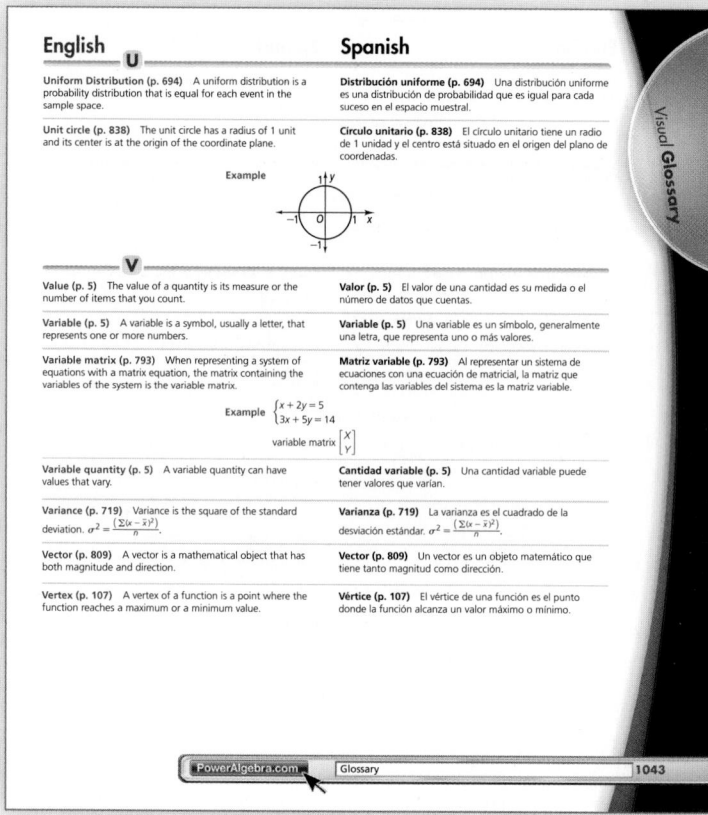

V

Value (p. 5) The value of a quantity is its measure or the number of items that you count.

Valor (p. 5) El valor de una cantidad es su medida o el número de datos que cuentas.

Variable (p. 5) A variable is a symbol, usually a letter, that represents one or more numbers.

Variable (p. 5) Una variable es un símbolo, generalmente una letra, que representa uno o más valores.

Variable matrix (p. 793) When representing a system of equations with a matrix equation, the matrix containing the variables of the system is the variable matrix.

Matriz variable (p. 793) Al representar un sistema de ecuaciones con una ecuación de matricial, la matriz que contenga las variables del sistema es la matriz variable.

Example $\begin{cases} x + 2y = 5 \\ 3x + 5y = 14 \end{cases}$
variable matrix $\begin{bmatrix} x \\ y \end{bmatrix}$

Variable quantity (p. 5) A variable quantity can have values that vary.

Cantidad variable (p. 5) Una cantidad variable puede tener valores que varían.

Variance (p. 719) Variance is the square of the standard deviation. $\sigma^2 = \frac{\left(\sum (x - \bar{x})^2\right)}{n}$.

Varianza (p. 719) La varianza es el cuadrado de la desviación estándar. $\sigma^2 = \frac{\left(\sum (x - \bar{x})^2\right)}{n}$.

Vector (p. 809) A vector is a mathematical object that has both magnitude and direction.

Vector (p. 809) Un vector es un objeto matemático que tiene tanto magnitud como dirección.

Vertex (p. 107) A vertex of a function is a point where the function reaches a maximum or a minimum value.

Vértice (p. 107) El vértice de una función es el punto donde la función alcanza un valor máximo o mínimo.

Vertex form of a quadratic function (p. 194) The vertex form of a quadratic function is $f(x) = a(x - h)^2 + k$, where $a \neq 0$ and (h, k) is the coordinate of the vertex of the function.

Forma del vértice de una función cuadrática (p. 194) La forma vértice de una función cuadrática es $f(x) = a(x - h)^2 + k$, donde $a \neq 0$ y (h, k) es la coordenada del vértice de la función.

Example $f(x) = x^2 + 2x - 1 = (x + 1)^2 - 2$
The vertex is $(-1, -2)$.

Vertex of a parabola (p. 194) The vertex of a parabola is the point where the function for the parabola reaches a maximum or a minimum value. The parabola intersects its axis of symmetry at the vertex.

Vértice de una parábola (p. 194) El vértice de una parábola es el punto donde la función de la parábola alcanza un valor máximo o mínimo. La parábola y su eje de simetría se intersecan en el vértice.

Example
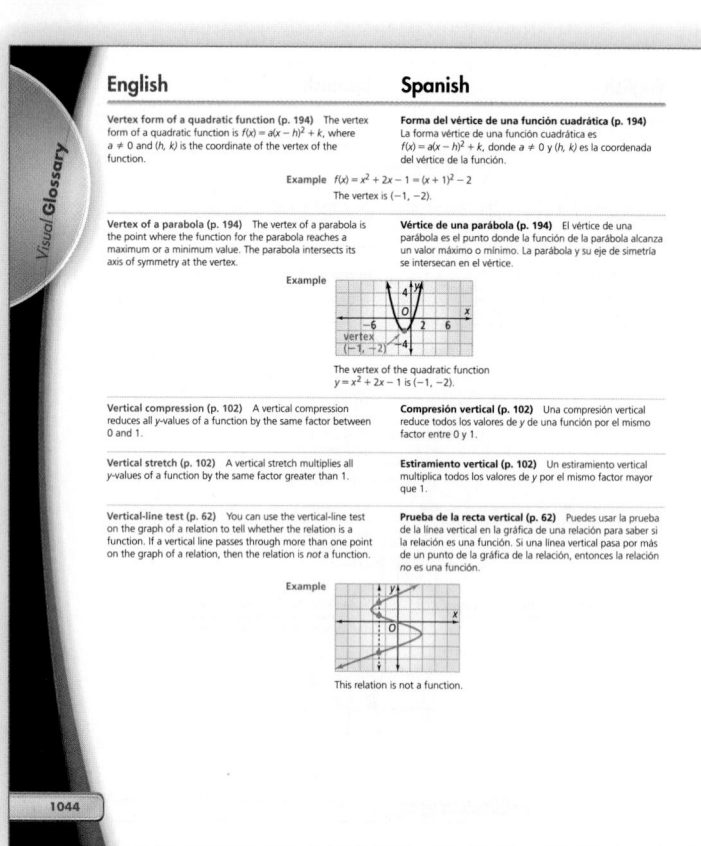
vertex $(-1, -2)$

The vertex of the quadratic function $y = x^2 + 2x - 1$ is $(-1, -2)$.

Vertical compression (p. 102) A vertical compression reduces all y-values of a function by the same factor between 0 and 1.

Compresión vertical (p. 102) Una compresión vertical reduce todos los valores de y de una función por el mismo factor entre 0 y 1.

Vertical stretch (p. 102) A vertical stretch multiplies all y-values of a function by the same factor greater than 1.

Estiramiento vertical (p. 102) Un estiramiento vertical multiplica todos los valores de y por el mismo factor mayor que 1.

Vertical-line test (p. 62) You can use the vertical-line test on the graph of a relation to tell whether the relation is a function. If a vertical line passes through more than one point on the graph of a relation, then the relation is *not* a function.

Prueba de la recta vertical (p. 62) Puedes usar la prueba de la línea vertical en la gráfica de una relación para saber si la relación es una función. Si una línea vertical pasa por más de un punto de la gráfica de la relación, entonces la relación *no* es una función.

Example

This relation is not a function.

Vertices of a hyperbola (p. 646) The endpoints of the transverse axis of a hyperbola are the vertices of the hyperbola.

Vértices de una hipérbola (p. 646) Los dos puntos de intersección de la hipérbola y su eje mayor son los vértices de la hipérbola.

Example
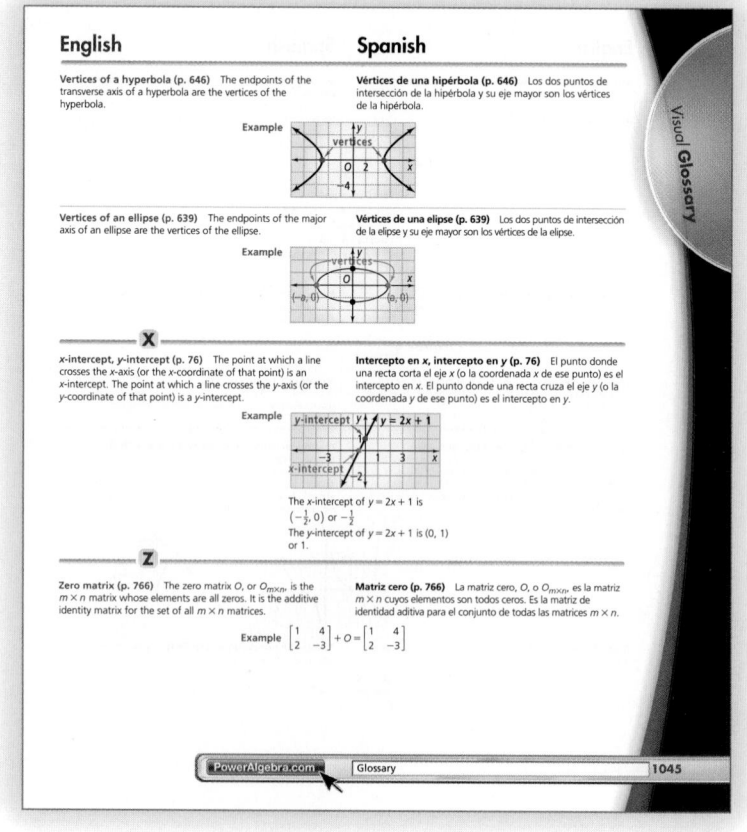
vertices

Vertices of an ellipse (p. 639) The endpoints of the major axis of an ellipse are the vertices of the ellipse.

Vértices de una elipse (p. 639) Los dos puntos de intersección de la elipse y su eje mayor son los vértices de la elipse.

Example
vertices

x-intercept, y-intercept (p. 76) The point at which a line crosses the x-axis (or the x-coordinate of that point) is an x-intercept. The point at which a line crosses the y-axis (or the y-coordinate of that point) is a y-intercept.

Intercepto en x, intercepto en y (p. 76) El punto donde una recta corta el eje x (o la coordenada x de ese punto) es el intercepto en x. El punto donde una recta cruza el eje y (o la coordenada y de ese punto) es el intercepto en y.

Example
y-intercept $y = 2x + 1$
x-intercept

The x-intercept of $y = 2x + 1$ is $\left(-\frac{1}{2}, 0\right)$ or $-\frac{1}{2}$
The y-intercept of $y = 2x + 1$ is $(0, 1)$ or 1.

Z

Zero matrix (p. 766) The zero matrix O, or $O_{m \times n}$, is the $m \times n$ matrix whose elements are all zeros. It is the additive identity matrix for the set of all $m \times n$ matrices.

Matriz cero (p. 766) La matriz cero, O, o $O_{m \times n}$ es la matriz $m \times n$ cuyos elementos son todos ceros. Es la matriz de identidad aditiva para el conjunto de todas las matrices $m \times n$.

Example $\begin{bmatrix} 1 & 4 \\ 2 & -3 \end{bmatrix} + O = \begin{bmatrix} 1 & 4 \\ 2 & -3 \end{bmatrix}$

English	Spanish
Zero of a function (p. 226) A zero of a function $f(x)$ is any value of x for which $f(x) = 0$.	**Cero de una función (p. 226)** Un cero de una función $f(x)$ es cualquier valor de x para el cual $f(x) = 0$.

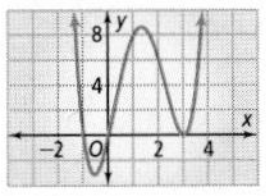

Example

Zero-Product Property (p. 226) If the product of two or more factors is zero, then one of the factors must be zero.	**Propiedad del cero del producto (p. 226)** Si el producto de dos o más factores es cero, entonces uno de los factores debe ser cero.

Example $(x - 3)(2x - 5) = 0$
$x - 3 = 0$ or $2x - 5 = 0$

z-score (p. 748) The z-score of a value is the number of standard deviations that the value is from the mean.	**Puntaje z (p. 748)** El puntaje z de un valor es el número de desviaciones normales que tiene ese valor de la media.

Example $\{0, 2, 3, 4, 6, 7, 8, 9, 10, 11\}$
$\bar{x} = 6$
standard deviation $= \sqrt{12} \approx 3.46$
For 8, z-score $= \frac{8 - 6}{\sqrt{12}} \approx 0.58$.

1046

Selected Answers

Chapter 1

Get Ready! pp. 1 1. 0 2. −2 3. −2.09 4. 8.05
5. $-\frac{3}{4}$ 6. $\frac{11}{12}$ 7. $10\frac{7}{10}$ 8. $3\frac{1}{9}$ 9. −42 10. 72 11. 9
12. −9.8 13. $-3\frac{1}{3}$ 14. $-\frac{1}{2}$ 15. $-4\frac{5}{9}$ 16. $-\frac{3}{4}$
17. −21 18. 7.35 19. $-\frac{1}{5}$ 20. $-\frac{3}{5}$ 21. −20 22. 8
23. 0.97 24. −5 25. 55 26. 3 27. because the placement of the parentheses changes the order of operations 28. 3 29. 3 terms 30. Calculate the answer numerically. 31. $\frac{-3}{n-3}$

Lesson 1-1 pp. 4–10

Got It? 1. The pattern shows a center square and a yellow square added to each side with the number of squares per side increasing by one.

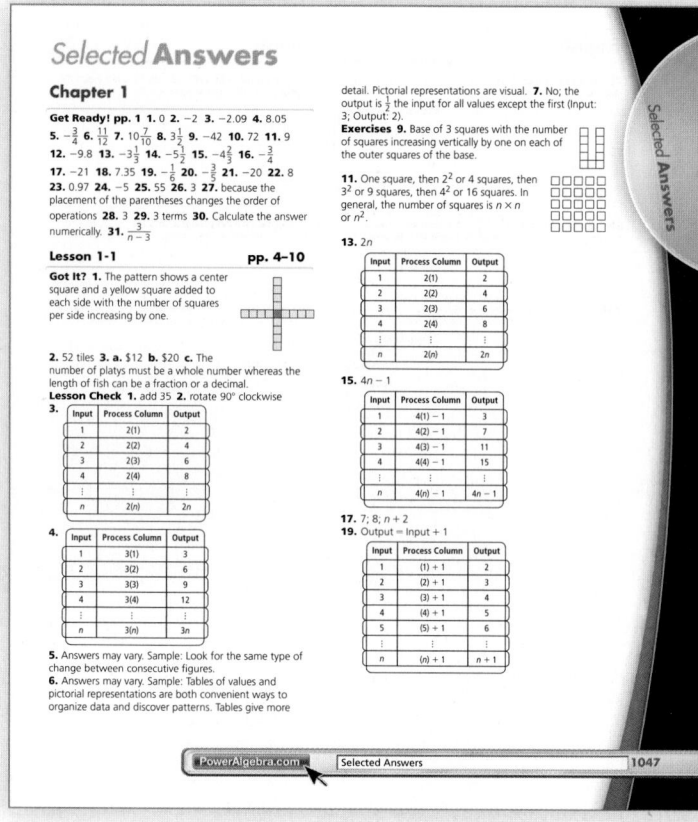

2. 52 tiles 3. a. $12 b. $20 c. The number of platys must be a whole number whereas the length of fish can be a fraction or a decimal.
Lesson Check 1. add 35 2. rotate 90° clockwise
3.

Input	Process Column	Output
1	2(1)	2
2	2(2)	4
3	2(3)	6
4	2(4)	8
⋮	⋮	⋮
n	2(n)	2n

4.

Input	Process Column	Output
1	3(1)	3
2	3(2)	6
3	3(3)	9
4	3(4)	12
⋮	⋮	⋮
n	3(n)	3n

5. Answers may vary. Sample: Look for the same type of change between consecutive figures.
6. Answers may vary. Sample: Tables of values and pictorial representations are both convenient ways to organize data and discover patterns. Tables give more detail. Pictorial representations are visual. 7. No; the output is $\frac{1}{3}$ the input for all values except the first (Input: 3; Output: 2).
Exercises 9. Base of 3 squares with the number of squares increasing vertically by one on each of the outer squares of the base.

11. One square, then 2^2 or 4 squares, then 3^2 or 9 squares, then 4^2 or 16 squares. In general, the number of squares is $n \times n$ or n^2.

13. 2n

Input	Process Column	Output
1	2(1)	2
2	2(2)	4
3	2(3)	6
4	2(4)	8
⋮	⋮	⋮
n	2(n)	2n

15. 4n − 1

Input	Process Column	Output
1	4(1) − 1	3
2	4(2) − 1	7
3	4(3) − 1	11
4	4(4) − 1	15
⋮	⋮	⋮
n	4(n) − 1	4n − 1

17. 7; 8; n + 2
19. Output = Input + 1

Input	Process Column	Output
1	(1) + 1	2
2	(2) + 1	3
3	(3) + 1	4
4	(4) + 1	5
5	(5) + 1	6
⋮	⋮	⋮
n	(n) + 1	n + 1

---

21. Output = Input − 1

Input	Process Column	Output
1	(1) − 1	0
2	(2) − 1	1
3	(3) − 1	2
4	(4) − 1	3
5	(5) − 1	4
⋮	⋮	⋮
n	(n) − 1	n − 1

23. 40 25. add 6 or 6n; 30, 36, 42 27. add 3, then add 4, then add 5, and so on; 21, 28, 36 29. multiply by 3; 243, 729, 2187 31. The black square and dot each move clockwise one block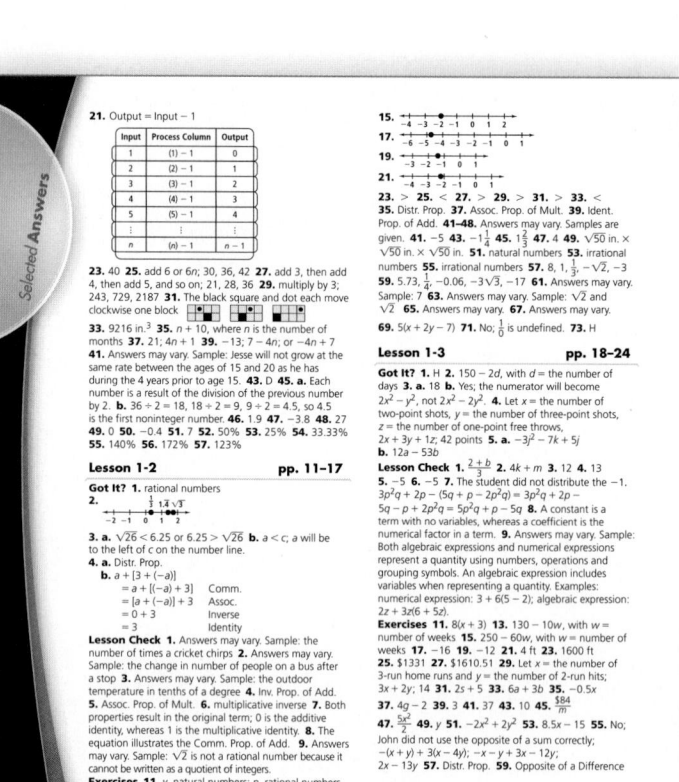
33. 9216 in.³ 35. n + 10, where n is the number of months 37. 21; 4n + 1 39. −13; 7 − 4n; or −4n + 7 41. Answers may vary. Sample: Jesse will not grow at the same rate between the ages of 15 and 20 as he has during the 4 years prior to age 15. 43. D 45. a. Each number is a result of the division of the previous number by 2. b. 36 ÷ 2 = 18, 18 ÷ 2 = 9, 9 ÷ 2 = 4.5, so 4.5 is the first noninteger number. 46. 1.9 47. −3.8 48. 27 49. 0 50. −0.4 51. 7 52. 50% 53. 25% 54. 33.33% 55. 140% 56. 172% 57. 123%

Lesson 1-2 pp. 11–17
Got It? 1. rational numbers
2. [number line]
3. a. $\sqrt{26} < 6.25$ or $6.25 > \sqrt{26}$ b. a < c; a will be to the left of c on the number line.
4. a. Distr. Prop.
b. $a + [3 + (-a)]$
$= a + [(-a) + 3]$ Comm.
$= [a + (-a)] + 3$ Assoc.
$= 0 + 3$ Inverse
$= 3$ Identity
Lesson Check 1. Answers may vary. Sample: the number of times a cricket chirps 2. Answers may vary. Sample: the change in number of people on a bus after a stop 3. Answers may vary. Sample: the outdoor temperature in tenths of a degree 4. Inv. Prop. of Add. 5. Assoc. Prop. of Mult. 6. multiplicative inverse 7. Both properties result in the original term; 0 is the additive identity, whereas 1 is the multiplicative identity. 8. The equation illustrates the Comm. Prop. of Add. 9. Answers may vary. Sample: $\sqrt{2}$ is not a rational number because it cannot be written as a quotient of integers.
Exercises 11. y, natural numbers; p, rational numbers
13. [number line]

15. [number line]
17. [number line]
19. [number line]
21. [number line]
23. > 25. < 27. > 29. > 31. > 33. <
35. Distr. Prop. 37. Assoc. Prop. of Mult. 39. Ident. Prop. of Add. 41–48. Answers may vary. Samples are given. 41. −5 43. $-1\frac{1}{4}$ 45. $1\frac{5}{9}$ 47. 49. $\sqrt{50}$ in. × $\sqrt{50}$ in. × $\sqrt{50}$ in. 51. natural numbers 53. irrational numbers 55. irrational numbers 57. $8, 1, \frac{1}{3}, -\sqrt{2}, -3$
59. $5.73, 1\frac{1}{4}, -0.06, -3\sqrt{3}, -17$ 61. Answers may vary. Sample: 7 63. Answers may vary. Sample: $\sqrt{2}$ and $\sqrt{2}$ 65. Answers may vary. 67. Answers may vary.
69. 5(x + 2y − 7) 71. No; $\frac{1}{0}$ is undefined. 73. H

Lesson 1-3 pp. 18–24
Got It? 1. H 2. 150 − 2d, with d = the number of days 3. a. 18 b. Yes; the numerator will become $2x^2 - y^2$, not $2x^2 - 2y^2$. 4. Let x = the number of two-point shots, y = the number of three-point shots, z = the number of one-point free throws, 2x + 3y + 1z; 42 points 5. a. $-3j^2 - 7k + 5j$ b. 12a − 53b
Lesson Check 1. $\frac{2 + b}{3}$ 2. 4k + m 3. 12 4. 13 5. −5 6. −5 7. The student did not distribute the −1. $3p^2q + 2p - (5q + p - 2p^2q) = 3p^2q + 2p - 5q - p + 2p^2q = 5p^2q + p - 5q$ 8. A constant is a term with no variables, whereas a coefficient is the numerical factor in a term. 9. Answers may vary. Sample: Both algebraic expressions and numerical expressions represent a quantity using numbers, operations and grouping symbols. An algebraic expression includes variables when representing a quantity. Examples: numerical expression: 3 + 6(5 − 2); algebraic expression: 2z + 3x(6 + 5z).
Exercises 11. 8(x + 3) 13. 130 − 10w, with w = number of weeks 17. −16 19. −12 21. 4 ft 23. 1600 ft 25. $1331 27. $1610.51 29. Let x = the number of 3-run home runs and y = the number of 2-run hits; 3x + 2y; 14 31. 2s + 5 33. 6a + 3b 35. −0.5x
37. 4g − 2 39. 3 41. 37 43. 10 45. $\frac{84}{m}$
47. $\frac{5x^2}{2}$ 49. y 51. $-2x^2 + 2y^2$ 53. 8.5x − 15 55. No; John did not use the opposite of a sum correctly; −(x + y) + 3(x − 4y); −x − y + 3x − 12y; 2x − 13y 57. Distr. Prop. 59. Opposite of a Difference

---

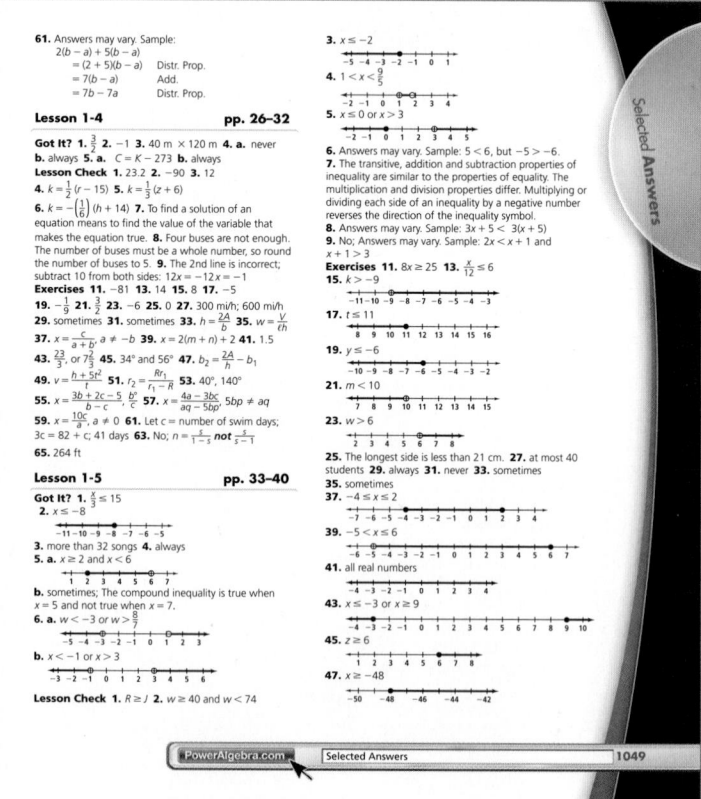

61. Answers may vary. Sample:
$2(b - a) + 5(b - a)$
$= (2 + 5)(b - a)$ Distr. Prop.
$= 7(b - a)$ Add.
$= 7b - 7a$ Distr. Prop.

Lesson 1-4 pp. 26–32
Got It? 1. $\frac{3}{2}$ 2. −1 3. 40 m × 120 m 4. a. never b. always 5. a. C = K − 273 b. always
Lesson Check 1. 23.2 2. −90 3. 12
4. $k = \frac{1}{2}(r - 15)$ 5. $k = \frac{1}{3}(z + 6)$
6. $k = -\left(\frac{1}{6}\right)(h + 14)$ 7. To find a solution of an equation means to find the value of the variable that makes the equation true. 8. Four buses are not enough. The number of buses must be a whole number, so round the number of buses to 5. 9. The 2nd line is incorrect; subtract 10 from both sides: 12x = −12x = −1
Exercises 11. −81 13. 14 15. 8 17. −5
19. $-\frac{1}{9}$ 21. $\frac{2}{3}$ 23. 25. 0 27. 300 mi/h; 600 mi/h
29. sometimes 31. sometimes 33. $h = \frac{2A}{b}$ 35. $w = \frac{V}{\ell h}$
37. $x = \frac{c}{a+b}, a \neq -b$ 39. x = 2(m + n) + 2 41. 1.5
43. $2\frac{3}{5}$, or $7\frac{3}{5}$ 45. 34° and 56° 47. $b_2 = \frac{2A}{h} - b_1$
49. $v = \frac{h + 5t^2}{t}$ 51. $r_2 = \frac{Rr_1}{r_1 - R}$ 53. 40°, 140°
55. $x = \frac{3b + 2c - 5}{b - c}$, c 57. $x = \frac{4a - 3bc}{aq - 5bp}$, $5bp \neq aq$
59. $x = \frac{10c}{a}, a \neq 0$ 61. Let c = number of swim days; 3c = 82 + c; 41 days 63. No; $n = \frac{k}{1 - 5}$ not $\frac{k}{5 - 1}$
65. 264 ft

Lesson 1-5 pp. 33–40
Got It? 1. $\frac{5}{9} \leq 15$
2. x ≤ −8
[number line]
3. more than 32 songs 4. always
5. a. x ≥ 2 and x < 6
[number line]
b. sometimes; The compound inequality is true when x = 5 and not true when x = 7.
6. a. $w < -3$ or $w > \frac{5}{2}$
[number line]
b. x < −1 or x > 3
[number line]
Lesson Check 1. R ≥ J 2. w ≥ 40 and w < 74

3. x ≤ −2
[number line]
4. $1 < x < \frac{5}{2}$
[number line]
5. x ≤ 0 or x > 3
[number line]
6. Answers may vary. Sample: 5 < 6, but −5 > −6.
7. The transitive, addition and subtraction properties of inequality are similar to the properties of equality. The multiplication and division properties differ. Multiplying or dividing each side of an inequality by a negative number reverses the direction of the inequality symbol.
8. Answers may vary. Sample: 3x + 5 < 3(x + 5)
9. No; Answers may vary. Sample: 2x < x + 1 and x + 1 > 3
Exercises 11. 8x ≥ 25 13. $\frac{x}{12} \leq 6$
15. k > −9
[number line]
17. t ≤ 11
[number line]
19. y ≤ −6
[number line]
21. m < 10
[number line]
23. w > 6
[number line]
25. The longest side is less than 21 cm. 27. at most 40 students 29. always 31. never 33. sometimes 35. sometimes
37. −4 ≤ x ≤ 2
[number line]
39. −5 < x ≤ 6
[number line]
41. all real numbers
[number line]
43. x ≤ −3 or x ≥ 9
[number line]
45. z ≥ 6
[number line]
47. x ≥ −48
[number line]

49. no solution **51.** 98 **53.** $2 < A8 < 6$ **55.** The classmate reversed the direction of the ≥ symbol to ≤ incorrectly. The correct answer is $y \le -20$. **57.** Distr. Prop.; arithmetic; Subtr. Prop. of Inequality; Mult. Prop. of Inequality
59. $-1 < x < 8$

61. $x < -2$ or $x > 2$

63. Answers may vary. Sample: $-3x + 1 > 4$
65. Answers may vary. Sample: $2x + 4 \le 0$ or $-3x - 3 \le 0$
67. D **69.** D **71.** $7a + 5$ **72.** $-2x + 14y$
73. $\frac{b}{12} + 1$ **74.** $1.61 - 0.1k$ **75.** 4
76. no solution **77.** $\frac{9}{10}$ **78.** -20

Lesson 1-6   pp. 41–48

Got It?
1. $\frac{5}{3}$, -2

2. -7, -11

3. -1 **4.** $-\frac{4}{3} \le x \le 4$

5. a. $x < -5$ or $x > 1$

b. The graph will have two closed circles with an arrow extending to the left of one and to the right of the other. **6.** $|h - 52.5| \le 0.5$
Lesson Check 1. -4, 4 **2.** -12, 4 **3.** $-\frac{6}{5}$
4. $-11 < x < 9$

5. $x \le -1$ or $x \ge 4$

6. A solution of an eq. is extraneous if it is a solution to a derived eq., but is not a solution to the original eq. **7.** when the number is positive or 0 **8.** Answers may vary. Sample: $d < -5$ and $5d > 25$ **9.** Answers may vary. Sample: An absolute value equation or inequality represents two equations or inequalities; each equation or inequality is solved in the same manner as a linear equation or inequality.
Exercises 11. -8, 8 **13.** $-\frac{5}{3}$, 3 **15.** no solution
17. -7, 17 **19.** $-\frac{3}{2}$ **21.** $\frac{3}{2}$ **23.** -1, $\frac{1}{2}$

25. $0 < y < 18$

27. $-2 < x < 6$

29. $-3\frac{1}{2} \le w \le \frac{1}{2}$

31. $x < -12$ or $x > 6$

33. $y \le -9$ or $y \ge 15$

35. $x \le -3$ or $x \ge 4$

37. $|h - 1.4| \le 0.1$ **39.** $|C - 27.5| \le 0.25$
41. $|m - 1250| \le 50$ **43.** no solution **45.** $-\frac{14}{3}$, $\frac{16}{3}$
47. no solution **49.** $\frac{11}{3}$, $\frac{1}{3}$ **51.** $-\frac{71}{36}$ **53.** $|c - 28.75| \le 0.25$; 0.25; 28.50 ≤ c ≤ 29.00 **55.** $|x| < 4$
57. $-6 \le x \le 8\frac{1}{2}$

59. all real numbers

61. all real numbers

63. $x \le -8.4$ or $x \ge 9.6$

65. $-5 < x < 11$

67. The graph of $|x| < a$ is the set of all points on the number line that lie between a and $-a$. The graph of $|x| > a$ has two parts; the left part consists of the points to the left of $-a$, and the right part consists of the points to the right of a. **69.** $|t - 350| \le 5$ **71.** $|t - 15| \le 30$ **73.** $|x - 9.55| \le 0.02$; $9.53 \le x \le 9.57$ **75.** never; absolute value is nonnegative **77.** sometimes; $|5| = 5$ but $|-5| \ne -5$ **79.** sometimes; $|-4 + 2| \ne -4 + 2$ **81.** The "3" in the second set of equations should be "-3."

$$-4x + 1 < -3$$
$$-4x < -4$$
$$x > 1 \text{ not } x > -\frac{1}{2}$$

83. $\frac{ab + d}{c}$, $\frac{-ab + d}{c}$, $c \ne 0$, $ab \ge 0$
85. $(-6 \le x \le -5)$ or $(5 \le x \le 6)$

---

87. $x \ge \frac{5}{2}$

89. Use *and* if the absolute value is less than a value and use *or* if the absolute value is greater than a value.
91. 0 **93.** 0.04
94. $y < 6$

95. $s < \frac{7}{15}$

96. $a > 4$

97. Each figure has 4 more squares than the previous figure.

98. Each figure n has n more circles than the previous figure.

99. 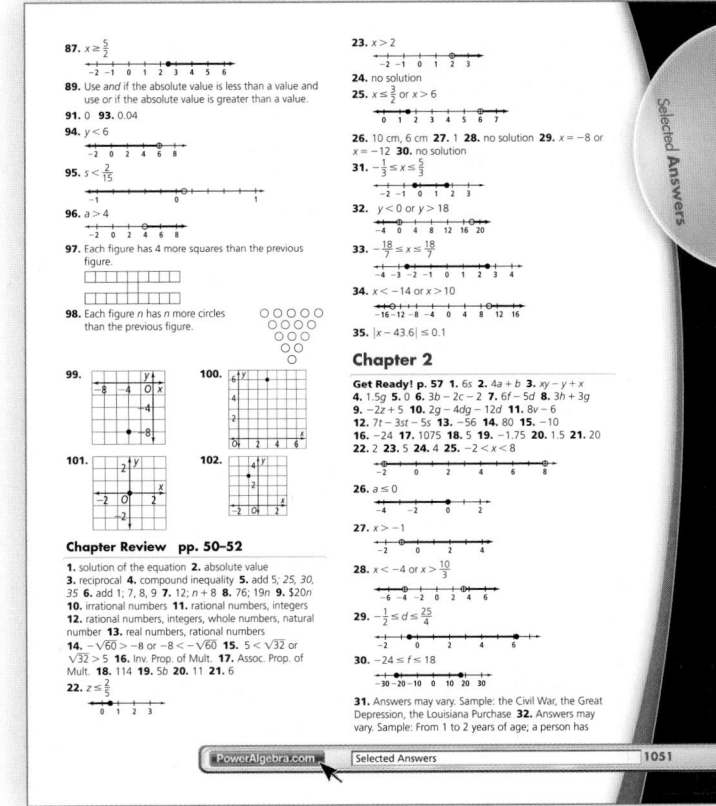 **100.**

101. **102.**

Chapter Review   pp. 50–52

1. solution of the equation **2.** absolute value **3.** reciprocal **4.** compound inequality **5.** add 5; 25, 30, 35 **6.** add 1; 7, 8, 9, 7, 12; $n + 8$ 8. 76; 19n **9.** $20n **10.** irrational numbers **11.** rational numbers, integers **12.** rational numbers, integers, whole numbers, natural number **13.** real numbers, rational numbers **14.** $-\sqrt{60} > -8$ or $-8 < -\sqrt{60}$ **15.** $5 < \sqrt{32}$ or $\sqrt{32} > 5$ **16.** Inv. Prop. of Mult. **17.** Assoc. Prop. of Mult. **18.** 114 **19.** $5b$ **20.** 11 **21.** 6
22. $z \le \frac{5}{2}$

---

23. $x > 2$

24. no solution
25. $x \le \frac{3}{2}$ or $x > 6$

26. 10 cm, 6 cm **27.** 1 **28.** no solution **29.** $x = -8$ or $x = -12$ **30.** no solution
31. $-\frac{1}{3} \le x \le \frac{5}{3}$

32. $y < 0$ or $y > 18$

33. $-\frac{18}{5} \le x \le \frac{18}{5}$

34. $x < -14$ or $x > 10$

35. $|x - 43.6| \le 0.1$

Chapter 2

Get Ready! p. 57 1. $6s$ **2.** $4a + b$ **3.** $xy - y + x$ **4.** $1.5g$ **5.** 0 **6.** $3b - 2c - 2$ **7.** $6f - 5d$ **8.** $3h + 3g$ **9.** $-2z + 5$ **10.** $2g - 4dg - 12d$ **11.** $8v - 6$ **12.** $7t - 3st - 5s$ **13.** -56 **14.** 80 **15.** -10 **16.** -24 **17.** 1075 **18.** 5 **19.** -1.75 **20.** 1.5 **21.** 20 **22.** 2 **23.** 5 **24.** 4 **25.** $-2 < x < 8$

26. $a \le 0$

27. $x > -1$

28. $x < -4$ or $x > \frac{10}{3}$

29. $-\frac{1}{2} \le d \le \frac{25}{4}$

30. $-24 \le f \le 18$

31. Answers may vary. Sample: the Civil War, the Great Depression, the Louisiana Purchase **32.** Answers may vary. Sample: From 1 to 2 years of age; a person has

---

usually stopped growing by age 30, but a baby is still growing at age 1. **33.** Answers may vary. Sample: The image is a reflection, left to right, of what other people see; the size is the same. **34.** Answers may vary. Sample: An inequality determines the limit of a value, or a boundary, for the solution on the number line.

Lesson 2-1   pp. 60–67

Got It?
1. Let Jan = 1, Feb = 2, Mar = 3, and Apr = 4.

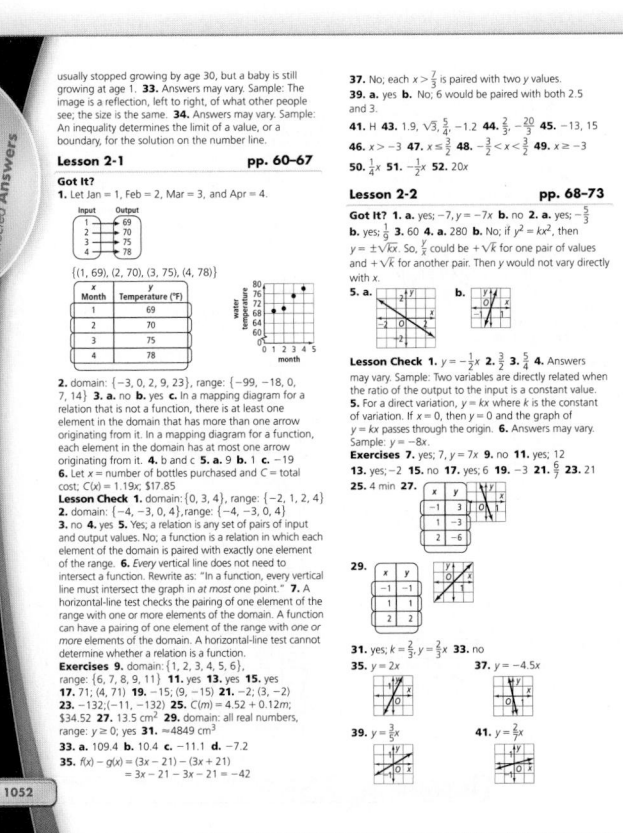

$\{(1, 69), (2, 70), (3, 75), (4, 78)\}$

Month	Temperature (°F)
1	69
2	70
3	75
4	78

2. domain: $\{-3, 0, 2, 9, 23\}$, range: $\{-99, -18, 0, 7, 14\}$ **3. a.** no **b.** yes **c.** In a mapping diagram for a relation that is not a function, there is at least one element in the domain that has more than one arrow originating from it. In a mapping diagram for a function, each element in the domain has at most one arrow originating from it. **4. b** and **c 5. a.** 9 **b.** 1 **c.** -19 **6.** Let $x = $ number of bottles purchased and $C = $ total cost; $C(x) = 1.19x$; \$17.85
Lesson Check 1. domain: $\{0, 3, 4\}$, range: $\{-2, 1, 2, 4\}$ **2.** domain: $\{-4, -3, 0, 4\}$, range: $\{-4, -3, 0, 4\}$ **3.** no **4.** yes **5.** Yes; a relation is any set of pairs of input and output values. No; a function is a relation in which each element of the domain is paired with exactly one element of the range. **6.** *Every* vertical line does not need to intersect a function. Rewrite as: "In a function, every vertical line must intersect the graph in *at most* one point." **7.** A horizontal-line test checks the pairing of one element of the range with one or more elements of the domain. A function can have a pairing of one element of the range with one or more elements of the domain. A horizontal-line test cannot determine whether a relation is a function.
Exercises 9. domain: $\{1, 2, 3, 4, 5, 6\}$, range: $\{6, 7, 8, 9, 11\}$ **11.** yes **13.** yes **15.** yes **17.** 71; (4, 71) **19.** -15; (9, -15) **21.** -2; (3, -2) **23.** -132; (-11, -132) **25.** $C(m) = 4.52 + 0.12m$; \$34.52 **27.** 13.5 cm² **29.** domain: all real numbers, range: $y \ge 0$; yes **31.** ≈ 4849 cm³
33. a. 109.4 **b.** 10.4 **c.** -11.1 **d.** -7.2
35. $f(x) - g(x) = (3x - 21) - (3x + 21)$
$= 3x - 21 - 3x - 21 = -42$

---

37. No; each $x > \frac{7}{3}$ is paired with two y values.
39. a. yes **b.** No; 6 would be paired with both 2.5 and 3.
41. H **43.** 1.9, $\sqrt{3}$, $\frac{2}{5}$, -1.2 **44.** $\frac{5}{2}$, $-\frac{20}{7}$ **45.** -13, 15
46. $x > -3$ **47.** $x \le \frac{5}{2}$ **48.** $-\frac{3}{2} < x < \frac{3}{2}$ **49.** $x \ge -3$
50. $\frac{1}{4}x$ **51.** $-\frac{1}{2}x$ **52.** $20x$

Lesson 2-2   pp. 68–73

Got It? 1. a. yes; -7, $y = -7x$ **b.** no **2. a.** yes; $-\frac{5}{3}$ **b.** yes; $\frac{1}{6}$ **3.** 60 **4. a.** 280 **b.** No; if $y^2 = kx^2$, then $y = \pm\sqrt{k}x$. So, $\frac{y}{x}$ could be $+\sqrt{k}$ for one pair of values and $+\sqrt{k}$ for another pair. Then y would not vary directly with x.
5. a. **b.**

Lesson Check 1. $y = -\frac{1}{2}x$ **2.** $\frac{2}{3}$ **3.** $\frac{4}{3}$ **4.** Answers may vary. Sample: Two variables are directly related when the ratio of the output to the input is a constant value. **5.** For a direct variation, $y = kx$ where k is the constant of variation. If $x = 0$, then $y = 0$ and the graph of $y = kx$ passes through the origin. **6.** Answers may vary. Sample: $y = -8x$
Exercises 7. yes; 7, $y = 7x$ **9.** no **11.** yes; 12 **13.** yes; -2 **15.** no **17.** yes; 6 **19.** -3 **21.** $\frac{6}{7}$ **23.** 21 **25.** 4 min **27.**

29.

31. yes; $k = \frac{2}{3}$, $y = \frac{2}{3}x$ **33.** no
35. $y = 2x$ **37.** $y = -4.5x$

39. $y = \frac{3}{8}x$ **41.** $y = \frac{1}{2}x$

---

43. 0.625 **45.** 0.225 **47.** First, it does not say that y varies directly with x. Second, every direct variation includes the point (0, 0), so k cannot be determined because k could be any value.
49. Answers may vary. Sample: $y = 3.2x$

51. Answers may vary. Sample: If y varies directly with x^2, and $y = 2$ when $x = 4$, then the slope of $\frac{81}{8}$ when $x = 9$.
53. $c = 0$, $a \ne 0$, $b \ne 0$
55. y is divided by 7; if x is divided by 7, $y = k\left(\frac{x}{7}\right)$ or $\frac{y}{7}$ the original value of y.
57. 1091 **59.** 0 **61.** -5
62. **63.**

domain: $\{-2, 0, 1, 3\}$; range: $\{-3, 1\}$

domain: $\{4, 7\}$; range: $\{-1, 0\}$

64. **65.**

domain: $\{1, 2, 4, 5\}$; range: $\{-2, -1, 1, 2\}$

domain: $\{1, 2, 3, 4\}$; range: $\{7, 8, 9, 10\}$

66. $8n$; 40, 48, 56 **67.** $7 - 2n$; -3, -5, -7
68. $12(13 - n)$; 96, 84, 72 **69.** $15(n + 1)$; 90, 105,120 **70.** $\frac{17}{2}$; 7; $\frac{23}{2}$; $\frac{29}{2}$ **71.** -3.2; -2; -1.4; 0.4 **72.** -5; 1; 4; 13 **73.** -9; -8; -7.5; -6

Lesson 2-3   pp. 74–80

Got It? 1. a. -1 **b.** 1 **c.** undefined **d.** $\frac{1 - 4}{8 - 5} = \frac{-3}{3} = -1 = \frac{3}{-3} = \frac{4 - 1}{5 - 8}$ **2. a.** $y = 6x + 5$
b. $y = -\frac{1}{2}x - 3$ **c.** No; any two points on a line can be used to calculate the slope.
3. a. $y = -\frac{3}{4}x + 9$; $-\frac{3}{4}$; (0, 9)
b. $y = -\frac{2}{5}x - 7$; $-\frac{2}{5}$; (0, -7)

---

4. $y = \frac{4}{3}x - 2$

Lesson Check 1. $y = \frac{1}{2}x + 1$ **2.** $y = \frac{4}{3}x + \frac{1}{3}$ **3.** -1 **4.** 1 **5.** The y-intercept of a line is the point at which the line crosses the y-axis. The x-intercept is the point at which the line crosses the x-axis. **6.** Since division by zero is undefined, the slope of a vertical line that passes through (a, b) and (a, c), $\frac{c - b}{0}$, is undefined. **7.** She subtracted the x-coordinates in the wrong order. The x- and y-coordinates of each point must be subtracted consistently.
Exercises 9. -2 **11.** $\frac{4}{11}$ **13.** 1 **15.** 0 **17.** $y = 3x + 2$ **19.** $y = \frac{5}{6}x + 12$ **21.** $y = -5x - 7$ **23.** $y = \frac{3}{2}x + \frac{7}{2}$, $\left(0, \frac{7}{2}\right)$ **25.** $y = -\frac{4}{3}x + \frac{5}{6}$, $\frac{4}{3}$, $\left(0, \frac{5}{6}\right)$ **27.** $y = 7$; 0, (0, 7)
29. **31.**

33. **35.**

37. **39.**

41. **43.**

45.

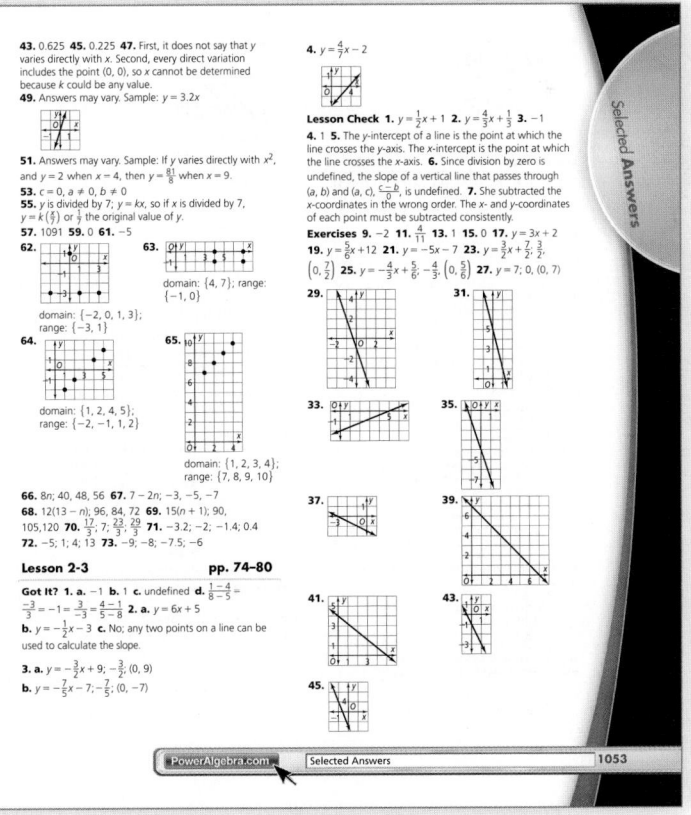

47. 0; (0, 3) **49.** $-\frac{1}{4}$; (0, 3) **51.** undefined slope; no y-intercept **53.** $-\frac{1}{2}$, $\left(0, -\frac{5}{2}\right)$ **55.** $-\frac{A}{B}$, $\left(0, \frac{C}{B}\right)$ **57. a.** 1 **b.** 1 **c.** 1 **d.** 1 **e.** Any two points on a line can be used to find the slope of the line. **59.** $-\frac{5}{13}$ **61.** $\frac{15}{2}$

Lesson 2-4 pp. 81–88

Got It? 1. $y + 1 = -3(x - 7)$ **2. a.** $y - 7 = \frac{2}{5}x$ **b.** $y = \frac{2}{5}(x + 5)$; Either point can be used to put the equation of the line in point-slope form. **3.** $-91x + 10y = 36$ **4.** (0, −2), (4, 0); **5. a.** Packs of Paper Left

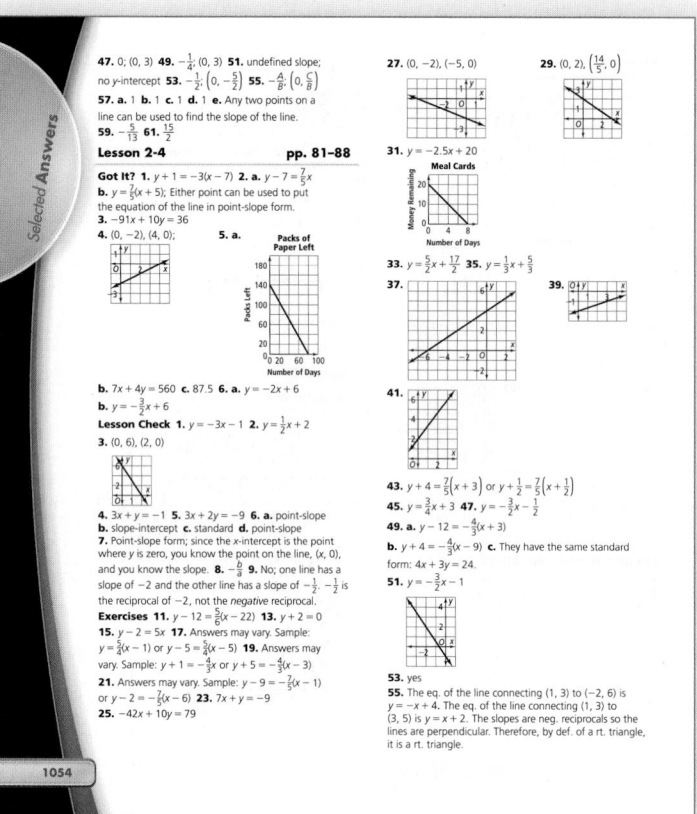

b. $7x + 4y = 560$ **c.** 87.5 **6. a.** $y = -2x + 6$ **b.** $y = -\frac{3}{2}x + 6$
Lesson Check 1. $y = -3x - 1$ **2.** $y = \frac{1}{2}x + 2$ **3.** (0, 6), (2, 0)
4. $3x + y = -1$ **5.** $3x + 2y = -9$ **6. a.** point-slope **b.** slope-intercept **c.** standard **d.** point-slope **7.** Point-slope form; since the x-intercept is the point where y is zero, you know the point on the line, (x, 0), and you know the slope. **8.** $-\frac{8}{9}$ **9.** No; one line has a slope of −2 and the other line has a slope of $-\frac{1}{2}$. $-\frac{1}{2}$ is the reciprocal of −2, not the negative reciprocal.
Exercises 11. $y - 12 = \frac{2}{8}(x - 22)$ **13.** $y + 2 = 0$ **15.** $y - 2 = 5x$ **17.** Answers may vary. Sample: $y = \frac{2}{3}(x - 1)$ or $y - 5 = \frac{2}{3}(x - 5)$ **19.** Answers may vary. Sample: $y + 1 = -\frac{4}{3}x$ or $y + 5 = -\frac{4}{3}(x - 3)$ **21.** Answers may vary. Sample: $y - 9 = -\frac{7}{2}(x - 1)$ or $y - 2 = -\frac{7}{2}(x - 6)$ **23.** $7x + y = -9$ **25.** $-42x + 10y = 79$

27. (0, −2), (−5, 0) **29.** (0, 2), $\left(\frac{14}{5}, 0\right)$
31. $y = -2.5x + 20$ Meal Cards
33. $y = \frac{2}{5}x + \frac{1}{2}$ **35.** $y = \frac{1}{3}x + \frac{5}{3}$
37. **39.**
41.
43. $y + 4 = \frac{7}{5}(x + 3)$ or $y + \frac{1}{2} = \frac{7}{5}\left(x + \frac{1}{2}\right)$
45. $y = \frac{3}{4}x + 3$ **47.** $y = -\frac{3}{2}x - \frac{1}{2}$
49. a. $y - 12 = -\frac{4}{3}(x + 3)$ **b.** $y + 4 = -\frac{4}{3}(x - 9)$ **c.** They have the same standard form: $4x + 3y = 24$.
51. $y = -\frac{3}{2}x - 1$
53. yes
55. The eq. of the line connecting (1, 3) to (−2, 6) is $y = -x + 4$. The eq. of the line connecting (1, 3) to (3, 5) is $y = x + 2$. The slopes are neg. reciprocals so the lines are perpendicular. Therefore, by def. of a rt. triangle, it is a rt. triangle.

Lesson 2-5 pp. 92–98

Got It?
1. a. strong negative correlation

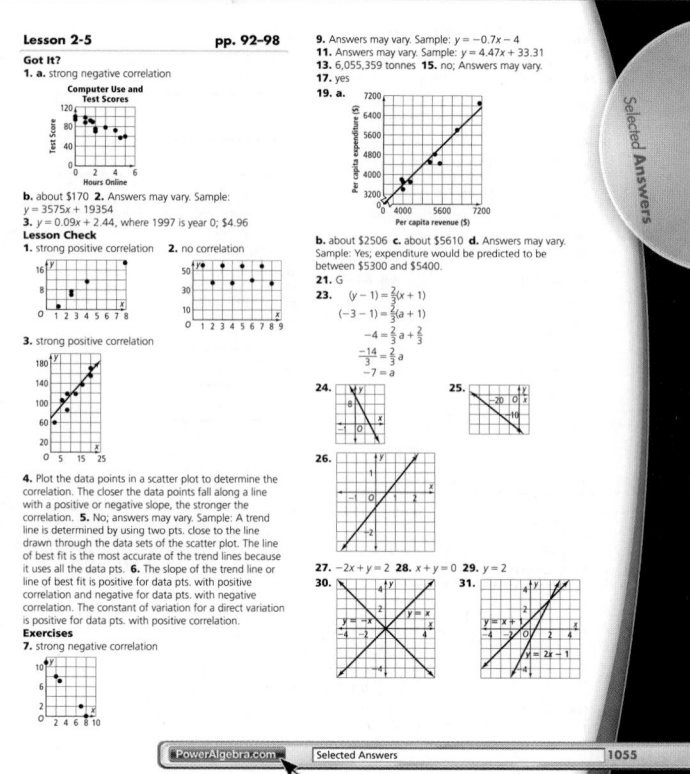

Computer Use and Test Scores
b. about $170 **2.** Answers may vary. Sample: $y = 3575x + 19354$ **3.** $y = 0.09x + 2.44$, where 1997 is year 0; $4.96
Lesson Check
1. strong positive correlation **2.** no correlation
3. strong positive correlation
4. Plot the data points in a scatter plot to determine the correlation. The closer the data points fall along a line with a positive or negative slope, the stronger the correlation. **5.** No; answers may vary. Sample: A trend line is determined by using two pts. close to the line drawn through the data sets of the scatter plot. The line of best fit is the most accurate of the trend lines because it uses all the data pts. **6.** The slope of the trend line or line of best fit is positive for data pts. with positive correlation and negative for data pts. with negative correlation. The constant of variation for a direct variation is positive for data pts. with positive correlation.
Exercises
7. strong negative correlation

9. Answers may vary. Sample: $y = -0.7x - 4$ **11.** Answers may vary. Sample: $y = 4.47x + 33.31$ **13.** 6,055,359 tonnes **15.** no; Answers may vary. **17.** yes
19. a. Per capita expenditure ($)
b. about $2506 **c.** about $5610 **d.** Answers may vary. Sample: Yes; expenditure would be predicted to be between $5300 and $5400.
21. G
23. $(y - 1) = \frac{2}{3}(x + 1)$
$(-3 - 1) = \frac{2}{3}(a + 1)$
$-4 = \frac{2}{3}a + \frac{2}{3}$
$-\frac{14}{3} = \frac{2}{3}a$
$-7 = a$
24. **25.**
26.
27. $-2x + y = 2$ **28.** $x + y = 0$ **29.** $y = 2$
30. **31.**

32.

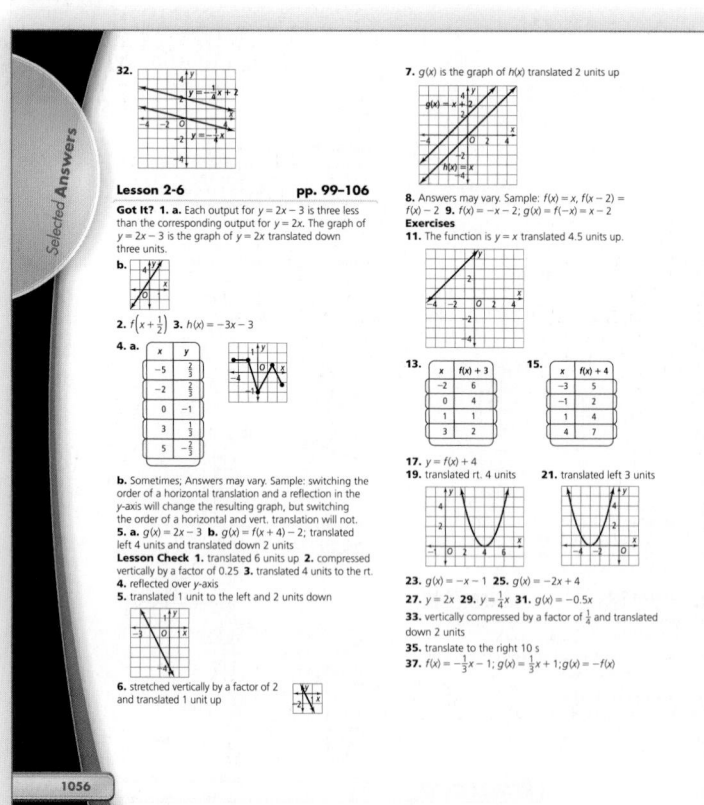

Lesson 2-6 pp. 99–106

Got It? 1. a. Each output for $y = 2x - 3$ is three less than the corresponding output for $y = 2x$. The graph of $y = 2x - 3$ is the graph of $y = 2x$ translated down three units.
b.
2. $f\left(x + \frac{1}{2}\right)$ **3.** $h(x) = -3x - 3$
4. a.

x	y
−5	$\frac{3}{5}$
−2	$\frac{3}{2}$
0	−1
2	$\frac{3}{2}$
5	$\frac{3}{5}$

b. Sometimes; Answers may vary. Sample: switching the order of a horizontal translation and a reflection in the y-axis will change the resulting graph, but switching the order of a horizontal and vert. translation will not.
5. a. $g(x) = 2x - 3$ **b.** $g(x) = f(x + 4) - 2$; translated left 4 units and translated down 2 units
Lesson Check 1. translated 6 units up **2.** compressed vertically by a factor of 0.25 **3.** translated 4 units to the rt. **4.** reflected over y-axis
5. translated 1 unit to the left and 2 units down
6. stretched vertically by a factor of 2 and translated 1 unit up

7. g(x) is the graph of h(x) translated 2 units up
8. Answers may vary. Sample: $f(x) = x$, $f(x - 2) = f(x) - 2$ **9.** $f(x) = -x - 2$; $g(x)$; $f(-x) = x - 2$
Exercises
11. The function is $y = x$ translated 4.5 units up.
13.

x	f(x) + 3
−2	6
0	4
1	4
4	7

15.

x	f(x) + 4
−3	5
1	4
1	4
4	7

17. $y = f(x) + 4$
19. translated rt. 4 units **21.** translated left 3 units
23. $g(x) = -x - 2$ **25.** $g(x) = -2x + 4$
27. $g(x) = 2x$ **29.** $y = \frac{1}{4}x$ **31.** $g(x) = -0.5x$
33. vertically compressed by a factor of $\frac{1}{4}$ and translated down 2 units
35. translate to the right 10 s
37. $f(x) = -\frac{1}{3}x - 1$; $g(x) = \frac{1}{3}x + 1$; $g(x) = -f(x)$

41. translated 6 units down **43.** translated 4 units up

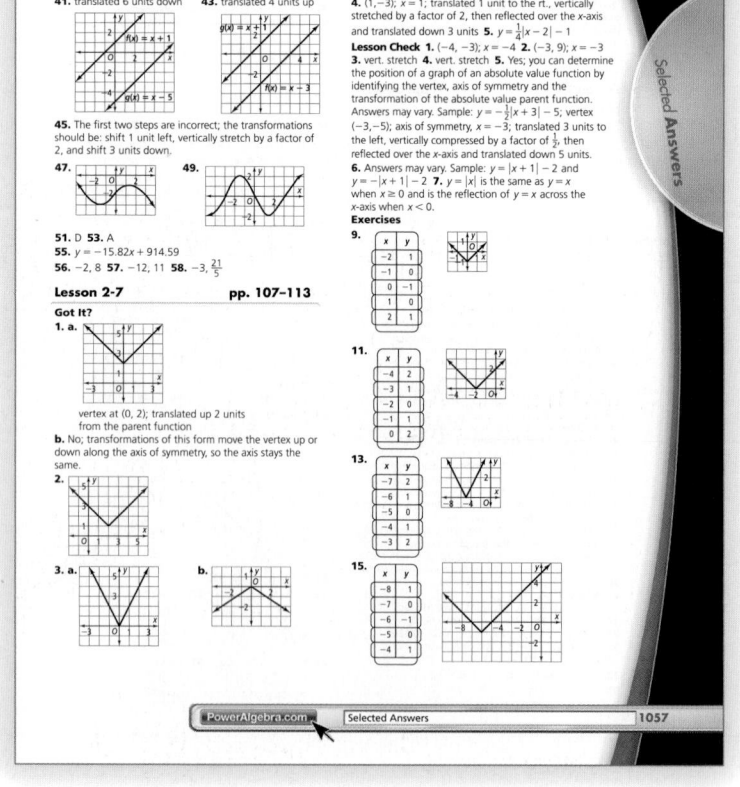

45. The first two steps are incorrect; the transformations should be: shift 1 unit left, vertically stretch by a factor of 2, and shift 3 units down.
47. **49.**
51. D **53.** A
55. $y = -15.82x + 914.59$
56. −2, 8 **57.** −12, 11 **58.** $-3, \frac{21}{5}$

Lesson 2-7 pp. 107–113

Got It?
1. a. vertex at (0, 2); translated up 2 units from the parent function
b. No; transformations of this form move the vertex up or down along the axis of symmetry, so the axis stays the same.
2.
3. a. **b.**

4. (1, −3); $x = 1$; translated 1 unit to the rt., vertically stretched by a factor of 2, then reflected over the x-axis and translated down 3 units **5.** $y = \frac{1}{4}|x - 2| - 1$
Lesson Check 1. (−4, −3); $x = -4$ **2.** (−3, 9); $x = -3$ **3.** vert. stretch **4.** vert. stretch **5.** Yes; you can determine the position of a graph of an absolute value function by identifying the vertex, axis of symmetry, and the transformation of the absolute value parent function. Answers may vary. Sample: $y = -\frac{1}{2}|x + 3| - 5$; vertex (−3, −5); axis of symmetry, $x = -3$; translated 3 units to the left, vertically compressed by a factor of $\frac{1}{2}$, then reflected over the x-axis and translated down 5 units.
6. Answers may vary. Sample: $y = |x + 1| - 2$ and $y = -|x + 1| - 2$ **7.** $y = |x|$ is the same as $y = x$ when $x \geq 0$ and is the reflection of $y = x$ across the x-axis when $x < 0$.
Exercises
9.

x	y
−2	1
−1	0
0	−1
1	0
2	1

11.

x	y
−4	2
−3	1
−2	0
−1	1
0	2

13.

x	y
−7	2
−6	1
−5	0
−4	1
−3	2

15.

x	y
−7	2
−6	1
−5	0
−4	1
−3	2

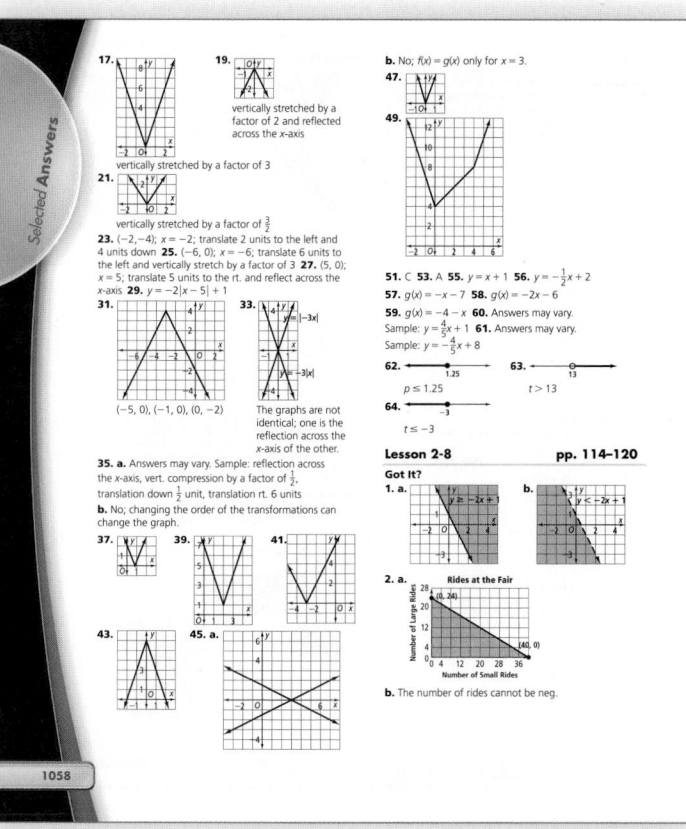

17. **19.** vertically stretched by a factor of 2 and reflected across the x-axis

vertically stretched by a factor of 3

21. vertically stretched by a factor of $\frac{3}{2}$

23. $(-2, -4)$; $x = -2$; translate 2 units to the left and 4 units down **25.** $(-6, 0)$; $x = -6$; translate 6 units to the left and vertically stretch by a factor of 3 **27.** $(5, 0)$; $x = 5$; translate 5 units to the rt. and reflect across the x-axis **29.** $y = -2|x - 5| + 1$

31. **33.** The graphs are not identical; one is the reflection across the x-axis of the other.

$(-5, 0), (-1, 0), (0, -2)$

35. a. Answers may vary. Sample: reflection across the x-axis, vert. compression by a factor of $\frac{1}{2}$, translation down $\frac{1}{2}$ unit, translation rt. 6 units **b.** No; changing the order of the transformations can change the graph.

37. **39.** **41.**

43. **45. a.**

b. No; $f(x) = g(x)$ only for $x = 3$.

47.

49.

51. C **53.** A **55.** $y = x + 1$ **56.** $y = -\frac{1}{2}x + 2$
57. $g(x) = -x - 7$ **58.** $g(x) = -2x - 6$
59. $g(x) = -4 - x$ **60.** Answers may vary.
Sample: $y = \frac{4}{5}x + 1$ **61.** Answers may vary.
Sample: $y = -\frac{4}{5}x + 8$

62. $p \le 1.25$ **63.** $t > 13$

64. $t \le -3$

Lesson 2-8 pp. 114–120

Got It?
1. a. **b.**

2. a. Rides at the Fair

b. The number of rides cannot be neg.

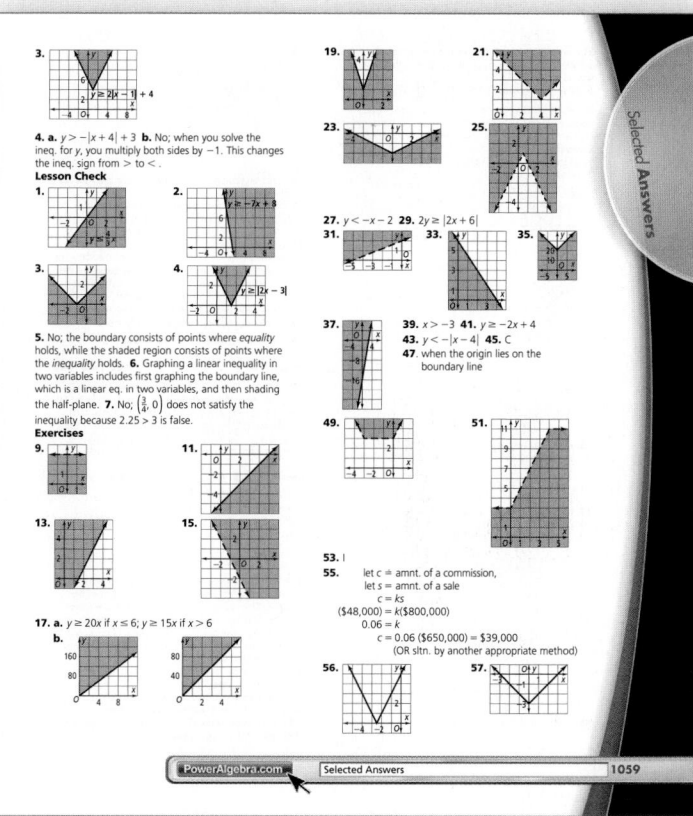

3.

4. a. $y > -|x + 4| + 3$ **b.** No; when you solve the ineq. for y, you multiply both sides by -1. This changes the ineq. sign from $>$ to $<$.

Lesson Check
1. **2.**

3. **4.**

5. No; the boundary consists of points where *equality* holds, while the shaded region consists of points where the *inequality* holds. **6.** Graphing a linear inequality in two variables includes first graphing the boundary line, which is a linear eq. in two variables, and then shading the half-plane. **7.** No; $\left(\frac{2}{3}, 0\right)$ does not satisfy the inequality because $2.25 > 3$ is false.

Exercises
9. **11.**

13. **15.**

17. a. $y \ge 20x$ if $x \le 6$; $y \ge 15x$ if $x > 6$
b.

19. **21.**

23. **25.**

27. $y < -x - 2$ **29.** $2y \ge |2x + 6|$
31. **33.** **35.**

37. **39.** $x > -3$ **41.** $y \ge -2x + 4$
43. $y < -|x - 4|$ **45.** C
47. when the origin lies on the boundary line

49. **51.**

53. I
55. let c = amnt. of a commission,
let s = amnt. of a sale
$c = ks$
$(\$48,000) = k(\$800,000)$
$0.06 = k$
$c = 0.06 \ (\$650,000) = \$39,000$
(OR sltn. by another appropriate method)

56. **57.**

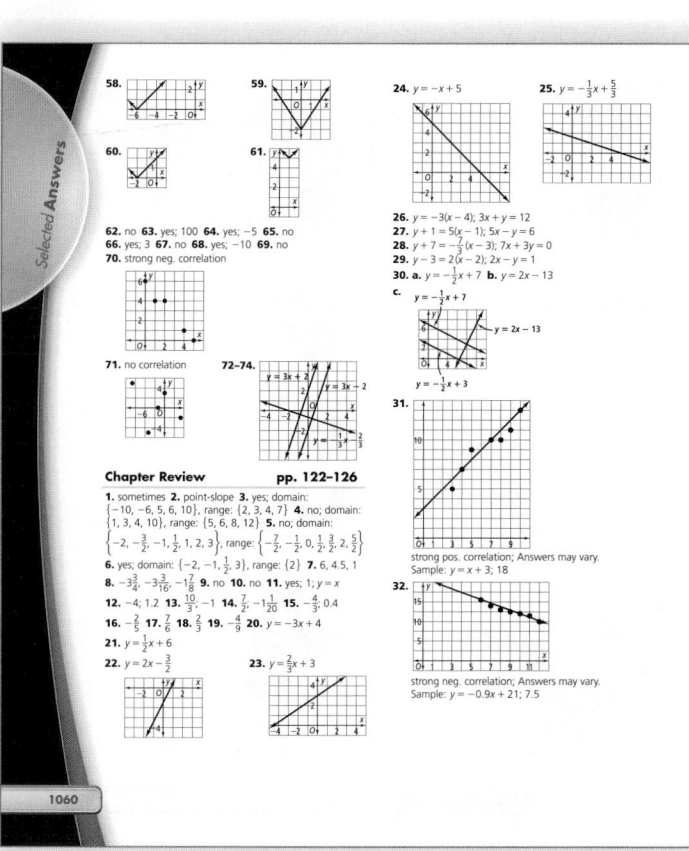

58. **59.**

60. **61.**

62. no **63.** yes; 100 **64.** yes; -5 **65.** no
66. yes; 3 **67.** no **68.** yes; -10 **69.** no
70. strong neg. correlation

71. no correlation **72–74.**

Chapter Review pp. 122–126

1. sometimes **2.** point-slope **3.** yes; domain: $\{-10, -6, 5, 6, 10\}$, range: $\{2, 3, 4, 7\}$ **4.** no; domain: $\{1, 3, 4, 10\}$, range: $\{5, 6, 8, 12\}$ **5.** no; domain: $\left\{-2, -\frac{3}{2}, -1, \frac{1}{2}, 1, 2, 3\right\}$, range: $\left\{-\frac{7}{2}, -\frac{1}{2}, 0, \frac{1}{2}, \frac{3}{2}, 2, \frac{5}{2}\right\}$
6. yes; domain: $\left\{-2, -1, \frac{1}{2}, 3\right\}$, range: $\{2\}$ **7.** 6, 4.5, 1
8. $-3\frac{3}{4}, -3\frac{3}{16}, -1\frac{7}{8}$ **9.** no **10.** no **11.** yes; 1; $y = x$
12. -4; 1.2 **13.** $\frac{10}{3}$; -1 **14.** $\frac{7}{2}$; $-1\frac{1}{20}$ **15.** $-\frac{4}{3}$; 0.4
16. $-\frac{2}{5}$ **17.** $\frac{2}{5}$ **18.** $\frac{2}{5}$ **19.** $-\frac{4}{9}$ **20.** $y = -3x + 4$
21. $y = \frac{1}{2}x + 6$
22. $y = 2x - \frac{3}{2}$
23. $y = \frac{2}{3}x + 3$

24. $y = -x + 5$ **25.** $y = -\frac{1}{3}x + \frac{5}{3}$

26. $y = -3(x - 4)$; $3x + y = 12$
27. $y + 1 = 5(x - 1)$; $5x - y = 6$
28. $y + 7 = -\frac{2}{3}(x - 3)$; $7x + 3y = 0$
29. $y - 3 = 2(x - 2)$; $2x - y = 1$
30. a. $y = -\frac{1}{2}x + 7$ **b.** $y = 2x - 13$
c. $y = -\frac{1}{2}x + 7$

$y = 2x - 13$

31. strong pos. correlation; Answers may vary. Sample: $y = x + 3$; 18

32. strong neg. correlation; Answers may vary. Sample: $y = -0.9x + 21$; 7.5

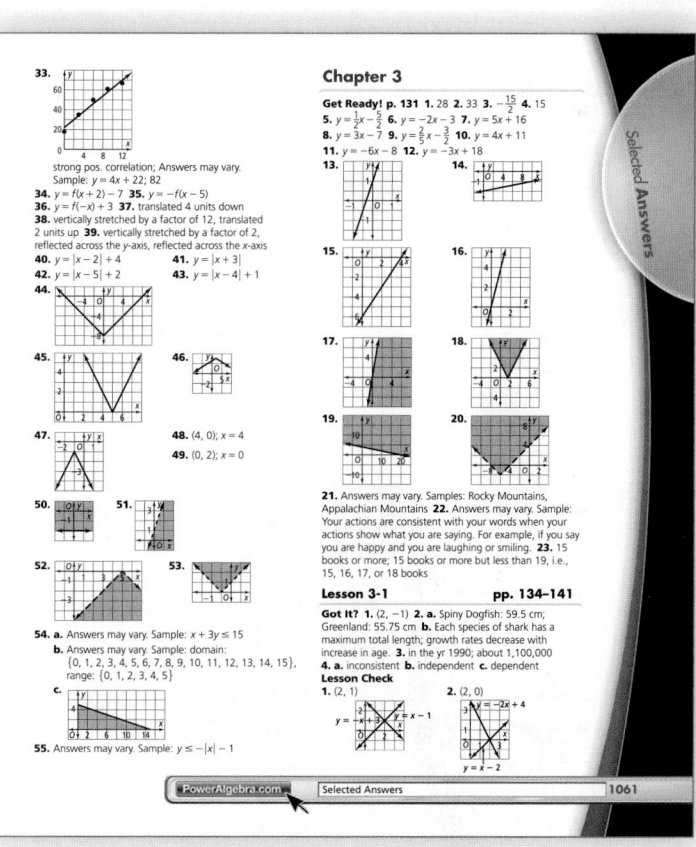

33. strong pos. correlation; Answers may vary. Sample: $y = 4x + 22$; 82
34. $y = f(x + 2) - 7$ **35.** $y = -f(x - 5)$
36. $y = f(-x) + 3$ **37.** translated 4 units down
38. vertically stretched by a factor of 12, translated 2 units up **39.** vertically stretched by a factor of 2, reflected across the y-axis, reflected across the x-axis
40. $y = |x - 2| + 4$ **41.** $y = |x + 3|$
42. $y = |x - 5| + 2$ **43.** $y = |x - 4| + 1$
44.

45. **46.**

47. **48.** $(4, 0)$; $x = 4$
49. $(0, 2)$; $x = 0$

50. **51.**

52. **53.**

54. a. Answers may vary. Sample: $x + 3y \le 15$
b. Answers may vary. Sample: domain: $\{0, 1, 2, 3, 4, 5, 6, 7, 8, 9, 10, 11, 12, 13, 14, 15\}$, range: $\{0, 1, 2, 3, 4, 5\}$
c.

55. Answers may vary. Sample: $y \le -|x| - 1$

Chapter 3

Get Ready! p. 131 1. 28 **2.** 33 **3.** $-\frac{15}{2}$ **4.** 15
5. $y = \frac{1}{2}x - \frac{5}{2}$ **6.** $y = -2x - 3$ **7.** $y = 5x + 16$
8. $y = 3x - 7$ **9.** $y = \frac{6}{5}x - \frac{3}{2}$ **10.** $y = 4x + 11$
11. $y = -6x - 8$ **12.** $y = -3x + 18$

13. **14.**

15. **16.**

17. **18.**

19. **20.**

21. Answers may vary. Samples: Rocky Mountains, Appalachian Mountains **22.** Answers may vary. Sample: Your actions are consistent with your words when your actions show what you are saying. For example, if you say you are happy and you are laughing or smiling. **23.** 15 books or more; 15 books or more but less than 19, i.e., 15, 16, 17, or 18 books

Lesson 3-1 pp. 134–141

Got It? 1. $(2, -1)$ **2. a.** Spiny Dogfish: 59.5 cm; Greenland: 55.75 cm **b.** Each species of shark has a maximum total length; growth rates decrease with increase in age. **3.** in the yr 1990; about 1,100,000
4. a. inconsistent **b.** independent **c.** dependent
Lesson Check
1. $(2, 1)$ **2.** $(2, 0)$

3. 2 pens; 4 pencils **4.** No; an independent system has a unique solution whereas an inconsistent system has no solution.
5. Answers may vary. Sample: $\begin{cases} y = 2x + 1 \\ y = 2x - 3 \end{cases}$
6. Independent; if the slope of one equation is the negative reciprocal of the slope of the other equation, the lines are perpendicular and intersect at a unique point.
Exercises 7–11. How solutions are determined may vary (graphing or using a table).
7. (3, 1)

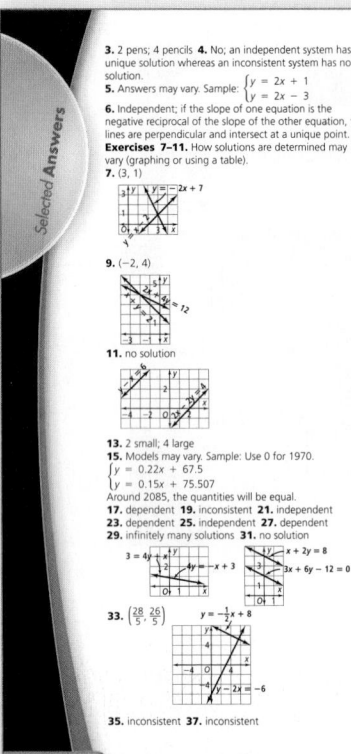

9. (−2, 4)

11. no solution

13. 2 small; 4 large
15. Models may vary. Sample: Use 0 for 1970.
$\begin{cases} y = 0.22x + 67.5 \\ y = 0.15x + 75.507 \end{cases}$
Around 2085, the quantities will be equal.
17. dependent **19.** inconsistent **21.** independent
23. dependent **25.** independent **27.** dependent
29. infinitely many solutions **31.** no solution

33. $\left(\dfrac{28}{5}, \dfrac{26}{5}\right)$ $y = -\tfrac{1}{2}x + 8$

35. inconsistent **37.** inconsistent

39.

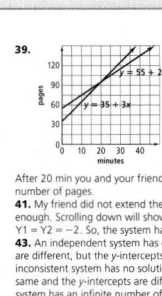

After 20 min you and your friend will have read the same number of pages.
41. My friend did not extend the table of values far enough. Scrolling down will show that when $x = 4$, then Y1 = Y2 = −2. So, the system has a solution, (4, −2).
43. An independent system has one solution. The slopes are different, but the y-intercepts could be the same. An inconsistent system has no solution. The slopes are the same and the y-intercepts are different. A dependent system has an infinite number of solutions. The slopes and y-intercepts are the same. **45.** sometimes **47.** never
49. Answers may vary. Sample: $5x + 2y = 5$
51. They are equivalent eqs. **53.** A **55.** C

Lesson 3-2   pp. 142–148
Got It? 1. (−2.5, 2.5) **2.** $.95 per download; $5.50 one-time registration fee **3.** (4, 0) **4. a.** (−2, 3) **b.** Yes; the solution (−5, 2) is a solution to both eqs. in the system, so substituting $y = 2$ into either equation will result in $x = -5$. **5. a.** no solution; The eq. is always false. **b.** infinite number of solutions; The eq. is always true.
Lesson Check 1. (1, 2) **2.** (−6, −6) **3.** (2, 1)
4. (5, −3) **5.** $\left(-\dfrac{1}{5}, \dfrac{19}{5}\right)$ **6.** (2, 1)
7. Answers may vary. Sample:
$\begin{cases} 4x - 3y = -2 \\ 3x - 2y = -1 \end{cases}$
$\begin{cases} -8x + 6y = 4 \\ 9x - 6y = -3 \end{cases}$
8. In the substitution method of solving a system of equations, you first solve one equation for one of the variables. Then substitute for this variable in the other equation and solve for the other variable. In the elimination method, you create an equivalent system of equations that contain a pair of additive inverses so that you can eliminate one variable and solve for the remaining variable.
9. Let r = number of regular cups of coffee and c = number of large cups of coffee. First, $r + c = 5$: because a total of 5 cups of coffee were purchased. Second, $r + 1.5c = 6$: because each regular cup of coffee is $1, each large cup is $1.50, and the total spent is $6. Then, solve the system of equations using elimination by

subtracting the first equation from the second to eliminate r and solve for $c = 2$; 2 large cups
Exercises 11. (−2, 4) **13.** (0.75, 2.5) **15.** (8, −1)
17. (−2, −5) **19.** seven $1-bills; eight $5-bills
21. 3 vans and 2 sedans **23.** (2, 4) **25.** (2, −2)
27. (4, 1) **29.** (1, 1) **31.** infinite number of solutions; $\{(x, y)\,|\,{-2x} + 3y = 13\}$ **33.** (3, 2) **35.** (5, 4)
37. $\left(\dfrac{20}{17}, \dfrac{19}{17}\right)$ **39.** (4, 1) **41.** no solution
43. 10 deliveries **45.** (4, −3) **47.** (−3, 4)
49. (300, 150) **51.** (0.5, 0.25)
53. Error in 5th line: $-4(-7 - x) = 28 + 4x$ not $-28 - 4x$; Lines 5–9 should be: $3x + 28 + 4x = 14$; $7x = -14$; $x = -2$; $y = -7 - (-2)$; $y = -5$
55. Answers may vary. Sample:
$\begin{cases} -3x + 4y = 12 \\ 5x - 3y = 13 \end{cases}$ (8, 9)
57. In determining whether to use substitution or elimination to solve an equation, look at the equations to determine if one is solved or can be easily solved for a particular variable. If that is the case, substitution can easily be used. Otherwise, elimination might be easier.
59. Substitution; the second equation is solved for y; (−7, −26) **61.** Elimination; substitution would be difficult since no coefficient is 1 in the original system. Dividing the first equation by 3 and dividing the second equation by 5 results in an equivalent system where y would be eliminated from the system if the equations were subtracted; (−1, −3)
63. yes; −40 degrees **65.** 0 **67.** 2 **69.** 6 **71.** 4

Lesson 3-3   pp. 149–155
Got It? 1. (4, 1), (5, 0), (6, 0), (7, 0)
2.

3. 5 meats and no vegetables; 4 meats and 1 or 2 vegetables; 3 meats and 2, 3, or 4 vegetables; 2 meats and 3, 4, 5, or 6 vegetables; 1 meat and 4 – 8 vegetables; no meat 5 – 10 vegetables
4. $y > 2|x - 1|$

Lesson Check
1. [graph] $2x + y \le 5$
2. [graph]
3. [graph] $y \le x + 2$; $y = -3x - 1$
4. 0 h TV and 1, 2, or 3 h football; 1 h TV and 1 or 2 h football; or 2 h TV and 1 h football **5.** Intersection; the solution of two inequalities is the overlap or the intersection of the graphs of the individual inequalities.
6. The graphical solution of a system of inequalities consists of the overlap or intersection of the individual half-planes and corresponding boundary lines (either dotted or solid). The graphical solution of a system of equations includes only the intersection of the lines, not the half-planes. **7.** For each inequality, the wrong half-plane has been shaded. The half-plane below $y = \tfrac{1}{2}x - 1$ should be shaded and the half-plane above $y = -3x + 3$ should be shaded. Also, both boundary lines should be dashed because the inequalities are < and >
Exercises 9. (0, 0), (0, 1), (0, 2), (0, 3), (0, 4), (0, 5), (0, 6), (0, 7), (1, 0), (1, 1), (1, 2), (1, 3), (1, 4), (1,5), (1, 6), (2, 0), (2, 1), (2, 2), (2, 3), (2, 4), (2, 5), (3, 3), (3, 4)
11. [graph]

13. [graph] $y \le x$ **15.** [graph] $x + 2y \le 10$

---

17. [graph] **19.** no solution
21. Let r = number of rose plants and t = number of tulip plants.
$\begin{cases} t + r \ge 50 \\ r \le 80 \end{cases}$
Because the number of plants must be a whole number, only the points in the overlap that represent whole numbers are solutions of the problem.

23. [graph] $y < -1...$; $y \le |2x + 1|$

25. [graph] **27.** [graph] $y \le -|x - 3|$; $y > ...$

29. [graph] $-x \ge ...$; $y \ge |3x - 6|$

31. (0, 4), (0, 5), (0, 6), (1, 3), (1, 4), (1, 5), (2, 3), (2, 4); the sum of the servings must be greater than or equal to 4 and less than or equal to 6.

33. Answers may vary. Sample: $\begin{cases} x < 5 \\ y \ge 1 \end{cases}$
35. Use test pts. that are not on either of the boundary lines and that make the calculations as easy as possible (e.g., the origin). **37.** A, B **39.** A, B **41.** B, C **43.** A **45.** A
47. [graph]
49. [graph]

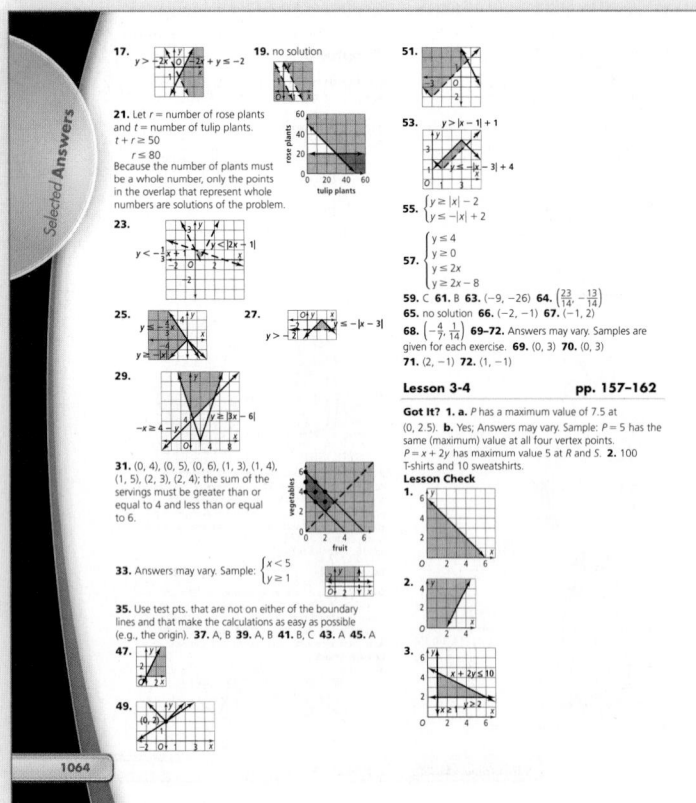

51. [graph]
53. [graph] $y > |x - 1| + 1$; $y \le -|x - 3| + 4$
55. $y \ge |x| - 2$; $y \le -|x| + 2$
57. $\begin{cases} y \le 4 \\ y \ge 0 \\ y \le 2x \\ y \ge 2x - 8 \end{cases}$
59. C **61.** B **63.** (−9, −26) **64.** $\left(\dfrac{23}{14}, -\dfrac{13}{14}\right)$
65. no solution **66.** (−2, −1) **67.** (−1, 2)
68. $\left(-\dfrac{4}{7}, \dfrac{1}{14}\right)$ **69–72.** Answers may vary. Samples are given for each exercise. **69.** (0, 3) **70.** (0, 3)
71. (2, −1) **72.** (1, −1)

Lesson 3-4   pp. 157–162
Got It? 1. a. P has a maximum value of 7.5 at (0, 2.5). **b.** Yes; Answers may vary. Sample: $P = 5$ has the same (maximum) value at all four vertex points. $P = x + 2y$ has maximum value 5 at R and S. **2.** 100 T-shirts and 10 sweatshirts.
Lesson Check
1. [graph]
2. [graph]
3. [graph]

---

4. [graph] $2x + 3y \le 18$; $-x \le 5$
5. (0, 0), (0, 4), (5, 0), (5, 4)
[graph] $y \le 4$; $x \le 5$
6. (0, 8), (3, 5), (0, 5)
[graph] $x + y \le 8$; $y \ge 5$
7. Constraints are limits or restrictions on the variables in the objective function in a linear programming problem. These constraints are written as linear inequalities.
8. Linear programming is an extension of solving linear inequalities. For each, you are given constraints represented by linear inequalities that are graphed. All the points in the overlapping region are solutions, but linear programming problems are usually looking for maximum or minimum values of some quantity modeled with an objective function.
9. Answers may vary. Sample: $\begin{cases} y \le x \\ y \le -x + 4 \\ 0 \le y \le 1 \end{cases}$
$P = 2x + 3y$, $P(0, 0) = 0$, $P(1, 1) = 5$, $P(3, 1) = 9$, $P(4, 0) = 8$; maximum value of P is 9 at (3, 1)

Exercises
11. [graph] vertices: (8, 0), (2, 3); minimized at (8, 0)

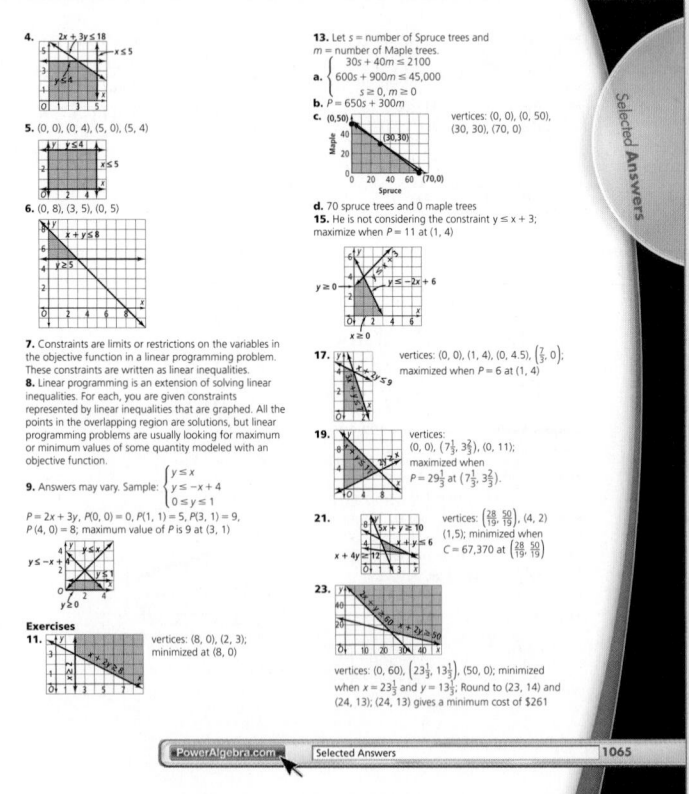

13. Let s = number of Spruce trees and m = number of Maple trees.
a. $\begin{cases} 30s + 40m \le 2100 \\ 600s + 900m \le 45,000 \\ s \ge 0,\ m \ge 0 \end{cases}$
b. $P = 650s + 300m$
c. [graph] vertices: (0, 0), (0, 50), (30, 30), (70, 0)
d. 70 spruce trees and 0 maple trees
15. He is not considering the constraint $y \le x + 3$; maximize when $P = 11$ at (1, 4)
[graph] $y \ge 0$; $y \le -2x + 6$; $x \ge 0$
17. [graph] vertices: (0, 0), (1, 4), (0, 4.5), $\left(\tfrac{7}{2}, 0\right)$; maximized when $P = 6$ at (1, 4)
19. [graph] vertices: (0, 0), $\left(7\tfrac{1}{3}, 3\tfrac{2}{3}\right)$, (0, 11); maximized when $P = 29\tfrac{1}{3}$ at $\left(7\tfrac{1}{3}, 3\tfrac{2}{3}\right)$
21. [graph] vertices: $\left(\dfrac{28}{19}, \dfrac{50}{19}\right)$, (4, 2), (1,5); minimized when $C = 67{,}370$ at $\left(\dfrac{28}{19}, \dfrac{50}{19}\right)$
23. [graph] vertices: (0, 60), $\left(23\tfrac{1}{3}, 13\tfrac{1}{3}\right)$, (50, 0); minimized when $x = 23\tfrac{1}{3}$ and $y = 13\tfrac{1}{3}$; Round to (23, 14) and (24, 13); (24, 13) gives a minimum cost of $261

25. C

27.

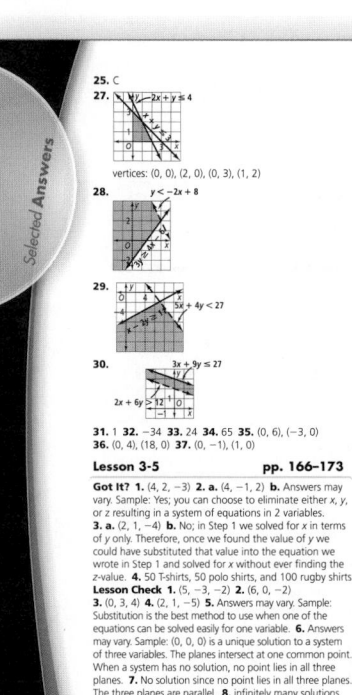

vertices: (0, 0), (2, 0), (0, 3), (1, 2)

28.

29.

30.

31. 1 **32.** −34 **33.** 24 **34.** 65 **35.** (0, 6), (−3, 0)
36. (0, 4), (18, 0) **37.** (0, −1), (1, 0)

Lesson 3-5   pp. 166–173

Got It? 1. (4, 2, −3) **2. a.** (4, −1, 2) **b.** Answers may vary. Sample: Yes; you can choose to eliminate either x, y, or z resulting in a system of equations in 2 variables.
3. a. (2, 1, −4) **b.** No; in Step 1 we solved for x in terms of y only. Therefore, once we found the value of y we could have substituted that value into the equation we wrote in Step 1 and solved for x without ever finding the z-value. **4.** 50 T-shirts, 50 polo shirts, and 100 rugby shirts
Lesson Check 1. (5, −3, −2) **2.** (6, 0, −2)
3. (0, 3, 4) **4.** (2, 1, −5) **5.** Answers may vary. Sample: Substitution is the best method to use when one of the equations can be solved easily for one variable. **6.** Answers may vary. Sample: (0, 0, 0) is a unique solution to a system of three variables. The planes intersect at one common point. When a system has no solution, no point lies in all three planes. **7.** No solution since no point lies in all three planes. The three planes are parallel. **8.** infinitely many solutions
Exercises 9. (4, 2, −3) **11.** (2, 1, −5) **13.** $\left(\frac{1}{2}, -3, 1\right)$
15. (1, −4, 3) **17.** (4, −1, 2) **19.** $\left(-\frac{10}{13}, -\frac{2}{13}, \frac{4}{13}\right)$

---

21. (8, −4, 2) **23.** (−2, −1, −3) **25.** (0, 1, 7)
27. (5, −2, 0) **29.** (1, 3, 2) **31.** $m\angle P = 32°$;
$m\angle Q = 96°$; $m\angle R = 52°$ **33.** (8, 1, 3)
35. $\left(\frac{1}{2}, 2, -3\right)$ **37.** no solution **39.** (2, 4, 6)
41. (0, 2, −3)
43. Answers may vary. Sample: Solution is (1, 2, 3).
$$\begin{cases} x + y + z = 6 \\ 2x - y + 2z = 6 \\ 3x + 3y + z = 12 \end{cases}$$
45. Let E, F, and V represent the number of edges, faces, and vertices, respectively. From the first statement, $E = \frac{6}{5}F$. From the second statement, $V = \frac{2}{5}F$. From the third statement, $V + F + E + 2$. Solving this system of 3 equations yields $E = 30$, $F = 12$, and $V = 20$.

Lesson 3-6   pp. 174–181

Got It? 1. 17
2. a. $\begin{bmatrix} -4 & -2 & | & 7 \\ 3 & 1 & | & -5 \end{bmatrix}$ **b.** $\begin{bmatrix} 4 & -1 & 2 & | & 1 \\ 0 & 1 & 5 & | & 20 \\ 2 & 1 & 0 & | & 7 \end{bmatrix}$
3. $\begin{cases} 2x = 6 \\ 5x - 2y = 1 \end{cases}$
4. a. (1, 2) **b.** elimination; you use the same steps to solve **5.** $\left(1, \frac{1}{2}, 3\right)$
Lesson Check 1. 2 × 1 **2.** 2 × 4
5. $\begin{bmatrix} 3 & 5 & | & 0 \\ 1 & 1 & | & 2 \end{bmatrix}$ $\begin{bmatrix} 1 & 3 & -1 & | & 2 \\ 1 & 0 & 2 & | & 8 \\ 0 & 2 & -1 & | & 1 \end{bmatrix}$
5. 16 **6.** a_{21} is 0, the element in row 2, column 1. a_{12} is −9, the element in row 1 and column 2. **7.** Answers may vary. Sample: The entry fee to a school play is $2 for adults. Jamie paid a total of $8 for 4 student entry fees and 2 adult entry fees. What is the student entry fee?
Exercises 9. 1 **11.** 8
13. $\begin{bmatrix} 3 & 2 & | & 16 \\ 0 & 1 & | & 5 \end{bmatrix}$ **15.** $\begin{bmatrix} 1 & -1 & 1 & | & 150 \\ 2 & 0 & 1 & | & 425 \\ 0 & 1 & 3 & | & 0 \end{bmatrix}$
17. $\begin{bmatrix} 3 & 1 & 0 \\ 1 & -2 & -1 & | & 5 \\ -1 & 2 & 1 & | & 8 \end{bmatrix}$ **19.** $\begin{cases} 5x + y = -3 \\ -2x + 2y = 4 \end{cases}$
21. $\begin{cases} 2x + y + z = 1 \\ x + y + z = 2 \\ x - y + z = -2 \end{cases}$ **23.** $\begin{cases} 5x + 2y + z = 5 \\ 4x + y + 2z = 8 \\ x + 3y - 6z = 2 \end{cases}$
25. (−1, 0) **27.** (4, 6) **29.** (2, 3)

---

31. $10,000 at 4% and $15,000 at 6%;
Let x = amount invested at 4% and y = amount invested at 6%.
$$\begin{cases} x + y = 25,000 \\ 0.04x + 0.06y = 1300 \end{cases}$$
$$\begin{bmatrix} 1 & 1 & | & 25000 \\ 0.04 & 0.06 & | & 1300 \end{bmatrix} = \begin{bmatrix} 1 & 0 & | & 10000 \\ 0 & 1 & | & 15000 \end{bmatrix}$$
33. (3, 1, 1) **35.** (35, −22, −16) **37.** (1, 1, 1)
39. (2, 3) **41.** 1 qt. of red paint: $7.75; 1 qt. of yellow paint: $5.75 **43.** Answers may vary. Sample: 0; 0
45. (8, 2) **47.** $\left(\frac{1}{8}, -\frac{1}{17}\right)$ **49.** G
51. $x \le -\frac{3}{7}$;
52. $x \ge -35$;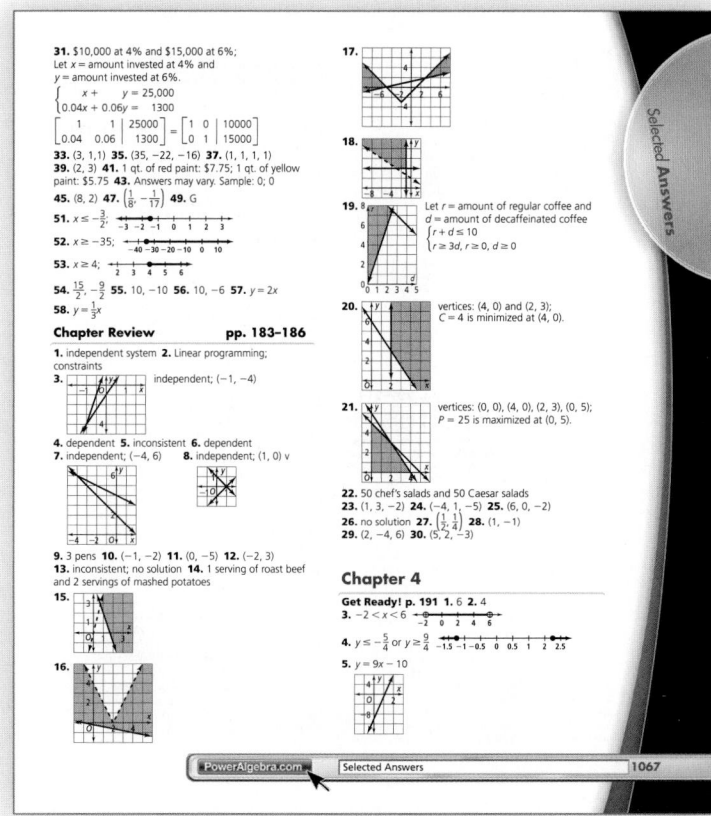
53. $x \ge 4$;
54. $\frac{15}{2}, -\frac{9}{2}$ **55.** 10, −10 **56.** 10, −6 **57.** $y = 2x$
58. $y = \frac{1}{3}x$

Chapter Review   pp. 183–186

1. independent system **2.** Linear programming; constraints
3. independent; (−1, −4)
4. dependent **5.** inconsistent **6.** dependent
7. independent; (−4, 6) **8.** independent; (1, 0) v
9. 3 pens **10.** (−1, −2) **11.** (0, −5) **12.** (−2, 3)
13. inconsistent; no solution **14.** 1 serving of roast beef and 2 servings of mashed potatoes
15.
16.

17.

18.

19. Let r = amount of regular coffee and d = amount of decaffeinated coffee
$$\begin{cases} r + d \le 10 \\ r \ge 3d, r \ge 0, d \ge 0 \end{cases}$$

20. vertices: (4, 0) and (2, 3); $C = 4$ is minimized at (4, 0).

21. vertices: (0, 0), (4, 0), (2, 3), (0, 5); $P = 25$ is maximized at (0, 5).

22. 50 chef's salads and 50 Caesar salads
23. (1, 3, −2) **24.** (−4, 1, −5) **25.** (6, 0, −2)
26. no solution **27.** $\left(\frac{1}{2}, \frac{1}{4}\right)$ **28.** (1, −1)
29. (2, −4, 6) **30.** (5, 2, −3)

Chapter 4

Get Ready! p. 191 1. 6 **2.** 4
3. −2 < x < 6
4. $y \le -\frac{5}{4}$ or $y \ge \frac{9}{4}$
5. $y = 9x − 10$

---

6. $y = \frac{1}{2}x + 8$

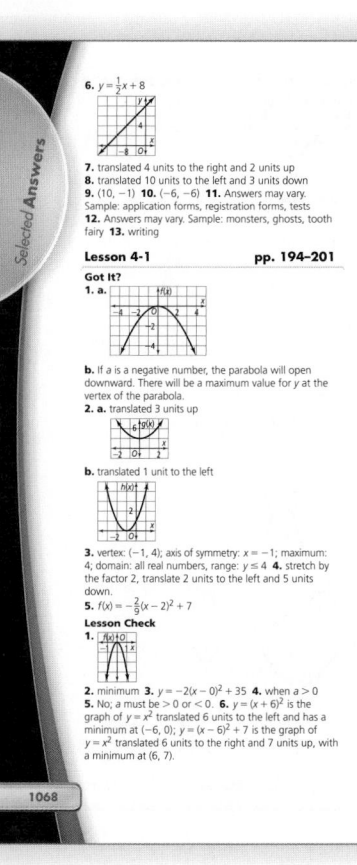

7. translated 4 units to the right and 2 units up
8. translated 10 units to the left and 3 units down
9. (10, −1) **10.** (−6, −6) **11.** Answers may vary. Sample: application forms, registration forms, tests
12. Answers may vary. Sample: monsters, ghosts, tooth fairy **13.** writing

Lesson 4-1   pp. 194–201

Got It?
1. a.

b. If a is a negative number, the parabola will open downward. There will be a maximum value for y at the vertex of the parabola.
2. a. translated 3 units up

b. translated 1 unit to the left

3. vertex: (−1, 4); axis of symmetry: $x = -1$; maximum: 4; domain: all real numbers, range: $y \le 4$ **4.** stretch by the factor 2, translate 2 units to the left and 5 units down.
5. $f(x) = -\frac{2}{9}(x - 2)^2 + 7$
Lesson Check
1.

2. minimum **3.** $y = -2(x - 0)^2 + 35$ **4.** when $a > 0$
5. No; a must be > 0 or < 0. **6.** $y = (x + 6)^2$ is the graph of $y = x^2$ translated 6 units to the left and has a minimum at (−6, 0); $y = (x − 6)^2 + 7$ is the graph of $y = x^2$ translated 6 units to the right and 7 units up, with a minimum at (6, 7).

Exercises
7.

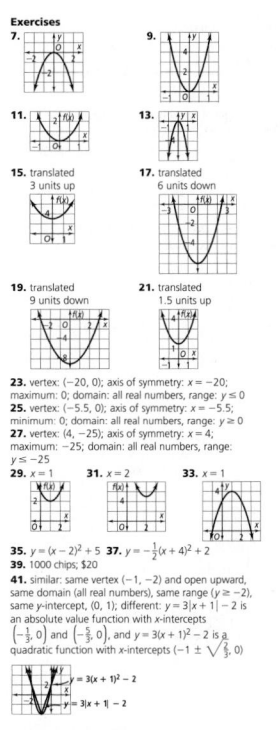

9.

11.

13.

15. translated 3 units up
17. translated 6 units down

19. translated 9 units down
21. translated 1.5 units up

23. vertex: (−20, 0); axis of symmetry: $x = -20$; maximum: 0; domain: all real numbers, range: $y \le 0$
25. vertex: (−5.5, 0); axis of symmetry: $x = -5.5$; minimum: 0; domain: all real numbers, range: $y \ge 0$
27. vertex: (4, −25); axis of symmetry: $x = 4$; maximum: −25; domain: all real numbers, range: $y \le -25$
29. $x = 1$ **31.** $x = 2$ **33.** $x = 1$

35. $y = (x - 2)^2 + 5$ **37.** $y = -\frac{1}{2}(x + 4)^2 + 2$
39. 1000 chips; $20
41. similar: same vertex (−1, −2) and open upward, same domain (all real numbers), same range ($y \ge -2$), same y-intercept, (0, 1); different: $y = 3|x + 1| − 2$ is an absolute value function with x-intercepts $\left(-\frac{1}{3}, 0\right)$ and $\left(-\frac{5}{3}, 0\right)$, and $y = 3(x + 1)^2 − 2$ is a quadratic function with x-intercepts $\left(-1 \pm \sqrt{\frac{2}{3}}, 0\right)$

---

43. similar: same vertex (−3, 0) and open upward, same domain (all real numbers), same range ($y \ge 0$), same x-intercept, (−3, 0); different: $y = |x + 3|$ is an absolute value function with y-intercept (0, 3), and $y = (x + 3)^2$ is a quadratic function with y-intercept (0, 9)

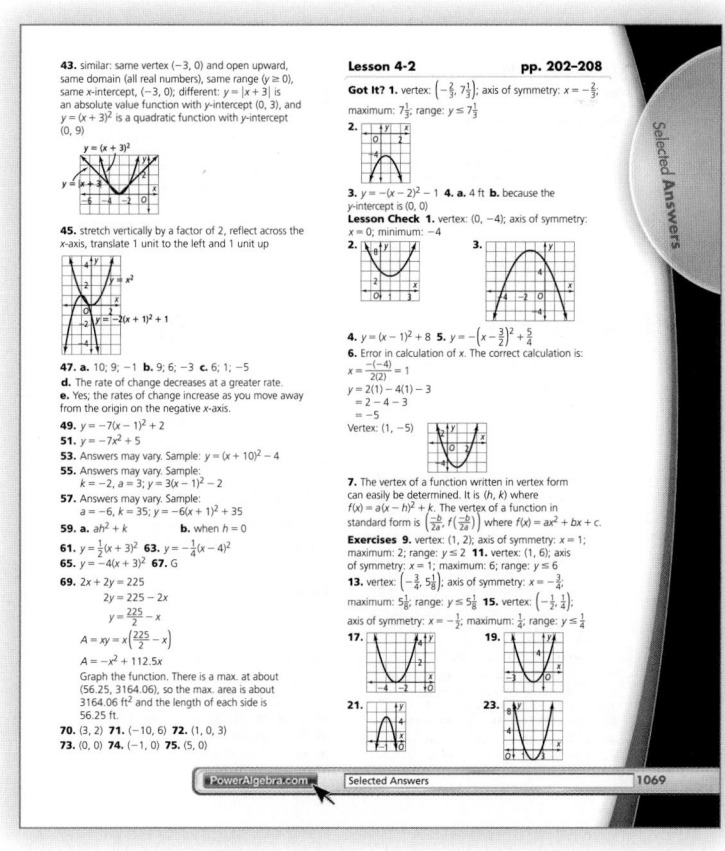

$y = (x + 3)^2$

45. stretch vertically by a factor of 2, reflect across the x-axis, translate 1 unit to the left and 1 unit up

$y = -2(x + 1)^2 + 1$

47. a. 10; 9; −1 **b.** 9; 6; −3 **c.** 6; 1; −5
d. The rate of change decreases at a greater rate.
e. Yes; the rates of change increase as you move away from the origin on the negative x-axis.
49. $y = -7(x - 1)^2 + 2$
51. $y = -7x^2 + 5$
53. Answers may vary. Sample: $y = (x + 10)^2 − 4$
55. Answers may vary. Sample:
$k = -2$, $a = 3$; $y = 3(x − 1)^2 − 2$
57. Answers may vary. Sample:
$a = -6$, $k = 35$; $y = -6(x + 1)^2 + 35$
59. a. $ah^2 + k$ **b.** when $h = 0$
61. $y = \frac{1}{2}(x + 3)^2$ **63.** $y = -\frac{1}{4}(x − 4)^2$
65. $y = -4(x + 3)^2$ **67.** G
69. $2x + 2y = 225$
$$2y = 225 − 2x$$
$$y = \frac{225}{2} − x$$
$$A = xy = x\left(\frac{225}{2} − x\right)$$
$$A = -x^2 + 112.5x$$
Graph the function. There is a max. at about (56.25, 3164.06), so the max. area is about 3164.06 ft^2 and the length of each side is 56.25 ft.
70. (3, 2) **71.** (−10, 6) **72.** (1, 0, 3)
73. (0, 0) **74.** (−1, 0) **75.** (5, 3)

Lesson 4-2   pp. 202–208

Got It? 1. vertex: $\left(-\frac{5}{2}, 7\frac{1}{2}\right)$; axis of symmetry: $x = -\frac{5}{2}$; maximum: $7\frac{1}{2}$; range: $y \le 7\frac{1}{2}$
2.

3. $y = -(x − 2)^2 − 1$ **4. a.** 4 ft **b.** because the y-intercept is (0, 0)
Lesson Check 1. vertex: (0, −4); axis of symmetry: $x = 0$; minimum: −4
2.   **3.**

4. $y = (x − 1)^2 + 8$ **5.** $y = -\left(x − \frac{3}{2}\right)^2 + \frac{5}{4}$
6. Error in calculation of x. The correct calculation is:
$$x = \frac{-(-4)}{2(2)} = 1$$
$$y = 2(1) − 4(1) − 3$$
$$= 2 − 4 − 3$$
$$= -5$$
Vertex: (1, −5)

7. The vertex of a function written in vertex form can easily be determined. It is (h, k) where $f(x) = a(x − h)^2 + k$. The vertex of a function in standard form is $\left(\frac{-b}{2a}, f\left(\frac{-b}{2a}\right)\right)$ where $f(x) = ax^2 + bx + c$.
Exercises 9. vertex: (1, 2); axis of symmetry: $x = 1$; maximum: 2; range: $y \le 2$ **11.** vertex: (1, 6); axis of symmetry: $x = 1$; maximum: 6; range: $y \le 6$
13. vertex: $\left(-\frac{3}{4}, \frac{5}{8}\right)$; axis of symmetry: $x = -\frac{3}{4}$; maximum: $5\frac{5}{8}$; range: $y \le 5\frac{5}{8}$ **15.** vertex: $\left(-\frac{1}{2}, \frac{1}{4}\right)$; axis of symmetry: $x = -\frac{1}{2}$; maximum: $\frac{1}{4}$; range: $y \le \frac{1}{4}$
17.   **19.**

21.   **23.**

25.
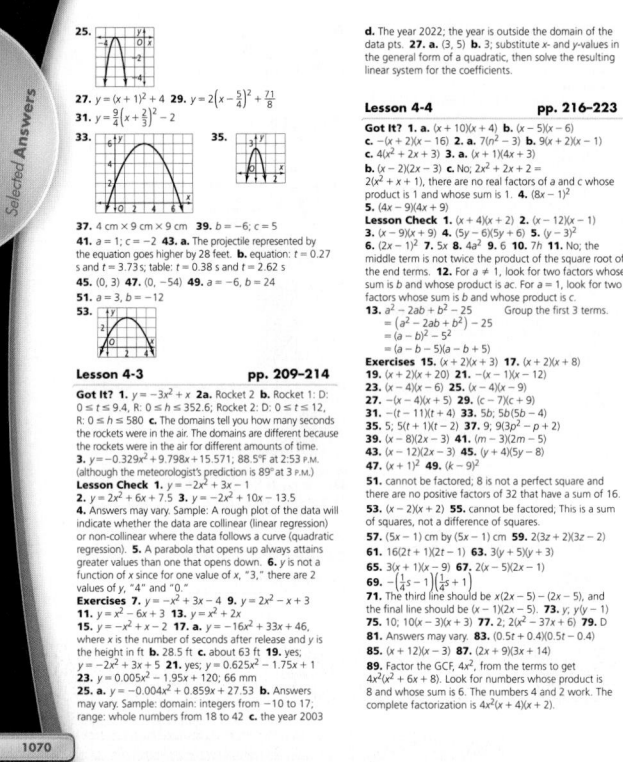

27. $y = (x + 1)^2 + 4$ **29.** $y = 2\left(x - \frac{5}{2}\right)^2 + \frac{71}{8}$
31. $y = \frac{9}{4}\left(x + \frac{5}{3}\right)^2 - 2$

33. **35.**

37. $4 \text{ cm} \times 9 \text{ cm} \times 9 \text{ cm}$ **39.** $b = -6; c = 5$
41. $a = 1; c = -2$ **43. a.** The projectile represented by the equation goes higher by 28 feet. **b.** equation: $t = 0.27$ s and $t = 3.73$ s; table: $t = 0.38$ s and $t = 2.62$ s
45. (0, 3) **47.** (0, −54) **49.** $a = -6$, $b = 24$
51. $a = 3$, $b = -12$
53.

Lesson 4-3 pp. 209–214

Got It? 1. $y = -3x^2 + x$ **2a.** Rocket 2 **b.** Rocket 1: D: $0 \le t \le 9.4$, R: $0 \le h \le 352.6$; Rocket 2: D: $0 \le t \le 12$, R: $0 \le h \le 580$ **c.** The domains tell you how many seconds the rockets were in the air. The domains are different because the rockets were in the air for different amounts of time.
3. $y = -0.329x^2 + 9.798x + 15.571$; 88.5°F at 2:53 P.M. (although the meteorologist's prediction is 89° at 3 P.M.)
Lesson Check 1. $y = -2x^2 + 3x - 1$
2. $y = 2x^2 + 6x + 7.5$ **3.** $y = -2x^2 + 10x - 13.5$
4. Answers may vary. Sample: A rough plot of the data will indicate whether the data are collinear (linear regression) or non-collinear where the data follows a curve (quadratic regression). **5.** A parabola that opens up always attains greater values than one that opens down. **6.** y is not a function of x since for one value of x, "3," there are 2 values of y, "4" and "0."
Exercises 7. $y = -x^2 + 3x - 4$ **9.** $y = 2x^2 - x + 3$
11. $y = x^2 - 6x + 3$ **13.** $y = x^2 + 2x$
15. $y = -x^2 + x - 2$ **17a.** $y = -16x^2 + 33x + 46$, where x is the number of seconds after release and y is the height in ft **b.** 28.5 ft **c.** about 63 ft **19.** yes; $y = -2x^2 + 3x + 5$ **21.** yes; $y = 0.625x^2 - 1.75x + 1$
23. $y = 0.005x^2 - 1.95x + 120$; 66 mm
25. a. $y = -0.004x^2 + 0.859x + 27.53$ **b.** Answers may vary. Sample: domain: integers from −10 to 17; range: whole numbers from 18 to 42 **c.** the year 2003

d. the year 2022; the year is outside the domain of the data pts. **27. a.** (3, 5) **b.** 3; substitute x- and y-values in the general form of a quadratic, then solve the resulting linear system for the coefficients.

Lesson 4-4 pp. 216–223

Got It? 1. a. $(x + 10)(x + 4)$ **b.** $(x - 5)(x - 6)$
c. $-(x + 2)(x - 16)$ **2. a.** $7(n^2 - 3)$ **b.** $9(x + 2)(x - 1)$
c. $4(x^2 + 2x + 3)$ **3. a.** $(x + 1)(4x + 3)$
b. $(x - 2)(2x - 3)$ **c.** No; $2x^2 + 2x + 2 = 2(x^2 + x + 1)$, there are no real factors of a and c whose product is 1 and whose sum is 1. **4.** $(8x - 1)^2$
5. $(4x - 9)(4x + 9)$
Lesson Check 1. $(x + 4)(x + 2)$ **2.** $(x - 12)(x - 1)$
3. $(x - 9)(x + 9)$ **4.** $(5y - 6)(5y + 6)$ **5.** $(y - 3)^2$
6. $(2x - 1)^2$ **7.** $5x$ **8.** $4a^2$ **9.** 6 **10.** $7h$ **11.** No; the middle term is not twice the product of the square root of the end terms. For $a \ne 1$, look for two factors whose sum is b and whose product is ac. For $a = 1$, look for two factors whose sum is b and whose product is c.
13. $a^2 - 2ab + b^2 - 25$ Group the first 3 terms.
$= (a^2 - 2ab + b^2) - 25$
$= (a - b)^2 - 25$
$= (a - b - 5)(a - b + 5)$
Exercises 15. $(x + 2)(x + 3)$ **17.** $(x + 2)(x + 8)$
19. $(x + 2)(x + 20)$ **21.** $-(x - 1)(x - 12)$
23. $(x - 4)(x - 6)$ **25.** $(x - 4)(x - 9)$
27. $-(x - 4)(x + 5)$ **29.** $(c - 7)(c + 9)$
31. $-(t - 11)(t + 4)$ **33.** $5b$; $5b(5b - 4)$
35. $5(t + 1)(t - 2)$ **37.** 9; $9(3p^2 - p + 2)$
39. $(x - 8)(2x - 3)$ **41.** $(m - 3)(2m - 5)$
43. $(x - 12)(2x - 3)$ **45.** $(y + 4)(5y - 8)$
47. $(x + 1)^2$ **49.** $(x - 9)^2$
51. cannot be factored; 8 is not a perfect square and there are no positive factors of 32 that have a sum of 16.
53. $(x - 2)(x + 2)$ **55.** cannot be factored; This is a sum of squares, not a difference of squares.
57. $(5x - 1) \text{ cm}$ by $(5x - 1) \text{ cm}$ **59.** $2(3z + 2)(3z - 2)$
61. $16(2t + 1)(2t - 1)$ **63.** $3(y + 5)(y + 3)$
65. $3(x + 1)(x - 9)$ **67.** $2(x - 5)(2x + 1)$
69. $-\left(\frac{1}{5}s - 1\right)\left(\frac{1}{5}s + 1\right)$
71. The third line should be $x(2x - 5) - (2x - 5)$, and the final line should be $(x - 1)(2x - 5)$. **73.** y; $y(y - 1)$
75. 10; $10(x - 3)(x + 3)$ **77.** 2; $2(x^2 - 37x + 6)$ **79.** D
81. Answers may vary. **83.** $(0.5t + 0.4)(0.5t - 0.4)$
85. $(x + 12)(x - 3)$ **87.** $(2x + 9)(3x + 14)$
89. Factor the GCF, $4x^2$, from the terms to get $4x^2(x^2 + 6x + 8)$. Look for numbers whose product is 8 and whose sum is 6. The numbers 4 and 2 work. The complete factorization is $4x^2(x + 4)(x + 2)$.

91. $(2x - 5y)(2x + 5y)(4x^2 + 25y^2)$
93. $(x - 8)(x + 3)$ **95.** B **97. a.** By entering the given lists into a graphing calculator and then calculating the quadratic regression, you get $h = -16t^2 + 22t + 3$ as the quadratic model for the ball's height as a function of time.
b. $h = -16t^2 + 22t + 3$
$h = -[8t(2t - 3) + 1(2t - 3)]$
$h = -(2t - 3)(8t + 1)$
98. $y = -0.149x^2 + 5.171x + 16.971$ **99.** penny: 2.5g, nickel: 5g, dime: 2.3g
100.

101.

102.

Algebra Review p. 225 1. $3\sqrt{2}$ **3.** $-4\sqrt{2}$ **5.** $\frac{-\sqrt{91}}{13}$
7. $-10\sqrt{2}$ **9.** 108 **11.** $|xy|$ **13.** $-\frac{|x|\sqrt{35}}{5}$ **15.** $\frac{5\sqrt{14}}{7}$

Lesson 4-5 pp. 226–231

Got It? 1. 3, 4 **2.** 3, $\frac{1}{3}$ **3.** −6, 4 **4. a.** $53\frac{1}{3}$ m; $21\frac{1}{3}$ m; $0 \le y \le 30$ **b.** No; domains and ranges are constrained by real-world limits.
Lesson Check 1. 3, −3 **2.** −4, −9 **3.** $-\frac{5}{2}$, 1
4. 4.372, −1.372 **5.** 2.608, −2.108 **6.** −1; since $y = 0$ when $x = 5$, substitute these values into the equation to find b. **7.** when the coefficients are integers and a recognizable pattern of factoring is evident **8.** One solution: when the table's range consists of zero and all positive numbers or zero and all negative numbers. No solution: when the table does not include zero and the y-values are either all positive or all negative numbers
Exercises 9. −4, −2 **11.** −1, $\frac{5}{3}$ **13.** −2, −1 **15.** 0, 4
17. 0, 4 **19.** 3, 8 **21.** −1, −3 **23.** −4, 3 **25.** $-\frac{4}{5}, \frac{2}{3}$
27. $-\frac{10}{3}, \frac{5}{2}$ **29.** $\frac{1}{4}$ **31.** 100 **33.** 4 **35.** 6 ± $\sqrt{29}$
37. 1 ± $\sqrt{6}$ **39.** 5 ± $\sqrt{13}$ **41.** 3 ± $\sqrt{11}$
43. $-\frac{5}{4} \pm \frac{1}{4}\sqrt{37}$ **45.** $-\frac{3}{5} \pm \frac{\sqrt{21}}{5}$
47. $y = 2(x - 2)^2 - 7$ **49.** $y = (x + 2)^2 - 11$
51. $y = -(x - 2)^2 + 3$ **53.** 10, −10 **55.** 22, −22
57. 18, −18 **59.** 1, −61 **84.** −84
63. $\frac{-5 \pm \sqrt{37}}{2}$ **65.** $\frac{1 \pm \sqrt{21}}{5}$ **67.** $\frac{2 \pm \sqrt{10}}{3}$
69. $\frac{-3 \pm \sqrt{41}}{8}$ **71.** $-\frac{1}{2}, -\frac{7}{3}$ **73.** $-3 \pm \sqrt{7}$
75a. $-.01(x - 59)^2 + 36.81$; 36.81 ft **b.** 7.65 ft
c. about 120 ft **77.** $\frac{-a \pm a\sqrt{13}}{6}$

53. −1, $\frac{10}{3}$ **55.** (0, −2), (2, 2) **57.** Solve $(x - 4)(x - 6) = 0$ to find that the zeros of $y = x^2 - 10x + 24$ are 4 and 6. Average 4 and 6 to get 5. This is the x-coordinate of the vertex. Substitute 5 for x in $x^2 - 10x + 24$ to find that −1 is the y-coordinate of the vertex. The vertex is (5, −1).
59. a. 2.45m **b.** ≈ 1.56 **61.** H
63. reflection across the x-axis, followed by a vertical translation 2 units up, and stretched by a factor of 3

Lesson 4-6 pp. 233–239

Got It? 1. a. $\sqrt{5}$, $-\sqrt{5}$ **b.** $\sqrt{2}$, $-\sqrt{2}$
2. 42 in. × 67.2 in. **3.** 2, 12 **4. a.** 9 **b.** No; $\left(\frac{b}{2}\right)^2 = \frac{b^2}{4}$, which is a function of b. **5.** $\frac{1}{2} \pm \frac{\sqrt{13}}{2}$
6. $y = \left(x + \frac{3}{2}\right)^2 - \frac{33}{4}$; vertex: $\left(-\frac{3}{2}, -\frac{33}{4}\right)$; y-intercept: (0, −6)
Lesson Check 1. 6, −6 **2.** 3, −3 **3.** 1, 4 **25.** 5, 4
6. 36 **7.** 2500 **8.** 256 **9.** First, you rewrite the eq. to get all terms with x on one side. Then, you find $\left(\frac{b}{2}\right)^2$ and add it to both sides of the eq. Then, you factor the resulting trinomial.
10. $x^2 + 12x + 5 = 3$ Rewrite to get all terms with x
$x^2 + 12x = -2$ on one side of the eq.
$\left(\frac{12}{2}\right)^2 = 6^2 = 36$ Find $\left(\frac{b}{2}\right)^2 = 36$.
$x^2 + 12x + 36 = -2 + 36$ Add 36 to each side.
$(x + 6)^2 = 34$ Factor the trinomial.
11. Your friend should have subtracted 49; $(x^2 - 14x + 49) + 36 - 49 = (x - 7)^2 - 13$
Exercises 13. 2, −2 **15.** $\frac{5}{3}, -\frac{5}{3}$ **17.** $2\sqrt{2}, -2\sqrt{2}$
19. −4, −2 **21.** −1, 3 **23.** −4, 3 **25.** $-\frac{4}{3}, \frac{2}{3}$

Lesson 4-9 pp. 258–264

Got It? 1. (−3, 0), (−2, 1) **2.** (−5, 6), (1, 6)
3. a. (0, 5), (2, 1) **b.** no solution
4. a. **b.** infinite, one, or none

Lesson Check 1. (1, 2), (2, 3) **2.** (1, −1), (2, 0)
3. (2, −5), $\left(-\frac{4}{3}, \frac{25}{9}\right)$
4. **5.**

6. For each system of eqs., linear or quadratic, to solve the system you need to find the pt. (or pts.) of intersection or, in the case of inequalities, the regions of intersection. A linear system of eqs. can have one, infinite, or no solutions, whereas a quadratic systems of eqs. can have one, two, infinite, or zero solutions.
7. a. two, one, or zero

b. two, one, or zero

c. four, three, two, one, or zero

79. $-\frac{3}{2a}, -\frac{1}{2a}, a \ne 0$ **81.** $-\frac{5}{3a}, \frac{5}{3a}, a \ne 0$
83. $y = -4\left(x + \frac{5}{8}\right)^2 + \frac{73}{16}; \left(-\frac{5}{8}, \frac{73}{16}\right)$
85. $y = -\frac{1}{3}(x - 2)^2 + 3; (2, 3)$ **87.** G
89. $\sqrt{b^2 - 9} = -8x$
$x^2 + 8x = 9$ Move the variables to the left side and the constant to the right by using the Add. Prop. of Eq.
$\left(\frac{8}{2}\right)^2 = 4^2 = 16$ Find $\left(\frac{b}{2}\right)^2 = 16$.
$x^2 + 8x + 16$ Add 16 to each
$= 9 + 16$ side.
$(x + 4)^2 = 25$ Factor left side. Simplify right side.
$x + 4 = \pm 5$ Take the square root of each side.
$x = -4 \pm 5$ Add −4 to each side.
$x = -9, 1$ Simplify.
90. $\frac{1}{2}, 1$ **91.** −4, 1 **92.** 8, $-\frac{5}{3}$
93. yes; $y = \frac{1}{2}x^2 + \frac{7}{2}x + 9$ **94.** yes;
$y = -\frac{1}{2}x^2 + x + 2$ **95.** yes; $y = 3x^2 - 5x + 2$
96. (2, 0) **97.** (3, 1) **98.** (3, 1) **99.** 24 **100.** 84

Lesson 4-7 pp. 240–247

Got It? 1. a. −2 **b.** −2 ± $\sqrt{7}$ **2. a.** $10.74 ft **b.** Yes; a neg. profit means more money was spent than earned.
3. a. no real solutions **b.** two real solutions **4.** Yes; $b^2 - 4ac = (85)^2 - 4(-16)\left(-109\frac{11}{12}\right) = 190\frac{1}{3}$. The discriminant is pos. So the eq. has two real solutions.
Lesson Check 1. $\frac{5 \pm \sqrt{53}}{2}$ **2.** $\frac{-3 \pm \sqrt{61}}{2}$ **3.** 3, $-\frac{1}{2}$
4. no real solutions **5.** −32; no real solutions **6.** 273; two real solutions **7.** 0; one real solution **8.** $k = \pm 6$ for one real solution; $k > 6$ or $k < -6$ for two real solutions **9.** Answers may vary. Sample: The discriminants of eqs. with one real solution are all zero and thus equal, but the solutions may or may not be equal. An example is $x^2 - 8x + 16$ and $x^2 - 4x + 4$. Each has a discriminant of zero, but the solutions are 4 and 2. **10.** Yes; the eqs. can share common factors such as for $x^2 + 2x - 8$ where the discriminant is 36 and the solutions are 2 and −4, and $x^2 - 4x + 4$ where the discriminant is zero and the solution is 2.
Exercises 11. 1, 3 **13.** $-\frac{7}{2}$, 1 **15.** −5 **17.** $\frac{3 \pm \sqrt{5}}{2}$
19. $\frac{2 \pm \sqrt{10}}{3}$ **21.** 1, 4 **23.** $16.34 **25.** −4; no real solutions **27.** 0; one **29.** 169; two **31.** 1; two
33. 0; one **35.** −23; no real solutions **37.** no
39. 2.29 in. × 15.71 in. **41.** $-\frac{1}{6}$, 1 **43.** −2.49, 0.89
45. −0.19, 2.69 **47.** 1, 10 **49.** $-\frac{3}{2}, \frac{1}{2}$ **51.** −1.70, 4.70
53. −8.47, 0.47 **55.** 1.47, −7.47 **57.** about 1.89 s

59. one **61.** two **63.** two **65.** two **67. a.** k such that $|k| < 12$ **b.** 12 or −12 **c.** k such that $|k| > 12$
69. a. $x^2 = 100\pi$ **b.** 17.72 cm
71. Answers may vary. Sample: $x^2 + 5x + 3 = 0$
73. 0, ± $\sqrt{5}$ **75.** −5, 1 **77.** The absolute value of $\frac{\sqrt{b^2 - 4ac}}{2a}$ is the distance from the axis of symmetry to the x-intercepts, if the discriminant is nonnegative.
79. 3 **81.** 15 **82.** −10 **83.** $\frac{2 \pm \sqrt{2}}{2}$ **84.** $\frac{3 \pm \sqrt{41}}{2}$
85. $9z^2 + 3z$ **86.** $4x + x$ **87.** $2y - 8$
88. $2\sqrt{17}$ **89.** 5 **90.** 13

Lesson 4-8 pp. 248–255

Got It? 1. a. $2i\sqrt{3}$ **b.** $5i$ **c.** $i\sqrt{7}$ **d.** $8i \ne -8$
2. a. ; $\sqrt{26}$

b. ; $\sqrt{13}$ **c.** ; $\sqrt{17}$

3. a. $4 - i$ **b.** $-2 + 7i$ **c.** $12i$ **d.** $18i$ **4. a.** -21
b. $23 - 2i$ **c.** 41 **5. a.** $-\frac{7}{25} - \frac{26}{25}i$ **b.** $-\frac{1}{6} - \frac{5}{6}i$
c. $\frac{15}{113} - \frac{112}{113}i$ **6. a.** $5(x + 2i)(x - 2i)$
b. $(x + 9i)(x - 9i)$ **7. a.** $\frac{1 \pm i\sqrt{23}}{6}$
b. $2 \pm i$
Lesson Check 1. $5i\sqrt{2}$ **2.** 5 **3.** $(x + 4i)(x - 4i)$
4. 7 − 3i **5.** 13 − 6i **6.** The add. inv. of a complex number, $a + bi$, is the opposite of the complex number, or $-a - bi$. The complex conjugate of a complex number, $a + bi$, is the real part plus the opposite of the imaginary part of the complex number, or $a - bi$. **7.** error in the sign of the last term of the first line, which carries through to the end of the calculation; the line should be: " . . . $= 16 + 28i - 28i - 49i^2$
$= 16 + 49$
$= 65$."
Exercises 9. $i\sqrt{7}$ **11.** 9i
13. ; $2\sqrt{2}$ **15.** ; $2\sqrt{2}$

17. ; $3\sqrt{5}$ **19.** $1 - 7i$ **21.** $10 + 6i$
23. $9 + 58i$ **25.** −36 **27.** $-\frac{2}{5} - \frac{2}{5}i$ **29.** $\frac{8}{17} + \frac{19}{17}i$
31. $\frac{8}{13} + \frac{12}{13}i$ **33.** $(5 + 5i)(5 - 5i)$ **35.** $3(s + 5i)(s - 5i)$ **37.** $(2b + i)(2b - i)$

39. $-1 \pm i\sqrt{2}$ **41.** $1 \pm i\frac{\sqrt{10}}{5}$ **43.** $2 \pm i$
45. a. A: −5; B: 3 + 2i; C: −2 − i; D: 3i; E: −6 − 4i; F: −1 + 5i **b.** A: 5; B: −3 − 2i; C: −2 + i; D: −3i; E: 6 + 4i; F: 1 − 5i **c.** A: −5; B: 3 − 2i; C: 2 + i; D: −3i; E: −6 + 4i; F: −1 − 5i **d.** A: 5; B: $\sqrt{13}$; C: $\sqrt{5}$; D: 3; E: $2\sqrt{13}$; F: $\sqrt{26}$ **47.** −5, 5 **49.** −1 + 5i
51. $\frac{8}{13} - 2i$, $\frac{8}{13}$ **53.** 5 + 10i **55.** 10 + 11i **57.** trapezoid
59. $\frac{7}{26} + \frac{3}{52}i$ **61.** sum: 2; product: 3
63. sum: $\frac{3}{2}$; product: $\frac{3}{4}$ **65.** Answers may vary. Sample: $x^2 - 4x + 29 = 0$ **67.** $x = -7$, $y = 3$
69. $x = -7$, $y = -3$ **71.** all nonzero numbers x and y such that $|x| = |y|$ **73.** 8 **75.** A
77. $\frac{-3 \pm \sqrt{41}}{4}$ **78.** $\frac{-1 \pm \sqrt{17}}{8}$ **79.** $\frac{-7 \pm \sqrt{17}}{2}$
80. ; axis of symmetry: $x = -1$

81. ; axis of symmetry: $x = 4$

82. ; axis of symmetry: $x = 1$

83. $y = 3x - 4$ **84.** $y = -0.5x - 2$
85. $y = -7x + 10$ **86.** $y = 2x + 8$
87. **88.**

89.

no solution

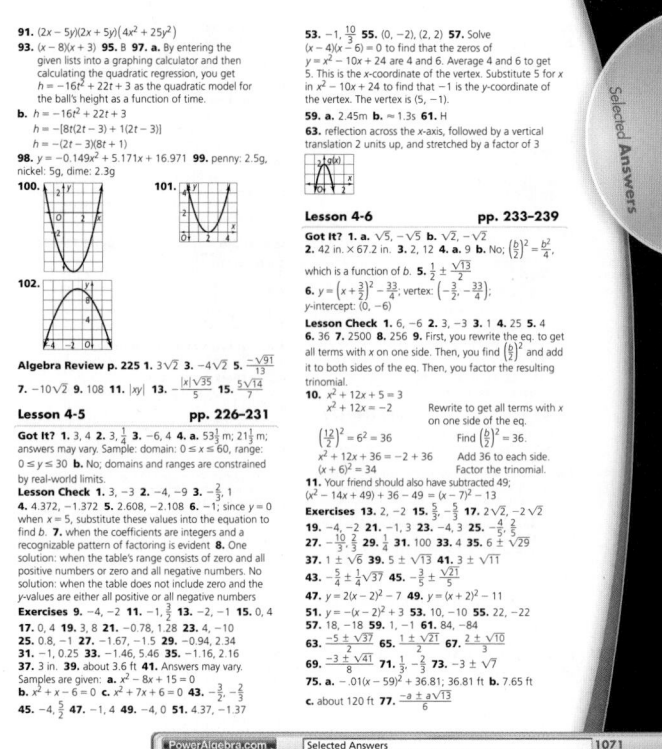
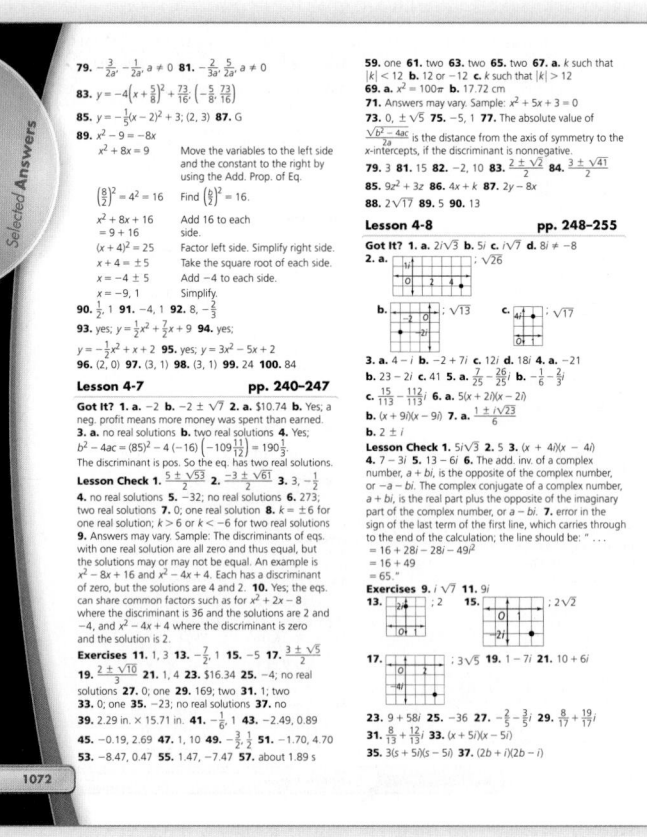
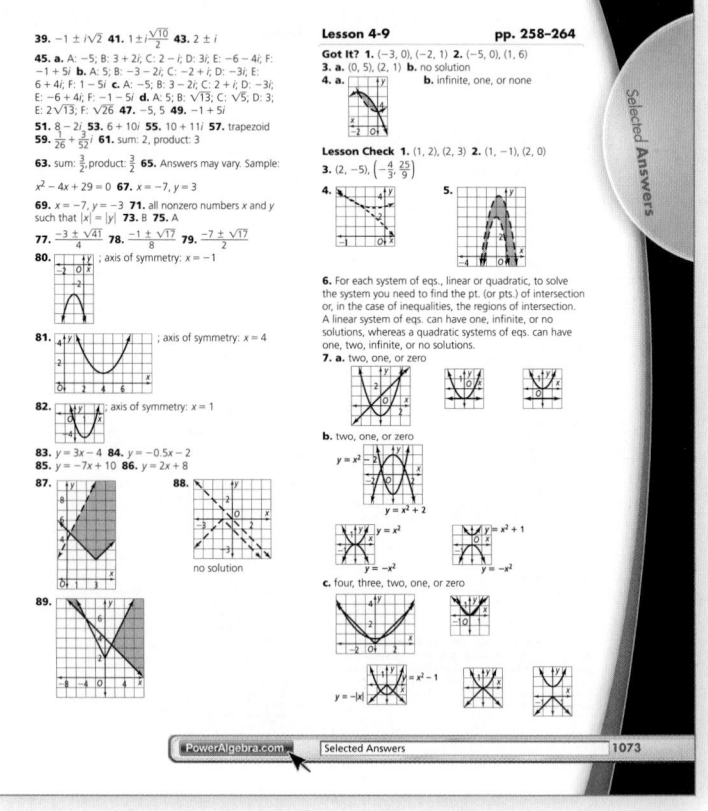

Exercises

9. (0, 1), (4, 9); 11. (0, 1), $\left(-\frac{5}{2}, 6\right)$;

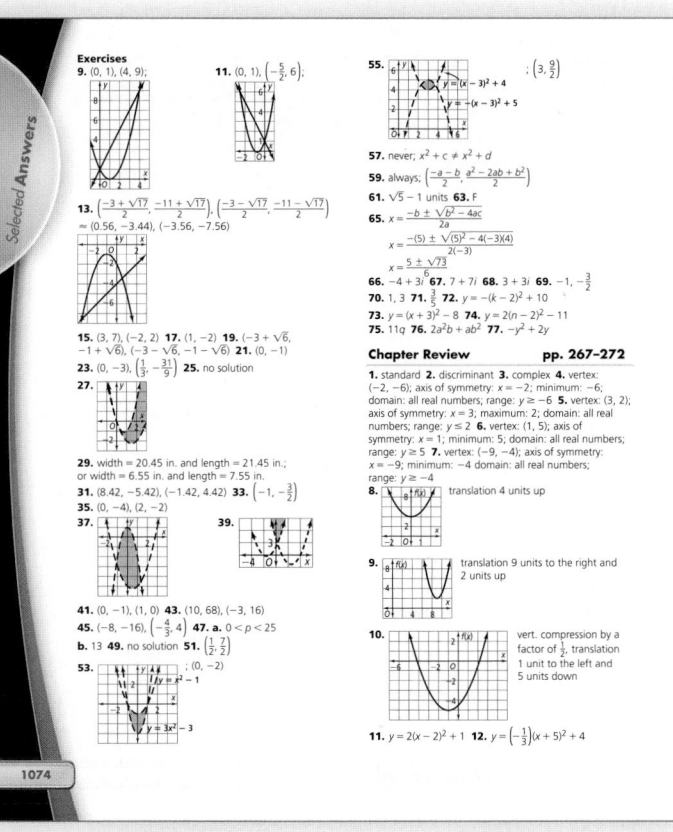

13. $\left(\frac{-3+\sqrt{17}}{2}, \frac{-11+\sqrt{17}}{2}\right), \left(\frac{-3-\sqrt{17}}{2}, \frac{-11-\sqrt{17}}{2}\right)$
≈ (0.56, -3.44), (-3.56, -7.56)

15. (3, 7), (-2, 2) 17. (1, -2) 19. $(-3 + \sqrt{6}, -1 + \sqrt{6})$, $(-3 - \sqrt{6}, -1 - \sqrt{6})$ 21. (0, -1)
23. $(0, -3), \left(\frac{1}{3}, -\frac{31}{9}\right)$ 25. no solution
27.

29. width = 20.45 in. and length = 21.45 in.; or width = 6.55 in. and length = 7.55 in.
31. (8.42, -5.42), (-1.42, 4.42) 33. $\left(-1, -\frac{3}{2}\right)$
35. (0, -4), (2, -2)
37. 39.
41. (0, -1), (1, 0) 43. (10, 68), (-3, 16)
45. $(-8, -16), \left(-\frac{4}{3}, 4\right)$ 47. a. 0 < p < 25
b. 13 49. no solution 51. $\left(\frac{1}{2}, \frac{7}{2}\right)$
53.

55. ; $\left(3, \frac{9}{2}\right)$

57. never; $x^2 + c \neq x^2 + d$
59. always; $\left(\frac{-a-b}{2}, \frac{a^2-2ab+b^2}{2}\right)$
61. $\sqrt{5} - 1$ units 63. F
65. $x = \frac{-b \pm \sqrt{b^2-4ac}}{2a}$
$x = \frac{-(5) \pm \sqrt{(5)^2-4(-3)(4)}}{2(-3)}$
$x = \frac{5 \pm \sqrt{73}}{6}$
66. -4 + 3i 67. 7 + 7i 68. 3 + 3i 69. $-1, -\frac{3}{2}$
70. 1, 3 71. $\frac{2}{5}$ 72. $y = -(k-2)^2 + 10$
73. $y = (x+3)^2 - 8$ 74. $y = 2(n-2)^2 - 11$
75. 11q 76. $2a^2b + ab^2$ 77. $-y^2 + 2y$

Chapter Review pp. 267–272

1. standard 2. discriminant 3. complex 4. vertex: (-2, -6); axis of symmetry: x = -2; minimum: -6; domain: all real numbers, range: y ≥ -6 5. vertex: (3, 2); axis of symmetry: x = 3; maximum: 2; domain: all real numbers; range: y ≤ 2 6. vertex: (1, 5); axis of symmetry: x = 1; minimum: 5; domain: all real numbers; range: y ≥ 5 7. vertex: (-9, -4); axis of symmetry: x = -9; minimum: -4 domain: all real numbers; range: y ≥ -4
8. translation 4 units up
9. translation 9 units to the right and 2 units up
10. vert. compression by a factor of $\frac{1}{2}$, translation 1 unit to the left and 5 units down
11. $y = 2(x-2)^2 + 1$ 12. $y = \left(-\frac{1}{3}\right)(x+5)^2 + 4$

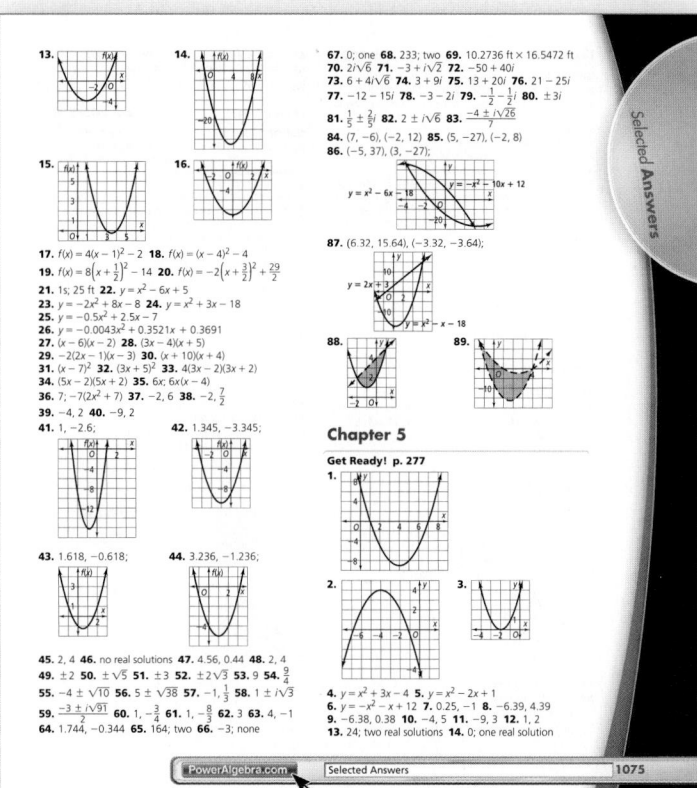

13. 14.
67. 0; one 68. 233; two 69. 10.2736 ft × 16.5472 ft
70. $2\sqrt{6}$ 71. $-3 + \sqrt{2}$ 72. -50 + 40i
73. $6 + 4i\sqrt{6}$ 74. 3 + 9i 75. 13 + 20i 76. 21 - 25i
77. -12 - 15i 78. -3 - 2i 79. $-\frac{1}{2} - \frac{1}{2}i$ 80. ± 3i
81. $\frac{1}{5} \pm \frac{2}{5}i$ 82. $2 \pm i\sqrt{3}$ 83. $\frac{-4 \pm i\sqrt{26}}{7}$
84. (7, -6), (-2, 12) 85. (5, -27), (-2, 8)
86. (-5, 37), (3, -27);
15. 16.
$y = x^2 - 6x$ $y = -x^2 - 10x + 12$
87. (6.32, 15.64), (-3.32, -3.64);
$y = 2x + 15$ $y = x^2 - x - 18$
88. 89.

17. $f(x) = 4(x-1)^2 - 2$ 18. $f(x) = (x-4)^2 - 4$
19. $f(x) = 8\left(x + \frac{1}{2}\right)^2 - 14$ 20. $f(x) = -2\left(x + \frac{3}{2}\right)^2 + \frac{29}{2}$
21. 1s; 25 ft 22. $y = x^2 - 6x + 5$
23. $y = -2x^2 + 8x - 8$ 24. $y = x^2 + 3x - 18$
25. $y = -0.5x^2 + 2.5x - 7$
26. $y = -0.0043x^2 + 0.3521x + 0.3691$
27. (x - 6)(x - 2) 28. (3x - 4)(x + 5)
29. -2(2x - 1)(x - 3) 30. (x + 10)(x + 4)
31. $(x - 7)^2$ 32. $(3x + 5)^2$ 33. 4(3x - 2)(3x + 2)
34. (5x - 2)(5x + 2) 35. 6x(x - 4)
36. 7; -2(2x + 7) 37. -2, 6 38. $-2, \frac{7}{2}$
39. -4, 2 40. -9, 2
41. 1, -2.6; 42. 1.345, -3.345;

43. 1.618, -0.618; 44. 3.236, -1.236;

45. 2, 4 46. no real solutions 47. 4.56, 0.44 48. 2, 4
49. ±2 50. $\pm \sqrt{5}$ 51. ±3 52. $\pm 2\sqrt{3}$ 53. $\frac{y}{4}$ 54. $\frac{9}{4}$
55. $-4 \pm \sqrt{10}$ 56. $5 \pm \sqrt{38}$ 57. $-1, \frac{1}{3}$ 58. $1 \pm i\sqrt{3}$
59. $\frac{-3 \pm i\sqrt{91}}{10}$ 60. $1, -\frac{3}{4}$ 61. $1, -\frac{8}{3}$ 62. 3, 4, -1
64. 1.744, -0.344 65. 164; two 66. 3; none

Chapter 5

Get Ready! p. 277

1.

2. 3.

4. $y = x^2 + 3x - 4$ 5. $y = x^2 - 2x + 1$
6. $y = -x^2 - x + 12$ 7. 0.25, -1 8. -6.39, 4.39
9. -6.38, 0.38 10. -4, 5 11. -9, 3 12. 1, 2
13. 2; two real solutions 14. 0; one real solution

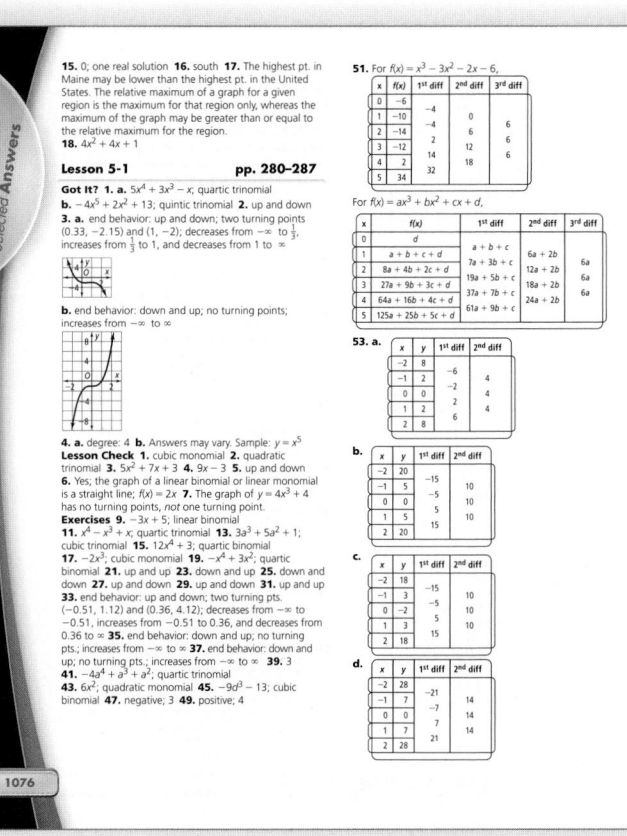

15. 0; one real solution 16. south 17. The highest pt. in Maine may be lower than the highest pt. in the United States. The relative maximum of a graph for a given region is the maximum for that region only, whereas the maximum of the graph may be greater than or equal to the relative maximum for the region.
18. $4x^2 + 4x + 1$

Lesson 5-1 pp. 280–287

Got It! 1. a. $5x^4 + 3x^3 - x$; quartic trinomial
b. $-4x^5 + 2x^2 + 13$; quintic trinomial 2. up and down
3. a. end behavior: up and down; two turning points (0.33, -2.15) and (1, -2); decreases from $-\infty$ to $\frac{1}{3}$, increases from $\frac{1}{3}$ to 1, and decreases from 1 to ∞

b. end behavior: down and up; no turning points; increases from $-\infty$ to ∞

4. a. degree: 4 b. Answers may vary. Sample: $y = x^5$
Lesson Check 1. cubic monomial 2. quadratic trinomial 3. $5x^2 + 7x + 3$ 4. 9x - 5. up and down
6. Yes; the graph of a linear binomial or linear monomial is a straight line; f(x) = 2x 7. The graph of $y = 4x^3 + 4$ has no turning points, not one turning point.
Exercises 9. -3x + 5; linear binomial
11. $x^4 - x^3 + x$; quartic trinomial 13. $3a^3 + 5a^2 + 1$; cubic trinomial 15. $12x^4 + 3$; quartic binomial
17. $-2x^3$; cubic monomial 19. $-x^4 + 3x^2$; quartic binomial 21. up and up 23. down and up 25. down and down 27. up and down 29. up and up 31. up and up
33. end behavior: up and down; two turning pts. (-0.51, 1.12) and (0.36, 4.12); decreases from $-\infty$ to -0.51, increases from -0.51 to 0.36, and decreases from 0.36 to ∞ 35. end behavior: down and up; no turning pts.; increases from $-\infty$ to ∞ 37. end behavior: down and up; no turning pts.; increases from $-\infty$ to ∞ 39. 3
41. $-4a^4 + a^3 + a^2$; quartic trinomial
43. $6x^2$; quadratic monomial 45. $-9d^3 - 13$; cubic binomial 47. negative; 3 49. positive; 4

51. For $f(x) = x^3 - 3x^2 - 2x - 6$,

x	f(x)	1st diff	2nd diff	3rd diff
0	-6			
		-4		
1	-10		0	
		-4		6
2	-14		6	
		2		6
3	-12		12	
		14		6
4	2		18	
		32		
5	34			

For $f(x) = ax^3 + bx^2 + cx + d$,

x	f(x)	1st diff	2nd diff	3rd diff
0	d			
		a + b + c		
1	a + b + c + d		6a + 2b	
		7a + 3b + c		6a
2	8a + 4b + 2c + d		12a + 2b	
		19a + 5b + c		6a
3	27a + 9b + 3c + d		18a + 2b	
		37a + 7b + c		6a
4	64a + 16b + 4c + d		24a + 2b	
		61a + 9b + c		
5	125a + 25b + 5c + d			

53. a.

x	y	1st diff	2nd diff
-2	8		
		-6	
-1	2		4
		-2	
0	0		2
		0	4
1	2		4
		4	
2	34		

b.

x	y	1st diff	2nd diff
-2	20		
		-15	
-1	5		10
		-5	
0	0		10
		5	
1	5		10
		15	
2	20		

c.

x	y	1st diff	2nd diff
-2	18		
		-15	
-1	3		10
		-5	
0	-2		10
		5	
1	3		10
		15	
2	18		

d.

x	y	1st diff	2nd diff
-2	28		
		-21	
-1	7		14
		-7	
0	0		14
		7	
1	7		14
		21	
2	28		

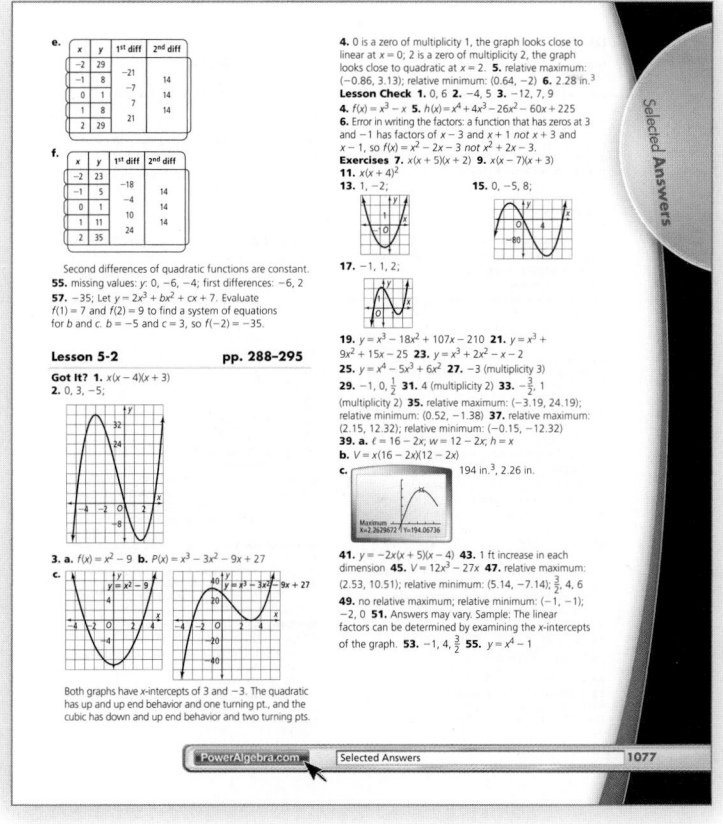

e.

x	y	1st diff	2nd diff
-2	29		
		-21	
-1	8		14
		-7	
0	1		14
		7	
1	8		14
		21	
2	29		

f.

x	y	1st diff	2nd diff
-2	23		
		-18	
-1	5		14
		-4	
0	1		14
		10	
1	11		14
		24	
2	35		

Second differences of quadratic functions are constant.
55. missing values: y, 0, -6, -4; first differences: -6, 2
57. -35; Let $y = 2x^3 + bx^2 + cx + 7$. Evaluate f(1) = 7 and f(2) = 9 to find a system of equations for b and c. b = -5 and c = 3, so f(-2) = -35.

Lesson 5-2 pp. 288–295

Got It! 1. x(x - 4)(x + 3)
2. 0, 3, -5;

3. a. $f(x) = x^2 - 9$ b. $P(x) = x^3 - 3x^2 - 9x + 27$
c.

$y = x^2 - 9$ $y = x^3 - 3x^2 - 9x + 27$

Both graphs have x-intercepts of 3 and -3. The quadratic has up and up end behavior and one turning pt., and the cubic has down and up end behavior and two turning pts.

4. 0 is a zero of multiplicity 1, the graph looks close to linear at x = 0; 2 is a zero of multiplicity 2, the graph looks close to quadratic at x = 2. 5. relative maximum: (-0.86, 3.13); relative minimum: (0.64, -2) 6. 2.28 in.³
Lesson Check 1. 0, 6 2. -4, 5 3. -12, 7, 9
4. $f(x) = x^3 - x$ 5. $h(x) = x^4 + 4x^3 - 26x^2 - 60x + 225$
6. Error in writing the factors: a function that has zeros at 3 and -1 has factors of x - 3 and x + 1 not x + 3 and x - 1, so $f(x) = x^2 - 2x - 3$ not $x^2 + 2x - 3$.
Exercises 7. x(x + 5)(x + 3) 9. x(x - 7)(x + 3)
11. $x(x + 4)^2$
13. 1, -2; 15. 0, -5, 8;

17. -1, 1, 2;

19. $y = x^3 - 18x^2 + 107x - 210$ 21. $y = x^3 + 9x^2 + 15x - 25$ 23. $y = x^3 + 2x^2 - x - 2$
25. $y = x^4 - 5x^3 + 6x^2$ 27. -3 (multiplicity 3)
29. $-1, 0, \frac{1}{2}$ 31. 4 (multiplicity 3) 33. $-\frac{3}{2}$ (multiplicity 2) 35. relative maximum: (-3.19, 24.19); relative minimum: (0.52, -1.38) 37. relative maximum: (2.15, 12.32); relative minimum: (-0.15, -12.32)
39. a. $\ell = 16 - 2x$; w = 12 - 2x; h = x
b. V = x(16 - 2x)(12 - 2x)
c. 194 in.³, 2.26 in.
41. y = -2x(x + 5)(x - 4) 43. 1 ft increase in each dimension 45. $V = 12x^3 - 27x$ 47. relative maximum: (2.53, 10.51); relative minimum: (5.14, -7.14); $\frac{3}{2}$, 4, 6
49. no relative maximum; relative minimum: (-1, -1); -2, 0 51. Answers may vary. Sample: The linear factors can be determined by examining the x-intercepts of the graph. 53. $-1, 4, \frac{3}{2}$ 55. $y = x^2 - 1$

Lesson 5-3 pp. 296–302

Got It? 1. a. $\pm 1, \pm 2i$ **b.** 0, 2, 3 **2. a.** $\pm 2, \pm 2i$ **b.** 0, −4, 2 **c.** $2, -1 \pm i\sqrt{3}$ **3. a.** −1.84 **b.** The second method seems to be a more reliable way to find the solutions because you do not risk missing a pt. of intersection. **4.** 7, 8, 9
Lesson Check 1. $(x-6)(x+3)$ **2.** $(x-3)(x^2+3x+9)$ **3.** $(x^2+4)(x+3)$ **4.** $(x-2)(x+2)(x^2+2)$ **5.** $-4, \frac{1}{2}$ **6.** −2, 0, 1 **7. a.** difference of squares **b.** sum of cubes **c.** difference of cubes **d.** difference of squares **8.** Graphing; imaginary numbers don't exist on the *x*-axis. **9.** Method 1: Graph $y = x^6 - x^2$. Find the zeros for the real solutions.

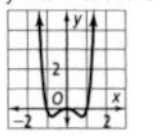

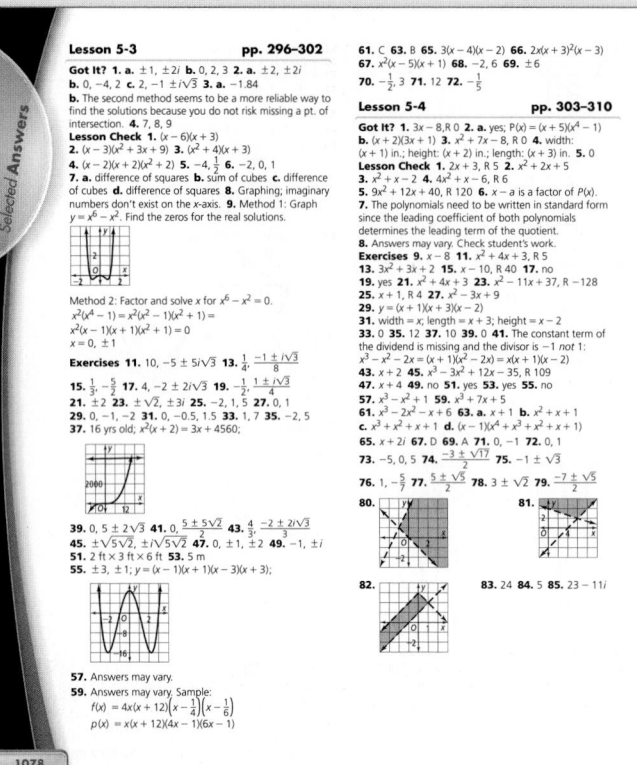

Method 2: Factor and solve *x* for $x^6 - x^2 = 0$.
$x^2(x^4-1) = x^2(x^2-1)(x^2+1) =$
$x^2(x-1)(x+1)(x^2+1) = 0$
$x = 0, \pm 1$

Exercises 11. $10, -5 \pm 5i\sqrt{3}$ **13.** $\frac{1}{4}, \frac{-1 \pm i\sqrt{3}}{8}$ **15.** $\frac{1}{3}, -\frac{5}{2}$ **17.** $4, -2 \pm 2i\sqrt{3}$ **19.** $-\frac{1}{2}, \frac{1 \pm i\sqrt{3}}{4}$ **21.** ± 2 **23.** $\pm\sqrt{2}, \pm 3i$ **25.** −2, 1, 5 **27.** 0, 1 **29.** 0, −1, −2 **31.** 0, −0.5, 1.5 **33.** 1, 7 **35.** −2, 5 **37.** 16 yrs old; $x^2(x+2) = 3x + 4560$;

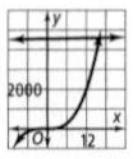

39. $0, 5 \pm 2\sqrt{3}$ **41.** $0, \frac{5 \pm 5\sqrt{2}}{2}$ **43.** $\frac{4}{3}, \frac{-2 \pm 2i\sqrt{3}}{3}$ **45.** $\pm\sqrt{5\sqrt{2}}, \pm i\sqrt{5\sqrt{2}}$ **47.** $0, \pm 1, \pm 2$ **49.** $-1, \pm i$ **51.** 2 ft × 3 ft × 6 ft **53.** 5 m **55.** $\pm 3, \pm 1$; $y = (x-1)(x+1)(x-3)(x+3)$;

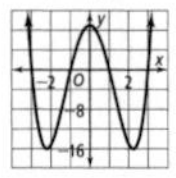

57. Answers may vary.
59. Answers may vary. Sample:
$f(x) = 4x(x+12)\left(x - \frac{1}{4}\right)\left(x - \frac{1}{6}\right)$
$p(x) = x(x+12)(4x-1)(6x-1)$

61. C **63.** B **65.** $3(x-4)(x-2)$ **66.** $2x(x+3)^2(x-3)$ **67.** $x^2(x-5)(x+1)$ **68.** −2, 6 **69.** ± 6 **70.** $-\frac{1}{2}, 3$ **71.** 12 **72.** $-\frac{1}{5}$

Lesson 5-4 pp. 303–310

Got It? 1. $3x - 8$, R 0 **2. a.** yes; $P(x) = (x+5)(x^4-1)$ **b.** $(x+2)(3x+1)$ **3.** $x^2 + 7x - 8$, R 0 **4.** width: $(x+1)$ in.; height: $(x+2)$ in.; length: $(x+3)$ in. **5.** 0
Lesson Check 1. $2x + 3$, R 5 **2.** $x^2 + 2x + 5$ **3.** $x^2 + x - 2$ **4.** $4x^2 + x - 6$, R 6 **5.** $9x^2 + 12x + 40$, R 120 **6.** $x - a$ is a factor of $P(x)$. **7.** The polynomials need to be written in standard form since the leading coefficient of both polynomials determines the leading term of the quotient. **8.** Answers may vary. Check student's work.
Exercises 9. $x - 8$ **11.** $x^2 + 4x + 3$, R 5 **13.** $3x^2 + 3x + 2$ **15.** $x - 10$, R 40 **17.** no **19.** yes **21.** $x^2 + 4x + 3$ **23.** $x^2 - 11x + 37$, R −128 **25.** $x + 1$, R 4 **27.** $x^2 - 3x + 9$ **29.** $y = (x+1)(x+3)(x-2)$ **31.** width = *x*; length = $x + 3$; height = $x - 2$ **33.** 0 **35.** 12 **37.** 10 **39.** 0 **41.** The constant term of the dividend is missing and the divisor is −1 *not* 1: $x^3 - x^2 - 2x = (x+1)(x^2-2x) = x(x+1)(x-2)$ **43.** $x + 2$ **45.** $x^3 - 3x^2 + 12x - 35$, R 109 **47.** $x + 4$ **49.** no **51.** yes **53.** yes **55.** no **57.** $x^3 - x^2 + 1$ **59.** $x^3 + 7x + 5$ **61.** $x^3 - 2x^2 - x + 6$ **63. a.** $x + 1$ **b.** $x^2 + x + 1$ **c.** $x^3 + x^2 + x + 1$ **d.** $(x-1)(x^4 + x^3 + x^2 + x + 1)$ **65.** $x + 2i$ **67.** D **69.** A **71.** 0, −1 **72.** 0, 1 **73.** −5, 0, 5 **74.** $\frac{-3 \pm \sqrt{17}}{2}$ **75.** $-1 \pm \sqrt{3}$ **76.** $1, -\frac{5}{7}$ **77.** $\frac{5 \pm \sqrt{5}}{2}$ **78.** $3 \pm \sqrt{2}$ **79.** $\frac{-7 \pm \sqrt{5}}{2}$

80.
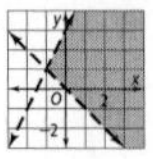

81.
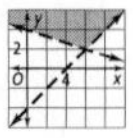

82.
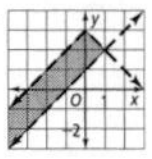

83. 24 **84.** 5 **85.** $23 - 11i$

Lesson 5-5 pp. 312–317

Got It? 1. $\frac{2}{3}$ **2.** $2, -1, -\frac{3}{2}$ **3.** $3 + 2i$ **4.** $P(x) = x^4 - 14x^3 + 69x^2 - 194x + 208$ **5. a.** There are three or one positive real roots and one negative real root. The graph confirms one negative and one positive real root. **b.** Real roots can be confirmed graphically because they are *x*-intercepts. Complex roots cannot be confirmed graphically because they have an imaginary component.
Lesson Check 1. $\pm 1, \pm 2$ **2.** $\pm 1, \pm 2, \pm 3, \pm 6, \pm\frac{1}{2}, \pm\frac{3}{2}$ **3.** $\pm 1, \pm 2, \pm 3, \pm 4, \pm 6, \pm 12, \pm\frac{1}{3}, \pm\frac{2}{3}, \pm\frac{4}{3}$ **4.** $P(x) = x^2 - 14x + 45$ **5.** $P(x) = x^3 + 4x^2 + 4x + 16$ **6.** Answers may vary. Samples: $1 + 2i, 1 - 2i$; $1 + \sqrt{2}, 1 - \sqrt{2}$ **7. a.** never; 5 does not divide 8 evenly **b.** always; −2 divides 8 evenly **8.** Complex number roots come in pairs; if $-4i$ is a root, so is $4i$.
Exercises 9. ± 1; no rational roots **11.** $\pm 1, \pm 2$; 1 **13.** $\pm 1, \pm 2, \pm\frac{1}{5}, \pm\frac{2}{5}; -1, \frac{1}{5}, 2$ **15.** $\pm 1, \pm 2, \pm 4, \pm\frac{1}{7}, \pm\frac{2}{7}, \pm\frac{4}{7}; \frac{2}{7}$ **17.** $\pm 1, \pm 2, \pm 3, \pm 6, \pm\frac{1}{2}, \pm\frac{1}{3}, \pm\frac{1}{6}, \pm\frac{2}{3}, \pm\frac{3}{2}; -\frac{3}{2}, -1, -\frac{1}{3}, 2$ **19.** $14 + \sqrt{2}, 6i$ **21.** $\sqrt{3}, 5 + \sqrt{11}$ **23.** $P(x) = x^2 + 24x + 135$ **25.** $P(x) = x^2 - 18x + 90$ **27.** $P(x) = x^4 - 10x^3 + 294x^2 - 1690x + 21{,}125$ **29.** $P(x) = x^4 - 58x^3 + 1290x^2 - 13{,}066x + 51{,}545$ **31.** two or no positive real roots; one negative real root **33.** no rational roots **35.** $\frac{1}{7}$ **37.** $-1, -\frac{1}{3}, \frac{1}{2}$ **39.** $P(x) = x^4 + 3x^3 + 207x^2 + 675x - 4050$ **41.** $P(x) = x^4 + 6x^3 + 27x^2 - 366x - 518$ **43.** Error in second line, sign of second term; the line should be: $P(-1) = -x^3 + x^2 - x + 1$. Since there are three sign changes in $P(-x)$, there are three or one negative real roots. **45.** height: 5 ft; bases: 10 ft, 14 ft **47.** Answers may vary. Samples: **a.** $x - 1 - \sqrt{2} = 0$ **b.** $x^2 - 2(1 + \sqrt{2})x + (1 + \sqrt{2})^2 = 0$ **c.** −1 **49.** Answers may vary. Sample: You cannot use the Conjugate Root Theorem for irrational roots unless the equation has rational coefficients.

Lesson 5-6 pp. 319–324

Got It? 1. 0, 1, −5, 2 **2. a.** $-1, 2, \frac{1 \pm i\sqrt{23}}{4}$ **b. i.** A 5th degree polynomial function has four, two, or no turning pts. Three turning pts. are visible, so there must be a fourth one. This will turn the graph back across the *x*-axis. **ii.** The Fundamental Thm. of Algebra states there will be five roots, and the Conjugate Root Thm. requires pairs of irrational or complex roots. Only two zeros appear in the graph, so there are three zeros remaining. Of the remaining roots, either there are three real roots, or one real and two complex roots. Either way, there is at least one real root that does not appear in the graph.
Lesson Check 1. four roots **2.** fourteen roots **3.** $5, \pm 4i$ **4.** $0, 2, \pm i$ **5.** By the Fundamental Thm. of Algebra, polynomial equation of degree *n* has exactly *n* roots. **6.** Answers may vary. Sample: $y = x^4 + 8x^2 + 16$ **7.** Use synthetic division to test for and factor out linear factors until a quadratic factor is obtained. Then use the Quadratic Formula if the quadratic factor cannot be factored further.
Exercises 9. $-1, \pm 2i$ **11.** −1, 2, 4 **13.** $2, \pm\sqrt{3}$ **15.** $0, \pm 3, \pm i$ **17.** $3, \pm i$ **19.** $2, \pm\sqrt{3}$ **21.** $\pm 2, \pm i$ **23.** $-6, \pm i$ **25.** $\pm 4, \frac{-1 \pm i\sqrt{3}}{2}$ **27.** five complex roots; one, three, or five real roots; possible rational roots: $\pm 1, \pm 2, \pm 3, \pm 6, \pm 9, \pm 18$ **29.** six complex roots; zero, two, four, or six real roots; possible rational roots: $\pm\frac{1}{4}, \pm\frac{1}{2}, \pm\frac{3}{4}, \pm 1, \pm\frac{3}{2}, \pm 2, \pm 3, \pm 4, \pm 6, \pm 8, \pm 12, \pm 24$ **31.** $-2, \pm\sqrt{5}$ **33.** $-2, \frac{4}{3}, 3$ **35.** $3, -1 \pm i\sqrt{2}$ **37.** $-\frac{1}{2}, -1, \pm 3$ **39.** 3 bridges **41.** sometimes **43.** always **45.** Answers may vary. Sample: $y = x^4 + 3x^2 + 2$
47. Given any polynomial eq. of odd degree $n \geq 1$, the eq. has exactly *n* roots. Since imaginary roots occur in pairs, a polynomial of odd degree *n* will have an even number of imaginary roots and thus an odd number of real roots. So, any odd degree polynomial eq. with real coefficients has at least one real root.
49. 5th degree; rational zero:
$-\frac{5}{6}(x - \sqrt{2})(x + \sqrt{2})(x - \sqrt{3})(x + \sqrt{3})(x + \frac{5}{6})$
$= x^5 + \frac{5}{6}x^4 - 5x^3 - \frac{25}{6}x^2 + 6x + 5.$
51. G **53.** Substitute (2, −2) into both inequalities to see if the pt. satisfies both inequalities. If it does, then (2, −2) is a solution of the system. If one or both inequalities are not satisfied by the pt.(2, −2), then (2, −2) is not a solution of the system.
54. $x^4 + 6x^3 + 14x^2 + 24x + 40 = 0$
55. $3 \pm 2\sqrt{2}$ **56.** $\frac{-5 \pm i\sqrt{47}}{4}$
57. $\frac{3 \pm i\sqrt{23}}{4}$ **58.** $f(x) = -x^2 + 2x + 3$ **59.** $f(x) = 2x^2 + 24x + 75$ **60.** $x^3 + 3x^2 + 3x + 1$ **61.** $x^3 - 9x^2 + 27x - 27$ **62.** $x^4 - 8x^3 + 24x^2 - 32x + 16$ **63.** $x^2 - 2x + 1$ **64.** $x^3 + 15x^2 + 75x + 125$ **65.** $-x^3 + 12x^2 + 48x + 64$

Lesson 5-7 pp. 326–330

Got It? 1. $a^8 + 8a^7b + 28a^6b^2 + 56a^5b^3 + 70a^4b^4 + 56a^3b^5 + 28a^2b^6 + 8ab^7 + b^8$ **2. a.** $16x^4 - 96x^3 + 216x^2 - 216x + 81$ **b.** If you express 11 as (10 + 1) and calculate the powers using Pascal's triangle, it will be the coefficients.
Lesson Check 1. $x^3 + 3x^2a + 3xa^2 + a^3$ **2.** $x^5 - 10x^4 + 40x^3 - 80x^2 + 80x - 32$ **3.** $4x^2 + 16x + 16$ **4.** $27a^3 - 54a^2 + 36a - 8$ **5. a.** yes **b.** yes **c.** no **6.** The coefficients for the expansion of $(a + b)^n$ are equal to the numbers in the *n*th row of Pascal's Triangle, respectively. **7.** 13; $n + 1$
Exercises 9. $a^4 + 8a^3 + 24a^2 + 32a + 16$ **11.** $x^3 - 15x^2 + 75x - 125$ **13.** $x^{10} + 20x^9 + 180x^8 + 960x^7 + 3360x^6 + 8064x^5 + 13{,}440x^4 + 15{,}360x^3 + 11{,}520x^2 + 5120x + 1024$ **15.** $b^9 + 27b^8 + 324b^7 + 2268b^6 + 10{,}206b^5 + 30{,}618b^4 + 61{,}236b^3 + 78{,}732b^2 + 59{,}049b + 19{,}683$ **17.** $a^4 + 12a^3b + 54a^2b^2 + 108ab^3 + 81b^4$ **19.** $65{,}536 - 131{,}072x + 114{,}688x^2 - 57{,}344x^3 + 17{,}920x^4 - 3584x^5 + 448x^6 - 32x^7 + x^8$ **21.** $27a^3 - 189a^2 + 441a - 343$ **23.** $81y^4 - 1188y^3 + 6534y^2 - 15{,}972y + 14{,}641$ **25. a.** 6 **b.** 489,888 **27.** $135x^4$ **29.** $625b^8$ **31.** The challenge of the Binomial Theorem occurs when there is a coefficient with the *x*. However, it is much more efficient to use the Binomial Theorem than FOIL when expanding a binomial that is raised to a high power. **33.** $x^{20} + 40x^{18} + 720x^{16} + 7680x^{14} + 53{,}760x^{12} + 258{,}048x^{10} + 860{,}160x^8 + 1{,}966{,}080x^6 + 2{,}949{,}120x^4 + 2{,}621{,}440x^2 + 1{,}048{,}576$ **35.** $a^5 - 5a^4b^2 + 10a^3b^4 - 10a^2b^6 + 5ab^8 - b^{10}$ **37.** $256x^4 - 1792x^3y + 4704x^2y^2 - 5488xy^3 + 2401y^4$ **39.** $4096x^{18} + 12{,}288x^{15}y^2 + 15{,}360x^{12}y^4 + 10{,}240x^9y^6 + 3840x^6y^8 + 768x^3y^{10} + 64y^{12}$ **41.** $125a^3 + 150a^2b + 60ab^2 + 8b^3$ **43.** $-32y^{10} + 80y^8x - 80y^6x^2 + 40y^4x^3 - 10y^2x^4 + x^5$ **45.** Answers may vary. Sample: Since one of the terms is negative $(-y)$ and it is alternately raised to odd and even powers; the term is negative when raised to an odd power and positive when raised to an even power. **47.** $-29{,}113 + 17{,}684i$ **49.** $(x^{14} - 21x^{10} + 35x^6 - 7x^2) + i(-7x^{12} + 35x^8 - 21x^4 + 1)$ **51.** $\frac{1}{64}$ **53.** $(-1 + i\sqrt{3})^3 = -1 + 3i\sqrt{3} + 9 - 3i\sqrt{3} = 8$ **55.** G **57.** Let c_a = the first company's cost per month and let c_b = the second company's cost per month: $c_a = 2.25t + 7.95$ and $c_b = 2.75t$

$$c_a = c_b$$
$$2.25t + 7.95 = 2.75t$$
$$7.95 = 0.5t$$
$$15.9 = t$$

The cost will be equal after 15.9 hours of use.
58. $-3, -1, \frac{-3 \pm i\sqrt{11}}{2}$ **59.** $1, \pm i, \pm 3i$ **60.** $-4, \frac{-3 \pm i\sqrt{7}}{4}$ **61.** −1, 1, 2, 7 **62.** $-18 + 43i$ **63.** $600i$ **64.** −2 **65.** $\frac{7}{5} + \frac{31}{5}i$ **66.** $2x^3 + 5x^2 - x + 9$; cubic polynomial of 4 terms **67.** $-7x^2 + 4x + 1$; quadratic trinomial **68.** $12x^4 - 3x^3 - 9x^2 + x - 8$; quartic polynomial of 5 terms

Lesson 5-8 pp. 331–338

Got It? 1. $y = 1.667x^3 + 1.3 \times 10^{-12}x^2 - 4.667x + 5$ **2.** 22.52 billion lbs **3.** Answers may vary. Sample: The cubic model would fit the data better than the linear model because of the $(n + 1)$ Pt. Principle. Both models have down and up end behavior and increasing growth. The cubic shows slowing growth followed by rapidly increasing growth.
4. a. $y = 0.269867411x - 3.919692952$

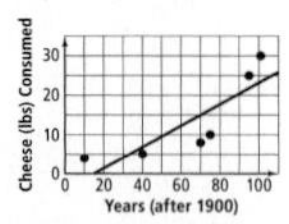

b. 1980: 17.7 lbs; 2000: 23.07 lbs; 2012: 26.31 lbs; most confident for the yrs 1980 and 2000, since they are within the domain of the data set; least confident for the yr 2012, since it is outside the domain of the data set
Lesson Check 1. linear **2.** quadratic **3.** cubic **4.** quartic **5.** interpolation since the data point is within the domain of the data set **6.** yes, since the four pts. pass the vertical-line test, a cubic function will fit the pts.; $y = -x^3 - 3x^2 - 3x$ **7.** cubic model; the closer R^2 is to 1, the better the fit
Exercises 9. $y = \frac{1}{2}x - 3$ **11.** $y = -0.929x^2 + 7.786x + 4$ **13.** $y = x^2 - 6x + 1$ **15.** $y = 2x^3 + x^2 - 4x + 6$ **17.** (where *x* = yrs after 1900) quadratic: $y = -1.25 \times 10^{-4}x^2 - 0.003x + 2.804$, cubic: $y = -8.33 \times 10^{-6}x^3 + 0.002x^2 - 0.190x + 8.142$; cubic; cubic **19.** linear: $y = -0.057x + 19.93$, quadratic: $y = -0.025x^2 + 0.14x + 19.595$; quadratic; quadratic **21.** 1950: 2.60%; 1988: 1.23%; 2010: 0.35%

23. January: 19.714 millions of barrels/day; March: 19.8 millions of barrels/day; October: 18.535 millions of barrels/day **25.** cubic: $y = 10.25x^3 + 5x^2 - 2.25x - 8.2$; quartic: $y = 2.042x^4 + 10.25x^3 - 4.042x^2 - 2.25x - 4$; quartic, $(R^2 = 1)$ **27.** $y = -0.275x^4 + 0.85x^3 - 4.025x^2 - 8.15x + 7$ **29.** $y = 0.0611511911x^3 - 0.9276466231x^2 + 6.184642324x + 1.750778723$; $R^2 = 0.9994739763$; good fit **31.** $y = 0.111x^4 - 45.618x^3 + 6997.73x^2 - 476{,}931.355x + 12{,}185{,}696.59$ **33.** A quadratic model would be more appropriate, given the real world context. According to the cubic model, there would be a negative number of students enrolled in the course in the year 2024.
35. a. −0.48; −0.75
b.
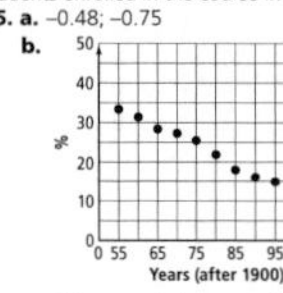

A linear model seems to be most appropriate.
c. Answers may vary. Sample: $y = -0.4464x + 57.77$ **d.** 4.2% **e.** No; although R^2 is close to 1, the model is not realistic since it predicts that the percentage will eventually become 0, and then negative.
37. $y = \frac{1}{8}(x^2 - 4)^2$

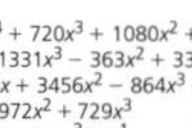

39. 1 **41.** $-\frac{7}{8}$ **43.** $32x^5 + 240x^4 + 720x^3 + 1080x^2 + 810x + 243$ **44.** $1331x^3 - 363x^2 + 33x - 1$ **45.** $4096 - 6144x + 3456x^2 - 864x^3 + 81x^4$ **46.** $64 + 432x + 972x^2 + 729x^3$ **47.** $|x - 8| < 1$ **48.** $|x - \frac{3}{8}| \leq \frac{1}{8}$ **49.** $|y - 2.8| < 1.1$ **50.** $|t - 750| < 250$ **51.** $s = \sqrt{A}$ **52.** $\ell = \frac{P}{2} - w$ **53.** $r = \frac{C}{2\pi}$ **54.** $b = \frac{A}{h}$

55.
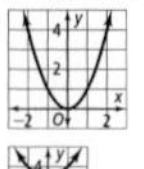

56.
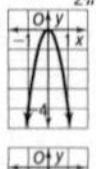

57.
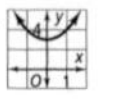

58.
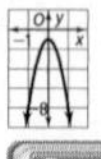

Lesson 5-9 pp. 339–345

Got It? 1. $y = 2(x+3)^3 - 4$ **2.** $1 - \sqrt[3]{2}$ **3. a.** Answers may vary. Sample: $y = x^4 - 6x^3 + x^2 - 6x$ **b.** Yes; $-f(x)$ is the function reflected across the *x*-axis, so the zeros will stay the same. **4.** 972 kW
Lesson Check 1. −2 **2.** 3 **3.** $\frac{1}{3}$ **4.** No; a power function is of the form $y = ax^b$, where *y* varies directly with the *b*th power of *x*. **5.** $y = x^3$ has end behavior of down and up with no turning pt. Thus, at most, there is one real root. **6.** Both $y = x^3$ and $y = 4x^3$ pass through the origin, have the same end behavior of down and up, and no turning pts. $y = 4x^3$ is $y = x^3$ stretched vertically by a factor of 4.
Exercises 7. $y = -3(x-1)^3 + 2$ **9.** $y = -(x+5)^3 - 1$ **11.** $y = -3\left(x + \frac{1}{2}\right)^3 + \frac{3}{4}$ **13.** $\frac{8}{3}$ **15.** $-\frac{2}{15}$ **17.** $1 - \frac{1}{2}\sqrt[3]{20}$ **For Exercises 19–24, answers may vary. Samples: 19.** $x^4 - x^3 - x^2 - x - 2$ **21.** $x^4 - 2x^3 - 2x^2 - 2x - 3$ **23.** $x^4 + 5x^3 + 5x^2 + 5x + 4$ **25.** $38.4 \approx 38$ slices **27.** $90\ \text{lb}\cdot\text{ft}^2/\text{s}^2$ **29.** Yes; using parent function $y = x^2$, stretch vertically by a factor of 2, then translate 5 units up and 3 units to the right. **31.** Yes; using parent function $y = x^2$, translate 9 units down and 4 units to the right. **33.** reflection across the *x*-axis, vert. stretch by a factor of 2, translation 1 unit up and 1 unit to the right **35.** vert. stretch by a factor of 3, translation 2 units down and 1 unit to the right **37.** reflection across the *x*-axis, translation 2 units up and 4 units to the right **39.** $40\ \text{lb}\cdot\text{ft}^2/\text{s}^2$ **41.** Some quartic polynomials have four *x*-intercepts and cannot be written in that form; $y = x^4 - 20x^2 + 64$; $y = x^4 - 5x^2 + 4$. **43.** 150 watts **45.** B
47. $y = (x-2)^2 - 1$
$= x^2 - 4x + 4 - 1$
$= x^2 - 4x + 3$
48. $y = -2x^3 + 3x^2 - x - 2$ **49.** $y = 3x^3 - 5x - 3$ **50.** $y = -\frac{4}{5}x + \frac{16}{5}$ **51.** $y = -3x + 5$ **52.** yes **53.** no **54.** $x^2(x^8 + 1)$ **55.** $(x - y)(x + y)(x^2 + y^2)$ **56.** $13x^3y^6(13x^3y^6 - 1)$

Chapter Review pp. 347–352

1. D **2.** B **3.** C **4.** A **5.** $y = -x^4 + 12$; quartic binomial; down and down **6.** $y = x^2 - x + 7$; quadratic trinomial; up and up **7.** $y = -x^4 + 2x^3 + 3x^2 - 6x + 12$; quartic polynomial of five terms; down and down **8.** $y = x^3 + 2x^2 - 4x + 8$; cubic polynomial of four terms; down and up **9.** $y = x^4 - 3x^3 + 3x^2 + 10$; quartic polynomial of four terms; up and up **10.** 3

11. If n is even there are an odd number of turning points; if n is odd there are an even number of turning points. **12.** $f(x) = x^3 - 4x^2 - 11x - 6$ **13.** $f(x) = x^3 - x^2 - 2x$ **14.** $f(x) = x^3 - 6x^2 + 11x - 6$ **15.** $f(x) = x^3 - 3x^2 - 6x + 8$ **16.** 0, −2 (multiplicity 3) **17.** 2 (multiplicity 2), −2 (multiplicity 2) **18.** $0, -\frac{1}{2}, 1$ **19.** 5, −2 (multiplicity 2) **20.** relative maximum: (0.8672, −1.9351); relative minimums: (0, −3), (2.8828, −12.1704); zeros: $x = -0.5992$, $x = 3.7115$ **21.** relative maximum: (−0.8441, 9.3023); relative minimum: (0.7108, −0.0964); zeros: $x = -1.6180$, $x = 0.6180$, $x = 0.8$ **22.** relative minimum: (1, −4); zeros: $x = -0.2491$, $x = 1.6633$ **23.** relative maximum: (−0.4142, −3.3432); relative minimum: (2.4142, −14.6569); zero: $x = 4$ **24.** 3, 8 **25.** $-\frac{1}{2}$ **26.** $0, \frac{-1 \pm \sqrt{37}}{2}$ **27.** $\frac{2 \pm i\sqrt{2}}{2}$ **28.** no real roots;

29. 2.3949;

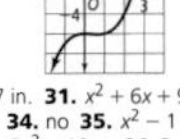

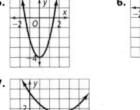

30. 4.87 in. × 2.87 in. × 2.87 in. **31.** $x^2 + 6x + 9$ **32.** $2x^2 + x - 3$, R 1 **33.** yes **34.** no **35.** $x^2 - 1$ **36.** $2x^2 - 6x + 2$, R −20 **37.** $5x^2 + 18x + 36$, R 12 **38.** −14 **39.** 2 **40.** ±1, ±2, ±3, ±6 **41.** $\pm 1, \pm 2, \pm\frac{1}{3}, \pm\frac{2}{3}$ **42.** $\pm 1, \pm 2, \pm 3, \pm 4, \pm 6, \pm 12, \pm\frac{1}{4}, \pm\frac{1}{2}, \pm\frac{3}{4}, \pm\frac{3}{2}$ **43.** $\pm 1, \pm 7, \pm\frac{1}{3}, \pm\frac{7}{3}$ **44.** −3 **45.** −5 **46.** $1, -4, -\frac{1}{2}$ **47.** $1, -2, -\frac{2}{3}$ **48.** $1 + i$ **49.** $5 - \sqrt{3}, \sqrt{2}$ **50.** $3i, -7i$ **51.** $-2 - \sqrt{11}, -4 + 6i$ **52.** $y = x^2 - 17x + 70$ **53.** $y = x^3 + 3x^2 + 25x + 75$ **54.** $y = x^2 - 12x + 37$ **55.** $y = x^4 - 4x^3 - 10x^2 + 68x - 80$ **56.** one positive real zero; two or no negative real zeros **57.** two or no positive real zeros; one negative real zero **58.** four, two, or no positive real zeros; no negative real zeros **59.** two or no positive real zeros; two or no negative real zeros **60.** 3 **61.** 4 **62.** 5 **63.** 6 **64.** $1, -3 \pm \sqrt{7}$ **65.** $2, \pm\sqrt{5}$ **66.** $1, \frac{1 \pm i\sqrt{15}}{4}$ **67.** $-3, 6, \frac{1 \pm \sqrt{5}}{2}$ **68.** 9 **69.** 1, 8, 28, 56, 70, 56, 28, 8, 1 **70.** 16 **71.** 105 **72.** $x^3 + 27x^2 + 243x + 729$ **73.** $b^4 + 8b^3 + 24b^2 + 32b + 16$ **74.** $27a^3 + 27a^2 + 9a + 1$ **75.** $x^3 - 15x^2 + 75x - 125$ **76.** $x^3 - 6x^2y + 12xy^2 - 8y^3$ **77.** $243a^5 + 1620a^4b + 4320a^3b^2 + 5760a^2b^3 + 3840ab^4 + 1024b^5$ **78.** $x^6 + 6x^5 + 15x^4 + 20x^3 + 15x^2 + 6x + 1$ **79.** $64x^6 - 192x^5 + 240x^4 - 160x^3 + 60x^2 - 12x + 1$ **80.** 108 **81.** $6a^2c^2$

82. $y = 3.5x^2 - 4.5x + 5$ **83.** $y = 2.082999x - 2.475234$; $y = 0.086232x^2 + 0.008929x + 5.963724$; $y = -0.002554x^3 + 0.178307x^2 - 0.913645x + 8.205128$; cubic is best fit since $R^2 = 1$. **84.** $y = -5.8667x^3 + 120.5333x^2 - 629.2667x + 1421$; $1097.2 \approx 1097$ **85.** $y = -(x - 2)^3 + 1$ **86.** $y = 6(x + 3)^3$ **87.** Answers may vary. Sample: $y = x^4 - 10x^3 + 25x^2 - 10x + 24$ **88.** $y = 0.3x^5 + 3$

Chapter 6

Get Ready! p. 357 **1.** domain: {1, 2, 3, 4}, range: {2, 3, 4, 5} **2.** domain: {1, 2, 3, 4}, range: {2} **3.** domain: all real numbers, range: $y \geq -8$ **4.** domain: all real numbers, range: $y \geq 3$

5.

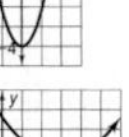

6.

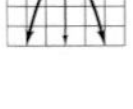

7.

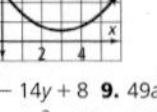

8. $3y^2 - 14y + 8$ **9.** $49a^2 - 100$ **10.** $x^3 + 4x^2 - 15x - 18$ **11.** −2, 7 **12.** $\frac{5}{2}, 3$ **13.** $-4, \frac{2}{3}$ **14.** $\frac{1}{2}$ **15.** $\pm\frac{7}{2}$ **16.** $\pm\sqrt{7}$ **17.** Yes; it is a better deal to first take 50% off the shirt and then use the $10 coupon. **18.** A "one-to-one function" is a function where there is exact correspondence of every element of the domain with exactly one element of the range. **19.** the non-negative root

Lesson 6-1 — pp. 361–367

Got It? **1. a.** 0; −1; 2 **b.** ±0.1; no real square root; $\pm\frac{6}{11}$ **c.** Any negative number multiplied by itself an even number of times will always be positive. Therefore, there can be no real nth roots (where n is even) for a negative number b. **2. a.** −3 **b.** no real root **c.** 7 **d.** no real root **3. a.** $9x^2$ **b.** a^4b^5 **c.** $|x^3|y^4$ **4.** 0; 100
Lesson Check **1.** ±5 **2.** ±0.4 **3.** no real root **4.** $3|b|$ **5.** $a^4|b^9|$ **6.** $-5a$ **7.** 16 has two real fourth roots, ±2. **8.** The real roots of a number are the positive and negative (but not imaginary) roots of the number; the principal root of a number is the nonnegative root of the number. **9.** n is odd.
Exercises **11.** ±0.07 **13.** $\pm\frac{8}{13}$ **15.** 0.5 **17.** 0.07

19. none **21.** $\pm\frac{10}{3}$ **23.** 0.5 **25.** −3 **27.** $3y^2$ **29.** $2y^2$ **31.** ±10 **33.** ±0.5 **35.** about 0.8 in. **37. a.** about 79.01 ft **b.** about 44.44 ft **39.** $\frac{1}{3}$ **41.** $\frac{1}{4}$ **43.** Answers may vary. Sample: $\sqrt[3]{-8x^6}, -\sqrt[4]{16x^8}, \sqrt[5]{-32x^{10}}$ **45.** always; x^2 is always nonnegative **47.** some; they are equal for $x = -1, 0, 1$ **49.** even: $|m|$; odd: m **51.** even: $|m^3|$; odd: m^3 **53.** 48 **55.** a diagonal of a square with side 5 **57.** G **59.** System: $-35 = (-3)^3a + (-3)^2b + (-3)c + d$, $1 = (0)^3a + (0)^2b + (0)c + d$, $3 = (2)^3a + (2)^2b + (2)c + d$, $7 = (4)^3a + (4)^2b + (4)c + d$ (OR equivalent system); solution: $a = 0.35$, $b = -1.85$, $c = 3.3$, $d = 1$, cubic polynomial: $y = 0.35x^3 - 1.85x^2 + 3.3x + 1$. **60.** $y = (x + 2)^3 + 3$ **61.** $y = \frac{1}{2}x^3 - 2$ **62.** $1, \frac{3}{4}$ **63.** $\frac{5 \pm i\sqrt{11}}{6}$ **64.** $\frac{11}{6}$ **65.** $2x^3y^3$ **66.** $\frac{ac}{3}$ **67.** $\frac{4}{x^2}$

Lesson 6-2 — pp. 367–373

Got It? **1. a.** No; the indexes are different. **b.** Yes; $\sqrt[5]{10}$ **2.** $4x^2\sqrt[3]{2x}$ **3.** $15x^3y^3\sqrt{7y}$ **4. a.** $5|x|$ **b.** yes; $\frac{3x^2\sqrt{2x}}{x\sqrt{2x}} = 3x$ **5. a.** $\frac{\sqrt[3]{175xy}}{5y}$ **b.** D; there is no y in the expression.
Lesson Check **1.** $\sqrt{10}$ **2.** $-3\sqrt[3]{4}$ **3.** Not possible, the indexes are different. **4.** not possible; $\sqrt{-4}$ is not a real number. **5.** $\sqrt[3]{3x}$ **6.** $x^2\sqrt{3x}$ **7.** $2x\sqrt[3]{4x}$ **8.** $x \leq 0$; for $x \leq 0$, $-4x^3 \geq 0$ and $\sqrt{-4x^3}$ is real. **9.** error in line 1: $\frac{\sqrt[7]{x^5}}{\sqrt[4]{x^2}} \neq \sqrt[7-4]{\frac{x^5}{x^2}}$
Exercises **11.** 4 **13.** not possible **15.** 5 **17.** 6 **19.** $2x\sqrt{5x}$ **21.** $5x^2\sqrt{2x}$ **23.** $3y^3\sqrt[3]{2y}$ **25.** $-5x^2y\sqrt[3]{2y^2}$ **27.** $-2xy\sqrt[5]{xy^2}$ **29.** $8y^3\sqrt{5y}$ **31.** $40x|y|\sqrt{3}$ **33.** $-2x^2y\sqrt[3]{30x}$ **35.** $4xy^2\sqrt[3]{y}$ **37.** 10 **39.** $2x^2y^2\sqrt{2}$ **41.** $\frac{2\sqrt[3]{x^2y}}{x}$ **43.** $\frac{\sqrt{2x}}{2}$ **45.** $\frac{\sqrt[3]{4x}}{2}$ **47.** $\frac{\sqrt[4]{250}}{5}$ **49.** $\frac{\sqrt{15y}}{5y}$ **51.** $\frac{\sqrt[3]{150ab^2c}}{5a}$ **53.** 6 cm² **55.** about 212 mi/h **57.** $5\sqrt{10}$ **59.** $3x^6y^5\sqrt{2y}$ **61.** $10 + 7\sqrt{2}$ **63.** $\frac{|x|\sqrt{10y}}{2y^2}$ **65.** $\frac{\sqrt[3]{3x^2}}{3x}$ **67.** $\frac{\sqrt[3]{2xy^2}}{xy}$ **69.** 4 g/cm³ **71.** Check students' work. **73.** always **75.** sometimes **77.** $2\sqrt{5}$ **79.** $a = -2c$, $b = -6d$ **81.** H **83.** F **85.** $11|a^{45}|$ **86.** $9c^{24}d^{32}$ **87.** $4a^{27}$ **88.** $2y^5$ **89.** $y^2 - 4y + 16$, $R - 128$ **90.** $6a^2 - 5a + 4$ **91.** 25 **92.** 25 **93.** $\frac{121}{4}$ **94.** $\frac{121}{4}$ **95.** $\frac{3}{5} + \frac{1}{5}i$ **96.** $\frac{10}{13} - \frac{15}{13}i$ **97.** $\frac{16}{17} - \frac{4}{17}i$ **98.** $-\frac{7}{74} - \frac{5}{74}i$

Lesson 6-3 — pp. 374–380

Got It? **1. a.** The indexes are different. You cannot combine the expressions. **b.** $7x\sqrt{xy}$ **c.** $2\sqrt[5]{3x^2}$ **2. a.** about 84.9 in. **b.** The length of the diagonal of a square of side 6 can be found using the Pythagorean Thm. to be $\sqrt{6^2 + 6^2} = \sqrt{72}$. Using this information you can calculate the perimeter of the window and simplify the expression at the end. **3.** $6\sqrt[3]{2}$ **4.** $46 + 16\sqrt{5}$ **5. a.** 24 **b.** 1 **6. a.** $-\sqrt{21} - \sqrt{35}$ **b.** $\frac{1}{3}(12x + 4x\sqrt{6})$ **c.** after rationalizing; When the numerator is multiplied by the conjugate of the denominator it is more convenient if $\sqrt{8}$ is not yet simplified.
Lesson Check **1.** $12\sqrt{6}$ **2.** cannot combine **3.** $3\sqrt{3x}$ **4.** $7\sqrt{3}$ **5.** 13 **6.** $75 + 34\sqrt{5}$ **7.** $-16 - 3\sqrt{2}$ **8. a.** not like radicals **b.** like radicals; $9\sqrt{3xy}$ **c.** not like radicals **9.** They are alike in that you can also use the FOIL method and Distr. Prop. to multiply binomial radical expressions; they are different in that you cannot multiply like radicands together if they do not have the same index.
Exercises **11.** $4\sqrt[3]{3}$ **13.** $-2\sqrt{x}$ **15.** $5\sqrt[3]{x^2}$ **17.** $33\sqrt{2}$ **19.** $7\sqrt{2}$ **21.** $9\sqrt[3]{3} - 6\sqrt[3]{2}$ **23.** $8 + 4\sqrt{5}$ **25.** $63 - 38\sqrt{2}$ **27.** $49 + 12\sqrt{13}$ **29.** 14 **31.** −40 **33.** $-2 + 2\sqrt{3}$ **35.** $13 + 7\sqrt{3}$ **37.** 140.3 in.² **39.** $8\sqrt{3}$ **41.** $5\sqrt{3} - 4\sqrt{2}$ **43.** $-2\sqrt[3]{2}$ **45.** $-11 + \sqrt{21}$ **47.** $84 + 24\sqrt{6}$ **49.** 2 **51.** $4x\sqrt{3}$ **53.** Answers may vary. Sample: Without simplifying first, you must estimate three square roots and then add the estimates. If they are first simplified, then they can be combined as $13\sqrt{2}$. Then only one square root need be estimated. **55.** Answers may vary. Sample: $(\sqrt{7} + 2)(\sqrt{7} - 2), (2\sqrt{2} + \sqrt{5})(2\sqrt{2} - \sqrt{5})$ **57.** $2\sqrt{3} - \sqrt{2}$ **59.** $11|x| - 3|x|\sqrt{11}$ **61.** $\frac{3\sqrt{5} + 2\sqrt{3}}{3}$ **63.** $\frac{x + 5\sqrt[4]{x^3}}{x}$ **65.** $-\frac{1}{2}$ **67.** $a = 0$ and $b \geq 0$, or $b = 0$ and $a \geq 0$ **69.** 13 **71.** $\frac{15}{7}$ **73.** 9 **74.** $3\sqrt[3]{2}$ **75.** $\frac{2\sqrt[3]{x^2}}{x}$ **76.** 4 **77.** 6 **78.** $2x$ **79.** $7x^2\sqrt{2}$ **80.** $x\sqrt{15}$ **81.** $15x^2$ **82.** $2, -1 \pm i\sqrt{3}$ **83.** $-10, 5 \pm 5i\sqrt{3}$ **84.** $\frac{1}{5}, \frac{-1 \pm i\sqrt{3}}{10}$ **85.** $\sqrt{7}$ (multiplicity 2), $-\sqrt{7}$ (multiplicity 2) **86.** $\frac{2\sqrt{5}}{5}$ (multiplicity 2), $-\frac{2\sqrt{5}}{5}$ (multiplicity 2) **87.** $\pm\frac{1}{3}, \pm\frac{1}{3}i$ **88.** x^6 **89.** p^5q^5 **90.** 2^9 or 512 **91.** 3^3 or 27

Lesson 6-4 — pp. 381–388

Got It? **1. a.** 8 **b.** 11 **c.** 6 **2. a.** $\frac{\sqrt[8]{w^3}}{w}, \sqrt[5]{w}$ **b.** $x^{\frac{3}{4}}, y^{\frac{4}{5}}$ **c.** If m is negative, a is in the denominator and $\frac{1}{a}$ is undefined when $a = 0$. **3. a.** The length of a Venusian

year is about 0.61 Earth years. **b.** The length of a Jovian year is about 12.76 Earth years. **4. a.** $\sqrt[4]{27}$ **b.** $\sqrt[6]{x^5}$ **c.** $\sqrt[6]{16{,}807}$ **5. a.** $\frac{1}{8}$ **b.** 8 **c.** $\frac{1}{2187}$ **6. a.** $\frac{1}{2x^5}$ **b.** $27x\sqrt[8]{x^4y^3}$
Lesson Check **1.** 5 **2.** 5 **3.** $\frac{1}{125}$ **4.** $\frac{1}{128}$ **5.** $\sqrt[4]{11^3}$ **6.** $\frac{\sqrt{x}}{x}$ **7.** $(1 + \sqrt{2})$ or any nonzero number times $(1 + \sqrt{2})$ **8.** error in third line, second term; $5(5^{\frac{1}{2}}) = 5^{\frac{3}{2}}$. The third and fourth lines should be: $20 - 5^{\frac{3}{2}}$ / $20 - 5\sqrt{5}$ **9.** $(-64)^{\frac{1}{3}} = \sqrt[3]{-64} = -4$ and $-64^{\frac{1}{3}} = -\sqrt[3]{64} = -4$; $(-64)^{\frac{1}{2}} = \sqrt{-64}$, is not a real number, but $-64^{\frac{1}{2}} = -\sqrt{64} = -8$ is a real number.
Exercises **11.** 3 **13.** 10 **15.** $7\sqrt{3}$ **17.** 3 **19.** $\sqrt[6]{x}$ **21.** $\sqrt[7]{x^2}$ or $(\sqrt[7]{x})^2$ **23.** $\frac{1}{\sqrt[8]{y^9}}$ or $\frac{1}{(\sqrt[8]{y})^9}$ **25.** $\sqrt{x^3}$ or $(\sqrt{x})^3$ **27.** $(-10)^{\frac{1}{3}}$ **29.** $(7x)^{\frac{3}{2}}$ **31.** $a^{\frac{1}{3}}$ **33.** $c^{\frac{1}{2}}$ **35.** ≈72.8 m **37.** ≈7.9 m **39.** $\sqrt[12]{6^7}$ **41.** $\sqrt[10]{5^7}$ **43.** $\frac{\sqrt[3]{4}}{2}$ **45.** $\frac{\sqrt[6]{7776}}{6}$ **47.** 4 **49.** 4 **51.** $\frac{1}{16}$ **53.** 64 **55.** $\frac{1}{x^2}$ **57.** $\frac{x^{\frac{1}{3}}}{3x}$ **59.** $-\frac{3}{x^3}$ **61.** $\frac{y^4}{x^3}$ **63.** $\frac{1}{x}$ **65.** x^3y^9 **67.** about 78%; 61%; 37% **69.** −7 **71.** 64 **73.** 2,097,152 **75.** $-\frac{1}{81}$ **77.** 125 **79.** $x^{\frac{1}{2}}$ **81.** $x^{\frac{3}{10}}$ **83.** $x^{\frac{1}{6}}y^{\frac{1}{4}}$ **85.** $\frac{4x^7}{9y^9}$ **87.** $\frac{2x^2}{3y^3}$ **89. a.** $(\sqrt{x})^4 = \sqrt{x} \cdot \sqrt{x} \cdot \sqrt{x} \cdot \sqrt{x} = x \cdot x = x^2$, so $\sqrt[4]{x^2} = \sqrt{x}$. **b.** $\sqrt[4]{x^2} = (x^2)^{\frac{1}{4}} = x^{\frac{2}{4}} = x^{\frac{1}{2}} = \sqrt{x}$ **91.** 49 **93.** $x^{2\pi}$ **95.** $3^{\sqrt{2}}$ **97.** 33.13 mi/h **99.** 12 **101.** 3

Lesson 6-5 — pp. 390–397

Got It? **1.** 6 **2.** 5, −11 **3.** 37,500,000 m³ **4. a.** 10 **b.** when you raise each side of an equation to a power **5.** 9
Lesson Check **1.** 12 **2.** 27 **3.** $\frac{1}{25}$ **4.** 4 **5.** 1 **6.** 512 **7.** 3; The solution of 3 yields a negative value for $x - 6$, but the right side of the equation $(\sqrt{3(3)})$ cannot be negative. **8.** Solving square root equations is different from solving absolute value equations in that you use a different technique to isolate the variable. In square root equations, you square each side. In absolute value equations, you write two new equations and solve both. Solving square root equations is similar to solving absolute value equations in that both can introduce extraneous solutions.
Exercises **9.** 16 **11.** 22 **13.** 5 **15.** 4 **17.** $\frac{2}{3}$ **19.** −29, 25 **21.** 78 **23.** 0 **25.** about 4 in. **27.** 1 **29.** 3 **31.** −3, −4 **33.** 1 **35.** 3 **37.** 1 **39.** −2 **41.** 1 **43.** 5 **45.** $10\sqrt[4]{3}$ or about 13.16 cm **47.** 5 **49.** 8 **51.** 5 **53.** 1 **55.** 9, −7 **57.** 9 **59.** $x = 4$ is a solution, but $x = 1$ is an extraneous solution. **61.** Answers may vary. Sample: $\sqrt{x - 3} = \sqrt{3x + 5}$ **63.** C **65.** 0, 2 **67.** 0 **69.** $\sqrt{6}$ **71.** $\sqrt{10}$ **73.** B **75.** D

Lesson 6-6 — pp. 398–404

Got It? **1.** $(f + g)(x) = 2x^2 + x + 5$, domain: all real numbers; $(f - g)(x) = 2x^2 - x + 11$, domain: all real numbers **2.** $(f \cdot g)(x) = 9x^3 - 30x^2 - 23x - 4$, domain: all real numbers; $\left(\frac{f}{g}\right)(x) = x - 4$, domain: all real numbers except $x = -\frac{1}{3}$ **3.** 4 **4.** Let $D(x)$ = cost after applying the 15% store discount, $E(x)$ = cost after applying the 20% employee discount, and x = cost of items. Then $D(x) = 0.85x$ and $E(x) = 0.80x$. **a.** $(E \circ D)(x) = 0.68x$ **b.** $(D \circ E)(x) = 0.68x$ **c.** The total discounts are the same.
Lesson Check **1.** $3x^3 - 2x^2 + 3x - 2$ **2.** $-x^2 + 3x - 3$ **3.** $3x^2 + 1$ **4.** $x^2 + 3x - 1$ **5.** $x^2 - 3x + 3$ **6.** $-x^2 + 3x - 3$ **7.** Answers may vary. Sample: $f(x) = 3x^2 + 1$, $g(x) = 2x + 1$; $(f \circ g)(x) = 12x^2 + 12x + 4$; $(g \circ f)(x) = 6x^2 + 3$ **8.** Answers may vary. Sample: $f(x) = 2x$, $g(x) = 0.5x$; $f(g(x)) = x$
Exercises **9.** $x^2 + 7x + 5$; domain: all real numbers **11.** $x^2 - 7x - 5$; domain: all real numbers **13.** $\frac{7x + 5}{x^2}$; domain: all real numbers except $x = 0$ **15.** $2 - x + \frac{1}{x}$; domain: all real numbers except $x = 0$ **17.** $\frac{1}{x} + x - 2$; domain: all real numbers except $x = 0$ **19.** $2x - x^2$; domain: all real numbers except $x = 0$ **21.** $2x^2 + 2x - 4$; domain: all real numbers **23.** $-2x^2 + 2$; domain: all real numbers **25.** $2x + 3$; domain: all real numbers except $x = 1$ **27.** 8 **29.** 20 **31.** 8 **33.** $4a$ **35.** $4a^2 + 4$ **37.** 25 **39.** 9 **41.** 0.25 **43.** $a^2 - 3$ **45. a.** $f(x) = 0.95x$ **b.** $g(x) = x - 200$ **c.** $1225 **d.** $1235 **47.** $x^2 - x + 7$; domain: all real numbers **49.** $x^2 - 5x - 3$; domain: all real numbers **51.** $-x^2 + 5x + 13$; domain: all real numbers **53.** $4x^2 - 14x + 3$; domain: all real numbers **55.** $2x^3 - x^2 - 11x + 10$; domain: all real numbers **57.** $\frac{2x + 5}{x^2 - 3x + 2}$; domain: all real numbers except $x = 1$ and 2 **59.** Substitute 5995x for y; $79,850 **61. a.** $g(x)$ is the bonus earned when x is the amount of sales over $5000. $h(x)$ is the excess sales over $5000. **b.** $(g \circ h)(x)$; you first need to find the excess sales over $5000 to calculate the bonus. **63.** 1 **65.** 0 **67.** 8 **69.** −2 **71. a.** ≈1963; The area after 2 seconds is about 1963 in.² **b.** ≈7854 in.² **73.** $x - 2$; $x - 2$ **75.** $x - 3$; $x - 6$ **77.** $\frac{x^2 + 5}{2}; \frac{x^2 + 10x + 25}{4}$

79. $x^7 - x^6 - 16x^5 + 10x^4 + 85x^3 - 25x^2 - 150x$; domain: all real numbers **81.** $\frac{x - 3}{x^2 + 2x}$; domain: all real numbers except $x = 0, -2, \sqrt{5}$, and $-\sqrt{5}$ **83.** 2 **85.** $8a + 4h$ **87.** H **89.** Look at the 5th number in Row 7 of Pascal's triangle to find the coefficient of the x^3y^4 term in the expansion of $(x + y)^7$. $35(3x)^3(-y)^4 = 945x^3y^4$, so 945 is the coefficient. **90.** 1 **91.** −3 **92.** 4 **93.** 3 **94.** 2 **95.** 3 **96.** $x^8 + 32x^7 + 448x^6 + 3584x^5 + 17{,}920x^4 + 57{,}344x^3 + 114{,}688x^2 + 131{,}072x + 65{,}536$ **97.** $x^6 + 6x^5y + 15x^4y^2 + 20x^3y^3 + 15x^2y^4 + 6xy^5 + y^6$ **98.** $16x^4 - 32x^3y + 24x^2y^2 - 8xy^3 + y^4$ **99.** $128x^7 - 1344x^6y + 6048x^5y^2 - 15{,}120x^4y^3 + 22{,}680x^3y^4 - 20{,}412x^2y^5 + 10{,}206xy^6 - 2187y^7$ **100.** $59{,}049 - 65{,}610x + 29{,}160x^2 - 6480x^3 + 720x^4 - 32x^5$ **101.** $1024x^5 - 1280x^4y + 640x^3y^2 - 160x^2y^3 + 20xy^4 - y^5$ **102.** $x^8 + 4x^7 + 6x^6 + 4x^5 + x^4$ **103.** $x^{12} + 12x^{10}y^3 + 60x^8y^6 + 160x^6y^9 + 240x^4y^{12} + 192x^2y^{15} + 64y^{18}$

104. no solution

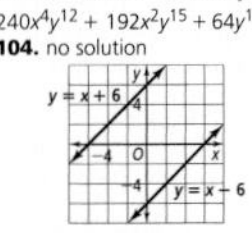

105. (2, 2)

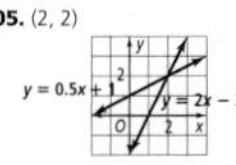

106. (1, 1)

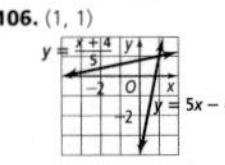

Lesson 6-7 — pp. 405–412

Got It?

1. a.

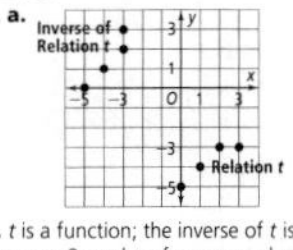

b. t is a function; the inverse of t is not a function; there are 2 y-values for one x-value **2.** $y = \frac{x}{2} - 4$

3.

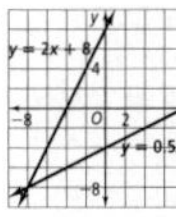

4. a. domain: all real numbers; range: all real numbers **b.** $g^{-1}(x) = -\frac{1}{4}x + \frac{3}{2}$ **c.** domain: all real numbers; range: all real numbers **d.** Yes; for each x in the domain of g^{-1}, there is only one value of y in the range. **5.** $v = \sqrt{19.6d}$; 21.7 m/s **6. a.** $g^{-1}(x) = \frac{4 - 2x}{x}$ **b.** 0 is not in the domain of g^{-1} so $(g \circ g^{-1})(0)$ does not exist. **c.** 0
Lesson Check **1.** $f^{-1}(x) = \frac{x - 3}{4}$; yes **2.** $f^{-1}(x) = \pm\sqrt{x + 1}$; no **3.** $f^{-1}(x) = -1 \pm \sqrt{x}$; no **4. a.** $h^{-1}(x) = -\frac{1}{x} - 2$ **b.** −2.25 **c.** 0 **5.** no; yes **6.** 2, 5 **7.** Answers may vary. Samples: $f(x) = 2x + 1$ and $g(x) = x - 2$; $f(x) = x^2$ and $g(x) = x + 1$

Exercises

9.

x	0	1	2	3
y	1	2	3	4

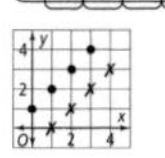

11.

x	2	2	2	2
y	−3	−2	−1	0

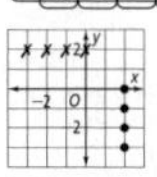

13. $y = \frac{1}{2}x + \frac{1}{2}$; yes **15.** $y = \pm\sqrt{\frac{5 - x}{2}}$; no **17.** $y = \pm\sqrt{\frac{x + 5}{3}}$; no **19.** $y = \frac{4 \pm \sqrt{x}}{3}$; no

21.

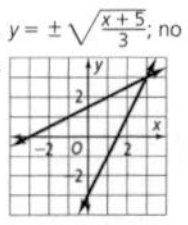

23.

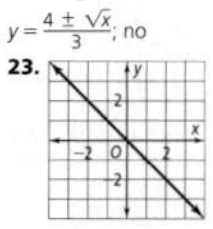

25.

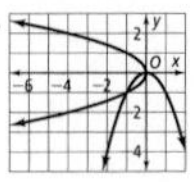

27.

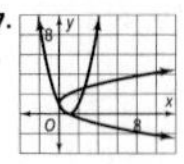

29.

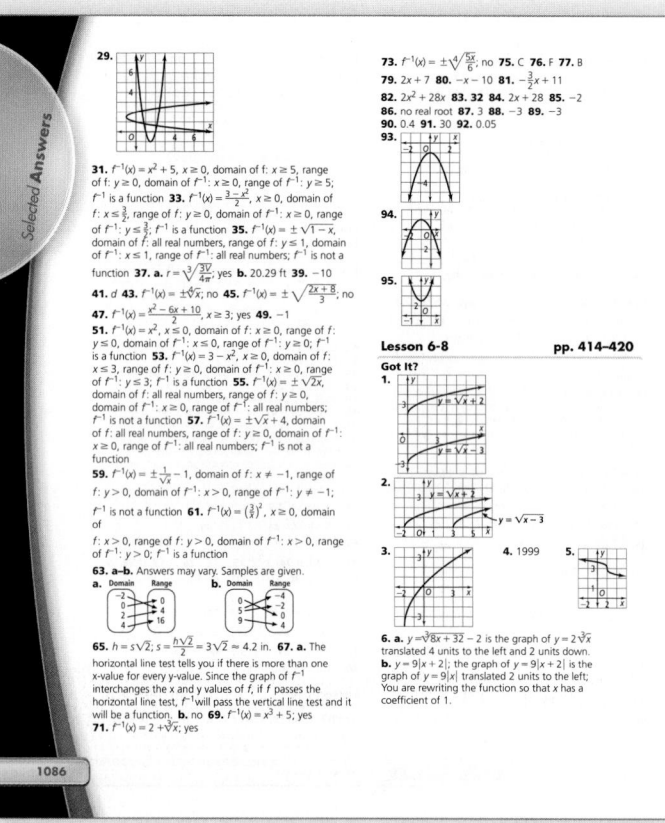

31. $f^{-1}(x) = x^2 + 5$, $x \ge 0$, domain of f: $x \ge 5$, range of f: $y \ge 0$, domain of f^{-1}: $x \ge 0$, range of f^{-1}: $y \ge 5$; f^{-1} is a function **33.** $f^{-1}(x) = \frac{3 - x^2}{2}$, $x \ge 0$, domain of f: $x \le \frac{3}{2}$, range of f: $y \ge 0$, domain of f^{-1}: $x \ge 0$, range of f^{-1}: $y \ge \frac{3}{2}$; f^{-1} is a function **35.** $f^{-1}(x) = \pm\sqrt{1 - x}$, domain of f: all real numbers, range of f: $y \le 1$, domain of f^{-1}: $x \le 1$, range of f^{-1}: all real numbers; f^{-1} is not a function **37. a.** $r = \sqrt[3]{\frac{3V}{4\pi}}$; yes **b.** 20.29 ft **39.** −10
41. d **43.** $f^{-1}(x) = \pm\sqrt[5]{x}$; no **45.** $f^{-1}(x) = \pm\sqrt{\frac{2x + 8}{3}}$; no
47. $f^{-1}(x) = \frac{x^2 - 6x + 10}{2}$, $x \ge 3$; yes **49.**
51. $f^{-1}(x) = x^2$, $x \le 0$, domain of f: $x \ge 0$, range of f: $y \le 0$, domain of f^{-1}: $x \le 0$, range of f^{-1}: $y \ge 0$; f^{-1} is a function **53.** $f^{-1}(x) = 3 - x^2$, $x \ge 0$, domain of f: $x \le 3$, range of f: $y \ge 0$, domain of f^{-1}: $x \ge 0$, range of f^{-1}: $y \le 3$; f^{-1} is a function **55.** $f^{-1}(x) = \pm\sqrt{2x}$, domain of f: all real numbers, range of f: $y \ge 0$, domain of f^{-1}: $x \ge 0$, range of f^{-1}: all real numbers; f^{-1} is not a function **57.** $f^{-1}(x) = \pm\sqrt{x} + 4$, domain of f: all real numbers, range of f: $y \ge 0$, domain of f^{-1}: $x \ge 0$, range of f^{-1}: all real numbers; f^{-1} is not a function
59. $f^{-1}(x) = \pm\frac{1}{\sqrt{x}} - 1$, domain of f: $x \ne -1$, range of f: $y > 0$, domain of f^{-1}: $x > 0$, range of f^{-1}: $y \ne -1$; f^{-1} is not a function **61.** $f^{-1}(x) = \left(\frac{3}{2}\right)^2$, $x \ge 0$, domain of f: $x > 0$, range of f: $y > 0$, domain of f^{-1}: $x > 0$, range of f^{-1}: $y > 0$; f^{-1} is a function
63. a–b. Answers may vary. Samples are given.

a.	Domain	Range
	−2	4
	4	16

b.	Domain	Range
	4	−4
	0	0
	4	

65. $h = s\sqrt{2}$; $s = \frac{h\sqrt{2}}{2} = 3\sqrt{2} \approx 4.2$ in. **67. a.** The horizontal line test tells you if there is more than one x-value for every y-value. Since the graph of f^{-1} interchanges the x and y values of f, if f passes the horizontal line test, f^{-1} will pass the vertical line test and it will be a function. **b.** no **69.** $f^{-1}(x) = x^3 + 5$; yes
71. $f^{-1}(x) = 2 + \sqrt[3]{x}$; yes

73. $f^{-1}(x) = \pm\sqrt[4]{\frac{5x}{6}}$; no **75.** C **76.** F **77.** B
79. $2x + 7$ **80.** $-x - 10$ **81.** $-\frac{3}{2}x + 11$
82. $2x^2 + 28x$ **83.** 32 **84.** $2x + 28$ **85.** -2
86. no real root **87.** 3 **88.** −3 **89.** −3
90. 0.4 **91.** 30 **92.** 0.05
93.

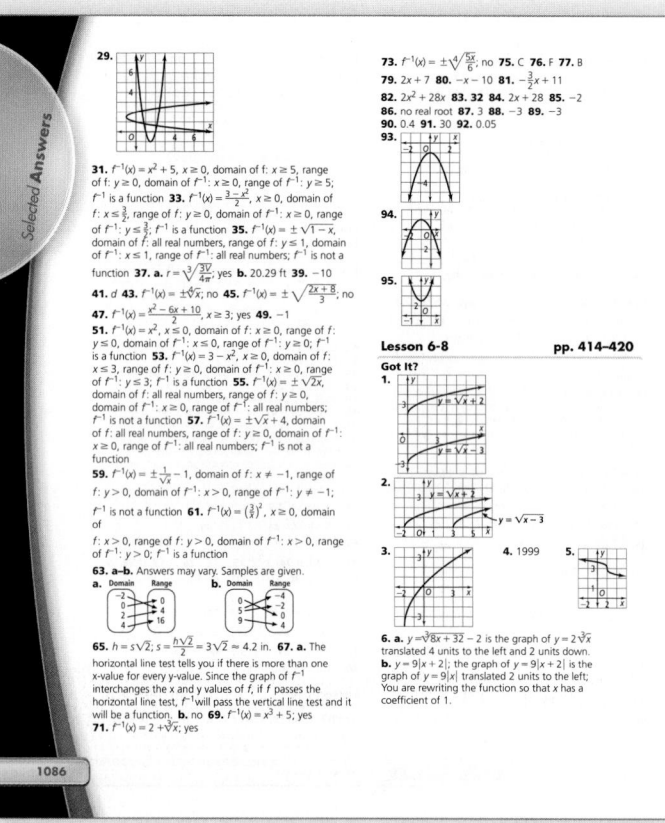

94.

95.

Lesson 6-8   pp. 414–420

Got It?
1.

2.

3.   **4.** 1999   **5.**

6. a. $y = \sqrt[3]{8x + 32} - 2$ is the graph of $y = 2\sqrt[3]{x}$ translated 4 units to the left and 2 units down. **b.** $y = 9|x + 2|$; the graph of $y = 9|x + 2|$ is the graph of $y = 9|x|$ translated 2 units to the left; You are rewriting the function so that x has a coefficient of 1.

Lesson Check
1.

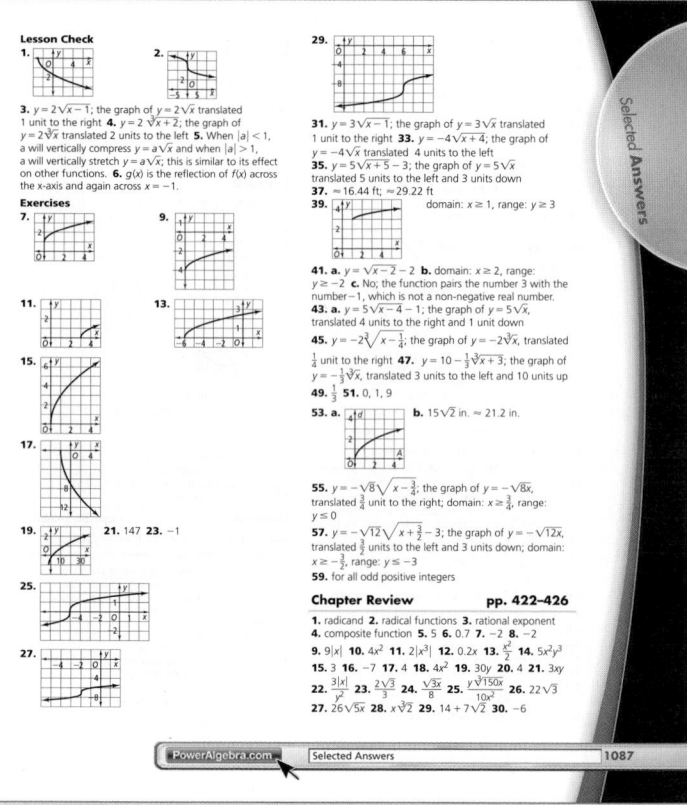

2.

3. $y = 2\sqrt{x - 1}$; the graph of $y = 2\sqrt{x}$ translated 1 unit to the right **4.** $y = 2\sqrt[3]{x + 2}$; the graph of $y = 2\sqrt[3]{x}$ translated 2 units to the left **5.** When $|a| < 1$, a will vertically compress $y = a\sqrt{x}$ and when $|a| > 1$, a will vertically stretch $y = a\sqrt{x}$; this is similar to its effect on other functions. **6.** $g(x)$ is the reflection of $f(x)$ across the x-axis and again across $x = -1$.

Exercises
7.   **9.**

11.   **13.**

15.

17.

19.   **21.** 147 **23.** −1

25.

27.

29.

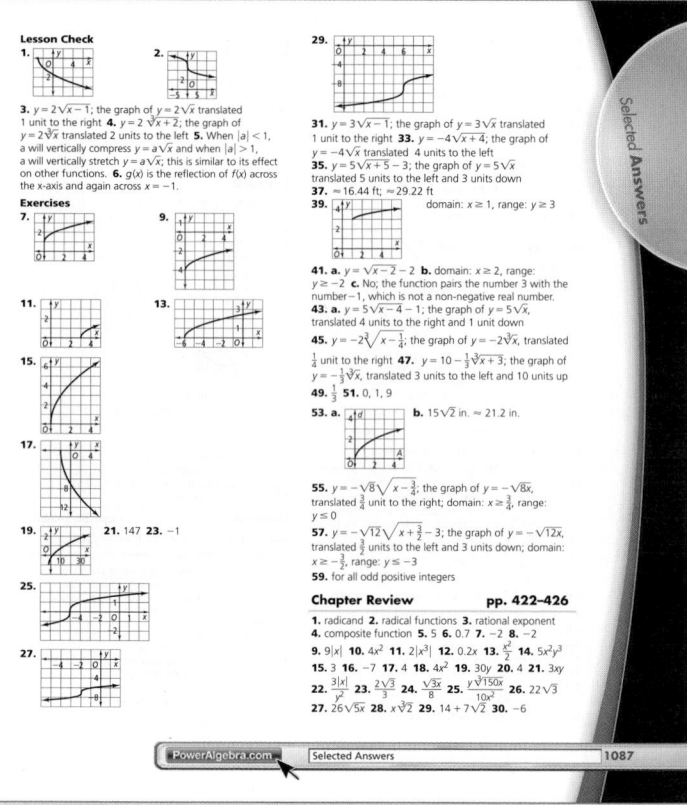

31. $y = 3\sqrt{x} - 1$; the graph of $y = 3\sqrt{x}$ translated 1 unit to the right **33.** $y = -4\sqrt{x + 4}$; the graph of $y = -4\sqrt{x}$ translated 4 units to the left
35. $y = 5\sqrt{x + 5} - 3$; the graph of $y = 5\sqrt{x}$ translated 5 units to the left and 3 units down
37. ≈16.44 ft; ≈29.22 ft
39.   domain: $x \ge 3$; range: $y \ge 3$

41. a. $y = \sqrt{x - 2} - 2$ **b.** domain: $x \ge 2$, range: $y \ge -2$ **c.** No; the function pairs the number 3 with the number −1, which is not a non-negative real number. **43. a.** $y = 5\sqrt{x - 4} - 1$; the graph of $y = 5\sqrt{x}$, translated 4 units to the right and 1 unit down
45. $y = -2\sqrt[3]{x - \frac{1}{4}}$; the graph of $y = -2\sqrt[3]{x}$, translated $\frac{1}{4}$ unit to the right **47.** $y = 10 - \frac{1}{3}\sqrt[3]{x + 3}$; the graph of $y = -\frac{1}{3}\sqrt[3]{x}$, translated 3 units to the left and 10 units up
49. $\frac{1}{3}$ **51.** 0, 1, 9
53. a.   **b.** $15\sqrt{2}$ in. ≈ 21.2 in.

55. $y = -\sqrt{8}\sqrt{x - \frac{1}{4}}$; the graph of $y = -\sqrt{8x}$, translated $\frac{1}{4}$ unit to the right; domain: $x \ge \frac{1}{4}$, range: $y \le 0$
57. $y = -\sqrt{12}\sqrt{x + \frac{2}{3}} - 3$; the graph of $y = -\sqrt{12x}$, translated $\frac{2}{3}$ units to the left and 3 units down; domain: $x \ge -\frac{2}{3}$, range: $y \le -3$
59. for all odd positive integers

Chapter Review   pp. 422–426
1. radicand **2.** radical functions **3.** rational exponent **4.** composite function **5.** 5 **6.** 0.7 **7.** −2 **8.** −2
9. $9|x|$ **10.** $4x^2$ **11.** $2|x^3|$ **12.** $0.2x$ **13.** $\frac{x^5}{y}$ **14.** $5x^2y^3$
15. 3 **16.** −7 **17.** 4 **18.** $4x^2$ **19.** 30 **20.** 4 **21.** $3xy$
22. $\frac{3|x|}{y^2}$ **23.** $\frac{2\sqrt{3}}{3}$ **24.** $\frac{\sqrt{3x}}{8}$ **25.** $\frac{y\sqrt[3]{150x}}{10x^2}$ **26.** $22\sqrt{3}$
27. $26\sqrt{5x}$ **28.** $x\sqrt[3]{2}$ **29.** $14 + 7\sqrt{2}$ **30.** −6

---

31. $100 + 10\sqrt{6} - 10\sqrt{3} - 3\sqrt{2}$ **32.** $\frac{5 + 2\sqrt{5}}{5}$
33. $\frac{9 + 3\sqrt{2}}{7}$ **34.** 5 **35.** 3 **36.** 4 **37.** 25 **38.** x
39. $-2y^3$ **40.** $81x^2y^4$ **41.** $\frac{1}{x^3y}$ **42.** $\frac{1}{2}$ **43.** x^3y^6 **44.** −1
45. 15 **46.** 5 **47.** 10, −8 **48.** 2, −1 **49.** −2 **50.** 0, 16
51. 0, 36 **52.** 9.05 W **53.** $x^2 + x - 20$; domain: all real numbers **54.** $x^2 - x - 12$; domain: all real numbers
55. $x^3 - 4x^2 - 16x + 64$; domain: all real numbers
56. $x + 4$; domain: all real numbers except x = 4 **57.** 50
58. 5 **59.** 23 **60.** $5a^2 + 5$ **61.** $D(C(x)) = 0.5x - 0.5$, $C(D(x)) = 0.5x - 1$; use the coupon after the store discount.
62. $f^{-1}(x) = \pm\sqrt{\frac{x + 8}{4}}$; no **63.** $f^{-1}(x) = 5 - \frac{1}{3}x$; yes
64. $f^{-1}(x) = x^2 - 6$, $x \ge 0$; yes **65.** $f^{-1}(x) = \frac{3 \pm \sqrt{x}}{2}$; no
66.   domain of f: all real numbers, range of f: all real numbers, domain of f^{-1}: all real numbers, range of f^{-1}: all real numbers
67. domain of f: all real numbers, range of f: $y \ge 0$; domain of f^{-1}: $x \ge 0$, range of f^{-1}: all real numbers
68. domain of f: $x \ge 3$, range of f: $y \ge 0$, domain of f^{-1}: $x \ge 0$, range of f^{-1}: $y \ge 3$

69. domain of f: all real numbers, range of f: $y \le 6$, domain of f^{-1}: $x \le 6$, range of f^{-1}: all real numbers

70. $s = \sqrt[3]{V}$; 4 ft

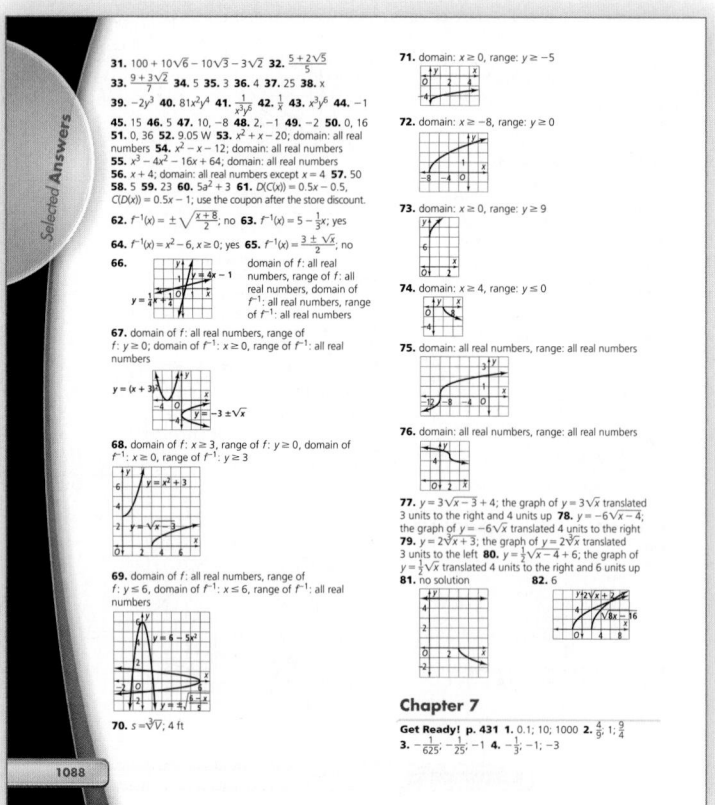

71. domain: $x \ge 0$, range: $y \ge -5$

72. domain: $x \ge -8$, range: $y \ge 0$

73. domain: $x \ge 0$, range: $y \ge 9$

74. domain: $x \ge 4$, range: $y \le 0$

75. domain: all real numbers, range: all real numbers

76. domain: all real numbers, range: all real numbers

77. $y = 3\sqrt{x - 3} + 4$; the graph of $y = 3\sqrt{x}$ translated 3 units to the right and 4 units up **78.** $y = -6\sqrt{x - 4}$; the graph of $y = -6\sqrt{x}$ translated 4 units to the right **79.** $y = 2\sqrt{x} + 3$; the graph of $y = 2\sqrt{x}$ translated 3 units to the left **80.** $y = \frac{1}{2}\sqrt{x - 4} + 6$; the graph of $y = \frac{1}{2}\sqrt{x}$ translated 4 units to the right and 6 units up
81. no solution   **82.** 6

Chapter 7
Get Ready! p. 431 1. 0.1; 10; 1000 **2.** $\frac{4}{9}$; 1; $\frac{9}{4}$
3. $-\frac{1}{625}$; $-\frac{1}{25}$; −1 **4.** $-\frac{1}{3}$; −1; −3

---

5.   ; $y = 2x + 2$

6.   ; $y = 25x + 25$

7. $y = x^2$

8. $y = x^3$

9. x^2 **10.** $16x^4$ **11.** $y = \pm\sqrt{\frac{10 - x}{2}}$; no
12. $y = -4 + \sqrt[3]{x + 1}$; **13.** decrease
14. increase **15.** no

Lesson 7-1   pp. 434–441
Got It?
1. a.   **b.**

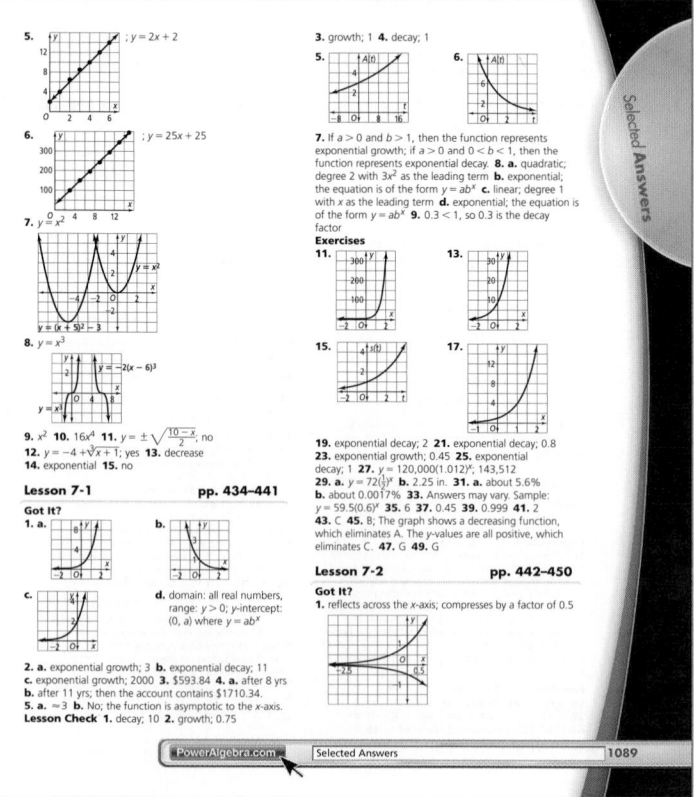

c.   **d.** domain: all real numbers, range: $y > 0$; y-intercept: $(0, a)$ where $y = ab^x$

2. a. exponential growth; 3 **b.** exponential decay; 11 **c.** exponential growth; 2000 **3.** $593.84 **4. a.** after 8 yrs **b.** after 11 yrs; then the account contains $1710.34.
5. a. ≈3 **b.** No; the function is asymptotic to the x-axis.
Lesson Check 1. decay; 10 **2.** growth; 0.75

3. growth; 1 **4.** decay; 1
5.   **6.**

7. If $a > 0$ and $b > 1$, then the function represents exponential growth; if $a > 0$ and $0 < b < 1$, then the function represents exponential decay. **8. a.** quadratic; degree 2 with $3x^2$ as the leading term **b.** exponential; the equation is of the form $y = ab^x$ **c.** linear; degree 1 with x as the leading term. **d.** exponential; the equation is of the form $y = ab^x$ **9.** $0.3 < 1$, so 0.3 is the decay factor
Exercises
11.   **13.**

15.   **17.**

19. exponential decay; 2 **21.** exponential decay; 0.8 **23.** exponential growth; 0.45 **25.** exponential decay; 1 **27.** $y = 120,000(1.012)^x$; 143,512
29. a. $y = 72(\frac{1}{2})^x$ **b.** 2.25 in. **31. a.** about 5.6% **b.** about 0.0017% **33.** Answers may vary. Sample: $y = 59.5(0.6)^x$ **35.** 6 **37.** 0.45 **39.** 0.999 **41.** 2
43. C **45.** B; The graph shows a decreasing function, which eliminates A. The y-values are all positive, which eliminates C **47.** G **49.** G

Lesson 7-2   pp. 442–450
Got It?
1. reflects across the x-axis; compresses by a factor of 0.5

Selected Answers

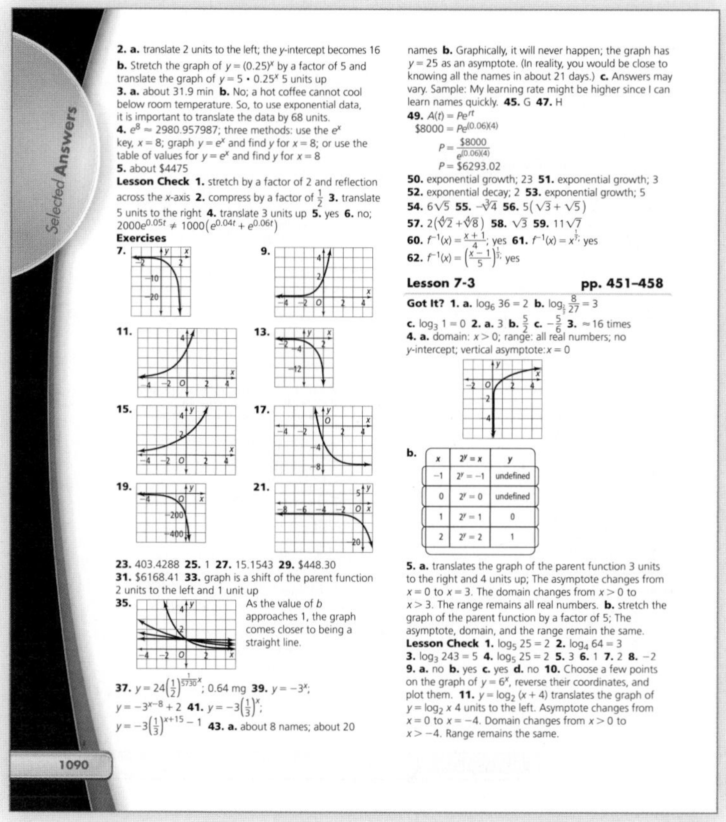

2. a. translate 2 units to the left; the y-intercept becomes 16 **b.** Stretch the graph of $y = (0.25)^x$ by a factor of 5 and translate the graph of $y = 5 \cdot 0.25^x$ 5 units up
3. a. about 31.9 min **b.** No; a hot coffee cannot cool below room temperature. So, to use exponential data, it is important to translate the data by 68 units.
4. $e^8 \approx 2980.957987$; three methods: use the e^x key, $x = 8$; graph $y = e^x$ and find y for $x = 8$; or use the table of values for $y = e^x$ and find y for $x = 8$
5. about \$4475
Lesson Check 1. stretch by a factor of 2 and reflection across the x-axis **2.** compress by a factor of $\frac{1}{2}$ **3.** translate 5 units to the right **4.** translate 3 units up **5.** yes **6.** no; $2000e^{0.05t} \neq 1000\left(e^{0.04t} + e^{0.06t}\right)$
Exercises
7. 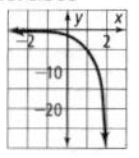
9. 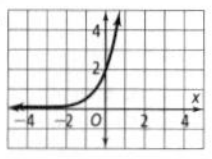
11. 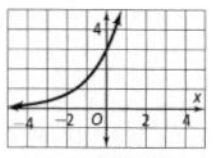
13. 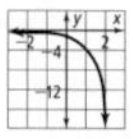
15. 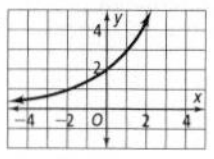
17. 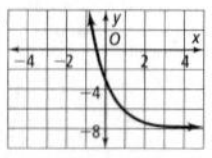
19. 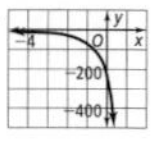
21. 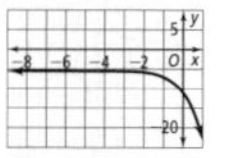

23. 403.4288 **25.** 1 **27.** 15.1543 **29.** \$448.30
31. \$6168.41 **33.** graph is a shift of the parent function 2 units to the left and 1 unit up
35. 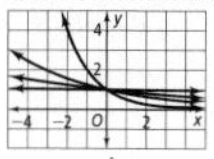
As the value of b approaches 1, the graph comes closer to being a straight line.

37. $y = 24\left(\frac{1}{2}\right)^{\frac{1}{5730}x}$; 0.64 mg **39.** $y = -3^x$; $y = -3^{x-8} + 2$ **41.** $y = -3\left(\frac{1}{3}\right)^x$; $y = -3\left(\frac{1}{3}\right)^{x+15} - 1$ **43. a.** about 8 names; about 20 names **b.** Graphically, it will never happen; the graph has $y = 25$ as an asymptote. (In reality, you would be close to knowing all the names in about 21 days.) **c.** Answers may vary. Sample: My learning rate might be higher since I can learn names quickly. **45.** G **47.** H
49. $A(t) = Pe^{rt}$

$$\$8000 = Pe^{(0.06)(4)}$$
$$P = \frac{\$8000}{e^{(0.06)(4)}}$$
$$P = \$6293.02$$

50. exponential growth; 23 **51.** exponential growth; 3
52. exponential decay; 2 **53.** exponential growth; 5
54. $6\sqrt{5}$ **55.** $-\sqrt[3]{4}$ **56.** $5\left(\sqrt{3} + \sqrt{5}\right)$
57. $2\left(\sqrt[4]{2} + \sqrt[4]{8}\right)$ **58.** $\sqrt{3}$ **59.** $11\sqrt{7}$
60. $f^{-1}(x) = \frac{x+1}{4}$; yes **61.** $f^{-1}(x) = x^{\frac{1}{7}}$; yes
62. $f^{-1}(x) = \left(\frac{x-1}{5}\right)^{\frac{1}{3}}$; yes

Lesson 7-3 pp. 451–458

Got It? 1. a. $\log_6 36 = 2$ **b.** $\log_{\frac{2}{3}} \frac{8}{27} = 3$ **c.** $\log_3 1 = 0$ **2. a.** 3 **b.** $\frac{5}{2}$ **c.** $-\frac{5}{6}$ **3.** ≈ 16 times
4. a. domain: $x > 0$; range: all real numbers; no y-intercept; vertical asymptote: $x = 0$

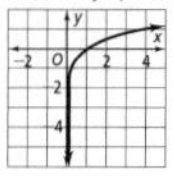

b.

x	$2^y = x$	y
−1	$2^y = -1$	undefined
0	$2^y = 0$	undefined
1	$2^y = 1$	0
2	$2^y = 2$	1

5. a. translates the graph of the parent function 3 units to the right and 4 units up; The asymptote changes from $x = 0$ to $x = 3$. The domain changes from $x > 0$ to $x > 3$. The range remains all real numbers. **b.** stretch the graph of the parent function by a factor of 5; The asymptote, domain, and the range remain the same.
Lesson Check 1. $\log_5 25 = 2$ **2.** $\log_4 64 = 3$ **3.** $\log_3 243 = 5$ **4.** $\log_5 25 = 2$ **5.** 3 **6.** 1 **7.** 2 **8.** −2 **9. a.** no **b.** yes **c.** yes **d.** no **10.** Choose a few points on the graph of $y = 6^x$, reverse their coordinates, and plot them. **11.** $y = \log_2 (x + 4)$ translates the graph of $y = \log_2 x$ 4 units to the left. Asymptote changes from $x = 0$ to $x = -4$. Domain changes from $x > 0$ to $x > -4$. Range remains the same.

Selected Answers

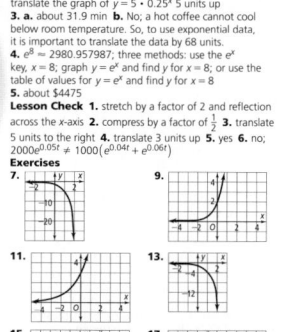

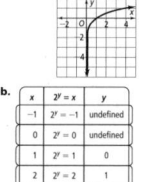

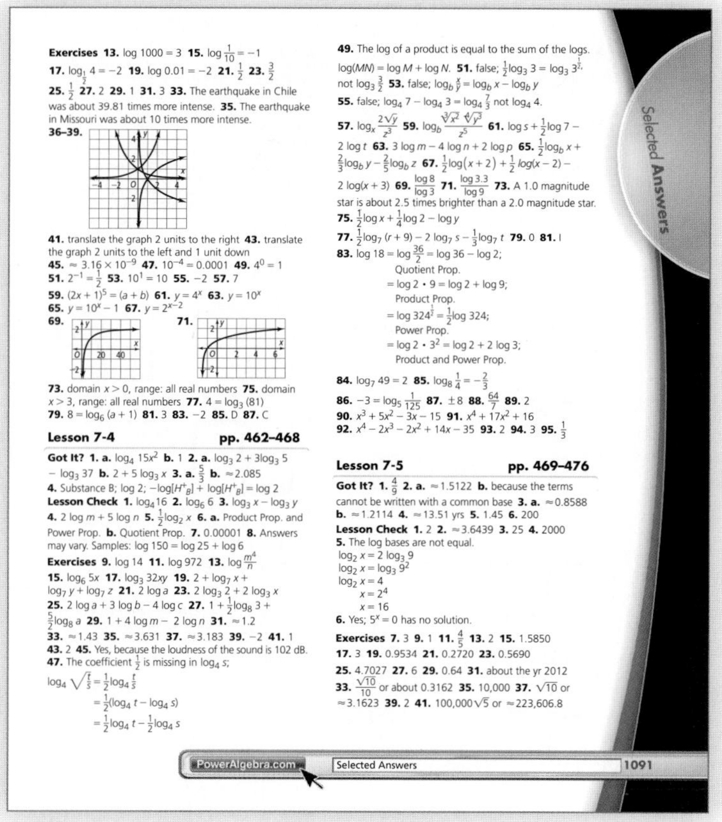

Exercises 13. $\log 1000 = 3$ **15.** $\log \frac{1}{10} = -1$ **17.** $\log_{\frac{1}{2}} 4 = -2$ **19.** $\log 0.01 = -2$ **21.** $\frac{1}{2}$ **23.** $\frac{3}{2}$ **25.** $\frac{1}{2}$ **27.** 2 **29.** 1 **31.** 3 **33.** The earthquake in Chile was about 39.81 times more intense. **35.** The earthquake in Missouri was about 10 times more intense.
36–39. 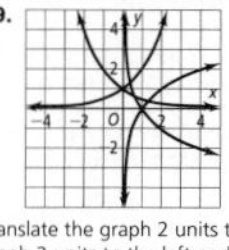

41. translate the graph 2 units to the right **43.** translate the graph 2 units to the left and 1 unit down
45. $\approx 3.16 \times 10^{-9}$ **47.** $10^{-4} = 0.0001$ **49.** $4^0 = 1$
51. $2^{-1} = \frac{1}{2}$ **53.** $10^1 = 10$ **55.** −2 **57.** 7
59. $(2x + 1)^5 = (a + b)$ **61.** $y = 4^x$ **63.** $y = 10^x$
65. $y = 10^x - 1$ **67.** $y = 2^{x-2}$
69. 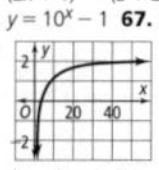
71. 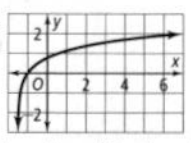

73. domain $x > 0$, range: all real numbers **75.** domain $x > 3$, range: all real numbers **77.** $4 = \log_3 (81)$
79. $8 = \log_6 (a + 1)$ **81.** 3 **83.** −2 **85.** D **87.** C

Lesson 7-4 pp. 462–468

Got It? 1. a. $\log_4 15x^2$ **b.** 1 **2. a.** $\log_3 2 + 3\log_3 5 - \log_3 37$ **b.** $2 + 5 \log_3 x$ **3. a.** $\frac{5}{3}$ **b.** ≈ 2.085
4. Substance B; log 2; $-\log[H^+{}_B] + \log[H^+{}_B] = \log 2$
Lesson Check 1. $\log_4 16$ **2.** $\log_6 6$ **3.** $\log_3 x - \log_3 y$ **4.** $2 \log m + 5 \log n$ **5.** $\frac{1}{2}\log_2 x$ **6. a.** Product Prop. and Power Prop. **b.** Quotient Prop. **7.** 0.00001 **8.** Answers may vary. Samples: $\log 150 = \log 25 + \log 6$
Exercises 9. log 14 **11.** log 972 **13.** $\log \frac{m^4}{n}$ **15.** $\log_6 5x$ **17.** $\log_3 32xy$ **19.** $2 + \log_7 x + \log_7 y + \log_7 z$ **21.** $2 \log a$ **23.** $2 \log_3 2 + 2 \log_3 x$ **25.** $2 \log a + 3 \log b - 4 \log c$ **27.** $1 + \frac{1}{2}\log_8 3 + \frac{5}{2}\log_8 a$ **29.** $1 + 4 \log m - 2 \log n$ **31.** ≈ 1.2
33. ≈ 1.43 **35.** ≈ 3.631 **37.** ≈ 3.183 **39.** −2 **41.** 1
43. 2 **45.** Yes, because the loudness of the sound is 102 dB.
47. The coefficient $\frac{1}{2}$ is missing in $\log_4 s$;

$$\log_4 \sqrt{\tfrac{t}{s}} = \tfrac{1}{2}\log_4 \tfrac{t}{s}$$
$$= \tfrac{1}{2}(\log_4 t - \log_4 s)$$
$$= \tfrac{1}{2}\log_4 t - \tfrac{1}{2}\log_4 s$$

49. The log of a product is equal to the sum of the logs. $\log(MN) = \log M + \log N$. **51.** false; $\frac{1}{2}\log_3 3 = \log_3 3^{\frac{1}{2}}$, not $\log_3 \frac{3}{2}$ **53.** false; $\log_b \frac{x}{y} = \log_b x - \log_b y$
55. false; $\log_4 7 - \log_4 3 = \log_4 \frac{7}{3}$ not $\log_4 4$.
57. $\log_x \frac{2\sqrt{y}}{z^3}$ **59.** $\log_b \frac{\sqrt[3]{x^2}\,\sqrt[4]{y^3}}{z^5}$ **61.** $\log s + \frac{1}{2}\log 7 - 2 \log t$ **63.** $3 \log m - 4 \log n + 2 \log p$ **65.** $\frac{1}{2}\log_b x + \frac{2}{3}\log_b y - \frac{2}{5}\log_b z$ **67.** $\frac{1}{2}\log(x + 2) + \frac{1}{2}\log(x - 2) - 2\log(x + 3)$ **69.** $\frac{\log 8}{\log 3}$ **71.** $\frac{\log 3.3}{\log 9}$ **73.** A 1.0 magnitude star is about 2.5 times brighter than a 2.0 magnitude star.
75. $\frac{1}{2}\log x + \frac{1}{4}\log 2 - \log y$
77. $\frac{1}{2}\log_7 (r + 9) - 2 \log_7 s - \frac{1}{3}\log_7 t$ **79.** 0 **81.** I
83. $\log 18 = \log \frac{36}{2} = \log 36 - \log 2$;
Quotient Prop.
$= \log 2 \cdot 9 = \log 2 + \log 9$;
Product Prop.
$= \log 324^{\frac{1}{2}} = \frac{1}{2}\log 324$;
Power Prop.
$= \log 2 \cdot 3^2 = \log 2 + 2 \log 3$;
Product and Power Prop.

84. $\log_7 49 = 2$ **85.** $\log_8 \frac{1}{4} = -\frac{2}{3}$
86. $-3 = \log_5 \frac{1}{125}$ **87.** ± 8 **88.** $\frac{64}{7}$ **89.** 2
90. $x^3 + 5x^2 - 3x - 15$ **91.** $x^4 + 17x^2 + 16$
92. $x^4 - 2x^3 - 2x^2 + 14x - 35$ **93.** 2 **94.** 3 **95.** $\frac{1}{3}$

Lesson 7-5 pp. 469–476

Got It? 1. $\frac{4}{9}$ **2. a.** ≈ 1.5122 **b.** because the terms cannot be written with a common base **3. a.** ≈ 0.8588 **b.** ≈ 1.2114 **4.** ≈ 13.51 yrs **5.** 1.45 **6.** 200
Lesson Check 1. 2 **2.** ≈ 3.6439 **3.** 25 **4.** 2000
5. The log bases are not equal.
$\log_2 x = 2 \log_3 9$
$\log_2 x = \log_3 9^2$
$\log_2 x = 4$
$x = 2^4$
$x = 16$
6. Yes; $5^x = 0$ has no solution.
Exercises 7. 3 **9.** 1 **11.** $\frac{4}{5}$ **13.** 2 **15.** 1.5850
17. 3 **19.** 0.9534 **21.** 0.2720 **23.** 0.5690
25. 4.7027 **27.** 6 **29.** 0.64 **31.** about the yr 2012
33. $\frac{\sqrt{10}}{10}$ or about 0.3162 **35.** 10,000 **37.** $\sqrt{10}$ or ≈ 3.1623 **39.** 2 **41.** $100{,}000\sqrt{5}$ or $\approx 223{,}606.8$

Selected Answers

43. $\frac{1}{4}$ **45.** 7 **47. a.** 18.9658 **b.** 18.9658 **c.** Answers may vary. Sample: You don't have to use the Change of Base Formula with the base-10 method, but there are fewer steps with the base-2 method. **49.** ≈ 7.6 *yrs* **51.** 3
53. 3 **55.** −2 **57.** $-\frac{1}{2}$ **59.** Answers may vary. Sample: $\log x = 1.6$; $x \approx 39.81$ **61.** 143.6 **63. a.** top up: 10^{-5} W/m² top down: $10^{-2.5}$ W/m² **b.** 99.68%
65. 625 **67.** 10 **69.** 1.5 **71.** 2.7944 **73.** 500 **75.** $114.\overline{3}$
77. $x = y = 2$ **79.** −2, 5 **81.** 1 **83 a.** bassoon, guitar, harp, violin, viola, cello **b.** bassoon, guitar, harp, cello, bass **c.** harp, violin **d.** harp **85.** 333 **87.** 4

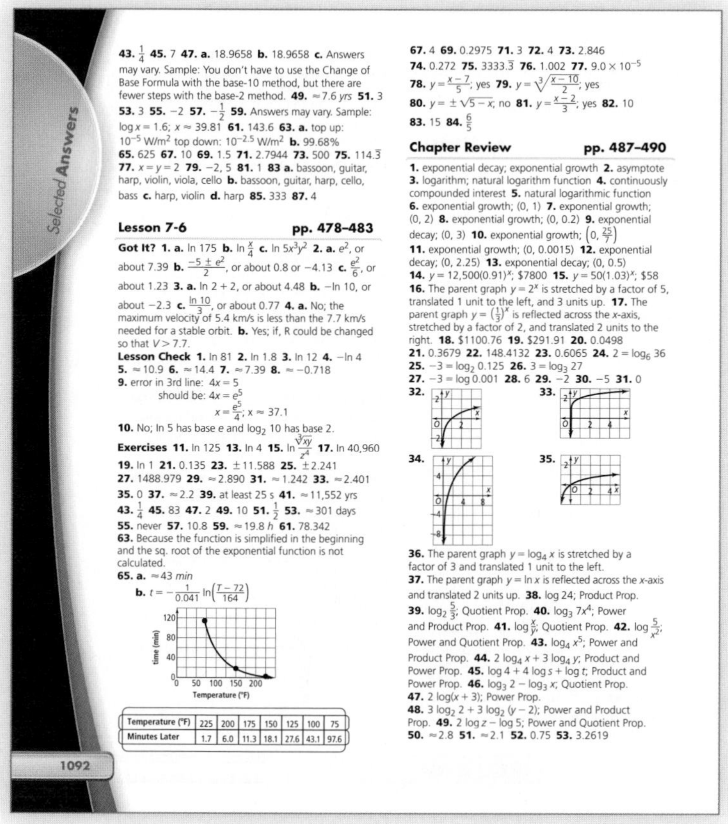

Lesson 7-6 pp. 478–483

Got It? 1. a. ln 175 **b.** $\ln \frac{x}{4}$ **c.** $\ln 5x^3y^2$ **2. a.** e^2, or about 7.39 **b.** $\frac{-5 \pm e^2}{2}$, or about 0.8 or −4.13 **c.** $\frac{e^2}{6}$, or about 1.23 **3. a.** $\ln 2 + 2$, or about 4.48 **b.** $-\ln 10$, or about −2.3 **c.** $\frac{\ln 10}{3}$, or about 0.77 **4. a.** No; the maximum velocity of 5.4 km/s is less than the 7.7 km/s needed for a stable orbit. **b.** Yes; if, R could be changed so that $V > 7.7$.
Lesson Check 1. ln 81 **2.** ln 1.8 **3.** ln 12 **4.** −ln 4
5. ≈ 10.9 **6.** ≈ 14.4 **7.** ≈ 7.39 **8.** ≈ -0.718
9. error in 3rd line: $4x = 5$
should be: $4x = e^5$
$x = \frac{e^5}{4}$; $x \approx 37.1$
10. No; ln 5 has base e and $\log_2 10$ has base 2.
Exercises 11. ln 125 **13.** ln 4 **15.** $\ln \frac{\sqrt[3]{xy}}{z^4}$ **17.** ln 40,960
19. ln 1 **21.** 0.135 **23.** ±11.588 **25.** ±2.241
27. 1488.979 **29.** ≈ 2.890 **31.** ≈ 1.242 **33.** ≈ 2.401
35. 0 **37.** ≈ 2.2 **39.** at least 25 s **41.** $\approx 11{,}552$ yrs
43. $\frac{1}{4}$ **45.** 83 **47.** 2 **49.** 10 **51.** $\frac{1}{2}$ **53.** ≈ 301 days
55. never **57.** 10.8 **59.** ≈ 19.8 *h* **61.** 78.342
63. Because the function is simplified in the beginning and the sq. root of the exponential function is not calculated.
65. a. ≈ 43 *min*
b. $t = -\frac{1}{0.041}\ln\left(\frac{T - 72}{164}\right)$

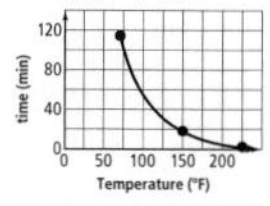

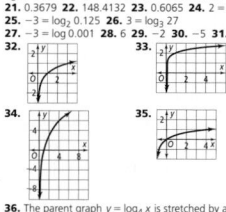

Temperature (°F)	225	200	175	150	125	100	75
Minutes Later	1.7	6.0	11.3	18.1	27.6	43.1	97.6

67. 4 **69.** 0.2975 **71.** 3 **72.** 4 **73.** 2.846
74. 0.272 **75.** $3333.\overline{3}$ **76.** 1.002 **77.** 9.0×10^{-5}
78. $y = \frac{x-7}{5}$; yes **79.** $y = \sqrt[3]{\frac{x-10}{2}}$; yes
80. $y = \pm\sqrt{5 - x}$; no **81.** $y = \frac{x-2}{3}$; yes **82.** 10
83. 15 **84.** $\frac{6}{5}$

Chapter Review pp. 487–490

1. exponential decay; exponential growth **2.** asymptote **3.** logarithm; natural logarithm function **4.** continuously compounded interest **5.** natural logarithmic function
6. exponential growth; (0, 1) **7.** exponential growth; (0, 2) **8.** exponential growth; (0, 0.2) **9.** exponential decay; (0, 3) **10.** exponential growth; $\left(0, \frac{25}{7}\right)$
11. exponential growth; (0, 0.0015) **12.** exponential decay; (0, 2.25) **13.** exponential decay; (0, 0.5)
14. $y = 12{,}500(0.91)^x$; \$7800 **15.** $y = 50(1.03)^x$; \$58
16. The parent graph $y = 2^x$ is stretched by a factor of 5, translated 1 unit to the left, and 3 units up. **17.** The parent graph $y = \left(\frac{1}{3}\right)^x$ is reflected across the x-axis, stretched by a factor of 2, and translated 2 units to the right. **18.** \$1100.76 **19.** \$291.91 **20.** 0.0498
21. 0.3679 **22.** 148.4132 **23.** 0.6065 **24.** $2 = \log_6 36$
25. $-3 = \log_2 0.125$ **26.** $3 = \log_3 27$
27. $-3 = \log 0.001$ **28.** 6 **29.** −2 **30.** −5 **31.** 0
32. 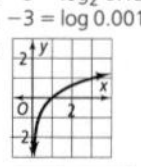
33. 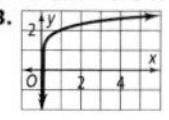
34. 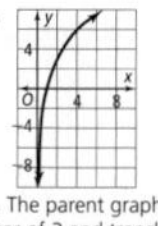
35. 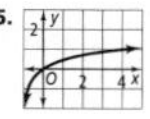

36. The parent graph $y = \log_4 x$ is stretched by a factor of 3 and translated 1 unit to the left.
37. The parent graph $y = \ln x$ is reflected across the x-axis and translated 2 units up. **38.** log 24; Product Prop.
39. $\log_2 \frac{5}{3}$; Quotient Prop. **40.** $\log_3 7x^4$; Power and Product Prop. **41.** $\log \frac{x}{y}$; Quotient Prop. **42.** $\log \frac{5}{x^2}$; Power and Quotient Prop. **43.** $\log_4 x^5$; Power and Product Prop. **44.** $2 \log_4 x + 3 \log_4 y$; Product and Power Prop. **45.** $\log 4 + 4 \log s + \log t$; Product and Power Prop. **46.** $\log_3 2 - \log_3 x$; Quotient Prop.
47. $2 \log(x + 3)$; Power Prop.
48. $3 \log_2 2 + 3 \log_2 (y - 2)$; Power and Product Prop. **49.** $2 \log z - \log 5$; Power and Quotient Prop.
50. ≈ 2.8 **51.** ≈ 2.1 **52.** 0.75 **53.** 3.2619

Selected Answers

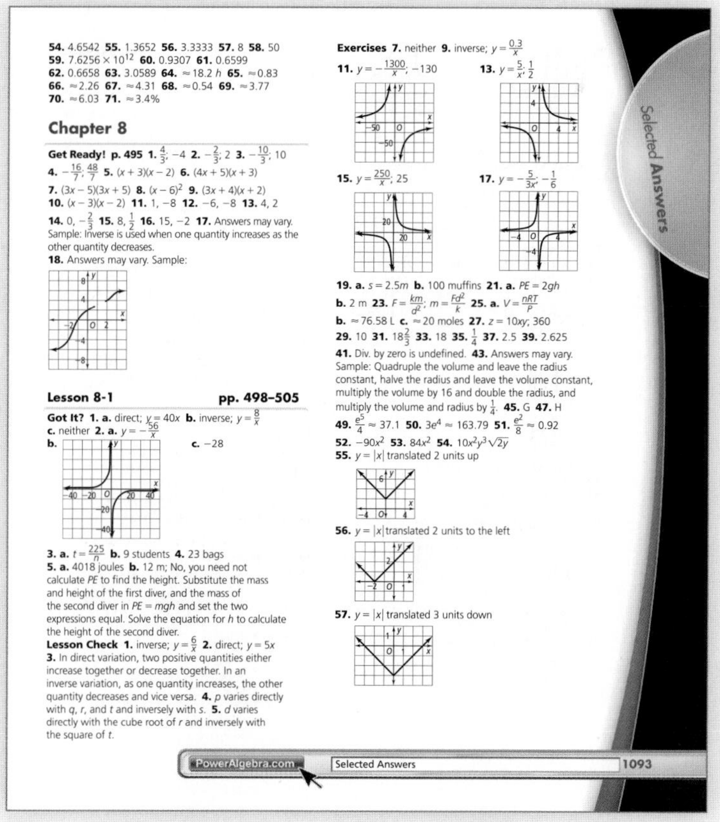

54. 4.6542 **55.** 1.3652 **56.** 3.3333 **57.** 8 **58.** 50
59. 7.6256×10^{12} **60.** 0.9307 **61.** 0.6599
62. 0.6658 **63.** 3.0589 **64.** ≈ 18.2 *h* **65.** ≈ 0.83
66. ≈ 2.26 **67.** ≈ 4.31 **68.** ≈ 0.54 **69.** ≈ 3.77
70. ≈ 6.03 **71.** $\approx 3.4\%$

Chapter 8

Get Ready! p. 495 1. $\frac{4}{3}$; −4 **2.** $-\frac{2}{3}$; 2 **3.** $-\frac{10}{3}$; 10
4. $-\frac{16}{7}$; $\frac{48}{7}$ **5.** $(x + 3)(x - 2)$ **6.** $(4x + 5)(x + 3)$
7. $(3x - 5)(3x + 5)$ **8.** $(x - 6)^2$ **9.** $(3x + 4)(x + 2)$
10. $(x - 3)(x - 2)$ **11.** 1, −8 **12.** −6, −8 **13.** 4, 2
14. 0, $-\frac{2}{3}$ **15.** 8, $\frac{1}{2}$ **16.** 15, −2 **17.** Answers may vary. Sample: Inverse is used when one quantity increases as the other quantity decreases.
18. Answers may vary. Sample:

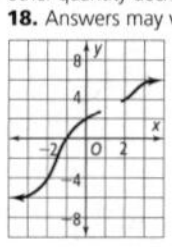

Lesson 8-1 pp. 498–505

Got It? 1. a. direct; $y = 40x$ **b.** inverse; $y = \frac{8}{x}$ **c.** neither **2. a.** $y = -\frac{56}{x}$
b. 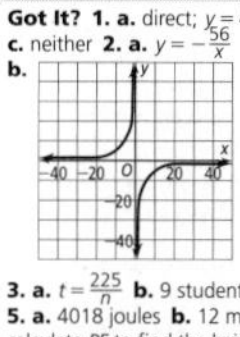
c. −28

3. a. $t = \frac{225}{n}$ **b.** 9 students **4.** 23 bags
5. a. 4018 joules **b.** 12 m; No, you need not calculate PE to find the height. Substitute the mass and height of the first diver, and the mass of the second diver in $PE = mgh$ and set the two expressions equal. Solve the equation for h to calculate the height of the second diver.
Lesson Check 1. inverse; $y = \frac{6}{x}$ **2.** direct; $y = 5x$
3. In direct variation, two positive quantities either increase together or decrease together. In an inverse variation, as one quantity increases, the other quantity decreases and vice versa. **4.** p varies directly with q, r, and t and inversely with s. **5.** d varies directly with the cube root of r and inversely with the square of t.

Exercises 7. neither **9.** inverse; $y = \frac{0.3}{x}$
11. $y = -\frac{1300}{x}$; −130 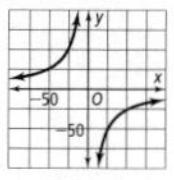
13. $y = \frac{5}{x}$; $\frac{1}{2}$ 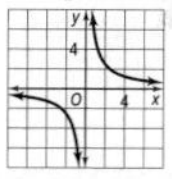
15. $y = \frac{250}{x}$; 25 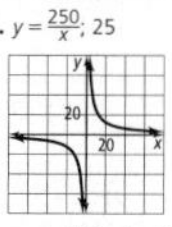
17. $y = -\frac{5}{3x}$; $-\frac{1}{6}$ 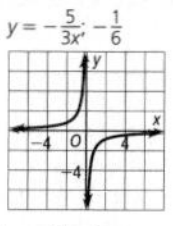

19. a. $s = 2.5m$ **b.** 100 muffins **21. a.** $PE = 2gh$ **b.** 2 m **23.** $F = \frac{km}{d^2}$; $m = \frac{Fd^2}{k}$ **25. a.** $V = \frac{nRT}{P}$ **b.** ≈ 76.58 L **c.** ≈ 20 moles **27.** $z = 10xy$; 360
29. 10 **31.** $18\frac{2}{3}$ **33.** 18 **35.** $\frac{1}{4}$ **37.** 2.5 **39.** 2.625
41. Div. by zero is undefined. **43.** Answers may vary. Sample: Quadruple the volume and leave the radius constant, halve the radius and leave the volume constant, multiply the volume by 16 and double the radius, and multiply the volume and radius by $\frac{1}{4}$. **45.** G **47.** H
49. $\frac{e^5}{4} \approx 37.1$ **50.** $3e^4 \approx 163.79$ **51.** $\frac{e^2}{8} \approx 0.92$
52. $-90x^2$ **53.** $84x^2$ **54.** $10x^2y^3\sqrt{2y}$
55. $y = |x|$ translated 2 units up

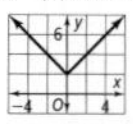

56. $y = |x|$ translated 2 units to the left

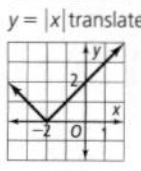

57. $y = |x|$ translated 3 units down

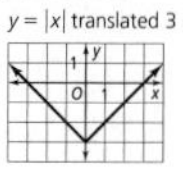

Selected Answers

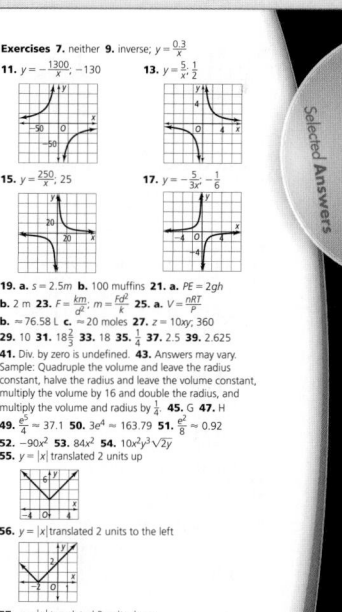

58. $y = |x|$ translated 3 units to the rt.

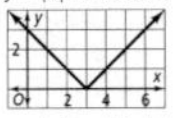

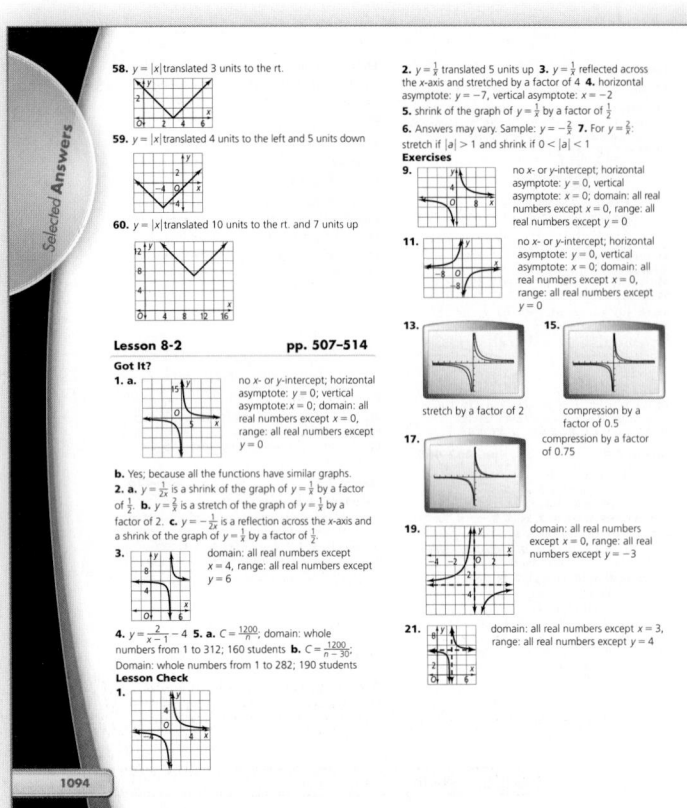

59. $y = |x|$ translated 4 units to the left and 5 units down

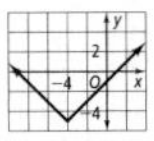

60. $y = |x|$ translated 10 units to the rt. and 7 units up

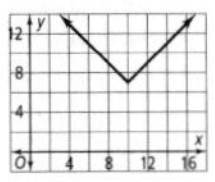

Lesson 8-2 pp. 507–514

Got It?

1. a.

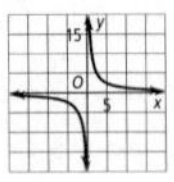

no x- or y-intercept; horizontal asymptote: $y = 0$; vertical asymptote: $x = 0$; domain: all real numbers except $x = 0$, range: all real numbers except $y = 0$

b. Yes; because all the functions have similar graphs. **2. a.** $y = \frac{1}{2x}$ is a shrink of the graph of $y = \frac{1}{x}$ by a factor of $\frac{1}{2}$. **b.** $y = \frac{2}{x}$ is a stretch of the graph of $y = \frac{1}{x}$ by a factor of 2. **c.** $y = -\frac{1}{2x}$ is a reflection across the x-axis and a shrink of the graph of $y = \frac{1}{x}$ by a factor of $\frac{1}{2}$.

3.

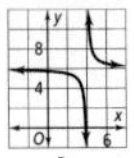

domain: all real numbers except $x = 4$, range: all real numbers except $y = 6$

4. $y = \frac{2}{x-1} - 4$ **5. a.** $C = \frac{1200}{n}$; domain: whole numbers from 1 to 312; 160 students **b.** $C = \frac{1200}{n-30}$; Domain: whole numbers from 1 to 282; 190 students

Lesson Check

1.

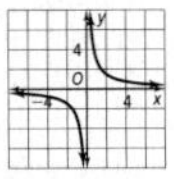

2. $y = \frac{1}{x}$ translated 5 units up **3.** $y = \frac{1}{x}$ reflected across the x-axis and stretched by a factor of 4 **4.** horizontal asymptote: $y = -7$, vertical asymptote: $x = -2$
5. shrink of the graph of $y = \frac{1}{x}$ by a factor of $\frac{1}{2}$
6. Answers may vary. Sample: $y = -\frac{2}{x}$ **7.** For $y = \frac{2}{x}$: stretch if $|a| > 1$ and shrink if $0 < |a| < 1$

Exercises

9.

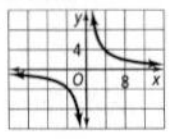

no x- or y-intercept; horizontal asymptote: $y = 0$, vertical asymptote: $x = 0$; domain: all real numbers except $x = 0$, range: all real numbers except $y = 0$

11.

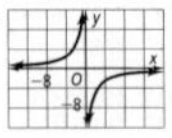

no x- or y-intercept; horizontal asymptote: $y = 0$, vertical asymptote: $x = 0$; domain: all real numbers except $x = 0$, range: all real numbers except $y = 0$

13.

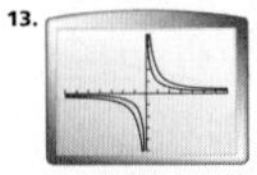

stretch by a factor of 2

15.

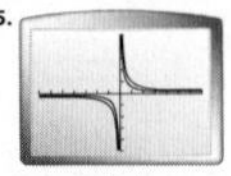

compression by a factor of 0.5

17.

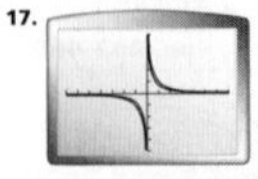

compression by a factor of 0.75

19.

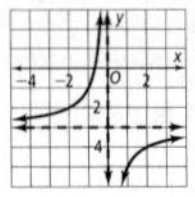

domain: all real numbers except $x = 0$, range: all real numbers except $y = -3$

21.

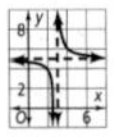

domain: all real numbers except $x = 3$, range: all real numbers except $y = 4$

23.

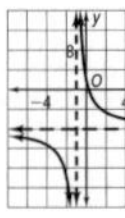

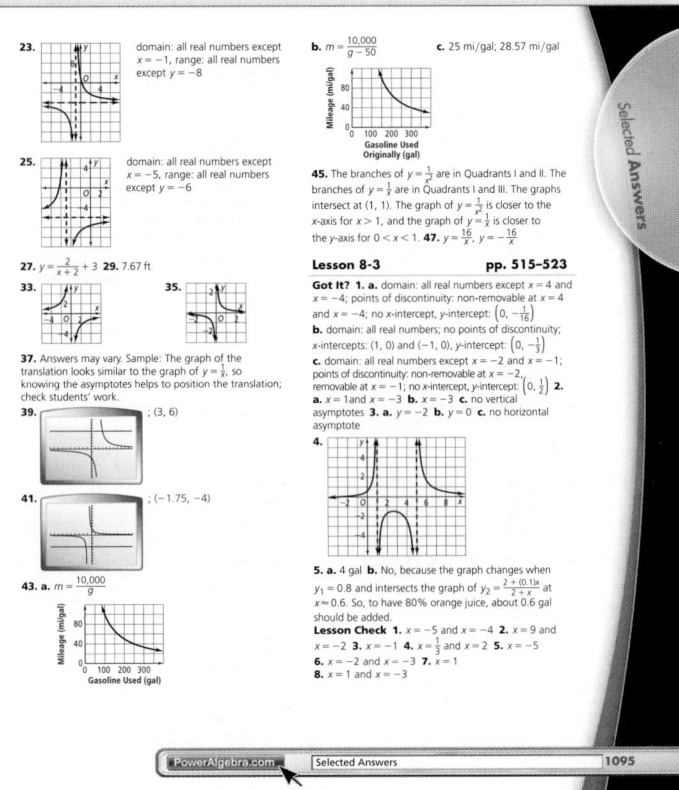

domain: all real numbers except $x = -1$, range: all real numbers except $y = -8$

25.

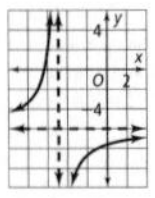

domain: all real numbers except $x = -5$, range: all real numbers except $y = -6$

27. $y = \frac{2}{x+2} + 3$ **29.** 7.67 ft

33.

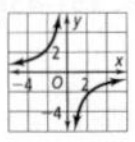

35.

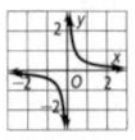

37. Answers may vary. Sample: The graph of the translation looks similar to the graph of $y = \frac{1}{x}$, so knowing the asymptotes helps to position the translation; check students' work.

39.

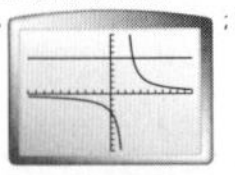

; (3, 6)

41.

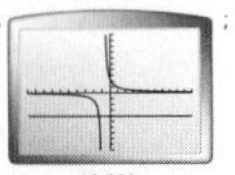

; (−1.75, −4)

43. a. $m = \frac{10{,}000}{g}$

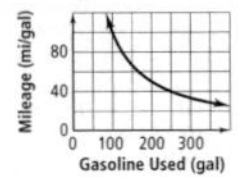
Mileage (mi/gal)
80
40
0
0 100 200 300
Gasoline Used (gal)

b. $m = \frac{10{,}000}{g - 50}$ **c.** 25 mi/gal; 28.57 mi/gal

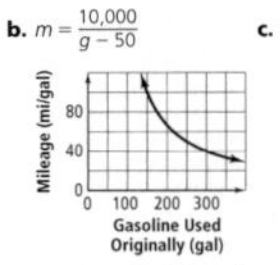
Mileage (mi/gal)
80
40
0
0 100 200 300
Gasoline Used
Originally (gal)

45. The branches of $y = \frac{1}{x^2}$ are in Quadrants I and II. The branches of $y = \frac{1}{x}$ are in Quadrants I and III. The graphs intersect at (1, 1). The graph of $y = \frac{1}{x^2}$ is closer to the x-axis for $x > 1$, and the graph of $y = \frac{1}{x}$ is closer to the y-axis for $0 < x < 1$. **47.** $y = \frac{16}{x}$, $y = -\frac{16}{x}$

Lesson 8-3 pp. 515–523

Got It? 1. a. domain: all real numbers except $x = 4$ and $x = -4$; points of discontinuity: non-removable at $x = 4$ and $x = -4$; no x-intercept, y-intercept: $\left(0, -\frac{1}{16}\right)$
b. domain: all real numbers; no points of discontinuity; x-intercepts: (1, 0) and (−1, 0), y-intercept: $\left(0, -\frac{1}{3}\right)$
c. domain: all real numbers except $x = -2$ and $x = -1$; points of discontinuity: non-removable at $x = -2$, removable at $x = -1$; no x-intercept, y-intercept: $\left(0, \frac{1}{2}\right)$ **2. a.** $x = 1$ and $x = -3$ **b.** $x = -3$ **c.** no vertical asymptotes **3. a.** $y = -2$ **b.** $y = 0$ **c.** no horizontal asymptote

4.

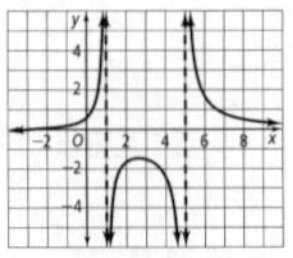

5. a. 4 gal **b.** No, because the graph changes when $y_1 = 0.8$ and intersects the graph of $y_2 = \frac{2 + (0.1)x}{2 + x}$ at $x \approx 0.6$. So, to have 80% orange juice, about 0.6 gal should be added.
Lesson Check 1. $x = -5$ and $x = -4$ **2.** $x = 9$ and $x = -2$ **3.** $x = -1$ **4.** $x = \frac{1}{3}$ and $x = 2$ **5.** $x = -5$
6. $x = -2$ and $x = -3$ **7.** $x = 1$
8. $x = 1$ and $x = -3$

9.

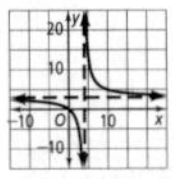

10.

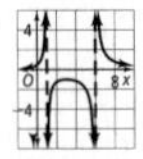

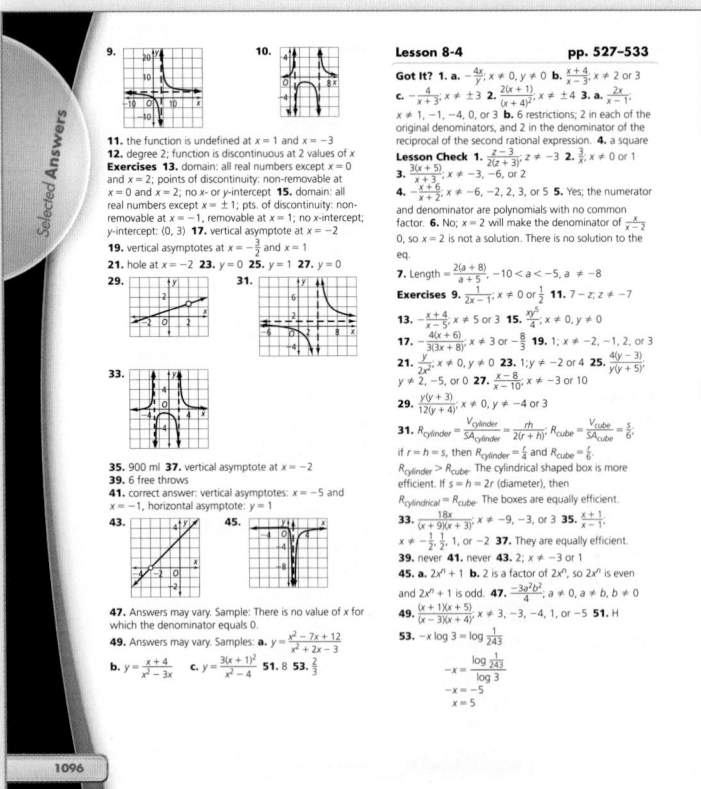

11. the function is undefined at $x = 1$ and $x = -3$
12. degree 2; function is discontinuous at 2 values of x
Exercises 13. domain: all real numbers except $x = 0$ and $x = 2$; points of discontinuity: non-removable at $x = 0$ and $x = 2$; no x- or y-intercept **15.** domain: all real numbers except $x = \pm 1$; pts. of discontinuity: non-removable at $x = -1$, removable at $x = 1$; no x-intercept; y-intercept: (0, 3) **17.** vertical asymptote at $x = -2$
19. vertical asymptotes at $x = -\frac{3}{2}$ and $x = 1$
21. hole at $x = -2$ **23.** $y = 0$ **25.** $y = 1$ **27.** $y = 0$

29.

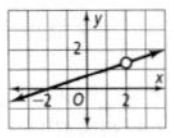

31.

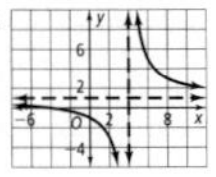

33.

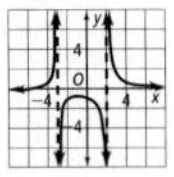

35. 900 ml **37.** vertical asymptote at $x = -2$
39. 6 free throws
41. correct answer: vertical asymptotes: $x = -5$ and $x = -1$, horizontal asymptote: $y = 1$

43.

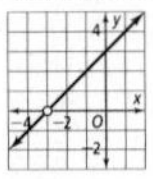

45.

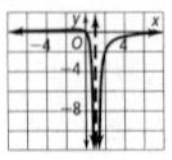

47. Answers may vary. Sample: There is no value of x for which the denominator equals 0.
49. Answers may vary. Samples: **a.** $y = \frac{x^2 - 7x + 12}{x^2 + 2x - 3}$
b. $y = \frac{x+4}{x^2 - 3x}$ **c.** $y = \frac{3(x+1)^2}{x^2 - 4}$ **51.** 8 **53.** $\frac{2}{3}$

Lesson 8-4 pp. 527–533

Got It? 1. a. $-\frac{4x}{y}$; $x \neq 0, y \neq 0$ **b.** $\frac{x+4}{x-3}$; $x \neq 2$ or 3 **c.** $-\frac{4}{x+3}$; $x \neq \pm 3$ **2.** $\frac{2(x+1)}{(x+4)^2}$; $x \neq \pm 4$ **3. a.** $\frac{2x}{x-1}$; $x \neq 1, -1, -4, 0$, or 3 **b.** 6 restrictions; 2 in each of the original denominators, and 2 in the denominator of the reciprocal of the second rational expression. **4.** a square
Lesson Check 1. $\frac{z-3}{2(z+3)}$; $z \neq -3$ **2.** $\frac{3}{x}$; $x \neq 0$ or 1
3. $\frac{3(x+5)}{x+3}$; $x \neq -3, -6$, or 2
4. $-\frac{x+6}{x+2}$; $x \neq -6, -2, 2, 3$, or 5 **5.** Yes; the numerator and denominator are polynomials with no common factor. **6.** No; $x = 2$ will make the denominator of $\frac{x}{x-2}$ 0, so $x = 2$ is not a solution. There is no solution to the eq.
7. Length $= \frac{2(a+8)}{a+5}$, $-10 < a < -5$, $a \neq -8$
Exercises 9. $\frac{1}{2x-1}$; $x \neq 0$ or $\frac{1}{2}$ **11.** $7 - z$; $z \neq -7$
13. $-\frac{x+4}{x-5}$; $x \neq 5$ or 3 **15.** $\frac{xy^5}{4}$; $x \neq 0, y \neq 0$
17. $-\frac{4(x+6)}{3(3x+8)}$; $x \neq 3$ or $-\frac{8}{3}$ **19.** 1; $x \neq -2, -1, 2$, or 3
21. $\frac{y}{2x^2}$; $x \neq 0, y \neq 0$ **23.** 1; $y \neq -2$ or 4 **25.** $\frac{4(y-3)}{y(y+5)}$; $y \neq 2, -5$, or 0 **27.** $\frac{x-8}{x-10}$; $x \neq -3$ or 10
29. $\frac{y(y+3)}{12(y+4)}$; $x \neq 0, y \neq -4$ or 3
31. $R_{cylinder} = \frac{V_{cylinder}}{SA_{cylinder}} = \frac{rh}{2(r+h)}$; $R_{cube} = \frac{V_{cube}}{SA_{cube}} = \frac{s}{6}$; if $r = h = s$, then $R_{cylinder} = \frac{r}{4}$ and $R_{cube} = \frac{r}{6}$. $R_{cylinder} > R_{cube}$. The cylindrical shaped box is more efficient. If $s = h = 2r$ (diameter), then $R_{cylindrical} = R_{cube}$. The boxes are equally efficient.
33. $\frac{18x}{(x+9)(x+3)}$; $x \neq -9, -3$, or 3 **35.** $\frac{x+1}{x-1}$; $x \neq -\frac{1}{2}, \frac{1}{2}, 1$, or -2 **37.** They are equally efficient.
39. never **41.** never **43.** 2; $x \neq -3$ or 1
45. a. $2x^n + 1$ **b.** 2 is a factor of $2x^n$, so $2x^n$ is even and $2x^n + 1$ is odd. **47.** $\frac{-3a^2b^2}{4}$; $a \neq 0, a \neq b, b \neq 0$
49. $\frac{(x+1)(x+5)}{(x-3)(x+4)}$; $x \neq 3, -3, -4, 1$, or -5 **51.** H
53.

$$-x \log 3 = \log \frac{1}{243}$$
$$-x = \frac{\log \frac{1}{243}}{\log 3}$$
$$-x = -5$$
$$x = 5$$

54. hole at $x = 3$ **55.** vertical asymptotes at $x = -\frac{2}{3}$ and $x = -1$ **56.** hole at $x = 4$, vertical asymptote at $x = -3$ **57.** 3 **58.** −5 **59.** $\frac{3}{2}$ **60.** $\frac{3}{4}$ **61.** 49 **62.** 168 **63.** 2 **64.** $\frac{17}{38}$ **65.** $\frac{19}{75}$ **66.** $\frac{11}{72}$ **67.** $\frac{137}{180}$

Lesson 8-5 pp. 534–541

Got It? 1. a. $2(x+2)(x-3)$
b. $(x-1)(x-2)^2(x+4)$ **2. a.** $\frac{x+2}{x}$, $x \neq 1$ or 0
b. $\frac{2(x-1)}{x^2-4}$; $x \neq \pm 2$ **c.** Yes, however the denominator could have to be factored more and there would be additional, incorrect limitations on x. **3. a.** $\frac{x-2}{x-1}$, $x \neq 1$ or 2 **b.** $\frac{x^2 - x - 4}{x^2 + 6x + 5}$; $x \neq -5$ or -1 **4. a.** $\frac{x^2y}{x+y}$
b. $\frac{(x-1)^2}{2x}$; $x \neq 0, -2$, or ± 1 **5.** Option 1 still gives the better combined mpg since Option 3 gives 18.46 mpg.
Lesson Check 1. $\frac{2a-10}{3a-5}$; $a \neq \frac{5}{3}$ **2.** $\frac{6x-11}{x^2-4}$; $x \neq \pm 2$
3. $\frac{-11m}{3m+6}$; $m \neq -2$ **4.** $\frac{-4(2b-5)}{(b-4)(b+4)(b-2)}$; $b \neq 2$ or ± 4
5. error in finding a common denominator:

$$\frac{1 + \frac{1}{x}}{\frac{3}{x}} = \frac{\frac{x+1}{x}}{\frac{3}{x}}$$
$$= \frac{x+1}{x} \cdot \frac{x}{3}$$
$$= \frac{x+1}{3}$$

6. Answers may vary. Sample: $\frac{x^2-1}{x^2-6x+5}$, $\frac{x^2+6x+5}{x^2-25}$
Exercises 7. $9(x+2)(2x-1)$ **9.** $5(y+4)(y-4)$
11. $\frac{1}{x}$; $x \neq 0$ **13.** $\frac{-3}{x}$; $x \neq 0$ **15.** $\frac{xy + 8y + 4}{2xy^2}$; $x \neq 0, y \neq 0$ **17.** $\frac{y-6}{2(y+2)}$; $y \neq -2$
19. $\frac{-x+6}{(x-3)(x+3)}$; $x \neq \pm 3$ **21.** $\frac{-2x(x+3)}{(x-2)(x-1)(x+1)}$; $x \neq \pm 1$ or 2 **23.** $\frac{15}{28}$ **25.** $\frac{b}{9}$ **27.** $\frac{3x}{2+xy}$ **29.** $\frac{3}{x-6}$
31. $\frac{3x-8}{4x^2}$; $x \neq 0$ **33.** $\frac{7x-17}{(x-3)(x+3)}$; $x \neq \pm 3$
35. $\frac{x(3x^2+x-1)}{x^2-2}$; $x \neq \pm\sqrt{2}$ **37.** 3.84 in. **39.** Yes; when you add, subtract, multiply, or divide rational expressions you get another rational expression. The restriction is that you must divide by a nonzero rational expression. **41.** $\frac{3x+2y}{7x-5y}$ **43.** x **45. a.** $\frac{2}{3}$ **b.** $\frac{3}{5}$ **c.** $\frac{2}{3}$ **d.** $\frac{1}{3}$
47. a. ≈ 1.18 ohms **b.** 6 ohms, 6 ohms, 3 ohms
49. G **51.** F

Lesson 8-6 pp. 542–548

Got It? 1. a. 1 **b.** 0 **2. a.** ≈ 4.47 m/h **b.** The direction of wind affects the speed (rate) of the bike. Since the speed is inversely related to time, change in speed will lead to change in time. Since there is no wind, the speed of the bike will remain same to and from the store, hence the time to and from the store will remain the same. **3.** $0.\overline{27}$
Lesson Check 1. 5 **2.** −1 **3.** −2 **4.** 310 mi/h
5. LCD was not found. The correct answer is

$$\frac{35 + 9x}{7x} = \frac{28(7)}{7x}, x \neq 0$$
$$9x = 161$$
$$x = \frac{161}{9} = 17.\overline{8}$$

6. Answers may vary. Sample: $\frac{2}{x-3} + \frac{1}{x+3} = \frac{5x}{x^2-9}$
7. Answers may vary. Sample: (1) Substitute the solution into the original equation. (2) Check to see if the solution is in the domain of the graph of the original equation.
Exercises 9. 10 **11.** 2 **13.** −1, 12 **15.** ≈ −1.45, ≈ 1.65 **17.** −3, −2 **19.** 1 **21.** 0.6 **23.** 1.5 **25.** 1.75 **27.** ±2 **29.** ≈ 1.69, ≈ −0.44 **31.** $E = mc^2$ **33.** $c = \pm\sqrt{a^2 - b^2}$ **35.** $B = \pm\sqrt{\frac{2\sqrt{m}}{r^2q}}$ **37.** $1\frac{5}{7}$ h **39.** 4 test scores **41. a.** $2250 **b.** $\frac{15{,}000}{24+x}(3.60)$ **c.** $2250 - \frac{15{,}000}{24+x}(3.60)$ **d.** ≈ 32.7 mpg
43. 3 **45.** no solution **47.** no solution **49.** no solution
51. $1, -\frac{2}{3}$ **53.** Answers may vary. **55.** Answers may vary. **57.** D **59.** B

Chapter Review pp. 553–556

1. simplest form **2.** combined variation **3.** complex fraction **4.** point of discontinuity **5.** branch **6.** 12
7. $y = \frac{72}{x}$ **8.** $y = 6x$ **9.** $z = \frac{7}{4}xy$; 56 **10.** $z = \frac{4x}{y}$; 2

11.

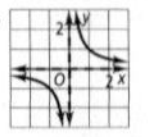

no x- or y-intercept; vert. asymptote: $x = 0$, horizontal asymptote: $y = 0$

12.

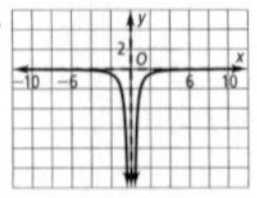

no x- or y-intercept; vert. asymptote: $x = 0$, horizontal asymptote: $y = 0$

13. 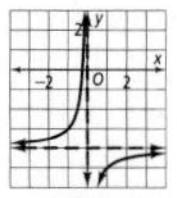 x-intercept: (−0.25, 0), no y-intercept; vert. asymptote: $x = 0$, horizontal asymptote: $y = -4$

14. 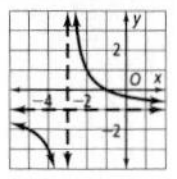 x-intercept: (−1, 0), y-intercept: $(0, -\frac{1}{3})$; vert. asymptote: $x = -3$, horizontal asymptote: $y = -1$

15. $y = \frac{4}{x} + 3$ **16.** $y = \frac{4}{x-2} + 2$ **17.** $y = \frac{4}{x+3} - 4$
18. $y = \frac{4}{x-4} - 3$
19. pts. of discontinuity: $x = -2, 1$;

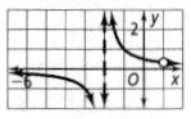

vert. asymptote: $x = -2$, horizontal asymptote: $y = 0$; hole at $x = 1$
20. 1, −1

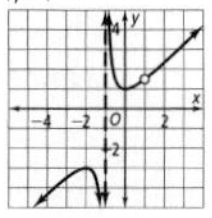

vert. asymptote: $x = -1$; hole at $x = 1$
21. no pts. of discontinuity

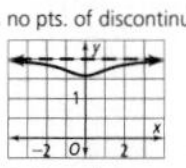

horizontal asymptote: $y = 2$
22. 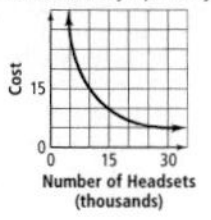

Cost
Number of Headsets (thousands)

≈31,056 headsets

23. $\frac{x+5}{x+4}$; $x \neq -4$ or -5 **24.** $\frac{(x-1)(x+1)}{x+3}$; $x \neq -4, -3$, or 6 **25.** $\frac{(2x-1)(x+1)}{x+4}$; $x \neq -4, -1$, or 0
26. $\frac{r}{3}$, where r is the radius **27.** $\frac{3(3x-4)}{(x-2)(x+2)}$; $x \neq \pm 2$
28. $\frac{-x^2+3x+2}{x(x+1)(x-1)(x+3)}$; $x \neq \pm 1, 0$, or -3
29. $\frac{2(x-1)}{3x-1}$ **30.** $\frac{1}{4(x+y)}$ **31.** −1 **32.** no solution
33. −12, 9 **34.** you: 10 mi/h friend: 8 mi/h

Chapter 9

Get Ready! p. 561 **1.** 9, 11, 13, 15 **2.** 1, 6, 11, 16 **3.** 0.9, 1.1, 1.3, 1.5 **4.** −2, −7, −12, −17 **5.** $3\frac{1}{3}, 7\frac{1}{3}, 11\frac{1}{3}, 15\frac{1}{3}$ **6.** −12, −15, −18, −21 **7.** subtract 5; −11, −16, −21 **8.** mult. by 2; 16, 32, 64 **9.** alternate subtract 9 and add 1; −7, −6, −15 **10.** add 3; 19, 22, 25 **11.** $\frac{4}{3}$ **12.** $\frac{3}{4}$ **13.** $\frac{5}{3}$ **14.** $\frac{5}{18}$ **15.** Answers may vary. Sample: $f(x) = 2x - 1$; 1, 3, 5, 7, 9 **16.** Answers may vary. Sample: $g(x) = 1 - 2x$; −1, −3, −5, −7, −9; yes; common difference: −2 **17.** Answers may vary. Sample: $h(x) = 5(2)^x$; 10, 20, 40, 80, 160; yes; common ratio: 2

Lesson 9-1 pp. 564–571

Got It? 1. 147 **2. a.** $a_1 = 1$ and $a_n = na_{n-1}$ **b.** $a_1 = 1$ and $a_n = a_{n-1} + n^2$ **3. a.** $a_n = n^2 - 1$; 399 **b.** To find the nth term using an explicit formula, you simply substitute for n in the formula. To find the nth term using a recursive definition may require many iterations. **4.** 18 months
Lesson Check 1. 2, 7, 12, 17, 22 **2.** −1, 0, 3, 8, 15 **3.** $a_1 = 3$ and $a_n = 2a_{n-1}$ **4.** $a_n = 2 + 3n$ **5.** A recursive formula defines the terms in a sequence by relating each term after the first term to the one before it and requires that the previous term be known to find a given term. An example of a recursive formula for the sequence 8, 4, 2, 1, … is $a_1 = 8$ and $a_n = \frac{1}{2}a_{n-1}$. An explicit formula describes the nth term of a sequence using the variable n and only requires the number of the term to be known. An example of an explicit formula for the sequence 1, 3, 5, 7, … is $a_n = 2n - 1$. **6.** The "+1" in $a_n = 3n + 1$ is incorrect for the sequence 1, 4, 7, 10, … . The correct explicit formula is $a_n = -2 + 3n$.
Exercises 7. 5, 8, 11, 14, 17, 20 **9.** $\frac{1}{2}, 1, \frac{3}{2}, 2, \frac{5}{2}, 3$ **11.** 2, 10, 24, 44, 70, 102 **13.** $-\frac{1}{2}, 3, \frac{25}{2}, 31, \frac{123}{2}, 107$ **15.** $a_1 = 80$ and $a_n = a_{n-1} - 3$ **17.** $a_1 = 0$ and $a_n = a_{n-1} + (n+1)$ **19.** $a_1 = 100$ and $a_n = \frac{1}{10}a_{n-1}$

21. $a_1 = 4$ and $a_n = -2a_{n-1}$ **23.** $a_1 = 1$ and $a_n = a_{n-1} + n^2$ **25.** $a_n = 3n + 1$; 31 **27.** $a_n = \frac{n-6}{2}$; 2 **29.** $a_n = n^2 + 1$; 101 **31.** $a_n = 3^{n-1}$; 19,683 **33.** 5 **35.** $\frac{5}{16}$ **37.** $\frac{9}{1024}$ **39.** −47 **41.** $-\frac{9}{8}$ **43.** recursive; 3, 9, 21, 45, 93 **45.** explicit; −24, −21, −16, −9, 0 **47.** explicit; −6, −18, −38, −66, −102 **49.** 25, 36, 49, 64 **51.** $\frac{16}{5}, \frac{25}{6}, \frac{36}{7}, \frac{49}{8}$ **53.** \$140 **55.** 20, 23; $a_n = 3n + 2$, explicit OR $a_n = a_{n-1} + 3$; $a_1 = 5$, recursive **57.** 216, 343; $a_n = n^3$, explicit **59.** 144, 169; $a_n = (n+6)^2$, explicit OR $a_n = a_{n-1} + 2n + 11$, $a_1 = 49$, recursive **61.** $-1, -\frac{1}{2}$; $a_n = \frac{-32}{2^n}$, explicit OR $a_n = \frac{a_{n-1}}{2}$, $a_1 = -16$, recursive **63.** −11, −19; $a_n = 29 - 8n$, explicit OR $a_n = a_{n-1} - 8$, $a_1 = 21$, recursive **65. a.** 25 boxes **b.** 110 boxes **c.** 9 levels **67.** $a_n = 10 \cdot 2^{n-1}$ **69.** $a_n = 1 + 4(n-1)$ **71.** 34.9 **73.** 2.19 **75.** 36.5 **76.** 2 **77.** 4 **78.** −5 **79.** −1 **80.** 1 **81.** 2 **82.** subtract 2; −2, −4, −6 **83.** add 17; 185, 202, 219 **84.** add $\frac{3}{7}$; $\frac{17}{7}, \frac{20}{7}, \frac{23}{7}$

Lesson 9-2 pp. 572–577

Got It? 1. a. not arithmetic **b.** arithmetic **2. a.** 93 **b.** 95, 110 **3. a.** 115 **b.** yes, use the formula for arithmetic mean and solve for a_7, $a_7 = 2a_6 - a_5$ **4.** 65 seats
Lesson Check 1. 56 **2.** 87 **3.** 13 **4.** 39 **5.** In an arithmetic sequence, the diff. between any two consecutive terms is always the same number. **6.** Answers may vary. Sample: 2, 4, 8, 16, 32, …
Exercises 7. yes; 10 **9.** yes; 3 **11.** yes; 4 **13.** 127 **15.** 240 **17.** 12.5 **19.** −7 **21.** 13 **23.** 7.5 **25.** \$135 **27.** 18 **29.** 36 **31.** 2 **33.** The student multiplied the third term by 2 instead of adding 2. The correct answer is 6. **35.** 120 **37.** 1.1 **39.** 0
41. $a_n = 2 + 2(n-1)$; $a_n = a_{n-1} + 2$, $a_1 = 2$
43. $a_n = -5 + 1(n-1)$; $a_n = a_{n-1} + 1$, $a_1 = -5$
45. $a_n = -5 + 1.5(n-1)$; $a_n = a_{n-1} + 1.5$, $a_1 = -5$
47. $a_n = 1 + \frac{1}{3}(n-1)$; $a_n = a_{n-1} + \frac{1}{3}$, $a_1 = 1$
49. $a_n = 27 - 12(n-1)$; $a_n = a_{n-1} - 12$, $a_1 = 27$
51. Answers may vary. Sample: An advantage of a recursive formula is that only the preceding term must be known to find the next term; a disadvantage is that many calculations may be required to find a term. An advantage of an explicit formula is that it is easy to find any term. Use the recursive formula when the previous term and common diff. are known. Use the explicit formula when the term number and common diff. are known. **53.** −4, −10, −16 **55.** −8, −17, −26 **57.** 17, 17, 17 **59.** −12.5, −8, −3.5 **61.** \$5055 **63.** 21st term **65.** 54 **67.** $a_1 = -1$, $d = 3$

69. $a_1 = 52$, $d = -10$ **71.** $a_1 = -100.5$, $d = 22$ **73.** $9k + 32$ **75.** D
77.
$$\frac{3}{(x-1)(x+1)} + \frac{4x(x-1)}{(x-1)(x+1)} = \frac{1.5(x+1)}{(x-1)(x+1)},\ x \neq \pm 1$$
$$3 + 4x^2 - 4x = 1.5x + 1.5$$
$$4x^2 - 5.5x + 1.5 = 0$$
$$x^2 - \frac{11}{8}x + \frac{3}{8} = 0$$
$$(x-1)\left(x - \frac{3}{8}\right) = 0$$
$$x = \frac{3}{8}$$
(Reject $x = 1$ because 1 is not in the domain.)
78. recursive; −2, −7, −12, −17, −22
79. explicit; 6, 18, 36, 60, 90 **80.** explicit; 0, 3, 8, 15, 24
81. recursive; −121, −108, −95, −82, −69
82. $y - 3 = \frac{8}{3}x$ or $y - 11 = \frac{8}{3}(x - 3)$
83. $y - 6 = 4(x - 4)$ or $y - 30 = 4(x - 10)$
84. $y - 10 = 8(x - 1)$ or $y - 42 = 8(x - 5)$
85. $r = \frac{\sqrt[3]{6\pi^2 V}}{2\pi}$ **86.** 32 **87.** 625 **88.** −81

Lesson 9-3 pp. 580–586

Got It? 1. a. yes; $a_1 = 2$, $r = 2$ **b.** no **c.** yes; $a_1 = 2^3$, $r = 2^4$ **2.** 6 or −6 **3. a.** explicit; it is easier to use because only one calculation is needed. **b.** about 16.8 cm, about 4 cm **4.** ±60
Lesson Check 1. no **2.** yes; 2 **3.** 729 **4.** 0.0064 **5.** The third term would be the geometric mean of 5 and 80 which is 20. Since a is pos. and r^2 is always pos., the third term, ar^2, cannot be neg. **6.** For both the arithmetic mean and the geometric mean, the middle term of any three consecutive terms can be determined using the first and last of the three terms. The arithmetic mean is the sum of the first and last terms divided by 2, whereas the geometric mean is the square root (or its opposite) of the product of the first and the last terms.
Exercises 7. yes; 2 **9.** yes; −2 **11.** yes; 0.4 **13.** yes; $-\frac{1}{3}$ **15.** yes; 1.5 **17.** yes; 6 **19.** 6561 **21.** 0.078125 **23.** $\frac{-3}{2048}$ **25.** about 656.1 g; about 182.5 g; about 96.2 g **27.** ±1530 **29.** ±1.5 **31.** ±6 **33.** $a_n = 100(-20)^{n-1}$; (100, −2000, 40,000, −800,000, 16,000,000 **35.** $a_n = 1024(0.5)^{n-1}$; 1024, 512, 256, 128, 64 **37.** $a_n = 10(-1)^{n-1}$; 10, −10, 10, −10, 10 **39.** arithmetic; 125, 150 **41.** geometric; −80, 160 **43.** neither; 25, 36 **45.** 7.5, 22.5, 67.5 or −7.5, 22.5, −67.5 **47.** −6.64, −11.02, −18.30 or 6.64, −11.02, 18.30 **49.** about 74.3 mi **51.** 768 **53.** 3×4^{19} or 824,633,720,832 **55.** 4 **57.** 10

59. Both the common diff. and the common ratio are used to find the next term in a sequence, but a common diff. is added and a common ratio is multiplied. **61.** 7 **63.** B **65.** C **67.** $x \neq -1, -5$; there's a hole in the graph at $x = -1$. There's a vert. asymptote at $x = -5$.

Lesson 9-4 pp. 587–593

Got It? 1. a. 1030 **b.** Yes; no; the sum of any number of even numbers is always even. The sum of an odd number of odd numbers is odd, but the sum of an even number of odd numbers is even. **2.** 59 sales; 1725 sales
3. a. $\sum_{n=1}^{40}(-12 + 7n)$ **b.** $\sum_{n=1}^{50}(510 - 10n)$ **4. a.** 2140 **b.** 100 **c.** 1 **5.** 41,650
Lesson Check 1. 91 **2.** 780 **3.** $\sum_{n=1}^{7} 3n$
4. $\sum_{n=1}^{12}(-3 + 4n)$ **5.** An arithmetic sequence is a list of numbers for which successive numbers have a common difference. **6.** The lower limit should not be 3, it should be one and the expression $5n - 2$ should be in parentheses. The correct summation notation is $\sum_{n=0}^{8}(3 + 5n)$. **7.** Yes; $44 = 2(a_1 + a_4)$, so any combination of a_1 and a_4 with a sum of 22 is a possible series.
Exercises 9. 92 **11.** 176 **13.** −165 **15.** $\sum_{n=1}^{5} 4n$ **17.** $\sum_{n=1}^{12}(2 + 3n)$ **19.** $\sum_{n=1}^{10}(-3n)$ **21.** 25 **23.** 20 **25.** −2 **27.** 2400 **29.** 682 **31.** −8556 **33.** 432 seats **35.** sequence; finite **37.** series; infinite **39.** series; finite **41.** −48 **43.** 35 **45.** −146 **47. a.** $a_n = n + 1$ **b.** $\sum_{n=1}^{9}(n + 1)$ **c.** 18 cans **d.** No; no; 13 rows have 104 cans, 14 rows have 119 cans, 15 rows have 135 cans, and 16 rows have 152 cans. The number of rows would not be an integer for 110 cans or 140 cans. **49.** −765 **51.** 300 **53.** 34 **55.** $10x + 45y$ **57.** C **59.** B
61. $\left(\frac{b}{2}\right)^2 = \left(\frac{10}{2}\right)^2 = 25$
$$x^2 + 10x + 25 = -35 + 25$$
$$(x+5)^2 = -10$$
$$x + 5 = \pm i\sqrt{10}$$
$$x = -5 \pm i\sqrt{10}$$
62. $a_n = 2^{n-1}$; 1, 2, 4 **63.** $a_n = -1(-1)^{n-1}$; −1, 1, −1 **64.** $a_n = 3\left(\frac{3}{2}\right)^{n-1}$; $3, \frac{9}{2}, \frac{27}{4}$ **65.** $\frac{x+3}{x-4}$; $x \neq 4$, $x \neq -1$ **66.** $\frac{c-2}{c-5}$; $c \neq 5$, $c \neq 6$ **67.** $\frac{z^2 + 12z + 20}{z - 1}$; $z \neq 1$, $z \neq 0$ **68.** $-\frac{1}{3}$ **69.** $\frac{3}{4}$ **70.** $-\frac{1}{2}$

Lesson 9-5 pp. 595–601

Got It? 1. a. 315 **b.** −1705 **2.** about \$2138.43 **3. a.** diverges **b.** converges; $\frac{1}{4}$ **c.** converges; 2 **d.** Yes; if $|r| < 1$, the series converges. If $|r| \geq 1$, the series diverges.
Lesson Check 1. $\frac{31}{80}$ **2.** $\frac{55}{9}$ **3.** converges **4.** diverges **5.** Since $r = 1.1 > 1$, the series diverges and does not have a sum. **6.** An infinite geometric series has a sum only when the series converges, which is when $|r| < 1$. **7.** The sum of a finite arithmetic series is $S_n = \frac{n}{2}(a_1 + a_n)$. The sum of finite geometric series is $S_n = \frac{a_1(1 - r^n)}{1 - r}$.
The formulas are similar in that each sum requires the first term and the number of terms in the series. The formulas are different in that the sum of a finite arithmetic series needs the last term, while the sum of a finite geometric series needs the common ratio.
Exercises 9. 1456 **11.** −5115 **13.** $\frac{15}{32}$ **15.** $\frac{121}{81}$ **17.** converges; $\frac{4}{3}$ **19.** converges; 8 **21.** diverges; no sum **23.** diverges; no sum **25.** diverges; no sum **27.** 1 **29.** $\frac{9}{2}$ **31.** $\frac{9}{5}$ **33.** arithmetic; 420 **35.** geometric; about 96.47 **37.** geometric; about 121.5
39. a.

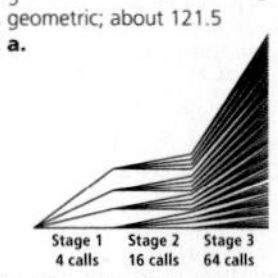

Stage 1
4 calls
Stage 2
16 calls
Stage 3
64 calls

b. 4 + 16 + 64 + 256 + 1024 + 4096 **c.** 5460 employees **41.** $\frac{5}{4}$ **43.** $\frac{3}{4}$ **45.** $0.8\overline{3}$ **47. a.** $\frac{7}{8}$ **b.** 10 **49. a.** Answers may vary. Sample: The student used $r - 1$ instead of $1 - r$ in the formula for the sum of an infinite geometric series. **b.** $\frac{1}{2}$
51. a. $rS_n = r(a_1 + a_1r + \cdots + a_1r^{n-1}) = a_1r + a_1r^2 + \cdots + a_1r^n$
b. $S_n - rS_n = a_1 + a_1r + a_1r^2 + \cdots + a_1r^{n-1} - a_1r - a_1r^2 - \cdots - a_1r^{n-1} - a_1r^n = a_1 - a_1r^n$
c. $S_n - rS_n = a_1 - a_1r^n$
$S_n(1 - r) = a_1 - a_1r^n$
$$S_n = \frac{a_1 - a_1r^n}{1 - r} = \frac{a_1(1 - r^n)}{1 - r}$$
53. $a_1 = \frac{9}{10}$, $r = \frac{1}{10}$; $S = \frac{\frac{9}{10}}{1 - \frac{1}{10}} = 1$

Chapter Review pp. 603–606

1. limits **2.** sequence **3.** converges **4.** common ratio **5.** explicit formula **6.** 1, −1, −3, −5, −7 **7.** 1, 0, −3, −8, −15 **8.** 2, 3, 5, 9, 17 **9.** 20, 10, 5, 2.5, 1.25 **10.** $a_n = a_{n-1} + 17$, $a_1 = 5$ **11.** $a_n = a_{n-1} + 9$, $a_1 = -2$ **12.** $a_n = 3n - 2$ **13.** $a_n = 6.5 - 2.5n$ **14.** no **15.** yes; $d = 15$, $a_{32} = 468$ **16.** yes; $d = 3$, $a_{32} = 100$ **17.** no **18.** 5 **19.** 101.5 **20.** 5 **21.** −4.9 **22.** −10.5, −8, −5.5 **23.** 1.4, 0.8, 0.2 **24.** $a_n = -2 + 9(n-1)$ **25.** $a_n = 62 - 3(n-1)$ **26.** yes; $r = \frac{1}{2}$; $\frac{1}{16}, \frac{1}{32}$ **27.** no **28.** yes; $r = 1.2$; 6.2208, 7.46496 **29.** ±6 **30.** ±0.04 **31.** ±10, −5, ±2.5 **32.** $a_n = 2^{n-1}$ **33.** $a_n = 25\left(\frac{1}{5}\right)^{n-1}$ **34.** 2560 **35.** 1536 **36.** $\sum_{n=1}^{5}(13 - 3n)$; 20 **37.** $\sum_{n=1}^{7}(45 + 5n)$; 455 **38.** $\sum_{n=1}^{11}(4.6 + 1.4n)$; 143 **39.** $\sum_{n=1}^{8}(23 - 2n)$; 112 **40.** 3; −8, 26; 27 **41.** 9; 4, 8; 54 **42.** 31 **43.** $53\frac{1}{8}$ **44.** $14\frac{7}{18}$ **45.** converges; $S = 187.5$ **46.** diverges **47.** diverges **48.** converges; $S = 2$

Chapter 10

Get Ready! p. 611
1. 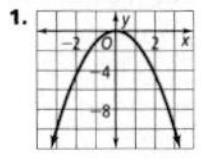 **2.** 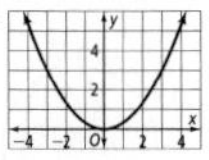
3. 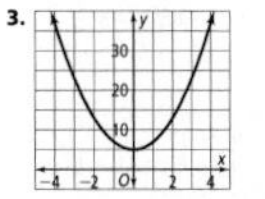 **4.** 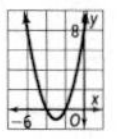

5. quadratic; $-x^2$, $6x$, 1 **6.** linear; none, $-12x$, −18 **7.** linear; none, x, $-\frac{13}{2}$ **8.** quadratic; $-8x^2$, $28x$, none **9.** quadratic; $-2x^2$, $-3x$, 6 **10.** linear; none, $-x$, −10 **11.** 16 **12.** $\frac{25}{4}$ **13.** 49

14. $y = (x+3)^2 - 2$ 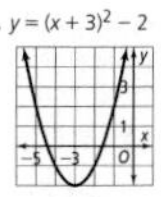
15. $y = 2(x-1)^2 + 8$ 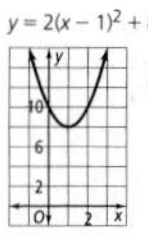
16. $y = -3\left(x - \frac{1}{6}\right)^2 + \frac{1}{12}$ 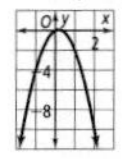
17. 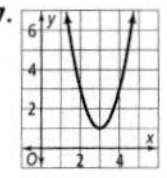 **18.** 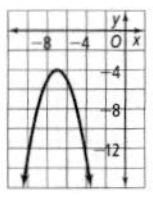
19. 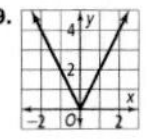 **20.** 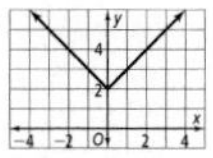

21. The radius of a circle is the distance from the center of the circle to any pt. on the circle. The radius extends in every direction from the center and ends on the circle. All radii of the same circle are equal. **22.** The vertex of a parabola is the lowest or highest pt. of a parabola; it is the pt. where the parabola changes direction.

Lesson 10-1 pp. 614–621

Got It?
1. a. 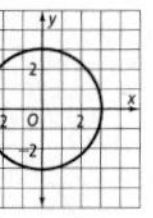 circle: center (0,0); radius 3; lines of sym.: every line through the origin; domain: $-3 \leq x \leq 3$, range: $-3 \leq y \leq 3$

b. 6 is outside the domain of x.

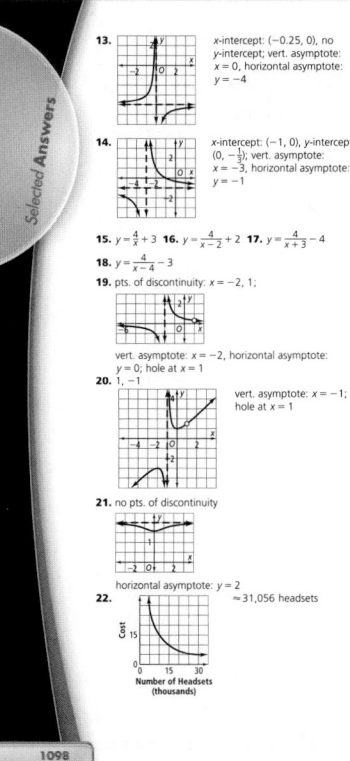

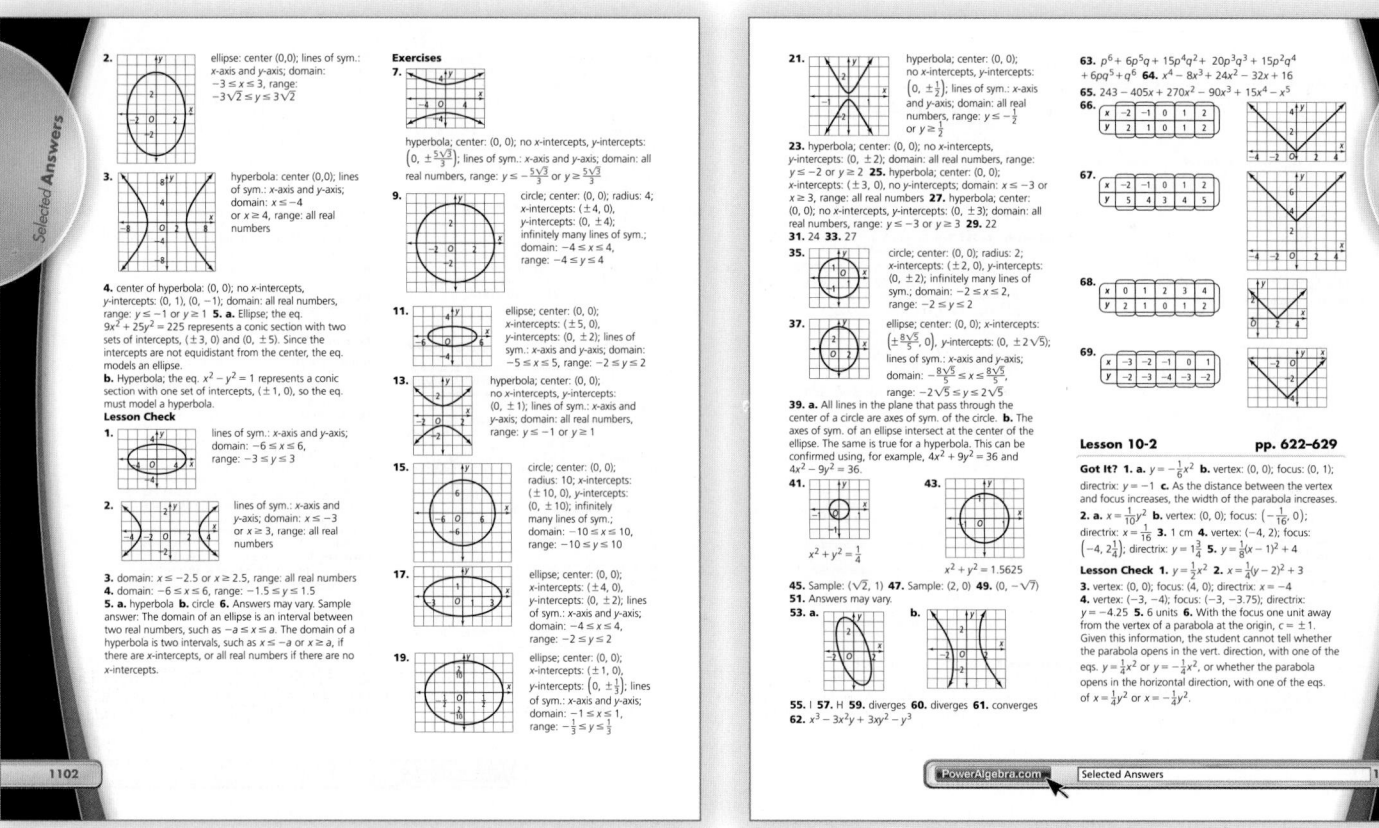

2. 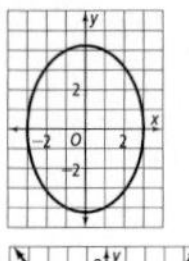
ellipse: center (0,0); lines of sym.: x-axis and y-axis; domain: $-3 \le x \le 3$, range: $-3\sqrt{2} \le y \le 3\sqrt{2}$

3. 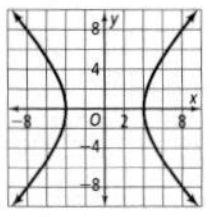
hyperbola: center (0,0); lines of sym.: x-axis and y-axis; domain: $x \le -4$ or $x \ge 4$, range: all real numbers

4. center of hyperbola: (0, 0); no x-intercepts, y-intercepts: (0, 1), (0, −1); domain: all real numbers, range: $y \le -1$ or $y \ge 1$ **5. a.** Ellipse; the eq. $9x^2 + 25y^2 = 225$ represents a conic section with two sets of intercepts, $(\pm 3, 0)$ and $(0, \pm 5)$. Since the intercepts are not equidistant from the center, the eq. models an ellipse.
b. Hyperbola; the eq. $x^2 - y^2 = 1$ represents a conic section with one set of intercepts, $(\pm 1, 0)$, so the eq. must model a hyperbola.

Lesson Check

1. 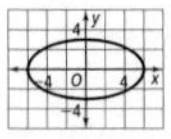
lines of sym.: x-axis and y-axis; domain: $-6 \le x \le 6$, range: $-3 \le y \le 3$

2. 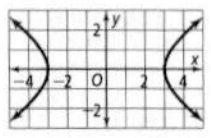
lines of sym.: x-axis and y-axis; domain: $x \le -3$ or $x \ge 3$, range: all real numbers

3. domain: $x \le -2.5$ or $x \ge 2.5$, range: all real numbers
4. domain: $-6 \le x \le 6$, range: $-1.5 \le y \le 1.5$
5. a. hyperbola **b.** circle **6.** Answers may vary. Sample answer: The domain of an ellipse is an interval between two real numbers, such as $-a \le x \le a$. The domain of a hyperbola is two intervals, such as $x \le -a$ or $x \ge a$, if there are x-intercepts, or all real numbers if there are no x-intercepts.

Exercises

7. 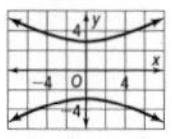
hyperbola; center: (0, 0); no x-intercepts, y-intercepts: $\left(0, \pm\frac{5\sqrt{3}}{3}\right)$; lines of sym.: x-axis and y-axis; domain: all real numbers, range: $y \le -\frac{5\sqrt{3}}{3}$ or $y \ge \frac{5\sqrt{3}}{3}$

9. 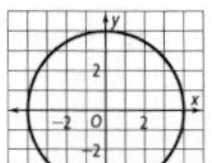
circle; center: (0, 0); radius: 4; x-intercepts: $(\pm 4, 0)$, y-intercepts: $(0, \pm 4)$; infinitely many lines of sym.; domain: $-4 \le x \le 4$, range: $-4 \le y \le 4$

11. 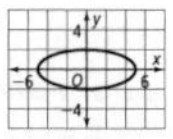
ellipse; center: (0, 0); x-intercepts: $(\pm 5, 0)$, y-intercepts: $(0, \pm 2)$; lines of sym.: x-axis and y-axis; domain: $-5 \le x \le 5$, range: $-2 \le y \le 2$

13. 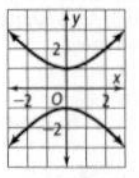
hyperbola; center: (0, 0); no x-intercepts, y-intercepts: $(0, \pm 1)$; lines of sym.: x-axis and y-axis; domain: all real numbers, range: $y \le -1$ or $y \ge 1$

15. 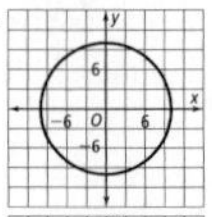
circle; center: (0, 0); radius: 10; x-intercepts: $(\pm 10, 0)$, y-intercepts: $(0, \pm 10)$; infinitely many lines of sym.; domain: $-10 \le x \le 10$, range: $-10 \le y \le 10$

17. 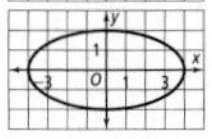
ellipse; center: (0, 0); x-intercepts: $(\pm 4, 0)$, y-intercepts: $(0, \pm 2)$; lines of sym.: x-axis and y-axis; domain: $-4 \le x \le 4$, range: $-2 \le y \le 2$

19. 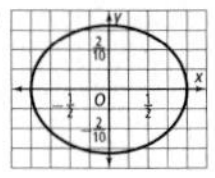
ellipse; center: (0, 0); x-intercepts: $(\pm 1, 0)$, y-intercepts: $\left(0, \pm\frac{1}{3}\right)$; lines of sym.: x-axis and y-axis; domain: $-1 \le x \le 1$, range: $-\frac{1}{3} \le y \le \frac{1}{3}$

21. 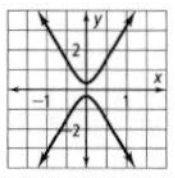
hyperbola; center: (0, 0); no x-intercepts, y-intercepts: $\left(0, \pm\frac{1}{2}\right)$; lines of sym.: x-axis and y-axis; domain: all real numbers, range: $y \le -\frac{1}{2}$ or $y \ge \frac{1}{2}$

23. hyperbola; center: (0, 0); no x-intercepts, y-intercepts: $(0, \pm 2)$; domain: all real numbers, range: $y \le -2$ or $y \ge 2$ **25.** hyperbola; center: (0, 0); x-intercepts: $(\pm 3, 0)$, no y-intercepts; domain: $x \le -3$ or $x \ge 3$, range: all real numbers **27.** hyperbola; center: (0, 0); no x-intercepts, y-intercepts: $(0, \pm 3)$; domain: all real numbers, range: $y \le -3$ or $y \ge 3$ **29.** 22 **31.** 24 **33.** 27

35. 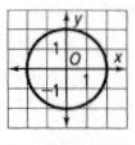
circle; center: (0, 0); radius: 2; x-intercepts: $(\pm 2, 0)$, y-intercepts: $(0, \pm 2)$; infinitely many lines of sym.; domain: $-2 \le x \le 2$, range: $-2 \le y \le 2$

37. 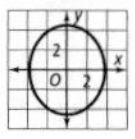
ellipse; center: (0, 0); x-intercepts: $\left(\pm\frac{8\sqrt{5}}{5}, 0\right)$, y-intercepts: $(0, \pm 2\sqrt{5})$; lines of sym.: x-axis and y-axis; domain: $-\frac{8\sqrt{5}}{5} \le x \le \frac{8\sqrt{5}}{5}$, range: $-2\sqrt{5} \le y \le 2\sqrt{5}$

39. a. All lines in the plane that pass through the center of a circle are axes of sym. of the circle. **b.** The axes of sym. of an ellipse intersect at the center of the ellipse. The same is true for a hyperbola. This can be confirmed using, for example, $4x^2 + 9y^2 = 36$ and $4x^2 - 9y^2 = 36$.

41. 43. 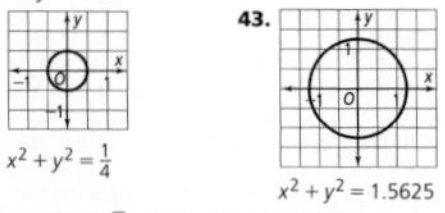
41. $x^2 + y^2 = \frac{1}{4}$ 43. $x^2 + y^2 = 1.5625$

45. Sample: $(\sqrt{2}, 1)$ **47.** Sample: (2, 0) **49.** $(0, -\sqrt{7})$
51. Answers may vary.
53. a. **b.** 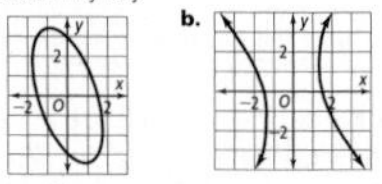

55. I **57.** H **59.** diverges **60.** diverges **61.** converges
62. $x^3 - 3x^2y + 3xy^2 - y^3$

63. $p^6 + 6p^5q + 15p^4q^2 + 20p^3q^3 + 15p^2q^4 + 6pq^5 + q^6$ **64.** $x^4 - 8x^3 + 24x^2 - 32x + 16$
65. $243 - 405x + 270x^2 - 90x^3 + 15x^4 - x^5$

66.

x	−2	−1	0	1	2
y	2	1	0	1	2

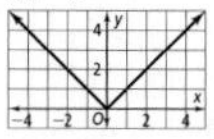

67.

x	−2	−1	0	1	2
y	5	4	3	4	5

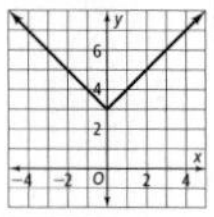

68.

x	0	1	2	3	4
y	2	1	0	1	2

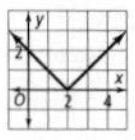

69.

x	−3	−2	−1	0	1
y	−2	−3	−4	−3	−2

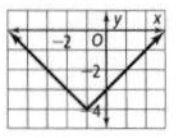

Lesson 10-2 pp. 622–629

Got It? 1. a. $y = -\frac{1}{6}x^2$ **b.** vertex: (0, 0); focus: (0, 1); directrix: $y = -1$ **c.** As the distance between the vertex and focus increases, the width of the parabola increases. **2. a.** $x = \frac{1}{10}y^2$ **b.** vertex: (0, 0); focus: $\left(-\frac{1}{16}, 0\right)$; directrix: $x = \frac{1}{16}$ **3.** 1 cm **4.** vertex: (−4, 2); focus: $\left(-4, 2\frac{1}{4}\right)$; directrix: $y = 1\frac{3}{4}$ **5.** $y = \frac{1}{8}(x - 1)^2 + 4$

Lesson Check 1. $y = \frac{1}{2}x^2$ **2.** $x = \frac{1}{4}(y - 2)^2 + 3$ **3.** vertex: (0, 0); focus: (4, 0); directrix: $x = -4$ **4.** vertex: (−3, −4); focus: (−3, −3.75); directrix: $y = -4.25$ **5.** 6 units **6.** With the focus one unit away from the vertex of a parabola at the origin, $c = \pm 1$. Given this information, the student cannot tell whether the parabola opens in the vert. direction, with one of the eqs. $y = \frac{1}{4}x^2$ or $y = -\frac{1}{4}x^2$, or whether the parabola opens in the horizontal direction, with one of the eqs. of $x = \frac{1}{4}y^2$ or $x = -\frac{1}{4}y^2$.

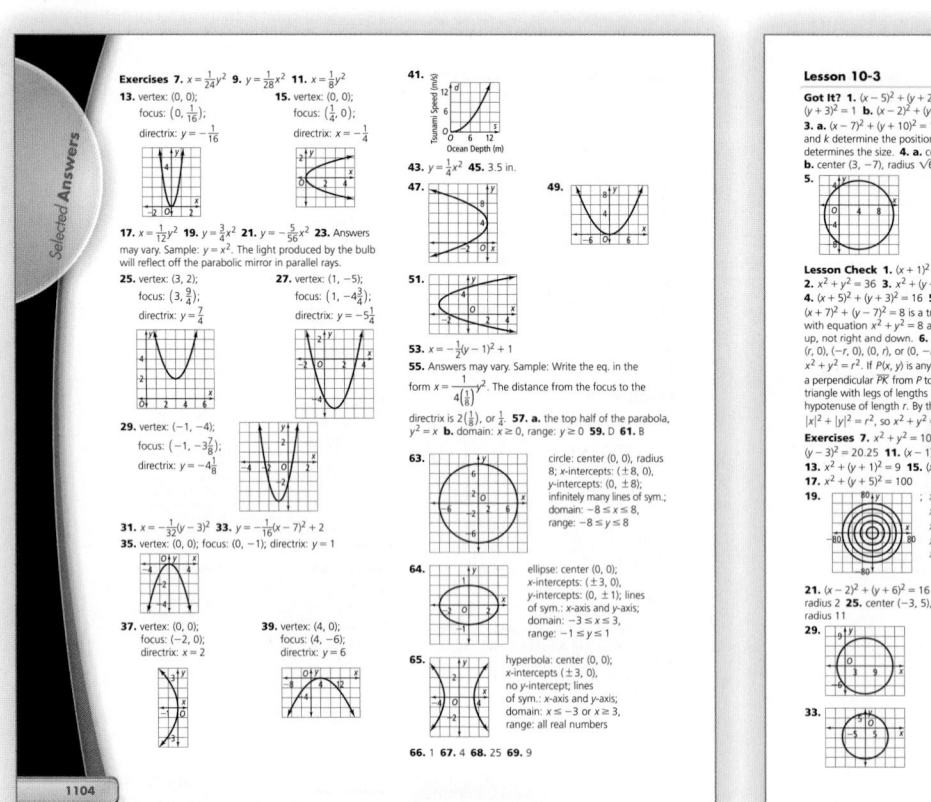

Exercises 7. $x = \frac{1}{24}y^2$ **9.** $y = \frac{1}{28}x^2$ **11.** $x = \frac{1}{8}y^2$

13. vertex: (0, 0); focus: $\left(0, \frac{1}{16}\right)$; directrix: $y = -\frac{1}{16}$ **15.** vertex: (0, 0); focus: $\left(\frac{1}{4}, 0\right)$; directrix: $x = -\frac{1}{4}$

17. $x = \frac{1}{12}y^2$ **19.** $y = \frac{3}{4}x^2$ **21.** $y = -\frac{5}{56}x^2$ **23.** Answers may vary. Sample: $y = x^2$. The light produced by the bulb will reflect off the parabolic mirror in parallel rays.

25. vertex: (3, 2); focus: $\left(3, \frac{9}{4}\right)$; directrix: $y = \frac{7}{4}$ **27.** vertex: (1, −5); focus: $\left(1, -4\frac{3}{4}\right)$; directrix: $y = -5\frac{1}{4}$

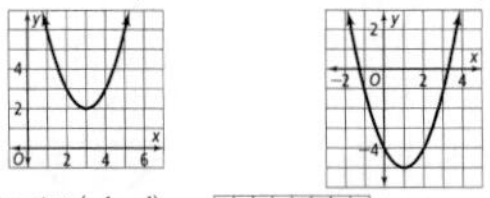

29. vertex: (−1, −4); focus: $\left(-1, -3\frac{7}{8}\right)$; directrix: $y = -4\frac{1}{8}$

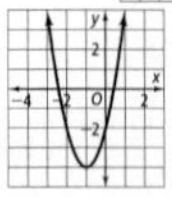

31. $x = -\frac{1}{32}(y - 3)^2$ **33.** $y = -\frac{1}{16}(x - 7)^2 + 2$
35. vertex: (0, 0); focus: (0, −1); directrix: $y = 1$

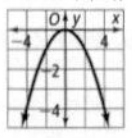

37. vertex: (0, 0); focus: (−2, 0); directrix: $x = 2$ **39.** vertex: (4, 0); focus: (4, −6); directrix: $y = 6$

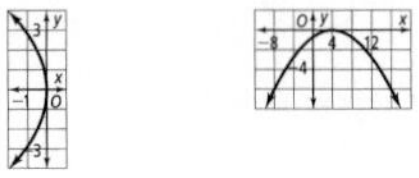

41. 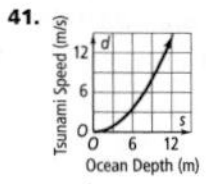
Tsunami Speed (m/s)
Ocean Depth (m)

43. $y = \frac{1}{4}x^2$ **45.** 3.5 in.

47. 49. 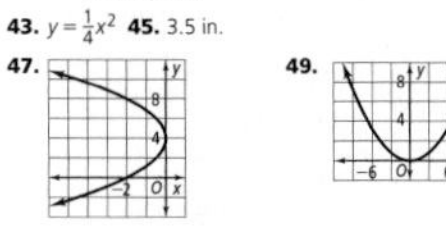

51. 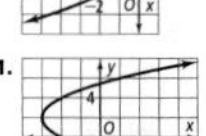

53. $x = -\frac{1}{2}(y - 1)^2 + 1$
55. Answers may vary. Sample: Write the eq. in the form $x = \frac{1}{4\left(\frac{1}{8}\right)}y^2$. The distance from the focus to the directrix is $2\left(\frac{1}{8}\right)$, or $\frac{1}{4}$. **57. a.** the top half of the parabola, $y^2 = x$ **b.** domain: $x \ge 0$, range: $y \ge 0$ **59.** D **61.** B

63. 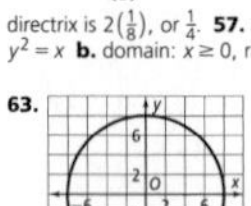
circle: center (0, 0), radius 8; x-intercepts: $(\pm 8, 0)$, y-intercepts: $(0, \pm 8)$; infinitely many lines of sym.; domain: $-8 \le x \le 8$, range: $-8 \le y \le 8$

64. 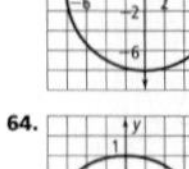
ellipse: center (0, 0); x-intercepts: $(\pm 3, 0)$, y-intercepts: $(0, \pm 1)$; lines of sym.: x-axis and y-axis; domain: $-3 \le x \le 3$, range: $-1 \le y \le 1$

65. 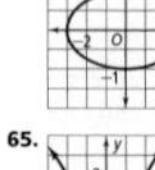
hyperbola: center (0, 0); x-intercepts $(\pm 3, 0)$, no y-intercept; lines of sym.: x-axis and y-axis; domain: $x \le -3$ or $x \ge 3$, range: all real numbers

66. 1 **67.** 4 **68.** 25 **69.** 9

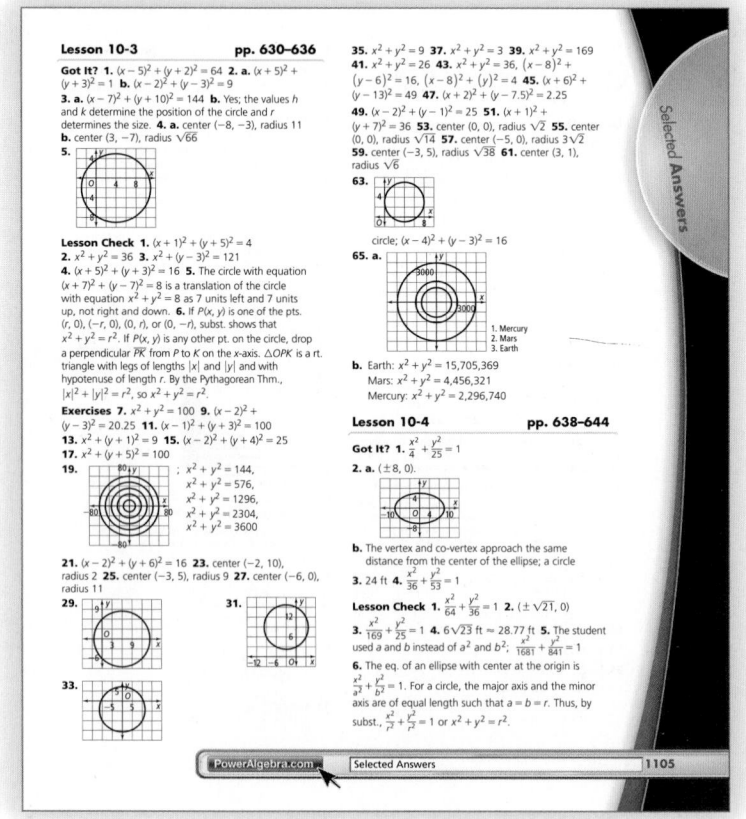

Lesson 10-3 pp. 630–636

Got It? 1. $(x - 5)^2 + (y + 2)^2 = 64$ **2. a.** $(x + 5)^2 + (y + 3)^2 = 1$ **b.** $(x - 2)^2 + (y - 3)^2 = 9$
3. a. $(x - 7)^2 + (y + 10)^2 = 144$ **b.** Yes; the values h and k determine the position of the circle and r determines the size. **4. a.** center (−8, −3), radius 11 **b.** center (3, −7), radius $\sqrt{66}$

5. 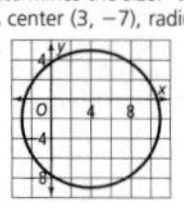

Lesson Check 1. $(x + 1)^2 + (y + 5)^2 = 4$ **2.** $x^2 + y^2 = 36$ **3.** $x^2 + (y - 3)^2 = 121$ **4.** $(x + 5)^2 + (y + 3)^2 = 16$ **5.** The circle with equation $(x + 7)^2 + (y - 7)^2 = 8$ is a translation of the circle with equation $x^2 + y^2 = 8$ as 7 units left and 7 units up, not right and down. **6.** If $P(x, y)$ is one of the pts. $(r, 0)$, $(-r, 0)$, $(0, r)$, or $(0, -r)$, subst. shows that $x^2 + y^2 = r^2$. If $P(x, y)$ is any other pt. on the circle, drop a perpendicular $\overline{PK}$ from P to K on the x-axis. $\triangle OPK$ is a rt. triangle with legs of lengths $|x|$ and $|y|$ and with hypotenuse of length r. By the Pythagorean Thm., $|x|^2 + |y|^2 = r^2$, so $x^2 + y^2 = r^2$.

Exercises 7. $x^2 + y^2 = 100$ **9.** $(x - 2)^2 + (y - 3)^2 = 20.25$ **11.** $(x - 1)^2 + (y + 3)^2 = 100$ **13.** $x^2 + (y + 1)^2 = 9$ **15.** $(x - 2)^2 + (y + 4)^2 = 25$ **17.** $x^2 + (y + 5)^2 = 100$

19. 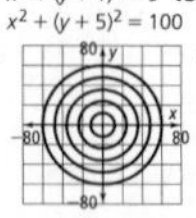
; $x^2 + y^2 = 144$, $x^2 + y^2 = 576$, $x^2 + y^2 = 1296$, $x^2 + y^2 = 2304$, $x^2 + y^2 = 3600$

21. $(x - 2)^2 + (y + 6)^2 = 16$ **23.** center (−2, 10), radius 2 **25.** center (−3, 5), radius 9 **27.** center (−6, 0), radius 11

29. 31. 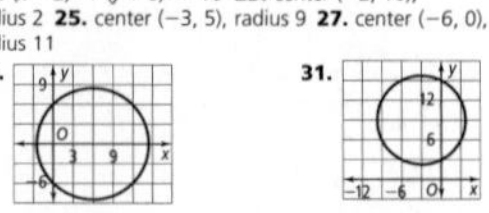

33. 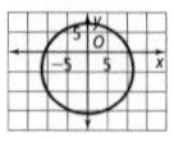

35. $x^2 + y^2 = 9$ **37.** $x^2 + y^2 = 3$ **39.** $x^2 + y^2 = 169$ **41.** $x^2 + y^2 = 26$ **43.** $x^2 + y^2 = 36$, $(x - 8)^2 + (y - 6)^2 = 16$, $(x - 8)^2 + (y)^2 = 4$ **45.** $(x + 6)^2 + (y - 13)^2 = 49$ **47.** $(x + 2)^2 + (y - 7.5)^2 = 2.25$ **49.** $(x - 2)^2 + (y - 1)^2 = 25$ **51.** $(x + 1)^2 + (y + 7)^2 = 36$ **53.** center (0, 0), radius $\sqrt{2}$ **55.** center (0, 0), radius $\sqrt{14}$ **57.** center (−5, 0), radius $3\sqrt{2}$ **59.** center (−3, 5), radius $\sqrt{38}$ **61.** center (3, 1), radius $\sqrt{6}$

63. 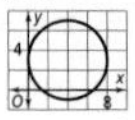
circle; $(x - 4)^2 + (y - 3)^2 = 16$

65. a. 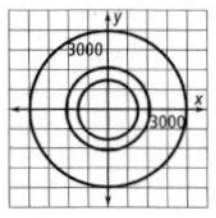
1. Mercury
2. Mars
3. Earth

b. Earth: $x^2 + y^2 = 15{,}705{,}369$
Mars: $x^2 + y^2 = 4{,}456{,}321$
Mercury: $x^2 + y^2 = 2{,}296{,}740$

Lesson 10-4 pp. 638–644

Got It? 1. $\frac{x^2}{4} + \frac{y^2}{25} = 1$
2. a. $(\pm 8, 0)$.

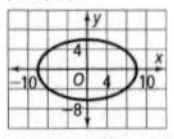

b. The vertex and co-vertex approach the same distance from the center of the ellipse; a circle
3. 24 ft **4.** $\frac{x^2}{36} + \frac{y^2}{53} = 1$

Lesson Check 1. $\frac{x^2}{64} + \frac{y^2}{36} = 1$ **2.** $(\pm\sqrt{21}, 0)$
3. $\frac{x^2}{169} + \frac{y^2}{25} = 1$ **4.** $6\sqrt{23}$ ft ≈ 28.77 ft **5.** The student used a and b instead of a^2 and b^2; $\frac{x^2}{1681} + \frac{y^2}{841} = 1$
6. The eq. of an ellipse with center at the origin is $\frac{x^2}{a^2} + \frac{y^2}{b^2} = 1$. For a circle, the major axis and the minor axis are of equal length such that $a = b = r$. Thus, by subst., $\frac{x^2}{r^2} + \frac{y^2}{r^2} = 1$ or $x^2 + y^2 = r^2$.

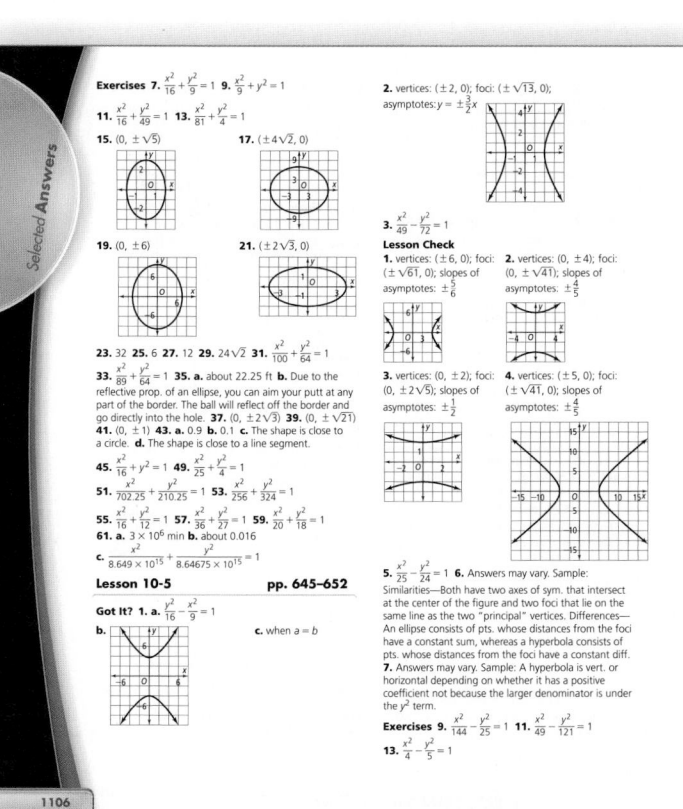

Exercises 7. $\frac{x^2}{16} + \frac{y^2}{9} = 1$ **9.** $\frac{x^2}{9} + y^2 = 1$

11. $\frac{x^2}{16} + \frac{y^2}{49} = 1$ **13.** $\frac{x^2}{81} + \frac{y^2}{4} = 1$

15. $(0, \pm\sqrt{5})$ **17.** $(\pm 4\sqrt{2}, 0)$

19. $(0, \pm 6)$ **21.** $(\pm 2\sqrt{3}, 0)$

23. 32 **25.** 6 **27.** 12 **29.** $24\sqrt{2}$ **31.** $\frac{x^2}{100} + \frac{y^2}{64} = 1$

33. $\frac{x^2}{89} + \frac{y^2}{64} = 1$ **35. a.** about 22.25 ft **b.** Due to the reflective prop. of an ellipse, you can aim your putt at any part of the border. The ball will reflect off the border and go directly into the hole. **37.** $(0, \pm 2\sqrt{3})$ **39.** $(0, \pm\sqrt{21})$ **41.** $(0, \pm 1)$ **43. a.** 0.9 **b.** 0.1 **c.** The shape is close to a circle. **d.** The shape is close to a line segment.

45. $\frac{x^2}{16} + y^2 = 1$ **49.** $\frac{x^2}{25} + \frac{y^2}{4} = 1$

51. $\frac{x^2}{702.25} + \frac{y^2}{210.25} = 1$ **53.** $\frac{x^2}{256} + \frac{y^2}{324} = 1$

55. $\frac{x^2}{16} + \frac{y^2}{21} = 1$ **57.** $\frac{x^2}{36} + \frac{y^2}{27} = 1$ **59.** $\frac{x^2}{20} + \frac{y^2}{18} = 1$

61. a. 3×10^6 min **b.** about 0.016

c. $\frac{x^2}{8.649 \times 10^{15}} + \frac{y^2}{8.64675 \times 10^{15}} = 1$

Lesson 10-5 pp. 645–652

Got It? 1. a. $\frac{y^2}{16} - \frac{x^2}{9} = 1$

b. **c.** when $a = b$

7. Answers may vary. Sample: A hyperbola is vert. or horizontal depending on whether it has a positive coefficient not because the larger denominator is under the y^2 term.

Exercises 9. $\frac{x^2}{144} - \frac{y^2}{25} = 1$ **11.** $\frac{y^2}{49} - \frac{x^2}{121} = 1$

13. $\frac{x^2}{4} - \frac{y^2}{5} = 1$

2. vertices: $(\pm 2, 0)$; foci: $(\pm\sqrt{13}, 0)$; asymptotes: $y = \pm\frac{3}{2}x$

3. $\frac{x^2}{49} - \frac{y^2}{72} = 1$

Lesson Check

1. vertices: $(\pm 6, 0)$; foci: $(\pm\sqrt{61}, 0)$; slopes of asymptotes: $\pm\frac{5}{6}$ **2.** vertices: $(0, \pm 4)$; foci: $(0, \pm\sqrt{41})$; slopes of asymptotes: $\pm\frac{4}{5}$

3. vertices: $(0, \pm 2)$; foci: $(0, \pm 2\sqrt{5})$; slopes of asymptotes: $\pm\frac{1}{2}$ **4.** vertices: $(\pm 5, 0)$; foci: $(\pm\sqrt{41}, 0)$; slopes of asymptotes: $\pm\frac{4}{5}$

5. $\frac{x^2}{25} - \frac{y^2}{24} = 1$ **6.** Answers may vary. Sample: Similarities—Both have two axes of sym. that intersect at the center of the figure and two foci that lie on the same line as the two "principal" vertices. Differences—An ellipse consists of pts. whose distances from the foci have a constant sum, whereas a hyperbola consists of pts. whose distances from the foci have a constant diff.

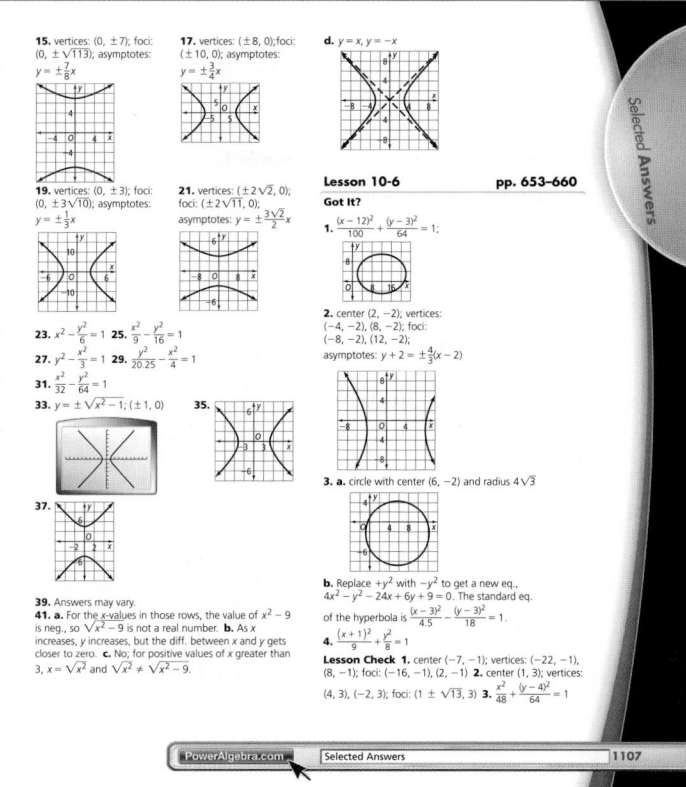

15. vertices: $(0, \pm 7)$; foci: $(0, \pm\sqrt{113})$; asymptotes: $y = \pm\frac{7}{8}x$ **17.** vertices: $(\pm 8, 0)$; foci: $(\pm 10, 0)$; asymptotes: $y = \pm\frac{3}{4}x$

19. vertices: $(0, \pm 3)$; foci: $(0, \pm\sqrt{10})$; asymptotes: $y = \pm\frac{1}{3}x$ **21.** vertices: $(\pm 2\sqrt{2}, 0)$; foci: $(\pm 2\sqrt{11}, 0)$; asymptotes: $y = \pm\frac{3\sqrt{2}}{2}x$

23. $x^2 - \frac{y^2}{6} = 1$ **25.** $\frac{x^2}{9} - \frac{y^2}{16} = 1$

27. $y^2 - \frac{x^2}{3} = 1$ **29.** $\frac{y^2}{20.25} - \frac{x^2}{4} = 1$

31. $\frac{x^2}{32} - \frac{y^2}{64} = 1$

33. $y = \pm\sqrt{x^2 - 1}$; $(\pm 1, 0)$ **35.**

37.

39. Answers may vary.
41. a. For the x-values in those rows, the value of $x^2 - 9$ is neg., so $\sqrt{x^2 - 9}$ is not a real number. **b.** As x increases, y increases, but the diff. between x and y gets closer to zero. **c.** No; for positive values of x greater than 3, $x = \sqrt{x^2}$ and $\sqrt{x^2} \neq \sqrt{x^2 - 9}$.

d. $y = x, y = -x$

Lesson 10-6 pp. 653–660

Got It?

1. $\frac{(x - 12)^2}{100} + \frac{(y - 3)^2}{64} = 1$;

2. center $(2, -2)$; vertices: $(-4, -2), (8, -2)$; foci: $(-8, -2), (12, -2)$; asymptotes: $y + 2 = \pm\frac{4}{3}(x - 2)$

3. a. circle with center $(6, -2)$ and radius $4\sqrt{3}$

b. Replace $+y^2$ with $-y^2$ to get a new eq., $4x^2 - y^2 - 24x + 6y + 9 = 0$. The standard eq. of the hyperbola is $\frac{(x - 3)^2}{4.5} - \frac{(y - 3)^2}{18} = 1$.

4. $\frac{(x + 1)^2}{9} + \frac{y^2}{8} = 1$

Lesson Check 1. center $(-7, -1)$; vertices: $(-22, -1)$, $(8, -1)$; foci: $(-16, -1), (2, -1)$ **2.** center $(1, 3)$; vertices: $(4, 3), (-2, 3)$; foci: $(1 \pm\sqrt{13}, 3)$ **3.** $\frac{x^2}{48} + \frac{(y - 4)^2}{64} = 1$

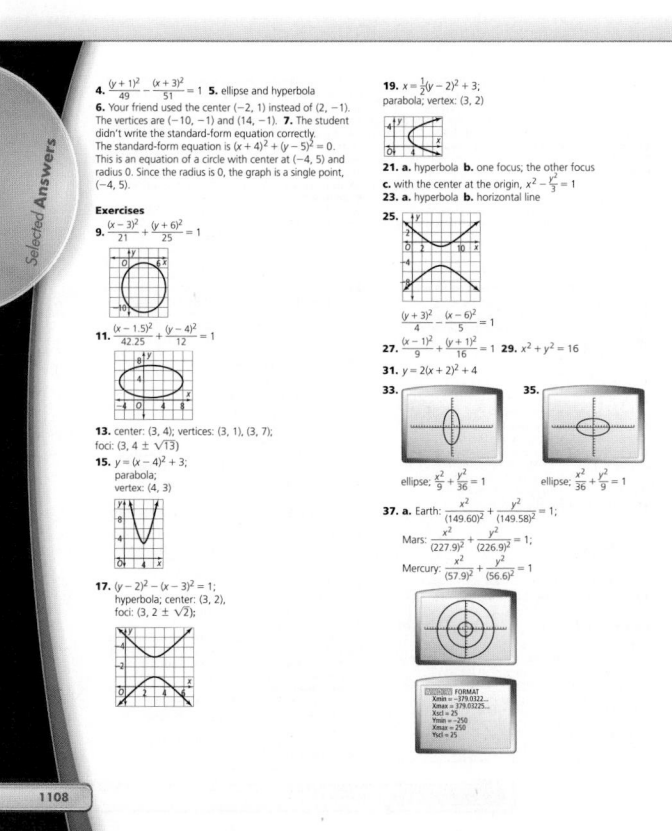

4. $\frac{(y + 1)^2}{49} - \frac{(x + 3)^2}{51} = 1$ **5.** ellipse and hyperbola **6.** Your friend used the center $(-2, 1)$ instead of $(2, -1)$. The vertices are $(-10, -1)$ and $(14, -1)$. **7.** The student didn't write the standard-form equation correctly. The standard-form equation is $(x + 4)^2 + (y - 5)^2 = 0$. This is an equation of a circle with center at $(-4, 5)$ and radius 0. Since the radius is 0, the graph is a single point, $(-4, 5)$.

Exercises

9. $\frac{(x - 3)^2}{21} + \frac{(y + 6)^2}{25} = 1$

11. $\frac{(x - 1.5)^2}{42.25} + \frac{(y - 4)^2}{12} = 1$

13. center: $(3, 4)$; vertices: $(3, 1), (3, 7)$; foci: $(3, 4 \pm\sqrt{13})$

15. $y = (x - 4)^2 + 3$; parabola; vertex: $(4, 3)$

17. $(y - 2)^2 - (x - 3)^2 = 1$; hyperbola, center: $(3, 2)$, foci: $(3, 2 \pm\sqrt{2})$;

19. $x = \frac{1}{3}(y - 2)^2 + 3$; parabola; vertex: $(3, 2)$

21. a. hyperbola **b.** one focus; the other focus **c.** with the center at the origin, $x^2 - \frac{y^2}{5} = 1$ **23. a.** hyperbola **b.** horizontal line

25.

$\frac{(y + 3)^2}{4} - \frac{(x - 6)^2}{5} = 1$

27. $\frac{(x - 1)^2}{9} + \frac{(y + 1)^2}{16} = 1$ **29.** $x^2 + y^2 = 16$

31. $y = 2(x + 2)^2 + 4$

33. **35.**

ellipse; $\frac{x^2}{9} + \frac{y^2}{36} = 1$ ellipse; $\frac{x^2}{36} + \frac{y^2}{9} = 1$

37. a. Earth: $\frac{x^2}{(149.60)^2} + \frac{y^2}{(149.58)^2} = 1$;

Mars: $\frac{x^2}{(227.9)^2} + \frac{y^2}{(226.9)^2} = 1$;

Mercury: $\frac{x^2}{(57.9)^2} + \frac{y^2}{(56.6)^2} = 1$

FORMAT
Xmin = -379.0322...
Xmax = 379.0225...
Xscl = 25
Ymin = -250
Ymax = 250
Yscl = 25

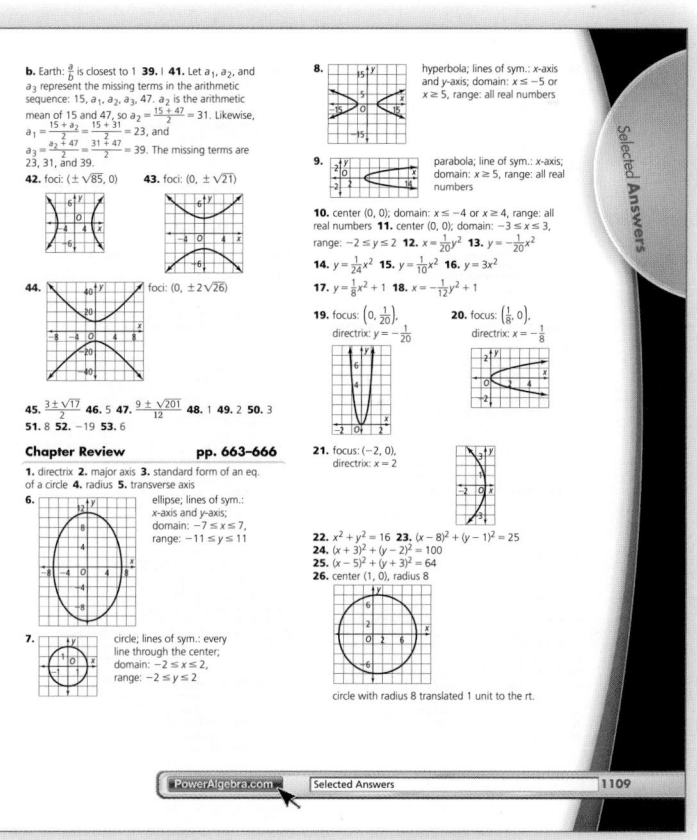

b. Earth: $\frac{8}{6}$ is closest to 1 **39.** 1 **41.** Let $a_1, a_2,$ and a_3 represent the missing terms in the arithmetic sequence: 15, $a_1, a_2, a_3,$ 47. a_2 is the arithmetic mean of 15 and 47, so $a_2 = \frac{15 + 47}{2} = 31$. Likewise, $a_1 = \frac{15 + a_2}{2} = \frac{15 + 31}{2} = 23$, and $a_3 = \frac{a_2 + 47}{2} = \frac{31 + 47}{2} = 39$. The missing terms are 23, 31, and 39.

42. foci: $(\pm\sqrt{85}, 0)$ **43.** foci: $(0, \pm\sqrt{21})$

44. foci: $(0, \pm 2\sqrt{26})$

45. $\frac{3 \pm\sqrt{17}}{2}$ **46.** 5 **47.** $\frac{9 \pm\sqrt{201}}{12}$ **48.** 1 **49.** 2 **50.** 3 **51.** 8 **52.** -19 **53.** 6

Chapter Review pp. 663–666

1. directrix **2.** major axis **3.** standard form of an eq. of a circle **4.** radius **5.** transverse axis

6.

ellipse; lines of sym.: x-axis and y-axis; domain: $-7 \leq x \leq 7$, range: $-11 \leq y \leq 11$

7.

circle; lines of sym.: every line through the center; domain: $-2 \leq x \leq 2$, range: $-2 \leq y \leq 2$

8.

hyperbola; lines of sym.: x-axis and y-axis; domain: $x \leq -5$ or $x \geq 5$, range: all real numbers

9.

parabola; line of sym.: x-axis; domain: $x \geq 5$, range: all real numbers

10. center $(0, 0)$; domain: $x \leq -4$ or $x \geq 4$, range: all real numbers **11.** center $(0, 0)$; domain: $-3 \leq x \leq 3$, range: $-2 \leq y \leq 2$ **12.** $x = \frac{1}{20}y^2$ **13.** $y = -\frac{1}{20}x^2$

14. $y = \frac{1}{24}x^2$ **15.** $y = \frac{1}{10}x^2$ **16.** $y = 3x^2$

17. $y = \frac{1}{8}x^2 + 1$ $x = -\frac{1}{12}y^2 + 1$

19. focus: $\left(0, \frac{1}{20}\right)$, directrix: $y = -\frac{1}{20}$ **20.** focus: $\left(\frac{1}{8}, 0\right)$, directrix: $x = -\frac{1}{8}$

21. focus: $(-2, 0)$, directrix: $x = 2$

22. $x^2 + y^2 = 16$ **23.** $(x - 8)^2 + (y - 1)^2 = 25$ **24.** $(x + 3)^2 + (y - 2)^2 = 100$ **25.** $(x - 5)^2 + (y + 3)^2 = 64$ **26.** center $(1, 0)$, radius 8

circle with radius 8 translated 1 unit to the rt.

27. center $(-7, -3)$, radius 7

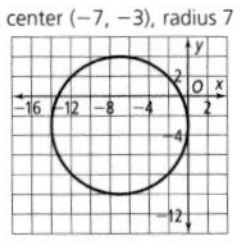

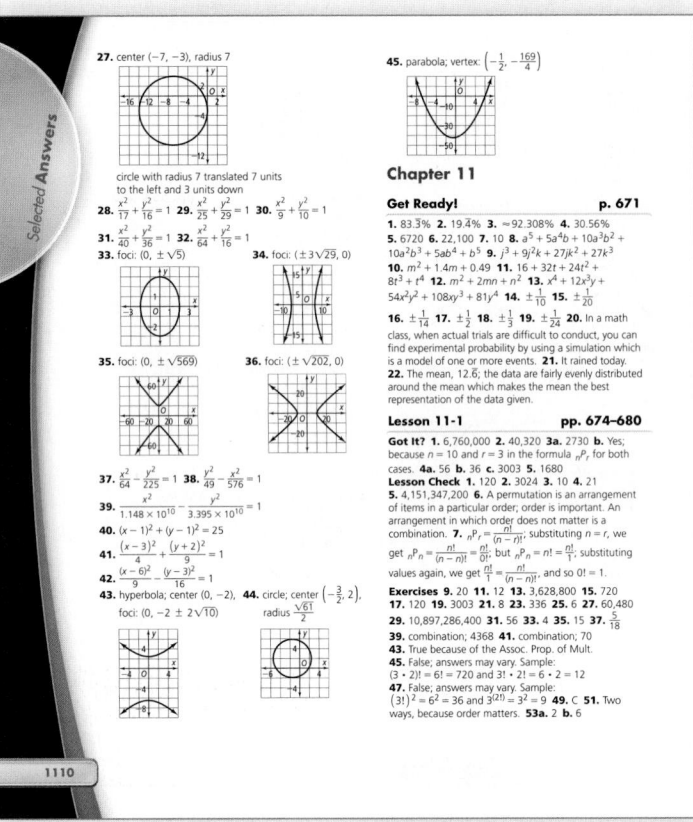

circle with radius 7 translated 7 units to the left and 3 units down

28. $\frac{x^2}{17} + \frac{y^2}{16} = 1$ **29.** $\frac{x^2}{25} + \frac{y^2}{29} = 1$ **30.** $\frac{x^2}{9} + \frac{y^2}{10} = 1$

31. $\frac{x^2}{40} + \frac{y^2}{36} = 1$ **32.** $\frac{x^2}{64} + \frac{y^2}{16} = 1$

33. foci: $(0, \pm\sqrt{5})$

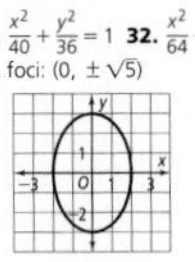

34. foci: $(\pm 3\sqrt{29}, 0)$

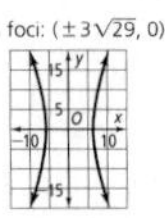

35. foci: $(0, \pm\sqrt{569})$

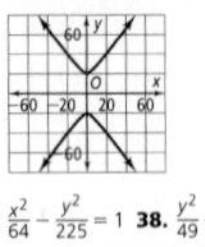

36. foci: $(\pm\sqrt{202}, 0)$

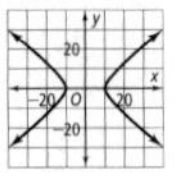

37. $\frac{x^2}{64} - \frac{y^2}{225} = 1$ **38.** $\frac{y^2}{49} - \frac{x^2}{576} = 1$

39. $\frac{x^2}{1.148 \times 10^{10}} - \frac{y^2}{3.395 \times 10^{10}} = 1$

40. $(x-1)^2 + (y-1)^2 = 25$

41. $\frac{(x-3)^2}{4} + \frac{(y+2)^2}{9} = 1$

42. $\frac{(x-6)^2}{9} - \frac{(y-3)^2}{16} = 1$

43. hyperbola; center $(0, -2)$, foci: $(0, -2 \pm 2\sqrt{10})$

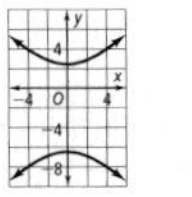

44. circle; center $\left(-\frac{3}{2}, 2\right)$, radius $\frac{\sqrt{61}}{2}$

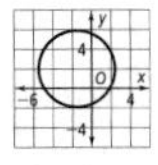

45. parabola; vertex: $\left(-\frac{1}{2}, -\frac{169}{4}\right)$

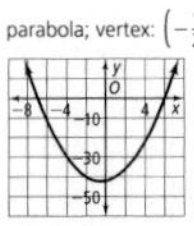

Chapter 11

Get Ready! p. 671

1. $83.\overline{3}\%$ **2.** $19.\overline{4}\%$ **3.** $\approx 92.308\%$ **4.** 30.56% **5.** 6720 **6.** 22,100 **7.** 10 **8.** $a^5 + 5a^4b + 10a^3b^2 + 10a^2b^3 + 5ab^4 + b^5$ **9.** $j^3 + 9j^2k + 27jk^2 + 27k^3$ **10.** $m^2 + 1.4m + 0.49$ **11.** $16 + 32t + 24t^2 + 8t^3 + t^4$ **12.** $m^2 + 2mn + n^2$ **13.** $x^4 + 12x^3y + 54x^2y^2 + 108xy^3 + 81y^4$ **14.** $\pm\frac{1}{10}$ **15.** $\pm\frac{1}{20}$ **16.** $\pm\frac{1}{14}$ **17.** $\pm\frac{1}{2}$ **18.** $\pm\frac{1}{3}$ **19.** $\pm\frac{1}{24}$ **20.** In a math class, when actual trials are difficult to conduct, you can find experimental probability by using a simulation which is a model of one or more events. **21.** It rained today. **22.** The mean, $12.\overline{6}$; the data are fairly evenly distributed around the mean which makes the mean the best representation of the data given.

Lesson 11-1 pp. 674–680

Got It? 1. 6,760,000 **2.** 40,320 **3a.** 2730 **b.** Yes; because $n = 10$ and $r = 3$ in the formula ${}_nP_r$ for both cases. **4a.** 56 **b.** 36 **c.** 3003 **5.** 1680
Lesson Check 1. 120 **2.** 3024 **3.** 10 **4.** 21 **5.** 4,151,347,200 **6.** A permutation is an arrangement of items in a particular order; order is important. An arrangement in which order does not matter is a combination. **7.** ${}_nP_r = \frac{n!}{(n-r)!}$; substituting $n = r$, we get ${}_nP_n = \frac{n!}{(n-n)!} = \frac{n!}{0!}$; but ${}_nP_n = n! = \frac{n!}{1}$; substituting values again, we get $\frac{n!}{1} = \frac{n!}{(n-n)!}$, and so $0! = 1$.
Exercises 9. 20 **11.** 12 **13.** 3,628,800 **15.** 720 **17.** 120 **19.** 3003 **21.** 8 **23.** 336 **25.** 6 **27.** 60,480 **29.** 10,897,286,400 **31.** 56 **33.** 4 **35.** 15 **37.** $\frac{5}{18}$ **39.** combination; 4368 **41.** combination; 70 **43.** True because of the Assoc. Prop. of Mult. **45.** False; answers may vary. Sample: $(3 \cdot 2)! = 6! = 720$ and $3! \cdot 2! = 6 \cdot 2 = 12$ **47.** False; answers may vary. Sample: $(3!)^2 = 6^2 = 36$ and $3^{(2!)} = 3^2 = 9$ **49.** C **51.** Two ways, because order matters. **53a.** 2 **b.** 6

c. $(n-1)!$ **55. a.** 35 **b.** 6 **c.** ${}_7C_3 = \frac{7!}{3!4!}$, so ${}_7C_3 \cdot 3! = \frac{7!}{4!}$, which is the permutation formula for ${}_7P_3$. **57.** H **59.** G **61.** center: (2, 1); vertices: (2, 6), (2, −4); co-vertices: (5, 1), (−1, 1); foci: (2, 5), (2, −3) **62.** $(x-1)^2 + (y-1)^2 = 36$ is a circle (not an ellipse) with center (1, 1) and radius 6. **63.** $4(x-1)^2$ **64.** $-(x+3)^2$ **65.** $3(x-5)(x+5)$ **66.** 30,240 **67.** $\frac{4}{5}$ **68.** 210

Lesson 11-2 pp. 681–687

Got It? 1. 0.40 or 40% **2.** 0.20 or 20% **3a.** $\frac{1}{2}$ **b.** The likelihood of getting an even or odd is the same, i.e. $\frac{1}{2}$. **4.** $\frac{48}{2{,}598{,}960}$ or 0.0000184689 or $\approx 0.00185\%$ **5.** 0.05 or 5%
Lesson Check 1. 0.75 or 75% **2.** 0.80 or 80% **3.** $\frac{1}{6}$ **4.** $\frac{1}{3}$ **5.** Experimental probabilities are calculated on the basis of data from an experiment, actual or simulated. Given equally likely outcomes, the basis for calculating theoretical probability is being able to determine the no. of ways that an event can occur within these outcomes. Comparisons of measures such as length and area are the basis of geometric probability. **6.** Answers may vary. Samples: Flip a coin; generate random numbers on a calculator; roll a die with odd numbers as true and even numbers as false. **7.** Because you are averaging over more samples, you are getting a more accurate average.
Exercises 9. the number 1: $\frac{21}{134} \approx 15.7\%$; the number 2: $\frac{11}{67} \approx 16.4\%$; the number 3: $\frac{45}{268} \approx 16.8\%$; the number 4: $\frac{11}{67} \approx 16.4\%$; the number 5: $\frac{47}{268} \approx 17.5\%$; the number 6: $\frac{23}{134} \approx 17.2\%$ **11.** Answers may vary. Sample: Toss 5 coins. Keep a tally of the times three or more heads are tossed. (A head represents a correct answer.) Do this 100 times. The total number of tally marks, as a percent, gives the experimental probability. The simulated probability should be about 50%. **13.** $\frac{3}{10}$, or 30% **15.** $\frac{4}{5}$, or 80% **17.** $\frac{48}{125}$, or 38.4% **19.** $\frac{103}{125}$, or 82.4% **21.** $\frac{77}{125}$, or 61.6% **23.** $\frac{{}_{30}C_3 \cdot {}_{120}C_6}{{}_{150}C_9} \approx 0.17879 \approx 17.9\%$ **25.** $\frac{5}{8}$, or 62.5% **27.** $\frac{3}{4}$, or 75% **29.** $\frac{116}{147} \approx 78.9\%$ **31.** $\frac{43}{147} \approx 29.3\%$ **33.** 1 chance in 2,869,685 or $\approx 0.00003485\%$ **35.** if there are any restrictions on the last digit of a ZIP code

Lesson 11-3 pp. 688–693

Got It? 1. Independent; the number of coins is the same after the coin is replaced. **2.** 0.20, or 20% **3a.** Not mutually exclusive; 2 is a prime number and an even number. **b.** Mutually exclusive; there is no even number less than 2 in the roll of a number cube. **4a.** 0.61, or 61% **b.** Yes; the percentage of students tells which language is chosen by more students. **5a.** $\frac{5}{9}$ **b.** $\frac{5}{9}$
Lesson Check 1. $\frac{1}{15}$, or $6.\overline{6}\%$ **2.** $\frac{27}{80}$, or 33.75% **3.** 1, or 100% **4.** $\frac{7}{8}$, or 87.5% **5.** $\frac{5}{8}$, or 62.5% **6.** Events A and B are independent if the outcomes of A do not affect the outcomes of B. The events are mutually exclusive if A and B cannot occur at the same time. For independent events, $P(A \text{ and } B) = P(A) \cdot P(B)$. For mutually exclusive events, $P(A \text{ and } B) = 0$. For any events, $P(A \text{ or } B) = P(A) + P(B) - P(A \text{ and } B)$. **7.** Since these are not mutually exclusive events, $P(A \text{ and } B) \neq 0$. The student should have multiplied to get the correct answer, which is 0.21 or 21%.
Exercises 9. independent **11.** dependent **13.** $\frac{1}{6}$ **15.** 0.54 **17.** $\frac{9}{25}$ **19.** mutually exclusive; if the numbers are equal, then the sum is even **21.** $\frac{3}{4}$ **23.** 39% **25.** $\frac{1}{2}$ **27.** $\frac{5}{6}$ **29.** $\frac{2}{3}$ **31.** $\frac{2}{5}$ **33.** 14.5% **35.** 87.4% **37.** $\frac{4}{15}$ **39.** $\frac{8}{15}$ **41.** not mutually exclusive **43.** $\frac{4}{9}$ **45.** $\frac{8}{11}$ **47.** 8 **49.** 5 **51.** $\frac{1}{6}$ **52.** $\frac{1}{2}$ **53.** $\frac{1}{2}$ **54.** $\frac{3}{7}$ **55.** $-\frac{3}{2}$, 2 **56.** $\frac{1}{6}$ **57.** $\frac{1}{2}e^3 \approx 10.04$ **58.** $\frac{1}{2}e^6 \approx 201.71$ **59.** $\pm e^2 \approx \pm 7.39$ **60.** $\frac{1}{16}$ **61.** $\frac{1}{16}$ **62.** $\frac{3}{16}$

Lesson 11-4 pp. 696–702

Got It? 1a. ≈ 0.57355 or $\approx 57.355\%$ **b.** Female; there are more females enrolled. **2a.** ≈ 0.026448 or $\approx 2.64\%$ **b.** ≈ 0.040302 or $\approx 4.03\%$ **3.** 0.2 **4.** 9%
Lesson Check 1. $\frac{1}{2}$ **2.** $\frac{1}{13}$, or 7.7% **3.** 0% **4.** 50% **5.** The sum of the probability of an event happening and the probability of an event not happening is 1. Each branch represents either the event happening or the event not happening. **7.** Answers may vary. Sample: You can use both to determine the number of ways a sequence of events can occur. A tree diagram can represent all outcomes for a given situation. If there are many branches, it may be easier to use the Fundamental Counting Principle to find the number of outcomes.
Exercises 9. 0.6 **11.** ≈ 0.085 **13.** ≈ 0.682 **15.** ≈ 0.709 **17.** $\approx 23\%$

19.

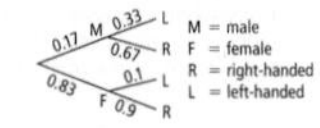

$P(L|F) = 10\%$, $P(M \text{ and } R) \approx 11.4\%$
21. 75% **23.** P(S and W) **25.** $\frac{2}{3}$, or 66.67% **27.** 0.08, or 8% **29.** 0.84 **31.** 0.16
33.

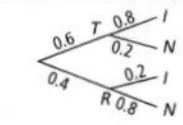

T = representative that completed training seminars
R = representative that didn't complete a training seminar
I = representative with increased sales
N = representative without increased sales

$P(I|N) = 0.2$

Lesson 11-5 pp. 703–709

Got It? 1. Answers may vary. Sample answer: No, it is not likely that both siblings have an equal chance of winning the race. **2. a.** 1, 6, 8, 9, 3 **b.** Yes, each student has an equal chance of being selected for either team. **3.** Answers may vary. Sample answer: Roll the cube until you get a 6. Keep track of the results. Repeat several times and take the average number of rolls needed. **4.** Answers may vary. Sample answer: No, almost as many volunteers who received the placebo reported improvement as received the drug. Fewer than half of those who received the drug reported improvement.
Lesson Check 1. about 0.89 **2.** about 0.86 **3.** Answers may vary. Sample answer: Flipping a coin to decide who has to wash the dishes is a fair decision. Arm wrestling to see who has to wash the dishes might be unfair if one brother is stronger than the other. **4.** Answers may vary. Sample answer: He only conducted 1 trial of the simulation, which is not enough to arrive at an accurate prediction. He should conduct the simulation at least 25 times and find the average number of boxes needed. **5.** Answers may vary. Sample answer: A simulation is an imitation or way of acting something out. In a mathematical simulation, a probability model is used to act out a situation that would be difficult or impractical to actually perform.
Exercises 7. Answers may vary. Sample answer: This will not result in a fair decision because the first person chooses the second person and might favor someone over someone else. **9.** 01, 05, 16, 03, 08 **11. a.** about 0.82 **b.** about 0.35 **c.** Sample answer: Yes, a high percentage of students who took the class passed the board exams on their first attempt so the class appears to be beneficial. **13.** 28 trials; about 1.14 correct answers per trial **15.** Answers may vary. Sample answer: Yes, the defensive driving course appears to be very effective and should be offered again. None of the drivers who took the course were involved in a major accident in the previous year. **17.** Answers may vary. Sample answer: Use a graphing calculator to generate random integers from 1 to 5. Let the integers 1, 2, 3, and 4 represent a made field goal, and let 5 represent a missed field goal. Generate random integers in groups of 3 to simulate the attempts in the next game. Perform the simulation at least 20 or 25 times and find the average number of field goals made. **19.** A **21.** C **23.** 0.35 **24.** 0.52 **25.** 0.7 **26.** 18

Lesson 11-6 pp. 711–718

Got It? 1. mean: 5.25, median: 5, mode: 5 **2a.** Yes; it is unlikely that the water temperature of a lake would change by 25 degrees. **b.** No; 98 would represent the busiest night of the week and it may relate to a weekly event. **3.** Dauphin Island: mean: $69.08\overline{3}$, mode: 84, range: 33, $Q_1 = 58$, median: 71, $Q_3 = 81$, interquartile range: 23; Grand Isle: mean: $73.41\overline{6}$, modes: 61, 70, 77, 83, 85, range: 24, $Q_1 = 64.5$, median: 73.5, $Q_3 = 83$, interquartile range: 18.5; The range and the interquartile range show the temperatures varying less at Grand Isle than at Dauphin Island. Also, the temperatures at Grand Isle are generally higher. **4a.** Use STAT PLOT, select a box-and-whisker plot. Enter data for the three remaining Gulf Coast sites. Enter the window values. Draw the box-and-whisker plots. Use TRACE on the plot to find quartiles Q_1, Q_2 and Q_3.

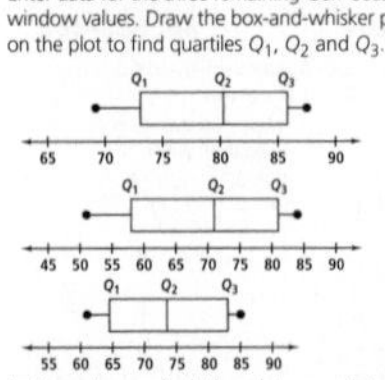

b. Yes, a box-and-whisker plot uses minimum and maximum values, the median, and the first and third quartiles to display the variability in a data set. **5a.** 79 **b.** 98
Lesson Check 1. outlier: 54; outlier included: mean: 22.8, median: 19.5, mode: 18; outlier not included: mean: $19.\overline{3}$, median: 19, mode: 18 **2.** outlier: 40; outlier included: mean: $92.\overline{6}$, median: 98, mode: 90; outlier not included: mean: 99.25, median: 99, mode: 90 **3.** the mean because the sum of the data values is affected and the mean depends on the sum **4.** 40%: 49 and below; 80%: 58 and below **5.** the mean; when data are somewhat sym, the best representation is the mean **6.** The error is in how to calculate the median. The median is the middle value or the 11th value which is 90.
Exercises 7. mean: $112.\overline{3}$, median: 95, mode: none **9.** 9.8 **11.** Jacksonville: mean: $67.991\overline{6}$, mode: none, range: 29.2, $Q_1 = 58.15$, median: 68.4, $Q_3 = 78.6$, interquartile range: 20.45; Austin: mean: $68.58\overline{3}$, mode: none, range: 36, $Q_1 = 56.85$, median: 70.5, $Q_3 = 80.75$, interquartile range: 23.9; the range and the interquartile range show the temperatures varying less at Jacksonville than at Austin.
13.

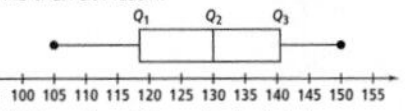

15. 5; 17 **17.** outlier: 381; outlier included: mean: ≈ 161.214, median: 158, mode: none; outlier not included: mean: ≈ 144.308, median: 142, mode: none
19.

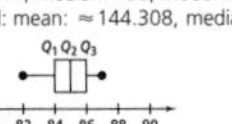

21. 30th **23.** 89 is at the 100th percentile, since 100% of the values are less than or equal to 89. **25.** The median; a few outliers can heavily influence the mean without drastically affecting the median. **27.** 83.9 **29.** Answers may vary. Sample: The range for women's shot put is greater than that for men's. The men are more consistent, as indicated by the shorter box and whiskers. Overall the men tend to throw farther. **31.** G
33. $P(H|I) = 0.40$, $P(H \text{ and } I) = 0.20$

$$P(H|I) = \frac{P(H \text{ and } I)}{P(I)}$$
$$0.40 = \frac{0.20}{P(I)}$$
$$P(I) = 0.50$$

34. 0.20 **35.** 0.56 **36.** yes; −9 **37.** yes; 17 **38.** no **39.** yes; 0 **40.** ± 16 **41.** ± 0.09 **42.** $\pm\frac{11}{4}$ **43.** $\pm\frac{19}{5}$

Lesson 11-7 pp. 719–724

Got It? 1. $\bar{x} = 69.8\overline{3}$, $\sigma^2 = 115.1389$, $\sigma = 10.7303$ **2.** $\bar{x} = 7.2\overline{6}$, $\sigma = 3.316$ **3a.** within 3 standard deviations of the mean **b.** FEMA can expect that the no. of hurricanes for a 15-year period will fall within 3 standard deviations of the mean.
Lesson Check 1. $\bar{x} = 10$, $\sigma^2 = 19.8$, $\sigma = 4.45$ **2.** within 2 standard deviations of the mean **3.** Measures of central tendency are specific data pts. which give a summary of the middle of the data set, whereas the measures of variation give a summary of the variation of the data set within the range of distribution. **4.** Standard deviation measures how widely spread the data values are. If the data pts. are close to the mean, the standard deviation is small; if the data pts. are far from the mean, the standard deviation is large. The data pts. of Set B are closer to the mean of 70 than the data pts. of Sets A and C; likewise, the data pts. of Set A are closer to 70 than the data pts. of Set C. **5.** The effect of an outlier on the standard deviation is to increase the standard deviation.
Exercises 7. $\bar{x} \approx 15.1$, $\sigma^2 \approx 12.4$, $\sigma \approx 3.5$ **9.** $\bar{x} = 43.8$, $\sigma^2 = 75.76$, $\sigma \approx 8.7$ **11.** $\bar{x} \approx 12320.00$, $\sigma \approx 273.71$ **13.** 3 standard deviations **15.** $\bar{x} = 53.8$, $\sigma \approx 3.4$; 1σ: 7; 2σ: 9; 3σ: 10 **17.** Overall farm income increased slightly, but there was less variability among the states in 2002. The income in 2001 clustered more tightly around the mean. (2001: $\sigma_x \approx 2679$, 2002: $\sigma_x \approx 2758$) **21.** Your first friend; one standard deviation encompasses all values within one standard deviation above and below the mean. The graph shows that all values are within 3 standard deviations of the mean. **23. a.** no change to σ **b.** σ increases by a factor of 10 **25.** 13 **27.** $\frac{5}{6}$
28.

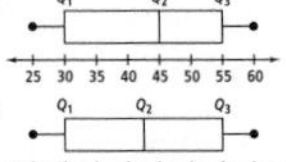

29.

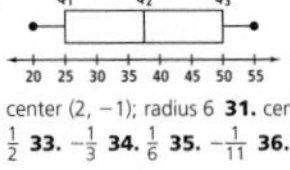

30. center (2, −1); radius 6 **31.** center (1, 1); radius 2 **32.** $\frac{1}{2}$ **33.** $-\frac{1}{3}$ **34.** $\frac{1}{6}$ **35.** $-\frac{1}{11}$ **36.** $-\frac{1}{9}$ **37.** $\frac{1}{7}$

Lesson 11-8 pp. 725–730

Got It? 1a. convenience sample; yes; since the location is at the food court in the mall, the sample may over-represent food court or fast food supporters. **b.** Answers may vary. Sample: population data for the US census **2.** Controlled study; If other factors of the volunteers are random, like age, gender, and overall health, are known, the results can be used to make a general conclusion. **3.** Answers may vary. Sample: Use a systematic sample. Go to every fifth house in your neighborhood. State the first and last names of the governor and ask a household member to identify the named person. A possible unbiased survey question is, "Who is this person?".
Lesson Check 1a. convenience sample **b.** Yes; since the location is near the exit of a history museum, the sample may over represent people who enjoy learning history and the results will have a bias. **2.** Yes; the question is leading and loaded. It suggests the person wants a particular answer. **3.** All members of the set are the population. A sample is a subset of the population.

Answers may vary. Sample: population: students in a high school; sample: students who like to snowboard **4.** It is important to have as little error as poss. in a sample, thus giving an unbiased sample. An unbiased sample is more representative of an entire population. **5.** A large sample size would give a better estimate. The size of the sample is important to the reliability of the sample.
Exercises 7. systematic sampling; no bias **9.** Survey; the statistics can be used to make a general conclusion about the population because the sample is randomly generated, and the survey question does not introduce a bias into the study. **11.** Controlled experiment; the statistics from this study can be used to make a general conclusion about the effectiveness of the plant food for this particular plant type as compared with giving no plant food at all. **13.** Answers may vary. Sample: Convenience sampling; interview students at a local high school.
15. Answers may vary. Sample: Self-selected sampling; a newspaper article invites females over the age of 21 to call the paper and express their opinions.
17. self-selected sampling; biased because only those who spend time online will respond. **19. a.** all students at the school **b.** every tenth student who enters the school building the day of the survey **c.** Answers may vary. Sample: A little over half of students favor the new dress code.
21. Answers will vary. Sample: No, because you would have to assume that all registered voters will actually vote on Election Day. **23. a.** convenience sample **b.** observational study **c.** Answers may vary. Sample: The statistics do not necessarily represent the school population because a random sample was not used to conduct the study. **25.** Yes, the question is leading the respondent to a particular desired answer, and it gives statistics that may elicit a strong reaction. Also, it requires the respondent to answer a question about whether a person *should* wear a safety belt, which may not necessarily influence whether they support the law.
27. G **29.** $\bar{x} \approx 2.83$, $\sigma \approx 2.54$ **30.** $\bar{x} \approx 5.62$, $\sigma \approx 3.67$
31. $y = \frac{1}{2}(x - 5)$; yes **32.** $y = \pm\sqrt{x}$; no
33. $y = \pm\sqrt{\frac{9x}{5}}$; no **34.** $y = \frac{x^2}{9}$, $x \geq 0$; yes **35.** 6
36. 1 **37.** 10 **38.** 792

Lesson 11-9 pp. 731–738

Got It?
1. $P(0) = 0.07776$; $P(1) = 0.2592$; $P(2) = 0.3456$; $P(3) = 0.2304$; $P(5) = 0.01024$
2. $81x^4 + 108x^3y + 54x^2y^2 + 12xy^3 + y^4$
3. ≈ 0.1035, or about 10.4%
Lesson Check 1. ≈ 0.3110, or $\approx 31.10\%$
2. ≈ 0.1641, or $\approx 16.41\%$ **3.** $20c^3d^3$ **4.** $-10x^4y$

5. 0.2646, or 26.46% **6.** Answers may vary. Sample: A binomial experiment has three important features: **a.** The situation involves repeated trials; flipping a coin 10 times has 10 trials. **b.** Each trial has two possible outcomes; in this case, heads or tails. **c.** The probability of success is constant throughout the trials; the trials of flipping a coin, are independent. **7.** The student wrote "5" instead of "4". It should be: ${}_nC_{(5-1)}a^{n-4}b^4 = {}_7C_4 j^3(-k)^4 = 35j^3k^4$
Exercises 9. ≈ 0.1361, or $\approx 13.61\%$
11. ≈ 0.0015, or $\approx 0.15\%$
13. $a^4 + 4a^3b + 6a^2b^2 + 4ab^3 + b^4$
15. $243x^5 + 810x^4y + 1080x^3y^2 + 720x^2y^3 + 240xy^4 + 32y^5$ **17.** $896g^6h$ **19.** e^6
21. $P(0) \approx 0.1176$, $P(1) \approx 0.3025$, $P(2) \approx 0.3241$, $P(3) \approx 0.1852$, $P(4) \approx 0.0595$, $P(5) \approx 0.0102$, $P(6) \approx 0.0007$
23. $P(0) \approx 0.000001$, $P(1) \approx 0.000054$, $P(2) \approx 0.0012$, $P(3) \approx 0.0146$, $P(4) \approx 0.0984$, $P(5) \approx 0.3543$, $P(6) \approx 0.5314$
25. 0.99328 **27.** ≈ 0.2824 **29.** ≈ 0.1109
31. ≈ 0.2461 **33.** ≈ 0.6230 **35a.** 0.0914 **b.** The probability that three boxes would be underweight is 0.0001. You can conclude that there might be a malfunction in the machinery or that the company's claim may be false. **37.** The probability of a group of 30 students having 4 or fewer left-handed students is about 77.05%. This means that more than three quarters of the classes will have enough left-handed desks; 4 is an adequate no.
39a. $P(0) = 0.001$, $P(1) = 0.027$, $P(2) = 0.243$, $P(3) = 0.729$

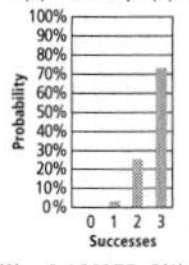

b. $P(0) = 0.166375$, $P(1) = 0.408375$, $P(2) = 0.334125$, $P(3) = 0.091125$

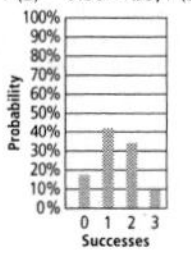

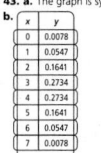

c. The probabilities of each graph sum to 1; $P(0) + P(1) + P(2) + P(3) = 1$. The probabilities of part (a) increase with increasing success numbers; the maximum probability occurring at $P(3)$. The probabilities of part (b) peak with a maximum at $P(1)$ and then decrease with increasing success numbers. **41.** Answers may vary.
43. a. The graph is sym. about the line $x = 3.5$.
b.

x	y
0	0.0078
1	0.0547
2	0.1641
3	0.2734
4	0.2734
5	0.1641
6	0.0547
7	0.0078

c. No; the bulge in the graph has shifted rt.

Lesson 11-10 pp. 739–745

Got It? 1a. 71% **b.** 88%
2.

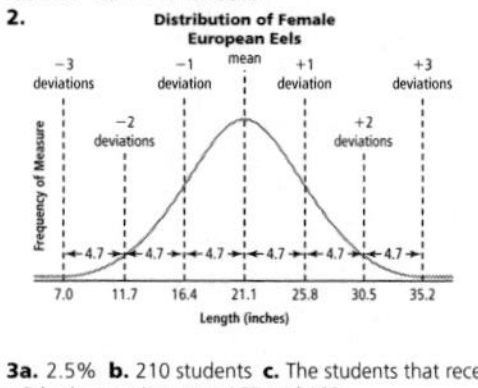

3a. 2.5% **b.** 210 students **c.** The students that received a B had scores between 165 and 180.
Lesson Check 1. 94%
2.

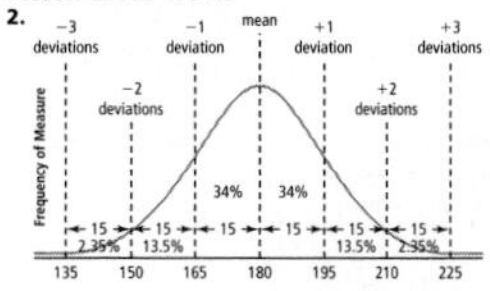

3. 47.5% **4.** Normal distribution means that most of the examples in a data set are close to the mean; the distribution of the data is within 1, 2, or 3 standard deviations of the mean. **5.** The mean and median are equivalent in a normal distribution. **6.** mean increases by 10: the bell curve is translated 10 units to the rt.; standard deviation and shape of the distribution do not change since each data value increases by the same amount.
Exercises 7. $\approx 43\%$ **9.** ≈ 43 men
11.

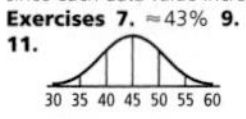

13.

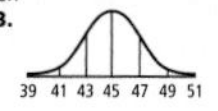

15. 68% **17.** 50% **19a.** Set 2
b. and c.

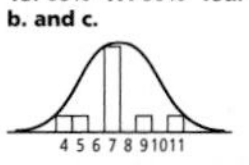

21. 59 min **23.** 47.5% **25.** 81.5% **27.** 84%
29a.

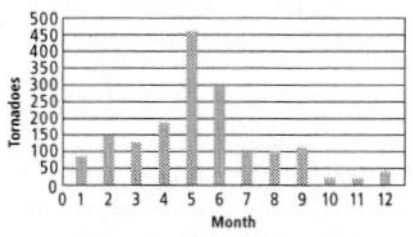

b. No; the curve is skewed to the left. **c.** No, mean and standard deviation are appropriate only for measuring normally distributed data. **31.** Yes; Elena scored within the top 10% of her group. Her score is 2.75 standard deviations above the mean, which places her in the top 1%. Jake did not score in the top 10%. His score is 1.16 standard deviations above the mean, or at the 88th percentile. **33.** A binomial distribution has a finite no. of probabilities, which sum to 1 and are a subset of a larger normal distribution. For example, using $n = 6$, $p = 0.5$, the binomial distribution probabilities are $P(0) \approx 0.0156$, $P(1) \approx 0.0938$, $P(2) \approx 0.2344$, $P(3) \approx 0.3125$, $P(4) \approx 0.2344$, $P(5) \approx 0.0938$, $P(6) \approx 0.0156$.

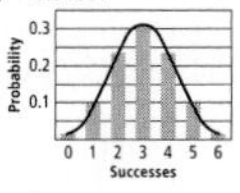

35. I **37.** For Distribution A with 50 data values, 25 values are at or below 40, which is the mean. For Distribution B with 30 data values, 15 values are at or below the mean 40. So Distribution A has more values at or below 40. **38.** 0.02867 **39.** 0.1612 **40.** 0.03676
41.

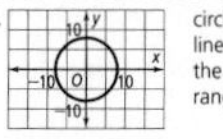

circle; center: (0, 0), radius: 8; lines of sym.: all lines through the center; domain: $-8 \leq x \leq 8$, range: $-8 \leq y \leq 8$
42.

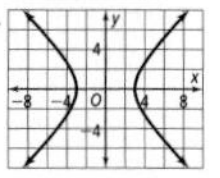

hyperbola; center: (0, 0), foci: $(\pm 3\sqrt{2}, 0)$; lines of sym.: $x = 0$, $y = 0$; domain: $x \leq -3$ or $x \geq 3$; range: all real numbers
43.

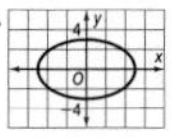

ellipse; center: (0, 0), foci: $(\pm 4, 0)$; lines of sym.: $x = 0$, $y = 0$; domain: $-5 \leq x \leq 5$, range: $-3 \leq y \leq 3$
44. $y = x - 3$;

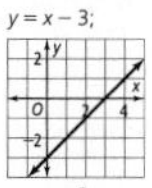

45. $y = x$;

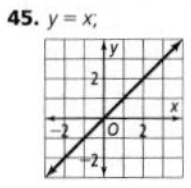

46. $y = x - \frac{5}{4}$;

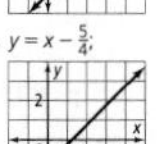

Chapter Review pp. 751–756

1. sample **2.** outlier **3.** probability distribution **4.** range of a set of data **5.** 6 **6.** 362,880 **7.** 12 **8.** 30 **9.** 21 **10.** 10 **11.** 30 **12.** 744 **13.** 220; 84; 20; 1 **14.** 3.315312×10^9 **15.** 216 **16.** $\frac{47}{70}$ **17.** 0 **18.** $\frac{2}{5}$ **19.** Not necessarily; you may pick a 5 zero times, one time, or more than once. Each time you pick, the prob. that it will be a 5 is $\frac{1}{20}$. **20.** dependent **21.** independent **22.** 0.21 **23.** 0.79 **24.** 0.3 **25.** 0.7 **26.** $\frac{1}{4}$ **27.** $\frac{1}{5}$ **28.** $\frac{1}{8}$ **29.** This will not necessarily result in a fair decision, because the principal may aim at a particular name, which means that not all students have an equally likely chance of being chosen. **30.** Yes, this will result in a fair decision, because the probabilities of each goalie being chosen are the same. **31.** Answers may vary. **32.** 9 **33.** mean: 6, median: 6, mode: 9 **34.** mean: $10.\overline{6}$, median: 7, modes: 3 and 7 **35.** mean: 15, median: 15, mode: 18 **36.** mean: 9.5, median: 9.5, mode: none **37.** range: 35; $Q_1 = 30$; $Q_3 = 55$ **38.** range: 35; $Q_1 = 25$; $Q_3 = 50$ **39.** range: 65; $Q_1 = 42$; $Q_3 = 87$ **40.** heights of 3 people **41.** ages of thirty college students **42.** gas mileage of 18 automobiles of various types
43. $\bar{x} \approx 6.64$, $\sigma \approx 5.12$ **44.** $\bar{x} \approx 17.14$, $\sigma \approx 3.52$
45. $\bar{x} = 7.5$, $\sigma \approx 2.67$ **46.** not a random sample; they will all begin with the letter "a" **47.** not a random sample; the lawyers will choose jurors that are likely to support their side **48.** random sample; all students have an equal chance to be chosen **49.** not a random sample; the five with the largest (or smallest) circulation size will be picked **50.** People at the bus station may be less likely to own a car and therefore less likely to be in favor of a new garage. **51.** $\frac{1}{2}$ **52.** $\frac{1}{3}$
53. ≈ 0.14 **54.** ≈ 0.0710 **55.** ≈ 0.2066 **56.** ≈ 0.1766
57. $21a^5b^2$ **58.** $56a^3b^5$ **59.** continuous **60.** discrete
61. discrete **62.** continuous **63.** 16%; 2.5%

Chapter 12

Get Ready! p. 761

1. 6 **2.** $\frac{1}{3}$ **3.** $-\frac{3}{8}$ **4.** $\frac{7}{72}$ **5.** −9 **6.** 11 **7.** 3 **8.** $\left(\frac{1}{2}, -4\right)$
9. $\left(-\frac{2}{3}, -\frac{2}{3}\right)$ **10.** $\left(\frac{3}{4}, \frac{11}{4}\right)$ **11.** (7, 9, −6) **12.** (0, 0, 8)
13. (7, 5, 0)

Lesson 12-1 pp. 764–770

Got It?
1a. $\begin{bmatrix} -15 & 25 \\ -1 & 1 \\ -2 & 15 \end{bmatrix}$ **b.** $\begin{bmatrix} -9 & 23 \\ -5 & 9 \\ 0 & 5 \end{bmatrix}$
c. Yes; it does not matter in which order you add matrices.
2. $A = \begin{bmatrix} 3 & 6 & -1 \\ 1 & 3 & 7 \\ 1 & 1 & 3 \end{bmatrix}$ **3a.** $\begin{bmatrix} 0 & 0 \\ 0 & 0 \end{bmatrix}$ **b.** $\begin{bmatrix} -1 & 10 & -5 \\ 0 & 2 & -3 \end{bmatrix}$
4a. $x = 6$, $y = -6$ **b.** $x = 4$, $y = -3$, $z = 2$
Lesson Check
1. $\begin{bmatrix} 1 & 1 \\ -2 & 8 \end{bmatrix}$ **2.** $\begin{bmatrix} 1 & -9 & 8 \\ -3 & -1 & 8 \end{bmatrix}$ **3.** $\begin{bmatrix} -3 & 4 \\ -5 & 11 \end{bmatrix}$ **4.** $\begin{bmatrix} 6 & 10 \\ 13 & -4 \end{bmatrix}$
5. Yes; the elements in each of the corresponding positions are equal.
6. The elements were not subtracted. The correct answer is $\begin{bmatrix} 6 \\ 5 \end{bmatrix} - \begin{bmatrix} 3 \\ 7 \end{bmatrix} = \begin{bmatrix} 3 \\ -2 \end{bmatrix}$
Exercises
7. $\begin{bmatrix} 6 & 5 & 4 \\ 2 & -1 & 7 \end{bmatrix}$ **9.** $\begin{bmatrix} 3.9 & -2.3 \\ -0.6 & 9.1 \end{bmatrix}$ **11.** $\begin{bmatrix} 4 & -8 \\ -1 & -1 \\ 11 & 1 \end{bmatrix}$

13. $\begin{bmatrix} 6 & 2 \\ -1 & 3 \end{bmatrix}$ **15.** $\begin{bmatrix} 2 & -3 & 4 \\ 5 & 6 & -7 \end{bmatrix}$
17. $x = -2$, $y = 3$, $z = 1$ **19.** $\begin{bmatrix} 0 & 5 \\ 8 & -6 \\ 0 & 5 \end{bmatrix}$ **21.** $\begin{bmatrix} 6 & 3 \\ -3 & 3 \end{bmatrix}$
23. $\begin{bmatrix} -4 & 1 \\ -3 & -1 \end{bmatrix}$ **25a.** $\begin{bmatrix} 952 \\ 720 \\ 1108 \\ 1172 \\ 1044 \end{bmatrix}$; $\begin{bmatrix} 760 \\ 832 \\ 1252 \\ 1144 \\ 1064 \end{bmatrix}$
b. Allen: 4996; Iagorashvili: 5052
27. Matrix B would have the same dimensions as A. Its elements would be the opposites of the corresponding elements in A.
29. $c = \frac{5}{2}$, $d = \frac{2}{5}$, $f = 7$, $g = 5$, $h = -1$
31. Consider any two 2×2 matrices, $A = \begin{bmatrix} a & b \\ c & d \end{bmatrix}$ and $B = \begin{bmatrix} w & x \\ y & z \end{bmatrix}$. By the definition of matrix addition and the Comm. Prop. of Add.

$$A + B = \begin{bmatrix} a & b \\ c & d \end{bmatrix} + \begin{bmatrix} w & x \\ y & z \end{bmatrix} = \begin{bmatrix} a+w & b+x \\ c+y & d+z \end{bmatrix}$$
$$= \begin{bmatrix} w+a & x+b \\ y+c & z+d \end{bmatrix} = \begin{bmatrix} w & x \\ y & z \end{bmatrix} + \begin{bmatrix} a & b \\ c & d \end{bmatrix}$$
$$= B + A$$

33. B **35.** B **37.** 68% **38.** 97.5% **39.** 47.5%
40. 2, −6 **41.** $\frac{2}{3}$, 2 **42.** $-\frac{1}{2}$, −6 **43.** 5, 0
44. $\begin{bmatrix} 9 & 15 \\ 6 & 24 \end{bmatrix}$ **45.** $\begin{bmatrix} -20 \\ 35 \end{bmatrix}$

Lesson 12-2 pp. 772–779

Got It?
1. $\begin{bmatrix} 8 & 24 & -19 \\ -3 & 9 & 10 \end{bmatrix}$ **2.** $\begin{bmatrix} 5 & -1 \\ \frac{7}{3} & 0 \end{bmatrix}$ **3a.** $\begin{bmatrix} -6 & 0 \\ -9 & 11 \end{bmatrix}$
b. $\begin{bmatrix} -3 & 7 \\ 6 & 8 \end{bmatrix}$ **c.** No; explanations may vary. Sample: For the matrices in parts (a) and (b), $AB = \begin{bmatrix} -6 & 0 \\ -9 & 11 \end{bmatrix}$ and $BA = \begin{bmatrix} -3 & 7 \\ 6 & 8 \end{bmatrix}$, so $AB \neq BA$. **4.** player from 1994: 100 pts., player from 2006: 81 pts. **5a.** no **b.** yes **c.** yes **d.** no **e.** yes
Lesson Check
1. $\begin{bmatrix} 6 & -2 \\ 4 & 0 \end{bmatrix}$ **2.** $\begin{bmatrix} -3 & 11 \\ -10 & 6 \end{bmatrix}$ **3.** $\begin{bmatrix} 5 & 7 \\ 2 & 6 \end{bmatrix}$ **4.** $\begin{bmatrix} 9 & -1 \\ -2 & 2 \end{bmatrix}$
5. Scalar; repeated matrix addition is repeated addition of each element of the matrix, which is the same as scalar multiplication of the matrix. **6.** The product of two matrices A and B exists only if the number of columns of A is equal to the number of rows of B. Since A is a 2×4 matrix with 4 columns and B is a 3×6 matrix with 3 rows and $4 \neq 3$, the product AB does not exist. Likewise, since $6 \neq 2$, the product BA does not exist.
Exercises
7. $\begin{bmatrix} 9 & 12 \\ 18 & -6 \\ 3 & 0 \end{bmatrix}$ **9.** $\begin{bmatrix} -3 & -6 \\ 9 & -3 \end{bmatrix}$ **11.** $\begin{bmatrix} 9 & 2 \\ 2 & 6 \\ 3 & -10 \end{bmatrix}$
13. $\begin{bmatrix} 19 & 11 \\ -12 & 10 \end{bmatrix}$ **15.** $\begin{bmatrix} 8 & -2.5 \\ -1.5 & -1 \end{bmatrix}$ **17.** $\begin{bmatrix} -4 & 8 \\ -22 & 2 \end{bmatrix}$
19. $\begin{bmatrix} 5 & -12 \\ 9 & -6 \end{bmatrix}$ **21.** $\begin{bmatrix} -8 & 0 \\ 0 & -8 \end{bmatrix}$ **23.** $\begin{bmatrix} 34 & 0 \end{bmatrix}$
25. $\begin{bmatrix} -15 & 0 \\ 25 & 0 \end{bmatrix}$ **27.** $\begin{bmatrix} -2 \\ 5 \end{bmatrix}$ **29.** yes **31.** yes **33.** yes
35a. River's Edge: 99 pts.; West River: 97 pts. **b.** West River
37. $\begin{bmatrix} 9 & -6 \\ 15 & -3 \\ -6 & -12 \end{bmatrix}$ **39.** $\begin{bmatrix} 17 & -24 \\ -33 & -7 \\ 69 & -18 \end{bmatrix}$ **41.** $\begin{bmatrix} 34 & -1 \\ 6 & -13 \\ -7 & 16 \end{bmatrix}$
43. $\begin{bmatrix} -90 & 0 \\ -78 & 42 \\ -30 & -30 \end{bmatrix}$ **45.** yes **47.** yes

Lesson 12-3 pp. 782–790

Got It? 1a. yes **b.** yes **c.** No; no matrix that is multiplied by the zero matrix will give an identity matrix.
2a. 3 **b.** 0 **c.** −48 **3a.** 12 units² **b.** 28 units²
4a. yes; $\begin{bmatrix} 1 & -1 \\ -\frac{3}{2} & 2 \end{bmatrix}$ **b.** no **c.** yes; $\begin{bmatrix} 3 & -4 \\ -5 & 7 \end{bmatrix}$
5a. 88, 68, 84, 60, 12, 32, 52, 72, 28, 30, 14, 18, 2, 8, 14, 20 **b.** Multiply the coded information by the inverse of the coding matrix: $\begin{bmatrix} 4 & 1 & 7 & 3 & 1 & 2 & 3 & 4 \\ 9 & 8 & 7 & 6 & 1 & 3 & 5 & 7 \end{bmatrix}$
Lesson Check 1. 16 **2.** 7 **3.** does not exist
4. yes; $\begin{bmatrix} 3 & -2 \\ -7 & 5 \end{bmatrix}$
5. The student did not subtract correctly.
$$\det\begin{bmatrix} 2 & 5 \\ -3 & 1 \end{bmatrix} = (2)(1) - (-3)(5) = 2 - (-15)$$
$$= 2 + 15 = 17$$
6. A 2×3 matrix does not have a multiplicative inverse because it is not a square matrix. The number of rows must equal the number of columns for a multiplicative inverse to be possible.
Exercises 7. yes **9.** yes **11.** no **13.** 0 **15.** $-\frac{11}{40}$
17. 11 **19.** −6 **21.** −5 **23.** 106 **25.** 6 **27.** 466,250 mi²
29. yes; $\begin{bmatrix} -1 & 3 \\ 1 & -2 \end{bmatrix}$ **31.** yes; $\begin{bmatrix} 0 & \frac{1}{2} \\ \frac{1}{3} & -\frac{1}{6} \end{bmatrix}$

Selected Answers

33. yes; $\begin{bmatrix} -\frac{1}{8} & -\frac{1}{2} \\ \frac{3}{16} & \frac{1}{4} \end{bmatrix}$ 35. yes; $\begin{bmatrix} 0 & \frac{1}{3} \\ -\frac{1}{2} & \frac{1}{6} \end{bmatrix}$
37. 2, 10, 10, 6, 9, 55, 15, 15, 9, 20 **39.** −120 **41.** 9 **43.** −3 **45.** 1 **47.** Answers may vary. Sample: Form a new matrix by switching the element in row 1, column 1 with the element in row 2, column 2. Then replace the other two elements with their opposites. Finally, divide each element by the determinant of the original matrix. **49.** 38 units^2
51. yes; $\begin{bmatrix} -5 & 7 \\ 3 & -4 \end{bmatrix}$ **53.** yes; $\begin{bmatrix} 0.5 & 0 \\ 0 & 0.5 \end{bmatrix}$
55. yes; $\begin{bmatrix} 0.4 & 0.4 & 0.2 \\ -0.6 & -0.6 & 0.2 \\ -0.2 & 0.8 & 0.4 \end{bmatrix}$
57. no inverse because the determinant equals zero
59. 6 **61.** $MN = \begin{bmatrix} ae+bg & af+bh \\ ce+dg & cf+dh \end{bmatrix}$
$\det MN = (ae+bg)(cf+dh) - (af+bh)(ce+dg)$
$= acef + adeh + bcfg + bdgh$
$- acef - adfg - bceh - bdgh$
$= adeh + bcfg - adfg - bceh$
Also, $\det M \cdot \det N = (ad - bc)(eh - fg)$
$= adeh - adfg - bceh + bcfg$.
So, $\det M \cdot \det N = \det MN$
63. $\frac{1}{2}$ **65.** 15 **67.** $\begin{bmatrix} 2 & 5 \\ 1 & 1 \end{bmatrix}$ **68.** $\begin{bmatrix} -10 & 19 \\ -20 & 7 \end{bmatrix}$ **69.** 720
70. 362,880 **71.** $1.08972864 \times 10^{10}$ **72.** 110,880
73. no solution **74.** (6, 0, −3) **75.** (3, −3, 9)
76. (−2, −1, −3)

Lesson 12-4 pp. 792–800

Got It?
1a. $\begin{bmatrix} -8 \\ 9 \end{bmatrix}$ **b.** $\begin{bmatrix} -14 & -20 \\ 19 & 28 \end{bmatrix}$
c. Since matrix A has no inverse, the eq. has no solution.
2a. $\begin{bmatrix} 3 & -7 \\ 5 & 1 \end{bmatrix}\begin{bmatrix} x \\ y \end{bmatrix} = \begin{bmatrix} 8 \\ -2 \end{bmatrix}$
b. $\begin{bmatrix} 1 & 3 & 5 \\ -2 & 1 & -4 \\ 7 & -2 & 0 \end{bmatrix}\begin{bmatrix} x \\ y \\ z \end{bmatrix} = \begin{bmatrix} 12 \\ -2 \\ 7 \end{bmatrix}$
c. $\begin{bmatrix} 2 & -8 \\ -1 & 1 \end{bmatrix}\begin{bmatrix} x \\ y \end{bmatrix} = \begin{bmatrix} -3 \\ -4 \end{bmatrix}$
3a. (5, −21) **b.** no solution **4.** run: 32 min; jog: 8 min
Lesson Check
1. $\begin{bmatrix} -6 & 3 \\ 4 & -2 \end{bmatrix}\begin{bmatrix} x \\ y \end{bmatrix} = \begin{bmatrix} 8 \\ 10 \end{bmatrix}$ **2.** $\begin{bmatrix} 2 & 3 & 0 \\ 1 & -2 & 1 \\ 0 & 6 & -4 \end{bmatrix}\begin{bmatrix} x \\ y \\ z \end{bmatrix} = \begin{bmatrix} 12 \\ 9 \\ 8 \end{bmatrix}$
3. (5, 3) **4.** (−6, −6) **5.** The student did not separate the coefficient matrix and the variable matrix. The matrix eq. should be written as $\begin{bmatrix} 2 & 3 \\ -4 & 5 \end{bmatrix}\begin{bmatrix} x \\ y \end{bmatrix} = \begin{bmatrix} 5 \\ 1 \end{bmatrix}$.
6. Use matrix multiplication to combine the coefficient matrix and the variable matrix into a product matrix. Then set the first element in the product matrix equal to the first element in the constant matrix and set the second element in the product matrix equal to the second element in the constant matrix. The result will be a system of equations.;
$-2p + 3q = 2$
$4p + q = -5$
Exercises
7. $\begin{bmatrix} -15 & -17 \\ 26 & 29 \end{bmatrix}$ **9.** $\begin{bmatrix} \frac{29}{31} \\ -\frac{66}{217} \\ \frac{34}{217} \end{bmatrix}$ **11.** $\begin{bmatrix} 1 & 1 \\ 1 & -2 \end{bmatrix}\begin{bmatrix} x \\ y \end{bmatrix} = \begin{bmatrix} 5 \\ -4 \end{bmatrix}$;
coefficient matrix: $\begin{bmatrix} 1 & 1 \\ 1 & -2 \end{bmatrix}$, variable matrix: $\begin{bmatrix} x \\ y \end{bmatrix}$,
constant matrix: $\begin{bmatrix} 5 \\ -4 \end{bmatrix}$ **13.** $\begin{bmatrix} 3 & 5 \\ 1 & 1 \end{bmatrix}\begin{bmatrix} a \\ b \end{bmatrix} = \begin{bmatrix} 0 \\ 2 \end{bmatrix}$; coefficient matrix: $\begin{bmatrix} 3 & 5 \\ 1 & 1 \end{bmatrix}$, variable matrix: $\begin{bmatrix} a \\ b \end{bmatrix}$, constant matrix: $\begin{bmatrix} 0 \\ 2 \end{bmatrix}$
15. $\begin{bmatrix} 1 & -1 & 1 \\ 2 & 0 & 1 \\ 0 & 1 & 3 \end{bmatrix}\begin{bmatrix} r \\ s \\ t \end{bmatrix} = \begin{bmatrix} 150 \\ 425 \\ 0 \end{bmatrix}$; coefficient matrix: $\begin{bmatrix} 1 & -1 & 1 \\ 2 & 0 & 1 \\ 0 & 1 & 3 \end{bmatrix}$, variable matrix: $\begin{bmatrix} r \\ s \\ t \end{bmatrix}$,
constant matrix: $\begin{bmatrix} 150 \\ 425 \\ 0 \end{bmatrix}$
17. (2, 1) **19.** $\left(\frac{1}{2}, 20\right)$ **21.** (3, 2) **23.** (2, −1, 3)
25. (1, 2, −2) **27.** 2.5 lb of almonds, 3.5 lb of peanuts, and 3 lb of raisins **29.** (−2, −1) **31.** (−1, 0) **33.** (5, 0, 1) **35.** (1, 0, 3) **37.** (1, 1, 1, 1) **39.** (6, 2) **41.** (16, −22) **43.** (5.4, 7.4) **45.** (6, 1) **47.** (2, −1, 4) **49.** length = 280 ft, width = 140 ft **51.** $\begin{bmatrix} -3 & 2 \\ -5 & 8 \end{bmatrix}$ **53.** $\begin{bmatrix} 10 \\ 3 \\ -2 \end{bmatrix}$ **55.** 14
57. Answers may vary. Sample: $y + z = 0$; $y + z = 1$
59. B **61.** A

Lesson 12-5 pp. 801–808

Got It? 1a. Subtract 8 from each x-coordinate and add 5 to each y-coordinate.
b. $\begin{bmatrix} 0 & -1 & -5 & 1 & 4 \\ -5 & -1 & 0 & 3 & 0 \end{bmatrix} + \begin{bmatrix} -3 & -3 & -3 & -3 & -3 \\ 2 & 2 & 2 & 2 & 2 \end{bmatrix}$
$= \begin{bmatrix} -3 & -4 & -8 & -2 & 1 \\ -3 & 1 & 2 & 5 & 2 \end{bmatrix}$; (−3, −3), (−4, 1), (−8, 2),

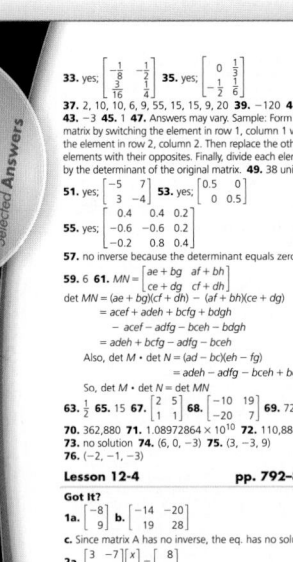

(−2, 5), (1, 2)
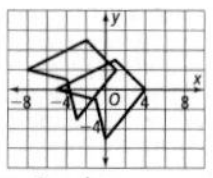

2. Answers may vary. Samples:
a. $\begin{bmatrix} 0 & 5 & 5 & 0 \\ 0 & 0 & 3 & 3 \end{bmatrix}$
b. $2\begin{bmatrix} 0 & 5 & 5 & 0 \\ 0 & 0 & 3 & 3 \end{bmatrix} = \begin{bmatrix} 0 & 10 & 10 & 0 \\ 0 & 0 & 6 & 6 \end{bmatrix}$;
(0, 0), (10, 0), (10, 6), (0, 6)
c. 4
3a. (0, 3), (4, 4), (1, −1);
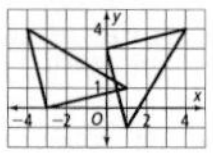

b. (−3, 0), (−4, 4), (1, 1);
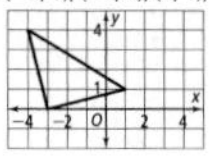

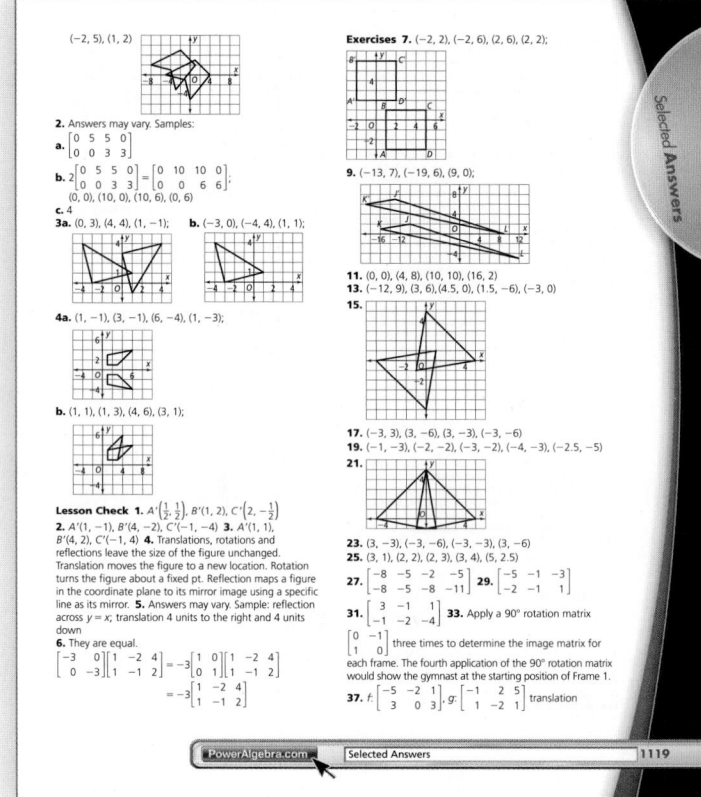

4a. (1, −1), (3, −1), (6, −4), (1, −3);
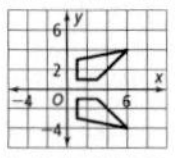

b. (1, 1), (1, 3), (4, 6), (3, 1);
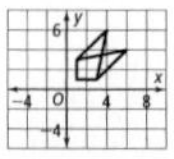

Lesson Check 1. $A'\left(\frac{1}{2}, \frac{1}{2}\right)$, $B'(1, 2)$, $C'\left(2, -\frac{1}{2}\right)$
2. $A'(1, -1)$, $B'(4, -2)$, $C'(-1, -4)$ **3.** $A'(1, 1)$, $B'(4, 2)$, $C'(-1, 4)$ **4.** Translations, rotations and reflections leave the size of the figure unchanged. Translation moves the figure to a new location. Rotation turns the figure about a fixed pt. Reflection maps a figure in the coordinate plane to its mirror image using a specific line as its mirror. **5.** Answers may vary. Sample: reflection across $y = x$; translation 4 units to the right and 4 units down
6. They are equal.
$\begin{bmatrix} -3 & 0 \\ 0 & -3 \end{bmatrix}\begin{bmatrix} 1 & -2 & 4 \\ 1 & -1 & 2 \end{bmatrix} = -3\begin{bmatrix} 1 & 0 \\ 0 & 1 \end{bmatrix}\begin{bmatrix} 1 & -2 & 4 \\ 1 & -1 & 2 \end{bmatrix}$
$= -3\begin{bmatrix} 1 & -2 & 4 \\ 1 & -1 & 2 \end{bmatrix}$

Exercises 7. (−2, 2), (−2, 6), (2, 6), (2, 2);
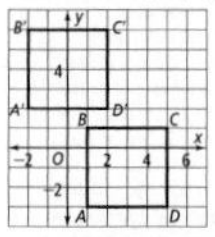

9. (−13, 7), (−19, 6), (9, 0);
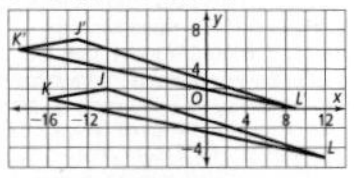

11. (0, 0), (4, 8), (10, 10), (16, 2)
13. (−12, 9), (3, 6),(4.5, 0), (1.5, −6), (−3, 0)
15.
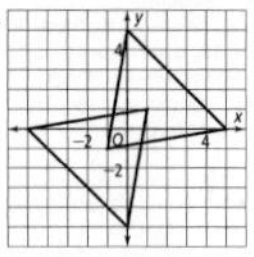

17. (−3, 3), (3, −6), (3, −3), (−3, −6)
19. (−1, −3), (−2, −2), (−3, −2), (−4, −3), (−2.5, −5)
21.
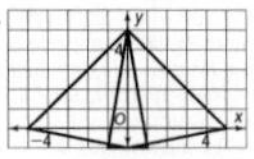

23. (3, −3), (−3, −6), (−3, −3), (3, −6)
25. (3, 1), (2, 2), (2, 3), (3, 4), (5, 2.5)
27. $\begin{bmatrix} -8 & -5 & -2 & -5 \\ -8 & -5 & -8 & -11 \end{bmatrix}$ **29.** $\begin{bmatrix} -5 & -1 & -3 \\ -2 & -1 & 1 \end{bmatrix}$
31. $\begin{bmatrix} 3 & -1 & 1 \\ -1 & -2 & -4 \end{bmatrix}$ **33.** Apply a 90° rotation matrix $\begin{bmatrix} 0 & -1 \\ 1 & 0 \end{bmatrix}$ three times to determine the image matrix for each frame. The fourth application of the 90° rotation matrix would show the gymnast at the starting position of Frame 1.
37. f: $\begin{bmatrix} -5 & -2 & 1 \\ 3 & 0 & 3 \end{bmatrix}$, g: $\begin{bmatrix} -1 & 2 & 5 \\ 1 & -2 & 1 \end{bmatrix}$ translation

39. $\begin{bmatrix} -1.5 & 0.25 & -2.5 \\ 0 & 1.5 & 1.5 \end{bmatrix}$
41. Answers may vary. Sample: The reflection of a matrix of pts. from a function table across the line $y = x$ interchanges the values of y and x in the function table. Finding the inverse of the matrix of pts. of a function from a function table also results in the interchanging of the values of y and x.
43. H **45.** G **47.** (3, −2) **48.** (1, −1, 2) **49.** (0, 1, −2)
50. $\begin{bmatrix} 16 \\ 12 \end{bmatrix}$ **51.** [12] **52.** [22]

Lesson 12-6 pp. 809–815

Got It? 1. $\mathbf{u} = \langle 3, 4 \rangle$; $\mathbf{v} = \langle -1, -6 \rangle$ **2a.** ⟨5, 3⟩
b. translation, reflection and dilation **3.** $\sqrt{74} \approx 8.60$
4a.
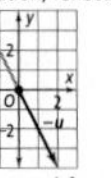

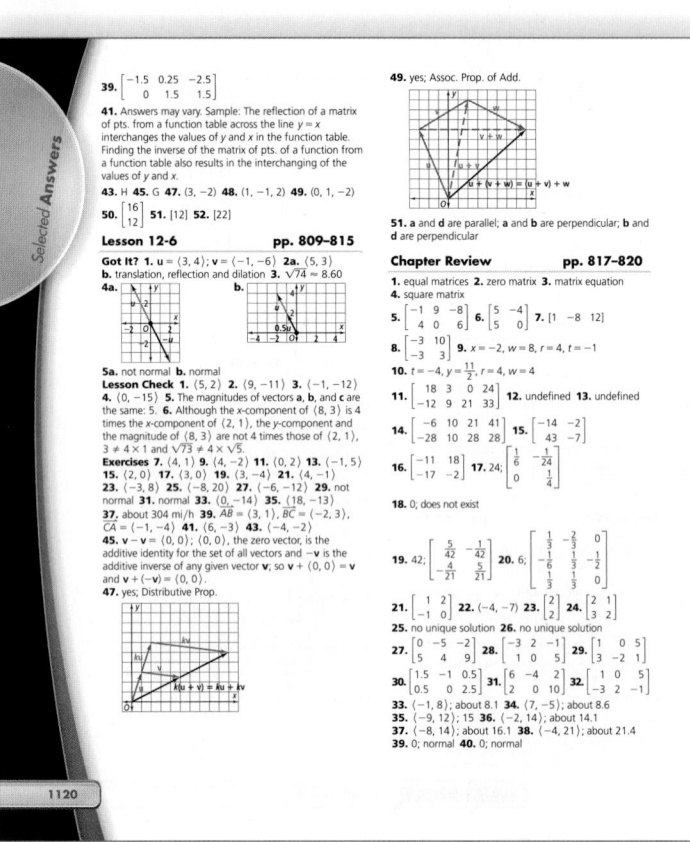

b.
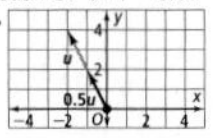

5a. not normal **b.** normal
Lesson Check 1. ⟨5, 2⟩ **2.** ⟨9, −11⟩ **3.** ⟨−1, −12⟩ **4.** ⟨0, −15⟩ **5.** The magnitudes of vectors **a**, **b**, and **c** are the same: 5. **6.** Although the x-component of ⟨8, 3⟩ is 4 times the x-component of ⟨2, 1⟩, the y-component and the magnitude of ⟨8, 3⟩ are not 4 times those of ⟨2, 1⟩, $3 \neq 4 \times 1$ and $\sqrt{73} \neq 4 \times \sqrt{5}$.
Exercises 7. ⟨4, 1⟩ **9.** ⟨4, −2⟩ **11.** ⟨0, 2⟩ **13.** ⟨−1, 5⟩ **15.** ⟨2, 0⟩ **17.** ⟨3, 0⟩ **19.** ⟨3, −4⟩ **21.** ⟨4, −1⟩ **23.** ⟨−3, 8⟩ **25.** ⟨−8, 20⟩ **27.** ⟨−6, −12⟩ **29.** not normal **31.** normal **33.** ⟨0, −14⟩ **35.** ⟨18, −13⟩ **37.** about 304 mi/h **39.** $\overrightarrow{AB} = \langle 3, 1 \rangle$, $\overrightarrow{BC} = \langle -2, 3 \rangle$, $\overrightarrow{CA} = \langle -1, -4 \rangle$ **41.** ⟨6, −3⟩ **43.** ⟨−4, −2⟩
45. $\mathbf{v} - \mathbf{v} = \langle 0, 0 \rangle$; ⟨0, 0⟩, the zero vector, is the additive identity for the set of all vectors and −**v** is the additive inverse of any given vector **v**; so $\mathbf{v} + \langle 0, 0 \rangle = \mathbf{v}$ and $\mathbf{v} + (-\mathbf{v}) = \langle 0, 0 \rangle$.
47. yes; Distributive Prop.
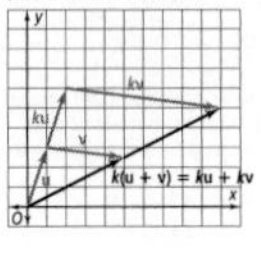

49. yes; Assoc. Prop. of Add.
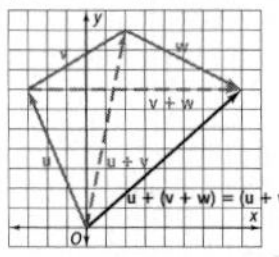

51. **a** and **d** are parallel; **a** and **b** are perpendicular; **b** and **d** are perpendicular

Chapter Review pp. 817–820

1. equal matrices **2.** zero matrix **3.** matrix equation **4.** square matrix
5. $\begin{bmatrix} -1 & 9 & -8 \\ 4 & 0 & 6 \end{bmatrix}$ **6.** $\begin{bmatrix} 5 & -4 \\ 5 & 0 \end{bmatrix}$ **7.** $\begin{bmatrix} 1 & -8 & 12 \end{bmatrix}$
8. $\begin{bmatrix} -3 & 10 \\ -3 & 3 \end{bmatrix}$ **9.** $x = -2, w = 8, r = 4, t = -1$
10. $t = -4, y = \frac{11}{2}, r = 4, w = 4$
11. $\begin{bmatrix} 18 & 3 & 0 & 24 \\ -12 & 9 & 21 & 33 \end{bmatrix}$ **12.** undefined **13.** undefined
14. $\begin{bmatrix} -6 & 10 & 21 & 41 \\ -28 & 10 & 28 & 28 \end{bmatrix}$ **15.** $\begin{bmatrix} -14 & -2 \\ 43 & -7 \end{bmatrix}$
16. $\begin{bmatrix} -11 & 18 \\ -17 & -2 \end{bmatrix}$ **17.** 24; $\begin{bmatrix} \frac{1}{6} & -\frac{1}{24} \\ 0 & \frac{1}{4} \end{bmatrix}$
18. 0; does not exist
19. 42; $\begin{bmatrix} \frac{5}{42} & -\frac{1}{42} \\ -\frac{4}{21} & \frac{5}{21} \end{bmatrix}$ **20.** 6; $\begin{bmatrix} \frac{1}{3} & -\frac{2}{3} & 0 \\ -\frac{1}{6} & \frac{1}{3} & -\frac{1}{2} \\ \frac{1}{3} & \frac{1}{3} & 0 \end{bmatrix}$
21. $\begin{bmatrix} 1 & 2 \\ -1 & 0 \end{bmatrix}$ **22.** (−4, −7) **23.** $\begin{bmatrix} 2 \\ 2 \end{bmatrix}$ **24.** $\begin{bmatrix} 2 & 1 \\ 3 & 2 \end{bmatrix}$
25. no unique solution **26.** no unique solution
27. $\begin{bmatrix} 0 & -5 & -2 \\ 5 & 4 & 9 \end{bmatrix}$ **28.** $\begin{bmatrix} -3 & 2 & -1 \\ 1 & 0 & 5 \end{bmatrix}$ **29.** $\begin{bmatrix} 1 & 0 & 5 \\ 3 & -2 & 1 \end{bmatrix}$
30. $\begin{bmatrix} 1.5 & -1 & 0.5 \\ 0.5 & 0 & 2.5 \end{bmatrix}$ **31.** $\begin{bmatrix} 6 & -4 & 2 \\ 2 & 0 & 10 \end{bmatrix}$ **32.** $\begin{bmatrix} 1 & 0 & 5 \\ -3 & 2 & -1 \end{bmatrix}$
33. ⟨−1, 8⟩; about 8.1 **34.** ⟨7, −5⟩; about 8.6
35. ⟨−9, 12⟩; 15 **36.** ⟨−2, 14⟩; about 14.1
37. ⟨−8, 14⟩; about 16.1 **38.** ⟨−4, 21⟩; about 21.4
39. 0; normal **40.** 0; normal

Chapter 13

Get Ready! p. 825

1. vert. asymptote: $x = 3$ **2.** vert. asymptotes: $x = -\frac{1}{2}$ and $x = 4$ **3.** $\frac{2b}{a}$ **4.** $\frac{55}{18}$ **5.** $\frac{3}{2(c+d)}$ **6.** $\frac{c}{16}$
7. $\frac{c+4}{9}$ **8.** $\frac{16}{x}$ **9.** $\frac{15}{7}$ **10.** 6 **11.** 4, 1; $a_n = 19 - 3n$, explicit or $a_1 = 16$, $a_n = a_{n-1} - 3$, recursive
12. −216, −343; $a_n = -n^3$, explicit
13. $(x-1)^2 + (y+4)^2 = 16$;
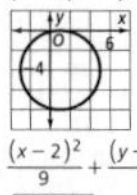

14. $\frac{(x-2)^2}{9} + \frac{(y-5)^2}{4} = 1$;
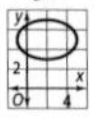

15. $y = \frac{1}{32}x^2 - 3$;
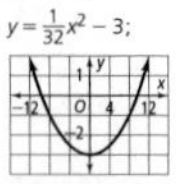

16. $\frac{(y-1)^2}{9} - \frac{(x-6)^2}{16} = 1$;
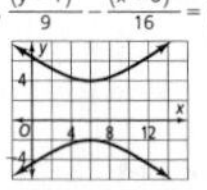

17. Answers may vary. Sample: Similar data tends to recur after a certain period has lapsed. In this case, 12 months.

Lesson 13-1 pp. 828–834

Got It? 1a. from $x = -3$ to $x = 1$ or from $x = 0$ to $x = 4$; 4 **b.** from $x = -4$ to $x = -1$ or from $x = 0$ to $x = 3$; 3 **2a.** no **b.** yes; 4 **c.** 15 cycles; $\frac{1}{3}$ s; $\frac{1}{440}$ s **3a.** 1.5; $y = -0.5$ **b.** 1.5; $y = 0.5$
4. period: 0.006; amplitude: 0.25; $y = -0.75$
Lesson Check 1. periodic; 5 **2.** no **3.** Answers may vary. Sample: hands of a clock, phases of the moon
4. The amplitude is not 2, but $\frac{2}{2} = 1$. **5.** $f(6) = f(11) = 2$; for any x, $f(x + 5)$ will always equal $f(x)$ because the period is 5. **6.** −4
Exercises 7. $x = -2$ to $x = 3$, $x = 2$ to $x = 7$; 5
9. $x = 0$ to $x = 4$, $x = 2$ to $x = 6$; 4 **11.** periodic; 12
13. not periodic **15.** periodic; 7 **17.** 3; $y = -1$
19.
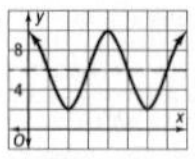

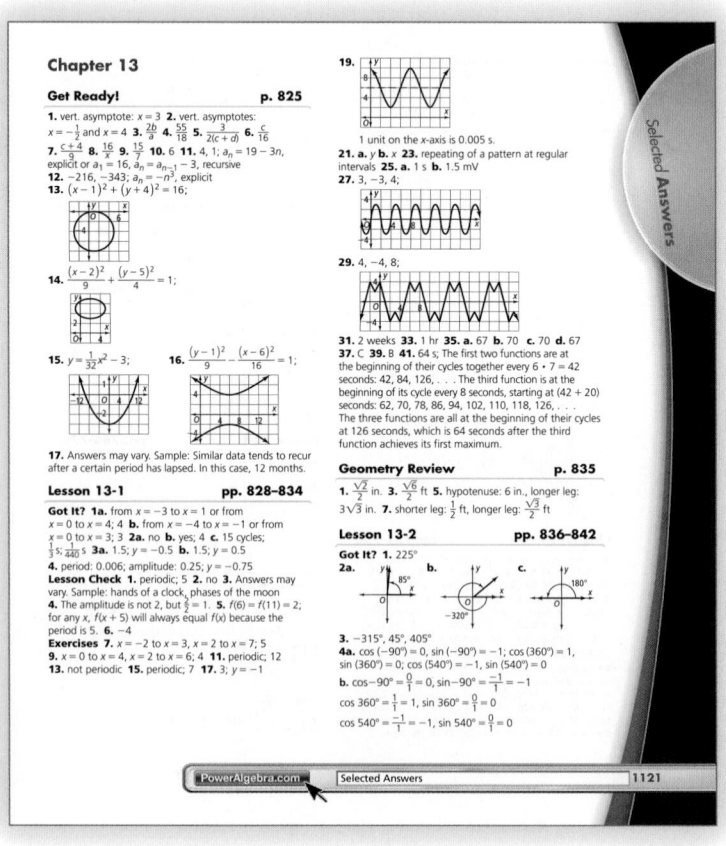

1 unit on the x-axis is 0.005 s.
21. a. y **b.** x **23.** repeating of a pattern at regular intervals **25. a.** 1 s **b.** 1.5 mV
27. 3, −3, 4;
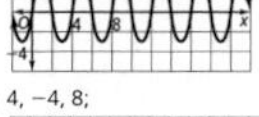

29. 4, −4, 8;
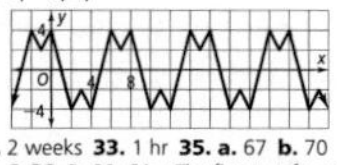

31. 2 weeks **33.** 1 hr **35. a.** 67 **b.** 70 **c.** 70 **d.** 67
37. C **39.** B **41.** 64 s; The first two functions are at the beginning of their cycles together every $6 \cdot 7 = 42$ seconds: 42, 84, 126, . . . The third function is at the beginning of its cycle every 8 seconds, starting at (42 + 20) seconds: 62, 70, 78, 86, 94, 102, 110, 118, 126, . . . The three functions are all at the beginning of their cycles at 126 seconds, which is 64 seconds after the third function achieves its first maximum.

Geometry Review p. 835

1. $\frac{\sqrt{2}}{2}$ in. **3.** $\frac{\sqrt{6}}{2}$ ft **5.** hypotenuse: 6 in., longer leg: $3\sqrt{3}$ in. **7.** shorter leg: $\frac{1}{2}$ ft, longer leg: $\frac{\sqrt{3}}{2}$ ft

Lesson 13-2 pp. 836–842

Got It? 1. 225°
2a.
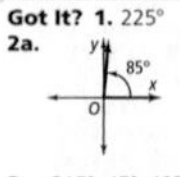

b.
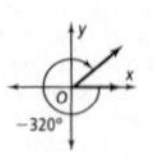

c.
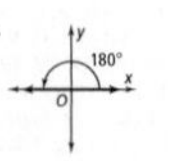

3. −315°, 45°, 405°
4a. $\cos(-90°) = 0$, $\sin(-90°) = -1$; $\cos(360°) = 1$, $\sin(360°) = 0$; $\cos(540°) = -1$, $\sin(540°) = 0$
b. $\cos -90° = \frac{0}{1} = 0$, $\sin -90° = \frac{-1}{1} = -1$
$\cos 360° = \frac{1}{1} = 1$, $\sin 360° = \frac{0}{1} = 0$
$\cos 540° = \frac{-1}{1} = -1$, $\sin 540° = \frac{0}{1} = 0$

5a. $\frac{\sqrt{2}}{2}, -\frac{\sqrt{2}}{2}$ **b.** $-\frac{\sqrt{3}}{2}, \frac{1}{2}$ **c.** Yes; for example, when $\theta = 45°$, $\sin\theta = \cos\theta$.
Lesson Check 1. 135° **2.** 240°
3. ; −332° **4.** ; −35°

5. Answers may vary. Sample: 45° and −315° **6.** The measure of the coterminal angle is not 310°; the measure of the coterminal angle is 50° − 360° = −310°.
Exercises 7. −315° **9.** 240° **11.** −30°
13. **15.**

17.

19. 215° **21.** 4° **23.** 150°
25. 180° **27.** $-\frac{\sqrt{2}}{2}, \frac{\sqrt{2}}{2}, -0.71, 0.71$
29. $-\frac{1}{2}, \frac{\sqrt{3}}{2}, -0.50, 0.87$ **31.** $\frac{\sqrt{2}}{2}, -\frac{\sqrt{2}}{2}$,
$0.71, -0.71$ **33.** $-\frac{\sqrt{2}}{2}, \frac{\sqrt{2}}{2}, -0.71, 0.71$ **35.** 0.98,
−0.17 **37.** 0.00, 1.00 **39.** 5
41–43. Answers may vary. Samples:
41. 370°, −350° **43.** 40°, −320° **45.** II
47. negative x-axis **49.** positive x-axis
51a.

Quadrant II
$\cos\theta$ is −
$\sin\theta$ is +

Quadrant I
$\cos\theta$ is +
$\sin\theta$ is +

Quadrant III
$\cos\theta$ is −
$\sin\theta$ is −

Quadrant IV
$\cos\theta$ is +
$\sin\theta$ is −

b. II **c.** If the terminal side of an angle is in Quadrants I or II, then the sine of the angle is positive. If the terminal side of an angle is in Quadrants I or IV, then the cosine of the angle is positive.
53.
60°, 300°; $\frac{1}{2}, \frac{\sqrt{3}}{2}$

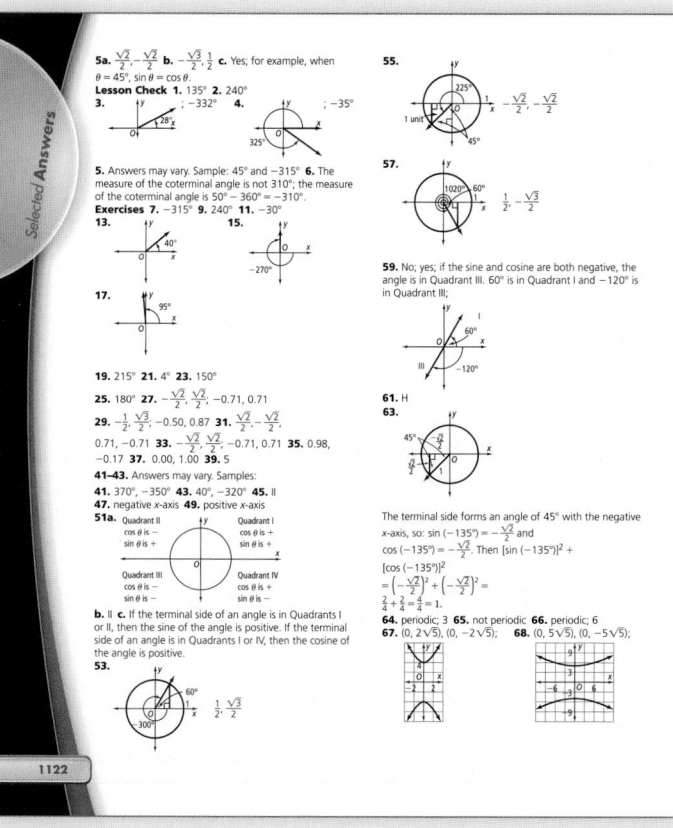

55.
225°; $-\frac{\sqrt{2}}{2}, -\frac{\sqrt{2}}{2}$
57.
1020°, 60°; $\frac{1}{2}, -\frac{\sqrt{3}}{2}$

59. No; yes; if the sine and cosine are both negative, the angle is in Quadrant III. 60° is in Quadrant I and −120° is in Quadrant III;

61. H
63.
45°

The terminal side forms an angle of 45° with the negative x-axis, so: $\sin(-135°) = -\frac{\sqrt{2}}{2}$ and $\cos(-135°) = -\frac{\sqrt{2}}{2}$. Then $[\sin(-135°)]^2 + [\cos(-135°)]^2$
$= \left(-\frac{\sqrt{2}}{2}\right)^2 + \left(-\frac{\sqrt{2}}{2}\right)^2 = \frac{2}{4} + \frac{2}{4} = \frac{4}{4} = 1$.
64. periodic; 3 **65.** not periodic **66.** periodic; 6
67. $(0, 2\sqrt{5}), (0, -2\sqrt{5})$; **68.** $(0, 5\sqrt{5}), (0, -5\sqrt{5})$;

1122

---

69. $(\sqrt{85}, 0), (-\sqrt{85}, 0)$;

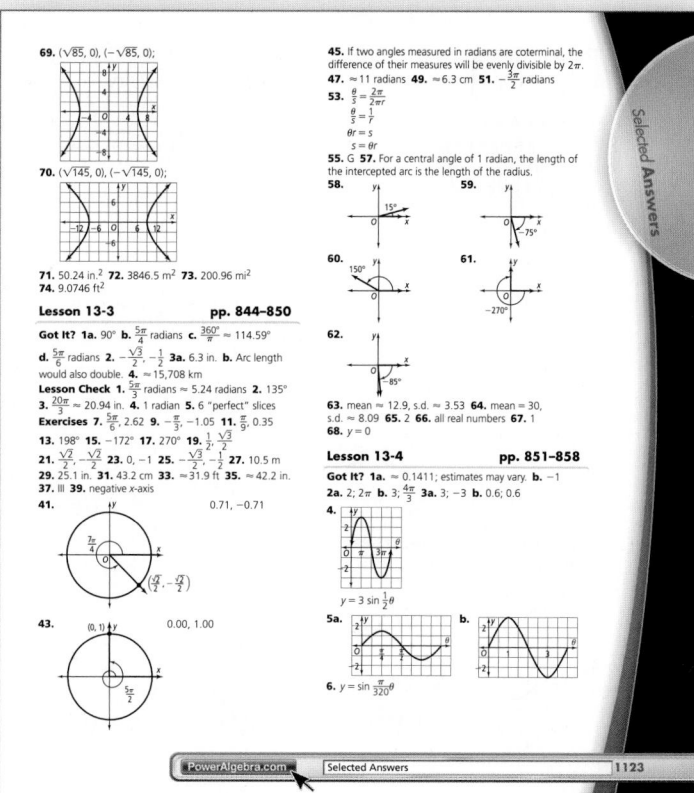

70. $(\sqrt{145}, 0), (-\sqrt{145}, 0)$;

71. 50.24 in.² **72.** 3846.5 m² **73.** 200.96 mi²
74. 9.0746 ft²

Lesson 13-3 pp. 844–850
Got It? 1a. 90° **b.** $\frac{5\pi}{9}$ radians **c.** $\frac{360°}{\pi} \approx 114.59°$
d. $\frac{5\pi}{6}$ radians **2.** $-\frac{\sqrt{3}}{2}, -\frac{1}{2}$ **3a.** 6.3 in. **b.** Arc length would also double. **4.** ≈15,708 km
Lesson Check 1. $\frac{5\pi}{6}$ radians ≈ 5.24 radians **2.** 135°
3. $\frac{20\pi}{3} \approx 20.94$ in. **4.** 1 radian **5.** 6 "perfect" slices
Exercises 7. $\frac{5\pi}{6}, 2.62$ **9.** $-\frac{\pi}{3}, -1.05$ **11.** $\frac{\pi}{9}, 0.35$
13. 198° **15.** −172° **17.** 270° **19.** $\frac{1}{2}, \frac{\sqrt{3}}{2}$
21. $\frac{\sqrt{2}}{2}, -\frac{\sqrt{2}}{2}$ **23.** 0, −1 **25.** $-\frac{\sqrt{3}}{2}, -\frac{1}{2}$ **27.** 10.5 m
29. 25.1 in. **31.** 43.2 cm **33.** ≈31.9 ft **35.** ≈ 42.2 in.
37. III **39.** negative x-axis
41.
0.71, −0.71
$\left(\frac{\sqrt{2}}{2}, -\frac{\sqrt{2}}{2}\right)$

43.
$(0, 1)$
0.00, 1.00

45. If two angles measured in radians are coterminal, the difference of their measures will be evenly divisible by 2π.
47. ≈11 radians **49.** ≈6.3 cm **51.** $-\frac{2\pi}{5}$ radians
53. $\frac{\theta}{s} = \frac{2\pi}{2\pi r}$
$\frac{\theta}{s} = \frac{1}{r}$
$\theta r = s$
$s = \theta r$
55. G **57.** For a central angle of 1 radian, the length of the intercepted arc is the length of the radius.
58. **59.**
15°
−75°

60. **61.**
150°
−270°

62.
−85°

63. mean ≈ 12.9, s.d. ≈ 3.53 **64.** mean = 30, s.d. ≈ 8.09 **65.** 2 **66.** all real numbers **67.** 1
68. $y = 0$

Lesson 13-4 pp. 851–858
Got It? 1a. ≈ 0.1411; estimates may vary. **b.** −1
2a. 2; 2π **b.** $\frac{2\pi}{3}$ **3a.** 3; −3 **b.** 0.6; 0.6
4.
$y = 3\sin\frac{1}{2}\theta$
5a. **b.**

6. $y = \sin\frac{\pi}{320}\theta$

Lesson Check 1a. 2 **b.** 3; π **c.** $y = 3\sin 2\theta$
2.

3. One cycle of a sine function is an interval on the x-axis with length equal to the period. The period is the length of one cycle. **4.** Answers may vary. Sample: $y = 5\sin\frac{\pi}{3}$
5. The amplitude is 3, and since $a < 0$, the graph is reflected across the x-axis. Also, the period is 2, not π.
Exercises 7. ≈0.1 **9.** ≈−1 **11.** ≈−0.7 **13.** $\frac{1}{2}, 1, 4\pi$
15.
$y = 2\sin 3\theta$
17.
$y = 4\sin\frac{1}{2}\theta$
19. **21.**
$y = \sin\pi\theta$
23. **25.**

27. 2π; $y = 2\sin\theta$ **29.** π; $y = \frac{5}{2}\sin 2\theta$ **31.** 1; $1, 2\pi$
33. π; $1, 2$ **35.** 1; $5, 2\pi$
37.

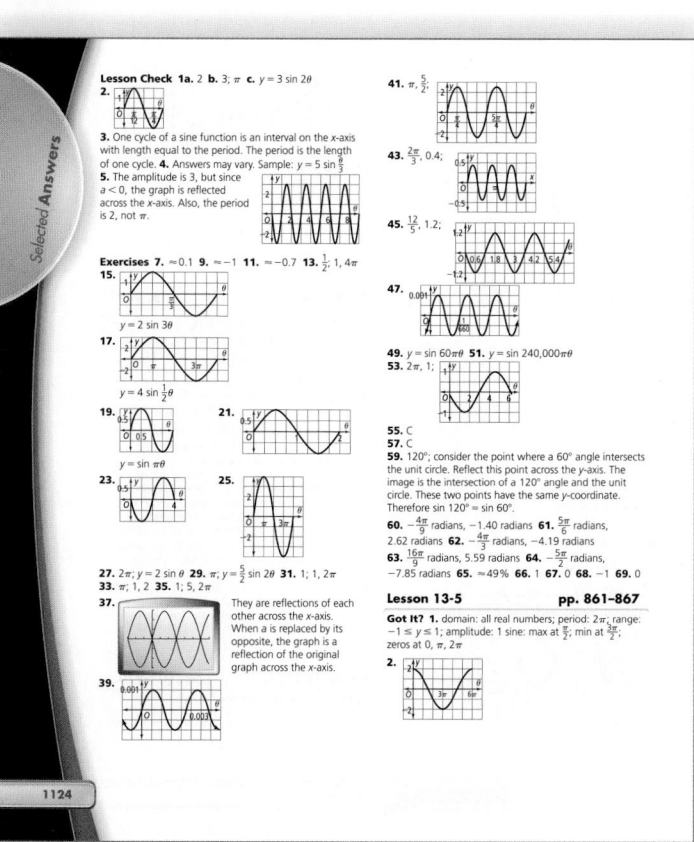

They are reflections of each other across the x-axis. When a is replaced by its opposite, the graph is a reflection of the original graph across the x-axis.
39.

41. $\pi, \frac{5}{2}$;

43. $\frac{2\pi}{3}, 0.4$;

45. $\frac{12}{5}, 1.2$;

47. 0.001;

49. $y = \sin 60\pi\theta$ **51.** $y = \sin 240,000\pi\theta$
53. 2π; 1;

55. C
57. C
59. 120°; consider the point where a 60° angle intersects the unit circle. Reflect this point across the y-axis. The image is the intersection of a 120° angle and the unit circle. These two points have the same y-coordinate. Therefore $\sin 120° = \sin 60°$.
60. $-\frac{4\pi}{9}$ radians, −1.40 radians **61.** $\frac{5\pi}{6}$ radians,
2.62 radians **62.** $-\frac{4\pi}{3}$ radians, −4.19 radians
63. $\frac{16\pi}{9}$ radians, 5.59 radians **64.** $-\frac{5\pi}{2}$ radians,
−7.85 radians **65.** ≈49% **66.** 1 **67.** 0 **68.** −1 **69.** 0

Lesson 13-5 pp. 861–867
Got It? 1. domain: all real numbers; period: 2π; range: $-1 \le y \le 1$; amplitude: 1 sine: max at $\frac{\pi}{2}$; min at $\frac{3\pi}{2}$; zeros at $0, \pi, 2\pi$
2.

1124

3a. $f(t) = -35\cos\left(\frac{4\pi}{25}t\right)$ **b.** The function would cross the midline at 3 hours, 7 minutes, 30 seconds. The midline represents average water level. **4a.** 1.15, 1.99, 4.29, 5.13 **b.** 2.21, 4.06 **c.** $0 \le \theta < 2.21$ and $4.06 < \theta \le 2\pi$; $2.21 < \theta < 4.06$
Lesson Check
1. **2.**

3. $y = 3\cos\theta$ **4.** $y = 1.5\cos 2\theta$ **5.** Answers may vary. Sample: $y = 5\cos\left(\frac{5}{2}\theta\right)$ **6a.** $0 \le \theta < \frac{\pi}{2}, \frac{3\pi}{2} < \theta \le 2\pi$
b. $\pi < \theta < 2\pi$ **c.** $y = 3\sin\left(\frac{2\pi}{3}x - \frac{\pi}{2}\right)$
Exercises 7. 2π; 3; max: 0, 2π; min: π; zeros: $\frac{\pi}{2}, \frac{3\pi}{2}$
9. π, 1; max: 0, π, 2π; min: $\frac{\pi}{2}, \frac{3\pi}{2}$; zeros: $\frac{\pi}{4}, \frac{3\pi}{4}, \frac{5\pi}{4}, \frac{7\pi}{4}$
11. **13.**

15.

17. $y = \frac{\pi}{2}\cos\frac{\pi}{2}\theta$ **19.** $y = -3\cos 2\theta$
21. 0.52, 2.62, 3.67, 5.76
23. 0.55, 1.45, 2.55, 3.45, 4.55, 5.45 **25.** 0.00
27. x, $-3 \le y \le 3$, 3 **29.** 4π, $-2 \le y \le 2$, 2
31. 6π, $-3 \le y \le 3$, 3 **33.** $\frac{4}{3}$, $-16 \le y \le 16$, 16
35. $y = 70 + 13\cos\frac{\pi}{6}(x - 1)$ where x represents the months of the year with January as 1, February as 2, March as 3, etc. **37.** 0.64, 2.50
39. 0.50, 2.50, 4.50
41a.

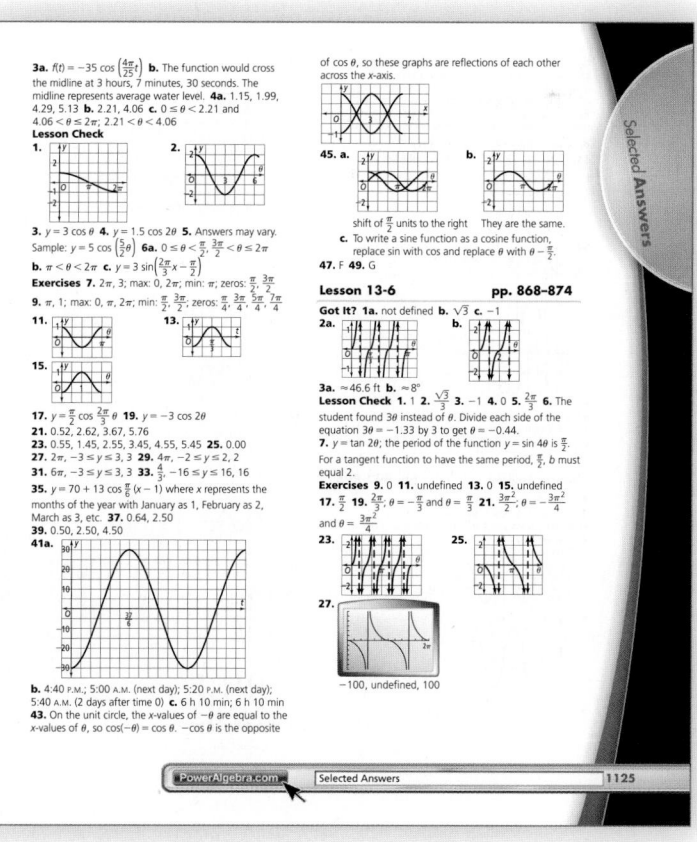

b. 4:40 P.M.; 5:00 A.M. (next day); 5:20 P.M. (next day); 5:40 A.M. (2 days after time 0) **c.** 6 h 10 min; 6 h 10 min
43. On the unit circle, the x-values of $-\theta$ are equal to the x-values of θ, so $\cos(-\theta) = \cos\theta$. $-\cos\theta$ is the opposite

of $\cos\theta$, so these graphs are reflections of each other across the x-axis.

45. a. **b.**
shift of $\frac{\pi}{2}$ units to the right   They are the same.
c. To write a sine function as a cosine function, replace sin with cos and replace θ with $\theta - \frac{\pi}{2}$.
47. F **49.** G

Lesson 13-6 pp. 868–874
Got It? 1a. not defined **b.** $\sqrt{3}$ **c.** −1
2a. **b.**

3a. ≈46.6 ft **b.** ≈ −8°
Lesson Check 1. 1 **2.** $\frac{\sqrt{3}}{3}$ **3.** −1 **4.** 0 **5.** $\frac{2\pi}{3}$ **6.** The student found 3θ instead of θ. Divide each side of the equation $3\theta = -1.33$ by 3 to get $\theta = -0.44$.
7. $y = \tan 2\theta$; the period of the function $y = \sin 4\theta$ is $\frac{\pi}{2}$. For a tangent function to have the same period, $\frac{\pi}{2}$, b must equal 2.
Exercises 9. 0 **11.** undefined **13.** 0 **15.** undefined
17. $\frac{\pi}{2}$ **19.** $\frac{2\pi}{3}$; $\theta = -\frac{\pi}{3}$ and $\theta = \frac{\pi}{3}$ **21.** $\frac{3\pi}{2}, \frac{\pi}{2}$; $\theta = -\frac{3\pi}{4}$ and $\theta = \frac{3\pi}{4}$
23. **25.**

27.
−100, undefined, 100

Page 1126

29a. 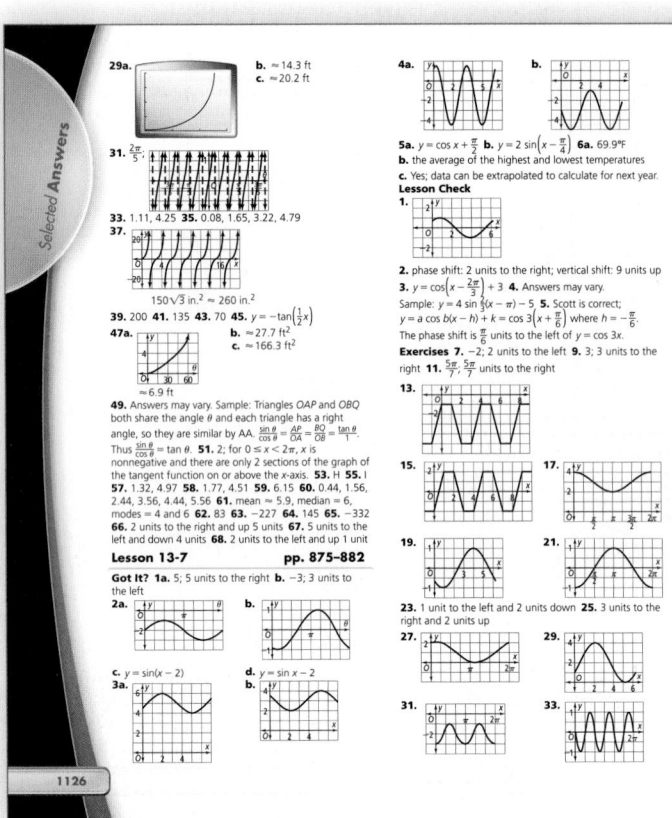 b. ≈14.3 ft c. ≈20.2 ft

31. $\frac{2\pi}{5}$;

33. 1.11, 4.25 35. 0.08, 1.65, 3.22, 4.79

37. $150\sqrt{3}$ in.² ≈ 260 in.²

39. 200 41. 135 43. 70 45. $y = -\tan\left(\frac{1}{3}x\right)$

47a. b. ≈27.7 ft² c. ≈166.3 ft² ≈6.9 ft

49. Answers may vary. Sample: Triangles OAP and OBQ both share the angle θ and each triangle has a right angle, so they are similar by AA. $\frac{\sin\theta}{\cos\theta} = \frac{AP}{OA} = \frac{BQ}{OB} = \frac{\tan\theta}{1}$. Thus $\frac{\sin\theta}{\cos\theta} = \tan\theta$. 51. 2; for $0 \le x < 2\pi$, x is nonnegative and there are only 2 sections of the graph of the tangent function on or above the x-axis. 53. H 55. I 57. 1.32, 4.97 58. 1.77, 4.51 59. 6.15 60. 0.44, 1.56, 2.44, 3.56, 4.44, 5.56 61. mean ≈ 5.9, median = 6, modes = 4 and 6 62. 83 63. −227 64. 145 65. −332 66. 2 units to the right and up 5 units 67. 5 units to the left and down 4 units 68. 2 units to the left and up 1 unit

Lesson 13-7 pp. 875–882

Got It? 1a. 5; 5 units to the right b. −3; 3 units to the left
2a. b.
c. $y = \sin(x - 2)$ d. $y = \sin x - 2$
3a. b.

4a. b.
5a. $y = \cos x + \frac{\pi}{3}$ b. $y = 2\sin\left(x - \frac{\pi}{2}\right)$ 6a. 69.9°F
b. the average of the highest and lowest temperatures
c. Yes; data can be extrapolated to calculate for next year.

Lesson Check
1.
2. phase shift: 2 units to the right; vertical shift: 9 units up
3. $y = \cos\left(x - \frac{2\pi}{3}\right) + 3$ 4. Answers may vary.
Sample: $y = 4\sin\frac{1}{2}(x - \pi) - 5$ 5. Scott is correct; $y = a\cos b(x - h) + k = \cos 3\left(x + \frac{\pi}{6}\right)$ where $h = -\frac{\pi}{6}$. The phase shift is $\frac{\pi}{6}$ units to the left of $y = \cos 3x$.

Exercises 7. −2; 2 units to the left 9. 3; 3 units to the right 11. $\frac{5\pi}{2}$; $\frac{5\pi}{2}$ units to the right
13.
15. 17.
19. 21.
23. 1 unit to the left and 2 units down 25. 3 units to the right and 2 units up
27. 29.
31. 33.

Page 1127

35.
37. 39. $y = \cos(x - 1.5)$ 41. $y = \cos(x + 3) +$ 43. $y = 1.5\cos\left[\frac{\pi}{3}(x - 6)\right] + 2$
45. $y = -10\cos\frac{\pi}{10}x$; $y = 10\sin\left(\frac{\pi}{10}x - \frac{\pi}{2}\right)$
49.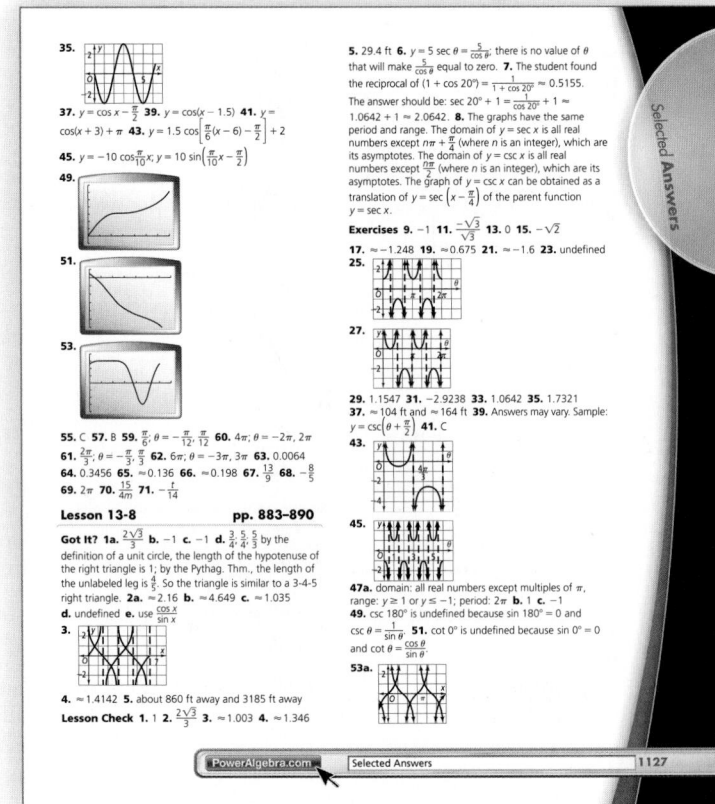
51.
53.
55. C 57. B 59. $\frac{\pi}{12}$; $\theta = -\frac{\pi}{12}, \frac{11\pi}{12}$ 60. 4π; $\theta = -2\pi, 2\pi$
61. $\frac{2\pi}{3}$; $\theta = -\frac{\pi}{3}, \frac{5\pi}{3}$ 62. 6π; $\theta = -3\pi, 3\pi$ 63. 0.0064
64. 0.3456 65. −0.136 66. −0.198 67. $\frac{13}{9}$ 68. $-\frac{\sqrt{10}}{10}$
69. 2π 70. $\frac{15}{4\pi}$ 71. $-\frac{7}{14}$

Lesson 13-8 pp. 883–890

Got It? 1a. $\frac{2\sqrt{3}}{3}$ b. −1 c. −1 d. $\frac{2}{4}, \frac{5}{4}, \frac{5}{2}$ by the definition of a unit circle, the length of the hypotenuse of the right triangle is 1; by the Pythag. Thm., the length of the unlabeled leg is $\frac{4}{5}$. So the triangle is similar to a 3-4-5 right triangle. 2a. ≈2.16 b. ≈4.649 c. ≈1.035
d. undefined e. use $\frac{\cos x}{\sin x}$
3.
4. ≈1.4142 5. about 860 ft away and 3185 ft away
Lesson Check 1. 1 2. $\frac{2\sqrt{3}}{3}$ 3. ≈1.003 4. ≈1.346

5. 29.4 ft 6. $y = 5\sec\theta = \frac{5}{\cos\theta}$; there is no value of θ that will make $\frac{5}{\cos\theta}$ equal to zero. 7. The student found the reciprocal of $(1 + \cos 20°) = \frac{1}{1 + \cos 20°} \approx 0.5155$. The answer should be: $\sec 20° + 1 = \frac{1}{\cos 20°} + 1 \approx 1.0642 + 1 \approx 2.0642$. 8. The graphs have the same period and range. The domain of $y = \sec x$ is all real numbers except $n\pi + \frac{\pi}{2}$ (where n is an integer), which are its asymptotes. The domain of $y = \csc x$ is all real numbers except $\frac{n\pi}{2}$ (where n is an integer), which are its asymptotes. The graph of $y = \csc x$ can be obtained as a translation of $y = \sec\left(x - \frac{\pi}{4}\right)$ of the parent function $y = \sec x$.
Exercises 9. −1 11. $-\frac{\sqrt{3}}{3}$ 13. 0 15. $-\sqrt{2}$
17. ≈ −1.248 19. ≈0.675 21. ≈ −1.6 23. undefined
25.
27.
29. 1.1547 31. −2.9238 33. 1.0642 35. 1.7321
37. ≈104 ft and ≈164 ft 39. Answers may vary. Sample: $y = \csc\left(\theta + \frac{\pi}{2}\right)$ 41. C
43.
45.
47a. domain: all real numbers except multiples of π, range: $y \ge 1$ or $y \le -1$; period: 2π b. 1 c. −1
49. $\csc 180°$ is undefined because $\sin 180° = 0$ and $\csc\theta = \frac{1}{\sin\theta}$. 51. $\cot 0°$ is undefined because $\sin 0° = 0$ and $\cot\theta = \frac{\cos\theta}{\sin\theta}$.
53a.

Page 1128

b. The domain of $y = \tan x$ is all real numbers except odd multiples of $\frac{\pi}{2}$, where its asymptotes occur. The domain of $y = \cot x$ is all real numbers except multiples of π, where its asymptotes occur. The range of both functions is all real numbers. c. The graphs have the same period and range. Their asymptotes are shifted $\frac{\pi}{2}$ units.
d. Answers may vary. Sample: $x = \frac{\pi}{4}$, $x = \frac{3\pi}{4}$
55. 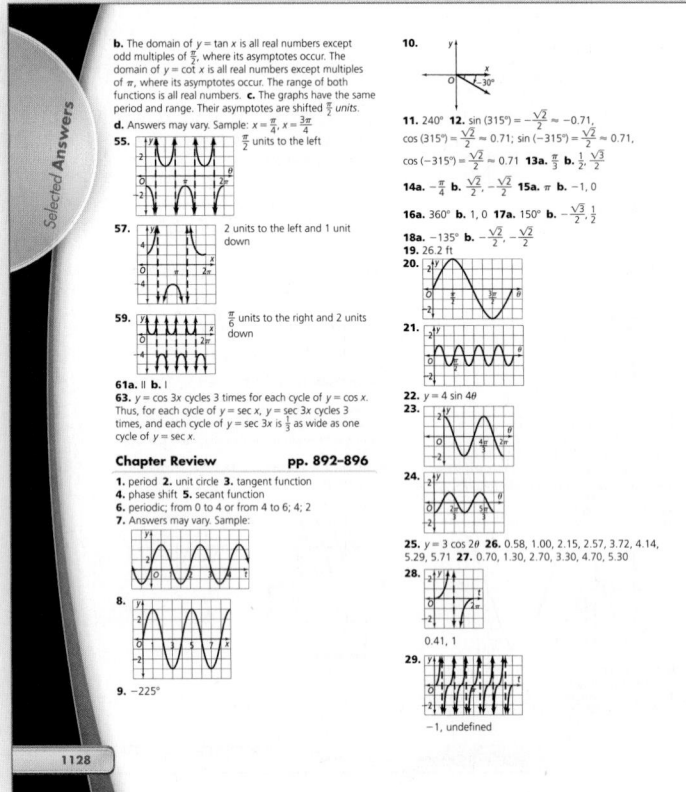 $\frac{\pi}{2}$ units to the left
57. 2 units to the left and 1 unit down
59. $\frac{\pi}{2}$ units to the right and 2 units down
61a. II b. I
63. $y = \cos 3x$ cycles 3 times for each cycle of $y = \cos x$. Thus, for each cycle of $y = \sec x$, $y = \sec 3x$ cycles 3 times, and each cycle of $y = \sec 3x$ is as wide as one cycle of $y = \sec x$.

Chapter Review pp. 892–896

1. period 2. unit circle 3. tangent function 4. phase shift 5. secant function 6. periodic; from 0 to 4 or from 4 to 6; 4; 2 7. Answers may vary. Sample:
8.
9. −225°

10.
11. 240° 12. $\sin(315°) = -\frac{\sqrt{2}}{2} \approx -0.71$, $\cos(315°) = \frac{\sqrt{2}}{2} \approx 0.71$; $\sin(-315°) = \frac{\sqrt{2}}{2} \approx 0.71$, $\cos(-315°) = \frac{\sqrt{2}}{2} \approx 0.71$ 13a. b. $\frac{1}{2}, \frac{\sqrt{3}}{2}$
14a. $-\frac{\pi}{4}$ b. $\frac{\sqrt{2}}{2}, -\frac{\sqrt{2}}{2}$ 15a. π b. −1, 0
16a. 360° b. 1, 0 17a. 150° b. $-\frac{\sqrt{3}}{2}, \frac{1}{2}$
18a. −135° b. $-\frac{\sqrt{2}}{2}, -\frac{\sqrt{2}}{2}$
19. 26.2 ft
20.
21.
22. $y = 4\sin 4\theta$
23.
24.
25. $y = 3\cos 2\theta$ 26. 0.58, 1.00, 2.15, 2.57, 3.72, 4.14, 5.29, 5.71 27. 0.70, 1.30, 2.70, 3.30, 4.70, 5.30
28. 0.41, 1
29. −1, undefined

Page 1129

30. 2, undefined
31.
32.
33.
34.
35.
36. $y = \sin\left(x - \frac{\pi}{4}\right)$ 37. $y = \cos x - 2$ 38. $\sqrt{2}$
39. $-\frac{\sqrt{3}}{3}$ 40. 2 41. $\sqrt{3}$
42.
43.

44.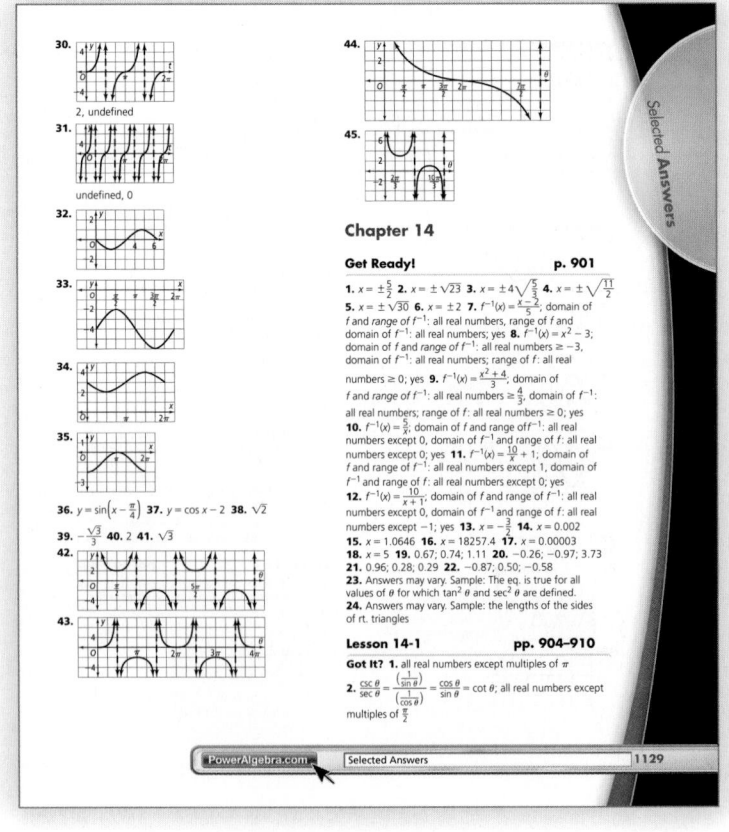
45.

Chapter 14

Get Ready! p. 901

1. $x = \pm\frac{5}{2}$ 2. $x = \pm\sqrt{23}$ 3. $x = \pm\frac{4\sqrt{5}}{5}$ 4. $x = \pm\sqrt{\frac{11}{2}}$
5. $x = \pm\sqrt{30}$ 6. $x = \pm 2$ 7. $f^{-1}(x) = \frac{x-2}{2}$, domain of f and range of f^{-1}: all real numbers, range of f and domain of f^{-1}: all real numbers; yes 8. $f^{-1}(x) = x^2 - 3$; domain of f and range of f^{-1}: all real numbers ≥ -3, domain of f^{-1}: all real numbers; range of f: all real numbers ≥ 0; yes 9. $f^{-1}(x) = \frac{x^2+4}{3}$, domain of f and range of f^{-1}: all real numbers $\ge \frac{4}{3}$, domain of f^{-1}; range of f: all real numbers ≥ 0; yes 10. $f^{-1}(x) = \frac{5}{x}$; domain of f and range of f^{-1}: all real numbers except 0, domain of f^{-1} and range of f: all real numbers except 0; yes 11. $f^{-1}(x) = \frac{10}{x} + 1$; domain of f and range of f^{-1}: all real numbers except 1, domain of f^{-1} and range of f: all real numbers except 0; yes
12. $f^{-1}(x) = \frac{10}{x+1}$; domain of f and range of f^{-1}: all real numbers except 0, domain of f^{-1} and range of f: all real numbers except −1; yes 13. $x = -\frac{3}{2}$ 14. $x = 0.002$
15. $x = 1.0646$ 16. $x = 18257.4$ 17. $x = 0.00003$
18. $x = 5$ 19. 0.67; 0.74; 1.11 20. −0.26; −0.97; 3.73
21. 0.96; 0.28; 0.29 22. −0.87; 0.50; −0.58
23. Answers may vary. Sample: The eq. is true for all values of θ for which $\tan^2\theta$ and $\sec^2\theta$ are defined.
24. Answers may vary. Sample: the lengths of the sides of rt. triangles

Lesson 14-1 pp. 904–910

Got It? 1. all real numbers except multiples of π
2. $\frac{\csc\theta}{\sec\theta} = \frac{\left(\frac{1}{\sin\theta}\right)}{\left(\frac{1}{\cos\theta}\right)} = \frac{\cos\theta}{\sin\theta} = \cot\theta$; all real numbers except multiples of $\frac{\pi}{2}$

Selected Answers

3a. $1 + \cot^2\theta = 1 + \left(\frac{\cos\theta}{\sin\theta}\right)^2$
$= 1 + \frac{\cos^2\theta}{\sin^2\theta}$
$= 1 + \frac{1-\sin^2\theta}{\sin^2\theta}$
$= 1 + \frac{1}{\sin^2\theta} - \frac{\sin^2\theta}{\sin^2\theta}$
$= 1 + \csc^2\theta - 1$
$= \csc^2\theta$

b. No; the domains of $\sin\theta$ and $\cos\theta$ are all real numbers, but the domains of $\tan\theta$, $\cot\theta$, $\sec\theta$, and $\csc\theta$ have restrictions.

4. $\sec^2\theta - \sec^2\theta\cos^2\theta$
$= \left(\frac{1}{\cos\theta}\right)^2 - \left(\frac{1}{\cos\theta}\right)^2\cos^2\theta$
$= \frac{1}{\cos^2\theta} - \frac{1}{\cos^2\theta}\cdot\cos^2\theta$
$= \frac{1}{\cos^2\theta} - \frac{\cos^2\theta}{\cos^2\theta}$
$= \frac{1-\cos^2\theta}{\cos^2\theta}$
$= \frac{\sin^2\theta}{\cos^2\theta}$
$= \tan^2\theta$

5. $\csc\theta$

Lesson Check

1. $\tan\theta\csc\theta$
$= \frac{\sin\theta}{\cos\theta}\cdot\frac{1}{\sin\theta}$
$= \frac{1}{\cos\theta}$
$= \sec\theta$

2. $\csc^2\theta - \cot^2\theta$
$= \left(\frac{1}{\sin\theta}\right)^2 - \left(\frac{\cos\theta}{\sin\theta}\right)^2$
$= \frac{1}{\sin^2\theta} - \frac{\cos^2\theta}{\sin^2\theta}$
$= \frac{1-\cos^2\theta}{\sin^2\theta}$
$= \frac{\sin^2\theta}{\sin^2\theta}$
$= 1$

3. $\sin\theta\tan\theta$
$= \sin\theta\cdot\frac{\sin\theta}{\cos\theta}$
$= \frac{\sin^2\theta}{\cos\theta}$
$= \frac{1-\cos^2\theta}{\cos\theta}$
$= \frac{1}{\cos\theta} - \frac{\cos^2\theta}{\cos\theta}$
$= \sec\theta - \cos\theta$

4. $\tan\theta\cot\theta - \sin^2\theta$
$= \tan\theta\frac{1}{\tan\theta} - \sin^2\theta$
$= \frac{\tan\theta}{\tan\theta} - \sin^2\theta$
$= 1 - \sin^2\theta$
$= \cos^2\theta$

5. Answers may vary. Sample: Letting *a* and *b* be the legs, and *c* the hypotenuse of a right triangle, the Pythagorean Theorem states that $a^2 + b^2 = c^2$. Dividing both sides by c^2, then $\frac{a^2}{c^2} + \frac{b^2}{c^2} = \left(\frac{a}{c}\right)^2 + \left(\frac{b}{c}\right)^2 = 1$. Calling the angle between *a* and *c* θ, then $\sin\theta = \frac{b}{c}$ and $\cos\theta = \frac{a}{c}$. By substitution, $\cos^2\theta + \sin^2\theta = 1$. **6.** wrong calculation: $2 - \cos^2\theta = 2 - (1 - \sin^2\theta) = 2 - 1 + \sin^2\theta = 1 + \sin^2\theta$

Exercises

7. $\cos\theta\cot\theta$
$= \cos\theta\left(\frac{\cos\theta}{\sin\theta}\right)$
$= \frac{1-\sin^2\theta}{\sin\theta}$
$= \frac{1}{\sin\theta} - \sin\theta$; all real numbers except multiples of π

9. $\cos\theta\tan\theta$
$= \cos\theta\left(\frac{\sin\theta}{\cos\theta}\right) = \sin\theta$; all real numbers except odd multiples of $\frac{\pi}{2}$

11. $\cos\theta\sec\theta$
$= \cos\theta\left(\frac{1}{\cos\theta}\right) = 1$; all real numbers except odd multiples of $\frac{\pi}{2}$

13. $\sin\theta\csc\theta$
$= \sin\theta\left(\frac{1}{\sin\theta}\right) = \frac{\sin\theta}{\sin\theta} = 1$; all real numbers except multiples of π

15. $\csc\theta - \sin\theta$
$= \frac{1}{\sin\theta} - \sin\theta$
$= \frac{1-\sin^2\theta}{\sin\theta}$
$= \frac{\cos^2\theta}{\sin\theta}$
$= \cot\theta\cos\theta$; all real numbers except odd multiples of $\frac{\pi}{2}$

17. $\sin^2\theta$ **19.** $-\cot^2\theta$ **21.** $\sin\theta$ **23.** 1 **25.** 1 **27.** 1 **29.** $\sec\theta$ **31.** $\sec^2\theta$ **33.** $\csc\theta$ **35.** $\sin^2\theta$ **37.** 1 **39.** 1 **41.** $\pm\sqrt{1-\cos^2\theta}$ **43.** $\pm\frac{\sqrt{1-\sin^2\theta}}{\sin\theta}$ **45.** $\pm\sqrt{\csc^2\theta - 1}$

47. $\sin^2\theta\tan^2\theta = \sin^2\theta\left(\frac{\sin^2\theta}{\cos^2\theta}\right)$
$= (1-\cos^2\theta)\left(\frac{\sin^2\theta}{\cos^2\theta}\right)$
$= \frac{\sin^2\theta - \sin^2\theta\cos^2\theta}{\cos^2\theta}$
$= \frac{\sin^2\theta}{\cos^2\theta} - \frac{\sin^2\theta\cos^2\theta}{\cos^2\theta}$
$= \tan^2\theta - \sin^2\theta$

49. $\sin\theta\cos\theta(\tan\theta + \cot\theta)$
$= \sin\theta\cos\theta\left(\frac{\sin\theta}{\cos\theta} + \frac{\cos\theta}{\sin\theta}\right)$
$= \frac{\sin^2\theta\cos\theta}{\cos\theta} + \frac{\cos^2\theta\sin\theta}{\sin\theta}$
$= \sin^2\theta + \cos^2\theta = 1$

51. $\frac{\sec\theta}{\cot\theta + \tan\theta}$
$= \frac{\frac{1}{\cos\theta}}{\frac{\cos\theta}{\sin\theta} + \frac{\sin\theta}{\cos\theta}}\cdot\frac{\sin\theta\cos\theta}{\sin\theta\cos\theta}$
$= \frac{\sin\theta}{\cos^2\theta + \sin^2\theta} = \frac{\sin\theta}{1} = \sin\theta$

53. $\frac{1-\sin^2\theta}{\sin^2\theta}$

55. $\sin^2\theta + \cos^2\theta = 1$
$(0.5)^2 + \cos^2\theta = 1$
$0.25 + \cos^2\theta = 1$
$\cos^2\theta = 1 - 0.25$
$\cos^2\theta = 0.75$
$\cos\theta = \pm\sqrt{0.75}$
Since θ is in the first quadrant, $\cos\theta$ is positive; $\cos\theta = 0.866025404$
$\tan\theta = \frac{\sin\theta}{\cos\theta}$
$= \frac{0.5}{0.866025404}$
$= 0.577350269$

57. $\sin^2\theta + \cos^2\theta = 1$
$\sin^2\theta + (-0.6)^2 = 1$
$\sin^2\theta + 0.36 = 1$
$\sin^2\theta = 1 - 0.36$
$\sin^2\theta = 0.64$
$\sin\theta = \pm\sqrt{0.64}$
Since θ is in the third quadrant, $\sin\theta$ is negative; $\sin\theta = -0.8$
$\tan\theta = \frac{\sin\theta}{\cos\theta}$
$= \frac{-0.8}{-0.6}$
$= 1.333333333$

59. $\tan\theta = \frac{\sin\theta}{\cos\theta}$, $\sin^2\theta + \cos^2\theta = 1$, which can be rewritten as $\sin^2\theta = 1 - \cos^2\theta$
$1.2 = \frac{\sin\theta}{\cos\theta}$
$1.2^2 = \frac{\sin^2\theta}{\cos^2\theta}$
$1.44(\cos^2\theta) = \sin^2\theta$
$1.44(\cos^2\theta) = 1 - \cos^2\theta$
$1.44(\cos^2\theta) + \cos^2\theta = 1$
$2.44(\cos^2\theta) = 1$
$\cos^2\theta = \frac{1}{2.44}$
$\cos^2\theta = 0.409836066$
$\cos\theta = \pm\sqrt{0.409836066}$
Since θ is in the first quadrant, $\cos\theta$ is positive; $\cos\theta = 0.640184400$
$\tan\theta = \frac{\sin\theta}{\cos\theta}$
$1.2 = \frac{\sin\theta}{0.640184400}$
$\sin\theta = 0.76822128$

61. $\sin^2\theta + \cos^2\theta = 1$
$(0.2)^2 + \cos^2\theta = 1$
$0.04 + \cos^2\theta = 1$
$\cos^2\theta = 1 - 0.04$
$\cos^2\theta = 0.96$
$\cos\theta = \pm\sqrt{0.96}$
Since $\sin\theta$ is positive and $\tan\theta$ is negative, θ is in the fourth quadrant, so $\cos\theta$ is positive; $\cos\theta = 0.97979590$

63. $\cos(\theta + \pi) = |\cos\theta|$, but is also in Quadrant III and is negative, so $\cos(\theta + \pi) = -\cos\theta$ **65.** 1

67. If $n_2 > n_1$, then $\theta_1 > \theta_2$; if $n_2 < n_1$, then $\theta_1 < \theta_2$; if $n_2 = n_1$, then $\theta_2 = \theta_1$. **69.** H **71.** F

73. By the Difference of Squares Property and the second Pythagorean Identity: $(\sec\theta + 1)(\sec\theta - 1) = \sec^2\theta - 1$
$= \tan^2\theta$

74.
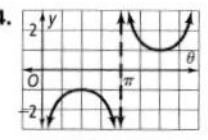

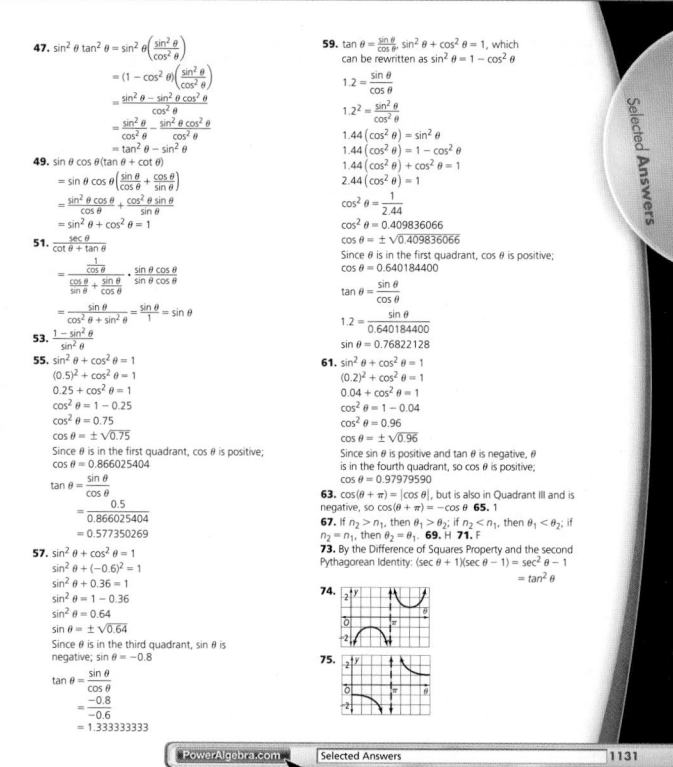

75.
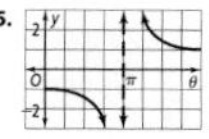

76.
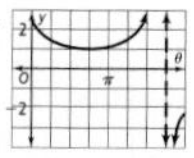

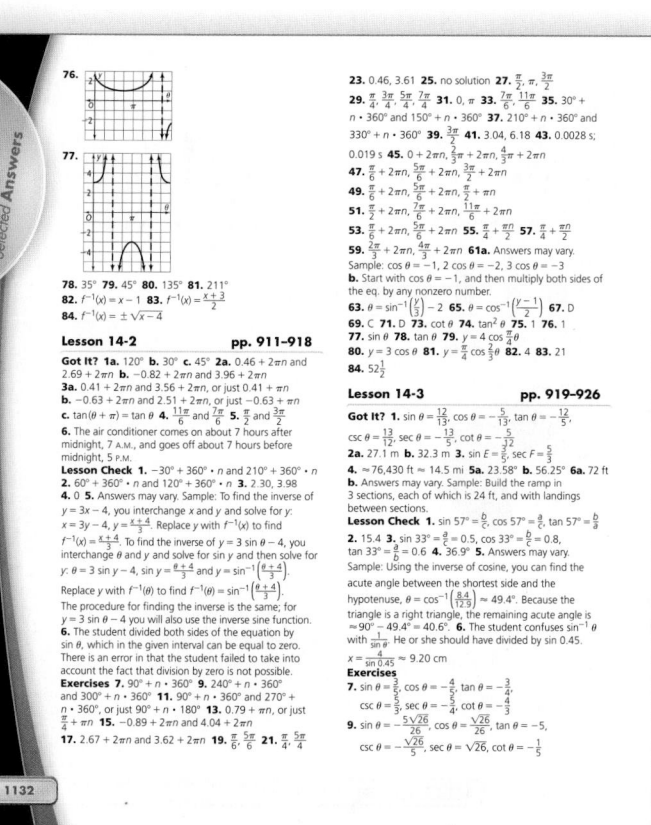

77.
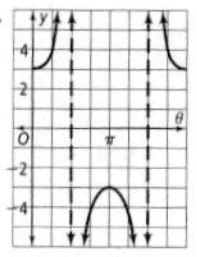

78. 35° **79.** 45° **80.** 135° **81.** 211° **82.** $f^{-1}(x) = x - 1$ **83.** $f^{-1}(x) = \frac{x+3}{2}$ **84.** $f^{-1}(x) = \pm\sqrt{x-4}$

Lesson 14-2 pp. 911–918

Got It? 1a. 120° **b.** 30° **c.** 45° **2a.** $0.46 + 2\pi n$ and $2.69 + 2\pi n$ **b.** $-0.82 + 2\pi n$ and $3.96 + 2\pi n$ **3a.** $0.41 + 2\pi n$ and $3.56 + 2\pi n$, or just $0.41 + \pi n$ **b.** $-0.63 + 2\pi n$ and $2.51 + 2\pi n$, or just $-0.63 + \pi n$ **c.** $\tan(\theta + \pi) = \tan\theta$ **4.** $\frac{11\pi}{6}$ and $\frac{7\pi}{6}$ **5.** $\frac{\pi}{2}$ and $\frac{3\pi}{2}$ **6.** The air conditioner comes on about 7 hours after midnight, 7 A.M., and goes off about 7 hours before midnight, 5 P.M.

Lesson Check 1. $-30° + 360°\cdot n$ and $210° + 360°\cdot n$ **2.** $60° + 360°\cdot n$ and $120° + 360°\cdot n$ **3.** 2.30, 3.98 **4.** 0 **5.** Answers may vary. Sample: To find the inverse of $y = 3x - 4$, you interchange *x* and *y* and solve for *y*: $x = 3y - 4$, $y = \frac{x+4}{3}$. Replace *y* with $f^{-1}(x)$ to find $f^{-1}(x) = \frac{x+4}{3}$. To find the inverse of $y = 3\sin\theta - 4$, you interchange θ and *y* and solve for sin *y* and then solve for *y*: $\theta = 3\sin y - 4$, $\sin y = \frac{\theta+4}{3}$ and $y = \sin^{-1}\left(\frac{\theta+4}{3}\right)$. Replace *y* with $f^{-1}(\theta)$ to find $f^{-1}(\theta) = \sin^{-1}\left(\frac{\theta+4}{3}\right)$. The procedure for finding the inverse is the same; for $y = 3\sin\theta - 4$ you will also use the inverse sine function. **6.** The student divided both sides of the equation by $\sin\theta$, which in the given interval can be equal to zero. There is an error in that the student failed to take into account the fact that division by zero is not possible.

Exercises 7. $90° + n\cdot 360°$ **9.** $240° + n\cdot 360°$ and $300° + n\cdot 360°$ **11.** $90° + n\cdot 360°$ and $270° + n\cdot 360°$, or just $90° + n\cdot 180°$ **13.** $0.79 + \pi n$, or just $\frac{\pi}{4} + \pi n$ **15.** $-0.89 + 2\pi n$ and $4.04 + 2\pi n$ **17.** $2.67 + 2\pi n$ and $3.62 + 2\pi n$ **19.** $\frac{\pi}{6}, \frac{5\pi}{6}$ **21.** $\frac{\pi}{4}, \frac{5\pi}{4}$ **23.** 0.46, 3.61 **25.** no solution **27.** $\frac{\pi}{2}, \pi, \frac{3\pi}{2}$ **29.** $\frac{\pi}{4}, \frac{3\pi}{4}, \frac{5\pi}{4}, \frac{7\pi}{4}$ **31.** $0, \pi$ **33.** $\frac{7\pi}{6}, \frac{11\pi}{6}$ **35.** $30° + n\cdot 360°$ and $150° + n\cdot 360°$ **37.** $210° + n\cdot 360°$ and $330° + n\cdot 360°$ **39.** $\frac{3\pi}{2}$ **41.** 3.04, 6.18 **43.** 0.0028 s; 0.019 s **45.** $0 + 2\pi n, \frac{2}{3}\pi + 2\pi n, \frac{4}{3}\pi + 2\pi n$ **47.** $\frac{\pi}{6} + 2\pi n, \frac{5\pi}{6} + 2\pi n, \frac{3\pi}{2} + 2\pi n$ **49.** $\frac{\pi}{6} + 2\pi n, \frac{5\pi}{6} + 2\pi n, \frac{\pi}{2} + \pi n$ **51.** $\frac{\pi}{2} + 2\pi n, \frac{7\pi}{6} + 2\pi n, \frac{11\pi}{6} + 2\pi n$ **53.** $\frac{\pi}{6} + 2\pi n, \frac{5\pi}{6} + 2\pi n$ **55.** $\frac{\pi}{4} + \frac{\pi n}{2}$ **57.** $\frac{\pi}{4} + \frac{\pi n}{2}$ **59.** $\frac{2\pi}{3} + 2\pi n, \frac{4\pi}{3} + 2\pi n$ **61a.** Answers may vary. Sample: $\cos\theta = -1$, $2\cos\theta = -2$, $3\cos\theta = -3$ **b.** Start with $\cos\theta = -1$, and then multiply both sides of the eq. by any nonzero number. **63.** $\theta = \sin^{-1}\left(\frac{y}{3}\right) - 2$ **65.** $\theta = \cos^{-1}\left(\frac{y-1}{2}\right)$ **67.** D **69.** C **71.** D **73.** $\cot\theta$ **74.** $\tan^2\theta$ **75.** 1 **76.** 1 **77.** $\sin\theta$ **78.** $\tan\theta$ **79.** $y = 4\cos\frac{\pi}{4}\theta$ **80.** $y = 3\cos\theta$ **81.** $y = \frac{\pi}{4}\cos\frac{2}{3}\theta$ **82.** 4 **83.** 21 **84.** $52\frac{1}{2}$

Lesson 14-3 pp. 919–926

Got It? 1. $\sin\theta = \frac{12}{13}$, $\cos\theta = -\frac{5}{13}$, $\tan\theta = -\frac{12}{5}$, $\csc\theta = \frac{13}{12}$, $\sec\theta = -\frac{13}{5}$, $\cot\theta = -\frac{5}{12}$ **2a.** 27.1 m **b.** 32.3 m **3.** $\sin E = \frac{3}{5}$, $\sec F = \frac{5}{3}$ **4.** ≈76,430 ft ≈ 14.5 mi **5a.** 23.58° **b.** 56.25° **6a.** 72 ft **b.** Answers may vary. Sample: Build the ramp in 3 sections, each of which is 24 ft, and with landings between sections.

Lesson Check 1. $\sin 57° = \frac{b}{c}$, $\cos 57° = \frac{a}{c}$, $\tan 57° = \frac{b}{a}$ **2.** 15.4 **3.** $\sin 33° = \frac{a}{c} = 0.5$, $\cos 33° = \frac{b}{c} = 0.8$, $\tan 33° = \frac{a}{b} = 0.6$ **4.** 36.9° **5.** Answers may vary. Sample: Using the inverse of cosine, you can find the acute angle between the shortest side and the hypotenuse, $\theta = \cos^{-1}\left(\frac{8.4}{12.9}\right) \approx 49.4°$. Because the triangle is a right triangle, the remaining acute angle is $\approx 90° - 49.4° = 40.6°$. **6.** The student confuses $\sin^{-1}\theta$ with $\frac{1}{\sin\theta}$. He or she should have divided by sin 0.45. $x = \frac{4}{\sin 0.45} \approx 9.20$ cm

Exercises

7. $\sin\theta = \frac{3}{5}$, $\cos\theta = -\frac{4}{5}$, $\tan\theta = -\frac{3}{4}$, $\csc\theta = \frac{5}{3}$, $\sec\theta = -\frac{5}{4}$, $\cot\theta = -\frac{4}{3}$

9. $\sin\theta = -\frac{5\sqrt{26}}{26}$, $\cos\theta = \frac{\sqrt{26}}{26}$, $\tan\theta = -5$, $\csc\theta = -\frac{\sqrt{26}}{5}$, $\sec\theta = \sqrt{26}$, $\cot\theta = -\frac{1}{5}$

11. $\sin\theta = \frac{\sqrt{7}}{4}$, $\cos\theta = -\frac{3}{4}$, $\tan\theta = -\frac{\sqrt{7}}{3}$, $\csc\theta = \frac{4\sqrt{7}}{7}$, $\sec\theta = -\frac{4}{3}$, $\cot\theta = -\frac{3\sqrt{7}}{7}$

13a. $\frac{15}{17} \approx 0.88$ **b.** $\frac{17}{8} \approx 2.13$ **c.** $\frac{8}{15} \approx 0.53$ **d.** $\frac{17}{8} \approx 2.13$ **e.** $\frac{17}{15} \approx 1.13$ **f.** $\frac{8}{15} \approx 0.53$ **15.** 41.8 **17.** 25.2 **19.** $a \approx 8.7$, $m\angle A = 60.0°$, $m\angle B = 30.0°$ **21.** $a = 9.0$, $m\angle A \approx 36.9°$, $m\angle B \approx 53.1°$ **23.** $a \approx 8.0$, $m\angle A \approx 61.8°$, $m\angle B \approx 28.2°$ **25a.** $m\angle A = \cos^{-1}\left(\frac{1200}{d}\right)$ **b.** 37° **c.** 53°

27.
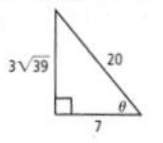

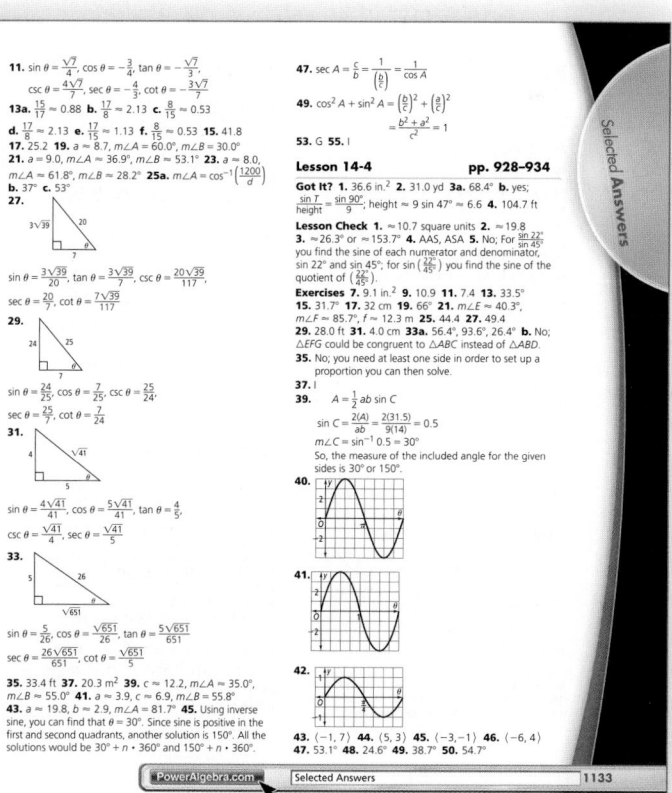

$\sin\theta = \frac{3\sqrt{39}}{20}$, $\tan\theta = \frac{3\sqrt{39}}{7}$, $\csc\theta = \frac{20\sqrt{39}}{117}$, $\sec\theta = \frac{20}{7}$, $\cot\theta = \frac{7\sqrt{39}}{117}$

29.
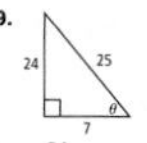

$\sin\theta = \frac{24}{25}$, $\cos\theta = \frac{7}{25}$, $\csc\theta = \frac{25}{24}$, $\sec\theta = \frac{25}{7}$, $\cot\theta = \frac{7}{24}$

31.
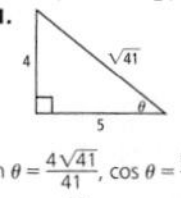

$\sin\theta = \frac{4\sqrt{41}}{41}$, $\cos\theta = \frac{5\sqrt{41}}{41}$, $\tan\theta = \frac{4}{5}$, $\csc\theta = \frac{\sqrt{41}}{4}$, $\sec\theta = \frac{\sqrt{41}}{5}$

33.
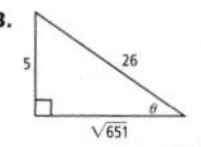

$\sin\theta = \frac{5}{26}$, $\cos\theta = \frac{\sqrt{651}}{26}$, $\tan\theta = \frac{5\sqrt{651}}{651}$, $\sec\theta = \frac{26\sqrt{651}}{651}$, $\cot\theta = \frac{\sqrt{651}}{5}$

35. 33.4 ft **37.** 20.3 m^2 **39.** $c \approx 12.2$, $m\angle A \approx 35.0°$, $m\angle B \approx 55.0°$ **41.** $a \approx 3.9$, $c \approx 6.9$, $m\angle B = 55.8°$ **43.** $a \approx 19.8$, $b \approx 2.9$, $m\angle A = 81.7°$ **45.** Using inverse sine, you can find that $\theta = 30°$. Since sine is positive in the first and second quadrants, another solution is 150°. All the solutions would be $30° + n\cdot 360°$ and $150° + n\cdot 360°$.

47. $\sec A = \frac{c}{b} = \frac{1}{\left(\frac{b}{c}\right)} = \frac{1}{\cos A}$

49. $\cos^2 A + \sin^2 A = \left(\frac{b}{c}\right)^2 + \left(\frac{a}{c}\right)^2$
$= \frac{b^2 + a^2}{c^2} = 1$

53. G **55.** I

Lesson 14-4 pp. 928–934

Got It? 1. 36.6 in.^{2} **2.** 31.0 yd **3a.** 68.4° **b.** yes; $\frac{\sin T}{\text{height}} = \frac{\sin 90°}{9}$; height ≈ 9 sin 47° ≈ 6.6 **4.** 104.7 ft

Lesson Check 1. ≈10.7 square units **2.** ≈19.8 **3.** ≈26.3° or ≈153.7° **4.** AAS, ASA **5.** No; For $\frac{\sin 22°}{\sin 45°}$ you find the sine of each numerator and denominator, sin 22° and sin 45°; for $\sin\left(\frac{22°}{45°}\right)$ you find the sine of the quotient of $\left(\frac{22°}{45°}\right)$.

Exercises 7. 9.1 in.^{2} **9.** 10.9 **11.** 7.4 **13.** 33.5° **15.** 31.7° **17.** 32 cm **19.** 66° **21.** $m\angle E \approx 40.3°$, $m\angle F \approx 85.7°$, $f \approx 12.3$ m **25.** 44.4 **27.** 49.4 **29.** 28.0 ft **31.** 4.0 cm **33a.** 56.4°, 93.6°, 26.4° **b.** No; $\triangle EFG$ could be congruent to $\triangle ABC$ instead of $\triangle ABD$.

35. No; you need at least one side in order to set up a proportion you can then solve.

37. I

39. $A = \frac{1}{2}ab\sin C$
$\sin C = \frac{2(A)}{ab} = \frac{2(31.5)}{9(14)} = 0.5$
$m\angle C = \sin^{-1} 0.5 = 30°$
So, the measure of the included angle for the given sides is 30° or 150°.

40.
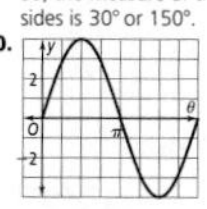

41.
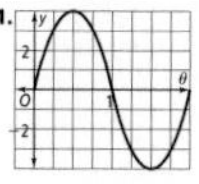

42.
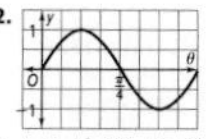

43. ⟨−1, 7⟩ **44.** ⟨5, 3⟩ **45.** ⟨−3, −1⟩ **46.** ⟨−6, 4⟩ **47.** 53.1° **48.** 24.6° **49.** 38.7° **50.** 54.7°

Lesson 14-5 pp. 936–942

Got It? 1a. 6.4
b. 1 mi to 6 mi;
$a^2 = 2.5^2 + 3.5^2 - 2(2.5)(3.5)\cos A$
$a^2 = 18.5 - 17.5\cos A$;
if $A = 0°$, then $\cos A = 1$ and $a = 1$; if $A = 180°$, then $\cos A = -1$ and $a = 6$. **2.** 75.3° **3.** 30.7°
Lesson Check 1. ≈11.85 in. **2.** ≈52.4° **3.** ≈34.1° **4.** ≈60.3° **5.** Use the Law of Sines when you have two sides and a non-included angle or two angles and a side; use the Law of Cosines when you have two sides and an included angle or three sides. **6.** The denominator should be negative. The answer should be:

$$\cos C = \frac{15^2 - 11^2 - 17^2}{-2(11)(17)} \approx 0.495$$
$$C = \cos^{-1}(0.495) \approx 60.3°$$

Exercises 7. 37.1 **9.** 13.7 **11.** 27.0 **13.** 33.7° **15.** 47.2° **17.** 50.8 **19.** 27.0° **21.** $b^2 = a^2 + c^2 - 2ac\cos B$ **23.** $\frac{\sin B}{b} = \frac{\sin C}{c}$ **25.** $\frac{\sin C}{c} = \frac{\sin A}{a}$ **27.** ≈ 59.1 nautical miles **29.** $b \approx 34.7$, $m\angle A \approx 26.7°$, $m\angle C \approx 33.3°$ **31.** $m\angle A \approx 56.1°$, $m\angle B \approx 70.0°$, $m\angle C \approx 53.9°$
33. For any two side lengths a and b, the ratio $\frac{a}{b}$ is equal to the ratio $\frac{\sin A}{\sin B}$, which can be found since A and B are given.
35a. ≈ 45.4 mi **b.** 14.4° left; 4.4° west of north
37. 11.0 cm **39.** 27.0° **41.** 13.0 cm **43.** 21.5° **45.** 8.3 ft **47.** 79.6° **49.** 18 cm
51. a. 2.1 m
b. 9.8 m^2
53. a. $\cos A > 0$ if $b^2 + c^2 > a^2$;
$\cos A = 0$ if $b^2 + c^2 = a^2$;
$\cos A < 0$ if $b^2 + c^2 < a^2$
b. acute △ if $\cos A > 0$; right △ if $\cos A = 0$; obtuse △ if $\cos A < 0$

Lesson 14-6 pp. 943–950

Got It?
1. $\cos\left(\theta - \frac{\pi}{2}\right) = \cos\left(-\left(\frac{\pi}{2} - \theta\right)\right) = \cos\left(\frac{\pi}{2} - \theta\right) = \sin\theta$
2. $\sec(90° - A) = \frac{1}{\cos(90° - A)} = \frac{1}{\sin\theta} = \csc\theta$
$\sec(90° - A) = \csc\theta$
3a. $0, \pi$ **b.** yes; πn
4. $\frac{\sqrt{6} - \sqrt{2}}{4}$
5. $\sin(A + B) = \sin(A - (-B))$
$= \sin A\cos(-B) - \cos A\sin(-B)$
$= \sin A\cos B - \cos A(-\sin B)$
$= \sin A\cos B + \cos A\sin B$
6. $-2 - \sqrt{3}$

Lesson Check
1. $\sin\left(\frac{\pi}{2} + \theta\right) + \sin\left(\frac{\pi}{2} - \theta\right)$
$= \sin\left(\frac{\pi}{2} - (-\theta)\right) + \sin\left(\frac{\pi}{2} - \theta\right)$
$= \cos(-\theta) + \cos\theta$
$= \cos\theta + \cos\theta$
$= 2\cos\theta$
2. $\frac{\pi}{4}, \frac{5\pi}{4}$ **3.** $\frac{\sqrt{2}}{2}$ **4.** $-\frac{\sqrt{2} + \sqrt{6}}{4}$
5. There are 2 solutions, $\frac{\pi}{2}$ and $\frac{3\pi}{2}$, between 0 and 2π because: $-\cos\theta = \cos\theta$
$2\cos\theta = 0$
$\cos\theta = 0;\ \theta = \frac{\pi}{2}, \frac{3\pi}{2}$
6. $\sin\left(\frac{\pi}{2} - \theta\right) = \sin\frac{\pi}{2}\cos\theta - \cos\frac{\pi}{2}\sin\theta = (1)\cos\theta - (0)\sin\theta = \cos\theta$

Exercises
7. $\csc\left(\theta - \frac{\pi}{2}\right) = \frac{1}{\sin\left(\theta - \frac{\pi}{2}\right)} = \frac{1}{\sin\left(-\left(\frac{\pi}{2} - \theta\right)\right)} = \frac{1}{-\sin\left(\frac{\pi}{2} - \theta\right)} = \frac{1}{-\cos\theta} = -\sec\theta$
9. $\cot\left(\frac{\pi}{2} - \theta\right) = \frac{\cos\left(\frac{\pi}{2} - \theta\right)}{\sin\left(\frac{\pi}{2} - \theta\right)} = \frac{\sin\theta}{\cos\theta} = \tan\theta$
11. $\tan\left(\theta - \frac{\pi}{2}\right) = \tan\left(-\left(\frac{\pi}{2} - \theta\right)\right) = -\tan\left(\frac{\pi}{2} - \theta\right) = -\cot\theta$
13. $\tan(90° - A) = \cot A$ **15.** $\cot(90° - A) = \tan A$
17. $\frac{\pi}{2}, \frac{3\pi}{2}$ **19.** π **21.** $\frac{\pi}{2}, \frac{3\pi}{2}$ **23.** $\frac{\sqrt{2}}{2}$ **25.** 0
27. $-\sqrt{3} - 2$ **29.** $\frac{\sqrt{2} + \sqrt{6}}{4}$
31. $-2 + \sqrt{3}$ **33.** $-\frac{1}{2}$ **35.** $\frac{1}{2}$
37. $\sin(A - B) = \cos\left[\frac{\pi}{2} - (A - B)\right]$
$= \cos\left[\left(\frac{\pi}{2} - A\right) + B\right]$
$= \cos\left(\frac{\pi}{2} - A\right)\cos B - \sin\left(\frac{\pi}{2} - A\right)\sin B$
$= \sin A\cos B - \cos A\sin B$

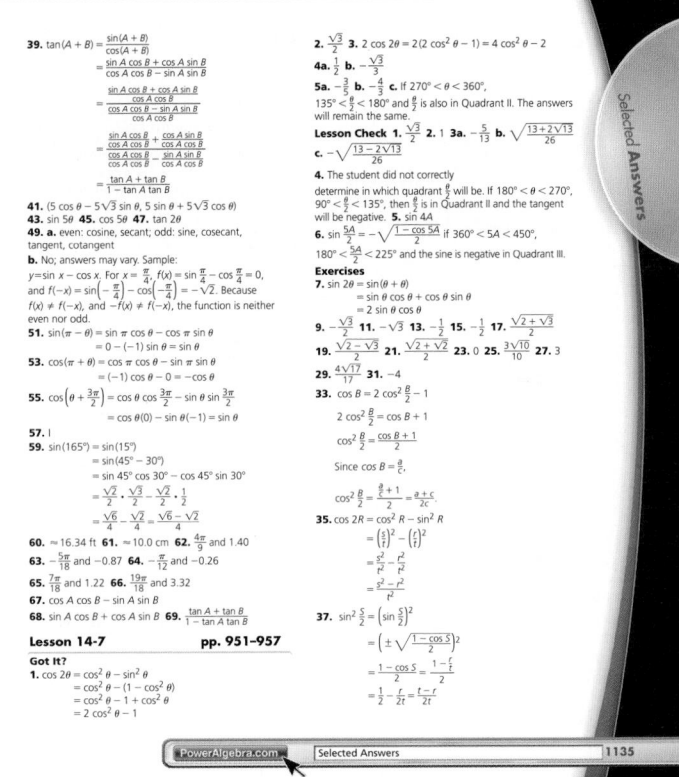

39. $\tan(A + B) = \frac{\sin(A + B)}{\cos(A + B)}$
$= \frac{\sin A\cos B + \cos A\sin B}{\cos A\cos B - \sin A\sin B}$
$= \frac{\frac{\sin A\cos B + \cos A\sin B}{\cos A\cos B}}{\frac{\cos A\cos B - \sin A\sin B}{\cos A\cos B}}$
$= \frac{\frac{\sin A\cos B}{\cos A\cos B} + \frac{\cos A\sin B}{\cos A\cos B}}{\frac{\cos A\cos B}{\cos A\cos B} - \frac{\sin A\sin B}{\cos A\cos B}}$
$= \frac{\tan A + \tan B}{1 - \tan A\tan B}$
41. $(5\cos\theta - 5\sqrt{3}\sin\theta, 5\sin\theta + 5\sqrt{3}\cos\theta)$
43. $\sin 5\theta$ **45.** $\cos 5\theta$ **47.** $\tan 2\theta$
49. a. even: cosine, secant; odd: sine, cosecant, tangent, cotangent
b. No; answers may vary. Sample: $y = \sin x - \cos x$. For $x = \frac{\pi}{4}$, $f(x) = \sin\frac{\pi}{4} - \cos\frac{\pi}{4} = 0$, and $f(-x) = \sin\left(-\frac{\pi}{4}\right) - \cos\left(-\frac{\pi}{4}\right) = -\sqrt{2}$. Because $f(x) \neq f(-x)$, and $-f(x) \neq f(-x)$, the function is neither even nor odd.
51. $\sin(\pi - \theta) = \sin\pi\cos\theta - \cos\pi\sin\theta$
$= 0 - (-1)\sin\theta = \sin\theta$
53. $\cos(\pi + \theta) = \cos\pi\cos\theta - \sin\pi\sin\theta$
$= (-1)\cos\theta - 0 = -\cos\theta$
55. $\cos\left(\theta + \frac{3\pi}{2}\right) = \cos\theta\cos\frac{3\pi}{2} - \sin\theta\sin\frac{3\pi}{2}$
$= \cos\theta(0) - \sin\theta(-1) = \sin\theta$
57. I
59. $\sin(165°) = \sin(15°)$
$= \sin(45° - 30°)$
$= \sin 45°\cos 30° - \cos 45°\sin 30°$
$= \frac{\sqrt{2}}{2} \cdot \frac{\sqrt{3}}{2} - \frac{\sqrt{2}}{2} \cdot \frac{1}{2}$
$= \frac{\sqrt{6}}{4} - \frac{\sqrt{2}}{4} = \frac{\sqrt{6} - \sqrt{2}}{4}$
60. ≈16.34 ft **61.** ≈10.0 cm **62.** $\frac{4\pi}{9}$ and 1.40
63. $-\frac{5\pi}{18}$ and −0.87 **64.** $-\frac{\pi}{12}$ and −0.26
65. $\frac{7\pi}{18}$ and 1.22 **66.** $\frac{19\pi}{18}$ and 3.32
67. $\cos A\cos B - \sin A\sin B$
68. $\sin A\cos B + \cos A\sin B$ **69.** $\frac{\tan A + \tan B}{1 - \tan A\tan B}$

Lesson 14-7 pp. 951–957

Got It?
1. $\cos 2\theta = \cos^2\theta - \sin^2\theta$
$= \cos^2\theta - (1 - \cos^2\theta)$
$= \cos^2\theta - 1 + \cos^2\theta$
$= 2\cos^2\theta - 1$
2. $\frac{\sqrt{3}}{2}$ **3.** $2\cos 2\theta = 2(2\cos^2\theta - 1) = 4\cos^2\theta - 2$
4a. $\frac{1}{2}$ **b.** $-\frac{\sqrt{3}}{3}$
5a. $-\frac{3}{5}$ **b.** $-\frac{4}{3}$ **c.** If $270° < \theta < 360°$, $135° < \frac{\theta}{2} < 180°$ and $\frac{\theta}{2}$ is also in Quadrant II. The answers will remain the same.
Lesson Check 1. $\frac{\sqrt{3}}{2}$ **2.** 1 **3a.** $-\frac{5}{13}$ **b.** $\sqrt{\frac{13 + 2\sqrt{13}}{26}}$
c. $-\sqrt{\frac{13 - 2\sqrt{13}}{26}}$
4. The student did not correctly determine in which quadrant $\frac{\theta}{2}$ will be. If $180° < \theta < 270°$, $90° < \frac{\theta}{2} < 135°$, then $\frac{\theta}{2}$ is in Quadrant II and the tangent will be negative. **5.** $\sin 4A$
6. $\sin\frac{5A}{2} = -\sqrt{\frac{1 - \cos 5A}{2}}$ if $360° < 5A < 450°$, $180° < \frac{5A}{2} < 225°$ and the sine is negative in Quadrant III.
Exercises
7. $\sin 2\theta = \sin(\theta + \theta)$
$= \sin\theta\cos\theta + \cos\theta\sin\theta$
$= 2\sin\theta\cos\theta$
9. $-\frac{\sqrt{3}}{2}$ **11.** $-\sqrt{3}$ **13.** $-\frac{1}{2}$ **15.** $-\frac{1}{2}$ **17.** $\frac{\sqrt{2 + \sqrt{3}}}{2}$
19. $\frac{\sqrt{2 - \sqrt{3}}}{2}$ **21.** $\frac{\sqrt{2 + \sqrt{2}}}{2}$ **23.** 0 **25.** $\frac{3\sqrt{10}}{10}$ **27.** 3
29. $\frac{4\sqrt{17}}{17}$ **31.** −4
33. $\cos B = 2\cos^2\frac{B}{2} - 1$
$2\cos^2\frac{B}{2} = \cos B + 1$
$\cos^2\frac{B}{2} = \frac{\cos B + 1}{2}$
Since $\cos B = \frac{a}{c}$,
$\cos^2\frac{B}{2} = \frac{\frac{a}{c} + 1}{2} = \frac{a + c}{2c}$.
35. $\cos 2R = \cos^2 R - \sin^2 R$
$= \left(\frac{s}{t}\right)^2 - \left(\frac{r}{t}\right)^2$
$= \frac{s^2}{t^2} - \frac{r^2}{t^2}$
$= \frac{s^2 - r^2}{t^2}$
37. $\sin^2\frac{S}{2} = \left(\sin\frac{S}{2}\right)^2$
$= \left(\pm\sqrt{\frac{1 - \cos S}{2}}\right)^2$
$= \frac{1 - \cos S}{2} = \frac{1 - \frac{r}{t}}{2}$
$= \frac{1}{2} - \frac{r}{2t} = \frac{t - r}{2t}$

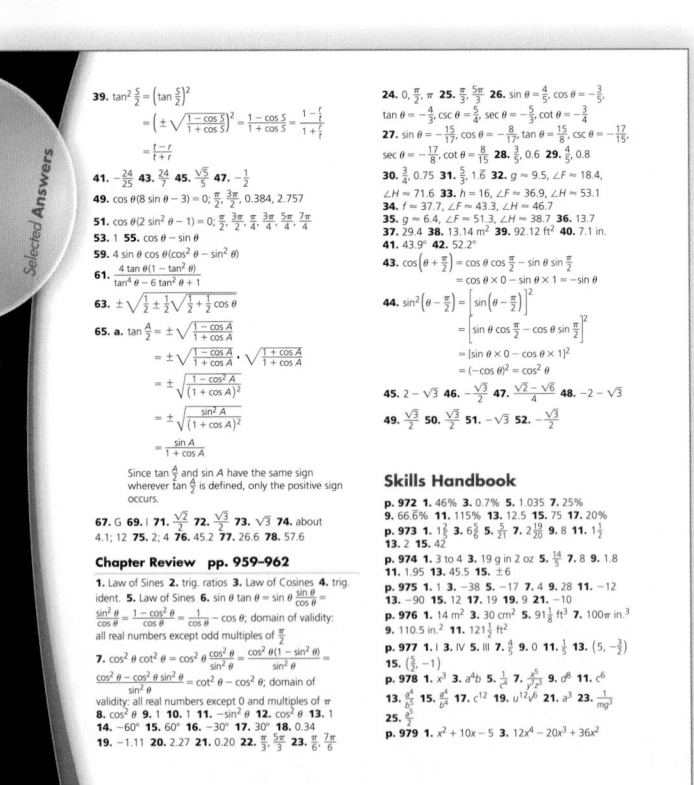

39. $\tan^2\frac{S}{2} = \left(\tan\frac{S}{2}\right)^2$
$= \left(\pm\sqrt{\frac{1 - \cos S}{1 + \cos S}}\right)^2 = \frac{1 - \cos S}{1 + \cos S} = \frac{1 - \frac{r}{t}}{1 + \frac{r}{t}}$
$= \frac{t - r}{t + r}$
41. $-\frac{24}{25}$ **43.** $\frac{24}{7}$ **45.** $\frac{\sqrt{5}}{5}$ **47.** $-\frac{1}{2}$
49. $\cos\theta(8\sin\theta - 3) = 0$; $\frac{\pi}{2}, \frac{3\pi}{2}$, 0.384, 2.757
51. $\cos\theta(2\sin^2\theta - 1) = 0$; $\frac{\pi}{2}, \frac{3\pi}{2}, \frac{\pi}{4}, \frac{3\pi}{4}, \frac{5\pi}{4}, \frac{7\pi}{4}$
53. 1 **55.** $\cos\theta - \sin\theta$
59. $4\sin\theta\cos\theta(\cos^2\theta - \sin^2\theta)$
61. $\frac{4\tan\theta(1 - \tan^2\theta)}{\tan^4\theta - 6\tan^2\theta + 1}$
63. $\pm\sqrt{\frac{1}{2} \pm \frac{1}{2}\sqrt{\frac{1}{2} + \frac{1}{2}\cos\theta}}$
65. a. $\tan\frac{A}{2} = \pm\sqrt{\frac{1 - \cos A}{1 + \cos A}}$
$= \pm\sqrt{\frac{1 - \cos A}{1 + \cos A}} \cdot \sqrt{\frac{1 + \cos A}{1 + \cos A}}$
$= \pm\sqrt{\frac{1 - \cos^2 A}{(1 + \cos A)^2}}$
$= \pm\sqrt{\frac{\sin^2 A}{(1 + \cos A)^2}}$
$= \frac{\sin A}{1 + \cos A}$
Since $\tan\frac{A}{2}$ and $\sin A$ have the same sign wherever $\tan\frac{A}{2}$ is defined, only the positive sign occurs.
67. G **69.** I **71.** $\frac{\sqrt{2}}{2}$ **72.** $\frac{\sqrt{3}}{2}$ **73.** $\sqrt{3}$ **74.** about 4.1; 12 **75.** 2; 4 **76.** 45.2 **77.** 26.6 **78.** 57.6

Chapter Review pp. 959–962

1. Law of Sines **2.** trig. ratios **3.** Law of Cosines **4.** trig. ident. **5.** Law of Sines **6.** $\sin\theta\tan\theta = \sin\theta\frac{\sin\theta}{\cos\theta} = \frac{\sin^2\theta}{\cos\theta} = \frac{1 - \cos^2\theta}{\cos\theta} = \frac{1}{\cos\theta} - \cos\theta$; domain of validity: all real numbers except odd multiples of $\frac{\pi}{2}$
7. $\cos^2\theta\cot^2\theta = \cos^2\theta\frac{\cos^2\theta}{\sin^2\theta} = \frac{\cos^2\theta(1 - \sin^2\theta)}{\sin^2\theta} = \frac{\cos^2\theta - \cos^2\theta\sin^2\theta}{\sin^2\theta} = \cot^2\theta - \cos^2\theta$; domain of validity: all real numbers except 0 and multiples of π
8. $\cos^2\theta$ **9.** 1 **10.** 1 **11.** $-\sin^2\theta$ **12.** $\cos^2\theta$ **13.** 1 **14.** −60° **15.** 60° **16.** −30° **17.** 30° **18.** 0.34 **19.** −1.11 **20.** 2.27 **21.** 0.20 **22.** $\frac{\pi}{3}, \frac{5\pi}{3}$ **23.** $\frac{\pi}{6}, \frac{7\pi}{6}$
24. $0, \frac{\pi}{2}, \pi$ **25.** $\frac{\pi}{3}, \frac{5\pi}{3}$ **26.** $\sin\theta = \frac{4}{5}$, $\cos\theta = -\frac{3}{5}$, $\tan\theta = -\frac{4}{3}$, $\csc\theta = \frac{5}{4}$, $\sec\theta = -\frac{5}{3}$, $\cot\theta = -\frac{3}{4}$
27. $\sin\theta = -\frac{15}{17}$, $\cos\theta = -\frac{8}{17}$, $\tan\theta = \frac{15}{8}$, $\csc\theta = -\frac{17}{15}$, $\sec\theta = -\frac{17}{8}$, $\cot\theta = \frac{8}{15}$ **28.** $\frac{3}{5}$, 0.6 **29.** $\frac{4}{5}$, 0.8
30. $\frac{3}{4}$, 0.75 **31.** $\frac{5}{3}$, $1.\overline{6}$ **32.** $g \approx 9.5$, $\angle F \approx 18.4$, $\angle H \approx 71.6$ **33.** $h = 16$, $\angle F \approx 36.9$, $\angle H \approx 53.1$
34. $f \approx 37.7$, $\angle F \approx 43.3$, $\angle H \approx 46.7$
35. $g \approx 6.4$, $\angle F \approx 51.3$, $\angle H \approx 38.7$ **36.** 13.7
37. 29.4 **38.** 13.14 m^2 **39.** 92.12 ft^2 **40.** 7.1 in.
41. 43.9° **42.** 52.2°
43. $\cos\left(\theta + \frac{\pi}{2}\right) = \cos\theta\cos\frac{\pi}{2} - \sin\theta\sin\frac{\pi}{2}$
$= \cos\theta \times 0 - \sin\theta \times 1 = -\sin\theta$
44. $\sin^2\left(\theta - \frac{\pi}{2}\right) = \left[\sin\left(\theta - \frac{\pi}{2}\right)\right]^2$
$= \left[\sin\theta\cos\frac{\pi}{2} - \cos\theta\sin\frac{\pi}{2}\right]^2$
$= [\sin\theta \times 0 - \cos\theta \times 1]^2$
$= (-\cos\theta)^2 = \cos^2\theta$
45. $2 - \sqrt{3}$ **46.** $-\frac{\sqrt{3}}{2}$ **47.** $\frac{\sqrt{2} - \sqrt{6}}{4}$ **48.** $-2 - \sqrt{3}$
49. $\frac{\sqrt{3}}{2}$ **50.** $\frac{\sqrt{3}}{2}$ **51.** $-\sqrt{3}$ **52.** $-\frac{\sqrt{3}}{2}$

Skills Handbook

p. 972 1. 46% **3.** 0.7% **5.** 1.035 **7.** 25% **9.** $66.\overline{6}$% **11.** 115% **13.** 12.5 **15.** 75 **17.** 20%
p. 973 1. $1\frac{2}{5}$ **3.** $6\frac{5}{6}$ **5.** $\frac{5}{21}$ **7.** $2\frac{19}{20}$ **9.** 8 **11.** $1\frac{1}{2}$ **13.** 2 **15.** 42
p. 974 1. 3 to 4 **3.** 19 g in 2 oz **5.** $\frac{14}{5}$ **7.** 8 **9.** 1.8 **11.** 1.95 **13.** 45.5 **15.** ±6
p. 975 1. 1 **3.** −38 **5.** −17 **7.** 4 **9.** 28 **11.** −12 **13.** −90 **15.** 12 **17.** 19 **19.** 9 **21.** −10
p. 976 1. 14 m^2 **3.** 30 cm^2 **5.** $91\frac{1}{8}$ ft^3 **7.** 100π $in.^3$ **9.** 110.5 $in.^2$ **11.** $121\frac{1}{2}$ ft^2
p. 977 1. I **3.** IV **5.** III **7.** $\frac{4}{5}$ **9.** 0 **11.** $\frac{1}{5}$ **13.** $\left(5, -\frac{3}{2}\right)$ **15.** $\left(\frac{5}{2}, -1\right)$
p. 978 1. x^3 **3.** a^4b **5.** $\frac{1}{c^4}$ **7.** $\frac{x^5}{y^7z^3}$ **9.** d^8 **11.** c^6 **13.** $\frac{a^4}{b^5}$ **15.** $\frac{a^4}{b^4}$ **17.** c^{12} **19.** $u^{12}v^6$ **21.** a^3 **23.** $\frac{1}{mg^3}$ **25.** $\frac{a^5}{2}$
p. 979 1. $x^2 + 10x - 5$ **3.** $12x^4 - 20x^3 + 36x^2$

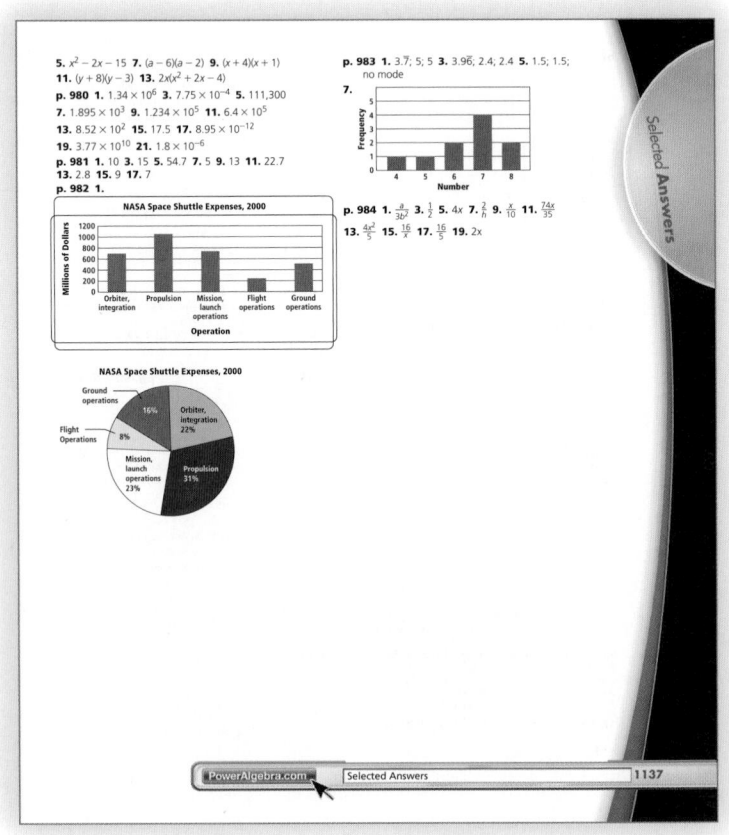

5. $x^2 - 2x - 15$ **7.** $(a - 6)(a - 2)$ **9.** $(x + 4)(x + 1)$ **11.** $(y + 8)(y - 3)$ **13.** $2x(x^2 + 2x - 4)$
p. 980 1. 1.34×10^6 **3.** 7.75×10^{-4} **5.** 111,300 **7.** 1.895×10^3 **9.** 1.234×10^5 **11.** 6.4×10^5 **13.** 8.52×10^2 **15.** 17.5 **17.** 8.95×10^{-12} **19.** 3.77×10^{10} **21.** 1.8×10^{-6}
p. 981 1. 10 **3.** 15 **5.** 54.7 **7.** 5 **9.** 13 **11.** 22.7 **13.** 2.8 **15.** 9 **17.** 7
p. 982 1.

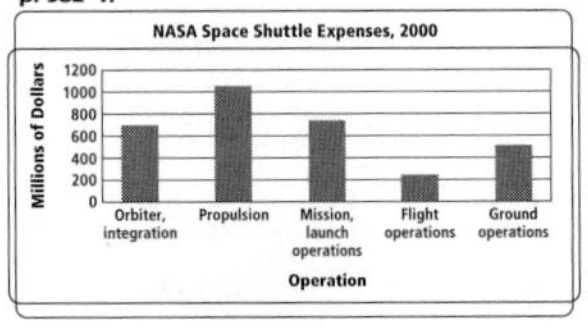
NASA Space Shuttle Expenses, 2000
Millions of Dollars
1200
1000
800
600
400
200
0
Orbiter, integration
Propulsion
Mission, launch operations
Flight operations
Ground operations
Operation

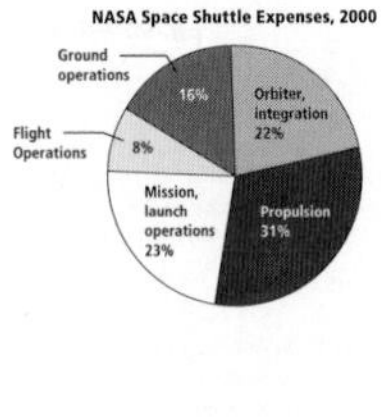
NASA Space Shuttle Expenses, 2000
Ground operations
16%
Orbiter, integration 22%
Flight Operations
8%
Mission, launch operations 23%
Propulsion 31%

p. 983 1. $3.\overline{7}$; 5; 5 **3.** $3.9\overline{6}$; 2.4; 2.4 **5.** 1.5; 1.5; no mode
7.

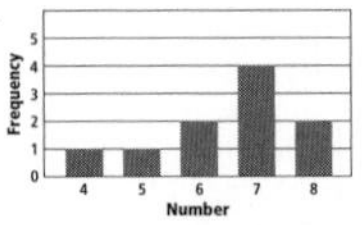
5
4
3
2
1
0
Frequency
4
5
6
7
8
Number

p. 984 1. $\frac{a}{3b^2}$ **3.** $\frac{1}{2}$ **5.** $4x$ **7.** $\frac{2}{h}$ **9.** $\frac{x}{10}$ **11.** $\frac{74x}{35}$ **13.** $\frac{4x^2}{5}$ **15.** $\frac{16}{x}$ **17.** $\frac{16}{5}$ **19.** $2x$

Additional Answers

Chapter 2

Lesson 2-7

page 112 Practice and Problem Solving Exercises

45. a.

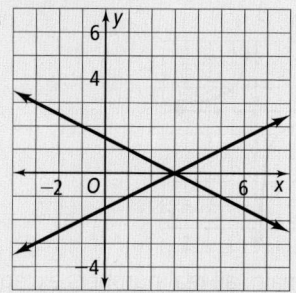

b. No; $f(x) = g(x)$ only for $x = 3$.

46. a. Check students' work.

    b. Check students' work.

    c. The graphs of y_1 and y_2 are the same for zero and positive values of k, and are mirror images for negative values of k.

47.

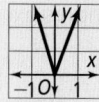

48.

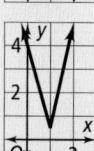

49.

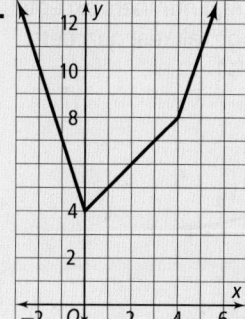

50. B

page 113 Standardized Test Prep

51. C

52. G

53. A

54. [2] No; both $(1, -1)$ and $(1, 1)$ are pts. on the graph of $|y| = x$. Since there is more than one y-value (-1 and 1) for a given x-value (1), $|y| = x$ is not a function. (OR equivalent explanation)

    [1] incomplete explanation

page 113 Mixed Review

55. $y = x + 1$

56. $y = -\frac{1}{2}x + 2$

57. $g(x) = -x - 7$

58. $g(x) = -2x - 6$

59. $g(x) = -4 - x$

60. Answers may vary. Sample: $y = \frac{4}{5}x + 1$

61. Answers may vary. Sample: $y = -\frac{4}{5}x + 8$

62.

$p \le 1.25$

63.

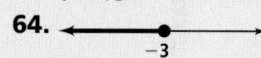

$t > 13$

64.

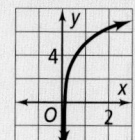

Chapter 5

Lesson 5-6

page 325 Concept Byte

5.

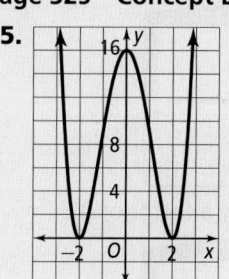

6.

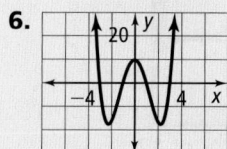

Chapter 7

Mid-Chapter Quiz

page 461 Mid-Chapter Quiz

24. domain: $x > 1$, range: all real numbers

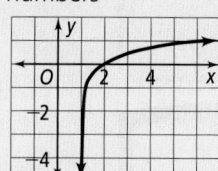

25. domain: all real numbers, range: all real numbers

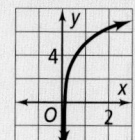

26. $y = 2144.23(0.95)^x$; about 6 minutes

27. The y-intercept is when $x = 0$ i.e. $(0, a)$.

28. If $a > 0$ and $b > 1$, the function represents exponential growth; if $a > 0$ and $0 < b < 1$, the function represents exponential decay.

29. The graphs are a reflection of each other over the line $y = x$. The domain of one is the range of the other, and vice-versa. They both share a common y-intercept, $(0, 0)$.

30. The annually compounded interest formula is $A = P(1 + r)^t$. The continuously compounded interest formula is $A = Pe^{rt}$.

Chapter 8

Lesson 8-2

page 506 Concept Byte

5.

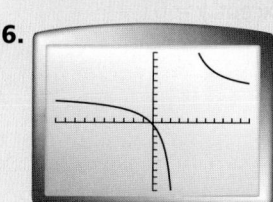

6.

7.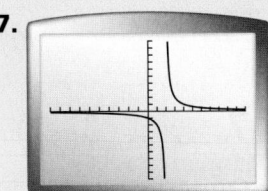

8.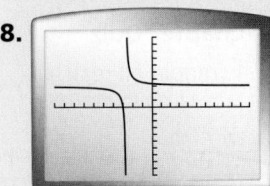

9.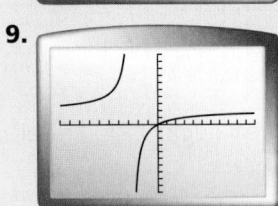

10.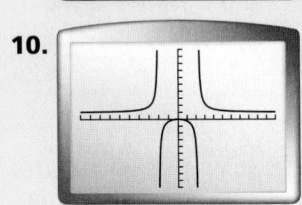

11.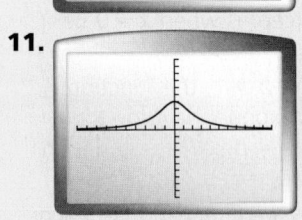

page 512 Practice and Problem Solving Exercises

10.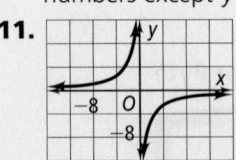

no x- or y-intercept; horizontal asymptote: $y = 0$, vertical asymptote: $x = 0$; domain: all real numbers except $x = 0$, range: all real numbers except $y = 0$

11.

no x- or y-intercept; horizontal asymptote: $y = 0$, vertical asymptote: $x = 0$; domain: all real numbers except $x = 0$, range: all real numbers except $y = 0$

12.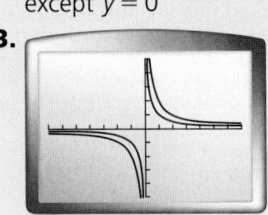

no x- or y-intercept; horizontal asymptote: $y = 0$, vertical asymptote: $x = 0$; domain: all real numbers except $x = 0$, range: all real numbers except $y = 0$

13.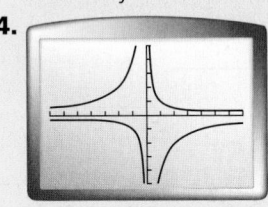

stretch by a factor of 2

14.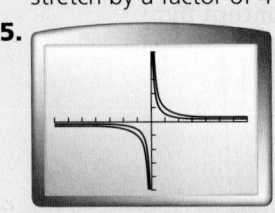

reflection across the x-axis and a stretch by a factor of 4

15.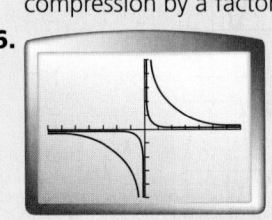

compression by a factor of 0.5

16.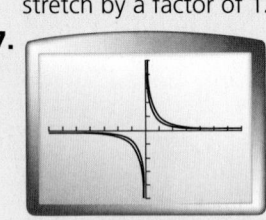

stretch by a factor of 12

17.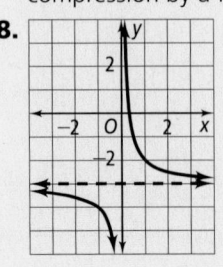

compression by a factor of 0.75

18.

domain: all real numbers except $x = 0$, range: all real numbers except $y = -3$

19.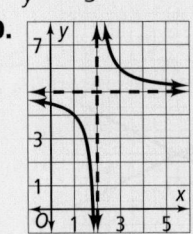

domain: all real numbers except $x = 0$, range: all real numbers except $y = -3$

20.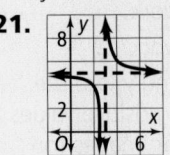

domain: all real numbers except $x = 2$, range: all real numbers except $y = 5$

21.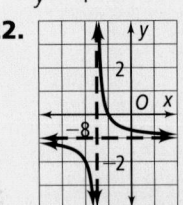

domain: all real numbers except $x = 3$, range: all real numbers except $y = 4$

22.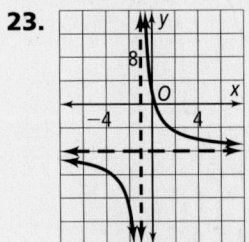

domain: all real numbers except $x = -6$, range: all real numbers except $y = -1$

23.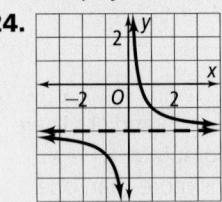

domain: all real numbers except $x = -1$, range: all real numbers except $y = -8$

24.

domain: all real numbers except $x = 0$, range: all real numbers except $y = -2$

25.

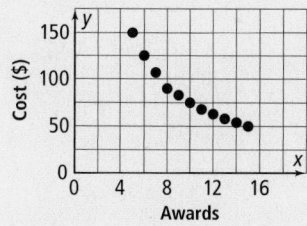

domain: all real numbers except $x = -5$, range: all real numbers except $y = -6$

26. $y = \frac{2}{x} + 4$

27. $y = \frac{2}{x + 2} + 3$

28. $y = \frac{2}{x - 4} - 8$

29. 7.67 ft

30.

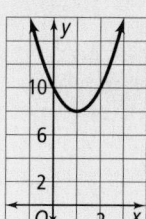

$c = \frac{750}{a}$; domain: whole numbers from 5 to 15, range: $50 \le c \le 750$

Chapter 10

Get Ready

page 611 Get Ready!

15. $y = 2(x - 1)^2 + 8$

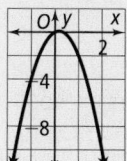

16. $y = -3\left(x - \frac{1}{6}\right)^2 + \frac{1}{12}$

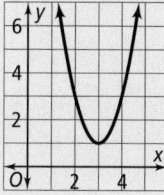

17.

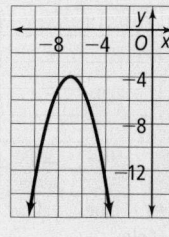

18.

19.

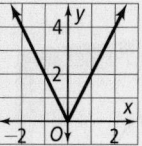

20.

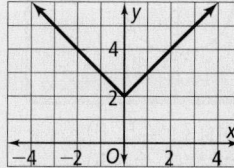

21. The radius of a circle is the distance from the center of the circle to any pt. on the circle. The radius extends in every direction from the center and ends on the circle. All radii of the same circle are equal.

22. The vertex of a parabola is the lowest or highest pt. of a parabola; it is the pt. where the parabola changes direction.

Lesson 10-1

page 619 Practice and Problem Solving Exercises

38. parabola: Hold the lamp so that the edge of the shade furthest from the wall is parallel to the plane of the wall.

circle: Hold the lamp so that the circular top rim of the shade is parallel to the wall.

hyperbola: Let the lamp sit in a normal, upright position, but close enough to the wall for the bottom rim of the shade to almost touch the wall.

ellipse: Hold the lamp at an angle so that the light from the top of the shade gives a closed, curved oblong area of light on the wall.

39. a. All lines in the plane that pass through the center of a circle are axes of sym. of the circle.

b. The axes of sym. of an ellipse intersect at the center of the ellipse. The same is true for a hyperbola. This can be confirmed using, for example, $4x^2 + 9y^2 = 36$ and $4x^2 - 9y^2 = 36$.

40.

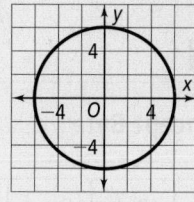

$x^2 + y^2 = 36$

41.

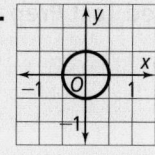

$x^2 + y^2 = \frac{1}{4}$

42.

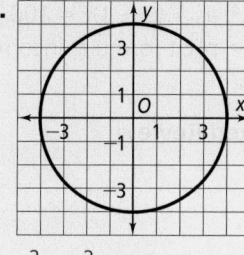

$x^2 + y^2 = 16$

43.

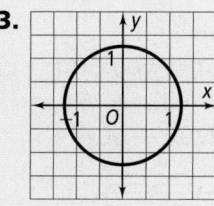

$x^2 + y^2 = 1.5625$

44–49. Answers may vary. Samples are given.

44. $(2, 4)$

45. $(\sqrt{2}, 1)$

46. $(-2, 2\sqrt{2})$

47. $(2, 0)$

48. $(3, \sqrt{51})$

49. $(0, -\sqrt{7})$

50. one branch of a hyperbola

51. Check students' work.

52. a.

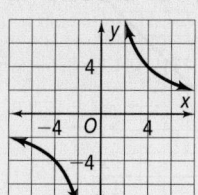

b. hyperbola

c. no intercepts; lines of symmetry: $y = x$ and $y = -x$

d. yes; $f(x) = \frac{16}{x}$

53. a.

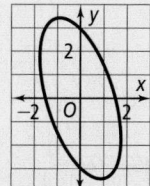

b.

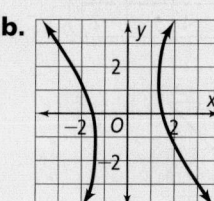

page 620 Standardized Test Prep

54. D

55. I

56. D

57. H

58. [2]

$a_n = (n + 1)^2$; $a_9 = (9 + 1)^2 = 100$

[1] correct explicit formula, incorrect ninth term

page 620 Mixed Review

59. diverges

60. diverges

61. converges

62. $x^3 - 3x^2y + 3xy^2 - y^3$

63. $p^6 + 6p^5q + 15p^4q^2 + 20p^3q^3 + 15p^2q^4 + 6pq^5 + q^6$

64. $x^4 - 8x^3 + 24x^2 - 32x + 16$

65. $243 - 405x + 270x^2 - 90x^3 + 15x^4 - x^5$

66.

x	−2	−1	0	1	2
y	2	1	0	1	2

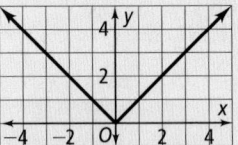

67.

x	−2	−1	0	1	2
y	5	4	3	4	5

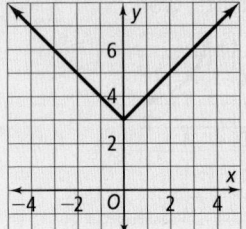

68.

x	0	1	2	3	4
y	2	1	0	1	2

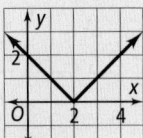

69.

x	−3	−2	−1	0	1
y	−2	−3	−4	−3	−2

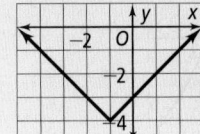

p. 621 Concept Byte

7. a.

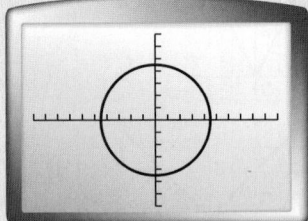

b. x-intercepts: (± 4.5, 0), y-intercepts: (0, ± 4.5)

c. Check students' work.

d. circle with center at the origin and radius 4.5

8.

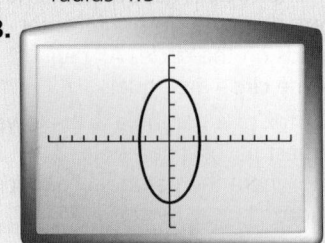

x-intercepts: (± 2.5, 0), y-intercepts: (0, ± 5)

9.

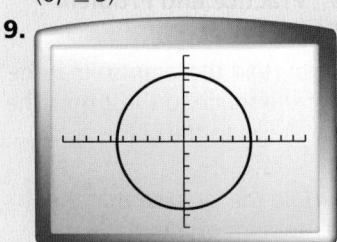

x-intercepts: ($\pm \sqrt{30}$, 0), y-intercepts: (0, $\pm \sqrt{30}$)

10.

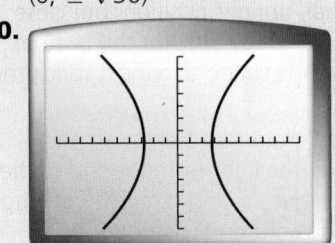

x-intercepts: ($\pm 2\sqrt{2}$, 0), no y-intercepts

11. Answers may vary. Sample: Graph on the same screen: $y = 3 - x$ where $x \geq 0$ and $y = 3 + x$ where $x \geq 0$.

12. Parabolas with a vert. axis of sym.; other conic sections have the x-axis as a line of sym., so they fail the vert. line test.

Chapter 11

pp. 694–695 Concept Byte

9.

Event: Color	Red	Green	Blue	Yellow
Frequency	1	3	2	1
Probability	$\frac{1}{7}$	$\frac{3}{7}$	$\frac{2}{7}$	$\frac{1}{7}$

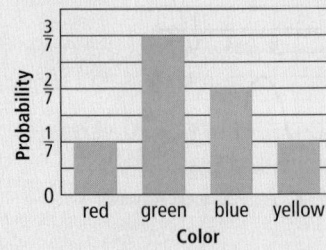

Chapter 14

Lesson 14-1

page 910 Practice and Problem Solving Exercises

62. a. In the unit circle, the coordinates of any point are (cos ϕ, sin ϕ) For P, $\phi = \theta + \pi$. Thus, the y-coordinate of point P is $\sin(\theta + \pi)$.

b. The triangles are right triangles by definition. The hypotenuse of each triangle is the radius of the unit circle, 1, and so they are congruent to each other. The acute angles with vertices at the origin are vertical angles and are congruent by the Vertical Angle Theorem. So, the two right triangles are congruent by HA; their hypotenuses and acute angles are congruent.

c. The legs opposite the vertical angles are congruent because they are corresponding parts of congruent triangles.

d. In Quadrant I, the y-coordinate is $y = \sin \theta$. In Quadrant III, the x- and y-coordinates are negative. Also, since the blue segments are congruent, the absolute values of the y-coordinates in Quadrants I and III are equal. So, the y-coordinate of P is $-\sin \theta$.

e. Since the y-coordinate of P is $\sin(\theta + \pi)$, which was shown in (a), and is also $-\sin \theta$, which was shown in (d), by transitivity: $\sin(\theta + \pi) = -\sin \theta$.

63. $\cos(\theta + \pi) = |\cos \theta|$, but is also in Quadrant III and is negative, so $\cos(\theta + \pi) = -\cos \theta$

64. $\tan(\theta + \pi) = \dfrac{\sin(\theta + \pi)}{\cos(\theta + \pi)} = \dfrac{-\sin \theta}{-\cos \theta} = \tan \theta$

65. 1

66. $\csc^2 \theta$

67. If $n_2 > n_1$, then $\theta_1 > \theta_2$; if $n_2 < n_1$, then $\theta_1 < \theta_2$; if $n_2 = n_1$, then $\theta_2 = \theta_1$.

page 910 Standardized Test Prep
68. C
69. H
70. C
71. F
72. C

73. [2] By the Difference of Squares Property and the second Pythagorean Identity:
$(\sec \theta + 1)(\sec \theta - 1) =$
$\sec^2 \theta - 1 = \tan^2 \theta$

[1] correctly worked out, but in more steps than used here

page 910 Mixed Review

74.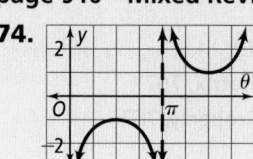

75.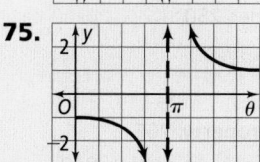

76.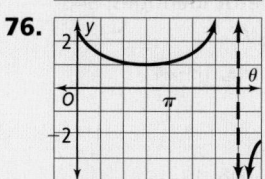

77.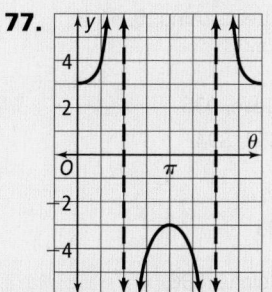

78. 35°   **79.** 45°
80. 135°   **81.** 211°
82. $f^{-1}(x) = x - 1$
83. $f^{-1}(x) = \dfrac{x + 3}{2}$
84. $f^{-1}(x) = \pm \sqrt{x - 4}$

p. 927 Mid-Chapter Quiz

40.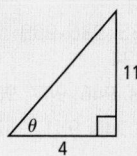

$\sin \theta = \dfrac{11\sqrt{137}}{137}$, $\cos \theta = \dfrac{4\sqrt{137}}{137}$,

$\csc \theta = \dfrac{\sqrt{137}}{11}$,

$\sec \theta = \dfrac{\sqrt{137}}{4}$, $\cot \theta = \dfrac{4}{11}$

41.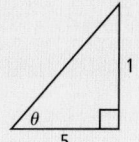

$\sin \theta = \dfrac{\sqrt{26}}{26}$, $\cos \theta = \dfrac{5\sqrt{26}}{26}$,

$\tan \theta = \dfrac{1}{5}$,

$\csc \theta = \sqrt{26}$, $\sec \theta = \dfrac{\sqrt{26}}{5}$

42. Answers may vary. Sample: In the eq. $x^2 - 3x + 2 = 0$, you isolate the variable x to get the solution. In the eq. $\tan^2 \theta - 3 \tan \theta + 2 = 0$, you first isolate the tangent function, but then you must continue to find the inverse tangent to solve for θ:
$x^2 - 3x + 2 = 0$
$\tan^2 \theta - 3 \tan \theta + 2 = 0$
$(x - 2)(x - 1) = 0$
$(\tan \theta - 2)(\tan \theta - 1) = 0$
$x - 2 = 0; x - 1 = 0$
$\tan \theta = 2; \tan \theta = 1$
$x = 2; x = 1$
$\theta \approx 63° + 180° \cdot n$;
$\theta = 45° + 180° \cdot n$

43. Answers may vary. Sample: Use the Pythagorean Theorem, $c^2 = a^2 + b^2$. Check students' work.

44. $\sin^2 \theta - \sin \theta - 6 = 0$
$(\sin \theta - 3)(\sin \theta + 2) = 0$
    $\sin \theta = 3; \sin \theta = -2$
There is no solution because the zeros of the eq. are 3 and −2, but the range of sine is between 1 and −1.

45. 76 in.

Index

D

data, describing, 729

data analysis, 711–718
- binomial distributions, 731–738
- binomial experiment, 731, 734, 755
- box-and-whisker plots, 714, 754
- exercises, 769
- interquartile range, 713
- mean, 711, 754
- measures of central tendency, 711, 719, 754
- measures of variation, 719, 754
- median, 711, 754
- mode, 711, 754
- normal distribution, 739–745, 756
- outliers, 712, 754
- percentiles, 715
- probability distributions, 694, 734, 739, 756
- quartile, 713, 754
- random sample, 725, 755
- range, 713, 754
- sample, 725–730, 751, 755
- standard deviation, 711, 719–724
- variance, 719, 720, 754
- z-score, 748

data collection and analysis, as Big Idea, 751

data modeling, 209–213, 269, 331–334, 352

data representation, as Big Idea, 750, 816, 817

data sets
- bimodal, 712
- comparing, 713
- range of, 713
- of scatter plots, 92, 93, 125

decay factor, 436, 488

decoding matrix, 787

degrees
- converting to and from radians, 844, 845
- of polynomials, 280–284

ΔTbl feature, 470

demography, 474

denominator
- least common (LCD), 535, 537
- rationalizing the, 369, 370, 377, 423

dependent
- events, 688, 698, 753
- system, 137, 184
- variable, 63

Descartes' Rule of Signs, 315, 350

design, 871

determinants, 782–790
- defined, 783
- of matrices, 784, 819

diagrams
- drawing and using for problem solving, 39, 53, 54, 55, 56, 60, 62, 65, 238, 294, 302, 316, 355, 375, 378, 379, 395, 421, 449, 453, 492, 532, 570, 594, 617, 628, 629, 631, 657, 814, 841, 921, 933, 938, 940
- mapping, 60
- tree, 699, 732

difference
- common, 572, 589, 604
- of cubes, factoring, 297
- opposite of a, 21

of squares, factoring, 220, 297
using to determine degree, 284

Differentiated Remediation 10A–B, 17A–B, 24A–B, 32A–B, 40A–B, 48A–B, 67A–B, 73A–B, 80A–B, 88A–B, 98A–B, 106A–B, 113A–B, 120A–B, 141A–B, 148A–B, 155A–B, 162A–B, 165A–B, 173A–B, 181A–B, 201A–B, 208A–B, 214A–B, 223A–B, 231A–B, 239A–B, 247A–B, 255A–B, 264A–B, 287A–B, 295A–B, 302A–B, 310A–B, 317A–B, 324A–B, 330A–B, 338A–B, 345A–B, 366A–B, 373A–B, 380A–B, 388A–B, 397A–B, 404A–B, 412A–B, 420A–B, 441A–B, 450A–B, 458A–B, 468A–B, 476A–B, 483A–B, 505A–B, 514A–B, 523A–B, 533A–B, 541A–B, 548A–B, 571A–B, 577A–B, 586A–B, 593A–B, 601A–B, 620A–B, 629A–B, 636A–B, 644A–B, 652A–B, 660A–B, 680A–B, 687A–B, 693A–B, 702A–B, 718A–B, 724A–B, 730A–B, 738A–B, 745A–B, 770A–B, 779A–B, 790A–B, 800A–B, 808A–B, 815A–B, 824A–B, 842A–B, 850A–B, 858A–B, 867A–B, 874A–B, 882A–B, 890A–B, 910A–B, 918A–B, 926A–B, 934A–B, 942A–B, 950A–B

Digital Resources. See **PowerAlgebra.com**

dilation, 801, 802, 803, 820

dimensional analysis, 845

dimensions, determining, 234

directrix of parabola, 622, 664

direct variation, 68–73, 123, 498–499

discontinuity
- non-removable, 516
- point of, 516–517, 555
- removable, 516

discontinuous function, 516

discrete
- function, 437
- probability distribution, 739, 756

discriminant, 242, 243, 244, 271

distribution
- binomial, 731–738
- continuous probability, 739, 756
- discrete probability, 739, 756
- normal, 739–745, 756
- probability, 694
- skewed, 740
- uniform, 694

Distributive Property
- of Matrix Multiplication, 776
- of Real Numbers, 14, 51
- of Scalar Multiplication, 773
- for Subtraction, 21

divergence of a series, 598, 606

division
- of algebraic expressions, 21
- of complex numbers, 251
- definition of, 21
- of functions, 398, 399
- inverse operation to, 27
- of logarithms, 462
- of polynomials, 302–310, 349
- of radical expressions, 367–373, 423
- of rational expressions, 529
- of square roots, 225
- synthetic, 303, 306–307, 349

Division Property
- of Equality, 27

of Inequality, 34
of Square Roots, 225

domain
- extrapolating, 334
- of functions, 62, 398, 399, 408, 414, 425, 434, 435, 515, 516
- predicting, 334
- of rational expressions, 527
- of relations, 61, 62, 123
- of validity, 904, 905

dot product, 812, 820

double-angle identities, 951–957, 962

drawing
- a diagram for problem solving, 814, 842, 921, 933, 938, 940
- a graph for problem solving, 36, 857, 862, 864, 865, 869, 873, 878, 881
- sketch angles in standard position, 837
- sketch sine curves, 854
- sketch solutions in a plane, 164, 184

DrawInv feature, 413

Dynamic Activities
- Absolute Value, 107
- Box-and-Whisker Plots, 712
- Circles, 630
- Cosine Function, 861
- Dilations, 801
- Ellipse, 639
- Factored-form, 226
- Geometric Probability, 682
- Growth/Decay, 435
- Hyperbola, 645
- Independent and Dependent Events, 689
- Inequality Systems, 149
- Linear Factors, 289
- Linear Programming, 158
- Log Functions, 451, 478
- Matrix Addition, 764
- Parabolas, 622
- Probability Binomial, 731
- Quadratic Functions, 203
- Radical Functions, 415
- Rational Functions, 515
- Real Number Line, 11
- Roots, 240
- Sequences, 572
- Simplifying, 361
- Sine Function, 851
- Special Solutions, 143
- Sum and Difference Identities for Sine and Cosine, 943
- Synthetic Division, 303
- Systems of Linear Equations, 135
- Tangent Function, 868
- Translation, 99, 507
- Trigonometric Functions, 875
- Trigonometric Identities, 904
- Variation, 499
- Vertex Form, 194

E

e
- base of exponential function, 442–444, 446
- natural logarithmic function, 478

earthquakes, 456, 474, 543

earth science, 392, 628

eccentricity, 643

economics, 140, 206, 402

EDIT option, 771

elimination, 144, 148, 166–173, 186

wind chill, 387
wind power, 327

fractions, complex, 536, 537

frequency, cumulative, 695

frog-jumping competition, 228

function(s). *See also* equation(s)
absolute value, 90, 107–113, 125, 126
adding, 398, 399
as Big Idea, 122, 133, 182, 183, 266, 267, 346, 347, 422, 486, 487, 552, 553, 892, 958, 959
composition of, 399, 400–401, 408, 409
continuous, 516
cosecant, 883
cosine, 875–882, 895
cotangent, 883
cube root, 417
cubic, 283–284, 339–340
defined, 62
dependent variable in, 63
discontinuous, 516
discrete, 437
dividing, 398, 399
domain of, 62, 398, 399, 408, 414, 425, 434, 435, 515, 516
exponential. *See* exponential functions
family of, 99–106, 125
graphing quadratic, 194–201
graphing trigonometric, 860, 886
greatest integer, 90
identifying, 60–65
independent variables in, 63
input of the, 63
inverse. *See* inverse functions
linear. *See* linear functions
logarithmic. *See* logarithmic functions
maximum and minimum values, 158, 185, 195, 291, 292
monomial, 352
multiplying, 398, 399
natural logarithmic, 478–483
objective, 157, 185
one-to-one, 408
operations with, 398–404, 425
parent. *See* Parent Function
periodic. *See* periodic function
piecewise, 90–91
polynomial. *See* polynomial functions
power, 341
quadratic. *See* quadratic functions
quartic, 341
radical, 414–420
rational. *See* rational functions
reciprocal. *See* reciprocal functions
reciprocal trigonometric, 883–890, 896
rewriting by completing the square, 233–239
secant, 883
simplest form of, 99, 125
sine, 851–858, 875–882, 894
square root, 414–420, 426
step, 90
subtracting, 398, 399
transformations. *See* transformations
translations. *See* translations
trigonometric, 860, 886
vertical-line test, 62–63
zeros of. *See* zero(s)

function notation, 62, 63, 407

function rule, 63

Fundamental Counting Principle, 674, 675

Fundamental Theorem of Algebra, 319–324, 351

G

Galton box, 731

GCF (greatest common factor), 218, 297

geography, 849

geometric
mean, 583, 605
probability, 684
series, 595–601, 606
transformations, 801–808, 820

geometric sequences, 580–586
analyzing, 581
arithmetic vs., 583
defined, 580
formula for, 565, 566, 567, 605
geometric series, 595–601, 606
identifying, 580–581

Geometry as Big Idea, 958, 959

Geometry exercises, 17, 30, 31, 39, 52, 66, 73, 88, 154, 173, 180, 213, 222, 238, 246, 294, 301, 308, 309, 329, 366, 379, 410, 411, 426, 449, 570, 577, 684, 686, 789, 799, 807, 808, 874, 889, 925, 933, 941

Geometry Review
Special Right Triangles, 825

Get Ready!
for chapters, 1, 57, 131, 191, 277, 431, 495, 561, 611, 671, 761, 825, 901
for lessons, 10, 17, 24, 32, 40, 48, 67, 73, 80, 88, 98, 106, 113, 120, 141, 148, 155, 162, 165, 173, 181, 201, 208, 214, 223, 231, 239, 247, 255, 264, 287, 295, 302, 310, 317, 324, 330, 338, 345, 366, 373, 380, 388, 397, 404, 412, 420, 441, 450, 458, 468, 476, 483, 505, 514, 523, 533, 541, 548, 571, 577, 586, 593, 601, 620, 629, 636, 644, 652, 660, 680, 687, 693, 702, 718, 724, 730, 738, 745, 770, 779, 780, 800, 808, 815, 834, 842, 850, 858, 867, 874, 882, 890, 910, 918, 926, 934, 942, 950

Glossary, 994

Got It? *See* assessment, Got It?

graph(s)
of absolute value functions, 107–113
of absolute value inequalities, 117
boundary lines, 107, 114, 115, 126
of circles, 615, 632, 633
complex number plane, 250
of conic sections, 616, 621
of cosine function, 861–863
of cube root function, 417
of cubic functions, 283–284
of direct variation equations, 70
drawing for problem solving, 857, 862, 864, 865, 869, 873, 878, 881
of ellipse, 615
end behavior of, 282–283
of exponential functions, 434–435, 437
of exponential functions with base *e*, 442–450
feasible region, 157, 185
of hyperbola, 616, 647
of inequalities, 33, 35, 114–120, 126
of inverse functions, 413, 508, 912
of linear equations, 77, 83, 84, 124
of linear inequalities, 115, 117, 150–151
line of best fit, 94, 95, 125
of logarithmic functions, 454–455
multiple zeros effect on, 291

numbers on a number line, 13
ordered pairs, 60, 110, 121–122, 123, 164
of parabola, 194, 197, 268
piecewise function, 90–91
points on a coordinate plane, 164
of polynomial functions, 283–284, 291, 339–345
of quadratic functions, 194–201
of quadratic functions in standard form, 202–208
of radical functions, 414–420, 426
of rational functions, 506, 515–523
of real numbers, 11, 13
of reciprocal functions, 507–511, 554
of reciprocal trigonometric functions, 886
of relations, 60–61, 406–407
scatter plot, 92–93, 125
of sine function, 851–858, 894
solving exponential equations using, 470
solving linear-quadratic system using, 259
solving linear systems using, 134–141, 166, 168
solving polynomial equations using, 296–302
solving quadratic equations using, 226–231
solving radical equations using, 416
solving systems of inequalities using, 115, 117, 150–151, 185
of square root function, 416
of tangent function, 870
in three-dimensions, 164–165, 166
transformations. *See* transformations
translations. *See* translations
of trigonometric functions, 860
turning point, 291
using for problem solving, 6, 9, 13, 16, 60, 61, 65, 70, 77, 78, 79, 83, 84, 87, 93, 94, 100, 105, 106, 109, 110, 111, 115, 116, 117, 118, 119, 121, 127, 129, 134, 141, 150, 152, 153, 154, 155, 156, 158, 159, 161, 162, 189, 190, 195, 196, 197, 199, 200, 205, 210, 227, 229, 230, 246, 250, 254, 257, 268, 275, 276, 286, 289, 291, 319, 333, 337, 338, 340, 341, 344, 345, 346, 352, 355, 356, 373, 406, 414, 415, 416, 418, 419, 429, 430, 434, 437, 440, 441, 442, 443, 444, 449, 450, 454, 455, 468, 484, 493, 494, 499, 508, 509, 510, 514, 515, 519, 533, 541, 554, 559, 593, 608, 609, 615, 616, 618, 623, 624, 632, 633, 635, 640, 641, 642, 644, 647, 649, 655, 656, 657, 659, 664, 668, 669, 670, 716, 721, 723, 740, 741, 742, 744, 789, 807, 811, 833, 852, 871, 912

graphing calculator. *See also* calculator
activity, 163
area of a polygon, 785
box-and-whisker plots, 714
CALC feature, 163, 202, 227
conic sections, 621
CONNECTED mode, 506
cosine equation, 864–865
CubicReg feature, 331, 332, 334
ΔTbl feature, 470
determinant of a matrix, 784
direct and inverse variation, 498–499, 500
DOT plotting mode, 506
DrawInv feature, 413
encoding and decoding with matrices, 787
exercises, 87, 88, 90, 97, 120, 121, 138, 139, 140, 151, 180, 213, 229, 265, 300, 337, 413, 418, 419, 420, 440, 448, 449,

Index

127, 140, 145, 147, 154, 171, 179, 180,
187, 207, 213, 222, 224, 245, 273, 294,
302, 310, 311, 317, 329, 336, 345, 353,
372, 379, 411, 413, 418, 427, 460, 461,
466, 474, 477, 482, 484, 491, 503, 505,
512, 513, 522, 540, 547, 557, 576, 585,
598, 600, 607, 621, 629, 636, 644, 661,
667, 679, 680, 685, 686, 701, 709, 717,
723, 728, 736, 744, 752, 757, 769, 778,
781, 789, 790, 791, 806, 807, 814, 821,
831, 833, 841, 849, 859, 860, 865, 871,
874, 889, 898, 915, 917, 923, 927, 934,
939, 941, 950, 956, 963
expressions, 20, 385
functions, 110, 451–458
inequalities, 33, 34, 117
technical writing, 525
Think/Write problems, 6, 35, 101, 108, 144,
168, 176, 198, 220, 234, 243, 252, 259,
300, 328, 364, 368, 376, 384, 417, 437,
465, 519, 529, 538, 543, 566, 582, 588,
648, 654, 677, 682, 698, 786, 795, 830,
870, 879, 884, 907, 914, 930, 938, 948
translations, 877

X

x-axis, 101, 102, 164, 195, 197, 226, 256,
435
x-coefficient, 175
x-coordinate, 61, 62, 74, 123, 124,
203, 416
x-intercept, 76, 243, 289, 291,
319, 348
Xmax feature, 413
Xmin feature, 413
xy-coordinate plane, 164

Y

y-axis, 101, 102, 164
y-coefficient, 175
y-coordinate, 61, 62, 74, 123, 124, 203
y-intercept, 76
YLIST feature, 477

Z

z-axis, 164
zero(s)
additive identity, 13
multiplication by, 21
multiplicative inverse and, 13
multiplicative property of, 773, 776
multiplicity of, 291
of polynomial functions, 288, 289,
348
properties of, 13, 226, 270, 289,
773
of quadratic equation, 226, 270
of quadratic function, 226
of quartic functions, 341
as a real number, 13
of transformed cubic function,
339–340
ZERO option, 163, 227, 299
Zero-Product Property, 226, 270, 288,
289, 349
zoology, 440, 740, 741
ZOOM feature, 460
z-score, 748

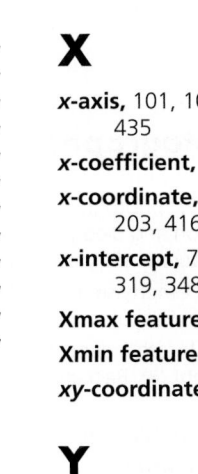
Index

Acknowledgments

Staff Credits

The people who made up the High School Mathematics team—representing composition services, core design digital and multimedia production services, digital product development, editorial, editorial services, manufacturing, marketing, and production management—are listed below.

Emily Allman, Dan Anderson, Scott Andrews, Christopher Anton, Carolyn Artin, Michael Avidon, Margaret Banker, Charlie Bink, Niki Birbilis, Suzanne Biron, Beth Blumberg, Tim Breeze-Thorndike, Kyla Brown, Rebekah Brown, Judith Buice, Sylvia Bullock, Stacie Cartwright, Carolyn Chappo, Christia Clarke, Mary Ellen Cole, Tom Columbus, Andrew Coppola, AnnMarie Coyne, Bob Craton, Nicholas Cronin, Patrick Culleton, Damaris Curran, Steven Cushing, Sheila DeFazio, Cathie Dillender, Emily Dumas, Patty Fagan, Frederick Fellows, Jorgensen Fernandez, Mandy Figueroa, Suzanne Finn, Sara Freund, Matt Frueh, Jon Fuhrer, Andy Gaus, Mark Geyer, Mircea Goia, Andrew Gorlin, Shelby Gragg, Ellen Granter, Jay Grasso, Lisa Gustafson, Toni Haluga, Greg Ham, Marc Hamilton, Chris Handorf, Angie Hanks, Scott Harris, Cynthia Harvey, Phil Hazur, Thane Heninger, Aun Holland, Amanda House, Chuck Jann, Linda Johnson, Blair Jones, Marian Jones, Tim Jones, Gillian Kahn, Matthew Keefer, Brian Keegan, Jim Kelly, Jonathan Kier, Jennifer King, Tamara King, Elizabeth Krieble, Meytal Kotik, Brian Kubota, Roshni Kutty, Mary Landry, Christopher Langley, Christine Lee, Sara Levendusky, Lisa Lin, Wendy Marberry, Dominique Mariano, Clay Martin, Rich McMahon, Eve Melnechuk, Cynthia Metallides, Hope Morley, Christine Nevola, Michael O'Donnell, Michael Oster, Ameer Padshah, Stephen Patrias, Jeffrey Paulhus, Jonathan Penyack, Valerie Perkins, Brian Reardon, Wendy Rock, Marcy Rose, Carol Roy, Irene Rubin, Hugh Rutledge, Vicky Shen, Jewel Simmons, Ted Smykal, Emily Soltanoff, William Speiser, Jayne Stevenson, Richard Sullivan, Dan Tanguay, Dennis Tarwood, Susan Tauer, Tiffany Taylor-Sullivan, Catherine Terwilliger, Mark Tricca, Maria Torti, Leonid Tunik, Ilana Van Veen, Lauren Van Wart, John Vaughan, Laura Vivenzio, Samuel Voigt, Kathy Warfel, Don Weide, Laura Wheel, Eric Whitfield, Sequoia Wild, Joseph Will, Kristin Winters, Allison Wyss, Dina Zolotusky

Additional Credits: Michele Cardin, Robert Carlson, Kate Dalton-Hoffman, Dana Guterman, Narae Maybeth, Carolyn McGuire, Manjula Nair, Rachel Terino, Steve Thomas

Illustration

Stephen Durke: 574; **Phil Guzy:** 596, 597; **Rob Schuster:** 4, 5, 11, 18, 26, 33, 39, 41, 48, 60, 68, 74, 81, 84, 99, 107, 114, 116, 134, 142, 143, 149, 157, 165, 166, 168, 171, 174, 194, 202, 207, 216, 226, 233, 240, 258, 280, 288, 294, 296, 303, 308, 312, 326, 331, 367, 374, 375, 381, 390, 395, 398, 405, 414, 429, 434, 449, 451, 469, 498, 515, 522, 527, 534, 542, 547, 564, 566, 567, 570, 571, 572, 580, 587, 595, 609, 614, 617, 619, 630, 638, 641, 653, 865; **Ted Smykel:** 209; **Pearson Education:** 596, 597; **Judi Pinkham:** 230; **Pronk&Associates:** 12, 362, 399, 462, 589; **XNR Productions:** 788

Technical Illustration

Aptara, Inc.; GGS Book Services

Photographs

Every effort has been made to secure permission and provide appropriate credit for photographic material. The publisher deeply regrets any omission and pledges to correct errors called to its attention in subsequent editions.

Unless otherwise acknowledged, all photographs are the property of Pearson Education, Inc.

Photo locators denoted as follows: Top (T), Center (C), Bottom (B), Left (L), Right (R), Background (Bkgd)

Cover

JL Klein & ML Hubert/Biosphoto

Front Matter

ix, x Peter Mason/Getty Images; **xii** Jeff Greenberg/PhotoEdit, Inc.

28 (T) BL Images Ltd/Alamy Images; **39** (TR) Richard Wahlstrom/Workbook/Jupiter Images/Getty Images; **45** (TR) UPI Photo/Roger Williams/NewsCom; **61** (TR, TCR, CR, CC) Jupiter Images/Brand X/Alamy, (TC) Roberto Mettifogo/Getty Images; **84** (BCR) William Harader, (BR) Zen Shui/SuperStock; **135** (CR) Doug Perrine/Peter Arnold Inc./PhotoLibrary Group, Inc./Getty Images, (TCR) Paul Nicklen/National Geographic Image Collection; **159** (TCR) Andy Crawford/©DK Images, (TCR) Getty Images, (TC) Steve Gorton/©DK Images; **164** (BR) Image Source/Getty Images; **198** (T) Design Pics Inc/Alamy; **205** (TR) Jeff Greenberg/PhotoEdit, Inc.; **228** (TR) ©Harvey Lloyd/Getty Images, (TCR) Andy Harmer/Photo Researchers, Inc.; **234** (TR) Rolf Hicker Photography/Alamy Images; **306** (BR) James Baigrie/Botanica/Jupiter Images/Getty Images; **333** (T) Andre Gallant/Getty Images, (TC) D. Hurst/Alamy, (TCR) Mark Sytes/Alamy, (TR) Peter Cade/Getty Images; **342** AF/Fotolia; **375** Wave Royalty Free/Alamy; **383** (TR) Detlev van Ravenswaay/Photo Researchers, Inc.; **392** (BC) Bob Llewellyn **408** (T) Bob Krist/Corbis; **438** (TR) John Cancalosi/Alamy Images; **453** (CR) Earth Imaging/Getty Images; **467** (BR) Jerry Lodriguss/Science Photo Library/Photo Researchers, Inc.; **476** (TR) Dave King/©DK Images; **480** (TR) JPL/NASA; **502** (TR) Chase Jarvis (R) Corbis Super RF/Alamy; **513** (TCR) NASA; **544** (TR) JPL/NASA; **578** (CR) ©DK Images, (L) Bob Gibbons/Alamy Images, (R) John Glover/Alamy Images, (CL) Peter Anderson/©DK Images; **582** (T) Thomas J. Peterson/Alamy Images; **625** (B) Hank Morgan/Photo Researchers, Inc.; **632** Guido Alberto Rossi/Tips Images/Tips Italia Srl a socio unico/Alamy; **641** (C) Museum of Science and Industry; **675** (T) Ron Chapple Stock; **684** (C) Koji Aoki/Aflo/Getty Images; **775** (TR, TL) iStockphoto; **803** (TC) Wolfgang Spunbarg/PhotoEdit, Inc.; **847** (CR) European Space Agency/Science Photo Library/Photo Researchers, Inc., (TCR) Steve Gorton/©DK Images; **848** (BL) David Zimmerman/Getty Images, (BR) Fnalphotos/Dreamstime LLC; **887** (TR) ART on FILE/Corbis; **889** (CR) Demetrio Carrasco/©DK Images; **921** (TR) age fotostock/SuperStock; **931** (C) mediacolor's/Alamy Images.